FUNDAMENTAL NEUROSCIENCE

Editors

Michael J. Zigmond, Ph.D.
Department of Neurology
University of Pittsburgh
Pittsburgh, Pennsylvania

Floyd E. Bloom, M.D.
Department of Neuropharmacology
The Scripps Research Institute
La Jolla, California

James L. Roberts, Ph.D.
Fishberg Research Center in Neurobiology
Mount Sinai School of Medicine
New York, New York

Story C. Landis, Ph.D.
National Institutes of Health/
National Institute of Neurological Disorders and Stroke
Bethesda, Maryland

Larry R. Squire, Ph.D.
VA Medical Center and University of California
San Diego, California

Section Editors

Thomas D. Albright, Ph.D. *Salk Institute, San Diego, CA*

John H. Byrne, Ph.D. *University of Texas Medical School, Houston, TX*

David R. Colman, Ph.D. *The Mount Sinai Medical Center, New York, NY*

Susan K. McConnell, Ph.D. *Stanford University, Stanford, CA*

Robert Y. Moore, M.D., Ph.D. *University of Pittsburgh School of Medicine, Pittsburgh, PA*

Michael I. Posner, Ph.D. *University of Oregon, Eugene, OR*

Edward M. Stricker, Ph.D. *University of Pittsburgh, Pittsburgh, PA*

Larry W. Swanson, Ph.D. *University of Southern California, Los Angeles, CA*

W. Thomas Thach, Ph.D. *Washington University, St. Louise, MO*

Leslie G. Ungerleider, Ph.D. *National Institute of Mental Health, Bethesda, MD*

FUNDAMENTAL NEUROSCIENCE

Edited by

MICHAEL J. ZIGMOND

FLOYD E. BLOOM

STORY C. LANDIS

JAMES L. ROBERTS

LARRY R. SQUIRE

Illustrations by
Robert S. Woolley

ACADEMIC PRESS

San Diego London Boston New York Sydney Tokyo Toronto

Cover photograph: Figure 17.25

This book is printed on acid-free paper. ♾

Academic Press
a division of Harcourt Brace & Company
525 B Street, Suite 1900, San Diego, California 92101-4495, USA
http://www.apnet.com

Academic Press
24-28 Oval Road, London NW1 7DX, UK
http://www.hbuk.co.uk/ap/

Library of Congress Catalog Card Number: 98-86877

International Standard Book Number: 0-12-780870-1

PRINTED IN THE UNITED STATES OF AMERICA
98 99 00 01 02 03 DO 9 8 7 6 5 4 3 2 1

Short Contents

I
NEUROSCIENCE

II
CELLULAR AND MOLECULAR NEUROSCIENCE

III
NERVOUS SYSTEM DEVELOPMENT

IV
SENSORY SYSTEMS

V
MOTOR SYSTEMS

VI
REGULATORY SYSTEMS

VII
BEHAVIORAL AND COGNITIVE NEUROSCIENCE

Full Contents

III
Nervous System Development

IV
Sensory Systems

V
Motor Systems

VII
BEHAVIORAL AND COGNITIVE NEUROSCIENCE

Authorship

I. Neuroscience

Fundamentals of Neuroscience: Floyd E. Bloom, Beth A. Fischer, Story C. Landis, James L. Roberts, Larry R. Squire, and Michael J. Zigmond

Organization of Nervous Systems: Larry W. Swanson, Thomas Lufkin, and David R. Colman

II. Cellular and Molecular Neuroscience

Section Editors: John H. Byrne and David R. Colman

The Cellular Components of Nervous Tissue: Patrick R. Hof, Bruce D. Trapp, Jean de Vellis, Luz Claudio, and David R. Colman

Subcellular Organization of the Nervous System: Organelles and Their Functions: Scott T. Brady, David R. Colman, and Peter Brophy

Electrotonic Properties of Axons and Dendrites: Gordon M. Shepherd

Membrane Potential and Action Potential: David A. McCormick

Release of Neurotransmitters: Robert S. Zucker, Dimitri M. Kullmann, and Mark Bennett

Neurotransmitters: Ariel Y. Deutch and Robert H. Roth

Neurotransmitter Receptors: M. Neal Waxham

Intracellular Signaling: Howard Schulman and Steven E. Hyman

Cell–Cell Communication via Gap Junctions: David C. Spray, Eliana Scemes, and Renato Rozental

Postsynaptic Potentials and Synaptic Integration: John H. Byrne

Information Processing in Dendrites: Gordon M. Shepherd

Brain Energy Metabolism: Pierre J. Magistretti

III. Nervous System Development

Section Editor: Susan K. McConnell

Neural Induction and Pattern Formation: Christopher Kintner and Andrew Lumsden

Neurogenesis and Migration: Mary E. Hatten and Nathaniel Heintz

Cellular Determination: William A. Harris and Volker Hartenstein

Growth Cones and Axon Pathfinding: Jonathan A. Raper and Marc Tessier-Lavigne

Synapse Formation and Elimination: Jeff W. Lichtman, Steven J. Burden, Susan M. Culican, and Rachel O. L. Wong

Programmed Cell Death: Ronald W. Oppenheim

Neurotrophic Factors: James E. Johnson

Early Experience and Critical Periods: Eric I. Knudsen

IV. Sensory Systems

Section Editor: Thomas D. Albright

Fundamentals of Sensory Systems: Stewart H. C. Hendry, Steven S. Hsiao, and M. Christian Brown

Sensory Transduction: Peter R. Mac Leish, Gordon M. Shepherd, Sue C. Kinnamon, and Joseph Santos-Sacchi

Chemical Senses: Taste and Olfaction: David V. Smith and Gordon M. Shepherd

Somatic Sensation: Stewart H. C. Hendry, Steven S. Hsiao, and Mary C. Bushnell

Audition: M. Christian Brown

Vision: R. Clay Reid

V. Motor Systems
Section Editor: W. Thomas Thach

Fundamentals of Motor Systems: W. Thomas Thach

Muscle, Motor Neurons, and Motor Neuron Pools: M. K. Floeter

Spinal Motor Control, Reflexes, and Locomotion: M. K. Floeter

Supraspinal Descending Control: The Medial "Postural" System: J. Baker

Voluntary Descending Control: Marc H. Schieber

Basal Ganglia: Jonathan W. Mink

Cerebellum: Amy J. Bastian, Enrico Mugnaini, and W. Thomas Thach

Eye Movements: Paul W. Glimcher

VI. Regulatory Systems
Section Editors: Robert Y. Moore, Edward M. Stricker, and Larry W. Swanson

The Hypothalamus: An Overview of Regulatory Systems: J. Patrick Card, Larry W. Swanson, and Robert Y. Moore

Central Control of Autonomic Functions: The Organization of the Autonomic Nervous System: Terry L. Powley

Cardiovascular System: Alan F. Sved

Neural Control of Breathing: Jack L. Feldman and Donald R. McCrimmon

Food Intake and Metabolism: Stephen C. Woods and Edward M. Stricker

Water Intake and Body Fluids: Edward M. Stricker and Joseph G. Verbalis

Neuroendocrine Systems I: Overview—Thyroid and Adrenal Axes: Huda Akil, Serge Campeau, William E. Cullinan, Ronald M. Lechan, Roberto Toni, Stanley J. Watson, and Robert Y. Moore

Neuroendocrine Systems II: Growth, Reproduction, and Lactation: Lawrence A. Frohman, Judy Cameron, Phyllis M. Wise

Circadian Timing: Robert Y. Moore

Sleep and Dreaming: J. Allan Hobson

Psychosexual Development: Michael J. Baum

Motivation and Reward: T. W. Robbins and B. J. Everitt

Drug Reward and Addiction: George F. Koob

VII. Behavioral and Cognitive Neuroscience
Section Editors: Michael I. Posner and Leslie G. Ungerleider

Human Brain Evolution: Todd M. Preuss and Jon H. Kaas

Cognitive Development: Marilyn S. Albert, Adele D. Diamond, Roslyn Holly Fitch, Helen J. Neville, Peter R. Rapp, and Paula A. Tallal

Object and Face Recognition: Martha J. Farah, Glynn Humphreys, and Hillary R. Rodman

Spatial Cognition: Carol L. Colby and Carl R. Olson

Attention: G. S. Aston-Jones, R. Desimone, J. Driver, S. J. Luck, and M. I. Posner

Learning and Memory: Basic Mechanisms: John M. Beggs, Thomas H. Brown, John H. Byrne, Terry J. Crow, Kevin S. LaBar, Joseph E. LeDoux, and Richard F. Thompson

Learning and Memory: Systems Analysis: Howard B. Eichenbaum, Lawrence F. Cahill, Mark A. Gluck, Michael E. Hasselmo, Frank C. Keil, Alex J. Martin, James L. McGaugh, Jaap Murre, Catherine Myers, Michael Petrides, Benno Roozendaal, Daniel L. Schacter, Daniel J. Simons, W. Carter Smith, and Cedric L. Williams

Language and Communication: David Caplan, Thomas Carr, James Gould, and Randi Martin

Hemispheric Specialization: Stephen M. Kosslyn, Michael S. Gazzaniga, Albert M. Galaburda, and Carolyn Rabin

Thinking and Problem Solving: Stanislas Dehaene, John Jonides, Edward E. Smith, and Manfred Spitzer

Preface

To our students, from whom we learn much.

Fundamental Neuroscience began with an ambitious set of objectives. We wished to produce a textbook that would: (1) introduce graduate students coming from diverse backgrounds to the full range of neuroscience, from molecular biology to clinical science; (2) assist instructors in offering an in-depth course in neuroscience to advanced undergraduates; (3) permit a research-oriented approach to neuroscience for medical students and others preparing for a professional career in the health sciences; and (4) provide a current resource for all who wish to familiarize themselves with this rapidly changing area. We also wished to contribute to the educational process in another way—by providing direct financial support.

This book reviews most of the major issues in neuroscience and some of the minor ones as well. We have included a large number of illustrations, almost all of them newly drawn. In addition, we have described many experiments to illustrate how information is gathered and conclusions are drawn and have included boxes that provide greater details and clinical correlations. Although we have focused on vertebrate neurobiology, particularly that of mammals, we have included examples from studies of invertebrates when that information was thought particularly useful to our objectives. And we have added a number of ethics cases for your consideration to emphasize our belief that good science and responsible conduct are inseparable.

To accomplish all this, the senior editors identified a group of section editors with experience both as researchers and as educators. These individuals were then asked to draft a table of contents for their sections and to find appropriate authors. Finally, the authors were asked to take part in an experiment—to try to produce a textbook that had the wisdom of a collection of individual reviews written by experts in their field and the cohesiveness of a single-authored volume. This required that the authors be willing to write material that would then be modified by others, often many others. We researchers don't like having our words—let alone our ideas—modified by anyone. And yet we assembled the team, and here, almost exactly six years after we began, our experiment has been completed.

The authors whom you will see listed under the titles of individual chapters and at the end of boxes are those people who accepted responsibility for preparing the initial drafts of material used in the textbook. In most cases they are listed in alphabetical order, although in some instances one individual played a substantially greater role than others and is listed first for that reason. There are instances in which the final chapter is very similar to that initially provided by the authors. In other cases a great deal of editing occurred. There are even chapters containing material taken from other chapters as well as chapters that were synthesized from several individual contributions. All this was done in an effort to provide you with the best possible textbook.

The Association of Neuroscience Departments and Programs (ANDP) was central to our efforts. The Council of the ANDP encouraged us to take on the task, and members of the ANDP provided critical input to the organization of the textbook. In particular, we thank the many individuals who commented on specific components of our project at various stages and thereby helped us to serve students and course instructors. These individuals include Yalchin Abdulaev, John Ashe, Jim Blankenship, John Bruno, Richard Burry, Dennis Choi, Avis Cohen, Gregory Cole, Ian Creese, Kathleen Dunlap, Gary Fiskum, Karen Gale, Glenn Hatton, John Hildebrand, John Kauer, James King, Kenneth Kratz, Richard Levine, Eve Marder, Alex Martin, Lorne Mendell, Ranney Mize, Sally Moody, Elisabeth Murray, Randolph Nudo, David Potter, Dale Purves, George Rebec, Nicholas Spitzer, Glenn Stanley, and Paula Tallal. One-third of the royalties generated by sales of this textbook will be contributed to the ANDP to support their educational projects.

A number of other neuroscientists also participated in the formulation of this project. Anthony Movshon played a major role in organizing the section on sensory systems and recruiting its authors. Dennis O'Leary was instrumental in formulating the section on development. In addition, Darcy Kelley, Tom Reese, Patricia Goldman-Rakic, Tom Carew, Paula Tallal, Karl Herrup, Joseph LeDoux, Nick Spitzer, Richard Thompson, and Stephen Waxman participated in early discussions concerning the book.

Many others should be acknowledged, as well. Perhaps chief among them is Bob Woolley, our illustrator. For two years this project was a central component of Bob's life as he struggled to convert authors' sketches into final products, sought their input, handled their feedback, and met our deadlines. We hope that the results of his efforts, and those of Patrick Hof, who collaborated on many of the illustrations, will enrich your reading of this textbook and, through the use of visual aids that we can provide, enrich the classroom experience as well.

Craig Panner, acquisitions editor, provided day-to-day (and year-to-year) coordination of the entire endeavor, working well beyond the call of professional duty to keep together the thousand pieces. Susan Giegel, working at the University of Pittsburgh, oversaw many aspects of the project, arranged conference calls and meetings, read and wrote memos, answered queries, and provided pleasant and effective encouragement to meet deadlines. Cindy MacDonald, editorial manager, orchestrated a team of developmental editors and moderated discussions with often fiercely independent authors to provide a consistent text. These outstanding editors, who challenged the authors to clarify and simplify and then clarify again, were Matt Lee, Arkady Mak, Philippa Solomon, Lee Young, and Patty Zimmerman. Jacqueline Garrett, desk editor, scheduled the final production of the book and then "made it happen." Debby Bicher provided the interface between the illustrators and the typesetters. Cathy Reynolds designed the book, inside and out. Suzanne Rogers developed the marketing designs that inspired the cover, while Karen Steele and Charlotte Brabants orchestrated the marketing and promotions. Jasna Markovac provided essential advice in the early stages of the project and continued encouragement throughout. Erika Conner provided assistance at the outset of this project, and Karen Dempsey provided key administrative help all along the way.

Finally, there is Graham Lees. It was Graham, neuroscientist by training, editor by profession, who provided the most essential ingredient for this project from the very beginning—faith. Graham did more than encourage us from the sidelines, he was an active participant, suggesting editors and authors, commissioning paragraphs and boxes, critiquing content and style—even approving expensive modifications (e.g., multicolor figures) when he felt it would help the students, and all the while sending out a cheery newsletter, *FuNews*. There would be no textbook without Graham.

We hope we have achieved our initial goal—a textbook that will be of value to virtually anyone interested in neuroscience. We invite all of you to join us in the adventure of studying the nervous system. Indeed, we hope you will be active participants in that adventure. Earlier in this preface we stated that our experiment had been completed. Of course, that is not entirely true. As you read this we are already beginning to prepare the next edition. And we hope that you will participate in that process by sending comments to us at FN@acad.com. You also are invited to stay in touch with us through our web site (www.academicpress.com/fun). Here we will post material to supplement the textbook, including study questions, updates, and corrections.

A story is told that Charles Darwin once received a letter from a student who was just beginning his studies as a naturalist. The student is said to have asked what advice Mr. Darwin might offer to someone just starting his career. Darwin wrote back, "Try to discover one new fact." This book contains many facts, along with unifying ideas and principles that reflect our current knowledge of the nervous system. But it is also true that there is still much, much more to understand and that in some cases we do not yet even know what the questions are. We hope—we believe—that from among those of you who use this book will come the next generation of neuroscientists, individuals who will take up Darwin's challenge to discover things about the brain that no one knew before. It is to you that we dedicate *Fundamental Neuroscience.*

The Senior Editors
La Jolla, California

SECTION I

NEUROSCIENCE

C H A P T E R

1

Fundamentals of Neuroscience

Floyd E. Bloom, Beth A. Fischer, Story C. Landis, James L. Roberts, Larry R. Squire, and Michael J. Zigmond

The name for the field of knowledge described in this book is **neuroscience,** the science of the nervous system. Studies of the nervous system have been ongoing since well before the 20th century. Neuroanatomists studied the brain's shape, its cellular structure, and its circuitry; neurochemists studied the brain's chemical composition; neurophysiologists studied the brain's bioelectric properties; and psychologists and neuropsychologists investigated the organization and neural substrates of behavior and cognition. Then in the late 1960s the term *neuroscience* was coined, signaling the beginning of an era in which each of these disciplines would work synergistically, sharing a common language, common concepts, and a common goal—to understand the structure and function of the normal and abnormal brain. Neuroscience today stretches from the molecular biology of nerve cells to the biological basis of normal and disordered behavior and cognition.

Neuroscience is currently one of the most rapidly growing areas of science. Indeed, the brain is sometimes referred to as the last frontier of biology. In 1971, 1100 scientists convened at the first Annual Meeting of the Society for Neuroscience. In 1997, 27,685 scientists participated at the Society's 27th Annual Meeting at which more than 14,000 research presentations were made.

THE FULL SCOPE OF THE FIELD

This book lays out our current understanding in each of the important domains that together define the full scope of modern neuroscience. **Cellular and Molecular Neuroscience** (Section II) concentrates on the structure and function of the neurons, glia, and synapses that are the building blocks of the nervous system. These chapters also highlight the remarkable techniques now being used to study the nervous system in cellular detail, including molecular biological techniques that are making it possible to study and manipulate genes.

Another major domain of our field is **Nervous System Development** (Section III). How does a simple epithelium differentiate into specialized collections of cells and ultimately into distinct brain structures? How do neurons grow processes that find appropriate targets some distance away? How does neuronal activity and experience shape activity?

Sensory Systems and Motor Systems (Sections IV and V) encompass how the nervous system receives information from the external world and how movements and actions are produced, for example, eye movements and limb movements. These questions range from the molecular level (how are odorants, photons, and sounds transduced into patterned neural activity?) to the systems and behavioral level (which brain structures control eye movements and what are the computations required by each structure?).

An evolutionarily old function of the nervous system is to regulate respiration, heart rate, sleep and waking cycles, food and water intake, and hormones. In this area of **Regulatory Systems** (Section VI), we explore how organisms remain in balance with their environment, ensuring that they obtain the energy resources needed to survive and reproduce. At the level of cells and molecules, the study of regulatory systems concerns the receptors and signaling pathways by which particular hormones or neurotransmitters prepare the organism to sleep, to cope with acute stress, or to seek food. At the level of brain systems, we ask such questions as what occurs in brain circuitry to produce thirst or to create a self-destructive problem such as drug abuse?

In recent years, the disciplines of psychology and biology have increasingly found common ground, and this convergence of psychology and biology defines the modern topics of **Behavioral and Cognitive Neuroscience** (Section VII). These topics concern the so-called higher mental functions: perception, attention, language, memory, thinking, and the ability to navigate in space. Work on these problems has traditionally drawn on the techniques of neuroanatomy, neurophysiology, neuropharmacology, and behavioral analysis. More recently, behavioral and cognitive neuroscience has benefited from several new approaches: the use of computers to perform detailed formal analyses of how brain systems operate and how cognition is organized; noninvasive neuroimaging techniques, such as positron emission tomography and functional magnetic resonance imaging, to obtain pictures of the living human brain in action; and molecular biological methods, such as single-gene knockouts in mice, which can relate genes to brain systems and to behavior.

CLINICAL ISSUES

Many fields of clinical medicine are directly concerned with the brain. The branches of medicine most closely tied to neuroscience are neurology (the study of the diseases of the brain), neurosurgery (the study of the surgical treatment of neurological disease), and psychiatry (the study of behavioral, emotional, and mental diseases). Other fields of medicine also make important contributions, including radiology (the use of radiation for such purposes as imaging the brain) and pathology (the study of pathological tissue). To make connections to the many facets of medicine that are relevant to neuroscience, this book details a number of clinical conditions in the context of basic knowledge in neuroscience.

THE SPIRIT OF EXPLORATION CONTINUES

At the threshold of the 21st century, the Hubble space telescope is providing us with information about as yet uncharted regions of the universe and the promise that we may learn something about the origin of the cosmos. This same spirit of adventure is also being directed to the most complex structure to exist in the known universe—the human brain. The complexity of the human brain is enormous, describable only in astronomical terms. For example, the number of neurons in the human brain (about 10^{12} or 100 billion) is approximately equal to the number of stars in our Milky Way galaxy. Whereas the possibility of understanding such a complex device is certainly daunting, it is nevertheless true that an enormous amount has already been learned. The promise and excitement of research on the nervous system have captured the attention of thousands of students and working scientists. What is at stake is not only the possibility of discovering how the brain works. It is estimated that diseases of the brain, including both neurological and psychiatric illnesses, affect as many as 50 million individuals annually in the United States alone, at an estimated societal cost of 40 billion dollars in clinical care and lost productivity. The prevention, treatment, and cure of these diseases will ultimately be founded in neuroscience research. Moreover, one must suppose that many of the issues currently challenging societies in the United States and around the world—instability within the family, illiteracy, poverty, and violence—could be illuminated by a better understanding of the brain.

PREPARED FOR A BROAD RANGE OF READERS

This textbook is for anyone interested in neuroscience. In preparing it we have focused primarily on graduate students just entering the field, understanding that some of you will have majored in biology, some in psychology, and some in mathematics or engineering. We hope that through the text, the explanatory boxes, and in some cases the supplementary readings, you will find the book to be both understandable and enlightening. In many cases, advanced undergraduate students will find this book useful as well. Medical students may find that they need additional clinical correlations that are not provided here. However, we hope that most of you will at least be able to use our textbook in conjunction with more clinically oriented material. Finally, to those who have completed their formal education, we hope that we can provide you with some useful information, whether you are active neuroscientists wishing to learn about areas of the field other than your own or individuals who wish to enter neuroscience from a different area of inquiry. We invite all of you to join us in the adventure of studying the nervous system.

NEUROSCIENCE TODAY: A COMMUNAL ENDEAVOR

As scientists, we draw from the work of those who came before us, using other scientists' work as a foundation for our own. We build on and extend previous observations and, we hope, contribute something to those who will come after us. The information presented in this book is the culmination of hundreds of years of research. To help acquaint you with some of this work, we have described many of the key experiments of neuroscience in the text or in boxes distributed throughout this book. We also have listed some of the classic papers of neuroscience and related fields at the end of each chapter and invite you to read some of them for yourselves.

The pursuit of science has not always been a communal endeavor. Initially, research was conducted in relative isolation. The scientific "community" that existed at the time consisted of intellectuals who shared the same general interests, terminology, and paradigms. For the most part, scientists were reluctant to collaborate or share their ideas broadly, because an adequate system for establishing priority for discoveries did not exist. However, with the emergence of scientific journals in 1665, scientists began disseminating their results and ideas more broadly, because the publication record could be used as proof of priority. Science then began to progress much more rapidly, as each layer of new information provided a higher foundation on which new studies could be built.

Gradually, an interactive community of scientists evolved, providing many of the benefits that contemporary scientists enjoy: Working as part of a community allows for greater specialization and efficiency of effort. This not only allows scientists to study a topic in greater depth, but also enables teams of researchers to attack problems from multidisciplinary perspectives. And the rapid feedback and support provided by the community help scientists refine their ideas and maintain their motivation. It is this interdependence across space and time that gives science much of its power.

With interdependence, however, comes vulnerability. In science, as in most communities, codes of acceptable conduct have evolved in an attempt to protect the rights of individuals while maximizing the benefits they receive. Some of these guidelines are concerned with the manner in which research is conducted, and other guidelines refer to the conduct of scientists and their interactions within the scientific community. Let us begin by examining how new knowledge is created.

THE CREATION OF KNOWLEDGE

Over the years, a generally accepted procedure for conducting research has evolved. This process involves examining the existing literature, identifying an important question, and formulating a research plan. Sometimes the plan is purely "descriptive," for example, determining the structure of a protein or the distribution of a neurotransmitter in brain. This type of research is essential to the **inductive phase** of experimentation, the movement from observations to theory. Descriptive experiments are valuable both because of the questions that they attempt to answer and because of the questions that their results allow us to ask. Information obtained from descriptive experiments provides a base of knowledge from which a scientist may draw to develop hypotheses about cause and effect in the phenomenon under investigation. For example, once we identify through descriptive work the distribution of a particular transmitter within the brain, we may then be able to develop a theory about what function that transmitter serves.

Once a hypothesis has been developed, the researcher then has the task of designing and performing experiments that are likely to disprove that hypothesis if it is incorrect. This is referred to as the **deductive phase** of experimentation, the movement from theory to observation. Through this paradigm the neuroscientist seeks to narrow down the vast range of alternative explanations for a given phenomenon. Only after attempting as thoroughly as possible to disprove the hypothesis may scientists be adequately assured that their hypothesis is a plausible explanation for the phenomenon under investigation.

A key point in this regard is that data may only lend support to a hypothesis rather than provide proof of its validity. In part, this is because the constraints of time, money, and technology only allow a scientist to test a hypothesis under a limited set of conditions. Variability and random chance also may contribute to the experimental results. Consequently, at the end of an experiment, scientists generally only report that there is a statistical probability that the effect measured was due to the intervention rather than to chance or variability.

Given that one can never prove a hypothesis, how do "facts" arise? At the conclusion of their experiments the researchers' first task is to report their findings to the scientific community. The dissemination of research findings often begins with an informal presentation at a scientific meeting that permits the rapid exchange of information. This is followed by a research

CASE 1: PROMOTIONAL PRESSURES

Mary Alexander is coming up for tenure. Despite the long hours she works, she has published only four papers in the five years since she started at Bradford University, which she knows is below the standards for tenure at that institution. However, she feels that her apparently low productivity is a result of her having invested the vast majority of her effort in a long-term project on the role of neurotrophic factors in the pathogenesis of neurodegenerative disease using a primate model of Huntington disease. That work is nearly ready for publication—in fact, she has already written a draft of the manuscript. She merely needs to increase the number of replications of some of the conditions she tested. She knows the results will be seen as ground-breaking but is worried that if she waits any longer to submit the manuscript, her suitability for tenure will be determined before the paper is published. Thus, she considers submitting a version of her manuscript that contains the means from the data she has collected but reports a larger number of replications. She reasons that she has, after all, tested each of the conditions—she just hasn't completed the tedious chore of replicating what she's already demonstrated. Moreover, she knows from past experience that her manuscript will go through at least one revision before it is accepted for publication, and even then it will be months before she receives the page proofs. Thus, there will be plenty of time to do the replications and insert the corrected data. How would you advise Dr. Alexander?

See Appendix for discussion questions.

article published in a peer-reviewed journal. Such publications are not simply a means to allow the authors to advance as professionals (though they are important in that respect, as well); publication is an essential component of the advancement of science. For as we have already stated, science depends on sharing information, replicating and thereby validating experiments, and then moving forward to solve the next problem. Indeed, "a scientific experiment, no matter how spectacular the results, is not completed until the results are published."[1]

RESPONSIBLE CONDUCT

Although individuals or small groups may perform experiments, new knowledge is ultimately the product of the larger community. Inherent in such a system is the need to be able to trust the work of other scientists—to trust their integrity in conducting and reporting research. Thus, it is not surprising that much emphasis is placed on the responsible conduct of research.

Research ethics encompasses a broad spectrum of behaviors, and where one draws the line between sloppy science and unethical conduct is a source of much debate within the scientific community. Some acts are considered to be so egregious that despite personal differences in defining what constitutes ethical behavior, the community generally agrees that these behaviors do not. These "high crimes" consist of fabrication, falsification, and plagiarism: *Fabrication* refers to making up data, *falsification* is defined as altering data, and *plagiarism* consists of using another person's ideas, words, or data without attribution. Each of these acts significantly harms the scientific community.

Fabrication and falsification in a research paper taint the published literature by undermining its integrity. Not only is the information contained in such papers misleading in itself, but other scientists may unwittingly use that information as the foundation for new research. If, when reported, these subsequent studies cite the previous, fraudulent publication, the literature is further corrupted. Thus, through a domino-like effect one paper may have a broad negative impact on the scientific literature. Moreover, when fraud is discovered, a retraction of the paper provides only a limited solution, as there is no guarantee that individuals who read the original article will see the retraction. Given the impact that just one fraudulent paper may have, it is not surprising that the integrity of the published literature is a primary ethical concern for scientists.

Plagiarism is also a major ethical infraction. Scientific publications provide a mechanism for establishing priority for a discovery. As such, they form the currency by which scientists gain positions, research support, students, and promotions. Plagiarism denies the original author of credit for his or her work. This hurts everyone: The creative scientist is robbed of credit, the scientific community is hurt by the disincentive to share ideas and research results, and the individual who has plagiarized—like the person who has fabricated or falsified data—may well find his or her career ruined.

In addition to the high crimes described above, there are a variety of "misdemeanors" in the conduct of research that can affect the scientific community. Like fabrication, falsification, and plagiarism, some of these actions are considered to be unethical because they violate a fundamental value, such as honesty. For example, we believe that *honorary authorship*—listing someone who did not make an intellectual contribution to the work as an author—is unethical because it misrepresents the origin of the research. In contrast, other behaviors may be termed unethical because they violate standards that the scientific community has adopted. For example, it is generally understood that material submitted to a peer-reviewed journal as part of a research manuscript has never been published in such a journal before, nor is it under consideration by another journal editor.

The high crimes of fabrication, falsification, and plagiarism are generally recognized throughout the scientific community. What constitutes a misdemeanor is less clear, however, because variations in the definitions of accepted practices are common. There are several sources of this variation. Because responsible conduct is based in part on conventions adopted by a field, it follows that there are differences among disciplines with regard to what is considered to be appropriate behavior. For example, students in neuroscience usually coauthor papers with their advisor, who typically works closely with them on their research. In contrast, students in the humanities often publish papers on their own even if their advisor has made a substantial intellectual contribution to the work reported. Within a discipline, the definition of acceptable practices may also vary from country to country. As a case in point, neuroscientists in the United Kingdom do relatively little work on stress in animals, whereas in the United States this topic is seen as an appropriate area of study so long as guidelines are followed to ensure that discomfort to the animals is minimized. The definition of responsible conduct also may change over time. For example, some protocols that were once performed on human and animal subjects may no longer be considered ethical. Indeed, ethics evolve alongside knowledge. We may not currently be able to know all of the risks involved in a procedure, but as new risks are identified (or previously identified risks refuted) we must be willing to reconsider the facts and adjust our policies as necessary. In sum, what is considered to be ethical behavior may not always be obvious, and therefore we must actively examine what is expected of us as scientists.

Having determined what is acceptable practice, we then must be vigilant. Each day neuroscientists are faced with a number of decisions having ethical implications, most of them at the level of misdemeanors: Should a data point be excluded because the apparatus might have malfunctioned? Have all the appropriate references been cited and are all the authors appropriate? Might the graphic representation of the data mislead the viewer? Are research funds being used efficiently? Although individually these decisions may not significantly affect the practice of science, cumulatively they can exert a great effect. At the level of the individual researcher, disregard for smaller ethical concerns may lead down a slippery slope, with the scientist gradually sliding further and further away from accepted practices. At the level of the scientific community, a general lack of attention to lesser ethical issues may lead to an environment that does little to discourage more serious unethical behaviors.

In addition to being concerned about the integrity of the published literature, we must be concerned with our public image. Despite concerns over the level of federal funding for research, neuroscientists are among the privileged few who have much of their work funded by taxpayer dollars. Highly publicized scandals damage the public image of our profession and hurt all of us who are dependent on continued public support for our work. They also reduce the public credibility of science and thereby lessen the impact that we can expect our findings to have. Thus, for our own good and that of our colleagues, the scientific community, and the public-at-large, we must strive to act with integrity.

BEHAVING RESPONSIBLY: INTEGRAL TO DOING GOOD SCIENCE

Research and research ethics are inseparable. In that spirit, ethics cases are distributed throughout this textbook. You are encouraged to think about these and other ethical issues as you explore neurosocience and to discuss your views with fellow students and faculty.

In some of these cases, as in real life, you may be faced with the need to choose between conflicting needs or obligations. In such situations, there is no magic formula for arriving at a resolution. However, ethicists have developed tools to assist us in analyzing such conflicts. The **Appendix** outlines a method for systematically examining the key components of an ethical dilemma, a process that often helps to clarify the situation and can aid you in determining your position. Such an approach is particularly useful in working though a novel dilemma, for example, one involving ethical issues arising from new technologies.

The ethics of human cloning is one such situation. Only a few years ago the idea of cloning humans was the stuff of science fiction, and researchers did not need to give much thought to its ethical dimensions. Now are faced with very real concerns over the use of such technologies.

Summary

You are about to embark on a tour of fundamental neuroscience. Enjoy the descriptions of the current state of knowledge, read the summaries of some of the classic experiments on which that information is based, and consult the references that the authors have drawn on to prepare their chapters. Think also about the ethical dimensions of the science you are studying—your success as a professional and the future of our field depend on it.

References

General

Boorstin, D. J. (1983). *The Discoverers.* Random House, New York.

Committee on the Conduct of Science (1995). *On Being a Scientist,* 2nd ed. National Academy Press, National Academy of Sciences, Washington, DC.

Kuhn, T. S. (1996). *The Structure of Scientific Revolutions,* 3rd ed. Univ. of Chicago Press, Chicago.

Popper, K. R. (1969). *Conjectures and Refutations: The Growth of Scientific Knowledge,* 3rd ed. Routledge and K. Paul, London.

Cited

1. Day, R. A. (1994). *How to Write and Publish a Scientific Paper,* 4th ed. Oryx Press, Phoenix, AZ.

CHAPTER

2

Organization of Nervous Systems

Larry W. Swanson, Thomas Lufkin, and David R. Colman

Structure and function are two sides of the same coin, and it is important to understand the relationship between them if we are to fully appreciate the organization of the nervous system. An object's structure imposes physical constraints on its function. For example, a piano is a harp laid on its side and enclosed in a resonating wooden box (its structure) that can produce a wide variety of music (its function). Because of the limits of its structure, however, a piano cannot possibly be made to sound like a brass instrument—for example, a trumpet. In this chapter, we will address two questions that relate to the functional architecture of nervous systems: What are the major structural components of the central nervous system (CNS), and how are these components interconnected? Answers to these questions should ultimately help explain how the brain works at a systems level rather than at the cellular or molecular levels.

The fundamental cellular unit in the nervous system is the nerve cell, or **neuron.** The cellular basis of nervous system organization was not appreciated until near the end of the 19th century, as discussed in Box 2.1. We will consider neurons in greater detail in Chapter 3, but a basic understanding of neuronal morphology is essential at this point. The nucleus of a neuron is located in a region called the cell body, or **soma** (Fig. 2.2). Most of the inputs a neuron receives are delivered to numerous thin extensions of the cell known as **dendrites.** In vertebrate neurons, the dendrites usually arise from the soma. Because they branch extensively, dendrites greatly increase the plasma membrane surface area available for receiving and integrating inputs. At the "output" end of a neuron is the **axon,** a single thin extension that can course uninterrupted for a meter or more and typically divides into a number of collateral branches. A portion of the output of thousands of neurons can converge onto the dendrites of a single neuron. Conversely, the output of each neuron can diverge to reach hundreds or thousands of other neurons. The principles of **convergence** and **divergence** are major themes in the organization of nervous systems.

There are roughly 100 billion neurons and 100 trillion interneuronal connections in the human brain. Faced with the task of analyzing systems as complex as this, biologists have traditionally tried to simplify matters by focusing on less complex organisms or animals at earlier developmental stages. Therefore, we will begin by examining current ideas about the evolution of nervous systems to illustrate fundamental principles of nervous system organization. Then we will discuss the embryogenesis of the vertebrate CNS, because it reveals a common structural plan in this most complex animal subphylum, which includes our own species among the mammals. Next, we will consider a simple model of how the nervous system's basic functional systems may be organized structurally. Finally, we will explore the major structural features of the vertebrate nervous system.

GENERAL PRINCIPLES FROM AN EVOLUTIONARY PERSPECTIVE

How does a nervous system add to or enhance the behavioral repertoire of an animal? From an evolutionary perspective, the answer is straightforward: a nervous system increases the chances that an individual animal will survive and reproduce, thereby increasing the chances for survival of the species. We will now examine some of the features that contribute to an increased likelihood of survival by focusing on nervous

BOX 2.1

THE NEURON DOCTRINE

The cell theory, which states that all organisms are composed of cells, was developed around the middle of the 19th century by Matthias Schleiden and Theodor Schwann. However, this unitary vision of the cellular nature of life was not immediately applied to the nervous system, as many biologists believed in the cytoplasmic continuity of cells in the nervous system. The most prominent advocate of this **reticularist view** was Camillo Golgi, who proposed that axons entering the spinal cord actually fuse with other axons (Fig. 2.1A). The reticularist view was challenged by Santiago Ramón y Cajal, a founder of contemporary neuroscience and without doubt the greatest observer of neuronal architecture. In beautifully written and carefully reasoned deductive arguments, Cajal presented us with what is now known as the **neuron doctrine.** This great concept in essence states that the cell theory also applies to the nervous system: each neuron is an individual entity (Fig. 2.1B). The acrimonious debate between the reticularists and the proponents of the neuron doctrine raged for decades. Over the years, the validity of the neuron doctrine has been supported by a wealth of accumulated data. Nevertheless, the reticularist view is not entirely incorrect, because some neurons do act syncytially via specialized intercellular junctions.

In 1897, Charles Sherrington postulated that neurons communicate with each other and with other cell types via a theoretical structure he called the **synapse** (Greek *synaptein,* to fasten together). It was not until 50 years later that the existence of synapses was demonstrated by electron microscopy. In the electron micrograph shown in Fig. 2.1C, two axon terminals (At1 and At2) form synaptic junctions (s1 and s2) with a dendrite (Den). On the presynaptic (axonal) side of the junctions, synaptic vesicles that hold chemical neurotransmitters cluster near the presynaptic membrane. The postsynaptic membrane, which is a specialization of the dendritic plasma membrane, has a prominent thickening that contains structural proteins, neurotransmitter receptors, intracellular signal transduction molecules, and cytoskeletal components. In the intercellular space that separates the pre- and postsynaptic plasma membranes, an electron-dense "fuzz" is observed; its molecular constituents probably are involved in adhesion between the membranes.

The synaptic complex is built around an *adhesive* junction, and in this and other respects the complex is quite similar to the desmosome and the adherens junction of epithelia (see Fannon and Colman[1]). In fact, similarities in ultrastructure between the adherens junction and the synaptic complex of central nervous tissue were noted even in early electron microscopic studies (see Peters *et al.*[2]).

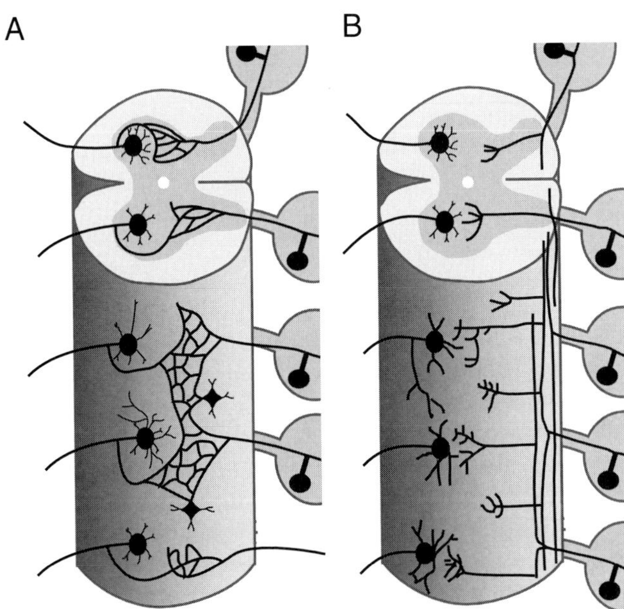

FIGURE 2.1 The nervous system is a reticulum *versus* the neuron doctrine. (A) Proponents of the reticularist's view of the nervous system believed that neurons were physically connected to one another, forming an uninterrupted network. (B) The neuron doctrine, in contrast, considers each neuron an individual entity that communicates with target cells across an appropriate intercellular gap. Adapted from Cajal.[3] (C) Electron micrograph of synaptic junctions.

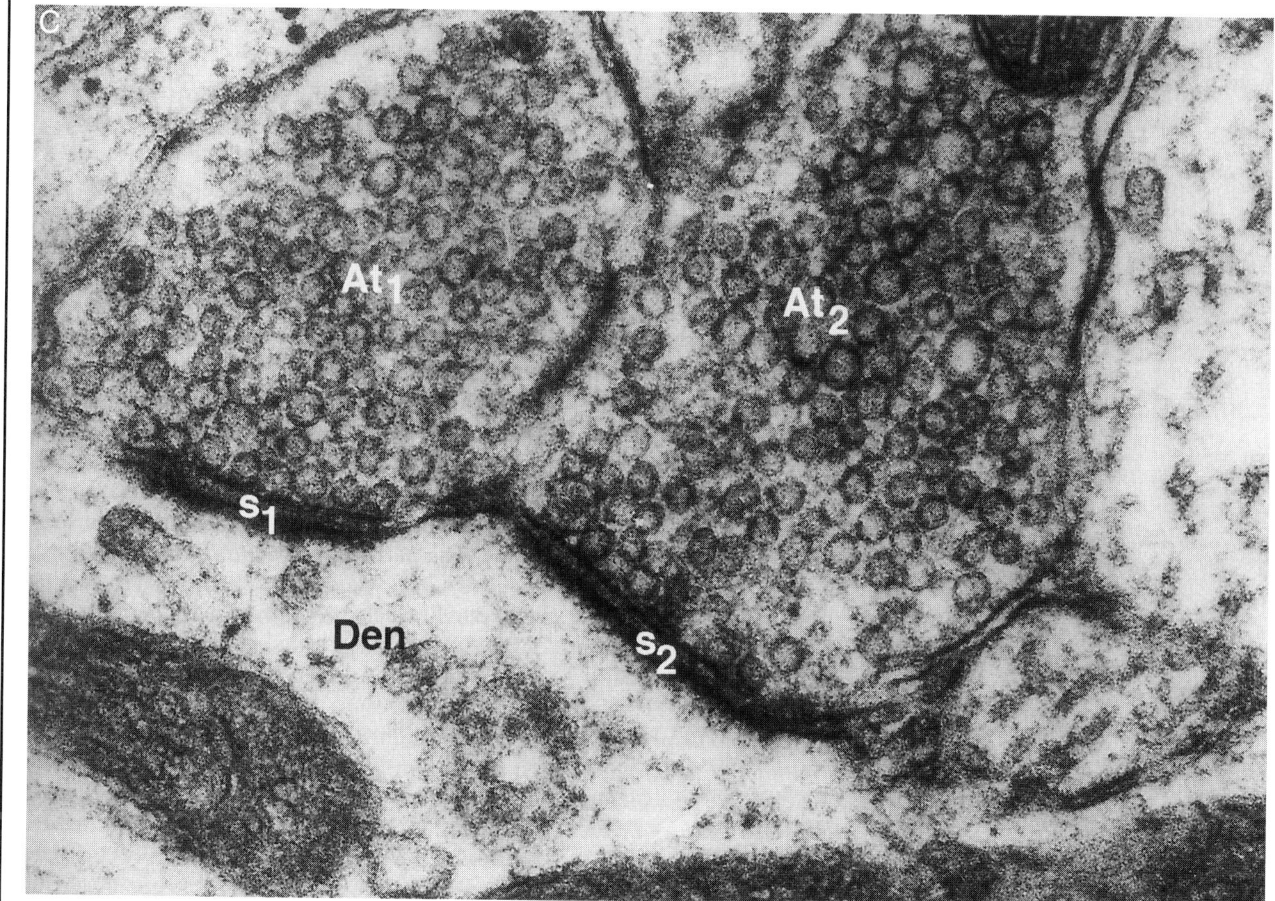

FIGURE 2.1—*Continued*

system organization in animals with relatively simple structures and behaviors.

The Nerve Net Is the Simplest Type of Nervous System

Sponges (phylum Porifera) are the only animals with no nervous system at all. Adult sponges are sessile (immobile), asymmetrical or radially symmetrical, aquatic animals. Their relatively simple physiology and behavior centers around creating a flow of environmental water through pores in the body wall, into the hollow center of the animal, and back out into the environment through a large opening called an **osculum.** The pores and osculum may be ringed with contractile cells, **myocytes,** which resemble smooth muscle cells and regulate water flow through the animal. These cells are described as independent **effectors** because they respond directly to stimuli (for example, stretch or certain chemicals in the water), although their response is rather slow and long-lasting (Fig. 2.3A).

Cnidarians, which include hydras, corals, sea anemones, and jellyfish, are the simplest animals to display the classic embryonic tissue layers (ectoderm, endoderm, and a primitive mesoderm) (Chapter 15). These radially symmetrical, aquatic animals have a mouth that leads to a gastrovascular cavity, and they may display locomotor behavior as adults. Cnidarians have a relatively simple, diffusely organized nervous system called a **nerve net** (Fig. 2.4).

An appealing scenario that explains the evolution of nerve nets was outlined by George Parker[4] in 1919. Parker proposed that **sensory neurons** were the first neurons to arise and differentiate in the ectodermal layer on the outside of the animal, facing the external environment (Fig. 2.3B). These cells are universally bipolar in shape, with a receptive process (a dendrite) and a transmitting process (an axon). In the simplest case, the axon ends on a set of contractile cells, which

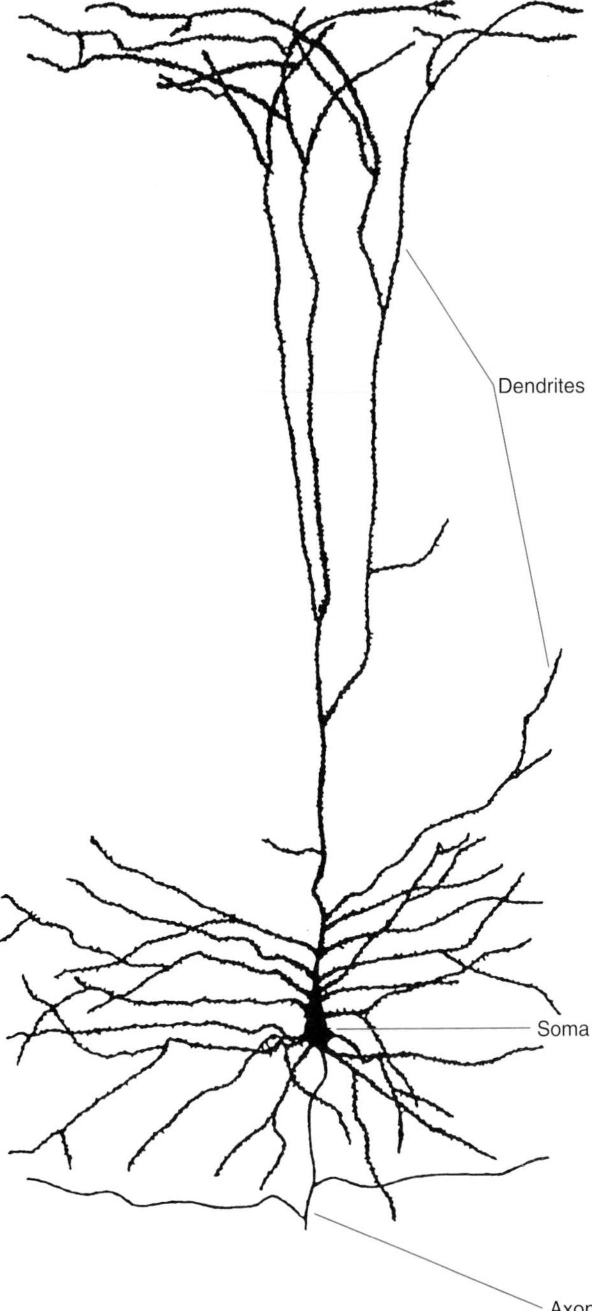

FIGURE 2.2 A typical neuron in the cerebral cortex. The soma gives rise to a single apical dendrite that branches, and many basal dendrites that emerge, near the base of the soma. A single branched axon with smooth contours is also observed. The jagged appearance of the dendrites is due to tiny protrusions termed "spines" where the synaptic apparatus is located. Adapted from Cajal.[3]

are thus no longer independent effectors. The sensory neurons are functionally polarized, conducting information in one direction only. Evidence such as this led Santiago Ramón y Cajal[3] to postulate at the end of the 19th century that information flow in most neurons is polarized, with the dendrites and soma being receptive and the axon transmissive (see Box 2.2).

Sensory neurons provide three major evolutionary advantages. First, they are specialized to detect stimuli, and are thus more sensitive to changes in input than independent effectors, triggering faster responses. Second, unlike effector cells, sensory neurons possess axons that can conduct action potentials, further decreasing response times. Third, the axon branches to innervate multiple contractile cells, thus providing divergence of information and amplified responses to a given stimulus.

Next, a second type of neuron, the **motor neuron,** may have evolved between the sensory neurons and effector cells (Fig. 2.3C). In the simple circuitry outlined so far, the motor neurons act essentially as amplifiers of input signals, leading to enhanced behavioral responses. They provide an additional level of divergence for sensory information and receive convergent information from more than one sensory neuron, or even more than one type of sensory neuron. In addition to innervating effector cells, nerve net motor neurons display a second important feature: they project to other motor neurons, providing further divergence and convergence of information in the system.

One characteristic of nerve nets is that information presumably flows in one direction in sensory neurons and in the processes connecting motor neurons to effector cells, but it flows in both directions in the processes that interconnect motor neurons. Therefore, information spreads through the nerve net in all directions from a stimulation site. Because they conduct information in both directions, the processes that interconnect motor neurons are neither axons nor dendrites. Such processes were called **amacrine processes** by Cajal, and remnants of nerve nets with amacrine processes can be found in many animals, including humans (in the retina and olfactory bulb, for example). Amacrine processes typically conduct graded potentials rather than action potentials (as explained in Chapter 6), so stronger stimuli are conducted farther through the nerve net than weaker stimuli and produce larger responses.

Flatworms Are the Simplest Animals Exhibiting Centralization and Cephalization

Flatworms, with their bilateral symmetry, dorsal and ventral surfaces, and rostral and caudal ends, are distinctly more complex than cnidarians. A flatworm's sensory receptors are more concentrated at the rostral end, where they encounter the oncoming environment as the animal swims or crawls along the substrate. Some flatworms are active predators. These changes

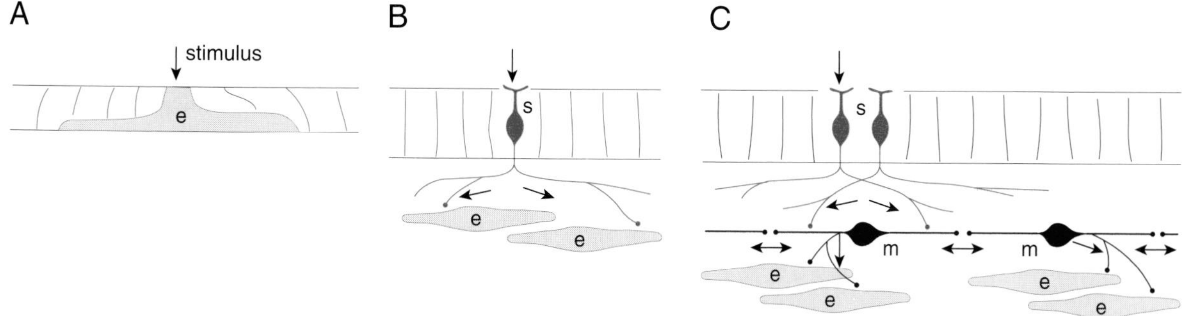

FIGURE 2.3 Activation of effector cells in simple animals. (A) Sponges lack a nervous system; stimuli act directly on effector cells (e), which are thus called independent effectors. (B) In cnidarians, bipolar sensory neurons (s) differentiate in the ectoderm (outer body layer). The outer process of the sensory neuron detects stimuli and is thus a dendrite. The inner process of some sensory neurons transmits information directly to effector cells and is thus an axon. Because this type of sensory neuron directly innervates effector cells, it is actually a sensorimotor neuron. (C) Most cnidarian sensory neurons send their axon to motor neurons (m), which in turn send an axon to effector cells. The motor neurons also have processes that interact with other motor neurons; these processes typically conduct information in both directions. Arrows show the direction of information flow.

in body plan and behavior are accompanied by equally important changes in nervous system organization.

The somata of most flatworm neurons are aggregated in clusters called **ganglia,** which are connected by longitudinal and transverse bundles of axons known as **nerve cords** (Fig. 2.5). This grouping of neuronal somata, called **centralization,** allows the communication between neurons to be faster and therefore more efficient, because cellular material is conserved and conduction times are reduced. The largest and most complex ganglia, the cephalic ganglia, are located in the rostral end of the animal, where they receive information from the specialized sensory receptors. These ganglia constitute the simplest form of a brain. The concentration of neurons and sensory receptors at the rostral end is termed **cephalization.** Centralization and cephalization are two fundamental organizational trends in nervous system evolution.

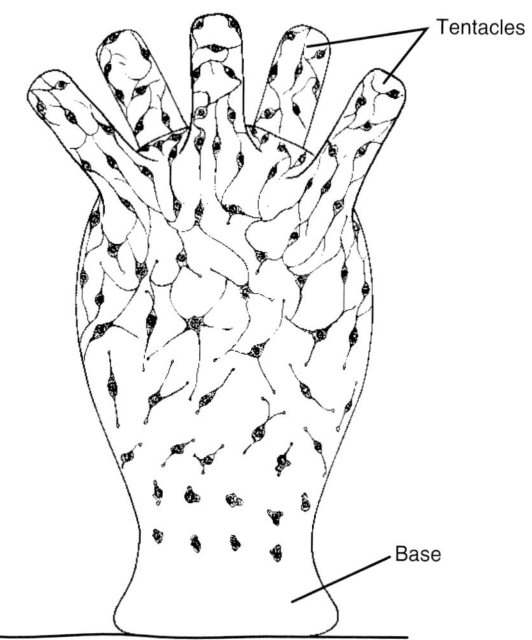

FIGURE 2.4 The nerve net of the hydra, a simple cnidarian, is spread diffusely around the animal. This drawing shows maturation of the nerve net in a hydra bud, starting near the base and finishing near the tentacles. Refer to McConnell.[5]

Flatworms are the simplest animals to have a third type of neuron, the **interneuron,** which is interpolated between sensory and motor neurons (Fig. 2.6). Unlike the amacrine processes of nerve nets, these are true neurons and transmit action potentials rather than graded potentials. Interneurons add another level of complexity to neural circuits, providing yet more opportunities for divergence and convergence. They also add two other interesting features with respect to information processing: They can act as excitatory or inhibitory "switches" in chains of neurons, and they can act as *pacemakers* if they generate intrinsic rhythmical changes in activity. All neurons throughout the animal kingdom may be classified as sensory neurons, interneurons, or motor neurons.

The omnidirectional flow of information that is typical of cnidarian nerve nets is unusual in the rest of the animal kingdom. The vast majority of neurons in other animals are functionally polarized, with information flowing from the dendrite and soma to the axon. In invertebrates, however, most motor neurons and interneurons are unipolar: a single process, the axon, arises from the soma. Dendrites branch from the axons in the center of the ganglion—the **neuropil**—where most synapses are made (Fig. 2.6). This arrangement

BOX 2.2

RAMÓN Y CAJAL: ICONOCLAST TO ICON

Santiago Ramón y Cajal (1852–1934) is considered by many people to be the founder of modern neuroscience—a peer of Darwin and Pasteur in 19th-century biology. He was born in the tiny Spanish village of Petilla de Aragon on May 1, 1852, and as related in his delightful autobiography, he was somewhat mischievous as a child and determined to become an artist, much to the consternation of his father, a respected local physician. However, he eventually entered the University of Zaragoza and received a degree in medicine in 1873. As a professor of anatomy in Zaragoza, his interests were mostly in bacteriology until 1887, when he visited Madrid and first saw through the microscope histological sections of brain tissue treated with the Golgi method, which had been introduced in 1873. Although very few workers had used this technique, Cajal saw immediately that it offered a great hope in solving one of the most vexing and fundamental problems in neurology: How do nerve cells interact with each other? This realization galvanized and directed the rest of his scientific life, which was extremely productive in originality, scope, and accuracy.

Shortly after Jacob Schleiden, Theodor Schwann, and Rudolf Virchow proposed the cell theory in the late 1830s, Joseph von Gerlach, Sr., and Otto Deiters suggested that nerve tissue was special in the sense that nerve cells are not independent units but instead form a continuous syncytium or reticular net. This concept was later refined by Camillo Golgi, who, based on the use of his silver chromate method, concluded that axons of nerve cells form a continuous reticular net, whereas dendrites serve a nutritive role, much like the roots of a tree. Using the same technique, Cajal almost immediately arrived at the opposite conclusion, based first on his examination of the cerebellum, and later of virtually all other parts of the nervous system. In short, he proposed that neurons interact by way of contract or contiguity rather than by continuity, and are thus independent units, which was finally proven when the electron microscope was used in the 1950s. This concept became known as the neutron doctrine.

Cajal's second major conceptual achievement was the theory of functional polarity, which stated that the dendrites and cell bodies of neurons receive information, whereas the single axon transmits information to other cells. This theory allows one to predict the direction of information flow through neural circuits based on the morphology or shape of individual neurons forming them, and it was the cornerstone of Charles Sherrington's revolutionary physiological analysis of reflex, organization in the mammal.

Around the close of the 19th century, Cajal made a remarkable series of discoveries at the cellular level. In addition to the two concepts outlined above, they include (1) the mode of axon termination in the adult central nervous system (1888), (2) the dendritic spine (1888), (3) the first diagrams of reflex pathways based on the neuron doctrine and functional polarity (1890), (4) the growth cone (1890), (5) the chemotactic theory of synapse specificity (1892), and (6) the suggestion that learning could be based on the selective strengthening of synapses (1895). In one of the great ironies in the history of neuroscience, Cajal and Golgi shared the Nobel Prize for Medicine in 1906 though they had used the same technique to elaborate fundamentally different views on nervous system organization! The meeting in Stockholm may not have diminished the great personal friction between them. In 1931 Cajal wrote: "What a cruel irony of fate to pair like Siamese twins united by the shoulders, scientific adversaries of such contrasting characters.

of axon and dendrites is different from that found in mammals, where neurons are generally multipolar, with several dendrites plus an axon extending from the soma or one of the dendrites.

The Nervous System of Annelids and Arthropods Is Segmented and Ventrally Located

Annelid worms and arthropods have even more complex body plans and behaviors than do flatworms, in part because of **segmentation.** Body segments, or metameres, are serially repeated along the rostrocaudal axis of the body. The segments presumably share a common underlying genetic program, although their terminal differentiation may vary. Because the same basic pattern is repeated in each segment, much of the genetic material from lower organisms is conserved even as a much more elaborate nervous system is produced. Annelids and all more complex invertebrates share another feature, a **ventral nerve cord,** consisting of a bilateral pair of ganglia (or a single fused ganglion) in each segment linked to ganglia in adjacent segments by axon bundles (Fig. 2.7). Nerves extend from each

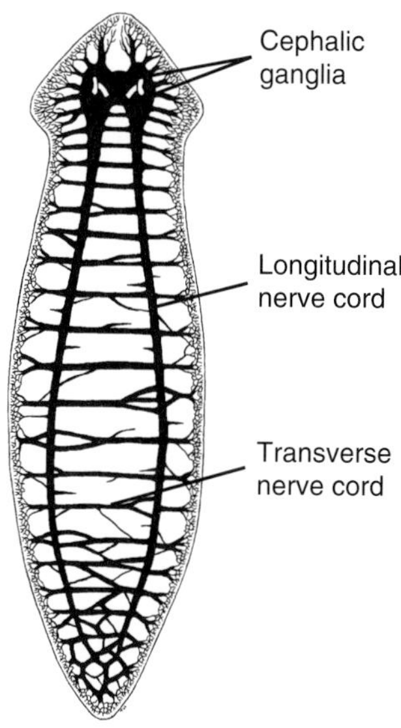

FIGURE 2.5 The nervous system of the planarian, a flatworm, includes longitudinal and transverse nerve cords associated with centralization and two fused cephalic ganglia in the rostral end associated with cephalization. Centralization and cephalization are probably related to the flatworm's bilateral symmetry and ability to swim forward rapidly. Refer to Lentz.[6] Reproduced with permission from Yale University Press.

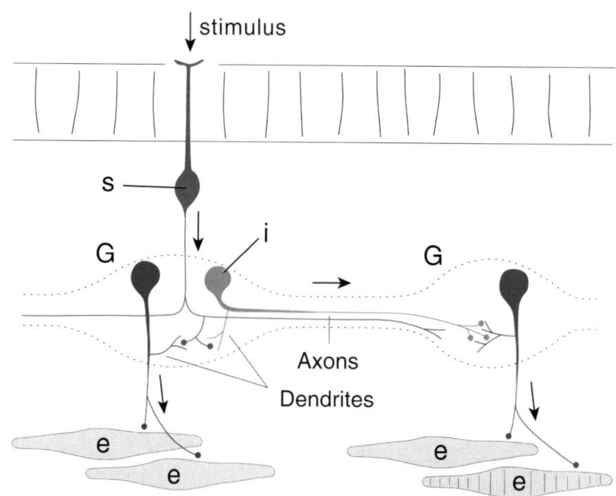

FIGURE 2.6 There are usually two kinds of neurons in invertebrate ganglia (G): motor neurons (m) and interneurons (i), both of which are typically unipolar, with dendrites arising from a single axon. In a typical invertebrate ganglion, neuronal somata are arranged around the outside and synapses occupy the central region, or neuropil. Sensory neurons (s) usually innervate motor neurons and interneurons but not effectors (e). Arrows show the direction of information flow.

ganglion to the sensory structures and muscles in the same segment.

The Basic Elements of the Vertebrate Nervous System Are Present in the Lancelet

Vertebrates, which constitute a subphylum of the phylum Chordata, are the most complex representatives of the animal kingdom in terms of both structure and behavior. All vertebrates are constructed according to a basic body plan in which common organ systems are placed in a relatively strict anatomical relationship with each other (see Box 2.3 and Fig. 2.8). Like other chordates, vertebrates possess two very important features during at least part of their life: a **notochord,** a stiff, cartilaginous rod that extends dorsally along the length of the body; and a more dorsal, hollow nerve cord. In most vertebrates, the body-stiffening and protective functions of the notochord are taken over by the vertebral column and the bony skull, and the notochord is reduced to a series of cartilaginous cushions between or within the vertebrae. The vertebrate nerve cord is tremendously expanded, thickened, and folded to form the brain and spinal cord.

The fundamental elements of the vertebrate nervous system are visible in the lancelet, a simple, nonvertebrate chordate (subphylum Cephalochordata). The lancelet is a slender, fishlike filter-feeder that lives half-buried in the sand in shallow, tropical marine waters (Fig. 2.9). The lancelet's dorsal nerve cord runs the length of the animal and sends out segmental nerves that innervate the muscles and organs. The body is stiffened by a dorsal notochord. Lancelets swim by alternately contracting segmental muscles, the **myotomes,** on the left and right sides of the body. Without the notochord, these contractions would shorten the animal but would not produce forward propulsive force.

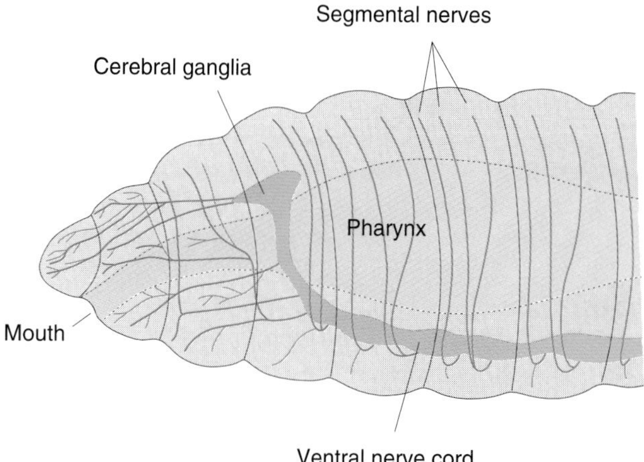

FIGURE 2.7 Organization of the nervous system in the rostral end of an annelid worm. A ventral nerve cord that contains more or less distinct ganglia connects with a fused pair of cerebral ganglia, which lie dorsal to the pharynx. Note the nerves arising from the ventral nerve cord and cerebral ganglia. Refer to Brusca and Brusca.[7]

Although the typical brain regions found in vertebrates are not apparent in the rostral end of the lancelet nerve cord, specific genes specifying the head that are expressed very early in vertebrate embryogenesis are also expressed in the rostral part of the lancelet body. Thus, certain components of the molecular program specifying head development in modern vertebrates were present very early in vertebrate evolution.

Summary

Most of the basic cellular features of nervous system organization, including convergence and divergence of sensory and motor information, are found in the cnidarian nerve net. In the more complex bilaterally symmetrical invertebrates, neurons and axons are aggregated in ganglia and nerve cords (centralization), and there is a higher concentration of neurons and sensory structures at the rostral end of the body (cephalization). Invertebrates with a segmented body have a ventral nerve cord that includes a bilateral pair of ganglia (or a single ganglion) in each segment. Basic features of vertebrate nervous system organization are found in the lancelet, a primitive chordate related to vertebrates.

DEVELOPMENT OF THE VERTEBRATE NERVOUS SYSTEM

One triumph of 19th-century biology was the demonstration that the early stages of embryogenesis are fundamentally the same in all vertebrates. See Boxes 2.4 and 2.5. Because along with the heart, the CNS is one of the first organ systems to differentiate in the embryo, its basic parts are therefore the same in all vertebrates, and the names and arrangement of these parts are the starting point for neuroanatomical nomenclature.

The Topographic Organization of the Nervous System Begins in the Neural Plate Stage

During embryogenesis, the CNS develops as a hollow cylinder from a flat sheet of cells, the **neural plate,** in a process called **neurulation.** The cellular and molecular mechanisms underlying neurulation will be discussed in Chapter 15. Here we will merely describe the overall structural changes that occur during this transformation.

The neural plate is a spoon-shaped region in the one-cell-thick ectodermal layer of the trilaminar embryonic disc (Fig. 2.10). The wide end of the neural plate lies rostrally and becomes the brain, while the narrow end lies caudally and becomes the spinal cord; these are the two major divisions of the CNS. A **neural groove** runs down the middle of the neural plate, dividing it into right and left halves. Thus, the neural plate displays three cardinal features of morphogenesis: polarity, bilateral symmetry, and regionalization. The neural plate differentiates in a rostrocaudal direction, so that the brain plate is the first to show signs of regionalization. These signs include the appearance of the **optic stalks,** which evaginate near the rostral end of the neural plate; a midline **infundibulum,** which evaginates just caudal to the optic stalks at the rostral end of the notochord; and the **otic rhombomere,** a swelling near the center of what will become the brainstem (Fig. 2.11, left).

At the junction between the neural plate and the

BOX 2.3

ANATOMICAL RELATIONSHIPS IN THE VERTEBRATE BODY

To describe the physical relationships between structures in the nervous system and the rest of the vertebrate body, we must use terms that accurately decribe the position of a given structure in three dimensions. The major axis of the body is the **rostrocaudal axis,** which passes through the rostral (anterior) and caudal (posterior) ends (Fig. 2.8). The rostrocaudal axis thus runs the length of the animal. In humans, the rostrocaudal axis bends forward in the head, so that rostral is toward the tip of the nose and caudal is toward the back of the head. The terms "superior" and "inferior" are essentially interchangeable with rostral and caudal, respectively, except when referring to structures within the head; in the head, superior means above and inferior means below. The second major axis is the **dorsoventral axis,** which passes through the dorsal (toward the back) and ventral (toward the stomach) sides of the body. The third major axis is the **mediolateral axis,** which extends between the medial (toward the middle) and lateral (toward the side) parts of the body.

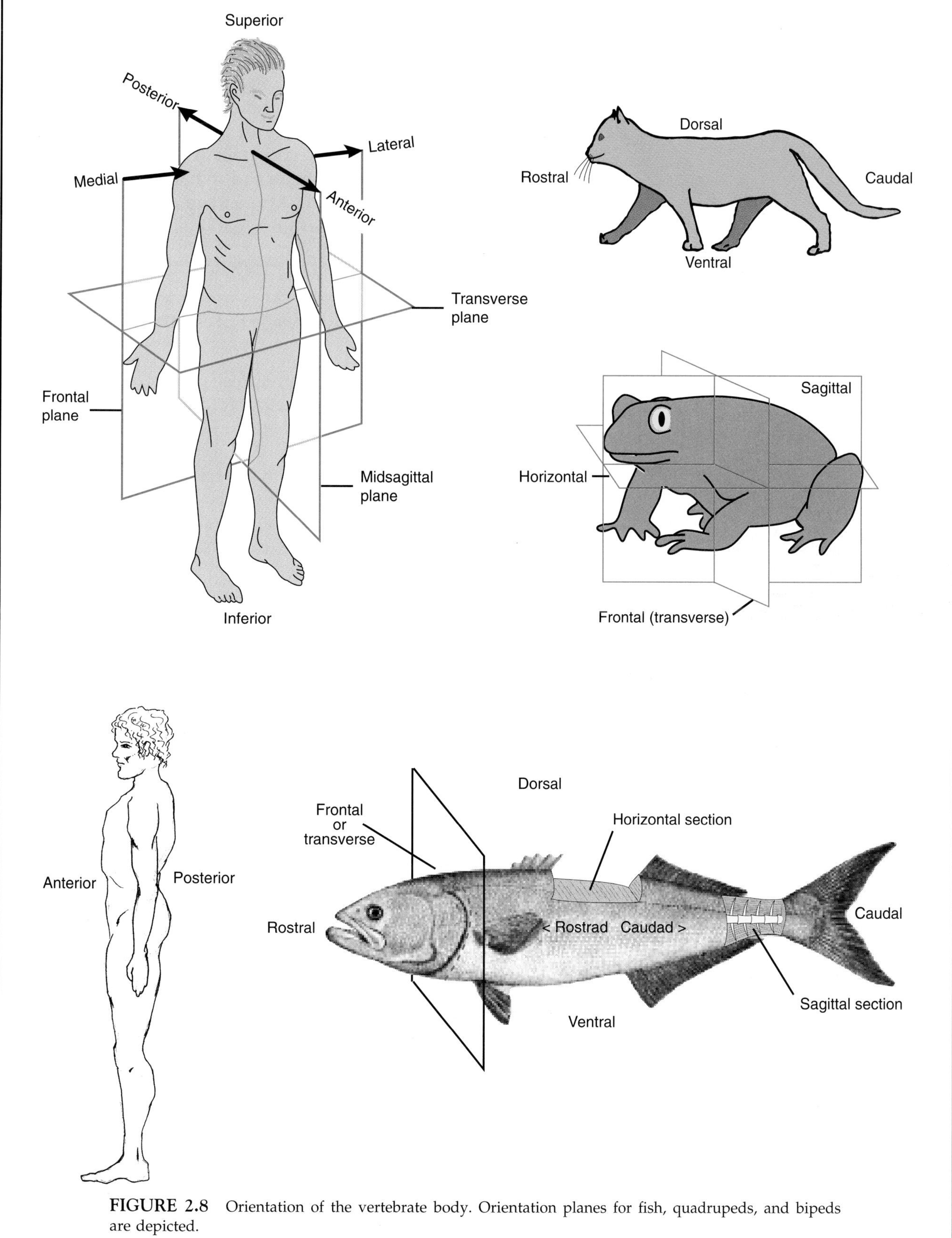

FIGURE 2.8 Orientation of the vertebrate body. Orientation planes for fish, quadrupeds, and bipeds are depicted.

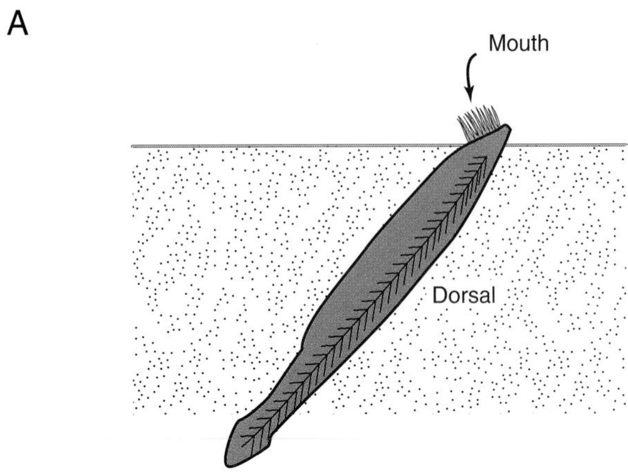

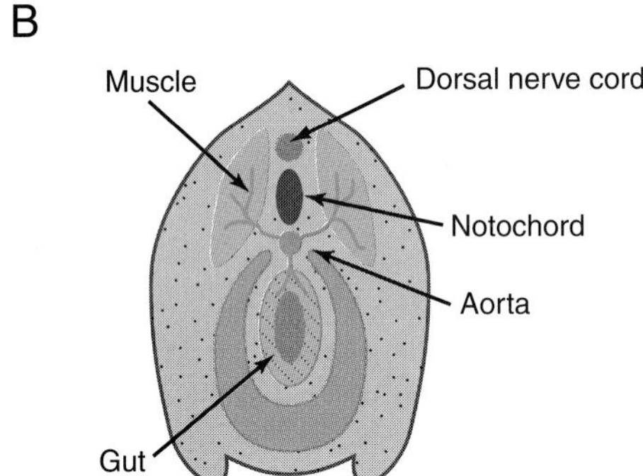

FIGURE 2.9 The lancelet is a prototypic vertebrate. (A) Lateral view of the animal in its native environment under the ocean floor, with its mouth protruding above the sand. (B) A cross-section of the lancelet showing the relationship between the dorsal nerve cord, the notochord, and the gut. Adapted from Cartmill *et al.*[8]

rest of the ectoderm (which forms the epidermal layer of skin on the outside of the adult body) lies a thin strip of tissue called the **neural crest** (Fig. 2.10). Extending around the spinal portion and approximately the caudal two-thirds of the brain portion of the neural plate, the neural crest is a distinctively vertebrate feature. It gives rise to a variety of adult structures, including neurons of the peripheral nervous system (PNS).

In summary, at the neural plate stage of vertebrate development the central and peripheral divisions of the nervous system are represented by the neural plate and neural crest, respectively. The two major divisions of the CNS—the brain and spinal cord—are also clear in the neural plate. At this stage the CNS is topologically quite simple: a bilaterally symmetrical, flat sheet that is one cell thick.

Further Regionalization Occurs in the Neural Tube Stage

As neurulation progresses, the two halves of the neural plate, called **neural folds,** extend dorsally, away from the endoderm and midline mesoderm, so that the plate becomes V- or U-shaped (Fig. 2.11, right). Eventually the tips of the folds fuse to form a tube with two open ends. Even later, the ends of the tube, called **neuropores,** also fuse to produce a completely closed **neural tube** whose wall, the **neuroepithelium,** is still only one cell thick.

Marcello Malphigi, the great 17th-century biologist who also discovered the capillary network between arteries and veins, recognized that the early neural tube displays three rostrocaudally arranged swellings now called the primary brain vesicles. They include the **forebrain** (prosencephalic) vesicle, which contains the optic stalks and infundibulum, the **midbrain** (mesencephalic) vesicle, and the **hindbrain** (rhombencephalic) vesicle, which contains the otic rhombomere (Fig. 2.12A). These vesicles are the fundamental structural divisions of the brain. The most characteristic feature of the hindbrain vesicle is the appearance and later disappearance of a series of transverse swellings

BOX 2.4

AMPHIHOX

The embryology of amphioxus is quite similar to that of vertebrates, the primary difference being a lack of craniofacial or head development in amphioxus. However, the amphioxus nervous system (nerve cord), although very primitive, appears to be homologous along the rostrocaudal axis with the mammalian central nervous system. *Hox* genes are present in all animals, and their expression domains in different organisms are reflective of homologous tissues. In amphioxus, the *Hox*3 gene is expressed in the developing nerve cord up to the limit parallel with the fourth somite; however, this is not to the end of the nerve cord. Comparison to *Hox*3 expression in mammals suggests that a large portion of the rostral nerve cord of amphioxus corresponds to what eventually became the fore and midbrain of vertebrates during evolution.[9]

BOX 2.5

HOW TO TURN A LOBSTER INTO A VERTEBRATE

In 1822, E. Geoffroy Saint-Hilaire suggested that an inversion of the dorsoventral axis had taken place during animal evolution. He believed that the ventral region of *Drosophila* and those of other members of the phylum Arthropoda (e.g., lobster) are homologous to the dorsal region of the vertebrates. Following the dissection of a lobster, Saint-Hilaire placed the animal upside down relative to its normal position with the ground and observed how the lobster's central nervous system was now located above the digestive tract, which itself was located above the heart, exactly as it is in vertebrates. Developmental studies on the extracellular signals that direct patterning of the dorsoventral axis have provided molecular evidence that such an inversion probably occurred in an animal that was the precursor to the arthropod and vertebrate lineages, which has been named Urbilateria.[10,11]

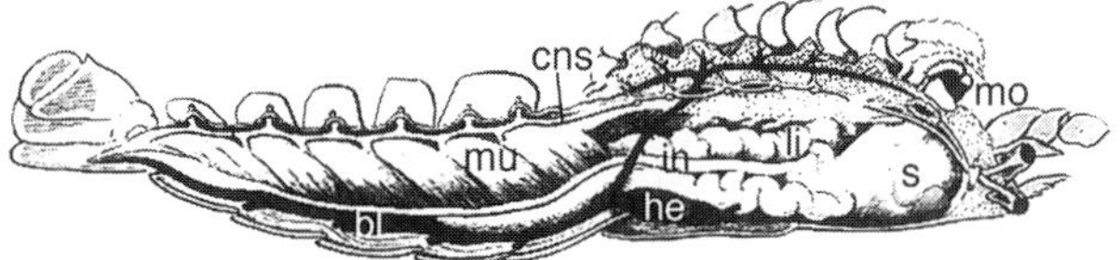

Geoffroy Saint-Hilaire's famous lobster. In this dissection the animal is presented in the orientation opposite to that it would normally have with respect to the ground. The central nervous system (CNS or nerve cord) is above and is traversed by the mouth (mo). Underneathh is the digestive tract, with the stomach (s), liver (li), and intestine (in). Below the gut are the heart (he) and main blood vessels (bl). Muscles (mu) flank the CNS. In this orientation the body plan of the arthropods resembles that of the vertebrate. Courtesy of the History and Special Collection Division, Louise M. Darling Biomedical Library, UCLA.

called rhombomeres, which develop in association with the pharyngeal pouches and are discussed more fully in Chapter 15. As embryogenesis continues, the forebrain vesicle divides into the **endbrain** (telencephalic) and **interbrain** (diencephalic) vesicles, whereas the hindbrain vesicle divides into a rostral pontine (metencephalic) region and a caudal medullary (myelencephalic) region (Fig. 2.12B). These divisions transform the "three primary vesicle stage" into the "five secondary vesicle stage."

The center of the neural tube remains in the adult as the ventricular system of the CNS (Fig. 2.12B). The shape of the ventricular system is determined by the differentiation of the five secondary brain vesicles and the spinal cord. The left and right endbrain vesicles each contain a lateral ventricle, which is connected by an interventricular foramen to the third ventricle in the center of the interbrain vesicle. The third ventricle leads into the cerebral aqueduct in the midbrain vesicle, and the aqueduct in turn leads into the fourth ventricle in the hindbrain. Finally, the fourth ventricle connects with the central canal of the spinal cord. In older embryos and adults, the ventricular system contains cerebrospinal fluid, much of which is elaborated by specialized, highly vascular regions of choroid plexus in the roof of the lateral, third, and caudal fourth ventricles.

Migrating Neurons Form the Mantle Layer

Through the five-secondary-vesicle stage, the cells in the neural tube proliferate mitotically, but the neural tube remains one cell thick. Shortly thereafter, however, many of these cells begin to differentiate into neurons, which migrate away from the proliferation zone near the ventricles to form a new, more superficial zone, the mantle layer (see Chapter 16). In some regions of the CNS, the neurons of the mantle layer become segregated into laminae that lie parallel to the surface of the CNS. In other regions, the neurons cluster in nuclei, relatively uniform collections of neurons that are structurally distinct from surrounding regions.

Mantle layer formation leads to further differentiation of the CNS (Fig. 2.12B). In the forebrain, the endbrain vesicle divides into the cerebral cortex (including the olfactory bulb) and basal nuclei or basal ganglia, and the interbrain vesicle divides into the thalamus dorsally and hypothalamus ventrally. The midbrain vesicle produces the laminated tectum dorsally and the nuclear tegmentum ventrally.

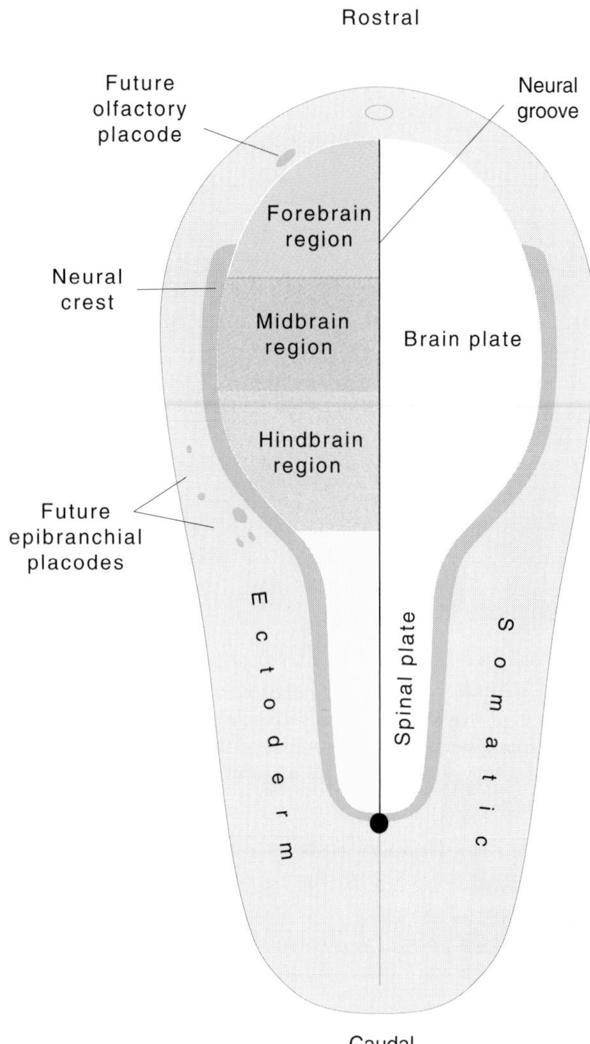

FIGURE 2.10 The neural plate is a spoon-shaped region of ectoderm (neural ectoderm) that forms the CNS. Ectoderm that lies outside the neural plate is called somatic ectoderm. The neural plate is polarized (the rostral end is wider than the caudal end), bilaterally symmetrical (divided by the neural groove), and regionalized (the rostral end forms the brain, and the caudal end forms the spinal cord). The neural crest lies along the junction between somatic and neural ectoderm, and a series of placodes develop as "islands" within the somatic ectoderm. The neural crest and placodes form the peripheral nervous system. The approximate location of future major brain divisions in the neural plate is shown in color on the left. The same color scheme is used in Figs. 2.11 and 2.12. Refer to Swanson.[12]

In the hindbrain and spinal cord, mantle layer formation results in clear regionalization, because motor neurons are generated first, and their site of differentiation is ventral in the neural tube (corresponding to medial in the neural plate). The early development of motor neurons correlates with the observation that gross, uncoordinated motor behavior in the embryo begins well before sensory reflex pathways are established, implying that this behavior is generated endogenously, that is, within the CNS itself.

The formation of a ventral mantle layer containing motor neurons is accompanied by the transient appearance of a longitudinal groove on the inner surface of the neural tube, the sulcus limitans. The great 19th-century Swiss embryologist Wilhelm His pointed out that the limiting sulcus divides much of the neural tube into a dorsal or alar plate and a ventral or basal plate, with sensory and motor functions, respectively (Fig. 2.13). His's observation complemented the earlier discovery by François Magendie and Charles Bell that sensory and motor fibers associated with the spinal cord are completely segregated within the spinal roots: Sensory fibers enter through the dorsal roots and motor fibers leave through the ventral roots. It is now clear that the alar and basal plates are not purely sensory and motor, because each contains interneurons. Nevertheless, it is helpful to think of the brainstem and spinal cord as consisting of three longitudinal zones: sensory,

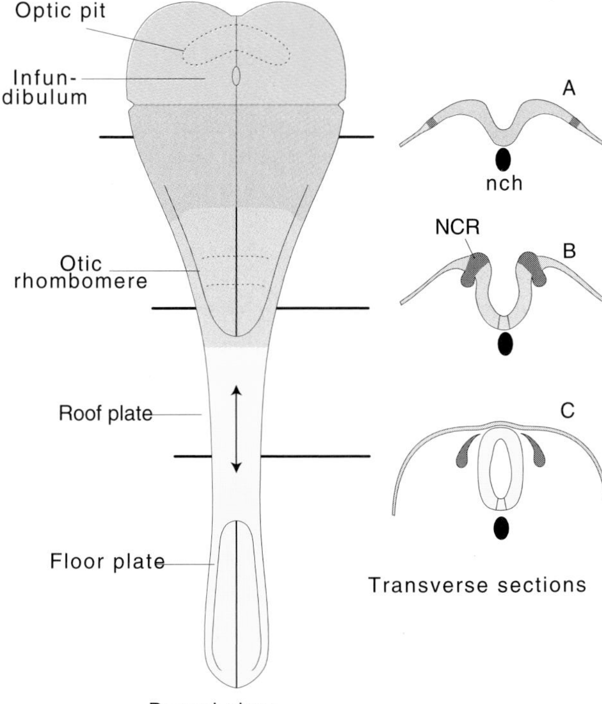

FIGURE 2.11 The optic pits, infundibulum, and otic rhombomere (dorsal view on left) are the earliest clear differentiations of the neural plate. The neural tube is formed by invagination of the neural ectoderm (transverse sections A and B), followed by fusion of the lateral edges of the neural plate (transverse section C). Fusion begins near the center of the neural plate (roughly the cervical region) and proceeds both rostrally and caudally (double arrow in roof plate). Note how the neural crest (NCR) pinches off in the process. Also note the position of the notochord (nch) just ventral to the neural groove. Refer to Swanson.[12]

integrative (reticular), and motor. Regionalization of the midbrain and forebrain does not fit as neatly into this scheme and is still poorly understood.

The most dorsal part of the hindbrain alar plate forms a unique structure, the rhombic lip. In the pons, the rhombic lip generates the granule cells of the cerebellum, whereas in more caudal parts of the hindbrain, the lip produces cell groups such as the precerebellar and vestibulocochlear nuclei. Cerebellar granule cells and neurons of the precerebellar nuclei are interesting because they migrate to their final destinations by traveling parallel to the surface of the neural tube rather than radially, like most CNS neurons (see Chapter 16).

This differentiation continues until the adult configuration of the CNS is achieved (Fig. 2.14). The most obvious late-developing structures are the cerebral hemispheres and the cerebellum.

Summary

The vertebrate central nervous system develops from a sheet of cells called the neural plate, which soon invaginates to form the neural tube. The rostral end of the tube then forms a series of swellings, or vesicles, that constitute the major parts of the brain. The caudal end of the tube forms the spinal cord. The neurons of the peripheral nervous system differentiate from the neural crest, which forms a narrow strip along the edge of the neural plate.

IDENTITY AND ORGANIZATION OF FUNCTIONAL SYSTEMS

How does the nervous system function from a systems rather than a cellular point of view? One way to approach this question is to analyze how the nervous system's basic functional subsystems are organized

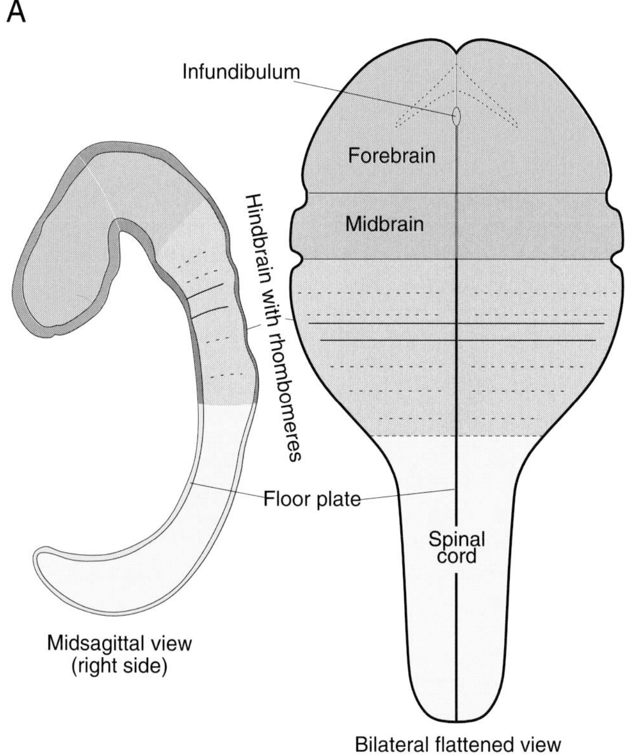

FIGURE 2.12 Formation and subdivision of the neural tube. (A) The brain region of the early neural tube develops three swellings: the forebrain, midbrain, and hindbrain vesicles. The hindbrain vesicle develops a series of transverse swellings called rhombomeres. (B) As neurulation continues, the forebrain vesicle differentiates into the right and left endbrain vesicles and a midline interbrain vesicle; the hindbrain vesicle differentiates into pontine and medullary regions. The endbrain vesicle further divides into the cerebral cortex (including the olfactory bulb) and basal nuclei; the interbrain vesicle divides into the thalamus, hypothalamus, and pretectum; the midbrain vesicle divides into the tectum and tegmentum; and the hindbrain divides into the basal plate (tegmentum), alar plate, and rhombic lip. At this stage of development, the major components of the adult ventricular system can be seen in the lumen of the neural tube. Refer to Swanson[12] and Alvarez-Bolado and Swanson.[15]

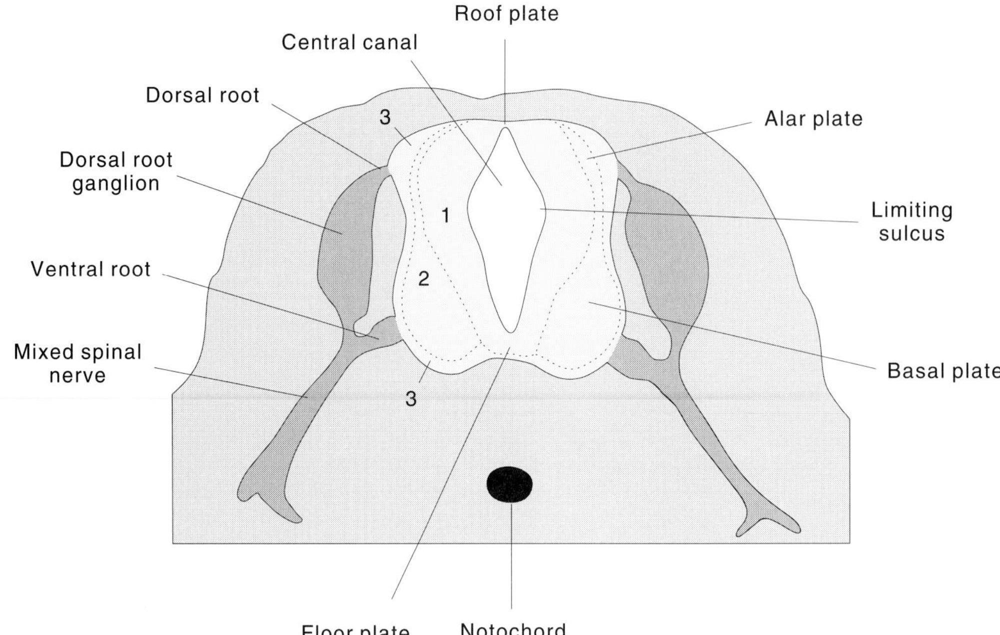

FIGURE 2.13 The early spinal cord and hindbrain are divided into dorsal (alar) and ventral (basal) plates by the limiting sulcus. This morphology reflects early ventral differentiation of the mantle layer (2), which is accompanied by an early ventral thinning of the ventricular (1) layer. This schematic drawing, which was traced from a transverse section of the spinal cord, also shows the dorsal (sensory) and ventral (motor) roots of the spinal cord; the dorsal root ganglia, which contain the somata of sensory neurons; and the mixed (sensory and motor) spinal nerves distal to the ganglia. The peripheral area (3) is called the marginal zone and develops into the spinal cord funiculi, which contain ascending and descending fiber tracts.

structurally. Such an approach should ultimately provide the fundamental circuit diagram for information processing in the nervous system. It seems prudent to begin this analysis without any biases or assumptions that may have been introduced by the strictly topographic considerations we dealt with in the preceding section.

One model of basic information processing in the nervous system is shown in Fig. 2.15. This model is a synthesis of basic neurobiological concepts pioneered by Cajal and Charles Sherrington and basic cybernetic concepts pioneered by Norbert Wiener[13] and John von Neumann.[14] In its simplest form, the model assumes that behavior is determined by the motor output of the CNS and that motor output is a function of three inputs: sensory (reflexive), cognitive (voluntary), and intrinsic. The relative importance of these inputs in controlling motor output varies from species to species and from individual to individual. Note that behavior elicits sensory feedback, which helps determine future motor activity and thus behavior. We will now consider in more detail each of the circuit's main components, bearing in mind that it is far beyond the scope of this chapter to place all known parts of the CNS within this framework.

Motor Systems Are Hierarchically Organized

There are three different types of motor systems: skeletal, autonomic, and neuroendocrine. The first controls skeletal muscles responsible for voluntary behavior, the second controls smooth muscles and cardiac muscles and some secretry glands, and the third controls hormonal secretion by the pituitary gland. Because the skeletal motor system is the best understood of the three, we will use it as a prototype for considering the basic organizing principles of motor systems, which are presumably similar for all three.

The skeletal motor system is hierarchically arranged, as diagrammed in Fig. 2.16. The lowest level in the hierarchy consists of alpha motor neurons, which synapse on skeletal muscle fibers. The motor neurons that innervate specific muscles are arranged in pools in the spinal cord and nuclei in the brainstem. The next-higher level consists of motor pattern generators (MPGs), circuits of interneurons that innervate unique sets of motor neuron pools or nuclei. The highest level is composed of motor pattern initiators (MPIs), which recognize specific input patterns and project to unique sets of MPGs. Ethologists refer to MPIs as "innate releasing mechanisms." One reason the organization of

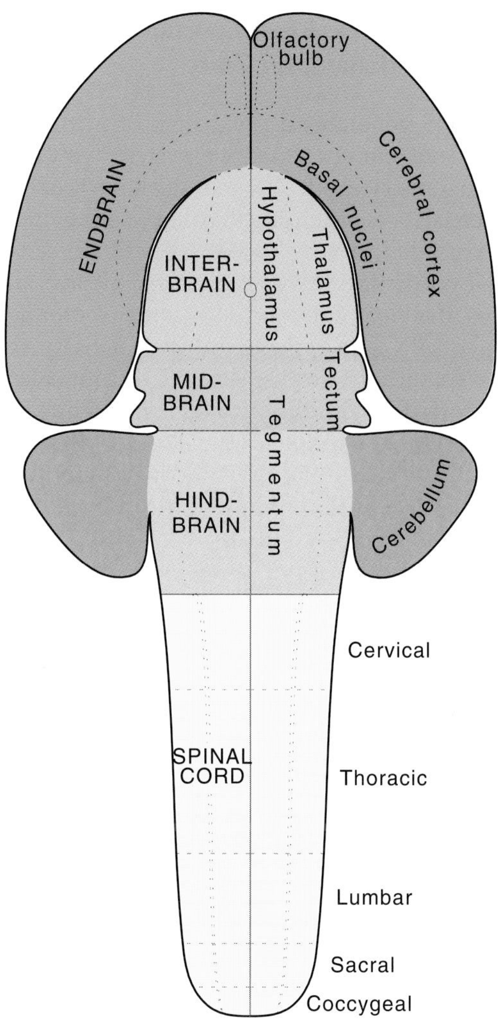

FIGURE 2.14 The major divisions of the adult central nervous system are derived from the regionalization of the neural plate and neural tube illustrated in Figs. 2.10–2.12. Modified from Swanson.[12]

central neural circuitry is so complex is that each of the three types of input may go directly to each of the three general levels in the motor system hierarchy.

A hierarchical organization also exists within the MPGs and MPIs themselves. At a conceptual level, this organization is particularly easy to understand for the MPGs serving locomotion. In the spinal cord, simple MPGs for locomotion coordinate the reciprocal innervation of antagonistic muscle pairs across individual joints, more complex MPGs coordinate the activity of simpler MPGs for all of the joints in a given limb, and still more complex MPGs coordinate the activity of the MPGs controlling all four limbs. Carrying the analysis to the next higher level, there is a separate MPI in the brain for locomotion, which is activated by specific patterns of input and projects to the locomotion pattern generator in the spinal cord.

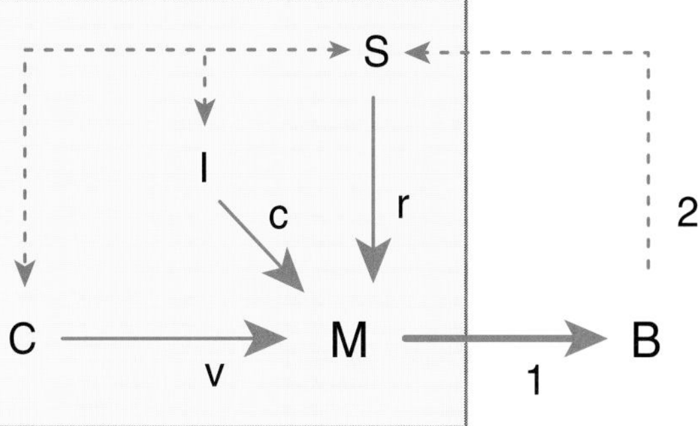

FIGURE 2.15 This model of information flow through the nervous system (inside the box) postulates that behavior (B) is determined by the motor system (M), which is influenced by three neural inputs: sensory (S), intrinsic (I), and cognitive (C). Sensory inputs lead to reflex responses (r), cognitive inputs produce voluntary responses (v), and intrinsic inputs act as control signals (c) to regulate the behavioral state. Motor system outputs (1) produce behaviors whose consequences are monitored by sensory feedback (2). Sensory feedback may be used by the cognitive system for perception and by the intrinsic system to generate affect. The cognitive, sensory, and intrinsic systems are all interconnected, hence the arrowheads at the end of each dashed line within the box (nervous system). Refer to Swanson.[16] Reprinted by permission of Oxford University Press.

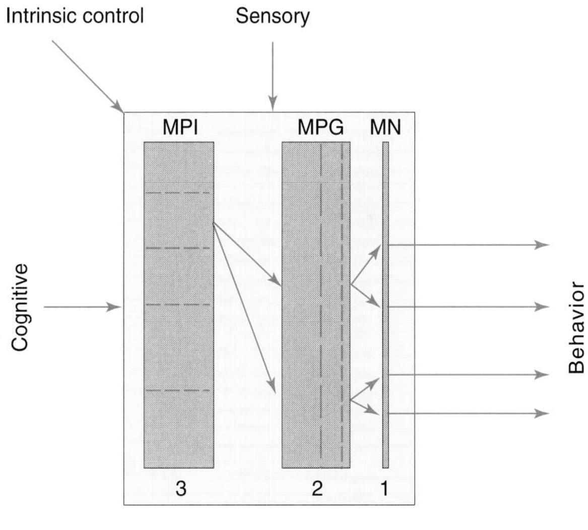

FIGURE 2.16 Hierarchical organization of the skeletal motor system. At the simplest level (1), pools of motor neurons (MNs) innervate individual muscles that generate individual components of behavior. At the next higher level (2), pools of interneurons referred to as motor pattern generators (MPGs) innervate specific sets of motor neuron pools. At the highest level (3), additional pools of interneurons referred to as motor pattern initiators (MPIs) innervate specific sets of MPGs. The MPIs can produce complex behaviors when they receive specific patterns of sensory, intrinsic, and cognitive inputs. Note that MPGs and MPIs may themselves be hierarchically organized as indicated by the dashed lines, and that sensory, intrinsic, and cognitive inputs may go directly to any level of the motor system. Refer to Swanson.[16] Reprinted by permission of Oxford University Press.

Multiple Sensory Systems Function in Parallel

A set of sensory systems provides information to the CNS from various classes of receptors, and all of these systems can function at the same time. Cajal noted that pathways carrying unimodal sensory information generally branch in such a way that part of the information goes directly to the motor system and part goes to the cerebral cortex for sensation and perception. Information going directly to the motor system is typically reflexive in nature, whereas information going to the cerebral cortex would reach the level of consciousness and play an important role in cognition.

The various types of sensory systems are dealt with extensively in Chapters 23–28, so we will mention only a few of their general features here. First, the CNS receives a wide range of information about the external environment as well as the internal state of the body itself. Thus, sensory receptors can be found on the surface of the body (e.g., touch receptors and olfactory receptors), deep within the body (e.g., stretch receptors in the aorta), and even within the brain itself (e.g., osmoreceptors). Second, each of the three types of motor systems receives a broad range of sensory inputs. Third, the range of sensory modalities is remarkably similar (though not identical) across vertebrate classes, and information relating to specific modalities enters the CNS through homologous cranial nerves in all vertebrates. And fourth, the number of synapses between a sensory receptor and the cerebral cortex may vary in different systems. For example, there is one synapse in the olfactory pathway and at least four in the visual pathway.

Cognitive Systems Produce Anticipatory Behavior

There seems little doubt that the cerebral cortex is the most important part of the cognitive system, if not the only part, and that it is responsible for planning, initiating, and evaluating the consequences of voluntary behavior (Chapter 59). The fundamental nature of voluntary behavior is obviously a difficult problem to address, but one useful approach is to compare it with reflexive behavior. Interestingly, many and perhaps all behaviors mediated by skeletal muscle can be initiated either reflexively or voluntarily, as René Descartes pointed out. What seems to distinguish reflexive and voluntary behavior most clearly is that the former is a stereotyped response to a defined stimulus, whereas the latter is anticipatory and impossible to predict with the same degree of certainty.

Intrinsic Systems Are Important in Controlling Behavioral State

The CNS generates a great deal of intrinsic activity—it is not merely a passive system waiting to respond to sensory input. In general, all parts of the CNS have a basal level of activity that can be either increased or decreased. In many cases, we still do not know whether particular cell types generate intrinsic activity patterns. It is clear, however, that either motor neurons or related MPGs do generate intrinsic activity; the embryonic spinal cord produces motor output before sensory circuits develop, as we noted above. Thus, in addition to the three extrinsic types of input to the motor system illustrated in Fig. 2.15, intrinsic activity within the motor system itself can produce behavior that is neither reflexive nor voluntary.

Certain regions of the CNS generate intrinsic activity patterns that are rhythmic. From a behavioral perspective, the most important rhythmic pattern is the sleep–wake cycle, which is entrained to the light–dark cycle by an endogenous circadian clock, the hypothalamic suprachiasmatic nucleus (see Chapters 45 and 46). The sleep–wake cycle is profoundly significant because during sleep the body is maintained entirely by ongoing intrinsic and reflexive systems that control such behaviors as respiration and the sustained contraction of sphincters. In contrast, voluntary mechanisms come into play during periods of wakefulness, although reflexive and intrinsic mechanisms are vitally important then as well.

The control of behavioral state is thus a fundamental intrinsic property of the brain. One other aspect of behavioral state, arousal, is especially important during wakefulness (Chapter 54). Arousal level is correlated in a general way with the motivational state—the level of drive—of an animal (Chapter 48). The neural system mediating drive or motivation has not been elucidated, but it almost certainly involves the hypothalamus. On the other hand, the attainment of specific goals in motivated behavior almost certainly involves the cognitive system. Therefore, arousal and drive may be controlled by subcortical systems, whereas the actual direction of behavior is mainly determined cortically.

One of the great mysteries of neuroscience is how systems elaborating pleasure and pain are organized. Many regard pleasure and pain as the conscious expression of positive and negative reinforcement, which determine whether a particular voluntary behavior is likely to be repeated or avoided in the future. Reinforcement, of course, depends on sensory feedback related to the consequences of a particular behavior, and one suggestion is that the sensations of pain and pleasure, like those associated with drive, are elaborated subcortically in intrinsic control systems. According to this view, thinking or cognition is a product of the cerebral cortex, while feeling or affect is produced subcortically. (See Chapters 51 and 59.)

Pharmacological Systems and Genetic Networks May Help Define Functional Systems

The incorporation of specific neurotransmitter systems into models of CNS function has become increasingly frequent over the last 25 years. Two such systems are the cholinergic and noradrenergic systems, defined as sets of neurons in the CNS that release acetylcholine or noradrenalin, respectively, as a neurotransmitter (Chapter 8). In general, these systems are not correlated in a straightforward way with traditional functional systems or with topographic divisions of the CNS. That is, they are not typically restricted to one functional system or one major division of the brain, although there may be some exceptions. Thus, neurotransmitter systems are not functional systems in the traditional sense. However, they are conceptually important in helping to define the circuits that are influenced by the direct action of particular drugs. For example, the administration of a centrally acting antagonist of acetylcholine receptors will influence synapses in a variety of traditional functional systems, and the set of these functional systems could be defined as a pharmacological system with a specific set of behavioral as well as other responses.

Extending this line of thought further, the distribution of any gene product can be used to define a chemical or molecular system in the brain, although the heuristic value of this approach is usually greater at the cellular and molecular levels than at the functional systems level. For example, one could define a system in terms of the presence of calbindin or μ-opioid receptors. It is important to remember, however, that a genetic program is responsible for constructing the basic circuitry of the brain during embryogenesis. Determining the correspondence between genetic and neural networks may be the ultimate achievement of systems neuroscience.

Summary

There does not appear to be a simple relationship between the topographic organization of the CNS and its functional organization. Thus, it is a mistake to think that information is processed in the CNS in a simple hierarchical way, with the spinal cord at the lowest level and the cerebral cortex at the highest level. An alternative view is that motor systems are driven by sensory, cognitive, and intrinsic inputs and that future motor activity is determined in part by sensory feedback related to the consequences of the initial behavior.

Two major features complicate this simple model. First, the motor system itself clearly displays aspects of hierarchical organization; the sensory system transmits a wide range of modalities in parallel, and this sensory information may reach each level in the motor hierarchy directly. Second, sensory information also reaches the intrinsic and cognitive systems. In fact, all three input systems are bidirectionally interconnected. The traditional functional organization of the CNS may be extended to include pharmacological systems and genetic networks.

THE BASIC STRUCTURAL FEATURES OF THE NERVOUS SYSTEM

Although the gross anatomical structure of nervous tissue was observed by early Greek physicians and scientists (see Box 2.6), the astounding complexity of the interconnections in the brain was not appreciated until techniques for isolating CNS tracts and nuclei from one another were developed. In the mid-19th century, general histological stains adapted from the European textile dye industry demonstrated the vast number of neuronal somata in the brain. However, these stains revealed only the most general features of the neuropil, where dendrites and axons intertwine and communicate.

Silver impregnation methods perfected in the second half of the 19th century, particularly the **Golgi method,** made the fine structure of the nervous system visible in great detail (Fig. 2.17). For the first time, neuroanatomists could see the smallest projections of the neuronal pathways that lay embedded in the brain, including even the synaptic endings themselves. The Golgi method involves placing fresh brain tissue alternately in solutions of potassium dichromate and silver nitrate over a period of several weeks, months, or years. Mysteriously—the chemistry of the reaction is still elusive—only one of every few hundred neurons is filled (seemingly at random) with a dense precipitate. The precipitate reveals the entire architecture of each metal-impregnated cell, from the tiniest dendritic branch to the tips of the axon, against a clear background of unstained tissue. Thus, the Golgi method reveals more by staining less. Today, selective labeling of individual

BOX 2.6

EARLY VIEWS OF BRAIN

The Greek physician Galen (131–201 A.D.) knew that nerves were related to movement, although the sinewy character of both nerves and tendons led him to confuse the two. He founded the science of nervous system physiology and recognized that nerves originate in the brain and spinal cord, not in the heart, as Aristotle had maintained. Galen believed that blood was successively distilled in the heart, liver, and brain into "animal spirits." These spirits were the agents of movement, and their reservoir was the ventricular system of the brain, which in Galen's view was filled with the purest essence of the animal spirit. The formless, watery interior of the brain was for the Galenists the repository of the mind! Incredibly, this was the prevailing view of nervous system organization for the next 1500 years. Galenic anatomy remained unchallenged—it was heresy to do so—until the middle of the 16th century, when Andreas Vesalius published the *Fabric of the Human Body,* the first original medical book to emerge out of the Renaissance. In his treatise, Vesalius expanded and deepened our anatomical perceptions of the nervous system, and the woodcuts from this work (see Fig. 2.23) are still used today in anatomy (and art) classes.

René Descartes (1596–1650) postulated that the conscious mind—the soul—resided in the only unpaired organ in the human brain, the pineal gland, a pea-sized structure perched in the middle of the head. Harkening back to Galen, Descartes reiterated the existence of animal spirits stored in the ventricles of the brain. He believed that for one to be aware of or conscious of something, the senses must funnel this information through the pineal gland. Although he knew of the existence of automatic, uncontrollable reflexes, Descartes believed that these impulses bypassed the pineal gland and thus never reached a conscious level of control. Descartes had a "mechanistic" view of the body and brain:

> If, for example, fire comes near the foot, the minute particles of this fire which, as you know, move with great velocity, have the power to set in motion the spot of skin of the foot which they touch, and by this means pulling upon the delicate thread which is attached to the spot of skin, they open up at the same instant the pore against which the delicate thread ends, just as by pulling at one end of a rope one causes to strike at the same instant a bell which hangs on the other end. When this pore is opened the animal spirits of the cavity enter into the tube and are carried by it partly to the muscles which pull back the foot from the fire, partly to those which turn the eyes and the head in order to regard it, and partly to those which serve to advance the hands and to bend the whole body in order to shield itself.

A great revolution in the study of the brain and the nerves occurred in the last part of the 17th century. Thomas Willis (1621–1675) of Oxford coined the term "neurology" and proceeded to reinvent the anatomy and physiology of the brain. Willis realized that the gray matter was the source of the "animal spirits." With great perception, he recognized that the white matter served only to connect the masses of gray matter. He argued for this new view by observing that the blood supply to the gray matter was much more extensive than that to the white matter. Willis also proposed the revolutionary idea that the more rostral centers of the brain exert conscious influences on reflexive actions. He described the brain's vasculature, and in particular the wreath of anatomizing arteries that surrounds the brainstem, now known as the circle of Willis.

neurons can also be achieved by injecting a dye or other marker into the living cell with a micropipette, which may be used simultaneously to study the neuron's electrical activity.

Methods for selectively staining degenerating nerve fibers have also yielded a wealth of information about the structural organization of the nervous system. These degeneration methods evolved from studies by Augustus Waller, who showed in 1850 that transection of a nerve eventually caused degeneration of the nerve's distal segment. About 30 years later, Gudden showed that this degeneration is accompanied by pathological changes in the somata of neurons whose axons were in the nerve. The first selective degeneration method, developed in 1885 by Vittorio Marchi and Algeri, revealed degenerating myelin sheaths around severed axons as black particles on a light background, effectively isolating the degenerating sheaths from healthy ones in a tissue section. After producing discrete brain lesions in experimental animals and waiting a few weeks for axonal degeneration to occur, anatomists could use this method to reveal the nerve tracts that originate in specific regions of the brain. The method was limited, however, because it did not stain

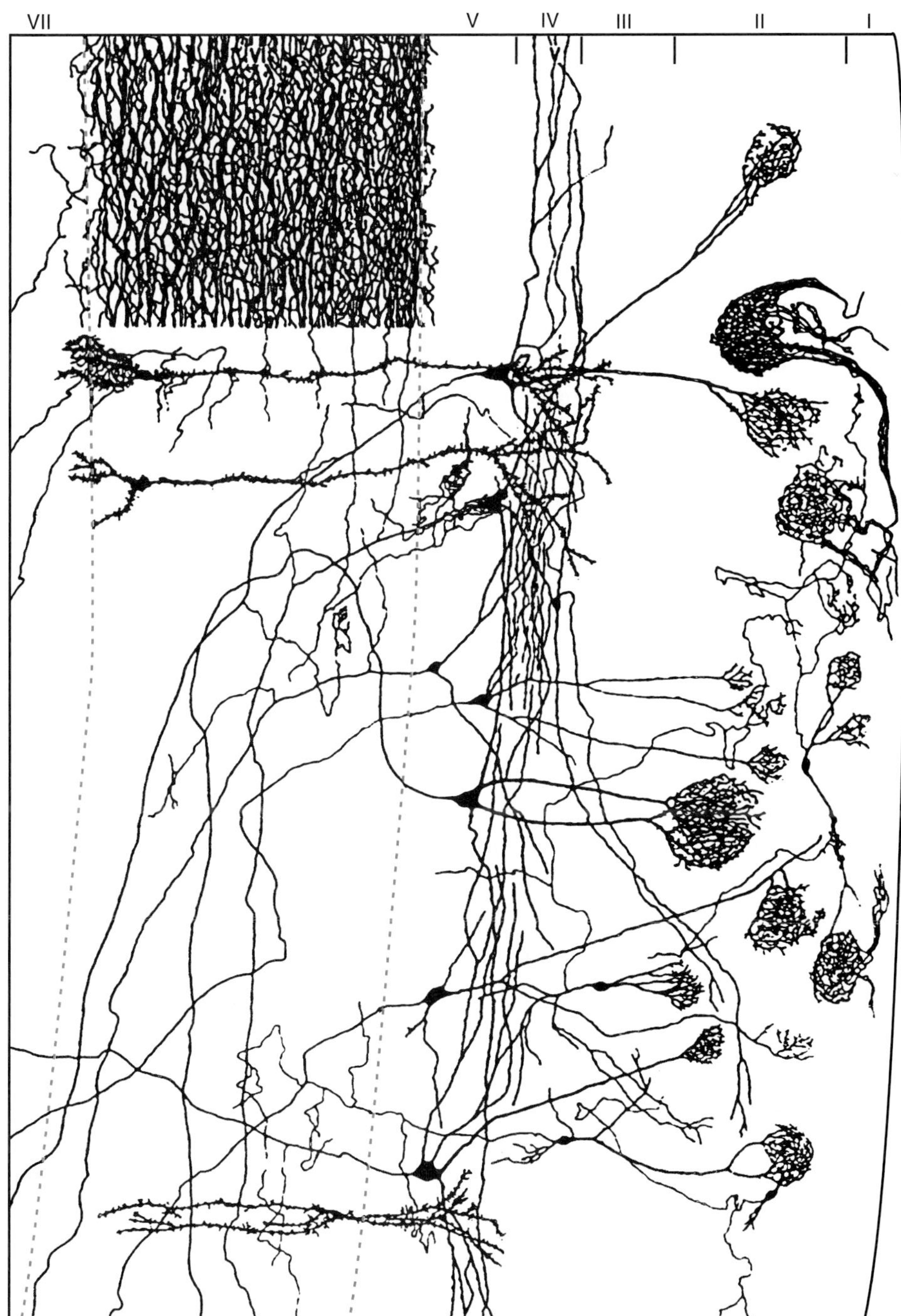

FIGURE 2.17 A horizontal section through the olfactory bulb of the rat (9 days postnatal). This is a composite of several Golgi-stained preparations that integrates the cellular and synaptic interrelationships in the bulb. The Golgi method reveals terminal ramifications of dendrites and axons in exquisite detail. Adapted from Valverde.[17]

unmyelinated or thinly myelinated axons. It also failed to reveal the terminal synaptic fields of myelinated axons, because the terminal branches of axons lack myelin.

In the middle of the 20th century, the silver impregnation and degeneration methods were combined in techniques that revealed degenerating cytoplasm in all types of axons, even down to the smallest synaptic terminals. These techniques, which are still in use, allow axonal pathways to be mapped in considerably more detail than was possible with earlier methods.

Another great technical advance in the study of neuronal connections was the introduction of **autoradiography,** a procedure in which radiolabeled amino acids and lipids are injected into the vicinity of neuronal somata. The neurons take up these radioactive precursors and incorporate them into proteins and membranes that are then distributed throughout the neuron (see Chapter 4). After tissue sections are prepared, a liquid photographic emulsion is applied to the sections and allowed to dry. Days or weeks later, the emulsion is developed so that silver grains appear over the areas in which radioactive material is concentrated. One advantage of autoradiography is that it relies on normal physiological processes in healthy neurons rather than the poorly understood and capricious phenomenon of degeneration-related staining. Moreover, in vertebrates, radiolabeled amino acids and lipids do not label axons that are simply passing through an injection site; because there are no ribosomes in axons, no protein synthesis can take place. In contrast, degeneration methods stain axons of passage as well as neurons whose somata are in the area of the lesion, making it difficult to interpret the staining.

Beginning around 1970, a related method for studying connections in the CNS was developed to expose specific regions of the CNS to macromolecular tracers such as enzymes and plant lectins, which are picked up by endocytosis and pinocytosis from the extracellular space. Neurons that acquire the tracers transport them intracellularly in vesicles whose presence can be revealed histochemically far from the site of application. If the tracers are placed in a synaptic field, they will be taken up by axon terminals and moved within the axon to the soma, where they accumulate. Thus, all of the neurons whose axons terminate in that synaptic field will be labeled. In contrast, if the tracers are applied in the vicinity of the dendrites or soma, they will be taken up and moved within the axon away from the soma, revealing the locations of the neuron's synaptic targets.

Beginning in the 1950s, the electron microscope opened a whole world of ultrastructure that was previously only guessed at. It provided the first images of synapses, myelin sheaths, and many organelles. It also allowed biologists to examine in detail the biosynthetic apparatus that resides within each cell.

The methods described above have given us an exceedingly detailed picture of the neural connectivity patterns in many species of animals, especially when these methods are combined with histochemical methods for cellular localization of molecules such as neurotransmitters and neurotransmitter receptors. As a result, comparative neuroanatomy has flourished and forms a solid structural foundation on which contemporary physiological and behavioral studies are based.

The Peripheral Nervous System Is Divided into Somatic, Autonomic, and Enteric Divisions

Early in embryogenesis, the cells that make up the neural crest bud off laterally from the neural tube and begin to migrate throughout the embryo. The neural crest ultimately gives rise to major portions of the head and jaw as well as the entire peripheral nervous system (PNS). Thus, migrating neural crest cells lay down all of the peripheral ganglia and their derivatives, the interconnections between them, and the neurons that comprise the enteric nervous system in the wall of the digestive tract. Other neural crest cells penetrate the adrenal gland and develop into the adrenal medulla, which secretes neuroactive hormones.

Functionally, the PNS is divided into the somatic innervation and the autonomic nervous system (ANS) and enteric nervous system. The somatic innervation consists of the peripheral nerves that supply the body wall (Fig. 2.18). These nerves carry both **afferent** information (traveling into the CNS) and **efferent** information (traveling away from the CNS). Somatic afferents are sensory neurons that respond to stimuli in the environment outside the body and in the skin, skeletal muscles, tendons, and joints. Somatic efferents are motor neurons whose axons innervate the skeletal muscles in the body wall and the limbs. The autonomic and enteric nervous system subdivisions consist of a network of efferent pathways and ganglia that control peristaltic movements of the gut, glandular secretions that accompany digestion, dilation and constriction of blood vessels, and many other functions involving the deep organs. Output from these nervous system subdivisions is controlled both by somatic afferents and by visceral afferents, which innervate the deep organs. Somatic and visceral afferents enter the spinal cord via the same nerves. Thus, a typical peripheral nerve carries a mixture of afferents and efferents that innervate the body wall and the deep organs.

Somatic afferents are distributed near the body surface in a manner that reflects the segmental origins of the nervous system. Each spinal nerve innervates a relatively narrow mediolateral band of skin called a **dermatome** (Fig. 2.19). The segmental pattern of the dermatomes is best seen in the torso, where very little growth of the body wall occurs. In contrast, dermatomes in the upper and lower limbs are distorted because they are put in place before the limbs grow out. In humans, the lower limbs also rotate after they are formed, causing the dermatomes to rotate as well.

Peripheral nerves often ramify and join with nerves

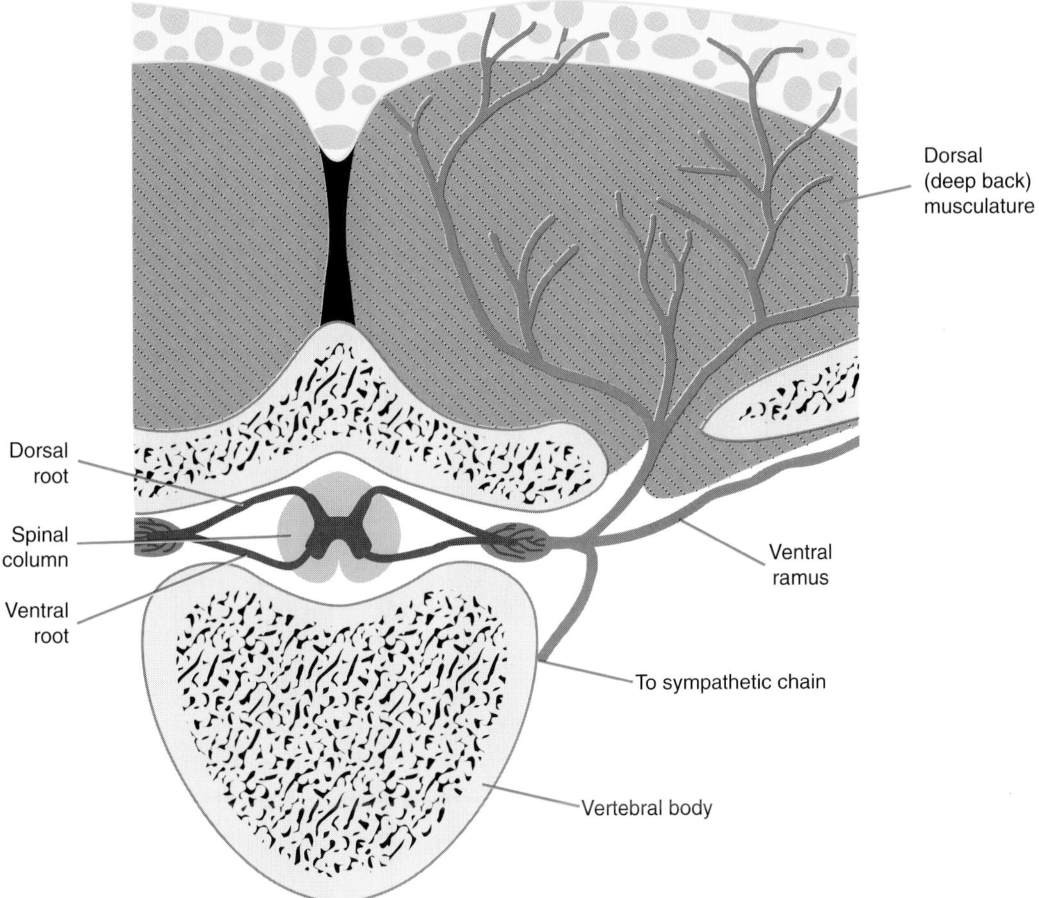

FIGURE 2.18 A cross section of the mid thoracic region in the human illustrating the appearance of the spinal cord *in situ* with dorsal and ventral roots coalescing to form the mixed spinal nerve. This nerve sends fibers dorsally to the postural (deep) muscles of the back by way of dorsal rami and ventral rami that innervate the muscles and skin of the thoracic cage. The mixed spinal nerve also sends fibers to the sympathetic chain, which is part of the autonomic nervous system.

from other segments to form **plexi** (singular: plexus; literally, a "braid"). Plexi serve as crossroads and distribution centers for peripheral nerves, allowing axons to reorganize themselves into complex nerve bundles that innervate body structures. The brachial and lumbosacral plexi at the base of the upper and lower limbs, respectively, are the largest examples of these structures. The ANS also has a variety of plexi in which nerves converge and redistribute axons to their target organs.

The Two Divisions of the ANS Generally Exert Opposing Actions

The ANS consists of two anatomically and functionally distinct systems, the **sympathetic** and **parasympathetic** divisions (Chapter 38). The pathways of the sympathetic division originate with neurons whose somata lie in the thoracic and upper lumbar segments of the spinal cord. In the parasympathetic division, the neurons of origin are in the brainstem and the sacral segments of the spinal cord. Therefore, the sympathetic and parasympathetic divisions are sometimes called the thoracolumbar and craniosacral divisions, respectively. Anatomically, the two divisions are constructed quite differently, and their anatomy reveals much about the differences in their function.

The sympathetic and parasympathetic divisions generally innervate the same organs but produce opposite effects. For example, the sympathetic division stimulates the heart, increasing the heart rate and the force of contraction, while the parasympathetic division inhibits the heart, decreasing the heart rate. In the gastrointestinal tract, motility is inhibited by the sympathetic division and stimulated by the parasympathetic division.

The two divisions function in a kind of "push–pull" relationship with each other. It is never the case that

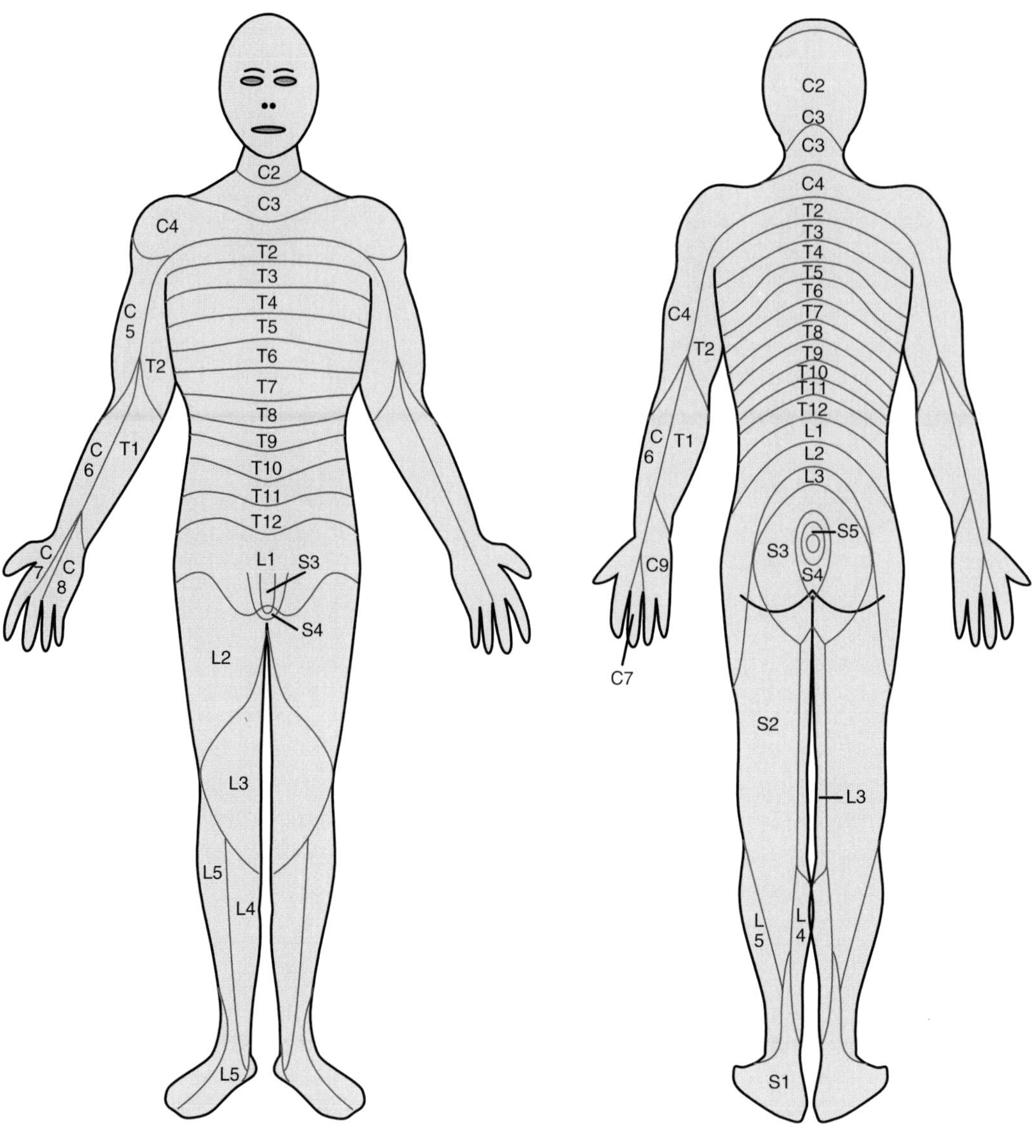

FIGURE 2.19 A dermatome map of the human body. The spinal cord level that selectively innervates each dermatome is indicated. Note the twisting of the dermatomes of the lower limb, which arises from rotation of that limb as it develops to accommodate bipedal motion.

one is completely on or off. Rather, there are degrees of sympathetic and parasympathetic "tone." During sleep, certain involuntary functions such as digestion are accelerated. The glands that take part in digestion are activated parasympathetically, and sympathetic tone is correspondingly decreased. On the other hand, as noted by Walter B. Cannon, during the characteristic "fight or flight" reaction in defensive behavior, sympathetic tone is markedly enhanced and parasympathetic tone is sharply reduced.

Sympathetic outflow is vastly amplified through a series of sympathetic ganglia and the adrenal medulla. As a consequence of this amplification, sympathetic function occurs more or less synchronously throughout the body. In contrast, the parasympathetic system is quite finely tuned. For example, digestion requires the coordinated stimulation of glandular secretion and smooth muscle contraction progressively through the gastrointestinal tract, from the stomach and the small intestine to the large bowel. This coordination is accomplished partly through local increases in parasympathetic tone.

The Spinal Cord Generates a Series of Dorsal and Ventral Roots

The spinal cord, roughly the thickness of an adult's little finger, is surrounded and protected by the vertebral column (Fig. 2.20), which forms during early embryogenesis from sclerotome cells. These cells initially

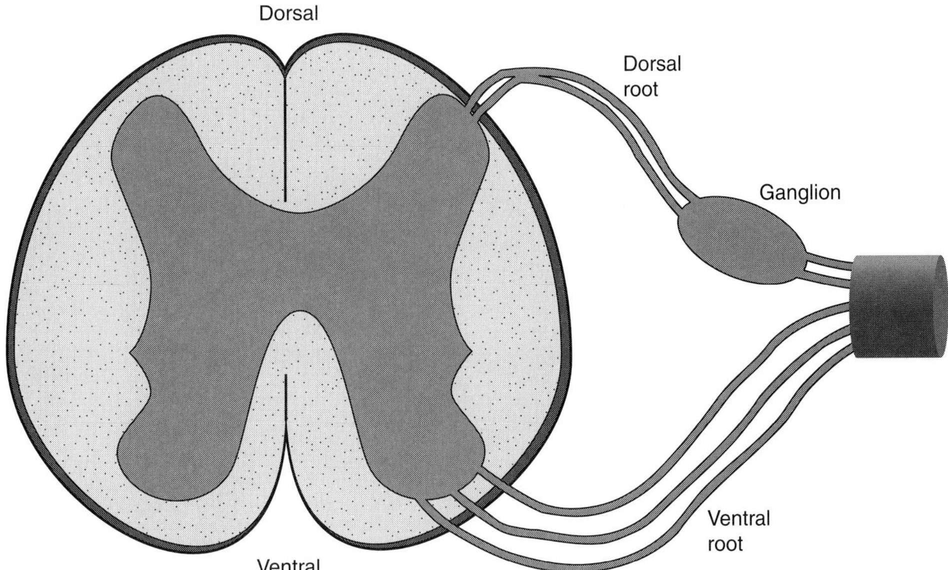

FIGURE 2.20 Cross section of the spinal cord. The "H" or butterfly-shaped gray matter containing neuronal cell bodies, and for the most part unmyelinated neuronal processes, is shown surrounded by white matter containing myelinated tracts. Dorsal and ventral rootlets, which coalesce to form dorsal and ventral roots, are apparent, as is the swelling of the dorsal root where the dorsal root ganglion cells are located.

enclose the neural tube, but later they form clefts at regularly spaced intervals that eventually separate adjacent vertebrae. In cross section, the spinal cord can be seen to contain two basic types of nervous tissue: **gray matter** and **white matter.** Gray matter occurs in a "butterfly" configuration surrounding the central canal and is composed primarily of neuronal somata and neuropil. White matter surrounds the gray matter and consists mostly of axons collected into poorly differentiated bundles. Many of the axons are surrounded by a myelin sheath, a uniquely vertebrate feature that allows very rapid conduction of nerve impulses (see Chapter 3). The paracrystalline arrangement of the lipids and proteins in myelin, together with myelin's unusually high lipid/protein ratio, give white matter its pale appearance.

The adult spinal cord has a segmented appearance, with a bilateral pair of dorsal and ventral roots attached at regular intervals along its length. The segments have been artificially grouped into five sets: cervical, thoracic, lumbar, sacral, and coccygeal. As we noted earlier, the dorsal roots in each segment contain sensory axons and the ventral roots contain motor axons. The dorsal and ventral roots unite a short distance from the spinal cord to form mixed (sensory and motor) spinal nerves, which pass through the vertebral column via the intervertebral foramina. Thus, one left and one right spinal nerve are associated with each spinal segment. In humans, there are 31 pairs of spinal nerves (8 cervical, 12 thoracic, 5 lumbar, 5 sacral, and 1 coccygeal), which are named according to the intervertebral foramen through which they pass (Fig. 2.21A).

In the early fetus, the spinal cord extends the full length of the vertebral column, but as development proceeds, the vertebral column outgrows the spinal cord. At birth, the spinal cord ends at the level of the third lumbar vertebra, and by adulthood it reaches only to the first lumbar vertebra. This differential growth does not affect the correct distribution of spinal nerves through the intervertebral foramina, however. As a result, the spinal nerves from the caudal segments of the cord travel long distances inside the vertebral canal (Fig. 2.21B). Their parallel arrangement caudal to the termination of the spinal cord gives them the appearance of a horsetail and is the basis for their name, *cauda equina*. It is at the level of the cauda equina where a sample of cerebrospinal fluid may be removed for analysis by aspiration through a lumbar puncture. This "spinal tap" is done at or below the level of the second lumbar vertebra to avoid the risk of injuring the spinal cord.

Cranial Nerves Carry Sensory and Motor Information between the Brain and the Periphery

Vertebrates have 12 pairs of **cranial nerves** (Fig. 2.22), which are numbered with Roman numerals according to the rostrocaudal level at which they enter the brain. In humans, seven cranial nerves carry infor-

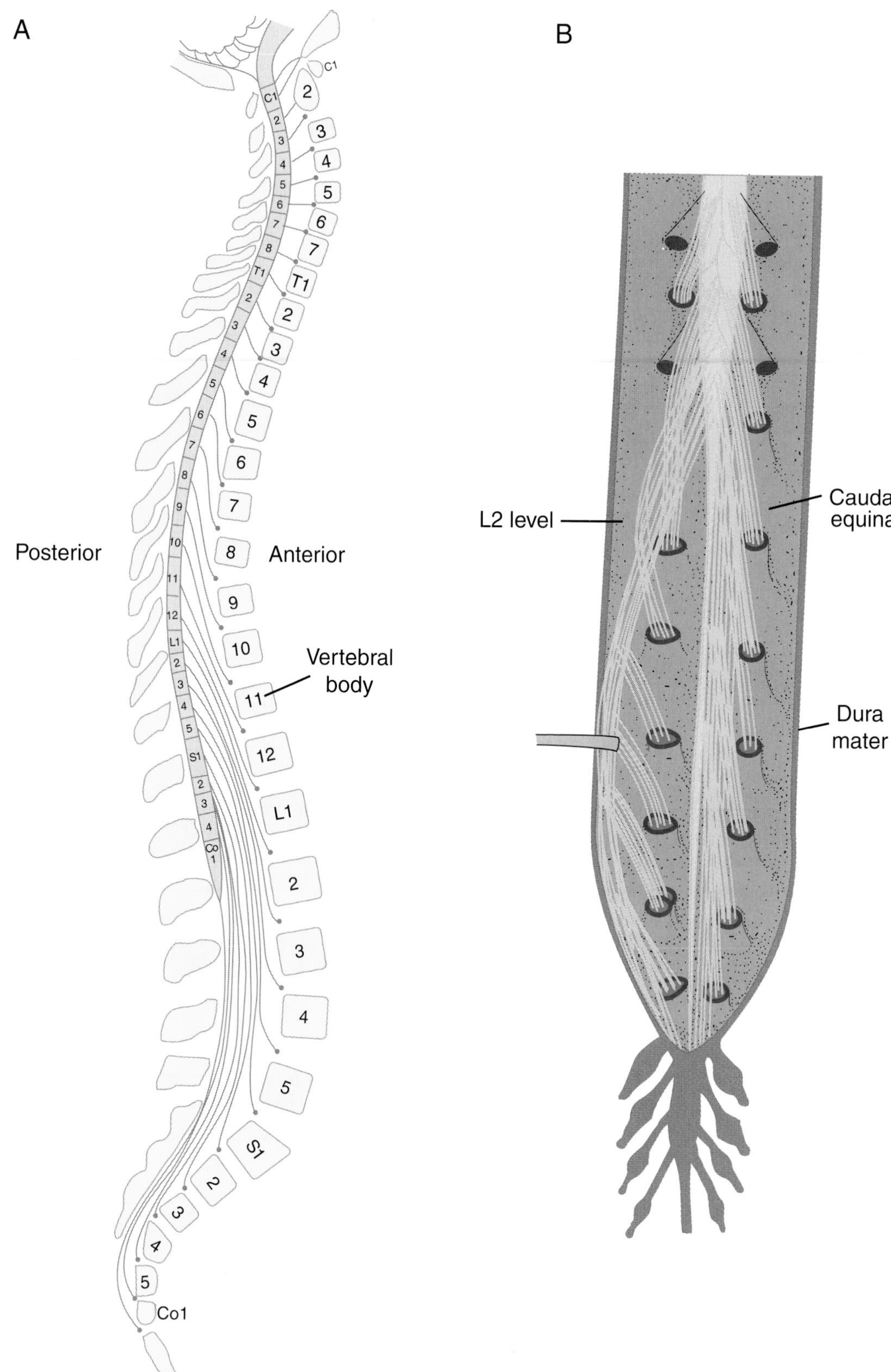

FIGURE 2.21 The spinal cord within the spinal column. (A) Mid-sagittal section of the back in the human. The spinal cord is considerably shorter than the vertebral column that encases it. The spinal cord extends only to level L1–L2, but the nerve rootlets emanating from each segment continue down to the appropriate vertebral column exit point. (B) The cauda equina ("horse tail") is formed from the collected nerve roots. The cauda equina exits the vertebral canal through the dura mater, which surrounds the spinal column.

mation about the so-called special senses: olfaction (I, the olfactory nerve), vision (II, the optic nerve), hearing and balance (VIII, the vestibuloacoustic nerve), and taste (V, VII, IX, and X). Nerves III, IV, and VI primarily control eye movement, while nerve III is also involved in the pupillary light reflex. Nerve V carries sensory axons from the face and motor axons that innervate the muscles used in mastication (chewing). The facial nerve, VII, controls the muscles of facial expression and also innervates the salivary and lacrimal glands. Nerve IX, the glossopharyngeal nerve, innervates the pharynx and mediates the swallowing reflex. Nerve X,

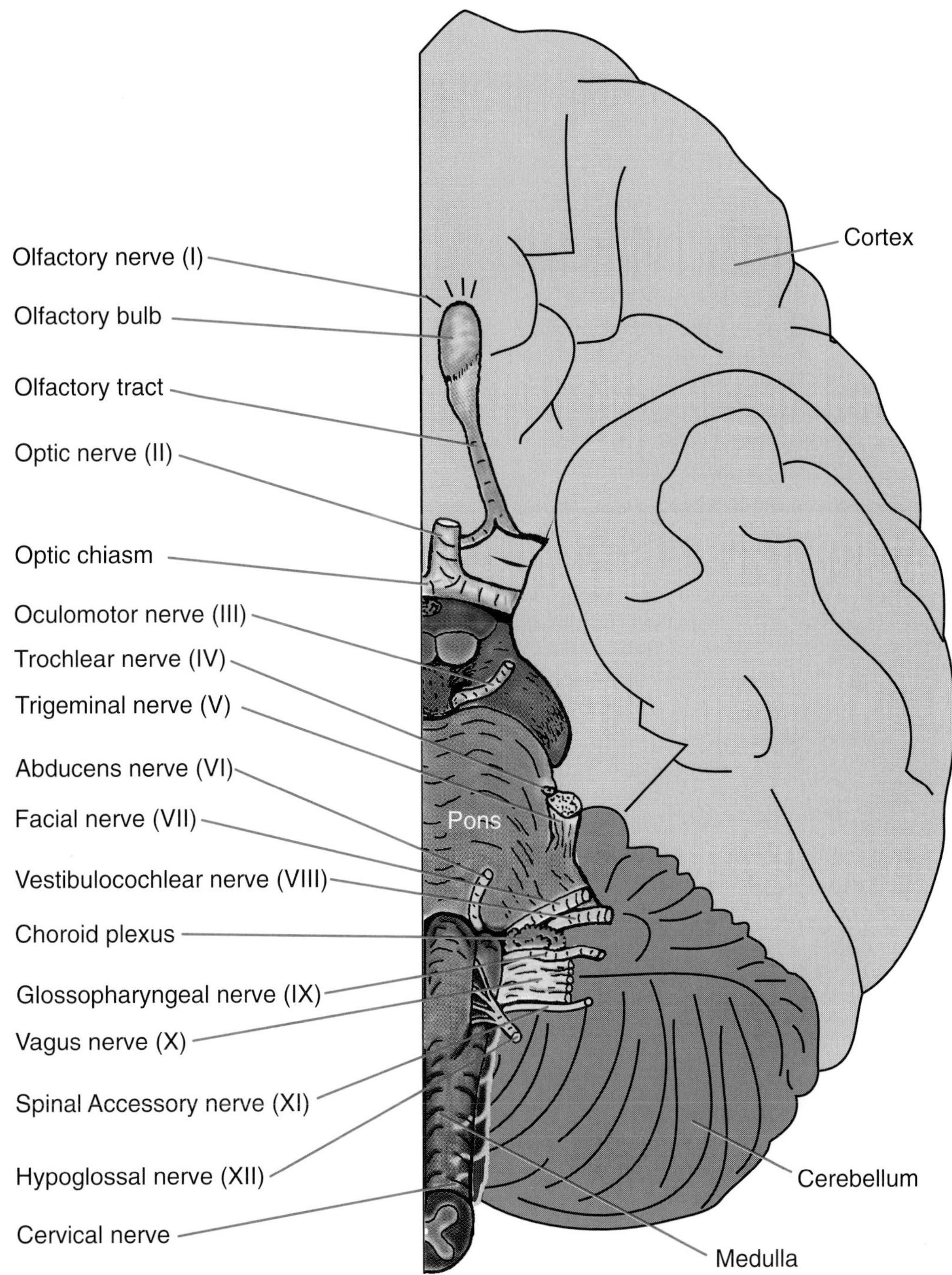

FIGURE 2.22 The cranial nerves at the base of the brain. The 12 pairs of cranial nerves are seen as they exit from the brain.

the vagus nerve ("the wanderer"), innervates the larynx and carries parasympathetic efferents to viscera in the thorax and abdomen. When stimulated, the vagus nerve slows the heart by increasing parasympathetic tone. Nerve XI, the spinal accessory nerve, innervates the trapezius, a trapezoid-shaped muscle that sits high on the back. The most caudal cranial nerve, XII, is the hypoglossal nerve, which moves the tongue. The cranial nerves may have evolved through the specialization and fusion of segmental nerves, so it should not be surprising that most of them are complex in terms of the functional components they contain.

The Cerebral Hemispheres Are Divided into Lobes

The most extraordinary growth of the brain occurs in the endbrain, or cerebral hemispheres. The cerebral hemispheres develop more or less as mirror images of each other and are divided down the dorsal midline by the interhemispheric (longitudinal) fissure. Their size is restricted by the capacity of the cranium within which the brain develops. As the hemispheres grow, they develop folds called gyri separated by invaginations known as sulci (singular: gyrus and sulcus; see Fig. 2.23). The folding gives the hemispheres a greater surface area and is very pronounced in primates, especially humans. The locations of particular sulci and gyri are stereotyped within a species, although like any trait, there is slight variation from one individual to another. Two major sulci, the central sulcus and the lateral sulcus, are used as anatomical landmarks in the human cerebral hemispheres. The central sulcus extends laterally from the interhemispheric fissure to the lateral midline, where it contacts the lateral sulcus. The sulci divide the surface of the cerebral hemispheres into four lobes—frontal, parietal, temporal, and occipital—which are named after the cranial bones that lie over them. In addition, the insular lobe is folded inside the hemispheres, and the limbic lobe forms the medial border of the hemispheres. Many of the functions of the cerebral cortex have been localized to specific lobes.

Each cerebral hemisphere generally oversees activities on the opposite, or contralateral, side of the body. Bundles of axons called commissures connect structures in one hemisphere to the same or related structures in the opposite hemisphere. In general, commissures enable the two hemispheres to integrate and compare information. Communication between the hemispheres is completely eliminated by commissurotomy, the surgical division of all of the commissures. Commissurotomy is sometimes performed as a treatment for severe cases of epilepsy, to prevent epileptic activity that originates in one hemisphere from spreading to the other hemisphere and thus affecting both sides of the body. Incredibly, commissurotomy patients function extremely well under most conditions, and behavioral studies on such patients have yielded some remarkable information about cerebral cortical

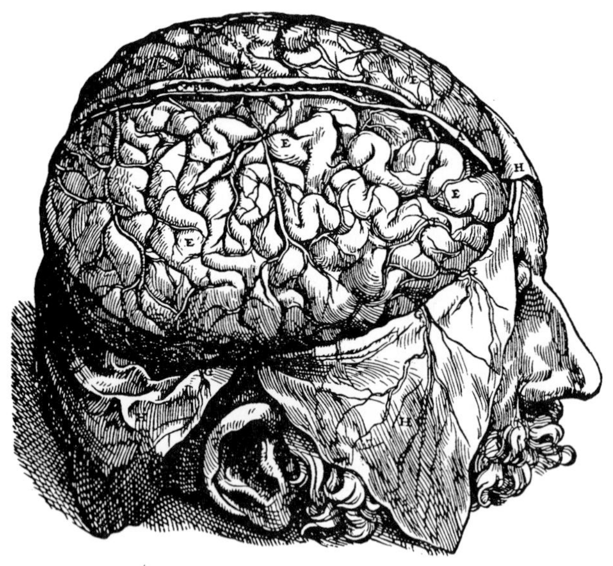

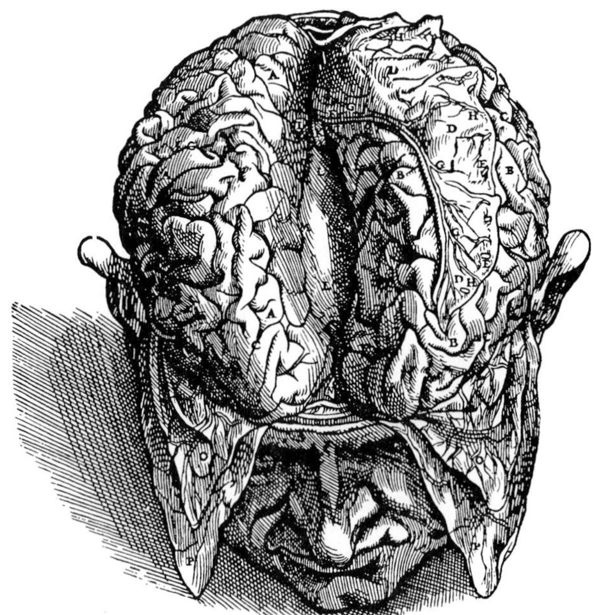

FIGURE 2.23 The surface structure of the cerebral cortex. The cortex is thrown into folds (gyri) separated by depressions (sulci). From Vesalius, 1543.

organization (see Chapter 58). Other axon bundles, known as decussations, connect structures in one hemisphere to contralateral structures in more caudal regions of the CNS.

The Nervous System Is Protected by Membranous Coverings

The brain and spinal cord are completely surrounded by three membranes: the **pia mater,** the **arachnoid mater,** and the **dura mater.** Collectively, these three membranes are known as the **meninges.** The pia (''faithful'') mater is very thin and, as its name suggests, adheres closely to the surface of the CNS, even in regions where there are substantial invaginations, such as the surface of the cerebellum and cerebral hemispheres. Exterior to the pia mater is the arachnoid (''spidery'') mater, which has a tenuous, weblike structure. The dura (''hard'' or ''strong'') mater is a thick, inelastic covering that is closely apposed to the inner surface of the skull and vertebral canal. The membranes covering the CNS are continuous with similar coverings in the PNS, although the terminology in the PNS is different.

In certain regions of the CNS, neural tissue is absent but the meninges persist. In these regions, the ependymal cells of the ventricular system fuse with the pia mater and arachnoid mater, forming a structure known as the **choroid plexus** (Fig. 2.24). The choroid plexus contains blood vessels and serves as a component in the blood–brain barrier. It also produces cerebrospinal fluid, which fills the ventricles of the brain and the central canal of the spinal cord. Cerebrospinal fluid passes out of the interior of the brain through paired foramina near the cerebellum and through a single median foramen in the roof of the medulla. All of these openings lead to the subarachnoid space, which lies between the pia mater and the arachnoid mater.

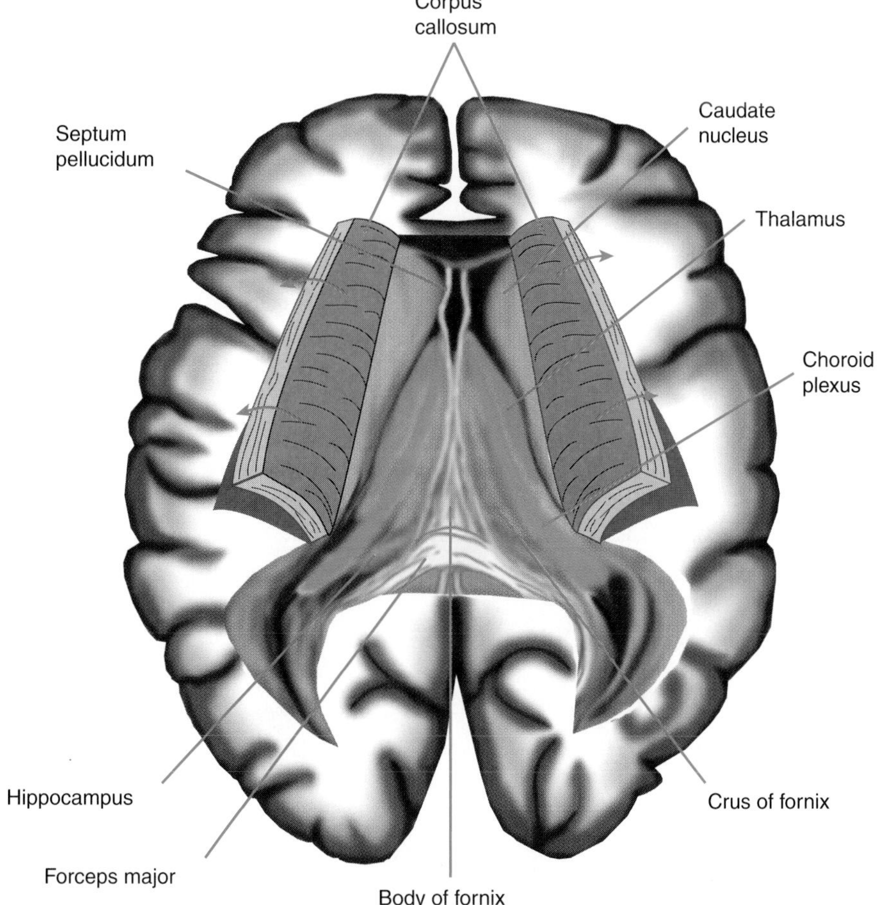

FIGURE 2.24 The choroid plexus of the ventricular system. In this horizontal section of the brain, the ventricular system, normally filled with cerebrospinal fluid (CSF), is opened and the choroid plexus, which produces the CSF, is visible in the lateral ventricles (in red).

The Brain Is a Well-Vascularized Structure

The human brain consumes a full 20% of the body's oxygen supply at rest. Therefore, it must continuously receive a voluminous blood supply, on the order of one liter per minute. Blood reaches the brain through two paired arterial roots, the **vertebral** and **internal carotid arteries.** These arteries anastomose at the circle of Willis, located at the base of the brain (Fig. 2.25). The importance of this anastomosis cannot be overemphasized, because after this point there is a marked reduction in the extent of anastomoses between brain arteries. As a result, blockages of even a small artery or arteriole can rapidly deprive a brain region of oxygen, producing the condition known as a stroke.

After entering the skull through the foramen magnum, the paired vertebral arteries fuse into a single basilar artery, giving off the cerebellar arteries and the posterior cerebral arteries, which supply caudal regions of the cerebral hemispheres. The internal carotid arteries divide to form the anterior and middle cerebral arteries; the former supplies the medial surface of each cerebral hemisphere, where it presses against the other hemisphere, while the latter supplies the rest of the hemispheres. For the most part, the major arteries course along the cerebral surface before abruptly diving into the brain and ramifying into arterioles and capillaries.

Numerous large venous sinuses collect blood from the capillary beds in the brain and return it to the heart, mostly via the internal jugular vein. The major venous sinuses lie within the dura mater, whose inelasticity essentially holds the sinuses open. Blood flow through the sinuses is not very rapid, nor is it under great pressure. The presence of thin-walled venous sinuses surrounded by the tough and immovable dura sets the stage for serious injury to the sinuses when the head is subjected to physical trauma. Perhaps the best-known example is the traumatic injury to the midline great cerebral vein that can occur when a boxer is struck in the head. The impact of the blow causes the brain to recoil in its cerebrospinal fluid cushion, exerting a shearing force against the dura, which remains attached to the skull. This force effectively ruptures the great cerebral vein, leading to serious hemorrhage of venous blood into the subdural space.

Summary

In this chapter we have considered some approaches to the problem of understanding the fundamental structure and wiring diagram of the nervous system. One approach is to examine a series of increasingly complex animals from an evolutionary perspective to gain insight into basic organizing principles. Such an

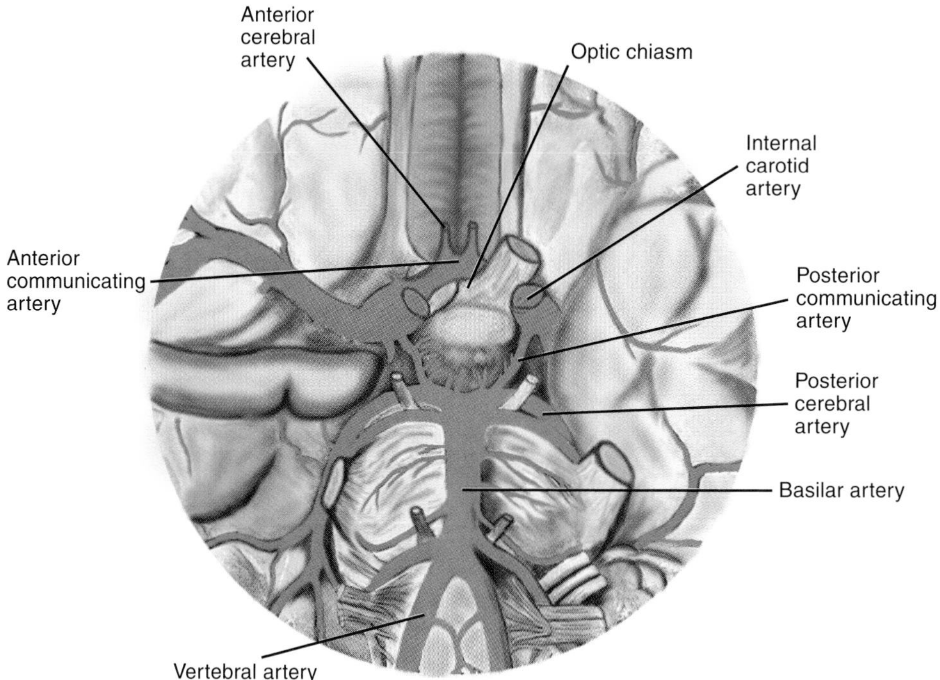

FIGURE 2.25 The circle of Willis (circulosis arteriosis) is located at the base of the brain. The circle consists of several arteries, which anastomose with each other, forming an alternative circulatory pathway when one of the arteries is obstructed.

examination reveals tendencies toward centralization, cephalization, bilateral symmetry, and regionalization of the nervous system. It also suggests that basic cellular mechanisms of neuronal function have changed little since the appearance of the simplest nervous systems.

Another approach is to follow the development of the vertebrate nervous system from embryo to adult. At early stages of development, the CNS of all vertebrates has the same basic structure. A polarized, bilaterally symmetrical, regionalized neural plate invaginates to form a neural tube. The neural tube has three swellings at its rostral end—the forebrain, midbrain, and hindbrain vesicles—and a primitive spinal cord at the caudal end. These four basic divisions of the CNS go on to subdivide repeatedly, until all of the laminated and nuclear cell groups of the adult CNS are formed. A topographic description of the CNS emerges from such a developmental approach.

How the functional systems of the CNS are arranged into a unified whole is an unsolved problem. In the model we have discussed in this chapter, behavior is equated with motor output, which is driven by sensory, intrinsic, and cognitive inputs as well as by endogenous activity within the motor system itself. Future behavior is determined in part by sensory feedback related to the consequences of the original behavior. In our present state of knowledge, the relationship between functional systems and the topographic organization of the CNS is not obvious.

References

General

Bergquist, H., and Källén, B. (1954). Notes on the early histogenesis and morphogenesis of the central nervous system in vertebrates. *J. Comp. Neurol.* **100:** 627–659.

Björklund, A., and Hökfelt, T. (1983–present). *Handbook of Chemical Neuroanatomy.* Elsevier, Amsterdam.

Brodal, A. (1981). *Neurological Anatomy, In Relation to Clinical Medicine,* 3rd ed. Oxford University Press, New York.

Churchland, P. M. (1995). *The Engine of Reason, the Seat of the Soul. A Philosophical Journey into the Brain,* pp. 7–8. MIT Press, Cambridge.

Descartes, R. (1972). *Treatise of Man.* French text with translation by T. S. Steele. Harvard University Press, Cambridge.

Hamburger, V. (1973). Anatomical and physiological basis of embryonic motility in birds and mammals. In *Studies on the Development of Behavior and the Nervous System* (G. Gottlieb, ed.), Vol. I, pp. 51–76. Academic Press, New York.

Herrick, C. J. (1948). *The Brain of the Tiger Salamander.* University of Chicago Press, Chicago.

Kingsbury, B. F. (1922). The fundamental plan of the vertebrate brain. *J. Comp. Neurol.* **34:** 461–491.

Lorenz, K. (1978). *Behind the Mirror.* Harcourt Brace Jovanovich, Orlando.

Nieuwenhuys, R., Voogd, J., and van Huijzen, C. (1988). *The Human Central Nervous System: A Synopsis and Atlas,* 3rd ed. Springer-Verlag, Berlin.

Russell, E. S. (1916). *Form and Function: A Contribution to the History of Animal Morphology.* John Murray, London.

Sherrington, C. S. (1947). *The Integrative Action of the Nervous System.* Cambridge University Press, Cambridge.

Tinbergen, N. (1951). *The Study of Instinct.* Oxford University Press, London.

Cited

1. Fannon, A., and Colman, D. R. (1996). A model for central synaptic junctional complex formation based on the differential adhesive specificities of the cadherins. *Neuron* **17:** 423–434.
2. Peters, A., Palay, S. L., and Webster, H. deF. (1991). *The Fine Structure of the Nervous System: Neurons and Their Supporting Cells,* 3rd ed. Oxford University Press, New York.
3. Cajal, S. Ramón y (1995). *Histology of the Nervous System of Man and Vertebrates,* in 2 Vols. Translation of *Histologie du système nerveux de l'homme et des vertébrés,* 1909–1911, by N. Swanson and L. W. Swanson. Oxford University Press, New York.
4. Parker, G. H. (1919). *The Elementary Nervous System.* Lippincott, Philadelphia.
5. McConnell, C. H. (1932). Development of the ectodermal nerve net in the buds of *Hydra. Quart. J. Micr. Sci.* **75:** 495–509.
6. Lentz, T. L. (1968). *Primitive Nervous Systems.* Yale University Press, New Haven.
7. Brusca, R. C., and Brusca, G. J. (1990). *Invertebrates.* Sinauer Associates, Sunderland.
8. Cartmill, M., Hylander, W. L., and Shafland, J. (1987). *Human Structure.* Harvard University Press, Cambridge.
9. Holland, L. Z., and Holland, N. D. (1996). Expression of AmphiHox-1 and AmphiPax-1 in amphioxus embryos treated with retinoic acid: insights into evolution and patterning of the chordate nerve cord and pharynx. *Development* **122:** 1829–1838.
10. De Robertis, E. M., and Sasai, Y. (1996). A common plan for dorsoventral patterning in Bilateria. *Nature* **380:** 37–40.
11. Hogan, B. L. M. (1996). Upside-down ideas vindicated. *Nature* **376:** 210–211.
12. Swanson, L. W. (1992). *Brain Maps: Structure of the Rat Brain.* Elsevier, Amsterdam.
13. Wiener, N. (1948). *Cybernetics, or Control and Communication in the Animal and Machine.* Wiley, New York.
14. Von Neumann, J. (1958). *The Computer and the Brain.* Yale University Press, New Haven.
15. Alvarez-Bolado, G., and Swanson, L. W. (1996). *Developmental Brain Maps: Structure of the Embryonic Rat Brain.* Elsevier, Amsterdam.
16. Swanson, L. W. (1999). *Thinking about Neural Circuits.* Oxford University Press, Oxford, in press.
17. Valverde, F. (1965). *Studies on the Piriform Lobe.* Harvard University Press, Cambridge.

S E C T I O N II

CELLULAR AND MOLECULAR NEUROSCIENCE

C H A P T E R

3

The Cellular Components of Nervous Tissue

Patrick R. Hof, Bruce D. Trapp, Jean de Vellis, Luz Claudio, and David R. Colman

Several types of cellular elements are anatomically, biochemically, and physiologically integrated to yield normally functioning brain tissue. The neuron is the hallmark communicating cell, and its functional properties are strongly shaped and sustained by the neuroglial cells. A wide variety of neuronal subtypes are connected to one another via complex circuitries usually involving multiple synaptic connections. Neuronal physiology is supported and maintained by the neuroglial cells, which have highly diverse and incompletely understood functions. These include myelination, secretion of trophic factors, maintenance of the extracellular milieu, and scavenging of molecular and cellular debris from it. Neuroglial cells also participate in the formation and maintenance of the blood–brain barrier, a multicomponent structure that is interposed between the circulatory system and the brain substance and that serves as the molecular gateway to the brain parenchyma.

THE NEURON

Neurons are highly polarized cells, meaning that they develop, in the course of maturation, distinct subcellular domains that subserve different functions. Morphologically, in a typical neuron, three major functional domains can be defined: (1) the **cell body,** or **perikaryon,** which contains the nucleus and the major cytoplasmic organelles; (2) a variable number of **dendrites,** which emanate from the perikaryon and ramify over a certain volume of gray matter and which differ in size and shape, depending on the neuronal type; and (3) a single **axon,** which extends in most cases much farther from the cell body than does the dendritic arbor (Fig. 3.1). The dendrites may be spiny (as in pyramidal cells) or nonspiny (as in most interneurons), whereas the axon is generally smooth and emits a variable number of branches (collaterals).[1] Many axons are surrounded by an insulating **myelin sheath,** which facilitates rapid impulse conduction. The axon terminal region, where contacts with other cells are made, displays a wide range of morphological specializations, depending on its target area in the central or peripheral nervous system. Classically, two major morphological types of contacts, or synapses, can be recognized by electron microscopy: the **asymmetric** synapses, responsible for transmission of excitatory inputs, and the **symmetric,** inhibitory synapses.

The morphology of the neuronal perikaryon and, most importantly, of its dendritic arborizations reflects its receptive field. The cell body and the dendrites are the two major domains of the cell that receive inputs, and the dendrites play a very important role in greatly expanding the receptive surface of the neuron. In addition, the particular shape of the dendritic tree, which can be used to classify neurons into morphological types, provides the neuron with the specificity of its synaptic contacts. Thus, both the structure of the dendritic arbor and the distribution of axonal terminal ramifications confer a high level of subcellular specificity in the localization of particular synaptic contacts on a given neuron. The three-dimensional distribution of the dendritic arborization is also a very important factor with respect to the type of information transferred to the neuron. A neuron with a dendritic tree restricted to a particular cortical layer may be receptive to a very limited pool of afferents, whereas the widely expanded dendritic arborizations of a large pyramidal neuron will receive highly diversified inputs within the different cortical layers in which segments of the dendritic tree are present (Fig. 3.2).[2–7] The structure of

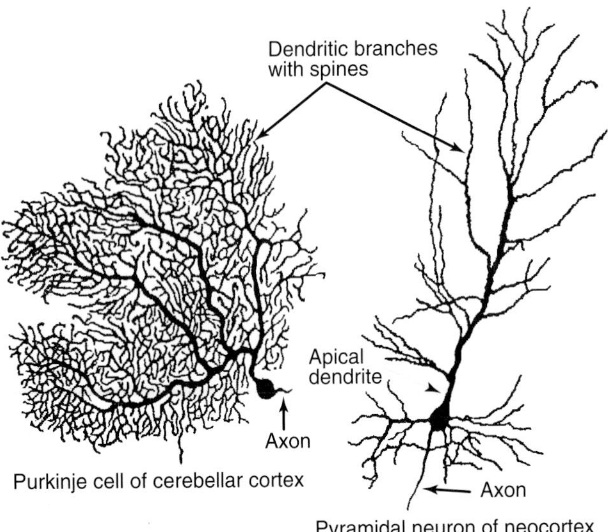

FIGURE 3.1 Typical morphology of projection neurons. On the left is a Purkinje cell of the cerebellar cortex and on the right a pyramidal neuron of the neocortex. These neurons are highly polarized. Each has an extensively branched, spiny apical dendrite, shorter basal dendrites, and a single axon emerging from the basal pole of the cell.

the dendritic tree is thought to be maintained by a complex array of cytoskeletal proteins (microtubules, neurofilaments, and associated proteins), which also take part in the movement of organelles within the dendritic cytoplasm.

An important specialization of the dendritic arbor of certain neurons is the presence of large numbers of dendritic **spines,** which are membrane-limited organelles that project from the surface of the dendrites. They are abundant in large pyramidal neurons and are much sparser on the dendrites of interneurons. Spines are more numerous on the apical shafts of the pyramidal neurons than on the basal dendrites. As many as 30,000 to 40,000 spines are present on the largest pyramidal neurons. Spines constitute the region of the dendritic arborization that receives most of the excitatory input. Each spine generally contains one asymmetric synapse; thus, the approximate density of excitatory input on a neuron can be inferred from an estimate of its number of spines. The cytoplasm within the spines is characterized by the presence of polyribosomes and a variety of filaments, including actin and α- and β-tubulin, as well as a spine apparatus consisting of cisternae, membrane vesicles, and stacks of dense lamellar material (see Box 3.1).[8–13]

The perikaryon contains the nucleus, which is generally round or ovoid and pale, and a large variety of cytoplasmic organelles. Stacks of rough endoplasmic reticulum rich in ribosomes are conspicuous in large neurons and are referred to as **Nissl substance** owing to their affinity for basic aniline dyes such as cresyl violet and toluidine. Another feature of the perikaryal cytoplasm is the presence of a rich cytoskeleton composed primarily of neurofilaments and microtubules, discussed in detail in Chapter 4. These cytoskeletal elements are dispersed in "bundles" within the cytoplasm and extend into the axon and dendrites.[3]

Whereas the dendrites and the cell body can be characterized as the domains of the neuron that receive afferents, the axon, at the other pole of the neuron, is responsible for transmitting neural information. This information may be primary, in the case of a sensory receptor, or processed information that has already been modified through a series of integrative steps. The morphology of the axon and its course through the nervous system are correlated with the type of information processed by the particular neuron and by its connectivity patterns with other neurons. The axon leaves the cell body from a small swelling called the **axon hillock.** This structure is particularly apparent in large pyramidal neurons; in other cell types, the axon sometimes emerges from one of the main dendrites. At the axon hillock, microtubules are packed

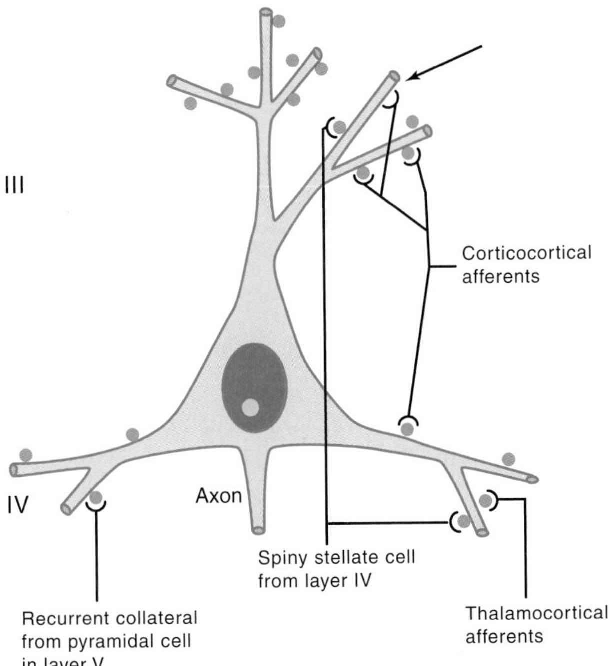

FIGURE 3.2 Schematic representation of four major excitatory inputs to pyramidal neurons. A pyramidal neuron in layer III is shown as an example. Note the preferential distribution of synaptic contacts on spines. Spines are labeled in red. Arrow shows a contact directly on the dendritic shaft.

into bundles that enter the axon as parallel fascicles. The axon hillock is the part of the neuron from which the action potential is generated. The axon is generally unmyelinated in local-circuit neurons (such as inhibitory interneurons), but it is myelinated in neurons that furnish connections between different parts of the nervous system. Axons usually have higher numbers of neurofilaments than do dendrites, although this distinction can be difficult to make in small elements that contain fewer neurofilaments. In addition, the axon may be extremely ramified, as in certain local-circuit neurons; it may give out a large number of recurrent collaterals, as in neurons connecting different cortical regions; or it may be relatively straight in the case of projections to subcortical centers, as in cortical motor neurons that send their very long axons to the ventral horn of the spinal cord. At the interface of axon terminals with target cells are the synapses, which represent specialized zones of contact consisting of a presynaptic (axonal) element, a narrow synaptic cleft, and a postsynaptic element on a dendrite or perikaryon. We consider the fine structure of synapses later in this chapter. In the next section, we turn our attention to the principal morphologic features of several neuronal types from the cerebral cortex, subcortical structures, and periphery as typical examples of the cellular diversity in the nervous system.

Pyramidal Cells Are the Main Excitatory Neurons in the Cerebral Cortex

All of the cortical output is mediated through pyramidal neurons, and the intrinsic activity of the neocortex can be viewed simply as a means of finely tuning their output. A **pyramidal cell** is a highly polarized neuron, with a major orientation axis perpendicular, or orthogonal, to the pial surface of the cerebral cortex. In cross section, the cell body is roughly triangular (Fig. 3.2), although a large variety of morphologic types exist with elongate, horizontal, or vertical fusiform, or inverted perikaryal shapes. A pyramidal neuron typically has a large number of dendrites that emanate from the apex and form the base of the cell body. The span of the dendritic tree depends on the laminar localization of the cell body, but it may, as in giant pyramidal neurons, spread over several millimeters. The cell body and dendritic arborization may be restricted to a few layers or, in some cases, may span the entire cortical thickness.[14]

In most cases, the axon of a large pyramidal cell extends from the base of the perikaryon and courses toward the subcortical white matter, giving off several collateral branches that are directed to cortical domains generally located within the vicinity of the cell of origin (as explained later in this section). Typically, a pyramidal cell has a large nucleus, a cytoplasmic rim that contains, particularly in large pyramidal cells, a collection of granular material chiefly composed of lipofuscin. The deposition of lipofuscin augments with age and is considered a benign change. Although all pyramidal cells possess these general features, they can also be subdivided into numerous classes based on their morphology, laminar location, and connectivity (Fig. 3.4).[15] For instance, small pyramidal neurons in layers II and III of the neocortex have restricted dendritic trees and form vast arrays of axonal collaterals with neighboring cortical domains, whereas medium-to-large pyramidal cells in deep layer III and layer V have much more extensive dendritic trees and furnish long corticocortical connections. Layer V also contains very large pyramidal neurons arranged in clusters or as isolated, somewhat regularly spaced elements. These neurons project to subcortical centers such as the basal ganglia, brain stem, and spinal cord. Finally, layer VI pyramidal cells exhibit a greater morphologic variability than do pyramidal cells in other layers and are involved in certain corticocortical as well as corticothalamic projections.[16–18]

The excitatory inputs to pyramidal neurons can be divided into **intrinsic afferents,** such as recurrent collaterals from other pyramidal cells and excitatory interneurons, and **extrinsic afferents** of thalamic and cortical origin. The neurotransmitters in these excitatory inputs are thought to be glutamate and possibly aspartate. Although this division may appear relatively simplistic, the complexity and heterogeneity of excitatory transmission in the neocortex may not be derived from the presynaptic side, but rather from the postsynaptic side of the synapse. In other words, at the molecular level, a variety of glutamate receptor subunit combinations may confer different functional capacities on a given glutamatergic synapse (see Chapter 9).

Pyramidal cells not only furnish the major excitatory output of the neocortex, but also act as a major intrinsic excitatory input through axonal collaterals. The collaterals of the main axonal branch that exits from the cortex are referred to as recurrent collaterals because they ascend back to superficial layers; thus, the collateral branches of a pyramidal cell synapse in layers superficial to their origin, although a deep or local system of branches is also present (see Fig. 3.4). Although many of these branches ascend in a radial, vertical pattern of arborization, there is a separate set of projections that travels horizontally over long distances (in some instances as much as 7–8 mm). One of the major functions of the vertically oriented component of the recurrent collaterals may be to interconnect layers III and V, the two major output layers of the neocortex. In layer III pyramidal cells, 95% of the synaptic targets of the recurrent cells are other pyramidal cells. This is true of both the vertical and the distant horizontal recurrent projections. In addition, the majority of these synapses are on dendritic spines and to some degree on dendritic shafts. It is possible that there are regional and laminar specificities to these synaptic arrangements, although such fine patterns are not yet fully elucidated.[4–6,19,19a] These recurrent projections function to set up local excitatory patterns and coordinate multineuronal assemblies into an excitatory output.

Spiny Stellate Cells Are Excitatory Interneurons

The other major excitatory input to pyramidal cells of cortical origin is provided by the interneuron class referred to as **spiny stellate cells,** small multipolar neurons with local dendritic and axonal arborizations. These neurons resemble pyramidal cells in that they are the only other cortical neurons with large numbers of dendritic spines, but they differ from pyramidal neurons in that they lack an apical dendrite. Although the dendritic arbor of these neurons tends to be local, it can vary from a primarily radial orientation to one that is more horizontal. The relatively restricted dendritic arbor of these neurons is presumably a manifestation of the fact that they are high-resolution neurons that gather afferents to a very restricted region of cortex. The dendrites rarely leave the layer in which the cell body resides. The spiny stellate cell also resembles the pyramidal cell in that it provides asymmetric synapses that are presumed to be excitatory, and, like pyramidal cells, these neurons are thought to use either glutamate or aspartate as their neurotransmitter.

Spiny stellate cells exhibit extensive regional and laminar specificities in their distribution. Spiny stellate cells are found in highest concentration in layers IVC and IVA of the primary visual cortex, where they constitute the predominant neuronal type. They are also found in high numbers in layer IV of other primary sensory areas. However, several cortical regions have relatively few of these neurons, and even in areas in which these neurons are well represented, they are vastly outnumbered by aspiny interneurons.[3,6]

The axons of spiny stellate neurons are primarily intrinsic in their targets and radial in orientation and appear to play an important role in forming links between layer IV, the major thalamorecipient layer, and layers III, V, and VI, the major projection layers (Fig. 3.5). In some respects, the axonal arbor of spiny stellate

BOX 3.1

SPINES

Spines are protrusions on the dendritic shafts of neurons and are the site of a large number of axonal contacts. The use of the silver impregnation techniques of Golgi or of the methylene blue used by Ehrlich in the late 19th century led to the discovery of spiny appendages on dendrites of a variety of neurons. The best known are those on pyramidal neurons and Purkinje cells, although spines occur on neuron types at all levels of the central nervous system. In 1896 Berkley[8] observed that terminal boutons were closely apposed on spines (a fact that was later confirmed by Gray in 1959[9] using electron microscopy) and suggested that spines may be involved in conducting impulses from neuron to neuron. In 1904, Santiago Ramón y Cajal[10] suggested that spines could collect the electrical charge resulting from neuronal activity. He also noted that spines substantially increase the receptive surface of the dendritic arbor, which may represent an important factor in receiving the contacts made by the axonal terminals of other neurons. It has been calculated that the approximately 4000 spines of a pyramidal neuron account for more than 40% of its total surface area.[1]

More recent analyses of spine electrical properties have demonstrated that spines are dynamic structures that can regulate many neurochemical events related to synaptic transmission and modulate synaptic efficacy.[11] Spines are also known to undergo pathologic alterations and have a reduced density in a number of experimental manipulations (such as deprivation of a sensory input) and in many developmental, neurologic, and psychiatric conditions (such as dementing illnesses, chronic alcoholism, schizophrenia, trisomy 21).[12] Morphologically, spines are characterized by a narrow portion emanating from the dendritic shaft, the neck, and an ovoid bulb or head. Spines have an average length of 2 μm despite considerable variability in morphology. At the ultrastructural level (Fig. 3.3), spines are characterized by the presence of asymmetric

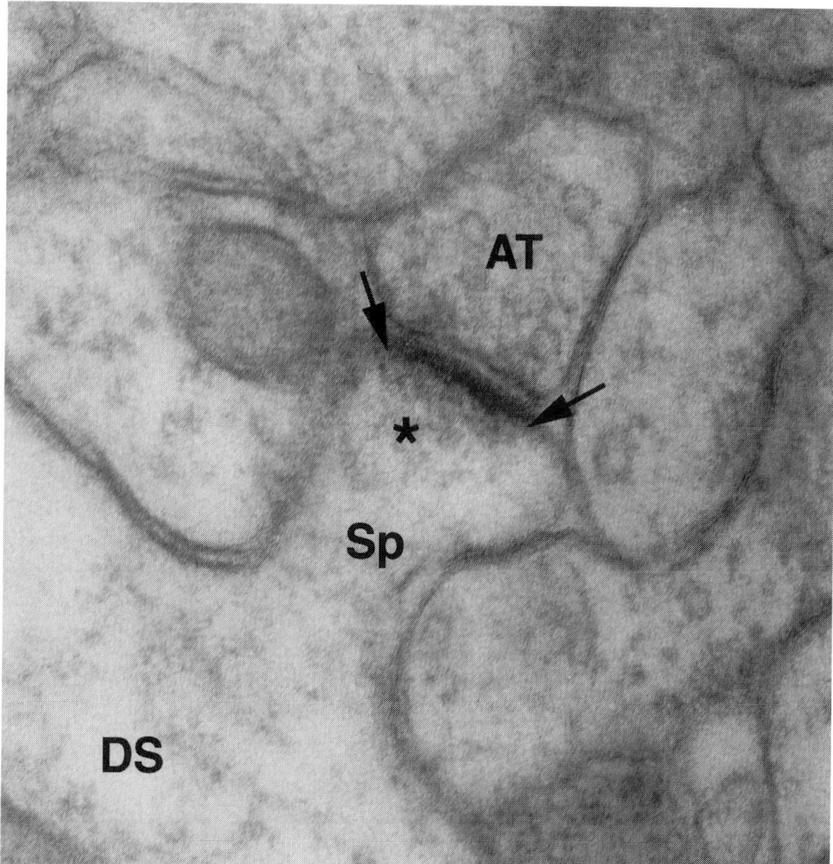

FIGURE 3.3 Ultrastructure of a single dendritic spine (Sp). Note the narrow neck emanating from the main dendritic shaft and the spine head containing filamentous material, the cisterns of the spine apparatus, and the postsynaptic density of an asymmetric synapse (arrows). AT, axon terminal.

synapses and a few vesicles and contain fine and quite indistinct filaments. These filaments most likely consist of actin and α- and β-tubulins. The microtubules and neurofilaments present in the dendritic shafts do not penetrate the spines. Mitochondria and free ribosomes are infrequent, although many spines contain polyribosomes in their head and neck. Interestingly most polyribosomes in dendrites are located at the bases of spines, where they are associated with endoplasmic reticulum, indicating that spines possess the machinery necessary for the local synthesis of proteins.[13]

Another classic feature of the spine is the presence in the spine head of confluent tubular cisterns that represent an extension of the dendritic smooth endoplasmic reticulum. Those cisterns are referred to as the spine apparatus. The function of the spine apparatus is not fully understood but may be related to storage of calcium ions during synaptic transmission.

cells mirrors the vertical plexuses of recurrent collaterals; however, they are more restricted than recurrent collaterals. Given its axonal distribution, the spiny stellate neuron appears to function as a high-fidelity translator of thalamic inputs, maintaining strict topographic organization and setting up initial vertical links of information transfer within sensory areas. Presumably, both pyramidal cells and aspiny nonpyramidal cells receive these radially limited inputs of the spiny stellate neuron, suggesting that this interneuron plays a key role in setting up the excitatory component of a functional cortical domain.[3]

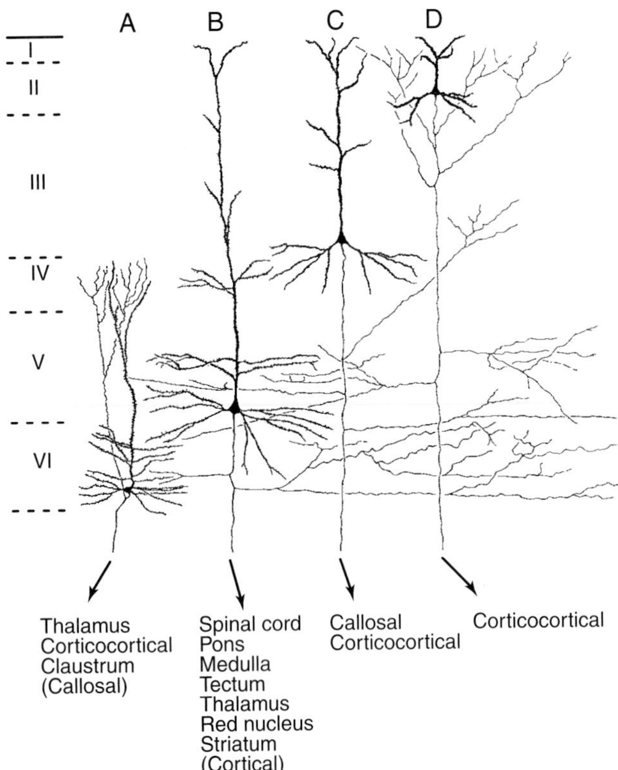

FIGURE 3.4 Morphology and distribution of neocortical pyramidal neurons. Note the variability in cell size and dendritic arborization as well as the presence of axon collaterals, depending on the laminar localization (I–VI) of the neuron. Also, different types of pyramidal neurons with a precise laminar distribution project to different regions of the brain. Adapted from Jones.[14]

Basket, Chandelier, and Double Bouquet Cells Are Inhibitory Interneurons

A large variety of inhibitory interneuron types are present in the cerebral cortex and in subcortical structures. These neurons contain the inhibitory neurotransmitter **γ-aminobutyric acid (GABA)** and exert strong local inhibitory effects. Three major subtypes of cortical interneurons are discussed in this section as examples. In all three cases, the dendritic and axonal arborizations offer important clues to their role in the regulation of pyramidal cell function.[20,21] In addition, for several GABAergic interneurons, a subtype of a given morphologic class can be further defined by a particular set of neurochemical characteristics.[21a] Although the following examples are taken from neurons prevalent in the neocortex and hippocampus of primates, inhibitory interneurons are present throughout the cerebral gray matter and exhibit a rich variety of morphologies, depending on the brain region as well as on the species studied.

Basket Cells

This class of GABAergic interneuron takes its name from the fact that its axonal endings form a basket of terminals surrounding a pyramidal cell soma (see Fig. 3.6).[22] Basket cells can be divided into large and small cells. This cell class provides most of the inhibitory GABAergic synapses to the somas and proximal dendrites of pyramidal cells, although the basket cells also synapse on the shaft of the apical dendrite. One basket cell may contact numerous pyramidal cells, and, in turn, several basket cells can contribute to the pericellular basket of one pyramidal cell. The basket cells have relatively large somas and multipolar morphology, with dendrites extending in all directions for several hundred micrometers such that the vertically oriented dendrites cross several layers. The axonal pattern is the defining characteristic of this cell. The axon arises vertically, quickly bifurcates, and travels long distances (1–2 mm), forming multiple pericellular arrays as it spreads horizontally. The basket cells predominate in layers III and V in the neocortex and preferentially innervate the pyramidal cells within these layers, al-

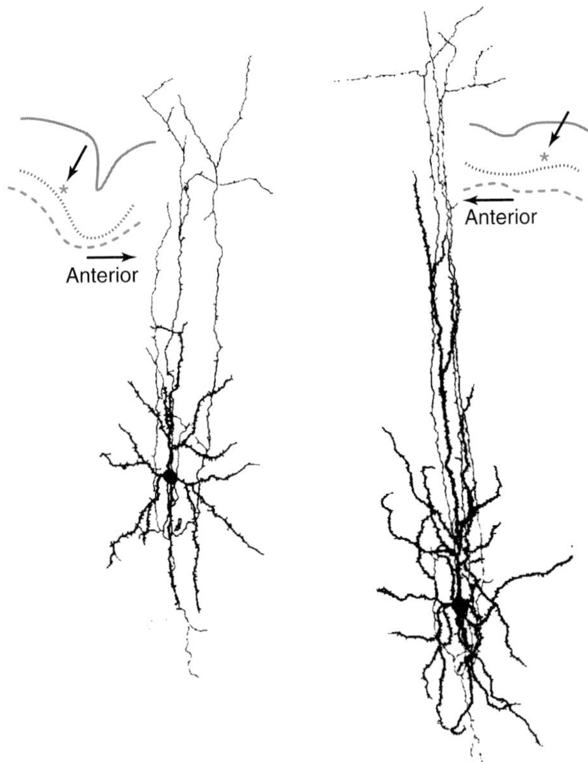

FIGURE 3.5 Drawing of Golgi-impregnated spiny stellate neurons in layer IV of the primary somatosensory cortex. The insets show the cortical localization of each neuron. The coarse branches represent the dendrites and fine branches represent the axonal plexus. Note that the axon is organized vertically. Adapted from Jones.[15]

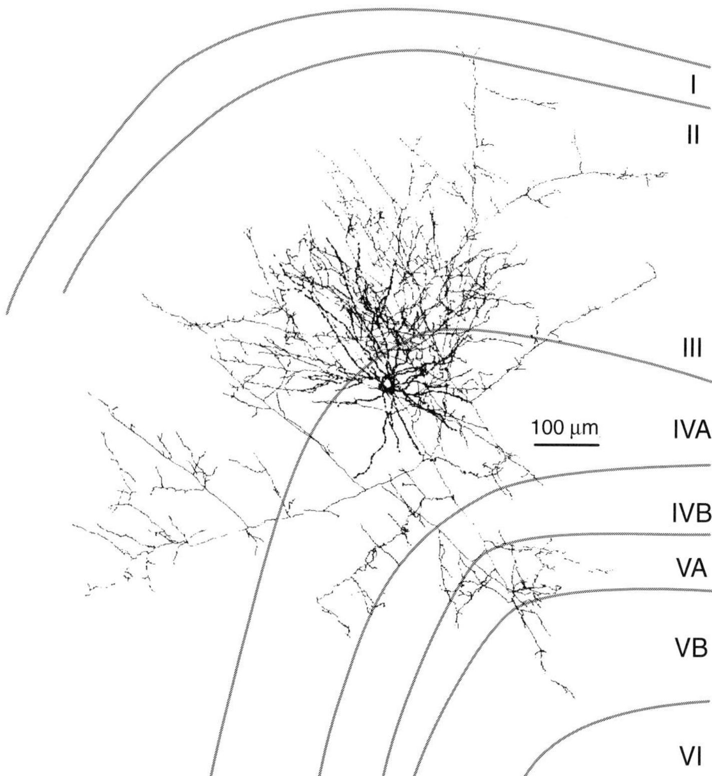

FIGURE 3.6 Drawing of a Golgi-impregnated basket cell from layer IVA of the primary visual cortex. Note the widely ramified dendritic tree and the wide horizontal spread of the axon that makes contact with many local neuronal perikarya. Cortical layers are indicated by Roman numerals. Adapted from Somogyi *et al.*[22]

though they do not synapse exclusively on pyramidal cells. They are also numerous amid pyramidal neurons in the hippocampus. Thus, the basket cell is the primary source of horizontally directed inhibitory inputs to the soma, proximal dendrites, and apical shaft of a pyramidal neuron. Interestingly, these cells are also characterized by certain biochemical features in that the majority of them contain the calcium-binding protein parvalbumin, and cholecystokinin appears to be the most likely neuropeptide in the large basket cells.

Chandelier Cells

The chandelier cell generally has a bitufted or multipolar dendritic tree, but the dendritic tree of this neuron is quite variable (Fig. 3.7).[23] The defining characteristic of this cell class is the very striking appearance of its axonal endings. In Golgi or immunohistochemical preparations, the axon terminals appear as vertically oriented "cartridges," each consisting of a series of axonal boutons, or swellings, linked together by thin connecting pieces. These axonal specializations look like old-style chandeliers, which explains why this cell type is so named. The most salient characteristic of the chandelier cell is the extraordinary specificity of its synaptic target. These neurons synapse exclusively on the axon initial segment of pyramidal cells. This characteristic is responsible for their alternate name, **axoaxonic cells.**[23a] Most of the chandelier cells are located in layer III, and their primary target appears to be layer III pyramidal cells, although they also synapse to a lesser extent on pyramidal cells in the deep layers. One pyramidal cell may receive inputs from multiple chandelier cells, and one chandelier cell may innervate more than one pyramidal cell. Because of the high density of chandelier cell axon endings in layer III, this particular neuron may be highly involved in controlling corticocortical circuits. In addition, because the strength of the synaptic input is correlated directly with its proximity to the axon initial segment, there can be no more powerful inhibitory input to a pyramidal cell than that of the chandelier cell. Presumably, this interneuron is in a position that enables it to completely shut down the firing of a pyramidal cell.[17,22–24]

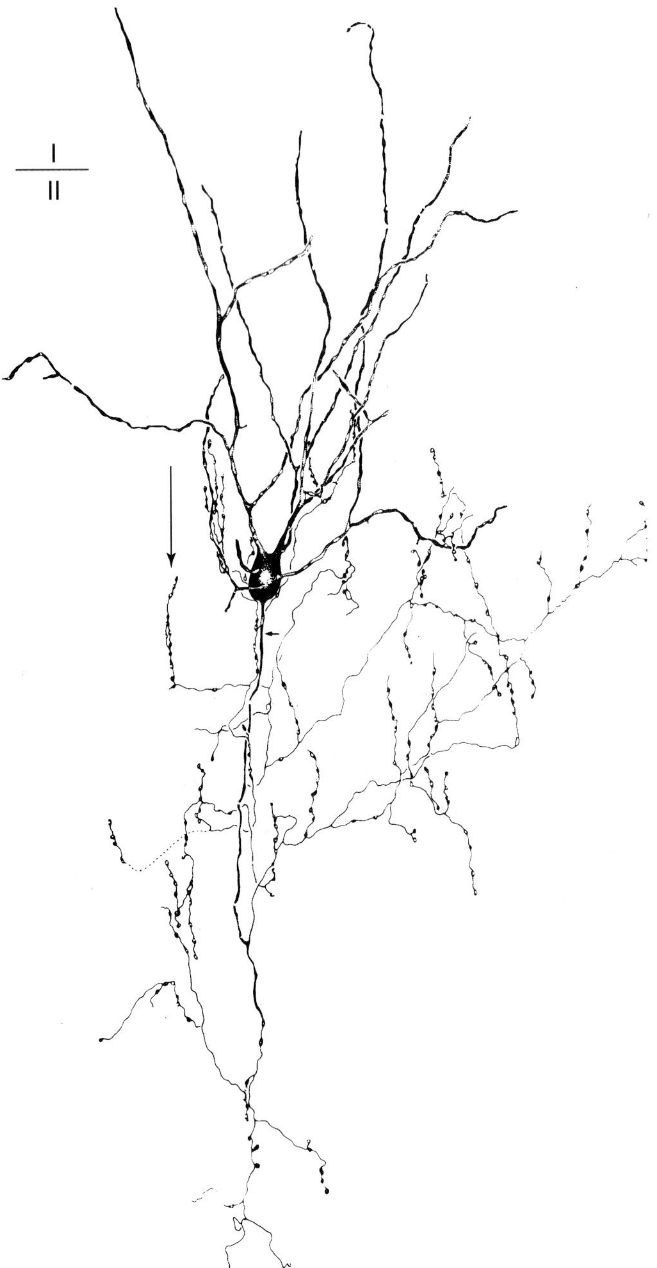

FIGURE 3.7 Drawing of an axoaxonic chandelier neuron from layer II of the primary visual cortex. The dendritic spread of this neuron is quite limited. Note the typical axon terminal specializations (arrow). Adapted from Freund *et al.*[23]

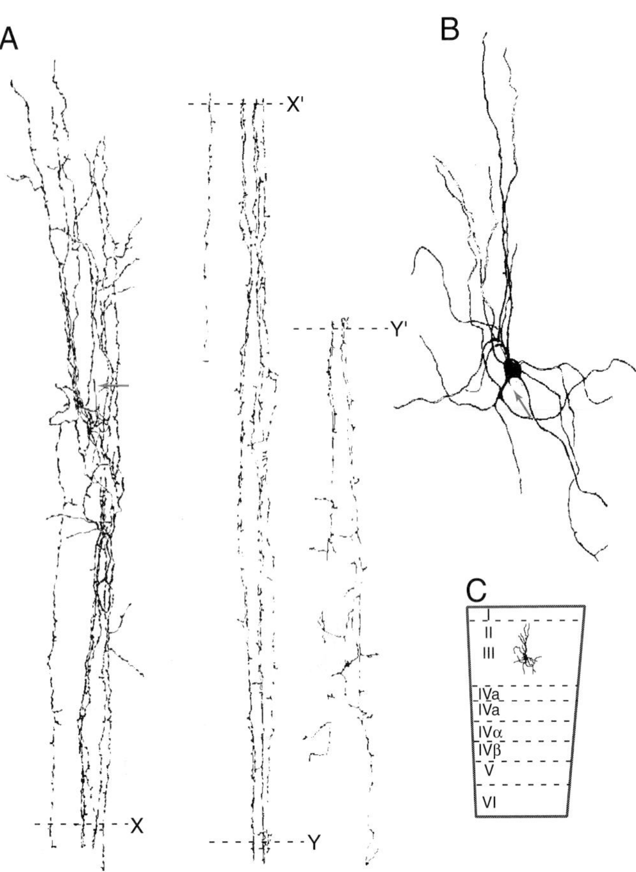

FIGURE 3.8 Drawing of a double bouquet cell in layer III of the primary visual cortex. The axonal tree (A) has been broken into three segments contiguous at X-X′ and Y-Y′, in order to display its entire radial extent. The arrow in B corresponds to the arrow in A. This neuron has very long radial axonal extensions, but very limited horizontal spread. Its location is shown in the inset C. Adapted from Somogyi and Cowey.[25]

Double Bouquet Cells

The cell bodies of double bouquet cells are most prevalent in layers II and III, as well as being present in layer V of the neocortex. These interneurons are characterized by a vertical bitufted dendritic tree and a tight bundle of vertically oriented varicose axon collaterals that traverse layers II through V (Fig. 3.8)[25] and are therefore entirely different from those of chandelier and basket cells.

Of the inhibitory interneurons, the double bouquet cell serves as perhaps the best example of the emerging concept of cell typology in which connectivity, location, morphology, and neurochemical phenotype are all features that are considered in "typing" a given cell.[25a] It is clear that neurochemical phenotype subdivides the double bouquet cell into multiple classes. For example, a GABA–calbindin–somatostatin double bouquet cell appears to be localized primarily in layers II and III and has 40% of its synapses on spines and the remaining synapses primarily on distal shafts of pyramidal and nonpyramidal cells. Large numbers of this particular subtype of double bouquet cell are present in association cortices, with fewer in primary sensory cortices. Its regional, laminar, and synaptic organization suggests that it plays a crucial role in the regulation of pyramidal cells that furnish corticocortical projections. A different subclass of double bouquet cell contains calbindin and tachykinins as peptide neuromodulators. This subclass appears to have similar synaptic targets but is present primarily in layer V and thus presumably regulates the activity of a different group of pyramidal cells.

Other Types of Interneurons

Several other subtypes of interneurons can be distinguished on the basis of their morphology and neurochemical characteristics. A particularly interesting neuron is the poorly understood "clutch cell," which is driven primarily by thalamocortical inputs and, in turn, targets the spiny stellate cell of layer IV. Thus, this inhibitory interneuron is in essence situated so that it can regulate the firing rate of the spiny stellate cell in a fashion similar to how the three GABAergic neurons (basket, chandelier, and double bouquet) regulate the firing rate of pyramidal cells. Another important interneuron type is the bipolar neuron, which is characterized by elongated apical and basal dendrites and a locally ramifying axonal plexus, presumably making contacts with the apical dendrites of neighboring pyramidal cells. This cell is highly prevalent in the neocortex of rodents and has a modulatory role in the integration of cortical activity with noradrenergic projections from the brainstem. In the rat brain, some of these bipolar neurons may also contain the calcium-binding protein calretinin, but their homolog, if any, in the primate cortex remains to be determined.

Noncortical Neurons Have Distinct Morphological Characteristics

In this section, we review characteristics of four neuronal types found in subcortical structures: the medium-sized spiny cells of the basal ganglia, the dopaminergic neurons of the pars compacta of the substantia nigra, the Purkinje cell of the cerebellum, and the alpha motor neuron of the ventral horn of the spinal cord. The rationale for choosing these particular neurons as representative is that each plays a determinant role in the pathogenetic mechanisms of severe neurologic disorders that affect humans. Thus, degeneration of the medium-sized spiny neurons is a central feature of Huntington disease; the death of dopaminergic neurons is the neuropathologic signature of Parkinson disease; the loss of Purkinje cells is seen in familial cerebellar cortical degeneration; and degeneration of spinal cord motor neurons is the hallmark of lower motor neuron disease, a form of amyotrophic lateral sclerosis.

Medium-Sized Spiny Cells

These neurons are unique to the **striatum,** a part of the basal ganglia that comprises the caudate nucleus and putamen (see Chapter 34), where they are present in large numbers (as many as 10^8 in humans). Medium-sized spiny cells are scattered throughout the caudate nucleus and putamen and are recognized by their relatively large size, compared with other cellular elements of the basal ganglia, and by the fact that they are generally isolated neurons.[26] These neurons differ from all others in the striatum in that they have a highly ramified dendritic arborization radiating in all directions and densely covered with spines (Fig. 3.9).[27] Medium-sized spiny neurons are central to the function of the basal ganglia because they furnish a major output from the caudate nucleus and putamen and receive a highly diverse input from, among other sources, the cerebral cortex, thalamus, and certain dopaminergic neurons of the substantia nigra. They have long axons that leave the basal ganglia and also form a large array of recurrent collaterals that innervate neighboring medium-sized spiny cells. These neurons are neurochemically quite heterogeneous, contain GABA, and may contain several neuropeptides such as enkephalin, dynorphin, substance P, and the calcium-binding protein calbindin. In **Huntington disease,** a neurodegenerative disorder of the striatum characterized by involuntary movements and progressive dementia, an early and dramatic loss of medium-sized spiny cells occurs. Interestingly, medium-sized spiny neurons that contain somatostatin appear to be relatively resistant to the degenerative process.

Dopaminergic Neurons of the Substantia Nigra

The substantia nigra is characterized by a rich diversity of neuronal types that exhibit differential distributions among the various functional compartments. Of

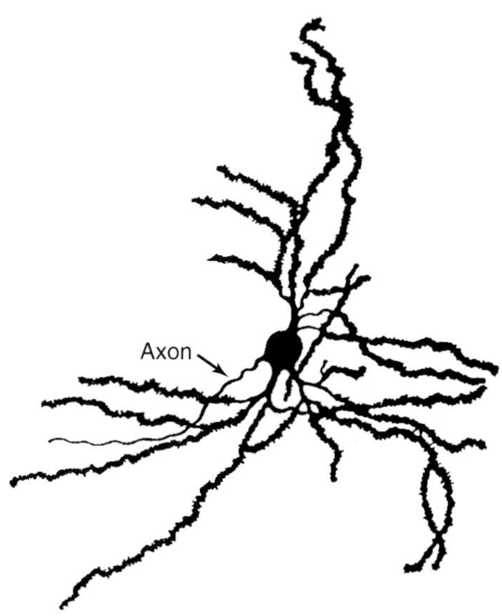

FIGURE 3.9 Drawing of a medium-size spiny neuron from the striatum. Note the highly ramified dendritic arborization radiating in all directions and the very high density of spines. Adapted from Carpenter and Sutin.[27]

these neurons, the most conspicuous are the large dopaminergic neurons that reside mostly within the pars compacta of the substantia nigra and in the ventral tegmental area. A distinctive feature of these cells is the presence of a pigment, neuromelanin, in compact granules in the cytoplasm. These neurons are medium-sized to large, fusiform, and frequently elongated; they have several large radiating dendrites. The axon emerges from the cell body or from one of the dendrites and projects to large expanses of cerebral cortex and to the basal ganglia. These neurons contain the catecholamine-synthesizing enzyme tyrosine hydroxylase, as well as the monoamine dopamine as their neurotransmitter; some of them colocalize calbindin and calretinin. These neurons are severely and selectively affected in **Parkinson disease**—a movement disorder different from Huntington disease and characterized by resting tremor and rigidity—and their specific loss is the neuropathologic hallmark of this disorder.[28]

Purkinje Cells

The structure of the cerebellar cortex, in contrast with that of the cerebral cortex, is basically identical all over; it is composed of three layers that contain very distinct neuronal types. One of these layers contains the Purkinje cells, which are the most salient cellular elements of the cerebellar cortex. They are arranged in a single row throughout the entire cerebellar cortex between the molecular (outer) layer and the granular (inner) layer. They are the largest cerebellar neurons and have a round perikaryon with a highly branched dendritic tree shaped like a candelabrum and extending into the molecular layer where they are contacted by incoming systems of afferent, parallel fibers from the granule neurons as well as other afferents from the brainstem (see Chapter 35). The apical dendrites of Purkinje cells have an enormous number of spines (more than 80,000 per cell). A particular feature of the dendritic tree of the Purkinje cell is that it is distributed in one plane, perpendicular to the longitudinal axes of the cerebellar folds, and each dendritic arbor determines a separate domain of cerebellar cortex (Fig. 3.1). The axons of Purkinje neurons course through the cerebellar white matter and contact the deep cerebellar nuclei or the vestibular nuclei. They also furnish recurrent collaterals, mostly within the granular layer. Humans have approximately 15 million Purkinje cells.[29] These neurons contain the inhibitory neurotransmitter GABA and the calcium-binding protein calbindin. A severe disorder combining ataxic gait and impairment of fine hand movements, accompanied by dysarthria and tremor, has been documented in some families and is related directly to Purkinje cell degeneration.

Spinal Motor Neurons

The motor cells of the ventral horns of the spinal cord, also called alpha motor neurons, have their cell bodies within the spinal cord and send their axons outside the central nervous system to innervate the muscles. Different types of motor neurons are distinguished by their targets. The alpha motor neurons innervate skeletal muscles, but smaller motor neurons (the gamma motor neurons, forming about 30% of the motor neurons) innervate the spindle organs of the muscles (see Chapter 31). The alpha motor neurons are some of the largest neurons in the entire central nervous system and are characterized by a multipolar perikaryon and a very rich cytoplasm that renders them very conspicuous on histological preparations. They have a large number of spiny dendrites that arborize locally within the ventral horn. The alpha motor neuron axon leaves the central nervous system through the ventral root of the peripheral nerves. The cell bodies are arranged in a nonrandom fashion in the ventral horn so that they are grouped in functional vertical columns that span a certain number of spinal segments. This disposition corresponds to a somatotopic repre-

CASE 2: TO BE OR NOT TO BE . . . A CONSULTANT?

Parker Pharmaceuticals has been receiving a lot of bad press. Critics are saying that their new drug for the treatment of myasthenia gravis has serious side effects, including cardiac arrhythmia. Chen Wong, a prominent researcher at Jackson Medical College, has been contacted by the firm and asked to run tests on the compound in his laboratory to see if he can detect any reactions that may lead to the reported side effects. The contract specifies that Dr. Wong must provide the company with 60 days in which to review any resulting manuscript prior to submission for publication. However, realizing that testing their compound would take time away from his current research, the company offers to provide Dr. Wong with a renewable $100,000 grant for his current work, in addition to the funds necessary to test their product. What issues should Dr. Wong consider when deciding whether or not to accept the company's proposal?

See Appendix for discussion questions.

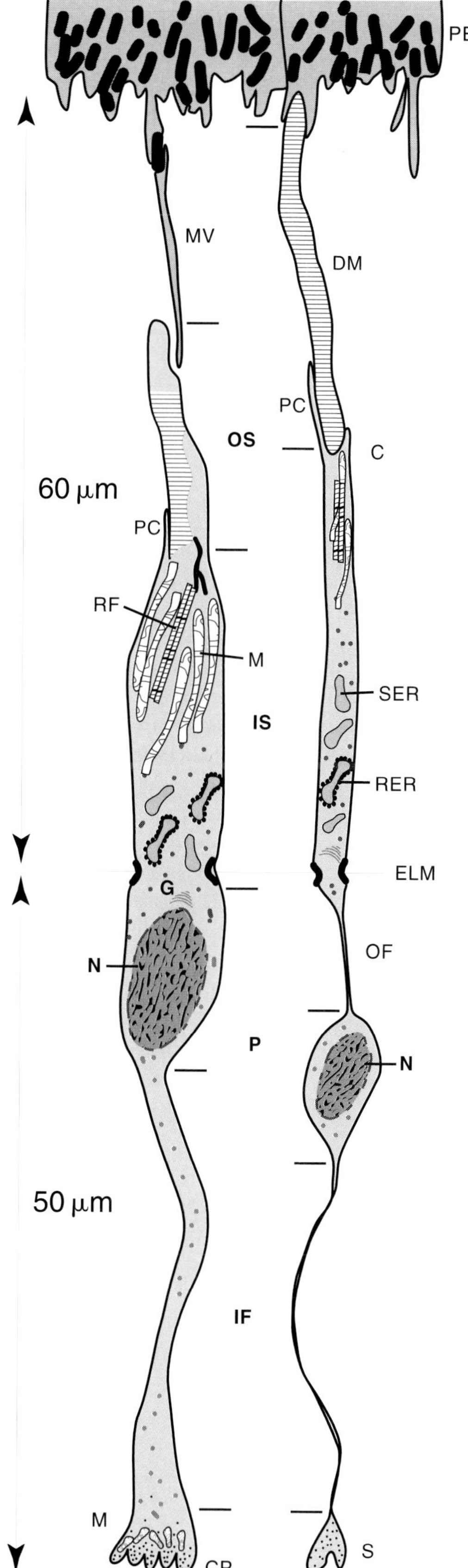

FIGURE 3.10 Drawing of a cone (left) and a rod (right) from the monkey retina. Note the difference in shape and size of these cells. They are composed of an outer segment (OS), an inner segment (IS), a perikaryon (P), and the inner fiber (IF). The outer segment is connected to the inner segment by a thin connecting cilium (C). The outer fiber (OF) is thin and well visible in rods, whereas the perikaryon of both cell types has a comparable appearance. In cones the inner fiber is thicker and ends as a large cone pedicle, while in rods the inner fiber is rather thin and terminates in a unique spherule. Cone pedicles (CP) and rod spherules (S) are specialized synaptic endings where the photoreceptors make contact with specific subtypes of retinal relay neurons. DM, membranous discs (lamellae); ELM, external limiting membrane; G, Golgi apparatus; M, mitochondria, MV, microvilli of pigment epithelium; N, nucleus; PC, calycoid process; PE, pigment epithelium; RER, SER, rough and smooth endoplasmic reticulum; RF, rootlet fibers. Adapted from Krebs and Krebs.[31]

sentation of the muscle groups of the limbs and axial musculature.[30] The spinal motor neurons use acetylcholine as their neurotransmitter. Large motor neurons are severely affected in lower motor neuron disease (a form of **amyotrophic lateral sclerosis**), a neurodegenerative disorder characterized by progressive muscular weakness that affects, at first, one or two limbs and that can be initially asymmetric. As the disease progresses, it becomes symmetric and affects more and more of the body musculature, which shows signs of wasting as a result of denervation. Neuropathologically, a massive loss of ventral horn motor neurons occurs, and the remaining motor neurons appear shrunken and pyknotic.

Retinal Photoreceptors and Cochlear Hair Cells Are Examples of Specialized Sensory Receptors

Retinal photoreceptors and cochlear hair cells are modified neuroepithelial cells that are specialized in the initial transduction of visual and acoustic stimuli, respectively. Comparable specialized neuronal types exist for other sensory modalities—that is, olfactory, gustatory, and vestibular inputs. In contrast, somatosensory inputs are transmitted by peripheral nerve cells whose endings are associated with a variety of sensory structures in the peripheral tissues. Receptor neurons are extremely polarized cells, with one uniquely diversified end that is responsible for the reception of the sensory stimulus. This morphology is particularly well demonstrated in retinal photoreceptors. Photoreceptor cells are of two types, the **rod** and the **cone,** which are specialized for scotopic (light/dark) and color vision, respectively (see Chapter 28). The rods are slender cells, with an elongated cylindrical outer portion, whereas the cones are smaller elements, with shorter, conical outer portions (Fig. 3.10).[31] Each cell type consists of an outer and an inner segment.

The inner segments of both rods and cones contain the metabolic machinery necessary for protein and lipid synthesis and oxidative metabolism. In rods, the outer segment is composed of a very large number of parallel lamellae stacked perpendicularly to the main axis of the cylinder. These lamellae are closed, flattened membranous discs that appear in thin-section electron microscopy as pairs of parallel membranes. In cones, these lamellar stacks are less numerous. These structures are responsible for the mechanisms of phototransduction and contain several visual pigments, located inside the membranous discs, that are necessary for the absorption of light.

Cochlear (and vestibular) hair cells also are highly polarized and present striking apical differentiation specialized in the detection of endolymphatic movements in the inner ear. In the cochlea, receptor hair cells that detect stimuli produced by sound are short, goblet-like cells embedded in supporting cells (the phalangeal cells of Deiters). Their apical domain contains a U-shaped row of stereocilia (hairs) that are in contact with the tectorial membrane of the organ of Corti. The vibrations of this membrane, generated by sound waves in the endolymph, displace the hairs and initiate the transduction of the acoustic stimulus (see Chapter 37). The other pole of the hair cell contains the nucleus and a dense population of mitochondria and receives synaptic contacts from afferent and efferent fibers from the cochlear nerve, which spreads around the lower third of the receptor cell (Fig. 3.11).[32]

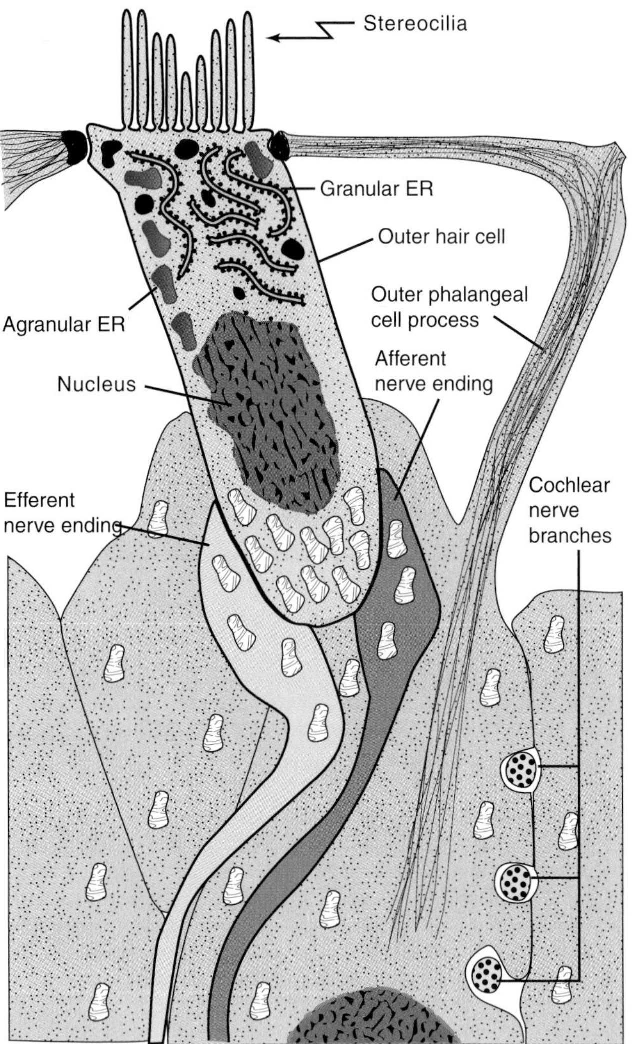

FIGURE 3.11 Schematic drawing of an electron micrograph of an outer hair cell and its relationships to supporting (outer phalangeal) cell and cochlear nerve endings. Note the apical domain containing stereocilia. The other pole of the hair cell contains the nucleus and a dense population of mitochondria and receives synaptic contacts from the cochlear nerve, which spread around the lower third of the receptor cell.

Enteric Motor Neurons Form an Independent Neural Plexus in the Gut Wall

The **enteric nervous system** constitutes a part of the autonomic nervous system that innervates the gastrointestinal tract, as do the sympathetic and parasympathetic systems. Although all three systems take part in the regulation of intestinal function, the enteric system is by far the most important and has the unique feature that it can function relatively independent of the control of higher centers.[33] The enteric system consists of an extremely rich plexus of nerve fibers and neurons disseminated among all of the layers that form the wall of the intestinal tract (Fig. 3.12). It contains nerve cells arranged in ganglia interconnected by complex bundles of fibers that extend from the lower third of the esophagus to the internal anal sphincter. In humans, this system contains about 10^7 to 10^8 neurons.

The principal enteric plexus is located between the circular and longitudinal layers of the muscularis and is known as the **myenteric plexus of Auerbach.** It is composed of ganglia, each containing from 3 to 50 neurons linked by unmyelinated fibers and forming a continuous network. The cells in this plexus are of two main morphological types. One is a large multipolar neuron with short dendrites in direct contact with similar nearby cells and a long axon that contacts different cell types in neighboring ganglia. These cells are thought to be association interneurons. The other cell type, considered an enteric motor neuron, is by far more dominant and demonstrates more variable morphology. These cells make extensive contacts with neurons of either type within the same ganglia or with distant cells. Other ganglia are found within the **submucosal plexus of Meissner.** Their relatively large multipolar neurons form a network interconnecting the outer nerve bundles with the submucosal tissue.

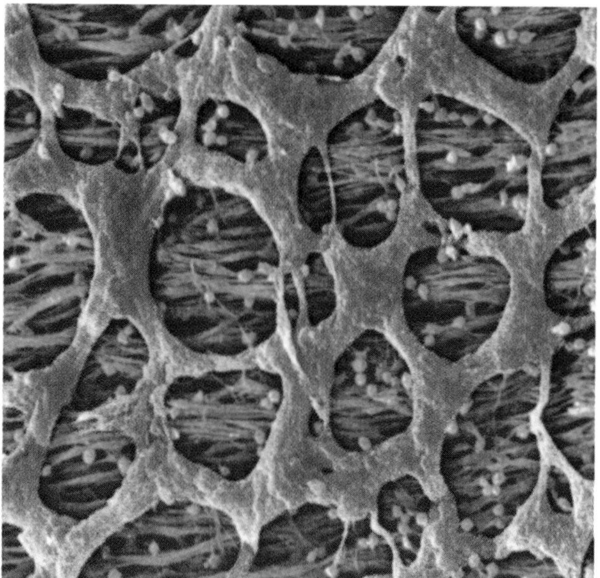

FIGURE 3.12 Scanning electron micrograph of the myenteric plexus in the intestine. Note the dense axonal bundles and synaptic boutons (pseudocolored green) and the network of large multipolar neurons with relatively short extensions contacting neighboring cells (pseudocolored red).

The neurochemistry of the enteric system is extremely complex and still poorly understood. A large number of classical neurotransmitters, such as acetylcholine, GABA, and noradrenaline, have been identified in enteric nerve fibers and ganglionic neurons. In addition, enteric neurons in both the myenteric and the submucosal plexuses contain a variety of neuropeptides. Neurons in the submucosal plexus are enriched in somatostatin, substance P, and vasoactive intestinal peptide but do not seem to contain Leu-enkephalin, which is observed in the myenteric nerve cells. It is not clear, however, whether these neuropeptides are the principal transmitters of subclasses of enteric neurons or are colocalized compounds that act as local neuromodulators.[33]

Summary

The neuron is one of the more highly specialized cell types and is the critical cellular element in the brain. All neurological processes are dependent on complex cell–cell interactions between single neurons and/or groups of related neurons. Neurons can be described according to their size, shape, neurochemical characteristics, location, and connectivity.

A neuron's size, shape, and neurochemistry are important determinants of that neuron's particular functional role in the brain. In this respect, there are three general classes of neurons: the inhibitory GABAergic interneurons that make local contacts, the local excitatory spiny stellate cells in the cerebral cortex, and the excitatory glutamatergic efferent neurons, exemplified by the cortical pyramidal neurons. Within these general classes, the structural variation of neurons is systematic, and careful analyses of the anatomic features of neurons have led to various categorizations and to the development of the concept of cell type. The grouping of neurons into descriptive cell types (such as chandelier, double bouquet, or bipolar cells) allows the analysis of populations of neurons and the linking of specified cellular characteristics with certain functional roles. The relevant characteristics may include morphology, location, connectivity, and biochemistry.

Also, neurons form circuits, and these circuits constitute the structural basis for brain function. Macrocircuits involve a population of neurons projecting from one brain region to a distant region, and microcircuits reflect the local cell–cell interactions within a brain region. The detailed analysis of these macro- and microcircuits is an essential step in understanding the neuronal basis of a given cortical function in the healthy and the diseased brain. Thus, these cellular characteristics allow us to appreciate the special structural and biochemical qualities of that neuron in relation to its neighbors and to place it in the context of a specific neuronal subset, circuit, or function.

THE NEUROGLIA

The term neuroglia, or "nerve glue," was coined in 1859 by Rudolph Virchow, who conceived of the neuroglia as an inactive "connective tissue" holding neurons together in the central nervous system (CNS). The metallic staining techniques developed by Santiago Ramón y Cajal and Pio del Río-Hortega allowed these two great pioneers to distinguish, in addition to the ependyma lining the ventricles and central canal, three types of supporting cells in the CNS: oligodendrocytes, astrocytes, and microglia. In the peripheral nervous system (PNS), the Schwann cell is the major neuroglial component.

Oligodendrocytes and Schwann Cells Synthesize Myelin

The more complex the brain, the more interconnections must be formed and maintained. As we will see in depth later, there is a practical limit to how fast an individual bare axon can conduct an action potential. Thus, neurons and their associated processes cannot communicate with each other extremely rapidly

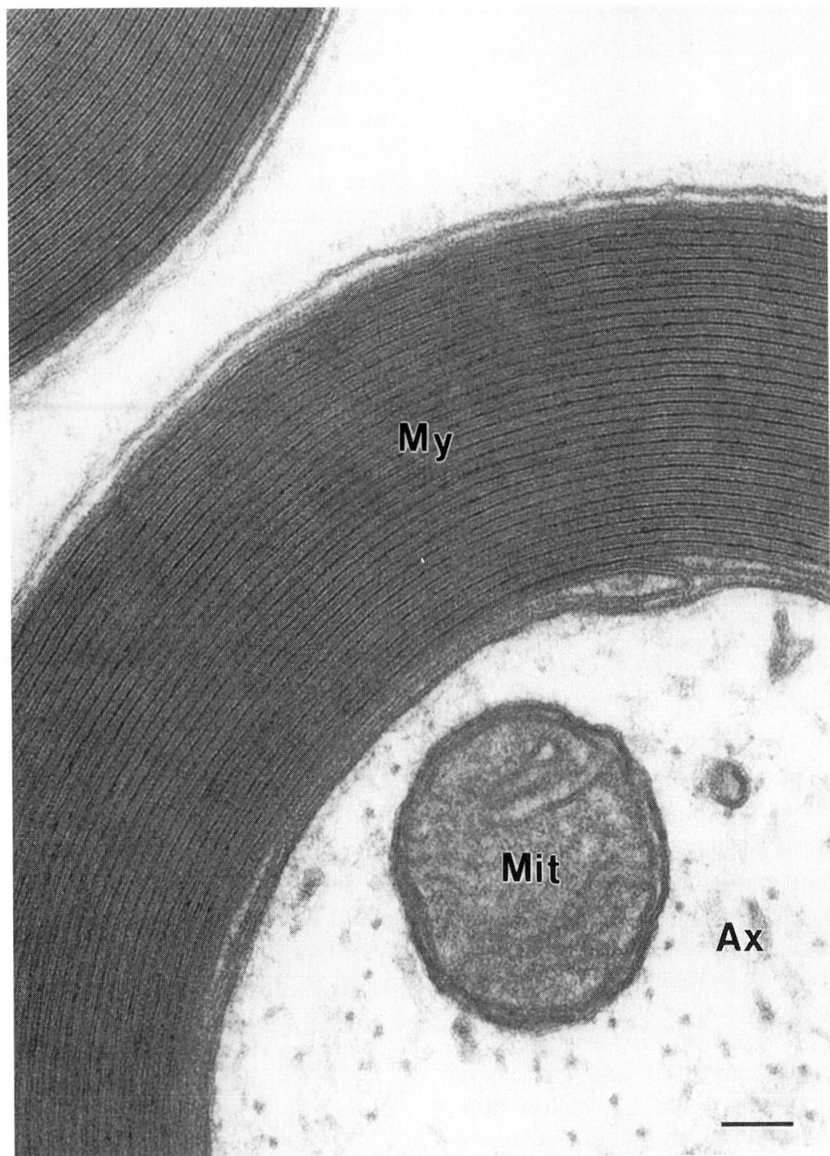

FIGURE 3.13 An electron micrograph of a transverse section through part of a myelinated axon from the sciatic nerve of a rat. The tightly compacted multilayer myelin sheath (My) surrounds and insulates the axon (Ax). Mit, mitochondria. Scale bar = 75 nm.

through the action potential without some help. Organisms have developed two kinds of solutions for enhancing rapid communication between neurons and their effector organs. In invertebrates, the diameters of individual axons that must conduct rapidly are enlarged. In vertebrates, the myelin sheath (Fig. 3.13) has evolved to permit rapid nerve conduction.

Axon enlargement greatly accelerates the rate of conduction of the action potential, which increases with axonal diameter. The net effect, therefore, is that small axons conduct at a much slower rate than larger ones. The largest axon in the invertebrate kingdom is the squid giant axon, which is about the thickness of a mechanical pencil lead. It conducts the action potential extremely rapidly, and the axon itself mediates an escape reflex, which must be rapid if the animal is to survive. An obvious trade-off in a nervous system with 10^{11} neurons, as in the human brain, is that all axons cannot be as thick as pencil lead, or each human head would be very large indeed.

Thus, along the invertebrate evolutionary line, there is a natural, insurmountable limit—a constraint imposed by axonal size—to increasing the processing capacity of the nervous system beyond a certain point. Vertebrates, however, devised a way to get around this problem through the evolution of the myelin sheath,

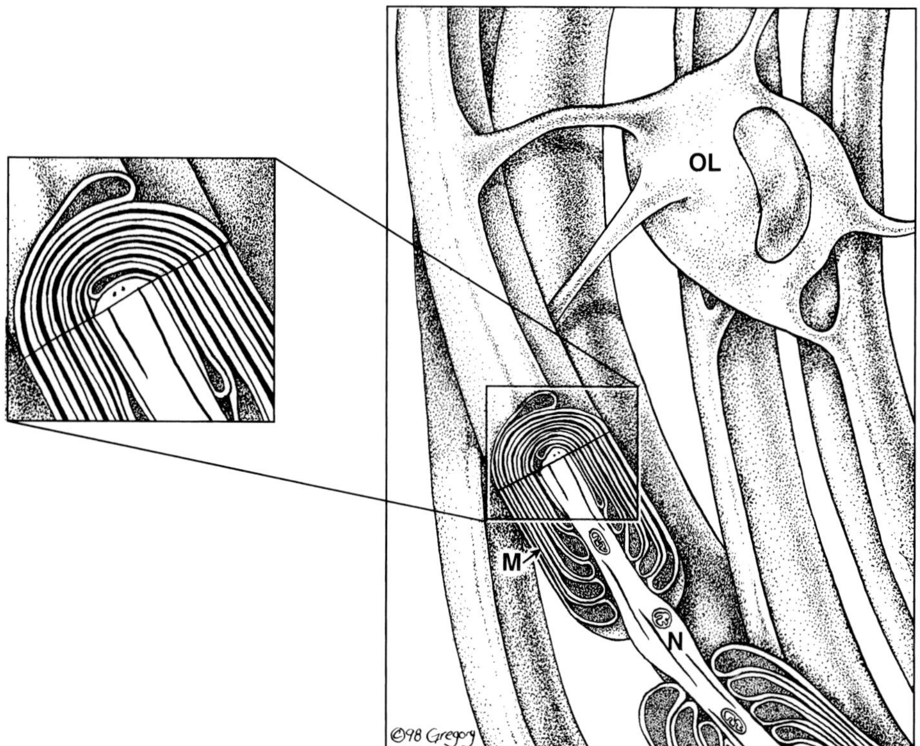

FIGURE 3.14 An oligodendrocyte (OL) in the central nervous system is depicted myelinating several axon segments. A cut away view of the myelin sheath is shown (M). Note that the internode of myelin terminates in paranodal loops that flank the node of Ranvier (N). The inset shows an enlargement of compact myelin with alternating dark and light electron-dense lines that represent the intracellular (major dense lines) and extracellular (intraperiod line) plasma membrane appositions, respectively.

allowing the tremendous evolutionary advantage of increased rapidity of conduction of the nerve impulse along axons with fairly minute diameters.[34] As we know, neurons interact in complex ways with the other cell types that exist within the nervous system. Virtually all axons, for example, are wrapped or ensheathed by cells that subserve what is vaguely termed a "supportive" or "trophic" function. This is true in invertebrate as well as vertebrate nervous systems. Along the vertebrate lineage, however, certain ensheathing cells have become highly specialized to generate vast quantities of plasma membrane that is compacted to form the myelin sheath, which supports rapid nerve conduction.

Not all axons in central or peripheral nervous systems are myelinated, and one of the puzzles is to determine why some are selected for myelination and others remain unmyelinated. It is believed that early in the nervous system development of an organism, signals relayed between the axon and the myelinating cell determine whether the "myelination program" is triggered in that cell. These signals have not yet been identified.

In the central nervous system, the myelin sheath (Fig. 3.14) is elaborated by **oligodendrocytes,** nonneuronal glial cells that, during brain development, send out a few cytoplasmic processes that engage adjacent axons, some of which go on to become myelinated.[35] Myelin itself consists of a single sheet of oligodendrocyte plasma membrane, which is wrapped tightly around an axonal segment.[36] Each myelinated segment of an axon is termed an **internode** because, at the end of each segment, there is a bare portion of the axon, the **node of Ranvier,** that is flanked by another internode. Physiologically, myelin has insulating properties such that the action potential can "leap" from node to node and therefore does not have to be regenerated continually along the axonal segment that is covered by the myelin membrane sheath. This leaping of the action potential from node to node allows axons with fairly small diameters to conduct extremely rapidly.[37] The jumping of the action potential from node to node along a given axon is called **saltatory conduction** (from the Latin *saltare,* to dance). The same Latin root can be found in the words sauté, somersault, and assault.

The evolution of a system in which a single oligo-

FIGURE 3.15 An "unrolled" Schwann cell in the PNS is illustrated in relation to the single axon segment that it myelinates. The broad stippled region is compact myelin surrounded by cytoplasmic channels that remain open even after compact myelin has formed, allowing exchange of materials among the myelin sheath, the Schwann cell cytoplasm, and perhaps the axon as well.

dendrocyte cell body is responsible for the construction and maintenance of several myelin sheaths (Fig. 3.14) and the removal of the cytoplasm between each turn of the myelin lamellae so that only the thinnest layer of plasma membrane is left have resulted in saving a huge amount of space. Brain volume is thus reserved for further expansion of neuronal populations.[38]

Conservation of space in the peripheral nervous system does not seem to have presented such a pressing problem. Myelin in the PNS is generated by **Schwann cells** (Fig. 3.15), each of which wraps only a single axonal segment. The biochemical composition of the myelin derived in the CNS and the composition of that derived in the PNS differ somewhat, although there are common proteins found in each nervous system subdivision. Myelin has a high lipid-to-protein ratio, and the lipids are specialized. The myelin sheath has become an excellent model system for studying the generation or formation of specialized plasma membrane and membrane adhesion, because each layer of the multilayered myelin sheath must adhere to the adjacent layers. This adhesion is largely accomplished by protein–protein interactions, which have been best studied in the PNS.

The major integral membrane protein of peripheral nerve myelin is Protein zero (P_0), a member of a very large family of proteins termed the immunoglobulin gene superfamily. These proteins have in common recognition or adhesion functions or both and, although the primary amino acid sequences differ among the members of this family, all members are related to one another by certain common structural motifs. Members of the immunoglobulin (Ig) gene superfamily have one or more Ig-like domains that contain cysteines placed about 100 amino acids or so apart. These cysteines are linked to one another by disulfide bridges. Most of these Ig domains are displayed on the extracellular surfaces of cells, where they can act as ligands or receptors. Protein zero is relatively simple in primary structure, consisting of a single Ig-like domain, a transmembrane segment, and a highly charged (basic) cytoplasmic domain.[39] This protein makes up about 80% of the protein complement of peripheral nerve myelin. The interactions between the extracellular domains of P_0 molecules expressed on one layer of the myelin sheath with those of the apposing layer yield a characteristic regular periodicity that can be seen by thin-section electron microscopy (Fig. 3.13). This zone, called the **intraperiod line,** represents the extracellular apposition of the myelin bilayer as it wraps around itself. On the other side of the bilayer, the cytoplasmic side, the highly charged P_0 cytoplasmic domain probably functions to neutralize the negative charges on the polar head groups of the phospholipids that make up the plasma membrane itself, allowing the membranes of the myelin sheath to come into close apposition with one another. In electron microscopy, this cytoplasmic apposition is a bit darker than the intraperiod line and is termed the **major dense line.** In peripheral nerves, although other molecules are present in small quantities in compact myelin and may have important functions, **compaction** (i.e., the close apposition of membrane surfaces without intervening cytoplasm) is accomplished solely by P_0–P_0 interactions at both extracellular and intracellular (cytoplasmic) surfaces.[40]

Protein zero is a "perfect" plasma-membrane compactor,[41] allowing the close apposition of adjacent bilayers such that the space between them effectively prevents the passage of anything but small ions and water along the compacted bilayer surfaces. It is in effect a "streamlined" Ig superfamily molecule that probably arose *de novo* with the development of the myelin sheath.[38] Curiously, P_0 is not present in all myelin sheaths in the central nervous system of every species—an evolutionary paradox that has attracted much attention. In fish, P_0 is present in both the central and the peripheral nervous systems, where it performs its compaction function, as the major integral membrane protein. However, in terrestrial vertebrates (reptiles, birds, and mammals), P_0 is limited to the PNS, and so is not found in the central nervous system. Instead, the compaction function is probably subserved by totally unrelated molecules, the **DM-20** protein and its insertion isoform, the myelin **proteolipid protein** (PLP).[42] These two proteins are generated from the same gene and are identical to each other with the exception that the proteolipid protein has, in addition, a positively charged segment exposed on the cytoplasmic aspect of the bilayer.[43,44] Both PLP and DM20 are extremely hydrophobic and traverse the bilayer four times, and so have hydrophilic segments exposed on both cytoplasmic and extracellular surfaces of the bilayer. In this respect, the topology of these molecules is very similar to that of connexins and other polypeptides (see Chapters 9 and 11) that are known to function in channel or pore formation.

A large number of naturally occurring neurological mutations can affect the proteins specific to the myelin sheath. These mutations have been named according to the phenotype that is produced: the *shiverer* mouse, the *shaking* pup, the *rumpshaker* mouse, the *jimpy* mouse, the *myelin-deficient* rat, the *quaking* mouse, and so forth. Many of these mutations have been well characterized, and their analyses have allowed us to begin to understand at a molecular level what the proteins affected by each mutation actually do in the formation and maintenance of the myelin sheath (see Box 3.2).[45]

The first neurologic mutation that was studied in this respect was the *shiverer* mouse, in which the gene that encodes a major set of peripheral membrane proteins, the myelin basic proteins (MBPs), is damaged. Normally, these proteins serve to seal the cytoplasmic aspects of the myelin bilayer, possibly by charge neutralization similar in function to the cytoplasmic tail of P_0. When the gene is functionally deleted, as in the *shiverer*, the cytoplasmic aspects fail to appose and do not fuse, and a mouse that exhibits tremors and convulsions ("shivers") as it walks is produced. This is a naturally occurring mutation and was the first neurological mutation whose effects were cured by gene transfer. This was accomplished by the introduction of an intact MBP gene into the *shiverer* genome.[46] The *shiverer* mutation is an autosomal recessive, but even a single allele of the gene (i.e., the heterozygote MBP^+/MBP^-) produces sufficient myelin to phenotypically at least "cure" the *shiverer* of its overtly abnormal behavior. These heterozygotes myelinate to somewhat less extent than normal, but the fact that the *shiverer* phenotype is eliminated in the heterozygote even though the number of myelin sheaths around each axon is reduced indicates that there is a built-in safety factor in the normal situation.

Astrocytes Play Important Roles in CNS Homeostasis

As the name suggests, **astrocytes** are star-shaped process-bearing cells distributed throughout the central nervous system. They constitute from 20 to 50% of the volume of most brain areas. Astrocytes come in many shapes and forms. The two main forms, **protoplasmic** and **fibrous** astrocytes, predominate in gray and white matter, respectively (Fig. 3.16). Embryonically, astrocytes develop from radial glial cells, which transversely compartmentalize the neural tube. Radial glial cells serve as scaffolding for the migration of neurons and play a critical role in defining the cytoarchitecture of the CNS (Fig. 3.17). As the CNS matures, radial glia retract their processes and serve as progenitors of astrocytes. However, some specialized astrocytes of a radial nature are still found in the adult cerebellum and the retina and are known as Bergmann glial cells and Müller cells, respectively.

Astrocytes "fence in" neurons and oligodendrocytes.[47] The astrocytes achieve this isolation of the brain parenchyma by extending long processes projecting to the pia mater and the ependyma to form the glia limitans, by covering the surface of capillaries, and by making a cuff around the nodes of Ranvier. They also ensheath synapses and dendrites and project processes to cell somas (Fig. 3.18). Astrocytes are connected to each other by gap junctions, forming a syncytium that allows ions and small molecules to diffuse across the brain parenchyma. Astrocytes have in common unique cytological and immunological properties that make them easy to identify, including their star shape, the glial end feet on capillaries, and a unique population of large bundles of intermediate filaments. These filaments are composed of an astroglial-specific protein commonly referred to as GFAP (glial fibrillary acidic protein). S-100, a calcium-binding protein, and glutamine synthetase also are astrocyte markers. Ultrastructurally, gap junctions (connexins), desmosomes, glycogen granules, and membrane orthogonal arrays are distinct features used by morphologists to identify astrocytic cellular processes in the complex cytoarchitecture of the nervous system.

For a long time, astrocytes were thought to physically form the blood–brain barrier (considered later in this chapter), which prevents the entry of cells and diffusion of molecules into the CNS. In fact, astrocytes are indeed the blood–brain barrier in lower species. However, in higher species, the astrocytes are responsible for inducing and maintaining the tight junctions in endothelial cells that effectively form the barrier.[48,49] Astrocytes also take part in angiogenesis, which may be important in the development and repair of the

BOX 3.2

INHERITED PERIPHERAL NEUROPATHIES

The peripheral myelin protein-22 (PMP22) is a very hydrophobic glycoprotein and is highly expressed in compact PNS myelin. It has been mapped to the previously defined *Tr* locus on mouse chromosome 11. Comparison of marker genes on mouse chromosome 11 and human chromosome 17 revealed that PMP22 was also a candidate gene for the most common form of autosomal-dominant demyelinating hereditary peripheral neuropathy in humans, Charcot–Marie–Tooth disease type 1A (CMT1A). Indeed, the entire PMP22 gene is contained within a 1.5-Mb intrachromosomal duplication on chromosome 17p11.2, a genetic abnormality that had been linked to CMT1A by human molecular genetics. Consistent with these results, PMP22 is overexpressed in CMT1A patients who carry the characteristic duplication. The crucial role of PMP22 in the etiology of CMT1A was confirmed by generating transgenic mice and rats with increased PMP22 gene dosage, which resulted in severe PNS myelin deficits.

CMT is one of the more frequent hereditary diseases of the nervous system, with an overall prevalence of approximately 1 in 4000, and the CMT1A duplication accounts for around 70% of all cases. Why is this chromosomal abnormality so common? Detailed analysis of the CMT1A locus suggests that the duplication is due to crossing over involving repetitive sequences that flank the monomeric region. If correct, such a mechanism should also generate an allele carrying the reciprocal deletion of the same region. Indeed, the expected deletion is associated with the relatively mild recurrent neuropathy hereditary neuropathy with liability to pressure palsy (HNPP). Thus, overexpression and underexpression of the myelin protein PMP22 are associated with myelin deficiencies in distinct human diseases. Although one might speculate from these data that correct stochiometry of myelin protein expression is crucial for a myelinating Schwann cell, the exact disease mechanism remains to be clarified.

Interestingly, the finding that a myelin protein was responsible for CMT1A led to the discovery that two other components of PNS myelin are mutated in rare forms of CMT1. The adhesion protein P_0, which is largely responsible for PNS myelin compaction, is affected in CMT1B, and an X-linked form of CMT (CMTX) has been linked to mutations in the gap junction protein connexin-32. In contrast to PMP22 and P_0, connexin-32 is located in uncompacted lamellae of PNS myelin, where it is thought to facilitate the exchange of small molecules via reflexive gap junctions between adaxonal and abaxonal aspects of myelinating Schwann cells.

Finally, there is a striking correlation between the role of PMP22 in the PNS and that of PLP/DM20 in the CNS with respect to biology and involvement in disease; both genes can be affected by various genetic mechanisms, including gene duplication and gene deletion. However, despite our vast knowledge derived from human molecular genetics, the molecular functions of both proteins are largely unknown. Given the recent findings that PMP22 and PLP/DM20 are members of extended gene families and may be involved in the control of cell proliferation and cell death, these proteins may have broader functions than simply being stabilizing building blocks of compact myelin.

In summary, the combination of basic and clinical sciences has led to substantial progress in our current understanding of common hereditary neuropathies. Using clinical, genetic, and cell biology approaches in concert, we will continue to learn more about disease mechanisms involved in neuropathies to the benefit of the clinic as much as to our understanding of myelin biology.

Ueli Suter

CNS.[50] However, their role in this important process is still poorly understood.

Astrocytes Have a Wide Range of Functions

There is strong evidence for the role of radial glia and astrocytes in the migration and guidance of neurons in early development. Astrocytes are a major source of extracellular matrix proteins and adhesion molecules in the CNS; examples are nerve cell–nerve cell adhesion molecule (N-CAM), laminin, fibronectin, cytotactin, and the J-1 family members janusin and tenascin. These molecules participate not only in the migration of neurons, but also in the formation of neuronal aggregates, so-called nuclei, as well as networks.

Astrocytes produce, *in vivo* and *in vitro*, a very large number of growth factors. These factors act singly or in combination to selectively regulate the morphology, proliferation, differentiation, or survival, or all four, of distinct neuronal subpopulations. Most of the growth factors also act in a specific manner on the development and functions of astrocytes and oligodendrocytes. The

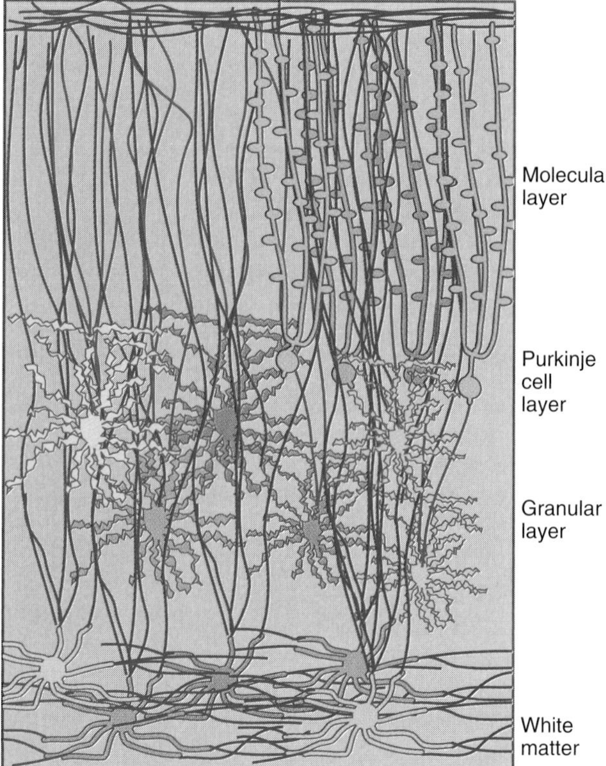

FIGURE 3.16 The arrangement of astrocytes in human cerebellar cortex. The Bergmann glial cells are in red, the protoplasmic astrocytes are in green, and the fibrous astrocytes are in blue.

production of growth factors and cytokines by astrocytes and their responsiveness to these factors are a major mechanism underlying the developmental function and regenerative capacity of the CNS.

During neurotransmission, neurotransmitters and ions are released at high concentration in the synaptic cleft. The rapid removal of these substances is important so that they do not interfere with future synaptic activity. The presence of astrocyte processes around synapses positions them well to regulate neurotransmitter uptake and inactivation.[51] These possibilities are consistent with the presence in astrocytes of transport systems for many neurotransmitters. For instance, glutamate reuptake is performed mostly by astrocytes, which convert glutamate into glutamine and then release it into the extracellular space. Glutamine is taken up by neurons, which use it to generate glutamate and γ-aminobutyric acid, potent excitatory and inhibitory neurotransmitters, respectively (Fig. 3.19). Astrocytes contain ion channels for K^+, Na^+, Cl^-, HCO_3, and Ca^{2+}, as well as displaying a wide range of neurotransmitter receptors. K^+ ions released from neurons during neurotransmission are soaked up by astrocytes and moved away from the area through astrocyte gap junctions. This is known as "spatial buffering." The astrocytes play a major role in detoxification of the CNS by sequestering metals and a variety of neuroactive substances of endogenous and xenobiotic origin.

In response to stimuli, intracellular calcium waves are generated in astrocytes. The propagation of the Ca^{2+} wave can be visually observed as it moves across the cell soma and from astrocyte to astrocyte. The generation of Ca^{2+} waves from cell to cell is thought to be mediated by second messengers, diffusing through gap junctions (see Chapter 11). Because they develop postnatally in rodents, gap junctions may not play an important role in development. In the adult brain, gap junctions are present in all astrocytes. Some gap junctions have also been detected between astrocytes and neurons. Thus, they may participate, along with astroglial neurotransmitter receptors, in the coupling of astrocyte and neuron physiology.

In a variety of CNS disorders—neurotoxicity, viral infections, neurodegenerative disorders, HIV, AIDS, dementia, multiple sclerosis, inflammation, and trauma—astrocytes react by becoming hypertrophic and, in a few cases, hyperplastic. A rapid and huge upregulation of GFAP expression and filament formation is associated with astrogliosis. The formation of reactive astrocytes can spread very far from the site of origin. For instance, a localized trauma can recruit astrocytes from as far as the contralateral side, suggesting the existence of soluble factors in the mediation process. Tumor necrosis factor α (TNFα) and ciliary neurotrophic factors (CNTF) have been identified as key factors in astrogliosis.

Microglia Are Mediators of Immune Responses in Nervous Tissue

The brain has traditionally been considered an "immunologically privileged site," mainly because the blood–brain barrier (see below) normally restricts the access of immune cells from the blood. However, it is now known that immunological reactions do take place in the central nervous system, particularly during cerebral inflammation. Microglial cells have been termed the tissue macrophages of the CNS, and they function as the resident representatives of the immune system in the brain. These cells are perhaps the least understood of the CNS cells. Although the function of microglia in the normal adult CNS remains to be clarified, a rapidly expanding literature describes microglia as major players in CNS development and in the pathogenesis of CNS disease. The notion that the CNS is an immune-privileged organ is no longer valid. A hallmark of microglia cells is their ability to become reactive and to respond to pathological challenges in a variety of ways.

The first description of microglia cells can be traced

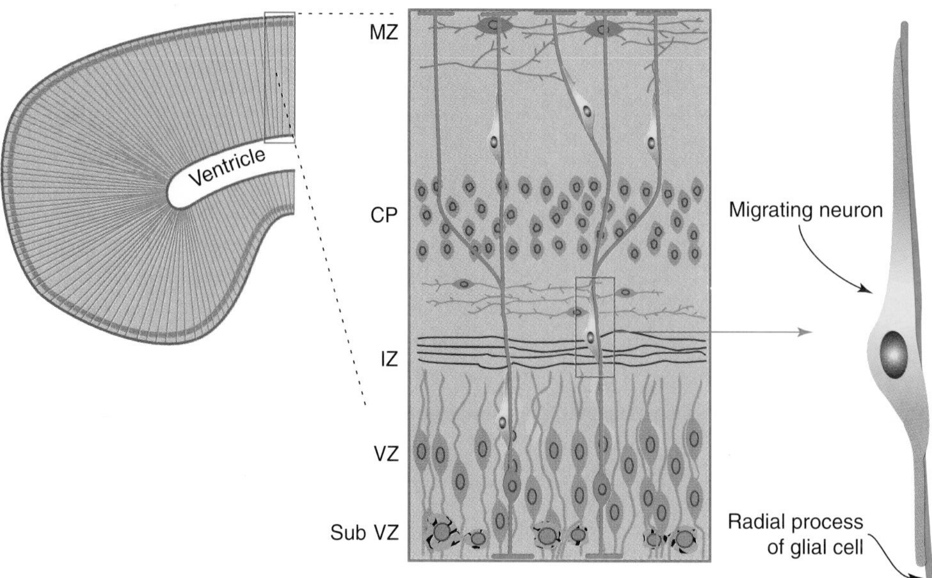

FIGURE 3.17 Radial glia perform support and guidance functions for migrating neurons. In early development, the radial glia span the thickness of the expanding brain parenchyma. The inset shows defined layers of the neural tube from the ventricular to the outer surface: VZ, ventricular zone; IZ, intermediate zone; CP, cortical plate; MZ, marginal zone. The radial process of the glial cell is indicated in blue, and a single attached migrating neuron is depicted at the right.

to Franz Nissl,[52] who used the term "rod cell" (Stäbchenzellen) to describe a population of glial cells that reacted to brain pathology. He postulated that rod-cell function was similar to that of leukocytes in other organs. Cajal described microglia as part of his "third element" of the CNS—cells that he considered to be of mesodermal origin and distinct from neurons and astrocytes.[53]

Del Río-Hortega[54] divided Cajal's third element into oligodendrocytes and microglia, two cell types with different morphology, function, and origin. He used silver impregnation methods to visualize the ramified appearance of microglia in the adult brain, and he concluded that ramified microglia could transform into cells that were migratory, ameboid, and phagocytic. A fundamental question raised by del Río-Hortega's studies was the origin of microglial cells. Although he provided evidence that microglia originated from cells that migrate into the brain from the pial surface, he also raised the possibility that microglia originate from blood "mononuclears." Controversy over the lineage of microglia still exists today.

Microglia Have Diverse Functions in Developing and Mature Nervous Tissue

Four different sources of microglia have been proposed[55]: (1) bone-marrow derived monocytes, (2) mesodermal pial elements, (3) neural epidermal cells, and (4) capillary-associated pericytes. On the basis of current knowledge, it appears that most ramified microglia cells are derived from bone-marrow derived monocytes, which enter the brain parenchyma during early stages of brain development. These cells help phagocytose degenerating cells that undergo programmed cell death as part of normal development. They retain the ability to divide and have the immunophenotypic properties of monocytes and macrophages. In addition to their role in remodeling the CNS during early development, microglia may secrete cytokines or growth factors that are important in fiber-tract development, gliogenesis, and angiogenesis. After the early stages of development, ameboid microglia cells transform into the ramified microglia cells that persist throughout adulthood.[56]

Little is known about microglial function in the normal adult vertebrate CNS. Microglia constitute a formidable percentage (5–20%) of the total cells in the mouse brain. Microglia are found in all regions of the brain, and there are more in gray than in white matter. The phylogenetically newer regions of the CNS (cerebral cortex, hippocampus) have more microglia than do older regions (brainstem, cerebellum).[57] Species variations also have been noted, as human white matter has three times more microglia than does rodent white matter.

Microglia usually have small rod-shaped somas from which numerous processes extend in a rather symmetrical fashion. Processes from different microglia rarely overlap or touch, and specialized contacts

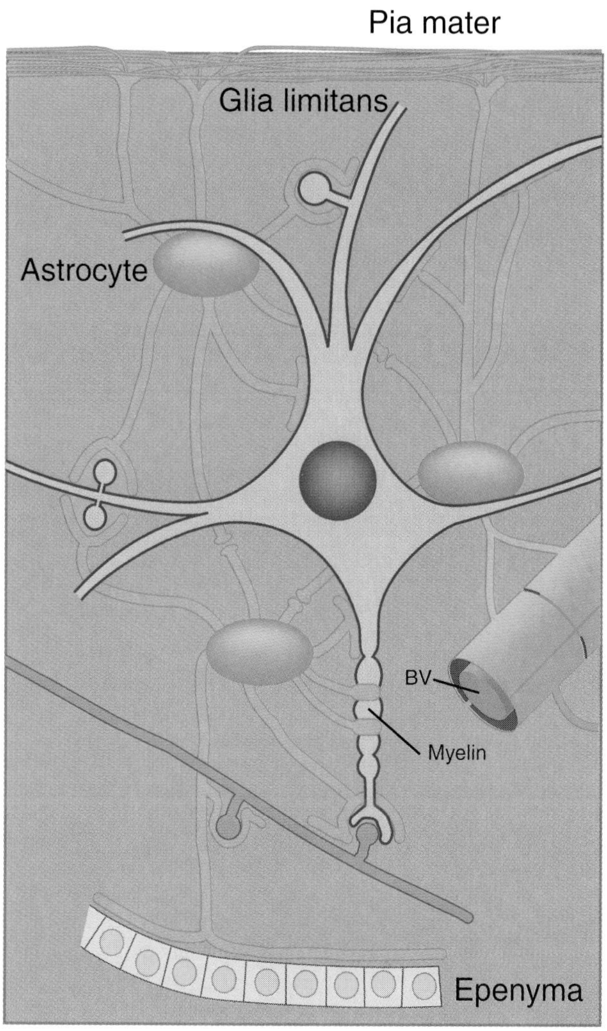

FIGURE 3.18 Astrocytes (in orange) are depicted *in situ* in schematic relationship with other cell types with which they are known to interact. Astrocytes send processes that surround neurons and synapses, blood vessels, and the region of the node of Ranvier and extend to the ependyma as well as to the pia mater, where they form the glial limitans.

between microglia and other cells have not been described in the normal brain. Although each microglial cell occupies its own territory, microglia collectively form a network that covers much of the CNS parenchyma. Because of the numerous processes, microglia present extensive surface membrane to the CNS environment. Regional variation in the number and shape of microglia in the adult brain suggests that local environmental cues can affect microglial distribution and morphology. On the basis of these morphological observations, it is likely that microglia play a role in tissue homeostasis. The nature of this homeostasis remains to be elucidated. It is clear, however, that microglia can respond quickly and dramatically to alterations in the CNS microenvironment.

Microglia Become Activated in Pathological States

"Reactive" microglia can be distinguished from resting microglia by two criteria: (1) change in morphology and (2) upregulation of monocyte–macrophage molecules (Fig. 3.20). Although the two phenomena generally occur together, reactive responses of microglia can be diverse and restricted to subpopulations of cells within a microenvironment. Microglia not only respond to pathological conditions involving immune activation, but also become activated in neurodegenerative conditions that are not considered immune mediated.[58] This latter response is indicative of the phagocytic role of microglia. Microglia change their morphology and antigen expression in response to almost any form of CNS injury.

Summary

Neuroglia are a set of cell types that together subserve supportive and trophic roles critical for the normal functioning of nervous tissue. Certain glial cells—the myelinating cells, for example—have clearly shaped nervous system evolution and development in that they evolved to facilitate rapid conduction of the action potential along small-caliber axons. The coordinated integrative functions of the vertebrate brain therefore depend on a normal complement of myelinated axons. Astrocytes and microglial cells also have major and extremely important functions in development and in tissue injury, but these roles are not as well understood as yet. In pathological states of all kinds (autoimmune, toxic insult, trauma), these cells react to contain and limit tissue damage. They also contribute in a major way to repair mechanisms.

THE CEREBRAL VASCULATURE

Blood vessels form an extremely rich network in the central nervous system, particularly in the cerebral cortex and subcortical gray masses, whereas the white matter is less densely vascularized (Fig. 3.21).[59] The vascular bed is supplied by perforating arteries that arise from a relatively small number of large, peripheral arterial trunks. The main trunks give off smaller cerebral arteries whose branches penetrate the subarachnoidal space, where they divide into many subbranches before penetrating the brain tissue. Within the cerebral gray matter, these penetrating arteries divide into a large number of small arterioles that eventually form an extremely rich, highly anastomotic capillary bed. At the other end of the capillary network are veinules, draining into larger cerebral veins, which are

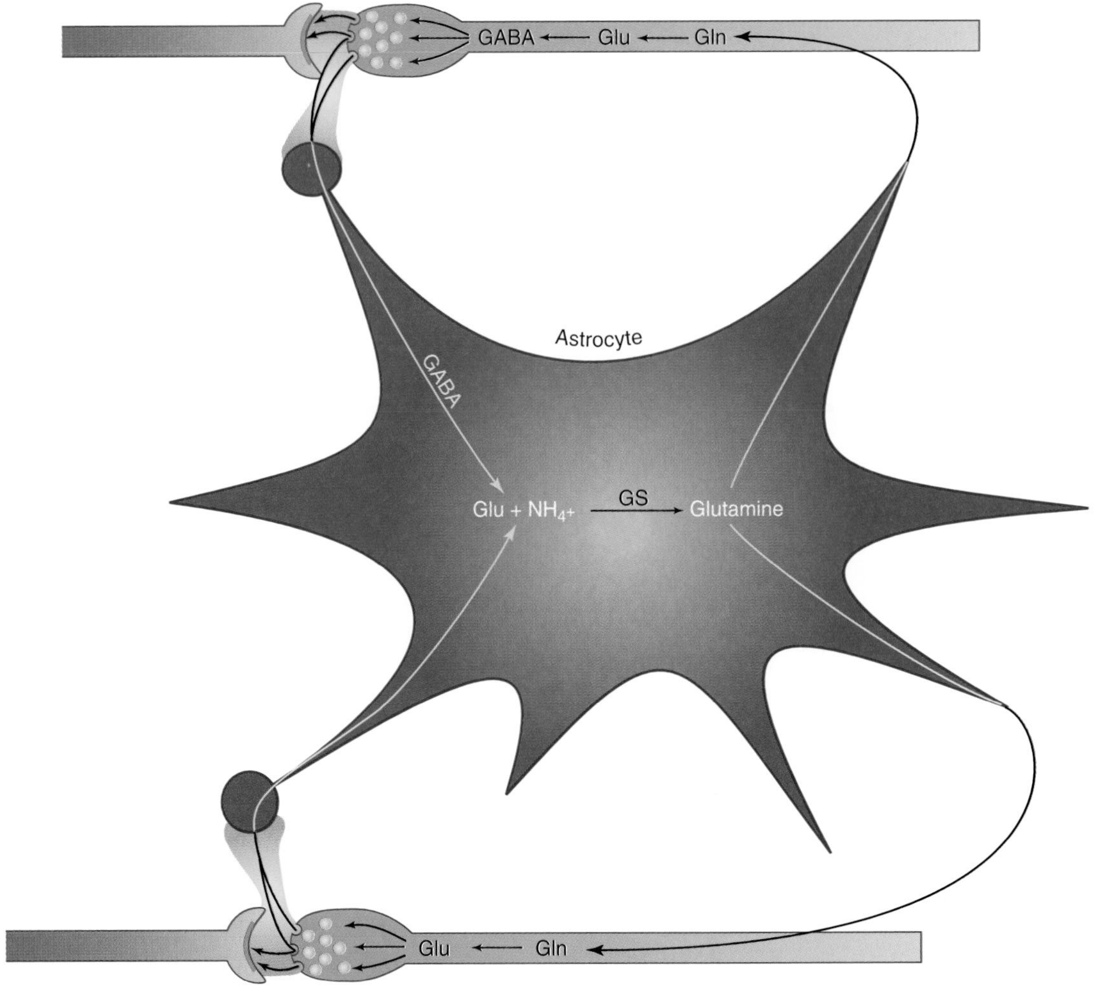

FIGURE 3.19 The glutamate–glutamine cycle is an example of a complex mechanism that involves an active coupling of neurotransmitter metabolism between neurons and astrocytes. The systems of exchange of glutamine, glutamate, GABA, and ammonia between neurons and astrocytes are highly integrated. The postulated detoxification of ammonia and inactivation of glutamate and GABA by astrocytes are consistent with the exclusive localization of glutamine synthetase in the astroglial compartment.

the tributaries of large venous sinuses responsible for returning blood to the general circulation. The brain vascular system has no end arteries, and there is a relatively free circulation throughout the central nervous system. There are, however, distinct regional patterns of microvessel distribution in the brain. These patterns are particularly clear in certain subcortical structures that constitute discrete vascular territories and in the cerebral cortex, where regional and laminar patterns are striking. For example, layer IV of the primary visual cortex possesses an extremely rich capillary network, in comparison with other layers and adjacent regions (Fig. 3.21). Interestingly, most of the inputs from the visual thalamus terminate in this particular layer. Whether similar functional correlations may be derived from comparable vascular patterns in other brain regions remains to be determined. Nonetheless, capillary densities are higher in regions containing large numbers of neurons and where synaptic density is high. Penetrating arteries and draining veins have well-defined, tree-shaped branching patterns.[59] With regard to cortical vessels, some arteries divide in the upper cortical layers, whereas others penetrate to the lower layers before dividing. The branches of penetrating arteries define local vascular fields of approximately similar size and shape around the vessel of origin, which cover the entire cortical mantle in a continuous network.

Pathologic factors that affect the patency of brain microvessels may result in the development of an ischemic injury localized to a variable amount of tissue, depending on the size and location of the affected arter-

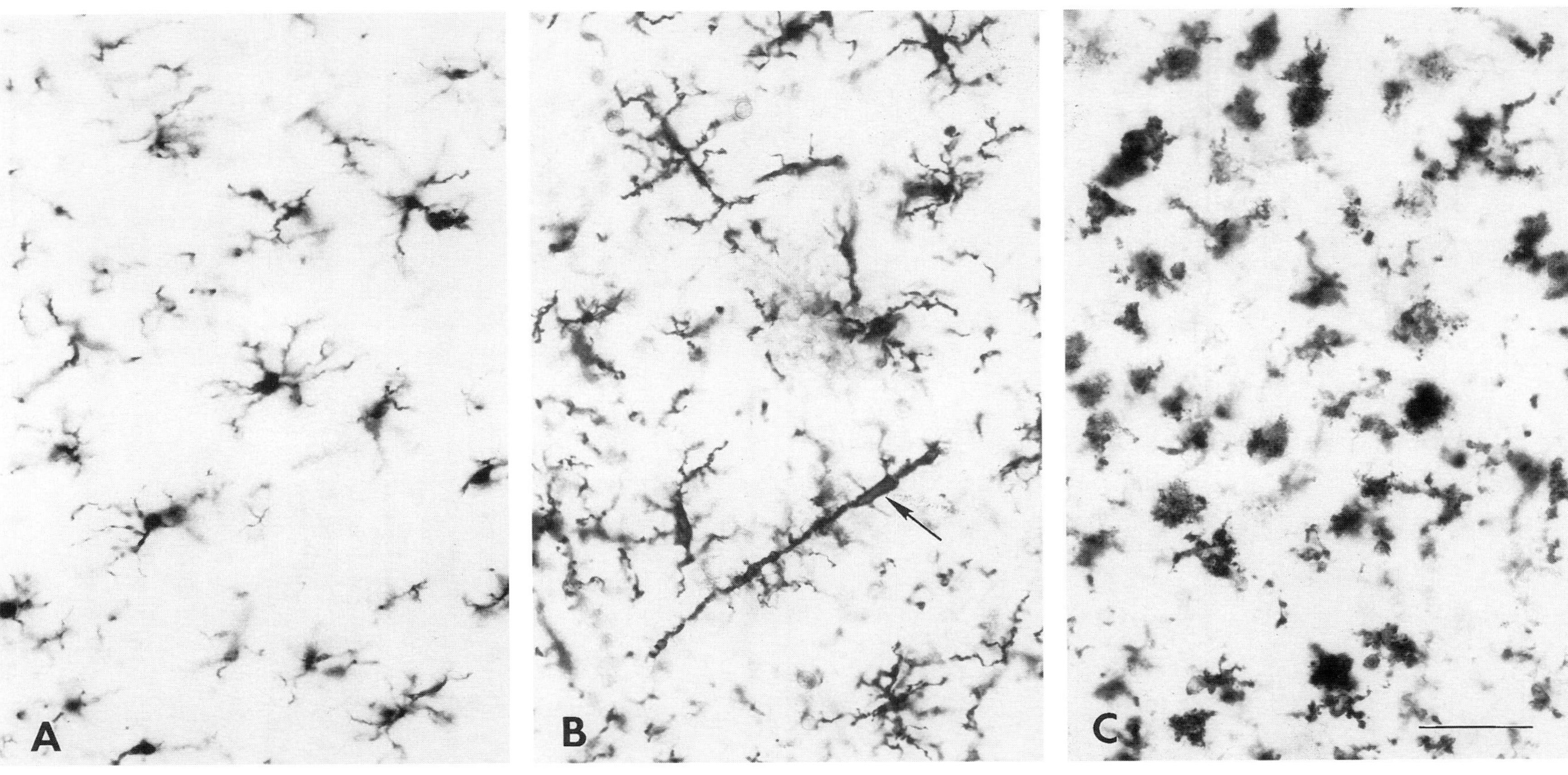

FIGURE 3.20 Activation of microglial cells in a tissue section from human brain. Resting microglia in normal brain (A). Activated microglia in diseased cerebral cortex (B) have thicker processes and larger cell bodies. In regions of frank pathology (C) microglia transform into phagocytic macrophages, which can also develop from circulating monocytes that enter the brain. Arrow in B indicates rod cell. Sections stained with antibody to ferritin. Scale bar = 40 μm.

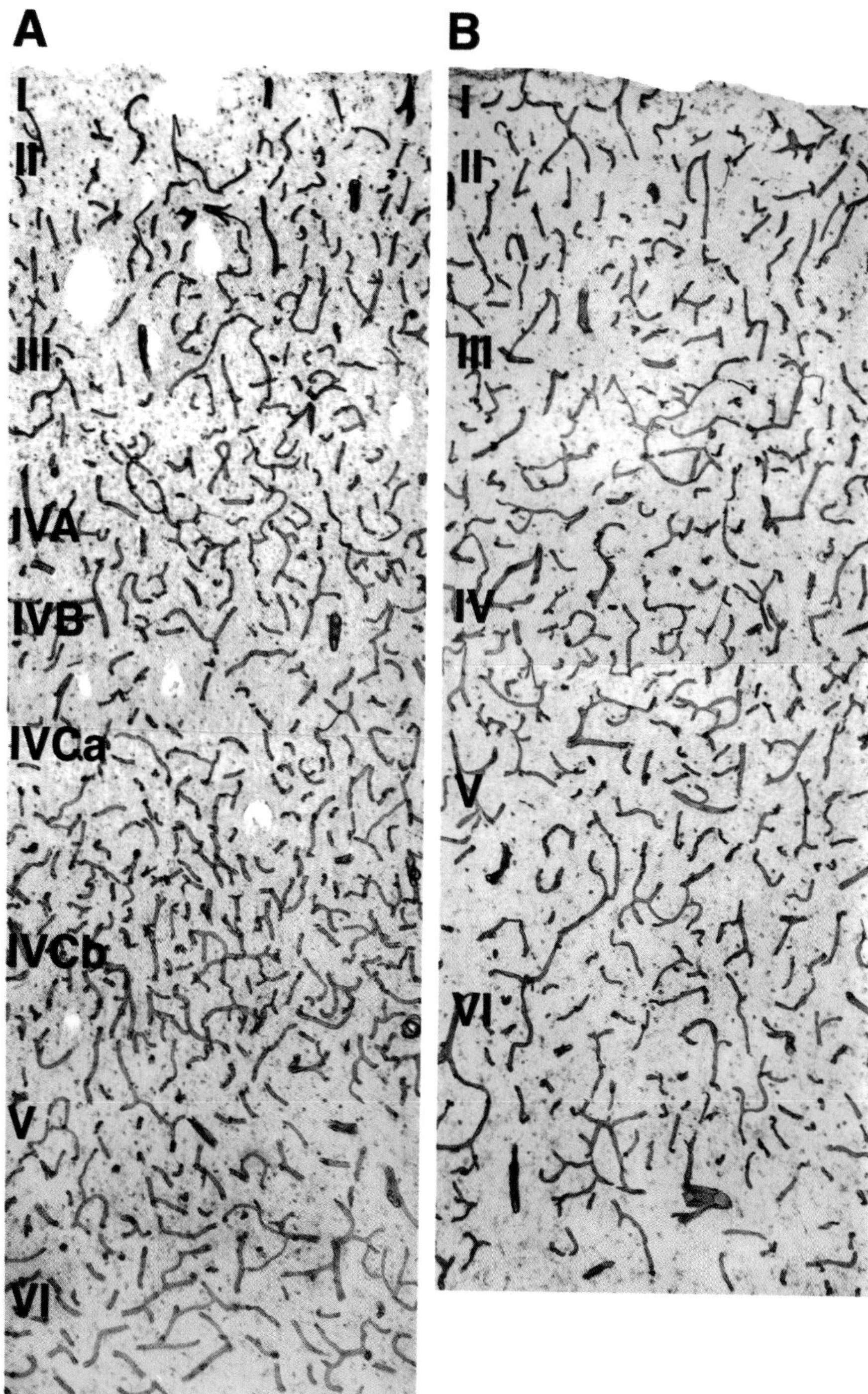

FIGURE 3.21 Microvasculature of the human neocortex. (A) The primary visual cortex (area 17). Note the presence of segments of deep penetrating arteries that have a larger diameter than the microvessels and run from the pial surface to the deep cortical layers, as well as the high density of microvessels in the middle layer (layers IVB and IVCb). (B) The prefrontal cortex (area 9). Cortical layers are indicated by Roman numerals. The microvessels are stained using an antibody against heparan sulfate proteoglycan core protein, a component of the extracellular matrix.

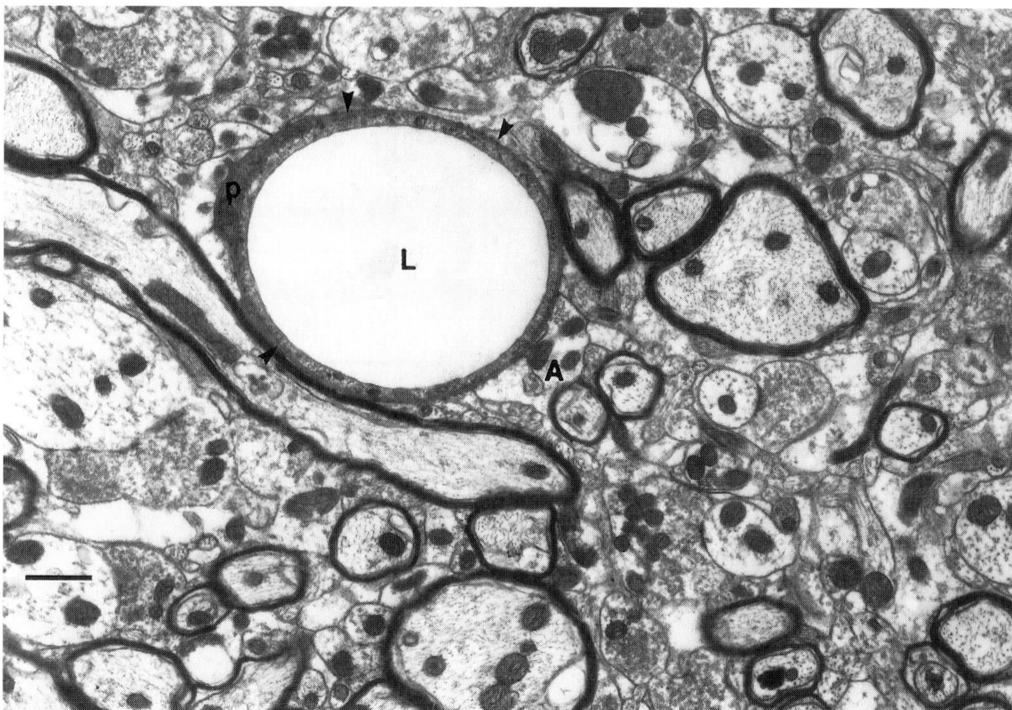

FIGURE 3.22 Electron micrograph of a blood–brain barrier capillary. Endothelial cells joined by tight junctions form continuous capillaries with no fenestrations and restrict the passage of solutes between blood and brain. Pericytes (P) are present within the basement membrane (arrowheads) of these capillaries, serve to control vascular tone, and can also be phagocytic in the brain. Astrocyte foot processes (A) surround the basement membrane and are responsible for the induction of BBB properties on endothelial cells. Bar = 2 μm.

ies. For instance, the progressive occlusion of a large arterial trunk, as seen in stroke, induces an ischemic injury that may eventually lead to necrosis of the brain tissue. The size of the resulting infarction is determined in part by the worsening of the blood circulation through the cerebral microvessels. In fact, occlusion of a large arterial trunk results in rapid swelling of the capillary endothelium and surrounding astrocytes, which may reduce the capillary lumen to about one-third of its normal diameter, preventing red blood cell circulation and oxygen delivery to the tissue. The severity of these changes subsequently determines the time course of neuronal necrosis, as well as the possible recovery of the surrounding tissue and the neurological outcome of the patient. In addition, the presence of multiple microinfarcts caused by occlusive lesions of small cerebral arterioles may lead to a progressively dementing illness, referred to as **vascular dementia,** affecting elderly humans.

The Blood–Brain Barrier Maintains the Intracerebral Milieu

The capillaries of the central nervous system form a protective barrier that restricts the exchange of solutes between blood and brain. This distinct function of brain capillaries is called the blood–brain barrier (Figs. 3.22 and 3.23).[60] The capillaries of the retina have similar properties and are termed the blood–retina barrier. It is thought that the blood–brain and blood–retina barriers function to maintain a constant intracerebral milieu, critical for neuronal function. This function is important because of the nature of intercellular communication in the CNS, which includes chemical signals across intercellular spaces. Without a blood–brain barrier, circulating factors in the blood such as certain hormones, which can also act as neurotransmitters, would interfere with synaptic communication.

When the blood–brain barrier is disrupted, edema fluid accumulates in the brain, leading to neurological impairments. Increased permeability of the blood–brain barrier plays a central role in many neuropathological conditions, including multiple sclerosis, AIDS, and childhood lead poisoning, and may also play a role in Alzheimer disease.[61,62] The blood–brain barrier is composed of three cellular components—endothelial cells, pericytes, and astrocytes—and one noncellular component—the basement membrane. These components interact with each other to

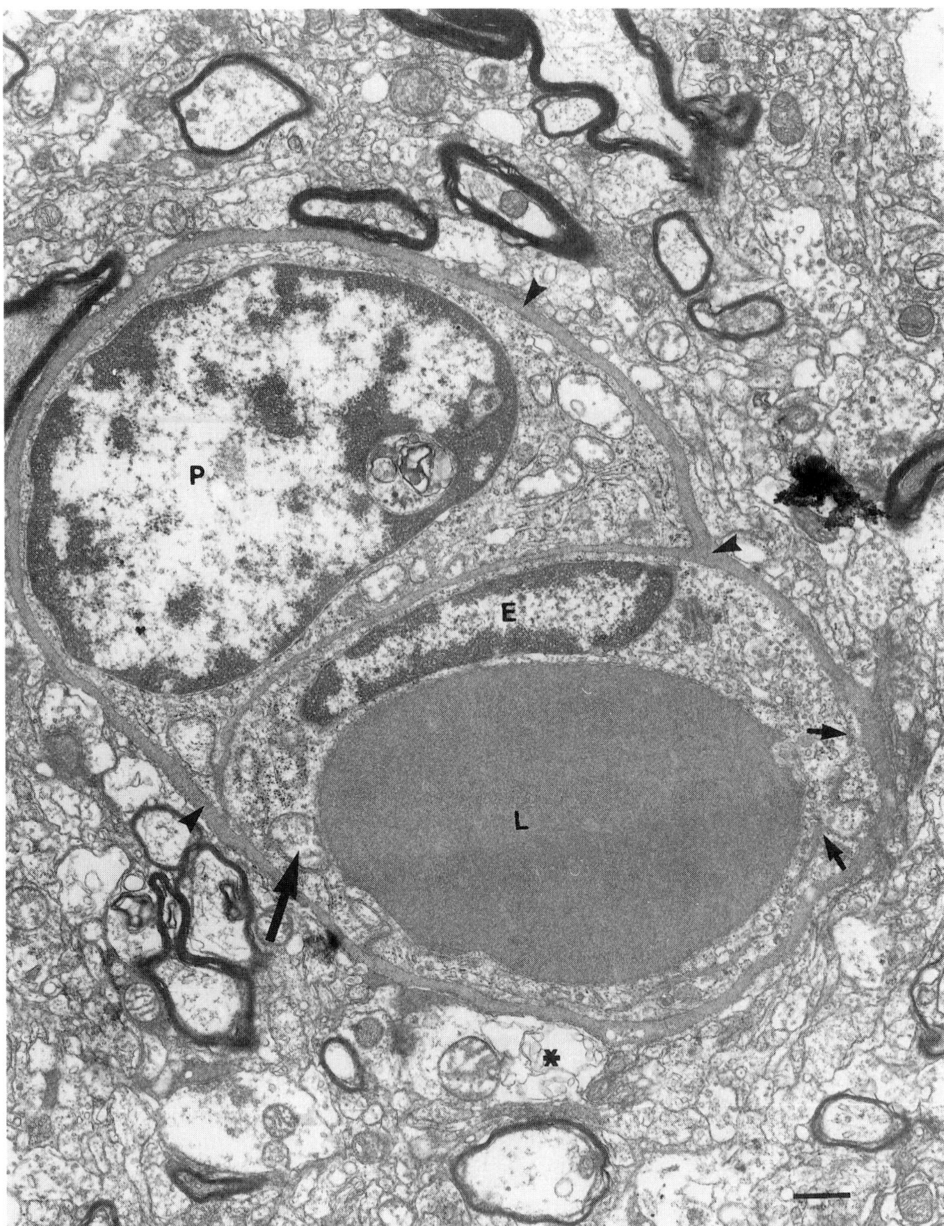

FIGURE 3.23 Human cerebral capillary obtained at biopsy. Blood–brain barrier (BBB) capillaries are characterized by the paucity of transcytotic vesicles in endothelial cells (E), a high mitochondrial content (large arrow), and the formation of tight junctions (small arrows) between endothelial cells that restrict the transport of solutes through the interendothelial space. The capillary endothelium is encased within a basement membrane (arrowheads), which also houses pericytes (P). Outside the basement membrane are astrocyte foot processes (asterisk), which may be responsible for induction of BBB characteristics on the endothelial cells. L, lumen of the capillary. Bar = 1 μm. From Claudio *et al.*[61]

produce a highly selective and dynamic barrier system.

In general, the cerebral capillaries are comparable to those seen in other tissues.[1] The capillary wall is composed of an endothelial cell surrounded by a very thin (about 30 nm) basal lamina, similar to that seen in capillaries in peripheral tissues. End feet of perivascular astrocytes are apposed against this continuous basal lamina. Around the capillary lies a virtual perivascular space occupied by another cell type, the pericyte, which surrounds the capillary walls. The endothelial cell forms a thin monolayer around the capillary lumen, and a single endothelial cell can completely surround the lumen of the capillary (Fig. 3.23). The cytoplasm is rich in actin filaments and contains an extensive Golgi apparatus and high numbers of mitochondria.

A fundamental difference between brain endothelial cells and those of the systemic circulation is the presence in brain of interendothelial tight junctions, also known as **zonula occludens.**[1] In the systemic circulation, the interendothelial space serves as a diffusion pathway that offers little resistance to most blood solutes entering the surrounding tissues. In contrast, blood–brain barrier tight junctions effectively restrict the intercellular route of solute transfer. The blood–brain barrier interendothelial junctions are not static seals; rather they are a series of active gates that can allow certain small molecules to penetrate. One such molecule is the lithium ion, used in the control of manic depression.

Another characteristic of endothelial cells of the brain is their low transcytotic activity. This is illustrated by the paucity of transcytotic vesicles in the cytoplasm, compared with endothelial cells of the systemic circulation. The frequency of transcytotic vesicles tends to increase with increasing permeability of an endothelium. Brain endothelium, therefore, is by this index not very permeable.

It is of interest that certain regions of the brain, such as the area postrema and periventricular organs, lack a blood–brain barrier. In these regions, the perivascular space is in direct contact with the nervous tissue, and the endothelial cells are fenestrated and show many pinocytotic vesicles. In these brain regions, neurons are known to secrete hormones and other factors that require rapid and uninhibited access to the systemic circulation.

Because of the high metabolic requirements of the brain, blood–brain barrier endothelial cells must have transport mechanisms for the specific nutrients needed for proper brain function. One such mechanism is glucose transporter isoform 1 (GLUT-1), which is asymmetrically expressed on the surface of blood–brain barrier endothelial cells. During Alzheimer disease, the expression of GLUT-1 on brain endothelial cells is reduced. This reduction may be due to a lower metabolic requirement of the brain after extensive neuronal loss. Other specific transport mechanisms on the cerebral endothelium include the large neutral amino acid carrier–mediated system that transports, among other amino acids, L-3,4-dihydroxyphenylalanine (L-dopa), used as a therapeutic agent in Parkinson disease. Also on the surface of blood–brain barrier endothelial cells are transferrin receptors that allow transport of iron into specific areas of the brain. The amount of iron that is transported into the various areas of the brain appears to depend on the concentration of transferrin receptors on the surface of endothelial cells of that region. Thus, the transport of specific nutrients into the brain is regulated during physiological and pathological conditions by blood–brain barrier transport proteins distributed according to the regional and metabolic requirements of brain tissue.

The Basement Membrane, Pericytes, and Astrocytes Are Also Blood–Brain Barrier Components

The basement membranes are not true membranes but are extracellular matrices with a width varying from 20 to 300 nm, composed mainly of collagens, glycoproteins, laminin, proteoglycans, and other proteins. In the cerebral microvasculature, the basement membrane surrounds the endothelium and the adjacent pericytes. The nature of the basement membrane surrounding the blood vessels varies with the type of vasculature and during pathological conditions. The composition and structure of the basement membrane affect the permeability of the vessel. For example, *in vitro* studies of endothelial monolayers in which the underlying matrix was composed primarily of collagen type I restricted passage of albumin, suggesting a role for the basement membrane in blood–brain barrier permeability.[63] Replacement of collagen type I with fibronectin resulted in increased permeability to albumin. This finding correlates with the lack of fibronectin around blood–brain barrier vessels.

Pericytes (Fig. 3.22) are present within the basement membrane of all vessels in the body, including the nervous system.[1] The functions of pericytes include the secretion of basement membrane components, the regulation of revascularization and repair, and the regulation of vascular tone in capillaries. In the central nervous system, pericytes may act as part of the vascular barrier by increased phagocytosis after blood–brain barrier injury.

The processes of astrocytes form a sheath around blood–brain barrier microvessels. These processes are termed astrocyte foot processes or end feet, and they assist in inducing the blood–brain barrier properties of brain endothelia.[64,65]

Disruption of the Blood–Brain Barrier Causes Edema

In general, disruption of the blood–brain barrier causes perivascular or vasogenic edema, which is the accumulation of fluids from the blood around the blood vessels of the brain. This is one of the main features of multiple sclerosis. In multiple sclerosis, inflammatory cells, primarily T cells and macrophages, invade the brain by migrating through the blood–brain barrier and attack cerebral elements as if these elements were foreign antigens.[61] It has been observed by many investigators that it is the degree of edema accumulation that causes the neurological symptoms experienced by people suffering from multiple sclerosis.

Studying the regulation of blood–brain barrier permeability is important for several reasons. Therapeutic treatments for neurological disease need to be able to cross the barrier. Attempts to design drug delivery systems that take therapeutic drugs directly into the brain have been made by using chemically engineered carrier molecules that take advantage of receptors such as that for transferrin, which normally transports iron into the brain. Development of an *in vitro* test system of the blood–brain barrier is of importance in the creation of new neurotropic drugs that are targeted to the brain. This could be especially useful in the treatment of neurodegenerative diseases and the AIDS dementia complex.

Summary

The hallmark of the brain vasculature is the blood–brain barrier, a multicomponent gateway between brain tissue and other organ systems. We can consider the blood–brain barrier the gateway to the brain because it restricts access to macromolecules present in the blood. It also serves as the interface between the immune and the nervous systems, acting as the "meeting site" for communication between the two.

References

General

Brightman, M. W., and Reese, T. S. (1969). Junctions between intimately apposed cell membranes in the vertebrate brain. *J. Cell Biol.* **40:** 648–677.

Broadwell, R. D., and Salcman, M. (1981). Expanding the definition of the BBB to protein. *Proc. Natl. Acad. Sci. U.S.A.* **78:** 7820–7824.

Fernandez-Moran, H. (1950). EM observations on the structure of the myelinated nerve sheath. *Exp. Cell Res.* **1:** 143–162.

Filbin, M., Walsh, F., Trapp, B., Pizzey, J., and Tennekoon, G. (1990). Role of myelin P_0 protein as a homophilic adhesion molecule. *Nature (London)* **344:** 871–872.

Gehrmann, J., Matsumoto, Y., and Kreutzberg, G. W. (1995). Microglia: Intrinsic immuneffector cell of the brain. *Brain Res. Rev.* **20:** 269–287.

Ikenaka, K., Furuichi, T., Iwasaki, Y., Moriguchi, A., Okano, H., and Mikoshiba, K. (1988). Myelin proteolipid protein gene structure and its regulation of expression in normal and jimpy mutant mice. *J. Mol. Biol.* **1991:** 587–596.

Kimbelberg, H., and Norenberg, M. D. (1989). Astrocytes. *Sci. Am.* **26:** 66–76.

Kirschner, D. A., Ganser, A. L., and Caspar, D. W. (1984). Diffraction studies of molecular organization and membrane interactions in myelin. In *Myelin* (P. Morell, ed.), pp. 51–96. Plenum, New York.

Lum, H., and Malik, A. B. (1994). Regulation of vascular endothelial barrier function. *Am. J. Physiol.* **267:** L223–L241.

Remahl, S., and Hildebrand, C. (1990). Relation between axons and oligodendroglial cells during initial myelination. Part 2. The individual axon. *J. Neurocytol.* **19:** 883–898.

Rosenbluth, J. (1980). Central myelin in the mouse mutant shiverer. *J. Comp. Neurol.* **194:** 639–728.

Rosenbluth, J. (1980). Peripheral myelin in the mouse mutant shiverer. *J. Comp. Neurol.* **194:** 729–753.

Williams, A. F. (1987). A year in the life of the immunoglobulin superfamily. *Immunol. Today* **8:** 298–303.

Cited

1. Peters, A., Palay, S. L., and Webster, H. de F. (1991). *The Fine Structure of the Nervous System: Neurons and Their Supporting Cells,* 3rd ed. Oxford University Press, New York.
2. Mountcastle, V. B. (1978). An organizing principle for cerebral function: the unit module and the distributed system. In *The Mindful Brain: Cortical Organization and the Group-Selective Theory of Higher Brain Function* (V. B. Mountcastle and G. Eddman, eds.), pp. 7–50. MIT Press, Cambridge, MA.
3. Peters, A., and Jones, E. G., eds. (1984). Vol. 1. *Cellular Components of the Cerebral Cortex.* Plenum, New York.
4. Schmitt, O. F., Worden, F. G., Adelman, G., and Dennis, S. G. (1981). *The Organization of the Cerebral Cortex.* MIT Press, Cambridge, MA.
5. Szentágothai, J., and Arbib, M. A. (1974). Conceptual models of neural organization. *Neurosci. Res. Program Bull.* **12:** 306–510.
6. Lund, J. S., Wu, Q., Hadingham, P. T., and Levitt, J. B. (1995). Cells and circuits contributing to functional properties in area I of macaque monkey cerebral cortex: Bases for neuroanatomically realistic models. *J. Anat.* **187:** 563–581.
7. Björklund, A., Hökfelt, T., Wouterlood, F. G., and Van den Pol, A. N., eds. (1990). *Handbook of Chemical Neuroanatomy,* Vol. 8. Elsevier, Amsterdam.
8. Berkley, H. J. (1896). The psychical nerve cell in health and disease. *Bull. Johns Hopkins Hosp.* **7:** 162–164.
9. Gray, E. G. (1959). Axo-somatic and axo-dendritic synapses of the cerebral cortex: An electron microscope study. *J. Anat.* **93:** 420–433.
10. Ramón y Cajal, S. (1955). *Histologie du système nerveux de l'homme et des vertébrés.* CSIC, Instituto Cajal, Madrid.
11. Coss, R. G., and Perkel, D. H. (1985). The function of dendritic spines: A review of theoretical issues. *Behav. Neural Biol.* **44:** 151–185.
12. Scheibel, M. E., and Scheibel, A. B. (1968). On the nature of dendritic spines—Report of a workshop. *Commun. Behav. Biol.* **A1:** 231–265.
13. Steward, O., and Falk, P. M. (1986). Protein-synthetic machinery at postsynaptic sites during synaptogenesis. A quantitative study of the association between polyribosomes and developing synapses. *J. Neurosci.* **6:** 412–423.
14. Jones, E. G. (1984). Laminar distribution of cortical efferent cells. In *Cellular Components of the Cerebral Cortex* (A. Peters and E. G. Jones, eds.), Vol. 1, pp. 521–553. Plenum, New York.
15. Jones, E. G. (1975). Varieties and distribution of non-pyramidal cells in the somatic sensory cortex of the squirrel monkey. *J. Comp. Neurol.* **160:** 205–267.
16. Feldman, M. L. (1984). Morphology of the neocortical pyramidal neuron. In *Cellular Components of the Cerebral Cortex* (A. Peters and E. G. Jones, eds.), Vol. 1, pp. 123–200. Plenum, New York.
17. Hof, P. R., Mufson, E. J., and Morrison, J. H. (1995). The human

orbitofrontal cortex: cytoarchitecture and quantitative immunohistochemical parcellation. *J. Comp. Neurol.* **359:** 48–68.

18. Hof, P. R., Nimchinsky, E. A., and Morrison, J. H. (1995). Neurochemical phenotype of corticocortical connections in the macaque monkey: Quantitative analysis of a subset of neurofilament protein-immunoreactive projection neurons in frontal, parietal, temporal, and cingulate cortices. *J. Comp. Neurol.* **362:** 109–133.
19. Kisvárday, Z. F., Cowey, A., and Somogyi, P. (1986). Synaptic relationships of a type of GABA-immunoreactive neuron (clutch cell), spiny stellate cells and lateral geniculate nucleus afferents in layer IVC of the monkey striate cortex. *Neuroscience* **19:** 741–761.

19a. Kisvárday, Z. F., Martin, K. A. C., Freund, T. F., Maglóczky, Z., Whitteridge, D., and Somogyi, P. (1986). Synaptic targets of HRP-filled layer III pyramidal cells in the cat striate cortex. *Exp. Brain Res.* **64:** 541–552.

20. Cobb, S. R., Buhl, E. H., Halasy, K., Paulsen, O., and Somogyi, P. (1995). Synchronization of neuronal activity in hippocampus by individual GABAergic interneurons. *Nature (London)* **378:** 76–79.
21. Sik, A., Penttonen, M., Ylinen, A., and Buzsáki, G. (1995). Hippocampal CA1 interneurons: An *in vivo* intracellular labeling study. *J. Neurosci.* **15:** 6651–6665.

21a. Somogyi, P., Hodgson, A. J., Smith, A. D., Nunzi, M. G., Gorio, A., and Wu, J. Y. (1984). Different populations of GABAergic neurons in the visual cortex and hippocampus of cat contain somatostatin- or cholecystokinin-immunoreactive material. *J. Neurosci.* **4:** 2590–2603.

22. Somogyi, P., Kisvárday, Z. F., Martin, K. A. C., and Whitteridge, D. (1983). Synaptic connections of morphologically identified and physiologically characterized large basket cells in the striate cortex of cat. *Neuroscience* **10:** 261–294.
23. Freund, T. F., Martin, K. A. C., Smith, A. D., and Somogyi, P. (1983). Glutamate decarboxylase-immunoreactive terminals of Golgi-impregnated axoaxonic cells and of presumed basket cells in synaptic contact with pyramidal neurons of the cat's visual cortex. *J. Comp. Neurol.* **221:** 263–278.

23a. Somogyi, P., Freund, T. F., and Cowey, A. (1982). The axoaxonic interneuron in the cerebral cortex of the rat, cat and monkey. *Neuroscience* **7:** 2577–2607.

24. DeFelipe, J., Hendry, S. H. C., and Jones, E. G. (1989). Visualization of chandelier cell axons by parvalbumin immunoreactivity in monkey cerebral cortex. *Proc. Natl. Acad. Sci. U.S.A.* **86:** 2093–2097.
25. Somogyi, P., and Cowey, A. (1981). Combined Golgi and electron microscopic study on the synapses formed by double bouquet cells in the visual cortex of the cat and monkey. *J. Comp. Neurol.* **195:** 547–566.

25a. DeFelipe, J., and Jones, E. G. (1992). High-resolution light and electron microscopic immunocytochemistry of colocalized GABA and calbindin D-28k in somata and double bouquet cell axons of monkey somatosensory cortex. *Eur. J. Neurosci.* **4:** 46–60.

26. Braak, H., and Braak, E. (1982). Neuronal types in the striatum of man. *Cell Tissue Res.* **227:** 319–342.
27. Carpenter, M. B., and Sutin, J. (1983). *Human Neuroanatomy.* Williams & Wilkins, Baltimore, MD.
28. van Domburg, P. H. M. F., and ten Donkelaar, H. J. (1991). The human substantia nigra and ventral tegmental area. *Adv. Anat. Embryol. Cell Biol.* **121:** 1–132.
29. Palay, S. L., and Chan-Palay, V. (1974). *Cerebellar Cortex: Cytology and Organization.* Springer-Verlag, Berlin.
30. Brodal, A. (1981). *Neurological Anatomy in Relation to Clinical Medicine,* 3rd ed. Oxford University Press, New York.
31. Krebs, W., and Krebs, I. (1991). *Primate Retina and Choroid: Atlas of Fine Structure in Man and Monkey.* Springer-Verlag, New York.
32. Hudspeth, A. J. (1983). Transduction and tuning by vertebrate hair cells. *Trends Neurosci.* **6:** 366–369.
33. Furness, J. B., and Costa, M. (1980). Types of nerves in the enteric nervous system. *Neuroscience* **5:** 1–20.
34. Morell, P., and Norton, W. T. (1980). Myelin. *Sci. Am.* **242:** 88–118.
35. Bunge, R. P. (1968). Glial cells and the central myelin sheath. *Physiol. Rev.* **48:** 197–251.
36. Bunge, M. B., and Bunge, R. P., and Pappas, G. D. (1962). Electron microscopic demonstration of connections between glia and myelin sheaths in the developing central nervous system. *J. Cell Biol.* **12:** 448–456.
37. Ritchie, J. M. (1984). Physiological basis of conduction in myelinated nerve fibers. In *Myelin* (P. Morell, ed.) pp. 117–146. Plenum, New York.
38. Colman, D. R., Doyle, J. P., D'Urso, D., Kitagawa, K., Pedraza, L., Yoshida, M., and Fannon, A. M. (1996). Speculations on myelin sheath evolution. In *Glial Cell Development* (K. R. Jessen and W. D. Richardson, eds.), pp. 85–100. Bios Scientific Publishers, Oxford.
39. Lemke, G., and Axel, R. (1985). Isolation and sequence of the gene encoding the major structural protein of peripheral myelin. *Cell (Cambridge, Mass.)* **40:** 501–513.
40. Giese, K. P., Martini, R., Lemke, G., Soriano, P., and Schachner, M. (1992). Mouse P_0 gene disruption leads to hypomyelination, abnormal expression of recognition molecules, and degeneration of myelin and axons. *Cell (Cambridge, Mass.)* **71:** 565–576.
41. Shapiro, L., Fannon, A. M., Kwong, P. D., Thompson, A., Lehmann, M. S., Grübel, G., Legrand, J.-F., Als-Nielson, J., Colman, D. R., and Hendrickson, W. A. (1995). Structural basis of cell-cell adhesion by cadherins. *Nature (London)* **374:** 327–337.
42. Folch-Pi, J., and Lees, M. B. (1951). Proteolipids, a new kind of tissue lipoproteins. *J. Biol. Chem.* **191:** 807–813.
43. Milner, R., Lai, C., Nave, K.-A., Lenoir, D., Ogata, J., and Sutcliffe, J. (1985). Nucleotide sequences of two mRNAs for rat brain myelin proteolipid protein. *Cell (Cambridge, Mass.)* **42:** 931–942.
44. Nave, K.-A., Lai, C., Bloom, F. E., and Milner, R. J. (1987). Splice site selection in the proteolipid protein (PLP) gene transcript and primary structure of the DM20 protein of central nervous system myelin. *Proc. Natl. Acad. Sci. U.S.A.* **84:** 5665–5669.
45. Nave, K.-A. (1994). Neurological mouse mutants and the genes of myelin. *J. Neurosci. Res.* **38:** 607–612.
46. Readhead, C., Popko, B., Takahashi, N., Shine, H. D., Saavedra, R. A., Sidman, R. L., and Hood, L. (1987). Expression of a myelin basic protein gene in transgenic shiverer mice: Correction of the dysmyelinating phenotype. *Cell (Cambridge, Mass.)* **48:** 703–712.
47. Arenander, A. T., and de Vellis, J. (1983). Frontiers of glial physiology. In *The Clinical Neurosciences* (R. Rosenberg, ed.), Sect. 5, pp. 53–91. Churchill-Livingstone, New York.
48. Goldstein, G. W. (1988). Endothelial cell-astrocyte interactions: A cellular model of the blood-brain barrier. *Ann. N.Y. Acad. Sci.* **529:** 31–39.
49. Raub, T. J., Kuentzel, S., and Sawada, G. A. (1992). Permeability of bovine brain microvessel endothelial cells *in vitro:* Barrier tightening by a factor released from astroglioma cells. *Exp. Cell Res.* **199:** 330—340.
50. Holash, J. A., and Stewart, P. A. (1993). The relationship of astrocyte-like cells to the vessels that contribute to the blood-ocular barriers. *Brain Res.* **629:** 218–224.

51. Kettenman, H., and Ransom, B. R., eds. (1995). *Neuroglia*. Oxford University Press, Oxford.
52. Nissl, F. (1899). Üeber einige Beziehungen zwischen Nervenzellenerkränkungen und gliösen Erscheinungen bei verschiedenen Psychosen. *Arch. Psychol.* **32:** 1–21.
53. Ramón y Cajal, S. (1913). Contribución al conocimiento de la neuroglia del cerebro humano. *Trab. Lab. Invest. Biol.* **11:** 255–315.
54. del Río-Hortega, P. (1932). Microglia. In *Cytology and Cellular Pathology of the Nervous System* (W. Penfield, ed.), Vol. 2, pp. 481–534. Harper (Hoeber), New York.
55. Dolman, C. L. (1991). Microglia. In *Textbook of Neuropathology* (R. L. Davis and D. M. Robertson, eds.), pp. 141–163. Williams & Wilkins, Baltimore, MD.
56. Altman, J. (1994). Microglia emerge from the fog. *Trends Neurosci.* **17:** 47–49.
57. Lawson, L. J., Perry, V. H., Dri, P., and Gordon, S. (1990). Heterogeneity in the distribution and morphology of microglia in the normal adult mouse brain. *Neuroscience* **39:** 151–170.
58. Banati, R. B., and Graeber, M. B. (1994). Surveillance, intervention and cytotoxicity: Is there a protective role of microglia? *Dev. Neurosci.* **16:** 114–127.
59. Duvernoy, H. M., Delon, S., and Vannson, J. L. (1981). Cortical blood vessels of the human brain. *Brain Res. Bull.* **7:** 519–579.
60. Bradbury, M. W. B. (1979). *The Concept of a Blood–Brain Barrier*, pp. 381–407. Wiley, Chichester.
61. Claudio, L., Raine, C. S., and Brosnan, C. F. (1995). Evidence of persistent blood–brain barrier abnormalities in chronic-progressive multiple sclerosis. *Acta Neuropathol.* **90:** 228–238.
62. Buée, L., Hof, P. R., Bouras, C., Delacourte, A., Perl, D. P., Morrison, J. H., and Fillit, H. M. (1994). Pathological alterations of the cerebral microvasculature in Alzheimer's disease and related dementing disorders. *Acta Neuropathol.* **87:** 469–480.
63. Rubin, L. L., Hall, D. E., Porter, S., Barbu, K., Cannon, C., Horner, H. C., Janatpour, M., Liaw, C. W., Manning, K., Morales, J., Tanner, L. I., Tomaselli, K. J., and Bard, F. (1991). A cell culture model of the blood-brain barrier. *J. Cell Biol.* **115:** 1725–1735.
64. Arthur, F. E., Shivers, R. R., and Bowman, P. D. (1987). Astrocyte-mediated induction of tight junctions in brain capillary endothelium: An efficient *in vitro* model. *Dev. Brain Res.* **36:** 155–159.
65. Janzer, R. C., and Raff, M. C. (1987). Astrocytes induce blood-brain barrier properties in endothelial cells. *Nature (London)* **325:** 235–256.

CHAPTER

4

Subcellular Organization of the Nervous System: Organelles and Their Functions

Scott Brady, David R. Colman, and Peter Brophy

Cells have many features in common, but each cell type also possesses a functional architecture related to its unique physiological functions. In fact, cells may become so specialized in fulfilling a particular function that virtually all cellular components may be devoted to it. For example, the architecture and molecular composition of mammalian erythrocytes are completely dedicated to the delivery of oxygen to the tissues and the removal of carbon dioxide. Toward this end, the erythrocyte has evolved a specialized plasma membrane, an underlying cytoskeletal matrix that molds the cell into a biconcave disk, and a cytoplasm that is rich in hemoglobin. Modification of the cell machinery extends even to the discarding of structures such as the nucleus and the protein synthetic apparatus, which are not needed after the red blood cell matures. In many respects, the terminally differentiated, highly specialized cells of the nervous system exhibit comparable commitment—the extensive development of subcellular components reflects the roles that each plays.

The neuron serves as the cellular correlate of information processing and, in aggregate, all neurons act together to integrate responses of the entire organism to the external world. It is therefore not surprising that the specializations found in neurons are more diverse and complex than those found in any other cell type. Single neurons commonly interact in specific ways with hundreds of other cells—other neurons, astrocytes, oligodendrocytes, immune cells, muscle, and glandular cells. In this chapter, the major functional domains of the neuron are defined, the subcellular elements that compose the building blocks of these domains are described, and the processes that create and maintain neuronal functional architecture are examined.

AXONS AND DENDRITES: UNIQUE STRUCTURAL COMPONENTS OF NEURONS

Neurons and glial cells are remarkable for their size and complexity, but they do share many features with other eukaryotic cells.[1] As discussed in Chapter 3, the perikaryon, or cell body, contains a nucleus and its associated protein synthetic machinery. Most neuronal nuclei are large, and they typically contain a preponderance of euchromatin. This is consistent with the need to create and maintain a large cellular volume. Because protein synthesis must be kept at a high level just to maintain the neuronal extensions, transcription levels in neurons are generally high. In turn, the wide variety of different polypeptide constituents associated with the cellular domains in a neuron requires that a large number of different genes be constantly transcribed.

When specific mRNAs have been synthesized and processed, they move from the nucleus into a subcellular region that can be termed the **translational cytoplasm**[2] comprising cytoplasmic ("free") and membrane-associated polysomes, the intermediate compartment of the smooth endoplasmic reticulum, and the Golgi complex. The constituents of translational cytoplasm are thus associated with the synthesis and processing of proteins. Neurons in particular have relatively large amounts of translational cytoplasm to accommodate a high level of protein synthesis. This protein synthetic machinery is arranged in discrete intracellular "granules" termed **Nissl substance** (Box 4.1) after the histologist who first discovered these structures in the 19th century. The Nissl substance is actually a combination of stacks of rough endoplasmic reticulum (RER), interposed with rosettes of free polysomes (Box 4.1 and Fig. 4.1). This arrangement is unique to neurons, and its functional significance is unknown. Most, but by no means all, proteins used throughout the neuron are synthesized in the perikaryon. During or after synthesis and processing, proteins are packaged into membrane-limited organelles, incorporated into cytoskeletal elements, or remain as soluble constituents of the cytoplasm. After proteins have been packaged appropriately, they are transported to their sites of function.

With a few exceptions, vertebrate neurons have two discrete functional domains or compartments, the axonal and the somatodendritic compartments, each of which encompasses a number of sub- or microdomains (Fig. 4.2). The **axon** is perhaps the most familiar functional domain of a neuron[2] and is classically defined as the cellular process by which a neuron makes contact with a target cell to transmit information, providing a conducting structure for transmitting the action potential to a **synapse,** a specialized subdomain for transmission of a signal from neuron to target cell (neuron, muscle, etc.), most often by release of appropriate neurotransmitters. Consequently, most axons end in a **presynaptic terminal,** although a single axon may have many (hundreds or even thousands in some cases) presynaptic specializations known as *en passant* synapses along its length. Characteristics of presynaptic terminals are presented in greater detail later in this chapter.

The axon is the first neuronal process to differentiate during development. A typical neuron has only a single axon that proceeds some distance from the cell body before branching extensively. Usually the longest process of a neuron, axons come in many sizes. In a human adult, axons range in length from a few micrometers for small interneurons to a meter or more for large motor neurons, and they may be even longer in large animals (such as giraffes, elephants, and whales). In mammals and other vertebrates, the longest axons generally extend approximately half the body length.

Axonal diameters also are quite variable, ranging from 0.1 to 20 μm for large myelinated fibers in vertebrates. Invertebrate axons grow to even larger diameters, with the giant axons of some squid species routinely reaching diameters of 750 μm. Invertebrate axons reach such large diameters because they lack the myelinating glia that speed conduction of the action potential. As a result, axonal caliber must be increased if higher rates of conduction for action potentials are needed for the reflexes that permit escape from predators and capture of prey. Although axonal caliber is closely regulated in both myelinated and nonmyelinated fibers, this parameter is critical for those organisms that are unable to produce myelin.

The region of the neuronal cell body where the axon originates has several specialized features. This domain, called the **axon hillock,** is most readily distinguished by a deficiency of Nissl substance. Therefore, protein synthesis cannot take place to any appreciable degree in this region. Cytoplasm in the vicinity of the axon hillock may have a few polysomes but is dominated by the cytoskeletal and membranous organelles that are being delivered to the axon. Microtubules and neurofilaments begin to align roughly parallel to each other, helping to organize membrane-limited organelles destined for the axon. The hillock is a region where materials either are committed to the axon (cytoskeletal elements, synaptic vesicle precursors, mitochondria, etc.) or are excluded from the axon (RER and free polysomes, dendritic microtubule-associated proteins). The molecular basis for this sorting is not understood. Cytoplasm in the axon hillock does not appear to contain a physical "sizing" barrier (like a filter) because large organelles such as mitochondria readily enter the axon whereas only a small number of essentially excluded structures such as polysomes are occasionally seen only in the initial segment of the axon and not in the axon proper. An exception to this general rule is during development when local protein synthesis does take place at the axon terminus or growth cone. In the mature neuron, the physiological significance of this barrier must be considerable, because axonal structures are found to accumulate in this region in many neuropathologies, including those due to degenerative diseases (such as amyotrophic lateral sclerosis) and to exposure to neurotoxic compounds (such as acrylamide).

The **initial segment** of the axon is the region of the axon adjacent to the axon hillock. Microtubules generally form characteristic fascicles, or bundles, in the initial segment of the axon. These fascicles are not seen elsewhere. The initial segment and to some extent the axon hillock also have a distinctive specialized plasma membrane. Initially, the plasmalemma was thought to have a thick electron-dense coating actually attached to the inner surface of the membrane, but this dense undercoating is in reality separated by 5–10 nm from the plasma membrane inner surface and has a complex ultrastructure. Neither the composition nor the function of this undercoating is known. Curiously, the undercoating is present in the same regions of the initial segment as the distinctive fasciculation of microtubules, although the relationship is not understood. The plasma membrane is specialized in the initial segment and axon hillock in that it contains voltage-sensi-

BOX 4.1

THE NISSL SUBSTANCE

"It is interesting that Nissl recognized the composite nature of the substance named for him, although he could not have resolved either of its components . . ."

The preceding quote and the following discussion of the Nissl substance appeared in L. Sanford, M. D. Palay, and G. E. Palade (1955). The fine structure of neurons. *J. Biophys. Biochem. Cytol.* **88:** 69–88.

> As imaged in the electron microscope, the crowded cytoplasm of the neuron contrasts sharply with the relatively open cytoplasm of many other cell types. As this compact appearance stems largely from the extensive meshwork of Nissl substance, the neuron resembles, even at the electron microscope level, certain protein-secreting glandular cells, such as those of the pancreatic acini and the salivary glands. . . .
>
> Like the basophilic substance or ergastoplasm of glandular cells, the Nissl substance is a composite material constructed of endoplasmic reticulum and fine granules, both of which have been revealed by electron microscopy. The first component of the Nissl substance appears to be part of the general endoplasmic reticulum of the neuron. The reticulum extends through-out the entire cytoplasm, but is considerably more condensed within the area of the Nissl bodies than in the rest of the cell. These condensations not only determine the size and shape of each Nissl body, but also constitute a membranous framework upon which the other components are arranged. In many types of neurons, the meshes of the endoplasmic reticulum are distributed at random in three dimensions but in all neurons, and especially in the large motor neurons, the endoplasmic reticulum may display a distinctly orderly arrangement within the Nissl bodies. This orientation consists of a layering of reticular sheets, at more or less regular intervals. Each sheet is a reticulum developed predominantly in two dimensions and comprising tubules, strings of vesicles, and numerous large and flat cisternae. Even in such highly ordered forms as the Nissl bodies of motor neurons, the continuity of the reticulum persists, as indicated by frequent branches and anastomoses between layers.
>
> The second component of the Nissl substance is represented by small granules disposed in patterned arrays either in close contact with the outer membranes of the endoplasmic reticulum or scattered in the intervening matrix. This matrix may be considered as a third component of the Nissl substance. It is evident, therefore, that although the Nissl bodies are differentiated parts of the cytoplasm, they are continuous with it by virtue of the continuity of the endoplasmic reticulum and the matrix. No interface or membrane separates them from the rest of the cytoplasm. In this respect, as well as in general architecture, they are comparable to the ergastoplasm of glandular cells. The only differences lie in (a) a different intracellular distribution, (b) a lesser degree of preferred orientation of the endoplasmic reticulum, and (c) an apparently greater concentration of fine granules within the areas of the Nissl bodies.

We now recognize that the electron-dense "granules" are ribosomes, arranged in cytoplasmic "free" polysomal rosettes (see box, in the accompanying figure), or attached to the surface of the endoplasmic reticulum membrane. The lumen of the ER compartment (arrow) contains a "fuzz" that probably is formed by the numerous nascent chains being cotranslationally inserted into the ER lumen, some resident proteins that take part in the translation process, and certain structural components of the ER membrane.

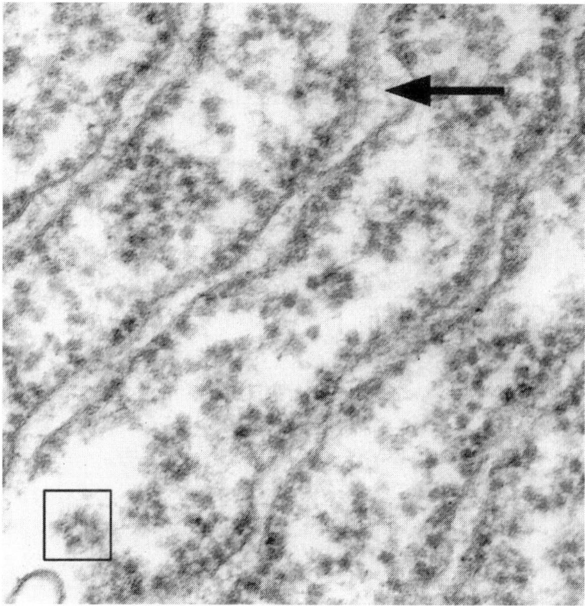

FIGURE 4.1 The "Nissl body" in neurons is an array of cytoplasmic free polysomal rosettes (boxed) interspersed between rows of rough endoplasmic reticulum (RER) studded with membrane-bound ribosomes. Nascent polypeptide chains emerging from the ribosomal tunnel on the RER are inserted into the lumen (arrow), where they may be processed before transport out of the RER. The relationship between the polypeptide products of these "free" and "bound" polysome populations in the Nissl body, an arrangement that is unique to neurons, is unknown.

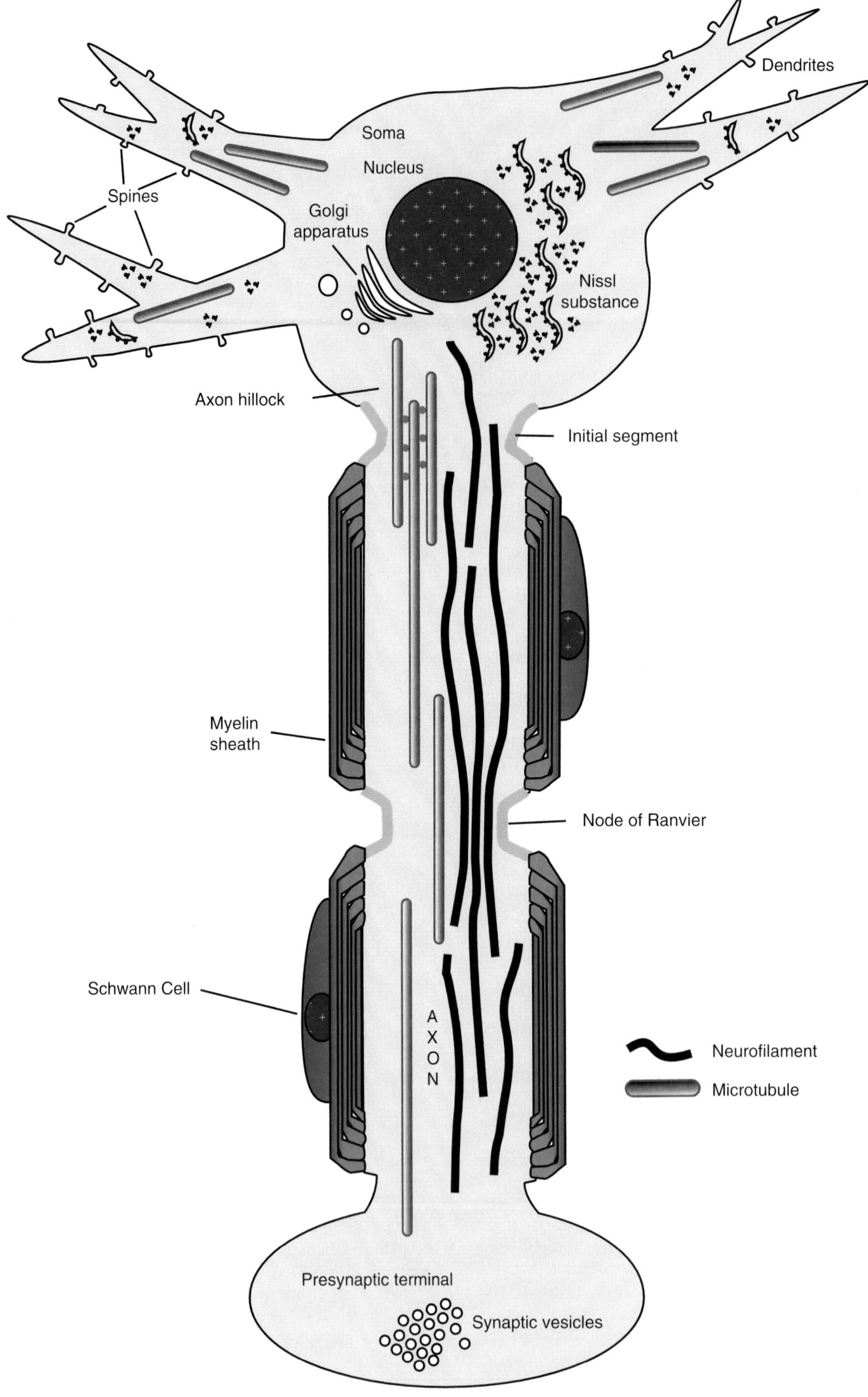
Dendrites
Soma
Nucleus
Spines
Golgi apparatus
Nissl substance
Axon hillock
Initial segment
Myelin sheath
Node of Ranvier
Schwann Cell
AXON
Neurofilament
Microtubule
Presynaptic terminal
Synaptic vesicles

tive ion channels in large numbers, and most action potentials originate in this domain.

Ultimately, axonal structure is geared toward the efficient conduction of action potentials at a rate appropriate to the function of that neuron. This can be seen from both the ultrastructure and the composition of axons. Axons are roughly cylindrical in cross section with little or no taper. As discussed later in this chapter, this diameter is maintained by regulation of the cytoskeleton. Even at branch points, daughter axons are comparable in diameter to the parent axon. This constant caliber helps ensure a consistent rate of conduction. Similarly, the organization of membrane components is regulated to this end. Voltage-gated ion channels are distributed to maximize conduction. Sodium channels are distributed more or less uniformly in small nonmyelinated axons, but are concentrated at high density in the regularly spaced unmyelinated gaps, known as **nodes of Ranvier.** An axon so organized will conduct an action potential or train of spikes long distances with high fidelity at a defined speed. These characteristics are essential for maintaining the precise timing and coordination seen in neuronal circuits.

Most vertebrate neurons have multiple **dendrites** arising from their perikarya. Unlike axons, dendrites continuously branch and taper extensively with a reduction in caliber in daughter processes at each branching. In addition, the surface of dendrites is covered with small protrusions, or **spines,** which are postsynaptic specializations. Although the surface area of a dendritic arbor may be quite extensive, dendrites in general remain in the relative vicinity of the perikaryon. A dendritic arbor may be contacted by the axons of many different and distant neurons or innervated by a single axon making multiple synaptic contacts.

The base of a dendrite is continuous with the cytoplasm of the cell body. In contrast to the axon, Nissl substance extends into dendrites, and certain proteins are synthesized predominantly in dendrites. There is evidence for the selective placement of some mRNAs in dendrites as well.[2a] For example, whereas RER and polysomes extend well into the dendrites, the mRNAs that are transported and translated in dendrites are a subset of the total neuronal mRNA, deficient in some mRNA species (such as neurofilament mRNAs) and enriched in mRNAs with dendritic functions (such as microtubule-associated protein mRNAs, MAP2). Also, certain proteins appear to be targeted, postsynthesis, to the dendritic compartment as well.

The shapes and complexity of dendritic arborizations may be remarkably plastic. Dendrites appear relatively late in development and initially have only limited numbers of branches and spines. As development and maturation of the nervous system proceed, the size and number of branches increase. The number of spines increases dramatically, and their distribution may change. This remodeling of synaptic connectivity may continue into adulthood, and environmental effects can alter this pattern significantly. Eventually, in the aging brain, there is a reduction in complexity and size of dendritic arbors, with fewer spines and thinner dendritic shafts. These changes correlate with changes in neuronal function during development and aging.

As defined by classical physiology, axons are the structural correlates for neuronal output, and dendrites constitute the domain for receiving information. A neuron without an axon or one without dendrites might therefore seem paradoxical, but such neurons do exist. Certain **amacrine** and **horizontal** cells in the vertebrate retina have no identifiable axons, although they do have dendritic processes that are morphologically distinct from axons. Such processes may have both pre- and postsynaptic specializations or they may have gap junctions that act as direct electrical connections between two cells. Similarly, the **pseudounipolar sensory neurons** of dorsal root ganglia (DRG) have no dendrites. In their mature form, these DRG sensory neurons give rise to a single axon that extends a few hundred micrometers before branching. One long branch extends to the periphery, where it may form a sensory nerve ending in muscle spindles or skin. Large DRG peripheral branches are myelinated and have the morphological characteristics of an axon, but they contain neither pre- nor postsynaptic specializations. The other branch extends into the central nervous system, where it forms synaptic contacts. In DRG neurons, the action potential is generated at distal sensory nerve endings and then transmitted along the peripheral branch to the central branch and the appropriate CNS targets, bypassing the cell body. The functional and morphological hallmarks of axons and dendrites are listed in Table 4.1.

FIGURE 4.2 The basic elements of neuronal subcellular organization. The neuron consists of a soma, or cell body, in which the nucleus, multiple cytoplasm-filled processes termed dendrites, and the (usually single) axon are placed. The neuron is highly extended in space; a neuron with a cell body of the size shown here could easily maintain an axon several *miles* in length! The unique shape of each neuron is the result of a cooperative interplay between plasma membrane components (the lipid matrix and associated proteins) and cytoskeletal elements. Most large neurons in vertebrates are myelinated by oligodendrocytes in the CNS and Schwann cells in the PNS. The compact wraps of myelin encasing the axon distal to the initial segment permit the rapid conduction of the action potential by a process termed "saltatory conduction" (see Chapter 3).

TABLE 4.1 Functional and Morphological Hallmarks of Axons and Dendrites

Axons	Dendrites
With rare exceptions, each neuron has a single axon.	Most neurons have multiple dendrites arising from their cell bodies.
Axons appear first during neuronal differentiation.	Dendrites begin to differentiate only after the axon has formed.
Axon initial segments are distinguished by a specialized plasma membrane containing a high density of ion channels and distinctive cytoskeletal organization.	Dendrites are continuous with the perikaryal cytoplasm, and the transition point cannot be readily distinguished.
Axons typically are cylindrical in form with a round or elliptical cross section.	Dendrites usually have a significant taper and small spinous processes that give them an irregular cross section.
Large axons are myelinated in vertebrates, and the thickness of the myelin sheath is proportional to the axonal caliber.	Dendrites are not myelinated, although a few wraps of myelin may occur rarely.
Axon caliber is a function of neurofilament and microtubule numbers with neurofilaments predominating in large axons.	The dendritic cytoskeleton may appear less organized, and microtubules dominate even in large dendrites.
Microtubules in axons have a uniform polarity with plus ends distal from the cell body.	Microtubules in proximal dendrites have mixed polarity, with both plus and minus ends oriented distal to the cell body.
Axonal microtubules are enriched in tau protein with a characteristic phosphorylation pattern.	Dendritic microtubules may contain some tau protein, but MAP2 is not present in axonal compartments and is highly enriched in dendrites.
Ribosomes are excluded from mature axons, although a few may be detectable in initial segments.	Both rough endoplasmic reticulum and cytoplasmic polysomes are present in dendrites, with specific mRNAs being enriched in dendrites.
Axonal branches tend to be distal from the cell body.	Dendrites begin to branch extensively near the perikaryon and form extensive arbors in the vicinity of the perikaryon.
Axonal branches form obtuse angles and have diameters similar to the parent stem.	Dendritic branches form acute angles and are smaller than the parent stem.
Most axons have presynaptic specializations that may be *en passant* or at the ends of axonal branches.	Dendrites are rich in postsynaptic specializations, particularly on the spinous processes that project from the dendritic shaft.
Action potentials are usually generated at the axon hillock and conducted away from the cell body.	Some dendrites can generate action potentials, but more commonly they modulate the electrical state of the perikaryon and initial segment.
Traditionally, axons are specialized for conduction and synaptic transmission, i.e., neuronal output.	Dendritic architecture is most suitable for integrating synaptic responses from a variety of inputs, i.e., neuronal input.

Note. Neurons typically have two classes of cytoplasmic extensions that may be distinguished using electrophysiological, morphological and biochemical criteria. Although some neuronal processes may lack one or more of these features, enough parameters can generally be defined to allow unambiguous identification.

Summary

Neurons are polarized cells that are specialized for membrane and protein synthesis as well as for conduction of the nerve impulse. In general, neurons have a cell body, a dendritic arborization that is usually located near the cell body, and an extended axon that may branch considerably before terminating to form synapses with other neurons.

PROTEIN SYNTHESIS IN NERVOUS TISSUE

Both neurons and glial cells have strikingly extended morphologies. This cytoarchitecture is ideal for a tissue whose functions depend on multiple intercellular contacts locally and at great distances. Protein and lipid components are synthesized and assembled into the membranes of these cell extensions through pathways of membrane biogenesis that have been elucidated primarily in other cell types, including the yeast *Saccharomyces cerevisiae.* However, some adaptations of these general mechanisms have been necessary, owing to the specific requirements of cells in the nervous system. Neurons, for example, have devised mechanisms for ensuring that the specific components of the axonal and dendritic plasma membranes are selectively delivered (targeted) to each plasma membrane subdomain.

The distribution to specific loci of organelles, receptors, and ion channels is critical to normal neuronal function. In turn, these loci must be "matched" appropriately to the local microenvironment and specific cell–cell interactions. Similarly, in myelinating glial cells during the narrow developmental window when the myelin sheath is being formed, these cells synthesize vast sheets of insulating plasma membrane at an unbelievably high rate. To understand how the plasma membrane of neurons and glia might be modeled to fit individual functional requirements, it is necessary to review the progress that has been made so far in our understanding of how membrane components and organelles are generated in eukaryotic cells.

There are two major categories of membrane proteins, integral and peripheral. **Integral membrane proteins,** which include the receptors for neurotransmitters (e.g., the acetylcholine receptor subunits) and polypeptide growth factors (e.g., the dimeric insulin receptor), have segments that are either embedded in the lipid bilayer or covalently bound to molecules that insert into the membrane, such as those proteins linked to glycosyl phosphatidylinositol at their C-termini (e.g., Thy-1). A protein with a single membrane-embedded segment and an N-terminus exposed at the extracellular surface is said to be of Type I, whereas Type II proteins retain their N-termini on the cytoplasmic side of the plasma membrane. **Peripheral membrane proteins** are localized on the cytoplasmic surface of the membrane and do not cross any membrane during their biogenesis. They interact with the membrane either by means of their associations with membrane lipids or the cytoplasmic tails of integral proteins or by means of their affinity for other peripheral proteins (e.g., **platelet-derived growth factor receptor–Grb2-Sos-Ras complex**). In some cases, they may bind directly to the polar head groups of the lipid bilayer (e.g., myelin basic protein).

Integral Membrane and Secretory Polypeptides Are Synthesized *de Novo* in the Rough Endoplasmic Reticulum

The subcellular destinations of integral and peripheral membrane proteins are determined by their sites of synthesis.[3,4] In the secretory pathway, integral membrane proteins, like secretory proteins, are synthesized in the rough endoplasmic reticulum, whereas the mRNAs encoding peripheral proteins are translated on cytoplasmic "free" polysomes, which are not membrane associated but which may interact with cytoskeletal structures.

The pathway by which secretory proteins are synthesized and exported was first postulated through the elegant ultrastructural studies on the pancreas by George Palade and colleagues.[5–7] Pancreatic acinar cells were an excellent choice for this work because they are extremely active in secretion, as revealed by the abundance of their RER network, a property they share with neurons. Nissl deduced, in the 19th century, that pancreatic cells and neurons would be found to have common secretory properties because of similarities in the distribution of the Nissl substance (Fig. 4.3).

Pulse–chase autoradiography has revealed that

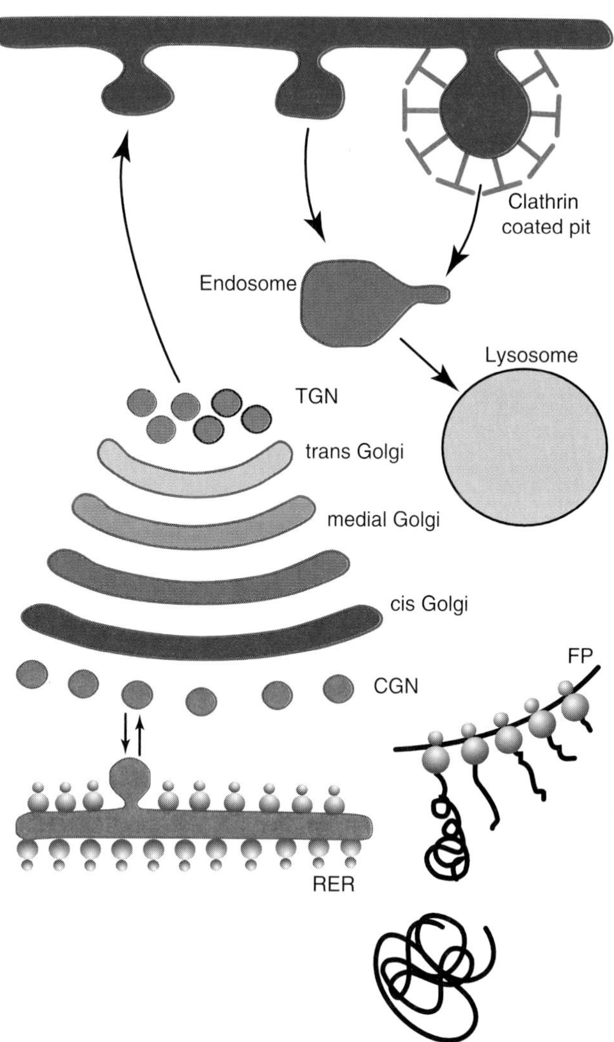

FIGURE 4.3 The secretory pathway. Transport and sorting of proteins in the secretory pathway occur as they pass through the Golgi complex before reaching the plasma membrane. Sorting occurs in the *cis*-Golgi network (CGN), also known as the intermediate compartment, and in the *trans*-Golgi network (TGN). Proteins exit from the Golgi complex at the TGN. The default pathway is the direct route to the plasma membrane. Proteins bound for regulated secretion or for transport to endosomes and from there to lysosomes are diverted from the default path by means of specific signals. In endocytosis, one population of vesicles is surrounded by a clathrin cage and is destined for late endosomes. Another population appears to be coated in a lacelike structure whose composition is yet to be defined.

newly synthesized secretory proteins move from the RER to the Golgi apparatus, where the proteins are packaged into secretory granules and transported to the plasma membrane from which they are released by exocytosis.[5–7] Pulse–chase studies in neurons reveal a similar sequence of events for proteins transported into the axon.[8] The unraveling of the detailed molecular mechanisms of the pathway began with the successful reconstitution of secretory protein biosynthesis *in vitro* and the direct demonstration that, very early during synthesis, secretory proteins are translocated into the lumen of RER vesicles, prepared by cell fractionation, termed **microsomes.**[9,10] A key observation here was that the fate of the protein was sealed as a result of encapsulation in the lumen of the RER at the site of synthesis. This cotranslational insertion model provided a logical framework for understanding the synthesis of integral membrane proteins with a transmembrane orientation.[4]

The process by which integral membrane proteins are synthesized closely follows the secretory pathway, except integral proteins are of course not released from the cell, but instead remain within cellular membranes. Synthesis of integral proteins begins with synthesis of the nascent chain on a polysome that is not yet bound to the RER membrane (Fig. 4.4). The emergence of the N-terminus of the nascent protein from the protein-synthesizing machinery allows a ribonucleoprotein, a **signal recognition particle** (SRP), to bind to an emergent hydrophobic signal sequence and prevent further translation.[11–14] Translation arrest is relieved when SRP docks with its cognate receptor in the RER and dissociates from the signal sequence in a process that requires GTP. Synthesis of transmembrane proteins on RER is an extremely energy efficient process. The passage of a fully formed and folded protein through a membrane is, thermodynamically, formidably expensive[15]; it is infinitely "cheaper" for cells to thread amino acids, in tandem, through a membrane during initial protein synthesis.

Protein synthesis then resumes, and the emerging polypeptide chain is translocated into the RER membrane through a conceptualized "aqueous pore" termed the **translocon.** Several proteins have been identified in cross-linking experiments as possible components of the translocon, including TRAM (translocating chain-associating membrane protein) and TRAP (translocon-associated protein a) which is a component of the mammalian homolog of the yeast sec 61 complex. Many others are strikingly similar to proteins that were originally discovered in yeast, revealing the common conserved nature of this process in organisms as diverse as yeasts and humans.

A few polypeptides deviate from the common pathway for secretion. For example, certain peptide growth factors, such as basic fibroblast growth factor and ciliary neurotrophic factor, are synthesized without signal peptide sequences but are potent biological modulators of cell survival and differentiation. These growth factors appear to be released under certain conditions, although the mechanisms for such release are still controversial. One possibility is that release of these factors may be associated primarily with cellular injury.

Two cotranslational modifications are commonly associated with the emergence of the polypeptide on the luminal face of the RER. First, an N-terminal hydrophobic signal sequence that is used for insertion into the RER is usually removed by a signal peptidase. Second, oligosaccharides rich in mannose sugars are transferred from a lipid carrier, **dolichol phosphate,** to the side chains of asparagine residues.[16] The asparagines must be in the sequence N X T (or S), and they

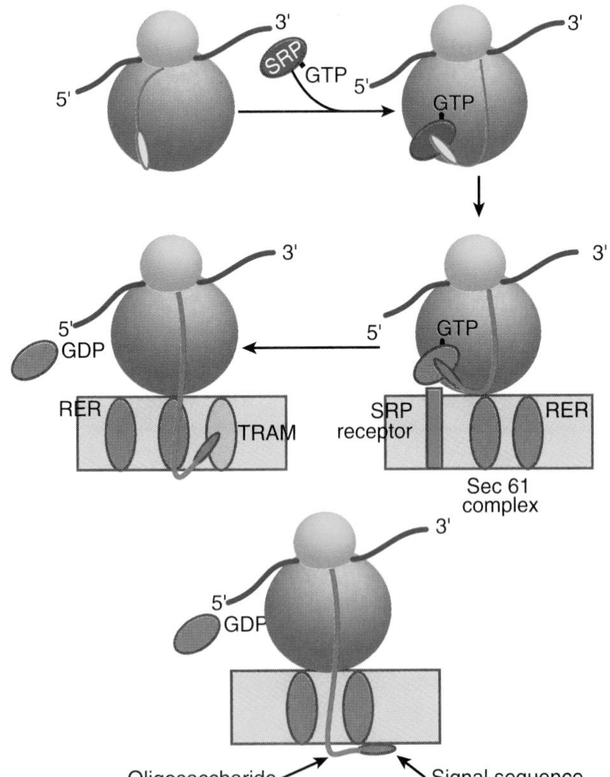

FIGURE 4.4 Translocation of proteins across the rough endoplasmic reticulum (RER). Integral membrane and secretory protein synthesis begins with partial synthesis on a free polysome not yet bound to the RER. The N-terminus of the nascent protein emerges and allows a ribonucleoprotein, signal recognition particle (SRP), to bind to the hydrophobic signal sequence and prevent further translation. Translation arrest is relieved once the SRP docks with its receptor at the RER and dissociates from the signal sequence in a process that requires GTP. Once protein synthesis resumes, translocation occurs through an aqueous pore termed the translocon, which includes translocating chain-associating membrane protein (TRAM) and translocon-associated protein a (TRAP). The signal sequence is removed by a signal peptidase located in the lumen of the RER.

are linked to the mannose sugars by two molecules of *N*-acetylglucosamine. Although the prevention of glycosylation of some proteins causes their aggregation and accumulation in the RER and Golgi apparatus, for most glycoproteins, the significance of glycosylation is not apparent. Neither is it a universal feature of integral membrane proteins: some proteins, such as the proteolipid proteins of CNS myelin, neither lose their signal sequence nor become glycosylated. One clear case of a proved function for a carbohydrate moiety is the targeting of proteins to lysosomes in the *trans*-Golgi by means of the mannose 6-phosphate receptor. Intercellular adhesion molecules such as the **selectins,** which effect the sticking of lymphocytes to blood vessel walls, appear to interact with lectin-like proteins through their oligosaccharide chains. Similarly, the sialic acid side chains of NCAM (neural cell adhesion molecule) are essential for modulation of cell–cell adhesion mediated by NCAMs. Thus, for the vast majority of polypeptides destined for release from the cell (secretory polypeptides), an N-terminal "signal sequence" first mediates the passage of the protein into the RER and is immediately cleaved from the polypeptide by a signal peptidase residing on the luminal side of the RER. For proteins destined to remain as permanent residents of cellular membranes (and these form a particularly important and diverse category of plasma membrane proteins in neurons and myelinating glial cells), however, many variations on this basic theme have been found. Simply stated:

1. Signal sequences for membrane insertions need not be only N-terminal; those that lie within a polypeptide sequence are not cleaved.
2. A second type of signal, a "halt" or "stop" transfer signal, functions to arrest translocation through the membrane bilayer. The halt transfer signal is also hydrophobic and is usually flanked by positive charges. This arrangement effectively stabilizes a polypeptide segment in the RER membrane bilayer.
3. The sequential display in tandem of insertion and halt transfer signals in a polypeptide as it is being synthesized ultimately determines its disposition with respect to the phospholipid bilayer, and thus its final topology in its target membrane. By synthesizing transmembrane polypeptides in this way, virtually any topology may be generated.

Newly Synthesized Polypeptides Exit from the RER and Are Moved through the Golgi Apparatus

When the newly synthesized protein has established its correct transmembrane orientation in the RER, it is incorporated into vesicles and must pass through the Golgi complex before reaching the plasma membrane (Fig. 4.3). For membrane proteins, the Golgi serves two major functions: first, it sorts and targets proteins and, second, it performs further posttranslational modifications, particularly on the oligosaccharide chains that were added in the RER.[17] Sorting takes place in the *cis*-Golgi network (CGN), also known as the intermediate compartment, and in the *trans*-Golgi network (TGN) whereas sculpting of the oligosaccharides is primarily the responsibility of the *cis*-, *medial*-, and *trans*-Golgi stacks. The TGN is a tubulovesicular network wherein proteins are targeted to the plasma membrane or to organelles.[18,19]

In addition to the processing of carbohydrates in the Golgi, posttranslational modifications can take place in other subcellular compartments. Some protein glycosylations are modified further post-Golgi in components of the smooth endoplasmic reticulum or transport vesicles, as described later in this section. Finally, some neuropeptides (adrenocorticotropic hormone, enkephalins, etc.) are synthesized as sequence domains in large precursor proteins that must be cleaved in transit by specific proteases to form the biologically active form.

The CGN serves an important sorting function for proteins entering the Golgi from the RER. Because most proteins that move from the RER through the secretory pathway do so by default, any resident endoplasmic reticulum proteins must be restrained from exiting or promptly returned to the RER from the CGN should they escape. Although no retention signal has been demonstrated for the endoplasmic reticulum, two retrieval signals have been identified, a Lys-Asp-Glu-Leu or KDEL sequence in type I proteins and the Arg-Arg or RR motif in the first five amino acids of proteins with a Type II orientation in the membrane. The KDEL tetrapeptide binds to a receptor called *Erd 2* in the CGN, and the receptor–ligand complex is returned to the RER. There may also be a receptor for the N arginine dipeptide; alternatively, this sequence may interact with other components of the retrograde transport machinery, such as microtubules.

Movement of proteins between Golgi stacks proceeds by means of vesicular budding and fusion.[20] Through the use of a cell-free assay containing Golgi-derived vesicles, the essential mechanisms for budding and fusion have been shown to require **coat proteins** (COPs) in a manner that is analogous to the role of clathrin in endocytosis. Currently, two main types of COP complex, COPI and COPII, have been distinguished. Although both have been shown to coat vesicles that bud from the endoplasmic reticulum, they may have different roles in membrane trafficking. Coat proteins provide the external framework into which a region of a flattened Golgi cisternae can bud and vesiculate.[21,22] A complex of these COPs forms the **coatomer** (coat protomer) together with a p200 protein, AP-1 adaptins, and a family of GTP-binding proteins called ADP-ribosylation factors (ARFs), originally named for their role in the action of cholera toxin. Immunolocalization of one of the coatamer proteins, β-COP, predominantly to the CGN and *cis*-Golgi indicates that these proteins may also take part in vesicle transport into the Golgi (Fig. 4.5). The function of ARF is to drive the assembly of the coatamer and therefore vesicle budding in a GTP-dependent fashion. Dissociation of the coat is triggered when hydrolysis of the GTP bound to ARF is stimulated by a GTPase-activating protein (GAP) in the Golgi membrane. The cycle of coat assembly and disassembly can continue when the replacement of GDP on ARF by GTP is catalyzed by a guanine-nucleotide exchange factor (GEF). The importance of this GDP–GTP exchange to normal vesicular traffic is dramatically illustrated by the effects of brefeldin A, a fungal metabolite that specifically inhibits GTP exchange and disperses the Golgi complex by preventing the return of Golgi components from the intermediate compartment.

Fusion of vesicles with their target membrane in the Golgi apparatus is believed to be regulated by a series of proteins, *N*-ethylmaleimide-sensitive factor (NSF), soluble NSF attachment proteins (SNAPs), and SNAP receptors (SNAREs), which together assist the vesicle in docking with its target membrane. In addition, the **Rabs,** a family of membrane-bound GTPases, act in concert with their own GAPs, GEFs, and a cytosolic protein that dissociates Rab–GDP from membranes after fusion called guanine-nucleotide dissociation inhibitor. Rabs are believed to regulate the action of SNAREs, the proteins directly engaged in membrane–membrane contact prior to fusion. The tight control necessary for this process and the importance of ensuring that vesicle fusion takes place only at the appropriate target membrane may explain why eukaryotic cells contain so many Rabs, some of which are known to specifically take part in the internalization of endocytic vesicles at the plasma membrane (Fig. 4.3).[23]

Exocytosis of neurotransmitter at the synapse must occur in an even more finely regulated manner than endocytosis. The proteins first identified in vesicular fusion events in the secretory pathway (viz., NSF, SNAPs, and SNAREs or closely related homologs) appear to play a part in the fusion of synaptic vesicles with the active zones of the presynaptic neuronal membrane (Fig. 4.6).

The synaptic counterpart of v-SNARE is synaptobrevin (also known as vesicle-associated membrane protein, or VAMP), and syntaxin corresponds to t-SNARE. SNAP-25 is an accessory protein that binds to syntaxin. In the constitutive pathway such as between the RER and Golgi apparatus, assembly of the complex at the target membrane promotes fusion. However, at the presynaptic membrane, Ca^{2+} influx is required to stimulate membrane fusion at the presynaptic membrane. Synaptotagmin is believed to be the Ca^{2+}-sensitive regulatory protein in the complex that binds syntaxin. The **neurexins** appear to have a role in regulation as well, because, in addition to interacting with synaptotagmin, they are the targets of black widow spider venom α-latrotoxin, which deregulates Ca^{2+}-dependent exocytosis of neurotransmitter.

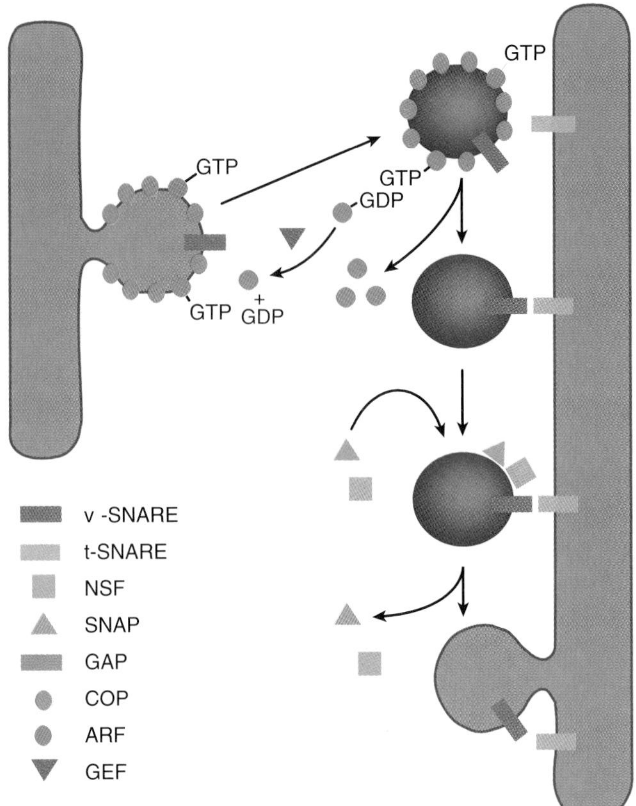

FIGURE 4.5 General mechanisms of vesicle targeting and docking in the ER and Golgi. The assembly of coat proteins (COPs) around budding vesicles is driven by ADP-ribosylation factors (ARFs) in a GTP-dependent fashion. Dissociation of the coat is triggered when hydrolysis of the GTP bound to ARF is stimulated by a GTPase-activating protein (GAP) in the Golgi membrane. The cycle of coat assembly and disassembly can continue when the replacement of GDP on ARF by GTP is catalyzed by a guanine-nucleotide exchange factor (GEF). Fusion of the vesicles with their target membrane in the Golgi is regulated by a series of proteins, *N*-ethylmaleimide-sensitive factor (NSF), soluble NSF attachment proteins (SNAPs), and SNAP receptors (SNAREs), which together assist the vesicle in docking with its target membrane. SNAREs on the vesicle (v-SNAREs) are believed to associate with corresponding t-SNAREs on the target membrane.

The comparison between secretion in slow-releasing

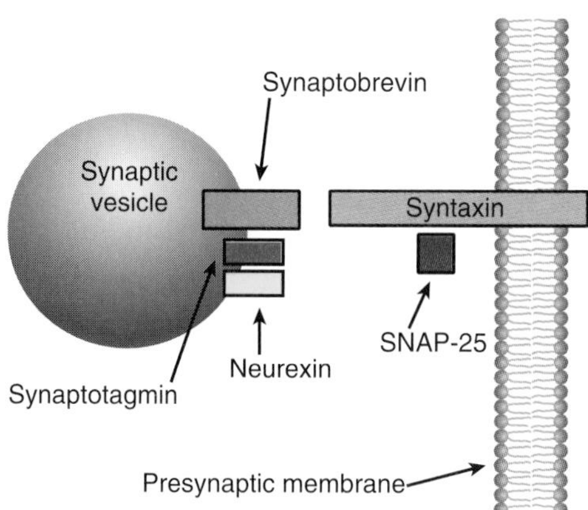

FIGURE 4.6 Mechanisms of vesicle targeting and docking in the synaptic terminal. The synaptic counterpart of v-SNARE is synaptobrevin (also known as vesicle-associated membrane protein), and syntaxin corresponds to the t-SNARE. SNAP-25 is an accessory protein that binds to syntaxin. Synaptotagmin is believed to be the Ca^{2+}-sensitive regulatory protein in the complex that binds to syntaxin. The neurexins appear to have a role in conferring Ca^{2+} sensitivity to these interactions.

cells, such as the pancreatic β-cell, and neurotransmitter release at the neuromuscular junction is much like the comparison between a hand-held pocket calculator for balancing a checkbook and a state-of-the-art desktop computer. Two differences stand out. First, the speed of neurotransmitter release is much greater both in release from a single vesicle and in total release in response to a specific signal. Releasing the contents of a single synaptic vesicle at a mouse neuromuscular junction takes from 1 to 2 milliseconds (ms) and the response to an action potential involving the release of many synaptic vesicles is over in approximately 5 ms. In contrast, releasing the insulin in a single secretory granule by a pancreatic β-cell takes from 1 to 5 *s*, and the full release response may take from 1 to 5 *min.* A 103- to 105-fold difference in rate is an extraordinary range, making neurotransmitter release one of the fastest biological events routinely encountered, but this speed is critical for a properly functioning nervous system.

A second major difference between slow secretion and fast secretion is seen in the recycling of vesicles. In the pancreas, secretory vesicles carrying insulin are used only once, and so new secretory vesicles must be assembled *de novo* and released from the TGN to meet future requirements. In the neuron, the problem is that the synapse may be at a distance of 1 m or more from the protein synthetic machinery of the perikaryon, and so newly assembled vesicles even traveling at rapid axonal transport rates (see below) may take more than a day to arrive. Now, the number of synaptic vesicles released in 15 min of constant stimulation at a single frog neuromuscular junction has been calculated to be on the order of 10^5 vesicles, but a single terminal may have only a few hundred vesicles at any one time. These measurements would make no sense if synaptic vesicles had to be constantly replaced through new synthesis in the perikaryon, as is the case with insulin-carrying vesicles. The reason that these numbers are possible is that synaptic vesicles are taken up *locally* by endocytosis, refilled with neurotransmitter, and *reutilized* at a rate fast enough to keep up with normal physiological stimulation levels. This takes place within the presynaptic terminal, and there is evidence that these recycled synaptic vesicles are used preferentially.[34] Such recycling does not require protein synthesis, because the classical neurotransmitters are small molecules, such as acetylcholine, or amino acids, such as glutamate, that can be synthesized or obtained locally.

Significantly, neurons have fast and slow secretory pathways operating in parallel in the presynaptic terminal.[25] Synapses that release classical neurotransmitters (acetylcholine, glutamate, etc.) with these fast kinetics also contain dense core granules containing neuropeptides (calcitonin gene-related peptide, substance P, etc.) that are comparable to the secretory granules of the pancreatic β-cell. These are used only once, because neuropeptides are produced from large polypeptide precursors that must be made by protein synthesis in the cell body. Release of neuropeptides is relatively slow; as is the case in endocrine release, the neuropeptides serve primarily as modulators of synaptic function. The small clear synaptic vesicles containing the classic neurotransmitters can in fact be pharmacologically depleted from the presynaptic terminal, while the dense core granules remain. These observations indicate that even though fast and slow secretory mechanisms have many similarities and may even have common components, in neurons they can operate independent of one another.

Proteins Exit the Golgi Complex at the *trans*-Golgi Network

Most of the N-linked oligosaccharide chains acquired at the RER are remodeled in the Golgi cisternae, and while the proteins are in transit, another type of glycosyl linkage to serine or threonine residues through *N*-acetylgalactosamine also can be made. Modification of existing sugar chains by a series of glycosidases and the addition of further sugars by glycosyl transferases occur from the *cis*- to the *trans*-stacks. Some of these enzymes have been localized to particular cisternae. For example, the enzymes β-1,4-galactosyltransferase and α-2,6-sialyltransferase are concentrated in the *trans*-Golgi. How they are retained there is a matter of some debate. One idea is that these proteins are anchored by oligomerization. Another view is that the progressively rising concentration of cholesterol in membranes more distal to the ER in the secretory pathway increases membrane thickness, which in turn anchors certain proteins and causes an arrest in their flow along the default route.[26]

The default or constitutive pathway seems to be the direct route to the plasma membrane taken by vesicles that bud from the TGN (Fig. 4.3). This is how, in general, integral plasma membrane proteins reach the cell surface. Proteins bound for regulated secretion or for transport to endosomes and from there to lysosomes are diverted from the default path by means of specific signals.[27] It has been assumed that sorting of proteins for their eventual destination takes place at the TGN itself.[28] However, recent analyses of the three-dimensional structure of the TGN have provoked a revision of this view. These studies have shown that the TGN is tubular, with two major types of vesicles that bud from distinct populations of tubules. The implication is that sorting may already have occurred in the *trans*-Golgi prior to the proteins' arrival at the TGN. One population of vesicles consists of those surrounded by the familiar clathrin cage, which are destined for late endosomes. The other population appears to be coated in a lacelike structure, which may prove to be made from the elusive coat protein required for vesicular transport to the plasma membrane. The β-COP protein and related coatomer proteins active in more proximal regions of the secretory pathway are absent from the TGN.

Endocytosis and Membrane Cycling Occurs in the *trans*-Golgi Network

Two types of membrane invagination occur at the surface of mammalian cells and are clearly distinguishable by electron microscopy. The first type is a **caveola,** which has a threadlike structure on its surface made of the protein **caveolin.** Caveolae mediate the uptake of small molecules such as the vitamin folic acid by a process called **potocytosis.** They may also have a role in concentrating proteins linked to the plasma membrane by the glycosylphosphatidylinositol anchor. Recent demonstration of the targeting of protein tyrosine kinases to caveolae by the tripeptide signal MGC (Met-Gly-Cys) also suggests that caveolae may function in signal transduction cascades.[29,30]

The other type of endocytic vesicle at the cell surface is that coated with the distinctive meshwork of **clathrin triskelions.** The triskelion[31] comprises three copies of a clathrin heavy chain and three copies of a clathrin light chain. The ease with which these triskelions can assemble into a cage structure demonstrates how they promote the budding of a vesicle from a membrane invagination. Clathrin binds selectively to regions of the cytoplasmic surface of membranes that are selected by adaptins. The AP-2 complex, which is primarily active at the plasma membrane, consists of 100-kDa α and β subunits and two subunits of 50 and 17 kDa each. AP-1 complexes localize to the TGN and have γ and β subunits of 100 kDa together with smaller polypeptides of 46 and 19 kDa. Adaptins bind to the cytoplasmic tails of membrane proteins, thus recruiting clathrin for budding at these sites.

A further component of the endocytic complex at the plasma membrane is the GTPase **dynamin,** which seems to be required for normal budding of coated vesicles during endocytosis. The dynamins[32] are a family of 100-kDa GTPases found in both neuronal and nonneuronal cells and may interact with the AP-2 component of a clathrin-coated pit. Dynamin I is found primarily in neurons, whereas dynamin II has a widespread distribution. Oligomers of dynamin form a ring at the neck of a budding clathrin-coated vesicle, and GTP hydrolysis appears to be necessary for the coated vesicle to pinch off from the plasma membrane. The existence of a specific neuronal form of dynamin may be a manifestation of the unusually rapid rate of synaptic vesicle recycling.

The primary function of clathrin-coated vesicles at the plasma membrane is to deliver membrane proteins together with any ligands bound to them to the early endosomal apparatus. The other major site of action of clathrin is in the vesicles that bud from the TGN carrying lysosomal enzymes en route to late endosomes. Early endosomes have a tubulovesicular morphology. Receptors that will be recycled back to the plasma membrane partition into the tubules; those endocytosed proteins destined for lysosomes concentrate in the vesicular regions. Recycling seems to be the default pathway, whereas proteins must be actively targeted to lysosomes. However, the precise signals for this are unknown.

Regulation of membrane cycling in the endosomal compartment is likely to include the Rab family of small GTP-binding proteins. Indeed, each stage of the endocytic pathway may have its own Rab protein to ensure efficient targeting of the vesicle to the appropriate membrane. Rab6 is believed to have a role in transport from the TGN to endosomes, whereas Rab9 may regulate vesicular flow in the reverse direction. In neurons, Rab5a has a role in regulating fusion of endocytic vesicles and early endosomes and appears to function in endocytosis from both somatodendritic domains and the axon. The association of the protein with synaptic vesicles in nerve terminals, attached presumably by means of its isoprenoid tail, also suggests that early endosomal compartments may have a role in the packaging and recycling of synaptic vesicles.

The Lysosome Is the Target Organelle in Several Inherited Diseases That Affect the Nervous System

Lysosomes were first isolated and characterized as a distinct organelle fraction bounded by a single membrane and separable from mitochondria by differential and sucrose-gradient centrifugation.[33,34] Because of their high content of acid hydrolases, the classic view is that lysosomes are organelles of terminal degradation. Indeed, the latency of hydrolase activity before membrane permeabilization by agents such as nonionic detergents has been used biochemically as a measure of the purity and intactness of lysosomal preparations. However, in addition to their well-established function in lipid and protein breakdown, tubulovesicular lysosomes may overlap in sorting functions with early endosomes, particularly during antigen processing in macrophages.

Inherited deficiencies in lipid metabolism in the lysosome often have particularly devastating consequences on the nervous system because of the abundance of the lipid-rich membrane myelin. **Metachromatic leukodystrophy** is an autosomal recessive disease caused by a deficiency in arylsulfatase A activity, which is also responsible for degrading the myelin lipid cerebroside sulfate (sulfatide). Oligodendrocytes accumulate sulfatide in metachromatic granules, causing severe disruption of myelination. Peripheral nerve myelination also is affected, as are other organs that normally contain much lower amounts of sulfatide, such as the kidney, the liver, and the endocrine system. **Krabbe disease,** or globoid cell leukodystrophy, also is a dysmyelinating disease in which there is an almost complete lack of oligodendrocytes and therefore myelin, caused by a deficiency in the β-galactosidase responsible for hydrolyzing galactocerebroside to ceramide and galactose. Galactocerebroside is particularly abundant in myelin, constituting about 25% of myelin lipid. Mice that lack galactocerebroside have the ability to assemble multilamellar myelin; however, this myelin does not support adequate nerve conduction, neither is it stable.[35] Unlike metachromatic leukodystrophy, Krabbe disease is limited to the CNS and PNS. However, why a build-up of galactocerebroside should prove particularly toxic to oligodendrocytes is not entirely clear. One hypothesis is that a metabolite of galactocerebroside, galactosphingosine (psychosine), is the primary culprit. Because there is an authentic mouse model for Krabbe disease, *twitcher*, gene therapy provides some hope of correcting the disease.

How are proteins destined to operate in lysosomes targeted to these organelles? Soluble lysosomal hydrolase enzymes acquire a phosphorylated mannose on their oligosaccharide chains by a two-step process in the Golgi apparatus. This mannose 6-phosphate label is recognized by specific mannose 6-phosphate receptors, which carry the proteins to late endosomes.[36] In contrast, lysosomal membrane proteins are targeted by means of cytoplasmic tail signals that contain either leucine or tyrosine of Type LJ or Type YXXJ or NXXY, where J is any hydrophobic amino acid. The LJ signal seems to be essential for efficient delivery directly to endosomes, whereas the second type of signal seems to be more important in the recovery of proteins destined for lysosomes from the plasma membrane. The majority of lysosomal membrane proteins have the YXXJ but do not have the LJ signal. The implication of these observations is that many of the lysosomal membrane proteins make their way to lysosomes from the TGN endosomes through the plasma membrane.

What are the receptors for the Type LJ or the Type YXXJ or NXXY motifs at the TGN? Because transport from the TGN to the endosomes occurs in clathrin-coated vesicles, the proteins that link such vesicles to membranes, the adaptins, may play a role. The weight of the evidence suggests that AP-1 recognizes the LJ sequence, whereas AP-2 identifies the YXXJ and NXXY motifs. Once the ligands are bound, these adaptins would direct transport of their respective ligands to the endosomes from the TGN or through the plasma membrane, respectively.[37]

At present, it is not clear how proteins in the late endosome, such as mannose 6-phosphate receptors, that cycle back to the Golgi are sorted from those whose ultimate destination is a lysosome.

How Are Peripheral Membrane Proteins Targeted to Their Appropriate Destinations?

Peripheral membrane proteins are synthesized in the same type of free polysome in which the bulk of the cytosolic proteins are made. However, the cell must ensure that these membrane proteins are sent to the plasma membrane rather than allowed to attach in a haphazard way to other intracellular organelles. The fact that a complex machinery has evolved to ensure the correct delivery of integral membrane proteins suggests that some equivalent targeting mechanism must exist for proteins that attach to the cytoplasmic surface of the plasma membrane. Such proteins are translated on "free" polysomes, but these polysomes are associated with cytoskeletal structures and are not uniformly distributed throughout the cell body. In a number of cases, mRNAs that encode soluble cytosolic proteins are concentrated in discrete regions of the cell, resulting in a local accumulation of the translated protein close to the site of action. For some peripheral membrane proteins, this is the plasma membrane.

Evidence that this mechanism might operate in peripheral membrane protein synthesis came from studies showing biochemically and by *in situ* hybridization that mRNAs encoding the **myelin basic proteins** are concentrated in the myelinating processes that extend from the cell body of oligodendrocytes.[38] Myelin basic protein may be a special case because of its very strong positive charge and consequent propensity for binding promiscuously to the negatively charged polar head groups of membrane lipids. Nevertheless, the fact that actin mRNAs are localized to the leading edge of cultured myocytes and the mRNA for the microtubule-associated protein MAP2b is concentrated in the dendrites of neurons suggests that targeting by local synthesis is more common than originally thought.[39,40,2a] This mechanism is probably less important for peripheral membrane proteins that associate with the cytoplasmic surface of the plasma membrane by means of strong specific associations with proteins already located at the membrane, because such proteins would act as specific receptors. Because only selected cytoplasmic mRNAs are localized to the periphery, the process is specific. However, no mRNAs are localized exclusively to the periphery, and a significant fraction are typically localized proximal to the nucleus in a region rich with the translational and protein-processing machinery of the cell (the Nissl substance or translational cytoplasm).

Special Mechanisms Are Used to Target Proteins to Mitochondria and Peroxisomes

The inner membrane of the mitochondrion is the site of oxidative phosphorylation in which the step-by-step transfer of electrons from oxygen intermediary metabolites to molecular oxidation is coupled to proton transport and ATP synthesis. Thus, this organelle has an essential role in providing the large amount of ATP required for the electrical activity of neurons. The fact that, in a resting adult, about 40% of the total energy consumption is required for ion pumping in the CNS accounts for the exquisite sensitivity of the brain to damage from oxygen deprivation. The sensitivity of neurons to interruptions in the provision of ATP by the mitochondrion is also seen in cases of **uremia,** where a build-up of ammonium ions depletes the Krebs cycle of α-oxoglutaric acid by converting it into glutamate.

Although the mitochondrion has its own circular DNA that encodes some proteins, most mitochondrial proteins are synthesized in the nucleocytoplasmic system.[41,42] This poses the problem of how these proteins once made in the cytoplasm gain entry into the mitochondrion. Furthermore, because the mitochondrion has an inner and an outer membrane, some proteins must cross two membranes to gain access to the inner matrix.[43,44] This group of proteins includes the enzymes of the Krebs cycle and the fatty acid β-oxidation pathway.

Unlike proteins inserted into the RER, mitochondrial proteins can be imported either posttranslationally or cotranslationally with the use of a cleavable amphipathic helical signal sequence usually at the N-terminus.[45,46] At the RER, the signal sequence of a nascent polypeptide chain can be translocated across the membrane, because the polypeptide remains small and unfolded owing to the arrest of translation caused by a signal-recognition particle. However, mitochondrial proteins are typically synthesized on cytoplasmic or free polysomes and must be folded at least partially to prevent degradation. For posttranslational import, mitochondria rely on a group of **molecular chaperones** to prevent complete folding of the polypeptides. These hsp70 and hsp60 proteins were originally identified because they are upregulated during heat shock. Their role in binding to proteins and maintaining them in specific conformations helps to explain why these proteins have an important function in protecting proteins against the stress of elevated temperatures as well as facilitating the proper folding of newly synthesized polypeptides. In yeast, a second protein, Ydj1p, whose bacterial homolog DnaJ regulates chaperone function has been identified. Ydj1p possesses an isoprenoid tail linked to its C-terminal amino acid and this may serve to anchor the protein to the outer membrane. The third factor that has been implicated is the mitochondrial stimulation factor, which is a heterodimer possessing an ATP-dependent protein "unfoldase" activity. This factor may be more important in cotranslational import where polysomes are known to be associated with the mitochondrial outer membrane.[47,48]

Most of our current understanding of protein translocation from the mitochondrial outer membrane inward has come from studies on either the fungus *neurospora crassa* or the yeast *Saccharomyces cerevisiae.* In both yeast and higher eukaryotes, the partially folded polypeptide targeted for the mitochondrion may be stabilized by a cytoplasmic chaperone that is a member of the hsp70 family, but this interaction is not required for import. However, several proteins in the outer membrane form an essential complex that acts as a receptor and pore for protein translocation. This complex can in turn interact with an inner membrane complex at specialized contact sites that minimize the distance across the two membranes, thereby facilitating the movement of proteins to the inner matrix. Although both pores can function independently, they contact and cooperate when there is a transmembrane potential across the inner membrane. This accounts for early observations showing that importation of subunits of the F1-ATPase, an inner membrane protein, required an active electron transport chain but did not need ATP synthesis. The mitochondrial import sequence extends through the pore into the inner matrix, where a second member of the hsp70 family binds and facilitates movement into the inner matrix. After proteins have crossed into the inner matrix, they must dissociate from hsp70 in order to fold properly, a process that requires another kind of molecular chaperone, hsp60.

Peroxisomes are so named because they contain oxidases that generate H_2O_2 and the enzyme catalase, which is responsible for detoxifying it. In addition, these organelles contain many other enzymes that take part in lipid, purine, and amino acid metabolism. Peroxisomes are of interest because of the number of inherited diseases associated with defects either in certain enzymes or indeed in the assembly of the organelle itself.[49] Some of these diseases manifest as particularly damaging to the nervous system and include **adrenoleukodystrophy** (accumulation of very long chain fatty acids due to insufficient lignoceryl-CoA ligase activity caused by inefficient import of the protein) and **Refsum disease** (build-up of phytanic acid due to defective α-oxidation), both of which cause demyelination.

Like many mitochondrial proteins, peroxisomal proteins are imported posttranslationally.[50] Although cytosolic factors are implicated in peroxisomal biogenesis, no peroxisomal chaperones analogous to the hsp70 family have yet been shown to function in protein import. Therefore unfolding and refolding are assumed not to play a role in the accumulation of proteins inside the peroxisome. Among these cytosolic proteins is presumed to be the receptor for the tripeptide C-terminal import signal SKL (Ser-Lys-Leu) known as peroxisomal targeting signal 1 (PTS1). In addition to the C-terminal PTS1, some peroxisomal proteins have a cleavable N-terminal sequence called PTS2, which signals their import. A quite distinct translocation machinery appears to operate for PTS1 and PTS2 proteins. Two possible receptor proteins in the peroxisomal membrane, one of which is the adrenoleukodystrophy protein (ALDP), have been identified. ALDP is a member of a larger family known as the ABC ATP-dependent membrane transporters.[51,52]

A characteristic feature of peroxisomal biogenesis is that it is stimulated by drugs whose detoxification requires peroxisomal activity. It is possible that mature peroxisomes are recruited from a pool of precursor organelles, and there is some evidence for the existence of such a population in rat liver. Although the mature organelle appears to be spherical, electron microscopic evidence suggests a peroxisomal reticulum at which synthesis and protein import may take place. Mature peroxisomes might then arise from this reticulum by a process of budding.

Cytoplasmic Proteins Are Also Compartmentalized

Membrane-bound organelles are the most familiar form of compartmentation in cells, but cytoplasmic regions of the cell containing metabolic compartments exist as well. Regions of the neuronal or glial cytoplasm may have highly specialized polypeptide compositions that are important for function. For example, the neuronal phosphoprotein **synapsin** is highly enriched in presynaptic terminals, where it participates in localization and targeting of synaptic vesicles. Similarly, **calmodulin** and the glycolytic enzyme **aldolase** have been localized in muscle cells to the region of the I-band, where they are thought to facilitate coupling of ATP production to contractility.

As mentioned earlier, cytoplasmic proteins are synthesized on cytoplasmic polysomes, termed "free" polysomes to reflect an absence of underlying ER membrane, even though they may be restricted to specific domains of the cell cytoplasm. This restriction is particularly obvious in the neuronal perikaryon, where both cytoplasmic polysomes and membrane-associated polysomes are concentrated in areas near the nucleus and Golgi complex. In addition, cytoplasmic polysomes containing specific mRNAs may be localized to certain regions of the cell such as the proximal dendrite (those encoding the microtubule-associated protein MAP-2) and the processes of oligodendrocytes (those encoding myelin basic protein). In contrast, the protein synthetic machinery of the polysome appears to be effectively excluded from the mature axon. Therefore, cytoplasmic polysomes are representative of cytoplasmic compartmentation for proteins and nucleic acids.

In most cases, localized cytoplasmic proteins interact with cytoskeletal structures in the cytoplasm (see next section), but macromolecular complexes that form in order to make a cellular process more efficient or free from error have been described. Evidence exists that glycolytic enzymes of neurons and muscle cells may be organized in a labile complex that facilitates energy metabolism, but the existence of such complexes remains controversial.

Perhaps the best-characterized cytoplasmic macromolecular complex is the **proteasome,** which is a large protein complex (2×10^6 Da, sedimenting as a 20S particle) that contains several distinct enzymatic activities, including catalytic sites for both ubiquitin-dependent and ubiquitin-independent proteolysis.[53,54] Ubiquitin is a small, highly conserved polypeptide that is covalently added to cytoplasmic proteins targeted for degradation. The catalytic core of the proteasome is a barrel-shaped structure formed by four heptameric stacked rings, but additional proteins (about 16 polypeptides) may interact with the 20S core to form a larger 26S particle. Because proteasomes constitute the primary cytoplasmic pathway for protein degradation (i.e., nonlysosomal pathways), they serve a number of important physiological functions, including regulation of cell proliferation and processing of antigens for presentation. In the nervous system, however, proteasomes are likely to be most important for homeostasis, allowing turnover of cytoplasmic polypeptides at specific sites so that the elaborate cellular extensions of neurons and glia may be maintained.

Cytoplasmic proteins may also be effectively compartmentalized by posttranslational modification. Two types of modification may be particularly important for this kind of compartmentalization. Local activation of kinases can lead to phosphorylation of proteins in specific domains of the neuron. For example, the reversible phosphorylation of synapsin in the presynaptic terminal appears to be responsible for the targeting of synaptic vesicles to the terminal and for the mobilization of vesicles during prolonged stimulation. An impressive variety of cytoplasmic protein kinases that may be selectively activated to modify serines or threonines presented in distinctive consensus sequences have been described. Distinct from these serine or threonine kinases, a number of other kinases that specifically modify tyrosines can be found in the brain. In some cases, the tyrosine kinase is linked directly to a membrane-spanning receptor and phosphorylates cytoplasmic proteins in the vicinity of the receptor after activation. Completing the cycle of phosphorylation and dephosphorylation are a number of phosphatases with varying specificities. The properties and physiological roles for kinases and phosphatases are discussed in greater detail later.

A second common posttranslational modification of cytoplasmic proteins is the addition of carbohydrate moieties. Whereas modification of membrane-associated proteins in the Golgi complex proceeds by the addition of complex carbohydrates through N-linkages on selected asparagines, glycosylated cytoplasmic proteins have simpler carbohydrates added through O-linkages to serine or threonine hydroxyls. This modification was first recognized as a feature of many nuclear proteins and components of the nuclear membrane, but subsequent studies showed that a number of cytoplasmic proteins also have O-linked carbohydrates. Unlike phosphorylation, relatively little is known about the functional significance of cytoplasmic glycosylation. Remarkably, however, serines and threonines subject to O-linked glycosylation would also be good sites for phosphorylation by various kinases as well. This congruence raises the possibility that glycosylation and phosphorylation of some cytoplasmic proteins may serve complementary functions.

Summary

Membrane biogenesis and protein synthesis in neurons and glial cells are accomplished by the same mechanisms that have been worked out in great detail in other cell types. Integral membrane proteins are synthesized in the rough endoplasmic reticulum, and peripheral membrane proteins are products of cytoplasmic free ribosomes that are found in the cell sap. For transmembrane proteins and secretory polypeptides, synthesis in the RER is followed by transport to the Golgi apparatus, where membranes and proteins are sorted and targeted for delivery to precise intracellular locations. It is likely that the neuron and glial cell have evolved additional highly specialized mechanisms for membrane and protein sorting and targeting because these cells are so greatly extended in space, although these additional mechanisms have yet to be fully described. The basic features of the process of secretion, which includes neurotransmitter delivery to presynaptic terminals, are beginning to be understood as well. The key features of this process are apparently common to all cells, including yeast, although the neuron has developed certain specializations and modifications of the secretory pathway that reflect its unique properties as an excitable cell.

THE CYTOSKELETONS OF NEURONS AND GLIAL CELLS

The cytoskeleton of eukaryotic cells is an aggregate structure formed by three classes of cytoplasmic structural proteins: microtubules (tubulins), microfilaments (actins), and intermediate filaments (Fig. 4.7). Each of these elements exists concurrently and independently in overlapping cellular domains. Most cell types contain one or more examples of each class of cytoskeletal structure, but there are exceptions. For example, mature mammalian erythrocytes contain neither microtubules nor intermediate filaments, but they do have

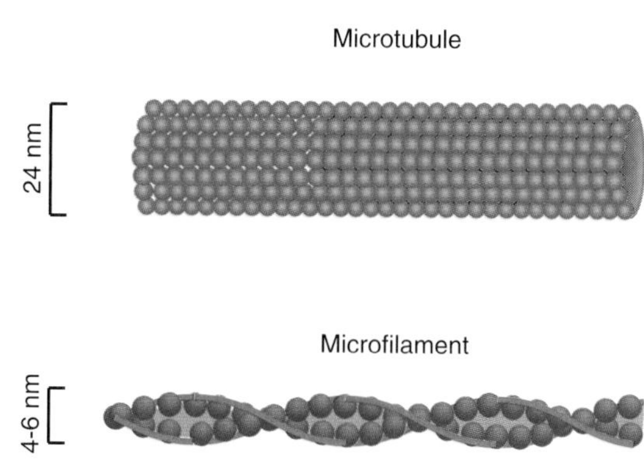

FIGURE 4.7 Two major classes of cytoskeletal structures found in all cellular components of the nervous system are microtubules and microfilaments. These structures constitute the substrates for the various motor proteins of cells. In electron micrographs, microtubules appear as hollow tubes with walls formed by 12–14 protofilaments. Each protofilament consists of a series of α- and β-tubulin dimers organized in a polar fashion, giving the microtubule a plus (fast growing) end and a minus (slow growing) end. In axons, the microtubules have their plus ends distal from the cell body, while dendritic microtubules may have either polarity. Microtubules are approximately 24 nm in diameter and may be more than 100 μm in length. Various polypeptides called microtubule-associated proteins (MAPs) are typically associated with the surface of the microtubule. These MAPs may help regulate the assembly and organization of the microtubules. In contrast, actin microfilaments form from two twisted strands of actin subunits that form filaments only 4–6 nm in diameter. The length of microfilaments is quite variable, but most neuronal filaments are short, in the range 20–50 nm. Many different proteins have been shown to interact with microfilaments in cells, including cross-linking, bundling, severing, and capping proteins (see Table 4.3).

elaborate and highly specialized actin cytoskeletons. Among cells of the nervous system, the oligodendrocyte is unusual in that it contains no cytoplasmic intermediate filaments. Typically, each cell type in the nervous system has a unique complement of cytoskeletal proteins that are important for the differentiated function of that cell type.

Although the three classes of cytoskeletal elements interact with each other and with other cellular structures, all three are dynamic structures rather than passive structural elements. Their aggregate properties form the basis of cell morphologies and plasticity in the nervous tissue. In many cases, biochemical specialization in the cytoskeleton is characteristic of a particular cell type, function, and developmental stage. Each type of cytoskeletal element has unique functions that are essential for a working nervous system.

Microtubules Are an Important Determinant of Cell Architecture

Microtubules (Fig. 4.7) are nearly ubiquitous components of the cytoskeleton in eukaryotes.[55] They play key roles in intracellular transport, are a primary determinant of cell morphology, are the structural correlate of the mitotic spindle, and form the functional core of cilia and flagella. Microtubules are very abundant in the nervous system, and the tubulin subunits of microtubules may constitute more than 10% of total brain protein. As a result, many fundamental properties of microtubules have been defined by using microtubule protein prepared from brain extracts. At the same time, the microtubule cytoskeleton of the neuron has a variety of biochemical specializations that meet the unique demands imposed by the size and shape of the neuron.

Of the various functions defined for microtubules, intracellular transport and the generation of cellular morphology are the most important roles played by microtubules in cells of the nervous system. In part, this comes from their ability to organize cytoplasmic polarity. Microtubules *in vitro* are dynamic, polar structures with plus and minus ends that correspond to the fast- and slow-growing ends, respectively. In contrast, both stable and labile microtubules can be identified *in vivo*, where they help define both microscopic and macroscopic aspects of intracellular organization in cells. Microtubule organization, stability, and composition in nervous tissue are all highly regulated in the nervous system.

By electron microscopy, microtubules appear as hollow tubes 25 nm in diameter and in axons can be up to hundreds of micrometers in length. High-resolution electron micrographs also reveal that the walls of microtubules typically comprise 13 protofilaments formed by a linear arrangement of globular subunits, although microtubules with 12 to 14 protofilaments exist in some tissues and organisms. The globular subunits in the walls of a microtubule are heterodimers of α- and β-tubulin, whereas a variety of microtubule-associated proteins bind to the surface of microtubules.

Neuronal microtubules are remarkable for their genetic and biochemical diversity. Multiple genes exist for both α- and β-tubulins. These genes are differentially expressed according to cell type and developmental stage. Some of these genetic isotypes are expressed ubiquitously, whereas others are only turned on at specific times in development or in specific cell types or both. Most tubulin genes are expressed in nervous tissue, and some appear to be enriched or specific to neurons. When specific isotypes are prepared in a pure form, they show variability in assembly kinetics and ability to bind ligands. However, when more than one isotype is expressed in a single cell such as a neuron, they coassemble into microtubules with mixed composition.

A variety of posttranslational modifications of the tubulins have been described, the most common of which are tyrosination-detyrosination, acetylation-deacetylation, and phosphorylation. The first two of these pathways are intimately associated with assembly of microtubules, but relatively little is known about physiological functions for any of these modified tubulins. Most α-tubulin isotypes are synthesized with a Glu-Tyr dipeptide at the C-terminus (Tyr-tubulin), but the tyrosine can be removed by a specific tubulin carboxypeptidase after assembly into a microtubule, leaving a terminal glutamate (Glu-tubulin). When microtubules containing detyrosinated α-tubulins are disassembled, the liberated α-tubulins are rapidly retyrosinated by a specific tubulin tyrosine ligase. The result is that microtubules that have been assembled for an extended period of time will tend to be rich in Glu-tubulin. The tyrosination state of α-tubulin does not affect its assembly–disassembly kinetics *in vitro,* but recent evidence suggests that detyrosination may affect the interaction of microtubules with other cellular structures. In parallel with detyrosination, α-tubulins are also substrates for a specific acetylation reaction. Acetylation of tubulin was initially described for flagellar tubulins, but subsequent work demonstrated that this modification was widespread in neurons and many other cell types. Because the acetylase acts preferentially on α-tubulin assembled into microtubules, long-lived or stable microtubules tend to be rich in acetylated α-tubulin. However, the distribution of microtubules rich in acetylated tubulin may not be identical with that of Glu-tubulin. Acetylated α-tubulin also is rapidly deacetylated upon disassembly of microtubules, although acetylation does not alter the stability of microtubules *in vitro.*

In contrast with these modifications, tubulin phosphorylation involves a β-tubulin and appears to be restricted to an isotype preferentially expressed in neurons and neuron-like cells. A variety of kinases have been shown to phosphorylate tubulin *in vitro,* but the endogenous kinase has not been identified. The effect of phosphorylation on assembly is unknown, but phosphorylation is upregulated during neurite outgrowth. As with the α-tubulin modifications, the physiological role of phosphorylation on neuronal β-tubulin has yet to be determined. A variety of additional posttranslational modifications have been reported, but their significance and distribution in the nervous system are not well documented.

The biochemical diversity of microtubules is increased through the association of different MAPs with different populations of microtubules (Table 4.2). The significance of microtubule diversity is not completely understood, but it may include functional differences as well as variations in assembly and stability. In particular, MAP composition may be used to define specific neuronal domains. For example, one type of MAP, MAP-2, appears to be restricted to dendritic regions of the neuron, whereas another class of MAPs, tau proteins, are differentially modified in axons. A recently identified isoform of MAP-2 is similar to MAP-2c but includes an additional repeat within the microtubule-binding site; hence it is known as 4-repeat MAP-2c, or MAP-2d.[57] Oligodendrocyte progenitors transiently express this novel isoform of MAP-2c in their cell bodies but not in their processes, suggesting that MAP-2d might have a role separate from its known capacity to bundle microtubules.[56–58]

MAPs in nervous tissue fall into two heterogeneous groups: tau proteins and high-molecular-weight MAPs. Tau proteins have recently been the subject of intense interest, because posttranslationally modified tau proteins are the primary polypeptide constituents of neurofibrillary tangles from the brains of Alzheimer patients. Tau proteins appear to be neuronal MAPs, although reports of tau immunoreactivity outside neurons have appeared. Tau proteins bind to microtubules during assembly–disassembly cycles with a constant stoichiometry and can promote microtubule assembly and stabilization. Tau exists in a number of molecular-weight isoforms that vary with region of the nervous system and developmental stage. For example, tau proteins in the adult CNS are typically from 60 to 75 kDa, whereas PNS axons contain a higher-molecular-weight tau of approximately 100 kDa. The different isoforms of tau protein are generated from a single mRNA by alternative splicing, and additional heterogeneity is produced by phosphorylation.

In contrast with tau MAPs, high-molecular-weight MAPs are a diverse group of largely unrelated proteins found in a variety of tissues, although some are brain specific. All have apparent molecular weights >300 kDa and form side arms protruding from the walls of microtubules. Many of them may participate in microtubule assembly and cytoskeletal organization. Traditionally, the high-molecular-weight MAPs comprise five polypeptides: MAPs 1a, 1b, 1c, 2a, and 2b. MAP-2 proteins are closely related and are located primarily in dendrites. In contrast, the three polypeptides known as MAP-1 are unique polypeptides with little sequence homology. MAP-1c is a cytoplasmic form of dynein (see the section on molecular motors later in this chapter). MAPs 1a and 1b are widespread and appear to be developmentally regulated. MAPs 1a, 1b, and 2 are all thought to play important roles in stabilizing and organizing the microtubule cytoskeleton.

In most cell types, cytoplasmic microtubules appear to be relatively dynamic structures, although stable microtubules or microtubule segments are found in all cells. In nonneuronal cells such as astrocytes and other

TABLE 4.2 Major Microtubule Proteins and Microtubule Motors in Mammalian Brain

	Location and function
Tubulins	
α-Tubulins and β-tubulins	Neurons, glia, and nonneuronal cells except mature mammalian erythrocytes. Multigene family with some genes expressed preferentially in brain, while others are ubiquitous. Primary structural polypeptides of microtubules.
γ-Tubulin	Present in all microtubule-containing cells, but restricted to region of microtubule-organizing center. Needed for nucleation of microtubules.
Microtubule-associated proteins (MAPs)	
MAP-1a/1b	Widely expressed in neurons and glia, including both axons and dendrites. Forms are developmentally regulated phosphoproteins.
MAP-2a/2b MAP-2c	Dendrite-specific MAPs. The smaller MAP-2c is developmentally regulated, becoming restricted to spines in adults, while 2a and 2b are major phosphoproteins in adult brain.
LMW tau HMW tau	Tau proteins are enriched in axons and have a distinctive phosphorylation pattern in the axon, but may be found in other compartments. A single gene with multiple forms due to alternative splicing. The HMW tau is found in adult peripheral axons.
Motor proteins	
Kinesin Neuron-specific kinesin	Present in all microtubule-containing cells. Associated with membrane-bound organelles and serves to move them along microtubules in fast axonal transport. The neuron-specific form is the product of a specific gene expressed in nervous tissue.
Kinesin-related proteins	A diverse set of motor proteins with a kinesin-related motor domain and varied tails. Some are developmentally regulated and some are restricted to dividing cells, where they act as mitotic motors.
Axonemal dynein Cytoplasmic dynein (MAP-1c)	A set of minus-end-directed microtubule motors. The axonemal forms are associated with cilia and flagella. In nervous tissue, these may be associated with the ependyma. The cytoplasmic forms may be involved in the transport of either organelles or cytoskeletal elements.

glial cells, microtubules are typically anchored in centrosomal regions that serve as microtubule-organizing centers. As a result, their cytoplasmic microtubules are oriented so that plus ends are distal to the cell center. The biochemistry of microtubule-organizing centers is not fully understood, but they contain a novel tubulin subunit, γ-tubulin, which is thought to function as a nucleating site for microtubules.

In contrast, the dendritic and axonal microtubules of neurons are not continuous with the microtubule-organizing center, so alternate mechanisms must exist for stabilization and organization of these microtubules. The situation is complicated further by the fact that dendritic and axonal microtubules differ in both composition and organization. Recent studies show that both axonal and dendritic microtubules are nucleated at the microtubule-organizing center but are subsequently released for delivery to the appropriate compartment. Surprisingly, axonal and dendritic compartments are not equivalent. There are two striking differences. First, the MAPs of dendritic and axonal microtubules are different in both identity and phosphorylation state. Second, microtubule orientation in axons is similar to that seen in other cell types with plus end distal, but microtubules in dendrites may exhibit both polarities. Perhaps owing to these differences, dendritic microtubules are less likely to be aligned with one another and appear less regular in their spacing.

Stabilization of axonal and dendritic microtubules is essential because of the volume of cytoplasm and distance from sites of protein synthesis for tubulin. Because microtubules play critical roles in both dendritic and axonal function, mechanisms to ensure their proper extent and organization must exist. A common side effect of one class of antineoplastic drugs, the vinca alkaloids, underscores the importance of microtubule stability in axons. Vincristine and other vinca alkaloids act by destabilizing spindle microtubules, but dosage must be carefully monitored to prevent development of peripheral neuropathies due to loss of axonal microtubules.

Axonal microtubules contain a particularly stable subset of microtubule segments that are resistant to depolymerization by antimitotic drugs, cold, and calcium. The stable microtubule segments are biochemically distinct and may constitute more than half of the axonal tubulin. Stable domains in microtubules may serve to regulate the axonal cytoskeleton by nucleating and organizing microtubules as well as stabilizing them. The biochemical basis of microtubule stability is not completely understood but probably includes posttranslational modification of the tubulin or the presence of stabilizing proteins or both. There are indications that levels of cold-insoluble tubulin correlate with axonal plasticity. In contrast, relatively little is known about regulation of dendritic microtubules, but local synthesis of MAP-2 in dendrites may play a role in regulating their stability.

Microfilaments and the Actin-Based Cytoskeleton Are Involved in Intracellular Transport and Cell Movement

The actin cytoskeleton is universally present in eukaryotes, although actin microfilaments are most familiar as the thin filaments of skeletal muscle. Microfilaments (Table 4.3) play a critical role in contractility for both muscle and nonmuscle cells. **Actin** and its contractile partner **myosin** are particularly abundant in nervous tissue relative to other nonmuscle tissues. In fact, one of the earliest descriptions of nonmuscle actin and myosin was in brain.[59] In neurons, actin microfilaments are most abundant in presynaptic terminals, dendritic spines, growth cones, and the subplasmalemmal cortex. Although concentrated in these regions, microfilaments are also present throughout the cytoplasm of both neurons and glia in the form of short filaments from 4 to 6 nm in diameter and from 400 to 800 nm in length.

TABLE 4.3 Selected Proteins of the Microfilament Cytoskeleton in Brain

Actins
α-Actin (smooth muscle)
β-Actin and γ-actin (neuronal and nonneuronal cells)
Actin monomer binding proteins
Profilin
Thymosin β4 and β10
Capping proteins
Ezrin/radixin/moesin
Schwannomin/merlin
Gelsolin family
Gelsolin
Villin
Scinderin
Cross-linking and bundling proteins
Spectrin (fodrin)
Dystrophin, utrophin, and related proteins
α-Actinin
Tropomyosin
Proteins with nonmicrofilament functions
MAP-2
Tau
Myosins
Myosin Iβ
Myosin II
Myosin V
Myosin VI
Myosin VII

As with tubulin, multiple actin genes exist in both vertebrates and invertebrates.[60] Four α-actin human genes have been cloned. Each of these α-actin genes is expressed specifically in a different muscle cell type (skeletal, cardiac, vascular smooth, and enteric smooth muscle). In addition to the α-actins, two nonmuscle actin genes (β- and γ-actin) are present in humans. β-Actin and γ-actin genes are expressed ubiquitously, and both are abundant in nervous tissue. The functional significance of these different genetic isotypes is not clear, because the actins are highly conserved proteins. Across the range of known actin sequences, the amino acids are identical at approximately two of three positions. Even the positions of introns within different actin genes are highly conserved across many species and genes. Despite this high degree of conservation, differences in the distribution of specific isotypes within a single neuron have been reported. For example, β-actin may be enriched in growth cones. The prominent actin bundles seen in fibroblasts and some other nonneuronal cells in culture are not characteristic of neurons, and most neuronal actin microfilaments are less than 1 μm in length.

Many microfilament-associated proteins have been described in nervous tissue (myosin, tropomyosin, spectrin, α-actinin, etc.), but less is known about their distribution and normal function in neurons and glia. The myosins and myosin-associated proteins are considered later in this chapter in the section on molecular motors, but several categories of actin-binding proteins can be defined (Table 4.3). Monomer actin-binding proteins such as profilin and thymosin β4 or β10 are abundant in the developing brain and are thought to help regulate the amount of actin assembled into microfilaments by sequestering actin monomers. These monomers can be rapidly mobilized in response to appropriate signals. For example, phosphatidylinositol 4,5-bisphosphate causes the actin–profilin complex to dissociate, freeing the monomer for microfilament assembly. Such regulation may play a key role in growth-cone motility, where actin assembly is an important mechanism for filopodial extension.

Several proteins that can cap actin microfilaments, serving to anchor them to other structures or to regulate microfilament length, have been identified. The ezrin-radixin-moesin gene family encodes barbed-end capping proteins that are concentrated at sites where the microfilaments meet the plasma membrane, suggesting a role in anchoring microfilaments or linking them to extracellular components through membrane proteins. A mutation in a member of this family expressed in Schwann cells, merlin or schwannomin, is thought to be responsible for the human disease neurofibromatosis Type 2. Development of numerous tumors with a Schwann cell lineage in neurofibromatosis Type 2 suggests that this microfilament-binding protein acts normally as a tumor suppressor.

Whereas some membrane proteins can interact directly with the actin microfilaments of the membrane cytoskeleton, others interact with the actin cytoskeleton through intermediaries such as spectrin. Proteins such as spectrin (fodrin), α-actinin, and dystrophins cross-link, or bundle, microfilaments, giving rise to higher-order complexes. Spectrin is enriched in the cortical membrane cytoskeleton and is thought to have a role in the localization of integral membrane proteins such as ion channels and receptors. Dystrophin is the best known member of a family of related proteins that all appear to be essential for the clustering of receptors in muscle and nervous tissue. A mutation in dystrophin is responsible for Duchenne muscular dystrophy. Positioning of integral membrane proteins on the cell surface is likely to be an essential function of the actin-rich membrane cytoskeleton, acting in concert with a new class of proteins that contain the protein-binding module, the PDZ domain.

Members of the gelsolin family have multiple activities. They can not only cap the barbed end of a microfilament, but also sever microfilaments and nucleate microfilament assembly under some circumstances. These severing–capping proteins may be essential for reorganizing the actin cytoskeleton. Because gelsolin severing activity is Ca^{2+} activated, it may provide a mechanism for altering the membrane cytoskeleton in response to Ca^{2+} transients. Other second messengers, such as phosphatidylinositol 4,5-bisphosphate, may also serve as regulators of gelsolin function, suggesting an interplay between different classes of actin-binding proteins such as gelsolin and profilin. Oligodendrocytes are the only neural cells in the CNS that express significant amounts of the actin-binding and microfilament-severing protein gelsolin.[61]

Proteins with other functions may also interact directly with actin or actin microfilaments. For example, the enzyme DNase I binds actin tightly, inhibiting both DNase activity and actin assembly. The physiological function of this interaction is unclear, but it has proved a useful tool for probing actin structure and function. Some membrane proteins, such as the epidermal growth factor receptor, bind actin microfilaments directly, which may be important in anchoring these membrane components at a particular location on the cell surface. Other cytoskeletal structures may have specific interactions. Both MAP-2 and tau microtubule-associated proteins have been shown to interact with actin microfilament *in vitro* and have the potential to mediate interactions between microtubules and microfilaments. Finally, the synaptic vesicle–associated phosphoprotein, synapsin I, has a phosphorylation-sensitive interaction with microfilaments that appears to be important for the targeting and storage of synaptic vesicles in the presynaptic terminal.[61a] Many of these interactions have been defined by *in vitro* binding studies, and their physiological significance is not always clearly established. However, there is little doubt that interactions occur between the actin cytoskeleton and a variety of other cellular structures.

The presence of actin as a major component of both pre- and postsynaptic specializations as well as in the growth cone gives the actin cytoskeleton special significance in the nervous system. The enrichment of microfilaments and associated proteins in the membrane cytoskeleton means that they are the cytoskeletal components most subject and most responsive to changes in the local external environment of the neuron. Microfilaments also play a critical role in positioning the various receptors and ion channels at specific locations on the neuronal surface. Although many studies have emphasized the enrichment of the microfilament cytoskeleton at the plasma membrane, microfilaments are also abundant in the deep cytoplasm. In many respects, the microfilaments may be best regarded as a uniquely plastic component of the neuronal cytoskeleton that plays a critical role in local trafficking of both cytoskeletal and membrane components.

Intermediate Filaments Are Prominent Constituents of Nervous Tissue

Intermediate filaments of the nervous system appear as solid, ropelike fibrils from 8 to 12 nm in diameter that may be many micrometers long.[62] Intermediate filament proteins constitute a superfamily of five classes, which have distinctive patterns of expression specific to cell type and developmental stage (Table 4.4).

Type I and Type II intermediate filament proteins are the **keratins,** which are hallmarks of epithelial cells. The keratins are not associated with nervous tissue and will not be considered further here. In contrast, all nucleated cells contain Type V intermediate filament proteins, the **nuclear lamins.** The lamins are encoded

TABLE 4.4 Intermediate Filament Proteins of the Nervous System

Class and name	Cell type
Types I and II	
Acidic and basic keratins	Epithelial and endothelial cells
Type III	
Glial fibrillary acidic protein	Astrocytes and nonmyelinating Schwann cells
Vimentin	Neuroblasts, glioblasts, fibroblasts, etc.
Desmin	Smooth muscle
Peripherin	A subset of peripheral and central neurons
Type IV	
NF triplet (NFH, NFM, NFL)	Most neurons, expressed at highest level in large myelinated fibers
α-Internexin	Developing neurons, parallel fibers of cerebellum
Nestin	Early neuroectodermal cells. The most divergent member of this class; some have classified it as a sixth type.
Type V	
Nuclear lamins	Nuclear membranes

by the most evolutionarily divergent of the intermediate filament genes, with a distinctive pattern of introns and exons, as well as having a different polypeptide domain structure. Intermediate filaments in the nervous system are all produced by either Type III or Type IV intermediate filament proteins.

Type III intermediate filaments are a diverse family that includes, among others, **vimentin** (characteristic of fibroblasts and many embryonic tissues such as embryonic neurons) and **glial fibrillary acidic protein** (GFAP, a marker for astrocytes and Schwann cells). Type III intermediate filament subunits typically have a molecular weight between 45 and 60 kDa and consist of a conserved rod domain and relatively small gene-specific amino- and carboxy-terminal sequences. As a result, intermediate filaments formed from Type III subunits form smooth filaments without side arms. Type III polypeptides can form homopolymers but may also coassemble with other Type III intermediate filament subunits.

A recently described Type III intermediate filament protein, peripherin, is unique to neurons and may be coexpressed with the neurofilament triplet proteins. Peripherin has a characteristic expression during development and regeneration in specific neuronal populations. It has been shown to coassemble with neurofilament triplet proteins both *in vitro* and *in vivo,* where presumably it can substitute for the low-molecular-weight neurofilament (NFL). However, whether coassembly is generally the case is not known. Physiological roles for neuron-specific Type III intermediate filament polypeptides are uncertain. Unlike Type IV intermediate filaments, intermediate filaments made from Type III subunits tend to disassemble more readily under physiological conditions. Thus, the presence of Type III intermediate filament subunit proteins may produce more dynamic structures, which could be important during development or regeneration.

Although other Type III intermediate filament proteins are found in the nervous system, they are generally restricted to glia or to neurons at early stages of differentiation. Vimentin is abundant in a wide variety of cells during early development, including both glioblasts and neuroblasts. Some Schwann cells and astrocytes contain vimentin. Curiously, mature oligodendrocytes do not appear to have any intermediate filaments, an exception to the general rule that most metazoan cells contain all three classes of cytoskeletal structures. Oligodendrocyte precursors do, however, express vimentin and may transiently express GFAP.

In neurons, intermediate filaments typically have side arms that limit packing density, whereas glial intermediate filaments lack side arms and may be very tightly packed. Neuronal intermediate filaments have an unusual degree of metabolic stability, which makes them well suited to the role of stabilizing and maintaining neuronal morphology. The existence of neurofilaments was established for many years before much was known about their biochemistry or function. Neurofilaments could be seen in early electron micrographs, and many traditional histological procedures visualize neurons as a result of a specific interaction of metals with neurofilaments. Recent work on the biochemistry and molecular genetics of intermediate filaments has illuminated many aspects of their function in the nervous system.

The primary type of intermediate filament in neurons is formed from three subunits, the **neurofilament triplet,** each encoded by a separate gene. The neurofilament triplet proteins are from Type IV intermediate filament genes, which are generally expressed only in neurons and have a characteristic domain structure that can be recognized in both primary sequence and gene structure. The polypeptides were initially identified from axonal transport studies. The apparent molecular weights for the neurofilament subunits vary widely across species, but mammalian forms typically range from 180 to 200 kDa for the high-molecular-weight subunit (NFH), from 130 to 170 kDa for the medium subunit (NFM), and from 60 to 70 kDa for the low-molecular-weight subunit (NFL). Interestingly, Schwann cells in damaged peripheral nerves also transiently express NFM and NFL. Neurofilament subunits are phosphorylated in axons, with NFM and NFH having unusually high levels of phosphorylation. In some species, NFH has 50 or more repeats of a consensus phosphorylation site at its carboxy terminus, and levels of NFH phosphorylation indicate that most of these sites are phosphorylated *in vivo*. This high level of phosphorylation in neurofilament subunit tail domains is a distinctive characteristic of neurofilaments.

A second motif characteristic of neurofilaments is the presence of a glutamate-rich region in the tail adjacent to the core rod domain. This glutamate region has particular significance for neuroscientists because it appears to be the basis for the reaction of the classic neurofibrillary silver stains for neurons. These stains were first introduced in the late 19th century and have been used extensively by neurohistologists and neuroanatomists from Ramón y Cajal's time to the present day. However, the molecular basis of these neurofibrillary stains was not known until 1968, when F. O. Schmitt showed that neurofibrils were formed by the 10-nm-diameter neurofilaments. Remarkably, the ability of isolated neurofilament subunits to react with silver histological stains is retained even after separation in gel electrophoresis for neurofilaments from organisms as diverse as humans, squid, and the marine fanworm, *Myxicola*. Conservation of the glutamate-rich domain suggests both an important functional role for this motif and the early divergence of neurofilaments from the other intermediate filament families.

The neurofilaments formed from the neurofilament triplet proteins play a critical role in determining axonal caliber. As mentioned earlier, neurofilaments have characteristic side arms, unique among intermediate filaments; these side arms are formed by NFM and NFH carboxy-terminal regions. Although all three neurofilament subunits contribute to the neurofilament central core, the side arms are formed only by the NFM and NFH subunits. Phosphorylation of NFH and NFM side arms alters charge density on the neurofilament surface, repelling adjacent neurofilaments with similar charge. The high density of surface charge due to phosphate groups on neurofilaments makes it difficult to imagine a stable interaction between neurofilaments and other structures of like charge. Although many reports refer to cross bridges between neurofilaments, direct studies of interactions between neurofilaments provide little evidence of stable cross-links between neurofilaments or between neurofilaments and other cytoskeletal structures. However, dynamic interactions between neurofilaments and cellular structures or proteins may be critical for many aspects of neurofilament function and metabolism.

Alteration in expression levels for neurofilament subunits or mutations in neurofilament genes can lead to specific neuropathologies. Overexpression of genes encoding normal NFH or expression of some mutant NFL genes in transgenic mouse models leads to the accumulation of neurofilaments in the cell body and proximal axon of spinal motor neurons. These accumulations are similar to those seen in amyotrophic lateral sclerosis and related motor neuron diseases, leading to the hypothesis that disruption of normal neurofilament function is a common intermediate in the pathogenesis of motor neuron disease. Similarly, an early indicator of neuropathies caused by neurotoxins such as acrylamide and hexanedione is the accumulation of neurofilaments in either proximal or distal regions of the axon. Disruption of neurofilament organization is a hallmark of pathology for many degenerative diseases of the nervous system, particularly those affecting large myelinated axons such as those of spinal motor neurons. Although pathology can be produced by altering neurofilament organization, the question whether neurofilament defects are a primary event in pathogenesis or a manifestation of an underlying metabolic pathology remains controversial in most cases.

Another member of the Type IV intermediate filament family, **α-internexin,** also has been identified. Like neurofilament triplet proteins, α-internexin is expressed only in neurons. Unlike the triplet proteins, α-internexin is preferentially expressed early in development of the nervous system and then disappears from most neurons during maturation. Intermediate filaments containing α-internexin do persist in portions of the adult nervous system, such as the branched axons of granule cells in the cerebellar cortex. There is evidence that α-internexin can coassemble with members of the neurofilament triplet, but it also forms homopolymeric filaments. The primary sequence of α-internexin has features in common with both NFL and NFM that are thought to form the basis for assembly properties distinct from those of other Type IV intermediate filaments.

The final type of intermediate protein present in the

nervous system is **nestin,** which is expressed transiently during early development. Nestin is also expressed in Schwann cells and in the progenitors of oligodendrocytes, which appear late in the development of the embryonic nervous system.[63] Remarkably, nestin appears to be expressed almost exclusively in ectodermal cells after commitment to the neuroglial lineage, but prior to terminal differentiation. At >250 kDa, nestin is the largest intermediate filament subunit and is the most divergent in sequence with several distinctive features, leading some to classify nestin as a sixth type of intermediate filament protein whereas others group it with Type IV intermediate filaments. Relatively little is known about the assembly properties of nestin *in vivo* or the physiological function of nestin intermediate filaments in neuroectodermal cells.

How Do the Various Cytoskeletal Systems Interact?

Each class of cytoskeletal structures may be found without the others in some cellular domains, but all three classes—microtubules, microfilaments, and intermediate filaments—coexist in many domains. As a result, they inevitably interact. This is not to say that individual cytoskeletal elements are necessarily crosslinked to one another. As mentioned earlier, microtubules and neurofilaments have highly phosphorylated side arms that project from their surfaces. The high density of negative charge on the surface tends to repel structures with a like charge such as other microtubules and neurofilaments. This does not mean that microtubules and neurofilaments do not interact with each other, but it does suggest that such interactions may be transient.

One location containing longer microfilaments and more elaborate organization is the growth cone, which contains bundles of microfilaments in the filopodia as well as a more dispersed actin network. Neurofilaments are largely excluded from the growth cone, typically extending no further than the neck of the growth cone. In contrast, microtubules and microfilaments play complementary roles in the growth cone itself. Microfilaments are critical in sprouting but appear less critical for elongation, at least over short distances. Disruption of microtubules in the distal neurite does not affect sprouting but does inhibit neurite elongation.

Summary

The intracellular framework that gives shape to the neuron and glial cell is the cytoskeleton, a complicated set of filaments and tubules and their associated proteins. These organelles are responsible as well for intracellular movement of materials and, during development, for cell migration and plasma membrane extension within nervous tissue.

MOLECULAR MOTORS IN THE NERVOUS SYSTEM

Until 1985, our knowledge of molecular motors in vertebrate cells of any type was restricted to **myosins** and flagellar **dyneins.** Myosins had been identified in nervous tissue, but their functions were uncertain. Because the preponderance of evidence indicated that fast axonal transport was microtubule based, there was considerable interest in dyneins in cell cytoplasm. Despite a number of studies, no evidence for a functional cytoplasmic dynein emerged. Worse yet, the characteristic properties of fast organelle movements appeared inconsistent with both myosins and dyneins. Over the past decade, however, we have developed a good but still incomplete understanding of how these motors may work inside cells.[64,65]

Myosins and dyneins can be distinguished pharmacologically by their differential susceptibility to inhibitors of ATPase activity, but the spectrum of inhibitors active against fast axonal transport fails to match the properties of either myosin or dynein. The most striking difference between inhibitor effects on axonal transport and on myosin or dynein motors was seen in the effect of a nonhydrolyzable analog of ATP. Adenylyl-imidodiphosphate (AMP-PNP) is a weak competitive inhibitor of both myosin and dynein, requiring a 10- to 100-fold excess of analog. In contrast, within minutes of AMP-PNP perfusion into isolated axoplasm, both anterograde and retrograde axonal transport stop. Inhibition by AMP-PNP occurs even in the presence of stoichiometric concentrations of ATP. Organelles moving in both directions freeze in place and remain attached to microtubules. AMP-PNP weakens the interaction of myosin with microfilaments and of dynein with microtubules, but stabilizes the binding of membrane-bound organelles to microtubules. Thus, the effects of AMP-PNP indicate that movement of membrane-bound organelles in fast axonal transport must require another type of motor, distinct from the myosins and dyneins.

The effects of AMP-PNP both demonstrated the existence of a new type of mechanochemical ATPase and provided a basis for identifying its constituent polypeptides. Binding of the ATPase to microtubules should be increased by AMP-PNP and decreased by ATP. Polypeptides meeting this criterion were soon identified. The new ATPase was named **kinesin,** based initially on an ability to move microtubules across glass coverslips as first described in axoplasmic extracts. Studies soon established that kinesin was a microtubule-activated ATPase with minimal basal activity. This combination of ATPase activity and motility *in vitro* confirmed that kinesin was a new class of microtubule-based motor.[65,66]

Kinesin has now been identified in a variety of organisms and tissues, leading to an extensive characterization of many biochemical, pharmacological, immunochemical, and molecular properties. Electron microscopic and biophysical analyses reveal kinesin as a long, rod-shaped protein, approximately 80 nm in length. Neuronal kinesin is a heterotetramer with two heavy chains (molecular weight 115–130 kDa) and two light chains (62–70 kDa). Localization of antibodies specific for kinesin subunits by high-resolution electron microscopy of bovine brain kinesin indicates that the two heavy chains are arranged in parallel, forming the heads and much of the shaft, whereas light chains are localized to the fan-shaped tail region (Fig. 4.8).

A variety of approaches have demonstrated that the ATP-binding and microtubule-binding domains of kinesin are in the head regions of the heavy chains, whereas the light chains in the tail region of kinesin appear to bind to membranes. When *in vitro* motility assays are employed for analysis of brain kinesins, movements are directed toward the plus ends of microtubules. Because axonal microtubules are oriented with their plus ends distal from the cell body, this movement would be appropriate for a motor that moves organelles in the anterograde direction.

Neuronal kinesin appears associated with a variety of membrane-bound organelles, including synaptic vesicles, mitochondria, coated vesicles, and lysosomes. The interaction of kinesin and other molecular motors with membrane surfaces is not well understood. In the case of kinesin, the interaction is thought to involve the light chains of kinesin along with the carboxy termini of the heavy chains.

The kinesins have now been shown to be a family of related proteins with a highly conserved domain that includes the ATP- and microtubule-binding domains. Many of these kinesin-related polypeptides appear associated with cell division, and kinesin-related proteins in vertebrate tissues are not well characterized. However, multiple members of the kinesin superfamily are expressed in both adult and developing brains. This proliferation of motor proteins has dramatically altered the questions being asked about motor function in the brain. The discovery that ncd, a kinesin-related protein from *Drosophila,* can move structures toward the minus end of microtubules increases the number of potential functions that kinesin family members might serve in nervous tissue still further, perhaps including a role in retrograde transport. Further study is needed to establish specific functions for each member of the kinesin superfamily expressed in neurons or glial cells.

As an indirect result of the discovery of kinesin, one of the high-molecular-weight microtubule-associated proteins of brain, MAP-1c, was found to be the long sought cytoplasmic form of dynein. Both MAP-1c dynein and kinesin can be isolated from bovine brain by incubation of microtubules with nucleotide-free soluble extracts. Both are bound to microtubules under these conditions and released by ATP. MAP-1c dynein moved microtubules *in vitro* with a polarity opposite that seen with kinesin and was identified as a two-headed cytoplasmic dynein by using both structural and biochemical criteria. Concurrently, a similar protein was identified in nematodes.

MAP-1c dyneins form a 40-nm-long complex of molecular mass 1.6×10^6 Da, which includes two heavy chains and a number of light chains (Figs. 4.8 and 4.9)[65,67,68] Less information is available about the distribution and properties of MAP-1c dyneins than about kinesin. Immunocytochemical studies in nonneuronal cells showed immunoreactivity on mitotic spindles. In addition, a punctate pattern of immunoreactivity also present in interphase cells was thought to be due to dynein bound to membrane-bound organelles. Dyneins are widely thought to be the motor for fast retrograde axonal transport but are also a candidate for a motor in slow axonal transport.

Myosins from muscle were the first molecular motors identified, but in recent years interest in nonmuscle myosins has increased.[69,70,70a] Nonmuscle myosins may be categorized as belonging to one of eight classes, but only a subset has been clearly demonstrated in the nervous system. The nonmuscle myosins in this subset share considerable homology in their motor domains but diverge widely in other domains.

The most familiar of the myosins are the myosin II proteins (Fig. 4.10), which are found in the thick filaments of smooth and skeletal muscle but are also present in nonmuscle cells. Two heavy chains of myosin II form a dimer that may interact with other myosin II dimers to form bipolar filaments. Under tissue culture conditions, many cells contain bundles of actin microfilaments, known as stress fibers, that exhibit a characteristic distribution of myosin II into distinct patterns that may be sarcomeric equivalents, but stress fibers are not apparent in neurons and other cells of the nervous system *in situ.* However, bipolar thick filaments assembled from myosin II dimers can be isolated from nervous tissues. Many of the cellular contractile

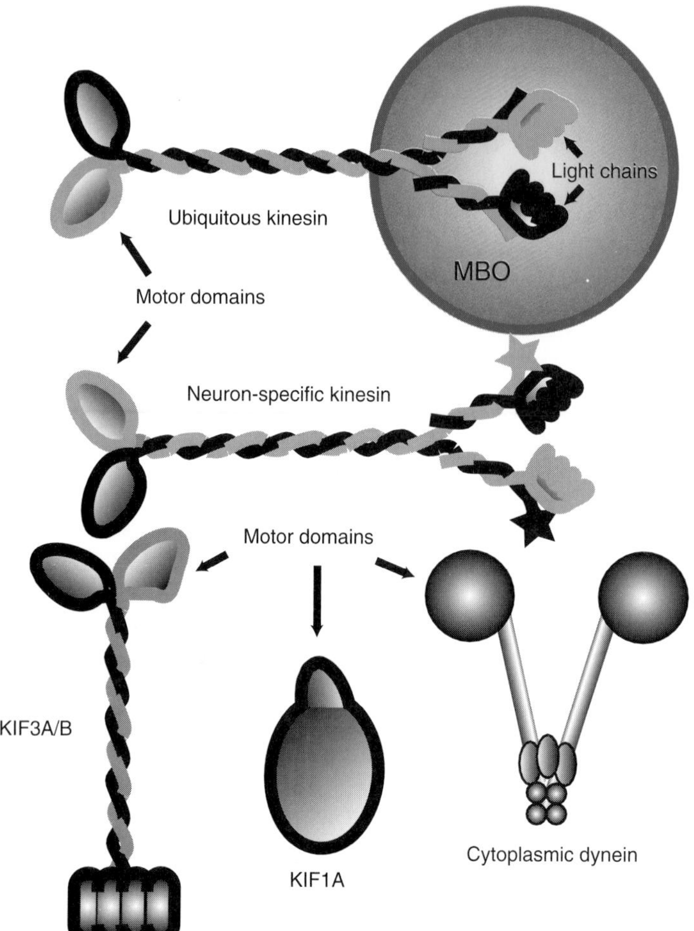

FIGURE 4.8 Examples of microtubule motor proteins in the mammalian nervous system. The first microtubule motor identified in nervous tissue was the ubiquitous form of kinesin, but subsequent studies showed that a neuron-specific form of kinesin was found in mammalian brain. The motor domains are well conserved by the tail domains and appear to be specialized for interaction with various targets, such as different membrane-bound organelles. After the sequence of the kinesin heavy chain was established, the presence of additional genes that contained sequences homologous to the motor domain of kinesin was soon recognized. The molecular organization of these various motor proteins is quite diverse, including monomers (KIF1A), trimers (KIF3A / 3B), and tetramers (ubiquitous and neuron-specific kinesins). Many kinesin-related proteins have been implicated in the processes of cell division, but a number can also be found in postmitotic cells such as neurons.

events described in nonneuronal cells, such as the contractile ring in mitosis, are thought to include myosin II. Although brain myosin II was one of the first nonmuscle myosins to be described, relatively little is known about the function of myosin II in neurons. Myosin II has been localized in the neurites of neurons in primary culture.

Myosin I proteins have a single, smaller heavy chain that does not form filaments but possesses a homologous actin-activated ATPase domain. One exciting aspect of myosin I is its ability to interact directly with membrane surfaces, which may generate movements of plasma membrane components or intracellular organelles. Myosin I has been purified from neural and neuroendocrine tissues. At least three genes in this family have been found in mammals, and multiple forms are present in brain. An interesting aspect of myosin IB is its expression in the stereocilia of hair cells in the cochlea and vestibular system, where it may play a role in mechanotransduction. Both myosin I and myosin II molecules have been proposed to have a role in the motility of lamelipodia at the leading

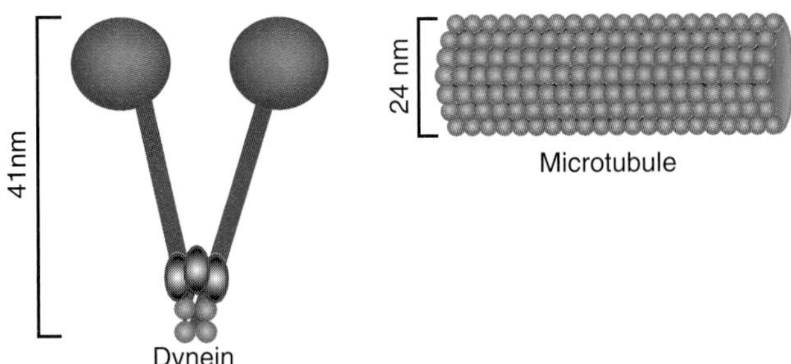

FIGURE 4.9 Biochemical studies on kinesin in brain led to the description of a cytoplasmic form of dynein that was distinct from axonemal dyneins. Cytoplasmic dynein may interact with membrane-bound organelles and cytoskeletal structures. Genetic methods have established that there may be as many as 30 kinesin-related proteins and 15 dynein heavy chains in a single organism. The diversity of microtubule-based motors is consistent with the extent of the microtubule cytoskeleton in the nervous system.

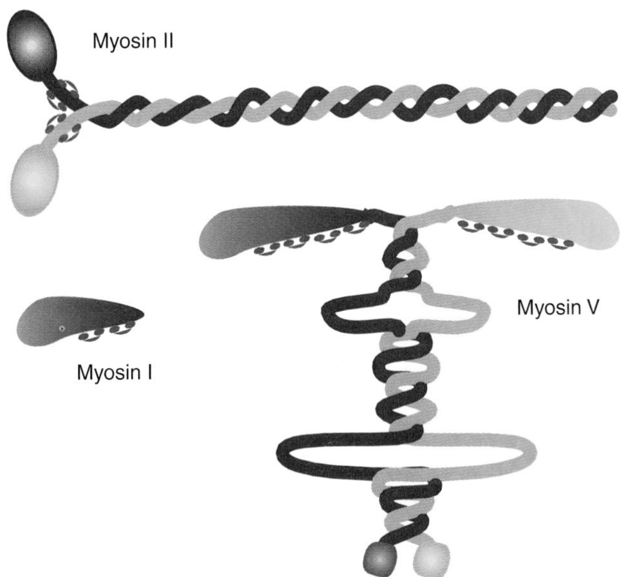

FIGURE 4.10 Examples of myosin motor proteins found in the mammalian nervous system. Myosin heavy chains contain the motor domain, whereas the light chains serve to regulate motor function. Myosin II was the first molecular motor characterized biochemically from skeletal muscle and brain. Biochemical and genetic approaches have now defined 11 classes of myosin, many of which can be found in brain. Myosin II is a classic two-headed myosin that forms thick filaments in nonmuscle cells. Myosin I motors have single motor domains, but may interact with actin microfilaments or membranes. Myosin V motors were initially identified as a mouse mutation that affected coat color and produced seizures. Myosin V has multiple binding sites for calmodulin that act as light chains. Mutations in other classes of myosin have been linked to deafness. Other myosins, including myosins I, II, and V, have been detected in growth cones as well as mature neurons. The specific roles of these various myosins in the nervous system remain to be established.

edge of growth cones, but they are also expressed at substantial levels in adult nervous tissue in which growth cones are rare.

The mouse mutation *dilute,* which affects coat color, was shown to result from a mutation in a gene that encodes a novel myosin heavy chain distinct from both myosins I and II. Similar myosin molecules have been identified in other cell types and organisms and are classified as myosin V. The change in coat color seen in the *dilute* mouse is due to an inability of skin dendritic pigment cells to deliver the pigment to developing hairs. There are complex neurological deficits in *dilute* mutants, including seizures that eventually lead to death in severely altered alleles of the *dilute* mutation. Myosin V was also discovered independently in extracts from chicken and mammalian brain. The specific cellular localization and function of myosin V in the nervous system remain unclear, although it has been reported in growth cones. However, neurons in *dilute* mice without one allele of myosin V clearly develop axons and make connections. The seizures do not begin until early adulthood.

Recently, representatives from two more classes of myosin have been identified in nervous tissue. Genes for a myosin VI and a myosin VIIA have been identified in brain as well as in other tissues. Both have been implicated in forms of congenital deafness. Myosin VI appears to be the gene responsible for **Snell's Waltzer deafness,** and myosin VIIA has been identified as the gene responsible for a human disease involving both deafness and blindness, **Usher syndrome Type 1B.** Both of these myosins are expressed in the mechanosensory hair cells of the cochlea and vestibular apparatus, and they exhibit a different localization from each other and from myosin IB.

The diversity of brain myosins and their distinctive localization suggests that the various myosins may have narrowly defined functions. However, relatively little is known about specific neuronal functions for the myosins despite intensive study of myosins in the nervous system. The axonal transport of myosin II-like proteins has been described, but little further progress has been made on the functions of myosin II in the mature nervous system. Even less is known about myosin I in the nervous system. However, myosins are likely to play roles in growth cone motility, synaptic plasticity, and even neurotransmitter release.

There are few instances in our knowledge of neuronal function in which we fully understand the role played by specific molecular motors, but members of all three classes are abundant in nervous tissue. This proliferation of different motor molecules and their isoforms suggests that some physiological activities may require multiple classes of motor molecules.

Summary

The concept is now firmly in place that neurons and glial cells, like other cells, contain certain molecular motors responsible for moving discrete populations of molecules, particles, and organelles through intracellular compartments.

BUILDING AND MAINTAINING NERVOUS SYSTEM CELLS

The functional architecture of neurons comprises many specializations in cytoskeletal and membranous components. Each of these specializations is dynamic, constantly changing and being renewed at a rate determined by the local environment and cellular metabolism. The processes of axonal transport represent a key to understanding neuronal dynamics and provide a basis for exploring neuronal development, regeneration, and neuropathology. Recent advances are important sources of insight into the molecular mechanisms underlying axonal transport, although many questions remain.

Slow Axonal Transport Moves Soluble Components and Cytoskeletal Structure

Slow axonal transport has two major components, both representing movement of cytoplasmic constituents (Fig. 4.11). The cytoplasmic and cytoskeletal elements of the axon in axonal transport move at rates at least two orders of magnitude more slowly than fast transport. Slow component a is composed largely of cytoskeletal proteins, neurofilaments, and microtubule protein. Slow component b is a complex and heterogeneous rate component, including hundreds of distinct polypeptides ranging from cytoskeletal proteins such as actin (and tubulin in some nerves) to soluble enzymes of intermediary metabolism (such as the glycolytic enzymes). Many characteristics of axonal transport have been described, and these characteristics provide the foundation for our understanding of mechanisms.

Neurofilaments and microtubules move as discrete cytological structures.[71] Recent studies on transport of neurofilament protein indicate that little degradation or metabolism occurs until neurofilaments reach nerve terminals, where they are rapidly degraded. Comparable results have been obtained in studies labeling microtubule protein by radioactivity or fluorescence. Under favorable conditions, movement of individual microtubules can be detected in neurites or growth cones. Both radiolabeling studies and direct observations of individual microtubules indicate that all microtubules and neurofilaments move down the axon, but the motor protein involved is uncertain. Differential metabolism appears to be a key to the targeting of cytoplasmic and cytoskeletal proteins. Proteins with slow degradative rates accumulate and reach higher steady-state concentrations. Alteration of degradation rates changes the steady-state concentration of a protein. Concentration of actin in presynaptic terminals is explained by slower turnover in terminals relative to neurofilament proteins and tubulin, and inhibition of calpain causes neurofilament rings to appear in presynaptic terminals. Differential turnover may be accomplished by specific proteases or posttranslational modifications that affect susceptibility to degradation.

The coherent movement of neurofilaments and microtubule proteins provides strong evidence for the "structural hypothesis." For example, pulse-labeling experiments show that radiolabeled neurofilament proteins move as a bell-shaped wave with little or no trailing of neurofilament protein. This fits with the observed stability of neurofilaments under physiological conditions, which suggests that any soluble pool of neurofilament subunits is negligible. Similarly, the coherent transport of tubulin and MAPs makes sense only if microtubules are moved, because MAPs do not interact with unpolymerized tubulin.

A striking demonstration of microtubule movement can be seen with fluorescent analogs of tubulin.[72,72a] Tubulin labeled with caged fluorescein can be injected into one cell of a fertilized *Xenopus* oocyte at the two-cell stage. Such tubulins are fluorescent only after pho-

→

FIGURE 4.11 Slow axonal transport represents the delivery of cytoskeletal and cytoplasmic constituents to the periphery. Cytoplasmic proteins are synthesized on free polysomes and organized for transport as cytoskeletal elements or macromolecular complexes (1). The microtubules are formed by nucleation at the microtubule-organizing center near the centriolar complex (2) and then released for migration into the axon or dendrites. The molecular mechanisms are not as well understood as those for fast axonal transport, but slow transport appears to be unidirectional with no retrograde component. Recent studies suggest that motors like cytoplasmic dynein may interact with the axonal membrane cytoskeleton to move the microtubules with their plus ends leading (3). Neurofilaments do not appear able to move on their own, but may hitchhike on the microtubules (4). Other cytoplasmic proteins may do the same or they may be moved by other motors. Once cytoplasmic structures reach their destinations, they are degraded by local proteases (5) at a rate that allows either growth (in the case of growth cones) or maintenance of steady-state levels. The different composition and organization of the cytoplasmic elements in dendrites suggest that different pathways may be involved in delivery of cytoskeletal and cytoplasmic materials to the dendrite (6). In addition, some mRNAs are transported into the dendrites, but not into axons.

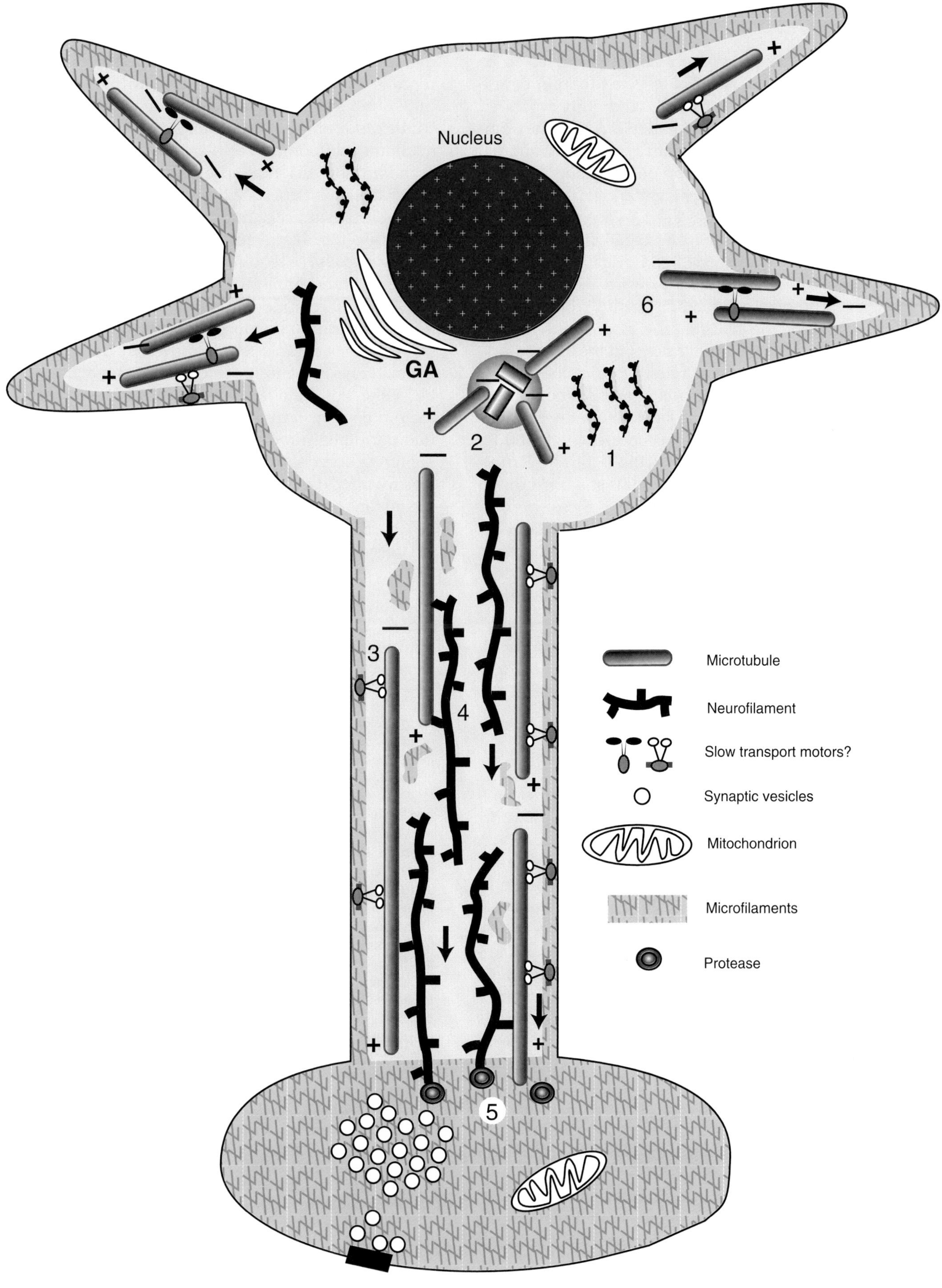

Nucleus
GA
1
2
3
4
5
6
Microtubule
Neurofilament
Slow transport motors?
Synaptic vesicles
Mitochondrion
Microfilaments
Protease

toactivation. The injected oocyte is then allowed to develop into an embryo. The injected tubulin equilibrates with endogenous tubulin and is incorporated into the microtubules of all cells derived from the original injected cell. Because protein synthesis is minimal in early cell divisions of embryonic development, the labeled tubulin is reused by daughter cells until diluted out by newly synthesized tubulin. When early embryonic neurons are cultured, the caged fluorescent tubulin may be photoactivated and visualized.

When local segments of an axon are photoactivated, patches of fluorescent tubulin can be seen to move down the growing neurite. The fluorescent patches remain discrete during movements in the anterograde direction at slow transport rates. Observations of full microtubules can also be made in embryonic *Xenopus* neurons by using rhodamine-labeled tubulin. In favorable areas of axons and growth cones, individual fluorescent microtubules can be visualized. Such microtubules can be seen to move down axons and into growth cones. The forces are sufficient to bend these microtubules in conjunction with growth cone movements. When studies of axonal transport using radiolabels are combined with direct observations of individual microtubules by video microscopy, there is little doubt that microtubules and neurofilaments can and do move in the axon as intact, individual cytoskeletal elements.

Fast Axonal Transport Is the Means by Which Membrane Vesicles and Their Contents Are Rapidly Moved Long Distances within a Neuron

Early biochemical and morphological studies established that the material moving in fast axonal transport was associated with membrane-bound organelles (Fig. 4.12).[2,71] A variety of materials could be shown to move in fast transport. In anterograde transport, materials being moved include membrane-associated enzyme activities, neurotransmitters, and neuropeptides. Many of the materials moving down the axon in anterograde transport are returned in retrograde transport,[73,74] in some cases after modification in the terminal. In addition, a number of exogenous materials taken up in the distal regions of the axon are moved back to the cell body by retrograde transport (Fig. 4.12). Exogenous materials in retrograde transport include neurotrophic factors, such as nerve growth factor, and viral particles invading the nervous system. The uptake of neurotrophic factors may play a critical role in the process of regeneration.

Electron microscopic analysis of materials accumulated at a ligation or crush demonstrated that the organelles moving in the anterograde direction were morphologically distinct from those moving in the retrograde direction.[75,76] Consistent with the ultrastructural differences, radiolabel and immunocytochemical studies indicate that there are both quantitative and qualitative differences between anterograde and retrograde moving material. The differences between anterograde and retrograde transport indicate that some processing or repackaging events must occur as part of turnaround in axonal transport. Turnaround processing appears to require a proteolytic event, because certain protease inhibitors inhibit turnaround without affecting anterograde and retrograde transport.

Biochemical and morphological approaches resulted in considerable progress toward a description of the materials being transported in fast axonal transport but were not suitable for identifying the molecular motors used in translocation. A different technology that permitted direct observation of organelle movements and precise control of experimental conditions was required. Such experiments became possible with the advent of video microscopic techniques.[64]

An early use of video-enhanced contrast (VEC) microscopy was to characterize the bidirectional move-

FIGURE 4.12 Fast axonal transport represents transport of membrane-associated materials, having both anterograde and retrograde components. For anterograde transport, most polypeptides are synthesized on membrane-bound polysomes, also known as rough endoplasmic reticulum (1), and then transferred to the Golgi apparatus for processing and packaging into specific classes of membrane-bound organelles (2). Proteins following this pathway include both integral membrane proteins and secretory polypeptides in the lumen of vesicles. Cytoplasmic peripheral membrane proteins like the kinesins are synthesized on the cytoplasmic or free polysomes. Once vesicles have been assembled and the appropriate motors associate with them, they are moved down the axon at a rate of 100–400 mm per day (3). Different membrane structures are delivered to different compartments and may be regulated independently. For example, dense core vesicles and synaptic vesicles are both targeted for the presynaptic terminal (4), but release of vesicle contents involves distinct pathways. After vesicles merge with the plasma membrane, their protein constituents are taken up by coated pits and vesicles via the receptor-mediated endocytic pathway and delivered to a sorting compartment (5). After proper sorting into appropriate compartments, membrane proteins are either committed to retrograde axonal transport or recycled (6). Retrograde moving organelles are morphologically and biochemically distinct from anterograde vesicles. These larger vesicles have an average velocity about half that of anterograde transport. The retrograde pathway is an important mechanism for delivery of neurotrophic factors to the cell body. Material delivered by retrograde transport typically fuses with cell body compartments to form mature lysosomes (7), where most constituents are recycled. However, neurotrophic factors and neurotrophic viruses can act at the level of the cell body. Although there is evidence that vesicle transport also occurs into dendrites (8), less is known about this process. Dendritic vesicle transport is complicated by the fact that dendritic microtubules may have mixed polarity.

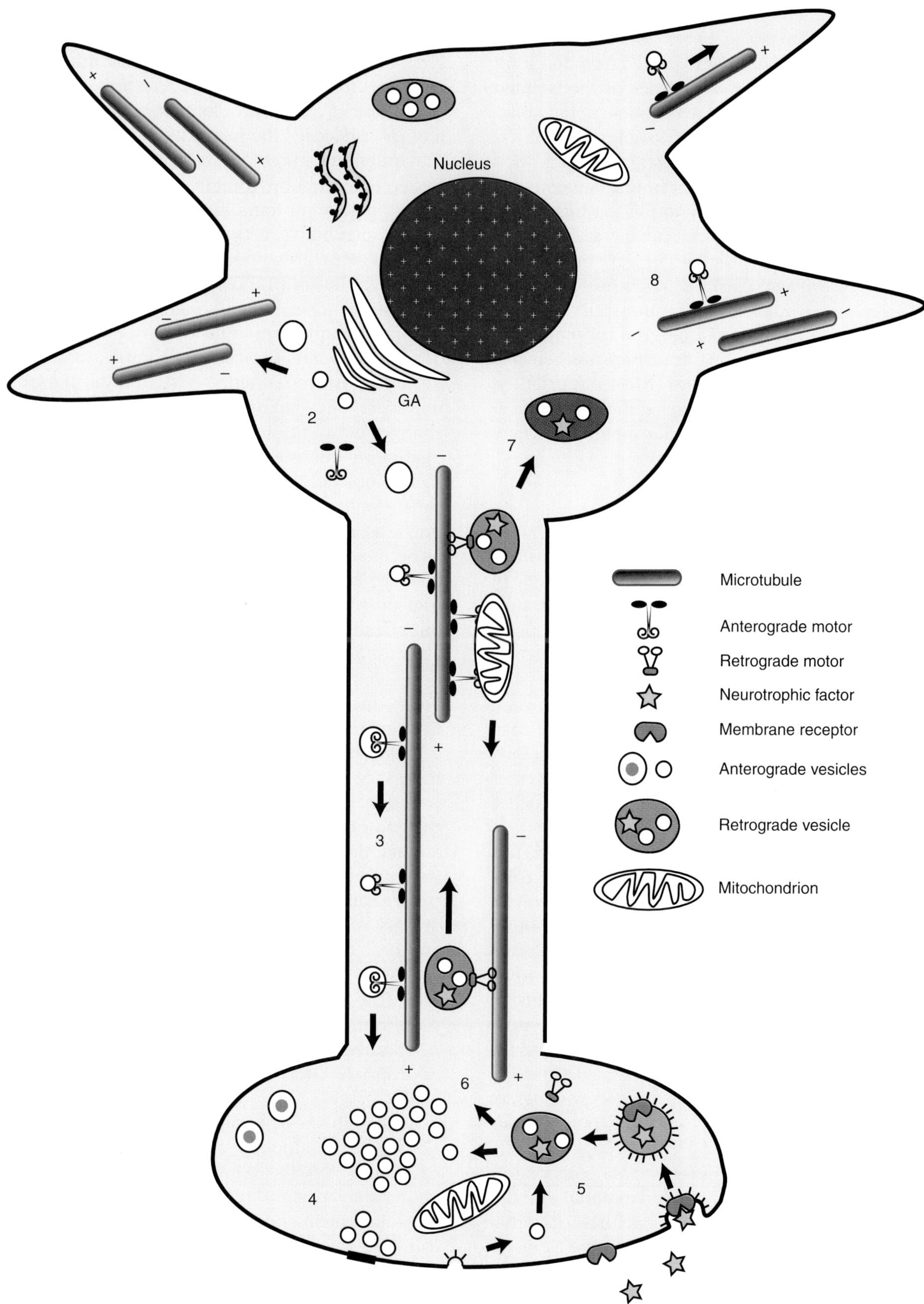
Nucleus
GA
1
2
3
4
5
6
7
8
Microtubule
Anterograde motor
Retrograde motor
Neurotrophic factor
Membrane receptor
Anterograde vesicles
Retrograde vesicle
Mitochondrion

ment of membrane-bound organelles in giant axons from the squid *Loligo pealeii.* Years before, studies had shown that axoplasm could be extruded from the giant axon as an intact cylinder. Properties of the isolated axoplasm had been characterized in some detail, making VEC microscopic analysis of axoplasm a natural choice. Remarkably, fast axonal transport continued unabated in isolated axoplasm for hours. Isolated axoplasm from the giant axon has no plasma membrane or other permeability barriers but can be readily maintained in an active state. Combining VEC microscopy with isolated axoplasm permitted rigorous dissection of the mechanisms for fast axonal transport with the use of biochemical and pharmacological approaches. A number of insights into axonal transport mechanisms have resulted from these studies. Most importantly, studies in isolated axoplasm have led to the identification of several families of molecular motors that may take part in axonal transport.[64,65]

How Is Axonal Transport Regulated?

The diversity of polypeptides in each axonal transport rate component and the coherent movement of proteins having many different molecular weights produce a conundrum. How can so many different polypeptides move down the axon as a group? In theory, one could propose that each protein has a motor of its own. In that case, each rate component might represent movements due to a specific class of motors or to variable affinities for a smaller number of motors. However, the relatively small numbers of motor molecules and the logistical difficulties associated with such a model effectively preclude this possibility.

The structural hypothesis mentioned earlier was formulated in response to the observation that rate components of axonal transport move as discrete waves, each with a characteristic rate and a distinctive composition (Figs. 4.11 and 4.12). The hypothesis is deceptively simple[71]: Axonal transport represents the movement of discrete cytological structures. Proteins in axonal transport do not move as individual polypeptides. Instead, they move as part of a cytological structure or in association with a cytological structure. The only assumption made is that a limited number of elements can interact directly with transport motors, so transported material must be packaged appropriately to be moved. The different rate components result from packaging of transported material into different cytologically identifiable structures. In other words, membrane-associated proteins move as membrane-bound organelles (vesicles, mitochondria, etc.), whereas tubulin and MAPs move as microtubules, and neurofilaments move as neurofilaments.

The structural hypothesis does not require movement of a cross-linked microtubule–neurofilament complex in the form of a solid axoplasmic column. The evidence for existence of a cross-linked complex of microtubules and neurofilaments is not compelling in any case. Instead, the hypothesis specifically predicts that individual microtubules and neurofilaments move rather than tubulin dimers or neurofilament monomers. No assumptions are made about higher-order interactions between cytoskeletal structures or membranous structures. Indeed, one variant of the structural hypothesis proposes that cytoskeletal proteins move in the form of small oligomers rather than polymers, although there is no evidence for the presence of such oligomers *in vivo*. For example, to the limits of detection, neurofilaments exist only as the polymer under *in vivo* conditions. Similarly, tubulin interchanges between dimer and polymer with no known oligomeric intermediate. Because a number of experiments indicate that microtubules and neurofilaments can move *in vivo* as intact polymers, there is no compelling reason to postulate additional oligomeric forms.

Because synthesis of proteins takes place at some distance from many functional domains of a neuron, transport to distal regions of the neuron is necessary, but not sufficient, for proper function. Specific materials must also be delivered to their proper site of utilization and should not be left in inappropriate locations. For example, a synaptic vesicle has no known function in axons or the cell body, so it must be delivered to a presynaptic terminal along with other components necessary for regulated neurotransmitter release. The traditional picture places the presynaptic terminal at the end of an axonal process. Such images imply that a synaptic vesicle need only move along the axonal microtubules until it reaches microtubule ends in the presynaptic terminal. However, many CNS synapses are not at the end of an axon. Numerous terminals are located sequentially along a single axon, making *en passant* contacts with multiple target cells along the way. Targeting of synaptic vesicles then becomes a more complex problem and targeting ion channels or neurotransmitter receptors to nodes of Ranvier or other appropriate sites on the neuronal surface is equally challenging.

Although the specific details of this targeting are not well understood, a simple model for the targeting of synaptic vesicles serves to illustrate how such targeting may occur (Fig. 4.13). Synapsin I[32] is a cytoplasmic protein enriched in presynaptic terminals that can bind reversibly to both actin microfilaments and synaptic vesicles. Both binding activities are regulated by phosphorylation of synapsin, and this phosphorylation is known to be increased during stimulation. If

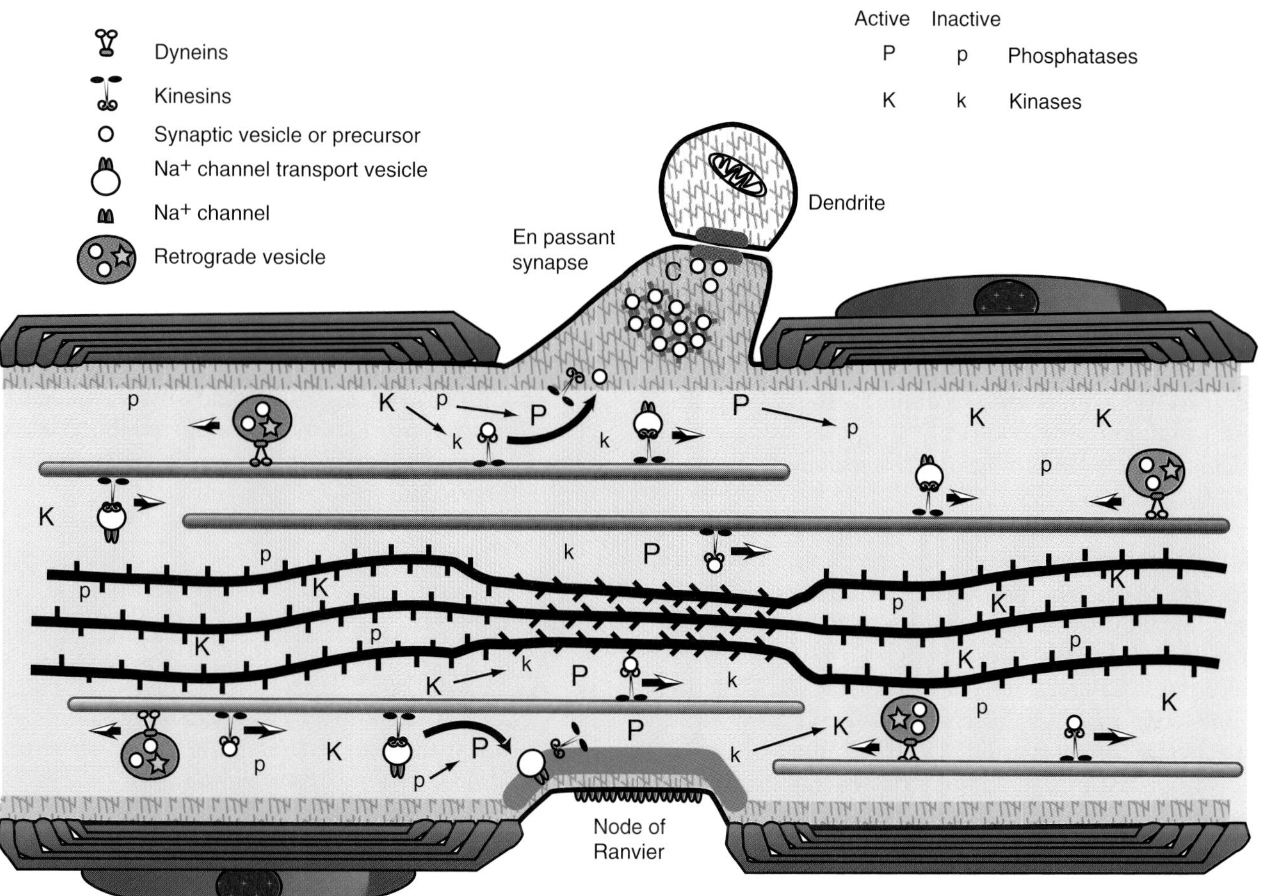

FIGURE 4.13 Axonal dynamics in a myelinated axon from the peripheral nervous system (PNS). Axons are in a constant flux with many concurrent dynamic processes. This diagram illustrates a few of the many dynamic events occurring at a node of Ranvier in a myelinated axon from the PNS. Axonal transport moves cytoskeletal structures, cytoplasmic proteins, and membrane-bound organelles from the cell body toward the periphery (from right to left). At the same time, other vesicles return to the cell body by retrograde transport (retrograde vesicle). Membrane-bound organelles are moved along microtubules by motor proteins such as the kinesins and cytoplasmic dyneins. Each class of organelles must be directed to the correct functional domain of the neuron. Synaptic vesicles must be delivered to a presynaptic terminal to maintain synaptic transmission. In contrast, organelles containing sodium channels must be targeted specifically to nodes of Ranvier for saltatory conduction to occur. Cytoskeletal transport is illustrated by microtubules (rods in the upper half of the axon) and neurofilaments (bundle of ropelike rods in the lower half of the axon) representing the cytoskeleton. They move in the anterograde direction as discrete elements and are degraded in the distal regions. Microtubules and neurofilaments interact with each other transiently during transport, but their distribution in axonal cross sections suggest that they are not stably cross-linked. In axonal segments without compact myelin, such as the node of Ranvier or following focal demyelination, a net dephosphorylation of neurofilament side arms allows the neurofilaments to pack more densely. Myelination is thought to alter the balance between kinase (K indicates an active kinase; k is an inactive kinase) and phosphatase (P indicates an active phophatase; p is an inactive phosphatase) activity in the axon. Most kinases and phosphatases have multiple substrates, suggesting a mechanism for targeting vesicle proteins to specific axonal domains. Local changes in the phosphorylation of axonal proteins may alter binding properties of proteins. The action of synapsin I in squid axoplasm suggests that dephosphorylated synapsin cross-links synaptic vesicles to microfilaments. When a synaptic vesicle encounters the dephosphorylated synapsin and actin-rich matrix of a presynaptic terminal, the vesicle is trapped at the terminal by inhibition of further axonal transport, effectively targeting the synaptic vesicle to a presynaptic terminal. Similarly, a sodium channel-binding protein may be present at nodes of Ranvier in a high-affinity state (i.e., dephosphorylated). Transport vesicles for nodal sodium channels (Na channel vesicle) would be captured upon encountering this domain, effectively targeting sodium channels to the nodal membrane. Interactions between cells could in this manner establish the functional architecture of the neuron.

nonphosphorylated synapsin were present at the border between the axon and the presynaptic terminal, then a fraction of the synaptic vesicles (or their precursors) traveling down the axon in fast axonal transport would be bound and cross-linked to the actin cytoskeleton that is enriched in the presynaptic terminal. These bound synaptic vesicles would become part of the reserve pool in the terminal at some distance from active zones. As the terminal was stimulated, local calmodulin-activated kinases would phosphorylate synapsin and allow these reserve synaptic vesicles to be mobilized. Consistent with this model, dephosphorylated synapsin has been shown to inhibit fast axonal transport when introduced directly into the axoplasm at concentrations comparable to those seen in the presynaptic terminal.

Although such a model is speculative at present, it does satisfy several criteria that any mechanism for targeting to specific neuronal subdomains must address. Specifically, the mechanism must be local, because distances to the cell body can be quite large. There must be some means to connect the targeting signal to an external microenvironment, such as an appropriate target cell. Finally, there must be a way of distinguishing subdomains so that synaptic vesicles are not delivered to nodes of Ranvier and voltage-gated sodium channels are not all targeted to the presynaptic terminal. The careful segregation of different organelles and polypeptides to different regions within a neuron suggests that highly efficient targeting mechanisms do exist.

Summary

A well-studied feature of the neuron is the phenomenon of axonal transport, which has been described in both the anterograde and the retrograde directions. The axonal transport system is responsible for delivery of materials from the cell body to distant parts of the neuron, for membrane retrieval and circulation, and for uptake of materials from presynaptic terminals and dendrites and their delivery to the cell soma. The precise molecular mechanisms by which anterograde and retrograde transport can be targeted within an individual dendrite and/or axon are not understood at present.

Neurons and glial cells may have unusually large cell volumes enclosed within extensive plasma membrane surfaces. Nature has evolved a number of "universal" mechanisms in other systems and adapted them for the special needs of nervous tissue cells. The synthesis and delivery of components, and in particular proteins, to cytoplasmic organelles and cell surface subdomains engage general and evolutionarily conserved molecular mechanisms and pathways that are employed in single-cell yeasts as well as in the cells in complex nervous tissue.

Once synthesized and sorted, most intracellular organelles (vesicles destined for axonal or dendritic domains, mitochondria, cytoskeletal components) must be distributed, and *targeted,* to precise intracellular locations. Neurons and glial cells, because they are so extended in space, have adapted and developed to a high degree common mechanisms that operate to distribute components within all cells. In the neuron, movement of materials within the axon has been the central focus of most studies. The phenomenon of axoplasmic flow or transport is now in some measure understood at the molecular level.

References

1. Peters, A., Palay, S. L., and Webster, H. D. (1991). *The Fine Structure of the Nervous System: Neurons and Their Supporting Cells,* 3rd ed. Oxford University Press, New York.
2. Lasek, R. J., and Brady, S. T. (1982). The Axon: A prototype for studying expressional cytoplasm. In *Organization of the Cytoplasm,* pp. 113–124. Cold Spring Harbor Lab. Press, Cold Spring Harbor, NY.

2a. Steward, O. 1995. Targeting of mRNAs to subsynaptic microdomains in dendrites. [Review]. *Curr. Opin. Neurobiol.* **5:** 55–61.

3. Blobel, G. (1980). Intracellular protein topogenesis. *Proc. Natl. Acad. Sci. U.S.A.* **77:** 1496.
4. Sabatini, D. D., Kreibich, G., Morimoto, T., and Adesnik, M. (1982). Mechanisms for the incorporation of proteins into membranes and organelles. *J. Cell Biol.* **92:** 1.
5. Palade, G. E. (1975). Intracellular aspects of the process of protein synthesis. *Science* **189:** 347–358.
6. Jamieson, J. D., and Palade, G. E. (1967). Intracellular transport of secretory proteins in the pancreatic exocrine cell. I. Role of the peripheral elements of the Golgi complex. *J. Cell Biol.* **34:** 577.
7. Jamieson, J. D., and Palade, G. E. (1967). Intracellular transport of secretory proteins in the pancreatic exocrine cell. II. Transport to condensing vacuoles and zymogen granules. *J. Cell Biol.* **34:** 597.
8. Droz, B., and Leblond, C. P. (1963). Axonal migration of proteins in the central nervous system and peripheral nerves as shown by radioautography. *J. Comp. Neurol.* **121:** 325–346.
9. Blobel, G., and Dobberstein, B. (1975). Transfer of proteins across membranes. *J. Cell Biol.* **67:** 835–851.
10. Rothman, J. E., and Lodish, H. F. (1977). Synchronised transmembrane insertion and glycosylation of a nascent membrane protein. *Nature* (*London*) **269:** 775–780.
11. Walter, P., and Blobel, G. (1981). Translocation of proteins across the endoplasmic reticulum: III. Signal recognition protein causes signal sequence-dependent and site-specific arrest of chain elongation that is released by microsomal membranes. *J. Cell Biol.* **91:** 557–561.
12. Walter, P., and Johnson, A. E. (1994). Signal sequence recognition and protein targeting to the endoplasmic-reticulum membrane. *Annu. Rev. Cell Biol.* **10:** 87–119.
13. Gilmore, R., Blobel, G., and Walter, P. (1982). Protein transloca-

C H A P T E R

5

Electrotonic Properties of Axons and Dendrites

Gordon M. Shepherd

We have seen, in Chapter 3, that most neurons are characterized by elaborate dendritic trees and by single axons having complex branching patterns. With this structural apparatus, neurons carry out five basic functions (Fig. 5.1):

1. Reception of synaptic inputs (mostly in dendrites; to some extent in cell bodies; in some cases in axon terminals)
2. Generation of intrinsic activity at any given site on the neuron through voltage-dependent membrane properties and internal second-messenger mechanisms
3. Integration of synaptic responses with intrinsic membrane activity
4. Generation of patterns of impulse discharges in axon, cell body, and dendrites, encoding outputs from the cell
5. Distribution of synaptic outputs (mostly from axon arborizations; in some cases from cell bodies and dendrites).

In addition to specific interactions through synaptic inputs and outputs, neurons may receive and send nonsynaptic signals through chemical messengers (e.g., hormones) and electrical fields.

A fundamental goal of neuroscience is to develop quantitative descriptions of how each region of the neuron mediates its operations and how these operations are coordinated within the neuron so that it can function as an integrated information-processing unit. Such quantitative description is the necessary basis for understanding the functional organization of the neuron. It is also the basis for constructing realistic models to test hypotheses and simulate the roles of neurons, neural systems, and networks in information processing and behavior.

This chapter deals mainly with the spread of activity within and between neuronal regions. Subsequent chapters will focus on specific properties—membrane receptors, internal receptors, synaptically gated membrane channels, intrinsic voltage-gated channels, and second-messenger systems—that mediate the neuron's operations. Slow spread of activity is by diffusion or active transport; rapid spread is by electric current. Many factors determine this rapid spread at any given point in a neuron; the most basic are the passive **electrotonic** properties.

The origins of our understanding of electrotonic properties were succinctly described by Wilfrid Rall,[1] whose brief account (adapted in Box 5.1)[2–16] highlights the interesting fact that our understanding of electrotonus has arisen from a merging of the study of the flow of current in nerve cells and muscle with the development of cable theory for transmission through electrical cables on the ocean floor. As mentioned in Box 5.1, electrotonic theory was first applied mathematically to the nervous system in the late 19th century for the simplest case of spread of electric current through a single nerve fiber. By the 1930s and 1940s, it was applied to simple invertebrate (crab and squid) axons—the first steps toward the development of the Hodgkin–Huxley equations for the impulse in the axon. The analytical approach is impractical for the complexity of dendritic systems, but the development of computational compartmental models by Rall,[17–21] beginning in the 1960s, opened the way to **compartmental models.** Together with the analytical methods, these models have provided a sound basis for a theory of dendritic function.[21,22] A variety of software packages now make it possible for even a beginning student to explore functional properties and construct realistic neuron models.[23–26] We therefore present modern elec-

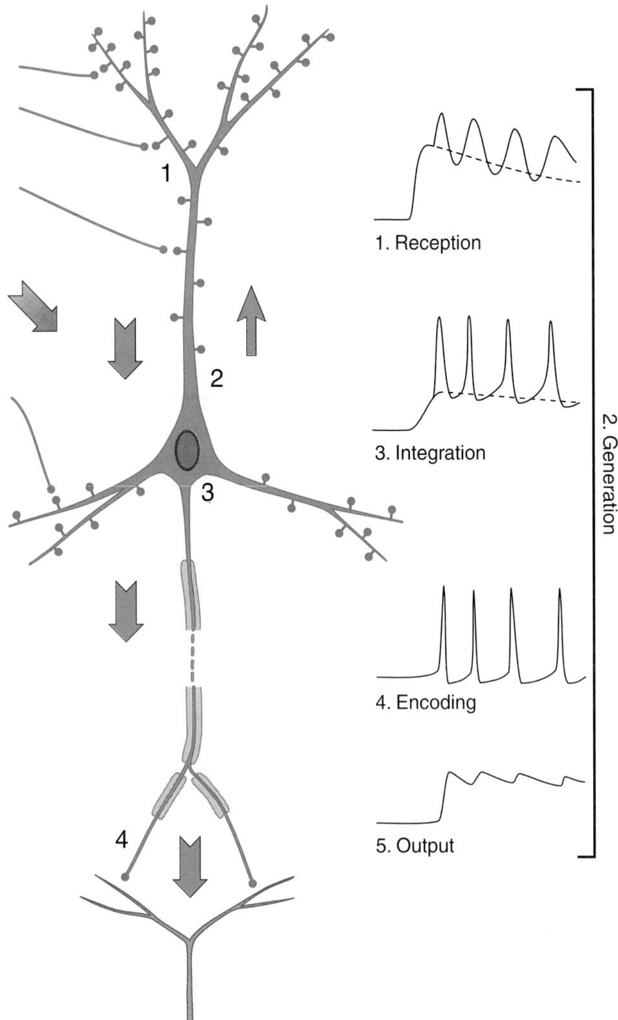

FIGURE 5.1 Nerve cells have four main regions and five main functions. Electrotonic potential spread is fundamental for coordinating the regions and their functions.

trotonic theory within the context of constructing these compartmental models.

SPREAD OF STEADY-STATE SIGNALS

Modern Electrotonic Theory Depends on Simplifying Assumptions

The successful application of cable theory to nerve cells requires that it be based as closely as possible on the structural and functional properties of neuronal processes. The problem confronting the neuroscientist is that most of these processes are quite complicated. As discussed in Chapter 4, a segment of axon or dendrite may be filled with various organelles, bounded by a plasma membrane with its own complex structure and irregular outline (Fig. 5.2A), and surrounded by myriad neighboring processes. Constructing a model of the spread of electric current through a segment of the neuron therefore requires some carefully chosen simplifying assumptions. These assumptions allow the construction of an **equivalent circuit** of the electrical properties of such a segment. The critical assumptions are as follows[1,22,27,28]:

1. *Segments are cylinders.* A segment is assumed to be a cylinder with constant radius. This is the simplest assumption; however, compartmental simulations can readily incorporate different geometrical shapes with differing radii if needed (Fig. 5.2B).
2. *The electrotonic potential is due to a change in the membrane potential.* At any instant of time, the "resting" membrane potential (E_r) at any point on the neuron can be changed by several means: injection of current into the cell, extracellular stimulation that causes current to cross the membrane, and a change in membrane conductance (caused by a driving force different from that responsible for the membrane potential). Electric current then begins to flow between that point and the rest of the neuron, in accord with the equation

$$V = V_m - E_r,$$

where V is the electrotonic potential and V_m is the changed membrane potential. Modern neurobiologists recognize that the membrane potential is rarely at rest. In practice, "resting" potential means the membrane potential at any given instant of time other than during an action potential or rapid synaptic potential.
3. *Electrotonic current is ohmic.* All passive electrotonic current flow is assumed to be ohmic—that is, in accord with the simple linear equation

$$E = IR,$$

where E is the potential, I is the current, and R is the resistance. This relation is largely inferred from macroscopic measurements of the conductance of solutions having the composition of the intracellular medium, but is rarely measured directly for a given nerve process. Also largely untested is the likelihood that at the smallest dimensions (0.1-μm diameter or less), the processes and their internal organelles may acquire submicroscopic electrochemical properties that deviate significantly from macroscopic fluid conductance values; compartmental models permit the incorporation of estimates of these properties.

BOX 5.1

THE ORIGINS OF ELECTROTONUS

The mathematical treatment of axonal electrotonus began in the 1870s with the work of Hermann,[2,3] supported by Weber's[4] mathematical analysis of the external field in the surrounding volume conductor. Hermann recognized the mathematical analogy of this problem with the problems in heat conduction, but the analogy with Kelvin's treatment of the submarine telegraph cable in the 1850s[5,6] was first recognized by Hoorweg in 1898.[7] This cable analogy was developed independently by Cremer[8,9] and by Hermann[10] early in the 20th century and has been widely used since that time. These mathematical analogies are important because of the extensive literature devoted to both general mathematical methods and special solutions applicable to problems of this kind.[11] Important papers on the steady-state distributions of axonal electrotonus are those of Rushton[12,13] and of Cole and Hodgkin,[14] published in the 1920s and 1930s. The two most useful mathematical presentations of axonal electrotonus (including consideration of transients) are those provided by Hodgkin and Rushton[15] and by Davis and Lorente de No[16] in the 1940s. (From Rall, 1958[1])

Wilfrid Rall

4. *In the steady state, membrane capacitance is ignored.* The simplest case of electrotonic spread assumes spread from the point of a **steady-state change** (due to injected current, a change in synaptic conductance, or a change in voltage-gated conductance), so that time-varying properties due to the capacitance of the membrane can be ignored (Fig. 5.2C).

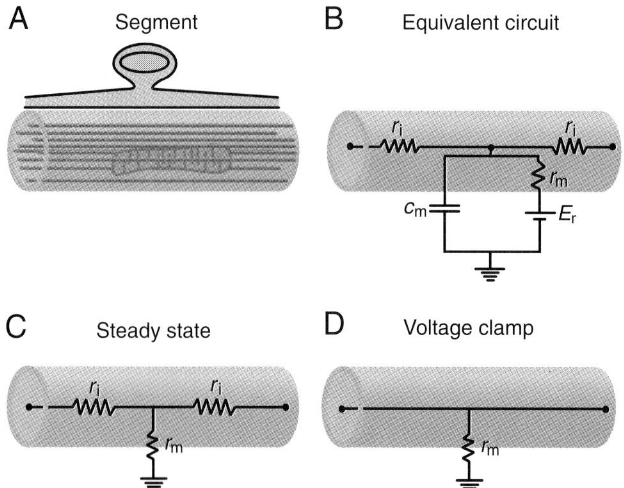

FIGURE 5.2 Construction of a compartmental model of the passive electrical properties of a nerve-cell process begins with (A) identification of a segment of the process and its organelles followed by (B) abstraction of an equivalent electrical circuit based on the membrane capacitance (c_m), membrane resistance (r_m), resting membrane potential (E_r), and internal resistance (r_i); (C) abstraction of the circuit for steady-state electrotonus, in which c_m and E_r can be ignored. (D) The space clamp used in voltage-clamp analysis reduces the equivalent circuit even further to only the membrane resistance (r_m), usually depicted as the membrane conductances (g) for different ions. In a compartmental modeling program, the equivalent circuit parameters are scaled to the size of each segment.

5. *The resting membrane potential can usually be ignored.* In the simplest case, we consider the spread of electrotonic potential (V) relative to a uniform resting potential (E_r), so that the value of the resting potential can be ignored. Where the resting membrane potential may vary spatially, V must be defined for each segment as $V_m - E_r$.
6. *Electrotonic current divides between internal and membrane resistances.* In the steady state, at any point on a process, current divides into two local resistance paths: further within the process through an internal (axial) resistance (r_i) or across the membrane through a membrane resistance (r_m) (see Fig. 5.2C).
7. *Axial current is inversely proportional to diameter.* Within the volume of the process, current is assumed to be distributed equally (the resistance across the process, in the Y and Z axes, is essentially zero). Because resistances in parallel sum to decrease the overall resistance, axial current (I) is inversely proportional to cross-sectional area ($I \propto 1/A \propto 1/\pi r^2$); thus, a thicker process has a lower overall axial resistance than does a thinner process. Because the axial resistance (r_i) is assumed to be uniform throughout the process, the total cross-sectional axial resistance of a segment is represented by a single resistance,

$$r_i = \frac{R_i}{A},$$

where r_i is the internal resistance per unit length of cylinder (in ohms per centimeter of axial length), R_i is the specific internal resistance (in ohms centimeter, or Ω cm), and A (= πr^2) is the cross-sectional area. The internal structure of a process may contain membranous or filamentous organelles that can raise the effective internal resistance or provide high-conductance submicroscopic pathways that can lower it. In voltage-clamp experiments, the space clamp eliminates current through r_i, so that the only current remaining is through r_m, thereby permitting isolation and analysis of different ionic membrane conductances (Fig. 5.2D).

8. *Membrane current is inversely proportional to membrane surface area.* For a unit length of cylinder, the membrane current (i_m) and the membrane resistance (r_m) are assumed to be uniform over the entire surface. Thus, by the same rule of the summing of parallel resistances, the membrane current is inversely proportional to the membrane area of the segment, so that a thicker process has a lower overall membrane resistance. Thus,

$$r_m = \frac{R_m}{c},$$

where r_m is the membrane resistance for unit length of cylinder (in Ω cm of axial length), R_m is the specific membrane resistance (in Ω cm^2), and c (= $2\pi r$) is the circumference. For a segment, the entire membrane resistance is regarded as concentrated at one point; that is, there is no axial current flow within a segment but only between segments (see Fig. 5.2C).

Modern compartmental simulations recognize that membrane current passes through ion channels in the membrane and that the density and types of these channels vary in different processes and indeed may vary locally in different segments and branches. These differences are readily incorporated into compartmental representations of the processes.

9. *The external medium along the process is assumed to have zero resistivity.* In contrast with the internal axial resistivity (r_i), which is relatively high because of the small dimensions of most nerve processes, the external medium has a relatively low resistivity for current because of its large volume. For this reason, the resistivity of the paths either along a process or to ground is regarded as negligible, and the potential outside the membrane is assumed to be everywhere equivalent to ground (see Fig. 5.2C). This greatly simplifies the equations that describe the spread of electrotonic potentials inside and along the membrane.

Modern compartmental models can simulate any arbitrary distribution of properties, including significant values for extracellular resistance. Particular cases in which external resistivity may be very large, such as the special membrane caps around synapses on the cell body or axon hillock of a neuron, can be addressed by suitable representation in the simulations. However, for most simulations, the assumption of negligible external resistance is a useful simplifying first approximation.

10. *Driving forces on membrane conductances are assumed to be constant.* It is usually assumed that ion concentrations across the membrane are constant during activity. However, changes in ion concentrations with activity may occur, particularly in constricted extracellular or intracellular compartments; these changes may cause deviations from the assumptions of constant driving forces for the membrane currents, as well as the assumption of uniform E_r. For example, accumulations of extracellular K^+ may change local E_r,[29] and intracellular accumulations of ions within the tiny volumes of spine heads may change the driving force on synaptic currents.[30] These special properties are easily included in most compartmental models.

11. *Cables have different boundary conditions.* In classical cable theory, a cable such as one used for long-distance telecommunication is very long and can be considered of infinite length (one customarily assumes a semi-infinite cable with $V = 0$ at $x = 0$ and only positive values of length x). This assumption carries over to the application of cable theory to long axons, but most dendrites are relatively short. This imposes **boundary conditions** on the solutions of the cable equations, and these boundary conditions have very important effects on electrotonic spread. In highly branched dendritic trees, they are difficult to deal with analytically but are readily represented in compartmental models.

In summary, even the simplest representation of the passive spread of electrotonic potential during a steady-state input to a neuron requires a number of specific assumptions. We will see that an understanding of these assumptions is critical to describing electrotonic spread under the different conditions that the nervous system presents.

Electrotonic Spread Depends on the Characteristic Length (λ)

Let us first consider the spread of electrotonic potential under steady-state conditions. Using the preceding assumptions, we represent a segment of a process as an internal resistance r_i connected both to the r_i of the next segment and through the membrane resistance r_m to ground (see Fig. 5.2C). In standard cable theory, the steady-state spread of electrotonic potential along this process is described by

$$V = \frac{r_m}{r_i} \cdot \frac{d^2V}{dx^2}. \tag{5.1}$$

This equation states that if there is a steady-state current input at point $x = 0$, the electrotonic potential (V) spreading along the cable is proportional to the second derivative of the potential (d^2V) with respect to distance and the ratio of the membrane resistance (r_m) to the internal resistance (r_i) over that distance. A solution of this equation for a cable of infinite extension for positive values of x gives

$$V = V_0 e^{-x/\lambda}, \tag{5.2}$$

where lambda (λ) is defined as the square root of r_m/r_i (in centimeters) and V_0 is the value of V at $x = 0$.

Inspection of this equation shows that when $x = \lambda$, the ratio of V to the V_0 is $e^{-1} = 1/e = 0.37$. Thus, λ is a critical parameter defining the length over which the electrotonic potential spreading along an infinite cable with given values for internal and membrane resistance decays (is attenuated) to a value of 0.37 of the value at the site of the input. It is accordingly referred to as the **characteristic length** (space constant, or length constant) of the cable. The higher the value of the specific membrane resistance (R_m), the higher the value of r_m for that segment, the larger the value for λ, and the greater the spread (the less the attenuation) of electrotonic potential through that segment (Fig. 5.3). Specific membrane resistance (R_m) is thus an important variable in determining the spread of activity in a neuron. Most of the passive electrotonic current may be carried by K^+ "leak" channels, which are open at "rest" and are largely responsible for holding the cell at its resting potential. However, as mentioned earlier, many cells or regions within a cell are seldom at "rest" but are constantly active, in which case electrotonic current is carried by a variety of open channels. Thus, the effective R_m can vary from values of less than 1000 Ω cm^2 to more than 100,000 Ω cm^2 in different neurons and in different parts of a neuron. Note that λ varies with the square root of R_m, and so a 100-fold difference in R_m translates into only a 10-fold difference in λ.

Conversely, the higher the value of the specific internal resistance (R_i), the higher the value of r_i for that segment, the smaller the value of λ, and the less the spread of electrotonic potential through that segment (see Fig. 5.3). Traditionally, the value of R_i has been believed to be in the range of approximately 50–100 Ω cm based on muscle cells and the squid axon. In mammalian neurons, estimates now tend toward a

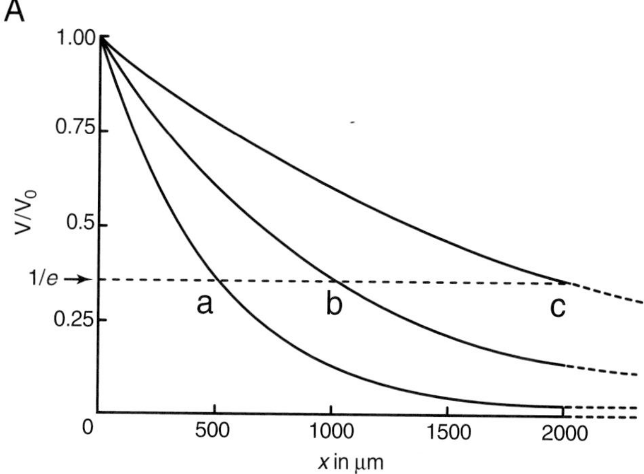

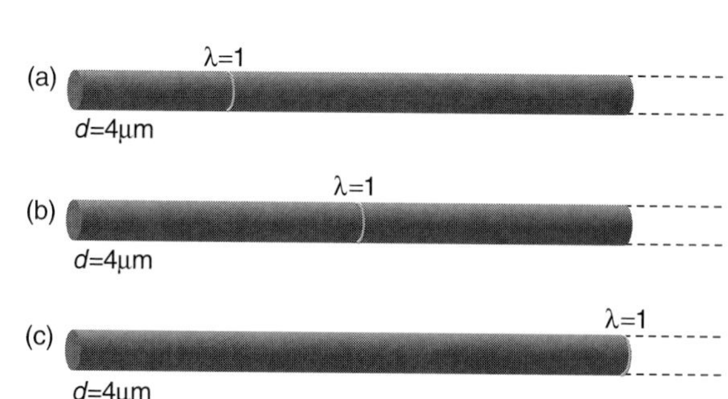

FIGURE 5.3 The space constant governing the spread of electrotonic potential through a nerve-cell process depends on the square root of the ratio between the specific membrane resistance (R_m) and the specific internal resistance (R_i). (A) Potential profiles for processes with three different values of λ. (B) Dotted lines represent the location of λ on each of the three processes.

value of 200 Ω cm. This limited range may suggest that R_i is less important than R_m in controlling passive current spread in a neuron. The square-root relation further reduces the sensitivity of λ to R_i. However, as noted in assumption 7 in the preceding section, the membranous and filamentous organelles in the cytoplasm may alter the effective R_i. The presence of these organelles in very thin processes, such as distal dendritic branches, spine stems, and axon preterminals, may thus have potentially significant effects on the spread of electrotonic current through them. Furthermore, the relative significance of R_i and R_m greatly depends on the length of a given process, as will be seen shortly.

Electrotonic Spread Depends on the Diameter of a Process

The space constant (λ) depends not only on the internal and membrane resistance, but also on the diameter of a process. Thus, from the relations between r_m and R_m, and r_i and R_i, discussed in the preceding section,

$$\lambda = \sqrt{\frac{r_m}{r_i}} = \sqrt{\frac{R_m}{R_i} \cdot \frac{d}{4}}. \quad (5.3)$$

Neuronal processes vary widely in diameter. In the mammalian nervous system, the thinnest processes are the distal branches of dendrites, the necks of some dendritic spines, and the cilia of some sensory cells; these processes may have diameters of only 0.1 μm or less (the thinnest processes in the nervous system are approximately 0.02 μm). In contrast, the largest processes in the mammal are the largest myelinated axons and the largest dendritic trunks, which may be from 20 to 25 μm. This means that the range of diameters is approximately three orders of magnitude. Note, again, that the relation to λ is the square root; thus, over a 10-fold difference in diameter, the difference in λ is only about 3-fold (Fig. 5.4).

Electrotonic Properties Must Be Assessed in Relation to the Lengths of Neuronal Processes

As noted earlier, application of classical cable theory to neuronal processes assumes that the processes are

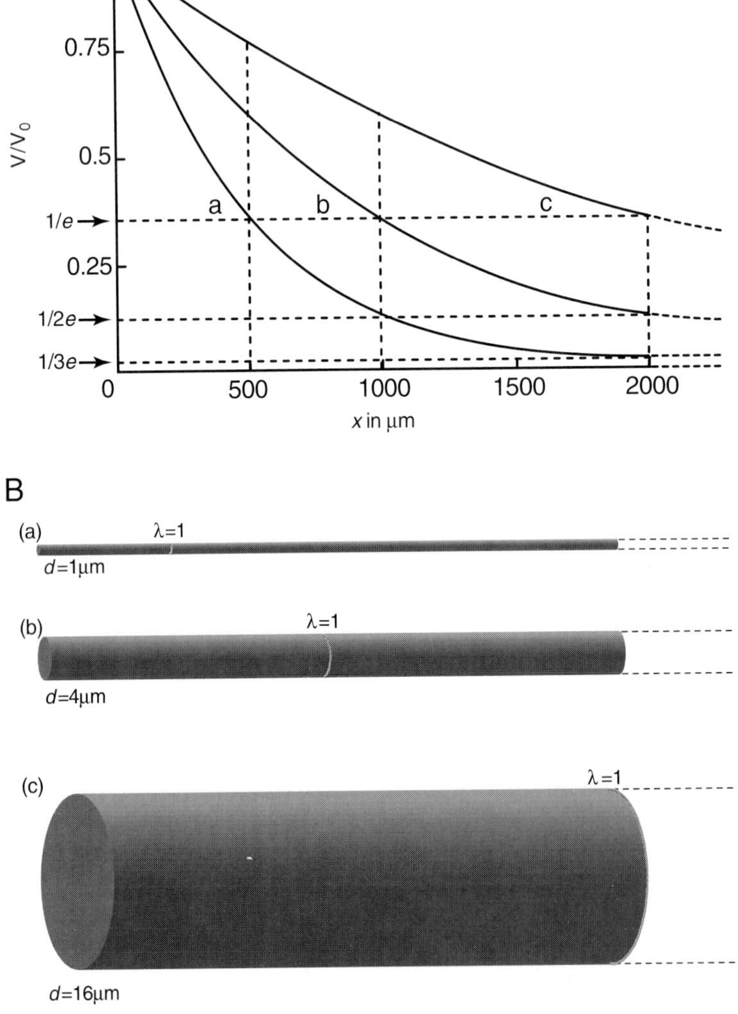

FIGURE 5.4 The space constant governing the spread of electrotonic potential through a nerve-cell process also depends on the square root of the diameter of the process. (A) Potential profiles for processes with three different diameters but fixed values of R_i and R_m. (B) The three axon profiles in (A). Note that to double λ, the diameter must be quadrupled.

infinitely long. However, because neuronal processes have finite lengths, the length of a given process must be compared with λ to assess the extent to which λ accurately describes the actual electrotonic spread in that process. For example, one of the largest processes in any nervous system, the squid giant axon, has a diameter of approximately 1 mm. For this axon, R_m has been estimated as 600 Ω cm^2 (a very low value compared to most values of R_m in mammals), and R_i is approximately 80 Ω cm, the value of Ringer solution (note that the very large diameter is counterbalanced by the very low R_m). Putting these values into Eq. (5.3) gives a λ of approximately 4.5 mm. The real length of the giant axon is several centimeters; to relate real length to characteristic length, we define **electrotonic length**[1,20,27] as

$$L = x/\lambda. \tag{5.4}$$

Thus, if x = 30 mm, then L = 30 mm/4.5 mm = 7; that is, the real length of the giant axon is seven characteristic lengths. However, by only three characteristic lengths, the electrotonic potential decays to only a small percentage of the original value (see Fig. 5.4); so for this case the assumption of an infinite length is justified. A reason often given for why the nervous system needs impulses is that impulses enable it to overcome the severe attenuation of passively spreading potentials that occurs over the considerable lengths required for transmission of signals by axons.

The relative importance of R_i and R_m in controlling current spread depends on the length of a segment relative to its characteristic length λ. Consider, for example, a neuronal process (large axon or dendrite) 10 μm in diameter, with R_i = 100 Ω cm and R_m = 10,000 Ω cm^2.[22] By the preceding definitions, the longitudinal resistance r_i per unit length (1 cm) would equal 130 MΩ, whereas the membrane resistance r_m would be only 3 MΩ. Thus, the relatively low specific internal resistance has a relatively large effect over the unit distance (1 cm) because of the small diameter of the nerve process. Such a process would have a characteristic length of 1500 μm, where, by definition, $r_m = r_i$, and the current would be equally divided between the two. At shorter distances, more current tends to flow through r_i as the membrane area is reduced (and r_m thereby increases); this becomes an important factor in shaping current flow through small dendritic branches and dendritic spines (as will be seen shortly and in Chap. 13).

Summary

Passive spread of electrical potential along the cell membrane underlies all types of electrical signaling in the neuron. It is thus the foundation for understanding how the diverse functions of the neuron are coordinated within the neuron, so that the neuron can generate, receive, encode, and send signals in interacting with its neighboring neurons and glial cells.

Electrotonic spread shares properties with electrical transmission through electrical cables; the study of cable transmission for over a century has put these properties on a sound quantitative basis. The theoretical basis for extension of cable theory to complex dendritic trees has been developed in parallel with compartmental modeling methods for simulating dendritic signal processing.

Steady-state electrotonus in dendrites depends on passive resistance, branch diameter, and impedance matching at branch points. Local electrotonic currents underlie the continuous spread of the impulse in unmyelinated axons and the discontinuous spread from node to node in myelinated axons. In dendrites, synaptic potentials are delayed and attenuated by passive membrane properties, exquisitely dependent on the electrotonic properties.

SPREAD OF TRANSIENT SIGNALS

Electrotonic Spread of Transient Signals Depends on Membrane Capacitance

Until now, we have considered only the passive spread of steady-state inputs. However, the essence of many neural signals is that they change rapidly. Fast impulses characteristically last from 1 to 5 ms, and fast synaptic potentials last from 5 to 30 ms. How do the electrotonic properties affect spread of these rapid signals?

Rapid signal spread depends not only on all of the factors discussed thus far, but also on the membrane capacitance (c_m), which is due to the lipid moiety of the plasma membrane. Classically, the value of the specific membrane capacitance (C_m) has been 1 microfarad per square centimeter (1 μF cm^{-2}). However, a value of 0.6–0.75 μF cm^{-2} is now preferred for the lipid moiety itself, the remainder being due to gating charges on membrane proteins.[22]

The simplest case demonstrating the effect of the membrane capacitance on transient signals is that of a cell body with no processes (a very unrealistic assumption, but a simple starting point). In the equivalent electrical circuit for a neural process, the membrane capacitance is placed in parallel with the ohmic components of the membrane conductance and the driving potentials for ion flows through those conductances (see Fig. 5.2B). Again neglecting the resting membrane potential, we take as an example the injection of a current step into a soma; in this case, the time course of the current spread to ground is described by the sum of the capacitative and resistive current (plus the input current, I_{pulse}):

$$C\frac{dV_{\text{m}}}{\text{dt}} + \frac{V_{\text{m}}}{R} = I_{\text{pulse}}. \tag{5.5}$$

By rearrangement,

$$RC\frac{dV_{\text{m}}}{dt} + V_{\text{m}} = I_{\text{pulse}} \cdot \text{R}, \tag{5.6}$$

where $RC = \tau$ (τ is the **time constant** of the membrane).

A solution of this equation is

$$V_{\text{m}}(T) = I_{\text{pulse}}R(1 - e^{-T}), \tag{5.7}$$

where $T = t/\tau$. This gives the initial response of the membrane to an injected current (I) pulse. When the pulse is terminated, the decay of the initial potential (V_0) to rest is given by

$$V_{\text{m}}(T) = V_0 e^{-T}. \tag{5.8}$$

These "on" and "off" transients are shown in Fig. 5.5. The significance of τ is shown in the diagram; it is the time required for the voltage change across the membrane to reach $1/e = 0.37$ of its final value. This time constant of the membrane defines the transient voltage response of a patch of membrane to a current step in terms of the electrotonic properties of the patch, analogous to the way that the length constant defines the spread of voltage change over distance in terms of the electrotonic properties of a segment.

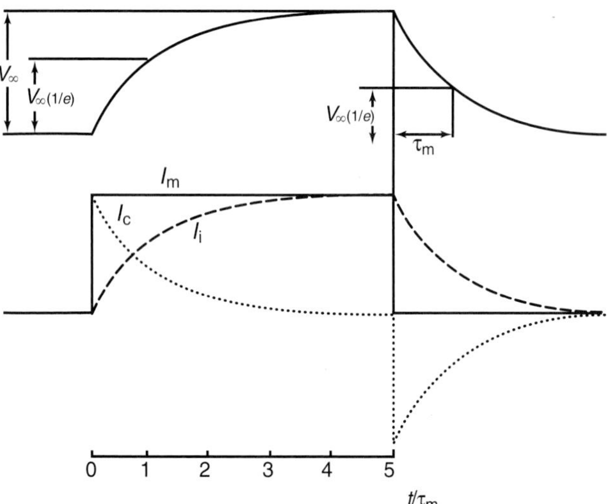

FIGURE 5.5 The equivalent circuit of a single isolated compartment responds to an injected current step by charging and discharging along a time course determined by the time constant τ. In actuality, nerve-cell segments are parts of longer processes (axonal or dendritic) or larger branching trees, so the actual time courses of charging or discharging are modified. Abbreviations: V_∞, steady-state voltage; I_{m}, injected current applied to membrane; I_{c}, current through the capacitance; I_{i}, current through the ionic leak conductance; τ_{m}, membrane time constant.

A Two-Compartment Model Defines the Basic Properties of Signal Spread

These spatial and temporal cable properties can be combined in a two-compartment model[31] that will apply to the generation and spread of any arbitrary transient signal (Fig. 5.6).

In the simplest case, current is injected into one of the compartments. For a positive current pulse, the positive charge injected into compartment A attempts to flow outward across the membrane, partially opposing the negative charge on the inside of the lipid membrane (this is the charge responsible for the negative resting potential), thereby depolarizing the membrane capacitance (C_{m}) at that site. At the same time, the charge begins to flow across the membrane through the resistance of the ionic membrane channels (R_{m}) that are open at that site. The proportion of charge divided between C_{m} and R_{m} determines the rate of charge of the membrane—that is, the membrane time constant, τ. However, charge also starts to flow through the internal resistance (R_{i}) into compartment B, where the same events take place. The charging (and discharging) transient in compartment A departs from the time constant of a single isolated compartment and is faster because of the impedance load (e.g., current sink) of the rest of the cable (represented by compartment B). Thus, the time constant of the system no longer describes the charging transient, which is faster because of the conductance load of one compartment on another (note that this is analogous to the way that the conductance load makes the electrotonic potential more attenuated than the space constant). The system is entirely passive and invariant; the response to a second current pulse sums linearly with that of the first.

Understanding this case is useful because an experimenter often uses electrical currents as stimuli in analyzing nerve function; however, it is not the way in which a neuron normally generates current flows. This usually occurs by means of a localized **conductance change** across the membrane. Consider such a change in the example of compartment A in Fig. 5.6. Assume a change in the ionic conductance for Na^+, as in the initiation of an action potential or an excitatory postsynaptic potential, producing an inward positive current in compartment A. The charge transferred to the interior surface of the membrane attempts to follow the same paths followed by the injected current just described: opposing the negativity inside the mem-

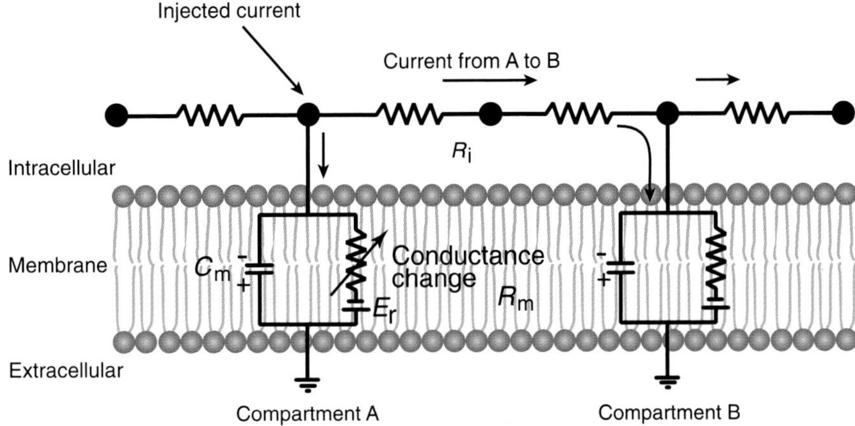

FIGURE 5.6 The equivalent circuit of two neighboring compartments or segments (A and B) of an axon or dendrite shows the pathways for current spread in response to an input (injected current or increase in membrane conductance) at segment A.

brane capacitance; crossing the membrane through the open membrane channels to ground; and spreading through the internal resistance to the next compartment, where the charge flows are similar. Thus, the two cases start with different means of transferring positive charge within the cell, but from that point the current paths and the associated spread of the electrotonic potential are similar. The electrotonic current that spreads between the two segments is also referred to as the **local current.** Note again that the charging transient in compartment A is faster than the time constant of the resting membrane; this difference is due both to the conductance load of compartment B and to the fact that the imposed conductance increase in compartment A reduces the time constant of compartment A (by reducing effective R_m). This illustrates a critical point first emphasized by Rall: changes in membrane conductance alter the system so that it is no longer strictly a linear system even though it is a passive system.[17] Nonlinear summation of synaptic responses is further discussed later in this chapter.

Summary

In addition to the properties underlying steady-state electrotonus, passive spread of transient potentials depends on the membrane capacitance. Initiation of electrotonic spread by intracellular injection of a transient electrical current pulse produces an electrotonic potential that spreads by passive local currents from point to point. It is more attenuated in amplitude than the steady-state case as it spreads along an axon or dendrite, due to the low-pass filtering action of the membrane capacitance. Simultaneous current pulses at that site or other sites produce potentials that add linearly, because the passive properties are invariant. However, electrotonic potentials produced by a transient conductance change do not sum linearly because of the nonlinear interactions of the conductances.

ELECTROTONIC PROPERTIES UNDERLYING PROPAGATION IN AXONS

Impulses Propagate in Unmyelinated Axons by Means of Local Electrotonic Currents

Let us now consider how knowledge of these electrotonic current properties helps us to understand the propagation of an impulse in an axon. (Details on the ionic mechanisms of the nerve impulse can be found in Chapter 6.) The local current spreading through the internal resistance to the neighboring compartment enables the impulse to spread along the membrane of the axon. The rate of spread is determined by both the passive electrotonic properties and the kinetics of the action potential mechanism. For an unmyelinated axon (i.e., one that is not surrounded by myelin or other membranes that restrict the spread of extracellular current), the relevant passive properties are the specific membrane resistance (R_m), the specific internal resistance (R_i), the diameter (d) of the axon, and the specific membrane capacitance (C_m).

Each of these properties is relevant in specific ways. For brief signals such as the action potential, C_m is critical in controlling the rate of change of the membrane potential. For long processes such as axons, R_i opposes electrotonic current flow as the value of R_i increases beyond the characteristic length, as stated earlier. This effect is greater in thinner axons, which have shorter characteristic lengths. Finally, R_m is a parameter that can vary widely; in addition, the effective membrane resistance encountered by electrotonic current is greatly increased by myelin sheathing. Thus, each of these parameters must be assessed in order to understand the exquisite effects of passive variables on the rates of impulse spread in axons.

A high value of R_m, for example, forces current further along the membrane, increasing the characteristic length and consequently the spread of electrotonic potential; however, at the same time, it increases the membrane time constant, thus slowing the response of a neighboring compartment to a rapid change. Increasing the diameter of the axon (d) lowers the effective internal resistance of a compartment, thereby also increasing the characteristic length. Because these effects are achieved without a concomitant effect on the time constant, changing the diameter is a direct way of affecting the rate of impulse propagation through changes in passive electrotonic properties. The conduction rate of any given axon depends on the particular combination of these properties.[32,33] For example, in the squid giant axon, the very large diameter (as large as 1 mm) promotes rapid impulse propagation; the very low value of R_m (600 Ω cm^2) lowers the time constant (promoting rapid spread) but also decreases the length constant (limiting the spatial extent of spread).

The effects of these passive properties on impulse velocity also depend on other factors. For example, on the basis of the cable equations, we can show that the conduction velocity should be related to the square root of the diameter.[32] However, the density of Na^+ channels in fibers of different diameters is not constant; thus, the binding of saxitoxin molecules, for example, to Na^+ channels varies greatly with diameter, from almost 300 μm^{-2} in the squid axon to only 35 μm^{-2} in the garfish olfactory nerve.[33] Both active and passive properties must be assessed in order to understand a particular functional property.

Myelinated Axons Have Membrane Wrappings and Booster Sites for Faster Conduction

The evolution of larger brains to control larger bodies and more complex behavior required communication over longer distances within the brain and body. This requirement placed a premium on the ability of axons to conduct impulses as rapidly as possible. As noted in the preceding section, a direct way of increasing the rate of conduction is by increasing the diameter, but larger diameters mean fewer axons within a given space, and complex behavior must be mediated by many axons. Another way of increasing the rate of conduction is to make the kinetics of the impulse mechanism faster; that is, make the rate of increase in Na^+ conductance with increasing membrane depolarization faster. The Hodgkin–Huxley equations for the impulse in mammalian nerves in fact have this faster rate.

As we have seen, rapid spread of local currents is promoted by an increase in R_m but opposed by an associated increase in the time constant. What is needed is an increase in R_m with a concomitant decrease in C_m. This is brought about by putting more resistances in series with the membrane resistance (resistances in series add) while putting more capacitances in series with the membrane capacitance (capacitances in series add as the reciprocals, much like resistances in parallel, as noted earlier). The way the nervous system does this is through a special satellite cell called a Schwann cell, a type of glial cell. As described in Chapter 4, Schwann cells wrap many layers of their plasma membranes around an axon. The membranes contain special constituents and together are called myelin. Myelinated nerves contain the fastest conducting axons in the nervous system. A general empirical finding known as the Hursh factor[34] states that the rate of propagation of an impulse in meters per second is six times the diameter of the axon in micrometers. Thus, the largest axons in the mammalian nervous system are approximately 20 μm in diameter, and their conduction rate is approximately 120 m s^{-1}, whereas the thin myelinated axons of about 1 μm in diameter have conduction rates of approximately 5 to 10 m s^{-1}.

As discussed in Chapter 4, myelinated axons are not myelinated along their entire length; at regular intervals (approximately 1 mm in peripheral nerves), the myelin covering is interrupted by a node of Ranvier. The node has a complex structure. The density of voltage-sensitive Na^+ channels at the node is high (10,000 μm^{-2}), whereas it is very low (20 μm^{-2}) in the internodal membrane. This difference in density means that the impulse is actively generated only at the node; the impulse jumps, so to speak, from node to node, and the process is therefore called **saltatory conduction.** In faster-conducting axons, the impulse may extend over considerable lengths; for example, in a 20-μm-diameter axon conducting at 120 m s^{-1}, at any instant of time an impulse of 1-ms duration extends over a 120-mm length of axon, which includes more than 100 nodes of Ranvier. It is therefore more appropriate to think of the impulse as being generated simultaneously by many nodes, which adds to local currents spreading to the next adjacent nodes to activate them. A myelinated axon therefore resembles a passive cable with active booster stations. The specific membrane resistance (R_m) at the node is estimated to be only 50 Ω cm^2, owing to a large number of open ionic channels at rest. This value of R_m reduces the time constant of the nodal membrane to approximately 50 ms, which enables the nodal membrane to charge and discharge quickly, greatly aiding rapid impulse generation. For axons of equal cross-sectional area, myelination is estimated to increase the impulse conduction rate 100-fold.

In all axons, a critical relation exists between the amount of local current spreading down an adjacent axon and the threshold for opening Na^+ channels in the membrane of the adjacent axon so that propagation of the impulse can continue. This introduces the notion of a **safety factor,** that is, the amount by which the electrotonic potential exceeds the threshold for activating the impulse. The safety factor must allow for a wide range of operating conditions, including adaptation (during high-frequency firing), fatigue, injury, infection, degeneration, and aging. Normally, an excess of local current ensures an adequate margin of safety against these factors. In the squid axon, the safety factor ranges from 4 to 5. In myelinated axons, an exquisite matching between the internodal electrotonic properties and the nodal active properties ensures that the electrotonic potential reaching a node has an adequate amplitude and the node has sufficient Na^+ channels to generate an impulse that will spread to the next node. The safety factors for myelinated axons range from 5 to 10. Thus, the interaction of passive and active properties underlies the safety factors for impulse propagation in axons. Similar considerations apply to the orthodromic spread of signals in dendritic branches and the backpropagation of impulses from the axon hillock into the soma and dendrites.

Theoretically, the conduction velocity, space constant, and impulse wavelength of myelinated fibers scale linearly with fiber diameter,[32,33] as indeed is indicated in the aforementioned Hursh factor. This difference between myelinated and unmyelinated fibers in their dependence on diameter is thus related to the scaling of the internodal length. At approximately 1 μm in diameter, the Hursh factor breaks down; at less than 1 μm in diameter, there is an advantage, all other factors being equal, for an axon to be unmyelinated. However, myelinated axons are found down to a diameter of only 0.2 μm, and this has been correlated with shorter internodal distances.[35] Thus, conduction velocity in myelinated nerve depends on a complex interplay between passive and active properties.

Summary

Electrotonic potentials are said to *spread* by means of passive local currents, whereas action potentials (impulses) are said to *propagate* by means of active local currents. Impulses propagate continuously through unmyelinated fibers because the active local currents spread directly to neighboring sites on the membrane. This rate of propagation is directly determined by the electrotonic properties of the fiber. In myelinated fibers, the impulse propagates discontinuously from node to node. The electrotonic properties of both the nodal and internodal regions determine not only the rate of impulse propagation but also the safety factor for impulse transmission.

ELECTROTONIC SPREAD IN DENDRITES

Dendrites are the main neuronal compartment for reception of synaptic inputs. Spread of synaptic responses through the dendritic tree depends critically on the electrotonic properties of the dendrites. Because dendrites are branching structures, understanding the rules governing dendritic electrotonus and the resulting integration of synaptic responses in dendrites is much more difficult than understanding those of simple spread in axons.

Dendritic Electrotonic Spread Depends on Boundary Conditions of Dendritic Termination and Branching

Compared with axons, dendrites are relatively short. Their length is an important factor in assessing their electrotonic properties. Consider, in the mammalian nervous system, a moderately thin dendrite of 1 μm (three orders of magnitude smaller than the squid axon) that has a typical R_m of 60,000 Ω cm^2 (two orders of magnitude larger than that of the squid axon) and an R_i of 240 Ω cm (three times the squid value). Inserting these values into the equation for characteristic length (Eq. 5.3) gives a λ of approximately 790 μm. This illustrates that although λ is short in thin dendrites, in absolute terms it is relatively long in comparison with the actual lengths of the dendrites; in other words, because of the relatively high membrane resistance, electrotonic spread of potentials is relatively effective within a dendritic branching tree. This essential property underlies the integration of signals in dendrites. However, with this property, the assumption of infinite length no longer holds; dendritic branches are bounded by their terminations, on the one hand, and the nature of their branching, on the other, and an assessment of the spread of electrotonic potentials through them must take these boundary conditions into account.

This problem is approached most easily by considering two extreme types of termination of a dendritic branch. First, consider that at $x = a$ the branch ends in an infinite resistance. In this case, the axial component of the current can spread no further and must therefore seek the only path to ground, which is across the membrane of the cylinder. This current is added to the current already crossing the membrane; in the equation for Ohm's law ($E = IR$), I is increased, giving a larger E. The membrane will thus be more depolarized up to the terminal point a; in fact, near point a, axial current is negligible and almost all the current is across the membrane, which amounts to a virtual space clamp near point a (Fig. 5.7). If at point a the infinite resistance is replaced by the more realistic assumption of an end that is sealed with surface membrane, only a small amount of current crosses this membrane and attenuation of electrotonic potential is correspondingly slightly greater; thus, the infinite resistance is a useful approximation for assessing the effects of a sealed end on electrotonic spread in a terminal dendritic branch.

At the other extreme, consider that at point a a small dendritic branch opens out into a very large conductance. Examples are a very small dendritic branch on a large soma and a small branch or spine on a large dendritic branch. Recall that large processes have their resistances in parallel, which gives low current density and small voltage changes. Therefore, a current spreading through the high resistance of a small branch into a large branch encounters a very low resistance. For steady-state current spread, this situation is referred to as a large **conductance load;** for a transient current, we refer to it as a **low impedance** (which includes the effect of the membrane capacitance). Thus, an **impedance mismatch** exists between the high-impedance thin branch and the lower-impedance thick branch. This mismatch reduces any voltage change due to the current and, in the extreme, effectively clamps the membrane to the resting potential (E_r) at that point. The electrotonic potential is thus attenuated through the branch much more rapidly than would be predicted by the characteristic length (see Fig. 5.7). This does not invalidate λ as a measure of electrotonic properties; rather, it means that, as with the time constant, each cable property must be assessed within the context of the size and branching of the dendrites.

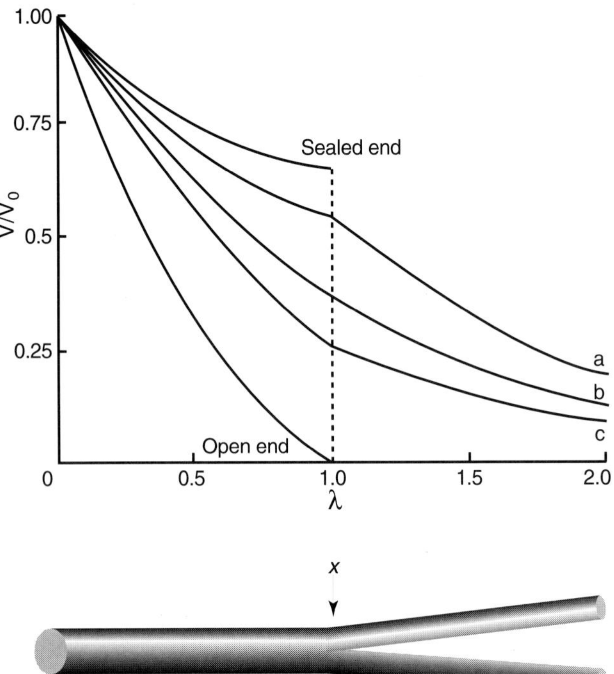

FIGURE 5.7 The spread of electrotonic potential through a short nerve-cell process such as a dendritic branch is governed by the space constant and by the size of the branches; the latter imposes a boundary condition at the branch point. The graph shows three assumptions about the size of the branches relative to the size of the stem, together with the limiting conditions of an open circuit (corresponding to an infinite conductance load) and a closed circuit (corresponding to a sealed tip).

All the different types of branching found in neuronal dendrites lie between these two extremes and give rise to a corresponding range of boundary conditions at $x = a$. Consider a segment of dendrite that divides into two branches at $x = a$. We can appreciate intuitively that the amount of spread of electrotonic potential into the two branches will be governed by the factors just considered. One possibility is that the two branches have very small diameters, so their input impedance is higher than that of the segment; in this case, the situation will tend toward the sealed-end case. In contrast, the segment may give rise to two very fat branches, so the situation will tend toward the large-conductance-load case (see Fig. 5.7).

For many cases of dendritic branching, the input impedance of the branches is in between the two extremes, providing for a reasonable degree of impedance matching between the stem branch and its two daughter branches. This situation thus approximates the infinite-cylinder case, in which by definition the input impedance at one site matches that at its neighboring site along the cylinder. The general rules for impedance matching at branch points were worked out by Rall,[17,20,21,27] who showed that the input conductance of a dendritic segment varies with the diameter raised to the $\frac{3}{2}$ power; there is electrotonic continuity at a branch point equivalent to the infinitely extended cylinder if the diameter of the segment raised to the $\frac{3}{2}$ power equals the sum of the diameters raised to the $\frac{3}{2}$ power of all the daughter branches. A branching pattern that satisfies this rule is shown in Fig. 5.8. Not only does the $d^{3/2}$ relation give a rule for constructing an **equivalent cylinder** for a segment and its daughter branches, but iterative application of the rule leads to an equivalent cylinder for an entire dendritic tree if there are similar orders of branching (see Fig. 5.8).

Dendritic Synaptic Potentials Are Delayed and Attenuated by Electrotonic Spread

We are now in a position to assess the effects of cable properties on the time course of the spread of synaptic potentials through dendritic branches and trees. The simplest case is a chain of equal compartments; this chain can simulate a single long dendritic branch or it can simulate an entire dendritic tree if the tree satisfies the $d^{3/2}$ branching rule, as described in the preceding section (Fig. 5.8). Consider the case of recording from a soma while delivering a brief excitatory synaptic conductance change to different locations in the dendritic tree. The response to the nearest site is a rapidly rising synaptic potential that peaks near the end of the conductance change and then rapidly decays toward baseline. When the input is delivered to the middle of the chain of compartments, the response in the soma begins only after a delay, rises more slowly, reaches a much lower peak (which is reached after the end of the conductance change in the soma), and decays slowly toward baseline. For input to the terminal compartment, the voltage delay at the soma is so long that the response has scarcely started by the end of the conductance change in the distal dendrite; the response rises slowly to a delayed (several milliseconds) and prolonged plateau that subsides very slowly.

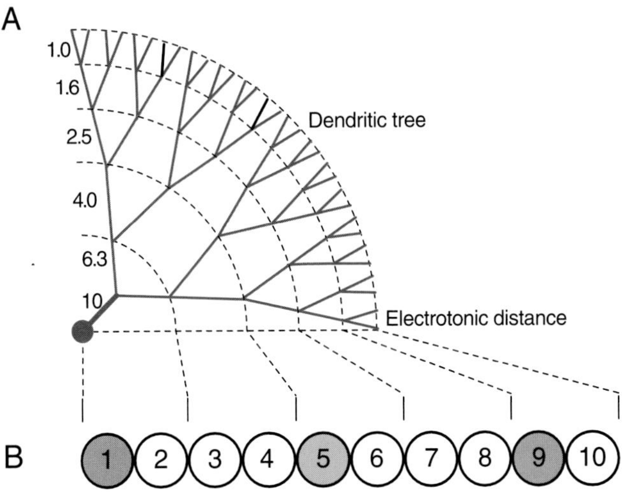

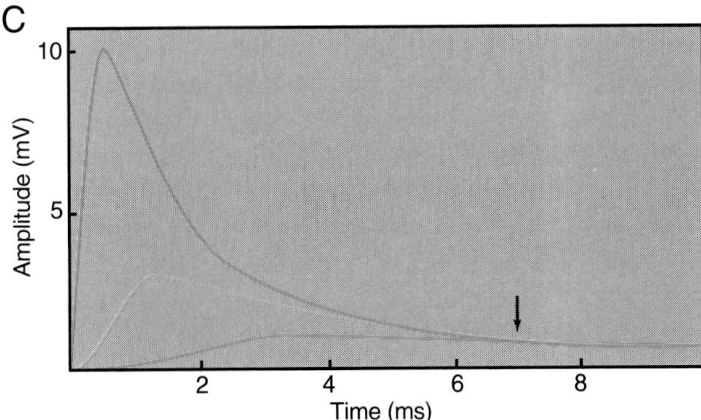

FIGURE 5.8 The spread of electrotonic potentials is accompanied by a delay and an attenuation of amplitude. (A), dendritic diameters (left) satisfy the $\frac{3}{2}$ rule, so that the tree can be portrayed by an equivalent cylinder. An excitatory postsynaptic potential (EPSP) is generated in compartment 1, 5, or 9 (B) while recordings are made from compartment 1. The graph (C) shows the short latency, large amplitude, and rapid transient response in compartment 1 at the site of input, as well as the later, smaller, and slower responses recorded in compartment 1 for the same input to compartments 5 and 9. Despite the initial differences in time course, the responses converge at the arrow to decay together. Based on Rall[17]; computer simulation in (C) by K. L. Marton.

Although the synaptic potentials thus decrease in amplitude as they spread, the rate of spread can be calculated in terms of the half-amplitude at any point. If distance is expressed in units of λ and time in units of τ, then for spread through a semi-infinite cable, we have the simple equation

$$\text{Velocity} = 2\frac{\lambda}{\tau}. \tag{5.9}$$

Thus, if we ignore boundary effects, for the 10-mm process mentioned earlier in which $\lambda = 1500$ and $\tau = 10$ ms, the velocity of spread would be 0.3 m s^{-1}, or 300 mm s^{-1}. It can be seen that spread can be relatively fast over short distances within a dendritic tree but is very slow in comparison with impulse transmission for an axon of this diameter (60 m s^{-1}). Thus, both the severe decrement and the slow velocity make passive spread by itself ineffective for transmission over long distances.

These general rules of delay and attenuation govern the passive spread of all transient potentials in dendritic branches and trees. From a functional point of view, what matters is the linkage between a response in one part of a branch or branching system and a related site or sites where integration of this signal with other signals takes place. As a rule of thumb, spread within one space constant (see the decrement between compartments 1 and 5 in Fig. 5.8) mediates relatively effective linkage for rapid signal integration, whereas spread over one or two space constants (see the decrement between compartments 1 and 9 in Fig. 5.8) is limited to slower background modulation. In

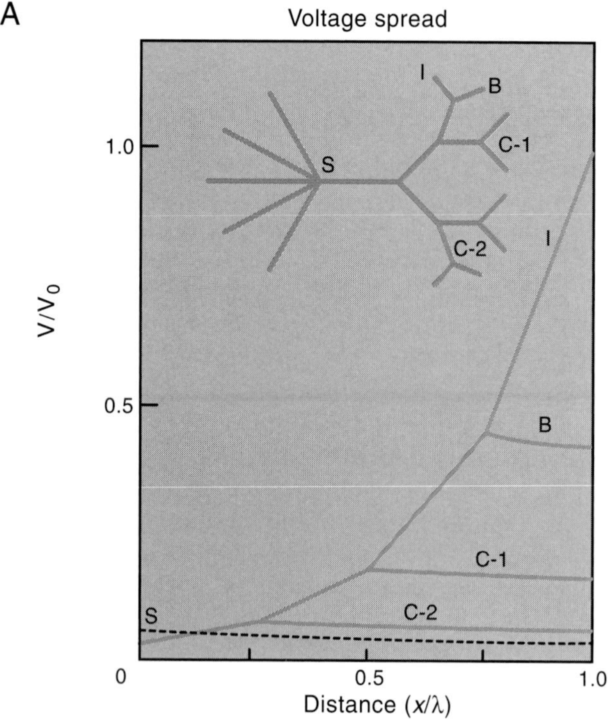

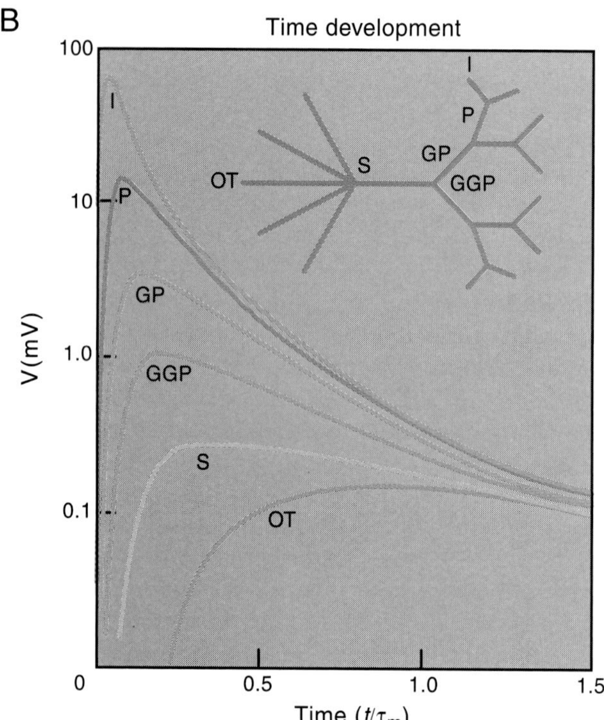

FIGURE 5.9 (A) For steady-state inputs (*I*) to a distal dendritic branch, the electrotonic potential spreads through the dendritic tree with large decrements into the parent branch (due to the large conductance load) but small decrements into neighboring branches B, C-1, and C-2 (due to the small conductance loads). The resulting potential in the soma (S) is much reduced, as is the response to the same input delivered directly to the soma (because of the low input resistance at the soma and the large conductance load of the dendritic tree). (B) For transient inputs (*I*) to a distal branch, the transient electrotonic potentials decrease sharply in amplitude and are delayed and slower as they spread toward the soma through the parent (P), grandparent (GP), and great-grandparent (GGP) branches, eventually reaching the soma (S) and output trunk (OT). Modified from Segev[28] based on Rall and Rinzel.[36,37]

real dendrites, these limitations are often overcome through boosting the signals by voltage-gated properties (see Chap. 13).

The spread of electrotonic potential from a locus of input involves the equalization of charge on the membrane throughout the system. After cessation of the input, a time is reached when charge has become equalized and the entire system is equipotential; from this time on, the remaining electrotonic potential decays equally at every point in the system. This time is indicated by the vertical arrow in Fig. 5.8C. Before this time, the decaying transients are governed by **equalizing time constants,** indicating electrotonic spread, which can be identified by "peeling" on semilogarithmic plots of the potentials.[20] After this time, the decay of electrotonic potential is governed solely by the membrane time constant, τ. In experimental recordings of synaptic potentials, the overall electrotonic length of the dendritic system, considered an "equivalent cylinder," can be estimated from measurements of the membrane time constant and the equalizing time constants. The electrotonic lengths of the dendritic trees of many neuron types lie between 0.3 and 1.5.

What is the spread of the postsynaptic potential throughout the system when a synaptic input is delivered to a single terminal dendritic branch (Fig. 5.9)?[36,37] Let us begin by considering a steady-state potential. Two main factors are involved. First, in the terminal branch, both the effective membrane resistance and the internal resistance are very large; hence, the branch has a very **high input resistance,** which produces a very large voltage change for any given synaptic conductance change. Balanced against this high input resistance is a second factor: the small branch has a very large **conductance load** on it because of the rest of the dendritic tree. As a result, there is a steep decrement in the electrotonic potential spreading from the branch through the tree to the cell body (see Fig. 5.9A). For comparison, a direct input to the soma produces only a small potential change there because of the relatively very low input resistance at that site.

For a transient synaptic input, a third factor—the **membrane capacitance**—must be taken into account. The small surface area of a terminal branch has little capacitance, and so the amplitude of a transient response differs little from a steady-state response in the branch. However, in spreading out from a small process (such as a distal dendritic twig or spine), the transient synaptic potential is attenuated by the impedance mismatch between the process and the rest of the dendritic tree. Spread of the transient through the dendritic tree is further attenuated by the need to charge the capacitance of the dendritic membrane and is slowed by the time taken for the charging. The amount of slowing is so precise that the relative distance of a synapse in the dendritic tree from the soma can be calculated from experimental measurements in the soma of the time to peak of the recorded synaptic potential.[20,38] For these reasons, the peak of a synaptic potential transient spreading from the distal dendrites toward the soma may be severely attenuated, severalfold more than for the case of steady-state attenuation. However, the integrated response (the area under the transient voltage) is approximately equivalent to the steady-state amplitude, indicating that there is only a small loss of total charge (see Fig. 5.9B).

The Electrotonic Structure of the Neuron Changes Dynamically

These considerations show that, compared with the anatomical structure of a dendritic system, which is relatively fixed, the electrotonic properties have complex and subtle effects on signal integration. The effects depend on multiple factors, including the directions of signal spread, inhomogeneities in passive properties, rates of signal transfer, and interactions between synaptic or active conductances, to name a few. The effects can be illustrated in a graphic fashion for the entire soma–dendritic system by taking a stained neuron and replacing it with a representation based on its electrotonic properties. This is termed a morpho-electrotonic transform (MET)[39] or neuromorphic transform.[40]

The method is illustrated in Fig. 5.10 for a CA1 hippocampal pyramidal cell. The problem is to compare the spread of a signal from the soma to the dendrites (voltage out, V_{out}) with spread from the dendrites to the soma (voltage in, V_{in}). On the left is the stained neuron, giving rise to a long apical dendrite with many branches and shorter basal dendrites and their branches. On the right, lower diagram, is an electrotonic representation of the neuron for signals spreading from the distal dendrites toward the soma. As shown in Fig. 5.9, there is severe decrement from each distal branch, so that apical and basal dendritic trees have electrotonic lengths of approximately 3 and 2, respectively. By comparison, on the right, upper diagram, is an electrotonic representation of this neuron for a signal spreading from the soma to the dendrites. The basal dendrites have shrunk to almost nothing, indicating that they are nearly isopotential. This is because they are relatively short compared with their electrotonic lengths and because the sealed-end boundary condition greatly reduces the decrement of electrotonic potential through them (see Fig. 5.7). The apical dendrite has shrunk to an electrotonic length of approximately 1. This analysis helps in understanding that distal synaptic responses decrease considerably in spreading to the soma, which active properties can help to overcome, as we shall see in Chapter 13. On the other hand, signals at the soma "see" a relatively compact dendritic tree.

The analysis in Fig. 5.10 applies to spread of steady-state or very slowly changing signals. What about spread of rapid signals? We have seen that the membrane capacitance makes the dendrites act as a low-pass filter, further reducing rapid signals. The electrotonic transforms can include this effect, as shown in Fig. 5.11. On the left, the electrotonic representation of a pyramidal neuron is shown for a slow (100 Hz) current injected in the soma. The form is similar to that of the cell in Fig. 5.10, with tiny, virtually isopotential basal dendrites, and a longer apical dendritic tree of electrotonic length of approximately 1.5. By comparison, a rapid (500 Hz) signal is severely attenuated in spreading into the dendrites, as shown by the basal dendrites with L of approximately 1 and the apical dendritic tree electrotonic lengths of 4–5. Thus, a somatic action potential could backpropagate into the basal dendrites rather effectively, but would require active properties to invade very far into the apical dendrites. There is direct evidence for these properties underlying backpropagating action potentials in apical dendrites (Chapter 13).

The electrotonic structure of a neuron is not necessarily fixed, but may vary under synaptic control. An example is shown in Fig. 5.12 for the case of a medium spiny cell in the basal ganglia. During low levels of resting excitatory synaptic input, the electrotonic transform of this cell type is relatively large (left) because of the action of a specific K^+ current in the dendrites that holds them relatively hyperpolarized (see arrow at −90 mV). When synaptic excitation increases, the K^+ current is deactivated, reducing the membrane conductance and thereby increasing the input resistance of the cell; the dendritic tree becomes more compact electrotonically (middle) so that synaptic inputs are more effective in activating the cell. As the cell responds to the synaptic excitation, the resulting depolarization activates other K^+ currents, which expand the electrotonic structure again (right). This example illustrates how cable properties and voltage-gated properties interact to control the integrative actions of the neuron.

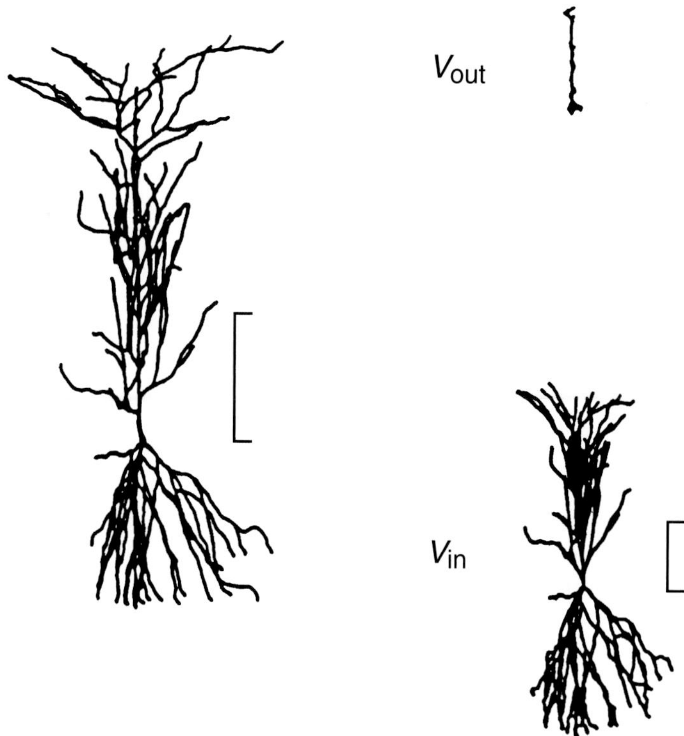

FIGURE 5.10 The electrotonic structure of a neuron varies with the direction of spread of signals. (Left) Stained CA1 pyramidal neuron. (Right) Electrotonic transform of the stained morphology for the case of a voltage spreading toward the cell body (below, V_{in}) and away from the cell body (above, V_{out}). Calibration, 1 electrotonic length. See text. From Carnevale *et al.*[40]

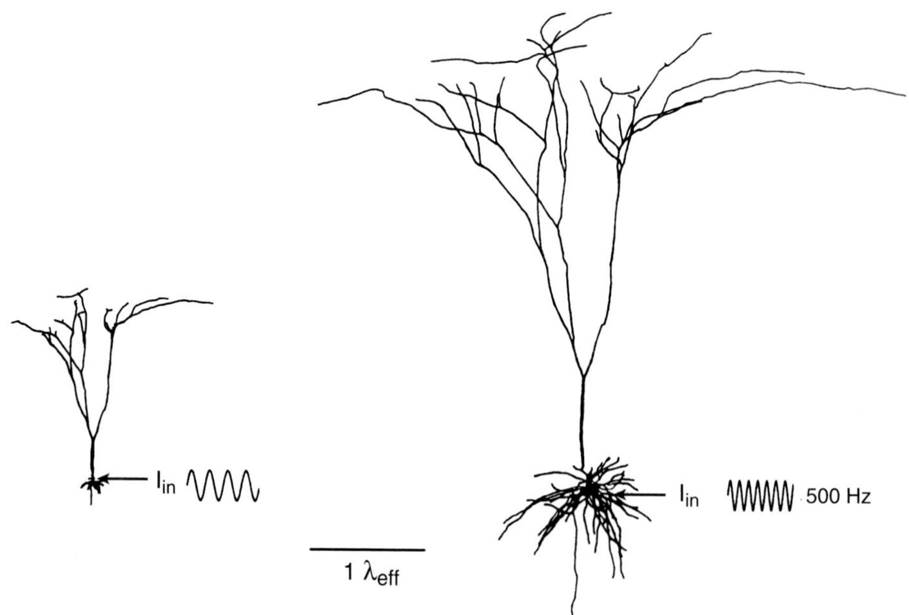

FIGURE 5.11 The electrotonic structure of a neuron varies with the rapidity of signals. (Left) Electrotonic transform of a pyramidal neuron in response to a sinusoidal current of 100 Hz injected into the soma (i.e., this is an example of V_{out}). (Right) Electrotonic transform of same cell in response to 500 Hz. Calibration, 1 electrotonic length. See text. From Zador *et al.*[39]

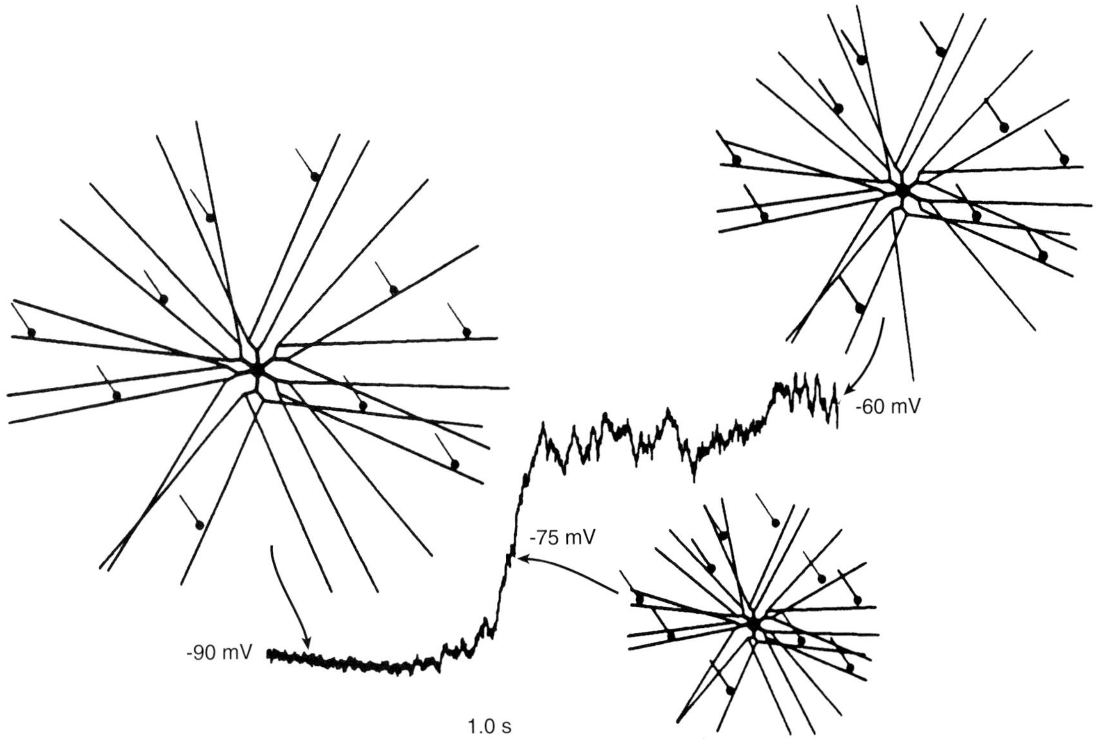

FIGURE 5.12 The electrotonic structure of a neuron can vary with shifts in the resting membrane potential. In this medium spiny cell, the electrotonic transform varies with the resting membrane potential, which in turn reflects the combination of resting voltage-gated K^+ currents and excitatory synaptic currents. See text. From Wilson.[41]

Synaptic Conductances in Dendrites Tend to Interact Nonlinearly

It is often assumed that synaptic responses sum linearly, but this is not generally true. In an electrical cable, responses to simultaneous current inputs sum linearly because the cable properties remain invariant at all times; this type of case was considered in Fig. 5.6. However, as noted in regard to that case, synaptic responses in real neurons generate current by means of changes in the membrane conductance at the synapse. In addition to generating current, the change in synaptic conductance alters the overall membrane resistance of that segment and with it the input resistance, thereby changing the electrotonic properties of the whole system. As pointed out by Rall, excitatory and inhibitory conductance changes involve "a change in a conductance which is an element of the system; the system itself is perturbed; the value of a constant coefficient in the linear differential equation is changed; hence the simple superposition rules do not hold."[17]

This effect is easily illustrated by the two-compartment model of Fig. 5.6. Consider a synaptic input to compartment A, which decreases the membrane resistance of that compartment. Now consider a simultaneous synaptic input to compartment B, which has the same effect on the membrane resistance of that compartment. The internal current flowing between the two compartments will then encounter a much lower impedance and hence have much less effect on the membrane potential than would have been the case for current injection. The integration of these two responses will therefore give a smaller summed potential than the summation of the two responses taken individually. This effect is referred to as **occlusion.** In essence, each compartment partially short circuits the other through a larger conductance load, thus reducing the combined response.

These properties mean that synaptic integration in dendrites in general is not linear even for purely passive electrotonic properties. The further apart the synaptic sites, the fewer the interactions between the conductances, and the more linear the summation becomes (see Fig. 5.13). These nonlinear properties of passive dendrites combined with the nonlinear properties of voltage-gated channels at local sites on the membrane contribute to the complexity of signal processing that takes place in dendrites, as will be discussed in Chapter 13.

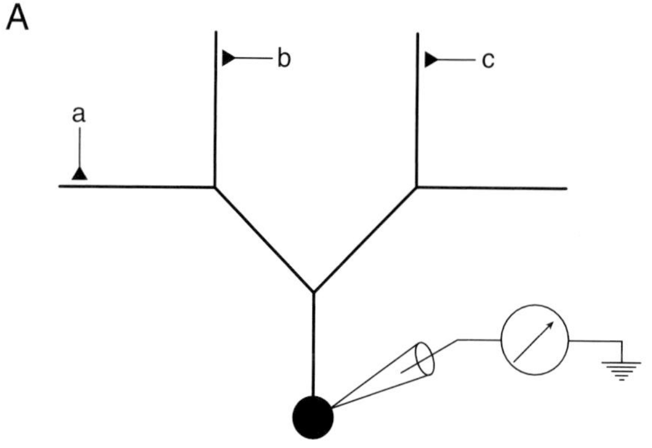

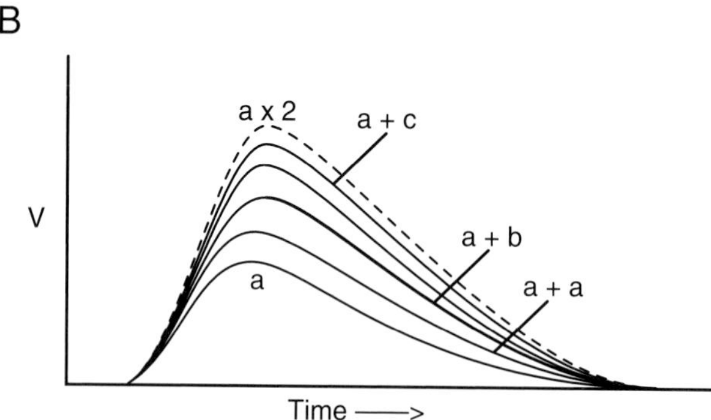

FIGURE 5.13 Schematic diagram of a dendritic tree to illustrate graded effects of nonlinear interactions between synaptic conductances. (A) Three sites of synaptic input (a–c) are shown, with recording site in the soma. (B) The voltage response (V) is shown for the response to a single input at a, the theoretical linear summation for two inputs at a (a × 2), and the gradual reduction in summation from c to a due to increasing shunting between the conductances. See text. From Shepherd and Koch.[31]

The Significance of Active Conductances in Dendrites Depends on Their Relation to Cable Properties

In electrophysiological recordings from the cell body, dendritic synaptic responses often appear small and slow. However, at their sites of origin in the dendrites, the responses tend to have a large amplitude (because of the high input resistances of the thin distal dendrites) and a rapid time course (because of the small membrane capacitance), as the electrotonic simulations in Fig. 5.9 suggest. These properties have important implications for the signal processing that takes place in dendrites. In particular, the fact that the distal dendrites contain sites of voltage-gated channels means that local integration, local boosting, and local threshold operations can take place. These most distal responses need spread no further than to neighboring local active sites to be boosted by these sites; thus, a rapid integrative sequence of these actions ultimately produces significant effects on signal integration at the cell body. These properties will be considered further in Chapter 13.

In addition to their role in orthodromic signal processing, the cable properties of the neuron are also important for controlling the spread of synaptic potentials from the dendrites through the soma to the site of impulse initiation in the axon hillock initial segment and for backpropagation of an impulse into the soma–dendritic compartments, where it can activate dendritic outputs and interact with the active properties involved in signal processing. These properties will be discussed further in Chapter 13.

Dendritic Spines Form Electrotonic and Biochemical Compartments

The rules governing electrotonic interactions within a dendritic tree also apply at the level of the smallest process of a nerve cell, called a **spine.** This may vary from a bump on a dendritic branch to a twig to a lollipop-shaped process several micrometers long (Fig. 5.14). A dendritic spine usually receives a single excitatory synapse; an axonal spine characteristically receives an inhibitory synapse.

Spines receive most of the excitatory inputs to pyramidal neurons in the cerebral cortex and to Purkinje cells in the cerebellum, as well as to a variety of other neuron types, so an understanding of their properties is critical for understanding brain function.[43–46] As with the whole dendritic tree, one begins with their electrotonic properties. Given the rules we have built earlier in this chapter, by simple inspection of spine morphol-

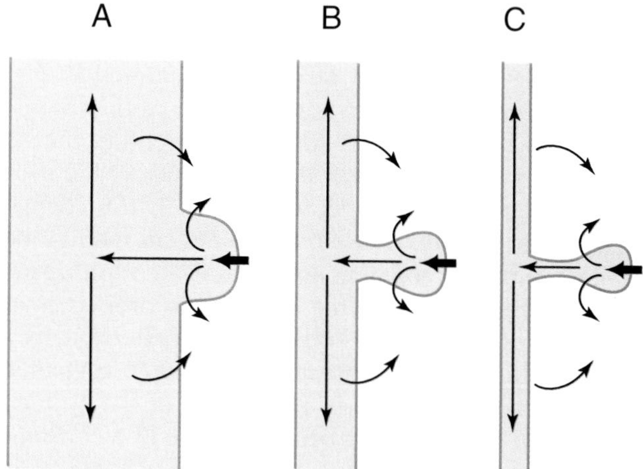

FIGURE 5.14 Diagrams illustrating different types of spines and the current flows generated by a synaptic input. (A) Stubby spine arising from a thick process. (B) Moderately elongated spine from a medium diameter branch. (C) Spine with a long stem originating from a thin branch. Parallel considerations apply to diffusion between the spine head and dendritic branch. Modified from Shepherd.[42]

ogy as shown in Fig. 5.14, we can postulate several distinctive features that may have important functional implications. First, the smaller the size and the narrower the stem, the higher the input resistance; this gives a large amplitude synaptic potential for a given synaptic conductance. A large depolarizing EPSP could have powerful effects on the local environment within the spine. Second, the small size also means a small capacitance, implying that synaptic (and any active) potentials may be rapid; this means that spines on dendrites can potentially be involved in rapid information transmission. Third, there is an impedance mismatch between the spine head and its parent dendrite; this means that potentials spreading from the spine to the dendrite will suffer considerable decrement, unless there are active properties of the dendrite or of neighboring spines to boost the signal. Fourth, the other side of this impedance mismatch is that potentials spreading through the dendrite will spread into the spine with little decrement; thus, the spine will tend to follow the potential of its dendrite, except for the transient large amplitude responses to its own synaptic input. This means that a spine can serve as a coincidence detector for nearby synaptic responses or for a back-propagating impulse.

In addition to it electrotonic properties, the spine may have interesting parallel biochemical properties. This is because the same cable equations that govern electrotonic properties also have their counterparts in describing the diffusion of substances (as well as the flow of heat). Thus, as already noted, accumulations of only small numbers of ions are needed within the tiny volumes of spine heads to change the driving force on an ion species or to effect significant changes in the concentrations of subsequent second messengers. For this reason, interest in the biochemical properties of spines is increasing. This interest will undoubtedly intensify as the ability to image ion fluxes, such as for Ca^{2+}, and measure other molecular properties of individual spines increases in the near future. The interpretation of those results for the integrative properties of the neuron will require considerations in the biochemical domain that parallel those we have discussed in the electrotonic domain.

The range of properties and possible functions of spines are discussed further in Chapter 13.

Rational Analysis of Dendritic Integration Reveals the True Computational Power of the Neuron

The field of dendritic integration is still relatively young, having been established about 1960. However, as this chapter explains, a number of properties have emerged that enable us to begin to identify some general principles. Some of the main insights are summarized in the following list adapted from Segev.[28] Most of these insights can be seen to build on the principles presented in this chapter. Together, these principles constitute rules for dendritic integration that can be the basis for rational analysis of dendritic functions and serve as a guide for the construction of more realistic network models that will incorporate the true computational power and complexity of the individual neuron.

1. Because of its dendritic tree, the neuron is not isopotential in response to individual synaptic inputs. Compared with the soma, the dendritic tree is relatively compact; there are significant local electrotonic gradients in dendrites.
2. Dendritic attenuation implies the need for multiple synchronous excitatory synaptic inputs to sum and reach threshold for impulse activation at the axonal initial segment. The large local dendritic depolarization and attenuation through the dendritic tree imply that the tree is functionally separated into semiautonomous subunits.
3. In spreading through the dendrites to the soma, the amplitude of transient potentials undergoes severe attenuation, but the attenuation of the total charge is relatively small.
4. Linear system theory predicts that the voltage change at a given recording location will be the same for local current injection into different sites in a passive dendritic tree. However, the same current or conductance change in thin distal dendrites produces a larger change in membrane potential and a steeper attenuation than does a similar change in thick proximal dendrites and the cell body; thus attenuation between different points along the soma–dendritic axis is asymmetrical.
5. In addition to being attenuated, transient synaptic potentials are delayed and become broader as they spread through the dendritic tree. This means that there are multiple time windows for synaptic integration within the dendritic tree.
6. With the exception of the most distal inputs, the delay of a spreading synaptic potential is small compared with the membrane time constant. Thus, for most synapses, the significant time window for somatic integration is the time constant of the somatic membrane.
7. Synaptic inputs tend to sum nonlinearly because of interactions between their conductances. Linear summation is therefore enhanced by spatial distribution of synaptic inputs within the dendritic tree.

8. Inhibitory synapses are most effective when positioned between a more distal excitatory input and a proximal dendrite or soma. In this position, an inhibitory input can "veto" excitatory responses in more distal parts of the dendritic tree.
9. Because of synaptic delay and attenuation, activation of synaptic inputs in a temporal sequence from distal to proximal in the dendritic tree produces a larger summated potential at the soma than a sequence from proximal to distal. Output from neurons with these arrangements is thus inherently directionally selective.
10. The passive membrane properties of the dendritic tree are the net effect of background activity and specific inputs. By changing the net membrane conductance, background synaptic activity can dynamically modulate the input–output operations of the neuron.

Summary

In addition to being dependent on membrane properties, spread of electrotonic potentials in branching dendritic trees is dependent on the boundary conditions set by the modes of branching and termination within the tree. In general, other parts of the dendritic tree constitute a conductance load on activity at a given site; the spread of activity from that site is determined by the impedance match or mismatch between that site and the neighboring sites. Rules governing these impedance relations have been worked out relative to the case in which the sum of the daughter branch diameters raised to the $\frac{3}{2}$ power is equal to that of the parent branch, in which case the system of branches is an "equivalent cylinder," resembling a single continuous cable. Many dendritic trees approximate this relation, thus providing a starting point in analyzing synaptic integration within them.

Synchronous synaptic potentials in several branches spread relatively effectively through most dendritic trees. Responses in individual branches may be relatively isolated because of the decrement of passive spread and require local active boosting for effective communication with the rest of the tree. Passive spread can be characterized in terms of several measures, including characteristic length of the equivalent cylinder. There is scaling within individual branches, such that in finer branches electrotonic spread is relatively effective over their shorter lengths. Integration of synaptic potentials in passive dendrites is fundamentally nonlinear, because of interactions between the synaptic conductances. The rules for electrotonic spread in dendrites are the basis for understanding the contributions of active properties of dendrites.

References

1. Rall, W. (1958). Dendritic current distribution and whole neuron properties. *Nav. Med. Res. Inst. Res. Rep.* **NM 0105.01.02:** 479–525.
2. Hermann, L. (1872). *Arch. Gesamte Physiol. Menschen Tiere* **6:** 312.
3. Hermann, L. (1879). *Handbuch der Physiologie* (L. Hermann, ed.), Vogel, Leipzig.
4. Weber, H. (1873). Uber die stationaren stromungen der elektricitat in cylindren. *J. Reine Angewandte Math.* **76**(1): 1–20.
5. Kelvin, W. T. (1855). On the theory of the electric telegraph. *Proc. R. Soc. London* **7:** 382–399.
6. Kelvin, W. T. (1856). On the theory of the electric telegraph. *Philos. Mag.* [4] **11:** 146–160.
7. Hoorweg, J. L. (1898). Ueber die elektrischen Eigenschaften der Nerven. *Arch. Gesamte Physiol. Menschen Tiere* **71:** 128.
8. Cremer, M. (1899). Zum kernleiterproblem. *Z. Biol.* **37:** 550–553.
9. Cremer, M. (1909). Die allgemeine physiologie ner nerven. In *Handbuch der Physiologie des Menschen,* p. 793. Vieweg, Braunschweig.
10. Hermann, L. (1905). Beitrage zur physiologie und physik des nerven. *Arch. Gesamte Physiol. Menschen Tiere* **109:** 95.
11. Carslaw, H. S., and Jaeger, J. C. (1959). *Conduction of Heat in Solids.* Oxford University Press, London.
12. Rushton, W. A. H. (1927). The effect upon the threshold for nervous excitation of the length of nerve exposed and the angle between current and nerve. *J. Physiol.* (*London*) **63:** 357.
13. Rushton, W. A. H. (1934). A physical analysis of the relation between threshold and interpolar length in the electric excitation of medullated nerve. *J. Physiol.* (*London*) **82:** 332–352.
14. Cole, K. C., and Hodgkin, A. L. (1939). Membrane and protoplasm resistance in the squid giant axon. *J. Gen. Physiol.* **22:** 671–687.
15. Hodgkin, A. L., and Rushton, W. A. H. (1946). The electrical constants of a crustacean nerve fibre. *Proc. R. Soc. London, Ser. B* **133:** 444–447.
16. Davis, L., and Lorente de Nó, R. (1947). Contribution to the mathematical theory of electrotonus. *Stud. Rockefeller Inst. Med. Res.* **131:** 50–62.
17. Rall, W. (1964). Theoretical significance of dendritic trees for neuronal input–output relations. In *Neural Theory and Modelling* (R. F. Reiss, ed.), pp. 73–97. Stanford University Press, Stanford, CA.
18. Rall, W. (1967). Distinguishing theoretical synaptic potentials computed for different soma–dendritic distributions of synaptic input. *J. Neurophysiol.* **30:** 1138–1168.
19. Rall, W., and Shepherd, G. M. (1968). Theoretical reconstruction of field potentials and dendrodendritic synaptic interactions in olfactory bulb. *J. Neurophysiol.* **31**(6): 884–915.
20. Rall, W. (1977). Core conductor theory and cable properties of neurons. In *The Nervous System: Cellular Biology of Neurons* (E. R. Kandel, ed.), Vol. 1: pp. 39–97. Am. Physiol. Soc., Bethesda, MD.
21. Segev, I., Rinzel, J., and Shepherd, G. M., eds. (1995). *The Theoretical Foundation of Dendritic Function.* MIT Press, Cambridge, MA.
22. Jack, J. J. B., Noble, D., and Tsien, R. W. (1975). *Electrical Current Flow in Excitable Cells.* Oxford University Press (Clarendon), London.
23. Shepherd, G. M., and Brayton, R. K. (1979). Computer simulation of a dendrodendritic synaptic circuit for self- and lateral-inhibition in the olfactory bulb. *Brain Res.* **175:** 377–382.
24. Hines, M. (1984). Efficient computation of branched nerve equations. *Int. J. Bio-Med. Comput.* **15:** 69–76.
25. Bower, J., and Beeman, D., eds. (1995). *The Book of Genesis.* Springer-Verlag (Telos), New York.
26. Ziv, I., Baxter, D. A., and Byrne, J. H. (1994). Simulator for neural

networks and action potentials: description and application. *J. Neurophysiol.* **71:** 294–308.

27. Rall, W. (1959). Branching dendritic trees and motoneuron membrane resistivity. *Exp. Neurol.* **1:** 491–527.
28. Segev, I. (1995). Cable and compartmental models of dendritic trees. In *The Book of Genesis* (J. M. Bower and D. Beeman, eds.), pp. 53–82. Springer-Verlag (Telos), New York.
29. Pongracz, F., Poolos, N. P., Kocsis, J. D., and Shepherd, G. M. (1992). A model of NMDA receptor–mediated activity in dendrites of hippocampal CA1 pyramidal neurons. *J. Neurophysiol.* **68**(6): 2248–2259.
30. Qian, N., and Sejnowski, T. J. (1989). An electro-diffusion model for computing membrane potentials and ionic concentrations in branching dendrites, spines and axons. *Biol. Cybernet.* **62:** 1–15.
31. Shepherd, G. M., and Koch, C. (1990). Dendritic electrotonus and synaptic integration. In *The Synaptic Organization of the Brain* (G. M. Shepherd, ed.), 3rd ed., pp. 439–574. Oxford University Press, New York.
32. Rushton, W. A. H. (1951). A theory of the effects of fibre size in medullated nerve. *J. Physiol. (London)* **115:** 101–122.
33. Ritchie, J. M. (1995). Physiology of axons. In *The Axon: Structure, Function, and Pathophysiology* (S. G. Waxman, J. D. Kocsis, and P. K. Stys, eds.), pp. 68–69. Oxford University Press, New York.
34. Hursh, J. B. (1939). Conduction velocity and diameter of nerve fibers. *Am. J. Physiol.* **127:** 131–139.
35. Waxman, S. G., and Bennett, M. V. L. (1972). Relative conduction velocities of small myelinated and nonmyelinated fibres in the central nervous system. *Nat., New Biol.* **238:** 217.
36. Rall, W., and Rinzel, J. (1973). Branch input resistance and steady attenuation for input to one branch of a dendritic neuron model. *Biophys. J.* **13:** 648–688.
37. Rinzel, J., and Rall, W. (1974). Transient response in a dendritic neuron model for current injected at one branch. *Biophys. J.* **14:** 759–790.
38. Johnston, D., and Wu, S. M.-S. (1995). *Foundations of Cellular Neurophysiology.* MIT Press, Cambridge, MA.
39. Zador, A. M., Agmon-Snir, H., and Segev, I. (1995). The morphoelectrotonic transform: A graphical approach to dendritic function. *J. Neurosci.* **15:** 1169–1682.
40. Carnevale, N. T., Tsai, K. Y., Claiborne, B. J., and Brown, T. H. (1997). Comparative electrotonic analysis of 3 classes of rat hippocampal neurons. *J. Neurophysiol.*, in press.
41. Wilson, C. J. (1998). Basal ganglia. In *The Synaptic Organization of the Brain.* (G. M. Shepherd, ed.), 4th ed., pp. 329–376. Oxford Univ. Press, New York.
42. Shepherd, G. M. (1974). *The Synaptic Organization of the Brain.* Oxford Univ. Press, New York.
43. Shepherd, G. M. (1996). The dendritic spine: A multifunctional integrative unit. *J. Neurophysiol.* **75:** 2197–2210.
44. Zador, A., and Koch, C. (1994). Linearized models of calcium dynamics: Formal equivalence to the cable equation. *J. Neurosci.* **14:** 4705–4715.
45. Harris, K. M., and Kater, S. B. (1994). Dendritic spines: Cellular specializations imparting both stability and flexibility to synaptic function. *Annu. Rev. Neurosci.* **17:** 341–371.
46. Yuste, R., and Tank, D. (1996). Dendritic integration in mammalian neurons, a century after Cajal. *Neuron* **13:** 23–43.

C H A P T E R

6

Membrane Potential and Action Potential

David A. McCormick

The communication of information between neurons and between neurons and muscles or peripheral organs requires that signals travel over considerable distances. A number of notable scientists have contemplated the nature of this communication through the ages. In the second century AD, the great Greek physician Claudius Galen proposed that "humors" flowed from the brain to the muscles along hollow nerves. A true electrophysiological understanding of nerve and muscle, however, depended on the discovery and understanding of electricity itself. The precise nature of nerve and muscle action became clearer with the advent of new experimental techniques by a number of European scientists, including Luigi Galvini, Emil Du Bois-Reymond, Carlo Matteucci, and Hermann von Helmholtz, to name a few.[1,2] Through the application of electrical stimulation to nerves and muscles, these early electrophysiologists demonstrated that the conduction of commands from the brain to muscle for the generation of movement was mediated by the flow of electricity along nerve fibers.

With the advancement of electrophysiological techniques, electrical activity recorded from nerves revealed that the conduction of information along the axon was mediated by the active generation of an electrical potential, called the **action potential**. But what precisely was the nature of these action potentials? To know this in detail required not only a preparation from which to obtain intracellular recordings but also one that could survive *in vitro*. The squid giant axon provided precisely such a preparation, as was first demonstrated by J. Z. Young in 1936.[3] Many invertebrates contain unusually large axons for the generation of escape reflexes; large axons conduct more quickly than small ones and so the response time for escape is reduced (see Chapter 5). The squid possesses an axon approximately 0.5 mm in diameter, large enough to be impaled by even a course micropipette (Fig. 6.1). By inserting a glass micropipette filled with a salt solution into the squid giant axon, Alan Hodgkin and Andrew Huxley demonstrated in 1939 that axons at rest are electrically **polarized** exhibiting a resting **membrane potential** of approximately −60 mV inside versus outside.[4,5] In the generation of an action potential, the polarization of the membrane is removed (referred to as **depolarization**) and exhibits a rapid swing toward, and even past 0 mV (Fig. 6.1). This depolarization is followed by a rapid swing in the membrane potential to more negative values, a process referred to as **hyperpolarization.** The membrane potential following an action potential typically becomes even more negative than the original value of approximately −60 mV. This period of increased polarization is referred to as the **afterhyperpolarization** or the undershoot.

The development of electrophysiological techniques to the point that intracellular recordings could be obtained from the small cells of the mammalian nervous system revealed that action potentials in these neurons are generated through mechanisms similar to that of the squid giant axon.[6–9]

It is now known that action potential generation in nearly all types of neurons and muscle cells is accomplished through mechanisms similar to those first detailed in the squid giant axon by Hodgkin and Huxley. In this chapter, we consider the cellular

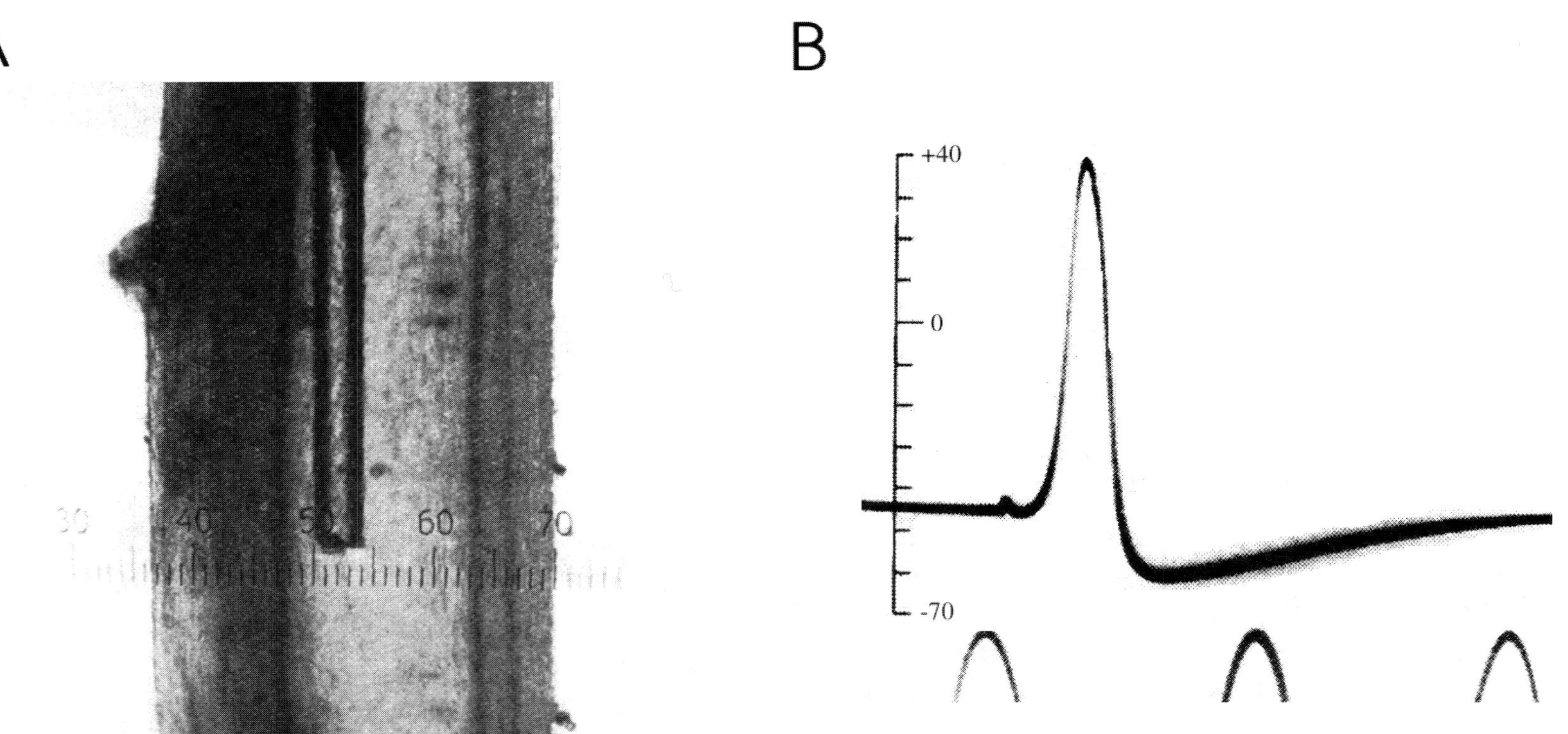

FIGURE 6.1 Intracellular recording of the membrane potential and action potential generation in the squid giant axon. (A) A glass micropipette, about 100 μm in diameter, was filled with seawater and lowered into a squid giant axon that had been dissected free. The axon, about 0.5 mm in diameter, was transilluminated from behind. (B) The nerve action potential. Note that the membrane potential becomes positive at the peak and that the repolarization is followed by an afterhyperpolarization. The sine wave at the bottom provides a scale for timing, with 2 ms between peaks. From Hodgkin and Huxley.[4]

mechanisms by which neurons and axons generate a resting membrane potential and how this membrane potential is briefly disrupted for the purpose of propagation of an electrical signal, the action potential.

THE MEMBRANE POTENTIAL

The Membrane Potential Is Generated by the Differential Distribution of Ions

Through the operation of ionic pumps and special ionic buffering mechanisms, neurons actively maintain precise internal concentrations of several important ions, including Na^+, K^+, Cl^-, and Ca^{2+}. The mechanisms by which they do so are illustrated in Figs. 6.2 and 6.3. The intracellular and extracellular concentrations of Na^+, K^+, Cl^-, and Ca^{2+} differ markedly (see Fig. 6.2); K^+ is actively concentrated inside the cell, and Na^+, Cl^-, and Ca^{2+} are actively extruded to the extracellular space. However, this does not mean that the cell is filled only with positive charge; anions (denoted A^-) to which the plasma membrane is impermeant are also present inside the cell and almost balance the high concentration of K^+. The osmolarity inside the cell is approximately equal to that outside the cell.

Electrical and Thermodynamic Forces Determine the Passive Distribution of Ions

Ions tend to move down their concentration gradients through specialized ionic pores, known as **ionic channels,** in the plasma membrane. Through simple laws of thermodynamics, the high concentration of K^+ inside glial cells, neurons, and axons results in a tendency for K^+ ions to diffuse down their concentration gradient and leave the cell or cell process (see Fig. 6.3). However, the movement of ions across the membrane also results in a redistribution of electrical charge. As K^+ ions move down their concentration gradient, the intracellular voltage becomes more negative, and this increased negativity results in an electrical attraction between the negative potential inside the cell and the positively charged, K^+ ions, thus offsetting the outward flow of K^+ ions. The membrane is **selectively permeable;** that is, it is impermeable to the large anions inside the cell, which cannot follow the potassium ions across the membrane. At some membrane potential, the "force" of the electrostatic attraction between the negative membrane potential inside the cell and the positively charged K^+ ions will exactly balance the thermal "forces" by which K^+ ions tend to flow down their concentration gradient (see Fig. 6.3). In this circumstance, it is equally likely that a K^+ ion exits the cell by movement down the concentration gradient as it is that a K^+ ion enters the cell owing to the attraction between the negative membrane potential and the positive charge of this ion. At this membrane potential, there is no *net* flow of K^+, and these ions are said to be in **equilibrium.** The membrane potential at which this occurs is known as the **equilibrium potential.** (See Box 6.1[10] for the calculation of the equilibrium potential.)

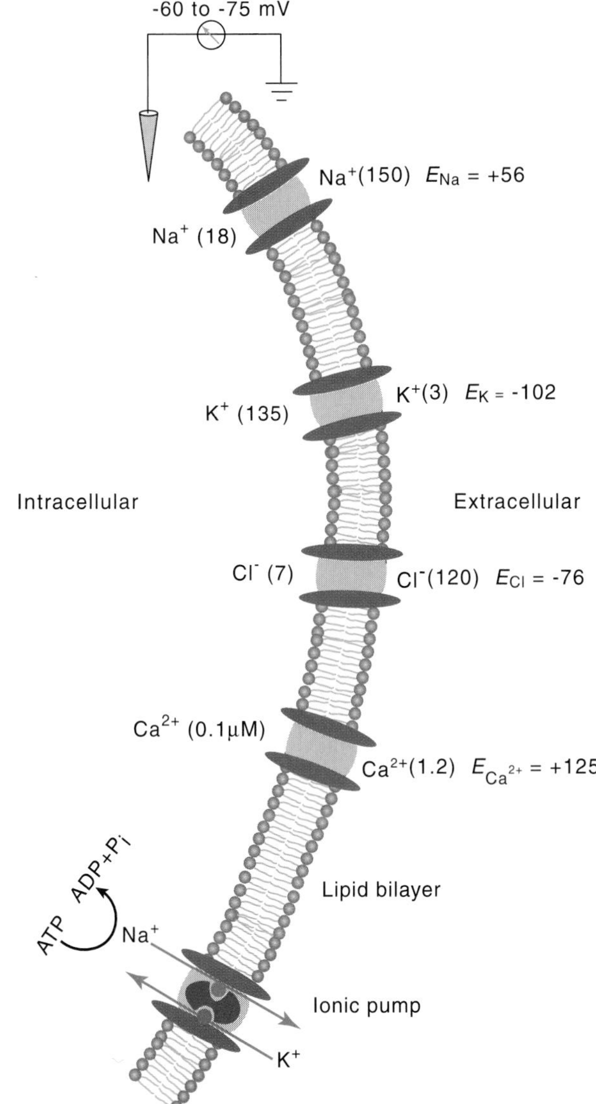

FIGURE 6.2 Differential distribution of ions inside and outside plasma membrane of neurons and neuronal processes, showing ionic channels for Na^+, K^+, Cl^-, and Ca^{2+}, as well as an electrogenic Na^+–K^+ ionic pump (also known as Na^+,K^+-ATPase). Concentrations (in millimoles except that for intracellular Ca^{2+}) of the ions are given in parentheses; their equilibrium potentials (E) for a typical mammalian neuron are indicated.

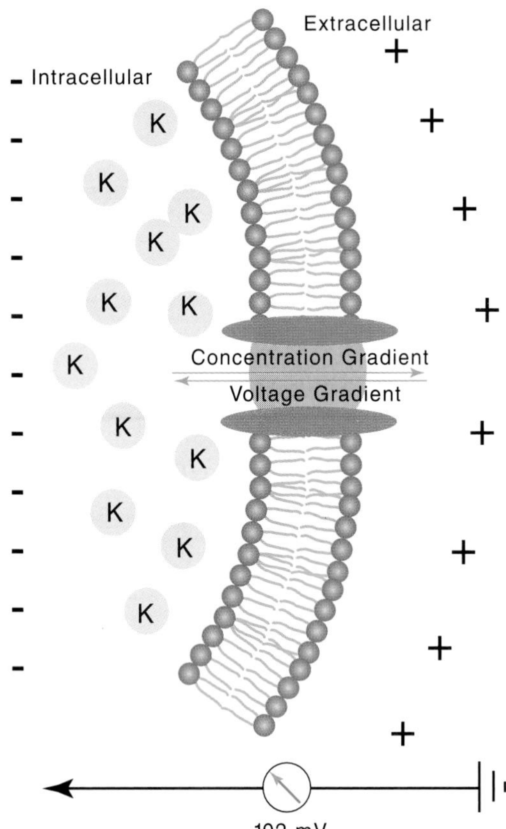

FIGURE 6.3 The equilibrium potential is influenced by the concentration gradient and the voltage difference across the membrane. Neurons actively concentrate K^+ inside the cell. These K^+ ions tend to flow down their concentration gradient from inside to outside the cell. However, the negative membrane potential inside the cell provides an attraction for K^+ ions to enter or remain within the cell. These two factors balance one another at the equilibrium potential, which in a typical mammalian neuron is −102 mV for K^+.

To illustrate, let us consider the passive distribution of K^+ ions in the squid giant axon as studied by Hodgkin and Huxley. The K^+ concentration $[K^+]$ inside the squid giant axon is about 400 m*M*, whereas the $[K^+]$ outside the axon is about 20 m*M* (Table 6.1). Because $[K^+]_i$ is greater than $[K^+]_o$ potassium ions will tend to flow down their concentration gradient, taking positive charge with them. The equilibrium potential (at which the tendency for K^+ ions to flow down their concentration gradient will be exactly offset by the attraction for K^+ ions to enter the cell because of the negative charge inside the cell) at a room temperature of 20°C is

$$E_K = 58.2 \log_{10}(20/400) = -76 \text{ mV}.$$

Therefore, at a membrane potential of −76 mV, K^+ ions have an equal tendency to flow either into or out of the axon. The concentrations of K^+ in mammalian neurons and glial cells differ considerably from that in the squid giant axon (see Table 6.1). By substituting 3.1 m*M* for $[K^+]_o$ and 140 m*M* for $[K^+]_i$ in the Nernst equation, with $T = 37°C$, we obtain

$$E_K = 61.5 \log_{10}(3.1/140) = -102 \text{ mV}.$$

Movements of Ions Can Cause either Hyperpolarization or Depolarization

In mammalian cells, at membrane potentials positive to −102 mV, K^+ ions tend to flow out of the cell. Increasing the ability of K^+ ions to flow across the membrane—that is, increasing the **conductance** of the membrane to K^+ (gK)—causes the membrane potential to become more negative, or **hyperpolarized,** owing to the exiting of positively charged ions from inside the cell (Fig. 6.4).

At membrane potentials negative to −102 mV, K^+ ions tend to flow into the cell; increasing the membrane conductance to K^+ causes the membrane potential to become more positive, or **depolarized,** owing to the flow of positive charge into the cell. The membrane potential at which the net current "flips" direction is referred to as the **reversal potential.** If the channels conduct only one type of ion (e.g., K^+ ions), then the reversal potential and the Nernst equilibrium potential for that ion coincide (see Fig. 6.4A). Increasing the membrane conductance to K^+ ions while the membrane potential is at the equilibrium potential for K^+ (E_K) does not change the membrane potential, because no net driving force causes K^+ ions to either exit or enter the cell. However, this increase in membrane conductance to K^+ decreases the ability of other species of ions to change the membrane potential, because any deviation of the potential from E_K increases the drive for K^+ ions to either exit or enter the cell, thereby drawing the membrane potential back toward E_K (see Fig. 6.4B).

The exiting and entering of the cell by K^+ ions during the generation of the membrane potential give rise to a curious problem. When K^+ ions leave the cell to generate a membrane potential, the concentration of K^+ changes both inside and outside the cell. Why does this change in concentration not alter the equilibrium potential, thus changing the tendency for K^+ ions to flow down their concentration gradient? The reason is that the number of K^+ ions required to leave the cell to achieve the equilibrium potential is quite small. For example, if a cell were at 0 mV and the membrane suddenly became permeable to K^+ ions, only about 10^{-12} mol of K^+ ions per square centimeter of membrane would move from inside to outside the cell in bringing the membrane potential to the equilibrium potential for K^+. In a spherical cell of 25-μm diameter, this would

BOX 6.1

THE NERNST EQUATION

The equilibrium potential is determined by (1) the concentration of the ion inside and outside the cell, (2) the temperature of the solution, (3) the valence of the ion, and (4) the amount of work required to separate a given quantity of charge. The equation that describes the equilibrium potential was formulated by a German physical chemist named Walter Nernst in 1888[10]:

$$E_{\text{ion}} = RT/zF \cdot \ln[\text{ion}]_o/[\text{ion}]_i.$$

Here, E_{ion} is the membrane potential at which the ionic species is at equilibrium, R is the gas constant [8.315 joules per Kelvin per mole (J K^{-1} mol^{-1})], T is the temperature in Kelvins ($T_{\text{Kelvin}} = 273.16 + T_{\text{Celcius}}$), F is Faraday's constant [96,485 coulombs per mole (C mol^{-1})], z is the valence of the ion, and $[\text{ion}]_o$ and $[\text{ion}]_i$ are the concentrations of the ion outside and inside the cell, respectively. For a monovalent, positively charged ion (cation) at room temperature (20°C), substituting the appropriate numbers and converting natural log (ln) into log base 10 ($\log_{10}$) result in the equation

$$E_{\text{ion}} = 58.2 \log_{10}[\text{ion}]_o/[\text{ion}]_i;$$

at a body temperature of 37°C, the Nernst equation is

$$E_{\text{ion}} = 61.5 \log_{10}[\text{ion}]_o/[\text{ion}]_i.$$

amount to an average decrease in intracellular K^+ of only about 4 μM (e.g., from 140 to 139.996 mM). However, there are instances when significant changes in the concentrations of K^+ may occur, particularly during the generation of pronounced activity, such as that related to an epileptic seizure. During the occurrence of a tonic-clonic generalized (grand mal) seizure, large numbers of neurons discharge throughout the cerebral cortex in a synchronized manner. This synchronous discharge of large numbers of neurons significantly increases the extracellular K^+ concentration, by as much as a couple of millimoles, resulting in a commensurate positive shift in the equilibrium potential for K^+.[11,12] This shift in the equilibrium potential can increase the excitability of affected neurons and neuronal processes and thus promote the spread of the seizure activity. Fortunately, the extracellular concentration of K^+ is tightly regulated and kept at normal levels through uptake by glial cells as well as by diffusion through the fluid of the extracellular space.[13]

TABLE 6.1 Ion Concentrations and Equilibrium Potentials

	Inside (mM)	Outside (mM)	Equilibrium potential (mV)
	Squid giant axon		
Na^+	50	440	+55
K^+	400	20	−76
Cl^-	40	560	−66
Ca^{2+}	0.4 μM	10	+145
	Mammalian neuron		
Na^+	18	145	+56
K^+	135	3	−102
Cl^-	7	120	−76
Ca^{2+}	100 nM	1.2	+125

As is true for K^+ ions, each of the different ions to which biological membranes are permeable possesses an equilibrium potential that depends on the concentration of the ions inside and outside the cell. Thus, equilibrium potentials may vary between different cell types, such as those found in animals adapted to live in salt water versus mammalian neurons (see Table 6.1). In mammalian neurons, the equilibrium potential is approximately +56 mV for Na^+, approximately −76 mV for Cl^-, and about +125 mV for Ca^{2+} (see Table 6.1 and Fig. 6.2). Thus, increasing the membrane conductance to Na^+ (gNa) through the opening of Na^+ channels depolarizes the membrane potential toward +56 mV; increasing the membrane conductance to Cl^- brings the membrane potential closer to −76 mV; and finally increasing the membrane conductance to Ca^{2+} depolarizes the cell toward +125 mV.

Na^+, K^+, and Cl^- Contribute to the Determination of the Resting Membrane Potential

If a membrane is permeable to only one ion and no electrogenic ionic pumps are operating (see next section), then the membrane potential is necessarily at

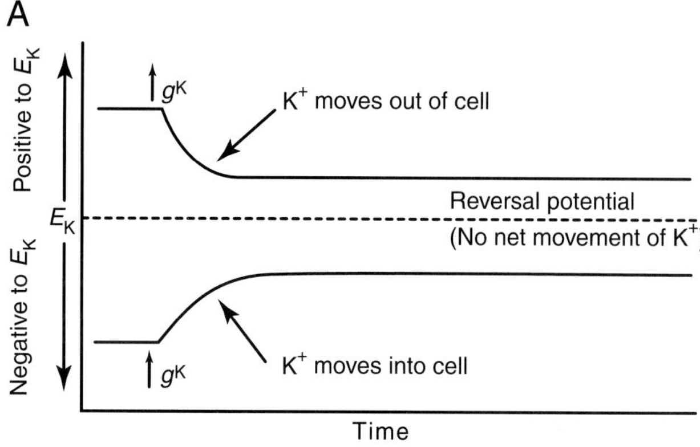

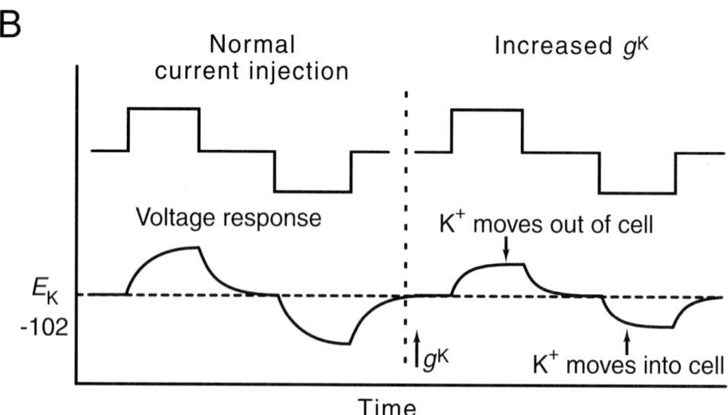

FIGURE 6.4 Increases in K^+ conductance can result in hyperpolarization, depolarization, or no change in membrane potential. (A) Opening K^+ channels increases the conductance of the membrane to K^+, denoted gK. If the membrane potential is positive to the equilibrium potential (also known as the reversal potential) for K^+, then increasing gK will cause some K^+ ions to leave the cell, and the cell will become hyperpolarized. If the membrane potential is negative to E_K when gK is increased, then K^+ ions will enter the cell, therefore making the inside more positive (more depolarized). If the membrane potential is exactly E_K when gK is increased, then there will be no net movement of K^+ ions. (B) Opening K^+ channels when the membrane potential is at E_K does not change the membrane potential; however, it reduces the ability of other ionic currents to move the membrane potential away from E_K. For example, a comparison of the ability of the injection of two pulses of current, one depolarizing and one hyperpolarizing, to change the membrane potential before and after opening K^+ channels reveals that increases in gK noticeably decrease the responses of the cell.

the equilibrium potential for that ion. At rest, the plasma membrane of most cell types is not at the equilibrium potential for K^+ ions, indicating that the membrane is also permeable to other types of ions. For example, the resting membrane of the squid giant axon is permeable to Cl^- and Na^+, as well as K^+, owing to the presence of ionic channels that not only allow these ions to pass but also are open at the resting membrane potential. Because the membrane is permeable to K^+, Cl^-, and Na^+, the resting potential of the squid giant axon is not equal to E_K, E_{Na}, or E_{Cl}, but is somewhere in-between these three. A membrane permeable to more than one ion has a steady-state membrane potential whose value is between those of the equilibrium potentials for each of the permeant ions (Box 6.2).[14,15]

Different Types of Neurons Have Different Resting Potentials

Intracellular recordings from neurons in the mammalian CNS reveal that different types of neurons exhibit different resting membrane potentials. Indeed, some types of neurons do not even exhibit a true "resting" membrane potential; they spontaneously and continuously generate action potentials even in the total lack of synaptic input. In the visual system, intracellular recordings have shown that the photoreceptor cells of the retina—the rods and cones—have a membrane potential of approximately −40 mV at rest and are hyperpolarized when activated by light.[16] Cells in the dorsal lateral geniculate nucleus, which receive axonal input from the retina and project to the visual cortex, have a resting membrane potential of approximately −70 mV during sleep and −55 mV during waking,[17–19] whereas pyramidal neurons of the visual cortex have a resting membrane potential of about −75 mV.[20] Presumably, the resting membrane potentials of different cell types in the central and peripheral nervous system are highly regulated and are functionally important. For example, the depolarized membrane potential of photoreceptors presumably allows the membrane potential to move in both negative and positive directions in response to changes in light intensity. The hyperpolarized membrane potential of thalamic neurons during sleep (−70 mV) dramatically decreases the flow of information from the sensory periphery to the cerebral cortex,[21,22] presumably to allow the cortex to be relatively undisturbed during sleep, and the 20-mV membrane potential between the resting potential and the action potential threshold in cortical pyramidal cells may permit the subthreshold computation and integration of multiple neuronal inputs in single neurons (see Chapters 5 and 13).

Ionic Pumps Actively Maintain Ionic Gradients

Because the resting membrane potential of a neuron is not at the equilibrium potential for any particular ion, ions constantly flow down their concentration gradients. This flux becomes considerably larger with the generation of electrical and synaptic potentials, because ionic channels are opened by these events. Although the absolute number of ions traversing the plasma membrane during each action potential or synaptic potential may be small in individual cells, the

BOX 6.2

THE GOLDMAN–HODGKIN–KATZ EQUATION

An equation developed by Goldman[14] and later used by Alan Hodgkin and Bernard Katz[15] describes the steady-state membrane potential for a given set of ionic concentrations inside and outside the cell and the relative **permeabilities** of the membrane to each of those ions:

$$V_m = RT/F \cdot \ln\{(p_K[K^+]_o + p_{Na}[Na^+]_o + p_{Cl}[Cl^-]_i)/(p_K[K^+]_i + p_{Na}[Na^+]_i + p_{Cl}[Cl^-]_o)\}.$$

The relative contribution of each ion is determined by its concentration differences across the membrane and the relative permeability (p_K, p_{Na}, p_{Cl}) of the membrane to each type of ion. If a membrane is permeable to only one ion, then the Goldman–Hodgkin–Katz equation reduces to the Nernst equation. In the squid giant axon, at resting membrane potential, the permeability ratios are

$$p_K : p_{Na} : p_{Cl} = 1.00 : 0.04 : 0.45.$$

The membrane of the squid giant axon, at rest, is most permeable to K^+ ions, less so to Cl^-, and least permeable to Na^+. (Chloride appears to contribute considerably less to the determination of the resting potential of mammalian neurons.) These results indicate that the resting membrane potential is determined by the resting permeability of the membrane to K^+, Na^+, and Cl^-. In theory, this resting membrane potential may be anywhere between E_K (e.g., −76 mV) and E_{Na} (+55 mV). For the three ions at 20°C, the equation is

$$V_m = 58.2 \log_{10}\{(1 \cdot 20 + 0.04 \cdot 440 + 0.45 \cdot 40)/(1 \cdot 400 + 0.04 \cdot 50 + 0.45 \cdot 560)\} = -62 \text{ mV}.$$

This suggests that the squid giant axon should have a resting membrane potential of −62 mV. In fact, the resting membrane potential may be a few millivolts hyperpolarized to this value through the operation of the electrogenic Na^+–K^+ pump.

collective influence of a large neural network of cells, such as in the brain, and the presence of ion fluxes even at rest can substantially change the distribution of ions inside and outside neurons. Cells have solved this problem with the use of active transport of ions against their concentration gradients. The proteins that actively transport ions are referred to as **ionic pumps,** of which the Na^+–K^+ pump is perhaps the most thoroughly understood.[23–26] The Na^+–K^+ pump is stimulated by increases in the intracellular concentration of Na^+ and moves Na^+ out of the cell while moving K^+ into it, achieving this task through the hydrolysis of ATP (see Fig. 6.2). Three Na^+ ions are extruded for every two K^+ ions transported into the cell. Owing to the unequal transport of ions, the operation of this pump generates a hyperpolarizing electrical potential and is said to be **electrogenic.** The Na^+–K^+ pump typically results in the membrane potential of the cell being a few millivolts more negative than it would be otherwise.

The Na^+–K^+ pump consists of two subunits, α and β, arranged in a tetramer $(\alpha\beta)_2$. The α subunit has a molecular mass of about 100 kDa and six hydrophobic regions capable of forming transmembrane helices.[27,28] The β subunit is smaller (about 38 kDa) and has only one hydrophobic membrane-spanning region. The Na^+–K^+ pump is believed to operate through conformational changes that alternatively expose a Na^+ binding site to the interior of the cell (followed by the release of Na^+) and a K^+ binding site to the extracellular fluid (see Fig. 6.2). Such a conformation change may be due to the phosphorylation and dephosphorylation of the protein.

The membranes of neurons and glia contain multiple types of ionic pumps, used to maintain the proper distribution of each ionic species important for cellular signaling.[29,30] Many of these pumps are operated by the Na^+ gradient across the cell, whereas others operate through a mechanism similar to that of the Na^+–K^+ pump (i.e., the hydrolysis of ATP). For example, the calcium concentration inside neurons is kept to very low levels (typically 50–100 n*M*) through the operation of both types of ionic pumps as well as special intracellular Ca^{2+} buffering mechanisms. Ca^{2+} is extruded from neurons through both a Ca^{2+},Mg^{2+}-ATPase and a Na^+–Ca^{2+} exchanger. The Na^+–Ca^{2+} exchanger is driven by the Na^+ gradient across the membrane and extrudes one Ca^{2+} ion for each Na^+ ion allowed to enter the cell.

The Cl^- concentration in neurons is actively maintained at a low level through the operation of a chloride–bicarbonate exchanger, which brings in one ion of Na^+ and one ion of HCO_3^- for each ion of Cl^- extruded.[31,32] Intracellular pH also can markedly affect neuronal excitability and is therefore tightly regulated, in part by a Na^+–H^+ exchanger that extrudes one proton for each Na^+ allowed to enter the cell.

Summary

The membrane potential is generated by the unequal distribution of ions, particularly K^+, Na^+, and Cl^-, across the plasma membrane. This unequal distribution of ions is maintained by ionic pumps and exchangers. K^+ ions are concentrated inside the neuron and tend to flow down their concentration gradient, leading to a hyperpolarization of the cell. At the equilibrium potential, the tendency of K^+ ions to flow out of the cell will be exactly offset by the tendency of K^+ ions to enter the cell owing to the attraction of the negative potential inside the cell. The resting membrane is also permeable to Na^+ and Cl^- and therefore the resting membrane potential is approximately −75 to −40 mV, in other words, substantially positive to E_K.

THE ACTION POTENTIAL

An Increase in Na^+ and K^+ Conductance Generates Action Potentials

Hodgkin and Huxley not only recorded the action potential with an intracellular microelectrode (see Fig. 6.1), but also went on to perform a remarkable series of experiments that qualitatively and quantitatively explained the ionic mechanisms by which the action potential is generated.[33–37] As mentioned earlier, these investigators found that during the action potential, the membrane potential of the cell rapidly overshoots 0 mV and approaches the equilibrium potential for Na^+. After the generation of the action potential, the membrane potential repolarizes and becomes more negative than before, generating an afterhyperpolarization. Kenneth Cole and Howard Curtis had previously shown that these changes in membrane potential during the generation of the action potential are associated with a large increase in conductance of the plasma membrane.[38] But to what does the membrane become conductive in order to generate the action potential? The prevailing hypothesis was that there was a nonselective increase in conductance causing the negative resting potential to increase toward 0 mV. Since publication of the experiments of E. Overton in 1902,[39] the action potential had been known to depend on the presence of extracellular Na^+. Reducing the concentration of Na^+ in the artificial seawater bathing the axon resulted in a marked reduction in the amplitude of the action potential. On the basis of these and other data, Hodgkin and Katz proposed that the action potential is generated through a rapid increase in the conductance of the membrane to Na^+ ions. A quantitative proof of this theory was lacking, however, because ionic currents could not be observed directly. The development of the **voltage-clamp** technique by Kenneth Cole at the Marine Biological Laboratory in Massachusetts resolved this problem and allowed quantitative measurement of the Na^+ and K^+ currents underlying the action potential[40] (Box 6.3).

Hodgkin and Huxley used the voltage-clamp technique to investigate the mechanisms of generation of the action potential in the squid giant axon. Axons and neurons have a threshold for the initialization of an action potential of about −45 to −55 mV. Increasing the voltage from −60 to 0 mV produces a large, but transient, flow of positive charge into the cell (known as **inward current**). This **transient** inward current is followed by a sustained flow of positive charge out of the cell (the **outward current**). By voltage-clamping the cell and substituting different ions inside or outside the axon or both, Hodgkin, Huxley, and colleagues demonstrated that the transient inward current is carried by Na^+ ions flowing into the cell and the sustained outward current is mediated by a sustained flux of K^+ ions moving out of the cell (Fig. 6.6).[33–37,41]

The Na^+ and K^+ currents (I_{Na} and I_K, respectively) can be blocked, allowing each current to be examined in isolation (see Fig. 6.6B). Tetrodotoxin (TTX), a powerful poison found in the puffer fish *Spheroides rubripes*,[42] selectively blocks voltage-dependent Na^+ currents (the puffer fish remains a delicacy in Japan and must be prepared with the utmost care by the chef). Using TTX, one can selectively isolate I_K and examine its voltage dependence and time course (see Fig. 6.6B).

Clay Armstrong, Bertil Hille,[43] and others demonstrated that tetraethylammonium (TEA) is a useful pharmacological tool for selectively blocking I_K (see Fig. 6.6B). The use of TEA to examine the voltage dependence and time course of the Na^+ current underlying action-potential generation (see Fig. 6.6B) reveals some fundamental differences between the Na^+ and the K^+ currents. First, the inward Na^+ current *activates*, or "turns on," much more rapidly than does the K^+ current (giving rise to the name "delayed rectifier" for this K^+ current). Second, the Na^+ current is transient; it *inactivates*, even if the membrane potential is maintained at 0 mV (see Fig. 6.6A). In contrast, the outward K^+ current, once activated, remains "on" as long as the membrane potential is clamped to positive levels; that is, the K^+ current does not inactivate; it is *sustained*. Remarkably, from one experiment, we see that the Na^+ current both rapidly *activates* and *inactivates*, whereas the K^+ current only slowly *activates*. These fundamental properties of the underlying Na^+ and K^+ channels allow the generation of action potentials.

BOX 6.3

THE VOLTAGE-CLAMP TECHNIQUE

In the voltage-clamp technique, two independent electrodes are inserted into the squid giant axon: one for recording the voltage difference across the membrane and the other for intracellularly injecting the current (Fig. 6.5). These electrodes are then connected to a feedback circuit that compares the measured voltage across the membrane with the voltage desired by the experimenter. If these two values differ, then current is injected into the axon to compensate for this difference. This continuous feedback cycle, in which the voltage is measured and current is injected, effectively "clamps" the membrane at a particular voltage. If ionic channels were to open, then the resultant flow of ions into or out of the axon would be compensated for by the injection of positive or negative current into the axon through the current-injection electrode. The current injected through this electrode is necessarily equal to the current flowing through the ionic channels. It is this injected current that is measured by the experimenter. The benefits of the voltage-clamp technique are twofold. First, the current injected into the axon to keep the membrane potential "clamped" is necessarily equal to the current flowing through the ionic channels in the membrane, thereby giving a direct measurement of this current. Second, ionic currents are both voltage and time dependent; they become active at certain membrane potentials and do so at a particular rate. Keeping the voltage constant in the voltage clamp allows these two variables to be separated; the voltage dependence and the kinetics of the ionic currents flowing through the plasma membrane can be directly measured.

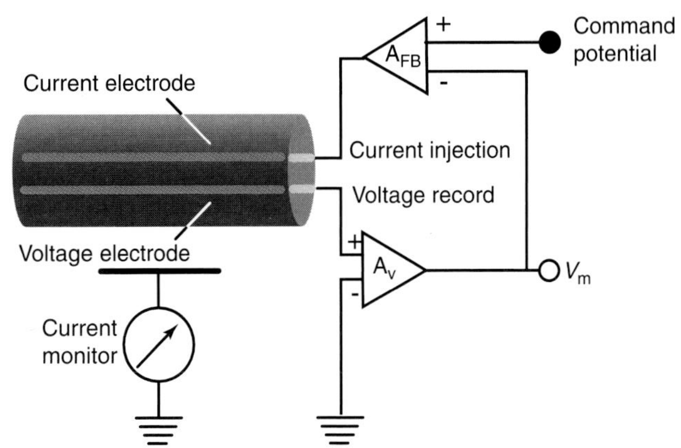

FIGURE 6.5 Voltage-clamp technique. The voltage-clamp technique keeps the voltage across the membrane constant so that the amplitude and time course of ionic currents can be measured. In the two-electrode voltage-clamp technique, one electrode measures the voltage across the membrane while the other injects current into the cell to keep the voltage constant. The experimenter sets a voltage to which the axon or neuron is to be stepped (the command potential). Current is then injected into the cell in proportion to the difference between the present membrane potential and the command potential. This feedback cycle occurs continuously, thereby clamping the membrane potential to the command potential. By measuring the amount of current injected, the experimenter can determine the amplitude and time course of the ionic currents flowing across the membrane.

Hodgkin and Huxley[33–36] proposed that the K^+ channels possess a voltage-sensitive "gate" that opens by the depolarization and closes by the subsequent repolarization of the membrane potential. This process of "turning on" and "turning off" the K^+ current came to be known as **activation** and **deactivation**. The Na^+ current also exhibits voltage-dependent activation and deactivation (see Fig. 6.6), but the Na^+ channels also become inactive despite maintained depolarization. Thus, the Na^+ current not only activates and deactivates, but also exhibits a separate process known as **inactivation,** whereby the channels become blocked even though they are activated. The removal of this inactivation is achieved by removal of the depolarization and is a process known as **deinactivation.** Thus, the Na^+ channels possess two voltage-sensitive processes: *activation–deactivation* and *inactivation–deinactivation*. The kinetics of these two properties of Na^+ channels are different: inactivation takes place at a slower rate than activation.

The functional consequence of the two mechanisms is that Na^+ ions are allowed to flow across the membrane only when the current is activated but not inactivated. Accordingly, Na^+ ions do not flow at resting membrane potentials, because the activation gate is closed (even though the inactivation gate is not). Upon depolarization, the activation gate opens, allowing Na^+ ions to flow into the cell. However, this depolarization also results in the closure (at a slower rate) of the inactivation gate, which then blocks the flow of Na^+ ions. Upon repolarization of the membrane potential, the activation gate once again closes and the inactiva-

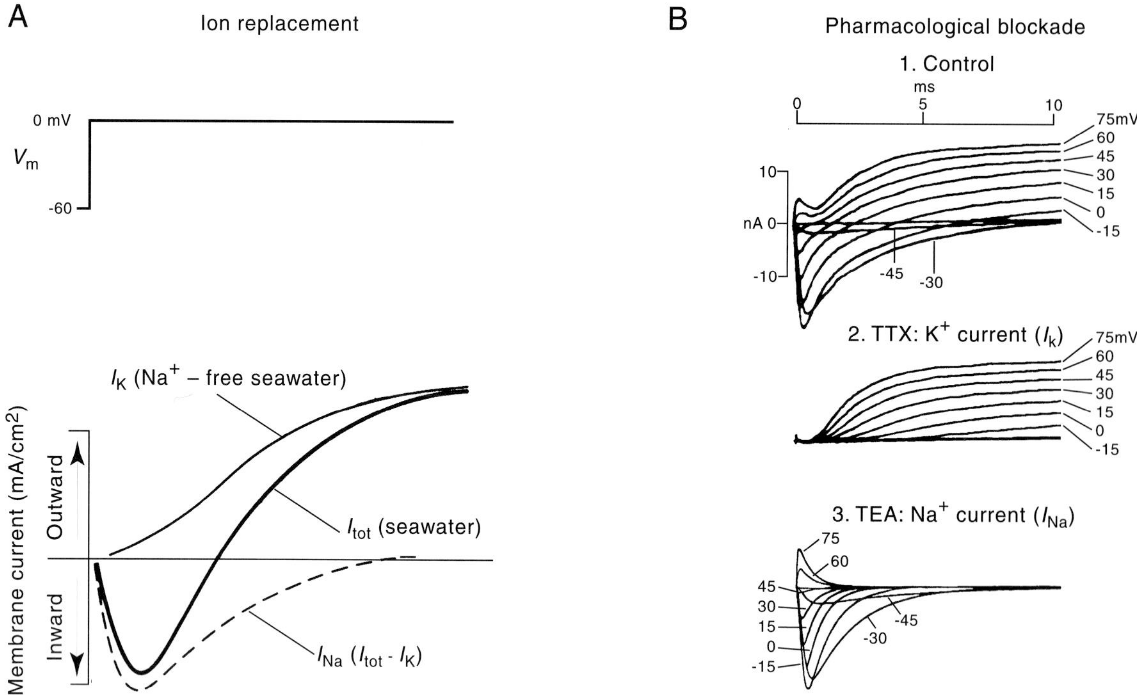

FIGURE 6.6 Voltage-clamp analysis reveals the ionic currents underlying action potential generation. (A) Increasing the potential from −60 to 0 mV across the membrane of the squid giant axon activates an inward current followed by an outward current. If the Na$^+$ in seawater is replaced by choline (which does not pass through Na$^+$ channels), then increasing the membrane potential from −60 to 0 mV results in only the outward current, which corresponds to I_K. Subtracting I_K from the recording in normal seawater illustrates the amplitude–time course of the inward Na$^+$ current, I_{Na}. Note that I_K activates more slowly than I_{Na} and that I_{Na} inactivates with time. (B) These two ionic currents can also be isolated from one another through the use of pharmacological blockers. (1) Increasing the membrane potential from −45 to +75 mV in 15-mV steps reveals the amplitude–time course of the inward Na$^+$ and outward K$^+$ currents. (2) After the block of I_{Na} with the poison tetrodotoxin (TTX), increasing the membrane potential to positive levels activates I_K only. (3) After the block of I_K with tetraethylammonium (TEA), increasing the membrane potential to positive levels activates I_{Na} only. Part A, from Hodgkin and Huxley[33]; part B from Hille.[41]

tion gate once again opens, preparing the axon for the generation of the next action potential (Fig. 6.7). Depolarization allows ionic current to flow by virtue of *activation* of the channel. The rush of Na$^+$ ions into the cell further depolarizes the membrane potential and more Na$^+$ channels become activated, forming a positive feedback loop that rapidly (within 100 μs or so) brings the membrane potential toward E_{Na}. However, the depolarization associated with the generation of the action potential also inactivates Na$^+$ channels, and, as a larger and larger percentage of Na$^+$ channels become inactivated, the rush of Na$^+$ into the cell diminishes. This inactivation of the Na$^+$ channels and the activation of K$^+$ channels result in the repolarization of the action potential. This repolarization deactivates the Na$^+$ channels. Then, the inactivation of the channel is slowly removed, and the channels are ready, once again, for the generation of another action potential (see Fig. 6.7).

By measuring the voltage sensitivity and kinetics of these two processes, activation–deactivation and inactivation–deinactivation of the Na$^+$ current, as well as the activation–deactivation of the delayed rectifier K$^+$ current, Hodgkin and Huxley generated a series of mathematical equations that quantitatively described the generation of the action potential (the calculation of the propagation of a single action potential required an entire week of cranking a mechanical calculator). According to these early experimental and computational neuroscientists, the action potential is generated as follows. Depolarization of the membrane potential increases the probability of Na$^+$ channels being in the activated, but not yet inactivated, state. At a particular membrane potential, the resulting inflow of Na$^+$ ions tips the balance of the net ionic current from outward to inward (remember that depolarization will also increase K$^+$ and Cl$^-$ currents by moving the membrane potential away from E_K and E_{Cl}). At this membrane

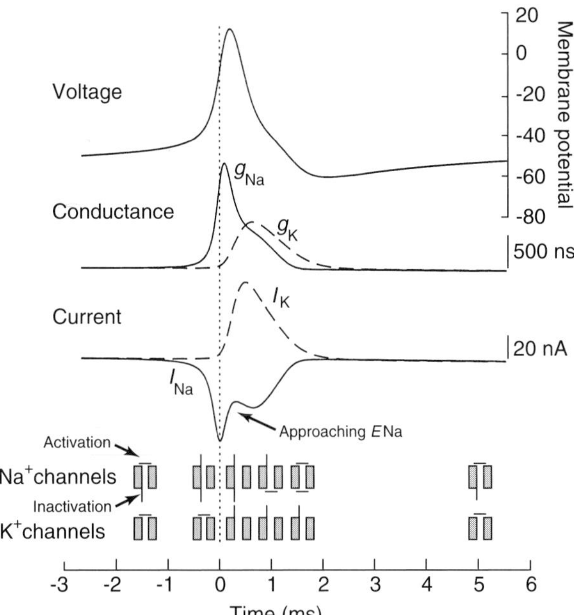

FIGURE 6.7 The generation of the action potential is associated with an increase in membrane Na^+ conductance and Na^+ current followed by an increase in K^+ conductance and K^+ current. Before action potential generation, Na^+ channels are neither activated nor inactivated (illustrated at the bottom of the figure). Activation of the Na^+ channels allows Na^+ ions to enter the cell, depolarizing the membrane potential. This depolarization also activates K^+ channels. After activation and depolarization, the inactivation particle on the Na^+ channels closes and the membrane potential repolarizes. The persistence of the activation of K^+ channels (and other membrane properties) generates an afterhyperpolarization. During this period, the inactivation particle of the Na^+ channel is removed and the K^+ channels close. From Huguenard and McCormick.[61]

potential, known as the action potential threshold (typically about −55 mV), the movement of Na^+ ions into the cell depolarizes the axon, and opens more Na^+ channels, causing yet more depolarization of the membrane; repetition of this process yields a rapid, positive feedback loop that brings the axon close to E_{Na}. However, even as more and more Na^+ channels are becoming activated, some of these channels are also inactivating and therefore no longer conducting Na^+ ions. In addition, the delayed rectifier K^+ channels also are opening, owing to the depolarization of the membrane potential, and allowing positive charge to exit the cell. At some point, close to the peak of the action potential, the inward movement of Na^+ ions into the cell is exactly offset by the outward movement of K^+ ions out of the cell. After this point, the outward movement of K^+ ions dominates, and the membrane potential is repolarized, corresponding to the fall of the action potential. The persistence of the K^+ current for a few milliseconds following the generation of the action potential generates the afterhyperpolarization. During this afterhyperpolarization, which is lengthened by the membrane time constant, the inactivation of the Na^+ channels is removed, preparing the axon for generation of the next action potential (see Fig. 6.7).

The occurrence of an action potential is not associated with substantial changes in the intracellular or extracellular concentrations of Na^+ or K^+, as we saw earlier for the generation of the resting membrane potential. For example, the generation of a single action potential in a 25-μm-diameter hypothetical spherical cell should increase the intracellular concentration of Na^+ by only approximately 6 μM (from about 31 to 31.006 mM). Thus, the action potential is an electrical event generated by a change in the distribution of charge across the membrane and not by a marked change in the intracellular or extracellular concentration of Na^+ or K^+.

Refractory Periods Prevent "Reverberation"

The ability of depolarization to activate an action potential varies as a function of the time since the last generation of an action potential, owing to the inactivation of Na^+ channels and the activation of K^+ channels. Immediately after the generation of an action potential, another action potential usually cannot be generated regardless of the amount of current injected into the axon. This period corresponds to the **absolute refractory period** and is largely mediated by the inactivation of Na^+ channels. The **relative refractory period** follows the absolute refractory period during the action potential afterhyperpolarization. This few-millisecond period is characterized by a requirement for the increased injection of ionic current into the cell to generate another action potential and results from the persistence of the outward K^+ current. The practical implication of refractory periods is that action potentials are not allowed to "reverberate" between the soma and the axon terminals.

The Speed of Action Potential Propagation Is Affected by Myelination

Axons may be either myelinated or unmyelinated. Invertebrate axons or small vertebrate axons are typically unmyelinated, whereas larger vertebrate axons are often myelinated. As described in Chapter 4, sensory and motor axons of the peripheral nervous system are myelinated by specialized cells (Schwann cells) that form a spiral wrapping of multiple layers of myelin around the axon (Fig. 6.8). Several Schwann cells wrap around an axon along its length; between the ends of successive Schwann cells are small gaps (nodes of Ranvier). In the central nervous system, a single **oligo-**

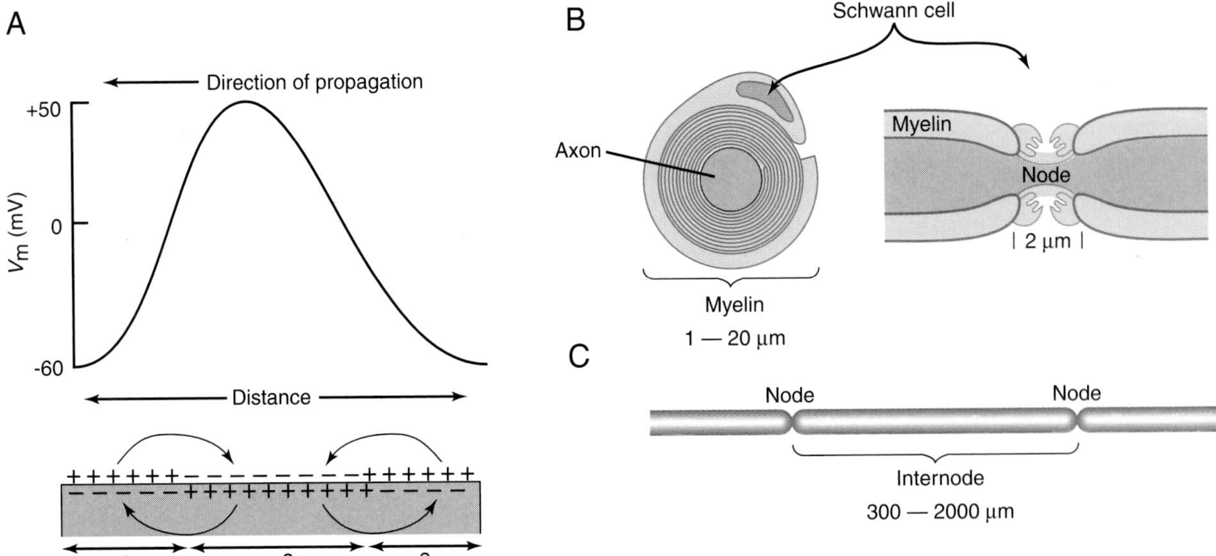

FIGURE 6.8 Propagation of the action potential in unmyelinated and myelinated axons. (A) Action potentials propagate in unmyelinated axons through the depolarization of adjacent regions of membrane. In the illustrated axon, region 2 is undergoing depolarization during the generation of the action potential, while region 3 has already generated the action potential and is now hyperpolarized. The action potential will propagate further by depolarizing region 1. (B) Vertebrate myelinated axons have a specialized Schwann cell that wraps around them in many spiral turns. The axon is exposed to the external medium at the nodes of Ranvier (Node). (C) Action potentials in myelinated fibers are regenerated at the nodes of Ranvier, where there is a high density of Na^+ channels. Action potentials are induced at each node through the depolarizing influence of the generation of an action potential at an adjacent node, thereby increasing the conduction velocity.

dendrocyte, a special type of glial cell, typically ensheaths several axonal processes.[44]

In unmyelinated axons, the Na^+ and K^+ channels taking part in action potential generation are distributed along the axon, and the action potential propagates along the length of the axon through local depolarization of each neighboring patch of membrane, causing that patch of membrane also to generate an action potential (see Fig. 6.8). In myelinated axons, on the other hand, the Na^+ channels are concentrated at the nodes of Ranvier.[45] The generation of an action potential at each node results in the depolarization of the next node and subsequently the generation of an action potential with an internode delay of only about 20 μs (see Chapter 5), referred to as **saltatory conduction** (from the Latin *saltare,* "to leap"). Growing evidence indicates that, between the nodes of Ranvier and underneath the myelin covering, K^+ channels may play a role in determining the resting membrane potential and the repolarization of the action potential. A cause of some neurological disorders, such as multiple sclerosis and Guillain–Barre syndrome, is the demyelination of axons, resulting in a block of conduction of the action potentials (see Chapter 3).

Ion Channels Are Membrane-Spanning Proteins with Water-Filled Pores

The generation of ionic currents useful for the propagation of action potentials requires the movement of significant numbers of ions across the membrane in a relatively short time. The rate of ionic flow during the generation of an action potential is far too high to be achieved by an active transport mechanism and results instead from the opening of ion channels. Although the existence of ionic channels in the membrane has been postulated for decades, their properties and structure have only recently become known in detail. The powerful combination of electrophysiological and molecular techniques has greatly enhanced our knowledge of the structure–function relations of ionic channels[46–51] (Box 6.4).

Various neural toxins were particularly useful in the initial isolation of ionic channels. For example, three subunits (α, $\beta1$, $\beta2$) of the voltage-dependent Na^+ channel were isolated with the use of a derivative of a scorpion toxin.[49,52] The α subunit of the Na^+ channel is a large glycoprotein with a molecular mass of 270 kDa, whereas the $\beta1$ and $\beta2$ subunits are smaller polypeptides of molecular masses 39 and 37 kDa, respectively (Fig. 6.9). The α subunit forms the water-filled pore of the ionic channel, whereas the β subunits have some other role, such as in the regulation or structure of the native channel.

The α subunit of the Na^+ channel contains four internal repetitions (see Fig. 6.9B). Hydrophobicity analysis of these four components reveals that each contains six hydrophobic domains that may span the membrane as an α-helix. Of these six membrane-spanning components, the fourth (S4) has been proposed to be critical to the voltage sensitivity of the Na^+ channels. Voltage-sensitive gating of Na^+ channels is accomplished by the redistribution of ionic charge ("gating charge") in the Na^+ channel.[53] Positive charges in the S4 region may act as voltage sensors such that an increase in the positivity of the inside of the cell results in a conformational change of the ionic channel. In support of this hypothesis, site-directed mutagenesis of the S4 region of the Na^+ channel to reduce the positive charge of this portion of the pore also reduces the voltage sensitivity of activation of the ionic channel.[49]

The mechanisms of inactivation of ionic channels have been analyzed with a combination of molecular and electrophysiological techniques. The most convincing hypothesis is that inactivation is achieved by a block of the inner mouth of the aqueous pore. Ionic channels are inactivated without detectable movement of ionic current through the membrane; thus inactivation is probably not directly gated by changes in the membrane potential alone. Rather, inactivation may be triggered or facilitated as a secondary consequence of activation. Site-directed mutagenesis or the use of antibodies has shown that the part of the molecule between regions III and IV may be allowed to move to block the cytoplasmic side of the ionic pore after the conformational change associated with activation.[54–56]

Neurons of the Central Nervous System Exhibit a Wide Variety of Electrophysiological Properties

The first intracellular recordings of action potentials in mammalian neurons by Sir John Eccles and colleagues revealed a remarkable similarity to those of the squid giant axon and gave rise to the assumption that the electrophysiology of neurons in the CNS was really rather simple: when synaptic potentials brought the membrane potential positive to action potential threshold, action potentials were produced through an increase in Na^+ conductance followed by an increase in K^+ conductance, as in the squid giant axon. The assumption, therefore, was that the complicated patterns of activity generated by the brain during the resting, sleeping, or active states were brought about as an interaction of the very large numbers of neurons present in the mammalian CNS.[6,57] However, intracellular recordings of invertebrate neurons revealed that different cell types exhibit a wide variety of different electrophysiological behaviors, indicating that neurons may be significantly more complicated than the squid giant axon.[58–60] The elucidation of the basic electrophysiology and synaptic physiology of different types of neurons and neuronal pathways within the mammalian CNS was facilitated by the *in vitro* slice technique, in which thin (~0.5 mm) slices of brain can be maintained for several hours. Intracellular recordings from identified cells revealed that neurons of the mammalian nervous system, such as those of invertebrate networks, can generate complex patterns of action potentials entirely through intrinsic ionic mechanisms and without synaptic interaction with other cell types. For example, Rodolfo Llinás and colleagues discovered that Purkinje cells of the cerebellum can generate high-frequency trains (>200 Hz) of Na^+- and K^+-mediated action potentials interrupted by Ca^{2+} spikes in the dendrites,[61,62] whereas a major afferent to these neurons, the inferior olivary cell, can generate rhythmic sequences of broad action potentials only at low frequencies (<15 Hz) through an interaction between various Ca^{2+}, Na^+, and K^+ conductances[63,64] (Fig. 6.10). These *in vitro* recordings confirmed a major finding obtained with earlier intracellular recordings *in vivo:* each morphologically distinct class of neuron in the brain exhibits its distinct electrophysiological features.[65] Just as cortical pyramidal cells are morphologically distinct from cerebellar Purkinje cells, which are distinct from thalamic relay cells, the electrophysiological properties of each of these different cell types also are markedly distinct.

Although no uniform classification scheme has been formulated in which all the different types of neurons of the brain can be classified, a few characteristic patterns of activity seem to recur. The first general class of action potential generation is characterized by those cells that generate trains of action potentials one spike at a time. The more prolonged the depolarization of these cells, the more prolonged their discharge. The more intensely these cells are depolarized, the higher the frequency of action potential generation. This type of relatively linear behavior is typical for brainstem and spinal cord motor neurons functioning in muscle contraction. A modification of this basic pattern of "regular firing" is characterized by the generation of trains of action potentials that exhibit a marked tendency to slow down in frequency with time, a process known as spike frequency adaptation. Examples of

BOX 6.4

ION CHANNELS AND DISEASE

Cells cannot survive without functional ion channels. It is therefore not surprising that an ever increasing number of diseases have been found to be associated with defective ion channel function. There are a number of different mechanisms by which this may occur.

1. Mutations in the coding region of ion channel genes may lead to gain or loss of channel function, either of which may have deleterious consequences. For example, mutations producing enhanced activity of the epithelial Na^+ channel are responsible for Liddle syndrome, an inherited form of hypertension, whereas other mutations in the same protein that cause reduced channel activity give rise to hypotension. The most common inherited disease in Caucasians is also an ion channel mutation. This disease is cystic fibrosis (CF), which results from mutations in the epithelial chloride channel, known as CFTR. The most common mutation, the deletion of a phenylalanine at position 508, results in defective processing of the protein and prevents it from reaching the surface membrane. CFTR regulates chloride fluxes across epithelial cell membranes, and this loss of CFTR activity leads to reduced fluid secretion in the lung, resulting in potentially fatal lung infections.

2. Mutations in the promoter region of the gene may cause under- or overexpression of a given ion channel.

3. Other diseases result from defective regulation of channel activity by cellular constituents or extracellular ligands. This defective regulation may be caused by mutations in the genes encoding the regulatory molecules themselves or defects in the pathways leading to their production. Some forms of maturity-onset diabetes of the young (MODY) may be attributed to such a mechanism. ATP-sensitive potassium (K-ATP) channels play a key role in the glucose-induced insulin secretion from pancreatic β cells, and their defective regulation is responsible for two forms of MODY.

4. Autoantibodies to channel proteins may cause disease by down-regulating channel function—often by causing internalization of the channel protein itself. Well-known examples are myasthenic gravis, which results from antibodies to skeletal muscle acetylcholine channels, and Eaton Lambert myasthenic syndrome, in which patients produce antibodies against presynaptic Ca channels.

5. Finally, a number of ion channels are secreted by cells as toxic agents. They insert into the membrane of the target cell and form large nonselective pores, leading to cell lysis and death. The hemolytic toxin produced by the bacterium *Staphylococcus aureus* and the toxin secreted by the protozoan *Entamoeba histolytica*, which causes amebic dysentery, are examples.

Natural mutations in ion channels have been invaluable for studying the relationship between channel structure and function. In many cases, genetic analysis of a disease has led to the cloning of the relevant ion channel. The first K channel to be identified (*Shaker*), for example, came from the cloning of the gene that caused *Drosophila* to shake when exposed to ether. Likewise, the gene encoding the primary subunit of a cardiac potassium channel (*KVLQT1*) was identified by positional cloning in families carrying mutations that caused a cardiac disorder known as long QT syndrome (see below). Conversely, the large number of studies on the relationship between Na channel structure and function have greatly assisted our understanding of how mutations in Na channels produce their clinical phenotypes.

Many diseases are genetically heterogeneous, and the same clinical phenotype may be caused by mutations in different genes. Long QT syndrome is a relatively rare inherited cardiac disorder that causes abrupt loss of consciousness, seizures, and sudden death from ventricular arrhythmia in young people. Mutations in three different genes, two types of cardiac muscle K channels (*HERG* and *KVLQT1*) and the cardiac muscle sodium channel (*SCN1A*), give rise to long QT syndrome. The disorder is characterized by a long QT interval in the electrocardiogram, which reflects the delayed repolarization of the cardiac action potential. As might therefore be expected, the mutations in the cardiac Na channel gene that cause long QT syndrome enhance the Na current (by reducing Na channel inactivation), while those in the potassium channel genes cause loss of function and reduce the K current.

Mutations in many different types of ion channels have been shown to cause human diseases. In addition to the examples listed above, mutations in water channels cause nephrogenic diabetes insipidus; mutations in gap junction channels cause Charcot–Marie–Tooth disease (a form of peripheral neuropathy) and hereditary deafness; mutations in the skeletal muscle Na channel cause a range of disorders known as the periodic paralyses; mutations in intracellular Ca-release channels cause malignant hyperthermia (a disease in which inhalation anaesthetics trigger a potentially fatal rise in body temperature); and mutations in neuronal voltage-gated Ca channels cause migraine and episodic ataxia. The list increases daily. As is the case with all single gene disorders, the frequency of these diseases in the general population is very low. However, the insight they have provided into the relationship between ion channel structure and function, and into the physiological role of the different ion channels, has been invaluable. As William Harvey said in 1657 "nor is there any better way to advance the proper practice of medicine than to give our minds to the discovery of the usual form of nature, by careful investigation of the rarer forms of disease."

Frances M. Ashcroft

cells that discharge in this manner are cortical and hippocampal pyramidal cells.[20,66,67]

In addition to these regular firing cells, many neurons in the central nervous system exhibit the intrinsic propensity to generate rhythmic bursts of action potentials (see Fig. 6.10). Examples of such neurons are thalamic relay neurons, inferior olivary neurons, and some types of cortical and hippocampal pyramidal cells.[18,19,63,64,68] In these cells, clusters of action potentials can occur together when the membrane is brought above firing threshold. These clusters of action potentials are typically generated through the activation of specialized Ca^{2+} currents that, through their slower kinetics, allow the membrane potential to be depolarized for a sufficient period to result in the generation of a burst of regular, Na^+- and K^+-dependent action potentials (discussed in the next section).

Yet another general category of neurons in the brain comprises cells that generate relatively short duration (<1 ms) action potentials and can discharge at relatively high frequencies (>300 Hz). Such electrophysiological properties are often found in neurons that release the inhibitory amino acid γ-aminobutyric acid[61,62] (see Fig. 6.10) and some types of interneurons in the cerebral cortex, thalamus, and hippocampus.[20,69,70] Finally, the last general category of neurons consists of those that spontaneously generate action potentials at relatively slow frequencies (e.g., 1–10 Hz). This type of electrophysiological behavior is often associated with neurons that release neuromodulatory transmitters, such as acetylcholine, norepinephrine, serotonin, and histamine.[71–73] Neurons that release these neuromodulatory substances often innervate wide regions of the brain and appear to set the "state" of the different neural networks of the CNS, in a manner similar to the modulation of the different organs of the body by the sympathetic and parasympathetic nervous systems.[22,74]

Each of these unique intrinsic patterns of activity in the nervous system is due to the presence of a distinct mixture and distribution of different ionic currents in the cells. As in the classical studies of the squid giant axon, these different ionic currents have been characterized, at least in part, with voltage-clamp and pharmacological techniques, and the basic electrophysiological properties have been replicated with computational simulations[75–77] (see Figs. 6.7 and 6.12).

Neurons Have Multiple Active Conductances

The search for the electrophysiological basis of the varying intrinsic properties of different types of neurons of vertebrates and invertebrates revealed a wide variety of ionic currents. Each type of ionic current is characterized by several features: (1) the type of ions conducted by the underlying ionic channels (e.g., Na^+, K^+, Ca^{2+}, Cl^-, or mixed cations), (2) their voltage and time dependence, and (3) their sensitivity to second messengers. In vertebrate neurons, two distinct Na^+ currents have been identified and five distinct Ca^{2+} currents and a plethora of distinct K^+ currents are known (Table 6.2; Fig. 6.11). In the following sections, we briefly review these classes of ionic currents and their ionic channels, relating them to the different patterns of behavior mentioned earlier for neurons in the mammalian CNS.

Na^+ Currents Are Both Transient and Persistent

Depolarization of many different types of vertebrate neurons results not only in the activation of the rapidly activating and inactivating Na^+ current (I_{Nat}) underlying action potential generation but also in the rapid activation of a Na^+ current that does not inactivate and is therefore known as the "persistent" Na^+ current (I_{Nap}).[65,78–80] The threshold for activation of the persistent Na^+ current is typically about −65 mV—that is, below the threshold for the generation of action potentials. This property gives this current the interesting ability to enhance or facilitate the response of the neuron to depolarizing, yet subthreshold, inputs. For example, synaptic events that depolarize the cell will activate I_{Nap}, resulting in an extra influx of positive charge and

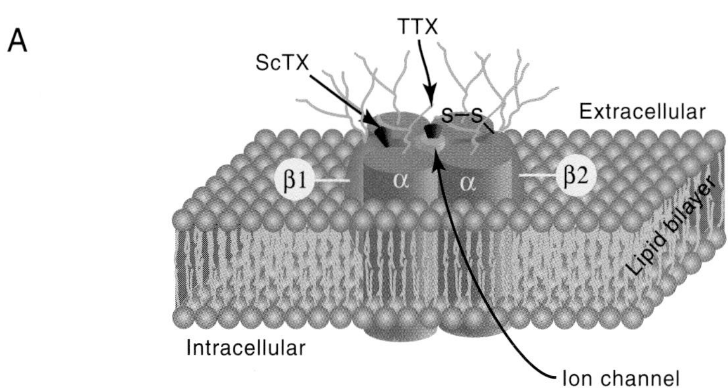

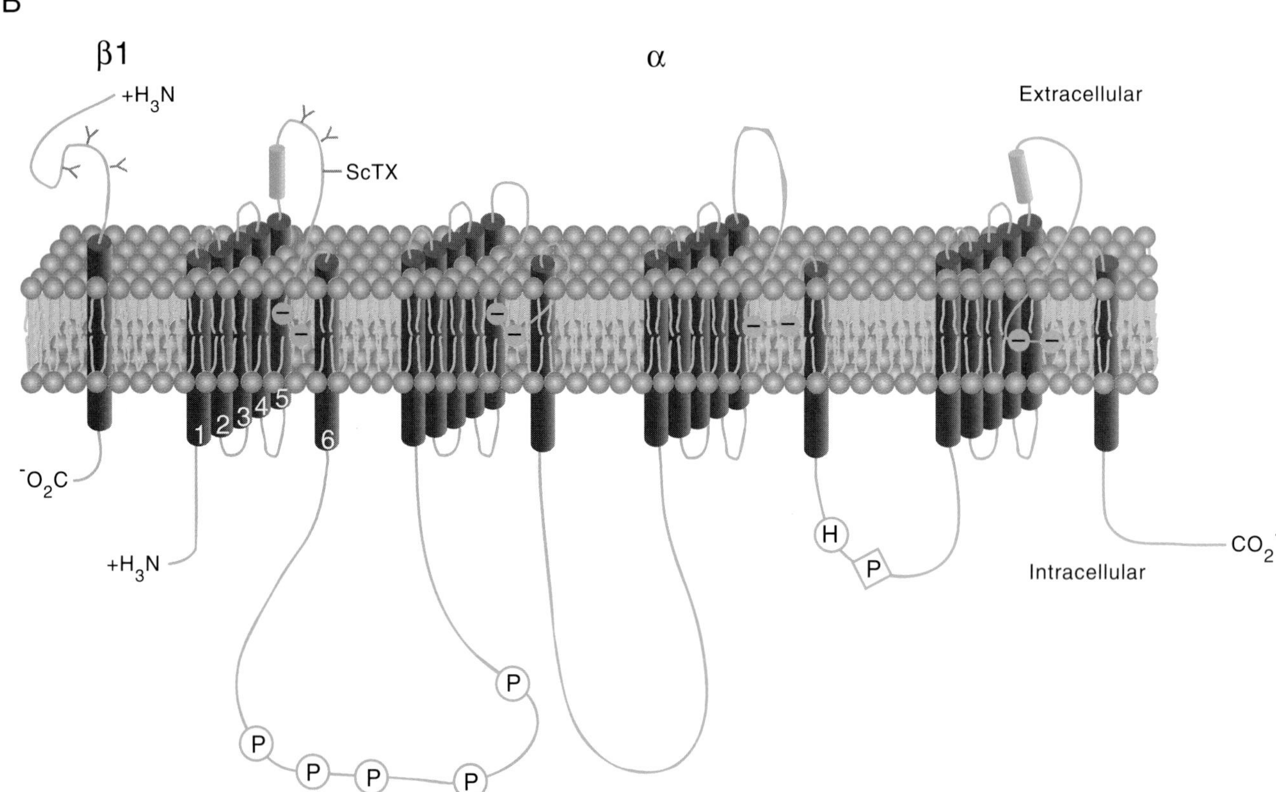

FIGURE 6.9 Structure of the sodium channel. (A) Cross section of a hypothetical sodium channel consisting of a single transmembrane α subunit in association with a $\beta 1$ subunit and a $\beta 2$ subunit. The α subunit has receptor sites for α-scorpion toxins (ScTX) and tetrodotoxin (TTX). (B) Primary structures of α and $\beta 1$ subunits of sodium channel illustrated as transmembrane folding diagrams. Cylinders represent probable transmembrane α-helices.

therefore a larger depolarization than otherwise would occur. Likewise, hyperpolarizations may result in deactivation of I_{Nap}, again resulting in larger hyperpolarizations than would otherwise occur. In this manner, the persistent Na^+ current may play an important regulatory function in the control of the functional responsiveness of the neuron to synaptic inputs and may contribute to the dynamic coupling of the dendrites to the soma.

Persistent activation of I_{Nap} may also contribute to another electrophysiological feature of neurons—namely, the generation of **plateau potentials.**[65] A plateau potential refers to the ability of many different types of neurons to generate, through intrinsic ionic

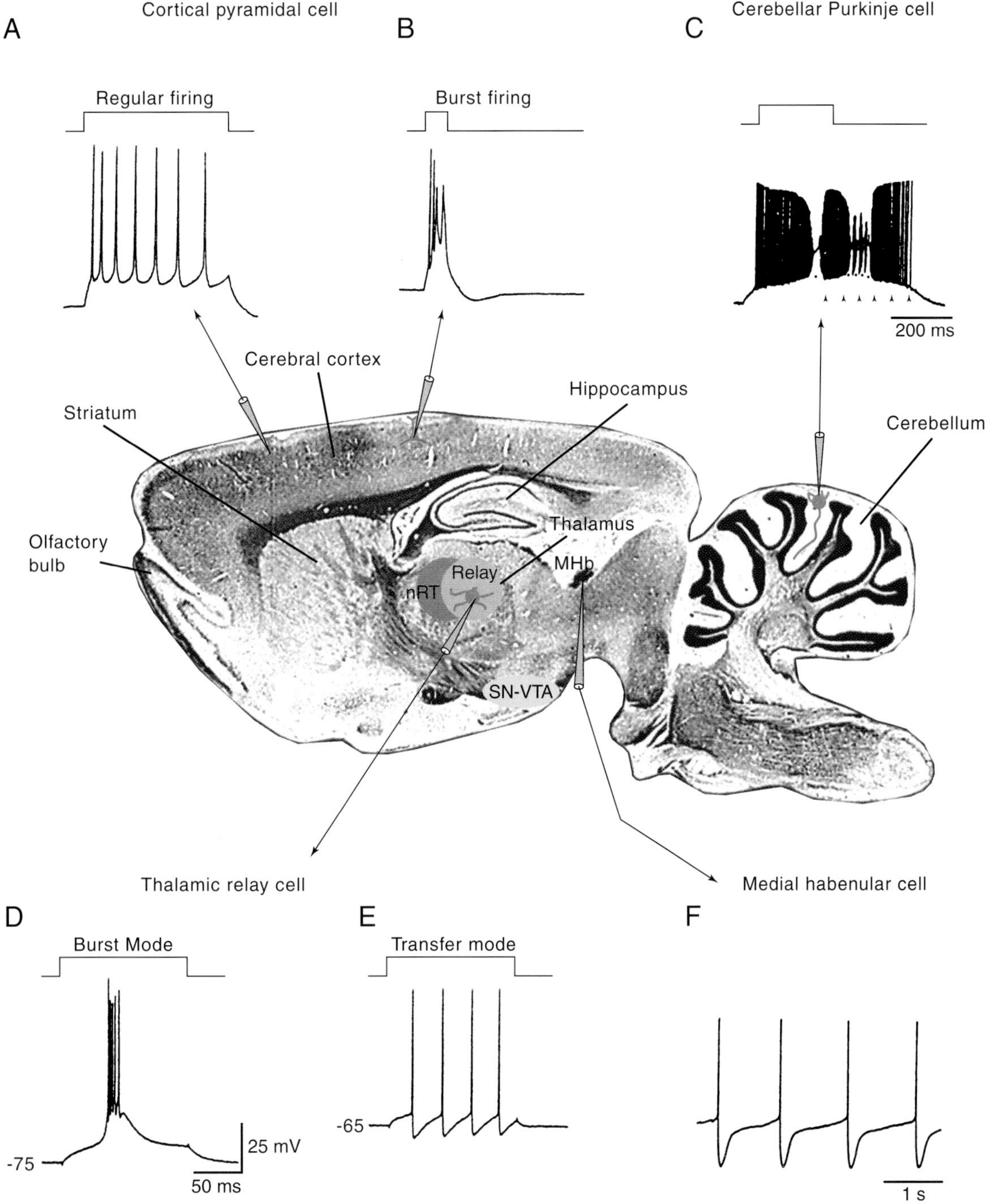

FIGURE 6.10 Neurons in the mammalian brain exhibit widely varying electrophysiological properties. (A) Intracellular injection of a depolarizing current pulse in a cortical pyramidal cell results in a train of action potentials that slow down in frequency. This pattern of activity is known as "regular firing." (B) Some cortical cells generated bursts of three or more action potentials, even when depolarized only for a short period of time. (C) Cerebellar Purkinje cells generate high-frequency trains of action potentials in their cell bodies that are disrupted by the generation of Ca^{2+} spikes in their dendrites. These cells can also generate "plateau potentials" from the persistent activation of Na^{+} conductances (arrowheads). (D) Thalamic relay cells may generate action potentials either as bursts (D) or as tonic trains of action potentials (E) owing to the presence of a large low-threshold Ca^{2+} current. (F) Medial habenular cells generate action potentials at a steady and slow rate, in a "pacemaker" fashion.

TABLE 6.2 Neuronal Ionic Currents

Current	Description	Function
Na^+ currents		
$I_{Na,t}$	Transient; rapidly activating and inactivating	Action potentials
$I_{Na,p}$	Persistent; noninactivating	Enhances depolarization; contributes to steady-state firing
Ca^{2+} currents		
I_T, low threshold	Transient; rapidly inactivating; threshold negative to −65 mV	Underlies rhythmic burst firing
I_L, high threshold	Long-lasting; slowly inactivating; threshold around −20 mV	Underlies Ca^{2+} spikes that are prominent in dendrites; involved in synaptic transmission
I_N	Neither; rapidly inactivating; threshold around −20 mV	Underlies Ca^{2+} spikes that are prominent in dendrites; involved in synaptic transmission
I_P	Purkinje; threshold around −50 mV	
K^+ currents		
I_K	Activated by strong depolarization	Repolarization of action potential
I_C	Activated by increases in $[Ca^{2+}]_i$	Action potential repolarization and interspike interval
I_{AHP}	Slow afterhyperpolarization; sensitive to increases in $[Ca^{2+}]_i$	Slow adaptation of action potential discharge; the block of this current by neuromodulators enhances neuronal excitability
I_A	Transient; inactivating	Delayed onset of firing; lengthens interspike interval; action potential repolarization
I_M	Muscarine sensitive; activated by depolarization; noninactivating	Contributes to spike frequency adaptation; the block of this current by neuromodulators enhances neuronal excitability
I_h	Depolarizing (mixed cation) current that is activated by hyperpolarization	Contributes to rhythmic burst firing and other rhythmic activities
$I_{K,leak}$	Contributes to neuronal resting membrane potential	Block of this current by neuromodulators can result in a sustained change in membrane potential

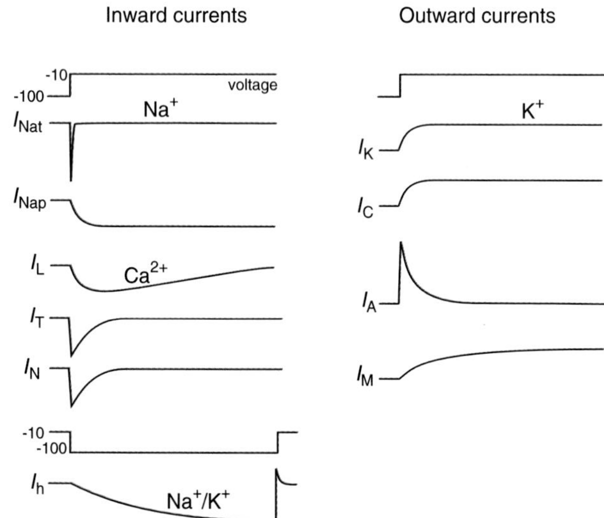

FIGURE 6.11 Voltage dependence and kinetics of different ionic currents in the mammalian brain. Depolarization of the membrane potential from −100 to −10 mV results in the activation of currents entering or leaving neurons.

mechanisms, a prolonged (from tens of milliseconds to seconds) depolarization and action potential discharge in response to a short-lasting depolarization (see Fig. 6.10C). One can wonder whether such plateau potentials contribute to persistent firing in neurons during the performance of visual memory tasks, as has been found in some types of neurons in the frontal neocortex and superior colliculus of behaving primates.[81]

K^+ Currents Vary in Their Voltage Sensitivity and Kinetics

Potassium currents that contribute to the electrophysiological properties of neurons are numerous and exhibit a wide range of voltage-dependent and kinetic properties.[51,82–84] Perhaps the simplest K^+ current is that characterized by Hodgkin and Huxley: this K^+ current, I_K, rapidly activates on depolarization and does not inactivate (see Fig. 6.11). Other K^+ currents activate with depolarization but also inactivate with time. For example, the rapid activation and inactivation of I_A give this current a transient appearance (see Fig. 6.11),

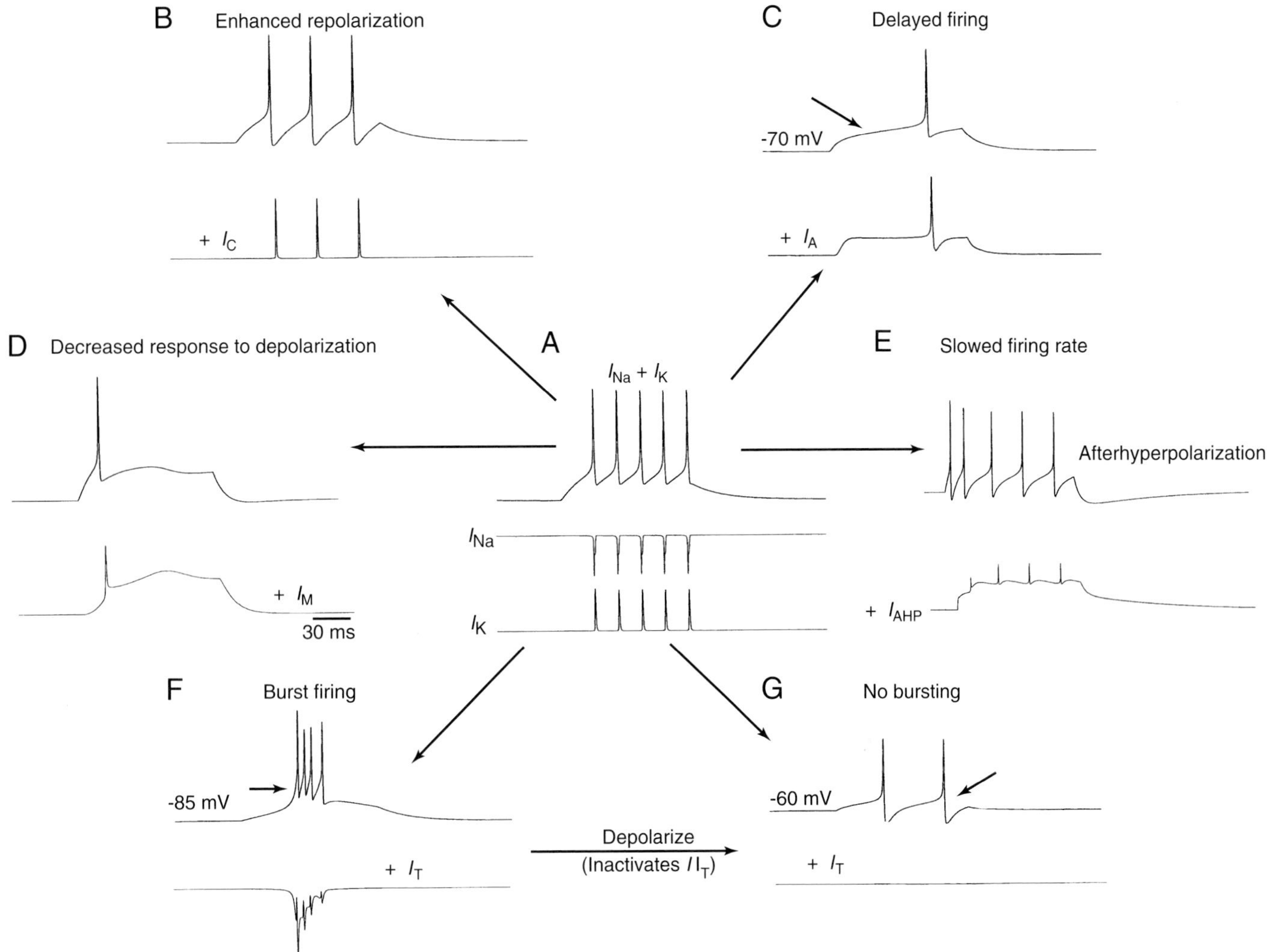

FIGURE 6.12 Simulation of the effects of the addition of various ionic currents to the pattern of activity generated by neurons in the mammalian CNS. (A) The repetitive impulse response of the classical Hodgkin–Huxley model (voltage recordings above, current traces below). With only I_{Na} and I_K, the neuron generates a train of five action potentials in response to depolarization. Addition of I_C (B) enhances action potential repolarization. Addition of I_A (C) delays the onset of action potential generation. Addition of I_M (D) decreases the ability of the cell to generate a train of action potentials. Addition of I_{AHP} (E) slows the firing rate and generates a slow afterhyperpolarization. Finally, addition of the transient Ca^{2+} current I_T results in two states of action potential firing: (F) burst firing at −85 mV and (G) tonic firing at −60 mV. From Huguenard and McCormick.[61]

and I_A is believed to be important in controlling the rate of action potential generation, particularly at low frequencies[85,86] (Fig. 6.12). Like the Na^+ channel, I_A channels are inactivated by the plugging of the inner mouth of the pore through the movement of an inactivation particle.[87,88]

Another broad class of K^+ channels consists of those that are sensitive to changes in the intracellular concentration of Ca^{2+}.[89,90] These K^+ currents are collectively referred to as I_{KCa} (see Fig. 6.11). Still other K^+ channels are not only activated by voltage but also modulated by activation of various modulatory neurotransmitter receptors (e.g., I_M; see Fig. 6.11). Between these classic examples of K^+ currents are a variety of other types that have not been fully characterized, including K^+ currents that vary from one another in their voltage sensitivity, kinetics, and response to various second messengers.

Recent molecular biological studies of voltage-sensitive K^+ channels, first done in *Drosophila* and later in mammals, have revealed the presence of four distinct gene families, *Shaker, Shab, Shaw,* and *Shal,*[51] that correspond to the newer nomenclature of Kv1, Kv2, Kv3, and Kv4 subfamilies.[91] These genes generate a wide variety of different K^+ channels through alternative RNA splicing and gene duplication. Functional expression of these different K^+ channels reveals remarkable variation in the rate of inactivation, such that *Shaker* channels are typically rapidly inactivating (A-current like), *Shal* channels inactivate more slowly, *Shab* channels inactivate very slowly, and *Shaw* channels typically do not inactivate, similar to I_K. These studies indicate that each type of neuron in the nervous system is likely to contain a unique set of functional voltage-sensitive K^+ channels, perhaps selected, modified, and placed in particular spatial locations in the cell in a manner to facilitate the unique role of that cell type in neuronal processing.

An additional current that also regulates the responsiveness of neurons to depolarizing inputs is the voltage-sensitive K^+ current known as the M-current (Figs. 6.11 and 6.12D). By investigating the ionic mechanisms by which the release of acetylcholine from preganglionic neurons in the brain results in prolonged changes in the excitability of neurons of the sympathetic ganglia, David Brown and Paul Adams[92] discovered a unique K^+ current that slowly (over tens of milliseconds) turns on with depolarization of the neuron (see Fig. 6.12D). The slow activation of this K^+ current results in a decrease in the responsiveness of the cell to depolarization, and therefore regulates how the cell responds to excitation. This K^+ current, like I_{AHP}, is reduced by the activation of a wide variety of receptors, including muscarinic receptors, for which it is named. Reduction of I_M results in a marked increase in responsiveness of the affected cell to depolarizing inputs and again may contribute to the mechanisms by which neuromodulatory systems control the state of activity in cortical and hippocampal networks.[74,93,94]

Ca^{2+} Currents Control Electrophysiological Properties and Ca^{2+}-Dependent Second-Messenger Systems

Ionic channels that conduct Ca^{2+} are present in all neurons. These channels are special in that they serve two important functions. First, Ca^{2+} channels are present throughout the different parts of the neuron (dendrites, soma, synaptic terminals) and contribute greatly to the electrophysiological properties of these processes.[65,95,96] Second, Ca^{2+} channels are unique in that Ca^{2+} is an important second messenger in neurons, and entry of Ca^{2+} into the cell can affect numerous physiological functions, including neurotransmitter release, synaptic plasticity, neurite outgrowth during development, and even gene expression.

On the bases of their voltage sensitivity, their kinetics of activation and inactivation, and their ability to be blocked by various pharmacological agents, Ca^{2+} currents can be separated into at least four separate categories, three of which are I_T ("transient"), I_L ("long lasting"), and I_N ("neither"),[97,98] illustrated in Fig. 6.11A. A fourth, I_P, is found in the Purkinje cells of the cerebellum, as well as in many different cell types of the CNS.[99] The wide variety of genes involved in the production of Ca^{2+} channels ensures that more Ca^{2+} currents are yet to be characterized.[100,101]

Neurons Possess Multiple Subtypes of High-Threshold Ca^{2+} Currents

High-voltage-activated Ca^{2+} channels are activated at membrane potentials positive to approximately -40 mV and include the currents I_L, I_N, and I_P. The L-type calcium currents exhibit a high threshold for activation (about -10 mV) and give rise to rather persistent, or long-lasting, ionic currents (see Fig. 6.11A). Dihydropyridines, Ca^{2+} channel antagonists, are clinically useful for their effects on the heart and vascular smooth muscle (e.g., for the treatment of arrhythmias, angina, and migraine headaches) and selectively block L-type Ca^{2+} channels.[102,103] In contrast with I_L, I_N is not blocked by dihydropyridines; rather it is selectively blocked by a toxin found in Pacific cone shells (ω-conotoxin-GVIA). The N-type Ca^{2+} channels have a threshold for activation of about -20 mV, inactivate with maintained depolarization, and are modulated by a variety of neurotransmitters. In some cell types, I_N has a role in the Ca^{2+}-dependent release of neurotransmitters at presynaptic terminals.[104] The P-type calcium channel is distinct from N and L types in that it is not blocked by either dihydropyridines or ω-conotoxin-GVIA but is blocked by a toxin (ω-agatoxin-IVA) present in the venom of the Funnel web spider.[99,103] This type of calcium channel activates at relatively high thresholds and does not inactivate. Prevalent in Purkinje cells as well as other cell types, as mentioned earlier, the P-type Ca^{2+} channel participates in the generation of dendritic Ca^{2+} spikes, which can strongly modulate the firing pattern of the neuron in which it resides (see Fig. 6.10C).

Collectively, the high-threshold-activated Ca^{2+} channels contribute to the generation of action potentials in mammalian neurons. The activation of Ca^{2+} currents adds somewhat to the depolarizing part of the action potential, but, more importantly, these channels allow Ca^{2+} to enter the cell and this has the secondary consequence of activation of various Ca^{2+}-activated K^+ currents[90] and protein kinases (see Chapter 10). As mentioned earlier, the activation of these K^+ currents modifies the pattern of action potentials generated in the cell (see Figs. 6.10 and 6.12).

High-threshold Ca^{2+} channels are similar to the Na^+ channel in that they are composed of a central $\alpha 1$ subunit that forms the aqueous pore and several regulatory or auxiliary subunits. As in the Na^+ channel, the primary structure of the α1 subunit of the Ca^{2+} channel consists of four homologous domains (I–IV), each containing six regions (S1–S6) that may generate transmembrane α-helices. The genes for at least five different Ca^{2+} channel α subunits have been cloned (α1A–E), and the properties of the products of these genes indicate that I_L is likely to correspond to α1C and α1D, whereas I_N corresponds to α1B and I_P may be related to α1A.[101,103]

Low-Threshold Ca^{2+} Currents Generate Bursts of Action Potentials

Low-threshold Ca^{2+} currents (see Fig. 6.11A) often take part in the generation of rhythmic bursts of action potentials (see Figs. 6.10 and 6.12). The low-threshold Ca^{2+} current is characterized by a threshold for activation of about −65 mV, which is below the threshold for generation of typical Na^+–K^+-dependent action potentials (−55 mV). This current inactivates with maintained depolarization. Owing to these properties, the role of low-threshold Ca^{2+} currents differs markedly from that of the high-threshold Ca^{2+} currents. Through activation and inactivation of the low-threshold Ca^{2+} current, neurons can generate slow (about 100 ms) Ca^{2+} spikes, which can result, owing to their prolonged duration, in the generation of a high-frequency "burst" of short-duration Na^+–K^+ action potentials (see Fig. 6.10 and Box 6.5).[105–109]

In the mammalian brain, this pattern is especially well exemplified by the activity of thalamic relay neurons; in the visual system, these neurons receive direct input from the retina and transmit this information to the visual cortex. During periods of slow wave sleep, the membrane potential of these relay neurons is relatively hyperpolarized, resulting in the removal of inactivation (deinactivation) of the low-threshold Ca^{2+} current. This deinactivation allows these cells to spon-

BOX 6.5

JELLYFISH—WHAT A NERVE!

Research on jellyfish provides an intriguing insight into how the properties and distribution of ion channels within a nerve membrane can affect the behavior of the whole animal. *Aglantha digitale* can swim slowly when feeding or quickly if escaping predators just through the "behavior" of a single muscle sheet coupled to a simply organized nervous system.

The jellyfish does this through an unusual form of signaling. Each "giant" motor nerve axon not only has voltage-dependent sodium channels and three types of potassium channel, but also crucial T-type calcium channels. *Aglantha* motor axons are unusual because they develop two entirely different propagating action potentials.[105] The T-type calcium channels contribute to a low-amplitude calcium-dependent spike that propagates along the motor axon without gaining amplitude or decrementing in the way that electrotonic potentials do.[106] The motor axon makes direct synaptic contact with the muscle epithelium that makes up the bell of the jellyfish and so the propagating calcium spike induces the weak contractions responsible for propulsion during the regular slow swimming the animal performs when feeding.

Aglantha lives in the colder waters of the world at a depth of about 100 m. Studied in their natural habitat, they are seen to avoid predators by generating an alltogether stronger form of swimming. In the laboratory this "escape" swimming can be reproduced by stimulating vibration-sensitive receptors at the base of the bell of the animal.[107] The strong synaptic depolarization that this stimulus induces in each of the eight giant motor axons drives its membrane potential beyond the peak of the calcium spike and induces a full-sized sodium action potential. As the sodium spike propagates more rapidly than the slow swim calcium spike, there is a coordinated contraction of the body wall that drives the animal forward.

Sodium and calcium spikes like those seen in *Aglantha* have been recorded from a variety of sites in the mammalian CNS.[64,108] However, unlike in *Aglantha*, the peak of the calcium spike always exceeds the threshold of the sodium spike and the two impulses form a single complex signal. Patch-clamp analysis of *Aglantha* axons has revealed a family of potassium channels that are responsible for setting thresholds and repolarizing each of the two different impulses. Each potassium channel class has an identical unitary conductance and appears to be organized in a mosaic fashion over the surface of the axon.[109] Sodium and T-type calcium channels are clustered together into well-defined "hot spots." George Mackie and I have suggested that the mosaic organization facilitates the turnover of ion channels; channels inserted into the membrane in clusters age together and are eliminated together.

Robert W. Meech

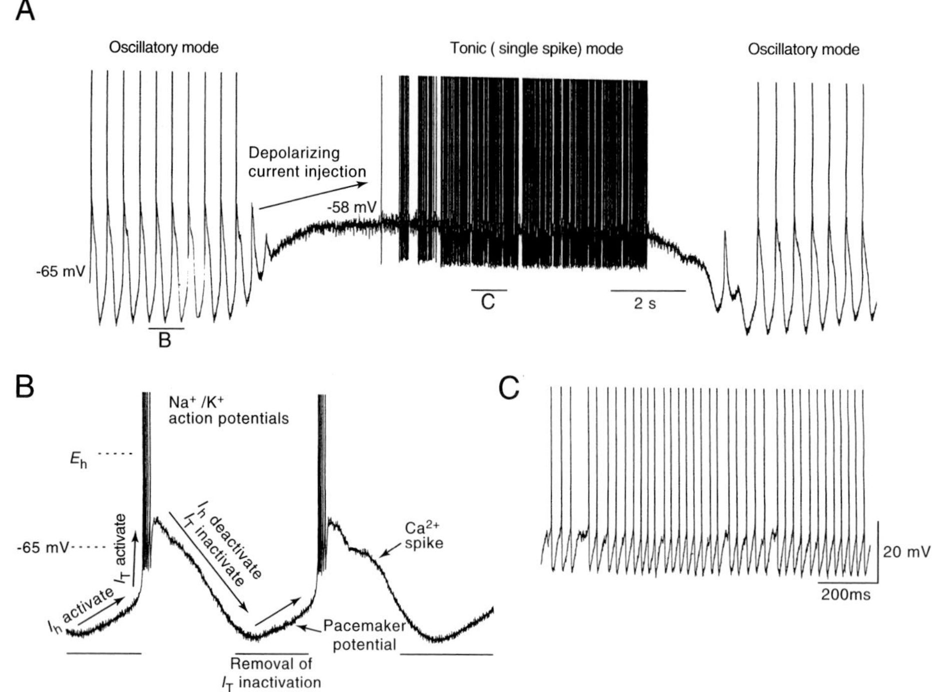

FIGURE 6.13 Two different patterns of activity generated in the same neuron, depending on membrane potential. (A) The thalamic neuron spontaneously generates rhythmic bursts of action potentials owing to the interaction of the Ca^{2+} current I_T and the inward "pacemaker" current I_h. Depolarization of the neuron changes the firing mode from rhythmic burst firing to tonic action potential generation in which spikes are generated one at a time. Removal of this depolarization reinstates the rhythmic burst firing. This transition from rhythmic burst firing to tonic activity is similar to that which occurs in the transition from sleep to waking. (B) Expansion of detail of rhythmic burst firing. (C) Expansion of detail of tonic firing. From McCormick and Pape.[110]

taneously generate low-threshold Ca^{2+} spikes and bursts of from two to five action potentials (Fig. 6.13).[110] The large number of thalamic relay cells bursting during sleep in part gives rise to the spontaneous synchronized activity that early investigators were so surprised to find during recordings from the brains of sleeping animals.[111] It has even proved possible to maintain one of the sleep-related brain rhythms (spindle waves) intact in slices of thalamic tissue maintained *in vitro*, owing to the generation of this rhythm by the interaction of a local network of thalamic cells and their electrophysiological properties.[112]

The transition to waking or the period of sleep when dreams are prevalent (rapid eye movement sleep) is associated with a maintained depolarization of thalamic relay cells to membrane potentials ranging from about −60 to −55 mV. The low-threshold Ca^{2+} current is inactivated and therefore the burst discharges are abolished. In this way, the properties of a single ionic current (I_T) help to explain in part the remarkable changes in brain activity taking place in the transition from sleep to waking (Fig. 6.13).

Low-threshold Ca^{2+} channels were recently cloned and shown to have some similarities to other Ca^{2+} channels.[117] Evidence suggests that some antiepileptic drugs may exert their therapeutic actions through a reduction in I_T. This is especially true of the drugs useful in the treatment of generalized absence (petit mal) seizures, which are known to rely on the thalamus for their generation.[113]

Hyperpolarization-Activated Ionic Currents Are Involved in Rhythmic Activity

In most types of neurons, hyperpolarization negative to approximately −60 mV activates an ionic current, known as I_h, that conducts both Na^+ and K^+ ions (see Fig. 6.11A). This current typically has very slow kinetics, turning on with a time constant on the order of tens of milliseconds to seconds. Because the channels underlying this current allow the passage of both Na^+ and K^+ ions, the reversal potential of I_h is typically about −35 mV—between E_{Na} and E_K. Because this current is activated by hyperpolarization below approximately −60 mV, it is typically dominated by the inward movement of Na^+ ions and is therefore depolarizing. For what purpose could neurons use a depolarizing current that activates when the cell is hyperpolarized? A clue comes from cardiac cells in which this current, known as I_f for "funny," is important for determining heart rate.[114] Activation of I_f results in a slow depolarization of the membrane potential between adjacent cardiac action potentials. The more that I_f is activated, the faster the membrane depolarizes between beats and therefore the sooner the threshold for the next action potential is reached and the next beat is generated. In this manner, the amplitude, or sensitivity to voltage, of I_f can modify heart rate. Interestingly, the sensitivity of I_f to voltage is adjusted by the release of noradrenaline and acetylcholine; the activation of β-adrenoceptors by noradrenaline increases I_f and therefore increases the heart rate, whereas the activation of muscarinic receptors decreases I_f, thereby decreasing the heart rate.[115,116] This continual adjustment of I_f results from a "push–pull" arrangement between β-adrenergic and muscarinic cholinergic receptors and is mediated by the adjustment of intracellular levels of cyclic AMP. Indeed, the recent cloning of H-channels reveals that its structure is similar to that of cyclic nucleotide gated channels.[118]

Could I_h play a role in neurons similar to that of I_f in the heart? Possibly. Synchronized rhythmic oscillations in the membrane potential of large numbers of neurons, in some respects similar to those of the heart, are characteristic of the mammalian brain. Oscillations of this type are particularly prevalent in thalamic relay neurons during some periods of sleep, as mentioned earlier. Intracellular recordings from these thalamic neurons reveal that they often generate rhythmic "bursts" of action potentials mediated by the activation of a slow spike that is generated through the activation of the low-threshold, or transient, Ca^{2+} current, I_T[76,110] (see Fig. 6.13). Between the occurrence of each low-threshold Ca^{2+} spike is a slowly depolarizing membrane potential generated by activation of the mixed Na^+–K^+ current I_h, as with I_f in the heart. The amplitude, or voltage sensitivity, of I_h adjusts the rate at which the thalamic cells oscillate, and, as with the heart, this sensitivity is adjusted by the release of modulatory neurotransmitters (see Fig. 6.13). In a sense, the thalamic neurons are "beating" in a manner similar to that of the heart.

Summary

An action potential is generated by the rapid influx of Na^+ ions followed by a slightly slower efflux of K^+ ions. Although the generation of an action potential does not disrupt the concentration gradients of these ions across the membrane, the movement of charge is sufficient to generate a large and brief deviation in the membrane potential. Propagation of the action potential along the axon allows communication of the output of the cell to its synapses. Neurons possess many different types of ionic channels in their membranes, allowing complex patterns of action potentials to be generated and complex synaptic computations to occur within single neurons.

References

1. Brazier, M. A. B. (1959). The historical development of neurophysiology. In *Handbook of Physiology* (J. Field, ed.), Sect. 1, Vol. 1, pp. 1–58. Am. Physiol. Soc., Washington, DC.
2. Brazier, M. A. B. (1988). *A History of Neurophysiology in the 19th Century*. Raven Press, New York.
3. Young, J. Z. (1936). The giant nerve fibers and epistellar body of cephalopods. *Q. J. Microsc. Sci.* **78:** 367.
4. Hodgkin, A. L., and Huxley, A. F. (1939). Action potentials recorded from inside a nerve fiber. *Nature* (*London*) **144:** 710–711.
5. Hodgkin, A. L. (1976). Chance and design in electrophysiology: An informal account of certain experiments on nerve carried out between 1934 and 1952. *J. Physiol.* (*London*) **263:** 1–21.
6. Brock, L. G., Coombs, J. S., and Eccles, J. C. (1952). The recording of potentials from motoneurones with an intracellular electrode. *J. Physiol.* (*London*) **117:** 431–460.
7. Buser, P., and Albe-Fessard, D. (1953). Premiers résultats d'une analyse l'activité électrique du cortex cérebral du Chat par microélectrodes intracellulaires. *C. R. Hebd. Seances Acad. Sci.* **236:** 1197–1199.
8. Tasaki, I., Polley, E. H., and Orrego, F. (1954). Action potentials from individual elements in cat geniculate and striate cortex. *J. Neurophysiol.* **17:** 454–474.
9. Phillips, C. G. (1956). Intracellular records from betz cells in the cat. *Q. J. Exp. Physiol.* **41:** 58–69.
10. Nernst, W. (1888). On the kinetics of substances in solution. Translated from *Z. Phys. Chem.* **2:** 613–622, 634–637. In *Cell Membrane Permeability and Transport* (G. R. Kepner, ed.), pp. 174–183. Dowden, Hutchinson & Ross, Stroudsburg, PA, 1979.
11. Hotson, J. R., Sypert, G. W., and Ward, A. A. (1973). Extracellular potassium concentration changes during propagated seizures in neocortex. *Exp. Neurol.* **38:** 20–26.
12. Prince, D. A., Lux, H. D., and Neher, E. (1973). Measurements of extracellular potassium activity in cat cortex. *Brain Res.* **50:** 489–495.
13. Kuffler, S. W., and Nicholls, J. G. (1966). The physiology of neuroglia cells. *Ergeb. Physiol.* **57:** 1–90.
14. Goldman, D. F. (1943). Potential, impedance, and rectification in membranes. *J. Gen. Physiol.* **27:** 37–60.
15. Hodgkin, A. L., and Katz, B. (1949). The effect of sodium ions on the electrical activity of the giant axon of the squid. *J. Physiol.* (*London*) **108:** 37–77.
16. Tomita, T. (1965). Electrophysiological study of the mechanisms subserving color coding in the fish retina. *Cold Spring Harbor Symp. Quant. Biol.* **30:** 559–566.
17. Hirsch, J. C., Fourment, A., and Marc, M. E. (1983). Sleep-related variations of membrane potential in the lateral geniculate body relay neurons of the cat. *Brain Res.* **259:** 308–312.
18. Jahnsen, H., and Llinás, R. (1984). Electrophysiological proper-

ties of guinea-pig thalamic neurons: an *in vitro* study. *J. Physiol. (London)* **349:** 205–226.
19. Jahnsen, H., and Llinás, R. (1984). Ionic basis for the electroresponsiveness and oscillatory properties of guinea-pig thalamic neurons *in vitro. J. Physiol. (London)* **349:** 227–247.
20. McCormick, D. A., Connors, B. W., Lighthall, J. W., and Prince, D. A. (1985). Comparative electrophysiology of pyramidal and sparsely spiny neurons of the neocortex. *J. Neurophysiol.* **54:** 782–806.
21. Livingstone, M. S., and Hubel, D. H. (1981). Effects of sleep and arousal on the processing of visual information in the cat. *Nature (London)* **291:** 554–561.
22. Steriade, M., and McCarley, R. W. (1990). *Brainstem Control of Wakefulness and Sleep.* Plenum, New York.
23. Hodgkin, A. L., and Keynes, D. (1955). Active transport of cations in giant axons from *Sepia* and *Loligo. J. Physiol. (London)* **128:** 28–60.
24. Skou, J. C. (1957). The influence of some cations on an adenosine triphosphatase from peripheral nerves. *Biochim. Biophys. Acta* **23:** 394–401.
25. Thomas, R. C. (1972). Electrogenic sodium pump in nerve and muscle cells. *Physiol. Rev.* **52:** 563–594.
26. Skou, J. C. (1988). Overview: The Na,K pump. In *Methods in Enzymology* (S. Fleischer and B. Fleischer, eds.), Vol. 156, pp. 1–25. Academic Press, Orlando, FL.
27. Mercer, R. W. (1993). Structure of the Na,K-ATPase. *Int. Rev. Cytol.* **137C:** 139–168.
28. Horisberger, J.-D., Lemas, V., Kraehenbühl, J.-P., and Rossier, B. C. (1991). Structure–function relationship of Na,K-ATPase. *Annu. Rev. Physiol.* **53:** 565–584.
29. Pedersen, P. L., and Carafoli, E. (1987). Ion motive ATPases. I. Ubiquity, properties, and significance to cell function. *Trends Biochem. Sci.* **12:** 146–150.
30. Läuger, P. (1991). *Electrogenic Ion Pumps.* Sinauer, Sunderland, MA.
31. Reithmeier, R. A. F. (1994). Mammalian exchangers and cotransporters. *Curr. Opin. Cell Biol.* **6:** 583–594.
32. Thompson, S. M., Deisz, R. A., and Prince, D. A. (1988). Relative contributions of passive equilibrium and active transport to the distribution of chloride in mammalian cortical neurons. *J. Neurophysiol.* **60:** 105–124.
33. Hodgkin, A. L., and Huxley, A. F. (1952). Currents carried by sodium and potassium ions through the membrane of the giant axon of *Loligo. J. Physiol. (London)* **116:** 449–472.
34. Hodgkin, A. L., and Huxley, A. F. (1952). The components of membrane conductance in the giant axon of *Loligo. J. Physiol. (London)* **116:** 473–496.
35. Hodgkin, A. L., and Huxley, A. F. (1952). The dual effect of membrane potential on sodium conductance in the giant axon of *Loligo. J. Physiol. (London)* **116:** 497–506.
36. Hodgkin, A. L., and Huxley, A. F. (1952). A quantitative description of membrane current and its application to conduction and excitation in nerve. *J. Physiol. (London)* **117:** 500–544.
37. Hodgkin, A. L., Huxley, A. F., and Katz, B. (1952). Measurement of current-voltage relations in the membrane of the giant axon of *Loligo. J. Physiol. (London)* **116:** 424–448.
38. Cole, K. S., and Curtis, H. J. (1939). Electric impedance of the squid giant axon during activity. *J. Gen. Physiol.* **22:** 649–670.
39. Overton, E. (1902). Beiträge zur allgemeinen Muskelund Nerven physiologie. II. Ueber die Urentbehrlichkeit von Natrium- (oder Lithium-) Ionen für den Contractsionact des Muskel. *Pfluegers Arch. Gesamte Physiol. Menschen Tiere* **92:** 346–386.
40. Cole, K. S. (1949). Dynamic electrical characteristics of the squid axon membrane. *Arch. Sci. Physiol.* **3:** 253–258.
41. Hille, B. (1977). Ionic basis of resting potentials and action potentials. In *Handbook of Physiology* (E. R. Kandel, ed.), Sect. 1, Vol. 1, pp. 99–136. Am. Physiol. Soc., Bethesda, MD.
42. Kao, C. T. (1966). Tetrodotoxin, saxotoxin and their significance in the study of excitation phenomena. *Pharmacol. Rev.* **18:** 997–1049.
43. Armstrong, C. M., and Hille, B. (1972). The inner quaternary ammonium ion receptor in potassium channels of the node of Ranvier. *J. Gen. Physiol.* **59:** 388–400.
44. Bunge, R. P. (1968). Glial cells and the central myelin sheath. *Physiol. Rev.* **48:** 197–251.
45. Ritchie, J. M., and Rogart, R. B. (1977). Density of sodium channels in mammalian myelinated nerve fibers and nature of the axonal membrane under the myelin sheath. *Proc. Natl. Acad. Sci. U.S.A.* **74:** 211–215.
46. Miller, C. (1989). Genetic manipulation of ion channels: A new approach to structure and mechanism. *Neuron* **2:** 1195–1205.
47. Anderson, O. S., and Koeppe, R. E., II (1992). Molecular determinants of channel function. *Physiol. Rev.* **72**(Suppl.): S89–S158.
48. Catterall, W. A. (1988). Structure and function of voltage-sensitive ion channels. *Science* **242:** 50–61.
49. Catterall, W. A. (1992). Cellular and molecular biology of voltage-gated sodium channels. *Physiol. Rev.* **72**(4, Suppl.): S15–S48.
50. Catterall, W. A. (1995). Structure and function of voltage-gated ion channels. *Annu. Rev. Biochem.* **64:** 493–531.
51. Salkoff, L., Baker, K., Butler, A., Covarrubias, M., Pak, M. D., and Wei, A. (1992). An essential "set" of K^+ channels conserved in flies, mice, and humans. *Trends Neurosci.* **15:** 161–166.
52. Beneski, D. A., and Catterall, W. A. (1980). Covalent labeling of protein components of the sodium channel with a photoactivable derivative of scorpion toxin. *Proc. Natl. Acad. Sci. U.S.A.* **77:** 639–643.
53. Armstrong, C. M. (1992). Voltage-dependent ionic channels and their gating. *Physiol. Rev.* **72**(Suppl.): 5–13.
54. Vassilev, P. M., Scheuer, T., and Catterall, W. A. (1988). Identification of an intracellular peptide segment involved in sodium channel inactivation. *Science* **241:** 1658–1661.
55. Vassilev, P., Scheuer, T., and Catterall, W. A. (1989). Inhibition of inactivation of single sodium channels by a site-directed antibody. *Proc. Natl. Acad. Sci. U.S.A.* **86:** 8147–8151.
56. Stuhmer, W., Conti, F., Suzuki, H., Wang, X., Noda, M., Yahadi, N., Kobu, H., and Numa, S. (1989). Structural parts involved in activation and inactivation of the sodium channel. *Nature (London)* **339:** 597–603.
57. Eccles, J. C. (1957). *The Physiology of Nerve Cells.* Johns Hopkins University Press, Baltimore, MD.
58. Alving, B. O. (1968). Spontaneous activity in isolated somata of *Aplysia* pacemaker neurons. *J. Gen. Physiol.* **51:** 29–45.
59. Arvanitaki, A., and Chalazonitis, N. (1961). Slow waves and associated spiking in nerve cells of *Aplysia. Bull. Inst. Oceanogr. Monaco* **58:** 1–15.
60. Jackelet, J. W. (1989). *Neuronal and Cellular Oscillators.* Dekker, New York.
61. Llinás, R., and Sugimori, M. (1980). Electrophysiological properties of *in vitro* Purkinje cell somata in mammalian cerebellar slices. *J. Physiol. (London)* **305:** 171–195.
62. Llinás, R., and Sugimori, M. (1980). Electrophysiological properties of *in vitro* Purkinje cell dendrites in mammalian cerebellar slices. *J. Physiol. (London)* **305:** 197–213.
63. Llinás, R., and Yarom, Y. (1981). Electrophysiology of mammalian inferior olivary neurones *in vitro:* Different types of voltage-dependent ionic conductances. *J. Physiol. (London)* **315:** 569–584.

64. Llinás, R., and Yarom, Y. (1981). Properties and distribution of ionic conductances generating electroresponsiveness of mammalian inferior olivary neurones *in vitro*. *J. Physiol.* (*London*) **315:** 569–584.
65. Llinás, R. R. (1988). The intrinsic electrophysiological properties of mammalian neurons: Insights into central nervous system function. *Science* **242:** 1654–1664.
66. Madison, D. V., and Nicoll, R. A. (1984). Control of repetitive discharge of rat CA1 pyramidal neurons *in vitro*. *J. Physiol.* (*London*) **354:** 319–331.
67. Pennefather, P., Lancaster, B., Adams, P. R., and Nicoll, R. A. (1985). Two distinct Ca-dependent K currents in bullfrog sympathetic ganglion cells. *Proc. Natl. Acad. Sci. U.S.A.* **82:** 3040–3044.
68. Wang, Z., and McCormick, D. A. (1993). Control of firing mode of corticotectal and corticopontine layer V burst-generating neurons by norepinephrine, acetylcholine, and 1S,3R-ACPD. *J. Neurosci.* **13:** 2199–2216.
69. Schwartzkroin, P. A., and Mathers, L. H. (1978). Physiological and morphological identification of a nonpyramidal hippocampal cell type. *Brain Res.* **157:** 1–10.
70. Pape, H.-C., and McCormick, D. A. (1995). Electrophysiological and pharmacological properties of interneurons in the cat dorsal lateral geniculate nucleus. *Neuroscience* **68:** 1105–1125.
71. Vandermaelen, C. P., and Aghajanian, G. K. (1983). Electrophysiological and pharmacological characterization of serotonergic dorsal raphe neurons recorded extracellularly and intracellularly in rat brain slices. *Brain Res.* **289:** 109–119.
72. Williams, J. T., North, R. A., Shefner, S. A., Nishi, S., and Egan, T. M. (1984). Membrane properties of rat locus coeruleus neurones. *Neuroscience* **13:** 137–156.
73. Reiner, P. B., and McGeer, E. G. (1987). Electrophysiological properties of cortically projecting histamine neurons of the rat hypothalamus. *Neurosci. Lett.* **73:** 43–47.
74. McCormick, D. A. (1992). Neurotransmitter actions in the thalamus and cerebral cortex and their role in neuromodulation of thalamocortical activity. *Prog. Neurobiol.* **39:** 337–388.
75. Belluzzi, O., and Sacchi, O. (1991). A five-conductance model of the action potential in the rat sympathetic neurone. *Prog. Biophys. Mol. Biol.* **55:** 1–30.
76. McCormick, D. A., and Huguenard, D. A. (1992). A model of the electrophysiological properties of thalamocortical relay neurons. *J. Neurophysiol.* **68:** 1384–1400.
77. Huguenard, J., and McCormick, D. A. (1994). *Electrophysiology of the Neuron*. Oxford University Press, New York.
78. Hotson, J. R., Prince, D. A., and Schwartzkroin, P. A. (1979). Anomalous inward rectification in hippocampal neurons. *J. Neurophysiol.* **42:** 889–895.
79. Stafstrom, C. E., Schwindt, P. C., and Crill, W. E. (1982). Negative slope conductance due to a persistent subthreshold sodium current in cat neocortical neurons *in vitro*. *Brain Res.* **236:** 221–226.
80. Alzheimer, C., Schwindt, P. C., and Crill, W. E. (1993). Modal gating of Na^+ channels as a mechanism of persistent Na^+ current in pyramidal neurons from rat and cat sensorimotor cortex. *J. Neurosci.* **13:** 660–673.
81. Goldman-Rakic, P. S. (1995). Cellular basis of working memory. *Neuron* **14:** 477–485.
82. Jan, L. Y., and Jan, Y. N. (1990). How might the diversity of potassium channels be generated? *Trends Neurosci.* **13:** 415–419.
83. Storm, J. F. (1990). Potassium currents in hippocampal pyramidal cells. *Prog. Brain Res.* **83:** 161–187.
84. Johnston, D., and Wu, S. M.-S. (1995). *Foundations of Cellular Neurophysiology*. MIT Press, Cambridge, MA.
85. Connor, J. A., and Stevens, C. F. (1971). Voltage clamp studies of a transient outward membrane current in gastropod neural somata. *J. Physiol.* (*London*) **213:** 21–30.
86. Connor, J. A., and Stevens, C. F. (1971). Prediction of repetitive firing behaviour from voltage clamp data on an isolated neurone soma. *J. Physiol.* (*London*) **213:** 31–53.
87. Hoshi, T., Zagotta, W. N., and Aldrich, R. W. (1990). Biophysical and molecular mechanisms of Shaker potassium channel inactivation. *Science* **250:** 533–538.
88. Zagotta, W. N., Hoshi, T., and Aldrich, R. W. (1990). Restoration of inactivation in mutants of Shaker potassium channels by a peptide derived from ShB. *Science* **250:** 568–571.
89. Blatz, A. L., and Magleby, K. L. (1987). Calcium-activated potassium channels. *Trends Neurosci.* **11:** 463–467.
90. Latorre, R., Oberhauser, A., Labarca, P., and Alvarez, O. (1989). Varieties of calcium-activated potassium channels. *Annu. Rev. Physiol.* **51:** 385–399.
91. Chandy, K. G., and Gutman, G. A. (1995). Voltage-gated potassium channel genes. In *Ligand- and Voltage-Gated Channels* (A. North, ed.), pp. 1–72. CRC Press, Boca Raton, FL.
92. Brown, D. A., and Adams, P. R. (1980). Muscarinic suppression of a novel voltage sensitive K^+ current in a vertebrate neurone. *Nature* (*London*) **283:** 673–676.
93. Nicoll, R. A. (1988). The coupling of neurotransmitter receptors to ion channels in the brain. *Science* **241:** 545–551.
94. Nicoll, R. A., Malenka, R. C., and Kauer, J. A. (1990). Functional comparison of neurotransmitter receptor subtypes in mammalian central nervous system. *Physiol. Rev.* **70:** 513–565.
95. Regehr, W. G., and Tank, D. W. (1994). Dendritic calcium dynamics. *Curr. Opin. Neurobiol.* **4:** 373–382.
96. Markram, H., Helm, P. J., and Sakmann, B. (1995). Dendritic calcium transients evoked by single back-propagating action potentials in rat neocortical pyramidal neurons. *J. Physiol.* (*London*) **485:** 1–20.
97. Nowycky, M. C., Fox, A. P., and Tsien, R. W. (1985). Three types of neuronal calcium channel with different calcium agonist sensitivity. *Nature* (*London*) **316:** 440–443.
98. Carbonne, E., and Lux, H. D. (1984). A low voltage–activated, fully inactivating Ca channel in vertebrate sensory neurones. *Nature* (*London*) **310:** 501–502.
99. Llinás, R., Sugimori, M., Hillman, D. E., and Cherksey, B. (1992). Distribution and functional significance of the P-type, voltage-dependent Ca^{2+} channels in the mammalian nervous system. *Trends Neurosci.* **15:** 351–355.
100. Tsien, R. W., Ellinor, P. T., and Horne, W. A. (1991). Molecular diversity of voltage-dependent Ca^{2+} channels. *Trends Pharmacol. Sci.* **12:** 349–354.
101. Birnbaumer, L., Campbell, K. P., Catterall, W. A., Harpold, M. M., Hofmann, F., Horne, W. A., Mori, Y., Schwartz, A., Snutch, T. P., Tanabe, T., and Tsien, R. W. (1994). The naming of voltage-gated calcium channels. *Neuron* **13:** 505–506.
102. Bean, B. P. (1989). Classes of calcium channels in vertebrate cells. *Annu. Rev. Physiol.* **51:** 367–384.
103. Stea, A. Soong, T. W., and Snutch, T. P. (1995). Voltage-gated calcium channels. In *Ligand and Voltage-Gated Ion Channels* (A. North, ed.), pp. 113–152. CRC Press, Boca Raton, FL.
104. Wheeler, D. B., Randall, A., and Tsien, R. W. (1994). Roles of N-type and Q-type Ca^{2+} channels in supporting hippocampal synaptic transmission. *Science* **264:** 107–111.
105. Mackie, G. O., and Meech, R. W. (1985). Separate sodium and calcium spikes in the same axon. *Nature* (*London*) **313:** 791–793.
106. Meech, R. W., and Mackie, G. O. (1995). Synaptic events underlying the production of calcium and sodium spikes in motor giant axons of Aglantha digitale. *J. Neurophysiol.* **74:** 1662–1669.

107. Arkett, S., Mackie, G. O., and Meech, R. W. (1988). Hair-cell mechanoreception in the jellyfish *Aglantha digitale*. *J. Exp. Biol.* **135:** 329–342.

108. Llinas, R., and Jahnsen, H. (1982). Electrophysiology of mammalian thalamic neurones *in vitro*. *Nature (London)* **297:** 406–408.

109. Meech, R. W., and Mackie, G. O. (1993). Potassium channel family in giant motor axons of *Aglantha digitale*. *Neurophysiology* **69:** 894–901.

110. McCormick, D. A., and Pape, H.-C. (1990). Properties of a hyperpolarization-activated cation current and its role in rhythmic oscillation in thalamic relay neurones. *J. Physiol. (London)* **431:** 291–318.

111. Steriade, M., McCormick, D. A., and Sejnowski, T. (1993). Thalamocortical oscillations in the sleep and aroused brain. *Science* **262:** 679–685.

112. von Krosigk, M., Bal, T., and McCormick, D. A. (1993). Cellular mechanisms of a synchronized oscillation in the thalamus. *Science* **261:** 361–364.

113. Coulter, D. A., Huguenard, J. R., and Prince, D. A. (1990). Differential effects of petit mal anticonvulsants and convulsants on thalamic neurones: Calcium current reduction. *Br. J. Pharmacol.* **100:** 800–806.

114. DiFrancesco, D. (1985). The cardiac hyperpolarizing-activated current, I_f: Origins and developments. *Prog. Biophys. Mol. Biol.* **46:** 163–183.

115. DiFrancesco, D. (1993). Pacemaker mechanisms in cardiac tissue. *Annu. Rev. Physiol.* **55:** 455–472.

116. DiFrancesco, D., Ducouret, P., and Robinson, R. B. (1989). Muscarinic modulation of cardiac rate at low acetylcholine concentrations. *Science* **243:** 669–671.

117. Perez-Reyes, E., Cribbs, L. L., Daud, A., Lacerda, A. E., Barclay, J., Williamson, M. P., Fox, M., Rees, M. and Lee, J.-H. (1998). Molecular characterization of a neuronal low-voltage-activated T-type calcium channel. *Nature* **391:** 896–900.

118. Ludwig, A., Zong, X., Jeglitsch, M., Hofmann, F., and Biel, M. (1998). A family of hyperpolarization-activated mammalian cation channels. *Nature* **393:** 587–591.

CHAPTER

7

Release of Neurotransmitters

Robert S. Zucker, Dimitri M. Kullmann, and Mark Bennett

The synapse is the point of functional contact between one neuron and another. It is the primary place at which information is transmitted from neuron to neuron in the central nervous system or from neuron to target (gland or muscle) in the periphery. The simplest way for one cell to inform another of its activity is by direct electrical interaction, in which the current generated extracellularly from the action potential in the first cell passes through neighboring cells. Owing to the shunting of current by the highly conductive extracellular fluid, a 100-mV action potential may generate only 10–100 μV in a neighboring neuron. This coupling can be improved if neighboring cells are joined by a specialized conductive pathway through gap junctions (see Chapter 11); even then, a presynaptic spike is not likely to generate more than about 1 mV postsynaptically, unless the presynaptic process is nearly as large or larger than the postsynaptic process. This biophysical constraint limits the number of presynaptic cells that can converge on and influence a postsynaptic cell, and such electrical connections can normally only be excitatory and short-lasting, are bidirectional in transmission, and show little plasticity or modifiability. They have limited potential for complex computation, but can be useful when a postsynaptic neuron must be activated with high reliability and speed or when concurrent activity in a large number of presynaptic afferents must be signaled.

ORGANIZATION OF THE CHEMICAL SYNAPSE

Most interneuronal communication relies on the use of a chemical intermediary, or **transmitter,** secreted subsequent to action potentials by presynaptic cells to influence the activity of postsynaptic cells. In chemical transmission, a single action potential in a small presynaptic terminal can generate a large **postsynaptic potential** (PSP) (as large as tens of millivolts). This is accomplished by the release of thousands to hundreds of thousands of molecules of transmitter that can bind to postsynaptic **receptor molecules** and open (or close) as many ion channels in about 1 ms. There is room for many afferents (often thousands) to interact and influence a postsynaptic neuron, and the effect can be either excitatory or inhibitory, depending on the ions that permeate the channels operated by the receptor. The resulting responses are either **excitatory postsynaptic potentials** (EPSPs) or **inhibitory postsynaptic potentials** (IPSPs), depending on whether they drive the cell toward a point above or below its firing threshold. Different afferents can have different effects, with different strengths and kinetics, on each other as well as on postsynaptic cells. These differences depend on the identity of the transmitter(s) released and the receptors present (see Chapters 8 and 9). Chemical synapses are often modified by prior activity in the presynaptic neuron. Chemical synapses are also particularly subject to modulation of presynaptic ion channels by substances released by the postsynaptic or neighboring neurons. This flexibility is essential for the complex processing of information that neural circuits must accomplish, and it provides an important locus for modifiability of neural circuits underlying adaptive processes such as learning (Chapters 55 and 56).

Transmitter Release Is Quantal

One of the first applications of the microelectrode was the discovery that transmitter release is *quantal* in nature.[1] Transmitter is released spontaneously in multimolecular packets called **quanta** in the absence of presynaptic electrical activity. Each packet generates a small postsynaptic signal—either a **miniature excitatory** or a **miniature inhibitory postsynaptic potential** (MEPSP or MIPSP, respectively, or just MPSP); under voltage clamp, a miniature excitatory or an inhibitory postsynaptic current (MEPSC or MIPSC, respectively, or just MPSC) is generated. An action potential tremendously, but very briefly, accelerates the rate of secretion of quanta and synchronizes them to evoke a PSP. Vertebrate skeletal neuromuscular junctions are frequently used as model synapses, because both receptors and nerve terminals are relatively accessible for anatomical, electrophysiological, and biochemical studies. At the neuromuscular junction, the motor nerve forms a cluster of small unmyelinated processes that lie in shallow gutters in the muscle to form a structure called an **end plate,** and PSPs, PSCs, MPSPs, and MPSCs are called **end-plate potentials** (EPPs), **end-plate currents** (EPCs), **miniature end-plate potentials** (MEPPs), and **miniature end-plate currents** (MEPCs), respectively.

Why is transmission quantized? Neural circuits must process complex and quickly changing information fast enough to generate timely appropriate responses. This requires rapid transmission across synapses. Fast-acting chemical synapses accomplish this by concentrating transmitter in membrane-bound structures, 50 nm in diameter, called **synaptic vesicles** and docking these vesicles at specialized sites called **active zones** along the presynaptic membrane (Fig. 7.1A). Vesicles not docked at the membrane are clustered behind it and associated with cytoskeletal ele-

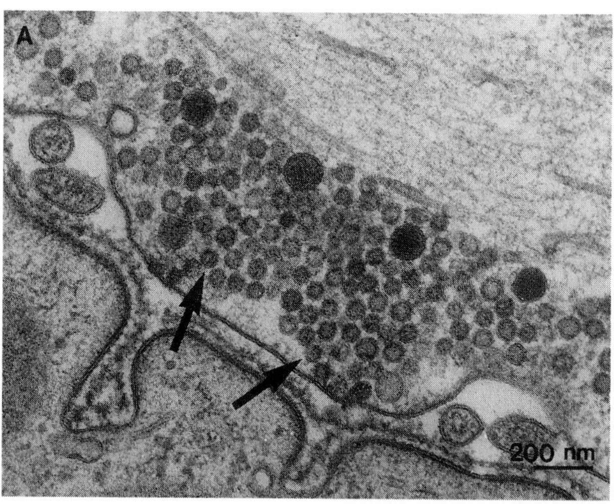

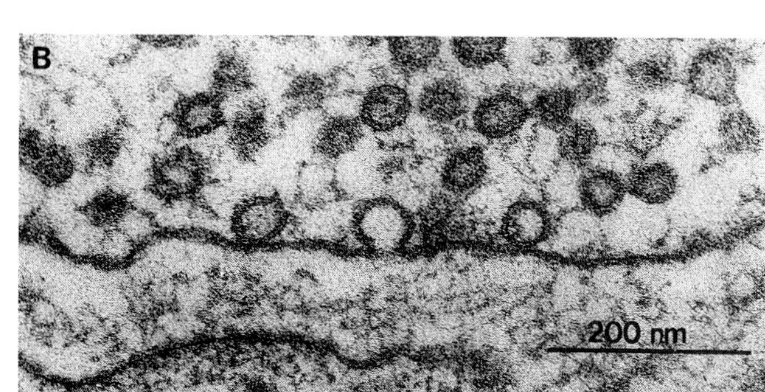

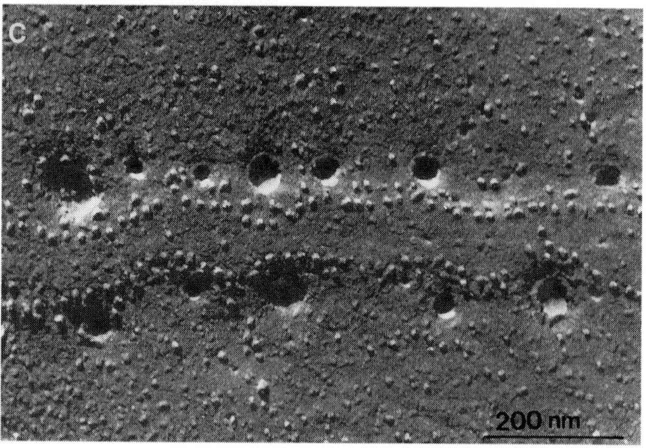

FIGURE 7.1 Ultrastructural images of synaptic vesicle exocytosis. Synapses from frog sartorius neuromuscular junctions were quick-frozen milliseconds after stimulation in 4-aminopyridine to broaden action potentials and enhance transmission. (A) A thin section from which water was replaced with organic solvents (*freeze substitution*) and fixed in osmium tetroxide, showing vesicles clustered in the active zone, some docked at the membrane (arrows). (B) Shortly (5 ms) after stimulation, vesicles were seen to fuse with the plasma membrane. (C) After freezing, presynaptic membranes were *freeze–fractured* and a platinum replica was made of the external face of the cytoplasmic membrane leaflet. Vesicles fuse about 50 nm from rows of intramembranous particles thought to include Ca^{2+} channels. Parts A and B from Heuser[2]; part C from Heuser and Reese.[4] Part B reproduced from the Journal of Cell Biology, 1981, 88, pp. 564–580.

BOX 7.1

EVIDENCE THAT A QUANTUM IS A VESICLE

Transmitter is released from vesicles:

1. All chemically transmitting synaptic terminals contain presynaptic vesicles.[8]
2. Synaptic vesicles concentrate and store transmitter.[9]
3. Rapid freezing of neuromuscular junctions during stimulation shows vesicle exocytosis occurring at the moment of transmitter release.[10]
4. Intravesicular proteins appear on the external terminal surface after secretion.[11,12]
5. Retarding the filling of vesicles by using transport inhibitors (e.g., vesamicol for acetylcholine) or by reducing the transvesicular pH gradient generates a class of small MEPSPs that probably represent partially filled vesicles; drugs that enhance vesicle loading increase MEPSP size.[13–15]
6. Quantal size is independent of membrane potential or cytoplasmic acetylcholine concentration altered osmotically.[16]
7. Synaptic vesicles formed by endocytosis load with extracellular electron-dense and fluorescent dyes (horseradish peroxidase and FM1-43, respectively) after nerve stimulation; the dye is released by subsequent stimulation.[17,18]
8. False transmitters synthesized from choline derivatives load slowly into cholinergic vesicles; they are coreleased with acetylcholine in proportion to their concentrations in vesicles.[19]
9. Clostridial toxins that interfere with the synaptic vesicle–plasma membrane interaction block neurosecretion.[20]

One quantum is one vesicle:

1. The number of acetylcholine molecules in isolated vesicles corresponds to the number of molecules released in a quantum.[5–7]
2. When release is enhanced and the collapse of vesicle fusion images is prolonged by treatment with the potassium channel blocker 4-aminopyridine to broaden action potentials, the number of vesicle fusions observed corresponds to the number of quanta released by an action potential.[21] Under these special circumstances, several vesicles are released at each active zone (Fig. 7.1C).
3. The number of vesicles present in nerve terminals corresponds to the total store of releasable quanta. When endocytosis is blocked by the temperature-sensitive *Drosophila* mutant *shibiri*[23] or pharmacologically[22] and the motor nerve is stimulated to exhaustion, the number of quanta released corresponds to the original number of presynaptic vesicles.

ments.[2] Action potentials release transmitter by depolarizing the presynaptic membrane and opening Ca^{2+} channels that are strategically colocalized with the synaptic vesicles in the active zone.[3] The local intense rise in Ca^{2+} concentration triggers the fusion of docked vesicles with the plasma membrane (called **exocytosis**; Figs. 7.1B and 7.1C[4]) and the release of their contents into the narrow **synaptic cleft** (about 100 nm wide) separating the presynaptic terminal from high concentrations of postsynaptic receptors. The fusion of one vesicle releases about 5000 transmitter molecules within a millisecond[5–7] and generates the quantal response recorded postsynaptically. No membrane carrier can release so much transmitter this fast, nor can a pore or channel unless some mechanism exists to concentrate the transmitter behind the pore, which may be regarded as the function of synaptic vesicles. Evidence that transmitter is released from vesicles and that one quantum is due to exocytosis of a vesicle is summarized in Box 7.1.[8–23]

At neuromuscular junctions, transmitter from one vesicle diffuses across the synaptic cleft in 2 μs and reaches a concentration of about 1 m*M* at the postsynaptic receptors.[24] These receptors bind transmitter rapidly, opening from 1000 to 2000 postsynaptic ion channels[25] (two molecules of transmitter must bind simultaneously to receptors to open each channel—see Chapter 14). Each channel has a 25-pS conductance and remains open for about 1.5 ms, admitting a net inflow of 35,000 positive ions. A single action potential in a motor neuron can release 300 quanta within about 1.5 ms along a junction that contains about 1000 active zones. The resulting postsynaptic depolarization, which begins after a **synaptic delay** of about 0.5 ms and reaches a peak of tens of millivolts, is typically sufficient to generate an action potential in the muscle fiber.

At fast central synapses, postsynaptic cells make contact with presynaptic axon swellings called **varicosities** when they occur along fine axons and **boutons** when they are located at the tips of terminals. Each varicosity or bouton contains one active zone or a few of them. The postsynaptic process is often on a fine dendritic branch or tiny spine with a length of a few micrometers, having a very high input resistance and capable of generating active propagating responses. At inhibitory GABAergic synapses and excitatory glutamatergic synapses,[26,27] each action potential releases from 5 to 10 quanta, and each quantum released elevates transmitter concentration [28–30] in the cleft to about 1 m*M* and activates about 30 ion channels. At excitatory synapses, this release may be sufficient to generate EPSPs of 1 mV or less in amplitude, clearly subthreshold for generating action potentials. But central neurons often receive thousands of inputs, each of which has a "vote" on how the cell should respond. No input has absolute, or even majority, control over postsynaptic cell activity, but the matching of quantal size to input resistance ensures that inputs are reasonably effective. Consequently, at synapses onto larger central neurons with lower input resistances, quanta open between 100 and 1000 postsynaptic channels.

Synaptic Vesicles Are Recycled

A constant supply of vesicles filled with transmitter must be available for release from the nerve terminal at all times. Maintaining this supply requires the efficient recycling of synaptic vesicles. For this purpose, two partly overlapping cycles are utilized: one for the components of the synaptic vesicle membrane and another for the vesicle contents (transmitter substances). The cycles overlap from the time of transmitter packaging into vesicles until exocytosis. The cycles are distinct during the stages in which vesicle membrane and transmitter are recovered for reuse. The various steps of these cycles are common to all chemical synapses and are summarized in Fig. 7.2.

Vesicle Membrane Cycle

The components of the synaptic vesicle membrane are initially synthesized in the cell body before being transported to nerve terminals by fast axoplasmic transport[31,32] (see Chapter 4). Within the nerve terminal, the synaptic vesicles are loaded with transmitter and either anchored to each other and actin filaments[33] or targeted to plasma membrane docking sites at active zones. These docking sites are also rich in clusters of high-voltage-activated Ca^{2+} channels[3,34] (mainly N-type, P-type, and Q-type Ca^{2+} channels, depending on the synapse[35,36]; see Chapter 6). Depolarization of the plasma membrane by an invading action potential opens these voltage-dependent Ca^{2+} channels to admit Ca^{2+} ions in the neighborhood of docked vesicles. The local high concentration of Ca^{2+} resulting from the opening of multiple Ca^{2+} channels triggers exocytosis. After exocytosis, some vesicles may rapidly reclose, whereas others fuse fully with the plasma membrane.[37,38] The latter are recovered by **endocytosis,** a budding off of the vesicular membrane to form a new "coated" vesicle covered by the protein *clathrin*. Endocytosis may also be regulated by presynaptic $[Ca^{2+}]$.[39,40] Recovered vesicular membrane often fuses to form large membranous sacs, called *endosomes* or *cisternae*, from which new synaptic vesicles are formed. Molecular mechanisms of the vesicle cycle of exo- and endocytosis are discussed later in this chapter.

Transmitter Cycle

The steps of the transmitter cycle vary with the type of transmitter. Some transmitters are synthesized from precursors in the cytoplasm before transport into synaptic vesicles, whereas other transmitters are synthesized in synaptic vesicles from transported precursors. Peptide transmitters are synthesized exclusively in the cell body and are not locally recycled. At most synapses, a transporter that harnesses the energy in the proton gradient across the vesicular membrane functions to concentrate transmitter (or transmitter precursors) in vesicles.[9] The pH gradient arises from the action of a vacuolar proton ATPase that uses the energy of ATP hydrolysis to transport protons into vesicles. After exocytosis, released transmitter diffuses across the synaptic cleft and rapidly binds to receptors. As transmitter falls off receptors, it is typically recovered from the synaptic cleft by sodium-dependent uptake transporters (see Chapters 8 and 9). At cholinergic

FIGURE 7.2 Steps in the life cycle of synaptic vesicles: (1) Na^+-dependent uptake of transmitter (XMTR) or XMTR precursors into the cytoplasm, (2) synthesis of XMTR, (3) delivery of vesicle membrane containing specialized transmembrane proteins by axoplasmic transport on microtubules, (4) production of transvesicular H^+ gradient by vacuolar ATPase, (5) concentration of XMTR in vesicles by H^+/XMTR antiporter, (6) synapsin I–dependent anchoring of vesicles to actin filaments near active zones, (7) releasable vesicles docked in active zones near Ca^{2+} channels, (8) depolarization of nerve terminal and presynaptic bouton by action potential, (9) opening of Ca^{2+} channels and formation of regions of local high $[Ca^{2+}]$ ("Ca^{2+} microdomains") in active zones, (10) triggering of exocytosis of docked vesicles comprising quantal units of XMTR release by overlapping Ca^{2+} microdomains, (11) nonquantal leakage of XMTR through vesicle membrane fused with plasma membrane and exposure of vesicle proteins to synaptic cleft, (12) recovery of vesicle membrane by dynamin-dependent endocytosis of clathrin-coated vesicles, (13) fusion of coated vesicles with endosomal cisternae, (14) formation of synaptic vesicles from endosomes. Also shown are postsynaptic receptors with multiple XMTR binding sites and extracellular XMTR-degradative enzymes in synaptic cleft.

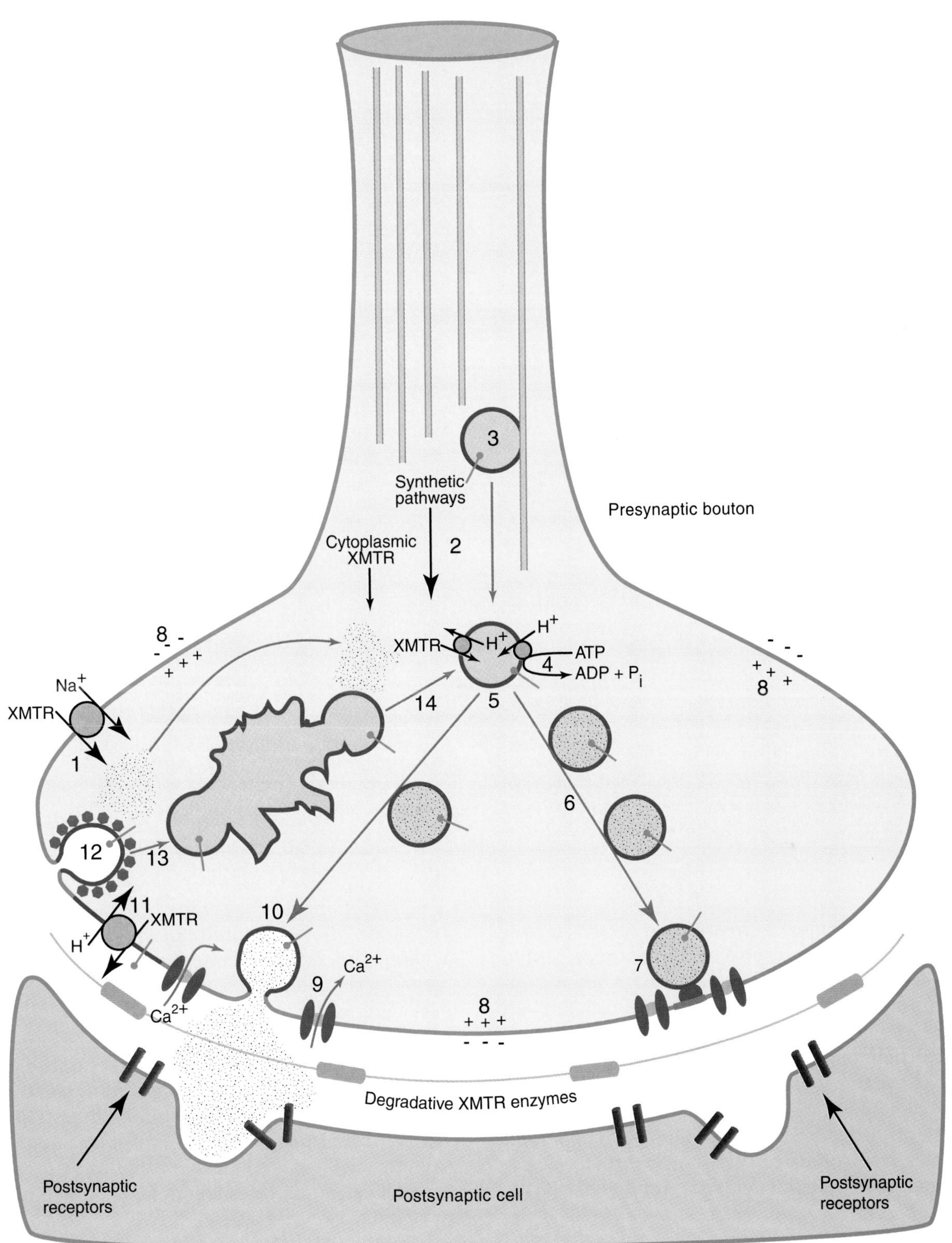

3
Synthetic pathways
Presynaptic bouton
Cytoplasmic XMTR
2
8
XMTR
H+
H+
ATP
4
ADP + Pi
Na+
XMTR
14
5
8
1
6
12
13
11
XMTR
10
H+
7
Ca2+
9
Ca2+
8
Degradative XMTR enzymes
Postsynaptic receptors
Postsynaptic cell
Postsynaptic receptors

BOX 7.2

EVIDENCE FOR SOME OF THE EVENTS IN THE LIFE HISTORY OF VESICLES

Numbers refer to the steps in Fig. 7.2.

1. Uptake of transmitter or transmitter precursors is prevented by specific inhibitors, such as *hemicholinium-3* block of choline uptake at cholinergic synapses, ultimately leading to failure of synaptic transmission.[41]
2. Cholinergic synapses can be identified by the presence of the synthetic enzyme choline acetyltransferase, GABAergic synapses by the enzyme *glutamic acid decarboxylase,* adrenergic synapses by the enzyme *dopamine β-hydroxylase,* and so forth.[42]
3. Vesicular transport into nerve terminals is blocked by inhibitors of axoplasmic transport such as antibodies to the microtubule motor protein *kinesin*.[31,32]

4, 5. The storage of transmitter in vesicles can be blocked by inhibitors of vacuolar ATPase, such as *bafilomycin* A_1, or of an H^+-dependent transporter, such as *vesamicol* for acetylcholine.[43]

6. Dephosphorylation of synapsin I inhibits vesicle movements and transmission, whereas its phosphorylation by Ca^{2+}–calmodulin-dependent kinase II protects against this inhibition.[33,44]
7. Toxins from *Clostridium* bacteria, which proteolyze the vesicular protein *synaptobrevin* or plasma membrane proteins *SNAP-25* and *syntaxin*, block exocytosis, whereas mutants deficient in the vesicle protein *synaptotagmin* and injection of peptides derived from synaptotagmin show defects in evoked transmitter release (more details later in this chapter).
8. Block of action potential propagation by local application of *tetrodotoxin* prevents transmission, and depolarization by elevating potassium in the bath accelerates MPSP frequency, as long as Ca^{2+} is present in the medium.[1]

9, 10. N- and P-type calcium channel antagonists, such as ω-conotoxin and ω-agatoxin IVA, prevent Ca^{2+} influx and block transmission at many synapses.[35,36]

11. Cholinergic synapses show a nonquantal leak of acetylcholine that is enhanced after stimulation; it is blocked by vesamicol, the vesicular acetylcholine transport inhibitor, indicating that the leak is due to transport through vesicular membrane fused with the plasma membrane.[45]
12. Endocytosis is blocked at high temperature in the *shibiri* mutant of *Drosophila*, which affects the protein *dynamin* in endocytosis of coated vesicles.[46,47]

Morphological evidence for steps 13 and 14 in Fig. 7.2 is given in the text.

synapses, acetylcholine is hydrolyzed to acetate and choline by the enzyme acetylcholinesterase present in the synaptic cleft. This enzyme is saturated by the initial gush of transmitter following exocytosis but can keep up with its subsequent slower release from receptors. The choline so produced is recovered by a presynaptic choline transporter and made available for the synthesis of new transmitter.

Much of the evidence for the steps outlined in Fig. 7.2 comes from ultrastructural and pharmacological experiments. Some of this evidence is outlined in Boxes 7.2[41–47] and 7.3.[48]

Summary

Chemical synapses are ideally suited to permit one neuron to rapidly and effectively excite or inhibit the activity of another cell. A diversity of transmitters and receptors guarantees a multiplicity of postsynaptic responses. The opportunity for presynaptic and postsynaptic interactions between inputs provides for marvelously complex computational capabilities. The packaging of transmitter into vesicles and its release in quanta enable a single action potential to secrete hundreds of thousands of molecules of transmitter almost instantaneously at a synapse onto another cell. Neurochemical and ultrastructural studies have provided a rich picture of the life cycle of synaptic vesicles from their exocytosis at active zones to their recovery by endocytosis, their refilling with transmitter, and redocking at release sites.

EXCITATION–SECRETION COUPLING

Shortly after an action potential invades presynaptic terminals at fast synapses, the synchronous release of many quanta of transmitter generates the postsynaptic potential. Since the work of Locke[49] in 1894, the presence of calcium in the external medium has been known to be a requirement for transmission. What is the central role of Ca^{2+} in triggering neurosecretion?

Calcium Triggers Release of Transmitters at Internal Sites

Calcium was originally believed to act at an external site to enable neurons to release transmitter. The pioneering work of Bernard Katz[1] and his co-workers showed that Ca^{2+} acts intracellularly. This conclusion is based on many lines of evidence:

1. Calcium must be present only at the moment of invasion of the nerve terminal by an action potential for transmitter to be released.
2. Calcium entry is retarded by a large presynaptic depolarization, and transmitter release is delayed until the voltage gradient is reversed at the end of the pulse, whereupon Ca^{2+} enters and release occurs as an off-EPSP until Ca^{2+} channels close. Sodium influx is not necessary for secretion, and K^+ ions have no role.
3. Elevation of intracellular $[Ca^{2+}]$ accelerates the spontaneous release of quanta of transmitter.[50,51] Stimulation in a Ca^{2+}-free medium reduces intracellular $[Ca^{2+}]$ and MEPSP frequency.
4. The presence of Ca^{2+} channels in presynaptic terminals is shown by the ability to stimulate local action potentials that trigger release in a high-$[Ca^{2+}]$ medium when Na^+ action potentials are blocked with tetrodotoxin and K^+ channels are blocked with tetraethylammonium.
5. Divalent cations that permeate Ca^{2+} channels, such as Ba^{2+} and Sr^{2+}, support transmitter release, although only weakly. Cations that block Ca^{2+} channels, such as Co^{2+} and Mn^{2+}, block transmission[52]; Mg^{2+} reduces transmission, perhaps by screening fixed surface charge and effectively hyperpolarizing the nerve.[53]
6. Transmission depends nonlinearly on $[Ca^{2+}]$ in the bath, varying with the fourth power of $[Ca^{2+}]$, whereas Ca^{2+} influx remains a linear function of

---

BOX 7.3

HISTOLOGICAL TRACERS CAN BE USED TO FOLLOW VESICLE RECYCLING

An elegant picture of the life history of synaptic vesicles comes from studies using electron-dense or fluorescent markers of intracellular regions that have been in contact with the extracellular space. *Horseradish peroxidase* (HRP) is an enzyme that catalyzes the oxidation of diaminobenzidine, forming an electron-dense product that can easily be identified in tissues fixed with osmium tetroxide for electron microscopy; *FM1-43* is an amphipathic styryl dye that becomes highly fluorescent on partitioning into cell membranes. When frog muscles were soaked in HRP and the motor neurons were stimulated at 10 Hz for 1 min, the enzyme appeared in coated vesicles in nerve terminals in regions outside active zones. After more prolonged stimulation, most of the HRP collected in endosomal cisternae, owing to the fusion of endocytotic vesicles with these organelles. When the HRP was washed out and the neurons were rested for an hour before fixation, HRP appeared in small clear synaptic vesicles in active zones. When rested neurons were stimulated again before fixation, this time in the absence of HRP, the filled vesicles gradually disappeared owing to their release by exocytosis.[17] Another study traced the uptake of FM1-43 into living motor nerve terminals with the use of confocal fluorescence microscopy. High-frequency stimulation for just 15 s in FM1-43 was marked by uptake of dye into nerve terminals. More prolonged stimulation followed by a period of rest without the dye in the bath resulted in the persistent staining of synaptic vesicles in active zones. Subsequent stimulation at 10 Hz gradually destained the terminals in minutes; destaining required the presence of Ca^{2+} in the medium and represented exocytosis of stained vesicles. After about 1 min, the rate of destaining decreased as the vesicle pool began to be diluted with unstained vesicles newly recovered by endocytosis.[18] Exposing dissociated hippocampal neurons to FM1-43 at various times after stimulation showed that endocytosis proceeded for about 1 min after exocytosis. Cells loaded with dye and then restimulated began to destain about 30 s after endocytosis, which is a measure of the time needed for recycling of recovered vesicles into the pool of releasable vesicles.[48] These experiments provide a dynamic view of the life cycle of synaptic vesicles.

[Ca^{2+}], indicating a high degree of Ca^{2+} cooperativity in triggering exocytosis.[52]

7. At giant synapses in the stellate ganglion of squid, voltage-clamp recording of the presynaptic Ca^{2+} current reveals a close correspondence between Ca^{2+} influx and transmitter release, including an association between the off-EPSP and a delay in Ca^{2+} current until the end of large pulses (called a tail current).[54]
8. Action potentials trigger no phasic release of transmitter when Ca^{2+} influx is blocked, even when presynaptic Ca^{2+} is tonically elevated by photolysis of photosensitive Ca^{2+} chelators; however, the elevated presynaptic [Ca^{2+}] accelerates the frequency of MEPSPs.[55]

Vesicles Are Released by Calcium Microdomains

Single action potentials generate a Ca^{2+} rise of about 10 n*M*, which lasts a few seconds.[56,57] This increment in [Ca^{2+}] is a small fraction of the typical resting [Ca^{2+}] of 100 n*M*. How can such a tiny change in [Ca^{2+}] trigger a massive synchronous release of quanta, and why is secretion so brief compared with the duration of the [Ca^{2+}] change?

As mentioned earlier, postsynaptic responses begin only 0.5 ms after an action potential invades nerve terminals. This synaptic delay includes the time taken for Ca^{2+} channels to begin to open after the peak of the action potential (300 μs),[54] leaving only about 200 μs after that for transmitter secretion and the start of a postsynaptic response. At this time, Ca^{2+} has barely begun to diffuse away from Ca^{2+} channel mouths. In an aqueous solution, [Ca^{2+}] would be mainly confined to within 1 μm of channel mouths—estimated roughly from the solution of the diffusion equation for a brief influx of *M* moles of Ca^{2+},

$$[Ca^{2+}] = M/8(\pi Dt)^{3/2} \exp(-r^2/4Dt),$$

where *t* is time after the influx, *r* is distance from the channel mouth, and *D* is the diffusion constant for Ca^{2+}, 6×10^{-6} cm^2 s^{-1}. In the cytoplasm, Ca^{2+} diffusion is retarded by intracellular organelles and the presence of millimolar concentrations of fast-acting protein-associated Ca^{2+}-binding sites with an average dissociation constant of a few micromolar. Together, these effects restrict Ca^{2+} microdomains to about 50 nm around channel mouths.

Furthermore, the 200 μs preceding the postsynaptic response must include not only the time required for Ca^{2+} to reach its target but also the time required for Ca^{2+} to bind and initiate exocytosis and for transmitter to diffuse across the synaptic cleft, bind to receptors, and begin to open channels. Thus, the presynaptic Ca^{2+} targets must be located within a few tens of nanometers of Ca^{2+} channel mouths. Neuromuscular junctions that are fast frozen during the act of secretion show vesicle fusion images in freeze–fracture planes of the presynaptic membrane about 50 nm from intramembranous particles thought to be Ca^{2+} channels (see Fig. 7.1C). Solution of the diffusion equation for a steady point source of Ca^{2+} influx in the presence of a nearly immobile fast-binding Ca^{2+} buffer reveals that approximately 100 μs after a Ca^{2+} channel opens, [Ca^{2+}] increases to more than 10 μM at 50 nm from its source and to over 100 μM at a distance of 10 nm.[58]

This calculation considers only what happens in the neighborhood of a single open Ca^{2+} channel. However, when individual Ca^{2+} channels are labeled with biotinylated ω-conotoxin tagged with colloidal gold particles, more than 100 channels per active zone are seen in terminals of chick parasympathetic ganglia.[34] Any vesicle docked at such an active zone is likely to be surrounded by as many as 10 Ca^{2+} channels within a 50-nm distance. Even though not all these channels will open during each action potential, more than one channel is likely to open, so a vesicle will be influenced by Ca^{2+} entering through several nearby channels. At the squid giant synapse, more than 50 channels open in each ~0.6-μm^2 active zone, whereas 10 channels open within the more compact active zones of frog saccular hair cells.[58,59] The Ca^{2+} microdomains of these channels overlap at single vesicles, and they cooperate in triggering secretion of a vesicle. Calculations of diffusion of Ca^{2+} ions from arrays of Ca^{2+} channels in the presence of a saturable buffer indicate that the [Ca^{2+}] at sites where neurotransmitter release is triggered is likely to reach 100–200 μM (Fig. 7.3).

Three indications that [Ca^{2+}] in fact reaches very high levels in active zones during action potentials are:

1. [Ca^{2+}] levels of over 100 μM have been measured in presynaptic submembrane regions of squid giant synapses likely to be active zones by using the low-affinity Ca^{2+}-sensitive photoprotein *n*-aequorin-J.[60]
2. Estimates of [Ca^{2+}] based on the activity of Ca^{2+}-activated K^+ channels in active zones of mechanosensory hair cells are similar.[61]
3. Transmitter release is blocked only by presynaptic injection of at least millimolar concentrations of fast high-affinity Ca^{2+} chelators, indicating that release is triggered locally by high concentrations of Ca^{2+}.[62]

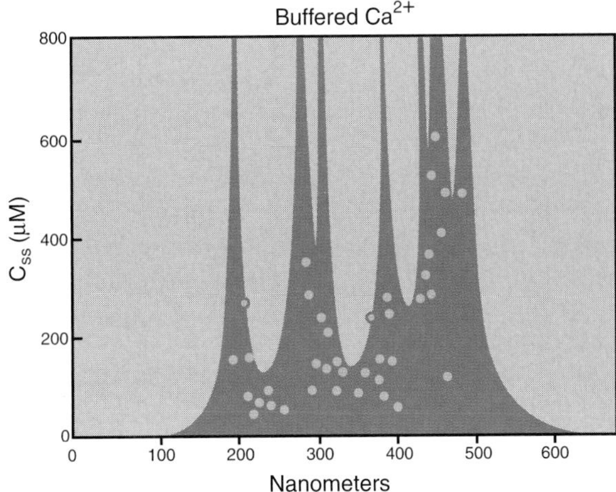

FIGURE 7.3 Computer simulations of steady-state [Ca^{2+}] (designated C_{ss}) just below the plasma membrane in an active zone in frog saccular hair cells that have been depolarized for 100 μs. Open circles represent Ca^{2+}-activated K^+ channels, whose activity confirmed the high levels of [Ca^{2+}]. Docked vesicles are likely to be located in the troughs between rows of Ca^{2+} channels located at the peaks of the [Ca^{2+}] profile. From Roberts.[58]

Vesicle Exocytosis Is Normally Triggered by Overlapping Ca^{2+} Channel Microdomains of High [Ca^{2+}]

Although release of a quantum of transmitter subsequent to the opening of a single presynaptic Ca^{2+} channel has been observed,[63] exocytosis may normally be due to Ca^{2+} entering through clusters of Ca^{2+} channels in active zones and contributing to local high [Ca^{2+}] at docked vesicles:

1. When transmitter release is increased under voltage clamp with pulses of increasing amplitude, a third-order power law relation exists between presynaptic Ca^{2+} current and postsynaptic response.[64] If each vesicle were released by Ca^{2+} entering through a single Ca^{2+} channel, then increasing depolarizations should recruit additional channel openings and proportionally more vesicle releases.[65] However, if Ca^{2+} channel microdomains from neighboring clustered Ca^{2+} channels overlap at docked vesicles, the [Ca^{2+}] at each vesicle will rise with increasing depolarization as more channels are recruited, and some cooperativity of Ca^{2+} action in triggering secretion will be expressed.[66]
2. In some neurons, more than one Ca^{2+} channel type contributes to secretion.[35,36] When contributions of each channel type are isolated pharmacologically, their combined effects add nonlinearly, much as would be predicted by a fourth-order cooperativity, indicating that the Ca^{2+} microdomains of different channels overlap and summate within individual active zones.
3. When transmitter release is increased by prolonging presynaptic depolarizations (e.g., by broadening action potentials with K^+ channel blockers), more channels are not likely to be opened simultaneously. Rather, as channels that open early in the action potential close, others open; so the pattern of presynaptic Ca^{2+} microdomains is not so much intensified as prolonged, leading to a more nearly linear relation between increases in Ca^{2+} influx and transmitter release.[57]
4. Large depolarizations admit little Ca^{2+} as they approach the Ca^{2+} equilibrium potential; they are therefore accompanied by a reduced Ca^{2+} current and reduced transmitter release during a pulse. However, large depolarizations can release more transmitter than can small depolarizations evoking a given macroscopic Ca^{2+} current.[54,67] This apparent voltage dependence of transmitter release may be due to the different spatial profiles of [Ca^{2+}] in the active zone, with greater overlap of [Ca^{2+}] from the larger number of more closely apposed open Ca^{2+} channels during large depolarizations.[66]

The Exocytosis Trigger Must Have Fast, Low-Affinity, Cooperative Ca^{2+} Binding

The brevity of the synaptic delay implies not only that Ca^{2+} acts near Ca^{2+} channels to evoke exocytosis but also that Ca^{2+} must bind to its receptor extremely rapidly. This is confirmed by the finding that presynaptic injection of relatively slow Ca^{2+} buffers such as ethylene glycol bis(β-aminoethyl ether) *N,N'*-tetraacetic acid (EGTA) have almost no effect on transmitter release to single action potentials. Only millimolar concentrations of fast Ca^{2+} buffers such as 1,2-bis(2-aminophenoxy)ethane-*N,N,N',N'*-tetraacetic acid (BAPTA), with on-rates of about 5×10^8 M^{-1} s^{-1}, can capture Ca^{2+} ions before they bind to the secretory trigger,[62] indicating that the on-rate of Ca^{2+} binding to this trigger is similarly fast. At a rate of 5×10^8 M^{-1} s^{-1}, 100 μM [Ca^{2+}] reaches equilibrium with its target in about 50 μs.

From the dependence of transmitter release on external [Ca^{2+}], we know that at least four Ca^{2+} ions cooperate in the release of a vesicle. The off-rate of Ca^{2+} dissociation from these sites also must be fast, at least 10^3 s^{-1}, to account for the rapid termination of transmitter release (0.25-ms time constant) after Ca^{2+}

channels close and Ca^{2+} microdomains collapse. The high temperature sensitivity of the time course of transmitter release ($Q_{10} \approx 3$) indicates that exocytosis is rate limited by a step with a high energy barrier.[59] This step is likely to be the process of exocytosis itself. If Ca^{2+} binding is not rate limiting, its dissociation rate must be substantially faster than $10^3\ s^{-1}$. This means that the affinity of the secretory trigger for Ca^{2+} is low, with a dissociation constant (K_D) above 10 μM.

The Ca^{2+}-binding trigger is not saturated under normal conditions, because increasing $[Ca^{2+}]$ in the bath increases release. Furthermore, because of the speed with which Ca^{2+} binds to its sites, this reaction will nearly equilibrate during the typical 0.5–1.0 ms that $[Ca^{2+}]$ remains high before Ca^{2+} channels close at the end of an action potential. If $[Ca^{2+}]$ reaches 100 μM or more in equilibrium with unsaturated release sites, the affinity of at least some of those sites binding Ca^{2+} must be similar to 100 μM or lower.

These predictions are consistent with experiments in which neurosecretion is triggered by photolysis of caged Ca^{2+} chelators such as DM-nitrophen. Partial flash photolysis of partially Ca^{2+}-loaded DM-nitrophen generates a $[Ca^{2+}]$ "spike" of a duration similar to the lifetime of Ca^{2+} microdomains around Ca^{2+} channels opened by an action potential.[68] This spike results in a postsynaptic response that closely resembles the normal EPSC at crayfish neuromuscular junctions, confirming that no presynaptic depolarization is necessary to obtain high levels of phasic transmitter release. As expected, secretion resembled a fourth-power function of peak $[Ca^{2+}]$. The peak presynaptic $[Ca^{2+}]$ needed for normal-amplitude postsynaptic responses was about 75 μM. This concentration is somewhat less than the level thought to normally trigger neurosecretion; however, in the photolysis experiments, all docked vesicles, not just those nearest Ca^{2+} channels that open, were uniformly activated.

In similar experiments on retinal bipolar neurons from fish,[69] fully loaded DM-nitrophen was photolyzed to produce a stepped increase in $[Ca^{2+}]$ while secretion was monitored as an increase in membrane capacitance, a measure of cell membrane area increased by fusion of vesicles. Calcium ion concentration had to be raised by more than 20 μM before a fast phase of secretion developed. The sharp Ca^{2+} dependence of release and short synaptic delays were fitted by a model with a high degree of positive Ca^{2+} cooperativity, in which four successive Ca^{2+} ions bind with affinities increasing (or K_D decreasing) from 140 to 9 μM, followed by a Ca^{2+}-independent rate-limiting step. These biophysical experiments provide a fairly detailed characterization of the Ca^{2+} receptor responsible for transmitter release.

Calcium Ions Must Mobilize Vesicles to Docking Sites at Slowly Transmitting Synapses

Most peptidergic synapses and some synapses releasing biogenic amines display kinetics remarkably different from those of fast synapses. In these slower synapses, single action potentials often have no discernible postsynaptic effect. During repetitive stimulation, postsynaptic responses rise slowly, often with a delay of seconds from the beginning of stimulation, and persist for just as long after stimulation ceases. Such slow responses are due to many factors: the postsynaptic receptors may have intrinsically sluggish second messengers or G proteins (Chapter 10); the postsynaptic receptors are often distant from release sites, so extracellular diffusion takes significant time; and release starts after the beginning of stimulation and continues after stimulation stops. Given these limitations, it is not surprising that single quanta are never discernible, either as spontaneous PSPs or as components of evoked responses.

The ultrastructural anatomy of presynaptic terminals of slowly transmitting synapses also is different from that of fast synapses. Transmitter is stored in large, dense core vesicles scattered randomly throughout the cytoplasm; vesicles do not tend to cluster at active zones or to line up at the membrane, docked and ready for release. Nevertheless, there is no doubt that transmitter is released from vesicles, because it is both stored and often synthesized in them, and they can be seen to undergo exocytosis during high-frequency stimulation causing high rates of release.[70]

A High-Affinity Calcium-Binding Step Controls Secretion of Slow Transmitters

Calcium ions are required for excitation–secretion coupling in slow synapses, but the dependence of release on $[Ca^{2+}]$ is linear, in contrast with fast synapses.[71] Furthermore, because few vesicles are predocked at active zones, most of those released by repetitive activity are not exposed to the local high $[Ca^{2+}]$ near Ca^{2+} channels. Thus, an important event triggered by Ca^{2+} influx in action potentials is likely to be the translocation of dense core vesicles to plasma membrane release sites, followed by exocytosis. This process has a very different dependence on $[Ca^{2+}]$ than does the release of docked vesicles. Measurements of $[Ca^{2+}]$ during stimulation indicate that release correlates well with $[Ca^{2+}]$ levels in the low micromolar range above a minimum, or threshold, level of a few hundred nanomolar.[72,73]

A striking difference between the release of fast

transmitters, such as GABA and glutamate, and peptide transmitters, such as cholecystokinin, was found in studies of **synaptosomes,** isolated nerve terminals prepared from homogenized brain tissue by differential centrifugation.[74] When terminals were depolarized to admit Ca^{2+} through Ca^{2+} channels, the amino acid transmitters GABA and glutamate were released at much lower levels of bulk cytoplasmic [Ca^{2+}] than when Ca^{2+} was admitted more uniformly and gradually across the membrane by use of the Ca^{2+}-transporting ionophore ionomycin. Peptides were released at the same low levels of [Ca^{2+}] no matter which method was used to elevate [Ca^{2+}]. Thus, only amino acids were sensitive to the difference in [Ca^{2+}] gradients imposed by the two methods and were preferentially released by local high submembrane [Ca^{2+}] caused by depolarization. Apparently, peptides are released by a high-affinity rate-limiting step not especially sensitive to submembrane [Ca^{2+}] levels.

Slow and Fast Transmitters May Be Coreleased from the Same Neuron Terminal

Some neurons have both small synaptic vesicles containing acetylcholine or glutamate and large, dense core vesicles containing neuropeptides.[75] Often, the two transmitters act on different targets. Single action potentials release only the fast transmitter, so different patterns of activity can have very different relative effects on the targets. For example, postganglionic parasympathetic nerves to the salivary gland release acetylcholine, which stimulates salivation, and vasoactive intestinal peptide, which stimulates vasodilation. Many examples of the corelease of multiple transmitters have been described.

Summary

Ca^{2+} acts as an intracellular messenger tying the electrical signal of presynaptic depolarization to the act of neurosecretion. At fast synapses, Ca^{2+} enters through clusters of channels near docked synaptic vesicles in active zones. It acts at extremely short distances (tens of nanometers) in remarkably little time (200 μs) and at very high local concentrations ($\geq 100\ \mu M$), in calcium microdomains, by binding cooperatively to a low-affinity receptor with fast kinetics to trigger exocytosis. Some transmitters, such as peptides and some biogenic amines, are stored in larger, dense core vesicles not docked at the plasma membrane in active zones. Release of these transmitters, as well as their diffusion to postsynaptic targets and their postsynaptic actions, is much slower than that of transmitters such as acetylcholine and amino acids at fast synapses. Release of slow transmitters depends linearly on [Ca^{2+}] and may be governed by a Ca^{2+}-sensitive rate-limiting step different from that triggering exocytosis of docked vesicles at fast synapses.

MOLECULAR MECHANISMS OF TRANSMITTER RELEASE

The primary function of the synaptic vesicle is transmitter exocytosis. This function is accomplished by the rapid, calcium-regulated fusion of the synaptic vesicle membrane with the presynaptic plasma membrane. After exocytosis, the components of the synaptic vesicle membrane are selectively recovered from the plasma membrane by endocytosis and recycled within the nerve terminal to generate new synaptic vesicles. This local recycling pathway, known as the **exo-endocytic cycle,** provides a mechanism by which neurons can maintain a constant supply of synaptic vesicles in the nerve terminal without reliance on the biosynthetic machinery in the cell body (which at some synapses can be more than 1 m away). The recycling capacity of the nerve terminal is thus essential for the consistent release of neurotransmitter in response to stimulation conditions of variable frequency and duration. The primary steps of the synaptic vesicle exo-endocytic cycle (illustrated in Fig. 7.2) include:

- Transmitter uptake from the cytoplasm
- Cytoskeletal and intervesicular anchoring
- Plasma membrane docking
- Membrane fusion (exocytosis)
- Endocytosis and recycling

Each step of the synaptic vesicle exo-endocytic cycle takes place at a site at which calcium or other second messengers may directly regulate or indirectly modulate transmitter secretion. Modulation of the strength or efficacy of synaptic signaling, commonly known as **synaptic plasticity,** plays an important role both in the development of synaptic connections and in the functioning of the mature nervous system. The synaptic vesicle exo-endocytic cycle is a prime target for such modulation. The combined use of biochemical, molecular genetic, and biophysical techniques is leading to an understanding of the molecular mechanisms that underlie the synaptic vesicle exo-endocytic cycle and the regulation of transmitter secretion.

Synaptic Vesicles Can Be Purified and Biochemically Characterized

How does one investigate the mechanisms that underlie transmitter release? A biochemical approach, one in which the components of the synaptic vesicle membrane are identified and characterized, has proved to be particularly powerful. The rationale behind this approach is that the molecular properties of synaptic vesicle components can be sources of insight into their function(s) in the exo-endocytic cycle. Synaptic vesicles are abundant in nervous tissue and, owing to their unique physical properties (uniform small diameter and low buoyant density), can be purified to homogeneity by simple subcellular fractionation techniques.[76,77] As a result, at a biochemical level, synaptic vesicles are among the most thoroughly characterized organelles. The most common sources for the purification of synaptic vesicles are mammalian brain and the electric organ of marine elasmobranchs. The latter, a specialized adaptation of the neuromuscular junction, is the tissue that served as the source for the purification of the nicotinic acetylcholine receptor (see Chapter 9). The protein compositions of synaptic vesicles from these sources are remarkably similar, demonstrating the evolutionary conservation of synaptic vesicle function. This similarity also points to the fact that many of the proteins present on the synaptic vesicle membrane perform general functions that are not restricted to a single class of transmitter.

Synaptic Vesicle Proteins Peform a Variety of Functions

The major protein constituents of the synaptic vesicle membrane are represented schematically in Fig. 7.4, and a brief summary of their functions is given in Table 7.1. Many of these proteins can be classified into three distinct groups according to function: (1) transmitter uptake, (2) vesicle cross-linking, and (3) membrane trafficking (docking, fusion, and endocytosis).[31,32] The functions of other components of the synaptic vesicle membrane remain unclear.

Transmitter Uptake

A central requirement of quantal synaptic transmission is the synchronous release of thousands of molecules of transmitter from the presynaptic nerve terminal. This requirement is partly met by the capacity of synaptic vesicles to accumulate and store high concentrations of transmitter. In cholinergic neurons, the concentration of acetylcholine within the synaptic vesicle can reach 0.6 *M*, more than 1000-fold greater than that in the cytoplasm.[76,77] Two synaptic vesicle proteins mediate the uptake of transmitter—the **vacuolar proton pump** and a family of **transmitter transporters.** The vacuolar proton pump is a multisubunit ATPase that catalyzes the translocation of protons from the cytoplasm into the lumen of a variety of intracellular organelles, including synaptic vesicles.[78] The resulting transmembrane electrochemical proton gradient is utilized as the energy source for the active uptake of transmitter by transmitter transporters. Transmitter uptake has been characterized in isolated synaptic vesicle preparations in which at least four types of distinct transporters have been identified—one for acetylcholine, another for biogenic amines (catecholamines and serotonin), a third for the excitatory amino acid glutamate, and the fourth for inhibitory amino acids (GABA and glycine).[9,79] These distinct transporters, which differ in their dependence on the ΔpH (proton gradient) and $\Delta\psi$ (potential difference) components of the proton electrochemical gradient, are differentially expressed by neurons. The type of transmitter stored in the synaptic vesicles of a particular neuron is dictated by the type of transporter expressed.

The molecular properties of several vesicular transmitter transporters have been deduced from their cDNA clones.[9,80] The vesicular transporters are integral membrane proteins with 12 membrane-spanning domains that display sequence similarity with bacterial drug-resistance transporters. The synaptic vesicle transporters are clearly distinct from the plasma membrane transmitter transporters that remove transmitter from the synaptic cleft and thereby contribute to the termination of synaptic signaling (see Fig. 7.2). The distinguishing characteristics include their transport topology, energy source, pharmacology, and structure[9,79] (see Chapter 8). Some nonquantal release of transmitter can be mediated by the activity of the vesicular transporter transiently localized to the plasma membrane after exocytosis or the reversal of the plasma membrane transporters induced by ionic and potential fluctuations. In most cases, however, this nonquantal release takes place at some distance from postsynaptic receptors and is unable to affect the properties of the postsynaptic cell.

In contrast with small chemical transmitters, proteinaceous signaling molecules, including neuropeptides and hormones, are typically stored in granules that are larger and have a higher electron density than synaptic vesicles. The contents of these granules are not recycled at the release sites; as a result, their replenishment requires new protein synthesis followed by packaging into secretory vesicles in the cell body. Because of the slow kinetics of their release, the slow responsiveness of their postsynaptic receptors, and their inability to be locally recycled, proteinaceous signaling molecules typically mediate regulatory functions.

Vesicle Cross-Linking

Although a fraction of the synaptic vesicles in a nerve terminal are found in close contact with the presynaptic plasma membrane at the active zone, most

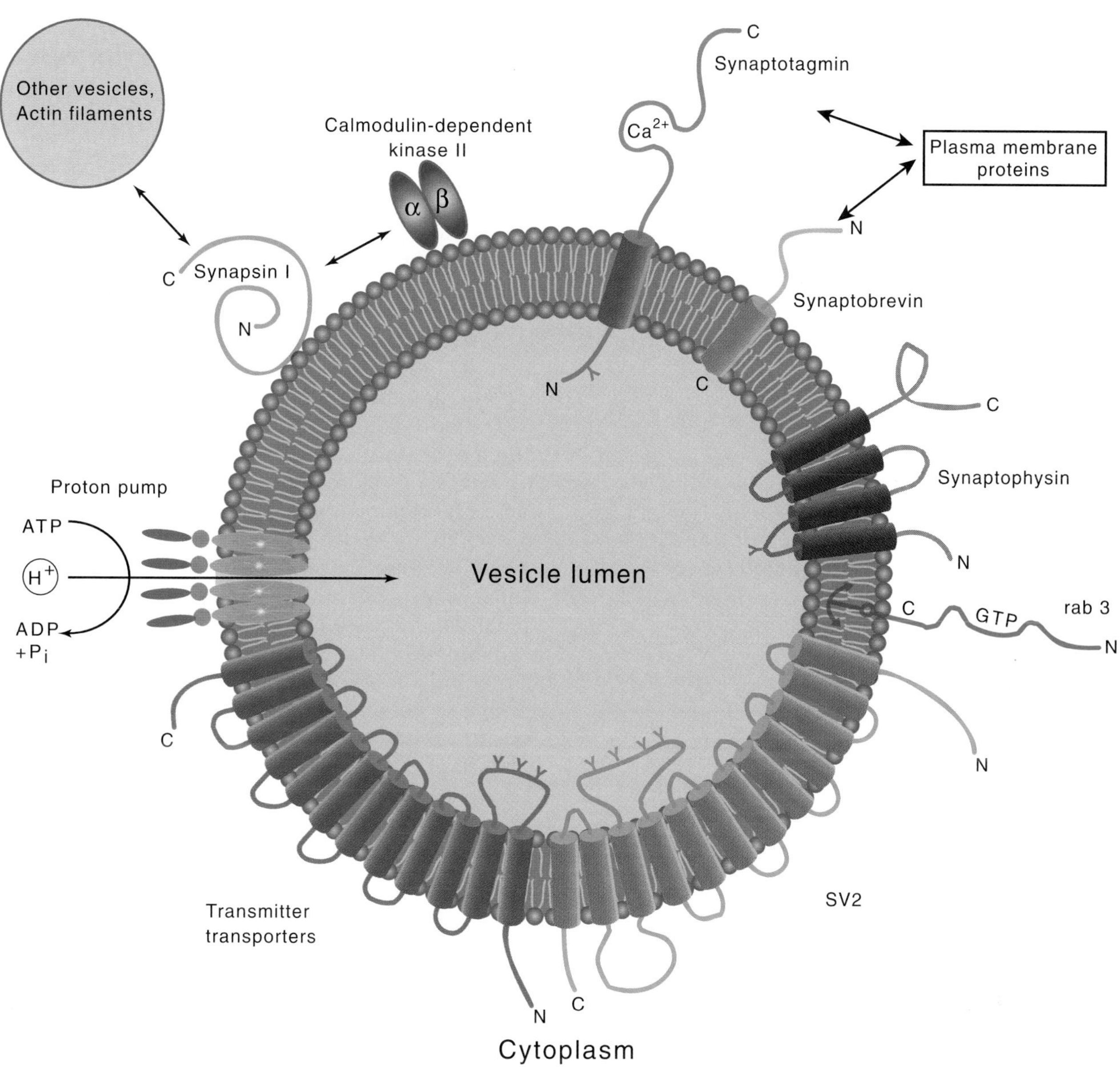

FIGURE 7.4 Schematic representation of the structure and topology of the major synaptic vesicle membrane proteins (see also Table 7.1). N, amino, and C, carboxy termini.

are clustered in the presynaptic cytoplasm, often connected to each other and to the actin cytoskeleton by thin cross-links[81,82] (Figs. 7.1A and 7.5).

These morphologically distinct populations of vesicles belong to functionally distinct pools. Synaptic vesicles closely associated with the presynaptic plasma membrane constitute a readily available pool for rapid fusion and release of transmitter in response to stimulation. The remaining synaptic vesicles make up a reserve pool from which vesicles are recruited to replenish those depleted after stimulation. **Synapsin I,** a protein peripherally associated with the synaptic vesicle membrane, possesses a number of properties consistent with a function in vesicle cross-linking. First, the morphological properties of the cross-links are similar to those of isolated synapsin I.[81,82] In addition, biochemical studies have demonstrated that synapsin I can bind both actin filaments and synaptic vesicles *in vitro.* These binding properties are negatively regulated by the phosphorylation of synapsin I by **calmodulin-dependent kinase II,**[83] an abundant neuronal calcium-regulated protein kinase that also functions in the localization of synapsin I to the synaptic vesicle[84] (see Fig. 7.4). Finally, injection of dephosphorylated synapsin I into the presynaptic terminal of the squid giant synapse reduces transmitter secretion, whereas injection of an activated form of calmodulin-dependent kinase II enhances secretion.[44] These results support a

TABLE 7.1 Function of Synaptic Vesicle Proteins

Protein	Function
	Transmitter uptake
Vacuolar proton pump	Generation of electrochemical proton gradient
Transmitter transporter	Transmitter uptake
	Vesicle crosslinking
Synapsin I	Vesicle crosslinking and anchoring to actin filaments
Calmodulin-dependent kinase II	Anchoring and phosphorylation-mediated regulation of synapsin I
	Membrane trafficking
Synaptotagmin	Interaction with plasma membrane proteins syntaxin and neurexin (vesicle docking or fusion), coated vesicle adaptor AP-2 (endocytosis), and calcium (calcium sensor)
Synaptobrevin	Interaction with plasma membrane proteins syntaxin and SNAP-25 (vesicle docking or fusion)
Rab3	Vesicle targeting or docking
	Other?
SV2	Transporter?
Synaptophysin	Fusion pore?

model in which synapsin I and calmodulin-dependent kinase II function to regulate the availability of synaptic vesicles for release. In mice, however, elimination of the gene encoding synapsin I by homologous recombination results in a rather modest phenotype.[85] The synapsin I–deficient mice develop and behave normally, clearly demonstrating that synapsin I is not essential for transmitter secretion. The mutant mice do exhibit an increase in a form of short-term synaptic plasticity known as paired pulse facilitation, suggesting that synapsin I functions to regulate the availability of synaptic vesicles during repetitive stimulation. Other roles for synapsin I may not be evident in the synapsin I–deficient mice owing to functional redundancy or compensatory changes.

Membrane Trafficking (Docking, Fusion, and Endocytosis)

Three central steps in the synaptic vesicle exo-endocytic cycle take place at or near the presynaptic plasma membrane: (1) synaptic vesicle docking; (2) regulated fusion; and (3) endocytosis. Several components of the synaptic vesicle membrane, as well as soluble and presynaptic plasma membrane proteins, have important functions in each of these steps. The processes of vesicle docking, fusion, and endocytosis are not restricted to the nerve terminal; rather, they are elements of membrane-trafficking pathways in all eukaryotic cells. Thus, numerous similarities between the molecular mechanisms mediating membrane trafficking in the nerve terminal and those operating in other regions of the cell or in other cell types have been identified.

Biophysical Measurements Place Constraints on the Molecular Mechanisms of Synaptic Vesicle Docking and Fusion

Biophysical studies have demonstrated that the fusion of synaptic vesicles with the presynaptic plasma membrane requires high calcium concentrations (≈ 100 μM)[62] and is extremely rapid (< 200 μs).[54] These measurements place constraints on the potential mechanisms responsible for synaptic vesicle docking and fusion. The extremely rapid time course eliminates the possibility that extensive biochemical cascades are required to trigger fusion. Even a single calcium-activated catalytic reaction (with a typical catalytic rate of 100 reactions per second) is unlikely to be fast enough. A more likely possibility is that calcium binding to its target induces a conformational change that triggers fusion—a possibility consistent with observations that calcium is the only factor necessary to trigger exocytosis. The rapid time course of exocytosis also indicates that some vesicles must be "primed" at the release sites. In contrast with fusion, the mechanisms that lead to vesicle docking can accommodate multiple catalytic reactions that ultimately prepare the vesicle for rapid exocytosis. The high calcium concentration required for transmitter release places additional constraints on the location of vesicle docking and fusion and on the molecular target(s) for calcium action. The high calcium levels necessary to trigger fusion are achieved only in a restricted region surrounding voltage-gated calcium channels.[86] Therefore, synaptic vesicle docking and fusion must take place in close proximity to the calcium channels. This proposal is supported by freeze–fracture studies at the frog neuromuscular junction showing that vesicle fusion occurs adjacent to parallel rows of intramembranous particles thought to be calcium channels[4] (see Fig. 7.1C). In addition, a direct interaction between N-type calcium channels (a class of voltage-gated calcium channel known to regulate transmitter secretion at some synapses) and a component of the synaptic vesicle docking and fusion machinery has been demonstrated.[87] The high calcium concentration requirement also indicates that the calcium sensor that triggers fusion must have a low affinity for calcium, which rules out a large number of high-affinity calcium-binding proteins. Finally, because transmitter secretion is nonlinearly dependent on the

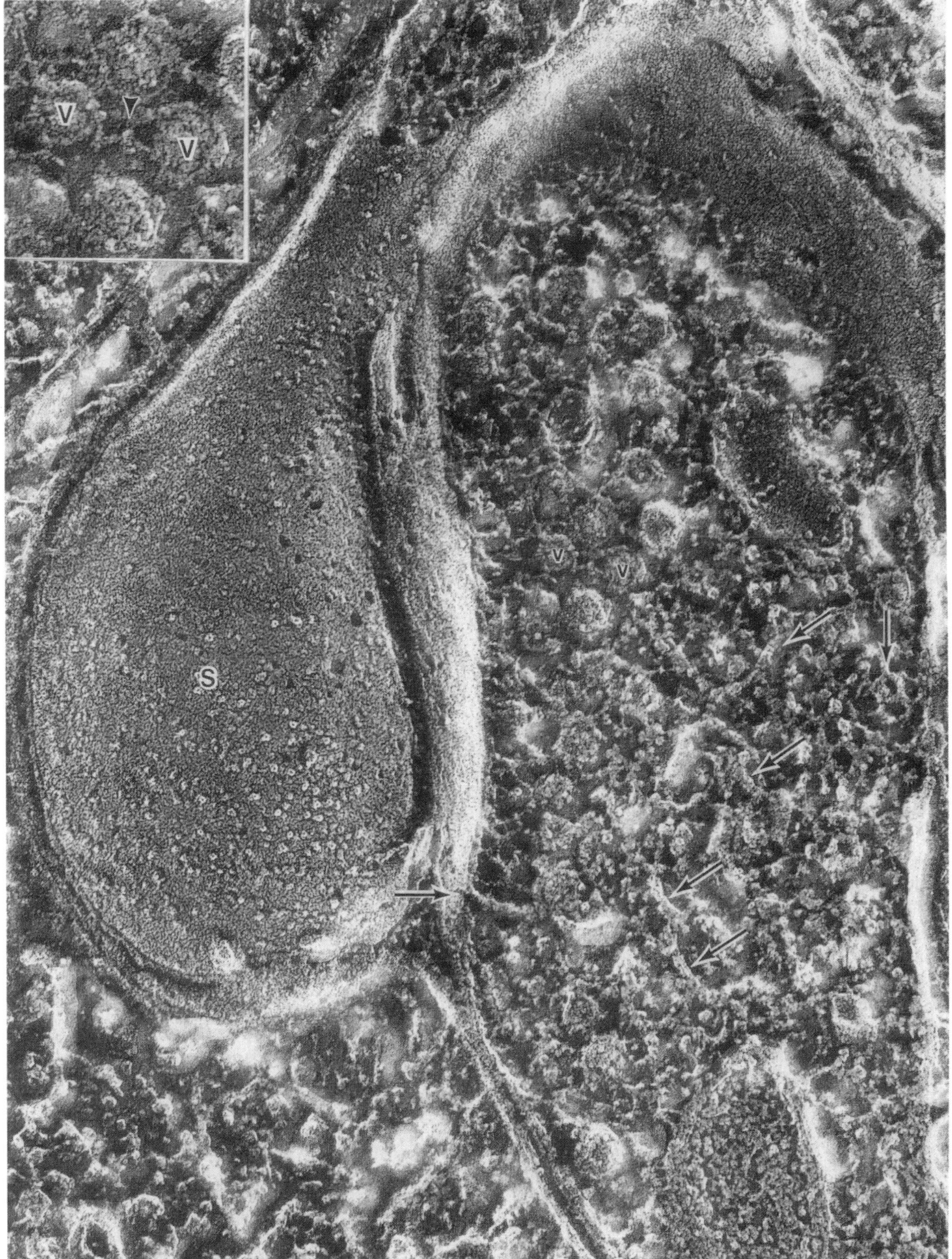

FIGURE 7.5 Structure of a synapse between a parallel fiber and a Purkinje cell spine in the cerebellum. The sample was rapidly frozen and then freeze–fractured, shallow-etched, and rotary-shadowed to reveal the details of the synaptic architecture. From Landis *et al.*[81] Copyright © by Cell Press.

influx of calcium,[52] the calcium sensor can be expected to exhibit cooperative calcium-binding properties.

Protein Complexes Mediate the Docking of Synaptic Vesicles at the Presynaptic Plasma Membrane

A prerequisite for the rapid, regulated secretion of transmitter is the precise docking of synaptic vesicles at the presynaptic plasma membrane. This docking is demonstrated morphologically by the close contact between the synaptic vesicle and the presynaptic plasma membranes (see Fig. 7.1A). The molecular basis for synaptic vesicle docking has been approached biochemically in studies aimed at identifying stable protein complexes that incorporate known synaptic vesicle proteins.[88] One such complex forms between two components of the synaptic vesicle membrane, **synaptobrevin** (also known as VAMP) and **synaptotagmin,** and two components of the presynaptic plasma membrane, **syntaxin** and **SNAP-25** (Fig. 7.6).

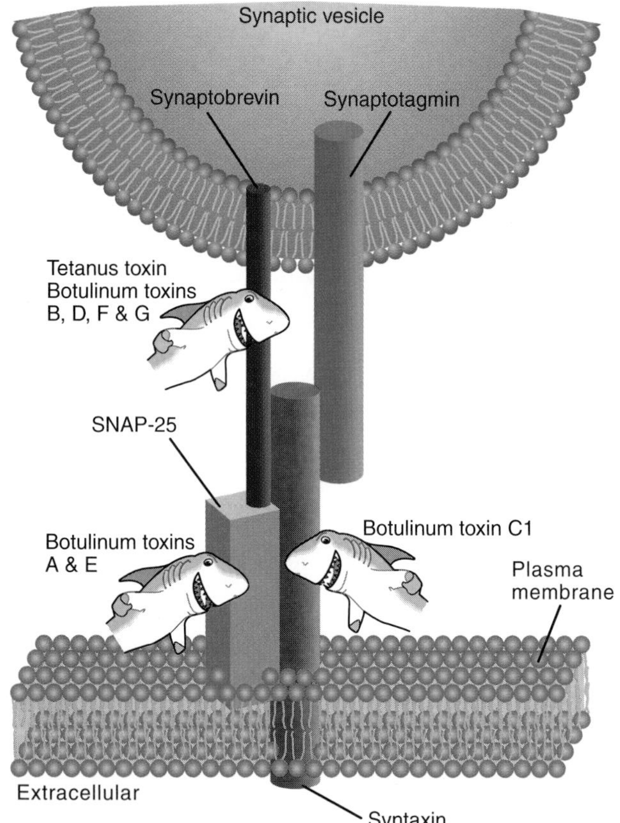

FIGURE 7.6 Schematic representation of synaptic vesicle docking mediated by a complex between components of the synaptic vesicle membrane (synaptobrevin and synaptotagmin) and the presynaptic plasma membrane (syntaxin and SNAP-25). Sharks indicate targets for the clostridial neurotoxins that inhibit transmitter release.

The importance of this complex for transmitter secretion is supported by the fact that three of its components (synaptobrevin, syntaxin, and SNAP-25) are targets for the action of neurotoxins produced by bacteria of the genus *Clostridium*.[20] These toxins, which include tetanus toxin and seven types of botulinum toxin, are extremely potent inhibitors of transmitter release. Each of the clostridial toxins is composed of disulfide-linked heavy and light chains. The heavy chains selectively bind to the surface of neurons and are responsible for the translocation of the toxins into the cytoplasm, where the reducing environment separates the two chains. The free light chains of the toxins function as endoproteases that selectively target synaptic proteins for cleavage (Fig. 7.6). Tetanus toxin and four classes of botulinum toxin cleave synaptobrevin, whereas two other classes of botulinum toxin cleave SNAP-25. The remaining class of botulinum toxin cleaves syntaxin. These results highlight the importance of these three proteins in synaptic vesicle docking or fusion or both.

In vitro, the complex incorporating synaptobrevin, synaptotagmin, syntaxin, and SNAP-25 can be recovered from detergent-solubilized membrane preparations (i.e., in the absence of lipid bilayers). The formation of a stable complex between these proteins *in vivo* would correspond to vesicle docking. However, it is important to note that vesicle docking is likely to be a highly regulated multistep process. The docked vesicles observed morphologically are likely to exist in multiple biochemically distinct states, only one of which corresponds to the current biochemical definition of vesicle docking.[89] The number and molecular composition of other protein complexes contributing to synaptic vesicle docking remain to be determined.

Molecular Mechanisms Underlying Membrane Trafficking Are Highly Conserved

Additional support for the importance of syntaxin, SNAP-25, and synaptobrevin in secretion comes from studies of other membrane-trafficking pathways. Several genes required for the proper functioning of the secretory pathway in the yeast *Saccharomyces cerevisiae* encode proteins that share sequence homology with syntaxin, SNAP-25, and synaptobrevin.[90] This remarkable evolutionary conservation emphasizes the fundamental role that these proteins play in the process of secretion. Another connection between the mechanisms of transmitter secretion and general membrane trafficking pathways is the role of two soluble proteins, NSF (*N*-ethylmaleimide sensitive factor) and α-SNAP (soluble NSF attachment protein). These two proteins, originally purified as factors required for the *in vitro* reconstitution of vesicle-mediated transport within the

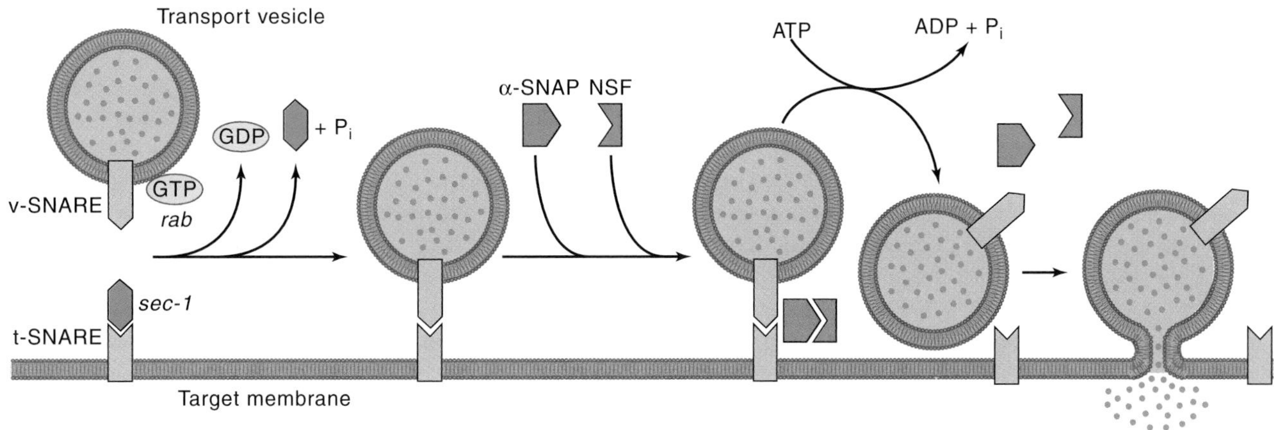

FIGURE 7.7 The SNARE hypothesis: a model depicting assembly and disassembly of the SNARE complex and its role in transport vesicle docking and fusion.

Golgi complex, are general factors required for most membrane-trafficking steps.[91] The function of NSF, an ATPase whose activity precedes membrane fusion, requires its association with α-SNAP and a complex of membrane proteins known as the **SNARE** (SNAP receptor) **complex.** In the nerve terminal, the SNARE complex consists of syntaxin, SNAP-25, and synaptobrevin.[92] In both yeast and animal cells, syntaxin and synaptobrevin homologs form small gene families whose members are required at distinct membrane-trafficking steps. This observation, coupled with the general role of NSF and α-SNAP in membrane trafficking, has led to a model of transport vesicle docking and fusion known as the **SNARE hypothesis** (Fig. 7.7).

According to the SNARE hypothesis, the inherent specificity of membrane-trafficking pathways is generated by the selective docking of a transport vesicle with its target membrane through the formation of a SNARE complex (composed of a vesicle membrane SNARE, or v-SNARE, and its cognate target membrane SNARE, or t-SNARE). When the SNARE complex has formed, α-SNAP and NSF are recruited to the vesicle membrane–target membrane interface. The hydrolysis of ATP by NSF causes the SNARE complex to dissociate in a reaction that may lead either directly or indirectly to membrane fusion.[93]

Two other elements of the nerve terminal that regulate synaptic vesicle docking with the plasma membrane are the synaptic vesicle protein **Rab3**[94] and the soluble protein **n-Sec1** (also known as munc18).[95,96] Like syntaxin and synaptobrevin, Rab3 and n-Sec1 are evolutionarily conserved and are members of protein families in both yeast and animal cells that contribute to the specificity of transport vesicle targeting. Rab3 is a low-molecular-weight GTPase, related to the *ras* oncogene, that functions as a GTP-regulated molecular switch. In its GTP-bound state, Rab3 is associated with the synaptic vesicle membrane. However, after GTP hydrolysis, the GDP-bound form of Rab3 is recycled as a soluble intermediate. The Rab protein GTPase cycle may serve to regulate SNARE complex formation, thereby ensuring the specificity of transport vesicle docking (Fig. 7.7). n-Sec1 is a hydrophilic protein that has a high affinity for syntaxin. When syntaxin is associated with n-Sec1, it is no longer able to interact with either SNAP-25 or synaptobrevin. Thus, members of the Sec1 family may function as negative regulators of SNARE complex formation (Fig. 7.7).

Regulatory Mechanisms Confer Specialized Properties on Synaptic Vesicle Docking and Fusion

It is clear that the fundamental mechanisms underlying membrane-trafficking processes are highly conserved in all eukaryotic cells. However, because most membrane-trafficking events are constitutive (i.e., they proceed in the absence of stimulation), additional regulatory mechanisms must account for the special temporal, spatial, and Ca^{2+}-sensitive properties of transmitter secretion. These regulatory mechanisms function in conjunction with the constitutive membrane-trafficking mechanisms to generate the unique characteristics of synaptic vesicle docking and fusion. For example, the docking of synaptic vesicles near voltage-gated calcium channels is the result of an interaction between syntaxin, a component of the vesicle-docking complex, and voltage-gated calcium channels.[87] This interaction ensures that synaptic vesicles are localized to sites that, on stimulation, will be exposed to calcium concentrations high enough to trigger fusion. **Neurexin** is another component of the presynaptic plasma membrane that interacts with the synaptic vesicle docking and fusion machinery.[97,98] Although the normal function of neurexin is not clear, it can serve as the receptor for a neurotoxin, known as *α-latrotoxin,* produced by black widow spiders. The binding of α-latrotoxin to neurexin stimulates massive, calcium-independent release of transmitter from the nerve terminal. This suggests that α-latrotoxin is able either to artificially activate or to bypass the normal regulatory mechanisms controlling transmitter release.

Calcium regulates multiple steps in the synaptic vesicle exo-endocytic cycle, including, most importantly, the fusion reaction. One of the targets for calcium action is synaptotagmin.[99–101] This synaptic vesicle membrane protein exhibits several of the properties expected of the calcium sensor that triggers exocytosis. *In vitro,* purified synaptotagmin exists as a homooligomer that cooperatively binds calcium (in the presence of acidic phospholipids) with relatively low affinity (10 μM). Furthermore, calcium binding induces a conformational change in synaptotagmin. Evidence that synaptotagmin plays an important role in the regulation of transmitter release *in vivo* is provided by studies of *Drosophila* and mouse mutants.[102–104] Disruption of the synaptotagmin gene in mice by homologous recombination causes severe deficits in synaptic transmission—the rapid synchronous release of transmitter is eliminated, whereas a much smaller calcium-dependent asynchronous release remains. Similarly, in *Drosophila* lacking synaptotagmin, calcium-dependent transmitter release is dramatically reduced but not entirely eliminated. Importantly, *Drosophila* expressing certain combinations of mutant synaptotagmin alleles exhibit an altered calcium dependence of transmitter release.[105] These results demonstrate that synaptotagmin is a major, but not exclusive, target for the regulation of transmitter release by calcium. Synaptotagmin may affect exocytosis by serving as a negative regulator, or "clamp," on the constitutive membrane-trafficking machinery. The binding of calcium may remove this clamp, allowing the constitutive machinery to catalyze the fusion reaction. Alternatively, synaptotagmin may play an active role in promoting membrane fusion in response to Ca^{2+}.

The Mechanism of Membrane Fusion Is Poorly Understood

Exocytosis requires the merging of the lipids in the membrane of the synaptic vesicle membrane with those in the plasma membrane. For this fusion reaction to take place, the two bilayers must be brought to within a few nanometers of each other—a process in which large hydration forces must be overcome. The reactions that contribute to vesicle docking and SNARE complex assembly–disassembly may perform this task. However, the mechanism by which fusion is initiated and the synaptic proteins taking part in this final step are not well understood. The most thoroughly characterized example of membrane fusion is that induced by the spike proteins of enveloped animal viruses, such as the hemagglutinin protein of influenza virus.[106,107] Hemagglutinin is anchored in the membrane of the virus particle and binds to a receptor on the surface of the target cell before being internalized. The low pH of the endosome compartment triggers a conformational change in hemagglutinin, resulting in the exposure of an amphipathic peptide known as the fusion peptide. The fusion peptide inserts into and perturbs the endosome membrane, thus initiating fusion with the viral membrane. Whether a similar calcium-induced conformational change initiates fusion of the synaptic vesicle with the presynaptic plasma membrane remains to be determined.

Capacitance measurements can be utilized to monitor the process of membrane fusion with high temporal resolution. Because membrane capacitance is directly proportional to membrane area, fusion reactions that add membrane to the cell surface will increase capacitance. Biophysical measurements of membrane capacitance have been used to monitor secretion (fusion) in several nonneuronal, slowly secreting systems, including mast cells and chromaffin cells.[108] In each case, the earliest sign of secretion is the formation of a gap-junction-sized pore, known as the **fusion pore,** that connects the lumen of the secretory granule with the extracellular space. This fusion pore can open and close, similar to an ion channel, before expanding irreversibly to produce full fusion. Cell–cell fusion artificially induced by influenza hemagglutinin also is initiated by a transient fusion pore,[109] suggesting that the fusion pore represents a mechanistic intermediate common to all membrane fusion reactions. However, the molecular nature of the fusion pore and its role in the rapid membrane fusion reaction responsible for transmitter secretion remain to be established.

Endocytosis Efficiently Recovers Synaptic Vesicle Components

After exocytosis, the components of the synaptic vesicle membrane must be recovered from the presynaptic plasma membrane. Vesicle recycling, which takes place in 30–60 s,[18,48] is accomplished by either of two mechanisms. The first is simply a reversal of the fusion process. In this case, a fusion pore opens to allow transmitter release and then rapidly closes to re-form a vesicle. Although this mechanism is employed in some systems,[108] the predominant pathway for synaptic vesicle recycling is endocytosis.[110] Endocytosis of synaptic vesicle components, like receptor-mediated endocytosis in other cell types, is mediated by vesicles coated with the protein clathrin,[111] as mentioned earlier. The cargo incorporated into these vesicles as they assemble is selected by accessory proteins. One class of accessory protein known as AP-2 displays a high affinity for synaptotagmin,[112] suggesting a potential role for synaptotagmin in endocytosis as well as exocytosis. The final pinching off of the clathrin-coated vesicle requires the protein dynamin. A crucial role for dynamin in synaptic vesicle recycling is most clearly demonstrated in a temperature-sensitive *Drosophila* mutant known as *shibire*. The *shibire* gene encodes the *Drosophila* homolog of dynamin.[46,47] At the nonpermissive temperature, the *shibire* mutant flies rapidly become paralyzed owing to a nearly complete depletion of synaptic vesicles from their nerve terminals. Dynamin is a GTPase whose activity is modulated by calcium-regulated phosphorylation and dephosphorylation.[113] Thus, the endocytic recycling of synaptic vesicles provides another site at which calcium regulates the synaptic vesicle exo-endocytic cycle. When the components of the synaptic vesicle membrane are recovered in clathrin-coated vesicles, recycling is completed by vesicle uncoating and, perhaps, passage through an endosomal compartment in the nerve terminal (see Fig. 7.2).

Summary

The synaptic vesicle life cycle consists of a series of membrane-trafficking events centered on the exocytotic release of transmitter. The molecular mechanisms that govern this synaptic vesicle exo-endocytic cycle have been elucidated through a combination of biochemical, molecular, and biophysical techniques. Components of the synaptic vesicle membrane, the presynaptic plasma membrane, and the cytoplasm all contribute to the regulation of synaptic vesicle function. Remarkably, many of the components taking part in transmitter release are evolutionarily conserved and include homologs required for constitutive secretion from yeast. In addition to these evolutionarily conserved elements, the synaptic vesicle exo-endocytic pathway utilizes specialized mechanisms that mediate regulatory events specific to the process of transmitter release. These elements provide the means for accomplishing the highly demanding membrane-trafficking events characteristic of the nerve terminal.

QUANTAL ANALYSIS

A quantitative description of the signal passing across a synapse is of utmost importance in understanding the function of the nervous system. This signal is the final output of all the integrative processes taking place in the presynaptic cell, and a complete statistical description should be able to capture the flow of information between neurons, as well as between neurons and effector cells. At many chemical synapses, a quantitative description is also a source of unique insight into the biophysics of transmission. The postsynaptic signal often fluctuates from trial to trial in a *quantal* manner; that is, it adopts preferred levels, which arise from the summation of various numbers of discrete events, thought to result from the release of individual vesicles of neurotransmitter.[1,114] Examination of the trial-to-trial amplitude fluctuation of the synaptic signal allows the size of the *quantum* to be estimated, as well as the average number of quanta released for a given presynaptic action potential. This approach is also a source of insight into the probabilistic processes underlying transmitter release from the presynaptic terminal and into the mechanisms by which transmission can be modified by physiological, pharmacological, and pathological phenomena.

Transmission at the Frog Neuromuscular Junction is Quantized

The quantal nature of transmission was first demonstrated in the early 1950s by Bernard Katz and his colleagues, who studied the frog motor end plate. By recording from a muscle fiber immediately under a branch of the motor axon, they measured the postsynaptic potential both at rest and in response to stimulation of the axon. Spontaneous signals were observed to occur at random intervals, measuring between 0.1 and 2 mV in amplitude, which was approximately 1/100 of the signal evoked by stimulating the presynaptic axon.[115] At any one site, these *spontaneous MEPPs* were of roughly the same amplitude, with a coefficient of variation of 30%, apparently resulting from the intermittent release of multimolecular packets of transmitter from the presynaptic terminal. In a comparison of the MEPPs with the signals evoked by stimulating the presynaptic axon under conditions designed to depress transmitter release to very low levels, the evoked EPP fluctuated from trial to trial between preferred amplitudes, which coincided with integral multiples of the MEPP amplitude[116] (see Fig. 7.8).[117,118] This implied that the MEPP is the *quantal building block*, variable numbers of which are released to make up the evoked signal. The relative numbers of trials resulting in 0, 1, 2, ... quanta were well described by a Poisson distribution—a statistical distribution that arises in many instances where a random process operates (Box 7.4), implying that the process governing quantal release may also depend on a simple underlying mechanism.

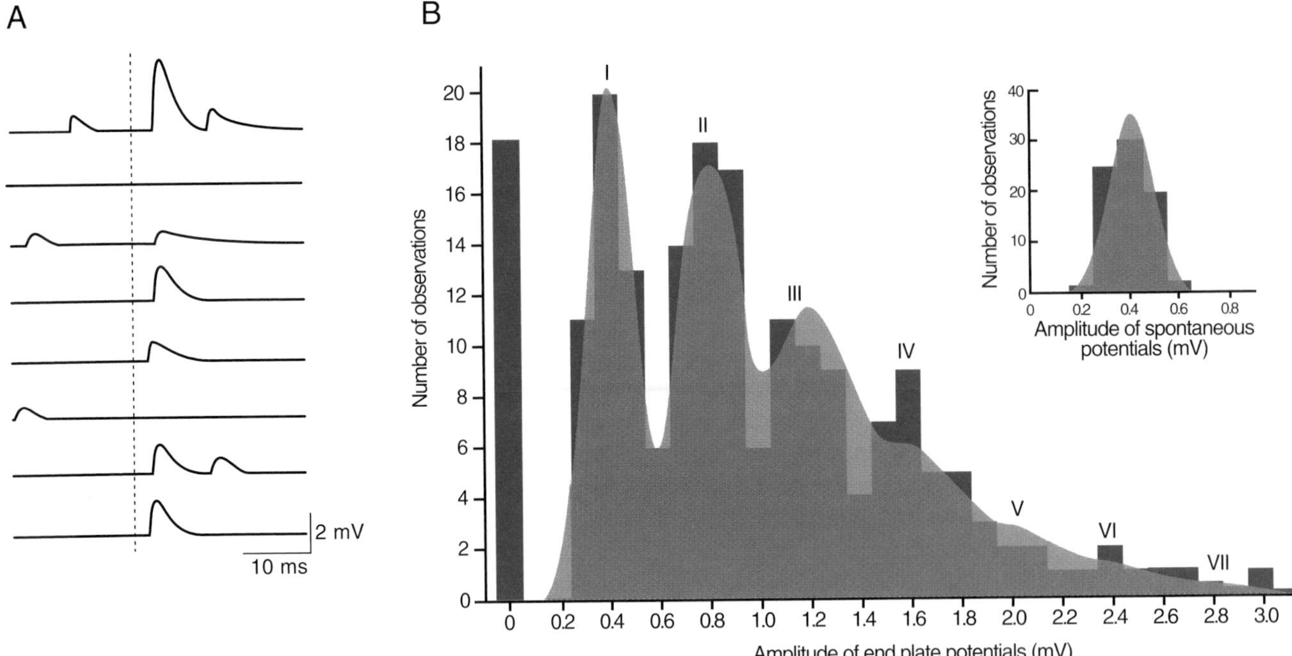

FIGURE 7.8 Quantal transmission at the neuromuscular junction. (A) Intracellular recordings from a rat muscle fiber in response to repeated presynaptic stimulation of the motor axon. Extracellular $[Ca^{2+}]$ and $[Mg^{2+}]$ were kept low and high, respectively, to depress transmission to a very low level. The size of the postsynaptic response, seen after the stimulus artifact, fluctuated from trial to trial, with some trials giving failures of transmission. Spontaneous MEPPs, occurring in the background, had approximately the same amplitude as the smallest evoked EPPs, implying that they arose from the release of single quanta of acetylcholine. (B) The peak amplitudes of 200 evoked EPPs from a similar experiment, plotted as an amplitude histogram. Eighteen trials resulted in failures of transmission (indicated by the bar at 0 mV), and the rest gave EPPs whose amplitude tended to cluster at integral multiples of 0.4 mV. This coincides with the mean amplitude of the spontaneous MEPPs, whose amplitude distribution is shown in the insert together with a Gaussian fit. The shading through the EPP histogram is a fit obtained by assuming a Poisson model of quantal release (see Box 7.4). The parameters describing this model were the average number of quanta released, m, obtained by dividing the mean EPP amplitude by the mean MEPP amplitude, and the quantal amplitude, Q, and its variance, Var_Q, obtained from the MEPP amplitude distribution. There is a good agreement with the observed amplitude distribution. The Poisson model predicts 19 failures. Roman numerals indicate the number of quanta corresponding to each component in the distribution. Part A from Liley[117]; Part B from Boyd and Martin.[118]

On the basis of this evidence, Katz and colleagues proposed the following model of transmission, which has gained wide acceptance and will be referred to as the **standard Katz model.**

- Arrival of an action potential at the presynaptic terminal briefly raises the probability of release of quanta of transmitter.
- Several quanta are available to be released, and every quantum gives roughly the same electrical signal in the postsynaptic cell. This is the quantal amplitude, Q, which sums linearly with all other quanta released.
- The average number of quanta released, m, is given by the product of n, the number of available quanta, and p, the average release probability: $m = np$. The relative probability of observing 0, 1, 2, . . . , n quanta released is then given by a binomial distribution, with parameters n and p (see Box 7.4).
- Under conditions of depressed transmission, p is low, and the system approximates a Poisson process. This is the limiting case of the binomial distribution where p tends to 0 and n tends to ∞ and is determined by the unique parameter m (see Box 7.4).

The standard Katz model has been supported by similar experiments in other preparations, which have shown that evoked EPSPs, IPSPs, EPSCs, or IPSCs tend to cluster near preferred values corresponding to integral multiples of a unit. In many cases, this quantal amplitude corresponds closely to the amplitude of spontaneous miniature postsynaptic signals (potentials or currents) occurring in the absence of presynaptic action potentials (Fig. 7.9).[119]

A major impetus for accurate measurement of quantal parameters is that it may help determine the locus of modulatory effects on synaptic transmission. An increase or decrease in the probability of presynaptic release should be detectable by a change in quantal content, m, whereas an alteration in the postsynaptic density or efficacy of receptors should be detectable by a change in quantal amplitude, Q.

BOX 7.4

BINOMIAL AND POISSON MODELS

Binomial Model

According to the binomial description, n quanta can be released in response to a presynaptic action potential, each of which has a probability, p, of being discharged. For convenience, let us define q as the probability that a given quantum is *not* discharged in a given trial: $q = 1 - p$. In any given trial, the number of quanta observed is between 0 and n. Imagine that only three quanta are available ($n = 3$), each of which has a 40% chance of being discharged in response to the action potential ($p = 0.4$, $q = 0.6$). The average number of quanta released is $m = np = 1.2$.

The probability that no quanta are released is $q^3 = 0.216$.

The probability that only one quantum is released is the sum of the probability that only the first is released, only the second is released, and only the third is released: $3pq^2 = 0.432$.

The probability that two of three are released is, conversely, $3p^2q = 0.288$.

Finally, the probability that all three are released is $p^3 = 0.064$.

The relative probabilities of observing 0, 1, ..., n quanta are the coefficients of the expansion of $G = (p + qz)^n = 0.216 + 0.432z + 0.288z^2 + 0.064z^3$. This is known as the generating function for the binomial distribution, and z is simply a "dummy variable"; that is, it serves no function except to allow the binomial expansion. These coefficients can be obtained from the binomial distribution, which gives the probability of observing 0, 1, ..., n quanta released for any n and p. Writing P_x for the probability of observing x quanta, we obtain

$$P_x = \frac{n!}{(n-x)!x!} p^x q^{n-x}.$$

Poisson Model

As n becomes very large and p very small, the probability of observing 0, 1, ... quanta is equally well described by a Poisson distribution. This is a limiting case of the binomial distribution when n tends to ∞ and p tends to 0, and, instead of two parameters (n and p), it is described by the sole parameter m. Again, m is the average value for P_x. The relative probability of observing 0, 1, ... quanta is now given by

$$P_x = \frac{m^x e^{-m}}{x!}.$$

For the same average quantal content m as that in the binomial model, the relative probabilities of observing 0, 1, ... quanta are now approximately

$$P_0 = 0.301$$
$$P_1 = 0.361$$
$$P_2 = 0.217$$
$$P_3 = 0.087$$
$$P_4 = 0.026$$
$$\vdots$$

Compound or Nonuniform Binomial Model

In the binomial model, what happens if different quanta have different, but still independent, release probabilities? Let us take the following example: $p_1 = 0.1$, $p_2 = 0.2$, $p_3 = 0.9$ (again defining $q_1 = 1 - p_1$, $q_2 = 1 - p_2$, $q_3 = 1 - p_3$). The average quantal content is again $p_1 + p_2 + p_3 = 1.2$.

$$P_0 = q_1q_2q_3 = 0.072$$
$$P_1 = p_1q_2q_3 + q_1p_2q_3 + q_1q_2p_3 = 0.674$$
$$P_2 = q_1p_2p_3 + p_1q_2p_3 + p_1p_2q_3 = 0.236$$
$$P_3 = p_1p_2p_3 = 0.018$$

Generally, P_x are again obtained from the coefficients of the polynomial expansion of the generating function: $G = (p_1 + q_1z)(p_2 + q_2z) \ldots (p_n + q_nz) = \Pi_k (p_k + q_kz)$, $k = 1, \ldots, n$.

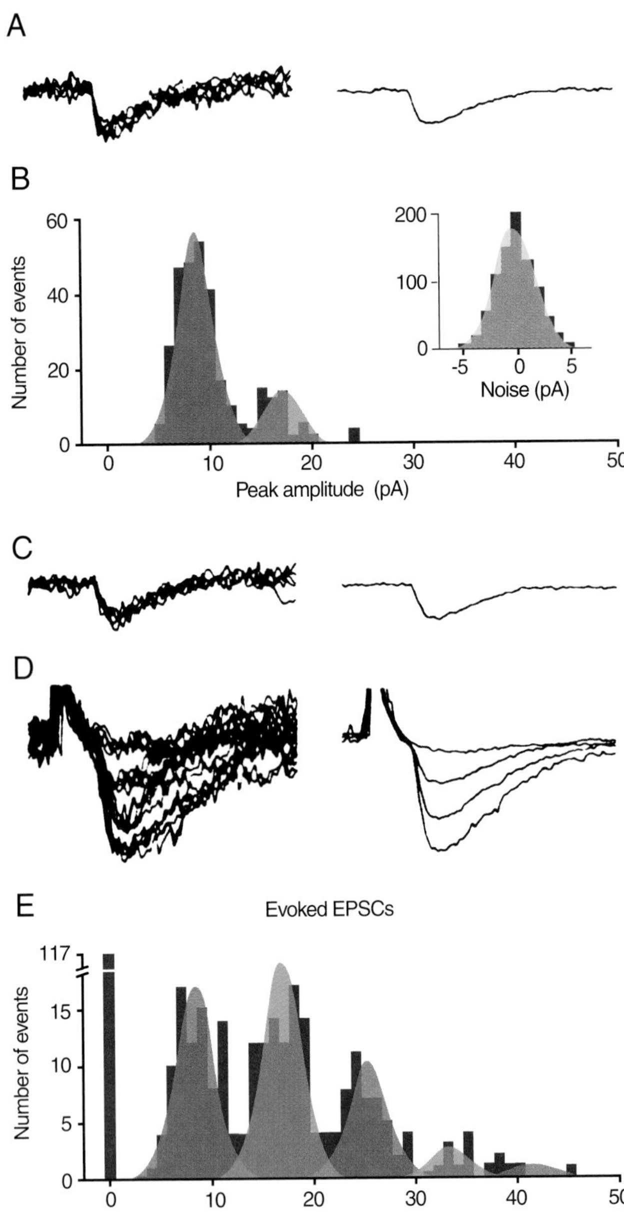

FIGURE 7.9 Quantal transmission in a thalamic neuron in a guinea pig brain slice. (A) Several spontaneous EPSCs superimposed (left), and the average time course (right). (B) An amplitude histogram showing that these events are clustered principally near 8.3 pA, with a smaller peak near 17 pA possibly representing the synchronous release of two quanta. (C) When presynaptic action potentials were abolished by tetrodotoxin, mean amplitudes of MEPSCs and spontaneous EPSCs were similar, implying that most were uniquantal. (D) EPSCs evoked by presynaptic stimulation in the optic tract. (E) Amplitude histogram of (D), showing clear clustering at integral multiples of approximately 8.3 pA. The superimposed Gaussian curves in (B) and (E) have approximately the same variance as the background noise, implying that quantal variability was negligible. From Paulsen and Heggelund.[119]

Underlying Processes Determine the Quantal Parameters

Considerable effort has been directed at establishing the physical correlates of the quantal parameters, Q, n, and p.

Quantal Parameter Q

A MEPP was thought to be too large to be accounted for by the release of an individual molecule of acetylcholine, because low doses of exogenous acetylcholine generated responses much smaller than a MEPP.[115] Vesicles were subsequently observed in electron micrographs of presynaptic terminals (see Chapter 9). Because these vesicles could act as packaging devices for transmitter, it was proposed that the quantal amplitude, Q, represents the discharge of one vesicle into the synaptic cleft. A large body of evidence (mentioned earlier) has since led to almost universal agreement that Q is the postsynaptic response to exocytosis of a single vesicle of transmitter.

Figure 7.10[120] shows a computer simulation of the diffusion of molecules of acetylcholine and binding to receptors at the neuromuscular junction: acetylcholine spreads out in a disc in the synaptic cleft and binds most of the underlying postsynaptic receptors, although many more spare receptors beyond the edge of the disc remain unoccupied by transmitter.[24]

Quantal Parameter n

The physical correlate of n has been more elusive. In the original description of quantal transmission, n represented the number of releasable quanta. As the ultrastructure of the presynaptic terminal was elucidated, however, vesicles were found to be clustered near specializations, or active zones, in the presynaptic membrane. Each active zone is composed of a dense bar on the cytoplasmic face of the terminal membrane, bordered by rows of intramembranous particles, thought to be voltage-sensitive calcium channels.[17] As stated earlier, entry of calcium ions through these channels raises the intracellular calcium concentration in a small volume immediately adjacent to the channels, triggering the exocytosis. Can n then be the number of active zones, if they are release sites? At the frog neuromuscular junction, evoked quanta seem to summate linearly, although the relation between depolarization and acetylcholine concentration is nonlinear when acetylcholine is added to the bath.[121] This result suggests that quanta rarely activate the same receptors, which would occur only if each active zone normally released only one quantum, and is consistent with the view that n is indeed the number of release sites. When acetylcholinesterase is inhibited, however, the falling

A

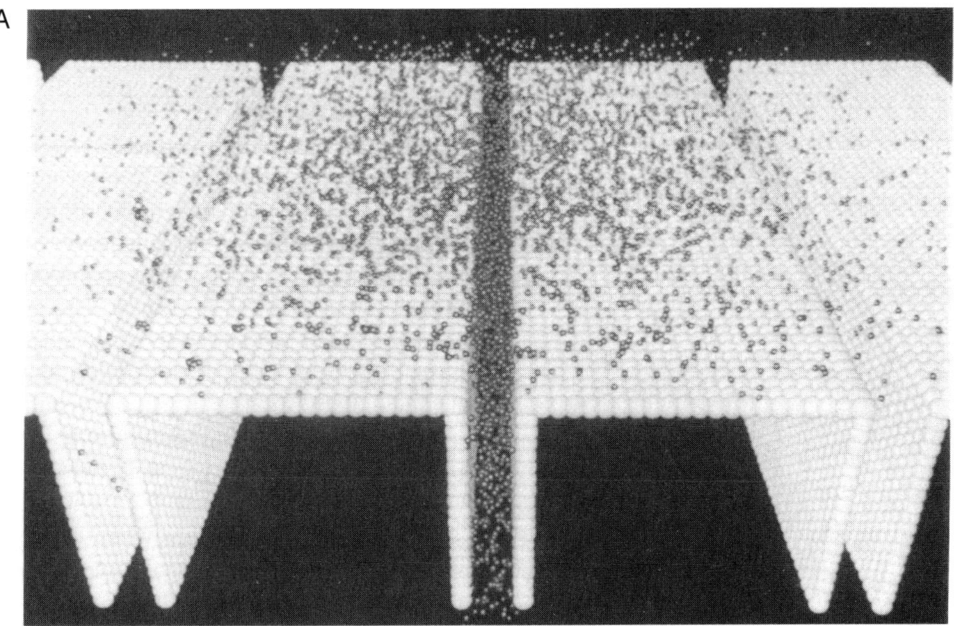

B

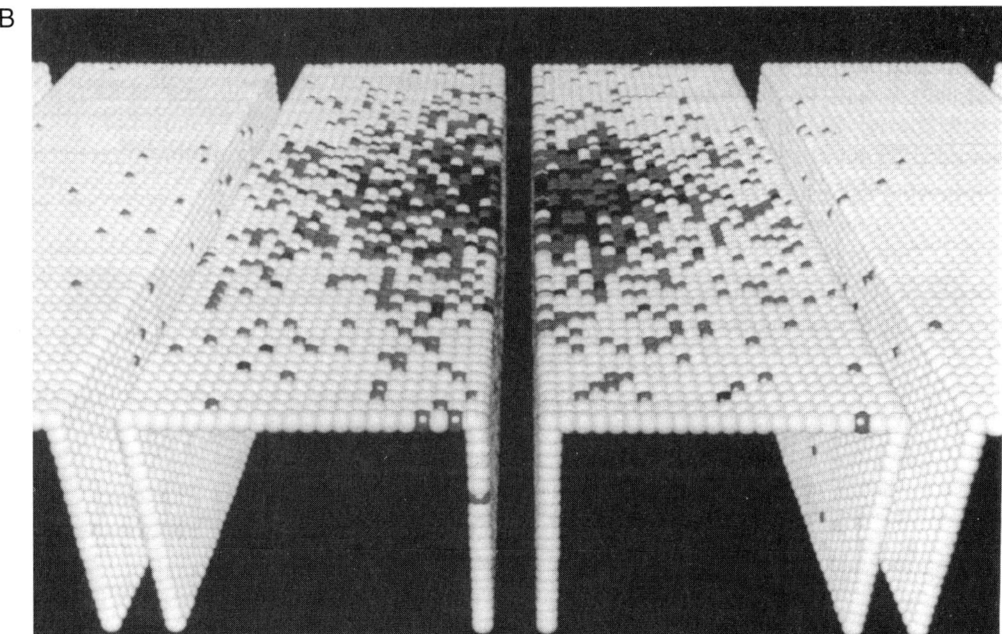

FIGURE 7.10 Monte Carlo simulation of quantal release of acetylcholine at the neuromuscular junction. The postsynaptic receptors are represented as a sheet of spheres—white if unliganded, gray if singly liganded, and black if doubly liganded. Presynaptic structures and the ends of the junctional folds are not shown, and the effect of acetylcholinesterase is not modeled. (A) Thirty microseconds after synchronous release of 9500 molecules of acetylcholine (small gray spheres) from a point source opposite the central fold. (B) Postsynaptic response, showing an effectively saturated area at the center, opposite the release site, surrounded by singly bound and unbound receptors. From Bartol *et al.*[120]

phases of the quanta do interact nonlinearly, implying that under these conditions transmitter molecules released from different sites can activate the same receptors. In contrast, in the goldfish CNS, an agreement between n, estimated by fitting the binomial model to evoked signals, and the number of terminals making contact with the postsynaptic cell was demonstrated.[122] In this system, each terminal has only one active zone defined microscopically, supporting the proposal that n is a measure of the number of active zones.

Quantal Parameter p

Parameter p is the probability of exocytosis in response to a presynaptic action potential. Because this interval is of finite duration, it is more strictly a time integral of the probability during this transient event.[123] Moreover, because discharge of a quantum may leave a release site empty, p should be treated as a product of two probabilities: (1) that a release site is occupied by a quantum and (2) that a presynaptic action potential will evoke release.[124]

The Standard Katz Model Does Not Always Apply

Before accepting the standard Katz model in all its details, we will more closely examine some of its implications to see how they tally with our knowledge of the underlying molecular mechanisms.

Quantal Uniformity

At the vertebrate neuromuscular junction, the amount of acetylcholine released into the synaptic cleft determines the quantal size.[5–7] Thus, in order for the quantal amplitude to be constant at different release sites, a uniform population of vesicles must be available to be released, as well as receptors with identical properties opposite each release site. Electron microscopic images of vesicles in the presynaptic terminal indicate that their diameters are indeed remarkably uniform, although whether the neurotransmitter content of the vesicles is unvarying is not known. Similarly, although postsynaptic receptors are clustered opposite the active zone, whether their properties are uniform between different sites is not clear.

Uniform and Independent Release Probabilities

The release sites must be identical, with a uniform probability of exocytosis. If this condition were not satisfied, evoked signals would still cluster at integral multiples of the quantal amplitude, but the relative proportion of trials resulting in $0, 1, \ldots, n$ quanta would no longer be described by a simple binomial (or Poisson) distribution. As a limiting case, if p at some sites is effectively 0, then the meaning of n is questionable.

Rapid and Synchronous Transmitter Release

All-or-none exocytosis is clearly necessary for quantization and is supported by freeze–fracture images of terminals taken during intense evoked release.[21] However, all-or-none exocytosis may not be the only mode of transmitter release, because secretory vesicles in mast cells can release some of their contents through a fusion pore that opens reversibly without necessarily leading to full exocytosis.[125] Whether this mode of release also occurs in synapses remains to be determined. Quantization in the size of the evoked response can also be concealed by asynchrony of transmitter release from individual sites.[126]

Ion Channel Noise

Stochastic properties of postsynaptic ligand-gated ion channels must not add excessive variability to the size of the postsynaptic signal. Again, if this condition were not satisfied, it would be difficult to identify the quantal amplitude, and clustering of amplitudes at integral multiples of the quantum would be concealed. If we assume that individual ionophores act independently of one another, the variance of the quantal current arising from their stochastic opening is described by the binomial formula

$$\text{Var} = i^2\, kp_o\, (1 - p_o),$$

where i, k, and p_o refer to the single channel current, the number of ionophores, and their probability of opening in response to transmitter release, respectively. Because the average number of ionophores opening is ikp_o, the coefficient of variation of the quantal amplitude is $[(1 - p_o)/kp_o]^{1/2}$. A low quantal variability, which is required for quantal behavior to be detected, therefore implies either a large number of ionophores, k, or a high probability of opening, p_o, in response to transmitter release. These parameters can be estimated indirectly by relating the quantal current to the open channel current. At the vertebrate neuromuscular junction, roughly 1000 to 2000 acetylcholine-receptor-gated ionophores open, so stochastic channel properties play a small part in determining quantal variability. Channel noise, however, becomes a potential source of appreciable quantal variability in the mammalian CNS, where fewer channels open (see below).

Postsynaptic Summation and Distortion of Signals

Postsynaptic currents or potentials arising from different release sites must sum linearly. If this is not satisfied, clustering of evoked postsynaptic signals may not occur at integral multiples of a quantal amplitude.

Stationarity

The state of the synapse must be relatively stable with time. A drift in the release probability with time could preclude a binomial or Poisson model, and changes in the quantal amplitude could prevent clear clustering in the distribution of evoked signals.

Thus, many of the requirements for the standard Katz model cannot realistically be expected to hold in all cases. In the presence of nonuniformity of release probability, the trial-to-trial amplitude fluctuation of the postsynaptic signal is unlikely to be described by a binomial or Poisson model. Indeed, the evidence that these simple probabilistic models are correct is far from compelling. On the other hand, the fact that evoked synaptic signals are often found clustered at integral multiples of an underlying unit strongly argues that vesicle filling and the postsynaptic phenomena determining the quantal amplitude are sufficiently uniform to ensure that a more general quantal description of transmission applies. It implies, moreover, that transmitter release through fusion pores is negligible and that postsynaptic currents do indeed sum linearly in certain cases.

Central Nervous System Synapses Behave Differently from the Frog End Plate

A number of differences have emerged between quantal transmission at the neuromuscular junction and in central synapses in vertebrates.

One-Quantum Release

A correlation of histological and electrophysiological evidence obtained in the same preparation led to the proposal that many individual terminals in the CNS have only one release site.[127–130] However, some synapses in the brainstem auditory pathway, for instance, have multiple active zones, and glutamate released from one release site can interact with transmitter released from neighboring sites.[131]

Nonuniform Release Probabilities

In the mammalian spinal cord, release probabilities may vary between individual sites supplied by an individual muscle afferent. Postsynaptic signals have been shown to fluctuate in a manner that cannot be described by a binomial model, unless the individual release probabilities are allowed to vary.[129,130,132] Because the release sites are often segregated in different terminals, they may be subject to differing amounts of tonic presynaptic inhibition mediated by axo-axonic synapses.

Determination of Quantal Amplitude and Variability

A major difference between vertebrate CNS synapses and the neuromuscular junction is that the quantal amplitude is often determined not by the vesicle contents but by the number of available receptors.[26,27,127–130] At some excitatory synapses, the glutamate content of a quantum appears to be sufficient to bind most available postsynaptic receptors.[28–30] The trial-to-trial variability of the quantal amplitude at an individual site is therefore determined principally by receptor and channel properties.[133] In the mammalian CNS, relatively few channels (fewer than 100) open, compared with 1000–2000 at the neuromuscular junction.[26,27] For the quantal coefficient of variation to be small, which is a necessary condition for observing clear quantal peaks in histograms of evoked signals, the opening probability of an individual receptor-gated channel must then be high. Some evidence that this is so has emerged from pharmacological studies of glutamate receptors that mediate rapid excitatory transmission.[27]

Spontaneous Miniature Postsynaptic Signals

In the central nervous system, spontaneous MEPSCs and MIPSCs vary widely in amplitude,[26,27,134] implying a quantal coefficient of variation considerably greater than that at the neuromuscular junction—between 40 and 80% instead of 30%. At first sight, this would preclude unambiguous peaks in histograms of evoked signals. However, quantal variability must be divided into variability from trial to trial at an individual release site (intrasite) and variability between sites (intersite). Spontaneous MEPSCs and MIPSCs arise from a large number of different sites, so their amplitude range includes both sources of quantal variability. If intrasite quantal variability were very large, then we would not expect to be able to detect quantal clustering in the amplitudes of evoked synaptic signals. The fact that such clustering is sometimes seen (see Fig. 7.9) implies that intrasite variability can be modest, and the wide range of amplitudes of miniature events principally indicates a large intersite variability. Thus, the mean amplitude of spontaneous miniature events cannot be used as a guide to the quantal amplitude underlying an evoked synaptic signal.

Quantal Parameters Can Be Estimated from Evoked and Spontaneous Signals

The goal is to establish, with a reasonable degree of precision, the quantal amplitude, Q, the average quantal content, *m*, and if appropriate the number of release sites, *n*, and the average release probability, *p*. The realization that release sites in the CNS may not always be uniform[129,130] makes a complete statistical description of transmission much more difficult to achieve. The parameters that need estimation must then include the release probability and the quantal amplitude and variability at each site. In principle, it should be possible to estimate the quantal parameters from the probability density of a statistic measured from the evoked postsynaptic signal. Most workers have measured the peak amplitude of the postsynaptic voltage or current on a large number of trials and displayed the results in the form of a histogram. Considerable information can also be obtained from the amplitude distribution of spontaneous miniature events. Two major obstacles, **sampling artifact** and **noise,** immediately arise.

Because the data sample is finite, the true probability density of a desired statistic is not known; only an approximation can be obtained from the recordings. This problem can be mitigated by obtaining a larger sample, but the sample is generally limited by nonstationarity in the recording and time constraints imposed by the experiment. Noise also conceals the true amplitude of spontaneous or evoked signals. If the noise amplitude is comparable to the quantal amplitude, then not only can spontaneous miniature events be missed, but features of the probability density of evoked signals also can be concealed. Relying entirely on visual inspection to determine whether the peaks and troughs in an amplitude histogram are "genuine" (i.e., that they do not arise from sampling artifact and noise) is misleading. A number of different computational approaches have been developed to overcome this obstacle. These approaches differ in the degree to which they rely on assumptions about the underlying probabilistic process. Clearly, if the assumptions are incorrect, then nothing has been achieved, because the parameters will have been estimated incorrectly.

Spontaneous Miniature Signals

If *Q* can be obtained from the amplitude distribution of MEPSCs or MIPSCs, then the average quantal content, *m*, can be obtained by dividing the average evoked signal amplitude by *Q*. This can be done only when the amplitude distribution of spontaneous signals is narrow, and when there is no a priori reason that the quanta underlying the evoked signals should be different.

Spontaneous miniature signals can also be used to detect changes in quantal parameters caused by a conditioning treatment affecting a large number of synapses; if the average amplitude of MEPSCs or MIPSCs becomes larger after an experimental perturbation, the implication is that a widespread increase in quantal amplitude has been distributed among the synapses that give rise to the miniature currents. Changes in the frequency of spontaneous miniature events usually imply an alteration in the average release probability.[13,23] An important difficulty with analysis of spontaneous miniature signals in CNS neurons is that their amplitude distribution is generally skewed, with a long tail toward larger values. At the other end of the distribution, small events often fall at the threshold for detection. To compare MEPSCs or MIPSCs obtained before and after a manipulation, cumulative distributions are generally easier to interpret than raw histograms.[13] A genuine widespread change in amplitude is then seen as a shift in the position of the cumulative distribution, whereas a change in frequency should have no effect on the position of the line, other than that which can be accounted for by sampling artifact (Fig. 7.11). The Kolmogorov–Smirnov test can then be applied to test the hypothesis that any difference between the two curves arose by chance.

Multimodal amplitude distributions have occasionally been described for spontaneous miniature signals.[26,27] When the modes are at equal intervals on the amplitude axis, multiquantal release, possibly arising from regenerative processes in the presynaptic terminal, is implied, although sampling error as a source of spurious peaks must be ruled out.

The principal shortcoming of miniature spontaneous signal analysis is that, generally, the synapses giving rise to the spontaneous signals cannot be identified unambiguously, although localized application of hypertonic sucrose or barium can selectively increase the frequency of discharge in relatively restricted areas.[115,135]

Quantal Amplitude Estimation

When *Q* cannot be estimated from the amplitude distribution of spontaneous MEPSCs or MIPSCs, it can often be obtained from the positions of the peaks in histograms of evoked signals. However, plotting data in the form of histograms can result in misleading estimates of *Q* in the presence of noise and finite sampling; spurious peaks and troughs can emerge, depending on the position and width of the bins. An approach for attacking this problem is to convolve the data with a *kernel*, generally a Gaussian function.[136] **Convolution** describes the mathematical equivalent of "smearing" one function across another. Gaussian kernel convolution has the effect of producing a smooth function with inflections that are no longer susceptible to *binning artifact*. The main pitfall of this approach is

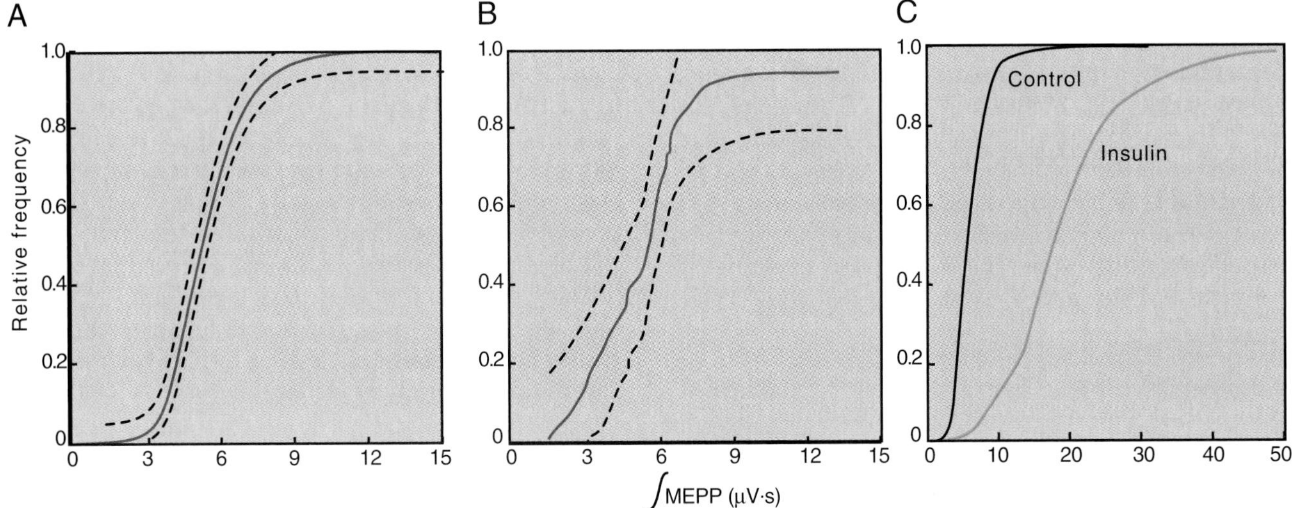

FIGURE 7.11 Cumulative distribution of MEPPs. (A) One thousand consecutive MEPPs recorded at the frog neuromuscular junction are plotted cumulatively. The dashed lines are the 95% confidence limits, calculated by applying Kolmogorov–Smirnov statistics. (B) The first 100 MEPPs are plotted in the same way, showing that, as the sample size is reduced, the confidence limits broaden. (C) The effect of insulin on the cumulative distribution. The curve is shifted to the right, indicating an increase in quantal amplitude. From Van der Kloot.[13]

that the optimal width of the smoothing kernel cannot be known a priori, and, if it is too narrow, artifactual inflections, arising from noise and finite sampling, will still appear in the convolved function.

Whatever method is used to display the data, the question remains whether all the inflections in the resulting function could have arisen by chance because of finite sampling. A testable null hypothesis is that the underlying function is in fact continuous; that is, transmission is not quantal. This hypothesis can be modeled by choosing a unimodal distribution with the same overall shape as that of the data distribution, but without any peaks or troughs. If this hypothesis can be rejected at a given degree of confidence, the implication is that the clustering in the data sample does indeed indicate a genuine underlying quantized process. An easily implemented general method is to draw random samples repeatedly from the smooth function, with a sample size equal to that of the data. If the peaks and troughs in these random samples are never or only rarely as prominent as those in the data sample, then the null hypothesis can be rejected. This is an example of a **Monte Carlo** test.[137]

Poisson Model

The assumption that a Poisson model holds must clearly be justified before it is used to estimate the quantal parameters. Several methods for obtaining m are:[138]

1. If Q is known, then m is simply obtained from the ratio of the average amplitude of the evoked signal to Q.
2. Alternatively, if the number of quanta released on each of a large number of trials can be easily detected, then m is simply the average of this number.
3. A further approach is to count the proportion of trials that result in a failure of transmission (N_o of N trials). The first term of the Poisson expansion (Box 7.4) gives the probability of observing zero quanta released and is equal to e^{-m}. Therefore, m is given by taking the natural logarithm of the inverse of this ratio: $m = \log_e (N/N_o)$.
4. Because the variance of a Poisson distribution is equal to its mean, m can be obtained from $m = 1/CV_m^2$, where CV_m is the coefficient of variation of the number of quanta (the standard deviation of the number of quanta released divided by the mean).
5. If the number of quanta released cannot be resolved, m can still be obtained from the coefficient of variation of the postsynaptic response, CV_R. However, CV_R must be corrected for two other sources of variability in the postsynaptic response: (1) variability in quantal size, expressed as the quantal coefficient of variation, CV_Q; and (2) background noise variance (Var_I), which can be measured separately by collecting data in the

absence of evoked activity. If we assume that the variances arising from the Poisson process, quantal variability, and noise add linearly, m is then given by the formula

$$m = (1 + CV_Q^2)/(CV_R^2 - Var_I/\overline{R}^2),$$

where $\overline{R}$ is the average evoked response amplitude. The *variance method* of estimation is often used incorrectly when the necessary corrections for quantal size and noise fluctuations are ignored.

Agreement among the estimates of m obtained with all these methods constitutes circumstantial evidence in favor of the model. A more formal test of the Poisson model is to compare the observed proportion of trials resulting in 0, 1, ... trials with the predicted values obtained from the Poisson expansion and apply a χ^2 test.

Binomial Models

The binomial model has more parameters than the Poisson (n and p replace m). If the number of trials resulting in 0, 1, ..., n trials is known unambiguously, yielding m, then the following methods give n and p:[138]

1. From the binomial theorem, the variance of the number of quanta, Var_m is equal to $np(1 - p)$. It follows that $p = 1 - Var_m/m$ and $n = m/p$.
2. p can also be obtained from the proportion of failures of transmission, from $N_o = N(1 - p)^n$. It follows that $p = 1 - (N_o/N)^{1/n}$, although the usefulness of this method is limited by the requirements that there be an appreciable proportion of failures and that n be known.
3. The variance method may be used, again with an appropriate correction for the quantal variability and background noise: $p = 1 + CV_Q^2 - (\overline{R} \cdot CV_R^2 - Var_I/\overline{R})/\overline{Q}$. This method requires that estimates be made of both the average quantal size, $\overline{Q}$, and its coefficient of variation, CV_Q, severely limiting its usefulness.

Again, the binomial model can be tested formally by comparing the observed proportion of trials resulting in different numbers of quanta with the predicted values obtained from the binomial expansion, although agreement does not necessarily mean that the model is correct.

If we relax the assumption of uniform release probabilities while continuing to assume that different sites are independent of one another, then a nonuniform or compound binomial model must be applied.[132] In this case, the desired parameters include the individual release probabilities: $p_1, p_2, \ldots, p_n$. If the sample was perfect, they could be obtained by treating the observed proportions of trials resulting in 0, 1, ..., n quanta as the polynomial expansion of $\Pi_k\ (p_k + q_k z)$ (see Box 7.4). Solving the polynomial would then yield $p_1, p_2, \ldots, p_n$.[132] In practice, however, the sample is incomplete; that is, some rare events may never have been observed, and others may be spuriously overrepresented. Root-finding algorithms generally yield complex roots in this situation. An alternative approach is to use a numerical optimization; that is, to find the release probabilities that give the best agreement with the data, taking into account the fact that the data sample is incomplete.[139]

Coefficient of Variation

With the use of the coefficient of variation of the evoked signal, the binomial and Poisson models allow inferences to be made about the site of modulation of transmission without the need to estimate the quantal parameters.[138] To correct for the background noise variance, Var_I, the coefficient of variation of the underlying signal, CV_S, is given by $CV_S = \sqrt{Var_R - Var_I}/\overline{R}$. CV_S is determined by probabilistic quantal release as well as by the quantal variability and is a useful statistic because it is dimensionless. It can be used to distinguish between changes in quantal amplitude and changes in quantal content. Briefly, if CV_S changes with a conditioning treatment that alters the average amplitude of the postsynaptic signal, the implication is a change in quantal content. If, conversely, CV_S is unaffected, the implication is that the conditioning treatment altered quantal amplitude.

If a Poisson model is assumed, further information can be obtained by plotting the ratio of $1/CV_S^2$ before and after a manipulation against the ratio of mean amplitudes[140] (Fig. 7.12).[141] Because the variance of a Poisson distribution is equal to its mean, a change in quantal content, m, should cause an excursion along the line of identity. A change in quantal amplitude, Q, on the other hand, should have no effect on $1/CV_S^2$, so the data points should fall on the horizontal line. If the points fall below the line of identity and above the horizontal line, then we can conclude that both quantal content and quantal amplitude increased. If a simple binomial model is assumed, then the results are slightly different, because the variance $np(1 - p)$ is less than the mean np. A plot of ratios of $1/CV_S^2$ against ratios of means in this case falls on the line of identity for manipulations that increase n and above it for manipulations that increase p.

This method, although easy to use, depends heavily on the assumption that a binomial or Poisson model applies. As soon as this assumption is relaxed, a wide range of explanations can be put forward for virtually

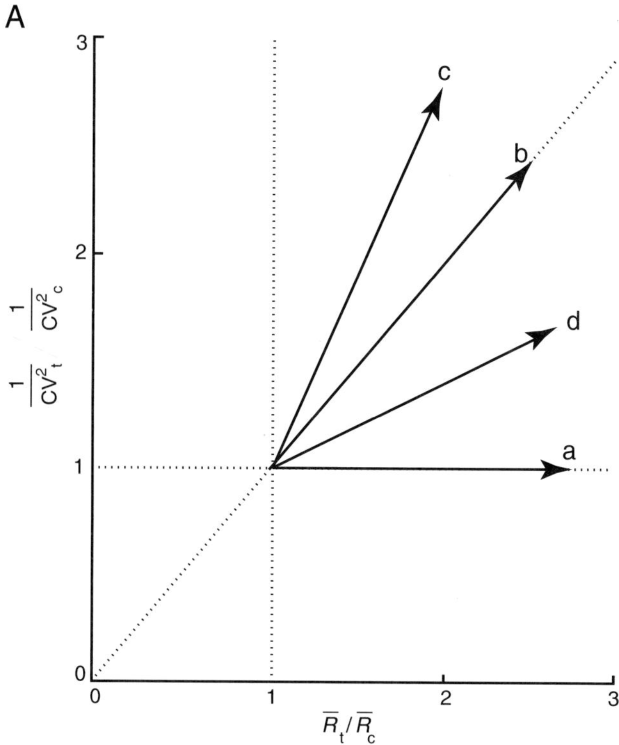

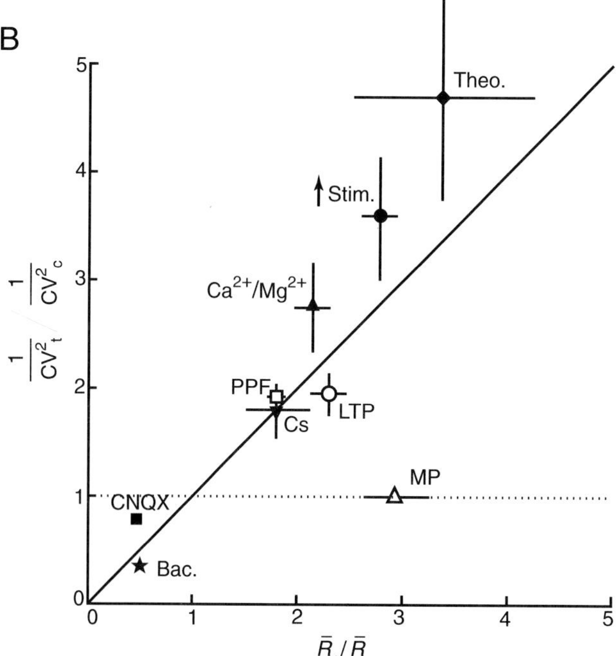

FIGURE 7.12 Coefficient of variation method for determining the site of modulation of synaptic transmission. (A) The possible excursions in the ratio of_1/CV_S^2 plotted against the ratio of the mean response amplitude $\bar{R}$ for a manipulation that increases synaptic strength. The subscripts "c" and "t" refer to the control and test conditions, respectively. A horizontal excursion (a) implies an increase in quantal amplitude, Q—for instance, through a postsynaptic increase in the number of receptors. If a Poisson model applies, an excursion along the 45° line (b) implies an increase in m. If a simple binomial model holds, the ratio should fall on the 45° line for an increase in n and above it (c) for an increase in p. Ratios falling below the 45° line and above the horizontal (d) imply an increase in both quantal content and quantal amplitude. Conversely, modulations that decrease synaptic strength should cause the ratios to fall to the left of the point (1, 1) and below it. These rules apply only if a Poisson or simple binomial model holds. (B) Experimental results obtained by recording from CA1 hippocampal pyramidal cells with various modulations. Each point shows the mean of several cells (with standard errors). Increasing the driving force for the synaptic current by changing the postsynaptic membrane potential (MP) produces no change in 1/CV_S^2, as expected from a purely postsynaptic modification. Extracellular theophylline or Cs^+, an increase in the extracellular Ca^{2+}/Mg^{2+} ratio, and facilitation by a conditioning prepulse (PPF) cause the ratios to fall in region (c) of (A), as expected from an increase in binomial p. Increasing the stimulus strength also causes the points to fall in region (c), although a simple binomial model predicts that an increase in n should cause the ratio to fall on the 45° line. Long-term potentiation of transmission causes the points to fall in region (d), implying an increase in both quantal content and quantal amplitude. Conversely, baclofen decreases transmitter release, and the glutamate receptor antagonist CNQX decreases quantal amplitude. From Manabe *et al.*[141]

any outcome.[142] The method is also sensitive to changes in the quantal coefficient of variation, so it must be assumed that changes in Q are accompanied by proportional changes in $\sqrt{\mathrm{Var}_Q}$.

Noise Deconvolution

In general, the proportion of trials resulting in 0, 1, ... trials cannot be determined unambiguously, and the assumption that Poisson or simple binomial statistics apply is untenable. Even if peaks and troughs, beyond what would be expected by chance, are present in the histogram, the amplitudes of many trials often fall between successive modes, because the trials are contaminated by noise. How then can one resolve the underlying quantal process at the synapses under investigation? The method of noise deconvolution[143] again relies on the assumption that noise adds linearly to the synaptic signal, which means that the sampled probability density function is a convolution of the underlying quantal density function with the noise density function. Because the noise can be measured independently, by recording the background signal in the absence of evoked synaptic activity, it should be possible to undo the convolution to reconstruct the probability density function that describes the underlying signal.

This operation is not trivial, because the data samples are finite; so the true probability density functions for the evoked signal and noise are not known, and only an approximation can be obtained from the measured signals. The underlying noise-free probability density function must therefore be estimated by applying an optimization method. The underlying function is generally assumed to comprise a number of discrete components, representing different numbers of quanta released. The task is then formally equivalent to solving a **mixture problem,** in which the data are sampled from a mixture of overlapping distributions, or components, each having a membership (probability), mean amplitude, and variance that need to be estimated. Optimization algorithms work as follows: (1) the data distribution is compared with an initial solution reconvolved with the noise function; (2) the solution is then adjusted to improve the goodness of fit; and (3) the cycle is repeated until no further improvement is detectable. The best results are obtained by *maximizing likelihood*, and a robust and versatile algorithm to use for this purpose is known as the expectation–maximization algorithm.[139,144] A number of constraints can be imposed on the solution to accommodate physiological assumptions. As a rule, as more constraints are imposed, the quantal parameters are more accurately estimated, but only as long as the underlying assumptions are justified.

A major obstacle is that the number of components in the solution is a critical parameter, which cannot generally be known a priori. As the number of parameters available to fit the data is increased, the maximum likelihood value increases, because finer details of the data distribution, many of which are due to sampling error and noise, can be accounted for. An alternative approach, which avoids the problem of overfitting, is to treat the underlying probability density function not as a mixture of discrete components but as a continuous function. The solution is biased toward the flattest, most featureless function that is just compatible with the data. This method, known as maximum entropy noise deconvolution, can give an estimate of quantal amplitude if there are periodic inflections in the solution.[145]

Figure 7.13 shows the results of applying several deconvolution methods to an amplitude histogram.

Model Discrimination

An important goal of parameter estimation is to choose between different models of transmission. The simplest approach is to ask if a given model is able to fit the data, by applying a conventional goodness-of-fit test, such as the χ^2 test, to the data and the maximum likelihood fit. If the fit is unsatisfactory, the model can tentatively be rejected with the corresponding degree of confidence. However, the model being in good agreement with the data does not necessarily mean that the assumptions underlying the solution are correct, because many alternative models also may give adequate fits.

Confidence Intervals

Confidence intervals must be estimated for quantal parameters, as for any statistic. Such an estimation can be difficult for any but the simplest model because the parameter space has many dimensions, and even the number of dimensions is often unknown. Resampling methods that rely on repeating the optimization on a large number of random samples drawn from the original data set[146] must be used with caution, and it is important in all cases to be aware of the limitations and biases of optimization algorithms by testing them extensively with Monte Carlo simulations.

Estimation of Transmitter Release Probability Does Not Rely Exclusively on Quantal Analysis

An ingenious method for estimating the release probability at glutamatergic synapses makes use of the pharmacological properties of *N*-methyl-D-aspartate (NMDA) receptors.[147,148] After application of MK-801, an irreversible open channel blocker, the size of the population synaptic signal mediated by NMDA receptors gradually decays with repeated stimulation of presynaptic fibers. Because the rate at which the postsynaptic signal decays is related to the probability that postsynaptic receptors are activated by released glutamate, this method gives an indirect estimate of the probability of transmitter release. Interestingly, the time course of the decay cannot be described by a single exponential, implying that the release probability must vary considerably across the population of synapses contributing to the signal.

Another indirect method for monitoring changes in transmitter release probability is to examine the response to paired presynaptic stimuli before and after a manipulation that alters the strength of the synapse. In general, either increasing or reducing the probability of transmitter release has a relatively greater effect on the size of the response to the first pulse than on that to the second. Therefore, a change in the ratio of the responses to the two pulses implies that at least part of the effect of the manipulation is mediated presynaptically.

Summary

Quantal analysis has greatly improved our understanding of biophysical and pharmacological mechanisms of transmission. Numerical methods can be used to estimate the probability of transmitter release and

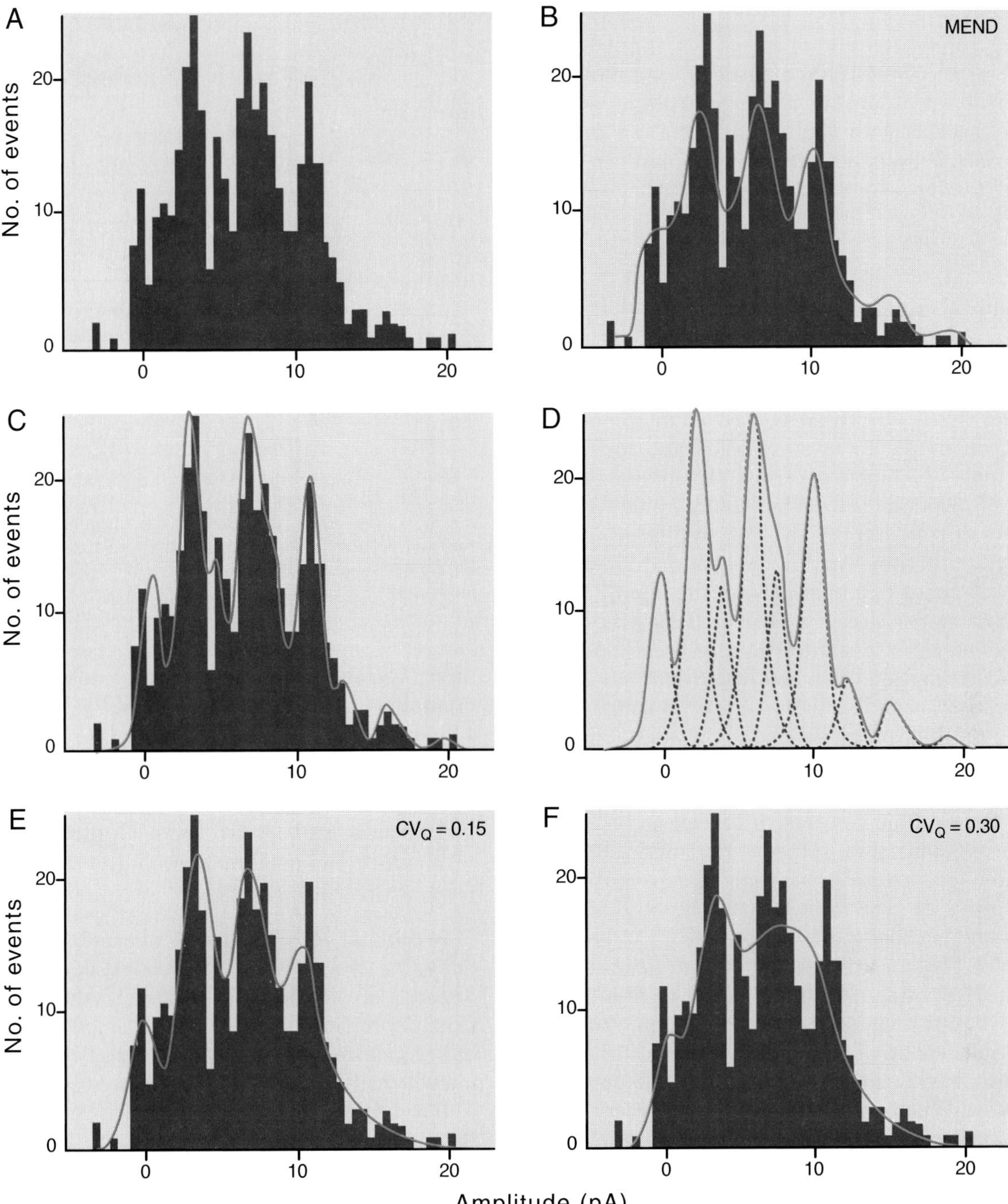

FIGURE 7.13 Noise deconvolution. (A) Amplitude histogram for 400 EPSCs recorded in a CA1 cell in a hippocampal slice in response to repeated stimulation of afferent fibers. EPSCs appear to cluster at integral multiples of approximately 3.6 pA. The continuous line in (B) is the maximum entropy noise deconvolution solution. This function, convolved with the noise, just fits the data at the $p = 0.05$ level of confidence (i.e., a curve any smoother and more featureless would have to be rejected at $p < 0.05$). The periodic inflections seen in this function imply that clustering results not simply from noise, sampling, and binning artifact but from an underlying quantal process. (C) The result of maximum likelihood deconvolution, with nine underlying components, each with the same variance as the background noise but with no constraint on their amplitudes and probabilities. The continuous line represents the solution reconvolved with the noise, showing a very good fit to the data. The underlying components (dashed lines) are plotted in (D), together with their sum (continuous line). Although the agreement of this solution with the data is excellent, some of its features may arise from sampling artifact and noise. (E and F) A quantal model has been fitted to the data; that is, the components have been constrained to occur at equal intervals, with the first component at 0, and with a quantal coefficient of variation (CV_Q) of 0.15 (E) or 0.3 (F). The maximum likelihood solution in (F), but not in (E), can be rejected at $p < 0.05$, implying that $CV_Q < 0.3$.

the size of the postsynaptic effect of an individual quantum of neurotransmitter. Although these methods must be applied with caution, they yield a unique insight into the mechanisms of synaptic plasticity, both at the neuromuscular junction and in the central nervous system.

SHORT-TERM SYNAPTIC PLASTICITY

Chemical synapses are not static transmitters of information. Their effectiveness waxes and wanes, depending on frequency of stimulation and history of prior activity.[149] At most synapses, repetitive high-frequency stimulation (called a tetanus) is initially dominated by a growth in successive PSP amplitudes, called **synaptic facilitation.** This process builds to a steady state within about 1 s and decays equally rapidly when stimulation stops. Decay is measured by single test stimuli given at various intervals after a conditioning train. Facilitation can often be divided into two exponential phases, called its first and second component, and may reach appreciable levels (e.g., a doubling of PSP size) after a single action potential. At most synapses, a slower phase of increase in efficacy, which has a characteristic time constant of several seconds and is called **augmentation,** succeeds facilitation. Finally, with prolonged stimulation, some synapses display a third phase of growth in PSP amplitude that lasts minutes and is called **potentiation.**

Often, a phase of decreasing transmission, called **synaptic depression,** is superimposed on these processes. Synaptic depression leads to a dip in transmission during repetitive stimulation, which often tends to overlap and obscure the augmentation and potentiation phases. When stimulation ceases, recovery from the various processes occurs in the same order as their development during the tetanus, with facilitation decaying first, then depression and augmentation, and finally potentiation (Fig. 7.14). Thus, potentiation is often visible in isolation only long after a tetanus and is thus called **posttetanic potentiation** (PTP). At some synapses, even longer-lasting effects (persisting for hours), named **long-term potentiation** (LTP),[150,151] have been observed. Long-term potentiation should not be confused with the form of synaptic plasticity bearing the same name and prominent at mammalian cortical synapses (Chapter 14). In almost all synapses in which a quantal analysis has been done, all these forms of synaptic plasticity (except some forms of cortical LTP) are due to changes in the number of quanta released by action potentials. When binomial parameters were estimated, correlated changes in $\overline{p}$ and n were usually observed. This result is expected if release sites with nonuniform p become more effective while "silent" sites are recruited during enhanced transmission, and vice versa during depression.

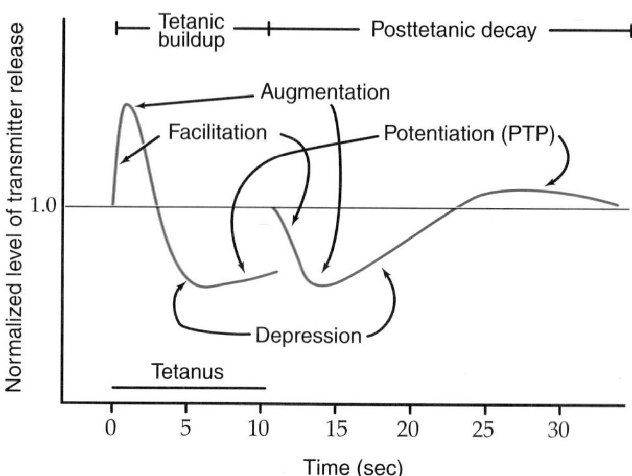

FIGURE 7.14 Accumulation of the effects of facilitation, augmentation, depression, and potentiation on transmitter release by each action potential in a tetanus, and the posttetanic decay of these phases of synaptic plasticity measured by single stimuli after the tetanus.

Depression May Arise from Depletion of Readily Releasable Transmitter or from Autoinhibition

In contrast with the growth phases in synaptic plasticity, the rate at which depression develops usually depends on stimulation frequency, whereas recovery from depression proceeds with a single time constant of seconds to minutes in different preparations. At many synapses, depression is relieved when transmission is reduced by lowering $[Ca^{2+}]$ or raising $[Mg^{2+}]$ in the medium. These characteristics are consistent with depression being due to the depletion of a readily releasable store of docked or nearly docked vesicles and recovery being due to their replenishment from a supply store (Fig. 7.15).[149] The parameters of such a depletion model can be estimated from the rate of recovery from depression, which gives the rate of refilling the releasable store, and the fractional drop in PSPs given at short intervals, which gives the fraction of the releasable store liberated by each action potential.

It is now clear that vesicle depletion cannot account for all forms of synaptic depression. Ultrastructural identification of a pool of vesicles that are actually depleted during short tetani and cause severe depression has never been possible. Moreover, at some synapses, depression is due to an inhibitory action of released transmitter on presynaptic receptors called

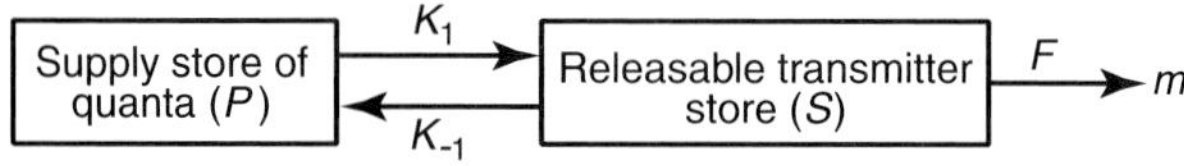

K_1 = Rate of refilling releasable store (S)
K_{-1} = Leakage rate out of S
F = Fraction of S released by an impulse
$m(t)$ = Number of quanta released by an impulse at time t
f = Frequency of stimulation

During a train:

$dS/dt = K_1P - K_{-1}S - fFS,\ m=FS$
$m(t) = FS_S - F(S_r - S_S)e^{-(fF + K_{-1})t}$
S_r = Resting level of $S = K_1P/K_{-1}$
S_S = Steady-state level of $S = K_1P/(fF + K_1)$

After a train of duration T:

$m(t) = FS_r - F(S_i - S_r)e^{-K_{-1}t}$
S_i = Level of S at end of train
$= S_S - (S_r - S_S)e^{-(fF + K_{-1})T}$

FIGURE 7.15 Depletion model of synaptic depression.

autoreceptors. For example, in rat hippocampal cortex, depression of GABA responses is blocked by antagonists of presynaptic $GABA_B$ receptors.[152] Presumably, GABA acts to hyperpolarize nerve terminals and block transmitter release. At frog neuromuscular junctions, ATP is coreleased with acetylcholine. Extracellular nucleotidases hydrolyze ATP to produce adenosine, which acts at presynaptic adenosine receptors to inhibit neurosecretion by an unknown mechanism. Antagonists of adenosine receptors and of nucleotidases eliminate one phase of synaptic depression to 1-Hz stimulation.[153] At synapses made by dorsal root ganglion neurons, depression appears to be due to inactivation of Ca^{2+} channels during repetitive activity;[154] this mechanism, however, has been specifically rejected at other synapses.[56] Finally, at some central synapses in the sea slug *Aplysia*, depression is due to desensitization of postsynaptic receptors rather than to a decline in transmitter release.[155]

Facilitation, Augmentation, and Potentiation Are Due to Effects of Residual Ca^{2+}

With few exceptions,[156] all the phases of increased short-term plasticity are Ca^{2+} dependent in the sense that little or no facilitation, augmentation, or potentiation is generated by stimulation in Ca^{2+}-free medium. Originally, these phases of increased transmission were thought to be due to the effect of residual Ca^{2+} remaining in active zones after presynaptic activity and summating with Ca^{2+} influx during subsequent action potentials to generate slightly higher peaks of $[Ca^{2+}]$.[149,157] Owing to the highly nonlinear dependence of transmitter release on $[Ca^{2+}]$, a small residual $[Ca^{2+}]$ could activate a substantial increase in phasic transmitter release during an action potential while having only a small effect on MPSP frequency itself. Temporal correlations between increased spike-evoked transmission after single action potentials or tetani and increases in MPSP frequency supported this idea. But the tetanic accumulation of facilitation, augmentation, and potentiation did not accord quantitatively with predictions of a model of the accumulation of Ca^{2+} acting at one site.[158] Simulations of expected levels of peak and residual $[Ca^{2+}]$ levels also were unable to account for the full magnitude of facilitation.[59] Presynaptic $[Ca^{2+}]$ measurements using fura-2 confirmed the persistence of residual $[Ca^{2+}]$ after repetitive stimulation during augmentation, PTP, and LTP, but showed that it was too weak to explain augmentation or potentiation by simply summating with peak $[Ca^{2+}]$ from Ca^{2+} channels at release sites.[159,160] These findings led to the proposal that, in addition to summating with peak $[Ca^{2+}]$ transients at release sites, Ca^{2+} acts to increase transmission at one or more targets distinct from the sites triggering exocytosis.

Two possibilities exist. Residual free Ca^{2+} could continue to act in equilibrium with such sites to increase transmission, or Ca^{2+} could bind to these targets and activate processes that increase release after residual Ca^{2+} has dissipated. The latter idea is suggested by experiments in which facilitation, augmentation, or potentiation persists when residual Ca^{2+} should be absorbed by presynaptic introduction of exogenous chelators; however, results of this sort of experiment have not been consistent.[161] The former idea is supported by experiments in which photolabile BAPTA derivatives were injected presynaptically at crayfish neuromuscular junctions.[162] Posttetanic photolysis to produce enough chelator to suddenly remove residual Ca^{2+} after conditioning stimulation sharply reduced facilitation within a few milliseconds, and it reduced augmentation and potentiation within about 1 s. These results suggest that Ca^{2+} can "prime" subsequent phasic release by action potentials by acting at two additional targets distinct from the exocytosis trigger—a fast site responsible for facilitation and a slow one for augmentation and potentiation.

Several additional indications of separate sites of Ca^{2+} action in synaptic plasticity are as follows:

1. Facilitation grows while secretion decays after one action potential at very low temperature at frog neuromuscular junctions.[163]
2. Sr^{2+} and Ba^{2+} selectively enhance facilitation and augmentation, respectively, of both evoked transmitter release and MEPP frequency at frog neuromuscular junctions.[164,165]

3. *Drosophila* mutants defective in enzymes affecting cAMP-dependent phosphorylation show reduced facilitation and potentiation.[166]
4. Other transformed *Drosophila* carrying an inhibitor of Ca^{2+}–calmodulin-dependent protein kinase II have impaired facilitation, augmentation, and potentiation.[167]
5. Mice lacking synapsin I show a specific defect in facilitation but not potentiation in hippocampal pyramidal cells.[85]

A particular site of Ca^{2+} action proposed to contribute to potentiation is the Ca^{2+}–calmodulin-dependent kinase II phosphorylation of synapsin I and the mobilization of vesicles to docking sites.[83] However, inhibitors of calmodulin and inhibitors or mutants with defects in the kinase failed to affect transmission, facilitation, augmentation, or potentiation at crayfish neuromuscular junctions and mammalian cortical synapses.[161] However, LTP in bull frog sympathetic ganglia may depend on this enzymatic pathway.[150,151]

Potentiation lasts for a long period after a strong tetanus because residual Ca^{2+} is present for the duration of PTP, presumably owing to overloading of the processes responsible for removing excess Ca^{2+} from neurons. These processes include Ca^{2+} extrusion pumps, such as the plasma membrane ATPase and Na^+–Ca^{2+} exchange, and Ca^{2+} uptake into organelles such as endoplasmic reticulum and mitochondria.[168] The accumulation of Na^+ during tetanic activity appears to play a role in prolonging residual Ca^{2+} by reducing its extrusion by Na^+–Ca^{2+} exchange.[169]

Summary

Short-term synaptic plasticity allows synaptic strength to be modulated as a function of prior activity. Synapses may show a decline in transmission (depression) or an increase in synaptic efficacy with time constants ranging from seconds (facilitation and augmentation) to minutes (potentiation or PTP) to hours (LTP); many synapses show a mixture of several of these phases. Depression may be due to depletion of a readily releasable supply of vesicles or to the inhibitory action of transmitter or enzymatically produced transmitter products on presynaptic autoreceptors. Depression makes synapses selectively responsive to brief stimuli or to changes in level of activity. Frequency-dependent increases in synaptic efficacy are due to the effects of residual presynaptic Ca^{2+} acting to modulate the release process. At least part of Ca^{2+} action is mediated by separate targets for facilitation and for augmentation and potentiation. PTP is prolonged after a long tetanus because residual Ca^{2+} remains in synaptic terminals for minutes after such stimulation. These frequency-dependent increases in synaptic efficacy allow synapses to distinguish significant signals from noise and respond to selected patterns of activity.

References

1. Katz, B. (1969). *The Release of Neural Transmitter Substances.* Thomas, Springfield, IL. (Describes the classical experiments on transmitter release.)
2. Heuser, J. E. (1977). Synaptic vesicle exocytosis revealed in quick-frozen frog neuromuscular junctions treated with 4-aminopyridine and given a single electrical shock. *Soc. Neurosci. Symp.* **2:** 215–239. (A fine anatomical analysis of vesicle recycling.)
3. Robitaille, R., Adler, E. M., and Charlton, M. P. (1990). Strategic location of calcium channels at transmitter release sites of frog neuromuscular synapses. *Neuron* **5:** 773–779.
4. Heuser, J. E., and Reese, T. S. (1981). Structural changes after transmitter release at the frog neuromuscular junction. *J. Cell Biol.* **88:** 564–580.
5. Kuffler, S. W., and Yoshikami, D. (1975). The number of transmitter molecules in a quantum: An estimate from iontophoretic application of acetylcholine at the neuromuscular junction. *J. Physiol. (London)* **251:** 465–482.
6. Fletcher, P., and Forrester, T. (1975). The effect of curare on the release of acetylcholine from mammalian motor nerve terminals and an estimate of quantum content. *J. Physiol. (London)* **251:** 131–144.
7. Whittaker, V. P. (1988). Model cholinergic systems: An overview. *Handb. Exp. Pharmacol.* **86:** 3–22.
8. Eccles, J. C. (1964). *The Physiology of Synapses.* Springer, Berlin. (A comprehensive summary of early work.)
9. Edwards, R. H. (1992). The transport of neurotransmitters into synaptic vesicles. *Curr. Opin. Neurobiol.* **2:** 586–594.
10. Torri-Tarelli, F., Grohovaz, F., Fesce, R., and Ceccarelli, B. (1985). Temporal coincidence between synaptic vesicle fusion and quantal secretion of acetylcholine. *J. Cell Biol.* **101:** 1386–1399.
11. von Wedel, R. J., Carlson, S. S., and Kelly, R. B. (1981). Transfer of synaptic vesicle antigens to the presynaptic plasma membrane during exocytosis. *Proc. Natl. Acad. Sci. U.S.A.* **78:** 1014–1018.
12. Torri Tarelli, F., Bossi, M., Fesce, R., Greengard, P., and Valtorta, F. (1992). Synapsin I partially dissociates from synaptic vesicles during exocytosis induced by electrical stimulation. *Neuron* **9:** 1143–1153.
13. Van der Kloot, W. (1991). The regulation of quantal size. *Prog. Neurobiol.* **36:** 93–130.
14. Searl, T., Prior, C., and Marshall, I. G. (1991). Acetylcholine recycling and release at rat motor nerve terminals studied using (-)-vesamicol and troxpyrrolium. *J. Physiol. (London)* **444:** 99–116.
15. Prior, C. (1994). Factors governing the appearance of small-mode miniature endplate currents at the snake neuromuscular junction. *Brain Res.* **664:** 61–68.
16. Van der Kloot, W. (1988). Acetylcholine quanta are released from vesicles by exocytosis (and why some think not). *Neuroscience* **24:** 1–7.
17. Heuser, J. E., and Reese, T. S. (1973). Evidence for recycling of synaptic vesicle membrane during transmitter release at the frog neuromuscular junction. *J. Cell Biol.* **57:** 315–344.
18. Betz, W. J., and Bewick, G. S. (1993). Optical monitoring of

transmitter release and synaptic vesicle recycling at the frog neuromuscular junction. *J. Physiol.* (*London*) **460:** 287–309.

19. Large, W. A., and Rang, H. P. (1978). Variability of transmitter quanta released during incorporation of a false transmitter into cholinergic nerve terminals. *J. Physiol.* (*London*) **285:** 25–34.
20. Schiavo, G., Rosetto, O., and Montecucco, C. (1994). Clostridial neurotoxins as tools to investigate the molecular events of transmitter release. *Semin. Cell Biol.* **5:** 221–229.
21. Heuser, J. E., Reese, T. S., Dennis, M. J., Jan, Y., Jan, L., and Evans, L. (1979). Synaptic vesicle exocytosis captured by quick freezing and correlated with quantal transmitter release. *J. Cell Biol.* **81:** 275–300.
22. Hurlbut, W. P., Iezzi, N., Fesce, R., and Ceccarelli, B. (1990). Correlation between quantal secretion and vesicle loss at the frog neuromuscular junction. *J. Physiol.* (*London*) **425:** 501–526.
23. Van der Kloot, W., and Molgó, J. (1994). Quantal acetylcholine release at the vertebrate neuromuscular junction. *Physiol. Rev.* **74:** 899–991. (An extremely comprehensive modern review.)
24. Matthews-Bellinger, J., and Salpeter, M. M. (1973). Distribution of acetylcholine receptors at frog neuromuscular junctions with a discussion of some physiological implications. *J. Physiol.* (*London*) **279:** 197–213.
25. Van der Kloot, W., Balezina, O. P., Molgó, J., and Naves, L. A. (1994). The timing of channel opening during miniature endplate currents at the frog and mouse neuromuscular junctions: Effects of fasciculin-2, other anti-cholinesterases and vesamicol. *Pfluegers Arch.* **428:** 114–126.
26. Edwards, F. A., Konnerth, A., and Sakmann, B. (1990). Quantal analysis of inhibitory synaptic transmission in the dentate gyrus of rat hippocampal slices: A patch-clamp study. *J. Physiol.* (*London*) **430:** 213–249.
27. Jonas, P., Major, G., and Sakmann, B. (1993). Quantal components of unitary EPSCs at the mossy fibre synapse on CA3 pyramidal cells of rat hippocampus. *J. Physiol.* (*London*) **472:** 615–663.
28. Clements, J. D., Lester, R. A. J., Tong, G., Jahr, C. E., and Westbrook, G. L. (1992). The time course of glutamate in the synaptic cleft. *Science* **258:** 1498–1501.
29. Tang, C.-M., Margulis, M., Shi, Q.-Y., and Fielding, A. (1994). Saturation of postsynaptic glutamate receptors after quantal release of transmitter. *Neuron* **13:** 1385–1393.
30. Tong, G., and Jahr, C. E. (1994). Multivesicular release from excitatory synapses of cultured hippocampal neurons. *Neuron* **12:** 51–59.
31. Bennett, M. K., and Scheller, R. H. (1994). A molecular description of synaptic vesicle membrane trafficking. *Annu. Rev. Biochem.* **63:** 63–100.
32. Jahn, R., and Südhof, T. C. (1994). Synaptic vesicles and exocytosis. *Annu. Rev. Neurosci.* **17:** 219–246.
33. McGuiness, T. L., Brady, S. T., Gruner, J. A., Sugimori, M., Llinás, R., and Greengard, P. (1989). Phosphorylation-dependent inhibition by synapsin I of organelle movement in squid axoplasm. *J. Neurosci.* **9:** 4138–4149.
34. Haydon, P. C., Henderson, E., and Stanley, E. F. (1994). Localization of individual calcium channels at the release face of a presynaptic nerve terminal. *Neuron* **13:** 1275–1280.
35. Wheeler, D. B., Randall, A., and Tsien, R. W. (1994). Roles of N-type and Q-type Ca^{2+} channels in supporting hippocampal synaptic transmission. *Science* **264:** 107–111.
36. Dunlap, K., Luebke, J. I., and Turner, T. J. (1995). Exocytotic Ca^{2+} channels in mammalian central neurons. *Trends Neurosci.* **18:** 89–98.
37. Zimmermann, H. (1979). Vesicle recycling and transmitter release. *Neuroscience* **4:** 1773–1804.
38. Ceccarelli, B., and Hurlbut, W. P. (1980). Ca^{2+}-dependent recycling of synaptic vesicles at the frog neuromuscular junction. *J. Cell Biol.* **87:** 297–303.
39. Thomas, P., Lee, A. K., Wong, J. G., and Almers, W. (1994). A triggered mechanism retrieves membrane in seconds after Ca^{2+}-stimulated exocytosis in single pituitary cells. *J. Cell Biol.* **124:** 667–675.
40. Von Gersdorff, H., and Matthews, G. (1994). Inhibition of endocytosis by elevated internal calcium in a synaptic terminal. *Nature* (*London*) **370:** 652–655.
41. Elmqvist, D., and Quastel, D. M. J. (1965). Presynaptic action of hemicholinium at the neuromuscular junction. *J. Physiol.* (*London*) **177:** 463–482.
42. Cooper, J. R., Bloom, F. E., and Roth, R. H. (1991). *The Biochemical Basis of Neuropharmacology*, 6th ed. Oxford University Press, New York.
43. Parsons, S. M., Prior, C., and Marshall, I. G. (1993). Acetylcholine transport, storage, and release. *Int. Rev. Neurobiol.* **35:** 279–390.
44. Llinás, R., Gruner, J. A., Sugimori, M., McGuiness, T. L., and Greengard, P. (1991). Regulation by synapsin I and Ca^{2+}-calmodulin-dependent protein kinase II of the transmitter release at the squid giant synapse. *J. Physiol.* (*London*) **436:** 257–282.
45. Edwards, C., Doležal, V., Tuček, S., Zemková, H., and Vyskočil, F. (1985). Is an acetylcholine system transport system responsible for nonquantal release of acetylcholine at the rodent myoneural junction? *Proc. Natl. Acad. Sci. U.S.A.* **82:** 3514–3518.
46. Van der Bliek, A. M., and Meyerowitz, E. M. (1991). Dynamin-like protein encoded by the *Drosophila shibire* gene associated with vesicular traffic. *Nature* (*London*) **351:** 411–414.
47. Chan, M. S., Obar, R. A., Schroeder, C., Austin, T. W., Poodry, C. A., Wadsworth, S. A., and Vallee, R. B. (1991). Multiple forms of dynamin are encoded by *shibire*, a *Drosophila* gene involved in endocytosis. *Nature* (*London*) **351:** 583–586.
48. Ryan, T. A., Reuter, H., Wendland, B., Schweizer, F. E., Tsien, R. W., and Smith, S. J. (1993). The kinetics of synaptic vesicle recycling measured at single presynaptic boutons. *Neuron* **11:** 713–724.
49. Locke, F. S. (1894). Notiz über den Einfluß physiologischer Kochsalzlösung auf die elektrische Erregbarkeit von Muskel und Nerv. *Zentralbl. Physiol.* **8:** 166–167.
50. Steinbach, J. H., and Stevens, C. F. (1976). Neuromuscular transmission. In *Frog Neurobiology* (R. Llinás and W. Precht, eds.), pp. 33–92. Springer, Berlin.
51. Rahamimoff, R., Lev-Tov, A., and Meiri, H. (1980). Primary and secondary regulation of quantal transmitter release: Calcium and sodium. *J. Exp. Biol.* **89:** 5–18.
52. Augustine, G. J., Charlton, M. P., and Smith, S. J. (1987). Calcium action in synaptic transmitter release. *Annu. Rev. Neurosci.* **10:** 633–693.
53. Muller, R. U., and Finkelstein, A. (1974). The electrostatic basis of Mg^{2+} inhibition of transmitter release. *Proc. Natl. Acad. Sci. U.S.A.* **71:** 923–926.
54. Llinás, R., Steinberg, I. Z., and Walton, K. (1981). Relationship between presynaptic calcium current and postsynaptic potential in squid giant synapse. *Biophys. J.* **33:** 323–351.
55. Mulkey, R. M., and Zucker, R. S. (1991). Action potentials must admit calcium to evoke transmitter release. *Nature* (*London*) **350:** 153–155.
56. Charlton, M. P., Smith, S. J., and Zucker, R. S. (1982). Role of presynaptic calcium ions and channels in synaptic facilitation and depression at the squid giant synapse. *J. Physiol.* (*London*) **323:** 173–193.
57. Zucker, R. S., Delaney, K. R., Mulkey, R., and Tank, D. W.

(1991). Presynaptic calcium in transmitter release and posttetanic potentiation. *Ann. N.Y. Acad. Sci.* **635:** 191–207.
58. Roberts, W. M. (1994). Localization of calcium signals by a mobile calcium buffer in frog saccular hair cells. *J. Neurosci.* **14:** 3246–3262.
59. Yamada, W. M., and Zucker, R. S. (1992). Time course of transmitter release calculated from simulations of a calcium diffusion model. *Biophys. J.* **61:** 671–682.
60. Llinás, R., Sugimori, M., and Silver, R. B. (1992). Microdomains of high calcium concentration in a presynaptic terminal. *Science* **256:** 677–679.
61. Roberts, W. M., Jacobs, R. A., and Hudspeth, A. J. (1991). Colocalization of ion channels involved in frequency selectivity and synaptic transmission at presynaptic active zones of hair cells. *J. Neurosci.* **11:** 1496–1507.
62. Adler, E. M., Augustine, G. J., Duffy, S. N., and Charlton, M. P. (1991). Alien intracellular chelators attenuate neurotransmitter release at the squid giant synapse. *J. Neurosci.* **11:** 1496–1507.
63. Stanley, E. F. (1993). Single Ca^{2+} channels and acetylcholine release at a presynaptic nerve terminal. *Neuron* **11:** 1007–1011.
64. Augustine, G. J., and Charlton, M. P. (1986). Calcium-dependence of presynaptic calcium current and post-synaptic response at the squid giant synapse. *J. Physiol. (London)* **381:** 619–640.
65. Simon, S. M., and Llinás, R. R. (1985). Compartmentalization of the submembrane calcium activity during calcium influx and its significance in transmitter release. *Biophys. J.* **48:** 485–498.
66. Zucker, R. S., and Fogelson, A. L. (1986). Relationship between transmitter release and presynaptic calcium influx when calcium enters through discrete channels. *Proc. Natl. Acad. Sci. U.S.A.* **83:** 3032–3036.
67. Augustine, G. J., Charlton, M. P., and Smith, S. J. (1985). Calcium entry and transmitter release at voltage-clamped nerve terminals of squid. *J. Physiol. (London)* **367:** 163–181.
68. Landò, L., and Zucker, R. S. (1994). Ca^{2+} cooperativity in neurosecretion measured using photolabile Ca^{2+} chelators. *J. Neurophysiol.* **72:** 825–830.
69. Heidelberger, R., Heinemann, C., Neher, E., and Matthews, G. (1994). Calcium dependence of the rate of exocytosis in a synaptic terminal. *Nature (London)* **371:** 513–515.
70. Verhage, M., Ghijsen, W. E. J. M., and Lopes da Silva, F. H. (1994). Presynaptic plasticity: The regulation of Ca^{2+}-dependent transmitter release. *Prog. Neurobiol.* **42:** 539–574.
71. Sakaguchi, M., Inaishi, Y., Kashihara, Y., and Kuno, M. (1991). Release of calcitonin gene-related peptide from nerve terminals in rat skeletal muscle. *J. Physiol. (London)* **434:** 257–270.
72. Lindau, M., Stuenkel, E. L., and Nordmann, J. J. (1992). Depolarization, intracellular calcium and exocytosis in single vertebrate nerve endings. *Biophys. J.* **61:** 19–30.
73. Peng, Y.-Y., and Zucker, R. S. (1993). Release of LHRH is linearly related to the time integral of presynaptic Ca^{2+} elevation above a threshold level in bullfrog sympathetic ganglia. *Neuron* **10:** 465–473.
74. Verhage, M., McMahon, H. T., Ghijsen, W. E. J. M., Boomsma, F., Scholten, G., Wiegant, V. M., and Nicholls, D. G. (1991). Differential release of amino acids, neuropeptides, and catecholamines from isolated nerve terminals. *Neuron* **6:** 517–524.
75. Lundberg, J. M., and Hökfelt, T. (1986). Multiple co-existence of peptides and classical transmitters in peripheral autonomic and sensory neurons—functional and pharmacological implications. *Prog. Brain Res.* **68:** 241–262.
76. Nagy, A., Baker, R. R., Morris, S. J., and Whittaker, V. P. (1976). The preparation and characterization of synaptic vesicles of high purity. *Brain Res.* **109:** 285–309.
77. Carlson, S. S., Wagner, J. A., and Kelly, R. B. (1978). Purification of synaptic vesicles from Elasmobranch electric organ and use of biophysical criteria to demonstrate purity. *Biochemistry* **17:** 1188–1199.
78. Nelson, N. (1992). The vacuolar H+-ATPase: One of the most fundamental ion pumps in nature. *J. Exp. Biol.* **172:** 19–27.
79. McMahon, H. T., and Nicholls, D. G. (1991). The bioenergetics of transmitter release. *Biochim. Biophys. Acta* **1059:** 243–264.
80. Alfonso, A., Grundahl, K., Duerr, J. S., Han, H. P., and Rand, J. B. (1993). The Ceonorhabditis unc-17 gene: A putative vesicular acetylcholine transporter. *Science* **261:** 617–619.
81. Landis, D. M. D., Hall, A. K., Weinstein, L. A., and Reese, T. S. (1988). The organization of cytoplasm at the presynaptic active zone of a central nervous system synapse. *Neuron* **1:** 201–209.
82. Hirokawa, N., Sobue, K., Kanda, K., Harada, A., and Yorifuji, H. (1989). The cytoskeletal architecture of the presynaptic nerve terminal and molecular structure of synapsin I. *J. Cell Biol.* **108:** 111–126.
83. Greengard, P., Valtorta, F., Czernik, A. J., and Benfenati, F. (1993). Synaptic vesicle phosphoproteins and regulation of synaptic function. *Science* **259:** 780–785.
84. Benfenati, F., Valtorta, F., Rubenstein, J. L., Gorelick, R. S., Greengard, P., and Czernik, A. J. (1992). Synaptic vesicle-associated Ca^{2+}/calmodulin-dependent protein kinase II is a binding protein for synapsin I. *Nature (London)* **359:** 417–420.
85. Rosahl, T. W., Geppert, M., Spillane, D., Herz, J., Hammer, R. E., Malenka, R. C., and Südhof, T. C. (1993). Short-term synaptic plasticity is altered in mice lacking synapsin I. *Cell (Cambridge, Mass.)* **75:** 661–670.
86. Smith, S. J., and Augustine, G. J. (1988). Calcium ions, active zones and synaptic transmitter release. *Trends Neurosci.* **11:** 458–464.
87. Bennett, M. K., Calcakos, N., and Scheller, R. H. (1992). Syntaxin: A synaptic protein implicated in docking of synaptic vesicles at presynaptic active zones. *Science* **257:** 255–259.
88. Bennett, M. K., and Scheller, R. H. (1994). Molecular correlates of synaptic vesicle docking and fusion. *Curr. Opin. Neurobiol.* **4:** 324–329.
89. Broadie, K., Prokop, A., Bellen, H. J., O'Kane, C. J., Schultz, K. L., and Sweeney, S. T. (1995). Syntaxin and synaptobrevin function downstream of vesicle docking in Drosophila. *Neuron* **15:** 663–673.
90. Ferro-Novick, S., and Jahn, R. (1994). Vesicle fusion from yeast to man. *Nature (London)* **370:** 191–193.
91. Rothman, J. E. (1994). Mechanisms of intracellular protein transport. *Nature (London)* **372:** 55–63.
92. Söllner, T., Whiteheart, S. W., Brunner, M., Erdjument-Bromage, H., Geromanos, S., Tempst, P., and Rothman, J. E. (1993). SNAP receptors implicated in vesicle targeting and fusion. *Nature (London)* **362:** 318–324.
93. Söllner, T., Bennett, M. K., Whiteheart, S. W., Scheller, R. H., and Rothman, J. E. (1993). A protein assembly-disassembly pathway in vitro that may correspond to sequential steps of synaptic vesicle docking, activation, and fusion. *Cell (Cambridge, Mass.)* **75:** 409–418.
94. Fischer von Mollard, G., Stahl, B., Li, C., Südhof, T. C., and Jahn, R. (1994). Rab proteins in regulated exocytosis. *Trends Biochem. Sci.* **19:** 164–168.
95. Hata, Y., Slaughter, C. A., and Südhof, T. C. (1993). Synaptic vesicle fusion complex contains unc-18 homologue bound to syntaxin. *Nature (London)* **366:** 347–351.
96. Pevsner, J., Hsu, S.-C., and Scheller, R. H. (1994). n-Secl: A

neural-specific syntaxin binding protein. *Proc. Natl. Acad. Sci. U.S.A.* **91:** 1445–1449.

97. Ushkaryov, Y. A., Petrenko, A. G., Geppert, M., and Südhof, T. C. (1993). Neurexins: Synaptic cell surface proteins related to the α-latrotoxin receptor and lamanin. *Science* **257:** 50–56.
98. Petrenko, A. G., Perin, M. S., Davletov, B. A., Ushkaryov, Y. A., Geppert, M., and Südhof, T. C. (1991). Binding of synaptotagmin to the α-latrotoxin receptor implicates both in synaptic vesicle exocytosis. *Nature* (*London*) **353:** 65–68.
99. DeBello, W. M., Betz, H., and Augustine, G. J. (1993). Synaptotagmin and transmitter release. *Cell* (*Cambridge, Mass.*) **74:** 947–950.
100. Brose, N., Petrenko, A. G., Südhof, T. C., and Jahn, R. (1992). Synaptotagmin: A calcium sensor on the synaptic vesicle surface. *Science* **256:** 1021–1025.
101. Davletov, B. A., and Südhof, T. C. (1994). Ca^{2+}-dependent conformational change in synaptotagmin I. *J. Biol. Chem.* **269:** 28547–28550.
102. Geppert, M., Goda, Y., Hammer, R. E., Li, C., Rosahl, T. W., Stevens, C. F., and Südhof, T. C. (1994). Synaptotagmin I: A major Ca^{2+} sensor for transmitter release at a central synapse. *Cell* (*Cambridge, Mass.*) **79:** 717–727.
103. DiAntonio A., Parfitt, K. D., and Schwarz, T. L. (1993). Synaptic transmission persists in synaptotagmin mutants of Drosophila. *Cell* (*Cambridge, Mass.*) **73:** 1281–1290.
104. Littleton, J. T., Stern, M., Schulze, K., Perin, M., and Bellen, H. J. (1993). Mutational analysis of Drosophila synaptotagmin demonstrates its essential role in Ca^{2+}-activated transmitter release. *Cell* (*Cambridge, Mass.*) **74:** 1125–1134.
105. Littleton, J. T., Stern, M., Perin, M., and Bellen, H. J. (1994). Calcium dependence of transmitter release and rate of spontaneous vesicle fusions are altered in Drosophila synaptotagmin mutants. *Proc. Natl. Acad. Sci. U.S.A.* **91:** 10888–10892.
106. White, J. M. (1990). Viral and cellular membrane fusion proteins. *Annu. Rev. Physiol.* **52:** 675–697.
107. Hughson, F. M. (1995). Structural characterization of viral fusion proteins. *Curr. Biol.* **5:** 265–274.
108. Monck, J. R., and Fernandez, J. M. (1992). The exocytotic fusion pore. *J. Cell Biol.* **119:** 1395–1404.
109. Spruce, A. E., Iwata, A., White, J. M., and Almers, W. (1989). Patch clamp studies of single cell-fusion events mediated by a viral fusion protein. *Nature* (*London*) **342:** 555–558.
110. Robinson, M. S. (1994). The role of clathrin, adaptors and dynamin in endocytosis. *Curr. Opin. Cell Biol.* **6:** 538–544.
111. Maycox, P. R., Link, E., Reetz, A., Morris, S. A., and Jahn, R. (1992). Clathrin-coated vesicles in nervous tissue are involved primarily in synaptic vesicle recycling. *J. Cell Biol.* **118:** 1379–1388.
112. Zhang, J. Z., Davletov, B. A., Südhof, T. C., and Anderson, R. G. W. (1994). Synaptotagmin I is a high affinity receptor for clathrin AP-2: Implications for membrane recycling. *Cell* (*Cambridge, Mass.*) **78:** 751–760.
113. Robinson, P. J., Liu, J.-P., Powell, K. A., Fyske, E. M., and Südhof, T. C. (1994). Phosphorylation of dynamin I and synaptic-vesicle recycling. *Trends Neurosci.* **17:** 348–353.
114. Martin, A. R. (1977). Junctional transmission. II. Presynaptic mechanisms. In *Handbook of Physiology* (E. Kandel, ed.), Sect. 1, pp. 329–355. Am. Physiol. Soc., Bethesda, MD.
115. Fatt, P., and Katz, B. (1952). Spontaneous sub-threshold activity at motor nerve endings. *J. Physiol.* (*London*) **119:** 109–128.
116. del Castillo, J., and Katz, B. (1954). Quantal components of the end-plate potential. *J. Physiol.* (*London*) **124:** 560–573.
117. Liley, A. W. (1956). The quantal components of the mammalian end-plate potential. *J. Physiol.* (*London*) **133:** 571–587.
118. Boyd, I. A., and Martin, A. R. (1956). Spontaneous subthreshold activity at mammalian neuromuscular junctions. *J. Physiol.* (*London*) **132:** 74–91.
119. Paulsen, O., and Heggelund, P. (1994). The quantal size at retinogeniculate synapses determined from spontaneous and evoked EPSCs in guinea-pig thalamic slices. *J. Physiol.* (*London*) **480:** 505–511.
120. Bartol, T. M., Land, B. R., Salpeter, E. E., and Salpeter, M. M. (1991). Monte Carlo simulation of miniature endplate current generation in the vertebrate neuromuscular junction. *Biophys. J.* **59:** 1290–1307.
121. Hartzell, H. C., Kuffler, S. W., and Yoshikami, D. (1975). Postsynaptic potentiation: Interaction between quanta of acetylcholine at the skeletal neuromuscular synapse. *J. Physiol.* (*London*) **251:** 427–463.
122. Korn, H., Mallet, A., Triller, A., and Faber, D. S. (1982). Transmission at a central inhibitory synapse. II. Quantal description of release, with a physical correlate for binomial n. *J. Neurophysiol.* **48:** 679–707.
123. Katz, B., and Miledi, R. (1965). The release of acetylcholine from nerve endings by graded electric pulses. *Proc. R. Soc. London, Ser. B* **167:** 28–38.
124. Zucker, R. S. (1973). Changes in the statistics of transmitter release during facilitation. *J. Physiol.* (*London*) **229:** 787–810.
125. Alvarez de Toledo, G., Fernandez-Chacon, R., and Fernandez, J. M. (1993). Release of secretory products during transient vesicle fusion. *Nature* (*London*) **363:** 554–558.
126. Isaacson, J. S., and Walmsley, B. (1995). Counting quanta: Direct measurements of transmitter release at a central synapse. *Neuron* **15:** 875–884.
127. Korn, H., and Faber, D. S. (1987). Regulation and significance of probabilistic release mechanisms at central synapses. In *Synaptic Function* (G. Edelman, W. E. Gall, and W. M. Cowan, eds.), pp. 57–108. Wiley, New York.
128. Korn, H., and Faber, D. S. (1991). Quantal analysis and synaptic efficacy in the CNS. *Trends Neurosci.* **14:** 439–445.
129. Redman, S. (1990). Quantal analysis of synaptic potentials in neurons of the central nervous system. *Physiol. Rev.* **70:** 165–198.
130. Walmsley, B. (1991). Central synaptic transmission: Studies at the connection between primary muscle afferents and dorsal spinocerebellar tract (DSCT) neurones in Clarke's column of the spinal cord. *Prog. Neurobiol.* **36:** 391–423.
131. Trussell, L. O., Zhang, S., and Raman, I. M. (1993). Desensitization of AMPA receptors upon multiquantal neurotransmitter release. *Neuron* **10:** 1185–1196.
132. Jack, J. J. B., Redman, S. J., and Wong, K. (1981). The components of synaptic potentials evoked in cat spinal motoneurones by impulses in single group Ia afferents. *J. Physiol.* (*London*) **321:** 65–96.
133. Faber, D. S., Young, W. S., Legendre, P., and Korn, H. (1992). Intrinsic quantal variability due to stochastic properties of receptor-transmitter interactions. *Science* **258:** 1494–1498.
134. Manabe, T., Renner, P., and Nicoll, R. (1992). Postsynaptic contribution to long-term potentiation revealed by the analysis of miniature synaptic currents. *Nature* (*London*) **355:** 50–55.
135. Bekkers, J. M., and Stevens, C. F. (1989). NMDA and non-NMDA receptors are co-localized at individual excitatory synapses in cultured rat hippocampus. *Nature* (*London*) **341:** 230–233.
136. Silverman, B. W. (1986). *Density Estimation for Statistics and Data Analysis.* Chapman & Hall, London.

137. Horn, R. (1987). Statistical methods for model discrimination. Applications to gating kinetics and permeation of the acetylcholine receptor channel. *Biophys. J.* **51:** 255–263.
138. McLachlan, E. M. (1978). The statistics of transmitter release at chemical synapses. *Int. Rev. Physiol.* **17:** 49–117.
139. Kullmann, D. M. (1989). Applications of the Expectation-Maximization algorithm to quantal analysis of postsynaptic potentials. *J. Neurosci. Methods* **30:** 231–245.
140. Malinow, R., and Tsien, R. W. (1990). Presynaptic enhancement shown by whole-cell recordings of long-term potentiation in hippocampal slices. *Nature* (*London*) **346:** 177–180.
141. Manabe, T., Wyllie, D. J. A., Perkel, D. J., and Nicoll, R. A. (1993). Modulation of synaptic transmission and long-term potentiation: Effects on paired pulse facilitation and EPSC variance in the CA1 region of the hippocampus. *J. Neurophysiol.* **70:** 1451–1459.
142. Faber, D. S., and Korn, H. (1992). Application of the coefficient of variation method for analyzing synaptic plasticity. *Biophys. J.* **60:** 1288–1294.
143. Edwards, F. R., Redman, S. J., and Walmsley, B. (1976). Statistical fluctuation in charge transfer at Ia synapses on spinal motoneurones. *J. Physiol.* (*London*) **259:** 665–688.
144. Stricker, C., and Redman, S. (1994). Statistical models of synaptic transmission evaluated using the Expectation-Optimization algorithm. *Biophys. J.* **67:** 656–670.
145. Kullmann, D. M., and Nicoll, R. A. (1992). Long-term potentiation is associated with increases in quantal content and quantal amplitude. *Nature* (*London*) **357:** 240–244.
146. Efron, B., and Tibshirani, R. (1993). *An Introduction to the Bootstrap.* Chapman & Hall, New York.
147. Rosenmund, C., Clements, J. D., and Westbrook, G. L. (1993). Nonuniform probability of glutamate release at a hippocampal synapse. *Science* **262:** 754–757.
148. Hessler, N. A., Shirke, A. M., and Malinow, R. (1993). The probability of transmitter release at a mammalian central synapse. *Nature* (*London*) **366:** 568–572.
149. Zucker, R. S. (1989). Short-term synaptic plasticity. *Annu. Rev. Neurosci.* **12:** 13–31.
150. Baxter, D. A., Bittner, G. D., and Brown, T. H. (1985). Quantal mechanism of long-term synaptic potentiation. *Proc. Natl. Acad. Sci. U.S.A.* **82:** 5978–5982.
151. Minota, S., Kumamoto, E., Kitakoga, O., and Kuba, K. (1991). Long-term potentiation induced by a sustained rise in the intraterminal Ca^{2+} in bull-frog sympathetic ganglia. *J. Physiol.* (*London*) **435:** 421–438.
152. Davies, C. H., Davies, S. N., and Collingridge, G. L. (1990). Paired-pulse depression of monosynaptic GABA-mediated inhibitory postsynaptic responses in rat hippocampus. *J. Physiol.* (*London*) **424:** 513–531.
153. Redman, R. S., and Silinsky, E. M. (1994). ATP released together with acetylcholine as the mediator of neuromuscular depression at frog motor nerve endings. *J. Physiol.* (*London*) **477:** 117–127.
154. Jia, M., and Nelson, P. G. (1986). Calcium currents and transmitter output in cultured spinal cord and dorsal root ganglion neurons. *J. Neurophysiol.* **56:** 1257–1267.
155. Wachtel, H., and Kandel, E. R. (1971). Conversion of synaptic excitation to inhibition at a dual chemical synapse. *J. Neurophysiol.* **34:** 56–68.
156. Wojtowicz, J. M., and Atwood, H. L. (1988). Presynaptic long-term facilitation at the crayfish neuromuscular junction: voltage-dependent and ion-dependent phases. *J. Neurosci.* **8:** 4667–4674.
157. Katz, B., and Miledi, R. (1968). The role of calcium in neuromuscular facilitation. *J. Physiol.* (*London*) **195:** 481–492.
158. Magleby, K. L., and Zengel, J. E. (1982). A quantitative description of stimulation-induced changes in transmitter release at the frog neuromuscular junction. *J. Gen. Physiol.* **30:** 613–638.
159. Delaney, K. R., Zucker, R. S., and Tank, D. W. (1991). Presynaptic calcium in motor nerve terminals associated with posttetanic potentiation. *J. Neurosci.* **9:** 3558–3567.
160. Delaney, K. R., and Tank, D. W. (1994). A quantitative measurement of the dependence of short-term synaptic enhancement on presynaptic residual calcium. *J. Neurosci.* **14:** 5885–5902.
161. Zucker, R. S. (1994). Calcium and short-term synaptic plasticity. *Neth. J. Zool.* **44:** 495–512.
162. Kamiya, H., and Zucker, R. S. (1994). Residual Ca^{2+} and short-term synaptic plasticity. *Nature (London)* **371:** 603–606.
163. Van der Kloot, W. (1994). Facilitation at the frog neuromuscular junction at 0°C is not maximal at time zero. *J. Neurosci.* **14:** 5722–5724.
164. Zengel, J. E., and Magleby, K. L. (1980). Differential effects of Ba^{2+}, and Sr^{2+}, and Ca^{2+} on stimulation-induced changes in transmitter release at the frog neuromuscular junction. *J. Gen. Physiol.* **76:** 175–211.
165. Zengel, J. E., and Magleby, K. L. (1981). Changes in miniature endplate potential frequency during repetitive nerve stimulation in the presence of Ca^{2+}, Ba^{2+}, and Sr^{2+} at the frog neuromuscular junction. *J. Gen. Physiol.* **77:** 503–529.
166. Zhong, Y., and Wu, C.-F. (1991). Altered synaptic plasticity in *Drosophila* memory mutants with a defective cyclic AMP cascade. *Science* **251:** 198–201.
167. Wang, J., Renger, J. J., Griffith, L. C., Greenspan, R. J., and Wu, C.-F. (1994). Concomitant alterations of physiological and developmental plasticity in Drosophila CaM kinase II-inhibited synapses. *Neuron* **13:** 1373–1384.
168. Miller, R. J. (1991). The control of neuronal Ca^{2+} homeostasis. *Prog. Neurobiol.* **37:** 255–285.
169. Mulkey, R. M., and Zucker, R. S. (1992). Posttetanic potentiation at the crayfish neuromuscular junction is dependent on both intracellular calcium and sodium accumulation. *J. Neurosci.* **12:** 4327–4336.

CHAPTER

8

Neurotransmitters

Ariel Y. Deutch and Robert H. Roth

Cells of the nervous system are anatomically and functionally specialized for the intercellular transmission of electrical and chemical signals and for the bulk transport of metabolites from one cell to another and solute from cell interior to extracellular space. Until the 20th century, basic neuroscience was primarily anatomical, with numerous milestone discoveries punctuating the evolution of the present-day concept of the nervous system as an intricately wired network of different cellular elements.[1] In this chapter, we briefly discuss the several mechanisms by which cells communicate with each other and then discuss one such mechanism—chemical synaptic transmission—in considerable detail. A second mechanism—electrical synaptic transmission via gap junction—will be discussed in Chapter 11 and, in particular, the forms of communication that they mediate.

THE MULTIPLE WAYS THAT NERVOUS SYSTEM CELLS INTERACT WITH EACH OTHER

The early history of neuroscience is summarized in Chapter 2 of this textbook and elsewhere.[1,2] By the beginning of this century, a silver-staining method developed by the Italian neuroanatomist Camillo Golgi and used extensively by the Spanish neuroanatomist Santiago Ramóny Cajal had revolutionized histology by allowing microscopists to view the details of entire individual brain cells *in situ* (also see Peinado *et al.*[3]). Because the Golgi method and other histological techniques demonstrated that the nervous system was composed of discrete cellular elements, the neuron doctrine became widely accepted by the end of the 19th century[1,2] (see Box 2.1).

A major question of the time became that of how activity was spread from one cell to another. The first hypothesis, initially formulated as the mechanism operating at neuromuscular synapses,[4] was that of electrical transmission (for a lively discussion of the early history summarized only briefly here, see Grundfest[2]). The term "synapse" was coined by Charles Sherrington to designate the site where transmission occurs from one cell (the presynaptic one) to another (the postsynaptic cell). Sherrington also noted that synaptic transmission was graded in strength and flexible, unlike conducted activity of nerve fibers, which exhibit all-or-none impulses (also called action potentials or "spikes"). To account for this difference, he proposed that synaptic transmission was chemically mediated.[5]

There Are Many Ways by Which Neurons Communicate with Each Other

The controversy surrounding whether the mode of transmission at the neuromuscular junction was electrical or chemical was finally resolved with pharmacological and electrophysiological approaches.[1] First, in 1849, Claude Bernard[6] found that the arrow poison curare blocked the transmission from nerve to muscle; this effect is now known to be due to binding of the drug to postsynaptic receptors, inhibiting excitation by the neurotransmitter acetylcholine (ACh). Second, in 1905, Thomas Elliott[7] observed that exogenous adrenaline application resulted in contraction of denervated smooth muscle, thereby indicating that muscle contraction depended on the action of chemical molecules

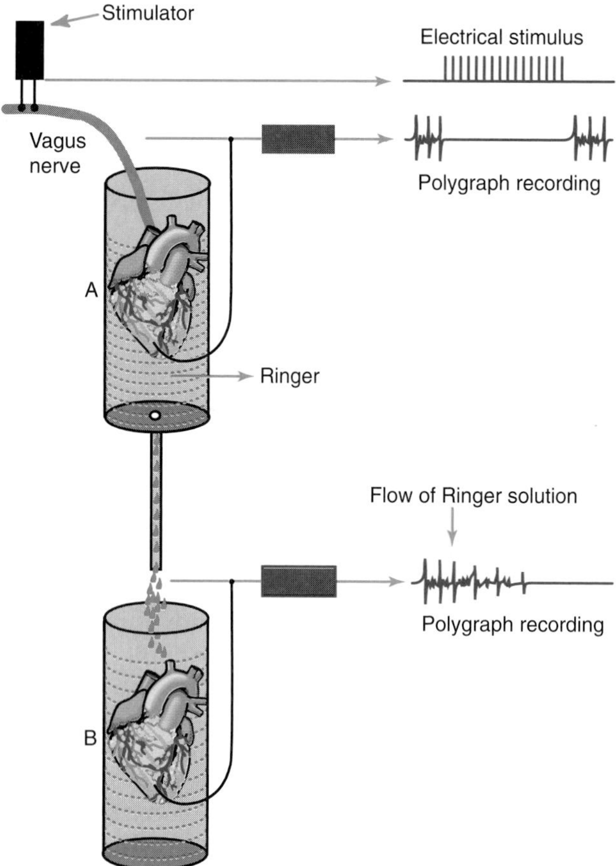

FIGURE 8.1 Otto Loewi's experimental paradigm by which chemical transmission was demonstrated. (A) Electrical stimulation of the vagus nerve of a frog heart suspended in Ringer solution reduces cardiac beat rate. (B) When the Ringer solution bathing the stimulated heart is introduced into a second chamber containing another frog heart (arrow indicates the time of addition), the beat rate of the second heart also decreases. This result, demonstrating that nerve stimulation liberated a substance that mimicked the action of electrical stimulation on the heart, led to the conclusion that neurotransmission is chemical in nature.

liberated from nerves. Otto Loewi's experiments on isolated frog heart (illustrated in Fig. 8.1) finally provided the conclusive proof that a substance (in this case now known to be ACh) was liberated by nerve impulse activity that affected a target.[8] This research finding, which revolutionized neuroscience, led to the revelation that nerve cells contain numerous neurotransmitter and neuromodulatory substances and ultimately resulted in the identification of gene families encoding the proteins forming presynaptic components of the release process (see Chapter 7) and the postsynaptic receptors (Chapter 9).

Before turning our attention to chemical synaptic transmission, we note that the nervous system uses several other processes for intracellular communication (Fig. 8.2). These include electrical synaptic transmission (Chapter 11), ephaptic interactions, and autocrine, paracrine, and long-range signaling, in which molecules produced by both neural and nonneural cells take part.

The nonsynaptic mode of intercellular communication having the longest range is humoral (hormonal) signaling. In this case certain peripheral hormones can gain entry into the central nervous system to drive, inhibit, or modulate neuronal activity (Fig. 8.2A1). The neuronal targets of these hormones possess specific high- and low-affinity receptors for these hormones. The actions of hormones may be either short term (to acutely change neuronal activity) or long term (through changes in gene expression).

Molecules generated endogenously within the nervous system can also be used in intercellular or intercompartmental communication that does not require synaptic specializations. Water-soluble factors that are secreted or diffuse from the cells in which they are generated include classical neurotransmitters, neuropeptides, and neurosteroids, as well as the gases nitric oxide (NO) and carbon monoxide (CO). These factors may act through autocrine mechanisms (activating receptors on the same cell that releases them: Fig. 8.2A3) or through paracrine pathways to nearby cells (Fig. 8.2A2), and the gases NO and CO in particular may act as retrograde neurotransmitters, signaling backward from postsynaptic to presynaptic elements. Soluble factors can act on high- or low-affinity

FIGURE 8.2 The multiple modes of intercellular signaling. (A) Substances (purple particles in this drawing) produced outside the nervous system (1) or by cells within the CNS (2, 3) can affect neuronal activity, acting through (1) humoral, (2) paracrine, and (3) autocrine mechanisms. (B) Ephaptic transmission. Two apposed cell membranes showing regions of low (1, green label indicating channels) and high (2, sawtooths, representing tight junctions) resistances. The electrical equivalent circuit is shown below. Communication between these cells is permitted through membrane regions of low resistance (1). The presence of tight junctions (2) between apposed cells favors an increase of current density by preventing current flow into the bulk extracellular space. Charges accumulate in the narrow intercellular space and affect capacitance and resistive components of the cell membranes. (C) Electrical synapses. Gap junction channels provide low-resistance pathways between adjacent cells, allowing direct communication between the cytoplasms of both cells. In contrast with the ephaptic mode of transmission, current flows directly from cell to cell and not through the extracellular space. The electrical equivalent circuit is shown below, differing from that of the ephapse in B primarily in the absence of a resistance to ground. (D) Chemical synapses. Neurotransmitters released from the presynaptic terminal (on the left) diffuse across the cleft to bind to postsynaptic receptors, thereby opening on channels and increasing conductance of the postsynaptic membrane, producing currents that excite or inhibit the cell.

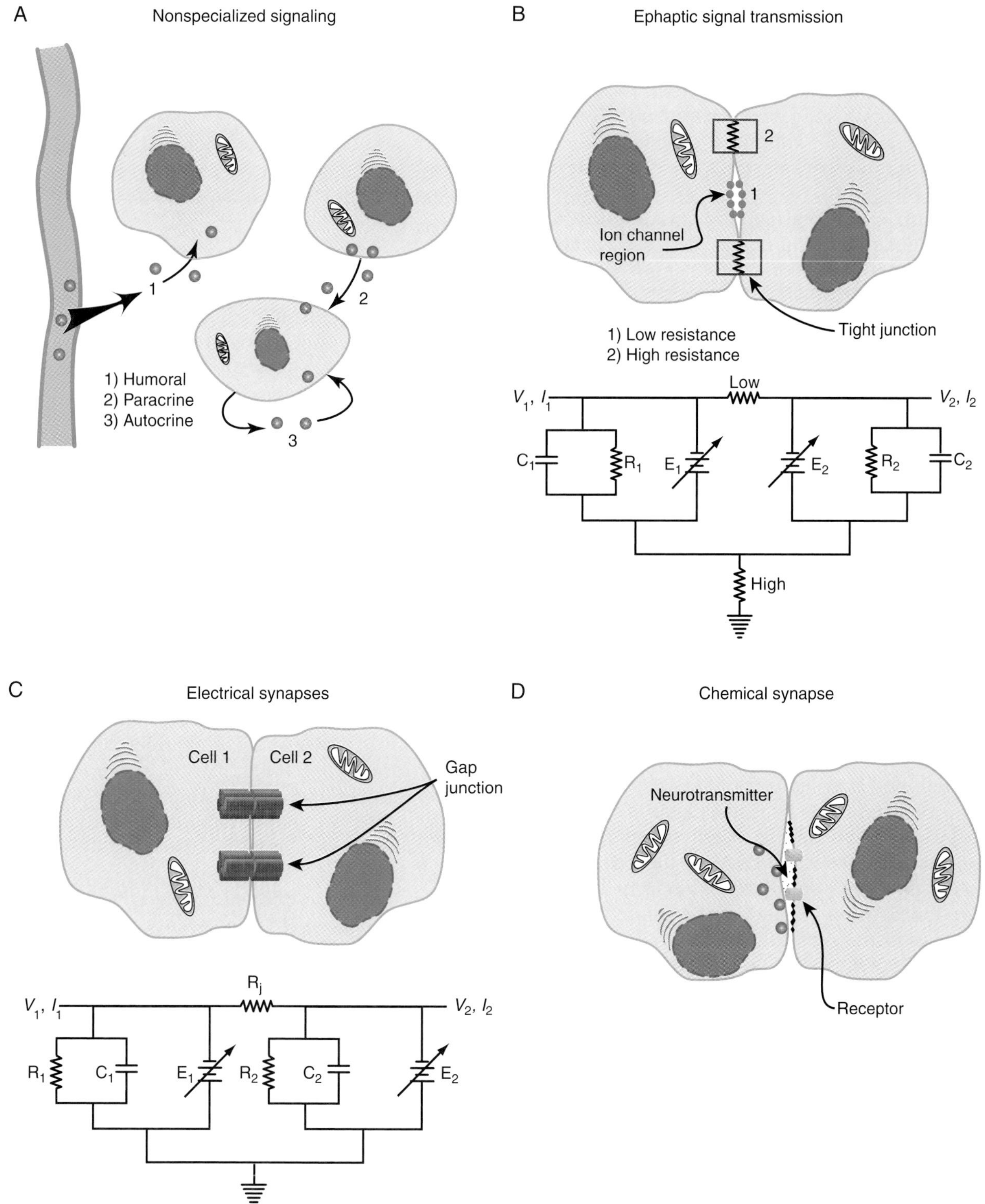
A
Nonspecialized signaling
1) Humoral
2) Paracrine
3) Autocrine
B
Ephaptic signal transmission
Ion channel region
Tight junction
1) Low resistance
2) High resistance
Low
High
C
Electrical synapses
Cell 1
Cell 2
Gap junction
D
Chemical synapse
Neurotransmitter
Receptor

FIGURE 8.2

receptors and can either act locally by volume transmission. The role of such molecules in nervous system function is believed to lie primarily in modulating neural activity, although they may also provide trophic support ("guidance cues") for neurons in the process of outgrowth and for the establishment and maintenance of synaptic connections (Chapter 21).

Cells also signal one another through structural components and adhesion molecules that are bound to cell surfaces. Adhesion molecules in general are transmembrane proteins, with extracellular segments that mediate adhesion interactions across the intercellular cleft, and cytoplasmic domains that communicate, either directly or indirectly, with signal transduction pathway components and/or the cytoskeleton. The intercellular domains of adhesion molecules may be "activated" by the binding of the extracellular segment to a cognate membrane-bound "ligand" protruding from another cell; in this respect adhesion molecules behave identically to growth factor receptors that are stimulated by binding of specific soluble ligands. Cell-specific adhesion molecules and extracellular matrix components are expressed in developmental patterns, where sequence and cell-type specificity provide inherent signals for cell differentiation. Binding of water-soluble hormones and other factors to matrix molecules may further enhance their role in acute responses and in alterations of gene expression.

The most intimate nonsynaptic mode of intercellular communication is the **ephapse,** in which electrical impulses in one cell or extracellular ionic accumulation in the vicinity of one cell can directly affect the activity of an adjacent cell. In this case, as illustrated in Fig. 8.2B, the only morphological requirement is closely apposed membranes. Ephaptic interactions are either transient or sustained. In the former case, the interaction is capacitative, with duration and amplitude dictated by the first derivative of the time course of the impulse (equivalent circuit, Fig. 8.2B). Sustained ephaptic interaction is due to local or focal ionic accumulation. Capacitative interactions are maximal at regions of high current density, and both transient and sustained ephaptic interactions are most effective when appositional membranes are specialized for low resistance and when ionic dissipation and current flow to the extracellular space are minimized by the presence of tight junctions (see Fig. 8.2B).

The two categories of intercellular communication considered to be true synaptic transmission are electrical (Chapter 11) and chemical synapses (Figs. 8.2C and 8.2D). Both are mediated by specialized structure, with families of genes encoding the protein components of each of these two types of synapses.

CHEMICAL TRANSMISSION

Chemically mediated transmission is the major means by which a signal is communicated from one nerve cell to another.

Several Criteria for a Neurotransmitter Have Been Established

The chemicals that transmit information between neurons or between neurons and effector cells are termed **neurotransmitters.** Neurotransmitters are endogenous substances that are released from neurons, act on receptor sites that are typically present on membranes of postsynaptic cells, and produce a functional change in the properties of the target cell. There is a consensus that several criteria should be met before a substance is designated a neurotransmitter.[9]

First, a neurotransmitter must be synthesized by and released from neurons. In many cases, this means that the presynaptic neuron should contain both the transmitter and the appropriate enzymes required for synthesis of the neurotransmitter. However, synthesis in the nerve terminal is not an absolute requirement; peptide transmitters are synthesized in the cell body and transported to the nerve terminal.

Second, the substance should be released from nerve terminals in a chemically or pharmacologically identifiable form.

Third, the putative neurotransmitter should reproduce at the postsynaptic cell the specific events (such as changes in membrane properties) observed to occur upon stimulation of the presynaptic neuron, and these effects should be realized in concentrations that approximate those seen after release of the neurotransmitter by nerve stimulation.

Fourth, the effects of a putative neurotransmitter should be blocked by known competitive antagonists of the transmitter in a dose-dependent manner.

Fifth, there should be appropriate active mechanisms to terminate the action of the putative neurotransmitter. These mechanisms can include enzymatic degradation, reuptake of the substance into the presynaptic neuron through specific transporter molecules, and uptake into glial cells.

Chemical Neurotransmission Involves Five Steps: Synthesis, Storage, Release, Receptor Binding, and Inactivation

The general mechanisms of chemical synaptic transmission are depicted in Fig. 8.3. Synaptic transmission

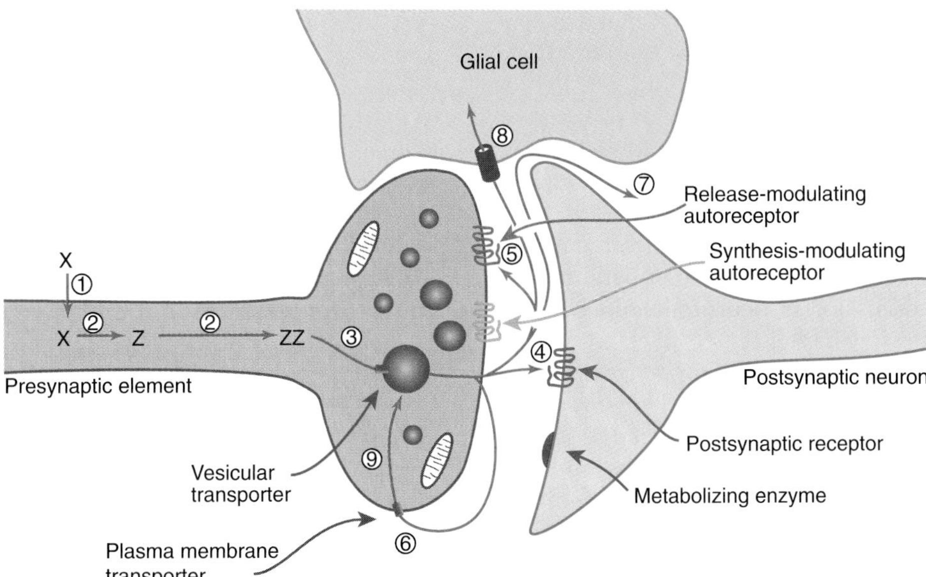

FIGURE 8.3 Schematic representation of the life cycle of a classical neurotransmitter. After accumulation of a precursor amino acid into the neuron (step 1), the amino acid precursor is sequentially metabolized (step 2) to yield the mature transmitter (22). The transmitter is then accumulated into vesicles by the vesicular transporter (step 3), where it is poised for release and protected from degradation. The released transmitter can interact with post-synaptic receptors (step 4) or autoreceptors (step 5) that regulate transmitter release, synthesis, or firing rate. Transmitter actions are terminated by means of a high-affinity membrane transporter (step 6) that is usually associated with the neuron that released the transmitter. Alternatively, the actions of the transmitter may be terminated by means of diffusion (step 7), or by accumulation into glia through a membrane transporter (step 8). When the transmitter is taken up by the neuron, it is subject to metabolic inactivation (step 9).

consists of a number of steps; each step constitutes a potential site of drug action.

1. *Biosynthesis of the neurotransmitter in the presynaptic neuron.* Biosynthesis requires that the precursors of the transmitter be available and appropriately localized in the neuron, that the enzymes taking part in the conversion of the precursor(s) into the transmitter also are present in the neuron and localized to the appropriate intraneuronal compartment, that the enzymes are in an active form, and, finally, that necessary cofactors for enzyme activity are present. The biosynthesis of neurotransmitters has long been an important site for clinically useful drugs. An example is the use of α-methyl-*p*-tyrosine in the treatment of pheochromocytoma, an adrenal tumor that releases massive amounts of catecholamines and thus causes hypertensive crises. α-Methyl-*p*-tyrosine prevents the synthesis of catecholamines, such as norepinephrine, and thus prevents their actions on target cells.

2. *Storage of the neurotransmitter or its precursor or both in the presynaptic nerve terminal.* Transmitters are stored in synaptic vesicles, where they are sequestered and thus protected from enzymatic degradation, and are available for ready release. In the case of so-called classical neurotransmitters (acetylcholine, biogenic amines, and amino acids), the synaptic vesicles are small ($\approx$50 nm in diameter). In contrast, neuropeptide transmitters are stored in large dense-core vesicles ($\approx$100 nm in diameter) and typically released in response to repetitive stimulation or burst firing of neurons. Because most neurotransmitters are synthesized in the cytosolic compartment of neurons, there must be some mechanism through which the transmitter gains entry into the vesicle. Recent studies have identified and cloned vesicular transporter proteins.

3. *Release of the neurotransmitter into the synaptic cleft.* This step includes fusion of the transmitter-containing vesicle and the cellular membrane and the subsequent exocytosis of the transmitter. Neurons use two pathways to secrete proteins. The release of neurotransmitters occurs by a regulated pathway controlled by extracellular signals. The neurotransmitter release process is discussed more fully in Chapter 7. This is contrasted to a second, constitutive pathway that is not triggered by extracellular stimulation and is used to secrete membrane components, viral proteins, and extracellular matrix molecules.

4. *Binding and recognition of the neurotransmitter by target receptors.* Released transmitters interact with receptors located on the target (postsynaptic) cell. These

receptors either are membrane proteins that are coupled to intracellular proteins that transduce the signal to the cell interior and thus alter intracellular processes (**metabotropic receptors**) or, alternatively, are proteins that form ion channels (**ionotropic receptors**). In addition to receptors located on postsynaptic neurons, **autoreceptors** may be present on a neuron. Autoreceptors respond to the transmitter released from the neuron and modulate transmitter release or synthesis. A more thorough discussion of neurotransmitter receptors may be found in Chapter 9.

5. *Inactivation and termination of the action of the released transmitter.* In the absence of mechanisms to terminate the actions of neurotransmitters, adverse sustained activation of postsynaptic targets, such as tetanus in muscles or seizure discharges in neurons, may occur. Cessation of chemical neurotransmission is accompanied by reuptake of the neurotransmitter through specific neuronal transporter proteins on the presynaptic neuron, enzymatic conversion into an inactive substance, or a combination of these processes. In addition, in certain cases glial cells can accumulate released transmitters. Finally, diffusion away from the synaptic region is a [potential] passive mechanism for inactivation of released transmitter.

These five steps form a logical scaffold for understanding chemical neurotransmission. However, there are particular and peculiar intricacies for each of the steps and for each of the many neurotransmitters. **Catecholamines**, a structurally defined group of neurotransmitters, have been extensively studied. Each of the aforedescribed five steps is relatively well understood in catecholamine-containing neurons. We therefore first consider the catecholamine neurotransmitters to illustrate the various steps of chemical neurotransmission. We then examine the particulars of chemical neurotransmission for other classical neurotransmitters. These include the **indoleamine serotonin** (5-hydroxytryptamine), **acetylcholine**, and the amino acids **GABA** (γ-aminobutyric acid) and **glutamate**. (Note: The catecholamines and the indoleamines are grouped together as **biogenic amines**.) We also note the key differences between classical and other (nonclassical) neurotransmitters or chemical messengers, among which are **peptide** neurotransmitters and unconventional transmitters such as **nitric oxide** and **growth factors**.

CLASSICAL NEUROTRANSMITTERS

The term *classical* is used to differentiate acetylcholine, the biogenic amines, and the amino acid transmitters from their *nonclassical* counterparts. In some respects, this designation is arbitrary. However, some generalization can help to differentiate the two groups. We have already mentioned that storage vesicles, when present, are smaller for classical transmitters. In addition, classical transmitters or their metabolic products are subject to reuptake by the presynaptic cell and can be viewed as homeostatically conserved. There is no energy-dependent high-affinity reuptake process for nonclassical transmitters.

Catecholamines Play Transmitter Roles

The term *catecholamine* refers generically to organic compounds that contain a catechol nucleus (a benzene ring with two adjacent hydroxyl substitutions) and an amine group. In practice, however, the term is usually used to describe the endogenous compounds **dopamine** (dihydroxyphenylethylamine), **norepinephrine**, and **epinephrine**. These three neurotransmitters are formed by successive enzymatic steps requiring distinct enzymes (see Fig. 8.4). In the central nervous system, there are distinct dopamine-, norepinephrine-, and epinephrine-containing neurons. The catecholamines also have transmitter roles in the peripheral nervous system and have certain hormonal functions. In the peripheral nervous system, dopamine is mainly present as a precursor for norepinephrine but also has important biological activity in the kidney. Norepinephrine is the postganglionic sympathetic neurotransmitter in mammals; in contrast, epinephrine is the sympathetic transmitter in frogs. Despite this species difference in sympathetic nervous system characteristics, the biochemical aspects of neurotransmission as a general rule are remarkably constant across vertebrate species and, indeed, invertebrates.

Biosynthesis of Catecholamines

The amino acids phenylalanine and tyrosine are precursors for catecholamines. These amino acids are present in the plasma and brain in high concentrations. In mammals, tyrosine can be derived from dietary phenylalanine by an enzyme (phenylalanine hydroxylase) that is found primarily in liver. Phenylketonuria, a disorder caused by insufficient amounts of phenylalanine hydroxylase, results in very high plasma and brain levels of phenylalanine and, unless dietary phenylalanine intake is restricted, intellectual impairment. See Box 8.1.

Catecholamines are formed in brain, adrenal chromaffin cells, and sympathetic nerves. In general, the processes regulating catecholamine synthesis are the same in the various tissues. Catecholamine synthesis is usually considered to begin with tyrosine, which

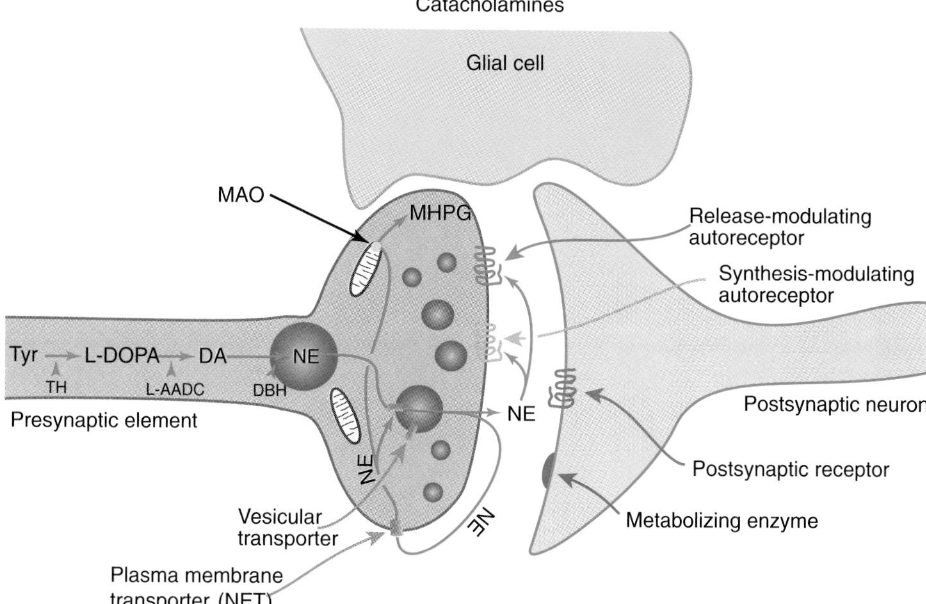

FIGURE 8.4 Characteristics of a norepinephrine-containing catecholamine neuron. Upon accumulation of tyrosine (Tyr) by the neuron, tyrosine is sequentially metabolized by tyrosine hydroxylase (TH) and *L*-aromatic amino acid decarboxylase (L-AADC) to dopamine (DA). The DA is then accumulated by the vesicular monoamine transporter. In dopaminergic neurons this is the final step. However, in this noradrenergic neuron, the DA is metabolized to NE by dopamine-β-hydroxylase (DBH), which is found in the vesicle. Once NE is released, it can interact with post-synaptic noradrenergic receptors or different types of presynaptic noradrenergic autoreceptors. The accumulation of NE by the high-affinity membrane norepinephrine transporter (NET) terminates the extracellular actions of NE. Once accumulated by the neuron, the NE can be metabolized to inactive species (for example, MHPG) by key degradative enzymes such as monoamine oxidase (MAO), or taken back up by the vesicular transporter.

represents a branch point for many important biosynthetic processes in animal tissues. The enzymatic processes in the formation of catecholamines have been extensively studied. The sequence of enzymatic steps in the synthesis of catecholamines from tyrosine was first postulated by Blaschko in 1939 and finally confirmed by Nagatsu and co-workers in 1964, when they demonstrated that the enzyme **tyrosine hydroxylase** (TH) converts the amino acid L-tyrosine into 3,4-dihydroxyphenylalanine (L-dopa). All of the component enzymes in the catecholamine biosynthetic pathway have now been purified to homogeneity. These purifications have allowed detailed analyses of the kinetics, substrate specificity, and cofactor requirements of these enzymes and have aided in the development of useful inhibitors of the enzymes. The development of antibodies against the purified enzymes has permitted the precise localization of the enzymes by immunohistochemical techniques.

After L-tyrosine has been hydroxylated by TH to the dopamine precursor **L-dopa**, the L-dopa formed is almost immediately metabolized to dopamine by **L-aromatic amino acid decarboxylase** (AADC). In dopamine-containing neurons, this is the final step in transmitter synthesis. However, in neurons using norepinephrine (also known as noradrenaline) or epinephrine (adrenaline) as transmitters, dopamine is oxidized by dopamine β-hydroxylase (DBH) to yield norepinephrine. Finally, in neurons in which epinephrine serves as the transmitter, a third enzyme, **phenylethanolamine *N*-methyltransferase** (PNMT), is present and converts norepinephrine into epinephrine. Thus, an **adrenergic neuron** (which uses epinephrine as its transmitter) contains four enzymes (TH, AADC, DBH, and PNMT) that sequentially metabolize tyrosine to epinephrine. Noradrenergic neurons express only the enzymes TH, AADC, and DBH, and thus norepinephrine cannot be further metabolized to epinephrine. Similarly, because dopamine neurons lack DBH and PNMT, the catecholamine end product is the transmitter dopamine. The transmitter of a catecholamine neuron is the final catecholamine that is formed, because, under basal conditions, the conversion of tyrosine into L-dopa is the rate-limiting step. The enzymes and cofactors taking part in the synthesis of the catecholamines are illustrated in Figs. 8.4 and 8.5.

BOX 8.1

PKU AND METABOLISM

Classic phenylketonuria (PKU) is a genetic disease caused by mutations in the enzyme phenylalanine hydroxylase (PAH) resulting in the loss of the enzyme's ability to hydroxylate phenylalanine (Phe) to tyrosine. This hydroxylase plays an integrated dual role in the metabolism of humans and other mammals. Not only does it provide them with an endogenous supply of tyrosine, thereby making the consumption of this amino acid unnecessary for normal growth, but, in addition, the reaction catalyzed by PAH is an essential step in the complete oxidation of Phe to CO_2 and water. When the hydroxylation reaction fails, as it does in PKU, massive amounts of Phe accumulate in the body, reaching blood levels that are 20- to 50-fold higher than normal. A tiny fraction of it is converted to the phenylketone phenylpyruvic acid, which is excreted in the urine; hence, the name of the disease. The accumulated Phe spares the body, but spoils—indeed, devastates—the developing brain, leading, with rare exceptions, to severe mental retardation.

The majority of untreated PKU patients suffer severe intellectual impairment (IQs less than 20). They also have a somewhat higher incidence of seizures and tend to have fair skin and hair. The latter effect is due to the inhibition of melanin formation by the excess Phe.

If one can dare say that there is anything fortunate about this dreadful disease, it is that it is extremely rare, with an average incidence of about 1/12,000. The frequency, however, varies widely among different ethnic groups, being only 1/200,000 in Japan but as high as 1/5000 in Ireland.

The other auspicious feature of the disease is that the affected infants are essentially normal at birth. This characteristic raised the hope that some way might be found to prevent the postnatal savaging of the brain. This hope was realized about 50 years ago with the introduction of a low-Phe diet (not a no-Phe diet!), that has proven to be largely if not totally effective in preventing brain damage, at least as reflected by the normal IQ of PKU patients who were started on the diet shortly after birth. Although it was once thought that the diet, which is a heavy burden for both the patients and their families, could be discontinued after 6 or 7 years, it is now clear that a longer period is beneficial. The goal of the diet is to keep blood Phe levels from rising no more than 5–6 $\times$ above normal.

For PKU women contemplating having children, the question of how long they should stay on the diet has been answered unambiguously. Even if they went off the diet at some earlier time, they must resume it *before* they become pregnant; otherwise, their fetuses face a serious risk of *in utero* damage caused by the mother's high levels of Phe, a condition called "maternal PKU."

Since the *sine qua non* of the successful dietary treatment of PKU is the initiation of the diet as soon as possible after birth, its success was closely tied to the development of a cheap and rapid test for the disease. The Guthrie test, which gives a semiquantitative measure of Phe levels in a drop of blood, which can be collected on a piece of filter paper and mailed to a medical center for evaluation, was introduced in 1961. It has been used successfully for the mass-screening of newborns before they leave the hospital.

A noteworthy feature of the disease is that the brain is the only organ that is damaged by mutations in an enzyme that occurs (in humans) only in the liver. This aspect of the pathophysiology of the disease teaches us a valuable lesson: metabolically, no organ in the body is an island unto itself. The mechanism by which hyperphenylalaninemia damages the developing brain is unknown, but it probably involves the interference by high levels of Phe with the uptake into the brain of other essential amino acids.

PKU is inherited as an autosomal recessive trait. The vast majority of PKU babies are conceived when both parents are heterozygotes, each one harboring one normal gene and one "PKU" gene. On average, one-fourth of the children born to such parents are PKU, one-fourth are normal, and one-half are heterozygotes. The incidence of heterozygozity for PKU is about 1 in 55.

PAH, the affected enzyme in PKU, functions *in vivo* as part of a complex multicomponent system consisting of two other enzymes, dihydropteridine reductase and pterin 4a-carbinolamine dehydratase, and a non-protein coenzyme, tetrahydrobiopterin (BH_4). During the hydroxylation reaction, BH_4 is stoichiometically oxidized, i.e., for every molecule of Phe converted to tyrosine by PAH, a molecule of BH_4 is oxidized. The function of the two ancillary enzymes is to regenerate BH_4.

With the realization that the hydroxylating system consists of four essential components, it was predicted that, in addition to the type of PKU caused by defects in PAH (i.e., classic PKU), there might also exist variant forms, caused by the lack of one of the other indispensable components. During the last 20 years, patients with these predicted variants were described. The ones traced to defects in the reductase or in one of the several enzymes essential for the synthesis of BH_4 (but not the one due to defects in the dehydratase) were originally called "lethal PKU" or "malignant PKU." In all probability, they are deadly because BH_4 and the reductase are also essential for the functions of tyrosine hydroxylase (TH) and tryptophan hydroxylase (TPH), the enzymes responsible for the synthesis of the neurotransmitters, dopamine, norepinephrine, and serotonin. These patients, therefore, suffer from three different metabolic lesions. Fortunately, these variants are extremely rare, accounting for between 1 and 2% of all PKU patients. They can be treated, with varying degrees of success, by feeding them the compounds beyond the metabolic blocks in TH and TPH (i.e., L-dopa and 5-hydroxytryptophan) and, when needed, large doses of BH_4.

Seymour Kaufman

Tyrosine hydroxylase. In human beings, a single tyrosine hydroxylase gene gives rise to four TH mRNA species through alternative splicing, resulting in four TH isoforms. In contrast, in most primates two TH isoforms are present, but the rat possesses a single form of TH. The different forms of TH in human beings may be associated with differences in activity of the enzyme, although this association remains unclear.

TH function is determined by two factors: changes in enzyme activity (the rate at which the enzyme converts the precursor into its product) and changes in the amount of enzyme protein present. One determinant of TH activity is phosphorylation of the enzyme (Fig. 8.5), which takes place at four different serine sites at the N-terminus of the protein. These four serine residues are differently phosphorylated by various kinases. A second means of regulation of activity of the enzyme is through end-product inhibition: catecholamines can inhibit the activity of TH through competition for the required pterin cofactor for the enzyme.

An increased demand for catecholamine synthesis can be met by inducing TH protein or by activating (by phosphorylation) the enzyme. The degree to which increases in catecholamine synthesis depend on *de novo* synthesis of new enzyme protein or changes in enzymatic activity differ across brain regions. For example, increased synthetic demand in noradrenergic neurons of the brainstem nucleus locus ceruleus appears to be primarily accomplished by increasing TH gene expression. In contrast, it is quite difficult to alter TH mRNA levels in dopamine neurons of substantia nigra; it appears that synthesis in these neurons is primarily changed by altering existing enzyme activity (i.e., by posttranslational events).

The entry of tyrosine into the brain depends on an energy-dependent uptake process for large neutral amino acids at which tyrosine competes with other substrates. Brain levels of tyrosine are sufficiently high to saturate TH under basal conditions, and thus synthesis cannot be enhanced by administration of the tyrosine precursor. TH is the rate-limiting step for catecholamine synthesis under basal conditions. However, under conditions of neuronal activation, the enzyme responsible for norepinephrine synthesis, DBH, becomes rate limiting.[10]

TH is a mixed-function oxidase that has moderate substrate specificity, hydroxylating phenylalanine as well as tyrosine. The major substrate in brain is tyrosine, with molecular oxygen required. TH actions require a biopterin cofactor and iron (Fe^{2+}). Because the levels of reduced tetrahydrobiopterin, the cofactor, are nonsaturating under basal conditions, levels of this cofactor are significant in regulating TH activity. The pterin cofactor is also of importance in certain neurological conditions. The genetic defect in a particular movement disorder called dopa-responsive dystonia has now been shown to be due to mutations in the gene encoding GTP-cyclohydrolase 1, the rate-limiting enzyme in the synthesis of the biopterin cofactor.[11]

L-Aromatic amino acid decarboxylase. The hydroxylation of tyrosine by TH generates L-dopa, which is then decarboxylated by AADC (also known in the brain as "dopa decarboxylase") to the neurotransmitter dopamine. AADC has low substrate specificity and decarboxylates tryptophan as well as tyrosine. In dopaminergic neurons, AADC is the final enzyme of the synthetic pathway.

In contrast with dopamine, which does not cross the blood–brain barrier, L-dopa readily enters the brain. Accordingly, this dopamine precursor has achieved fame as a means of treating Parkinson disease, which is due to loss of dopamine in the striatum (see Chapter 34). L-Dopa administration to parkinsonian patients increases brain levels of dopamine and thus offers symptomatic improvement. Because L-dopa is rapidly metabolized by decarboxylating enzymes present in the periphery, L-dopa is administered to parkinsonian patients along with a peripheral decarboxylase inhibitor that does not readily enter the brain. The administration of the peripheral decarboxylase inhibitor thus protects L-dopa from metabolism before it enters the brain.

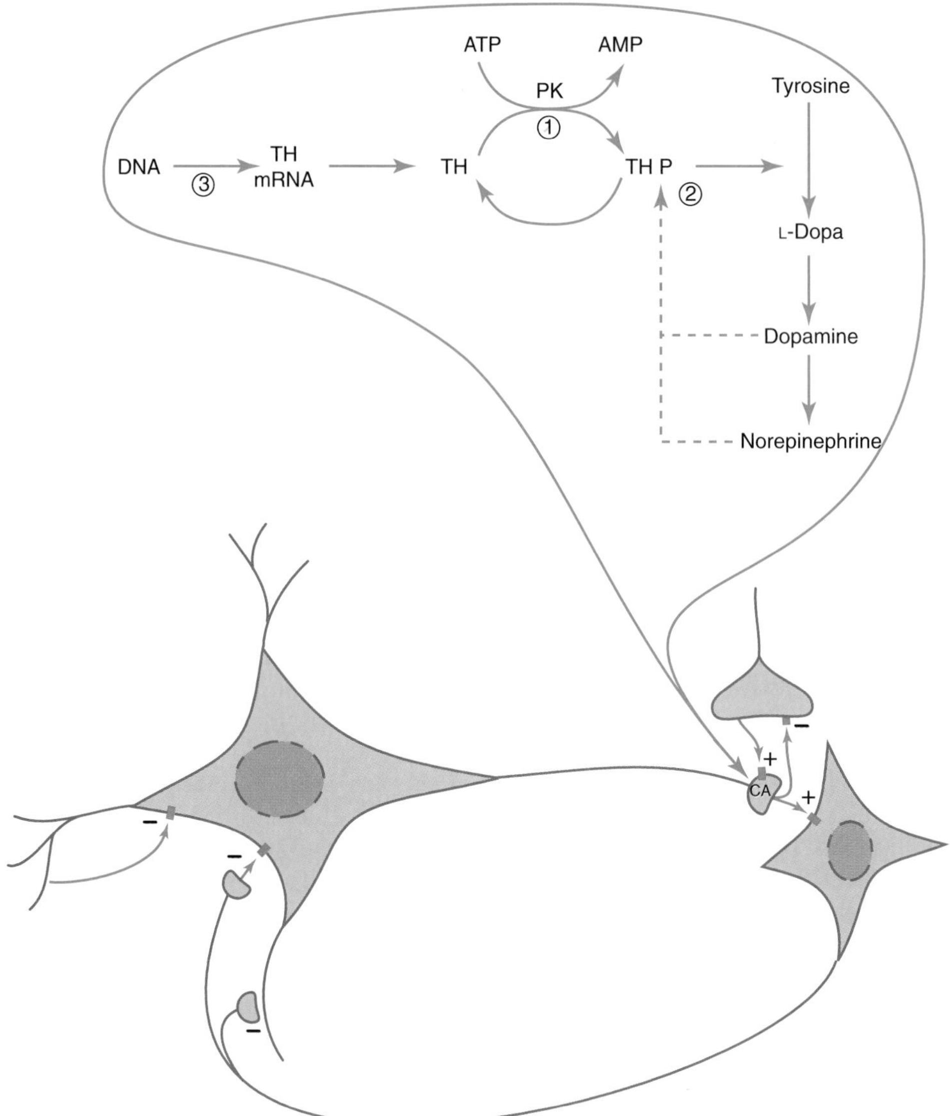

FIGURE 8.5 Schematic for the regulation of TH enzymatic activity. The numbered sites depict the 3 major types of regulation from TH phosphorylation (1), accomplished by the action of specific protein kinases (PK), to end-product inhibition (2) to changes in TH gene transcription and the subsequent increase in protein.

The AADC gene has been cloned. The AADC gene of the fruit fly *Drosophila* undergoes alternative splicing, but in mammalian organisms it appears that different transcripts are generated through different promoter sequences, leading to one transcript being expressed in the CNS and another in peripheral tissues. AADC mRNA is expressed in all catecholamine- and indoleamine-containing neurons in the CNS.

Levels of L-dopa are virtually unmeasurable in the CNS under basal conditions, because the activity of AADC is so high that L-dopa is converted into dopamine almost instantaneously. AADC requires pyridoxal 5-phosphate as a cofactor. The regulation of AADC has not been as intensively studied as that of TH, but converging data suggest that AADC is regulated primarily through induction of new protein rather than changes in activity. It is interesting to note that although L-dopa is used extensively in Parkinson disease, recent studies suggest that chronic administration of L-dopa or other dopamine agonists decreases endogenous AADC activity. As is frequently the case with therapeutic administration of drugs, these drugs can have side effects or even be counter-therapeutic.

Dopamine β-hydroxylase. Noradrenergic and adrenergic neurons contain the enzyme DBH, a mixed-function oxidase that converts dopamine into norepinephrine. In noradrenergic neurons, this conversion is the final step in catecholamine synthesis. Human beings appear to possess two different DBH mRNAs that are generated from a single gene. The presence of DBH mRNAs in the nervous system is restricted to noradrenergic and adrenergic neurons.

DBH is a copper-containing glycoprotein that requires ascorbic acid as the electron source during the hydroxylation of dopamine. Dicarboxylic acids such as fusaric acid are not absolute requirements but stimulate the enzymatic conversion of dopamine into norepinephrine. DBH does not show a high degree of substrate specificity and, *in vitro*, acts on a variety of substrates besides dopamine, oxidizing almost any phenylethylamine to its corresponding phenylethanolamine. For example, tyramine is converted into octopamine, and α-methyldopamine is converted into α-methylnorepinephrine. Interestingly, many of the resultant structurally analogous metabolites can replace norepinephrine at the noradrenergic nerve ending, acting as **false neurotransmitters**.

The regulation of DBH, like that of AADC, is less completely understood than that of TH. However, it now appears that under conditions that increase the activity of locus ceruleus noradrenergic neurons and increase TH activity, DBH (rather than TH) becomes saturated and is the rate-limiting step in catecholamine synthesis. This results in the accumulation of dopamine and acidic dopamine metabolites, which are then released from noradrenergic neurons.

Phenylethanolamine N-methyltransferase. Phenylethanolamine *N*-methyltransferase is present at high levels in the adrenal medulla, where it methylates norepinephrine to form epinephrine, the major adrenal catecholamine. PNMT is also formed in two nuclei of the brainstem. A single PNMT gene with three exons has been cloned. The transcript is present in the adrenal medulla and in the brainstem. PNMT requires *S*-adenosylmethionine as the methyl donor for the methylation of the amine nitrogen of norepinephrine. PNMT has modest substrate specificity and will transfer methyl groups to the nitrogen atom on a variety of β-hydroxylated amines. However, the adrenal PNMT is distinct from the nonspecific *N*-methyltransferases present in lung, which methylate indoleamines.

The regulation of PNMT activity in the brain has not been extensively studied. In the adrenal gland, glucocorticoids regulate activity of the enzyme, and activity is increased in response to nerve growth factor.

Storage of Catecholamines and Their Enzymes

Vesicular storage. It has been known since the 1960s that much of the norepinephrine in sympathetic nerve endings and in adrenal chromaffin cells is present in highly specialized subcellular particles termed granules. Most of the norepinephrine and other catecholamines in the CNS are also located within similar vesicles. These granules contain adenosine triphosphate (ATP) in a molar ratio of catecholamine/ATP of 4/1. The anionic phosphate groups of ATP are thought to form a salt link with norepinephrine, which exists as a cation at physiological pH and thereby serves as a means to bind the amines within the vesicles.

Vesicular storage of transmitters serves as a depot of the transmitter that can be released by appropriate physiological stimuli. Catecholamine transmitters are stored in small vesicles located near the synapse, where they are ready for fusion with the cellular membrane and subsequent exocytosis. Catecholamine storage in vesicles has two other key functions: (1) the ability to sequester catecholamines in vesicles retards their diffusion out of the neuron, and (2) it offers protection from metabolic inactivation by intraneuronal enzymes or attack by toxins that have gained entry into the neuron.

Because DBH is present in vesicles rather than the cytosol, dopamine is accumulated into the vesicles by the vesicular monoamine transporter (VMAT) and only then metabolized to norepinephrine. The vesicular storage of DBH has one other interesting consequence. In contrast with the other catecholamine-synthesizing enzymes, DBH is released from cells when its product, norepinephrine, is released.

Vesicular monoamine transporter. The ability of vesicles to take up dopamine depends on the presence of the VMAT. The VMAT is distinct from the neuronal membrane transporter that will be considered later. Two vesicular monoamine transporter genes have been cloned. One is found in the adrenal medulla, which synthesizes and releases monoamines. The other is present in catecholamine and serotonin neurons in the CNS. The CNS VMAT protein shows modest substrate specificity and can transport both catecholamines and indoleamines into vesicles. These VMATS are Mg^{2+}-dependent and are inhibited by reserpine, a drug that disrupts vesicular storage of monoamines.

Reserpine has been used in India for centuries as a folk medicine to treat hypertension and psychoses. The realization that reserpine depletes vesicular stores of monoamines was critical to our understanding of the mechanisms through which reserpine alleviates psychotic symptoms, and it shed light on the means through which certain toxins can cause a Parkinson disease-like syndrome. The use of reserpine in the treatment of hypertension and psychoses was reported in international journals in the early 1930s, but the therapeutic actions of reserpine were not widely appreciated in Western medicine until a generation later. At that time, Bernard Brodie and co-workers discovered that reserpine depleted brain stores of serotonin. Contemporaneously, it became known that the hallucinogen LSD (lysergic acid diethylamide) is an indolealkylamine, structurally related to serotonin. The antipsychotic actions of reserpine were then proposed to be due to its ability to deplete serotonin in the brain. However, it was soon realized that reserpine depletes both serotonin and catecholamine stores in the brain. Thus, antipsychotic effects might be realized by the depletion of serotonin or dopamine or both.

To test this hypothesis, Arvid Carlsson and colleagues administered catecholamine and serotonin precursors to reserpine-treated rats to replenish monoamine levels and then examined locomotor activity, which is severely depressed by reserpine treatment. Motor function was restored by the administration of the dopamine precursor. However, this did not occur when the serotonin precursor 5-hydroxytryptophan was used. Further neurochemical studies revealed that, despite the improvement in motor behavior, L-dopa treatment did not restore brain concentrations of norepinephrine and epinephrine. After the subsequent discovery of dopamine as a neurotransmitter, L-dopa treatment of reserpinized animals was shown to increase brain concentrations of dopamine. These data were interpreted to suggest that the primary mechanism through which reserpine exerts antipsychotic effects is through its ability to disrupt dopamine neurotransmission. These and subsequent studies led to the hypothesis that dysfunction of central dopamine systems underlies schizophrenia, which soon became the dominant view. Interestingly, recent data suggest that to best treat the full spectrum of psychotic symptoms in schizophrenia, drugs that are antagonists at both dopamine and serotonin receptors may be most efficacious.

Release of Catecholamines

In general, catecholamines are released by the same Ca^{2+}-dependent process (exocytosis) that has been described for other transmitters (see Chapter 7). This is assumed to occur at synapses made by the variocosities formed as the catecholaminergic axons course through their target region, although this view has been challenged. Such synapses **en passant** appear like beads along an axon string.

At least two other types of release have been described for catecholamines. First, catecholamines can be released by a reversal of the catecholamine transporters. This occurs in response to certain drugs (e.g., amphetamine) and has been reported to occur following the application of excitatory amino acids as well. Second, catecholamines (at least dopamine) can be released from dendrites through a process that may not always involve conventional exocytosis. Given the importance of release to our understanding of the nervous system, it is not surprising that researchers have developed a variety of approaches to study this process.

Regulation of Catecholamine Synthesis and Release by Autoreceptors

The enzymes that control the synthesis of catecholamines can be regulated, as noted earlier, at the transcriptional level and at the level of posttranslational modifications. In addition, the synthesis of dopamine can be regulated by the interaction of dopamine released from the nerve terminal with dopamine autoreceptors located on the dopamine terminals. Similarly, the release of catecholamines is regulated by autoreceptors, as is the firing rate of catecholaminergic neurons.

Dopamine autoreceptors are perhaps the best characterized of the catecholamine autoreceptors. Autoreceptors exist on most parts of the neuron, including the soma, the dendrites, and nerve terminals. They can be defined functionally in relation to the events that they regulate, that is, *synthesis*-modulating, *release*-modulating, and *impulse*-modulating autoreceptors. All three types of dopamine autoreceptors belong to the D2 family of dopamine receptors. Whether distinct receptor proteins modulate each of these functions or the same receptor protein is coupled to each function through distinct transduction mechanisms is unclear.

Dopamine that is released from the neuron interacts with an autoreceptor and dampens further release of the transmitter. The ability of the released transmitter to dampen subsequent transmitter release can be conceptualized as a homeostatic mechanism. Because intracellular levels of dopamine regulate tyrosine hydroxylase activity by binding the pterin cofactor, changes in the release of dopamine may also alter synthesis of transmitter. Release-modulating autoreceptors appear to be a common regulatory feature on catecholamine neurons and other neurons that use classical transmitters.

Dopamine autoreceptors also regulate the synthesis

of dopamine. The actions of released transmitter at dopamine autoreceptors act homeostatically to regulate synthesis: dopamine agonists decrease synthesis, whereas dopamine antagonists increase synthesis of the transmitter. Interestingly, synthesis-modulating autoreceptors are not found on all dopamine neurons; some midbrain dopamine neurons that project to the prefrontal cortex appear to lack synthesis-modulating autoreceptors, as do the tuberoinfundibular dopamine neurons of the hypothalamus. Because release-modulating autoreceptors may indirectly regulate synthesis, the presence of synthesis-modulating autoreceptors may not be necessary in certain neurons.

Impulse-modulating autoreceptors that are located on the soma and dendrites of dopamine neurons regulate the firing rate of dopamine neurons. As noted earlier, because the release of dopamine can alter dopamine synthesis, impulse-modulating autoreceptors can also be expected to change dopamine synthesis. Thus, all three types of dopamine autoreceptors may regulate synthesis.

Autoreceptors have also been shown to regulate release of norepinephrine in the brain. However, the direct regulation of synthesis by synthesis-modulating autoreceptors on noradrenergic neurons is not well established. We do know, however, that there are two norepinephrine autoreceptors. Whereas one, the α_2-receptor, inhibits norepinephrine release, the second, a β-receptor, actually facilitates release. Little is known about the role of autoreceptors in regulating epinephrine release in the CNS.

Inactivation of Released Catecholamine Neurotransmitters

The continuous stimulation of receptors on postsynaptic cells is not desirable, and there must be mechanisms that allow the brain to inactivate released transmitters. This can be most easily understood in regard to receptors that form ion channels, in which continued action of a neurotransmitter would lead to inappropriate ion concentrations across the membrane and thus disrupt neurotransmission. However, the principle for all neurotransmitters is simply that continued activation of target-cell receptors does not convey appropriate information about the dynamic state of the presynaptic neuron.

There are several different ways of terminating the actions of a catecholamine. Perhaps the simplest is diffusion away from the receptor sites followed by dilution in extracellular fluid or plasma to subthreshold concentrations. A second means of inactivation is for neurons to take up the catecholamine by a membrane-associated transporter protein. This may be followed by uptake of the catecholamines into storage vesicles, from where they can be reutilized, or catabolism by monoamine oxidase (MAO). A third possibility is direct catabolism by catechol-*o*-methyltransferase (COMT).

Enzymatic inactivation of catecholamines. Two major enzymes take part in catecholamine catabolism: (1) MAO and (2) COMT. These two enzymes can each act on the products of the other, leading to metabolites that have been deaminated, *o*-methylated, or both. Although none of these products is active at catecholamine receptors, deaminated catechols can bind to cysteine residues, with possible toxic consequences. This may help to explain the presence of two inactivating enzymes. COMT is a relatively nonspecific enzyme that transfers methyl groups from *S*-adenosylmethionine to the *m*-hydroxy group of catechols. COMT is the major means of inactivating circulating catecholamines released from the adrenal gland.

Two forms of MAO have been identified on the basis of substrate specificities and selective enzyme inhibitors. MAO_A has a higher affinity for norepinephrine and serotonin and is selectively inhibited by clorgyline. MAO_B has a higher affinity for *o*-phenylethylamines and is selectively inhibited by deprenyl. MAO_A and MAO_B are associated with the outer mitochondrial membrane and are abundant both in the CNS and in peripheral tissues such as liver. The MAOs oxidatively deaminate catecholamines and their *o*-methylated derivatives to form inactive and unstable aldehyde derivatives. These aldehydes can be further catabolized by dehydrogenases and reductases to form corresponding acids and alcohols.

The enzymatic inactivation of catecholamines appears to be the primary mode of terminating the action of circulating catecholamines. In the CNS, inactivation of catecholamines by means of reuptake mechanisms is more important. Nevertheless, drugs that alter the enzymatic inactivation of catecholamines have proved useful in the treatment of several disorders, including clinical **depression** and Parkinson disease (see Box 8.2).

Catecholamine reuptake (transport) processes. Neuronal reuptake of catecholamines is a major means of inactivation of the released transmitter in the brain. The reuptake process also allows intracellular enzymes that degrade catecholamines to act, thus bolstering the actions of extracellular enzymes. Neuronal reuptake of catecholamines, and indeed of all transmitters for which a reuptake process has been identified, has several characteristics.[12] The reuptake process is energy dependent, is saturable, and depends on Na^+ cotransport; in addition, extracellular Cl^- is necessary for

BOX 8.2

MAO INHIBITORS AND PHARMACOTHERAPY

Clinical Depression

One hypothesis concerning the pathophysiology of clinical depression posits a decrease in noradrenergic tone in the brain. MAO_A inhibitors such as tranylcypromine effectively increase norepinephrine levels and have been extensively used in the treatment of depression. The use of MAO inhibitors in depression has more recently been supplanted by the introduction of drugs that increase extracellular norepinephrine levels by blocking reuptake rather than decreasing enzymatic inactivation of catecholamines.

The eclipse of MAO_A inhibitor therapy for depression is due in part to the fact that the clinical use of these drugs is marred by a large number of side effects. Among the most serious side effects is hypertensive crisis. Patients who are treated with MAO_A inhibitors and eat foods that contain large amounts of tyramine (such as aged cheeses) cannot metabolize the ingested tyramine. Because tyramine releases catecholamines from nerve endings and relatively small amounts of tyramine increase blood pressure significantly, a marked increase in blood pressure and a high risk for stroke may develop.

Parkinson Disease

Deprenyl, a specific inhibitor of MAO_B, has been used in the initial treatment of Parkinson disease (see Chapter 34). The introduction of the use of deprenyl in the treatment of Parkinson disease and the rationale for its use were based on data from studies of a neurotoxin, 1-methyl-4-phenyl-1,2,3,6-tetrahydropyridine (known as MPTP). The systemic administration of MPTP to human beings and other primates results in a relatively specific degeneration of midbrain dopamine neurons and a marked parkinsonian syndrome. MPTP toxicity was first noted in a group of opiate addicts. In an attempt to synthesize a designer drug that is a meperidine (Demerol) derivative, the structurally related MPTP was inadvertently produced. Addicts who injected this drug developed a severe parkinsonian syndrome. Subsequent animal studies showed that MPTP is not toxic but that the active metabolite MPP^+ is highly toxic. The formation of MPP^+ from MPTP is catalyzed by MAO_B, and animal studies soon revealed that treatment with the MAO inhibition by deprenyl could prevent MPTP toxicity.

The realization that MPTP administration rather faithfully reproduces the cardinal signs and symptoms of Parkinson disease reawakened interest in an environmental toxin as the cause of Parkinson disease. This interest led to the idea that treatment with deprenyl might be useful in slowing the progression of Parkinson disease, putatively caused by an environmental toxin. Clinical trials of patients who were newly diagnosed as having Parkinson disease initially indicated that daily administration of deprenyl increased the amount of time required before patients needed other drugs for the relief of symptoms. However, when the drug was withdrawn, patients treated with deprenyl regressed and appeared no better than untreated subjects. It now appears that the actions of deprenyl are due at least in part to the symptomatic improvement that results from increasing dopamine levels by inhibiting degradation of the transmitter rather than to slowing of the progression of Parkinson disease. Moreover, low levels of methamphetamine are generated by the metabolism of deprenyl; because methamphetamine potently releases dopamine from nerve terminals, this would result in a symptomatic improvement.

---

transport. Because reuptake depends on coupling to the Na^+ gradient across the neuronal membrane, toxins that inhibit Na^+,K^+-ATPase inhibit reuptake. However, under certain conditions, the coupling of transporter function to Na^+ flow may lead to local changes in the membrane Na^+ gradient and result in the paradoxical extrusion of transmitter. In contrast with monoamine transporters associated with neuronal vesicles, the membrane catecholamine transporters are not Mg^{2+}-dependent and are not inhibited by reserpine. There does appear to be a reuptake process that accumulates catecholamines in glial cells, but the glial mechanism is not a high-affinity reuptake process and the functional significance of the glial reuptake of catecholamines is not known.

Two distinct catecholamine transporter proteins, the dopamine transporter (DAT) and the norepinephrine transporter (NET), have been identified and their genes cloned. These proteins share considerable sequence homology and are members of a class of transporter proteins (including serotonin and amino acid transmitter transporters) that have 12 transmembrane domains. Neither transporter has a very good substrate specificity, with both transporters accumulating both dopamine and norepinephrine. In fact, the NET has a higher affinity for dopamine than for norepinephrine. A specific transporter for epinephrine-containing neurons has been identified in the frog but not in mammalian species.

The regional distribution of catecholamine transporters in the CNS is largely consistent with DAT being present in dopamine neurons and NET being expressed in noradrenergic neurons. However, DAT does not appear to be expressed in all dopamine cells. The tuberoinfundibular dopamine neurons, which are hypothalamic cells that release dopamine into the pituitary portal blood system, lack demonstrable DAT mRNA and protein. Because dopamine released from tuberoinfundibular neurons is carried away in the vasculature, the existence of a transporter protein on these dopamine neurons would be superfluous.

Recent studies using antibodies generated against the DAT protein have surprisingly revealed that the transporter is not typically found in the synaptic area but is expressed in the extrasynaptic region of the axon terminal. This finding suggests that the transporter may be of importance in terminating the actions of dopamine that has escaped from the synaptic cleft and thus that diffusion is the initial process by which dopamine is removed from the synapse. This observation is consistent with recent studies indicating that the perisynaptic concentrations of dopamine can reach 1.0 μM or more, a value roughly comparable to the affinity of the cloned DAT for DA. It should also be remembered that receptors for dopamine and many other transmitters are found along the length of axons. This fact, the presence of extrasynaptic transporters, and the relatively high concentration of catecholamines in the extracellular region are among the reasons for believing that extrasynaptic (''paracrine'' or volume) neurotransmission may be of considerable importance for catecholaminergic signaling.

How neurotransmitter transporter proteins are regulated has only recently been studied. Chronic treatment with inhibitors of catecholamine reuptake alter the number of transporter sites, but the precise regulatory mechanisms remain unclear. There are phosphorylation sites on DAT and NET, and thus changes in neurotransmitter release may alter function through interaction with autoreceptors and subsequent activation of serine–threonine kinases.

In view of the fact that the catecholamine transporters critically determine extracellular transmitter levels, it is reasonable to assume that these proteins may be important targets of psychoactive drugs. This is indeed the case (see Chapter 49). Psychostimulant drugs, such as cocaine and amphetamine, block the dopamine transporter and thereby increase extracellular levels of catecholamines. In particular, cocaine shows a very high affinity for the dopamine transporter; amphetamine is not only a less-potent inhibitor of reuptake but also induces release of catecholamines from the cytoplasm. Methylplenidate, on the other hand, releases dopamine from vesicles. A group of drugs known as tricyclic antidepressants potently inhibits norepinephrine reuptake, with significantly weaker effects on the dopamine transporter, and is a mainstay in the pharmacotherapy of clinical depression.

Neuroanatomy of CNS Catecholamine Neurons

Cell bodies for catecholamines are present in the brainstem, midbrain, hypothalamus, olfactory bulb, and retina (Fig. 8.6). The groups of noradrenergic and dopaminergic cell bodies in different parts of the brain are designated A1–A16, with A1 neurons being present in the medulla and higher numbers encountered more anteriorly in the brain.

Dopamine cell bodies are present in the midbrain, where they are concentrated in the substantia nigra, ventral tegmental area, and retrorubral field. These dopamine neurons give rise to extensive forebrain dopamine innervations.[13] Among these are the projections to the caudate nucleus and putamen (dorsal striatum), nucleus accumbens and olfactory tubercle (ventral striatum), and several cortical regions (prefrontal, anterior cingulate, perirhinal, and entorhinal cortices) as well as limbic regions including the amygdala, lateral septum, and ventral hippocampus. The midbrain dopamine projections to the striatum have been among the most intensively studied catecholamine neurons, in part because when these dopamine neurons degenerate the result is Parkinson disease (see Chapter 34). This basic organization of midbrain dopamine neurons and their projections is consistent across most mammalian species and across many other species as well. One key difference is that the cortical dopamine projections are much more extensive in primate species than in the rat.

There are also several groups of dopamine cell bodies in the hypothalamus, including those in the arcuate nucleus (which give rise to the dopamine innervation of the median eminence), the periventricular dopamine neurons (which project to the spinal cord and medial thalamus among other sites), the preoptic area dopamine neurons, and dopamine cells in the zona incerta. Dopamine neurons in the olfactory bulb and retina have been extensively investigated because their well-defined anatomical organization and the relative ease with which they can be experimentally manipulated make them useful for functional studies.

Norepinephrine (NE)-containing cell bodies, in contrast to dopamine cell bodies, are found only in the pons and medulla. However, the pontine NE-con-

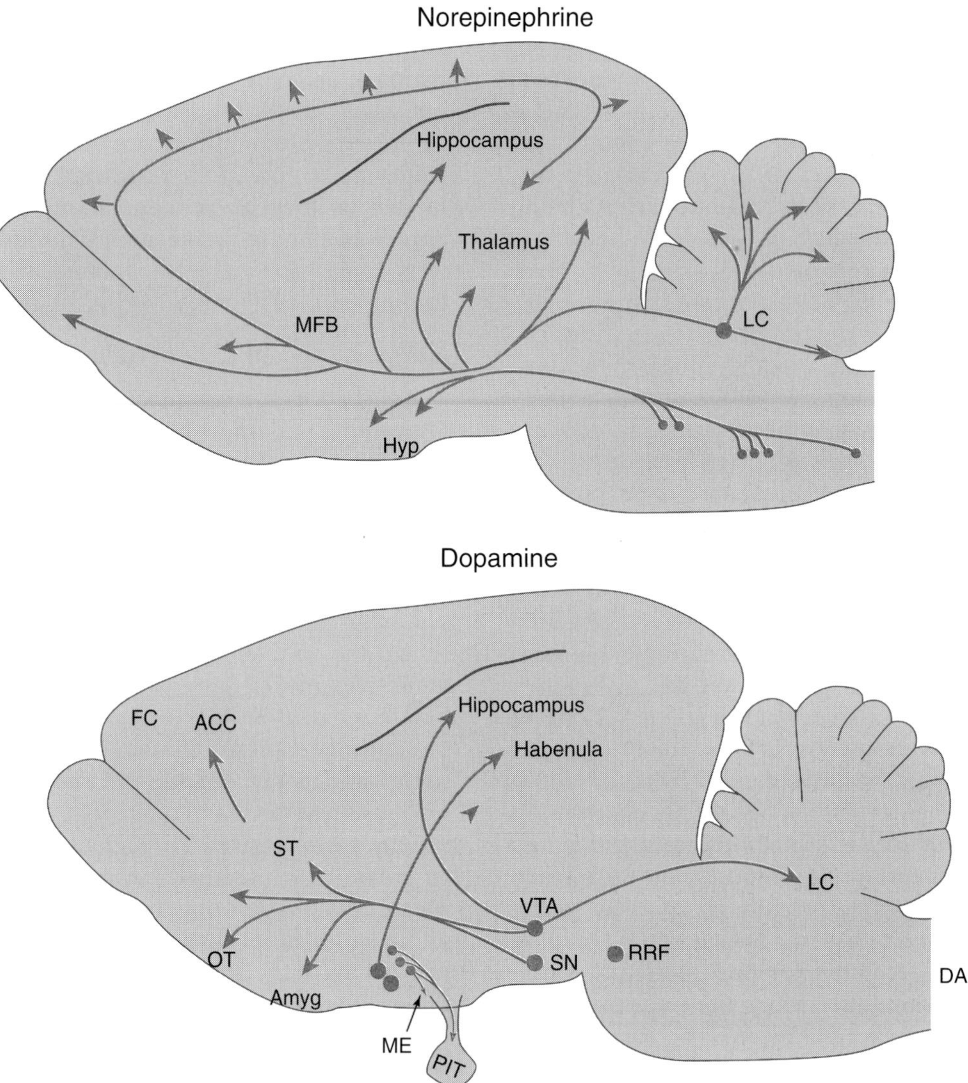

FIGURE 8.6 Schematic illustrating some of the major collection of noradrenergic (top panel) and dopaminergic (bottom panel) neurons (red circles) and their projection areas. Abbreviations: Hyp, hypothalamus; LC, locus coerleus; MFG, medial forebrain bundle; SN, substantia nigra; OT, optic tract; ST, striatum; FC, frontal cortex; VTA, ventral tegmental area; Amyg, amygdala RRF, retrorubral field; ME, median eminence; OB, olfactory bulb; PIT, pituitary.

taining cells, in the nucleus locus ceruleus, give rise to extensive projections to the hypothalamus, thalamus, limbic regions, and cortex. Medullary NE cells project to the hypothalamus, locus ceruleus, and spinal cord. A detailed discussion of the neuroanatomy of the catecholamine neurons in the brain can be found in Bloom and Moore.[13,14]

PNMT-containing cells are relatively few in the CNS and are limited to two medullary sites. These cells, which presumably use epinephrine as their transmitter, were discovered later than the dopamine- and NE-containing neurons in the CNS. Thus, the two clusters of PNMT neurons in the brain are called the C1 and C2 cell groups.

Serotonin Is a Neurotransmitter with Many Parallels to the Catecholamines

About 150 years ago, scientists were aware of a substance present in serum that induced powerful contractions of smooth muscle organs. More than a century passed before Page and his collaborators succeeded in isolating the substance, which they proposed to be a possible cause of high blood pressure, from platelets.

At the same time, investigators in Italy were characterizing a substance present in high concentrations in intestinal mucusa that caused contractions of gastrointestinal smooth muscle. The material isolated from blood platelets was given the name "serotonin"; that from the intestinal tract was called "enteramine." Subsequently, both materials were purified, crystallized, and shown to be 5-hydroxytryptamine (5-HT), which is now called serotonin. The laboratory synthesis of serotonin soon allowed the direct comparison of serotonin with the purified compound isolated from platelets, which conclusively demonstrated that serotonin possessed all the biological features of the natural substance.

Although the purification and identification of serotonin were based on studies of blood pressure regulation, the possible relation of serotonin to psychiatric disorders propelled research on the central effects of serotonin. The observation that the indole structure of serotonin was similar to that of the psychedelic agent LSD and a number of other psychotropic indoleamines led to theories linking abnormalities of serotonergic function to a number of psychiatric disorders, including schizophrenia and depression. This remains a major focus of research on central serotonergic systems.

The basic principles of the biochemical aspects of neurotransmission revealed by examination of catecholamines are applicable to serotonergic systems. Accordingly, we outline more briefly the serotonergic system, focusing on differences.

Synthesis of Serotonin

The biosynthesis of serotonin is in basic outline quite similar to that of the catecholamines. The precursor amino acid tryptophan gains entry to the serobnergic neuron and is hydroxylated by tryptophan hydroxylase, the rate-limiting step in serotonin synthesis (Fig. 8.7). The resultant serotonin precursor, 5-hydroxytryptophan (5-HTP), is decarboxylated by the aromatic amino acid decarboxylase. Thus, only two critical enzymes take part in the synthesis of serotonin, tryptophan hydroxylase and AADC.[9,15]

In the CNS, serotonin is the final product of this synthetic pathway, with no subsequent enzymes generating other transmitters. However, in the pineal gland, serotonin is metabolized further to the hormone melatonin. Finally, there is a kynurenic acid shunt from tryptophan metabolism that leads to the formation of several compounds that may be involved in neurotoxicity. Serotonin is found in many cells that are not neurons, such as platelets, mast cells, and enterochromaffin cells. In fact, the brain accounts for only about 1% of body stores of serotonin.

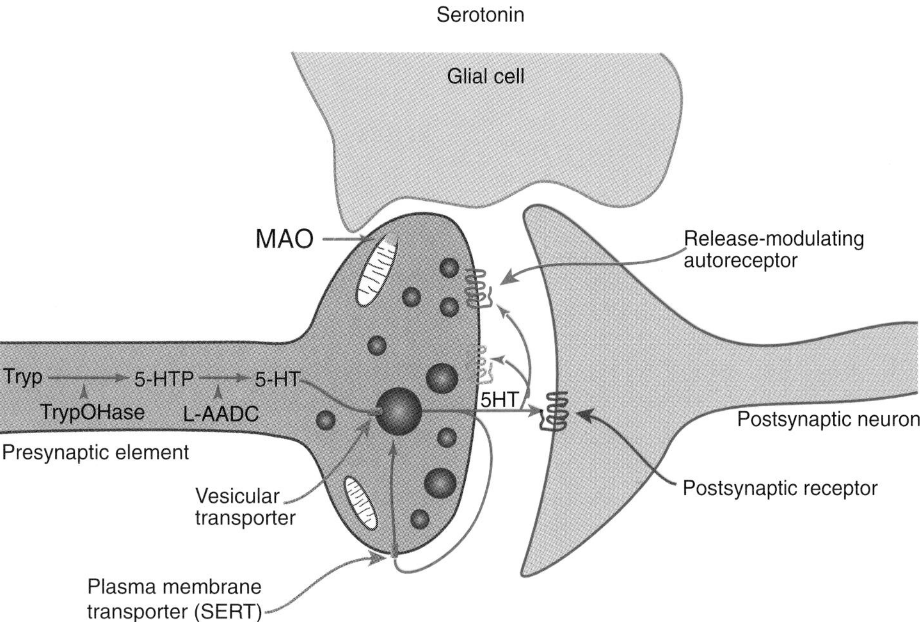

FIGURE 8.7 Depiction of a serotonergic neuron. Tryptophan (Trp) in the neuron is sequentially metabolized by tryptophan hydroxylase (TrypOHase) and L-AADC to yield serotonin (5-HT). The serotonin is accumulated by the vesicular monoamine transporter. When released, the serotonin can interact with both postsynaptic receptors and presynaptic autoreceptors. 5-HT is taken up by the high-affinity serotonin transporter (SERT), and once inside the neuron it can be re-accumulated by vesicular transporter or metabolically inactivated by MAO and other enzymes.

Tryptophan hydroxylase. The rate-limiting step in serotonin synthesis is enzymatic, requiring **tryptophan hydroxylase**. However, the availability of the precursor amino acid tryptophan plays an important role in regulating the synthesis of serotonin, contrasting sharply with catecholamine synthesis.

Because serotonin cannot cross the blood–brain barrier, it is clear that brain cells synthesize the amine. The precursor to serotonin is the amino acid tryptophan, which is present in high levels in plasma. Thus, for example, changes in dietary sources of tryptophan can substantially alter brain levels of serotonin. An active uptake process facilitates entry of tryptophan into the brain. However, other large, neutral, aromatic amino acids compete for this transport process. Accordingly, brain levels of tryptophan are determined by plasma concentrations of competing neutral amino acids as well as the plasma levels of tryptophan itself.

The gene encoding tryptophan hydroxylase has been cloned and sequenced. Although some differences in the biochemical properties of tryptophan hydroxylases present in the brain and peripheral tissues have been reported, these differences appear to be due to posttranslational modifications of the protein rather than to different mRNAs.

Neuronal systems need to be able to adapt to either short- or long-term demands on activity. In serotonergic neurons, the synthesis of serotonin from tryptophan is increased in a frequency-dependent manner in response to electrical stimulation of serotonergic cells. Tryptophan hydroxylase requires both molecular oxygen and a reduced pterin cofactor.

L-Aromatic amino acid decarboxylase. Aromatic amino acid decarboxylase metabolizes 5-HTP to the transmitter serotonin. This enzyme is the same as that found in catecholaminergic neurons. Just as in catecholamine cells, in which the precursor L-dopa is almost instantaneously converted into dopamine by AADC, the precursor 5-HTP is so rapidly decarboxylated in serotonergic cells that levels of 5-HTP are almost nil. Thus, because AADC is not saturated with 5-HTP under physiological conditions, it is possible to increase the content of serotonin in brain not only by increasing the dietary intake of tryptophan but also by administering 5-HTP, which readily enters the brain.

Alternative tryptophan metabolic pathways. Although serotonin is generally thought of as the final product of tryptophan synthesis, in the brain and periphery serotonin can be further metabolized to yield important active products. In the pineal gland, serotonin is metabolized to 5-methoxy-*N*-acetyltryptamine (**melatonin**), a hormone that is thought to play an important role in both sexual behavior and sleep. The production of melatonin from serotonin requires two enzymatic steps: *N*-acetylation of serotonin to form *N*-acetylserotonin, which is rapidly methylated by 5-hydroxyindole *o*-methyltransferase to melatonin.

In peripheral tissues, most tryptophan is not metabolized to serotonin but is instead metabolized in the kynurenine pathway. Recent data indicate that the kynurenine shunt is present in the CNS and leads to the accumulation of neuroactive substances that may be of clinical importance in cases of trauma and stroke.[16] The two major tryptophan metabolites that are generated by the kynurenine shunt are quinolinic acid and kynurenic acid. Quinolinic acid is a potent agonist at *N*-methyl-D-aspartate (NMDA) receptors and causes neurotoxicity and convulsions. In contrast, kynurenine is an antagonist at NMDA receptors. Considerable effort is being directed to determining the role that these tryptophan metabolites may play in neurological disorders.

Storage and Release of Serotonin

Serotonin is stored primarily in vesicles and is released by an exocytotic mechanism. The vesicular amine transporter that accumulates serotonin is identical with that present in catecholamine neurons, and, in most respects, vesicles that store serotonin resemble those that contain catecholamines. The serotonin-containing vesicles differ from catecholamine-containing vesicles in that they may express a specific high-affinity serotonin-binding protein.

Regulation of Serotonin Synthesis and Release

There are some important regulatory differences between catecholaminergic and serotonergic neurons. As noted earlier, serotonin neurons are sensitive to changes in plasma levels of the precursor amino acid tryptophan, and thus dietary changes can regulate serotonin levels in brain. In addition, it appears that increases in intracellular serotonin levels do not significantly alter serotonin synthesis *in vivo*, although in catecholaminergic neurons, transmitter synthesis is influenced by end-product inhibition. Short-term requirements for increases in serotonin synthesis appear to be accomplished by a Ca^{2+}-dependent phosphorylation of tryptophan hydoxylase, which changes its kinetic properties without necessitating the synthesis of more enzyme. In contrast, situations requiring long-term increases in serotonin availability appear to induce tryptophan hydroxylase protein.

Serotonin autoreceptors regulate serotonin release and synthesis. As is the case in catecholamine neurons, there are functionally dissociable somatodendritic and terminal autoreceptors on serotonin neurons. The release and impulse-modulating autoreceptor in serotonin neurons is a 5-HT1a receptor, which is also found as a postsynaptic receptor on nonserotonergic cells.

Inactivation of Released Serotonin

As in the case of the catecholamines, reuptake serves as a major means of terminating the action of serotonin. Released serotonin is taken up by a plasma membrane carrier, the serotonin transporter. In addition, the same enzymatic inactivation that is operative within catecholamine neurons is functional in serotonergic neurons.

Reuptake. Serotonin released into the synapse is inactivated primarily by the reuptake of the transmitter by a plasma membrane serotonin transporter. The serotonin transport (SERT) has been cloned and sequenced and belongs to the same family of 12-transmembrane-domain transporters as the catecholamine transporter. The SERT has in common with these other transporters an absolute requirement for Na^+ cotransport. Interestingly, just as the norepinephrine transporter is an important clinical target for tricyclic antidepressant drugs, the SERT is the target of the new class of antidepressant drugs termed selective serotonin reuptake inhibitors, which includes such drugs as fluoxetine (Prosac). The fact that antidepressant drugs alter monoamine inactivation by disrupting serotonin and norepinephrine reuptake and by disrupting enzymatic inactivation of both monoamines has led to the dominant theories of the pathogenesis of depression, which suggest a critical modulatory role for these monoamines.[17]

Enzymatic degradation. The primary catabolic pathway for serotonin is oxidative deamination by the enzyme monoamine oxidase. The product of this reaction, 5-hydroxyindole acid aldehyde, can be further oxidized to 5-hydroxyindole acetic acid (5-HIAA), the primary serotonin metabolite, or can be reduced to 5-hydroxytrypophol. In brain, 5-HIAA is the primary metabolite of serotonin. As previously mentioned, MAO_A is an important target of certain antidepressant medications.

The Anatomy of Serotonin-Containing Neurons in the CNS

The distribution of serotonin-containing cell bodies and the projections of these neurons were originally described using fluorescent histochemical methods, which revealed nine serotonin-containing cell groups (designated B1–B9) in the brainstem. These fluorescent methods have been supplanted by more sensitive immunohistochemical methods using antibodies generated against serotonin or tryptophan hydroxylase. In addition, neurons have been characterized by uptake of [^{3}H]serotonin; this method has identified some putative serotonergic neurons (in the hypothalamus) that the other methods have not noted.

The serotonergic neurons of the CNS have diverse rostral and caudal projections, with virtually all areas of the brain receiving serotonergic inputs (see Fig. 8.8). Serotonin-containing cell bodies in the ventral medulla and caudal pons provide descending projections to the dorsal horn of the spinal cord; these neurons are critically involved in pain sensation. The spinal cord also receives serotonergic afferents from the rostral serotonergic neurons at the postmesencephalic junc-

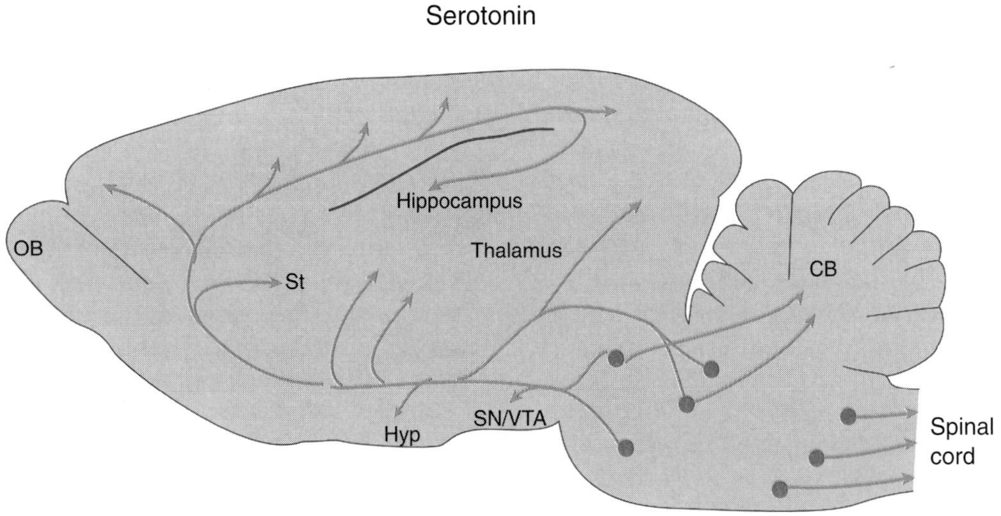

FIGURE 8.8 Schematic illustrating some of the major collection of serotonergic cell bodies (red circles) and projection areas. Abbreviations: as in Figure 8.6.

ture. Serotonin neurons in the pontine dorsal and median raphe provide extensive serotonergic innervations of the cortex, thalamus, hypothalamus, limbic regions, and midbrain.

γ-Aminobutyric Acid Is the Principal Inhibitory Transmitter in Brain

Several amino acids fulfill most of the criteria for neurotransmitters. Among them are γ-aminobutyric acid (GABA), the major inhibitory transmitter in brain; glutamate, which is the major excitatory transmitter in brain; and glycine, another inhibitory amino acid.[18] The broad principles outlined in the discussion of catecholamine neurotransmitters are also applicable to the amino acid transmitters, although certain aspects of the synthesis of amino acid transmitters are less completely understood than the catecholamines. A key difference between the catecholamine transmitters and the amino acid transmitters is that the latter are derived from intermediary glucose metabolism. This dual role for the amino acid transmitters means that there must be mechanisms to segregate the transmitter and general metabolic pools of the amino acid transmitters.[19] A second difference between amino acid and catecholamine transmitters is that amino acid transmitters are readily accumulated by glial cells as well as neurons. We review the life cycle of GABA as a prototypic amino acid transmitter and, in particular, focus on differences between catecholamines and GABA.

GABA was discovered in 1950 by Eugene Roberts, whose subsequent studies[20] revealed that GABA has a neurotransmitter role. GABA is ubiquitous in the CNS, as might be expected for a transmitter derived from the metabolism of glucose. Although the presence of GABA as a transmitter in neurons is widespread, it nonetheless has a distinct distribution. It was initially thought that, with few exceptions, GABA was a neurotransmitter found in local-circuit interneurons but not in projection neurons. However, it has become apparent that there are many examples of GABAergic projection neurons.

GABA Biosynthesis

Several aspects of the synthesis of GABA differ from that of the monoamines. These differences are due to GABA precursors being part of cellular intermediary metabolism rather than dedicated solely to a neurotransmitter synthetic pool.

The GABA shunt and GABA transaminase. GABA is ultimately derived from glucose metabolism. α-Ketoglutarate formed by the Krebs (tricarboxylic acid) cycle is transaminated to the amino acid glutamate by the enzyme GABA α-oxoglutarate transaminase (GABA-T). In those cells in which GABA is used as a transmitter, the presence of the enzyme glutamic acid decarboxylase (GAD) permits the formation of GABA from glutamate derived from α-ketoglutarate.

An unusual aspect of GABA synthesis is that intraneuronal GABA is inactivated by the actions of GABA-T, which appears to be associated with mitochondria (Fig. 8.9). Thus, GABA-T is both a key synthetic enzyme and a degradative enzyme. GABA-T metabolizes GABA to succinic semialdehyde but only if α-ketoglutarate is present to receive the amino group removed from GABA. This unusual GABA shunt serves to maintain supplies of GABA.

Glutamic acid decarboxylase. The critical biosynthetic enzyme for the neurotransmitter GABA is glutamic acid decarboxylase (GAD). Two isoforms of GAD are encoded by two distinct genes. These two isoforms, designated GAD65 and GAD67 in accord with their molecular masses, exhibit somewhat different intracellular distributions, suggesting that the two GAD forms may be regulated in different ways. This appears to be the case.

GAD requires a pyridoxal phosphate cofactor for activity. GAD65 and GAD67 differ significantly in their affinity for the pyridoxal cofactor. GAD65 shows a relatively high affinity for the cofactor, whereas the larger GAD isoform does not. The affinity of GAD65 for the cofactor results in the ability of GAD65 enzyme activity to be efficiently and quickly regulated. In contrast, the activity of GAD67 is regulated at the transcriptional level, through the induction of new enzyme protein rather than through posttranslational mechanisms.

A key question concerning amino acid transmitters is how the transmitter pools are kept distinct from the general metabolic pools in which the amino acids serve. GAD is necessary for the synthesis of the transmitter GABA, and the presence of the GAD mRNAs or the GAD proteins serves as an excellent marker of GABAergic neurons. GAD is a cytosolic enzyme, but GABA-T, which converts α-ketoglutarate into the GAD substrate glutamate, is present in mitochondria. Thus, the metabolic pool is present in the mitochondria, but glutamate destined for the transmitter pool must be exported from the mitochondria to the cytosolic compartment. This process remains pooly understood.

Glutamate not only serves as a precursor to GABA but is also a transmitter. GAD is not present in neurons in which glutamate functions as a transmitter, and thus glutamatergic neurons do not use GABA as a transmitter. What prevents GABA neurons from using the precursor glutamate as a transmitter is not well under-

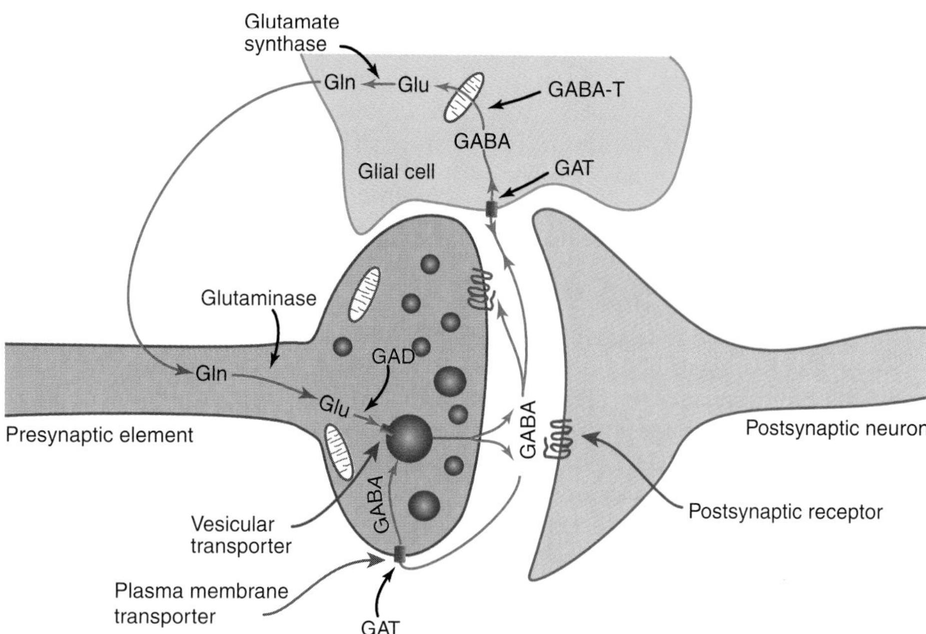

FIGURE 8.9 Schematic depiction of the life cycle of a GABAergic neuron. α-keto-glutarate formed in the Krebs cycle is transaminated to glutamate (Glu) by GABA-transaminase (GABA-T). The transmitter GABA is formed from the Glu by glutamic acid decarboxylase (GAD). GABA that is released is taken by high-affinity GABA transporters (GAT) present on neurons and glia.

stood but may require two different biosynthetic enzymes for glutamate as a transmitter and as a metabolic intermediary. A specific form of glutaminase, a phosphate-activated glutaminase, has been proposed to be responsible for the synthesis of the transmitter pool of glutamate; this glutaminase is localized to certain vesicles. Because both GABA and glutamate cause very rapid changes in postsynaptic neurons, one depolarizing neurons and the other hyperpolarizing them, it is not surprising (and probably fortunate) that the two amino acid transmitter pools are not colocalized.

Regulation of GABA Release by Autoreceptors

The major postsynaptic GABA receptor is the $GABA_A$ receptor, which contains the chloride ion channel (Chapter 9). Pharmacological studies indicate that autoreceptor-mediated regulation of GABA neurons takes place predominantly through $GABA_B$ receptors located on GABAergic nerve terminals. Immunohistochemical studies have revealed that $GABA_A$ receptor subunits also are present on GABAergic neurons in many regions of the brain. It is possible that these receptors respond to GABA released from a GABAergic cell that is presynaptic to the GABA neuron expressing the $GABA_A$ site. However, because this anatomical arrangement of one GABA neuron terminating on another GABA cell would have the same functional consequence as an autoreceptor (decreasing subsequent transmitter release), one cannot distinguish between true autoreceptors and heteroceptors.

Inactivation of Released GABA

Pharmacological studies have characterized uptake in both neurons and glia. This situation appears to be common for amino acid transmitters, because amino acids can play dual roles, functioning as transmitters and metabolic intermediaries. However, the ability of glia to avidly accumulate GABA and other amino acids distinguishes amino acid transmitters from other classical transmitters.

GABA transporter proteins. Reuptake of GABA is the primary mode of transmitter inactivation. At least three specific GABA transporter (GAT) proteins are expressed in the CNS.[10] In addition, a betaine transporter that accumulates GABA has been cloned. Two types of GATs were initially defined on pharmacological grounds: a glial and a neuronal transporter. However, the cloning of GAT genes, which belong to the same family of transporter genes that includes the catecholamine transporters, has led to unexpected findings. *In situ* hybridization and immunohistochemical studies revealed that a cloned CNS GAT, which on pharmacological grounds was defined as a "glial" transporter, is in fact present predominantly on neurons rather than glia. Moreover, the other GATs appear to be expressed in both neurons and glia. The discrepancy between the strong accumulation of GABA by glia and the predominant localization of known GATs to neurons opens the possibility that there may be other GATs that remain to be defined.

The presence of multiple transporter proteins for the same transmitter, all localized to neurons, differs from the situation for catecholamine transmitters, in which a single membrane-associated transporter protein with relatively poor substrate specificity is found in a neuron. An obvious question is, Why are there multiple transporters for GABA? There are several possible explanations. It appears that the GATs may be expressed in both GABAergic neurons and in non-GABAergic cells (presumably cells that receive a GABA innervation). However, it is not known if multiple GATs are present in the same cell, and the precise intracellular localization of the transporter proteins is not yet known. It is possible that different transporters are targeted differently in the cell. For example, one might be present in dendrites and another expressed in axons, with corresponding different functional requirements. Another possibility is that the GATs that have been cloned may serve as cotransporters for other amino acids. For example, transporters for β-alanine and taurine have not been cloned, but these amino acids are accumulated by GATS. Finally, it is possible that one or more of these transporters frequently works in the outward direction, serving as a mechanism for GABA release.

In catecholaminergic neurons, a vesicular monoamine transporter accumulates the transmitter, where it is poised for release but in a compartment that affords protection from enzymatic or xenobiotic degradation. However, a GABA vesicular transporter has not been identified. Many think it likely that there is a GABA vesicular transporter, but no specific data indicate a distinct vesicular GABA transporter, although a glutamate vesicular transporter has been pharmacologically characterized and purified.

Enzymatic inactivation of GABA. As noted earlier, GABA-T is both a synthetic and a degradative enzyme. This unusual dual role allows conservation of the transmitter pool of GABA. GABA-T is a particulate enzyme that is present in high concentration in GABAergic neurons. GABA-T is found in non-GABAergic as well as GABA-containing neurons and is present in a number of peripheral tissues. Electron microscope data suggest that GABA-T is associated with mitochondria. However, pharmacological studies of various subcellular fraction preparations suggest that the GABA-T activity associated with synaptosomes that contain mitochondria is less than that seen in synaptosomal membrane fractions, suggesting that GABA may be metabolized either extraneuronally or in postsynaptic neurons.

Neuroanatomy of GABA Neurons

GABA cells are among the best known of all neurons. GABA neurons are particularly prominent in the cortex, where they are local circuit interneurons. Indeed, for many years GABA cells were widely considered to be almost exclusively local circuit neurons. However, with the development of improved neuroanatomical methods and antibodies against GAD and GABA, it became apparent that there are many long-axoned GABA projection neurons.

The cortical GABAergic interneurons have received considerable attention because of their key role as inhibitory constraints over glutamatergic projection (pyramidal) cells of the cortex. The cortical interneurons are remarkably diverse, with over a dozen different types that can be defined on morphological grounds. These morphological differences translate into functional consequences, because some GABAergic interneurons have very narrow axon arbors that appear to be restricted to a single cortical column, whereas other types of interneurons can exert widespread influence over cells in many columns.

Among the long-axoned GABA cells are the neurons that project from the striatum (caudate nucleus and putamen) to the substantia nigra in the midbrain. In addition, GABA cells in the substantia nigra project to the superior colliculus and to the motor thalamus. Other examples of GABAergic projection neurons are two different groups of GABAergic cells in the zona incerta and midbrain ventral tegmental area that innervate the prefrontal cortex.

Glutamate and Aspartate Serve as Key Excitatory Transmitters

Excitatory amino acid transmitters account for most of the fast synaptic transmission that occurs in the mammalian CNS. **Glutamate** and **aspartate** are the major excitatory amino acid neurotransmitters; several related amino acids (e.g., homocysteic acid and *N*-acetylaspartylglutamate) also may have neurotransmitter roles. The excitatory amino acids participate in intermediary metabolism as well as cellular communication and thus share with GABA the problem of dissociating neurotransmitter from metabolic roles. The intertwining of the transmitter roles of amino acids and intermediary metabolism makes it difficult to fulfill all of the criteria that would give amino acids fully legitimate status as neurotransmitters. Despite these issues, it is now widely accepted that glutamate and aspartate function as excitatory transmitters in the CNS. We briefly consider glutamate biosynthesis and regulation, focusing on the differences between excitatory and inhibitory amino acid transmitters. Many of the general principles addressed in the section on GABA are clearly applicable to glutamate and therefore are not discussed in detail.

Biosynthesis of Glutamate

Glutamic acid is found in very high concentrations in the CNS. However, brain glutamate and aspartate levels are derived solely by local synthesis from glucose, because neither amino acid crosses the blood–brain barrier.

Two processes contribute to the synthesis of glutamate in the nerve terminal. As mentioned in the section on GABA neurons, glutamate is formed from glucose through the Krebs cycle and transamination of α-ketoglutarate. In addition, glutamate can be formed directly from glutamine (Fig. 8.10). Because glutamine is synthesized in glial cells, there is an unusual degree of interaction between glia and neurons in the regulation of availability of the transmitter pool of glutamate. The glutamine that is formed in glia is transported into nerve terminals and then locally converted by glutaminase into glutamate.[21]

The formation of glutamate from glutamine requires the actions of the enzyme glutaminase. A phosphate-activated glutaminase has been suggested to be the specific form of the enzyme making the transmitter pool of glutamate, but this remains controversial, since phosphate-activated glutaminase is present in several peripheral tissues (such as liver) in relatively high concentrations.[22] Glutaminase is localized to mitochondria; as discussed in the section on GABA, the process by which glutamate is exported to allow vesicular storage of the transmitter remains poorly understood.

In glutamate-containing nerve terminals, the amino acid is stored in synaptic vesicles from which the transmitter is released in a calcium-dependent manner upon depolarization of the nerve terminal. Although the vesicular storage of glutamate has been convincingly demonstrated, the vesicular transporter for these amino acids has not been cloned; a vesicular glutamate transporter has been characterized biochemically and purified to near homogeneity.[23]

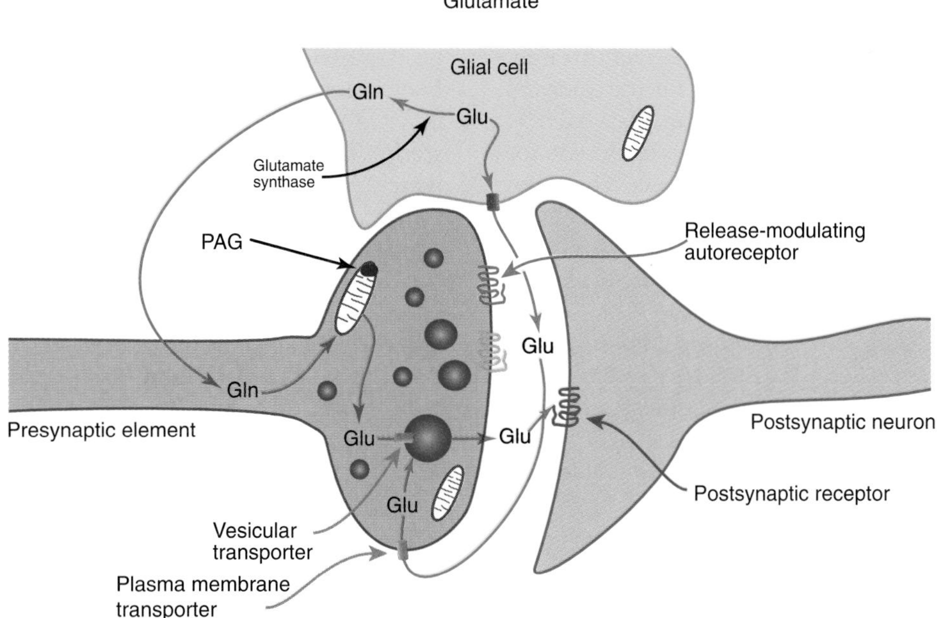

FIGURE 8.10 Depiction of an excitatory amino acid (glutamate) synapse. Glutamate, synthesized via metabolic pathways, is concentrated through a vesicular transporter into secretory granules. After release from the presynaptic terminal, glutamate can interact with postsynaptic and/or release-modulating receptors. Glutamate is then cleared from the synaptic region by the high-affinity plasma membrane transporters or by recycling through adjacent glia.

Regulation of Glutamate Release

The release of glutamate from nerve terminals is regulated by an autoreceptor. There are three types of postsynaptic excitatory amino acid receptors that form ion channels (see Chapter 9). However, the autoreceptor regulating glutamate release is a metabotropic rather than ionotrophic receptor. Eight different receptors that constitute three distinct classes of metabotropic receptors have been identified. Current data suggest that the release-modulating autoreceptor is a member of one class of metabotropic receptors (either an mGluR2 or mGluR3 receptor). In addition, electrophysiological studies have revealed an impulse-modulating glutamate autoreceptor. This receptor differs from a release-modulating glutamate autoreceptor and is thought to be either an mGluRl or mGluR5 site.

Inactivation of Released Glutamate

The major mode of glutamate inactivation is through reuptake of the amino acid by dicarboxylic acid transporters. In contrast to GABA and other classical transmitters, enzymatic inactivation of glutamate does not appear to play a significant role. The extent to which diffusion regulates synaptic and extracellular levels of glutamate is not clear.

Several glutamate transporters have been cloned; two are localized to glia, and one transporter has been reported to be present in neurons. Electron microscopic studies suggest that the glutamate transporters are heavily expressed in astrocytes but relatively weakly present in neurons. All three glutamate transporters accumulate L-glutamate and both D- and L-aspartate. The affinities of the three transporters are similar for glutamate but differ for other amino acids. The three transporters have distinct brain distributions, and even the glial transporters exhibit regional and intracellular differences in expression,[24] underscoring the heterogeneity of glia as well as neurons.

The glial localization of certain glutamate transporters is consistent with the intricate interplay of glial and neuronal elements in the synthesis of glutamate. Because glutamate that is released from neurons is accumulated by glia and then metabolized to glutamine, there is an ultimate recycling of the released amino acid. The fate of glutamate accumulated by the neuronal glutamate transporter is unclear. As is the case with GABA transporters, whether glutamate released from a neuron is accumulated by a neuronal transporter present on that particular neuron or, alternatively, by transporters on other neurons or by glial transporters remains to be established.

Localization of Excitatory Amino Acid Transmitter-Containing Cells

Excitatory amino acid-containing neurons are almost ubiquitously present in the CNS. Rare indeed is the region in which glutamate-containing neurons are not present. It has been somewhat difficult to unambiguously distinguish between glutamate- and aspartate-containing neurons, and hence most statements concerning the anatomy of glutamate-containing neurons may also reflect the presence of aspartate. The development of antibodies to other putative excitatory amino acid transmitters, such as *N*-acetylasparylglutamate, has revealed a more restricted distribution of immunoreactive cells that contain as transmitters these other amino acids.

The pyramidal cells of the cerebral cortex are the best characterized glutamate-containing neurons. These excitatory projection neurons of the cortex represent the counterpoint to the inhibitory GABAergic interneurons of the cortex. In addition to cortical pyramidal cells, relatively well-defined groups of glutamatergic neurons can be found throughout the neuraxis. Most appear to be projection neurons.

Acetylcholine Was the First Neurotransmitter Discovered

Much of our conceptual approach to neurotransmitters is based on lessons learned from studies of acetylcholine (ACh), partly because ACh was the first transmitter discovered (the vagal substance noted by Loewi[8] and subsequently demonstrated by Loewi and Navratil). However, the guiding role of ACh in our study of neurotransmitters is also due to the ease with which ACh can be studied. Acetylcholine is the transmitter at the neuromuscular junction, and thus both the nerve terminal and its target are in a peripheral site that can be easily accessed for experimental manipulations. Subsequent investigations also focused on another peripheral site, the superior cervical ganglion. These studies of peripheral tissues shaped our current approaches to the defining characteristics of neurotransmitters.

The ability to easily expose the neuromuscular junction and maintain isolated preparations of it allowed electrophysiological and biochemical studies of synaptic transmission. Electrophysiological studies revealed fast excitatory responses of muscle fibers to stimulation of the nerve innervating the muscle. The presence of miniature end-plate potentials (MEPPs) was noted, and Fatt and Katz[25] demonstrated that these MEPPs resulted from the slow "leakage" of ACh, with each MEPP representing the release of one vesicle's stores (termed a *quantum*) of transmitter. Overt depolarization generated an increase in the number of quanta released over a given period of time. In addition, studies of the neuromuscular junction allowed detailed analyses of the enzymatic inactivation of ACh, setting the reference for subsequent studies.

In the half-century or so since the initial studies of ACh and neurotransmission at the neuromuscular junction and superior cervical ganglion, many of the rules that apply to ACh transmission have been shown to be general principles that apply to other transmitters. For example, the concept of the quantal nature of neurotransmission is central to current ideas of transmitter release. Although the discovery of different neurotransmitters has expanded our knowledge, studies of ACh continue to provide a foundation for modern concepts of chemical neurotransmission.

Acetylcholine Synthesis

The synthesis of ACh is probably the simplest of all transmitter syntheses; in a single step, the acetyl group from acetyl-coenzyme A is transferred to choline by the enzyme choline acetyltransferase (ChAT). Thus, the requirements for ACh synthesis are few: the presence of the substrate choline, the donor acetyl-coenzyme A, and the enzyme ChAT. (See Fig. 8.11.)

The acetyl-CoA that serves as the donor is derived from pyruvate generated by glucose metabolism. This dependence on a metabolic intermediary is similar to that seen in GABA synthesis, where the immediate precursor glutamate is formed from α-ketoglutarate. Acetyl-CoA is localized to mitochondria. Because the cholinergic synthetic enzyme ChAT is cytoplasmic, acetyl-CoA must exit the mitochondria to gain access to ChAT; this process is poorly understood.

Choline. Choline is present in the plasma in high concentration. A low-affinity reuptake process for choline is widely distributed in the body. However, brain cholinergic neurons express a different sodium-dependent transporter that is saturated at plasma levels of choline. Although a few years ago a choline transporter appeared to have been cloned, this transporter was present in peripheral tissues as well as brain. More importantly, when the cloned transporter was expressed in cell lines, it displayed different kinetics from those found in CNS tissue and was not sensitive to hemicholinium 3, which blocks the high-affinity

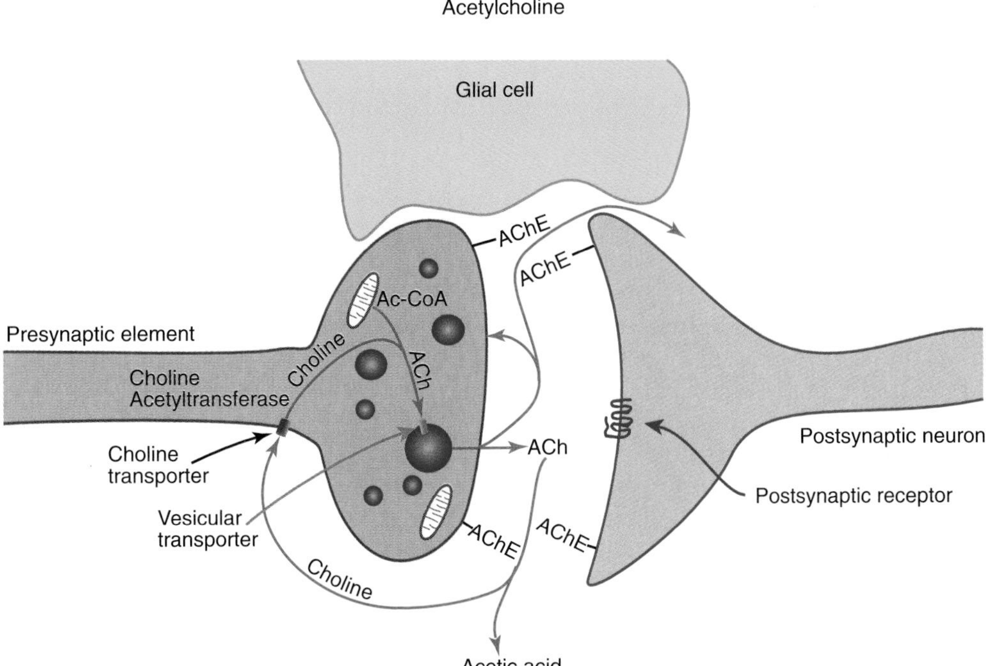

FIGURE 8.11 Acetylcholine (ACh) synthesis, release, and termination of action is shown. A choline transporter accumulates choline. The enzyme choline acetyltransferase (ChAT) acetylates the choline using acetyl-CoA (Ac-CoA) to form the transmitter ACh, which is accumulated into vesicles by the vesicular transporter. The released ACh may interact with postsynaptic muscarinic or nicotinic cholinergic receptors, or can be taken up into the neuron by a choline transporter. Acetylcholine can be degraded after release by the enzyme acetylcholine esterase (AChE).

cholinergic reuptake process. It now appears that the gene cloned encoded a creatinine transporter rather than the choline transporter.[26]

Choline acetyltransferase. Choline acetyltransferase is considered the definitive marker for cholinergic neurons.[27] Multiple mRNAs encode ChAT, resulting from differential use of three promoters and alternative splicing of the 5′ noncoding region. The functional significance of the different transcripts is not known; the multiple promoters suggest different regulation of the transcripts.

Although ChAT is the sole enzyme in ACh synthesis, it appears that ChAT is not the rate-limiting step in the synthesis of the transmitter. As in the case for TH in the synthesis of catecholamines, the full enzymatic activity of ChAT is not expressed *in vivo,* because the activity of ChAT *in vitro* is much greater than what would be predicted on the basis of the synthesis of ACh from choline *in vivo.* The transport of acetyl-CoA from the mitochondria to the cytoplasm may be rate limiting, or intracellular choline concentrations may ultimately determine the rate of ACh synthesis. This latter speculation has led to the use of choline precursors in attempts to enhance ACh synthesis in Alzheimer disease, in which there is a marked decrease of ACh in the cerebral cortex. Attempts have been made to treat Alzheimer disease with lecithin, a choline precursor; unfortunately, lecithin does not appear to diminish dementia, although it does markedly increase bad breath!

Vesicular cholinergic transporter. ACh is synthesized by ChAT and transported into vesicles by a vesicular cholinergic transporter, similar to the amine vesicular transporter. The vesicular cholinergic transporter is distinct from the membrane transporter that accumulates choline. A unique aspect of the vesicular cholinergic transporter is that its entire coding region is contained in the first intron of the ChAT gene.[28] This suggests that both genes are coordinately regulated, and this suspicion has been confirmed.[29]

Cholinergic autoreceptor function. As with the catecholamine transmitters, a cholinergic release-modulating autoreceptor has been identified both in peripheral tissues and in the CNS. This receptor is a muscarinic cholinergic receptor, rather than the nicotinic cholinergic receptor found at the neuromuscular junction. Most recent data suggest that the autoreceptor in the brain is an M2 cholinergic receptor, although the contribution of M4 autoreceptors has not been eliminated. The cholinergic autoreceptor in the guinea pig bladder has been suggested to be an M4 subtype of muscarinic receptor. Because there is little evidence for a synthesis-modulating cholinergic autoreceptor, it is not clear why two different receptor proteins (M2 and M4) might both serve as release-modulating autoreceptors.

Inactivation of Acetylcholine

The primary mode of inactivation of ACh appears to be enzymatic. Esterases that hydrolyze choline esters are the degradative enzymes. The esterases, including the relatively specific ones such as acetylcholinesterase (AChE), are quite diverse. See Box 8.3.

Acetylcholinesterase. The enzymatic inactivation of ACh includes the hydrolysis of ACh to choline. Two groups of cholinesterases have been defined on the basis of substrate specificity: (1) acetylcholinesterases and (2) butrylcholinesterases.[30] The former are relatively specific for ACh and are found in abundance in the brain. There are multiple AChE species.[31] The butylcholinesterases also efficiently hydrolyze choline esters but are found primarily in the liver, with lower concentrations present in the adult brain.

AChE is present in high concentration in cholinergic neurons. However, AChE is also present in moderately high concentration in certain noncholinergic neurons that receive cholinergic inputs (i.e., that are cholinoceptive). This is consistent with the fact that AChE is a secreted enzyme that is associated with the cell membrane. Thus, ACh hydrolysis takes place extracellularly, and the choline generated is conserved by the high-affinity reuptake process.

In addition to its role in inactivating released acetylcholine, AChE appears to function as a chemical messenger in the CNS.[32] The release of AChE from neurons in the substantia nigra and cerebellum is calcium dependent, and cerebellar release is enhanced by electrical stimulation of cerebellar afferents. Electrophysiological studies have revealed that AChE elicits changes in the threshold for Ca^{2+} spikes, and local administration of AChE enhances the responses of cerebellar neurons to glutamate and aspartate, the transmitters present in the climbing and mossy fiber innervations of the cerebellum.[33]

There are, as noted earlier, many AChE species, all of which are encoded by a single gene that is alternatively spliced.[34] Evidence exists for tissue-specific expression of different transcripts.[35] Among the multiple mRNAs encoding AChE is one that represents the primary form expressed in brain and muscle. Other forms are present in developing blood cells. The function of AChE in nonneural tissues is likely to be quite different from that in neurons. AChE mRNAs are present in high abundance in bone marrow stem cells and, in

BOX 8.3

AChE INHIBITORS, NERVE GASES, AND PHARMACOTHERAPY

The enzymatic inactivation of acetylcholine has been fertile ground for the development of a large number of pharmaceutical agents. Anticholinesterases such as sarin are potent neurotoxins and have been used as nerve gases since World War I. Other anticholinesterases include organophosphates (such as parathion), which are widely used insecticides. Anticholinesterases, whether the target is a human or a tomato hornworm, function in the same way: instead of the released ACh leading to discrete single depolarizations of muscle fibers, the accumulation of acetylcholine at the neuromuscular junction leads to muscle fibrillation and ultimately depolarization inactivation of the muscle.

Anticholinesterases have some less aggressive uses as well. Competitive neuromuscular blocking agents such as succinylcholine are used as an adjunct to anesthetics to increase muscle relaxation in certain surgical procedures; conversely, anticholinergics can be used to reverse the muscle paralysis caused by succinylcholine. Attempts have also been made to increase central AChE stores in Alzheimer disease by administration of an anticholinesterase. Unfortunately, this approach has not proved effective.

particular, in peripheral blood cells in certain leukemias.[36] Recent data indicate that inhibition of AChE gene expression in bone marrow cultures suppresses apoptosis (programmed cell death; see Chapter 20) and leads to progenitor cell expansion,[37] supporting a role of AChE in the development of leukemias.

Distribution and Anatomy of Acetylcholine-Containing CNS Neurons

Acetylcholine-containing cells are found in over 10 relatively well-defined populations of cholinergic neurons (Fig. 8.12). Most of these clusters of cholinergic cells represent projection neurons, although there are several very well-characterized populations of cholinergic interneurons.

Among the most widely studied of the central cholinergic neurons are those cholinergic neurons found in the basal forebrain and allied regions. Thus, cells in the nucleus basalis and related areas of the basal forebrain, together with cells in the diagonal band regions, form a continuum of cholinergic cells that project widely onto the cortex. These cells have been intensively studied because they undergo degeneration in Alzheimer disease.

Other cholinergic projection neurons include a continuum of cells in the pons that include neurons extending from the pedunculopontine tegmental nucleus to cells located in the tissue forming the floor of the fourth ventricle. These cells have widespread projections to forebrain sites, including some cortical projections, as well as descending projections to the spinal cord.

The large aspiny neurons of the striatum are probably the best-studied population of cholinergic interneurons. These cells are easily distinguished from the much smaller GABAergic projection neurons of the striatum. The use of cholinergic receptor antagonists to reduce motor symptoms in Parkinson disease is based on the disinhibition of striatal cholinergic interneurons due to the loss of dopaminergic regulation of these cells.

Summary

The classical neurotransmitters are small molecules that are derived from either amino acids or intermediary metabolism and share several characteristics. The classical transmitters are generally synthesized by the sequential actions of key enzymes. These transmitters are synthesized in the general vicinity of where they are to be released. Release is elicited by depolarization and is calcium dependent. Once released, the transmitter is inactivated by a specific reuptake mechanism, or by enzymatic means, or both.

The criteria for designation of a classical transmitter were in large part based on experiments that could be conducted in sites that were easily accessible (such as the neuromuscular junction). The relatively high concentrations of classical transmitters made measurement of transmitter release a key criterion but, unfortunately, one that would prove difficult to meet in the cases of transmitters discovered in and after the 1970s. Nevertheless, the increasing sensitivity of analytical techniques coupled with the ingenuity of neuroscien-

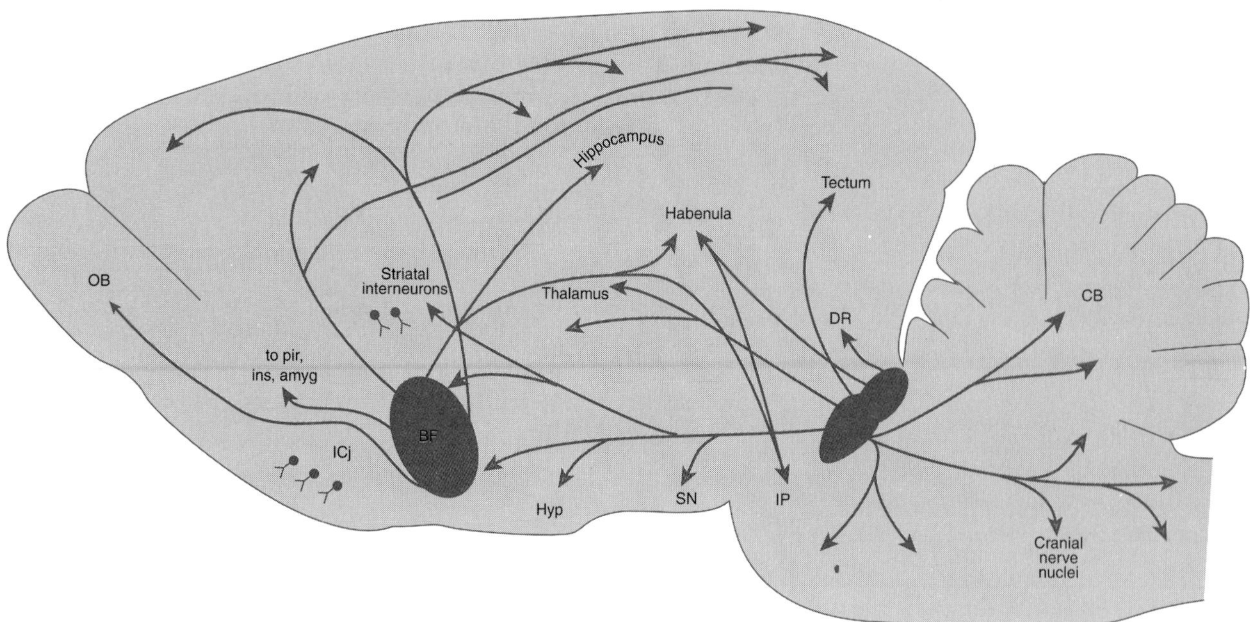

FIGURE 8.12 Schematic of acetylcholine cell bodies and projections in a saggital section of the rat. Abbreviations: as in Figure 8.6; BF, basal forebrain.

tists led to the uncovering of a large number of peptides, growth factors, and even gases that functioned as transmitters. We next explore the similarities and differences of the classical transmitters with these new kids on the block. These differences have often illuminated unknown fundamental processes of neurons and expanded our concept of information flow between neurons.

PEPTIDE TRANSMITTERS

There are many more peptide transmitters than classical transmitters. These two groups of transmitters have much in common. For example, both classical and peptide transmitters are typically well conserved across species. In fact, many of the peptide transmitters or closely related peptides were initially isolated from amphibian species. In addition, both classical and peptide transmitters are synthesized within nerves, stored in vesicles, and released in a calcium-dependent manner. However, the biosynthetic mechanisms, the nature of the stimulus required for release, and the modes of inactivation of peptide and classical transmitters are quite different. We consider the question of the significance of multiple neurotransmitters first. We then turn to the general principles of peptide transmitter biosynthesis and inactivation, which are illustrated by examining in detail the life cycle of one peptide transmitter, neurotensin.

Why Do Neurons Have So Many Transmitters?

About a dozen classical transmitters and literally dozens of neuropeptides function as transmitters. If the role of neurotransmitters is to serve as a chemical bridge that conveys information between two spatially distinct cells, why have so many chemical messengers? Several different factors, ranging from the intracellular localization of transmitters to the different firing rates and patterns of neurons, probably contribute to the need for multiple transmitters. In this section, we consider the characteristics of neurons and neuronal communication that may require multiple transmitters.

Afferent Convergence on a Common Neuron

Perhaps the simplest explanation for multiple transmitters is that many afferent nerve terminals abut on a single neuron. A neuron must be able to distinguish between the multiple afferent inputs that bring information to the neuron. To some degree, this can be accomplished by the site on a neuron at which an afferent terminates: at the soma, axon, or dendritic shaft or spine. However, because many afferents terminate in close proximity, another means of distinguishing the inputs and their information is necessary. One way in which this can be accomplished is by chemically coding afferent neurons. The information conveyed by distinct transmitters is then distinguished by the different receptors present on the targeted neuron and their various transduction mechanisms.

Colocalization of Neurotransmitters

A major conceptual change in the neurosciences has been the realization that a cell can use more than one neurotransmitter. The idea that a neuron is limited to one transmitter can be traced to Henry Dale, or, more properly, to an informal restatement of what is termed **Dale's principle**. About 60 years ago, Dale posited that a metabolic process that takes place in the cell body can reach or influence events in all the processes of the neuron. John Eccles restated Dale's view to suggest that a neuron releases the same transmitter at all its processes. Illustrating the dangers of the scientific equivalent of sound bites, this principle was soon misinterpreted to indicate that only a single transmitter can be present in a given neuron. This is clearly not the case. Neurons can colocalize two or more transmitters. For example, a neuron can use both a classical transmitter such as dopamine and a peptide transmitter such as neurotensin. Indeed, it now appears that few if any neurons contain only one transmitter, and in several cases three or even four transmitters have been found in a single neuron.

The presence of multiple transmitters in a single neuron may indicate that different transmitters are used by a neuron to signal different functional states to its target cell. For example, the firing *rates* of neurons differ considerably, and thus it may be useful for a neuron to encode fast firing by one transmitter and slower firing by another transmitter. In addition, the firing *pattern* of cells is of significance. For example, a neuron might show an absolute firing rate of 5 spikes every second. This frequency could result from a neuron discharging every 200 ms or from discharging five times in an initial 200-ms period followed by 800 ms of silence. Recent data indicate that in cases in which there is a colocalization of a peptide and a classical transmitter, peptide transmitters are often released at higher firing rates and particularly under burst-firing patterns.

In many ways, the different biosynthetic strategies used by peptides and classical transmitters may lead to differential release. Classical transmitters can be rapidly replaced because their synthesis occurs in nerve terminals. In contrast, peptide transmitters must be synthesized in the cell body and transported to the terminal. Thus, it is useful to conserve peptide transmitters for situations of high demand, because they would otherwise be rapidly depleted.

Transmitter Release from Different Processes

The restatement of Dale's principle by Eccles held that a transmitter or other protein is present in all processes of a neuron. However, it now appears that a transmitter can be specifically localized to different parts of a neuron. For example, in the marine mollusc *Aplysia*, different transmitters are targeted to different processes of a single neuron.[38] Although differential targeting of transmitters in mammalian neurons has not been conclusively demonstrated, if a transmitter were restricted to a particular part of a neuron, it follows that the neuron would need multiple transmitters to account for different release sites. Considerable evidence supports distinct spatial localizations of receptors (such as NMDA-type glutamate receptors and certain G-protein-coupled receptors) on a neuron.

Synaptic Specializations versus Nonjunctional Appositions between Neurons

In addition to the diversity in transmitters that may result from transmitters being targeted to different intraneuronal sites, the anatomical relations between one cell and its follower may contribute to the need for different transmitters. We typically think of synaptic specializations (see Chapter 3) as the morphological substrate of communication between two neurons. However, there may also be nonsynaptic communication between two neurons. These could occur across distances that are smaller or much larger than synaptic distances. In the latter case, the requirements for transmitter action would differ from those discussed previously because the distance traversed by the transmitter molecule would be larger than at a synaptic apposition. Thus, transmitters that lack an efficient reuptake system, such as peptide transmitters, might be favored at nonsynaptic sites. Because a single neuron can form both synaptic and nonsynaptic specializations, a single neuron may require more than one neurotransmitter.

Fast versus Slow Responses of Target Neurons to Neurotransmitters

We have seen that different firing rates or patterns may be accompanied by changes in the transmitter being released from a neuron. The postsynaptic response to a transmitter can occur over different time scales. For example, **ionotropic receptors** (i.e., those that form ion channels) lead to very rapid changes upon stimulation by a released transmitter, because the ionic gradients across the cell are almost instantaneously changed. In contrast, **metabotrophic receptors** that respond to catecholamines and peptide transmitters are coupled to intracellular events through specific transduction molecules, such as G proteins. Thus, metabotrophic receptors respond to neurotransmitter stimulation on a slower time scale than do ionotropic receptors. This difference in temporal response characteristics is useful, because it allows the receptive neuron to respond differently to a stimulus, depending on the antecedent activity in the cell. A transmitter can change the response characteristics of a particular cell to subsequent stimuli on the order of seconds or even minutes, and thus short-term changes can occur independent of changes in gene expression.

Synthesis and Inactivation of Peptide and Classical Transmitters Differ

There are two major differences between classical and peptide transmitters. Peptide transmitters are synthesized in the cell body, rather than at the terminal processes of neurons; this difference has significant functional consequences. In addition, peptide transmitters are inactivated by enzymatic actions and not by a reuptake process.

Synthesis and Storage of Peptide Transmitters

Whereas classical transmitters are synthesized in the process (axon, dendrite) from which they are released, peptide transmitters are frequently not synthesized locally. In most cases, the genes encoding peptide transmitters give rise to a **prohormone**, from which the peptide transmitter is subsequently cleaved. The prohormone is incorporated into **secretory granules** after transcription, where it can be acted on by **peptidases** to form the peptide transmitter. In contrast, classical transmitters are formed by successive small enzymatic transformations of a transmitter precursor, rather than from a larger precursor, and do not require transport to distal processes. Although the synthesis of a prohormone is the major strategy used to produce peptide transmitters, certain small peptides can be enzymatically synthesized. An example is carnosine (β-alanyl-L-histidine), which is synthesized by carnosine synthase.

The neuron meets demands for increased amounts of a classical transmitter by increasing local synthesis of the transmitter. However, increasing the amount of a peptide transmitter requires an increase in gene expression to yield a prohormone, and the subsequent delivery of the prohormone–peptide-containing granules to the terminal by axonal transport may take hours or even days. Thus, classical transmitters can respond to increased demand rapidly, but peptide transmitters cannot. This difference in biosynthetic strategies contributed to the initial difficulties in localizing the sources of peptide-containing innervations of certain brain regions. Because peptides or their prohormones are transported from the soma immediately after translation from mRNA, the cell-body regions and proximal processes of these neurons typically contain very low concentrations of the peptide transmitters. Although immunohistochemical methods can easily localize the cell bodies of classical transmitters, to demonstrate the cell bodies in which peptide transmitters are formed often requires the disruption of microtubule-mediated axonal transport, which allows the peptide to accumulate in the soma.

The storage of peptides and classical transmitters also differs. Classical neurotransmitters are generally stored in small (approximately 50 nm) synaptic vesicles. In contrast, neuropeptide transmitters are stored in large (approximately 100 nm) dense-core vesicles. Because peptide transmitters are typically released at high neuronal firing frequency or in a burst-firing pattern, it is reasonable to assume that there are different mechanisms for the exocytosis and subsequent release of peptide and classical transmitter vesicles. Although the release of peptide transmitters, like that of the classical transmitters, is calcium dependent, recent data suggest that distinct but related molecular mechanisms subserve release of small and large dense-core vesicles.[39]

Inactivation of Peptide Transmitters

The different strategies employed for the synthesis of peptide and classical transmitters are paralleled by differences in inactivation of the released transmitter. As discussed earlier, classical transmitters have high-affinity reuptake processes that remove the transmitter from the synaptic or extracellular space. In contrast, peptide transmitters are inactivated enzymatically or by diffusion but lack a high-affinity reuptake process. The enzymatic inactivation of peptide transmitters also differs from that of classical transmitters. Because peptide transmitters are short chains of amino acids, the inactivating enzymes show specificity for certain types of dipeptides but are not specific to any single peptide. For example, a metalloendopeptidase that inactivates enkephalins, small pentapeptide opioid-like transmitters, is frequently called enkephalinase but is also critically involved in the inactivation of other neuropeptides, including neurotensin and somatatostatin.

One final difference in the inactivation of peptide and classical transmitters is the product. In the case of classical transmitters that are catabolized, the product is inactive at the receptor site. However, in the case of peptide transmitters, certain peptide fragments derived from the enzymatic "inactivation" of the peptide are biologically active. An example is angiotensin, in which the peptide angiotensin I is metabolized to yield angiotensin II and III, each successively more active than the parent angiotensin I. It is therefore sometimes difficult to distinguish between synthetic processing (of a prohormone) and inactivation. The peptide that is stored in vesicles and then released is therefore considered the transmitter, although the actions of certain peptidases may lead to other biologically active fragments.

Approaches to Studying Neuropeptide Localization, Synthesis, Release, and Inactivation

The unusual aspects of peptide transmitter biosynthesis and inactivation have resulted in different methods being emphasized in the study of peptide transmitters and classical transmitters.

Localization. Anatomical approaches are used extensively to define the neurons in which peptides serve as neurotransmitters. Immunohistochemistry, with the use of antibodies generated against the prohormone, can be used to identify neurons in which peptide transmitters are synthesized. Similarly, antibodies against the peptide transmitter itself can be used to localize the peptide to cell bodies, particularly when axonal transport has been blocked by prior administration of colchicine. Recent anatomical studies have emphasized the use of *in situ* hybridization histochemistry, in which cRNA probes or oligonucleotides complementary to a defined sequence of a peptide mRNA are used to identify the cells in which the gene encoding a peptide prohormone is present.

Synthesis and Inactivation. Biochemical studies of peptide synthesis and inactivation also use different approaches from those undertaken in classical transmitters. The synthesis of peptide transmitters has been extensively studied by following the rapid incorporation of radiolabeled amino acids into peptides, in so-called pulse-chase experiments. More recent studies have emphasized molecular approaches, because the prohormone from which the peptide will be cleaved is directly transcribed from mRNA.

Release. The release of peptides has been studied in slices of brain, much as has been the case with classical transmitters. However, *in vivo* studies of release have not been possible until relatively recently. The measurement of metabolites as an index of transmitter release (which has been used extensively for monoamine neurons) is not applicable to peptidergic neurons for two reasons. The peptide fragments derived from the parent peptide may be similar to those of other peptides, thus confounding identification of the source. Moreover, larger peptide fragments are often further degraded to smaller peptide fragments. This situation requires antisera with exquisite specificity for the parent peptide but not fragments, which is rare indeed. Nonetheless, if one knows the principal peptide fragments derived from a released peptide, one can use immunoassays coupled with chromatographic separation methods to measure levels of the parent peptide and thereby gain an appreciation of the release of the peptide.

In vivo microdialysis methods are more directly useful for the measurement of extracellular concentrations of neuropeptides, particularly small neuropeptides. Because the released peptide quickly diffuses across the dialysis membrane, whereas the peptidases are generally too large to do so, one can obtain measurable levels of peptides in the dialysate. The dialysis approach, however, requires very sensitive analytic methods because of the poor recovery of peptides. In addition, dialysis does not offer good temporal or spatial resolution. Another *in vivo* approach is to insert electrodes coated with antibodies into a specific area of the brain for a short period of time. The removed probes are then exposed to a radiolabeled peptide, which will bind to receptors that are not already occupied by peptide that is released endogenously. This method does not allow repeated measurements and requires very precise experiments to optimize the time that the probe is left in the brain.

Pharmacological studies of neuropeptide transmitters have been hampered by the lack of specific compounds that interact with peptide receptors. Many specific analogs of neurotransmitter peptides have been synthesized. However, although these peptides interact specifically with appropriate receptors, peptides and proteins do not readily enter the brain and thus have been of very limited utility. Several nonpeptide antagonists that enter the CNS with relative ease have been developed. In contrast, there are almost no nonpeptide agonists that one can use to study central peptide transmitters; one key exception is morphine, which targets certain opioid receptors in the brain.

Neurotensin Is a Peptide Neurotransmitter

Neurotensin (NT) is widely expressed in the central nervous system and in peripheral tissues (particularly the small intestine). In addition, a hexapeptide termed neuromedin N (NMN) is transcribed from the gene that encodes NT in mammals (Fig. 8.13). NMN is nearly identical to a peptide called LANT-6 that is found in avian species. Many mammalian brain peptides are structurally similar to peptides that are found in nonmammalian organisms. In fact, examination of extracts of the skin of certain toads has resulted in the identification of a large number of peptides and has been a starting point for subsequent isolation of related peptides in mammals. An example is the neurotensin-like octapeptide xenopsin, which was isolated from the skin of a toad (*Xenopsis*).

Neurotensin Synthesis

A 170-amino-acid prohormone precursor of NT is encoded by a single gene that is transcribed to yield two mRNAs. The smaller transcript is the predominant form in the intestine, but both mRNA species are present in equal abundance in most brain areas.[40] The 170-amino-acid precursor contains one copy each of NT and NMN.

NT is present in very high concentrations in the small intestine and in lower amounts in the stomach and large intestine. NMN also is present in these tissues, but the molar ratios of NT/NMN differ across the different tissues, suggesting differential enzymatic processing of the prohormone or alternatively the generation of different transcripts. Because NT and NMN are contained in the same exon of the NT–NMN gene, differences in relative abundance of NT and NMN are due to differential processing of the precursor.

NT and NMN are stored in large dense-core vesicles. The characteristics of NT and NMN release have been examined by studying the levels of NT and NMN released from slices of the hypothalamus (an area of the brain enriched in NT and NMN). Superfusing hypothalamic tissue with high concentrations of K^+ to depolarize cells evokes the release of both NT and NMN[41]; the molar ratio of NT/NMN release is virtually identical with that in extracts of hypothalamic tissue. The release of NT and NMN is not seen in tissue perfused with a medium that lacks extracellular Ca^{2+}. Thus, the release of the peptides requires calcium (presumably indicating dependence of vesicular docking with the membrane and exocytosis on calcium) and is evoked by stimulation. These criteria are considered to be necessary for the designation of a compound as a neurotransmitter.

The impulse-dependent release of NT varies as a function of frequency and pattern of impulses. Higher frequencies of firing elicit greater NT release. More marked, however, is the release of the peptide seen in response to burst firing of neurons.[37]

Inactivation of Neurotensin

There is no high-affinity reuptake process for peptides. Accordingly, other than diffusion, the sole means of inactivating peptide transmitters that are released from a neuron is enzymatic.

Enzymatic inactivation of neurotensin. NT is enzymatically inactivated by a group of enzymes known as metalloendopeptidases. In particular, three of these **endopeptidases** (known with great flair as 24.11, 24.15, and 24.16) take part in the catabolism of NT. In both brain and gut, NT is hydrolyzed by combinations of the three endopeptidases.[41] Endopeptidase 24.11 (also known as enkephalinase for its well-characterized actions on the enkephalin peptides) cleaves NT at two sites, the Pro-10–Tyr-11 and the Tyr-11–Ile-12 residues, yielding a decapeptide. Endopeptidase 24.15 acts at the Arg-8–Arg-9 site, and 24.16 acts at the same Pro-10–Try-11 site as enkephalinase. Thus, the enzymes involved in peptide degradation do not exhibit much specificity. In contrast to NT, NMN is inactivated by an aminopeptidase at the amino-terminal Lys-1–Ile-2 site.

We noted earlier that certain proteins that have important functions in neurotransmission (such as AChE) may have very different functions in other (nonneural) systems. Enkephalinase, which hydrolyzes NT and somatostatin as well as enkephalins, appears to be similar to AChE by having a role in leukemia. The common acute lymphoblastic leukemia antigen (CALLA) is a protein expressed by most acute lymphoblastic leukemias and normal lymphoid progenitors. The human CALLA cDNA encodes a protein that appears to be nearly identical with that of enkephalinase.[42]

Internalization of neurotensin. As already noted, there is no high-affinity reuptake process for peptides. Nonetheless, certain peptides, including NT, have been shown to enter neurons. This is thought to occur by internalization of a peptide bound to its receptor. This process has been relatively well characterized for NT in the midbrain dopamine cells that project to the striatum. Perhaps most interestingly, NT that is accumulated by axon terminals in the striatum is retrogradely transported back to the cell bodies of origin in the midbrain.

The functional significance of internalization of NT and its subsequent retrograde transport is not clear. NT could conceivably serve as a growth factor, regulating the targeted ingrowth and survival of afferents to the striatum. An intriguing possibility is that the NT may function over a relatively extended period to alter the transmitter function of the cell. Local injections of NT into the striatum result in retrograde labeling of midbrain dopamine neurons and have been reported to increase the number of midbrain cells expressing tyrosine hydroxylase mRNA.

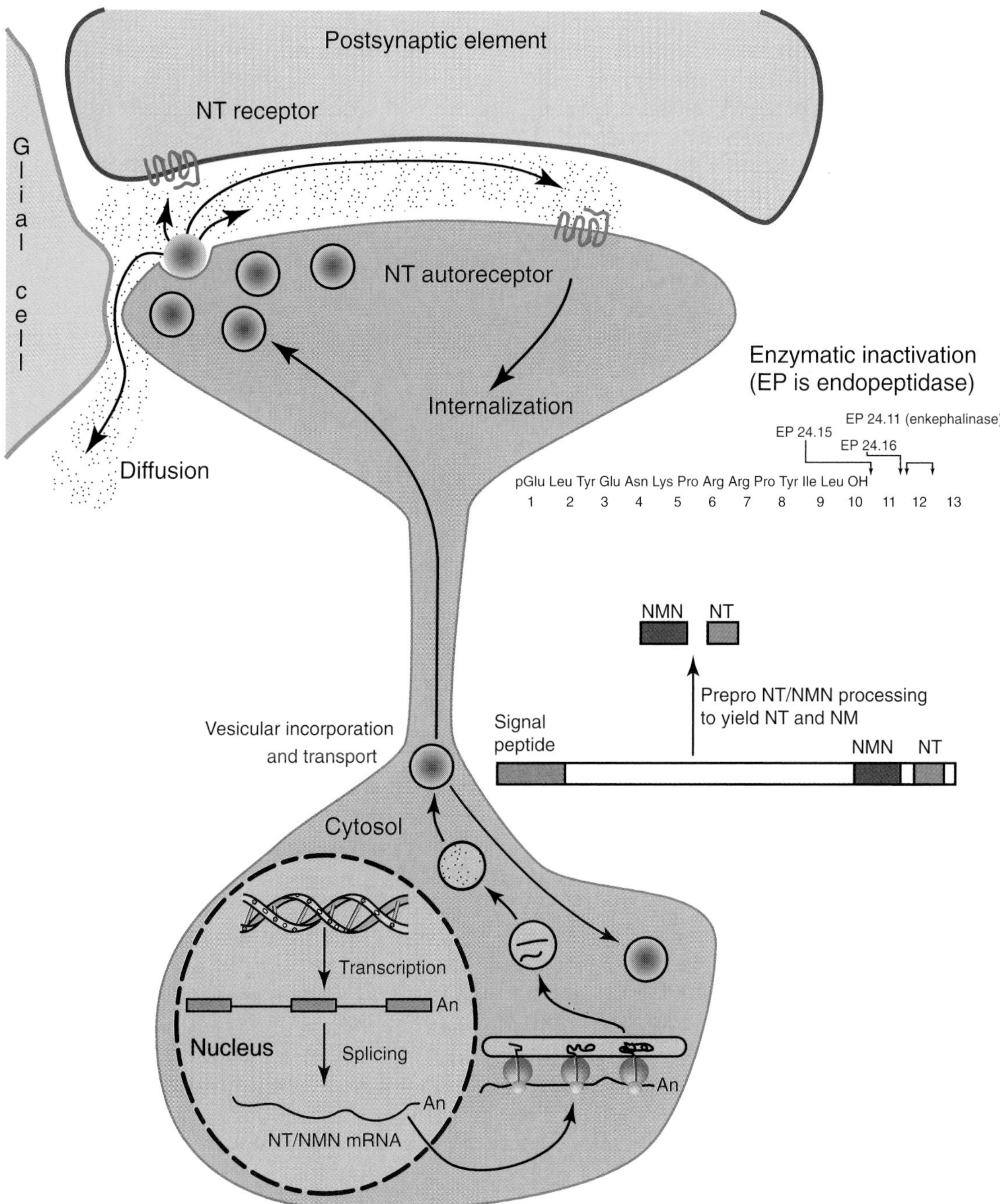

FIGURE 8.13 Schematic illustration of neurotensin (NT) and neuromedan (NMN) biosynthesis and action, from gene transcription to diffusion from the synaptic cleft and inactivation by a group of endopeptidases (EP).

Coexistence of Neurotensin and Classical Transmitters

Neurotensin is found in many dopaminergic neurons in mammalian species. It is present in certain hypothalamic dopamine cell groups and in the A10 dopamine cell group of the ventral tegmental area of the rat. In contrast, although neurotensin-containing cells are found in many areas of the primate brain, only a very few dopamine cells express the NT–NMN gene in primate species, and the projection target of these neurons is not known. Because all of the neurotensin in the prefrontal cortex of the rat is thought to be contained in dopamine axons, study of the rodent prefrontal cortex has afforded a unique opportunity to investigate interactions between colocalized transmitters *in vivo.* A series of studies has revealed that neurotensin release in the prefrontal cortex is increased when neuronal firing is increased or when dopamine neurons enter into a burst-like firing pattern.[37]

In addition, the dopaminergic autoreceptor present on dopamine axons in the prefrontal cortex appears to be closely associated with NT release from these axons. In contrast with most forebrain areas innervated by dopamine axons, transmitter release but not synthesis is regulated by dopamine autoreceptors in the prefrontal cortex. Low autoreceptor-selective doses of dopamine agonists, which decrease subsequent dopamine release, enhance NT release from these axons; conversely, antagonists at the release-modulating dopamine autoreceptor decrease NT release but enhance dopamine release. Thus, NT and dopamine release are regulated in a reciprocal fashion by autoreceptors in neurons in which both transmitters are present.

The intracellular mechanisms through which dopamine autoreceptors regulate NT release are not known. The NT receptor is a G-protein-coupled receptor, and thus some form of receptor–receptor interaction is possible.

Summary

There are over 20 peptide neurotransmitters. Peptide transmitters differ from classical transmitters by being synthesized in the soma and then transported in vesicles to the release site. Although there are a considerably larger number of peptide than classical transmitters, there is less specificity in the inactivation of peptide transmitters. Thus, termination of the action of peptide neurotransmitters is achieved by relatively nonspecific enzymatic inactivation or by diffusion. These differences between peptide and classical transmitters are important, and the common acceptance of peptides as transmitters met with considerable resistance. However, once this battle was won, it opened the door for consideration of radically different molecules as transmitters; these unconventional transmitters are discussed next.

UNCONVENTIONAL TRANSMITTERS

The designation of a substance as a neurotransmitter has traditionally rested on certain criteria, as discussed earlier in this chapter. However, these criteria were formulated early in the modern neuroscience era and are mainly based on studies conducted in peripheral tissues, particularly the neuromuscular junction and superior cervical ganglion. The marked advance in technical sophistication that allow us to measure substances in the brain that are present in minute quantities or are very unstable have opened the possibility that several substances that do not meet the established requirements for designation as a neurotransmitter may indeed be transmitters. This possibility obviously requires changing the definition of a transmitter. One simple approach would be to designate a chemical mediator a neurotransmitter if it allows information to flow from one neuron to another. This definition circumvents the matter of glial contribution to the ionic milieu of the neuron, which certainly imparts information concerning the function of the glia (and parenthetically points to the increasing awareness of the active roles that glia play in the CNS). On the other hand, such a definition also closely approximates the definition of a hormone, in which the temporal characteristics of transmitter action are not defined, nor is the distance of the target cell to the transmitter substance specified. Finally, this definition does not accommodate unconventional roles for transmitters, such as the regulation of neuronal development or intracellular trafficking of proteins. Because growth factors can clearly affect neuritic outgrowth and cell survival, as well as neuronal polarity and other various functions thought to involve changes in intracellular trafficking, the definition of a neurotransmitter changes as we discuss what are termed "unconventional" transmitters.

The discovery of peptidergic neurotransmitters more than a generation ago was accompanied by considerable debate over the definition of a transmitter. Yet peptide transmitters are quite similar to classical transmitters, sharing such features as conventional storage, calcium-dependent release, and the ability to influence the activity (e.g., the firing rate) of postsynaptic neurons over a relatively brief interval. Given these basic similarities and the broad acceptance of peptide transmitters into the language of neurotransmission, it seems necessary to contrast peptide transmitters with other novel substances that influence target cells in unique ways. Among these novel substances are neuroactive gases (nitric oxide and carbon monoxide), growth factors, and neurosteroids.

Nitric Oxide and Carbon Monoxide Are Unconventional Transmitters

Nitrates have long been used in the treatment of cardiovascular disorders. Nitrates dilate blood vessels of the heart and thereby relieve the symptoms of angina, but the mechanisms by which nitroglycerine and similar nitrates elicit vasodilatation were not known until recently. In 1980, an endothelial-derived relaxing factor in the cells lining blood vessels was shown to potently and rapidly dilate blood vessels. This endothelial factor was soon shown to be the gas nitric oxide (NO). In addition, glutamate, acting at NMDA receptors, was observed to release a factor that causes vasodilatation and increases cGMP levels in brain. It soon became apparent that the endothelial-derived relaxing factor and the glutamate-induced factor that causes vasodilatation were the same and that NO was present in neurons as well as vasculature. These data, coupled with the identification of neuronal as well as vascular isoforms of the NO synthetic enzyme (nitric oxide synthase), led to the concept that NO may serve as a molecule taking part in intercellular communication, including neurotransmission.

Nitric oxide is a well-known air pollutant and thus at the very least an unconventional candidate for a neurotransmitter. The idea that an unstable toxic gas could serve as a transmitter led to several questions concerning the nature of neurotransmission, the most obvious being how can a gas be stored for release in an impulse-dependent manner. The answer is rather simple: NO is not stored. Accordingly, the classical definition of a neurotransmitter has become blurred or untenable, depending on one's perspective. Many theories can accommodate one exception. However, the realization that NO is not the only gaseous neurotransmitter and that carbon monoxide and hydrogen sulfide play similar transmitter-like roles[43,44] has led to another realization—that the classical transmitters that meet the criteria of a neurotransmitter as defined in the middle of the 20th century may be the exception rather than the norm. The list of exceptions posed by NO to the dogma of traditional neurotransmitters is rather long. For example, NO is not stored in cells, is not released in an exocytotic manner, lacks an active process that terminates its action, does not interact with specific membrane receptors on target cells, and regulates the function of axon terminals presynaptic to the neuron in which NO is synthesized. It is therefore not difficult to understand the skepticism that first met the hypothesis that NO could be a neurotransmitter or to have some sympathy for those who expressed the view that NO is not a transmitter but an alien event, benign or otherwise, intent on making neuroscientists question their most cherished beliefs. See Box 8.4.

Synthesis of Nitric Oxide

The synthesis of NO rivals that of ACh in simplicity, consisting of only one step: the conversion of L-arginine into NO and citrulline (Fig. 8.14). The enzyme responsible for this step is nitric oxide synthase (NOS). Three distinct isoforms of NOS have been cloned: (1) macrophage-inducible NOS (iNOS) is present in microglia, (2) endothelial NOS (eNOS) is found in the endothelial cells that line blood vessels, and (3) the neuronal NOS (nNOS). All three forms require tetrahydrobiopterin as a cofactor and nicotinamide adenine dinucleotide phosphate (NADPH) as a coenzyme. In fact, NOS is identical with the enzyme NADPH-diaphorase, which is expressed in high concentrations in several different types of neurons.

Regulation of Nitric Oxide

NOS is among the most regulated enzymes, and NO levels in various tissues can be modified by several means. Although the general use of the term inducible NOS for iNOS may lead one to suspect that only macrophage-inducible NOS is regulated, all NOS isoforms are regulated. Other regulatory processes include phosphorylation (which decreases NOS activity) and hormonal control. In addition, levels of NOS can be modified by direct inhalation of NO.

Storage, Release, and Inactivation of Nitric Oxide

Classical transmitter status requires that the substance be synthesized in neurons and released from these cells in a calcium-dependent exocytotic fashion; these criteria imply an intermediary storage step as well. However, NO is not stored in vesicles, because NO is an uncharged molecule that diffuses freely across cell membranes. NO is also not released by a calcium-dependent exocytotic mechanism.

Although NO is synthesized in neurons, its ability to diffuse across membranes allows it to modify the activity of other cells. The lack of storage conditions and exocytotic release might suggest that NO simply modifies in a tonic fashion the activity of targets; however, the exquisite regulation of NOS and the critical observation that neuronal stimulation elicits NO release indicate a more phasic (and hence more transmitter-like) role.

NO is also different from conventional transmitters because no active process terminates the action of NO. Inactivation of NO is essentially passive; NO has a short half-life of less than 30 s and decays spontaneously to nitrite. Another means of terminating the action of NO is by reaction of the gas with iron-containing compounds, including hemoglobin.

Actions of Nitric Oxide Synthase on Receptive Neurons and Functional Effects

Another unique aspect of NO as a neurotransmitter-like compound is that NO, in contrast with traditional neurotransmitters and hormones, does not interact with specific membrane-associated receptor proteins

BOX 8.4

GOING FOR GASES AS NEUROTRANSMITTERS

One of the most rewarding experiences for a scientist is to find that long-held prejudices are altogether wrong and that a new, correct insight reveals a novel scientific principle. In the late 1950s, only acetylcholine and the biogenic amines were known to be neurotransmitters. In the mid- to late-1960s, amino acids were acknowledged as neurotransmitters, and scientists realized that, quantitatively, they are the predominant ones, being present in the majority of neurons in the brain, whereas the biogenic amines account for only a few percent. The discovery of the enkephalins and endorphins in the mid-1970s reinforced gradually accumulating evidence that peptides are neurotransmitters. Now we find that there are over a hundred different bioactive peptides in the brain.

At that time, nitric oxide (NO) was found to mediate the ability of macrophages to kill tumor cells and bacteria and to regulate blood vessel relaxation. A short report suggested that NO can be formed in brain tissue. The remarkable properties of NO led to an exploration of what it does in the brain. Progress in the NO field at that time was slow, because assaying NO synthase (NOS), the enzyme that oxidizes the amino acid arginine to NO, was quite tedious, based on the accumulation of nitrite formed from the NO. A much simpler approach was to monitor the conversion of [^{3}H]arginine into [^{3}H]citrulline, which is formed simultaneously with NO, which led to the development of an assay in which 100 or more samples could be processed in an hour. Research on blood vessels revealed that NO acts by stimulating cyclic GMP formation. In the brain, the excitatory neurotransmitter glutamate was known to augment cyclic GMP levels. Glutamate, acting through its NMDA receptor subtype triples NO synthase activity in a matter of seconds, and arginine derivatives that inhibit NOS activity block the elevation of cyclic GMP. This finding causally linked the actions of so prominent a neurotransmitter as glutamate to NO.

To determine if NO was a neurotransmitter, it was necessary to ascertain whether NOS was localized in neurons. The most straightforward approach would be to generate an antibody and do immunohistochemistry. However, purifying NOS protein to generate an antibody proved very difficult, because the enzyme lost activity in attempts to purify it. The addition of calmodulin was found to stabilize the enzyme. Because calmodulin is a calcium-binding protein, this finding immediately explained how NO formation can be triggered rapidly by synaptic activation through glutamate. When glutamate activates its NMDA receptor, calcium ion channels are opened. The calcium rushes into the cell, binds to calmodulin, and activates NOS.

With pure NOS protein, antibodies to the enzyme were soon developed, and NOS was localized by immunohistochemistry. The neuronal form of NOS (nNOS) is present in only about 1% of the neuronal cells in the brain. However, these cells give rise to processes that ramify so extensively that probably every neuron in the brain is exposed to NO.

With purified NOS protein, some amino acid sequence could be obtained and the gene for the enzyme could be cloned. The structure of NOS revealed that it is regulated by many more factors than virtually any other enzyme in biology, including at least five oxidative–reductive cofactors, four phosphorylating enzymes, and three binding proteins. This makes sense because of the unique properties of NO as a gaseous neurotransmitter. Most neurotransmitters are stored in synaptic vesicles with large storage pools so that only a few percent of the transmitter is released with each nerve impulse. By contrast, every time a neuron wishes to release a molecule of NO, it must activate NOS—hence, a requirement for exquisitely subtle regulation of the enzyme.

Neurotransmitters come in chemical classes with numerous biogenic amines, amino acids, and peptides. Might there be at least one other gaseous neurotansmitter? Carbon monoxide (CO) is normally formed in the body by the enzyme heme oxygenase, which is primarily responsible for degrading heme in aging red blood cells. It cleaves the heme ring to form biliverdin, which is rapidly reduced to bilirubin, the pigment that accounts for jaundice in patients with degradation of red blood cells. When the enzyme cleaves the heme ring, CO is released as a single carbon fragment.

The biosynthetic enzyme for a transmitter should be localized to selected neuronal populations. To determine whether CO is a neurotransmitter, with the use of conventional microscopic techniques, heme oxygenase-2, the neuronal form of the enzyme, was shown to be localized to discrete neuronal populations throughout the brain. To seek a neurotransmitter function, the peripheral nervous system, in which synaptic transmission is more readily characterized than in the brain, was used. The myenteric plexus of nerves regulates intestinal peristalsis. A previously unidentified neurotransmitter of myenteric plexus neurons accounts for the relaxation phase of peristalsis. nNOS had already been localized to neurons of the myenteric plexus, and there was some functional evidence that NO might be a neurotransmitter of this pathway. By immunohistochemistry, heme oxygenase-2 was found to be localized to the same plexus neurons as NOS. For functional studies, mice with targeted deletions of the genes for nNOS or heme oxygenase-2 were used (see Box 15.1 for a discussion of knockout technology). In both types of gene knockout mice, intestinal relaxation evoked by neuronal depolarization was reduced about 50%, implying that NO and CO each contribute half of the relaxation.

This finding, along with other evidence, established transmitter functions for both NO and CO. They seem to be functioning as cotransmitters, though exactly how they interact remains a mystery. Such a cotransmitter role reminds us of the surprising but well-established fact that most neurons in the brain contain at least two and sometimes more neurotransmitters. Cotransmission will surely turn out to be a crucial aspect of neurotransmission. Thus, besides overturning a number of dogmas about neurotransmission, NO and CO may help neuroscientists resolve the riddle of cotransmission.

Solomon H. Snyder

on postsynaptic target cells but instead interacts with second-messenger molecules in the target cell to effect a cascade of intracellular processes. In particular, NO stimulates guanlylyl cyclase to increase cGMP levels.

A final aspect of NO that confounds the traditional boundaries of neurotransmitters is its cellular target. Conventional neurotransmitters have effects on postsynaptic cells that are "downstream" of the neuron releasing the transmitter. In contrast, a body of data suggests that NO may be a retrograde messenger, modifying the metabolism and release of transmitter from presynaptic terminals. For example, NO appears to be released from certain hippocampal neurons after NMDA receptor stimulation and to enhance transmitter release from presynaptic elements. This role may be of critical importance in long-term potentiation[45] (see Chapter 55). The release of NO upon NMDA receptor stimulation may also underlie potential neurotoxic actions of NO, a highly reactive species. An excess release of NO associated with NMDA receptor stimulation may be particularly important in the cell loss caused by strokes.

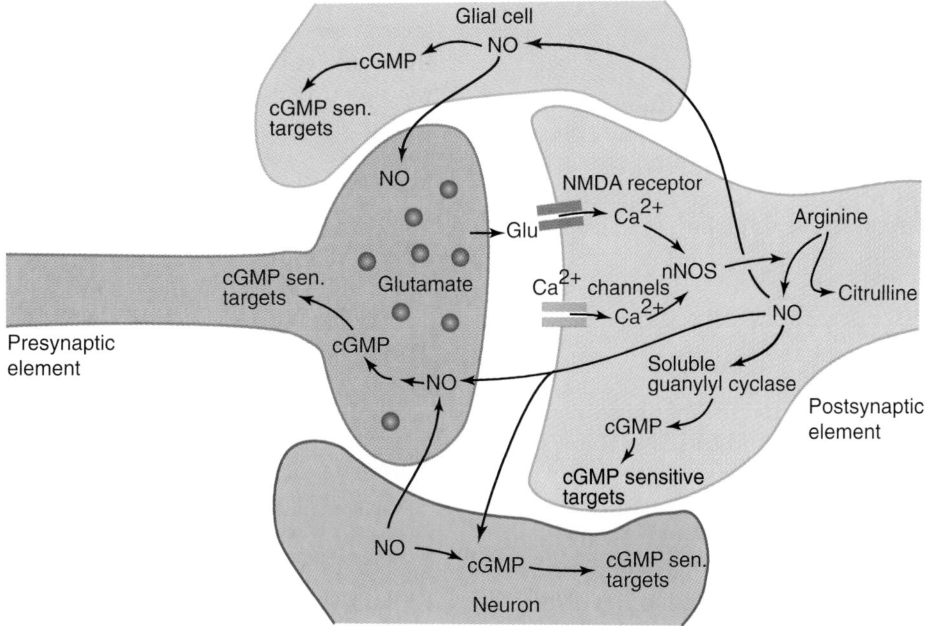

FIGURE 8.14 Schematic representation of a nitric oxide (NO)-containing neuron. NO is formed from arginine by the actions of different nitric oxide synthase (NOS). NO freely diffuses across cell membranes and can thereby influence both presynaptic neurons (such as the glutamatergic presynaptic neuron in the figure) or other cells that are not directly apposed to the NOS-containing neuron; these other cells can be neurons or glia.

Carbon Monoxide

A large and growing body of literature documents the function of NO in the brain and raises the case for consideration of NO as an unconventional neurotransmitter. However, despite this body of data, acceptance of NO as an unconventional transmitter would have been delayed considerably were it not for emerging data that indicate a sibling of NO as a neurotransmitter: carbon monoxide (CO).

There are several striking parallels between NO and CO. Carbon monoxide is a gas that diffuses across cells freely, targets guanlylyl cyclase rather than a membrane protein as a receptor, and lacks a cellular storage compartment. Although CO has not yet received the attention received by NO, awareness of the role of CO as an unconventional transmitter is growing.

CO is formed by the enzyme heme oxygenase (HO), which catalyzes the conversion of heme into biliverdin with the accompanying liberation of CO. The two major isoforms of heme oxygenase are HO-1 and HO-2. HO-1 is an inducible enzyme that is present in glia and a few neurons and present in very high concentrations in the liver and spleen. In contrast, HO-2 is constitutively active rather than inducible and is found in high concentration in neurons, particularly in the cerebellum and hippocampus.[45] Cytochrome P-450 reductase is a necessary electron donor for both HO and NOS.

It is difficult to gauge the degree to which CO may parallel NO, because functional studies of CO have only just started. Recent data, however, do suggest that CO (like NO) may be an endothelial-derived relaxing factor of blood vessels.[46] Moreover, studies of mice genetically engineered to lack eNOS have indicated that cerebral circulatory response is relatively normal, despite the absence of eNOS, and suggest that CO may function cooperatively with NO to maintain vascular tone.

The CNS Distribution of Nitric Oxide-Containing Neurons

Although it is not possible to talk about the distribution of NO-containing neurons in the CNS (NO is not stored and diffuses readily across membranes after being formed), NOS is discretely localized to several different populations of cells in the CNS. Histochemical studies of the distribution of NADPH–diaphorase, as well as subsequent studies using antibodies directed against NOS, reveal the presence of both projection neurons and interneurons. Among the latter is a distinct population of cortical neurons that contain NOS, as do certain hippocampal neurons; both of these populations of cells have been implicated in the pathogenesis of schizophrenia. Certain striatal interneurons also contain NOS.

Among the projection neurons that contain NOS are the cholinergic cells of the pons discussed earlier. The functional significance of colocalization of NOS and acetylcholine in these neurons is not known.

Growth Factors Act in Part as Unconventional Transmitters

The section on nitric oxide presented several striking differences between conventional and unconventional transmitters. Another class of unconventional transmitters, the **growth factors**, has certain features in common with the transmitter gases but differs in other ways. These molecules are discussed in detail in Chapter 21. However, we introduce them briefly now in order to contrast them with the other signaling molecules discussed above.

Growth factors are an extremely heterogeneous group of proteins that regulate the survival, differentiation, and growth of various cell types;[47] some growth factors specifically target neurons.[48,49] One similarity between the neurotrophic factors and NO is that both are capable of influencing presynaptic cells. Thus, NO has been shown to diffuse out of cells and alter transmitter release from presynaptic axons, and neurotrophic factors provide trophic support for developing axons innervating a region in which growth factors are expressed in cells (hence the term "trophic"). Growth factors are also unconventional in that the release of these proteins may be through both constitutive and regulated pathways.

There are several different classes of growth factors, each class comprising many different growth factors. For example, the neurotrophins include nerve growth factor (NGF), brain-derived neurotrophic factor (BDNF), neurotrophin-3 (NT-3), NT-4, and NT-5. Unfortunately, our knowledge of the basic cellular biology of any single growth factor, even one known as long as NGF, is incomplete. Accordingly, we draw on examples from several different growth factors to illustrate general characteristics of relevance.

Synthesis of Growth Factors

Growth factors have been identified historically by examining the effects of crude extracts of tissues or biological fluids on a bioassay of cell survival or growth. After the identification of some serum or tissue factor as being capable of sustaining cell survival or differentiation, the crude extract is further purified, culminating in the isolation and purification of the protein. The protein is then sequenced. This tedious approach requires very large amounts of starting material and a sensitive and reliable bioassay. It is essentially the same (and therefore confronted with the same difficulties) as the early methods used to discover and characterize pituitary and CNS peptides. Contemporary approaches to the identification of growth factors frequently emphasize cloning of growth factors on the basis of sequence homology; the cloned genes are then expressed in various cell lines and tested in various bioassays. This approach can be a source of insight into potential regulatory features of growth factors and their cellular biology.

Molecular approaches have often provided interesting and unexpected information on the synthesis of growth factors. For example, certain growth factors are translated from multiple mRNAs.[50] One such example is BDNF, a neurotrophin that has a heterogeneous distribution in the CNS and several distinct functions, some classically associated with growth factors and others more transmitter-like. The BDNF gene has five different exons that encode the mature BDNF protein. Each of four 5′ exons has a separate promoter, and alternative use of these promoters and differential splicing gives rise to eight different BDNF mRNAs. Despite the complexity of the molecular "synthesis" of BDNF, there is only one mature BDNF protein; it has been speculated that various BDNF transcripts may produce BDNF protein under different conditions or give rise to different amounts of protein.

Current knowledge of the posttranslational processing of growth factors is limited. In the case of NGF, the mature protein is cleaved from a prohormone, in a manner analogous to the formation of peptide transmitters. The processing of the NGF prohormone is unique, however, in that three subunits are present. One of them, the gamma subunit, is a serine protease that is thought to cleave the prohormone to yield the mature protein. Other neurotrophins, including BDNF and NT-3, also are formed by cleavage of a prohormone; the identity and degree of specificity of the responsible enzymes are only now being determined. One final aspect of the biosynthesis of growth factors (in its broad definition) resides in their assembly. The neurotrophins form biologically active heteromers *in vitro*, but *in vivo* have been thought to form exclusively homodimers. However, recent data suggest that heterodimers of NGF, BDNF, and NT-3 can be formed in mammalian cells and may also be formed *in vivo*.[51]

Storage and Release of Growth Factors

Surprisingly little is known about the storage and release of growth factors. Almost no studies of the storage of growth factors, particularly electron microscopic studies of intracellular localization, have been undertaken. In part, this lack is due to the difficulty in generating specific antibodies to growth factors, because individual growth factors (e.g., BDNF) within a family (neurotrophins) have in common a high degree of homology with other members of the family (e.g., NT-3). However, significant progress is now being made in generating specific antisera and, in conjunction with studies of localization of growth factors in cells transfected with specific growth factor genes, the intracellular localization of some growth factors can be tracked.

Neurons secrete proteins by two distinct processes (see Chapter 7). The constitutive pathway for secretion is not triggered by extracellular stimulation and is used to secrete membrane components, viral proteins, and extracellular matrix molecules. In this pathway, Golgi-derived vesicles continuously fuse with the plasma membrane. In contrast, the release of conventional neurotransmitters is controlled by extracellular signals and uses the so-called regulated pathway. For example, peptide protein precursors contain an N-terminal signal sequence that allows the protein to be targeted to the endoplasmic reticulum and then to the Golgi network to ultimately be packaged into vesicles.

Some growth factors lack a signal sequence, and thus growth factors have generally been considered to be processed by the constitutive pathway, despite the clear data indicating release of these proteins. Data from studies of neurotrophins suggest that BDNF and NGF are secreted through *both* constitutive and regulated pathways. With the use of antibodies to examine the localization of BDNF in a transfected cell line,[52] BDNF has been shown to be present in chromogranin-containing secretory granules. This observation suggests that BDNF may be present in certain vesicles in neurons.

Under basal conditions, BDNF and NGF may be constitutively released from the soma and proximal dendrites. However, depolarization induced by a high concentration of potassium or by glutamate leads to regulated release, which is seen in the distal as well as proximal processes of the neuron.[52,53] This activity-dependent release does not appear to depend on extracellular calcium but is critically dependent on intracellular calcium stores[54]; this dependency distinguishes BDNF and NGF from conventional transmitters, which are not released in the absence of extracellular calcium. Thus, the release of at least certain growth factors differs from that of conventional transmitters by occurring through both constitutive and regulated pathways and by not being dependent on extracellular calcium concentrations. After seizures, BDNF can be seen to move into the axons of hippocampal pyramidal cells and then into perikarya, suggesting that it is poised to be released; about 2 h after seizures, BDNF immunoreactivity is observed in the neuropil surrounding pyramidal cells and in the area where mossy fibers terminate, suggesting that the growth factor has been released from somatodendritic sites.[54] In the developing visual system, there is also evidence of anterograde transport and release of neurotrophins.[55]

Functional Significance of Growth Factors as Neurotransmitters

Growth factors have a wide array of functions (Chapter 21).[56] As indicated by their name, growth factors support the development and differentiation of neurons. Thus, the survival and axonal ingrowth of neurons to their final targets typically requires certain factors expressed in the targeted cells. After the axon of a neuron has reached its target and survives, it does not appear to require further support from growth factors under most conditions. This ability of growth factors to determine survival, differentiation, and final target destination is certainly not part of the normal list of functions ascribed to neurotransmitters, although recent data have suggested that conventional transmitters may also have trophic roles.[57,58] It is not clear that the release of the growth factor in this context is a chemical signal that conveys information to neurons or provides critical sustenance.

What information then supports the contention that growth factors may be unconventional transmitters, even under the broad definition that we have used? First, growth factors are stored and released from neurons. The release of growth factors is now thought to occur through the regulated as well as constitutive pathways, suggesting some specificity in release. Some data are consistent with the speculation that BDNF is stored in vesicles. The synthesis and release of growth factors are also under transynaptic control. For example, NGF and BDNF expression is controlled by neuronal activity, with glutamate and ACh increasing expression and GABA decreasing expression of these neurotrophic factors. Moreover, the induction of BDNF by various treatments is regionally, spatially, and temporally distinct. Thus, seizures result in patterns of increases of various BDNF exon-specific mRNAs that differ across hippocampal subregions, and the specific patterns of promotor activation depend on the stimulus. All these characteristics suggest that, in addition to the synthesis and storage of neurotrophins in neurons, the synthesis and release of these growth factors are regulated by neuronal activity, and thus growth factors may participate in both receiving information and conveying information across cells.

The second characteristic suggesting a transmitter role for growth factors is that they appear to regulate other neurons. The receptors for neurotrophins, the tyrosine kinase (trk) receptors, are expressed in neurons. The trk receptors are members of a class of transmembrane receptor protein tyrosine kinases and have an intracellular catalytic domain that is activated upon ligand binding. Neurotrophic factors regulate key intracellular signaling pathways upon stimulation of the appropriate receptor.[59] BDNF has been shown to stimulate phosphoinositide turnover in neurons[60] and thus has in common with NO the ability to regulate a key intracellular transduction mechanism. BDNF has also been shown to increase NT-3 expression in the cerebellum and hippocampus,[61,62] again suggesting that growth factors regulate the functional activity of target cells.

The aforedescribed data suggest that growth factors can regulate the functional activities of neurons but do not address a physiological role for growth factors independent of their effects on growth and survival. However, several recent studies have suggested that BDNF may regulate hippocampal function during the induction of long-term potentiation. Mice carrying a deletion in the coding region of the BDNF gene show significantly reduced long-term potentiation,[63] whereas BDNF administration to hippocampal slices markedly enhances long-term potentiation.[64] (Chapter 55).

Summary

The choice of the term "unconventional transmitters" to describe the gases and growth factors is quite restrained. These compounds seem to be designed as challenges to the criteria for classical transmitters. They may be synthesized by the constitutive rather than the regulated pathway, are not necessarily stored, do not obligatorily depend upon calcium for release, and make a mockery of the designation of neurons as pre- and postsynaptic, because they often influence afferents. These considerations suggest that the unconventional transmitters are probably unconventional in their functional roles as well as their metabolism.

SYNAPTIC TRANSMITTERS IN PERSPECTIVE

We have considered chemically coded synaptic transmission, focusing on the biochemical processes involved in synthesis, storage, release, and inactivation. Several things are apparent from this discussion. One is that it is difficult to discuss the biochemical nature of synaptic transmission without reference to other critical information about the structure and function of neurons. Neuroscience is multidisciplinary, requiring an understanding of several different aspects of cellular function to come to grips with the basic principles of the biochemical nature of synaptic transmission. In addition, concepts of synaptic transmission are still in flux, frequently requiring reevaluation and revision. This can be most clearly seen in the evolving definition of a neurotransmitter.

Through the years, the rather strict definition of a neurotransmitter, based on certain criteria derived primarily from studies of peripheral sites, has shifted. The status of classical transmitters as the sole members of the royal family of transmitters was challenged by the emergence of peptide transmitters, the pretenders to the throne. Sufficient data were amassed to establish that the peptides were at least cousins, if not siblings, of the classical transmitters. Soon after this upheaval came the unexpected finding that more than one transmitter is present in a neuron. And now we are just beginning to come to grips with the concept that some transmitters may be gases—and that growth factors essential in development can also serve as neurotransmitters!

The use of the terms "conventional" and "unconventional" in discussing transmitters is indicative of our current unease with the expanding definition of transmitters. This is not an isolated event: all aspects of neuroscience are similarly expanding, which is one of the characteristics that make neuroscience such a tremendously exciting (albeit occasionally frustrating) discipline.

References

1. Brazier, M. A. B. (1959). The historical development of neurophysiology. In *Handbook of Physiology* (J. Field, ed.), Sect. 1, Vol. 1, pp. 1–58. Am Physiol. Soc., Washington, DC.
2. Grundfest, H. (1959). Synaptic and ephaptic transmission. In *Handbook of Physiology* (J. Field, ed.), Sect. 1, Vol. 1, pp. 147–197. Am. Physiol. Soc., Washington, DC.
3. Peinado, A., Yuste, R., and Katz, L. C. (1993). Extensive dye coupling between rat neocortical neurons during the period of circuit formation. *Neuron* **10:** 103–114.
4. Kuehne, W. (1888). On the origin and causation of vital movement. *Proc. R. Soc. London, Ser. B* **44:** 427.
5. Sherrington, C. S. (1906). *The Integrative Action of the Nervous System.* Scribner's, New York.
6. Bernard, C. (1849). Action physiologique des venins (curare). *C. R. Seances Soc. Biol. Ses Fil.* **1:** 90.
7. Elliott, T. R. (1905). On the action of adrenaline. *J. Physiol.* **32:** 401.
8. Loewi, O. (1921). Uber Humorale Ubertragbarkeit Herznervenwirkung. *Pfluegers Arch. Gesamte Physiol. Menschen Tiere* **189:** 239.
9. Cooper, J. R., Bloom, F. E., and Roth, R. H. (1996). *The Biochemical Basis of Neuropharmacology,* 7th ed. Oxford University Press, New York.
10. Scatton, B., Dennis, T., and Curet, O. (1984). Increase in dopamine and DOPAC levels in noradrenergic nerve terminals after electrical stimulation of the ascending noradrenergic pathways. *Brain Res.* **298:** 193–196.
11. Ichinose, H., Ohye, T., Takahashi, E., Seki, N., Hori, T., Segawa, M., Nomura, Y., Endo, K., Tanaka, K., Tanaka, H., and Tsuji, S. (1994). Hereditary progressive dystonia with marked diurnal fluctuation caused by mutations in the GTP cyclohydrolase I gene. *Nat. Genet.* **8:** 236–242.
12. Clark, J. A., and Amara, S. G. (1993). Amino acid neurotransmitter transporters: Structure, function, and molecular diversity. *BioEssays* **15:** 323–332.
13. Moore, R. Y., and Bloom, F. E., (1978). *Central catecholamine neuron systems: Anatomy and physiology of the dopamine systems,* Vol. 1.
14. Moore, R. Y., and Bloom, F. E., (1979). *Central catecholamine neuron systems: Anatomy and physiology of the norepinepheine and epinephrine systems,* Vol. 2.
15. Frazer, A., and Hensler, J. G. (1994). Serotonin. In *Basic Neurochemistry* (G. J. Siegel, B. W. Agranoff, R. W. Albers, and P. B. Molinoff, eds.), pp. 283–309. 5th ed. Raven Press, New York.
16. Stone, T. W. (1993). Neuropharmacology of quinolinic and kynurenic acids. *Pharmacol. Rev.* **45:** 309–379.
17. Heninger, G. R., Delgado, P. L., Charney, D. S. (1996). The revised monoamine theory of depression: a modulatory role for monoamines, based on new findings from monoamine depletion experiments in humans. *Pharmacopsychiatry* **29:** 2–11.
18. Paul, S. P. (1995). GABA and glycine. In *Neuropyschopharmacology: The Fourth Generation of Progress* (F. E. Bloom and D. J. Kupfer, eds.), pp. 87–94. Raven Press, New York.
19. DeLorcy, T. N., and Olsen, R. W. (1994). GABA and glycine. In *Basic Neurochemistry* (G. J. Siegel, B. W. Agranoff, R. W. Albers, and P. B. Molinoff, eds.), pp. 389–400. 5th ed. Raven Press, New York.
20. Roberts, E. (1986). GABA: The road to neurotransmitter status. In *Benzodiazepine/GABA Receptors and Chloride Channels: Structural and Functional Properties* (Olsen and Venter, eds.), pp. 1–39. Liss, New York.
21. Dingeldine, R., and McBain, C. J. (1994). Excitatory amino acid transmitters. In *Basic Neurochemistry* (G. J. Siegel, B. W. Agranoff, R. W. Albers, and P. B. Molinoff, eds.), pp. 367–388. 5th ed. Raven Press, New York.
22. Conti, F., and Minelli, A. (1994). Glutamate immunoreactivity in rat cerebral cortex is reversibly abolished by 6-diazo-5-oxo-L-norleucine (DON), an inhibitor of phosphate-activated glutaminase. *J. Histochem. Cytochem.* **42:** 717–726.
23. Naito, S., and Ueda, T. (1985). Characterization of glutamate uptake into synaptic vesicles. *J. Neurochem.* **44:** 99–109.
24. Chaudhry, F. A., Lehre, K. P., van Lookeren Campagne, M., Otterson, O. P., Danbolt, N. C., and Storm-Mathisen, J. (1996). Glutamate transporters in glial plasma membranes: Highly differentiated localizations revealed by quantitative ultrastructural immunocytochemistry. *Neuron* **15:** 711–720.
25. Fatt, P., and Katz, B. (1952). Spontaneous subthreshold activities at motor nerve endings. *J. Physiol.* **117:** 109–128.
26. Happe, H. K., and Murrin, L. C. (1995). In situ hybridization analysis of CHOTT, a creatine transporter, in the rat central nervous system. *J. Comp. Neurol.* **351:** 94–103.
27. Wu, D., and Hersch, L. B. (1994). Choline acetyltransferase: celebrating its fiftieth year. *J. Neurochem.* **62:** 1653–1663.
28. Usdin, T. B., Elden, L. E., Bonner, T. I., and Erickson, J. D. (1995). Molecular biology of the vesicular ACh transporter. *Trends Neurosci.* **18:** 218–224.
29. Berrard, S., Varoqui, H., Cervine, R., Israel, M., Mallet, J., and Diebler, M. F. (1995). Coregulation of two embedded gene products, choline acetyltransferase and the vesicular acetylcholine transporter. *J. Neurochem.* **65:** 939–942.
30. Taylor, P., and Brown, J. H. (1994). Acetylcholine. In *Basic Neuro-*

chemistry (G. J. Siegel, B. W. Agranoff, R. W. Albers, and P. B. Molinoff, eds.), 5th ed. Raven Press, New York.

31. Fernandez, H. L., Moreno, R. D., and Inestrosa, N. C. (1996). Tetrametric (G4) acetylcholinesterase: Structure, localization, and physiological regulation. *J. Neurochem.* **66:** 1335–1346.
32. Greenfield, S. A. (1991). A non-cholinergic role of ACHE in the substantia nigra: From neuronal secretion to the generation of movement. *Mol. Cell. Neurobiol.* **11:** 55–77.
33. Appleyard, M., and Jahnsen, H. (1992). Actions of acetylcholinesterase in the guinea-pig cerebellar cortex in vitro. *Neuroscience* **47:** 291–301.
34. Schumacher, M., Maulet, Y., Camp, S., and Taylor, P. (1988). Multiple messenger RNA species give rise to the structural diversity of acetylcholinesterase. *J. Biol. Chem.* **263:** 18979–18987.
35. Seidman, S., Sternfeld, M., Ben Azziz-Aloya, R., Timberg, R., Kaufer-Nachum, D., and Soreq, H. (1995). Synaptic and epidermal accumulations of human acetylcholinesterase are encoded by alternative 3′-terminal exons. *Mol. Cell. Biol.* **15:** 2993–3002.
36. Lapidot-Lifson, Y., Prody, C. A., Ginzberg, D., Meytes, D., Zakut, H., and Soreq, H. (1989). Coamplification of human acetylcholinesterase and butrylcholinesterase genes in blood cells: Correlation with various leukemias and abnormal megakaryacytopoiesis. *Proc. Natl. Acad. Sci. U.S.A.* **86:** 4715–4719.
37. Soreq, H., Pantinkin, D., Lev-Lehman, E., Grifman, M., Ginzberg, D., Eckstein, F., and Zakut, H. (1994). Antisense oligonucleotide inhibiton of acetylcholinesterase gene expression induces progenitor cell expansion and suppresses hematopoeietic apoptosis ex vivo. *Proc. Natl. Acad. Sci. U.S.A.* **91:** 7907–7911.
38. Bean, A. J., and Roth, R. H. (1992). Dopamine-neurotensin interactions in mesocortical neurons. Evidence from microdialysis studies. *Ann. N. Y. Acad. Sci.* **668:** 43–53.
39. Sossin, W. S., Sweet-Cordero, A., and Scheller, R. H. (1990). Dale's hypothesis revisited: different neuropeptides derived from a common prohormone are targeted to different processes. *Proc. Natl. Acad. Sci. USA* **87:** 4845–4848.
40. Kislauskis, E., Bullock, B., McNeil, S., and Dobner, P. R. (1988). The rat gene encoding neurotensin and neuromedin N. Structure, tissue-specific expression, and evolution of exon sequences. *J. Biol. Chem.* **263:** 4963–4968.
41. Kitabgi, P., De Nadal, F., Rovere, C., and Bidard, J.-N. (1992). Biosynthesis, maturation, release, and degradation of neurotensin and neuromedin N. *Ann. N. Y. Acad. Sci.* **668:** 30–42.
42. Shipp, M. A., Vijayaraghavan, J., Schmidt, E. V., Masteller, E. L., D'Adamio, L., Hersch, L. B., and Reinherz, E. L. (1989). Common acute lymphoblastic leukemia antigen (CALLA) is active neutral endopeptidase 24.11 ("enkaphalinase"): Direct evidence by CDNA transfection analysis. *Proc. Natl. Acad. Sci. U.S.A.* **86:** 297–301.
43. Dawson, T. M., and Snyder, S. H. (1994). Gases as biological messengers: Nitric oxide and carbon monoxide in the brain. *J. Neurosci.* **14:** 5147–5159.
44. Abe., K., and Kimura, H. (1996). The possible role of hydrogen sulfide as an endogenous neuromodulator. *J. Neurosci.* **16:** 1066–1071.
45. O'Dell, T. J., Huang, P. L., Dawson, T. M., Dinnerman, J. L., Snyder, S. H., Kandel, E. R., and Fishman, M. C. (1994). Endothelial NOS and the blockade of LTP by NOS inhibitors lacking neuronal NOS. *Science* **265:** 542–546.
46. Zakhary, R., Gaine, S. P., Dinennan, J. L., Ruat, M., Flavahan, N. A., and Snyder, S. H. (1996). Heme oxygenase 2: Endothelial and neuronal localization and role in endothelial-dependent relaxation. *Proc. Natl. Acad. Sci. U.S.A.* **93:** 795–798.
47. Patterson, P. H. (1995). Neuronal growth and differentiation factors and synaptic plasticity. In *Neuropsychopharmacology: The Fourth Generation of Progress* (F. E. Bloom and D. J. Kupfer, eds.), pp. 619–630. Raven Press, New York.
48. Russell, D. S. (1995). Neurotrophins: Mechanisms of action. *Neuroscientist* **1:** 3–6.
49. Thoenen, H. (1995). Neurotrophins and neuronal plasticity. *Science* **270:** 593–598.
50. Lindvall, O., Kokaia, Z., Bengzon, J., Elmer, E., and Kokaia, M. (1994). Neurotrophins and brain insults. *Trends Neurosci.* **17:** 490–496.
51. Heymach, J. V., Jr., and Shooter, E. M. (1995). The biosynthesis of neurotrophin heterodimers by transfected mammalian cells. *J. Biol. Chem.* **270:** 12297–12304.
52. Goodman, L. J., Valverde, J., Lim, F., Geschwind, M. D., Federoff, H. J., Geller, A. I., and Hefti, F. (1996). Regulated release and polarized localization of brain-derived neurotrophic factor in hippocampal neurons. *Mol. Cell. Neurosci.* **7:** 222–238.
53. Thoenen, H. (1995). Neurotrophins and neuronal plasticity. *Science* **270:** 593–598.
54. Wetmore, C., Olson, L., and Bean, A. J. (1994). Regulation of brain-derived neurotrophic factor (BDNF) expression and release from hippocampal neurons is mediated by non-NMDA type glutamate receptors. *J. Neurosci.* **14:** 1688–1700.
55. von Bartheld, C. S., Byers, M. R., Williams, R., and Bothwell, M. (1996). Anterograde transport of neurotrophins and axodendritic transfer in the developing visual system. *Nature (London)* **379:** 830–833.
56. Ip, N. Y., and Yancopoulos, G. D. (1996). The neurotrophins and CNTF: Two families of collaborative neurotrophic factors. *Annu. Rev. Neurosci.* **19:** 491–515.
57. Whitaker-Azmitia, P. M., Druse, M., Walker, P., and Lauder, J. M. (1995). Serotonin as a developmental signal. *Behav. Brain Res.* **73:** 19–29.
58. Reinoso, B. S., Undie, A. S., and Levitt, P. (1996). Dopamine receptors mediate differential morphological effects on cerebral cortical neurons in vitro. *J. Neurosci. Res.* **43:** 439–453.
59. Segal, R. A., and Greenberg, M. E. (1996). Intracellular signaling pathways activated by neurotrophic factors. *Annu. Rev. Neurosci.* **19:** 463–489.
60. Widmer, H. R., Ohsawa, F., Knusel, B., and Hefti, F. (1993). Down-regulation of phosphatidylinositol response to BDNF and NT-3 in cultures of cortical neurons. *Brain Res.* **614:** 325–334.
61. Leingartner, A., Heisenberg, C. P., Kolbeck, R., Thoenen, H., and Lindholm, D. (1994). Brain-derived neurotrophic factor increase neurotrophin-3 expression in cerebellar granule cells. *J. Biol. Chem.* **269:** 828–830.
62. Lindholm, D., da Penha Berzaghi, M., Cooper, J., Thoenen, H., and Castren, E. (1994). Brain-derived neurotrophic factor and neurotrophin-4 increase neurotrophin-3 expressed in rat hippocampus. *Int. J. Dev. Neurosci.* **12:** 745–751.
63. Korte, M., Carroll, P., Wolf, E., Brem, G., Thoenen, H., and Bonhoeffer, T. (1995). Hippocampal long-term potentiation is unpaired in mice lacking brain-derived neurotrophic factor. *Proc. Natl. Acad. Sci. U.S.A.* **92:** 8856–8860.
64. Patterson, S. L., Grover, L. M., Schwartzkroin, P. A., and Bothwell, M. (1992). Neurotrophin expression in rat hippocampal slices: A stimulus paradigm inducing LTP in CAI evokes increases in BDNF and NT-3 mRNAs. *Neuron* **9:** 1081–1088.

CHAPTER

9

Neurotransmitter Receptors

M. Neal Waxham

Chemical synaptic transmission is the functional process for neuron-to-neuron and neuron-to-muscle communication. In its simplest form, chemical transmission can be reduced to a two-step process. First, transmitter is released from the presynaptic terminal (Chapter 7). Second, transmitter diffuses throughout the synaptic cleft and binds to specific receptors embedded in the presynaptic and postsynaptic cell membranes. The structure of these receptors and the nature of their response are the primary focus of this chapter and extend into Chapter 10.

The nature, magnitude, and sign of a neuron's response to a neurotransmitter are determined by the type of receptor(s) present in the plasma membrane. The nature of the response can be either the direct opening of an ion channel (ionotropic receptors) or the modulation of the concentration of intracellular metabolites (metabotropic receptors). The magnitude of the response is determined by receptor number, the state of the receptors, and the amount of transmitter released. Finally, the sign of the response can be inhibitory or excitatory. The temporal and spatial summation of information conveyed by the activation of the receptors determines whether the postsynaptic cell will fire an action potential or the muscle will contract. Transmitters that bind to metabotropic receptors may cause no apparent change in the synaptic potential. Rather, the binding of transmitter to receptor may activate a cascade of events that modulate the opening and closing of ion channels or regulate other cellular processes. On the presynaptic terminal, released transmitter can activate receptors (termed autoreceptors) that serve the important function of modifying the subsequent release of neurotransmitter.

The receptors that mediate the responses to transmitters are of two structurally distinct types. An **ionotropic receptor** is a relatively large, multisubunit complex composed of five individual proteins that combine to form an ion channel through the membrane (Fig. 9.1A). These ion channels are largely impermeable to ions in the absence of neurotransmitter. Neurotransmitter binding to an ionotropic receptor induces a series of very rapid conformational changes that open the channel and permit ions to flow down their electrochemical gradients. Changes in membrane current resulting from ligand binding to ionotropic receptors are measured on a submillisecond time scale. The ion flow ceases when transmitter dissociates from the receptor or when the receptor becomes desensitized, a process discussed in more detail later in this chapter.

In contrast, a **metabotropic receptor** is composed of a single polypeptide (Fig. 9.1B) and exerts its effects through a mechanism different from that of the ionotropic receptors. When a metabotropic receptor binds transmitter, it also undergoes a conformational change. However, instead of opening an ion channel, this conformational change produces a state of the receptor that, in the majority of cases, binds to and activates GTP-binding proteins (G proteins). Transmitters that activate metabotropic receptors typically produce responses of slower onset and longer duration (from tenths of seconds to potentially hours) owing to the series of enzymatic steps necessary to produce a response.

We consider the structure of the ionotropic receptor family first and then turn to a description of the structure of the metabotropic receptors. In each section, we present information to establish a general structural model of each receptor type, and then use this information to guide the description of other related neurotransmitter receptors. The order in which receptor types are presented is based predominantly on struc-

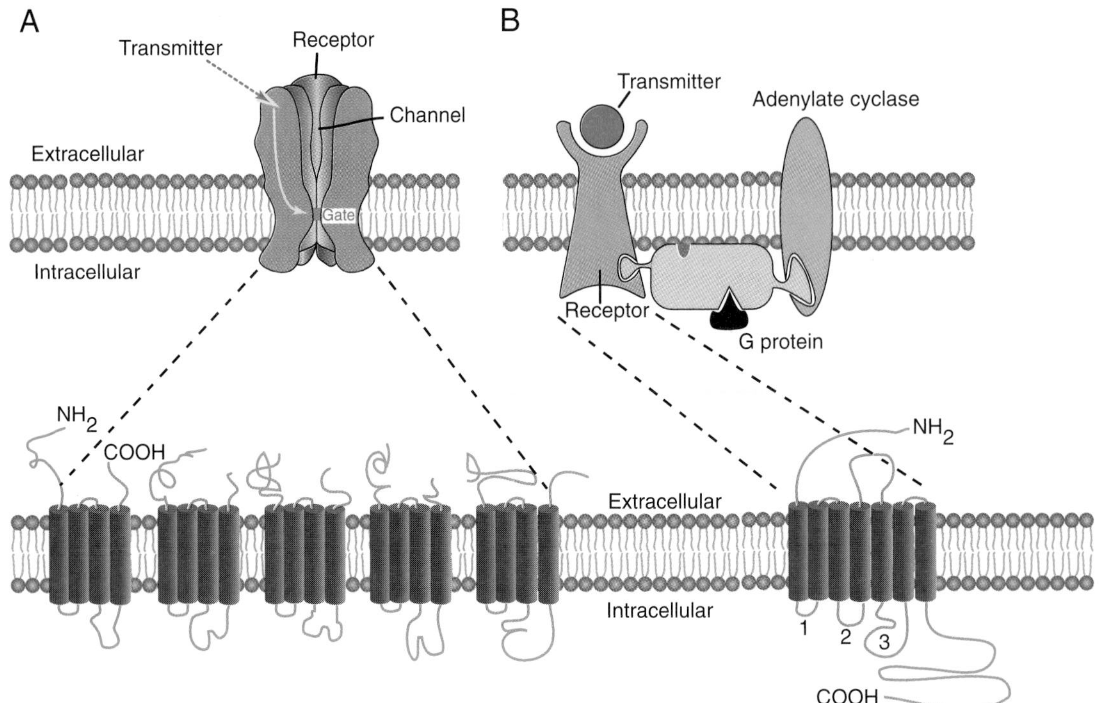

FIGURE 9.1 Structural comparison of ionotropic and metabotropic receptors. (A) Ionotropic receptors bind transmitter, and this binding directly translates into the opening of the ion channel through a series of conformational changes. Ionotropic receptors are composed of multiple subunits. Shown are the five subunits that together form the functional nAChR. Note that each of the nAChR subunits wraps back and forth through the membrane four times and the mature receptor has two copies of the α subunit. (B) Metabotropic receptors bind transmitter and, through a series of conformational changes, bind to G proteins and activate them. G proteins then activate enzymes such as adenylate cyclase to produce cAMP. Through the activation of cAMP-dependent protein kinase, ion channels become phosphorylated, which affects their gating properties. Metabotropic receptors are single subunits. They are predicted to have seven membrane-spanning segments, with the cytoplasmic loops formed between the segments providing the points of interaction for coupling to G proteins. Adapted from Ref. 97.

tural relatedness and should not be interpreted as representing their relative importance in the function of the nervous system.

IONOTROPIC RECEPTORS

All ionotropic receptors are membrane-bound protein complexes that form an ion-permeable pore in the membrane. A comparison of the deduced amino acid sequence of all of the cloned ionotropic receptors indicates a similar overall structure, although two independent ancestral genes likely gave rise to two major families of ionotropic receptors. One family includes the nicotinic acetylcholine receptor (nAChR), the γ-aminobutyric acid A ($GABA_A$) receptor, the glycine receptor, and one subclass of serotonin receptors.[1] The other family comprises the many types of ionotropic glutamate receptors.[2]

Our understanding of ionotropic receptor structure and function has expanded enormously in the past 20 years. Molecular approaches have provided elegant and extensive descriptions of gene families encoding different receptors. Systems for expressing cloned cDNAs have permitted detailed structure–function analysis of each receptor subtype. Expression of subunits independently and together has resulted in a detailed concept of the necessity and sufficiency of the multisubunit nature of the ionotropic receptor family. With the addition of biophysical and electron microscopic examination, events associated with the opening of at least one ionotropic receptor, the nAChR, are available at nearly atomic resolution.[3–5]

The nAChR Is a Model for the Structure of Ionotropic Receptors

The nAChR is so named because the plant alkaloid nicotine can bind to the ACh-binding site and activate the receptor. Nicotine is therefore called an **agonist** of ACh because it binds to the receptor and opens it. However, bear in mind that ACh is the endogenous neurotransmitter that normally opens this receptor. In contrast, **antagonists** are molecules that bind to the receptor and inhibit its function. Agonists and antagonists are powerful tools that permit characterization of the structure and function of individual receptor subtypes.

We know more about the structure of the nAChR than about any other ionotropic receptor, primarily because electric organs of certain species of fish, such as the *Torpedo* ray, contain nearly crystalline arrays of this molecule (Fig. 9.2). The electric organ is a specialized form of skeletal muscle that has the potential to generate large voltages (as much as 500 V in some cases) from the simultaneous opening of arrays of these ligand-gated ion channels. The electric organ is a rich source of nAChRs, and the majority of biochemical and structural analyses have been done on receptors isolated from it. The snake venom toxin α-bungarotoxin binds to the nAChR with high affinity and specificity; thus α-bungarotoxin affinity columns are used to purify almost homogeneous nAChRs.

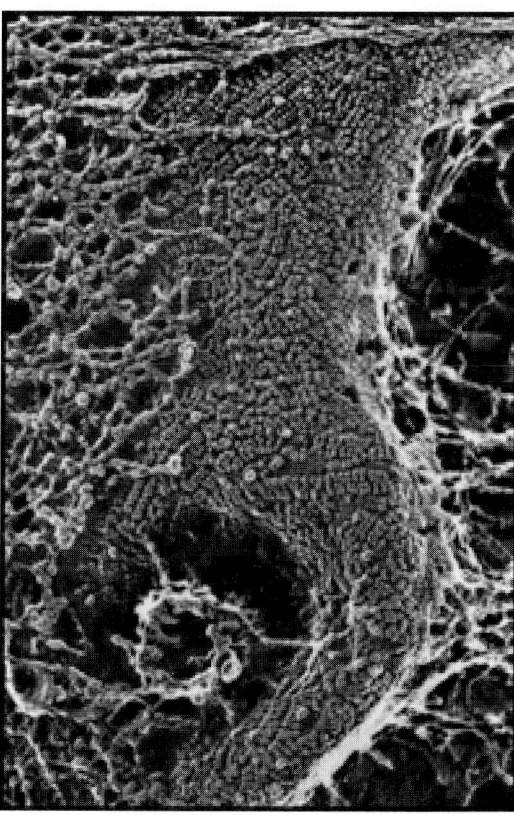

FIGURE 9.2 Panoramic view of the postsynaptic membrane of an electrocyte in the *Torpedo* electric organ, revealed by "deep-etch" electron microscopy. To the left, a lacelike basal lamina lies above the membrane, obscuring it from view. Near the bottom-center, the basal lamina assumes a ringlike appearance as it dips down into a dark postsynaptic invagination. In the center of the field, the basal lamina has been fractured away to reveal the true external surface of the postsynaptic membrane. Thereupon, clusters and linear arrays of 8- to 9-nm protrusions can be clearly seen. These represent the acetylcholine receptor oligomers. To the right, the postsynaptic membrane has been freeze-fractured away, thus revealing an underlying meshwork of cytoplasmic filaments that supports the postsynaptic membrane and its receptors. ×175,000. Adapted from Ref. 97. Original courtesy of J. Heuser.

The nAChR Is a Heteromeric Protein Complex with a Distinct Appearance

The structure of the nAChR is typical of ionotropic receptors. The nAChR from *Torpedo* is composed of five subunits (see Fig. 9.1) and has a native molecular mass of approximately 290 kDa. The subunits are designated α, β, γ, and δ, and each receptor complex contains two copies of the α subunit. The subunits are homologous membrane-bound proteins that congregate in the bilayer as a ring, forming a central pore. Pioneering electron microscopic analysis of nAChRs by Nigel Unwin has provided the best image of the structural appearance of this receptor (Fig. 9.3). The extracellular domains form a funnel-shaped opening that extends approximately 100 Å from the outer leaflet of the membrane, and the funnel has an inside diameter of 20–25 Å.[3] The funnel shape is thought to force ions to interact with amino acids in the limited space of the pore without producing a major barrier to diffusion. This funnel narrows near the center of the bilayer to form the domain of the receptor that determines the opened or closed state of the ion pore. The intracellular domain of the receptor forms a short exit for ions traveling into the cell and an entrance for ions traveling out of the cell. The intracellular domain also establishes the association of the receptor with other intracellular proteins that determine the subcellular localization of the nAChR. The arrangement of the subunits in the receptor is somewhat debatable; the two α subunits appear to be separated by either the β or the γ subunit. Much biochemical work supports a model in which the γ subunit lies between the two α subunits. However, electron microscopic studies assume that the β subunit lies between the two α subunits.[3–5]

Each nAChR Subunit Has Multiple Membrane-Spanning Segments

The primary structures of the nAChR subunits were obtained by the efforts of Shosaka Numa and his colleagues.[6,7] The deduced amino acid sequence from cloned mRNAs indicates that the nAChR subunits

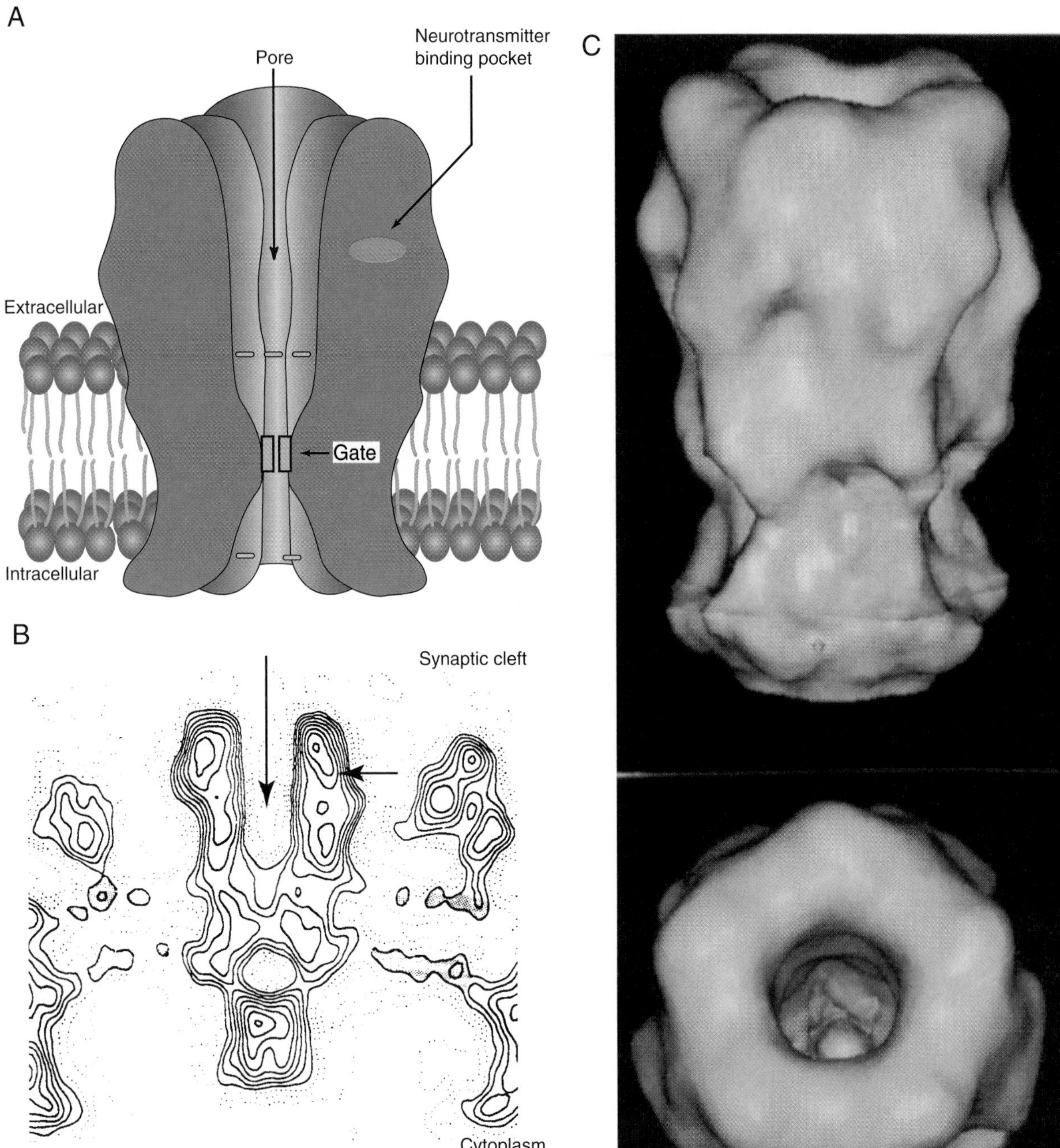

FIGURE 9.3 (A) Vertical section diagramming the structure of the nAChR as it is believed to exist in the membrane. Note that the funnel-shaped structure narrows to a central point referred to as the gate. Strategically placed rings of negatively charged amino acids on both sides of the gate form a large part of the selectivity of the channel for positively charged ions. The approximate position of the neurotransmitter-binding site in relation to the gate and plasma membrane is shown. (B) Protein-density map derived from reconstructions of the nAChR imaged by cryoelectron microscopy. The vertical arrow indicates the direction of ion flow from outside to inside within the funnel-shaped part of the receptor. The horizontal arrow indicates the predicted position of the neurotransmitter-binding site that resides approximately 30 Å above the bilayer surface. The additional protein density attached to the bottom of the receptor (bracket) is suggested to be a protein that helps anchor the nAChR to specific cellular localizations. The darkly stippled areas represent the lipid head groups of the membrane bilayer. Adapted from Unwin.[3] (C) Three-dimensional computer rendering of the nAChR imaged by cryo-electron microscopy. (Upper) Side view of the nAChR similar to that in (A). The dark-colored area indicates the approximate position of contact between the lipid bilayer and the receptor. (Lower) A view from above looking down into the funnel-shaped opening of the receptor. Note that, near the center of the pore, a restriction forms the gate for the nAChR.

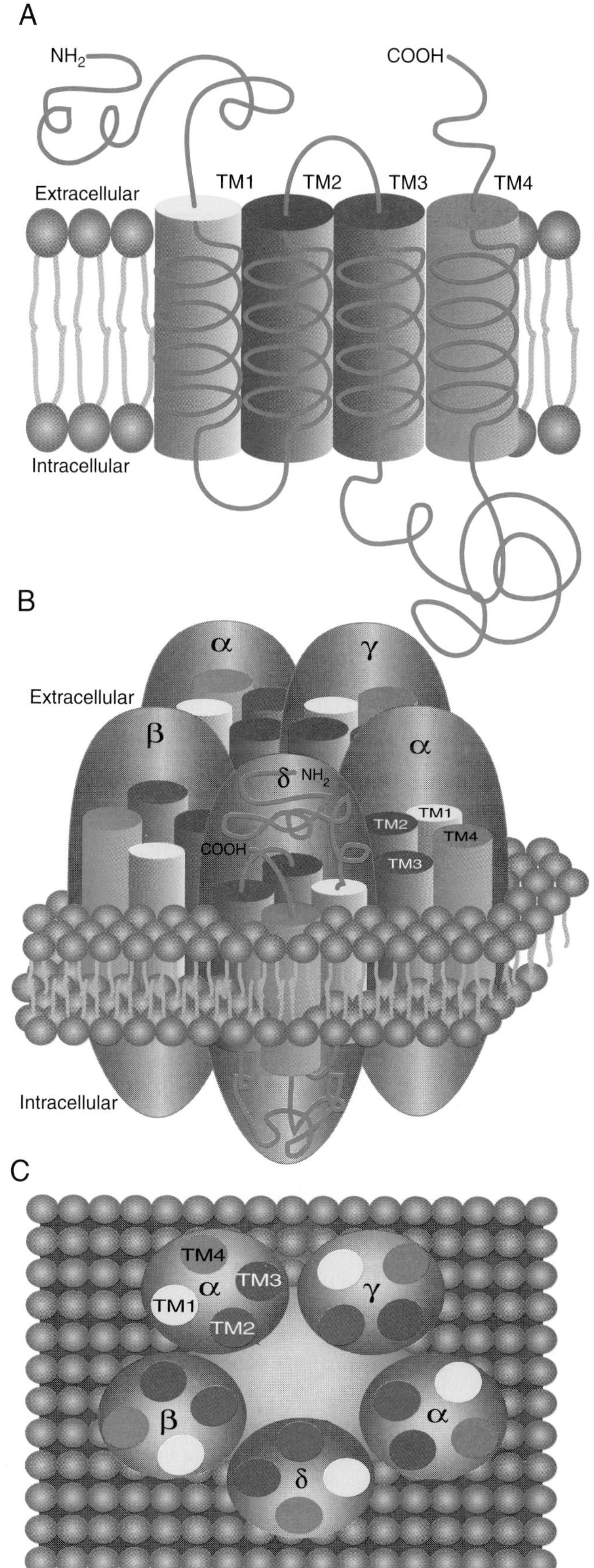

range in size from 40 to 65 kDa. A general domain structure for each subunit was derived from primary sequence data and toxin and antibody-binding studies. Each subunit consists of four transmembrane-spanning segments, or domains, referred to as TM1–TM4 (Fig. 9.4). Each segment is composed mainly of hydrophobic amino acids that stabilize the domain within the hydrophobic environment of the lipid membrane. The four transmembrane domains are arranged in an antiparallel fashion, wrapping back and forth through the membrane. The N-terminus of each subunit extends into the extracellular space, as does the loop connecting TM2 and TM3 as well as the C-terminus. The amino acids linking TM1 and TM2 and those linking TM3 and TM4 form short loops that extend into the cytoplasm.

The Structure of the Channel Pore Determines Ion Selectivity and Current Flow

In the model shown in Fig. 9.4C, each subunit of the nAChR can be seen to contribute one cylindrical component (representing a membrane-spanning segment) to a central core that forms the ion channel through the center of the complex. The membrane-spanning segments that line the pore are mainly the TM2 regions of each subunit. From analysis of the permeation of various sized cations, the dimensions of the pore were estimated to be approximately 6.5 × 6.5 Å.[8] This pore diameter is in excellent agreement with the measurements of 9–10 Å from images of the open state of the receptor.[5] The restricted dimensions of the pore contribute significantly to the selectivity for particular ions.

The amino acids that compose TM2 of each subunit are arranged in such a way that three rings of negatively charged amino acids are oriented toward the central pore of the channel (Fig. 9.5). These rings of negative charge appear to provide much of the selectivity filter so that only cations can pass through the central channel, whereas anions are largely excluded owing to charge repulsion.[9,10] The nAChR is permeable to most cations, such as Na^+, K^+, and Ca^{2+}, although

FIGURE 9.4 (A) Diagram highlighting the orientation of the membrane-spanning segments of one subunit of the nAChR. The amino and carboxy termini extend into the extracellular space. The four membrane-spanning segments are designated TM1–TM4. (B) Side view of the five subunits in their approximate positions within the receptor complex. The TM2 segment of each subunit is oriented toward the pore of the nAChR. (C) Top view of all five subunits highlighting the relative positions of their membrane-spanning segments, TM1–TM4. Amino acids in the TM2 segment of each subunit form the majority of the structure of the channel pore. Adapted from Ref. 97.

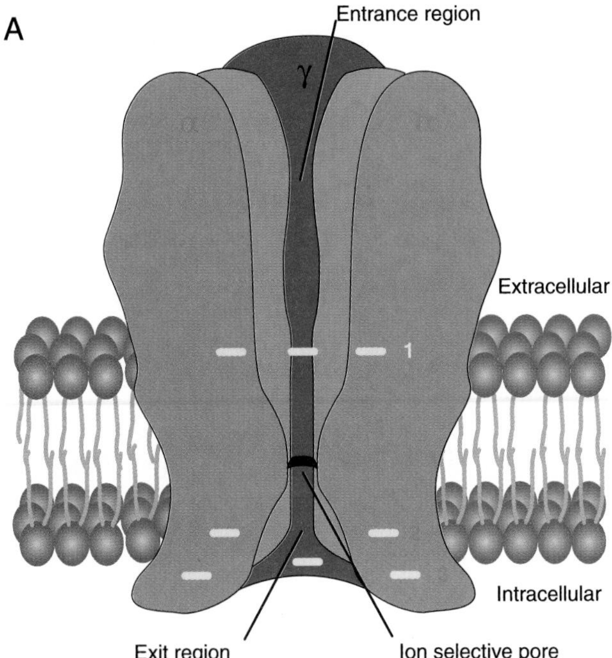

monovalent cations are selectively preferred. This mechanism for selectivity is poor in relation to the selectivity described for the family of voltage-gated ion channels (e.g., voltage-gated Ca^{2+} channels; see Chapter 8). When the pore of the nAChR opens, positively charged ions move down their respective electrochemical gradients, resulting in an influx of Na^+ and Ca^{2+} and an efflux of K^+. A coarse filtering that also contributes to selectivity appears to be a shielding effect produced by other negatively charged amino acids surrounding the outer channel region of the receptor.

There Are Two Binding Sites for ACh on the nAChR

Each receptor complex has two ACh-binding sites that reside in the extracellular domain and lie approximately 30 Å from the outer leaflet of the membrane[3] (see Fig. 9.3). Each ACh-binding site is formed for the most part by six amino acids in the α subunits; how-

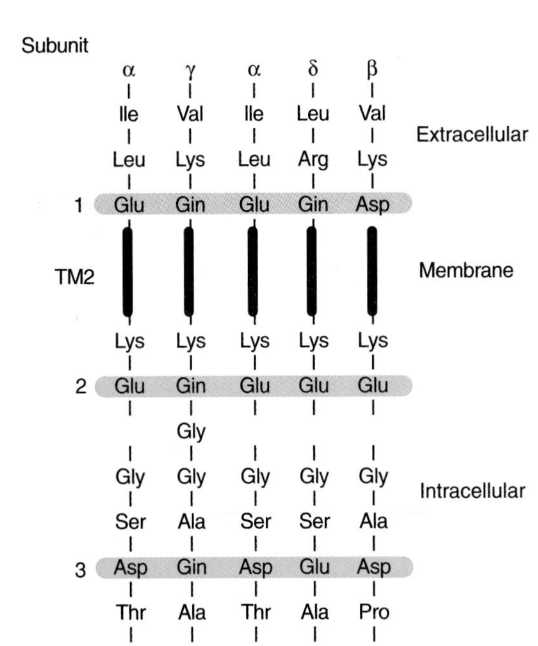

FIGURE 9.5 (A) Vertical section highlighting the relative positions of the three rings of negatively charged amino acids that help form the cation selectivity of the nAChR. (B) Amino acid sequence surrounding the TM2 membrane-spanning segment of the five nAChR subunits. Numbers 1–3 indicate the positions of amino acids taking part in the formation of the three rings of negatively charged amino acids that form the cation selectivity of the pore. Aspartate (Asp) and glutamate (Glu) are negatively charged amino acids. Adapted from Ref. 97.

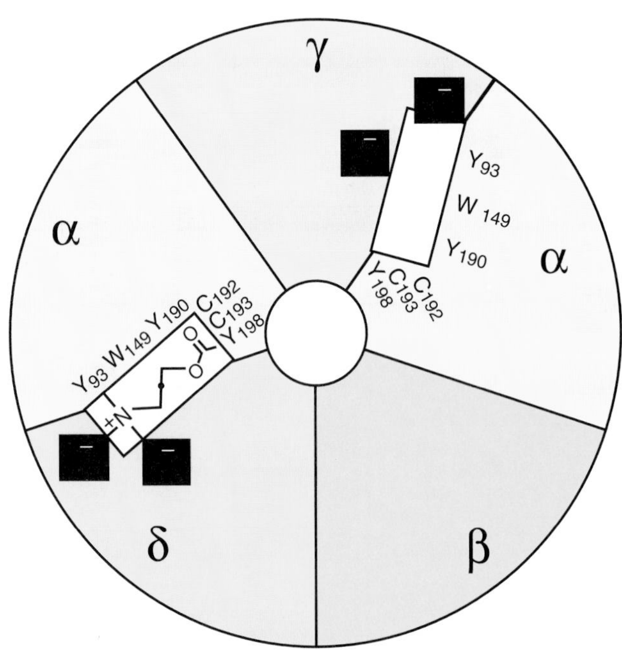

FIGURE 9.6 Diagram of the relative positions of amino acids that form a part of the ACh-binding site in the nAChR. The view is from above the receptor looking down into the pore. Each subunit is represented by a wedge. At the left, ACh is shown bound to its site on the nAChR at the interface between the α and δ subunits. The length of the binding site is shown contracted relative to the site (between the α and γ subunits) without bound ACh. Amino acids identified as important for binding ACh are indicated. Residues shown in dark boxes are amino acids predicted to make contact with the positively charged part of the ACh molecule. Note that many of the residues important for ACh binding are contributed by the α subunit. Cysteine (C) residues at positions 192 and 193 form a disulfide bond essential for stabilizing the ACh-binding site. Adapted from Ref. 9.

ever, amino acids in both the γ and the δ subunits also contribute to binding[9] (Fig. 9.6). Mutations introduced at these critical amino acids in the α subunit significantly attenuate ligand binding. The two binding sites are not equivalent because of the receptor's asymmetry due to the different neighboring subunits (either γ or δ) adjacent to the two α subunits. Significant cooperativity also exists within the receptor molecule, and so binding of the first molecule of ACh enhances binding of the second.[11] Two adjacent cysteine residues (Cys-192 and Cys-193) in each α subunit form a disulfide bond that also appears to contribute to a part of the ACh-binding pocket. These Cys residues are highly conserved in most ionotropic receptors and must form an essential stabilizing bond for high-affinity neurotransmitter binding. α-Bungarotoxin binds to the α subunit in close proximity to the two adjacent Cys residues.[9]

Opening of the nAChR Occurs through Concerted Conformational Changes Induced by ACh Binding

When the nAChR binds two molecules of ACh, the channel opens almost instantaneously (time constants for opening are approximately 20 μs[12,13]), thus permitting the flux of ions. A model developed from electron micrographic reconstructions of the nicotine-bound form of the nAChR indicates that the closed-to-open transition is associated with a rotation of the TM2 segments[5] (Fig. 9.7). The TM2 segments are α-helical and exhibit a kink in their structure that forces a Leu residue from each segment into a tight ring that effectively blocks the flow of ions through the central pore of the receptor. When the TM2 segments rotate because of ACh binding, the kinks also rotate, relaxing the constriction formed by the Leu ring, and ions can then permeate through the pore. The rotation also orients a series of Ser and Thr residues (amino acids with a polar character) into the central core of the pore, which presumably facilitates the permeation of water-solvated ions. Despite these structural studies, this model is somewhat incompatible with data from studies using biochemical and site-directed mutagenesis approaches. Except for minor refinements in this model that are likely to be forthcoming, the general structure of the nAChR seems well established and provides a structural framework with which all other ionotropic receptors can be compared.

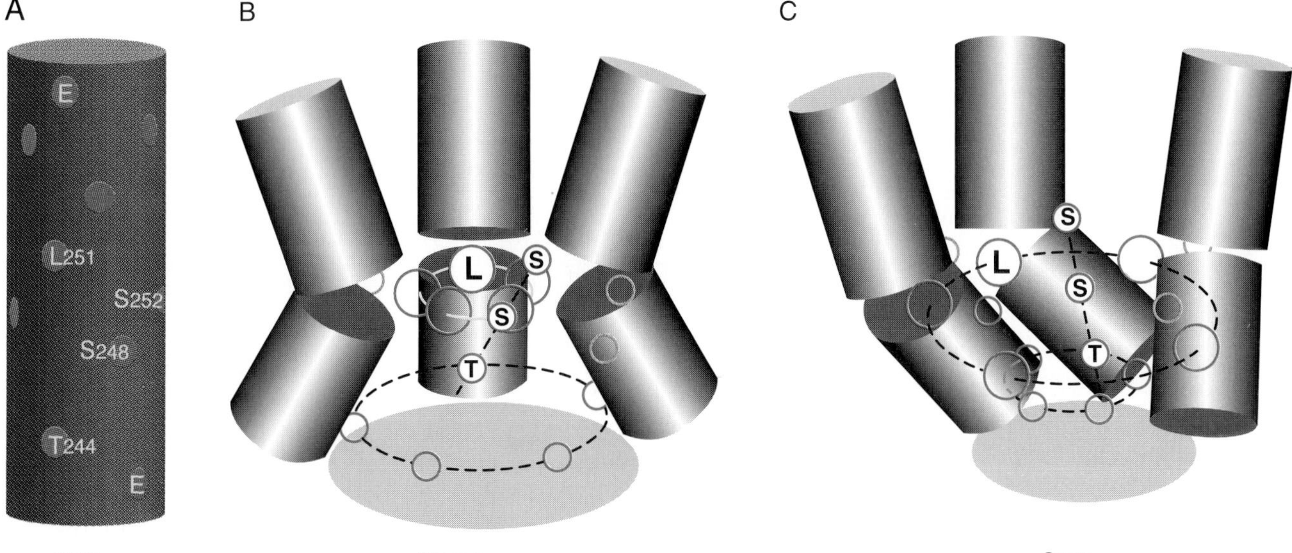

FIGURE 9.7 (A) Relative positions of amino acids in the TM2 segment of one of the nAChR α subunits modeled as an α-helix. The glutamate residues (E) that form parts of the negatively charged rings for ion selectivity are shown at the top and bottom of the helix. (B) Arrangement of three of the TM2 segments of the nAChR modeled with the receptor in the closed (ACh-free) configuration. In the closed conformation, leucine (L) residues form a tight ring in the center of the pore that blocks ion permeation. (C) Arrangement of the three TM2 segments after ACh binds to the receptor. In the open conformation, the constriction formed by the ring of leucine residues opens as the TM2 segments twist about their axes. Note that the polar serine (S) and threonine (T) residues align when ACh binds, which apparently helps the water-solvated ions travel through the pore. Adapted from Ref. 5.

The Muscle Form of the nAChR Is Very Similar to the nAChR from *Torpedo*

The nAChRs at the neuromuscular junction are a concentrated collection of homogeneous receptors having a structure similar to that of the *Torpedo* electric organ. This similarity is not surprising, because the electric organ is a specialized form of muscle tissue. The adult form of the muscle receptor has the pentameric structure $\alpha 2\beta\varepsilon\delta$. An embryonic form of the receptor has an analogous structure, except that the ε subunit is replaced by a unique γ subunit. The embryonic and adult subunits of both mouse and bovine muscle receptors have been cloned and expressed in heterologous systems, such as the *Xenopus laevis* oocyte (Box 9.1),[14] and the receptors differ in both channel kinetics and channel conductance. These differences in channel properties appear to be necessary for the proper function of the nAChRs as they undergo the transition from developing to mature synapses.

The nAChR Has Well-Ordered Assembly

The pathway of nAChR assembly is a tightly regulated process. For example, the five subunits of the nAChR have the potential to randomly assemble into 208 different configurations. Nevertheless, in vertebrate muscle, only one of these configurations ($\alpha 2\beta\varepsilon\delta$) is typically found in mature tissue, indicating a very high degree of coordinated assembly and, ultimately, little structural variability.[15,16] The assembly of specific intermediates is essential for this coordinated process, and the intermediates formed appear to start with a dimer between α and either ε (γ in mature muscle) or δ. The heterodimers then bind to β and to each other to form the final receptor.[17] An alternative pathway in which α, β, and γ first form a trimer has also been proposed.[16] All of this assembly takes place within the endoplasmic reticulum. Also during intracellular maturation, each subunit is glycosylated, and, if glycosylation is inhibited, the production of mature nAChRs decreases. Two highly conserved disulfide bonds in

BOX 9.1

THE *Xenopus* OOCYTE

The *Xenopus* oocyte has been used extensively to study the properties of cDNAs encoding receptor subunits and their mutated forms. In addition, the oocyte has been used to study how combinations of different subunits interact to produce receptors with different properties. The large size and efficient translational machinery of *Xenopus* oocytes make them ideal for electrophysiological analyses of cDNAs encoding prospective receptors and channels. For example, mRNAs produced by *in vitro* transcription of cDNAs encoding each of the individual nAChR subunits were introduced into oocytes by microinjection (part A of the accompanying illustration). Several days later, the oocytes were voltage clamped to study the properties of the expressed channels (part B). When ACh was applied through a separate pipette, a significant inward current was detected in the oocyte (part C, trace 1). The response was specifically blocked by addition of an antagonist, tubocurarine (part C, trace 2), and the block was reversed by a 15-min wash (part C, trace 3). Details of this study indicate that all four of the nAChR subunits (α, β, γ, and δ) were required for ACh to produce an electrophysiological response.[14] More recently, the patch-clamp technique has also been applied to oocyte expression of receptors to analyze the behavior of single channels.

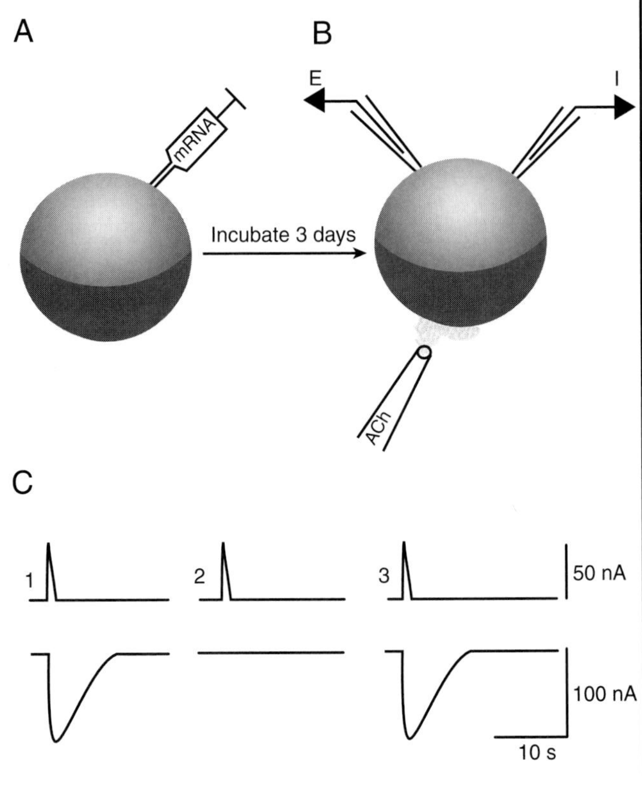

the N-terminal extracellular domain are essential for efficient assembly of the mature receptor. The first bond is between two adjacent Cys residues (Cys-192 and Cys-193) and, as noted, resides very close to the ACh-binding site on the receptor (see Fig. 9.6). The second bond is between two Cys residues 15 amino acids apart, forming a loop in the extracellular domain.

Posttranslational Processing Is Common to Receptors

Many ionotropic receptors, such as the nAChR, are phosphorylated, although the significance of the phosphorylation for receptor function is not clear in most cases. The nAChR is phosphorylated by at least three protein kinases—cAMP-dependent protein kinase (PKA; phosphorylates the γ and δ subunits), Ca^{2+}–phospholipid-dependent protein kinase (PKC; phosphorylates the δ subunit), and an unidentified tyrosine kinase (phosphorylates the β, γ, and δ subunits).[18] The phosphorylation sites are all found in the intracellular loop between the TM3 and TM4 membrane-spanning segments. Phosphorylation by all three protein kinases appears to increase the rapid phase of desensitization of the receptor. Desensitization of receptors is a common observation, and this process limits the amount of ion flux through a receptor by producing transitions into a closed state (one that does not permit ion flow) in the continued presence of neurotransmitter. For the nAChR, the rate of desensitization has a time constant of approximately 50–100 ms, a rate that appears to be too slow to have much significance in shaping the synaptic response at the neuromuscular junction, where the response typically lasts from 5 to 10 ms. This slow desensitization is not true of the brain forms of the nAChR and is discussed further in a later section of this chapter.

The Structures of Other Ionotropic Receptors Are Variations of nAChR Structure

On the basis of similarity of structure, clear evolutionary relationships exist for the family of ionotropic receptors. Figure 9.8 shows an evolutionary tree for the family of ionotropic receptors that are related to the nAChR. An early major subdivision separates those receptors permeable to anions from those permeable to cations. The former group includes the $GABA_A$ and glycine receptors, whereas the latter group includes the 5-hydroxytryptamine (5-HT3) and ACh receptors. One can begin to appreciate that structural similarities can predict a degree of functional similarity. Each of these receptor types is described in the next section.

Neuronal nAChRs Contain Two Types of Subunits

The neuronal nAChRs, though similar in structure to the *Torpedo* isoform of the receptor, are distinct from it (Fig. 9.8). For example, the neuronal nAChR appears to have only two types of subunits, α and β, that combine to produce the functional receptor, and the majority of these receptors do not bind to α-bungarotoxin. At least nine different α subtypes (α1 being the muscle α subunit) have been identified, and some are species specific (α8 is found only in chicken and α9 is found only in rat). Four different β subtypes (β1 being the muscle β subunit) have been identified. The neuronal β subunits are not closely related to the muscle β1 subunit and are sometimes referred to simply as non-α subunits. One structural feature that distinguishes the neuronal α subunits from β subunits is the presence of Cys residues in the extracellular domain of the α subunit. Two of these Cys residues are adjacent to one another and form a disulfide bond. The β subunits do not have these adjacent Cys residues. Because these Cys residues are critical for ACh binding, the α subunits of the neuronal AChRs, like the muscle α subunits, contain the main contact points for ACh binding. All of the α and β genes encode proteins with four transmembrane-spanning segments (TM1–TM4). Although the physical structure of this receptor family has not been well characterized, it appears that each functional receptor is a pentameric assembly of one or several subunits.

Structural Diversity of Neuronal nAChRs Produces Channels with Unique Properties

Neuronal nAChRs have diverse functions and are the receptors presumed to be responsible for the psychophysical effects of nicotine addiction. One major function of nAChRs in the brain is to modulate excitatory synaptic transmission through a presynaptic action.[19] The diversity in function can be related to the heterogeneous structure contributed by the thousands of possible combinations between the different α and β subunits. Control mechanisms for receptor assembly in neurons do not appear to be as stringent as those of the nAChR in *Torpedo* and muscle. Functional neuronal nAChRs can also be assembled from a single subunit (as in α7, α8, and α9), and a single type of α subunit can be assembled with multiple types of β subunits (e.g., α3 with β2 or β4 or both) and vice versa. These additional possibilities produce a staggering array of potential receptor molecules, each with distinct properties. This type of diversity is not unique to neuronal nAChRs. For most receptor classes studied in detail,

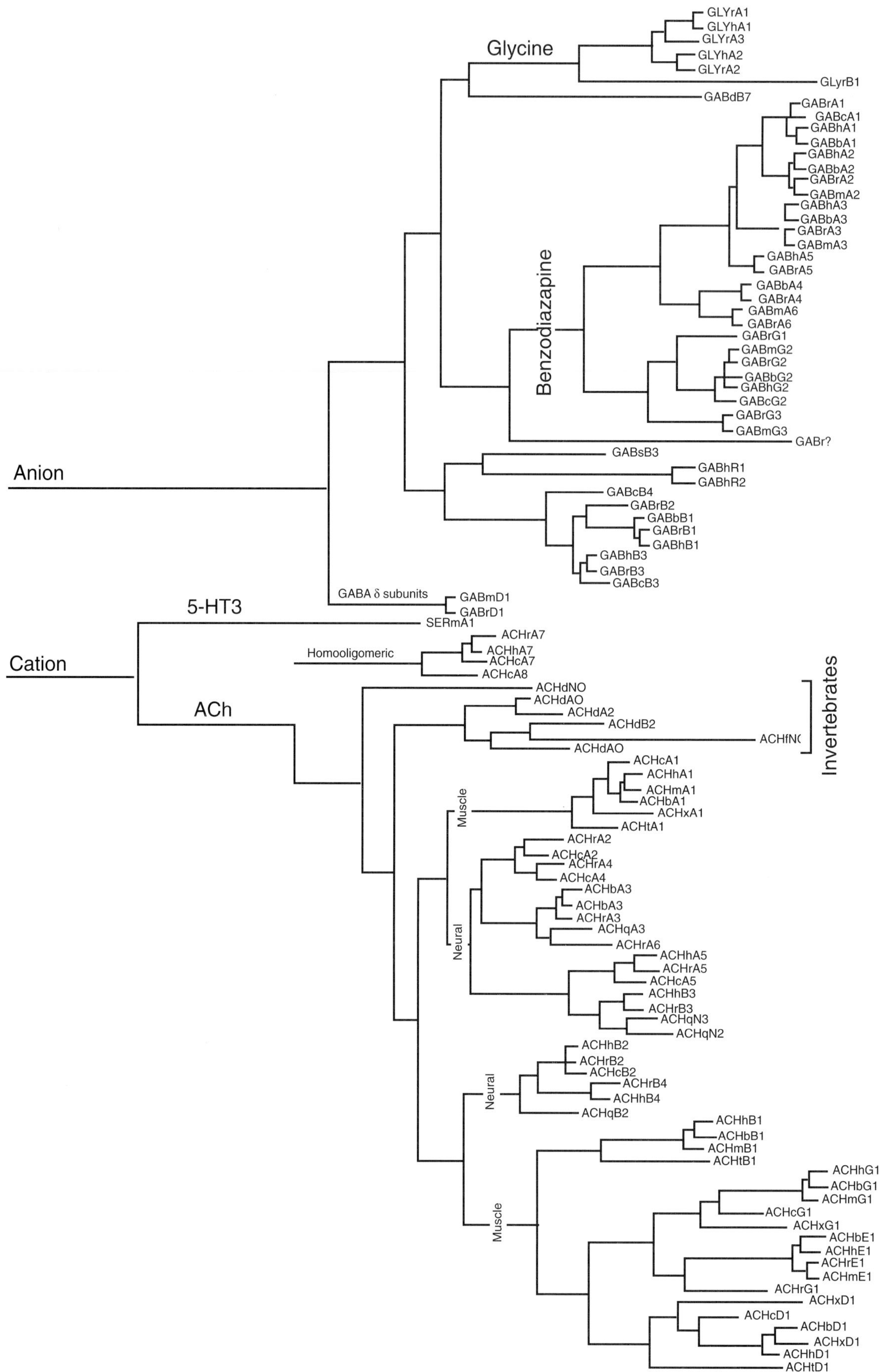

Glycine
GLYrA1
GLYhA1
GLYrA3
GLYhA2
GLYrA2
GLyrB1
GABdB7
GABrA1
GABcA1
GABhA1
GABbA1
GABhA2
GABbA2
GABrA2
GABmA2
GABhA3
GABbA3
GABrA3
GABmA3
GABhA5
GABrA5
GABbA4
GABrA4
GABmA6
GABrA6
GABrG1
GABmG2
GABrG2
GABbG2
GABhG2
GABcG2
GABrG3
GABmG3
GABr?
Benzodiazapine
Anion
GABsB3
GABhR1
GABhR2
GABcB4
GABrB2
GABbB1
GABrB1
GABhB1
GABhB3
GABrB3
GABcB3
GABA δ subunits
GABmD1
GABrD1
5-HT3
SERmA1
Cation
Homooligomeric
ACHrA7
ACHhA7
ACHcA7
ACHcA8
ACh
ACHdNO
ACHdAO
ACHdA2
ACHdB2
ACHfNO
ACHdAO
Invertebrates
Muscle
ACHcA1
ACHhA1
ACHmA1
ACHbA1
ACHxA1
ACHtA1
ACHrA2
ACHcA2
ACHrA4
ACHcA4
ACHbA3
ACHbA3
ACHrA3
ACHqA3
ACHrA6
Neural
ACHhA5
ACHrA5
ACHcA5
ACHhB3
ACHrB3
ACHqN3
ACHqN2
ACHhB2
ACHrB2
ACHcB2
ACHrB4
ACHhB4
ACHqB2
Neural
ACHhB1
ACHbB1
ACHmB1
ACHtB1
ACHhG1
ACHbG1
ACHmG1
ACHcG1
ACHxG1
Muscle
ACHbE1
ACHhE1
ACHrE1
ACHmE1
ACHrG1
ACHxD1
ACHcD1
ACHbD1
ACHxD1
ACHhD1
ACHtD1

diversity is the rule and not the exception. It is intriguing to speculate that subunit composition may also play roles in targeting the receptors to different intracellular locations.

Neuronal nAChRs exhibit a range of single-channel conductances between 5 and 50 pS, depending on the tissue analyzed or the specific subunits expressed. Most, but not all, are blocked by neuronal bungarotoxin, a snake venom distinct from α-bungarotoxin. All of the neuronal nAChRs are cation-permeable channels that, in addition to permitting the influx of Na^+ and the efflux of K^+, permit an influx of Ca^{2+}. This Ca^{2+} permeability is greater than that for the muscle nAChR[20] and is variable among the different neuronal receptor subtypes. Indeed, some receptors have very high Ca^{2+}/Na^+ permeability ratios; for example, $\alpha7$ nAChRs exhibit a Ca^{2+}/Na^+ permeability ratio of nearly 20.[21] The Ca^{2+} permeability of the $\alpha7$ nAChR can be eliminated by the mutation of a single amino acid residue in the second transmembrane domain (i.e., Glu-237 → Ala) without significantly affecting other aspects of the receptor.[22] This key Glu residue must lie within the pore of the receptor and presumably enhances the passage of Ca^{2+} ions through an interaction with its negatively charged side chain. Activation of $\alpha7$ receptors through the binding of ACh could therefore produce a significant increase in the level of intracellular Ca^{2+} without voltage-gated Ca^{2+} channels being open. Subunits $\alpha7$, $\alpha8$, and $\alpha9$ are also the α-bungarotoxin-binding subtypes of neuronal nAChRs. Other neuronal isoforms exhibit Ca^{2+}/Na^+ permeability ratios of about 1.0–1.5.

Neuronal nAChRs Desensitize Rapidly

For the nAChR from muscle or *Torpedo*, desensitization is minor and probably is not of physiological significance in determining the shape of the synaptic response at the neuromuscular junction. However, for some of the neuronal nAChRs, desensitization likely plays a major role in determining the effects of the actions of ACh. Receptors composed of $\alpha7$, $\alpha8$, and certain α/β combinations exhibit desensitization time constants of between 100 and 500 ms, whereas others exhibit desensitization constants between 2 and 20 s. Given the apparent diverse functions of the neuronal nAChRs, the variable rates of desensitization likely play important roles whereby properties inherent to the receptor shape the response generated from binding ACh.

←

FIGURE 9.8 Evolutionary relationships of the family of cloned ionotropic receptor subunits. The nomenclature used to describe each receptor subunit type is RRRsS#, where RRR represents the type of receptor, s the organism, S the subunit type, and # the subunit number. Type of receptor (RRR): ACH, acetylcholine; GAB, GABA, GLY, glycine; and SER, serotonin. Organism (s): b, bovine; c, chicken; d, *Drosophila*; f, filaria; g, goldfish; h, human; l; locust; m, mouse; n, nematode; r, rat; s, snail; t, *Torpedo*; and x, *Xenopus*. Subunit type (S): A, alpha; B, beta; G, gamma; D, delta; E, epsilon; R, rho; N, nonalpha; and ?, undetermined. Adapted from Ortells and Lunt (1995) *Trends Neurosci.* **18,** 122.

One Serotonin Receptor Subtype, 5-HT3, Is Ionotropic and Is a Close Relative of the nAChR

Serotonin (5-hydroxytryptamine; 5-HT) is historically thought of as a transmitter that binds to and activates metabotropic receptors (described in more detail later). However, the 5-HT3 subclass is an ionotropic receptor activated by binding serotonin. The 5-HT3 receptor is permeable to Na^+ and K^+ ions and is similar in many ways to the nAChR in that both desensitize rapidly and are blocked by tubocurarine. From expression studies of the cloned cDNA, it appears that the functional 5-HT3 receptor is a homomeric complex composed of five copies of the same subunit. The deduced amino acid sequence of the cDNA[23] indicates that the protein is 487 amino acids long (56 kDa) and has a structure most analogous to the $\alpha7$ subtype of neuronal nAChR (see Fig. 9.8), which also forms a homo-oligomeric receptor. However, receptor-binding and electrophysiological studies indicate the likelihood of other subunits of this receptor subclass being discovered.

The 5-HT3 receptor is mostly impermeable to divalent cations. For example, Ca^{2+} is largely excluded from permeation and in fact effectively blocks current flow through the pore, even though the predicted pore size of the channel (7.6 Å) is approximately the same as that for the nAChR (8.4 Å). Apparently, other physical or electrochemical barriers limit the capacity of divalent ions to permeate the 5-HT3 channel. Dose–response studies indicate that at least two ligand-binding sites must be occupied for the channel to open; however, the binding of agonist or activation of the channel appears to be approximately 10 times as slow as that for most other ligand-gated ion channels. The functional significance of this slow opening is not known. The native 5-HT3 receptor also exhibits desensitization (time constant 1–5 s), although the rate varies widely, depending on the methodology used for analysis and the source of receptor. Interestingly, this desensitization can be significantly slowed or enhanced by single amino acid substitutions at a Leu residue in the TM2 transmembrane-spanning segment.[24]

The 5-HT3 receptors are sparsely distributed on primary sensory nerve endings in the periphery and are widely distributed at low concentrations in the mammalian CNS. The 5-HT3 receptor is clinically significant because antagonists of 5-HT3 receptors have important applications as antiemetics, anxiolytics, and antipsychotics.

$GABA_A$ Receptors Are Related in Structure to nAChRs, but Exhibit an Inhibitory Function

Synaptic inhibition in the mammalian brain is mediated principally by GABA receptors. The most widespread ionotropic receptor activated by GABA is designated $GABA_A$. The subunits composing the $GABA_A$ receptor have sequence homology with the nAChR subunit family, and the two families have presumably diverged from a common ancestral gene.[1] In fact, the general structures of the two receptors appear to be quite similar. The $GABA_A$ receptor is composed of multiple subunits, probably forming a heteropentameric complex of approximately 275 kDa. Five different types of subunits are associated with $GABA_A$ receptors and are designated α, β, γ, δ, and ρ. The ρ subunit is found predominantly in the retina, whereas the other subunits are widely distributed in the brain. These subunit groups also have different subtypes; for example, six different α, four β, and three γ subunits have been identified. The predicted amino acid sequences indicate that each of these subunits has a molecular mass ranging between 48 and 64 kDa. Like the neuronal nAChR, these subunits mix in a heterogeneous fashion to produce a wide array of $GABA_A$ receptors with different pharmacological and electrophysiological properties. Expression of subunit cDNAs in oocytes indicates that the α subunit is essential for producing a functional channel. The α subunit also appears to contain the high-affinity binding site for GABA.[25]

The ion channel associated with the $GABA_A$ receptor is selective for anions (in particular, Cl^-), and the selectivity is provided by strategically placed positively charged amino acids near the ends of the ion channel.[26] When GABA binds to and activates this receptor, Cl^- flows into the cell, producing a hyperpolarization and moving the membrane potential away from the threshold for firing an action potential. The neuronal $GABA_A$ receptor exhibits multiple conductance levels, with the predominant conductance being 27–30 pS. Measurements and modeling of single-channel kinetics suggest that two sequential binding sites exist for anions within the pore.[27]

The $GABA_A$ Receptor Binds Several Compounds That Affect Its Properties

The $GABA_A$ receptor is an allosteric protein, its properties being modulated by the binding of a number of compounds. Two well-studied examples are barbiturates and benzodiazepines, both of which bind to the $GABA_A$ receptor and potentiate GABA binding. The net result is that in the presence of barbiturates or benzodiazepines or both, the same concentration of GABA will increase inhibition. Benzodiazepine binding is conferred on the receptor by the γ subunit,[28] but the presence of the α and β subunits can significantly affect the qualitative and quantitative aspects of benzodiazepine binding.

Picrotoxin, a potent convulsant compound, appears to bind within the channel pore of the $GABA_A$ receptor and prevent ion flow.[25] Single-channel experiments indicate that picrotoxin either slowly blocks an open channel or prevents the GABA receptor from undergoing a transition into a long-duration open state. Apparently, barbiturates produce smilar changes in channel properties, but they potentiate rather than inhibit $GABA_A$ receptor function. Bicuculline, another potent convulsant, appears to inhibit $GABA_A$ receptor channel activity by decreasing the binding of GABA to the receptor. Steroid metabolites of progesterone, corticosterone, and testosterone also appear to have potentiating effects on GABA currents that are similar in many ways to the action of barbiturates; however, the binding sites for these steroids and the barbiturates are distinct. Finally, penicillin directly inhibits GABA receptor function, apparently by binding within the pore and thus being designated an open channel blocker.

The physiological effects of compounds such as picrotoxin, bicuculline, and penicillin are striking. Each of these compounds at a sufficiently high concentration can produce widespread and sustained seizure activity. Conversely, many, but not all, of the sedative properties associated with barbiturates and benzodiazepines can be attributed to their ability to potentiate inhibition in the brain through enhancing GABA's inhibitory potency.

Interestingly, ρ-subunit-containing GABA receptors, found in abundance in the retina, are pharmacologically unique. They are resistant to bicuculline's inhibitory action, although they remain sensitive to blockage by picrotoxin. In addition, these retinal receptors are not sensitive to modulation by barbiturates or benzodiazepines. Thus, ρ-containing receptors are distinct from $GABA_A$ receptors and are similar to receptors earlier designated $GABA_C$.[29]

Several studies indicate that phosphorylation of the $GABA_A$ receptor likely modifies its functions; however, whether the receptor itself is phosphorylated *in vivo* and whether phosphorylation increases or decreases the current flowing through the channel remain unknown. $GABA_A$ receptors are modulated by protein kinase A, protein kinase C, Ca^{2+}–calmodulin-dependent protein kinase, and an undefined protein kinase.

Glycine Receptor Structure Is Closely Related to GABA$_A$ Receptor Structure

Glycine receptors are the major inhibitory receptors in the spinal cord.[30] However, within the CNS, particularly in the brainstem, glycine receptors provide similar inhibitory functions. Glycine receptors are similar to GABA$_A$ receptors in that both are ion channels selectively permeable to the anion Cl^- (see Fig. 9.8). The structure of the glycine receptor is indicative of this similarity in properties. The native complex is approximately 250 kDa and is composed of two main subunits, α (48 kDa) and β (58 kDa). The receptor appears to be pentameric, most likely composed of three α and two β subunits. Apparently, three molecules of glycine must bind to the receptor to open it to ion flow,[31] suggesting that the α subunit may contain the glycine-binding site. The glycine receptor has an open-channel conductance of approximately 35–50 pS, similar to that of the GABA$_A$ receptor, and the glycine receptor is effectively blocked by the compound strychnine.

Four distinct α subunits and one β subunit have been cloned. Each exhibits the typical predicted four transmembrane segments and they are approximately 50% identical with one another at the amino acid level. Expression of a single α subunit in oocytes is sufficient to produce functional glycine receptors, indicating that the α subunit is the pore-forming unit of the native receptor. The β subunits play exclusively modulatory roles, affecting, for example, sensitivity to the inhibitory actions of picrotoxin. They are widespread in the brain, and their distribution does not specifically colocalize with glycine receptor α subunit mRNA. The β subunits may serve other functions independent of their association with glycine receptor.

Certain Purinergic Receptors Are Also Ionotropic

Although not included in Fig. 9.8, purinergic receptors appear to be related to the family of ionotropic receptors. Purinergic chemical transmission is distributed throughout the body. The subtypes and myriad effects are considered in greater detail in the section on metabotropic receptors later in this chapter. Purinergic receptors bind to ATP (or other nucleotide analogs) or its breakdown product adenosine. ATP is released from some synaptic terminals in a quantal manner and is often packaged within synaptic vesicles containing another neurotransmitter.

Two subtypes of ATP-binding purinergic receptors (P2x and P2z) were recently discovered to be ionotropic receptors, but data on their functions or properties are sparse. P2x receptors appear to mediate a fast depolarizing response in neurons and muscle cells to ATP by the direct opening of a nonselective cation channel. cDNAs encoding the P2x receptor indicate that its structure comprises only two transmembrane domains, with some homology in its pore-forming region with K^+ channels.[32,33] The P2z receptor also is a ligand-gated channel; however, the channel permits permeation of either anions or cations and even molecules as large as 900 Da. Its primary structure has not yet been defined.

Glutamate Receptors Are Structurally Distinct from Other Ionotropic Receptors and Are Derived from a Different Ancestral Gene

Glutamate receptors are widespread in the nervous system. They are responsible for mediating the majority of excitatory synaptic transmission in the brain and spinal cord. Early pharmacological studies suggested that glutamate receptors were not homogeneous. In the 1970s, Jeffrey Watkins and his colleagues significantly advanced this field by developing agonists that could pharmacologically distinguish between different glutamate receptor subtypes. Four of these agonists—*N*-methyl-D-aspartate (NMDA), α-amino-3-hydroxy-5-methylisoxazoleproprionic acid (AMPA), kainate, and quisqualate—are distinct in the type of receptors to which they bind and have been used extensively to characterize the glutamate receptor family.[34] Quisqualate is unique within this group in having the capacity to activate both ionotropic and metabotropic glutamate receptor subtypes.[2] Historically, the ionotropic glutamate receptors have been described as either NMDA or non-NMDA subtypes, depending on whether they bind the agonist NMDA. A family tree of the glutamate receptors is shown in Fig. 9.9.

Non-NMDA Receptors Are a Diverse Family

In 1989, Stephen Heinemann and his colleagues reported the isolation of a cDNA that produced a functional glutamate-activated channel when expressed in

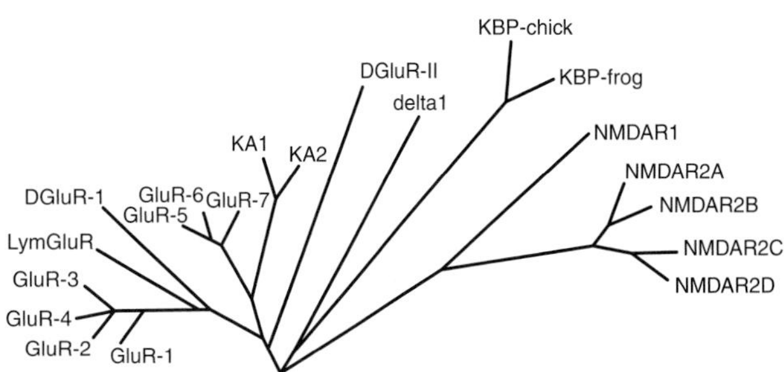

FIGURE 9.9 Evolutionary relationships of the ionotropic glutamate receptor family. Adapted from Ref. 2.

Xenopus oocytes.[35] The initial glutamate receptor was termed GluR-K1, and the cDNA encoded a protein with an estimated molecular mass of 99.8 kDa. Not long after this original report, Heinemann's group,[36] Peter Seeburg's group,[37] and Richard Axel's group[38] independently reported the isolation of families of glutamate receptor subunits, termed GluR1–GluR4 by Heinemann's group and GluRA–GluRD by Seeburg's group. Each GluR subunit consists of approximately 900 amino acids and has four predicted membrane-spanning segments (TM1–TM4). The native form of GluR subunits appears to be a pentameric complex with an approximate molecular mass of 600 kDa.[39,40] The size of the glutamate receptor complex is almost twice that of the nAChR, mostly because of the large extracellular domain found in all glutamate receptor subunits.

Unique Properties of Non-NMDA Receptors Are Determined by Assembly of Different Subunits

When the cDNAs encoding these receptors were expressed in either oocytes or HeK-293 cells, application of the non-NMDA receptor agonist AMPA produced substantial inward currents. In these same experiments, the agonist kainate was demonstrated to produce larger currents, mainly because of rapid and significant desensitization of the receptor when AMPA was used as the agonist. A striking observation from these expression studies was that when the GluR2 subunit alone was expressed in the oocytes, little current was obtained when GluR2 was exposed to agonist, unlike the large currents found when either GluR1 or GluR3 was expressed.[36,38,41] Apparently, GluR2 subunits by themselves form poorly conducting receptors; however, when GluR2 is expressed with either GluR1 or GluR3, the behavior of the heteromeric receptor is distinctly different. Examination of I/V plots indicates that when GluR1 and GluR3 are expressed alone or together, they produce channels with strong inward rectification. Coexpression of GluR2 with either GluR1 or GluR3 produces a channel with little rectification and a near linear I/V plot. Further analyses[2] indicated that GluR1 and GluR3, either independently or when coexpressed, exhibited channels permeable to Ca^{2+}. In contrast, any combination of receptor that included the GluR2 subunit produced channels impermeable to Ca^{2+}. Earlier single-channel analyses of glutamate receptors expressed in embryonic hippocampal neurons indicated that two distinct receptors are present: one relatively impermeable to Ca^{2+}, exhibiting a linear I/V plot, and another significantly permeable to Ca^{2+}, exhibiting a rectifying I/V plot.[42] Clearly, the properties of glutamate receptors can be quite different and can initiate quite different intracellular responses, depending on the subunit composition expressed in a particular neuron. In a series of elegant studies, the replacement of a single amino acid (Arg $\rightarrow$ Gln) in the second transmembrane region of the GluR2 subunit was shown to switch its behavior from a non-Ca^{2+}-permeable to a Ca^{2+}-permeable channel.[43,44] Apparently, an arginine at this position blocks Ca^{2+} from traversing the pore formed in the center of the GluR channel.

Functional Diversity in GluRs Is Produced by mRNA Splicing and RNA Editing

A mechanism in the neuronal nucleus appears to edit mRNAs posttranscriptionally, and at least three of the four GluR subunits are subjected to this editing mechanism.[45] One of the sites edited is the critical arginine residue regulating Ca^{2+} permeability in the GluR2 subunit. At another edited site, Arg-764 is replaced by Gly in the GluR2 subunit, and this editing also takes place in GluR3 and GluR4. The Arg-to-Gly conversion at amino acid 764 produces receptors that exhibit significantly faster rates of recovery from the desensitized state.[46] The extent to which other receptors or other protein molecules undergo this form of editing is an area rich for investigation. At a minimum, this editing mechanism produces dramatic differences in the function of GluRs.

Earlier analysis of the mRNAs encoding GluR subunits indicated that each can be expressed in one of two splice variants, termed flip and flop.[47] These flip and flop modules are small (38 amino acid) segments just preceding the TM4 transmembrane domain in all four GluR subunits. The receptor channel expressed has distinct properties, depending on which of these two modules is present. The fundamental finding appears to be that flop-containing receptors exhibit significantly greater magnitudes of desensitization during glutamate application. Therefore, GluRs with flop modules express smaller steady-state currents than GluRs with flip modules. Both flip- and flop-containing GluRs are widely expressed in the brain with a few exceptions. One unique cell type appears to be pyramidal CA3 cells in the rat hippocampus, where the GluRs are deficient in flop modules. In neighboring CA1 pyramidal cells and dentate granule cells, flop-containing GluRs appear to dominate. The functional significance of these splice variations is not known, but the prediction would be that CA3 neurons exhibit larger steady-state glutamate-activated currents owing to decreased desensitization from the absence of flop modules.

Glutamate Receptors May Not Conform to the Typical Four Transmembrane-Spanning Segment Structures Described for the nAChR

Although the field of glutamate receptors is advancing at a rapid pace, we have little structural data on the native molecule or on the topology of any single GluR subunit as it exists in the membrane. The region of the receptor originally thought to consist of four transmembrane segments has been conceptually challenged by a number of recent molecular and biochemical studies. To accommodate the most recent information, a new model was proposed suggesting that the TM2 membrane-spanning segment does not completely traverse the membrane (Figs. 9.10 and 9.11). Instead, it forms a kink within the membrane and enters back into the cytoplasm, similar in some ways to the pore-forming domain (P segment) of voltage-activated K^+ channels.[48] This model greatly affects the consideration of which parts of the receptor are exposed to the cell cytoplasm. In the original model, the C-terminal tail is outside the plasma membrane, and the loop (i2) between TM3 and TM4 is in the cytoplasm. In the more recent model, the C-terminus is in the cytoplasm, and the loop between TM3 and TM4 is extracellular. The differences between the two models raise important questions regarding the sites for ligand binding, protein phosphorylation, and glycosylation.[49]

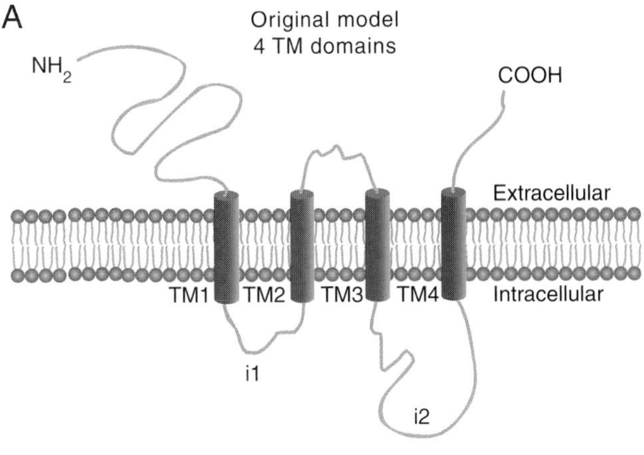

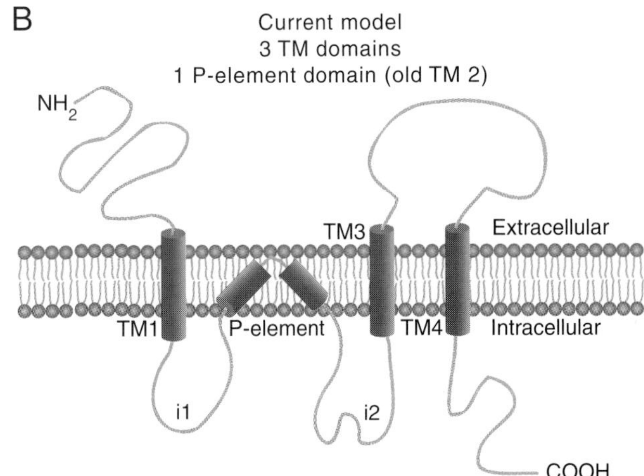

FIGURE 9.10 Alternative models for describing the transmembrane domain organization of the ionotropic glutamate receptors. (A) Original model in which the transmembrane domains were thought to be organized in a manner analogous to the nAChR. The NH_2 and COOH domains were proposed to be extracellular, and the two intracellular loops (i1 and i2) were proposed to reside between TM1 and TM2 and between TM3 and TM4, respectively. (B) Currently proposed model for the organization of the transmembrane domains of the ionotropic glutamate receptors. TM2 is now thought to form a kink in the membrane that causes the loop between TM2 and TM3 to become cytoplasmic. The COOH terminus also becomes cytoplasmic. The kink in TM2 shows some homology with a domain in K^+ channels called a P element. Adapted from Dani and Mayer (1995) *Curr. Opin. Neurobiol.*

Other Non-NMDA GluRs Have Poorly Characterized Functions

Three other members, GluR5–7, now form a second non-NMDA receptor subfamily, whose contribution to producing functionally distinct receptors is less well understood. Their overall structure is similar to that of the GluR1–4, and they exhibit about 40% sequence homology; however, their agonist-binding profile and their electrophysiological properties are distinct. They are expressed at lower levels in the brain than the GluR1–4 family.[2]

Two members of the glutamate receptor family, KA-1 and KA-2, are the high-affinity kainate-binding receptors found in brain. Clearly distinct from the glutamate receptors discussed so far, KA-1 and KA-2 are more similar to the GluR5–7 subfamily than to the GluR1–4 subfamily. Neither KA-1 nor KA-2 produces a functional channel when expressed in cells or oocytes, even though high-affinity kainate-binding sites were detected. KA-1 does not appear to form functional receptors or channels with any of the other GluR subunits, and its physiological relevance remains obscure. It is expressed at high concentrations in only two cell types, hippocampal CA3 and dentate granule cells. KA-2 exhibits interesting properties when combined with other GluR subunits. For example, coexpression of GluR6 and KA-2 produces functional receptors that respond to AMPA, although neither subunit itself responds to this agonist.[50] This information indicates that agonist-binding sites are at least partly formed at the interfaces between subunits.

Although other kainate-binding proteins and glutamate receptors have been described, their functions and biological significance are not currently understood. These receptors include two kainate-binding

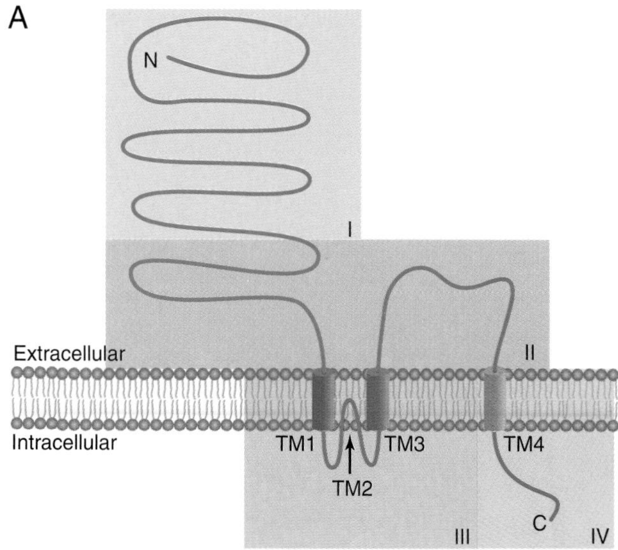

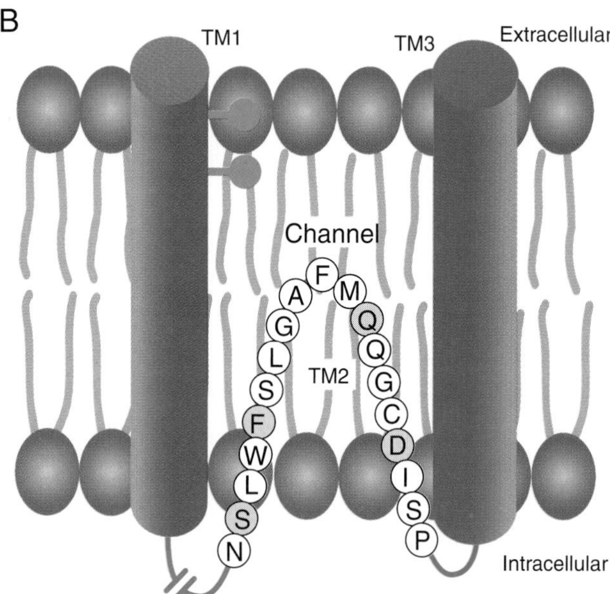

FIGURE 9.11 (A) Model of one of the subunits of the ionotropic glutamate receptor highlighting four domains with structures analogous to other proteins. Area I is homologous to a bacterial protein called the leucine, isoleucine, valine-binding protein–leucine-binding protein domain. Area II is homologous to another bacterial protein termed the lysine, arginine, ornithine-binding protein–glutamate-binding protein domain. Area III is homologous to the pore region of K^+ channels, and area IV is a regulatory domain of currently unknown function. The four transmembrane segments are labeled TM1 through TM4; however, TM2 forms a kink and does not completely traverse the membrane. (B) Enlarged area of the predicted structure and amino acid sequence of the TM2 region of the glutamate receptor, GluR3. TM1 and TM3 are drawn as cylinders flanking TM2. The residue that determines the Ca^{2+} permeability of the non-NMDA receptor is the glutamine residue (Q) highlighted in gray and is one of the amino acid changes produced by editing of the mRNA. In NMDA receptors, an asparagine residue at this same position is the proposed site of interaction with Mg^{2+} ions that produce the voltage-dependent channel block. The serine (S) and phenylalanine (F) are highly conserved in the non-NMDA glutamate receptor family. The aspartate (D) residue also is conserved and is thought to form a part of the internal cation-binding site. The break in the loop between TM1 and TM2 indicates a domain that varies in length among ionotropic glutamate receptors. Adapted from Ref. 48.

proteins, one from chicken and the other from frog, several invertebrate glutamate receptors, and two "orphan" receptors termed $\alpha 1$ and $\delta 2$.[2]

The NMDA Receptors Are a Family of Ligand-Gated Ion Channels That Are Also Voltage Dependent

NMDA receptors appear to be at least partly responsible for aspects of development, learning and memory, and neuronal damage due to brain injury. The significance of this receptor to neuronal function comes from two of its properties. First, the receptor exhibits associativity. For ions to flow, the receptor must bind glutamate and the membrane must be depolarized. This behavior is due to a Mg^{2+}-dependent block of the receptor at normal membrane resting potentials.[51,52] Second, the receptor permits a significant influx of Ca^{2+}, and increases in intracellular Ca^{2+} activate a variety of processes that alter the properties of the neuron. Excess Ca^{2+} is also toxic to neurons, and the hyperactivation of NMDA receptors is thought to contribute to a variety of neurodegenerative disorders.

Several hallucinogenic compounds, such as phencyclidine (PCP) and dizocilpine (MK-801), are effective blockers of the ion channel associated with the NMDA receptor (Fig. 9.12). These potent antagonists require the receptor channel to be open to gain access to their binding sites and are therefore referred to as open-channel blockers. They also become trapped when the channel closes and are therefore difficult to wash out of the NMDA receptor's channel. Although NMDA is a specific agonist for this receptor, it is one order of magnitude less potent than L-glutamate at activating the receptor. L-Aspartate can also activate NMDA receptors, as can an endogenous dipeptide in the brain, *N*-acetylaspartylglutamate.[2] Antagonists for the glutamate-binding site also have been developed, and some of the most well known are AP-5 and AP-7.

NMDA Receptor Subunits Show Similarity to Non-NMDA Receptor Subunits

The primary structure of the NMDA receptor was revealed in 1990 when Nakanishi and his colleagues

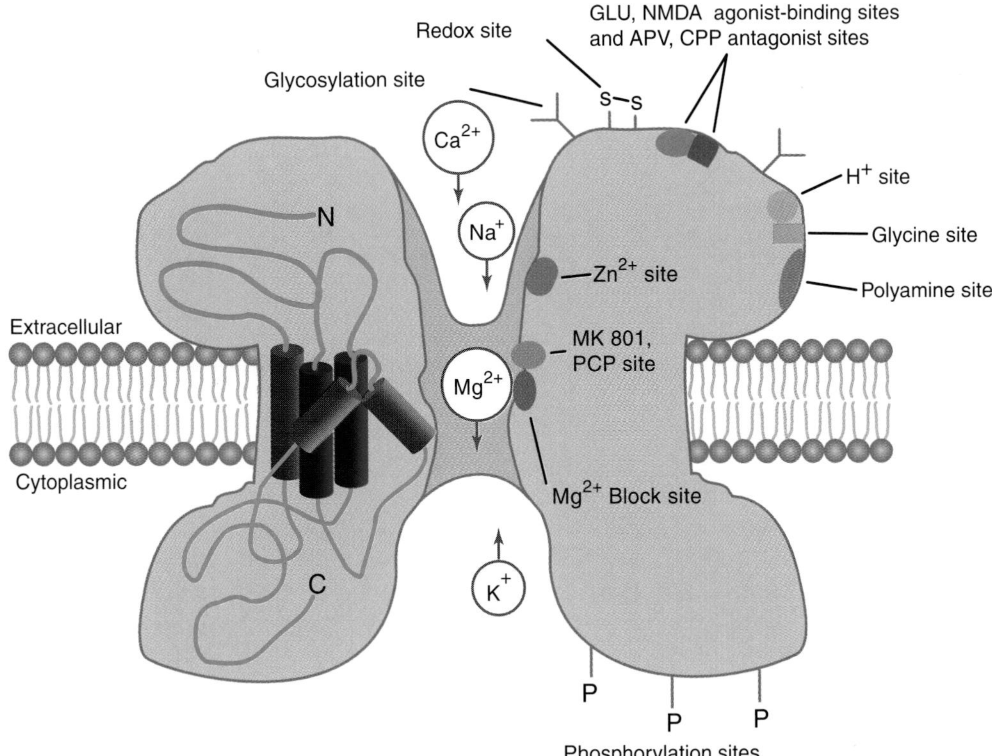

FIGURE 9.12 Diagram of NMDA receptor. Binding sites for numerous agonists, antagonists, and other regulatory molecules are identified. The locations of these bindings sites are approximate. Highlights include the Mg^{2+}-binding site that lies within the channel and produces the voltage-dependent block in ion permeation and the significant permeability to Ca^{2+}. Adapted from Ref. 2.

isolated the first cDNA encoding a subunit of the NMDA receptor.[53] The first cloned subunit was aptly named NMDAR1, and the deduced amino acid sequence indicated a protein of approximately 97 kDa, similar to other members of the GluR family. Four potential transmembrane domains were identified, and the current assumption is that five individual subunits compose the macromolecular NMDA receptor complex. However, recall that the transmembrane organization of GluR subunits currently suggests that TM2 does not fully transverse the membrane. Current thinking suggests that the NMDA receptor subunits will follow this recent modification of the model. The TM2 segment of each subunit also appears to line the pore of the NMDA receptor channel, as does the TM2 segment of the GluR subunits. In fact, a single asparagine residue, analogous to that in the GluR2 subunit, regulates the Ca^{2+} permeability of the NMDA receptor.[44,54] Mutation of this Asn residue markedly reduces Ca^{2+} permeability. Three of the best characterized facets of the NMDA receptor were found when the NMDAR1 subunit was expressed by itself in oocytes, although currents were relatively small. These characteristics are (1) a Mg^{2+}-dependent voltage-sensitive ion channel block, (2) a glycine requirement for effective channel opening, and (3) Ca^{2+} permeability.[53]

Functional Diversity of NMDA Receptors Occurs through RNA Splicing

At least eight splice variants have now been identified for the NMDAR1 subunit and these variants produce differences, ranging from subtle to significant, in the properties of the expressed receptor.[2] For example, NMDAR1 receptors lacking a particular N-terminal insert owing to alternative splicing exhibit enhanced blockade by protons and exhibit responses that are potentiated by Zn^{2+} in micromolar concentrations. Zn^{2+} has classically been described as an NMDA receptor antagonist that significantly blocks their activation. Clearly, the particular splice variant incorporated into the receptor complex affects the types of physiological response generated. Spermine, a polyamine found in neurons and in the extracellular space, also slightly increases the amplitude of NMDA responses, and this modulatory effect also appears to be associated with a particular splice variant. The physiologic role of spermine in regulating NMDA receptors remains unclear.

Multiple NMDA Receptor Subunit Genes Also Contribute to Functional Diversity

Four other members of the NMDA receptor family have been cloned (NMDAR2A–2D), and their deduced primary structures are highly related. These four NMDA receptor subunits do not form channels when expressed by themselves or in combination unless they are coexpressed with NMDAR1.[55–57] Apparently, NMDAR1 serves an essential function for the formation of a functional pore by which activation of NMDA receptors permits the flow of ions. NMDA receptors 2A–2D appear to play roles in modulating the receptor activity when mixed as heteromeric forms with NMDAR1. Coexpression of NMDAR1 with any of the other subunits produces much larger currents (from 5- to 60-fold greater) than when NMDAR1 is expressed in isolation, and NMDA receptors expressed in neurons are likely to be hetero-oligomers of NMDAR1 and NMDAR2 subunits. The C-terminal domains of NMDAR2A–2D are quite large relative to NMDAR1C termini, whose functions have not been determined.[2] All of the NMDAR subunits have an Asn residue at the critical point in the TM2 domain essential for producing Ca^{2+} permeability. This Asn residue also appears to form at least part of the binding site for Mg^{2+}, which suggests that the sites for Mg^{2+} binding and Ca^{2+} permeation overlap.[44,54]

The distribution of NMDAR2 subunits is generally more restricted than the homogeneous distribution of NMDAR1, with the exception of NMDAR2A, which is expressed throughout the nervous system. NMDAR2C is mostly restricted to cerebellar granule cells, whereas 2B and 2D exhibit broader distributions. The large size of the C-terminus of the NMDAR2 subunit suggests a potential role in association with other proteins, possibly to target or restrict specific NMDA receptor types to areas of the neuron. Mechanisms related to receptor targeting are not understood but will clearly play major roles in determining the efficacy of synaptic transmission.[58,59]

NMDA Receptors Exhibit Complex Channel Properties

The biophysical properties of the NMDA receptor are complex.[51,52] The single-channel conductance has a main level of 50 pS; however, subconductances are evident, and different subunit combinations produce channels with distinct single-channel properties. A binding site for the Ca^{2+}-binding protein calmodulin has also been identified on the NMDAR1 subunit.[60] Binding of Ca^{2+}–calmodulin to NMDA receptors produces a fourfold decrease in open-channel probability. Ca^{2+} influx through the NMDA receptor could induce calmodulin binding and lead to an immediate short-term feedback inhibition, decreasing ion flow through the receptor.

Summary

A general model for ionotropic receptors has emerged mainly from analyses of the nAChR. Ionotropic receptors are large membrane-bound complexes generally composed of five subunits. The subunits each have four transmembrane domains, and the amino acids in the transmembrane segment TM2 form the main lining of the pore. Transmitter binding induces rapid conformational changes that are translated into an increase in the diameter of the pore, permitting ion influx. Cation or anion selectivity is obtained through the coordination of specific negatively or positively charged amino acids at strategic locations in the receptor pore. How well the details of structural information obtained for the nAChR will generalize to other ionotropic receptors awaits structural analyses of these other members. However, it is already clear that this model does not adequately describe the orientation of the transmembrane domains of the glutamate receptor family. This is perhaps not surprising given that the nAChR family and the glutamate receptor family appear to have arisen from two different ancestral genes.

METABOTROPIC RECEPTORS

The number of receptors classified as metabotropic is enormous (250 cloned members and the number is growing). The term metabotropic describes the fact that intracellular *meta*bolites are produced when these receptors bind ligand. Metabotropic receptors produce their effects by interacting with the family of trimeric G proteins that, when activated, exchange GDP for GTP and activate other intracellular enzymes. These enzymes produce diffusible second messengers (metabolites) that stimulate secondary biochemical processes, including the activation of protein kinases (see Chapter 10). Time is required for each of these coupling events, and the effects of metabotropic receptor activation are typically slower than those observed after activation of ionotropic receptors. Most small neurotransmitters, such as ACh, glutamate, serotonin, and GABA, can bind to both ionotropic and metabotropic receptors and activate them. Thus, each of these transmitters can induce both fast responses (milliseconds), such as typical excitatory or inhibitory postsynaptic potentials, and slow-onset and longer-duration responses (from tenths of seconds to, potentially, hours). This ability provides the nervous system with a rich source for temporal information processing that is subject to constant modification. Currently, the metabotropic receptor family can be divided into three subfamilies on the basis of the structure: (1) the rhodopsin–β-adrenergic receptor subfamily, (2) the secretin–vasoactive intestinal peptide receptor subfamily, and (3) the metabotropic glutamate receptor subfamily.[61]

Metabotropic Receptor Structure Conforms to a General Model

A metabotropic receptor consists of a single polypeptide with a generally conserved structure. The receptor contains seven membrane-spanning α-helical segments that wrap back and forth through the membrane (Fig. 9.13). The G-protein-coupled receptors are homologous to bacteriorhodopsin, and detailed structural information on bacteriorhodopsin[61,62] has been used to provide a framework for developing models of metabotropic receptor structure. Aside from rhodopsin, two of the best structurally characterized metabotropic receptors are the β-adrenergic receptor (βAR) and the muscarinic acetylcholine receptor (mAChR), and biochemical data support the use of bacteriorhodopsin as a structural model for the βAR.[63] Information regarding these receptors serves as the basis for a generalized model of metabotropic receptor structure.

The N-terminus of the receptor extends into the extracellular space, whereas the C-terminus resides within the cytoplasm (Fig. 9.13). Each of the seven membrane-spanning domains between the N- and C-termini consists of approximately 24 mostly hydrophobic amino acids that form a circular ring within the plasma membrane (Fig. 9.14A). Between each transmembrane domain is a loop of amino acids of various sizes. The loops connecting TM1 and TM2, TM3 and TM4, and TM5 and TM6 are intracellular and are labeled i1, i2, and i3, respectively, in Fig. 9.13, whereas those between TM2 and TM3, TM4 and TM5, and TM6 and TM7 are extracellular and are labeled e1, e2, and e3, respectively.

The Neurotransmitter-Binding Site Lies in the Core of the Receptor

The neurotransmitter-binding site for metabotropic receptors (excluding the metabotropic glutamate and neuropeptide receptors) resides within the central pocket formed by the seven membrane-spanning segments (Fig. 9.14A). In the βAR, this pocket resides at least 10.9 Å into the hydrophobic core of the receptor, placing the ligand-binding site within the plasma membrane lipid bilayer.[63,64] Strategically positioned charged and polar residues in the membrane-spanning segments form the binding site for the ligand. For example, Asn residues in the second and third segments, two Ser residues in the fifth segment, and a Phe residue in the sixth segment provide major contact points in the βAR-binding site for the agonist[65] (Fig. 9.14B). Point mutations in which Glu replaces the TM3 Asp reduce agonist binding by more than 100-fold, and replacement with a nonacidic amino acid, such as Ser, reduces binding by more than 10,000-fold. Two Ser residues in the fifth transmembrane domain also are essential for efficient ligand binding and receptor activation, as is an Asp residue in TM2 and a Phe residue in TM6. In total, the two Asp, the two Ser, and the Phe residues are highly conserved in all receptors that bind biogenic amines. The amino acids in these five positions likely take part in ligand binding for many of the metabotropic receptors.

The neurotransmitter-binding site of mAChRs, like that of the β2AR, has been investigated in great detail (Fig. 9.14C). The Asp residue in TM3 is also critical for ACh binding to the mAChRs. Mutagenesis studies indicate important roles for Tyr and Thr residues in TM3, TM5, TM6, and TM7 in contributing to the ligand-binding site for ACh. Interestingly, many of these mutations do not affect antagonist binding, indicating that distinct amino acids participate in binding agonists and antagonists. When the transmembrane domains are examined from a side view (Fig. 9.15), all of the key amino acids implicated in agonist binding lie at about the same level within the core of the receptor structure, buried approximately 10–15 Å from the surface of the plasma membrane. An additional amino acid identified as essential for agonist binding of the mAChR is a Pro residue in TM4. This residue is also highly conserved among the metabotropic receptors, and structural predictions suggest that it affects ligand binding not by interacting with agonist but by stabilizing a conformation essential for high-affinity binding. Structural predictions also place this Pro residue in the same plane as the Asp, Tyr, and Thr residues that form the ligand-binding site of the mAChR (Fig. 9.15).

Transmitter Binding Causes a Conformational Change in the Receptor and Activation of G Proteins

Proposed models for metabotropic receptor activation assume that the receptor can spontaneously isomerize between the inactive and active states.[66,67] Only the active state interacts with G proteins in a produc-

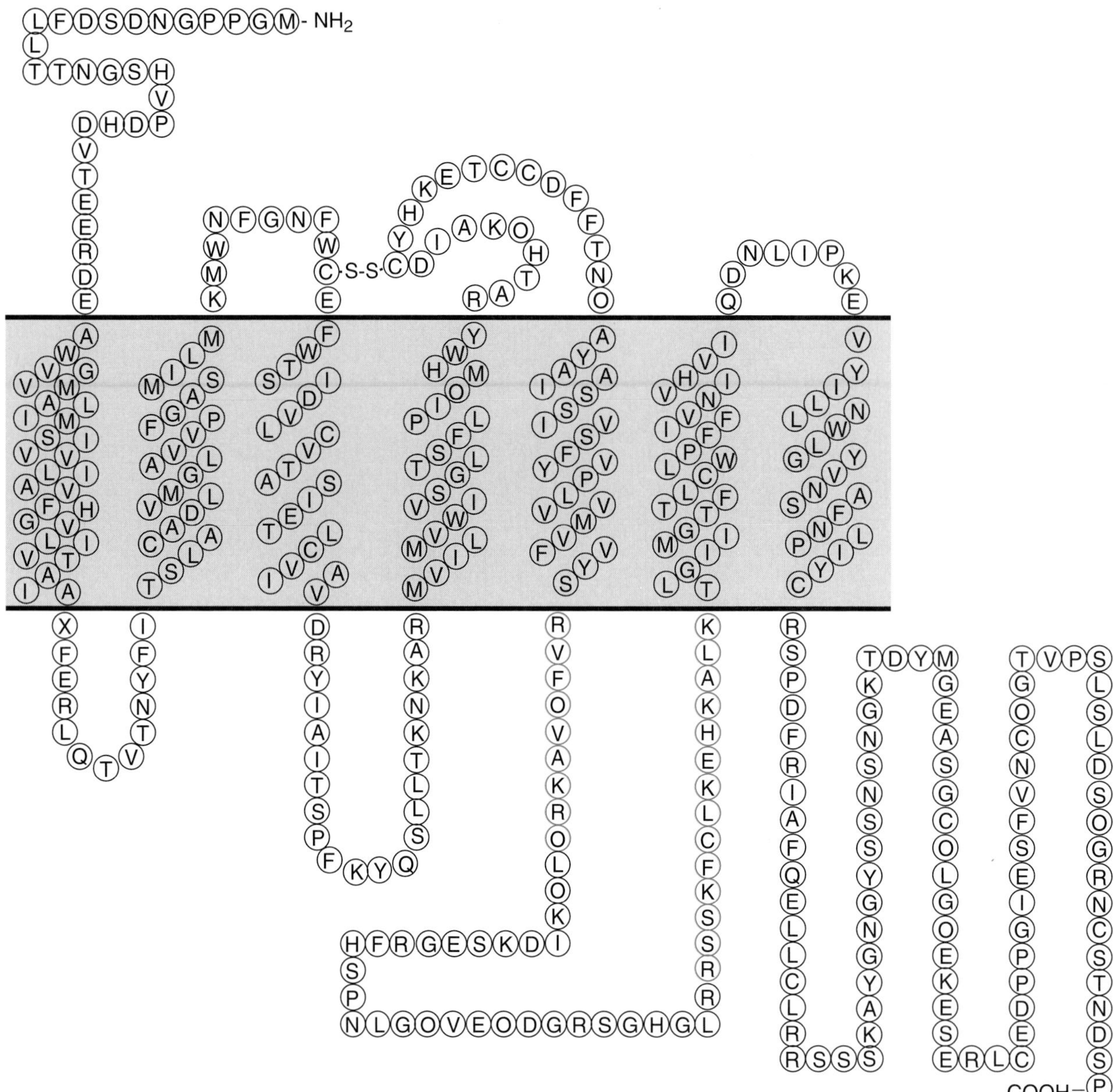

FIGURE 9.13 The β2AR serves as a structural model for metabotropic receptors. The NH_2 terminus of the receptor is extracellular (e1), and the receptor comprises seven transmembrane domains (TM1–TM7). Three loops of amino acids are extracellular (e2–e4), and three loops are intracellular (i1–i3). The COOH-terminal tail is intracellular (i4). Four of the key amino acid residues for ligand binding are identified in white circles in TM3, TM5, and TM6. A disulfide bond (–S–S–) between two cysteine (C) residues that stabilizes the structure of the receptor is shown linking e2 to e3. Areas in i3 and i4 proposed to be important for the association of the transmitter-bound form of the receptor with G proteins are indicated by amino acids enclosed in red circles. Adapted from Ref. 71.

tive fashion. This isomerization is analogous to the spontaneous isomerization proposed for ion channels that oscillate between open and closed states. At equilibrium, in the absence of agonist, the inactive state of metabotropic receptors is favored, and little G-protein activation occurs. Agonist binding stabilizes the active conformation and shifts the equilibrium toward the active form, and G-protein activation ensues. Conversely, receptor antagonists block G-protein activation through two proposed mechanisms: (1) negative antagonism in which antagonists bind to the inactive state of the receptor, thus favoring an equilibrium to

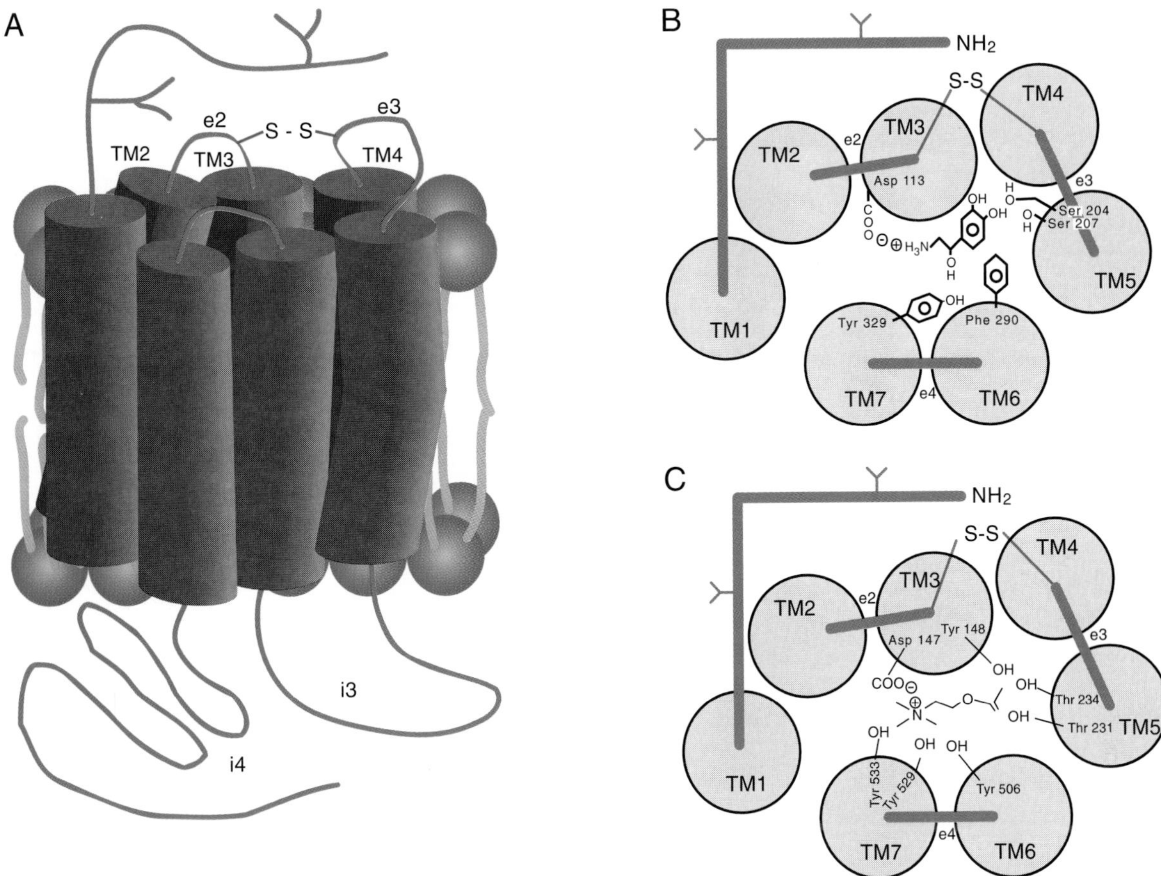

FIGURE 9.14 (A) Diagram showing the approximate position of the catecholamine-binding site in the βAR. The transmitter-binding site is formed by amino acids whose side chains extend into the center of the ring produced by the seven transmembrane domains (TM1–TM7). Note that the binding site exists at a position that places it within the plane of the lipid bilayer. (B) A view looking down from the top of a model of the βAR receptor identifying residues important for ligand binding. The seven transmembrane domains are represented as circles labeled TM1 through TM7. Amino acids composing the extracellular domains are represented as green bars labeled e1 through e4. The disulfide bond (–S–S–) that links e2 to e3 also is shown. Each of the specific residues indicated makes stabilizing contact with the transmitter. (C) A view looking down from the top of a model of the mAChR receptor identifying residues important for ligand binding. Stabilizing contacts, mainly through hydroxyl groups (–OH), are made with the transmitter on four of the seven transmembrane domains. The chemical nature of the transmitter (i.e., epinephrine versus ACh) determines the type of amino acids necessary to produce stable interactions in the receptor binding site (compare B and C). Adapted from Ref. 71.

the inactive form; and (2) neutral antagonism in which other antagonists bind to both the active and inactive forms, thus stabilizing both and preventing a transition into the active form. This kinetic model indicates that agonist binding is not necessary for the receptor to undergo a transition into the active state; instead, it stabilizes the receptor. In part, this model is based on observations of both spontaneously arising and engineered mutants of βAR and αAR receptors. Specific amino acid replacements were discovered to produce receptors that exhibit constitutive activity in the absence of agonists.[66,67] The amino acid changes apparently stabilize the active conformation of the molecule in a state more similar to the agonist-bound form of the receptor, leading to productive interactions with G proteins in the agonist-free state.

The Third Intracellular Loop Forms a Major Determinant for G-Protein Coupling

Extensive studies using site-directed mutagenesis and the production of chimeric molecules have revealed the domains and amino acids essential for G-protein coupling to metabotropic receptors. Receptor

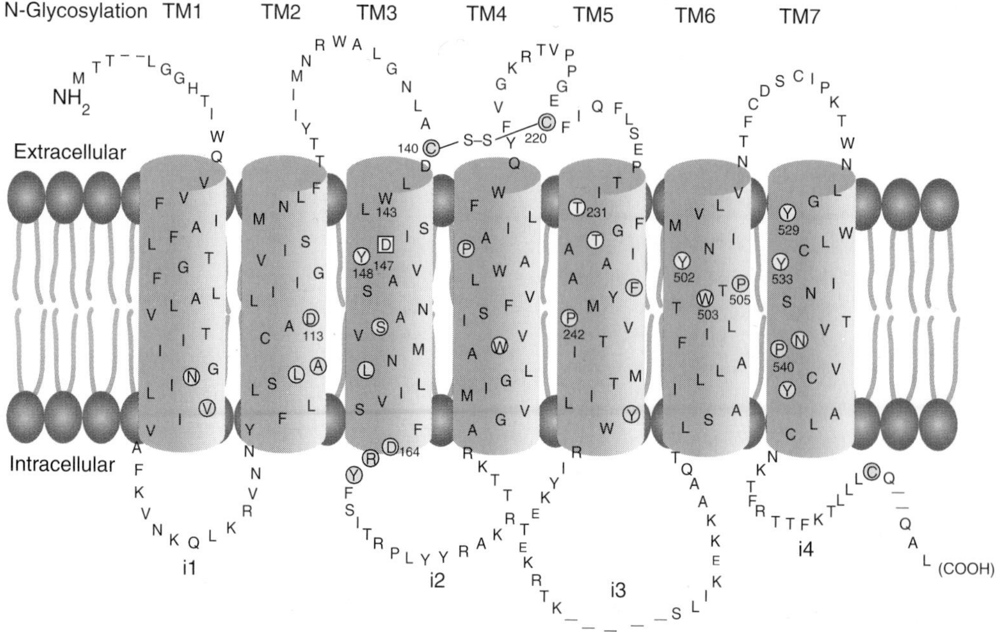

FIGURE 9.15 Amino acid sequence and predicted domain topology of the M3 isoform of the mAChR. The transmembrane domains are TM1–TM7. The NH_2 terminus of the protein is at the left and extends into the extracellular space. The COOH terminus is intracellular and is at the right; i1–i4 are the four intracellular domains. The conserved disulfide bond (–S–S–) connects extracellular loop 2 to loop 3. The dashes in the amino acid sequence represent inserts of various lengths that are not shown. Conserved amino acids for all members of the G-protein-coupled family of receptors are marked in purple. The amino acids taking part in ACh binding to the receptor are highlighted in yellow. Notice that all amino acids associated with ligand binding lie in approximately the same place across the receptor molecule. Adapted from *Trends Pharm. Sci.*, Vol. 14, 1993.

domains within the second (i2) and third (i3) intracellular loops (Fig. 9.13) appear largely responsible for determining the specificity and efficiency of coupling for adrenergic and muscarinic cholinergic receptors and are the likely sites for G-protein coupling of the entire metabotropic receptor family. In particular, the 12 amino acids of the N-terminal region of the third intracellular loop significantly affect the specificity of G-protein coupling. Other regions in the C-terminus of the third intracellular loop and the N-terminal region of the C-terminal tail appear to be more important for determining the efficiency of G-protein coupling than for determining its specificity.[64] The third intracellular loop varies enormously in size among the different G-protein-coupled receptors, ranging from 29 amino acids in the substance P (a neuropeptide) receptor to 242 amino acids in the mAChR.[65] The intracellular loop connecting TM5 and TM6 is the main point of receptor coupling to G proteins, and ligand binding to amino acids in TM5 and TM6 may be responsible for triggering the G protein–receptor interaction by transmitting a conformational change to the third intracellular loop (i3).

Specific Amino Acids Are Involved in Transmitting Ligand Binding into G-Protein Coupling

Residues associated with transmitting the conformational change induced by ligand binding to the activation of G proteins have been investigated with the use of mAChRs. These studies revealed that an Asp residue in TM2 is important for receptor activation of G proteins, and altering the Asp by site-directed mutagenesis has a major negative effect on G protein–receptor activation.[68,69] For mAChRs, a Thr residue in TM5 and a Tyr residue in TM6 also are essential; because these residues are connected by i3, they are assumed to play fundamental roles in transmitting the conformational change induced by ligand binding to the area of i3 essential for G-protein coupling and activation. When mutated, an additional Pro residue on TM7 produces a major impairment in the ability of the TM3 segment to induce activation of phospholipase C through a G protein and presumably is another key element in propagating the important conformational changes for efficient coupling to G proteins. A true molecular understanding of the conformational changes induced by agonist binding will likely require a structural approach similar to that applied by Nigel Unwin to the nAChR.

As mentioned earlier, the metabotropic receptors are single polypeptides; however, they are clearly separable into distinct functional domains. For example, the β2AR can be physically split, with the use of molecular techniques, into two fragments, one fragment containing TM1–TM5 and the other containing TM6 and TM7. In isolation, neither of these fragments can produce a functional receptor; however, when coexpressed in the same cell, functional β2ARs that can bind ligand and activate G proteins are produced.[70] This remarkable experiment indicates that physical contiguity in the primary sequence is not essential for producing functional β2ARs, but it does emphasize the contribution of domains in the separate fragments (TM1–TM4 and TM6–TM7) to both ligand binding and G-protein coupling. Like the β2AR, the m2 and m3 members of the mAChR family can form functional receptors even if split into two separate domains. A fragment containing the first five TM domains, when expressed with a fragment containing TM6 and TM7, forms a functional receptor[71] (Fig. 9.16).

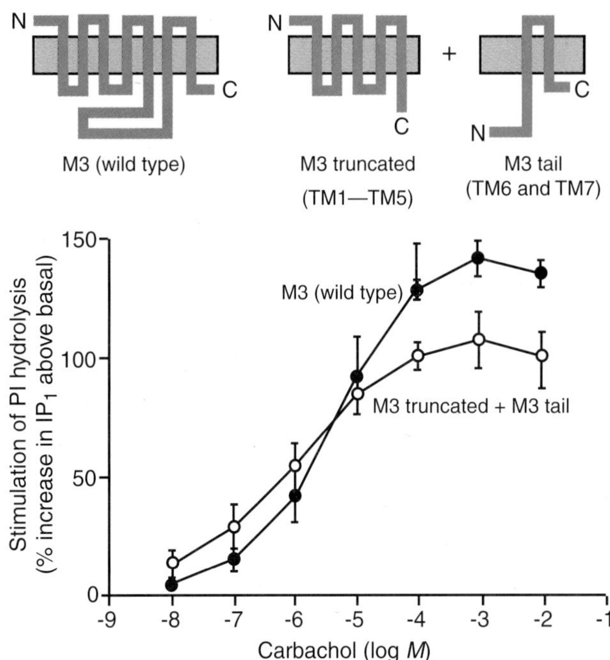

FIGURE 9.16 The mAChR can be split into two physically separated domains that retain the ability to bind transmitter and activate G proteins. (Upper left) Models of the full-length mAChR molecule; (upper right) two engineered pieces of the receptor. The graph indicates that, when coexpressed in the same cells, the two fragments can produce a functional mAChR that responds to the agonist carbachol by coupling to a G protein, which increases the activity of an enzyme that hydrolyzes phosphatidylinositol (PI). In fact, the receptor split into two pieces is nearly as effective as the full-length molecule in stimulating PI hydrolysis. Adapted from *Trends Pharm. Sci.*, Vol. 14, 1993.

G-Protein Coupling Increases the Affinity of the Receptor for Ligand

The affinity of a metabotropic receptor for an agonist increases when the receptor is coupled to the G protein. This positive feedback effectively increases the lifetime of the agonist-bound form of the receptor. An excellent demonstration of this effect comes from studies using engineered βAR receptors that are constitutively active in their ability to couple to G proteins and show an increased affinity for agonists.[66] When the G protein dissociates, the receptor returns to its lower affinity state. The changes induced by ligand binding apparently stabilize the receptor in a conformation with both higher affinity for ligand and higher affinity for coupling to G proteins.

The Specificity and Potency of G-Protein Activation Are Determined by Several Factors

Metabotropic receptors associate with G proteins to transduce ligand binding into intracellular effects. This coupling step can lead to diverse responses, depending on the type of G protein and the type of effector enzyme present. In addition, ligand binding to a single subtype of metabotropic receptor can activate multiple G-protein-coupled pathways. Activated α2ARs have been shown to couple to as many as four different G proteins in the same cell.[65] Some of the specificity for G-protein activation can be determined by the specific conformations assumed by the receptor, and a single receptor can assume multiple conformations. For example, α2ARs can apparently isomerize into at least two states. One state interacts only with a G protein that couples to phospholipase C, and a second state interacts with G proteins that can couple to both phospholipase C and phospholipase A2.[66]

Activated metabotropic receptors are free to couple to many G-protein molecules and thus permit a significant amplification of the initial transmitter-binding event.[72] This catalytic mechanism is referred to as "collision coupling,"[73] whereby a transient association between the activated receptor and the G protein is sufficient to produce the exchange of GDP for GTP, activating the G protein. Because enzymes such as adenylate cyclase appear to be tightly coupled even to the GTP-bound G protein, the rate-limiting step in the production of cAMP is the number of productive collisions between the receptor and the G protein. A constant GTPase activity hydrolyzes GTP, bringing the G protein and therefore the adenylate cyclase back to the basal state. Transmitter concentration clearly plays a role in the number of activated receptors present at any given time, and metabotropic receptors exhibit saturable dose–response curves. This apparent maximal rate is achieved when all of the G protein–cyclase complexes have become activated (more accurately, when the rate of formation is maximal with respect to the rate of GTP hydrolysis). A less intuitive consequence that evolves from these models is that receptor number can significantly affect the concentration of transmitter that produces a half-maximal response of cAMP accumulation. The larger the receptor number, the greater the probability that a productive collision will occur between an agonist-bound receptor and the G protein. Experimental evidence for this prediction was obtained for the βAR receptor expressed at various levels in eukaryotic cells. Increasing concentrations of βAR produced a decrease in the concentration of agonist required to produce half-maximal production of cAMP.[74] Apparently, the cell can adjust the magnitude of its response appropriately by regulating the number of receptors available for transmitter interaction. The number of available receptors for productive G-protein interactions is also regulated by the process of desensitization.

Receptor Desensitization Is a Built-in Mechanism for Downregulating the Cellular Response to Transmitter

Desensitization is a very important process whereby cells can decrease their sensitivity to a particular stimulus to prevent saturation of the system. Desensitization is a complex series of events.[64] For metabotropic receptors, desensitization is defined as an increase in the concentration of agonist required to produce half-maximal stimulation of, for example, adenylate cyclase. In practical terms, desensitization of receptors produces less response for a constant amount of transmitter.

There are two known mechanisms for desensitization. One mechanism is a decrease in response brought about by the covalent modifications produced by receptor phosphorylation and is quite rapid (seconds to minutes). The other mechanism is the physical removal of receptors from the plasma membrane (likely through a mechanism of receptor-mediated endocytosis) and tends to require greater periods of time (minutes to hours). The process can be either reversible (sequestration) or irreversible (downregulation).

The Rapid Phase of Metabotropic Receptor Desensitization Is Mediated by Receptor Phosphorylation

Desensitization of the βAR appears to involve at least three protein kinases—PKA, PKC, and β-adrenergic receptor kinase [βARK; also referred to as a G-protein receptor kinase (GRK)]. Phosphorylation of ARs by PKA does not require that agonist bind to the receptor and appears to be a general mechanism by which the cell can reduce the effectiveness of all available receptors, independent of whether they are in the agonist-bound or unbound state (Fig. 9.17). This process is also referred to as **heterologous desensitization** because the receptor does not require bound agonist. PKA and PKC phosphorylate sites on the third intracellular loop and possibly the C-terminal cytoplasmic domain. Phosphorylation of these sites functionally interferes with the receptor's ability to couple to G proteins, thus producing the desensitization. PKC has also been implicated in metabotropic receptor desensitization. Whether the same sites on the βAR are phosphorylated by both PKA and PKC is controversial. Some researchers conclude that the effects of phosphorylation by either kinase on decreasing coupling of the receptor to G proteins are similar (suggesting that the sites phosphorylated are similar).[18] Others find that the effects are additive.[75] Although the details of the role played by each of these kinases are ambiguous, phosphorylation by either enzyme desensitizes the receptor.

An additional pathway of metabotropic receptor desensitization includes the family of GRKs. The first member described was βARK, a Ser- and Thr-specific protein kinase initially identified by phosphorylation

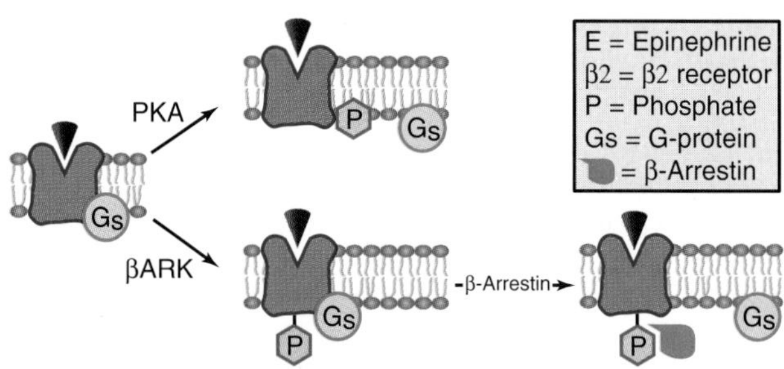

FIGURE 9.17 Different modes of desensitization of G-protein-coupled receptors. This diagram indicates that the epinephrine (E)-bound form of the β2AR normally couples to the G protein, G_S. PKA can phosphorylate the receptor, leading to an inhibition of the binding of G_S. βARK also can phosphorylate the receptor; however, this phosphorylation does not directly interfere with binding to G_S. βARK phosphorylation is needed for the binding of another protein, β-arrestin, which by its association with the receptor, prevents G_S from binding. Adapted from Ref. 64.

of the βAR. βARK phosphorylates only the agonist-bound form of the receptor, usually when agonist concentrations reach the micromolar level, as typically found in the synaptic cleft. This process is referred to as **homologous desensitization** because the regulation is specific for those receptor molecules that are in the agonist-bound state. Phosphorylation of the βAR by βARK does not substantially interfere with coupling to G proteins. Instead, an additional protein, β-arrestin, binds the βARK-phosphorylated form of the receptor with dramatically increased affinity, thus blocking receptor–G protein coupling (Fig. 9.17). This process is analogous to the desensitization of the light-sensitive receptor molecule rhodopsin produced by rhodopsin kinase phosphorylation and the binding of arrestin. The phosphorylation sites on the βAR for βARK reside on the C-terminal cytoplasmic domain and are distinct from those phosphorylated by PKA.

Even though the name implies specificity to the βAR, βARK can also phosphorylate other G-protein-coupled receptors, including the αAR and mAChR, to produce agonist-dependent desensitization. As noted earlier, the name G-protein receptor kinases, was adopted for this family of enzymes to describe their capacity to phosphorylate receptors that bind to G proteins.[76,77] Six members of the GRK family of kinases have been identified; rhodopsin kinase (GRK1), βARK (GRK2), and GRK3 through GRK6.[67,77] The mechanism of GRK activation appears to be related to agonist binding to the receptor because receptor activation simultaneously activates GRK catalytic activity. The addition of G-protein $\beta\gamma$ subunits also increases the activity of GRKs, primarily by promoting a translocation of the kinase to the membrane.

Homologous desensitization starts with the activation of a metabotropic receptor, which induces activation of G proteins and dissociation of the $\beta\gamma$ subunit complex from α subunits. At least one role for the $\beta\gamma$ complex appears to be to bind to GRKs, which leads to membrane association, presumably in the area of the locally activated G protein–receptor complex. Transmitter binding to receptors also activates GRKs, leading to receptor phosphorylation and binding of β-arrestin. The ensuing processes of uncoupling the activated receptor from G proteins and possibly sequestration follow.

Desensitization Can Also Be Produced by Loss of Receptors from the Cell Surface

Desensitization of metabotropic receptors is also produced by removal of the receptor from the cell surface. This process can be either reversible (sequestration, or internalization) or irreversible (downregulation). **Sequestration** is the term used to describe the rapid (within minutes) but reversible endocytosis of receptors from the cell surface after agonist application (Fig. 9.18). Neither G-protein coupling nor receptor phosphorylation appears to be essential for this process, but phosphorylation by GRKs clearly enhances the rate of sequestration.[78] The binding of arrestins to the phosphorylated receptor also enhances sequestration.[79] Thus, arrestin binding appears to promote not only rapid desensitization by disrupting the receptor–G protein interaction but also receptor sequestration. Because the receptor can be functionally uncoupled from the G protein through the rapid phosphorylation-dependent phase of desensitization, the physiological role(s) of sequestration remains an open issue, although decreasing the number of receptor molecules on the cell surface would contribute to the overall process of desensitization to agonist. One hypothesis is that the process of receptor cycling through sequestered vesicles is a trafficking mechanism that leads to an enhanced rate of dephosphorylation of the normally phosphorylated receptor, returning it to the cell surface in its basal state[80] (Fig. 9.18).

Downregulation occurs more slowly than sequestration and is irreversible (Fig. 9.18). The early phase (within 4 h) may be both a PKA-dependent and a PKA-independent process.[81,82] This early phase of downregulation is apparently due to receptor degradation after endocytotic removal from the plasma membrane. The later phases (>4 h) of downregulation appear to be further mediated by a reduction in receptor biosynthesis through a decrease in the stability of the receptor mRNA[81] and a decreased transcription rate.

Other Posttranslational Modifications Are Required for Efficient Metabotropic Receptor Function

Like many proteins expressed on the cell surface, metabotropic receptors are glycosylated, and the N-terminal extracellular domain is the site of carbohydrate attachment. Relatively little is known about the effect of glycosylation on the function of metabotropic receptors. Glycosylation does not appear to be essential to the production of a functional ligand-binding pocket,[65] although prevention of glycosylation may decrease membrane insertion and alter intracellular trafficking of the β2AR.

Another important structural feature of most metabotropic receptors is the disulfide bond formed between two Cys residues present on the extracellular loops (e2 and e3; Figs. 9.13 and 9.14). Apparently, the disulfide bond stabilizes a restricted conformation of

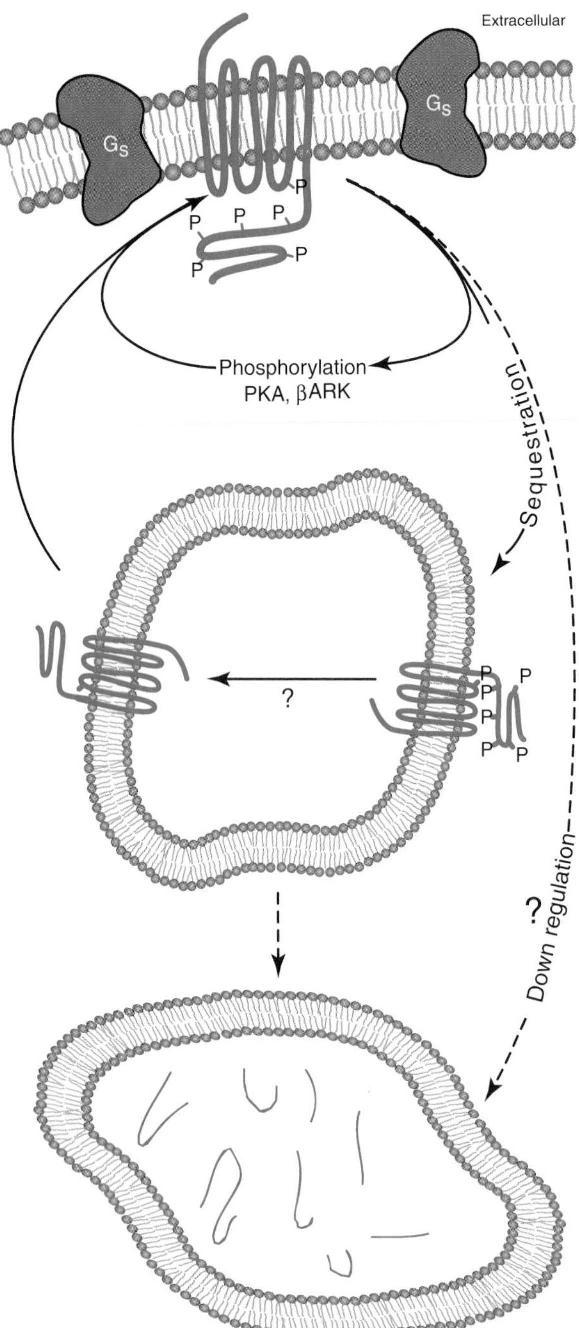

FIGURE 9.18 Intracellular pathways associated with desensitization of G-protein-coupled receptors. G-protein-coupled receptors are phosphorylated on their intracellular domains (P) by PKA, βARK, and other kinases. The phosphorylated forms of the receptor are removed from the cell surface by a process called sequestration; thus fewer binding sies remain on the cell surface for transmitter interactions. This cycle may be reversible and may help return the phosphorylated form of the receptor to the cell surface in its unphosphorylated state. Alternatively, the phosphorylated receptors can be downregulated, whereby they are removed from the cell surface and targeted to a compartment in which they are degraded. Downregulation is irreversible without new receptor synthesis. Adapted from Ref. 64.

the mature receptor by covalently linking the two extracellular domains, and this conformation favors ligand binding. Disruption of this disulfide bond significantly decreases agonist binding.[64]

A third Cys residue, in the C-terminal domain of metabotropic receptors, appears to serve as a point for covalent attachment of a fatty acid (often palmitate). Presumably, fatty acid attachment stabilizes an interaction between the C-terminal domain of a metabotropic receptor and the membrane.[83] The full consequences of this posttranslational modification are not understood, because replacing the normally palmitoylated Cys with an amino acid that cannot be acylated appears to have little effect on receptor binding; however, G-protein coupling may not be as efficient.[84]

Metabotropic Receptors All Exhibit Similar Structures

The family of metabotropic receptors exhibit structural similarities that permit the construction of "trees" describing the degree to which they are related (Fig. 9.19). Some remarkable relations become evident in such an analysis. For example, the D1 and D5 subtypes of dopamine receptors are more closely related to the α2-adrenergic receptors than to the D2, D3, and D4 dopamine receptors. The similarities and differences

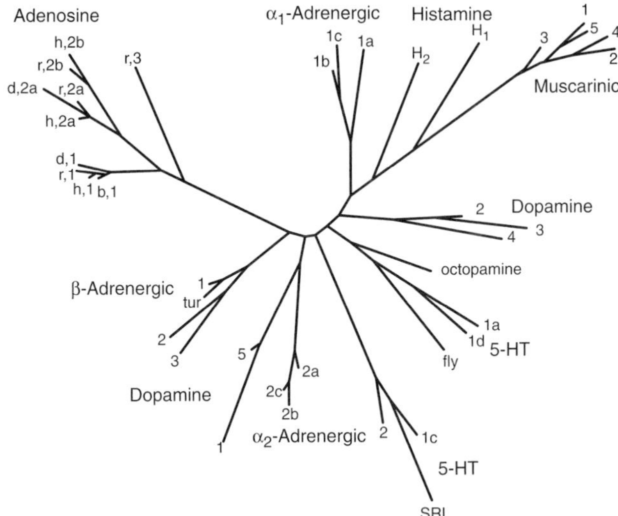

FIGURE 9.19 Evolutionary relationship of metabotropic receptor family. To assemble this tree, sequence homologies in the transmembrane domains were compared for each receptor. Distance determines the degree of relatedness. Abbreviations are: r, rat; d, dog, h, human; tur, turkey; SRL, a putative serotonin receptor; and 5-HT, 5-hydroxytryptamine (serotonin). Figure adapted from Linden, Chapter 21, figure 2, *Basic Neurochemistry*, 1993. Original tree construction by William Pearson and Kevin Lynch, University of Virginia.

among metabotropic receptor families are highlighted in the remainder of this chapter.

Muscarinic ACh Receptors

Muscarine is a naturally occurring plant alkaloid that binds to muscarinic subtypes of the AChRs and activates them. The mAChRs play a dominant role in mediating the actions of ACh in the brain, indirectly producing both excitation and inhibition through binding to a family of unique receptor subtypes. The mAChRs are found both presynaptically and postsynaptically and, ultimately, their main neuronal effects appear to be mediated through alterations in the properties of ion channels. The presynaptic mAChRs take part in important feedback loops that regulate neurotransmitter release. ACh released from the presynaptic terminal can bind to mAChRs on the same nerve ending, thus activating enzymatic processes that modulate subsequent neurotransmitter release. This modulation is typically an inhibition; however, activation of the m5 AChR produces an enhancement in subsequent release. These autoreceptors are an important regulatory mechanism for short-term (milliseconds to seconds) modulation of neurotransmitter release.

The family of mAChRs now includes five members (m1–m5), ranging from 55 to 70 kDa, and each of the five subtypes exhibits the typical architecture of seven membrane-spanning domains. Much of the diversity in this family of receptors resides in the third intracellular loop (i3) responsible for the specificity of coupling to G proteins. The m1, m3, and m5 mAChRs predominantly couple to G proteins that activate the enzyme phospholipase C. The m2 and m4 receptors couple to G proteins that inhibit adenylate cyclase, as well as to G proteins that directly regulate K^+ and Ca^{2+} channels. As is the case for other metabotropic receptors, the domain near the N-terminus of the third intracellular loop is important for the specificity of G-protein coupling. This domain is conserved in m1, m3, and m5 AChRs, but is unique in m2 and m4. Several other important residues also have been identified for G-protein coupling. A particular Asp residue near the N-terminus of the second intracellular loop (i2) is important for G-protein coupling, as are residues residing in the C-terminal region of the i3 loop.

The major mAChRs found in the brain are m1, m3, and m4, and each is diffusely distributed. The m2 subtype is the heart isoform and is not highly expressed in other organs. The genes for m4 and m5 lack introns, whereas those encoding m1, m2, and m3 contain introns, although little is known concerning alternatively spliced products of these receptors.

Atropine is probably the most widely utilized antagonist for the mAChR and binds to most subtypes, as does *N*-methylscopolamine. The antagonist pirenzipine appears to be relatively specific for the m1 mAChR, and other antagonists such as AF-DX116 and hexahydrosiladifenidol appear to be specific for the m2 and m3 subtypes.

Adrenergic Receptors

The catecholamines epinephrine (adrenaline) and norepinephrine (noradrenaline) produce their effects by binding to adrenergic receptors and activating them; in fact, both can bind to the same subtypes of adrenergic receptors. Adrenergic receptors are currently separated into three families, $\alpha1$, $\alpha2$, and β. Each of the $\alpha1$ and $\alpha2$ families is further subdivided into three subclasses. Similarly, the β family also contains three subclasses ($\beta1$, $\beta2$, and $\beta3$). The main adrenergic receptors in the brain are the $\alpha2$ and $\beta1$ subtypes. The $\alpha2$ARs have diverse roles, but the function that is best characterized (in both central and peripheral nervous tissue) is their role as autoreceptors (i.e., presynaptic receptors that bind transmitter and alter the release apparatus so that subsequent release is modulated, normally, but not always, in an inhibitory fashion). Different AR subtypes bind to G proteins that can alter the activity of phospholipase C, Ca^{2+} channels, and, probably best studied, adenylate cyclase. For example, activation of $\alpha2$ARs produces inhibition of adenylate cyclase, whereas all βARs activate the cyclase.

Only a few agonists or antagonists cleanly distinguish the AR subtypes. One of them, isoproterenol, is an agonist that appears to be highly specific for βARs. Propranolol is the best-known antagonist for β receptors, and phentolamine is a good antagonist for α receptors but weakly binds at β receptors.

The genomic organization of the different AR subtypes is unusual. Like many G-protein-coupled metabotropic receptors, $\beta1$ and $\beta2$ARs are encoded by genes lacking introns. $\beta3$ARs, which apparently have a role in lipolysis and are poorly characterized, are encoded by an intron-containing gene, as are $\alpha1$ARs, providing an opportunity for alternative splicing as a means of introducing functional heterogeneity into the receptor. This could explain why the exact identity of a cDNA encoding the $\alpha1$AR has not been determined.

Dopamine Receptors

Some 80% of the catecholamine dopamine in the brain is localized to the corpus striatum, which receives major input from the substantia nigra and takes part in coordinating motor movements. Dopamine is also found diffusely throughout the cortex, where its specific functions remain undefined. However, many neuroleptic drugs appear to exert their effects by blocking dopamine binding, and imbalances in the dopaminergic system have long been thought to be associated with neuropsychiatric disorders.

Dopamine receptors are found both pre- and postsynaptically, and their structure is homologous to that of the receptors for other catecholamines.[85,86] Five subtypes of dopamine receptors can be grouped into two main classes, D1-like and D2-like receptors. D1-like receptors include D1 and D5, and D2-like receptors include D2, D3, and D4 (see Fig. 9.19). The main distinction between these two classes is that D1-like receptors activate adenylate cyclase, whereas D2-like receptors inhibit adenylate cyclase. The D1-like receptors are also slightly larger in molecular mass than the D2-like receptors. The deduced amino acid sequence for the entire family ranges from 387 amino acids (D4) to 477 amino acids (D5). The main structural differences between the D1-like and D2-like receptors are that the intracellular loop between the sixth and seventh transmembrane segments is larger in the D2-like receptors and the D2-like receptors have smaller C-terminal intracellular segments after the seventh transmembrane segment. Two isoforms of the D2 receptor have been isolated; called D2 long and D2 short, these isoforms were generated by alternative splicing. D2 long contains a 29-amino-acid insert in the large intracellular loop between the fifth and sixth membrane-spanning segments. No functional or anatomical difference has yet been identified for the short and long forms of D2.

The D1-like receptors, like the βARs, are transcribed from intronless genes.[87] Conversely, all the D2-like receptors contain introns, thus providing for possibilities of alternatively spliced products. Posttranslational modifications include glycosylation at one or more sites, disulfide bonding of the two Cys residues in e2 and e3, and acylation of the Cys residue in the C-terminal tail (analogous to the β2AR). The dopamine-binding site may include two Ser residues in TM5 and an Asp residue in TM3, analogous to the βAR.

Because of dopamine's presumed role in neuropsychiatric disorders, enormous effort has been put into developing pharmacological tools for manipulating this system. Dopamine receptors bind amphetamines, bromocriptine, lisuride, clozapine, melperone, fluperlapine, and haloperidol. Because these drugs do not show great specificity for receptor subtypes, their usefulness for dissecting effects specifically related to binding to one or another dopamine receptor subtype is limited.

Purinergic Receptors

Purinergic receptors bind to ATP (or other nucleotide analogs) or its breakdown product adenosine. Adenosine is not found in synaptic vesicles and is therefore not considered a "classic" neurotransmitter. However, the multitude of receptors that bind and are activated by adenosine indicates that this molecule has important modulatory effects on the nervous system. Situations of high metabolic activity that consume ATP and situations of insufficient ATP-regenerating capacity can lead to the accumulation of adenosine. Because adenosine is permeable to membranes and can diffuse into and out of cells, a feedback loop is established in which adenosine can serve as a local diffusible signal that communicates the metabolic status of the neuron to surrounding cells and vice versa.[88]

The original nomenclature describing purinergic receptors defined adenosine as binding to P1 receptors and ATP as binding to P2 receptors. Families of both P1 and P2 receptors have since been described, and adenosine receptors are now identified as A-type purinergic receptors, consisting of A1, A2a, A2b, and A3. ATP receptors are designated as P type and consist of P2x, P2y, P2z, P2t, and P2u. Recall that P2x and P2z subtypes are ionotropic receptors.

A-type receptors exhibit the classic arrangement of seven transmembrane-spanning segments but are typically shorter than most metabotropic receptors, ranging in size between 35 and 46 kDa. The ligand-binding site of A-type receptors is unique in that the ligand, adenosine, has no inherent charged moieties at physiological pH. A-type receptors appear to utilize histidine residues as their points of contact with adenosine, and, in particular, a His residue in TM7 is apparently essential, because its mutation eliminates agonist binding. Other His residues in TM6 and TM7 are conserved in all A-type receptors and may serve as other points of contact with agonists. Work with chimeric A-type receptors has further substantiated the importance of residues in TM5, TM6, and TM7 for ligand binding.

A1 receptors are highly expressed in the brain, and their activation downregulates adenylate cyclase and increases phospholipase C activity. The A2a and A2b receptors are not as highly expressed in nervous tissue and are associated with the stimulation of adenylate cyclase and phospholipase C, respectively. The A3 subtype exhibits a unique pharmacological profile in that binding of xanthine derivatives, which blocks adenosine's action competitively, is absent. Very low levels of the A3 receptor are found in brain and peripheral nervous tissue. The A3 receptor appears to be coupled to the activation of phospholipase C.

The human A1 receptor has a unique mode of receptor expression.[89] Introns in the 5′ untranslated sequence of the mRNA, spliced in a tissue-specific manner, are capable of affecting the translational efficiency of the mRNA. Two extra start codons upstream from the start codon that initiates translation of the A1 receptor exert a negative effect on translation. The translational repression can be relieved by mutating these two extra start codons. This process is an effective way of controlling the level of receptor expression and may serve as a model for translational regulation for many mRNAs.

The P-type receptors, P2y, P2t, and P2u, are typical G-protein-linked metabotropic receptors, mostly localized to the periphery. However, direct effects of ATP have been detected in neurons, and often the response is biphasic—an early excitatory effect followed, with its breakdown to adenosine, by a secondary inhibitory effect. Interestingly, P-type receptors exhibit a higher degree of homology to peptide-binding receptors than they do to the A-type purinergic receptors. As in A-type receptors, P-type receptors have a His residue in the third transmembrane domain; however, other sites for ligand binding have not been specifically identified. Specific receptor antagonists for the subtypes are not available.

Serotonin Receptors

Serotonin-containing cell bodies are found in the raphe nucleus in the brainstem and in nerve endings distributed diffusely throughout the brain.[90] Serotonin has been implicated in sleep, modulation of circadian rhythms, eating, and arousal. Serotonin also has hormonelike effects when released in the blood stream, regulating smooth muscle contraction and affecting the platelet aggregating and immune systems.

Serotonin receptors are classified into four subtypes, 5-HT1–5-HT4, with a further subdivision of the 5-HT1 subtype. Recall that the 5-HT3 receptor is ionotropic. The other 5-HT receptors exhibit the typical seven transmembrane-spanning segments, and all couple to G proteins to exert their effects. For example, 5-HT1a, 1b, 1d, and 4 either activate or inhibit adenylate cyclase. 5-HT1c and 5-HT2 receptors preferentially stimulate activation of phospholipase C to produce increased intracellular levels of diacylglycerol and inositol 1,4,5-triphosphate.

Serotonin receptors can also be grossly distributed into two groups on the basis of their gene structures. Both 5-HT1c and 5-HT2 are derived from genes that contain multiple introns. In contrast, similar to the βAR family, 5-HT1 is coded by a gene lacking introns. Interestingly, 5-HT1a is more closely related ancestrally to the βAR family than it is to other membranes of the serotonin receptor family and was originally isolated by utilizing the cDNA for the β2AR as a molecular probe.[91] This observation helps explain some pharmacological data suggesting that both 5-HT1a and 5-HT1b can bind certain adrenergic antagonists.

$GABA_B$ Receptor

$GABA_B$ receptors are found throughout the nervous system, where they are sometimes colocalized with ionotropic $GABA_A$. $GABA_B$ receptors are present both pre- and postsynaptically. Presynaptically, they appear to mediate inhibition of neurotransmitter release through an autoreceptor-like mechanism by activating K^+ conductances and diminishing Ca^{2+} conductances. In addition, $GABA_B$ receptors may affect K^+ channels through a direct physical coupling to the K^+ channel, not mediated through a G-protein intermediate. Postsynaptically, $GABA_B$ receptor activation produces a characteristic slow hyperpolarization (termed the slow inhibitory postsynaptic potential) through the activation of a K^+ conductance. This effect appears to be through a pertussis-toxin-sensitive G protein that inhibits adenylate cyclase.

The recent cloning of the $GABA_B$ receptor[92] revealed that it has high sequence similarity to the family of metabotropic glutamate receptors, but shows little similarity to other G-protein-coupled receptors. Like those of the metabotropic glutamate receptors, the N-terminal extracellular domains of the $GABA_B$ receptor exhibit sequence similarity to bacterial amino acid transport proteins and are the presumed sites of GABA binding. Two isoforms of the $GABA_B$ receptor with predicted sizes of 960 and 844 amino acids were identified. With the exception of the large extracellular domain, the $GABA_B$ receptor structure is typical of the metabotropic receptor family, exhibiting seven TM domains. Identification of this initial cDNA will provide the means for characterizing the family of $GABA_B$ receptor subtypes. Cloning of the $GABA_B$ receptor was made possible by the development of a high-affinity, high-specificity antagonist termed CGP64213. This antagonist is several orders of magnitude more potent at inhibiting $GABA_B$ receptor function than the more widely known antagonist saclofen. Baclofen, an analog of saclofen, remains the best agonist for activating $GABA_B$ receptors.

Metabotropic Glutamate Receptors

The metabotropic glutamate receptors (mGluR) are similar in general structure (in having seven transmembrane-spanning segments) to other metabotropic receptors; however, they are divergent enough to be considered to have originated from a separate evolutionary-derived receptor family.[2,93] In fact, sequence homology between the mGluR family and the other

G-protein-linked, seven-transmembrane-segment receptors is minimal. The mGluR family is heterogeneous in size, ranging from 854 to 1179 amino acids. Both the N-terminal and C-terminal domains are unusually large for G-protein-coupled receptors. One great difference in the structures of mGluRs is that the binding site for glutamate appears to reside in the large N-terminal extracellular domain and is homologous to a bacterial amino acid-binding protein.[94] In most of the other families of metabotropic receptors, the ligand-binding pocket is formed by the transmembrane segments partly buried in the membrane. This significant structural distinction supports the idea that the mGluRs evolved separately from the other metabotropic receptors. The third intracellular loop (thought to be the major determinant responsible for G-protein coupling in other metabotropic receptors) of the mGluRs is relatively small, whereas the C-terminal domain is typically quite large. The coupling between mGluRs and their respective G proteins may be through unique determinants that likely exert their effects on the large C-terminal domain.

Currently, eight different metabotropic glutamate receptors can be subdivided into three groups on the basis of sequence homologies and their capacity to couple to specific enzyme systems. Both mGluR1 and mGluR5 activate a G protein coupled to phospholipase C. Expression of the mGluR1 cDNA receptors in eukaryotic cells reveals that activation of the receptor can lead to the production of cAMP and of arachidonic acid, by coupling to G proteins that activate adenylate cyclase and phospholipase A2.[95] mGluR5, coupling in a relatively specific fashion to the G-protein-activated phospholipase C, does not exhibit this behavior.

The other six mGluR subtypes are distinct from one another in favoring either *trans*-1-aminocyclopentane-1,3-dicarboxylate (mGluR2, 3, and 8) or 1-2-amino-4-phosphonobutyrate (mGluR4, 6, and 7) as agonists for activation. mGluR2 and mGluR4 can be further distinguished pharmacologically by using the newly developed agonist 2-(carboxycyclopropyl)glycine, which is more potent at activating mGluR2 receptors.[96] Much less is known about the mechanisms by which these receptors produce intracellular responses; however, they seem to specifically inhibit the production of cAMP by activating an inhibitory G protein.

mGluRs are widespread in the nervous system and are found both pre- and postsynaptically. Presynaptically, they serve as autoreceptors and appear to participate in the inhibition of neurotransmitter release. Their postsynaptic roles appear to be quite varied and depend on the specific G protein to which they are coupled. mGluR1 activation has been implicated in long-term synaptic plasticity at many sites in the brain, including long-term potentiation in the hippocampus and long-term depression in the cerebellum.

Peptide Receptors

Neuropeptide receptors are an immense family. Because of their diversity, they cannot be covered in detail in this chapter. Despite their diversity, none of the receptors that bind peptides appears to be coupled directly to the opening of ion channels. Neuropeptide receptors exert their effects either through the typical pathway of activation of G proteins or through a more recently described pathway related to activation of an associated tyrosine kinase activity.

The peptide-binding domain of neuropeptide receptors includes residues in both the large N-terminal extracellular domain and the transmembrane domain.[61] The additional stabilizing contacts presumably provide the receptors with their remarkably high affinity for neuropeptides (in the nanomolar range). For example, residues in the first and second extracellular domains, as well as those in at least four of the transmembrane domains of the NK1 neurokinin receptor, interact with substance P to form stabilizing contacts. Many small-molecule antagonists are known to inhibit activation of the NK1 neurokinin receptor, and these antagonists bind to some, but not all, of the same amino acids in the transmembrane segments as does substance P. The possible mechanisms for inhibition of the peptide receptors range from complete structural overlap between agonist and antagonist binding to complete allosteric exclusion.[61] Knowledge of the activated structure of the neuropeptide receptors provides remarkable opportunities for future drug design.

Summary

Metabotropic receptors are single polypeptides composed of seven transmembrane-spanning segments. In general, the binding site for neurotransmitter is located within the core of the circular structure formed by these segments. Transmitter binding produces conformational changes in the receptor that expose parts of the i3 region, among others, for binding to G proteins. G-protein binding increases the affinity of the receptor for transmitter. Desensitization is common among the metabotropic receptors and leads to decreased response of the receptor to neurotransmitter by several distinct mechanisms. The mGluRs are structurally distinct from other metabotropic receptors; mGluRs have large N-terminal extracellular domains that form the binding site for glutamate. Otherwise, the basic structure of mGluRs appears to be similar to that of the rest of the metabotropic receptor family.

References

1. Ortell, M. O., and Lunt, G. G. (1995). Evolutionary history of the ligand-gated ion-channel superfamily of receptors. *Trends Neurosci.* **18:** 121–128.
2. Hollmann, M., and Heinemann, S. (1994). Cloned glutamate receptors. *Ann. Rev. Neurosci.* **17:** 31–108.
3. Unwin, N. (1993). Neurotransmitter action: Opening of ligand-gated ion channels. (*Cambridge, Mass.*) *Cell* **72**(Suppl.), 31–41.
4. Unwin, N. (1993). Nicotinic acetylcholine receptor at 9 Å resolution. *J. Mol. Biol.* **229:** 1101–1124.
5. Unwin, N. (1995). Acetylcholine receptor channel imaged in the open state. *Nature* (*London*) **373:** 37–43.
6. Noda, M., Takahashi, H., Tanabe, T., Toyosato, M., Furutani, Y., Hirose, T., Asai, M., Inayama, S., Miyata, T., and Numa, S. (1982). Primary structure of alpha-subunit precursor of *Torpedo californica acetylcholine receptor deduced from cDNA sequence. Nature* (*London*) **299:** 793–797.
7. Noda, M., Takahashi, H., Tanabe, T., Toyosato, M., Kikyotani, S., Furtani, Y., Hirose, T., Takashima, H., Inayama, S., Miyata, T., and Numa, S. (1983). Structural homology of *Torpedo californica* acetylcholine receptor subunits. *Nature* (*London*) **302:** 528–532.
8. Hille, B. 1992. *Ionic Channels of Excitable Membranes.* Sinauer, Sunderland, MA.
9. Karlin, A. (1993). Structure of nicotinic acetylcholine receptors. *Curr. Opin. Neurobiol.* **3:** 299–309.
10. Imoto, K., Busch, C., Sakmann, B., Mishina, M., Konno, T., Nakai, J., Bujo, H., Mori, Y., Fukuda, K., and Numa, S. (1988). Rings of negatively charged amino acids determine the acetylcholine receptor channel conductance. *Nature* (*London*) **335:** 645–648.
11. Changeux, J. P., Devillers-Thiery, A., and Chemouilli, P. (1984). Acetylcholine receptor: An allosteric protein. *Science* **225:** 1335–1345.
12. Colquhoun, D., and Sakmann, B. (1985). Fast events in single-channel currents activated by acetylcholine and its analogues at the frog muscle end-plate. *J. Physiol.* (*London*) **369:** 501–557.
13. Colquhoun, D., and Ogden, D. C. (1988). Activation of ion channels in the frog end-plate by high concentrations of acetylcholine. *J. Physiol.* **395:** 131–159.
14. Mishina, M., Kurosaki, T., Tobimatsu, T., Morimoto, Y., Noda, M., Yamamoto, T., Terao, M., Lindstrom, J., Takahashi, T., Kuno, M., and Numa, S. (1984). Expression of functional acetylcholine receptor from cloned cDNAs. *Nature* (*London*) **307:** 604–608.
15. Paulson, H. L., Ross, A. F., Green, W. N., and Claudio, T. (1991). Analysis of early events in acetylcholine receptor assembly. *J. Cell Biol.* **113:** 1371–1384.
16. Green, W. N., and Claudio, T. (1993). Acetylcholine receptor assembly: Subunit folding and oligomerization occur sequentially. *Cell* (*Cambridge, Mass.*) **74:** 57–69.
17. Gu, Y., Forsayeth, J. R., Verrall, S., Yu, X. M., and Hall, Z. W. (1991). Assembly of the mammalian muscle acetylcholine receptor in transfected COS cells. *J. Cell Biol.* **114:** 799–807.
18. Huganir, R. L., and Greengard, P. (1990). Regulation of neurotransmitter receptor desensitization by protein phosphorylation. *Neuron* **5:** 555–567.
19. McGehee, D. S., Heath, M. J., Gelber, S., Devay, P. and Role, L. W. (1995). Nicotine enhancement of fast excitatory synaptic transmission in CNS by presynaptic receptors [see comments]. *Science* **269:** 1692–1696.
20. Vernino, S., Amador, M., Luetje, C. W., Patrick, J., and Dani, J. A. (1992). Calcium modulation and high calcium permeability of neuronal nicotinic acetylcholine receptors. *Neuron* **8:** 127–134.
21. Seguela, P., Wadiche, J., Dineley-Miller, K., Dani, J. A., and Patrick, J. W. (1993). Molecular cloning, functional properties, and distribution of rat brain alpha 7: A nicotinic cation channel highly permeable to calcium. *J. Neurosci.* **13:** 596–604.
22. Bertrand, D., Galzi, J. L., Devillers-Thiery, A., Bertrand, S., and Changeux, J. P. (1993). Mutations at two distinct sites within the channel domain M2 alter calcium permeability of neuronal alpha 7 nicotinic receptor. *Proc. Natl. Acad. Sci. U.S.A.* **90:** 6971–6975.
23. Maricq, A. V., Peterson, A. S., Brake, A. J., Myers, R. M., and Julius, D. (1991). Primary structure and functional expression of the 5HT3 receptor, a serotonin-gated ion channel. *Science* **254:** 432–437.
24. Yakel, J. L., Lagrutta, A., Adelman, J. P., and North, R. A. (1993). Single amino acid substitution affects desensitization of the 5-hydroxytryptamine type 3 receptor expressed in *Xenopus* oocytes. *Proc. Natl. Acad. Sci. U.S.A.* **90:** 5030–5033.
25. Seighart, W. (1992). $GABA_A$ receptors: Ligand-gated Cl- ion channels modulated by multiple drug-binding sites. *Trends Pharmacol. Sci.* **13:** 446–450.
26. Barnard, E. A., Darlison, M. G., and Seeburg, P. (1987). Molecular biology of the $GABA_A$ receptor: The receptor / channel superfamily. *Trends Neurosci.* **10:** 502–509.
27. Bormann, J. (1988). Electrophysiology of $GABA_A$ and $GABA_B$ receptor subtypes. *Trends Neurosci.* **11:** 112–116.
28. Pritchett, D. B., Sontheimer, H., Shivers, B. D., Ymer, S., Kettenmann, H., Schofield, P. R., and Seeburg, P. H. (1989). Importance of a novel GABAA receptor subunit for benzodiazepine pharmacology. *Nature* (*London*) **338:** 582–585.
29. Bormann, J., and Fiegenspan, A. (1995). $GABA_C$ receptors. *Trends Neurosci.* **18:** 515–519.
30. Betz, H. (1991). Glycine receptors: Heterogeneous and widespread in the mammalian brain. *Trends Neurosci.* **14:** 458–461.
31. Young, A. B., and Snyder, S. H. (1974). The glycine synaptic receptor: Evidence that strychnine binding is associated with the ionic conductance mechanism. *Proc. Natl. Acad. Sci. U.S.A.* **71:** 4002–4005.
32. Brake, A. J., Wagenbach, M. J., and Julius, D. (1994). New structural motif for ligand-gated ion channels defined by an ionotropic ATP receptor. *Nature* (*London*) **371:** 519–523.
33. Valera, S., Hussy, N., Evans, R. J., Adami, N., North, R. A., Surprenant, A., and Buell, G. (1994). A new class of ligand-gated ion channel defined by P2x receptor for extracellular ATP [see comments]. *Nature* (*London*) **371:** 516–519.
34. Watkins, J. C., Krogsgaard-Larsen, P., and Honore, T. (1990). Structure activity relationships in the development of excitatory amino acid receptor agonists and competitive antagonists. *Trends Pharmacol. Sci.* **11:** 25–33.
35. Hollmann, M., O'Shea-Greenfield, A., Rogers, S. W., and Heinemann, S. (1989). Cloning by functional expression of a member of the glutamate receptor family. *Nature* (*London*) **342:** 643–648.
36. Boulter, J., Hollmann, M., O'Shea-Greenfield, A., Hartley, M., Deneris, E., Maron, C., and Heinemann, S. (1990). Molecular cloning and functional expression of glutamate receptor subunit genes. *Science* **249:** 1033–1037.
37. Keinanen, K., Wisden, W., Sommer, B., Werner, P., Herb, A., Verdoorn, T. A., Sakmann, B., and Seeburg, P. H. (1990). A family of AMPA-selective glutamate receptors. *Science* **249:** 556–560.
38. Nakanishi, N., Shneider, N. A., and Axel, R. (1990). A family of glutamate receptor genes: Evidence for the formation of heteromultimeric receptors with distinct channel properties. *Neuron* **5:** 569–581.
39. Blackstone, C. D., Moss, S. J., Martin, L. J., Levey, A. I., Price, D. L., and Huganir, R. L. (1992). Biochemical characterization and localization of a non-*N*-methyl-D-aspartate glutamate receptor in rat brain. *J. Neurochem.* **58:** 1118–1126.

40. Wenthold, R. J., Yokotani, N., Doi, K., and Wada, K. (1992). Immunochemical characterization of the non-NMDA glutamate receptor using subunit-specific antibodies: Evidence for a hetero-oligomeric structure in rat brain. *J. Biol. Chem.* **267:** 501–507.
41. Verdoorn, T. A., Burnashev, N., Monyer, H., Seeburg, P. H., and Sakmann, B. (1991). Structural determinants of ion flow through recombinant glutamate receptor channels. *Science* **252:** 1715–1718.
42. Iino, M., Ozawa, S.. and Tsuzuki, K. (1990). Permeation of calcium through excitatory amino acid receptor channels in cultured hippocampal neurones. *J. Physiol. (London)* **424:** 151–165.
43. Hume, R. I., Dingledine, R., and Heinemann, S. F. (1991). Identification of a site in glutamate receptor subunits that controls calcium permeability. *Science* **253:** 1028–1031.
44. Burnashev, N., Schoepfer, R., Monyer, H., Ruppersberg, J. P., Gunther, W., Seeburg, P. H., and Sakmann, B. (1992). Control by asparagine residues of calcium permeability and magnesium blockade in the NMDA receptor. *Science* **257:** 1415–1419.
45. Sommer, B., Kohler, M., Sprengel, R., and Seeburg, P. H. (1991). RNA editing in brain controls a determinant of ion flow in glutamate-gated channels. *Cell (Cambridge, Mass.)* **67:** 11–19.
46. Lomeli, H., Mosbacher, J., Melcher, T., Hoger, T., Geiger, J. R., Kuner, T., Monyer, H., Higuchi, M., Bach, A., and Seeburg, P. H. (1994). Control of kinetic properties of AMPA receptor channels by nuclear RNA editing. *Science* **266:** 1709–1713.
47. Sommer, B., Keinanen, K., Verdoorn, T. A., Wisden, W., Burnashev, N., Herb, A., Kohler, M., Takagi, T., Sakmann, B., and Seeburg, P. H. (1990). Flip and flop: A cell-specific functional switch in glutamate-operated channels of the CNS. *Science* **249:** 1580–1585.
48. Wo, Z. G., and Oswald, R. E. (1995). Unraveling the modular design of glutamate-gated ion channels. *Trends Neurosci.* **18:** 161–168.
49. Hollmann, M., Maron, C., and Heinemann, S. (1994). *N*-Glycosylation site tagging suggests a three transmembrane domain topology for the glutamate receptor GluR1. *Neuron* **13:** 1331–1343.
50. Herb, A., Burnashev, N., Werner, P., Sakmann, B., Wisden, W., and Seeburg, P. H. (1992). The KA-2 subunit of excitatory amino acid receptors shows widespread. *Neuron* **8:** 775–785.
51. Ascher, P., and Nowak, L. (1988). The role of divalent cations in the *N*-methyl-D-aspartate responses of mouse central neurones in culture. *J. Physiol. (London)* **399:** 247–266.
52. Mayer, M. L., and Westbrook, G. L. (1987). Permeation and block of N-methyl-D-aspartic acid receptor channels by divalent cations in mouse cultured central neurones. *J. Physiol. (London)* **394:** 501–527.
53. Moriyoshi, K., Masu, M., Ishii, T., Shigemoto, R., Mizuno, N., and Nakanishi, S. (1991). Molecular cloning and characterization of the rat NMDA receptor. *Nature (London)* **354:** 31–37.
54. Mori, H., Masaki, H., Yamakura, T., and Mishina, M. (1992). Identification by mutagenesis of a Mg^{2+}-block site of the NMDA receptor channel. *Nature (London)* **358:** 673–675.
55. Monyer, H., Sprengel, R., Schoepfer, R., Herb, A., Higuchi, M., Lomeli, H., Burnashev, N., Sakmann, B., and Seeburg, P. H. (1992). Heteromeric NMDA receptors: molecular and functional distinction of subtypes. *Science* **256:** 1217–1221.
56. Kutsuwada, T., Kashiwabuchi, N., Mori, H., Sakimura, K., Kushiya, E., Araki, K., Meguro, H., Masaki, H., Kumanishi, T., Arakawa, M. and Mishina, M. (1992). Molecular diversity of the NMDA receptor channel [see comments]. *Nature (London)* **358:** 36–41.
57. Meguro, H., Mori, H., Araki, K., Kushiya, E., Kutsuwada, T., Yamazaki, M., Kumanishi, T., Arakawa, M., Sakimura, K., and Mishina, M. (1992). Functional characterization of a heteromeric NMDA receptor channel expressed from cloned cDNAs. *Nature (London)* **357:** 70–74.
58. Ehlers, M. D., Whittemore, G. T., and Huganir, R. L. (1995). Regulated subcellular distribution of the NR1 subunit of the NMDA receptor. *Science* **269:** 1734–1737.
59. Komau, H.-C., Schenker, L. T., Kennedy, M. B. and Seeburg, P. H. (1995). Domain interaction between NMDA receptor subunits and the postsynaptic density protein PSD-95. *Science* **269:** 1737–1740.
60. Ehlers, M. D., Zhang, S., Bernhardt, J. P., and Huganir, R. L. (1996). Inactivation of NMDA receptors by direct interaction of calmodulin with the NR1 subunit. *Cell (Cambridge, Mass.)* **84:** 745–755.
61. Strader, C. D., Fong, T. M., Graziano, M. P., and Tota, M. R. (1995). The family of G-protein–coupled receptors. *FASEB J.* **9:** 745–754.
62. Henderson, R., Baldwin, J. M., Ceska, T. A., Zemlin, F., Beckmann, E., and Downing, K. H. (1990). Model for the structure of bacteriorhodopsin based on high-resolution electron cryomicroscopy. *J. Mol. Biol.* **213:** 899–929.
63. Mizobe, T., Maze, M., Lam, V., Suryanarayana, S., and Kobilka, B. K. (1996). Arrangement of transmembrane domains in adrenergic receptors: Similarity to bacteriorhodopsin. *J. Biol. Chem.* **271:** 2387–2389.
64. Kobilka, B. (1992). Adrenergic receptors as models for G protein–coupled receptors. *Ann. Rev. Neurosci.* **15:** 87–114.
65. Strader, C. D., Fong, T. M., Tota, M. R., Underwood, D., and Dixon, R. A. (1994). Structure and function of G protein–coupled receptors. *Annu. Rev. Biochem.* **63:** 101–132.
66. Perez, D. M., Hwa, J., Gaivin, R., Manjula, M., Brown, F, and Graham, R. M. (1996). Constitutive activation of a single effector pathway: Evidence for multiple activation states of a G protein–coupled receptor. *Mol. Pharmacol.* **49:** 112–122.
67. Premont, R. T., Inglese, J., and Lefkowitz, R. J. (1995). Protein kinases that phosphorylate activated G protein–coupled receptors. *FASEB J.* **9:** 175–182.
68. Fraser, C. M., Chung, F. Z., Wang, C. D., and Venter, J. C. (1988). Site-directed mutagenesis of human beta-adrenergic receptors: Substitution of aspartic acid-130 by asparagine produces a receptor with high-affinity agonist binding that is uncoupled from adenylate cyclase. *Proc. Natl. Acad. Sci. U.S.A.* **85:** 5478–5482.
69. Fraser, C. M., Wang, C. D., Robinson, D. A., Gocayne, J. D., and Venter, J. C. (1989). Site-directed mutagenesis of m1 muscarinic acetylcholine receptors: Conserved aspartic acids play important roles in receptor function. *Mol. Pharmacol.* **36:** 840–847.
70. Kobilka, B. K., Kobilka, T. S., Daniel, K., Regan, J. W., Caron, M. G., and Lefkowitz, R. J. (1988). Chimeric alpha 2-beta 2-adrenergic receptors: Delineation of domains involved in effector coupling and ligand binding specificity. *Science* **240:** 1310–1316.
71. Strosberg, A. D. (1990). Biotechnology of beta-adrenergic receptors. *Mol. Neurobiol.* **4:** 211–250.
72. Cassel, D., and Selinger, Z. (1977). Mechanism of adenylate cyclase activation by cholera toxin: Inhibition of GTP hydrolysis at the regulatory site. *Proc. Natl. Acad. Sci. U.S.A.* **74:** 3307–3311.
73. Tolkovsky, A. M., Braun, S., and Levitzki, A. (1982). Kinetics of interaction between β-receptors, GTP protein, and the catalytic unit of turkey erythrocyte adenylate cyclase. *Proc. Natl. Acad. Sci. U.S.A.* **79:** 213–217.
74. Whaley, B. S., Yuan, N., Birnbaumer, L., Clark, R. B., and Barber, R. (1993). Differential expression of the β-adrenergic receptor modifies agonist stimulation of adenylyl cyclase: A quantitative evaluation. *Mol. Pharmacol.* **45:** 481–489.
75. Yuan, N., Friedman, J., Whaley, B. S., and Clark, R. B. (1994). cAMP-dependent protein kinase and protein kinase C consensus

site mutations of the β-adrenergic receptor. *J. Biol. Chem.* **269:** 23,032–23,038.

76. Inglese, J., Freedman, N. J., Koch, W. J., and Lefkowitz, R. J. 1993. Structure and mechanism of the G protein–coupled receptor kinases. *J. Biol. Chem.* **268:** 23735–23738.
77. Sterne-Marr, R., and Benovic, J. L. (1995). Regulation of G protein–coupled receptors by receptor kinases and arrestins. *Vitam. Horm. (N.Y.)* **51:** 193–234.
78. Ferguson, S. S. G., Menard, L., Barak, L. S., Koch, W. J., Colapietro, A.-M., and Caron, M. G. (1995). Role of phosphorylation in agonist-promoted β2-adrenergic receptor sequestration. *J. Biol. Chem.* **270:** 24782–24789.
79. Ferguson, S. S. G., Downey, W. E., Colapietro, A.-M., Barak, L. S., Menard, L., and Caron, M. G. (1996). Role of β-arrestin in mediating agonist-promoted G-protein coupled receptor internalization. *Science* **271:** 363–366.
80. Barak, L. S., Tiberi, M., Freedman, N. J., Kwatra, M. M., Lefkowitz, R. J., and Caron, M. G. (1994). A highly conserved tyrosine residue in G protein–coupled receptors is required for agonist-mediated beta 2-adrenergic receptor sequestration. *J. Biol. Chem.* **269:** 2790–2795.
81. Bouvier, M., Collins, S., O'Dowd, B. F., Campbell, P. T., de Blasi, A., Kobilka, B. K., MacGregor, C., Irons, G. P., Caron, M. G., and Lefkowitz, R. J. (1989). Two distinct pathways for cAMP-mediated down-regulation of the beta 2-adrenergic receptor: Phosphorylation of the receptor and regulation of its mRNA level. *J. Biol. Chem.* **264:** 16786–16792.
82. Proll, M. A., Clark, R. B., Goka, T. J., Barber, R., and Butcher, R. W. (1992). β-Adrenergic receptor levels and function after growth of S49 lymphoma cells in low concentrations of epinephrine. *Mol. Pharmacol.* **42:** 116–122.
83. Casey, P. J. (1995). Protein lipidation in cell signaling. *Science* **268:** 221–225.
84. O'Dowd, B. F., Hnatowich, M., Caron, M. G., Lefkowitz, R. J., and Bouvier, M. (1989). Palmitoylation of the human beta 2-adrenergic receptor: Mutation of Cys341 in the carboxyl tail leads to an uncoupled nonpalmitoylated form of the receptor. *J. Biol. Chem.* **264:** 7564–7569.
85. Bunzow, J. R., Van Tol, H. H., Grandy, D. K., Albert, P., Salon, J., Christie, M., Machida, C. A., Neve, K. A. and Civelli, O. (1988). Cloning and expression of a rat D2 dopamine receptor cDNA [see comments]. *Nature (London)* **336:** 783–787.
86. Civelli, O., Bunzow, J. R., and Grandy, D. K. (1993). Molecular diversity of the dopamine receptors. *Annu. Rev. Pharmacol. Toxicol.* **33:** 281–307.
87. Dohlman, H. G., Caron, M. G., and Lefkowitz, R. J. (1987). A family of receptors coupled to guanine nucleotide regulatory proteins. *Biochemistry* **19/26:** 2657–2664.
88. Linden, J. (1994). In *Basic Neurochemistry* (G. J. Siegel, B. W. Agranoff, R. W. Albers, and P. B. Molinoff, eds.), pp. 401–416. Raven Press, New York.
89. Olah, M. E., and Stiles, G. L. (1995). Adenosine receptor subtypes: Characterization and therapeutic regulation. *Annu. Rev. Pharmacol. Toxicol.* **35:** 581–606.
90. Julius, D. (1991). Molecular biology of serotonin receptors. *Annu. Rev. Neurosci.* **14:** 335–360.
91. Kobilka, B. K., Frielle, T., Collins, S., Yang-Feng, T., Kobilka, T. S., Francke, U., Lefkowitz, R. J., and Caron, M. G. (1987). An intronless gene encoding a potential member of the family of receptors coupled to guanine nucleotide regulatory proteins. *Nature (London)* **329:** 75–79.
92. Kaupman, K., Huggel, K., Heid, J., Flor, P. J., Bischoff, S., Mickel, S. J., McMaster, G., Angst, C., Bittiger, H., Froestl, W., and Bettler, B. (1997). Expression cloning of $GABA_B$ receptors uncovers similarity to metabotropic glutamate receptors. *Nature (London)* **386:** 239–246.
93. Nakanishi, S. 1994. Metabotropic glutamate receptors: Synaptic transmission, modulation, and plasticity. *Neuron* **13:** 1031–1037.
94. O'Hara, P. J., Sheppard, P. O., Thogersen, H., Venezia, D., Haldeman, B. A., McGrane, V., Houamed, K. M., Thomsen, C., Gilbert, T. L., and Mulvihill, E. R. (1993). The ligand-binding domain in metabotropic glutamate receptors is related to bacterial periplasmic binding proteins. *Neuron* **11:** 41–52.
95. Aramori, I., and Nakanishi, S. (1992). Signal transduction and pharmacological characteristics of a metabotropic glutamate receptor, mGluR1, in transfected CHO cells. *Neuron* **8:** 757–765.
96. Hayashi, Y., Tanabe, Y., Aramori, I., Masu, M., Shimamoto, K., Ohfune, Y., and Nakanishi, S. (1992). Agonist analysis of 2-(carboxycyclopropyl)glycine isomers for cloned metabotropic glutamate receptor subtypes expressed in Chinese hamster ovary cells. *Br. J. Pharmacol.* **107:** 539–543.
97. Kandel, E. R., Schwartz, J. H., and Jessell, T. M. (1991). *Principles of Neural Science,* 3rd ed. Elsevier, New York/Amsterdam.

CHAPTER

10

Intracellular Signaling

Howard Schulman and Steven E. Hyman

The response of a neuron to neurotransmitters is determined by its complement of receptors, pathways available for transducing signals into the neuron, and the enzymes, ion channels, cytoskeletal proteins, and transcription factors that ultimately mediate the effects of the neurotransmitters. Individual neuronal responses are further determined by the concentration and localization of signal transduction components and modified by the prior history of neuronal activity. Three primary classes of signaling systems, operating at different time courses and with different response specificities, provide great flexibility for intercellular communication. The first class comprises ligand-gated ion channels, such as the nicotinic receptor considered in Chapter 9. This class of signaling system provides fast transmission that is activated and deactivated within 10 ms. It forms the underlying "hard wiring" of the nervous system that makes rapid multisynaptic computations possible. The second class consists of receptor tyrosine kinases, which typically respond to growth factors and to trophic factors and produce major changes in the growth, differentiation, or survival of neurons (Chapter 19). The third class utilizes G-protein-linked signals and constitutes the largest number of receptors. This signaling system requires several steps for transduction and transmission of the signal, thus slowing the response from 100–300 ms to many minutes. The relatively slow speed is offset, however, by a richness in the diversity of its modulation and its inherent capacity for amplification and plasticity. The initial steps in this signaling system typically generate a second messenger inside the cell, and this second messenger then activates a number of proteins, including protein kinases that modify cellular processes. Signal transduction also modulates the level of transcription of genes, which determine the differentiated and functional state of cells.

SIGNALING THROUGH G-PROTEIN-LINKED RECEPTORS

Signal transduction through G-protein-linked receptors requires three membrane-bound components: (1) a cell-surface receptor that determines to which signal the cell can respond; (2) a G protein on the intracellular side of the membrane that is stimulated by the activated receptor; and (3) either an effector enzyme that changes the level of a second messenger or an effector channel that changes ionic fluxes in the cell in response to the activated G protein. As many as 1000 receptors for catecholamines, odorants, neuropeptides, and light couple to one or more of the 20 different G proteins. These, in turn, regulate one or more of more than a dozen different effector channels and enzymes. The key feature of this information flow is the ability of G proteins to detect the presence of activated receptors and to amplify the signal by altering the activity of appropriate effector enzymes and channels.

G proteins are GTP-binding proteins that couple the activation of seven-helix receptors by neurotransmitters at the cell surface to changes in the activity of effector enzymes and effector channels. A common effector enzyme is **adenylate cyclase,** which synthesizes cyclic AMP—an intracellular surrogate for the neurotransmitter, the first messenger. **Phospholipase C** (PLC), another effector enzyme, generates **diacylglycerol** (DAG) and **inositol trisphosphate** (IP_3), the latter of which releases intracellular stores of Ca^{2+}. Information from an activated receptor flows to the second messengers that typically activate protein kinases, which modify a host of cellular functions. Cyclic AMP Ca^{2+}, and DAG have in common the ability to activate protein kinases with broad substrate specificities. They phosphorylate key intracellular proteins, ion channels, enzymes, and transcription factors taking part in diverse cellular biological processes. The activities of protein kinases and phosphatases are in balance, constituting a highly regulated process, as revealed by the phosphorylation state of these targets of the signal transduction process. In addition to regulating protein kinases, second messengers such as cAMP, cGMP, Ca^{2+}, and arachidonic acid can directly gate, or modulate, ion channels. G proteins can also couple directly to ion channels without the interception of second messengers or protein kinases. In these diverse ways, a neurotransmitter outside the cell can modulate essentially every aspect of cell physiology and encode the history of cell stimuli in the form of altered activity and expression of its cellular constituents. An overview of G-protein signaling to protein kinases is presented in Fig. 10.1.

G-Protein Signaling Operates on Common Principles

The many types of G proteins and the many types of effector enzymes have certain features in common.[1] First, each receptor can couple to one or only a few G proteins, thus ensuring specificity of response. Second, the second messengers are typically synthesized in one or two steps from a precursor (e.g., ATP) that is readily available in those cells at high concentration but is itself inactive as a signaling molecule. G proteins can also stimulate enzymes that eliminate second messengers. Third, the initial signal can be greatly amplified: each receptor can activate many G-protein molecules; each adenylate cyclase can synthesize many cAMP molecules; and each protein kinase can phosphorylate many copies of each of its substrates. Fourth, the process is slower in onset and persists longer than ligand-gated ion-channel signaling.

A fifth feature of G-protein signaling is the ability to orchestrate a variety of effects through the same second messenger. For example, the cyclic AMP-dependent protein kinase (PKA), stimulated by serotonin activity on sensory neurons, phosphorylates and inhibits a K^+ channel. This inhibition results in a prolonged action potential and a greater influx of Ca^{2+} with each stimulation of the sensory neuron and in a sensitization of the gill response regulated by this circuit. On a slower time course, cAMP and PKA can also modify carbohydrate metabolism to keep up with activity and the transcription of genes and translation of proteins that ultimately modify the number of synaptic contacts made by the sensory neuron after prolonged periods of activity or inactivity.

A nervous system with information flow by fast transmission alone would be capable of stereotyped or reflex responses. Modulation of this transmission and changes in other cellular functions by G-protein-linked systems and by receptor–tyrosine kinase-linked systems enables an orchestrated response. The large diversity of signaling molecules and their intracellular targets offer nearly unlimited flexibility of response over a broad time scale and with high amplification. This signaling is a key feature of neuronal plasticity, regulating every step of the way from neurotransmitter receptors and ion channels, signal transduction pathways, neurotransmitter synthesis, and release to the expression of genes in the nucleus that underlie synaptic changes linked to learning and memory.

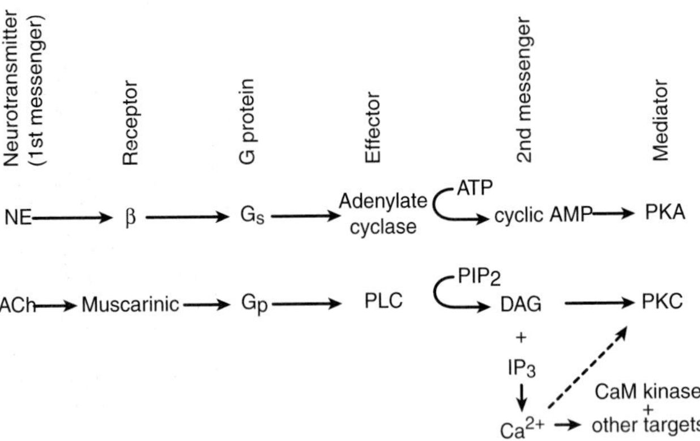

FIGURE 10.1 Overview of G-protein signaling to protein kinases. Norepinephrine (NE) and acetylcholine (ACh) can stimulate certain receptors that couple through distinct G proteins to different effectors, which results in increased synthesis of second messengers and activation of protein kinases (PKA and PKC). PLC, phospholipase C; PIP_2, phosphatidylinositol bisphosphate; DAG, diacylglycerol; CaM, Ca^{2+}–calmodulin-dependent; IP_3, inositol 1,4,5-triphosphate.

Receptors Catalyze the Conversion of G Proteins into the Active GTP-Bound State

G proteins undergo a molecular switch between two interconvertible states that are used to "turn on" or "turn off" downstream signaling. G proteins taking part in signal transduction utilize a regulatory motif that is seen in other GTPases engaged in protein synthesis and in intracellular vesicular traffic.[2] G proteins are switched on by stimulated receptors, and they switch themselves off after a time delay. Whether a G protein is turned on or off depends on the guanine nucleotide to which it is bound. The G proteins are

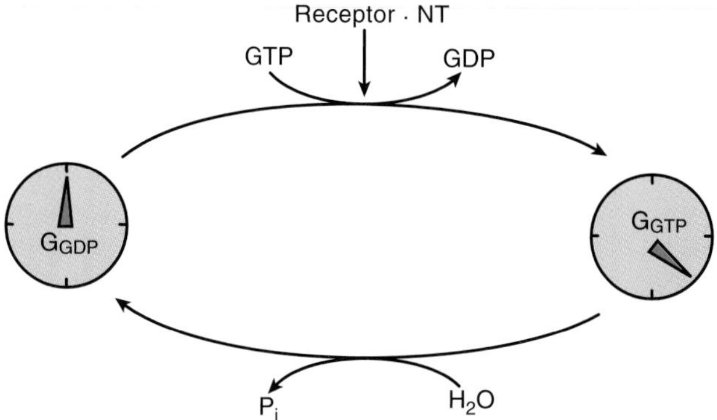

FIGURE 10.2 GTPase activity of G proteins serves as a timer and amplifier. Receptors activated by neurotransmitters (NT) initiate the GTPase timing mechanism of G proteins by displacement of GDP by GTP. Neurotransmitters thus convert G_{GDP} ("turned-off state") to G_{GTP} (time-limited "turned-on" state).

inactive when GDP is bound and are active when GTP is bound. The sole function of the seven-helix receptors in activating G proteins is to catalyze an exchange of GTP for GDP. This is a temporary switch because G proteins are designed with a GTPase activity that hydrolyzes the bound GTP and converts the G protein back into the GDP-bound, or inactive, state. Thus, a G protein must continuously sample the state of activation of the receptor, and it transmits downstream information only while the neuron is exposed to neurotransmitter. A fast GTPase means that the signal transduction pathway is very responsive to the presence of neurotransmitter outside, whereas a slow GTPase provides greater amplification but is less responsive to the elimination of the neurotransmitter. A cell cannot produce distinct responses to each stimulus presented at high frequency when the participating G protein has a slow GTPase. The benefit of a slow GTPase is that it allows amplification of the signal by permitting a given receptor to activate many G proteins and allows G proteins to produce changes in many effector enzymes for each G-protein cycle. The GTPase activity of G proteins serves both as a timer and as an amplifier (Fig. 10.2).

The G-Protein Cycle

G proteins are trimeric structures composed of two functional units: (1) an α subunit (39–52 kDa) that catalyzes the GTPase activity and (2) a $\beta\gamma$ dimer (35 and 8 kDa, respectively) that tightly interacts with the α subunit when bound to GDP.[3,4] The role of the three subunits in the G-protein cycle is depicted in Fig. 10.3. In the basal state, GDP is bound tightly to the α subunit, which is associated with the $\beta\gamma$ pair to form an inactive G protein. In addition to blocking interaction of the α subunit with its effector, the $\beta\gamma$ pair increases the affinity of the α subunit for activated receptors. Binding of the neurotransmitter to the receptor produces a conformational change that increases the affinity of the receptors for the inactive G protein. A given receptor can interact with only one or a limited number of G proteins, and the α subunit produces most of this specificity. Coupling with the activated receptor reduces the affinity of the α subunit for GDP, facilitating its dissociation and thus leaving the nucleotide-binding site empty. Either GDP or GTP can bind the vacant site; however, because the level of GTP in the cell is much greater than the level of GDP, the dissociation of GDP is usually followed by the binding of GTP. Thus, the receptor effectively catalyzes an exchange of GTP for GDP.[5] Binding of GTP has two consequences: (1) it dissociates the G protein into α-GTP and $\beta\gamma$[6] and (2) the α-GTP subunit has a reduced affinity for the stimulated receptor, leading to dissociation of the complex.

The GTP–GDP exchange is inherently very slow because the amount of activation energy required to open the nucleotide-binding site is large. This slow exchange ensures that very little of the G protein is in the on state under basal conditions. The stimulated receptor does not provide the energy for the cycle, but it lowers the amount of free energy for the dissociation from the nucleotide-binding site and greatly accelerates the exchange reaction. When the stimulated receptor increases the GTP–GDP exchange, the GTPase reaction becomes the rate-limiting step of the cycle and α-GTP accumulates. The level of G protein in the on state can increase from being 1% to being more than 50% of all G protein. The direction of the cycle is determined by the GTPase reaction, which uses the energy

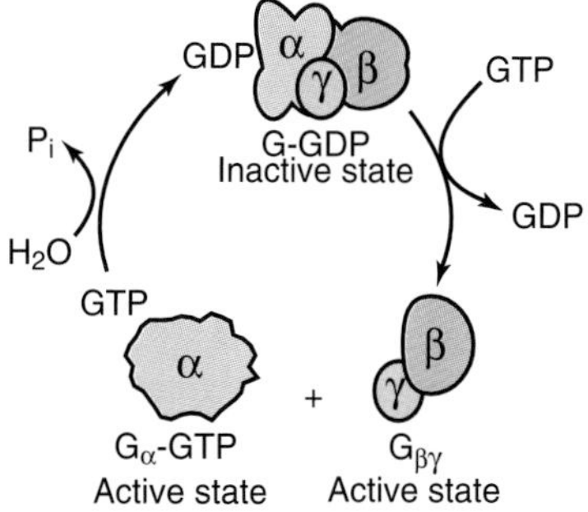

FIGURE 10.3 Interconversion, catalyzed by excited receptors, of G-protein subunits between inactive and active states. Displacement of GDP with GTP dissociates the inactive heterotrimeric G protein, generating α-GTP and $\beta\gamma$, both of which can interact with their respective effectors and activate them. The system converts into the inactive state after GTP has been hydrolyzed and the subunits have reassociated. From *Biochemistry*, 4th ed. by Stryer. © 1995 by Lubert Stryer. Used with permission of W. H. Freeman and Company.

of GTP to make the reaction irreversible and to maintain a low level of α-GTP in the basal state.[3]

Information Flow

One of the more tense and public debates in signal transduction has been the question whether the α subunit alone conveys information that specifies which effector is activated or whether the $\beta\gamma$ pair has a role. One of the contestants even paid for a vanity license plate proclaiming "α not β." The α subunit was thought to be responsible for specifying which effector enzyme was activated by a G protein, with $\beta\gamma$ playing a nonspecific role in keeping the α subunit inactive while presenting it to receptors for activation.[6] This notion was eventually changed because of the finding that $\beta\gamma$ can directly activate certain K^+ channels.[7,8] The historic association of G-protein function with α has persisted for the purpose of nomenclature, with G_s and α_s referring to the G protein and its corresponding α subunit, which stimulates adenylate cyclase. These names have been retained even though it is now apparent that α and $\beta\gamma$ subunits can both modify effector enzymes and channels and that a given α subunit may combine with a number of $\beta\gamma$ pairs. The α subunits may act either independently or in concert with $\beta\gamma$.[9] Furthermore, β and γ subunits in a $\beta\gamma$ pair can combine in many different ways. The terms G_i, G_p, and G_o were used for G-protein activities that inhibited adenylate cyclase, stimulated phospholipase, or were presumed to have other effects, respectively. At this stage, cloning has outpaced functional studies. At least 20 distinct cDNAs for α subunits, along with four βs and seven γs, are known.[4,10] The protein composition of most G proteins is not known, so a cell may contain $\alpha_i\beta_2\gamma_3$ and $\alpha_i\beta_1\gamma_4$, each having different properties. The inherent affinities of $\beta\gamma$ pairs for a particular α and spatial segregation of G proteins probably greatly limit the number of combinations of subunits. See Box 10.1.

Function of α subunits Determination of the crystal structures of different conformational states of some α subunits and $\beta\gamma$ subunits has been a source of insight into their functional domains and the critical GTPase activity of all α subunits.[11,12] The α subunits are compact molecules that must accommodate a number of protein–protein interactions in addition to their GTP-hydrolyzing activity. The β subunit consists of repeating motifs arranged like blades of a propeller or wedges of a pie with a central tunnel (see next subsection). In the trimeric GDP-bound state, the α subunit is docked to the β subunit; the α amino terminus interacts with one side of β while its catalytic domain interacts with the tunnel region of β.[12] Receptors interact with the carboxy terminus of the α subunit; this interaction, along with other contacts, specifies which receptors can activate which α subunits.[13] The guanine nucleotide-binding site is highly conserved and likely altered by interaction with ligand-bound receptors. Movement of the C terminus of the α subunit may reduce contacts with GDP to facilitate dissociation of the nucleotide and exchange for GTP, thus producing an activated α-GTP conformation. The γ phosphate present in GTP, but not in GDP, interacts with a region of α that participates in the docking of α to $\beta\gamma$. The resulting conformational changes reduce the affinity between this surface and $\beta\gamma$, resulting in dissociation of the trimer to produce α and $\beta\gamma$ capable of interacting with their respective effectors. Dissociation also releases the receptor, which can then catalyze activation of other G proteins. Thus, each functional half of the G protein inhibits the action of the other: $\beta\gamma$ does not convey information to its effectors in the presence of α-GDP, whereas α is ineffective at conveying information to its effectors when complexed with $\beta\gamma$ as the trimeric G protein. Dissociation of these subunits exposes the residues needed for interactions with effectors. GTP hydrolysis reverses the conformational changes, exposing a region of α that can interact with $\beta\gamma$ and creating a binding pocket for residues in the β subunit that bind α. Table 10.1 indicates the range of effectors that are regulated by G proteins through their α subunits.

Function of $\beta\gamma$ subunits The crystal structure of the $\beta\gamma$ heterodimer both in its inactive form bound to the α subunit and in its free active form has been determined.[11,12] The C-terminal half of the β subunit has a sevenfold repeat of a structural motif termed the WD repeat, which interacts with γ and is the likely site of interaction between β and its effector enzymes and channels. The WD repeat is a sequence of 25–40 amino acids and ends with the amino acids tryptophan (W) and aspartic acid (D). Each repeat forms a wedge of a circular disk with a central tunnel in both the free and the bound states. Whether each WD repeat specifies interaction with a particular target effector of β or whether several effectors can be bound simultaneously to a single β to form a large complex is not known. The γ subunit is in an extended conformation, circling and making contact with several WD domains of the β subunit. Prenylation of the C terminus of γ anchors the $\beta\gamma$ dimer to membranes.

The $\beta\gamma$ subunits regulate numerous effector enzymes and channels (Table 10.2), as well as participating in the overall function of G proteins. The identified effector targets or $\beta\gamma$ are several adenylate cyclases, the β isoform of phospholipase C, ion channels (for K^+ and Ca^{2+}), phospholipase A_2, and phosphatidylinositol 3-kinase.[9] The other functions of $\beta\gamma$ are as follows. First, they keep G proteins inactive in the basal state by complexing with α and reducing its intrinsic GTP–GDP exchange rate. Second, they help to target the α subunits to the membrane and increase the affinity of α-GDP for ligand-bound receptors. Third, both β and γ help to specify which receptors couple to the G protein. Fourth, the WD repeats of β serve as anchors for a protein kinase, called βARK, that terminates signaling by ligand-bound β-adrenergic receptors.

Examination and Manipulation of G-Protein-Coupled Signals

Neurotransmitters can produce their cellular effects by a variety of signal transduction pathways. A number of experimental tools and approaches must be used to delineate the pathway used in any system of interest. Table 10.3 summarizes some of these experimental tools.

Toxins Differential sensitivities to cholera toxin and pertussis toxin can be used to implicate a G-protein-mediated pathway. Both G_s and transducin are sensitive to cholera toxin, which selectively ADP-ribosylates α_s and α_t. The α subunits of G_i, G_o, and transducin, but not of G_s, are ADP-ribosylated by pertussis toxin. These toxins transfer the ADP–ribose moiety of NAD^+ to an arginine (cholera toxin) or cysteine (pertussis toxin) on the appropriate α subunit. The toxins act at distinct steps in the GTPase cycle to lock it in either the on or the off position (see Fig. 10.3). Cholera toxin reduces the GTPase activity to insignificant levels, thereby generating a persistently on state. For example, cholera toxin treatment of G_s stimulates robust and continuous production of cAMP by adenylate cyclase. In contrast, pertussis toxin acts on the inactive G protein, blocking its interaction with receptors so that it cannot be activated and thus remains in the GDP-bound, or off, state. Toxin sensitivity can be used to narrow the choice of possible G proteins taking part in a process or to block a known pathway.

Guanine nucleotides and NaF The GTPase cycle of all G proteins can also be modified by GTPγS or GDPβS. GTPγS is a nonhydrolyzable analog of GTP with high affinity for the α subunit. Activation of any of the G proteins in the presence of GTPγS leads to the exchange of GTPγS for GDP to produce α-GTPγS. The G protein is thereby activated for prolonged periods because the GTPase cycle is blocked and remains so until GDP exchanges with GTPγS. A similar response is obtained by addition of aluminum fluoride. Fluoride forms a complex with trace amounts of Al^{3+} and binds to α-GDP. The aluminum fluoride moiety simulates the γ phosphate of GTP so that, like GTPγS, α-GDP-AlF_3 persistently activates the G protein.[14,15] In contrast, GDPβS can exchange with GDP, leaving the G protein in the inactive state. GDPβS has a higher affinity than GDP for the G protein and, as a result, the GTPase cycle is slowed and spends more of its time with an inactive G protein.

Effector Enzymes, Channels, and Transporters Decode Receptor-Mediated Cell Stimulation in the Cell Interior

The function of the trimeric G proteins is to decode information about the concentration of neurotransmitters bound to appropriate receptors on the cell surface and convert this information into a change in the activity of enzymes and channels that mediate the effects of the neurotransmitter. The effector can be an enzyme that synthesizes or degrades a diffusible second messenger or it can be an ion channel. The number of identified effectors of G-protein signaling has increased markedly in the past few years and now also includes membrane-transport proteins.

Response Specificity in G-Protein Signaling

The modular design of G-protein signaling may appear to be incapable of providing specificity. Receptors can stimulate one or more G proteins, G proteins can couple to one or more effector enzymes or channels, and the resulting second messengers will affect many cellular processes. Signals originating from activated receptors can either converge or diverge, depending on the receptor and on the complement of G proteins and effectors in a given neuron (Fig. 10.5).[16]

How can a neurotransmitter produce a specific response if G-protein coupling has the potential for such a diversity of effectors? A given neuron has only a subset of receptors, G proteins, and effectors, thereby limiting possible signaling pathways. Transducin, for example, is confined to the visual system, where the predominant effector is the cGMP phosphodiesterase and not adenylate cyclase. A number of other factors combine to increase signal specificity.[1,4,16]

Specificity and choice. Receptors and G proteins have higher intrinsic affinities and efficacies for modulating the activity of the "correct" G protein(s) and effector(s), respectively. Some coupling obtained when high concentrations of these components are generated by overexpression in cell lines or in reconstitution experiments with purified proteins does not occur at concentrations found *in vivo.*

Spatial compartmentalization. Second-messenger systems can be compartmentalized, thus adding specificity and localized control of signaling. The same receptor may regulate a Ca^{2+} channel through one G protein at a nerve terminal and regulate PLCβ at a distal dendrite through another G protein. Although the addition of the neurotransmitter in culture would produce both effects, synaptic inputs would be able to elicit specific effects at nerve terminals or at dendrites.

GTPase activity. The degree of amplification by the G protein (based on GTPase) and by the effector (based on its specific activity or conductance) can determine which of the possible pathways is more prominent. Furthermore, some effectors appear to act as GTPase-activating proteins (GAPs), which modify the intrinsic GTPase activity of the G protein. Such an effector terminates signaling faster when stimulated by one G protein relative to another and fine-tunes the flow of information through the various forks of the signaling system.

BOX 10.1

WHY ARE G-PROTEIN-REGULATED SYSTEMS SO COMPLEX

Transmembrane signaling systems all contain two fundamental elements: one that recognizes an extracellular signal (a receptor) and another that generates an intracellular signal. These elements can be easily incorporated into a single molecule, for example, in receptor tyrosine kinases and guanylyl cyclases. Why then are G-protein-regulated systems so complex, minimally containing five gene products in the basic module (receptor, heterotrimeric G protein, and effector)? The design of these systems permits both integration and branching at its two interfaces—between receptor and G protein and between G protein and effector. Each component of the system can thus be regulated independently—transcriptionally, post-translationally, or by interactions with other regulatory proteins. Furthermore, hundreds of genes encode receptors for hormones and neurotransmitters, dozens of genes encode G-protein subunits (α, β, and γ), and dozens more genes encode G-protein-regulated effectors. Each cell in an organism thus has the opportunity to sample the genome and construct a highly customized and sophisticated switchboard in its plasma membrane, permitting the organism to make an extraordinary variety of responses to complex situations. The choices that each cell makes include much more than just the components of the basic modules, extending as well to regulators of G-protein-mediated pathways such as receptor kinases and GTPase-activating proteins. And, of course, the identity and concentrations of the components of the switchboard can be sculpted within minutes or hours to permit adaptation to developmental needs or environmental stresses.

The classical stress response of mammals to the hormone epinephrine provides an elegant example of the power of modular signal transduction systems. A single hormone is utilized to initiate responses of opposite polarity in very similar cells. Thus, vascular smooth muscle in skin contracts to minimize bleeding (if there is a wound) and to maintain blood pressure, whereas vascular smooth muscle in skeletal muscle relaxes to provide increased blood flow during heightened physical activity. Smooth muscle in the intestine relaxes, whereas cardiac muscle is powerfully stimulated. In addition, hepatocytes hydrolyze glycogen to glucose, adipocytes hydrolyze triglycerides and release free fatty acids for fuel, and certain endocrine and exocrine secretions are stimulated or inhibited. Several distinct receptors for epinephrine are selectively expressed in various cell types to achieve this beneficial orchestration of stimulatory and inhibitory events. These receptors vary in their capacities to interact with G proteins from three different subfamilies (G_s, G_i, G_q) and thus to activate or inhibit several effects to achieve the desired responses. Each cell's choices of particular receptors, G proteins, and effectors permit additional choices of regulators of each of these components to adjust the magnitude and/or the kinetics of the response.

The past two decades of research in this area have witnessed identification and characterization of the molecular players involved in G-protein-mediated signaling and appreciation of the basic mechanisms that underlie the protein–protein interactions that drive these systems. Current research is expanding this basic core of knowledge—on the one hand, toward greater understanding of how the individual modules contribute to the integrated networks of intact cells and, on the other, toward elucidation of the physical and structural bases of these complex cellular reactions. We can begin to construct a movie of G-protein-mediated signaling at atomic resolution, and many of its most important frames are shown in the accompanying figure.

(A) G proteins are held in an inactive state because of very-high-affinity binding of GDP to their α subunits. When activated by agonist, membrane-bound seven-

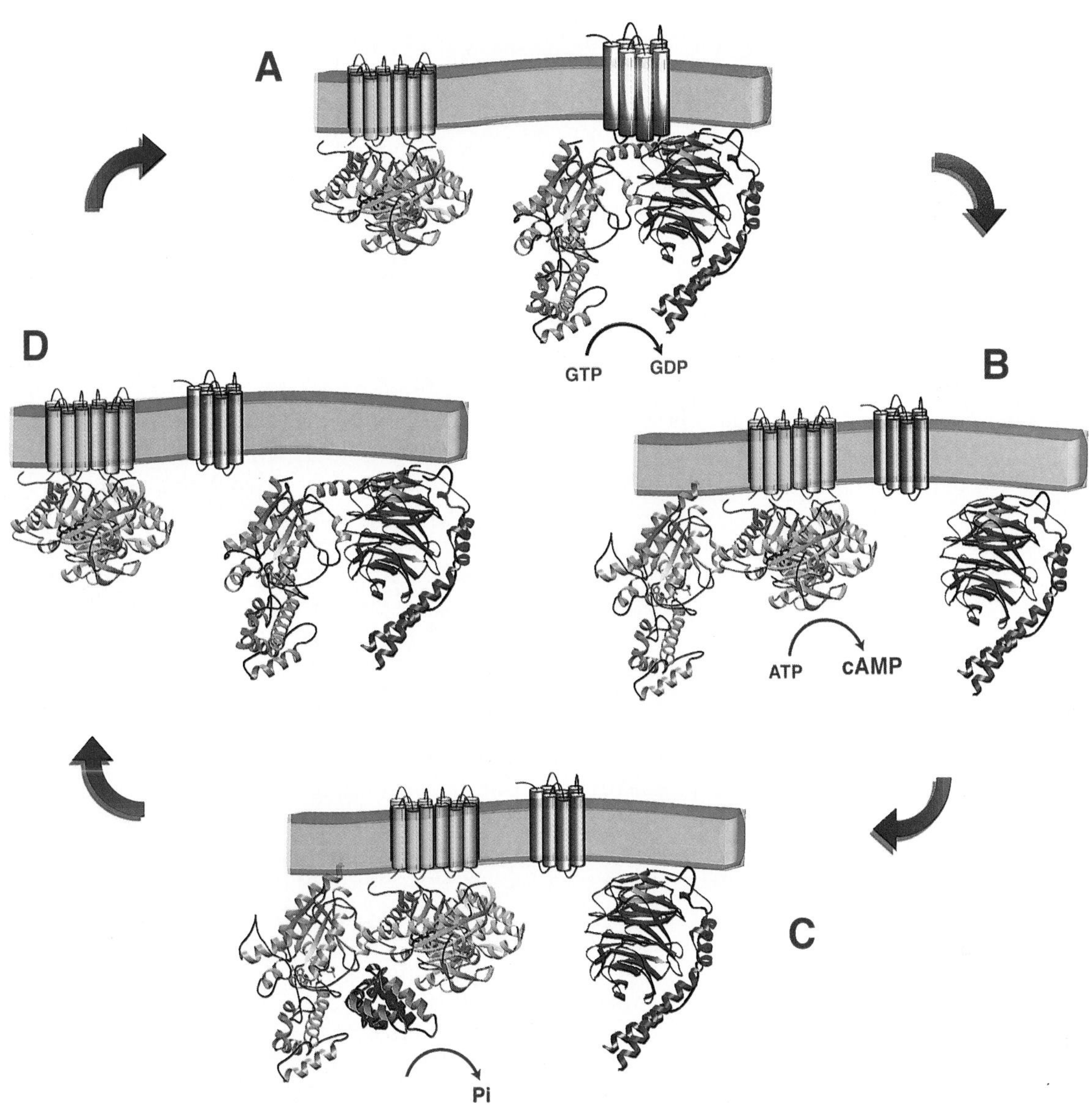

FIGURE 10.4

helical receptors (Fig. 10.4 right, glowing magenta) interact with heterotrimeric G proteins (α, amber; β, teal; γ, burgundy) and stimulate dissociation of GDP. This permits GTP to bind to and activate α, which then dissociates from the high-affinity dimer of β and γ subunits. (B) Both activated (GTP-bound) α (lime) and $\beta\gamma$ are capable of interacting with downstream effectors. Figure 10.4 shows the interaction of GTP-α_S with adenylate cyclase (catalytic domains are mustard and ash). Adenylate cyclase then catalyzes the synthesis of the second messenger cyclic AMP (cAMP) from ATP. (C) Signaling is terminated when α hydrolyzes its bound GTP to GDP. In some signaling systems GTP hydrolysis is stimulated by GTPase-activating proteins or GAPs (cranberry) that bind to α and stablize the transition state for GTP hydrolysis. (D) Hydrolysis of GTP permits GDP-α to dissociate from its effector and associate again with $\beta\gamma$. The heterotrimeric G protein is then ready for another signaling cycle if an activated receptor is present. The figure is based on the original work of Mark Wall and John Tesmer.

Alfred G. Gilman and Stephen R. Sprang

TABLE 10.1 Functions of α Subunits of G Proteins

Class	Member	Modifying toxin	Functions
α_S	α_S, α_{olf}	Cholera	Stimulate adenylate cyclase, regulate Ca^{2+} channels
α_i	$\alpha_{i\text{-}1}$, $\alpha_{i\text{-}2}$, $\alpha_{i\text{-}3}$, α_o, α_z	Pertussis	Inhibit adenylate cyclase, regulate K^+ and Ca^{2+} channels
α_t	α_{gust}, $\alpha_{t\text{-}1}$, $\alpha_{t\text{-}2}$	Cholera and pertussis	Activate cGMP phosphodiesterase
α_q	α_q, α_{11}, α_{14}, α_{15}, α_{16}		Activate PLC
α_{12}	α_{12}, α_{13}		Regulate Na^+–K^+ exchange

Source: Summarized from Neer.[4]

The signaling strength (i.e., the speed and efficiency) of any branch of the pathway can be modulated. Inherent affinities, level of expression of the various components, compartmentation, GTPase rates, and GAP activity combine to produce either a well-focused response by a single pathway or a richer and more diffuse response through several pathways.

Fine-Tuning of cAMP by Adenylate Cyclases

The level of cAMP is highly regulated owing to a balance between synthesis by adenylate cyclases and degradation by cAMP phosphodiesterases (PDEs). Each of these enzymes can be independently regulated and manipulated. Adenylate cyclase was the first G-protein effector to be identified, and now a group of related adenylate cyclases are known to be differentially regulated by both α and $\beta\gamma$ subunits.[17] G proteins can both activate and inhibit adenylate cyclases either synergistically or antagonistically.

Adenylate cyclases are large proteins of approximately 120 kDa. Their topology, shown in Fig. 10.6, has been deduced from sequence information.[18] All the known classes of adenylate cyclase consist of a tandem repeat of the same structural motif—a short cytoplasmic region followed by six putative transmembrane segments and then a highly conserved catalytic domain of approximately 35 kDa on the cytoplasmic side. The catalytic domains resemble each other as well as the catalytic domain of guanylate cyclase. It is therefore likely that these two domains interact with G_s, bind ATP, and catalyze its conversion into cyclic AMP. Some isoforms are activated by calmodulin and have one calmodulin-binding domain in the link between the first catalytic domain and the second set of transmembrane sequences.

Differential regulation of adenylate cyclase isoforms The most common and familiar pathway for modulating adenylate cyclase is activation through α_s. As more isoforms were cloned and studied, however, it became clear that, though all were activated by α_s, they differed in the degree and type of regulation by other G proteins. The activity of adenylate cyclase corresponds to input from receptors that are stimulatory or inhibitory and whose concurrent action can be additive or synergistic. Mammals have at least eight adenylate cyclase isoforms, designated I–VIII (not including alternative splicing), that differ in their regulatory properties and tissue distribution.[17,19] Many isoforms are found throughout the body, but Type I is largely restricted to nerve cells and Type III to the olfactory bulb. Additional isoforms, such as Type II, also are prominent in the brain. Types V and VI may be the predominant forms of adenylate cyclase in peripheral tissues.

TABLE 10.2 Effector Functions of $\beta\gamma$ Dimers of G Proteins

Inhibition of adenylate cyclase
Stimulation of adenylate cyclase Types II and IV (with α)
Stimulation of phospholipase Cβ (PLCβ)
Stimulation of K^+ channel
Inhibition of Ca^{2+} channel
Stimulation of phospholipase A_2 (PLA_2)
Stimulation of phosphatidylinositol 3-kinase (PI 3-kinase)

TABLE 10.3 Experimental Tools for and Approaches to Testing the Role of G Proteins

Cholera toxin and pertussis toxin
GTPγS or GDPβS, NaF
Antibody to G-protein subunits
Antisense oligonucleotides
Knockouts or other forms of gene disruption
Reconstitution from purified components

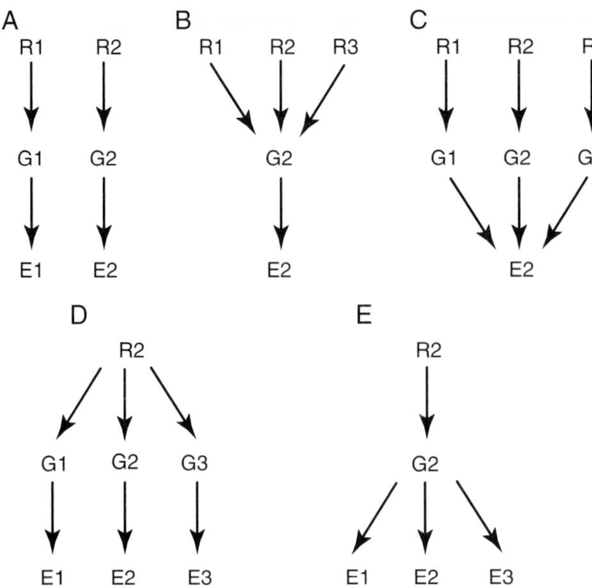

FIGURE 10.5. Signals can converge or diverge on the basis of interactions between receptors (R) and G proteins (G) and between G proteins and effectors (E). The complement of receptors, G proteins, and effectors in a given neuron determines the degree of integration of signals, as well as whether cell stimulation will produce a focused response to a neurotransmitter or a coordination of divergent responses. Adapted from Ross.[16]

All adenylate cyclase isoforms are stimulated by G_s through its α_s subunit. The known isoforms can be minimally divided into at least three groups on the basis of additional regulatory properties (Fig. 10.7). Group A (Types I, III, and VIII) possesses a calmodulin-binding domain and is activated by Ca^{2+}–calmodulin. Group B (Types II and IV) is weakly responsive to direct interaction with α_s or $\beta\gamma$ but is highly activated when both are present.[19] As described later, this synergistic effect enables this cyclase to function as a coincidence detector. Group C is typified by Types V and VI, which differ from group A cyclases in their inhibitory regulation.

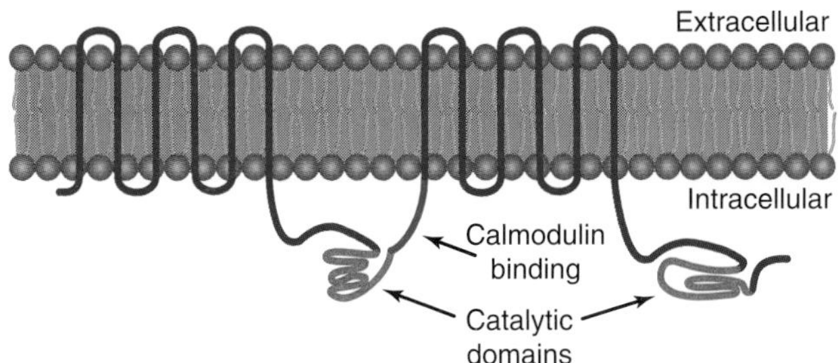

FIGURE 10.6 Domain structure of adenylate cyclase. Two sets of transmembrane segments with two catalytic sites are characteristic of mammalian adenylate cyclases. Some isoforms of the kinase also have a calmodulin-binding domain (shown in green).

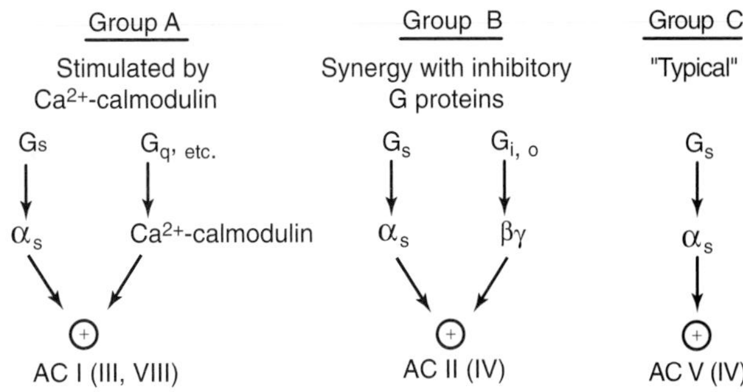

FIGURE 10.7 Isoforms of adenylate cyclase (AC). All isoforms are stimulated by α_s but differ in the degree of interaction with Ca^{2+}–calmodulin and with $\beta\gamma$ derived from inhibitory G proteins. Not shown is the ability of excess $\beta\gamma$ to complex with α_s and inhibit group A and group C adenylate cyclases. Adapted from Taussig and Gilman.[17]

Inhibition of adenylate cyclases Adenylate cyclases are also subject to several forms of inhibitory control. First, activation of all adenylate cyclases can be antagonized to some extent by $\beta\gamma$ released from abundant G proteins, such as G_i, G_o, and G_z, which complex with α_s-GTP and shift the equilibrium toward an inactive trimer by mass action.[6] Second, either α or $\beta\gamma$ subunits derived from G_i, G_o, or G_z can directly inhibit group A cyclases, and the α subunit from G_i or G_z can inhibit group C cyclases.[19]

Many G proteins can generate $\beta\gamma$ subunits capable of directly inhibiting group A and activating group B adenylate cyclases. However, not all G proteins are sufficiently abundant to produce enough $\beta\gamma$ to bring about these effects. The level of $\beta\gamma$ required for these actions is higher than the level needed for α subunits to produce their effects. The level of G_s in particular is low; thus, the α_s derived from G_s is sufficient to activate adenylate cyclases, but the $\beta\gamma$ derived from it is insufficient to directly inhibit or activate adenylate cyclases. Therefore, the sources of $\beta\gamma$ for modulation of Type I and II adenylate cyclases are likely the abundant G proteins, such as G_i and G_o. This explains the apparent paradox that receptors that couple to G_s produce effects only through α_s, whereas receptors that couple to G_i produce effects through both α_i and $\beta\gamma$ even though they can share the same $\beta\gamma$.

Receptors coupling to adenylate cyclase Dozens of neurotransmitters and neuropeptides work through cyclic AMP as a second messenger and do so by activation of either G_s to stimulate adenylate cyclase or G_i or G_o to inhibit adenylate cyclase. Among the neurotransmitters that increase cyclic AMP are the amines norepinephrine, epinephrine, dopamine, serotonin, and histamine and the neuropeptides vasointestinal peptide (VIP) and somatostatin. In the olfactory system, a special form of G-protein α subunit, termed α_{olf}, serves the same function as α_s. Odorants are detected by as many as 1000 seven-helix receptors that activate G_{olf}, which in turn activates the Type III adenylate cyclase in the neuroepithelium. Many of the same neurotransmitters activate distinct receptors that couple to G_i or G_o. They include acetylcholine, dopamine, serotonin, norepinephrine, and opiate peptides.

Adenylate cyclases as coincidence detectors The properties of adenylate cyclases described in Fig. 10.7 suggest an integrative capacity for adenylate cyclase. Type I and Type II adenylate cyclases appear to be specifically designed to detect concurrent stimulation of neurons by two or more neurotransmitters.[20]

Type I adenylate cyclase is stimulated by neurotransmitters that couple to G_s and by neurotransmitters that elevate intracellular Ca^{2+}. This adenylate cyclase can convert the depolarization of neurons into an increase in cAMP.[21] Cells possess many mechanisms for increasing intracellular Ca^{2+}, including voltage-gated Ca^{2+} channels that allow Ca^{2+} influx in response to depolarization and a G_q-coupled pathway. This class of adenylate cyclase has been implicated in several associative forms of learning, a role that may be related to its ability to link cAMP-based and Ca^{2+}-based signals.

Stimulation of Type II adenylate cyclase by α_s is conditional on the presence of $\beta\gamma$ derived from a G protein other than G_s, thus enabling the cyclase to serve as a coincidence detector.[19,22] As indicated earlier, $\beta\gamma$ derived from G_s is not sufficient to produce synergistic activation of this enzyme. Thus, activation of a second receptor, presumably coupled to the abundant G_i and G_o, is needed to provide the $\beta\gamma$. In tissues lacking the Type II adenylate cyclase, neurotransmitters can couple to G_i and inhibit the other adenylate cyclases. In tissues, such as cortex and hippocampus, that contain the type II adenylate cyclase, the same neurotransmitters can couple to G_i and potentiate increases in cyclic AMP resulting from concurrent stimulation by neurotransmitters coupled to G_s.

Sources of Second Messengers for G Proteins and Other Signaling Systems: Phospholipids

Two phospholipids, **phosphatidylinositol 4,5-bisphosphate** (PIP_2) and **phosphatidylcholine** (PC), are primary precursors for a G-protein-based second-messenger system. Three second messengers, diacylglycerol, arachidonic acid and its metabolites, and Ca^{2+}, are ultimately produced. A single step converts the inert phospholipid precursors into the lipid messengers.[23] The conversion of Ca^{2+} from an inert into an active form is accomplished by the regulated entry of Ca^{2+} from a concentrated pool sequestered in the endoplasmic reticulum or from outside the cell into the lumen of the cytosol or nucleus, where its concentration is low. DAG action is mediated by protein kinase C.[24,25] Ca^{2+} has many cellular targets but mediates most of its effects through **calmodulin**, a Ca^{2+}-binding protein that activates many enzymes after it binds Ca^{2+}. One class of calmodulin-dependent enzymes is a family of protein kinases that enable Ca^{2+} signals to modulate a large number of cellular process by phosphorylation.[26]

Generation of DAG and IP_3 from G_q and G_i coupled to PLCβ The phosphatidylinositide-signaling pathway is just as prominent in neuronal signaling as the cyclic AMP pathway and is similar to it in overall design. Stimulation of a large number of neurotransmitters and hormones [including acetylcholine (M1, M3), serotonin ($5HT_2$, $5HT_{1C}$), norepinephrine (α_{1A}, α_{1B}), glutamate (metabotropic), neurotensin, neuropeptide Y, and substance P] is coupled to the activation of a phosphatidylinositide-specific PLC. Turnover of phosphatidylinositol—its degradation followed by resynthesis in response to a large variety of neurotransmitters and hormones—has been a curiosity for decades. Only recently has it become clear that in addition to their function as membrane phospholipids, the phosphoinositides are precursors for second messengers.[27,28]

Phosphatidylinositol (PI) is composed of a diacylglycerol backbone with *myo*-inositol attached to the *sn*-3 hydroxyl by a phosphodiester bond (Fig. 10.8). The six positions of the inositol are not equivalent: the 1-position is attached by a phosphate to the DAG moiety. PI is phosphorylated by PI kinases at the 4-position and then at the 5-position to form PIP_2. In response to

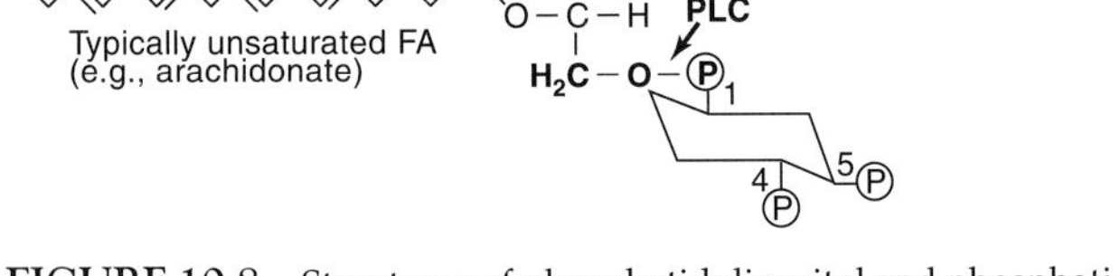

FIGURE 10.8 Structures of phosphatidylinositol and phosphatidylcholine. The sites of hydrolytic cleavage by PLC, PLD, and PLA_2 are indicated by arrows. FA, fatty acid.

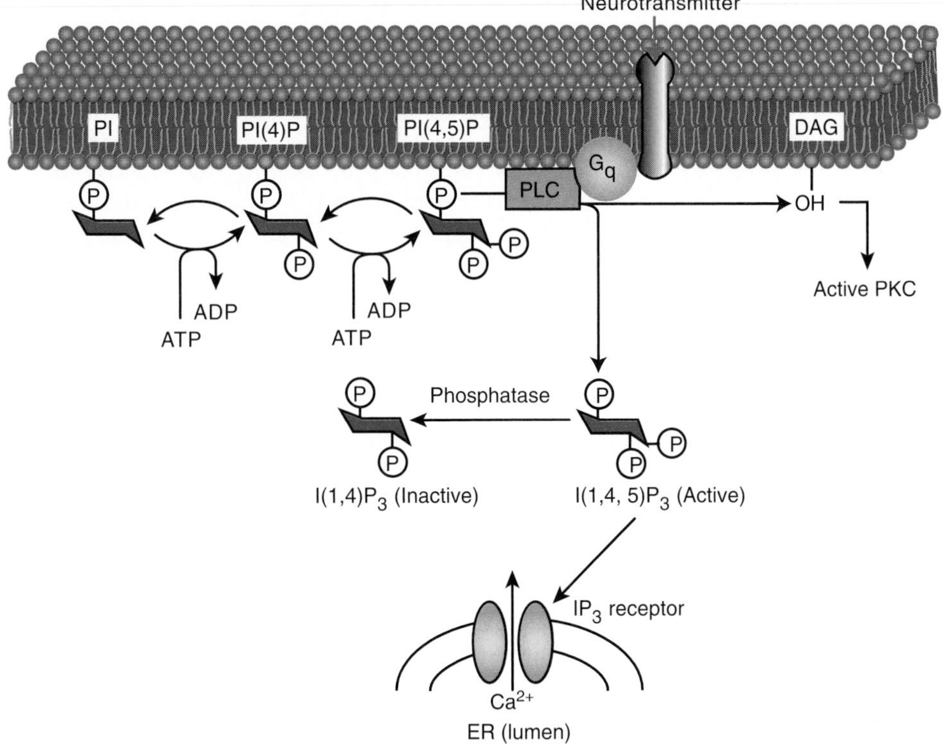

FIGURE 10.9. Schematic pathway of IP_3 and DAG synthesis and action. Stimulation of receptors coupled to G_q activates PLCβ, which leads to release of DAG and IP_3. DAG activates PKC, whereas IP_3 stimulates the IP_3 receptor in the endoplasmic reticulum (ER), leading to mobilization of intracellular Ca^{2+} stores. Adapted from Berridge.[24]

the appropriate G-protein coupling, PLC hydrolyzes the bond between the *sn*-3 hydroxyl of the DAG backbone and the phosphoinositol to produce DAG, a hydrophobic molecule, and inositol 1,4,5-trisphosphate (IP_3), which is water soluble[23,29] (Fig. 10.9). Three classes of PLC that hydrolyze PIP_2 with some selectivity have been cloned and characterized. Ten genes encode the three classes designated PLCβ, PLCγ, and PLCδ—soluble enzymes that have in common a catalytic domain structure but differ in their regulatory properties. G proteins couple to several variants of PLCβ. PLCγ is regulated by growth factor tyrosine kinases. In contrast, PLCδ in brain is primarily glial, and its mode of regulation is not well understood, although it may be activated by arachidonic acid.

PLCβ is coupled to neurotransmitters by G_i and G_q.[25] At least two G proteins were suspected because PLC stimulation was fully inhibited by pertussis toxin in some systems and only partially inhibited in others. The pertussis-toxin-sensitive pathway is mediated by G_i. However, the $\beta\gamma$ rather than the α subunit of G_i is responsible. The pertussis-toxin-insensitive pathway is mediated by a number of isoforms originally termed G_p, with the subscript "p" for PLC activation. Because the PLC-activating function resides in several cloned α subunits given the designation α_q, this activity is now more commonly referred to as G_q and α_q rather than G_p and α_p. G_q couples to PLCβ through its α subunit. There are several PLCβ isoforms, and they show distinct regulation by G proteins. One isoform is most sensitive to α_q; another is more sensitive to $\beta\gamma$ (e.g., from G_i), and a third shows little activation by either G protein.

DAG derived from activation of phospholipase D The time course of DAG production after cell stimulation suggests a complex process. DAG is initially derived from PIP_2 as a direct consequence of G-protein coupling to PLCβ. This DAG activates protein kinase C (PKC), and its action is quickly terminated by conversion into phosphatidic acid and recycling into phospholipids. However, a second phase of DAG synthesis often follows, and this phase produces a level of DAG far in excess of that available from PIP_2. This second phase can last many minutes and may include the hydrolysis of a major cellular phospholipid, phosphatidylcholine, by a phospholipase D (PLD) activity.[23,30] PLD cleaves phosphatidylcholine at the phosphodiester bond to produce phosphatidic acid and choline. Dephosphorylation of phosphatidic acid produces DAG. The PLD pathway may be used by some mitogens and growth factors and likely contains a variety of activation schemes that may include G proteins.

Stimulation of the cell generates a transient cleavage of IP_3 and DAG from PIP_2 and a transient rise in Ca^{2+} due to IP_3-mediated release of intracellular stores. This produces the early activation of PKC. Activation is sustained in the cell in which PLD is stimulated, leading to the second phase of DAG, from phosphatidylcholine. If PLA_2 is activated, arachidonic acid is released from PIP_2 and phosphatidylcholine.

Regulation of PLCγ by receptor tyrosine kinases DAG and IP_3 are also produced when certain receptor tyrosine kinases are activated. This G-protein-independent pathway utilizes PLCγ rather than PLCβ. Stimulation of receptor tyrosine kinases such as epidermal growth factor (EGF) leads to their autophosphorylation on tyrosine residues and activation. Specific phosphotyrosine moieties on the receptor then recruit effector enzymes, such as PLCγ, that possess Src homology 2 (SH2) domains. These structural elements specifically recognize certain protein sequences with phosphotyrosine and lead to the translocation of effectors such as PLCγ to the receptor at the membrane. After binding to the receptor, PLCγ is activated by phosphorylation on tyrosine and hydrolyzes PIP_2 to DAG and IP_3.

Additional lipid messengers PLA_2 cleaves the fatty acid at the *sn*-2 position of the DAG backbone (Fig. 10.8). The fatty acid composition of phospholipids is quite heterogeneous; PIP_2 is largely composed of stearic acid at the *sn*-1 position and arachidonic acid at the *sn*-2 position. Thus, arachidonic acid is released in response to PLA_2 hydrolysis of PIP_2. This fatty acid is a 20-carbon *cis*-unsaturated fatty acid with four double bonds. PLA_2 can be activated by $\beta\gamma$ and α subunits of G proteins, but the identity of the endogenous G proteins that mediate this activation is not known. A cytosolic PLA_2 has been cloned and shown to be activated by microtubule-associated protein (MAP) kinases in response to growth-factor signaling. Phosphorylation leads to its translocation to the membrane, where it can act on membrane phospholipids. Arachidonic acid has biological activity of its own in addition to serving as a precursor for prostaglandins and leukotrienes. Arachidonic acid and other *cis*-unsaturated fatty acids can modulate K^+ channels, PLCγ, and some forms of PKC. Other lipids also may generate signaling molecules. There is growing evidence that growth factors activate PI-3 kinase, which converts PIP_2 into phosphatidylinositol 3,4,5-trisphosphate and thus leads to active signaling molecules. Sphingomyelin also may be a precursor for intracellular signals.

IP_3, a potent second messenger that produces its effects by mobilizing intracellular Ca^{2+} The main function of IP_3 is to stimulate the release of Ca^{2+} from intracellular stores.[31] The concentration of cytosolic free Ca^{2+} is approximately 100 n*M* in unstimulated neurons, whereas its concentration in the extracellular space is 1.5–2.0 m*M*. This provides a tremendous driving force for movement down its concentration gradient; its reversal potential is more than 100 mV. Ca^{2+} is the most common second messenger in neurons, yet it can be neurotoxic. Neurons have therefore developed several mechanisms for maintaining a low interstimulus level of free Ca^{2+}. A Ca^{2+}-ATPase and a Na^+–Ca^{2+} exchanger in the plasma membrane catalyze the active transport of Ca^{2+} to the extracellular space, and a different Ca^{2+}-ATPase in the ER membrane sequesters Ca^{2+} in the ER network. Much of the Ca^{2+} in the ER is complexed with low-affinity-binding proteins that enable the ER to concentrate Ca^{2+} yet enable Ca^{2+} to readily flow down its concentration gradient into the cell lumen upon opening of Ca^{2+} channels in the ER. The ER is the major IP_3-sensitive Ca^{2+} store in cells (Fig. 10.9).

The IP_3 receptor is a macromolecular complex that functions as an IP_3 sensor and a Ca^{2+}-release channel. It has a broad tissue distribution but is highly concentrated in the cerebellum. Purification and cloning of the IP_3 receptor show it to be a 313-kDa membrane glycoprotein with a single IP_3-binding site at its N terminal, facing the cytoplasm. The functional channel is composed of four such subunits. The C-terminal half of the molecule contains eight putative transmembrane domains; four such sets of transmembrane segments combine to form a relatively nonselective channel or pore. Ca^{2+} release by IP_3 is highly cooperative, with a Hill coefficient of 2.7. Thus, a small change in IP_3 has a large effect on Ca^{2+} release from the ER. The IP_3 receptor has low activity at either high or low levels of cytoplasmic Ca^{2+}, with peak release requiring 200–300 n*M* Ca^{2+}, a property that may be used in the generation of some Ca^{2+} waves.[24,32] The mouse mutants *pcd* and *nervous* have deficient levels of the IP_3 receptor and exhibit defective Ca^{2+} signaling, and a genetic knockout of the IP_3 receptor leads to motor and other deficits.

The structure of the IP_3 receptor is quite similar to that found earlier for the ryanodine receptor, which serves as a Ca^{2+}-sensitive Ca^{2+} channel in muscle and brain. The ryanodine receptor is a tetramer composed of 560-kDa subunits. In muscle, it is activated by voltage changes that are detected by the dihydropyridine receptor and conveyed to the ryanodine receptor by direct protein–protein interaction. In other cells, the ryanodine receptor is gated by Ca^{2+} or by cyclic ADP-ribose. The localizations of the IP_3 and the ryanodine receptors in the brain are distinct, suggesting that they subserve different aspects of Ca^{2+} signaling. For example, the IP_3 receptor is more enriched in cerebellar Purkinje cells and hippocampal CA1 neurons, whereas the ryanodine receptor is more enriched in the dentate gyrus and CA3 neurons in hippocampus. Electron microscopy reveals that IP_3 receptors in the hippocampus are often on dendritic shafts and cell bodies, whereas ryanodine receptors are in axons and in dendritic spines and the nearby shaft.

Termination of the IP_3 signal IP_3 is a transient signal terminated by dephosphorylation to inositol. Inactivation is initiated either by dephosphorylation to inositol 1,4-bisphosphate (Fig. 10.9) or by an initial phosphorylation to a tetrakisphosphate form that is dephosphorylated by a different pathway. Both pathways have in common an enzyme that cleaves the phosphate on the 1-position. Complete dephosphorylation yields inositol, which is recycled in the biosynthetic pathway. Recycling is important because most tissues do not contain *de novo* biosynthetic pathways for making inositol. Thus, the phosphatases not only terminate the signal but also serve as a salvage step that may be particularly important when cells are actively undergoing PI turnover. It is intriguing that the simple salt Li^+ selectively inhibits the salvage of inositol by inhibiting the enzyme that dephosphorylates the 1-position and is common to the two pathways. This simple salt is the drug used to treat manic–depressive disorders. At therapeutic doses of Li^+, the reduced salvage of inositol in cells with high phosphoinositide signaling may lead to depletion of PIP_2 and a selective inhibition of this signaling pathway in active cells.

Calcium Ion

Calcium has a dual role as a carrier of electrical current and as a second messenger. Its effects are more diverse than those of other second messengers such as cyclic AMP and DAG because its actions are mediated by a much larger array of proteins, including protein kinases.[33] Furthermore, many signaling pathways directly or indirectly increase cytosolic Ca^{2+} concentration from 100 nM to 0.5–1.0 μM. The source of elevated Ca^{2+} can be either the ER or the extracellular space (Fig. 10.10). As indicated earlier, mobilization of ER Ca^{2+} is mediated by IP_3 derived from PLCβ activation through G proteins and from PLCγ activation by receptor tyrosine kinases acting on the IP_3 receptor. In addition, Ca^{2+} can activate its own mobilization through the ryanodine receptor on the ER. Mechanisms for Ca^{2+} influx from outside the cell include several voltage-sensitive Ca^{2+} channels and ligand-gated cation channels that are permeable to Ca^{2+} [e.g., nicotinic receptor and N-methyl-D-aspartate (NMDA) receptor]. In the *Drosophila* visual system and in nonexcitable mammalian cells, depletion of Ca^{2+} from the ER initiates an unknown signal that stimulates a low-conductance influx current called I_{CRAC} (Ca^{2+}-release-activated current) across the plasma membrane.[34] In mammalian cells, it provides a slow but prolonged rise in intracellular Ca^{2+} that not only serves as a second messenger but also replenishes ER stores. Ca^{2+} is efficiently sequestered in the ER and extruded out of the cell, which can rapidly lower Ca^{2+} to baseline levels.

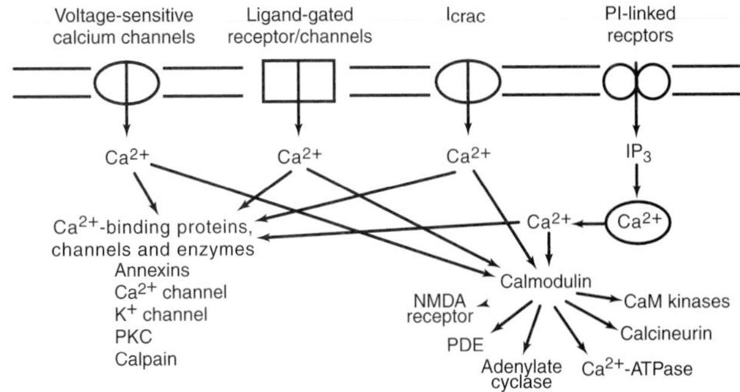

FIGURE 10.10 Multiple sources of Ca^{2+} converge on calmodulin and other Ca^{2+}-binding proteins. Cellular levels of Ca^{2+} can rise either by influx (e.g., through voltage-sensitive channels or ligand-gated channels) or by redistribution from intracellular stores triggered by IP_3. Calcium modulates dozens of cellular processes by the action of the Ca^{2+}–calmodulin complex on many enzymes, and calcium has some direct effects on enzymes such as PKC and calpain. CaM kinase, Ca^{2+}–calmodulin-dependent kinase.

Dynamics of Ca^{2+} signaling revealed by fluorescent Ca^{2+} indicators We know a great deal about the spatial and temporal regulation of Ca^{2+} signals because of the development of fluorescent Ca^{2+} indicators. A variety of fluorescent compounds related to the Ca^{2+} chelator ethylene glycol bis(β-aminoethyl ether)N,N'-tetraacetic acid selectively bind Ca^{2+} at various concentration ranges and change their fluorescent properties upon binding Ca^{2+}.[35] They have dissociation constants in the physiological range of Ca^{2+} and provide a rapid and fairly accurate measurement of ionized Ca^{2+}. Digital fluorescence imaging can be used to detect Ca^{2+} in subcellular compartments such as dendrites and spines, the nucleus, and the cytosol and has demonstrated localized changes in free Ca^{2+}. Some cells also undergo oscillations in free Ca^{2+} with a frequency that is increased by an increased concentration of hormone.

Stimulation of cultured astrocytes with glutamate generates Ca^{2+} oscillations, which propagate as a wave that spreads across a multicellular network and may coordinate some actions of glia.

Lack of uniformity in Ca^{2+} levels The concentration of Ca^{2+} entering the cytosol through voltage-sensitive Ca^{2+} channels in the plasma membrane or through the IP_3 receptor in the ER is extremely high because of the large concentration gradient across these membranes. Relatively low-affinity Ca^{2+}-dependent processes can produce effects of Ca^{2+} near the membrane, such as synaptic release and modulation of Ca^{2+} channels. However, by the time Ca^{2+} diffuses a few membrane diameters away, it is rapidly buffered by many Ca^{2+}-binding proteins, and its concentration drops from 100 to 1 μM or less. The diffusion of Ca^{2+} is greatly slowed in biological fluid because of the high concentration of binding proteins (0.2–0.3 mM). Ca^{2+} diffuses a distance of 0.1–0.5 μm, and diffusion lasts approximately 30 μs before Ca^{2+} is bound. Ca^{2+} is therefore a second messenger that acts locally, a feature that makes Ca^{2+} subdomains possible where Ca^{2+} signaling is spatially segregated. In contrast, IP_3 is a global intermediate with an effective range that can span a typical soma before being terminated by dephosphorylation.[36]

Calmodulin-Mediated Effects of Ca^{2+}

Ca^{2+} acts as a second messenger to modulate the activity of many mediators. The predominant mediator of Ca^{2+} action is calmodulin. This abundant and ubiquitous 17-kDa calcium binding is highly conserved across phyla. Ca^{2+} binds to calmodulin in the physiological range and converts it into an activator. Calmodulin has no intrinsic enzymatic activity. It serves a central regulatory role by modulating the activity of various cellular targets.[37] Binding of Ca^{2+} to calmodulin produces a conformational change that greatly increases its affinity for a number of target enzymes. Ca^{2+}-calmodulin binds and activates more than 20 eukaryotic enzymes, including cyclic nucleotide PDEs, adenylate cyclase, nitric oxide synthase, Ca^{2+}-ATPase, calcineurin (a phophoprotein phosphatase), and several protein kinases (Fig. 10.10). This activation of calmodulin allows neurotransmitters that change Ca^{2+} to affect dozens of cellular proteins, presumably in an orchestrated fashion. Ca^{2+} also affects proteins and enzymes independently of calmodulin, including calcium-binding proteins and enzymes such as calpain and PKC. Ion channels (K channels and IP_3 receptors or channels) are directly modulated by Ca^{2+} (Fig. 10.10). First discovered as a protein factor necessary for Ca^{2+}-dependent activation of a cyclic nucleotide PDE, the substance was renamed calmodulin (Ca^{2+} response modulator) when it was subsequently found to modulate many enzymes in addition to PDE.

Calmodulin interacts with its targets in several ways. The "conventional" interaction with enzyme targets requires a stimulated rise in Ca^{2+} so that the four Ca^{2+}-binding sites on calmodulin become occupied and it can bind. At basal Ca^{2+}, however, much of calmodulin may be bound to a diverse group of proteins such as GAP-43 (neuromodulin), neurogranin, and unconventional myosins. Interactions with these targets are not well understood and may serve to localize calmodulin near other targets or to "buffer" free calmodulin so that it is less likely to activate the conventional targets at basal Ca^{2+}. A third group of enzymes, which includes the inducible form of nitric oxide synthase, bind calmodulin in a manner that makes it sensitive to basal Ca^{2+}, and the enzymes are therefore active at basal Ca^{2+}.

Actions of enzymes and proteins modulated by calmodulin Calmodulin has four Ca^{2+}-binding sites, or binding folds, described as EF hands, a recurring Ca^{2+}-binding structural motif first identified in paravalbumin from carp muscle. Calmodulin is composed of a number of helical segments designated by capital letters and separated by loops. Orientation of the helix–loop–helix EF segment of 29 amino acids is similar to that of the thumb and index finger, which positions amino acids in the loop for coordination with Ca^{2+}, hence the name EF hand. Two EF hands, or calmodulin folds, stabilize each other to form two Ca^{2+}-binding sites. Binding of Ca^{2+} is cooperative, with binding to the first set of high-affinity sites facilitating binding to low-affinity sites (K_d approximately 1 μM). The ability of Ca^{2+} to be accommodated in an asymmetric coordination shell with multiple and distant amino acids, including uncharged oxygens, enables it to compete with Mg^{2+} and to produce large conformation changes that are the basis for interconversion between inactive and active states of proteins.

Calmodulin recognizes a short segment of the enzymes that it regulates; however, there is no strict consensus sequence for calmodulin binding. X-ray crystallography and NMR have provided a three-dimensional structure of Ca^{2+}–calmodulin with and without a peptide whose sequence is based on calmodulin-binding sites in several kinases. In the absence of a target protein, Ca^{2+}–calmodulin is in an extended structure composed of two globular regions, each containing a set of calmodulin folds separated by a long α-helical tether. Binding of Ca^{2+} allows movement of the globular regions around the calmodulin-binding site, "gripping" it as would hands around a rope.[38] The two lobes of this compact structure surround the target peptide, making dozens of hydrophobic contacts as well as ionic interactions between Arg and Lys typically found in target peptides and Glu residues in calmodulin. The large number of possible interactions allows calmodulin to accommodate many target sequences, with the calmodulin grip slightly differently in each case to maximize interactions. This binding likely produces the necessary displacement of the calmodulin-binding domain for activation of the target enzymes.

Regulation of guanylate cyclase by nitric oxide An important target of Ca^{2+}–calmodulin is the enzyme nitric oxide synthase (NOS) (see Chapter 8). This enzyme synthesizes one of the simplest known messengers, the gas NO.[39] Nitric oxide was first recognized as a signaling molecule that mediates the action of acetylcholine on smooth muscle relaxation.[40] An intercellular signal was necessary to explain how stimulation of endothelial cells by acetylcholine could produce a relaxation in tone of the underlying smooth muscle cells that surround the vessels. A labile substance operationally termed endothelium-derived relaxing factor (EDRF) was detected and has since been shown to be NO. Acetylcholine stimulates the PI signaling pathway in the endothelium to increase intracellular Ca^{2+}, which activates NOS so that more NO is made. NO then diffuses radially from the endothelial cells across two cell membranes to the smooth muscle cell, where it activates guanylate cyclase to make cyclic GMP. This in turn activates a cyclic GMP-dependent protein kinase that phosphorylates proteins, leading to a relaxation of muscle.[39] This intercellular signaling in which NO made in one cell increases cyclic GMP in a nearby cell is the conventional view of how NO works. In a related scheme, heme oxygenase may be stimulated to make carbon monoxide (CO), which also can act intercellularly through guanylate cyclase and cyclic GMP.

Let us now turn to the details of the NO pathway. We will see that other pathways can activate NOS, mediate the actions of NO, stimulate guanylate cyclases, and mediate the actions of cyclic GMP.

Nitric oxide is derived from L-arginine in a reaction catalyzed by NOS, a complex enzyme that has one equivalent each of flavin adenine dinucleotide (FAD), flavin mononucleotide (FMN), tetrahydrobiopterin, and heme (iron protoporphyrin IX) per monomer. NOS converts L-arginine and O_2 into NO and L-citrulline in a five-electron oxidation reaction that requires nicotinamide adenine dinucleotide phosphate (NADPH) as a cofactor. NOS likely produces the neutral free radical NO· as the active agent. As we have already seen in the generation of second messengers, stimulation of a single step converts a common inert precursor (in this case, L-arginine) into a powerful intercellular and intracellular signal (NO). Although NO is stable in oxygen-free water, it is labile and lasts only a few seconds in biological fluids because of its inactivation by superoxides and its complex formation with heme-containing proteins such as oxyhemoglobin. Thus, no specialized processes are needed to inactivate this particular signaling molecule.

As a gas, NO is soluble in both aqueous and lipid media and can readily diffuse from its site of synthesis across the cytosol or cell membrane and affect targets in the same cell or in nearby neurons, glia, and vasculature. Neuronal communication by synaptic vesicles is unidirectional, from presynaptic to postsynaptic neuron. NO provides the capability for a retrograde message and thus reverse the usual flow of information; that is, information can travel from a postsynaptic site of synthesis to a presynaptic site of modulation. When synaptic activity stimulates NO production at a spine, NO signals are unlikely to be restricted to that synapse alone, the consequences of which are important for models of long-term potentiation that propose NO as a messenger.

NO produces a variety of effects, including relaxation of smooth muscle (as mentioned earlier) of the peripheral vasculature and perhaps control of cerebral blood flow, relaxation of smooth muscle of the gut in peristalsis, and killing of foreign cells by macrophages.[39] It was first recognized as a neuronal messenger that couples glutamate receptor stimulation to increases in cyclic GMP. Analog of L-arginine, such as nitroarginine and monomethyl arginine, block NOS unless there is an excess of L-arginine. Such inhibitors of NO synthase have been used to implicate NO in long-term potentiation and long-term depression in the hippocampus and cerebellum, respectively[41].

Representative clones from three classes of NO synthase have been characterized. Two of them are constitutively expressed and activated by Ca^{2+}–calmodulin formed when intracellular Ca^{2+} is elevated. The constitutive forms are designated neuronal or endothelial on the basis of their original source, although they overlap in this tissue distribution. The third class of NOS is an inducible form; its level is markedly increased by transcription and protein synthesis in response to cell stimulation, and it is prominent in macrophages stimulated by cytokines. After translation, the inducible form is active at basal Ca^{2+} levels because it has a tightly bound calmodulin in a conformation that greatly enhances its Ca^{2+} sensitivity. Because NOS is a major flavin-containing enzyme, it possesses NADPH diaphorase activity. It reduces nitroblue tetrazolium to formazan, a reaction that can be used as a cytochemical stain for NOS because much of the diaphorase staining in the brain is due to this enzyme. This family of enzymes displays distinct regional distributions in the brain, suggesting some regional specificity in the use of NO as a signaling molecule in the brain. The constitutive neuronal isoform is concentrated in cerebellar granule cells and likely provides the NO that activates guanylate cyclase in nearby Purkinje cells during the induction of long-term depression in the cerebellum (Chapter 35).

The action of NO is often mediated by guanylate cyclase and cyclic GMP. However, a number of physiological and pathological effects of NO are independent of cyclic GMP. NO stimulates ADP-ribosylation of a number of proteins in the brain and other tissues. The nature of the ADP-ribosyltransferases and their effects is not known. Another effect of NO is stimulation of release of neurotransmitters, apparently in a Ca^{2+}-independent fashion.

Activation of guanylate cyclases Two types of guanylate cyclase, a soluble one regulated by NO and a membrane-bound enzyme directly regulated by neuropeptides,[42] synthesize cyclic GMP from GTP in a reaction similar to the synthesis of cyclic AMP from ATP. The soluble enzyme is a heterodimer, with catalytic sites resembling those of adenylate cyclase and a heme group. NO activates the soluble enzyme by binding to the iron atom of the heme moiety. This is the basic mechanism for regulation of soluble guanylate cyclases. Stimulation of guanylate cyclase is the major, but not only, effect of NO in the brain and other tissues. A number of therapeutic muscle relaxants, such as nitroglycerin and nitroprusside, are NO donors that produce their effects by stimulating cyclic GMP synthesis.

The membrane-bound guanyllate cyclases are transmembrane proteins with a binding site for neuroendocrine peptides on the extracellular side of the plasma membrane and a catalytic domain on the cytosolic side. Several isoforms of membrane-bound guanylate cyclase, each with a binding site for a distinct neuropeptide such as atrial natriuretic peptide and brain natriuritic peptide, have been characterized. In the periphery, these peptides regulate sodium excretion and blood pressure; in the brain, their functions are less clear.

Cyclic GMP Phosphodiesterase, an Effector Enzyme in Vertebrate Vision

The versatility of G-protein signaling is illustrated in vertebrate phototransduction, in which a specialized G protein called **transducin** (G_t) is activated by light rather than by a hormone or neurotransmitter. Without transducin, we would not be able to see. Transducin stimulates cyclic GMP phosphodiesterase, an effector enzyme that hydrolyzes cyclic GMP and ultimately turns off the dark current. Nature has devised an elegant mechanism for using photons of light to modify a hormone-like molecule, retinal, that activates a seven-helix receptor called **rhodopsin.** This receptor has a built-in prehormone that is converted into the active form by light. Light photoisomerizes the inactive 11-*cis*-retinal to the active all-*trans*-retinal, which functions as a neurotransmitter to activate its receptor. Activated rhodopsin triggers the GTP–GDP exchange of transducin, leading to dissociation of its α_t and $\beta\gamma$ subunits. The active species in transducin is the α subunit. It activates a soluble cyclic GMP phosphodiesterase by binding to and displacing an inhibitory subunit of the enzyme. In the dark, retinal rods contain high levels of cyclic GMP, which maintains a cyclic GMP-gated channel permeable to Na^+ and Ca^{2+} in the open state and thus provides a depolarizing dark current. As the levels of cyclic GMP drop, the channel closes to hyperpolarize the cell.

Rods can detect a single photon of light because the signal-to-noise ratio of the system is very low owing to a very low spontaneous conversion of the 11-*cis*- into the all-*trans*-retinal. Furthermore, the amplification factor is quite high; one rhodopsin molecule stimulated by a single photon can activate 500 transducins. Transducin remains in the "on"' state long enough to activate 500 PDEs. PDE is designed for speed and can hydrolyze 10^5 cyclic GMP molecules in the second before it is deactivated by GTP hydrolysis and dissociation from transducin.[43] Cyclic GMP in rods regulates a cyclic GMP-gated cation channel, leading to additional amplification of the signal.

Modulation of Ion Channels by G Protein

Each neuron has a set of ion channels that it uses to integrate incoming signals, propagate action potentials, and introduce Ca^{2+} into terminals specialized for the release of neurotransmitters. Because the repertoire of ion channels gives neurons their individual response signatures, it is not surprising that several types of mechanisms regulate these channels. Second messengers derived from G protein and other pathways activate protein kinases that phosphorylate ion channels. In addition, certain ion channels are effector proteins that are directly modulated by G proteins.

The first ion channel demonstrated to undergo regulation by G proteins was the cardiac K^+ channel that mediates slowing of the heart by acetylcholine released from the vagus nerve. When this I_{KACh} channel is examined in a membrane patch delimited by the seal of a cell-attached electrode, addition of acetylcholine within the electrode dramatically increases the frequency of channel opening, whereas addition of acetylcholine to the cell surface outside the seal does not. Although acetylcholine stimulates muscarinic M2 receptors when added either inside or outside the seal, the receptors outside do not have access to the channels being recorded in the sealed patch because this signaling pathway does not include diffusible second messengers that can affect the channel. The process is therefore described as membrane delimited, which is explained most simply by a direct interaction between the G protein and the channel. Subsequent studies have shown that the pathway is pertussis toxin sensitive and that purified G_i activated by GTPγS added to the underside of the patch will activate the channel.

Whether the active component of G_i is the α or the $\beta\gamma$ subunit is controversial. Dogmas do not die easily and, for many years, $\beta\gamma$ was not considered a direct activator or inhibitor of effector enzymes and channels. The I_{KACh} channel appears to be composed of heteromultimers of two types of subunits that can be activated either by α_i or by $\beta\gamma$. The α_i subunit is more potent in regulating the channel, but the membrane contains enough $\beta\gamma$ to enable $\beta\gamma$ to activate the channel as well.[8,44] Different combinations of channel subunits may be preferentially activated by α_i and by $\beta\gamma$ subunits.

Of the ion channels other than the K^+ channel, evidence is most compelling for the stimulation or inhibition of Ca^{2+} channel subtypes by G proteins. The central role played by Ca^{2+} in muscle contraction, in synaptic release, and in gene expression makes the modulation of Ca^{2+} influx a common target for regulation by neurotransmitters. In the heart, where L-type Ca^{2+} channels are critical for regulation of contractile strength, the Ca^{2+} current is enhanced by α_S formed by β-adrenergic stimulation of G_S. In contrast, N-type Ca^{2+} channels, which modulate synaptic release in nerve terminals, are often inhibited by muscarinic and α-adrenergic agents and by opiates acting at receptors coupled to G_i and G_o. In sympathetic ganglia, norepinephrine reduces synaptic release by inhibiting Ca^{2+} influx through the N channel. The G protein couples to the channel in a membrane-delimited process that shifts the temporal distribution of gating modes, favoring the time spent in a low-open probability mode, thereby effectively lowering the open time of the channel.[45]

Inhibition of L-type Ca^{2+} currents can exhibit strict G-protein specificity for both the α and $\beta\gamma$ subunits. In GH3 cells, a pituitary cell line, antisense oligonucleotides that eliminate expression of α_{o1} and α_{o2} block the inhibitory effect of muscarinic agents (at M4 receptors) and of somatostatin, respectively. Microinjection of antisense oligonucleotides to β_1 and β_3 blocked inhibition by somatostatin and muscarinic agents, respectively.[46] Finally, the γ subunit subtype also was critical. Thus, γ_3 was required for coupling to the somatostatin receptor, whereas γ_4 coupled to muscarinic receptors.[47] Thus, in the same cell, somatostatin couples to Ca^{2+} channels through $\alpha_{o2}\beta_1\gamma_3$, whereas the muscarinic receptor couples to $\alpha_{o1}\beta_3\gamma_4$. The $\beta\gamma$ subunits may directly affect the channels, perhaps in synergy with the α subunit or as a requirement for the appropriate presentation of the α subunits to the correct receptor.

G-Protein Signaling Gives Special Advantages in Neural Transmission

The G-protein-based signaling system provides several advantages over fast transmission.[1,4] These advantages include amplification of the signal, modulation of cell function over a broad temporal range, diffusion of the signal to a large cellular volume, cross talk, and coordination of diverse cell functions.

Amplification. Several thousandfold amplification can be initiated by a single neurotransmitter–receptor complex that activates numerous G proteins, each of which activates many effector enzymes and channels. Each enzyme can generate many second-messenger molecules, and each channel allows the flux of many ions. As we shall see in the next section, second messengers often activate protein kinases that phosphorylate many substrates before deactivation.

Temporal range. The sacrifice in speed relative to signaling by ligand-gated ion channels is compensated by a broad range of signaling that facilitates integration of signals by the G-protein system. Transmission through membrane-delimited coupling of ion channels to G proteins is relatively fast, with only some sacrifice in speed. Signaling that includes second messengers is much slower. It can be as fast as 100–300 ms, as in olfactory signaling in which cAMP and IP_3 take part, or it can take from seconds to minutes.

Spatial range. A slower time frame means that cellular processes that are quite distant from the receptor can be modulated. Diffusion of second messengers such as IP_3, Ca^{2+}, and DAG can extend neurotransmission through the cell body and to the nucleus to alter gene expression.

Cross talk. Both the signal transduction machinery and the ultimate mediators of their responses, such as the protein kinases, are capable of cross talk. This is seen in coincident detection of signals from two receptors converging on Type I and Type II adenylate cyclase.

Coordinated modulation. Neurotransmitters acting through G proteins can elicit a coordinated response of the cell that can modulate synaptic release, resynthesis of neurotransmitter, membrane excitability, the cytoskeleton, metabolism, and gene expression.

Summary

A major class of signaling utilizing G-protein-linked signals affords the nervous system a rich diversity of modulation, amplification, and plasticity. Signals are mediated through second messengers activating proteins that modify cellular processes and gene transcription. A key feature is the ability of G proteins to detect the presence of activated receptors and to amplify the signal through effector enzymes and channels. Phosphorylation of key intracellular proteins, ion channels, and enzymes activates diverse, highly regulated cellular processes. Specificity of response is ensured through receptors reacting only with a limited number of G proteins. The response of the system is determined by the speed of activation of GTPase. The function of G-protein subunits is now being elucidated. In addition to speed of response, the spatial compartmentalization of the system enables specificity and localized control of signaling. Phospholipids and phosphoinositols provide substrates for second-messenger signaling for G proteins. Stimulation of release of intracellular calcium is often the mediator of the signal. Calcium itself has a dual role as a carrier of electrical current and as a second messenger. Calmodulin is a key regulator that provides complexity and enhances specificity of the signaling system. Sensitivity of the system is imparted by an extremely robust amplification system, as seen in the visual system, which can detect single photons of light.

MODULATION OF NEURONAL FUNCTION BY PROTEIN KINASES AND PHOSPHATASES

Protein phosphorylation and dephosphorylation are key processes that regulate cellular function. They play a fundamental role in mediating signal transduction initiated by neurotransmitters, neuropeptides, growth factors, hormones, and other signaling molecules. The primary determinants of a cell's morphology and function are the protein constituents expressed in that cell. However, the functional state of many of these proteins is modified by phosphorylation–dephosphorylation, the most ubiquitous posttranslational modification in eukaryotes. About 4% of genes probably encode a kinase or phosphatase, and as many as a fifth of all proteins may serve as targets for kinases and phosphatases. Phosphorylation can rapidly modify the function of enzymes, structural and regulatory proteins, receptors, and ion channels taking part in diverse processes, without a need to change the level of their expression. Phosphorylation and dephosphorylation can also produce long-term alterations in cellular properties by modulating transcription and translation and changing the complement of proteins expressed by cells.

Protein kinases catalyze the transfer of the terminal, or γ, phosphate of ATP to the hydroxyl moieties of Ser, Thr, or Tyr residues at specific sites on target proteins. Most protein kinases are either Ser/Thr kinases or Tyr kinases, with only a few designed to phosphorylate both categories of acceptor amino acids. Protein phosphatases catalyze the hydrolysis of the phosphoryl groups from phosphoserine–phosphothreonine, phosphotyrosine, or both types of phosphorylated amino acids on phosphoproteins.

Protein phosphatases reverse the effects of protein kinases, and protein kinases reverse the effect of protein phosphatases (Fig. 10.11). This statement may seem odd only because signal transduction schemes typically depict unidirectional and not bidirectional regulation; that is, a stimulus activates a kinase that phosphorylates a substrate protein, and basal phosphatase activity dephosphorylates the substrate protein after kinase activity subsides. In fact, regulation of the phosphorylation state of proteins is bidirectional, and the phosphorylation state of proteins *in vivo* ranges widely, from minimal to almost fully phosphorylated, even in the absence of cell stimulation.[48,49] The phosphorylation state can be dynamically altered either upward or downward from the steady state, depending on the cell's inputs and its complement of kinases and phosphatases. Although phosphatases clearly serve to reverse a stimulated phosphorylation, our lack of understanding of phosphatase regulation is largely to

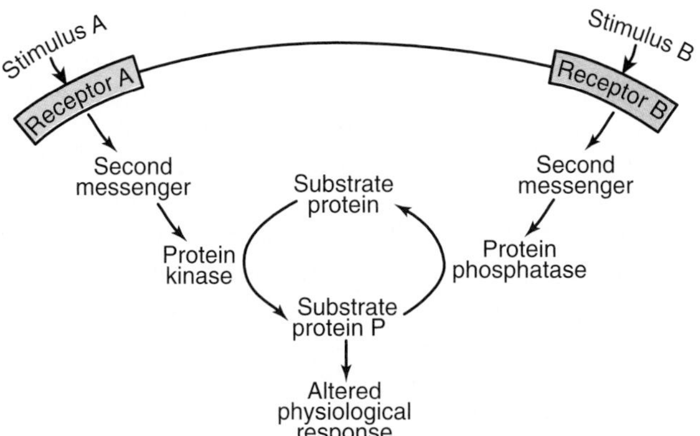

FIGURE 10.11 Regulation by protein kinases and protein phosphatases. Enzymes and other proteins serve as substrates for protein kinases and phosphoprotein phosphatases, which modify their activity and control them in a dynamic fashion. Multiple signals can be integrated at this level of protein modification. Adapted from Greengard *et al.*[49]

blame for our viewing phosphatases in this limited role.

The activity of protein kinases and protein phosphatases is typically regulated either by a second messenger (e.g., cAMP or Ca^{2+}) or by an extracellular ligand (e.g., nerve growth factor). In general, the second-messenger-regulated kinases modify Ser and Thr, whereas the receptor-linked kinases modify Tyr. Among the thousands of protein kinases and protein phosphatases in neurons, a relatively small number serve as master regulators to orchestrate neuronal function.

The cAMP-dependent protein kinase is a prototype for the known regulated Ser/Thr kinases; they are similar in overall structure and regulatory design. PKA is emphasized here because the experimental strategies currently being used in the study of kinases have come from the investigation of PKA-mediated processes. As its name implies, cyclic AMP-dependent protein kinase carries out the posttranslational modification of numerous protein targets in response to signal transduction processes that act through G proteins and alter the level of cAMP in cells. PKA is the predominant mediator for signaling through cAMP, the only other being a cAMP-liganded ion channel in olfaction. In a similar fashion, the related cGMP-dependent protein kinase (PKG) mediates most of the actions of cGMP. Ca^{2+}–calmodulin-dependent protein kinase II and several other kinases mediate many of the actions of stimuli that elevate intracellular Ca^{2+}. Finally, the PI signaling system increases both DAG and Ca^{2+}, which activate any of a family of protein kinases collectively called protein kinase C. Each of these kinases has a broad substrate specificity and is therefore able to phosphorylate diverse substrates throughout the cell. The activities of protein kinases and phosphatases are balanced, as revealed by the phosphorylation state of these targets of the signal transduction process. Here, again, although there are thousands of protein phosphatases, a relatively small number exemplified by protein phosphatase 1 (PP-1), protein phosphatase 2A (PP-2A), and protein phosphatase 2B (PP-2B, or calcineurin) are responsible for most of the dephosphorylation at Ser and Thr residues on phosphoproteins that are under the regulation of the aforementioned kinases. The Nobel Prize for Physiology and Medicine was awarded to Edwin G. Krebs and Edmund H. Fischer in 1992 for their pioneering work on regulation of cell function by protein kinases and phosphatases.

Certain Principles Are Common in Protein Phosphorylation and Dephosphorylation

Protein kinases and protein phosphatases are described either as multifunctional if they have a broad specificity and therefore modify many protein targets or as dedicated if they have a very narrow substrate specificity and may modify only a single protein target. The Ser/Thr kinases and phosphatases described here are multifunctional, giving them the ability to coordinate the regulation of many cellular processes in response to cell stimulation. But how is response specificity achieved with kinases and phosphatases that are designed to recognize many substrates? These enzymes are by no means promiscuous; their substrates conform either to a consensus sequence along the primary protein sequence (for the kinases) or to general features of the three-dimensional structure of the phosphoprotein (for the phosphatases). Furthermore, spatial positioning of kinases and their substrates in the cell either increases or decreases the likelihood of phosphorylation–dephosphorylation of a given substrate.

The amplification of signal transduction described earlier is continued during the transmission of the signal by protein kinases and protein phosphatases. In some cases (e.g., protein tyrosine kinases), the kinases are themselves subject to activation by phosphorylation in a cascade in which one activated kinase phosphorylates and activates a second, and so on, to provide amplification and a switchlike response termed ultrasensitivity.[49a]

Kinases and phosphatases integrate cellular stimuli and encode the stimuli as the steady-state level of phosphorylation of a large complement of proteins in the cell.[50] Phosphorylation and dephosphorylation are reversible processes, and the net activity of the two processes determines the phosphorylation state of each substrate. The phosphorylation state depends on the degree of activation or inactivation of the protein kinase or protein phosphatase, the affinity of the protein target for these enzymes, and the concentration and access of the kinase, phosphatase, and target protein. Some proteins are largely phosphorylated in the basal state and are primarily subject to regulation of phosphatases. Distinct signal transduction pathways can converge on the same or different target substrates. In some cases, these substrates can be phosphorylated by several kinases at distinct sites.

Phosphorylation produces specific changes in the function of a target protein, but these changes are completely dependent on the site of phosphorylation and the nature of the target protein. Phosphorylation may increase or decrease the catalytic activity of an enzyme or its affinity for its substrate or cofactor. It can modify interactions between the phosphoprotein and other proteins, DNA, phospholipids, or other cellular constituents and thereby alter the function of the phosphoprotein in gene expression, synaptic vesicle recycling, and membrane transport. Phosphorylation can regulate desensitization of receptors, their coupling to other signaling molecules, or their localization at synaptic sites. Any of several characteristics of ion channels can be altered by phosphorylation, including voltage dependence, probability of being opened, open and close time kinetics, and conductance. The number of possible effects is almost limitless and enables the fine-tuning of numerous cellular processes over broad time scales, from milliseconds to hours. Kinases and phosphatases do this fine-tuning by regulating the presence of a highly charged and bulky phosphoryl moiety on Ser, Thr, or Tyr at a precise location on the substrate protein. The phosphate may introduce a steric constraint at the surface of the protein in interactions with other cellular constituents, or the negative charge of the phosphoryl moiety may elicit a conformational change because of attractive or repulsive ionic interactions between the phosphorylated segment and other charged amino acids on the protein.

Finally, each of the three kinases described here is capable of functioning as a cognitive kinase, that is, a kinase capable of a molecular memory. Although each is activated by its respective second messenger, it can undergo additional modification that reduces its requirement for the second messenger. This molecular memory potentiates the activity of these kinases and may enable them to participate in aspects of neuronal plasticity.

cAMP-Dependent Protein Kinase Was the First Well-Characterized Kinase

Neurotransmitters that stimulate the synthesis of cAMP exert their intracellular effects primarily by activating PKA.[51] The functions (and substrates) regulated by PKA include gene expression (cAMP response element binding protein, or CREB), catecholamine synthesis (tyrosine hydroxylase), carbohydrate metabolism (phosphorylase kinase), cell morphology (microtubule-associated protein-2, or MAP-2), postsynaptic sensitivity (AMPA receptor), and membrane conductance (L-type Ca^{2+} channel).

PKA is a tetrameric protein composed of two types of subunits: (1) a dimer of regulatory (R) subunits (either two RI subunits for Type I PKA or two RII subunits for Type II PKA) and (2) two catalytic subunits (C subunit).[52] Two or more isoforms of the RI, RII, and C subunits have distinct tissue and developmental patterns of expression but appear to function similarly. The C subunits are 40-kDa proteins that contain the binding sites for protein substrates and ATP. The R subunits are 49- to 51-kDa proteins that contain two cAMP-binding sites. In addition, the R subunit dimer contains a region that interacts with cellular anchoring proteins that serve to localize PKA appropriately within the cell.

The binding of second messengers by PKA and the other second-messenger-regulated kinases relieves an inhibitory constraint and thus activates the enzymes (Fig. 10.12). The C subunit has intrinsic protein kinase activity that remains inhibited as long as the C subunit is complexed with the R subunits in the tetrameric holoenzyme. As each R subunit binds two molecules of cAMP, its affinity for the C subunit is greatly reduced, and the C subunit dissociates as a free active kinase. Cyclic AMP therefore activates the C subunit by relieving it of its inhibitory R subunits. The steady-state level of cAMP determines the fraction of PKA that is in the dissociated or active form. In this way PKA decodes cAMP signals into the phosphorylation of proteins and the resultant change in various cellular processes.

PKA is a member of a large family of protein kinases that have in common a significant degree of homology in their catalytic domains and are likely derived from an ancestral gene[53] (Fig. 10.13). This homology extends to the three-dimensional crystal structure, based on X-ray crystallography of PKA and a few other kinases. The catalytic domain comprises approximately 280 amino acids that may be in a subunit distinct from the regulatory domain, as in PKA, or in the same subunit, as in PKC and Ca^{2+}–calmodulin-dependent (CaM) kinases. The crystal structure of the C subunit complexed to a segment of protein kinase inhibitor (PKI), a selective high-affinity inhibitor of PKA, reveals that the C subunit is composed of two lobes. A small N-terminal lobe contains a highly conserved region that binds Mg^{2+}-ATP in a cleft between the two lobes. A larger C-terminal lobe contains the protein-substrate recogni-

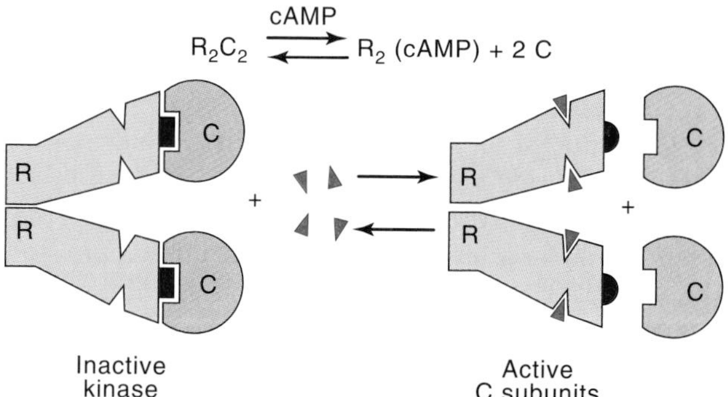

FIGURE 10.12 Activation of PKA by cyclic AMP. An autoinhibitory segment (blue) of the regulatory subunit (R) dimer interacts with the substrate-binding domain of the catalytic (C) subunits of PKA, blocking access of substrates to their binding site. Binding of four molecules of cyclic AMP reduces the affinity of R for C, resulting in dissociation of constitutively active C subunits.

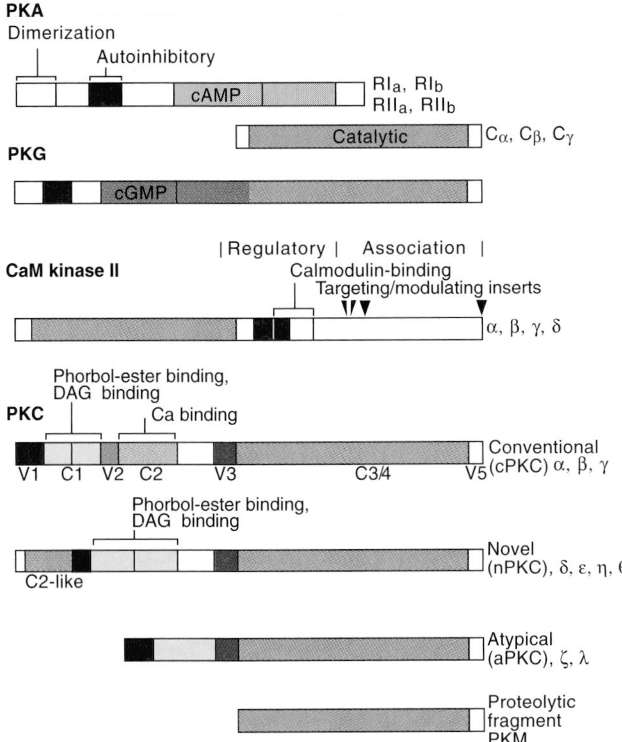

FIGURE 10.13 Domain structure of protein kinases. Protein kinases are encoded by proteins with recognizable structural sequences that encode specialized functional domains. Each of the kinases [PKA, PKG, CaM (Ca^{2+}–calmodulin-dependent) kinase II, and PKC] have homologous catalytic domains that are kept inactive by the presence of an autoinhibitory segment (blue lines). The regulatory domains contain sites for binding second messengers such as cAMP, cGMP, Ca^{2+}–calmodulin, DAG, and Ca^{2+}–phosphatidylserine. Alternative splicing creates additional diversity.

tion sites and the appropriate amino acids for catalyzing the transfer of the phosphoryl moiety from ATP to the polypeptide chain of the substrate. Inhibition by PKI is diagnostic of PKA involvement; PKI contains an autoinhibitory sequence resembling PKA substrates and is positioned in the catalytic site like a substrate, thus blocking access for substrates.

How can protein kinases have a common structural homology yet exhibit phosphorylation target specificity? Although the C-terminal lobes of all kinases may utilize a similar scaffold for their peptide-binding and catalytic sites, distinct amino acids are positioned on this scaffold to produce specificity in peptide binding. Dedicated protein kinases, such as myosin light chain kinase (MLCK), which phosphorylates only certain myosin light chains, have numerous sites of contact between the catalytic domain and substrate and therefore have high specificity. In contrast, PKA has a smaller number of contact sites, thus enabling a much larger yet specific set of substrates to bind.

PKA phosphorylates Ser or Thr at specific sites in dozens of proteins. The sequences of amino acids at the phosphorylation sites are not identical, but a consensus sequence can be deduced from a comparison of these sequences.[54] PKA phosphorylates at sites with the consensus sequence Arg-Arg-X-Ser/Thr-Y, in which X can be one of many different amino acids and Y is a hydrophobic amino acid. Each kinase has a characteristic consensus sequence that forms the basis for distinct substrate specificities (Table 10.4). These consensus sequences are often used to identify putative sites of phosphorylation on newly cloned proteins, although many substrates are phosphorylated at "anomalous" sites, thus reducing the reliability of these predictions. Secondary and tertiary structures probably have a role in substrate recognition, and the finding of anomalous phosphorylation sites may simply be due to our lack of knowledge of exactly how substrates are recognized.[55] The consensus sites of PKA, CaM kinase II, and PKC all include a basic residue on the substrate, and these kinases do share some target substrates.

A regulatory theme common to PKA, CaM kinase II, and PKC is that their second messengers activate them by displacing an autoinhibitory domain from the active site; that is, they relieve an inhibitory constraint rather than stabilizing a conformation of the kinase that has higher activity.[56] Some of the contacts between the C and R subunits of PKA resemble those between the C subunit with its protein substrates. The R subunit blocks access of substrates by positioning a pseudosubstrate or autoinhibitory domain in the catalytic site. This segment of R resembles a substrate and binds to C as would a substrate or PKI. Binding of cAMP to the R subunit near this autoinhibitory domain must disrupt its binding to the C subunit, thus leading to dissociation of an active C subunit.[57] CaM kinase II and PKC likewise have autoinhibitory segments that are near the second-messenger binding sites and may be activated similarly[56] (see Fig. 10.13).

TABLE 10.4 Consensus Phosphorylation Sites of Some Protein Kinases

Protein kinase	Consensus phosphorylation site
PKA	R-R/K-X-S*/T*
PKG	R/$K_{2\text{-}3}$-X-S*/T*
cPKC	(R/$K_{1\text{-}3}$,-$X_{2\text{-}0}$)-S*/T*-($X_{2\text{-}0}$,-R/$K_{1\text{-}3}$)
CaM kinase II	R-X-X-S*/T*
MLCK (smooth muscle)	(K/R_2-X)-$X_{1\text{-}2}$-K/R_3-$X_{2\text{-}3}$-R-X_2-S*-N-V-F

Source. Adapted from Kennelly and Krebs.[54]

R, Arg; K, Lys; S*, phospho-Ser; T*, phospho-Thr; X, polar amino acid; N, Asn; V, Val; F, Phe.

Functional differences between Type I and Type II PKA (which have C subunits in common but have different R subunits) may arise from differential targeting in cells and from differences in regulation by autophosphorylation. RII, but not RI, is autophosphorylated by its C subunit when it is in the holoenzyme form. This potentiates cAMP action by reducing the rate of reassociation of RII and C after a stimulus. Only anchoring proteins for RII have been characterized thus far.[58]

Multifunctional CaM Kinase II Decodes Diverse Signals That Elevate Intracellular Ca^{2+}

Most of the effects of Ca^{2+} in neurons and other cell types are mediated by calmodulin, and many of the effects of Ca^{2+}–calmodulin are mediated by protein phosphorylation–dephosphorylation. In contrast with the cAMP system, both dedicated and multifunctional kinases are found in the Ca^{2+}-signaling system.[59] Two kinases, MLCK and phosphorylase kinase, are each dedicated to the phosphorylation of a single substrate—myosin light chains and phosphorylase, respectively. The Ca^{2+}-signaling system also contains a family of Ca^{2+}–calmodulin-dependent protein kinases with broad substrate specificity, including CaM kinases I, II, and IV; of them, CaM kinase II is the best characterized. CaM kinase II phosphorylates tyrosine hydroxylase, MAP-2, synapsin I, calcium channels, Ca^{2+}-ATPase, transcription factors, and glutamate receptors and thereby regulates synthesis of catecholamines, cytoskeletal function, synaptic release in response to high-frequency stimuli, calcium currents, calcium homeostasis, gene expression, and synaptic plasticity, respectively. The enzyme is activated by Ca^{2+} regardless of whether it is elevated by influx through Ca^{2+} channels or ligand-gated Ca^{2+} channels or is released from intracellular stores following stimulation of the PI-signaling pathway. This kinase is found in every tissue but is particularly enriched in neurons, where it may account for as much as 2% of all hippocampal protein. This level is 50 times as high as the level of the kinase in other tissues; thus, CaM kinase II likely serves some special functions in such brain regions. It is found in the cytosol, in the nucleus, in association with cytoskeletal elements, and in postsynaptic thickening termed the postsynaptic density found in asymmetric synapses. It is a large multimeric enzyme, consisting of 10–12 subunits derived from four homologous genes (α, β, γ, and δ) that encode different isoforms of the kinase that range from 54 to 65 kDa per subunit. Multimers and heteromultimers of α- and β-CaM kinase II isoforms are found predominantly in brain, whereas the γ- and δ-CaM kinases are found throughout the body, including the brain.

The domain structure of CaM kinase II isoforms is shown in Fig. 10.13. Unlike those of PKA, the catalytic, regulatory, and targeting domains are all contained within a single polypeptide. The N-terminal half of each isoform contains the catalytic domain that is highly homologous to the catalytic subunit of PKA and other Ser/Thr kinases. The middle region constitutes the regulatory domain, which contains an autoinhibitory domain with an overlapping calmodulin-binding sequence. The C-terminal end contains an association domain that allows approximately 10 subunits to assemble into a multimer of 500–600 kDa, as well as targeting sequences that direct the kinase to distinct intracellular sites.

Regulation of the kinase by autophosphorylation is a critical feature of CaM kinase II. The basic three-dimensional conformation of the catalytic domain is likely to be similar to the structures determined for PKA and CaM kinase I. The kinase is inactive in the basal state because an autoinhibitory segment is positioned in the catalytic site, sterically blocking access to its substrates. Peptides corresponding to this region are useful inhibitors for functional studies and inhibit the kinase by competing for binding of both ATP and protein substrates. Elevation of Ca^{2+} generates a Ca^{2+}–calmodulin complex that wraps around the calmodulin-binding domain of the kinase. The overlapping of the autoinhibitory domain and calmodulin-binding domains is likely to displace the autoinhibitory domain from the catalytic site and thus activate the kinase by enabling ATP and protein substrates to bind. The site occupied by one particular amino acid in the autoinhibitory domain of all isoforms of this kinase, Thr-286 (in α-CaM kinase), must be crucial in allowing the autoinhibitory domain to keep the active site shut before activation. If the kinase is activated, it can autophosphorylate this particular Thr residue. Phosphorylation disables the autoinhibitory segment by preventing it from blocking the active site after calmodulin dissociates and thereby locks the kinase in a partially active state that is independent, or autonomous, of Ca^{2+}–calmodulin.[60–62]

An additional dramatic effect of autophosphorylation is that it enhances the affinity of the bound calmodulin by 400-fold, which it achieves by reducing the rate of dissociation of calmodulin from the kinase after Ca^{2+} levels are reduced below threshold.[63] In essence, autophosphorylation traps bound calmodulin for several seconds and keeps the kinase active for a while after Ca^{2+} levels decline to baseline. The consequence of calmodulin trapping and disruption of the autoinhibitory domain is to prolong the active state of the kinase, a potentiation that led to its description as a cognitive kinase.[59,64]

CaM kinase II responds to a large number of neurotransmitter receptors subserved by various signal transduction systems *in situ,* and stimulation of these pathways increases the autonomous activity of the enzyme. The level of autonomous activity (8–15% in brain) may correspond to the integration of multiple cellular inputs, and the autonomous activity may be adjusted either upward or downward.

CaM kinase II is targeted to distinct cellular compartments. Differences between the four genes encoding CaM kinase II and between the two or more isoforms that are encoded by each gene by apparent alternative splicing reside primarily in a variable region at the start of the association domain (see Fig. 10.13). In some isoforms, this region contains an additional sequence of 11 amino acids that targets those isoforms to the nucleus. The major neuronal isoform, α-CaM kinase, is largely cytosolic but is also found attached to postsynaptic densities and to synaptic vesicles and may therefore have several targeting sequences.

Protein Kinase C Is the Principal Target of the PI Signaling System

Protein kinase C (PKC) is a collective name for members of a relatively diverse family of protein kinases most closely associated with the PI-signaling system. PKC is a multifunctional Ser/Thr kinase capable of modulating many cellular processes, including exocytosis and endocytosis of neurotransmitter vesicles, neuronal plasticity, gene expression, regulation of cell growth and cell cycle, ion channels, and receptors. A major breakthrough in understanding of the PI-signaling pathway was the realization that DAG and Ca^{2+}, two products of this pathway, function as second messengers to activate PKC.[27,28] The role of DAG in PI signaling was unclear until its link to PKC was established. Many PKC isoforms also require an acidic phospholipid such as phosphatidylserine for appropriate activation. The kinase is also of interest because it is the target of a class of tumor promoters called phorbol esters. They activate PKC by simulating the action of DAG, bypassing the normal receptor-based pathway, and somehow inappropriately stimulating cell growth.

We now understand that the PKC family of kinases is diverse in structure and regulatory properties.[28] Unlike PKA, PKC is a monomeric enzyme (78–90 kDa) with catalytic, regulatory, and targeting domains all on one polypeptide. Each isoform has a regulatory domain, with several subdomains, in its N-terminal half and a catalytic domain at the C-terminal[65] (see Fig. 10.13). Only the first PKC isoforms to be characterized, now termed the conventional isoforms (or cPKC), have all of the domains. The domains are referred to as (1) V1, which contains the autoinhibitory or pseudosubstrate sequence present in all isoforms; (2) C1, a cysteine-rich domain that binds DAG and phorbol esters; (3) C2, a region necessary for Ca^{2+} sensitivity and for binding to phosphatidylserine and to anchoring proteins; (4) V3, a protease-sensitive hinge; (5) C3/4, the catalytic domain; and (6) V5, which may also mediate anchoring. Subsequent cloning revealed a larger and more diverse group of isoforms than that of cPKC (Fig. 10.13). One class of isoforms, termed novel PKCs (nPKC), lacks a true C2 domain and is therefore not Ca^{2+} sensitive. Another class is considered atypical (aPKC) because it lacks C2 and the first of two cysteine-rich domains that are necessary for DAG (or phorbol ester) sensitivity. This class is neither Ca^{2+} nor DAG sensitive.

Activation of PKC is best understood for the conventional isoforms. Generation of DAG resulting from stimulation of the PI-signaling pathway increases the affinity of cPKC isoforms for Ca^{2+} and phosphatidylserine. Although triglyceride lipases also generate DAG, the *sn*-1,2-diacylglycerol isomer is derived only from PI turnover, and it is the only isomer effective in activating PKC. Cell stimulation results in the translocation of cPKC from a variety of sites to the membrane or cytoskeletal elements where it interacts with PS–Ca^{2+}–DAG at the membrane.[66–68] Binding of the second messengers to the regulatory domain disrupts the nearby autoinhibitory domain, leading to a reversible activation of PKC by deinhibition, as is found for PKA and CaM kinase II.[69]

Translocation is not restricted to the plasma membrane. Some PKC isoforms translocate to intracellular sites enriched with certain anchoring proteins for the activated form of PKC, termed RACK (receptors for activated C kinase).[68,70] Distinct PKC isoforms can translocate to the cytoskeleton, membrane, perinuclear area, and nucleus, probably by binding of the C2 and/or the V1 and V5 domains to distinct anchoring proteins. In the inactive state, a segment of PKC may occupy this RACK-binding domain, thus preventing translocation until the activation of PKC exposes this domain. Activation may therefore consist of both displacement of the autoinhibitory segment to unblock the catalytic site and displacement of an "auto-anchoring" site to unblock the RACK-binding site. Whether DAG is synthesized only in the plasma membrane and the PKC–PS–DAG complex subsequently diffuses to distant RACKs or whether some DAG is generated intracellularly is not known. The early phase of DAG derived from PI is followed by a longer phase in which

DAG derived from PC is more prominent. After termination of the signal, DAG is recycled into phospholipids, and PKC is redistributed to its initial sites.

Prolonged activation of PKC can be produced by the addition of phorbol esters, which simulate activation by DAG but remain in the cell until they are washed out. In a matter of hours to days, such persistent activation by phorbol esters leads to a degradation of PKC. Either PKC may be more susceptible to proteolysis when activated or some of the compartments to which it translocates have a higher level of protease activity. This phenomenon is often used experimentally to produce a PKC-depleted cell (at least for phorbol-ester-binding isoforms) and thereafter to test for a loss of putative PKC functions.

Spatial Localization Regulates Protein Kinases and Phosphatases

Protein kinases and protein phosphatases are often spatially positioned near their substrates or they translocate to their substrates upon activation to improve speed and specificity in response to neurotransmitter stimulation. PKA is targeted to intracellular sites on the cytoskeleton, membrane, and Golgi through interactions between the RII subunit and specific anchoring proteins. MAP-2 is an anchoring protein for RII, which concentrates PKA near its substrate (including MAP-2) in dendrites. Anchoring proteins with no previously known function are referred to as A kinase anchoring proteins, or AKAPs.[58] One such anchor, AKAP79, is an anchor for PKA, for PKC, and for calcineurin, the Ca^{2+}–calmodulin-dependent phosphatase.[71] The three signaling molecules bind to different sites on this anchoring protein. Better coordination of the phosphorylation–dephosphorylation of the same or different substrates may be achieved by placing calcineurin, PKC, and PKA in the same compartment through AKAPs.

The use of anchoring proteins has several consequences. First, it enhances the rate of phosphorylation when kinases or phosphatases are placed near some substrates. Specificity is enhanced when these enzymes are concentrated near proteins that are to be substrates and away from other proteins that are not to be substrates in a given cell. Second, it increases the signal-to-noise ratio for substrates that are not near anchoring proteins because phosphorylation–dephosphorylation would be reduced in the basal state. For example, PKA is anchored on the Golgi away from the nucleus in the basal state. Brief stimuli lead to transient dissociation of C subunits and provide for localized regulation of nearby substrates but little phosphorylation of nuclear proteins. Prolonged stimuli enable some C subunits to passively diffuse through nuclear pores and into nuclei, where they can participate in regulation of gene expression.[72] Termination of the nuclear action of C subunits is aided by PKI, which binds and inhibits the C subunit in the nucleus and hastens its export out of the nucleus, where it can reassociate with R subunits.[73] A high signal-to-noise ratio can be achieved with PKC by translocation toward substrates only after activation. Interaction with anchoring proteins should increase the rate and specificity of phosphorylation and may also prolong the active state of PKC by stabilizing it. Third, anchoring enables significant basal phosphorylation of substrates near anchoring proteins. Basal phosphorylation would be high if PKA were highly concentrated by an anchoring protein near high-affinity substrates. For example, if an anchoring protein concentrates PKA 50-fold relative to the rest of the cell, then the local concentration of free C subunits will be high at basal cAMP even though the percentage of dissociated C subunits is low. Such an arrangement provides for novel ways of blocking the pathway through disruption of anchoring. When a peptide similar to the site at which RII binds to the AKAP is introduced into a neuron, it disrupts the ability of an AKAP to concentrate PKA near the AMPA receptor and leads to decreased modulation of the AMPA receptor in the basal state.[48]

PKA, CaM Kinase II, and PKC Are Cognitive Kinases

The ability of three major Ser/Thr kinases (PKA, CaM kinase II, and PKC) in brain to initiate or maintain synaptic changes that underlie learning and memory may require that they themselves undergo some form of persistent change in activity. As mentioned earlier, they have been described as cognitive kinases because they are capable of sustaining their activated states after their second messengers return to basal level and because their target substrates modulate synaptic plasticity.[74]

cAMP-Dependent Protein Kinase

A role for PKA as a cognitive kinase can be seen in long-term facilitation of the gill-withdrawal reflex in *Aplysia* and in long-term potentiation in the rodent hippocampus. In the gill withdrawal reflex, stimulation of the tail facilitates the withdrawal of the gill and siphon in response to a light touch. A shock to the tail stimulates the release of serotonin from tail sensory neurons onto motor neurons that control gill withdrawal, which increases cAMP and PKA activity in the motor neurons. Repetitive stimulation of the tail produces a sensitization, based on prolonged PKA activity, that can last for several days. Sensitization is an elementary form of learning in which a response to one stimulus is facilitated by another stimulus. This

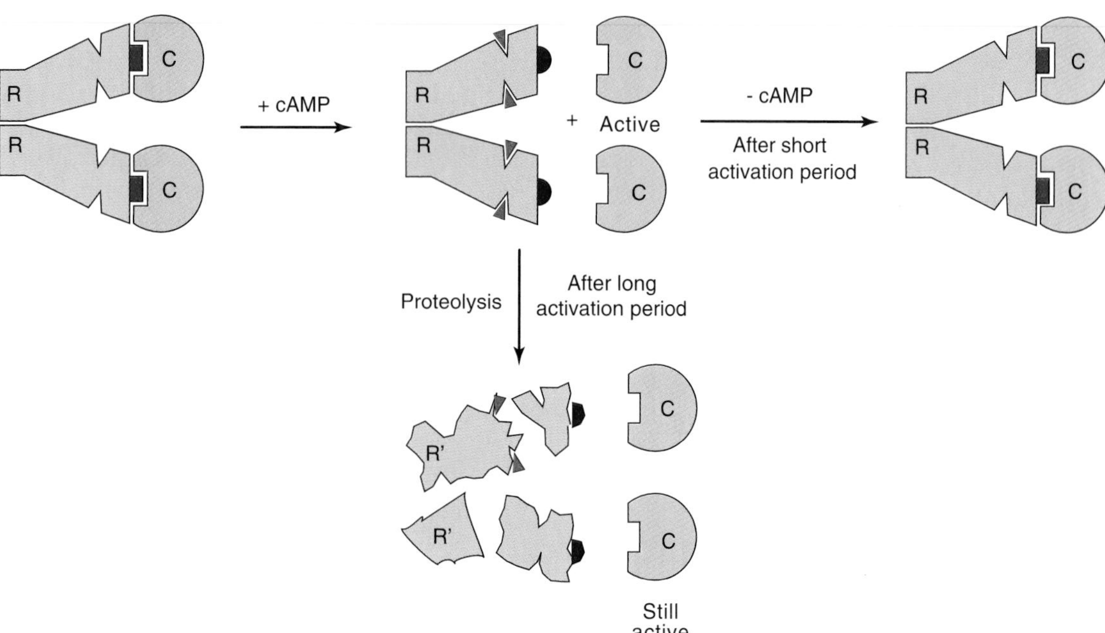

FIGURE 10.14 Long-term stimulation can convert PKA into a constitutively active enzyme. Dissociation of PKA R and C subunits is reversible with short-term elevation of cyclic AMP. More prolonged activation results in loss of R subunits to proteolysis, resulting in an insufficient amount of R subunits to associate with and inhibit all C subunits after the cAMP stimulus terminates.

pathway is a crude approximation of what happens when *Aplysia* finds itself in turbulent waters. Where is the molecular memory of tail stimulation retained? In motor-neuron cultures, a single exposure to serotonin or cAMP produces short-term facilitation and a short-term increase in the phosphorylation of more than a dozen PKA substrates in these cells. However, repeated or prolonged exposure to these agents leads to long-term facilitation and an enhanced state of phosphorylation of the same set of proteins. This phenomenon is due to a PKA that is persistently active despite the fact that cAMP is no longer elevated.[75] A possible scheme for this phenomenon is shown in Fig. 10.14. The RII subunit is autophosphorylated on its autoinhibitory segment by the C subunit in the holoenzyme. Phospho-RII and C subunits dissociate upon elevation of cAMP and reassociate when cAMP levels subside. However, the reassociation rate is greatly reduced by the presence of phosphate on the RII subunit, thus prolonging phosphorylation of various target proteins by the C subunit. Furthermore, the RII subunits are more susceptible than the C subunits to proteolytic degradation in their dissociated state. Thus, prolonged or repetitive stimulation leads to a preferential decrease in the inhibitory RII subunits and thus a slight excess of C subunits that remain persistently active because of insufficient RII subunits. The various targets of PKA can then be phosphorylated by this active C subunit long after cAMP levels return to basal or prestimulus levels. Prolonged activation of PKA enables the C subunit to enter the nucleus and induce gene expression, and one of these genes facilitates further proteolysis of RII. Although short-term facilitation does not require transcription of new genes or protein synthesis, the long-term effects on phosphorylation and on facilitation do require transcription of new genes and protein synthesis.[76] In this interesting process, a molecular memory of appropriate stimulation by serotonin is encoded by a persistence of PKA activity that is regenerative.

PKA may also function as a cognitive kinase in hippocampal long-term potentiation. This phenomenon is most clearly seen in the short- and long-term phases of long-term potentiation in CA3 neurons stimulated by means of the mossy fiber pathway, one of several sites of long-term potentiation in the hippocampus. Induction of both the early and the late phase of long-term potentiation at this site requires PKA.[77] The persistent phase of long-term potentiation requires both RNA synthesis and new protein synthesis, with the likelihood of PKA-mediated increases in gene expression. Although the induction of long-term potentiation requires a rise in Ca^{2+}, rather than of cAMP, one of the Ca^{2+}-stimulated adenylate cyclases appears to convert some of the Ca^{2+} signal into a rise in cAMP. Mutant mice lacking one such cyclase isoform show a marked reduction in Ca^{2+}-sensitive cyclase and cAMP accumulation, a reduced long-term potentiation in hippocampal slices, and a weaker spatial memory in behavioral tests.[78]

Ca^{2+}–Calmodulin-Dependent Protein Kinase

CaM kinase II has features of a cognitive kinase because it has a molecular memory of its activation that is based on autophosphorylation and it phosphorylates proteins that modulate synaptic plasticity.[64,74,79] The biochemical properties of CaM kinase II suggest mechanisms by which appropriate stimulus frequencies can generate an autonomous enzyme (Fig. 10.15). The critical site of phosphorylation is in the autoinhibitory segment that is part of the 10 or so catalytic–regulatory domains surrounding the central hub of the holoenzyme. Each subunit can bind and be activated by calmodulin independently but requires neighboring subunits for autophosphorylation. Autophosphorylation takes place within each holoenzyme but requires the phosphorylation of one subunit by a proximate neighbor. Furthermore, calmodulin must be bound to the subunit that is to be phosphorylated, perhaps to displace the autoinhibitory domain and expose the phosphorylation site to the active subunit. Individual stimuli may be too brief and available calmodulin may be limited, so a single stimulus may lead to binding and activation of only a few subunits per holoenzyme. Thus, each stimulus achieves only submaximal activation of the kinase. When two neighboring subunits are bound to calmodulin during a stimulus, autophosphorylation is achieved. Autophosphorylation leads to a potentiation because the phosphorylated subunit traps its bound calmodulin for several seconds and thus remains active, longer than the Ca^{2+} signal. Even after calmodulin dissociates, the autophorylated subunit remains partially active until dephosphorylated. At low stimulus frequency, the time between stimuli is sufficient for calmodulin to dissociate and the kinase to be dephosphorylated, and the same submaximal activation will occur with each stimulus. However, at higher frequencies, some subunits will remain autophosphorylated and bound to calmodulin, so successive stimuli will result in more calmodulin bound per holoenzyme, which will make autophosphorylation and subsequent calmodulin trapping more probable.[59,80] Thus, low-frequency stimulation leads to submaximal activation of the kinase at each stimulus, whereas higher frequencies exceed a threshold beyond which stimulation leads to recruitment of additional calmodulin and a higher level of activation and autonomy with each spike.[80a]

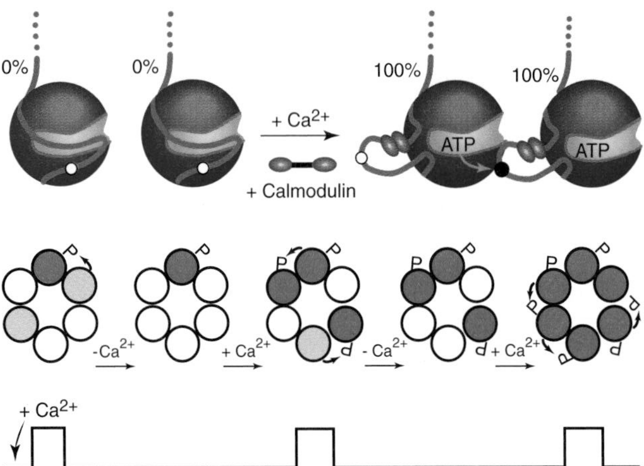

FIGURE 10.15 Frequency-dependent activation of CaM kinase II. Autophosphorylation occurs when both of two neighboring subunits in a holoenzyme are bound to calmodulin. At high frequency of stimulation (rapid Ca^{2+} spikes), the interspike interval is too short to allow significant dephosphorylation or dissociation of calmodulin, thereby increasing the probability of autophosphorylation with each successive spike. In a simplified CaM kinase with only six subunits, calmodulin-bound subunits are shown in pink, and autophosphorylated subunits with trapped calmodulin are shown in red. Adapted from Hanson and Schulman.[79]

CaM kinase phosphorylates a number of substrates that affect synaptic strength. For example, phosphorylation of **synapsin I,** a synaptic vesicle protein, by CaM kinase II reduces the attachment of synaptic vesicles to actin at nerve terminals. Phosphorylation of synapsin I by CaM kinase enables synaptic release to be maintained at high stimulus frequencies, perhaps by facilitating movement of vesicles toward release sites. Inhibition of CaM kinase II in hippocampal slices or elimination of α-CaM kinase by targeted knockout in mice blocks the induction of long-term potentiation.[81] Mice lacking α-CaM kinase are deficient in learning spatial navigational cues, one of the functions of the rodent hippocampus. The basis for its role is uncertain but may be the phosphorylation of AMPA receptors, leading to a greater postsynaptic response. Variations in the level of autonomous CaM kinase II in development and in mice expressing a recombinant CaM kinase II that is constitutively active suggest that this kinase modulates the threshold for synapse modification, an important element in some learning theories.[82] The enzyme can therefore be appropriately described as a cognitive kinase with regard to its own molecular memory as well as its functional role in mediating aspects of synaptic plasticity.

Protein Kinase C

PKC also can be converted into a form that is independent, or autonomous, of its second messenger and can be described as a cognitive kinase. Before Ca^{2+} and DAG were known to have roles in the reversible activation of PKC, the PKC was identified as an inactive precursor that was activated *in vitro* by Ca^{2+}-dependent proteolysis to a constitutively active fragment termed protein kinase M (PKM). Physiological activation of PKC may also convert it into a PKM-like species. Standard protocols lead to transient activation of both Ca^{2+}-dependent and Ca^{2+}-independent forms of PKC. However, during the persistent phase of long-term potentiation, some of the PKC remains active but is autonomous of Ca^{2+} and DAG. The activity appears to be a PKM or other modified form of an atypical PKC.[83] PKC has also been implicated in long-term potentiation, and its substrates include the NMDA and AMPA receptors.

Protein Tyrosine Kinases Take Part in Cell Growth and Differentiation

Protein kinases that phosphorylate tyrosine residues on key proteins participate in numerous cellular process and are usually associated with regulation of cell growth and differentiation. Signal transduction by protein tyrosine kinases often includes a cascade of kinases phosphorylating other kinases, eventually activating Ser/Thr kinases, which carry out the intended modification of a cellular process. There are two classes of protein tyrosine kinases. The first is a family of receptor tyrosine kinases that are activated by the binding of extracellular growth factors such as nerve growth factor, epidermal growth factor, insulin, and platelet-derived growth factor. The second family of protein tyrosine kinases such as c-Src are soluble kinases that also participate in regulation of cell growth but are indirectly activated by extracellular ligands.

Why have two sets of amino acids been chosen as targets for phosphorylation? First, the consequences of leaky, or "promiscuous," phosphorylation by a protein Ser/Thr kinase of an unintended target may affect metabolic activity or synaptic function but do not typically initiate irreversible and global functions such as cell growth and differentiation. The consequence of such inappropriate stimulation is seen in the effect of a variety of oncogenes that utilize altered forms of receptor tyrosine kinases or intermediates in their cascades to subvert normal cell growth. The cellular concentrations of protein Ser/Thr kinases and their targets are much higher than those of protein tyrosine kinases and their substrates. Inadvertent phosphorylation of targets that play critical roles in cell growth is less likely if these targets are regulated at tyrosine residues, which are not well recognized by the numerous protein Ser/Thr kinases. Second, introduction of a phosphotyrosine structure into a protein has a greater regulatory potential than does introduction of a phosphoserine or phosphothreonine. The three phosphorylated amino acids have in common an ability to produce conformational changes due to the extra charge or bulk of the phosphate. For example, in the activation of receptor tyrosine kinases, autophosphorylation displaces an inhibitory domain. In addition, however, the phosphotyrosine and nearby amino acid sequences can be recognized by various signal transduction effectors, such as PLCγ, that contain structural domains that bind to the tyrosine-phosphorylated kinase. The receptor tyrosine kinase thus becomes a platform for concentrating various signaling molecules at specific phosphotyrosine sites in its sequence. These signaling molecules either are activated directly by binding or are activated after having been phosphorylated by the receptor tyrosine kinase. It is easier to bind with the necessary strict specificity to segments of protein around phosphotyrosines, because of the aromatic side chain in tyrosine, and this may be an additional reason for use of Tyr as phosphotransferase targets.

Protein Phosphatases Undo What Kinases Create

Protein phosphatases in neuronal signaling are categorized as either phosphoserine–phosphothreonine phosphatases (PSPs) or phosphotyrosine phosphatases.[50,84] The enzymes catalyze the hydrolysis of the ester bond of the phosphorylated amino acids to release inorganic phosphate and the unphosphorylated protein. Phosphatases control all of the cellular processes of protein kinases, including neurotransmission, neuronal excitability, gene expression, protein synthesis, neuronal plasticity, and cell growth. A limited number of multifunctional PSPs account for most of such phosphatase activity in cells.[50] They are categorized into six groups (1, 4, 5, 2A, 2B, and 2C) on the basis of their substrates, inhibitors, and divalent cation requirements (Table 10.5). An additional historical distinction is that phosphatase 1 (PP-1) preferentially dephosphorylates the β subunit of phosphorylase kinase, whereas protein phosphatase 2A preferentially dephosphorylates its α subunit. Of these PSPs, only protein phosphatase 2B (PP-2B, or calcineurin) directly responds to a second messenger; it responds to increases in cellular Ca^{2+}. PP-1, -4, -5, -2A, and calcineurin are structurally related and differ from PP-2C. Little is known about the basis of substrate specificity of these phosphatases; examination of the primary sequences of their dephosphorylation sites reveals no obvious consensus. The specificity of PP-1 and PP-2A is particularly broad, and each can remove phosphates that were transferred by any of the protein kinases discussed herein as well as many other kinases. The phosphotyrosine phosphatases (PTPs) constitute a distinct and larger class of phosphatases, including PTPs with dual specificity for both phosphotyrosines and phosphoserine–phosphothreonines. PTPs are either soluble enzymes or membrane proteins with variable extra cellular domains that enable regulation by extracellular binding of either soluble or membrane-bound signals.

TABLE 10.5 Categories of Protein Phosphatases

Phosphatase	Characteristic	Other inhibitors
PP-1	Sensitive to phosphoinhibitor-1, phospho-DARPP-32, and inhibitor-2; has targeting subunits	Weakly sensitive to okadaic acid
PP-4	Nuclear	Highly sensitive to okadaic acid
PP-5	Nuclear	Mildly sensitive to okadaic acid
PP-2A	Regulatory subunits Does not require divalent cation	Highly sensitive to okadaic acid
PP-2B (calcineurin)	Ca^{2+}-calmodulin dependent CnB regulatory subunit	FK506, cyclosporin
PP-2C	Requires Mg^{2+}	EDTA
Receptor PTPs*	Plasma membrane	Vanadate, tyrphosphtin, erbstatin
Nonreceptor PTPs	Various cellular compartments	Vanadate, tyrphosphtin
Dual-specificity PTPs	Nuclear (e.g., cdc25A/B/C and VH family)	Vanadate

Source: Hunter.[50]
*Protein tyrosine phosphatases.

Structure and Regulation of PP-1 and Calcineurin

PP-1 and calcineurin are the best characterized phosphatases with regard to both structure and regulation. The domain structures of the catalytic subunits of PP-1 and calcineurin are depicted in Fig. 10.16. PP-1 is a protein of 35–38 kDa; most of the sequence forms the catalytic domain; its C terminal is the site of regulatory phosphorylation. The catalytic domains of PP-1, PP-2A, and calcineurin are highly homologous.[84]

Although PP-1 and PP-2A are usually prepared as free catalytic subunits, they are normally complexed in cells with specific anchoring or targeting subunits.[85] For example, PP-1 is attached to glycogen particles in liver, myofibrils in muscle, and unidentified targeting subunits in brain. Phosphorylation of the PP-1 targeting subunit in liver releases the catalytic subunit and results in reduced dephosphorylation of substrates near the targeting subunit because diffusion reduces the local concentration of PP-1. Targeting of PP-1 also modulates its regulation by natural inhibitors. As PP-1 dissociates from targeting subunits, it becomes susceptible to inhibition by inhibitor-2.

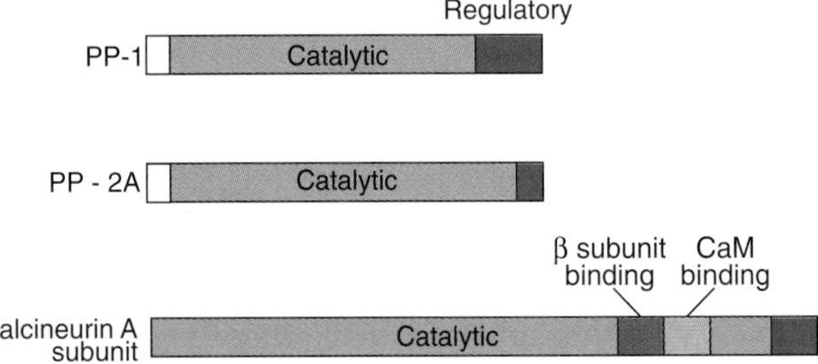

FIGURE 10.16 Domain structure of the catalytic subunits of some Ser/Thr phosphatases. The three major phosphoprotein phosphatases, PP-1, PP-2A, and calcineurin, have homologous catalytic domains but differ in their regulatory properties.

Inhibition of PP-1 by two other inhibitors, inhibitor-1 and its homolog DARPP-32 (dopamine and cAMP-regulated phosphoprotein; M_r 32,000), is conditional on the phosphorylation state of these inhibitors.[86] Inhibitor-1 has a broader distribution in brain than DARPP-32, which is largely found in the medium spiny neurons in the neostriatum and in their terminals in the globus pallidus and substantia nigra. Both proteins inhibit only after they are phosphorylated by PKA or PKG. PKA also increases the susceptibility of PP-1 to inhibition by stimulating its release from targeting subunits. Because the substrates for PKA and PP-1 overlap to a great extent, the rate and extent of phosphorylation of such substrates are enhanced by the ability of PKA to catalyze their phosphorylation while blocking their dephosphorylation. Inhibitor-1, DARPP-32, and inhibitor-2 are all selective for PP-1. Highly selective inhibitors capable of penetrating the cell membrane are available for these phosphatases. Okadaic acid, a natural product of marine dinoflagellates, is a tumor promoter but, unlike phorbol esters, it acts on PP-2A and PP-1, rather than on PKC. The steady-state level of phosphorylation of dozens of proteins is elevated when cells are treated by okadaic acid and its derivatives.

Protein phosphatase 1 The X-ray structure of the catalytic subunit of PP-1 bound to the toxin microcystin, a cyclic peptide inhibitor, reveals PP-1 to be a compact ellipsoid with hydrophobic and acidic surfaces forming a cleft for binding substrates.[87] PP-1 is a metalloenzyme requiring two metals in the active site that likely take part in electrostatic interactions with the phosphate on substrates that aid in catalyzing the hydrolytic reaction. The phosphate would be positioned at the intersection of two grooves on the surface of the enzyme where binding to amino acid residues on the substrate would occur. Such binding would be blocked when phosphoinhibitor-1 or microcrystin LR bind to this surface. The same general structure of the catalytic domain is seen in calcineurin.

Calcineurin (PP-2B) Calcineurin is a Ca^{2+}–calmodulin-dependent phosphatase that is highly enriched in the brain.[84] It is a heterodimer with a 60-kDa A subunit (CnA) that contains an N-terminal catalytic domain and a C-terminal regulatory domain that includes an autoinhibitory segment, a calmodulin-binding domain, and a binding site for the 19-kDa regulatory B subunit (CnB). CnB is a calmodulin-like Ca^{2+}-binding protein that binds to a hinge region of CnA. Regulation of calcineurin takes place in this region because it controls access of phosphoproteins to the catalytic site. Some activation of calcineurin is attained by binding of Ca^{2+} to CnB. Stronger activation is obtained by the binding of Ca^{2+}–camodulin.

The substrate specificity of calcineurin does not appear to be as broad as that of PP-1, and that of calcineurin and CaM kinase II has little overlap. Thus, a rise in Ca^{2+} does not lead to a futile cycle of phosphorylation and dephosphorylation by these Ca^{2+}–calmodulin-dependent enzymes. However, their Ca^{2+}–calmodulin sensitivity is quite different, and weak or low-frequency stimuli may selectively activate calcineurin, whereas strong or high-frequency stimuli activate CaM kinase II and calcineurin. This difference may play a role in bidirectional control of synaptic strength by low- and high-frequency stimulation.[64]

Additional regulation may be accorded by interaction of this hinge region with cyclophilin and FKBP, proteins that bind the immunosuppressive agents cyclosporin and FK506, respectively. The FK506-binding protein, or FKBP, is highly abundant in the brain, and its distribution resembles that of calcineurin. Both FK506 and cyclosporin A are membrane permeant and are highly potent and selective inhibitors of calcineurin. They are referred to as immunophilins because their ability to block the essential role of calcineurin in lymphocyte activation makes them effective immunosuppressants. The X-ray structure of calcineurin complexed with FK506 reveals a ternary complex in which FK506 is bound at the interface between FKBP and the regulatory domain of CnA.[88] Unlike calmodulin, CnB does not completely wrap around its target. CnB binds to one surface of an extended regulatory domain and FKBP–FK506 binds to the opposite surface. The FK506–FKBP complex is wedged between the regulatory domain and the catalytic site and likely inhibits calcineurin by making it difficult for phosphoproteins to have access to the catalytic site. The physiological role of FKBP and whether a natural ligand functions like FK506 to facilitate its interaction with calcineurin are not known.

Protein Kinases, Protein Phosphatases, and Their Substrates Are Integrated Networks

Cross talk between protein kinases and protein phosphatases is key to their ability to integrate inputs into neurons.[89] Such cross talk is exemplified by the interaction of cyclic AMP and Ca^{2+} signals through PKA and calcineurin, respectively. The medium spiny neurons in the neostriatum receive cortical inputs from glutamatergic neurons that are excitatory and nigral inputs by dopaminergic neurons that inhibit them. A possible signal transduction scheme for this regulation is shown in Fig. 10.17. The key to the regulation is the bidirectional control of DARPP-32 phosphorylation.[49] See Box 10.2. Glutamate activates calcineurin by increasing intracellular Ca^{2+}, leading to the dephosphor-

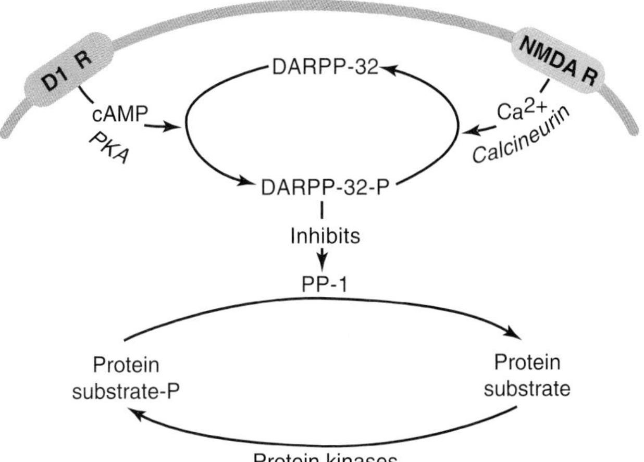

FIGURE 10.17. Cross talk between kinases and phosphatases. The state of phosphorylation of protein substrates is regulated dynamically by protein kinases and phosphatases. In the striatum, for example, dopamine stimulates PKA, which converts DARPP-32 into an effective inhibitor of PP-1. This increases the steady-state level of phosphorylation of a hypothetical substrate subject to phosphorylation by a variety of protein kinases. This action can be countered by NMDA receptor stimulation by another stimulus that increases intracellular Ca^{2+} and activates calcineurin. PP-1 is deinhibited and dephosphorylates the phosphorylated substrate when calcineurin deactives DARPP-32-P. Adapted from Greengard *et al.*[49]

BOX 10.2

INTERACTIONS OF SIGNAL TRANSDUCTION PATHWAYS IN THE BRAIN

An understanding of the signal transduction mechanisms by which neurotransmitters produce their effects on their target neurons, and of the mechanisms by which coordination of various signal transduction pathways is achieved, represents a major area of research in cellular neurobiology. The dopaminoceptive medium-sized spiny neurons, located in the neostriatum, have been studied in great detail with regard to these mechanisms. Figure 10.18 illustrates a portion of what is now known about interactions of signaling mechanisms in these neurons. Activation by dopamine of D1 receptors increases cAMP, causing activation of PKA (cAMP-dependent protein kinase) and phosphorylation of DARPP-32 (*d*opamine + c*A*MP-*r*egulated *p*hospho*p*rotein; M_r, 32,000) on threonine-34. Conversely, glutamate, acting on NMDA receptors, increases $[Ca^{2+}]_i$, leading to the activation of PP2B (protein phosphatase 2B; calcineurin) and dephosphorylation of phosphothreonine-34–DARPP-32. Neurotensin, VIP, NO (nitric oxide), and some other neurotransmitters increase the phosphorylation of DARPP-32 through a variety of signaling mechanisms. Dopamine (acting on D2 receptors), CCK, GABA, and some other neurotransmitters decrease the state of phosphorylation of DARPP-32 through a variety of other signaling mechanisms. CK1 (casein-kinase 1) and CK2 (casein-kinase 2) phosphorylate DARPP-32 on residues other than threonine-34, causing it to undergo conformational changes. These changes result in phosphothreonine-34–DARPP-32 becoming a poorer substrate for PP2B (in the case of CK1) or a better substrate for PKA (in the case of CK2). Antipsychotic drugs such as Haldol increase the state of phosphorylation of DARPP-32 by blocking the dopamine-induced D2 receptor-mediated activation of PP2B.

The physiological consequences of phosphorylation of DARPP-32 on threonine-34 are profound. Thus, DARPP-32 in its threonine-34 phosphorylated, but not dephosphorylated, form acts as a potent inhibitor of PP-1 (protein phosphatase 1). PP-1 is a major serine–threonine protein phosphatase, which controls the state of phosphorylation of a variety of phosphoprotein substrates in the brain. These substrates include Na^+ channels, L-, N-, and P-type Ca^{2+} channels, the electrogenic ion pump Na^+, K^+ATPase, the NR-1 subclass of glutamate receptors, and probably many more.

In summary, the DARPP-32/PP-1 cascade provides a mechanism by which a large number of neurotransmitters act in a complex, but coordinated, fashion to regulate the state of phosphorylation and activity of a variety of ion channels, ion pumps, and neurotransmitter receptors. Adapted from Greengard *et al.*[49]

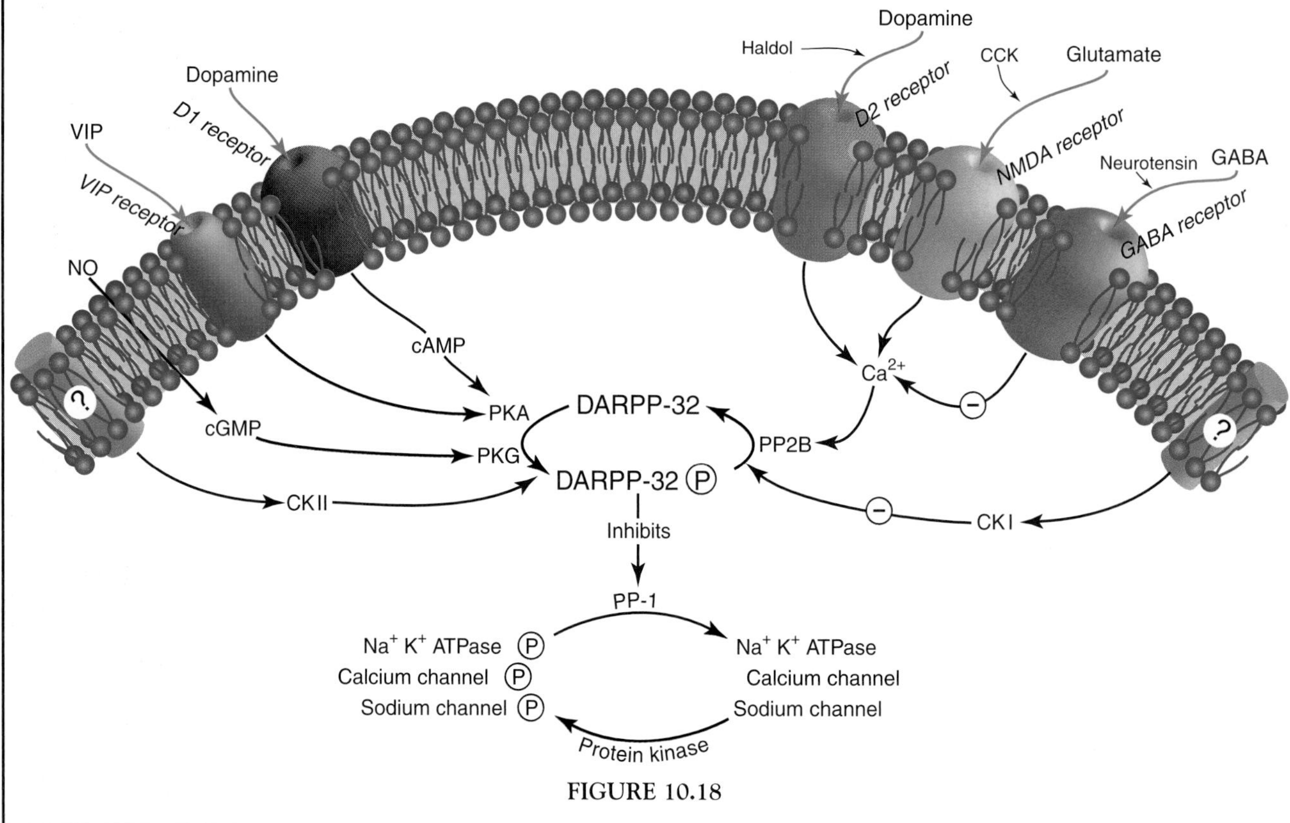

FIGURE 10.18

ylation and inactivation of phospho-DARPP-32. This releases inhibition of PP-1, which can then dephosphorylate a variety of substrates, including the Na^+,K^+-ATPase, and lead to membrane depolarization. This is countered by dopamine, which stimulates cAMP formation and activation of PKA, which then converts DARPP-32 into its phosphorylated (i.e., PP-1 inhibitory) state. Although PKA and calcineurin are acting in an antagonistic manner, they are not doing it by phosphorylating and dephosphorylating the ATPase. By their actions upstream, at the level of DARPP-32, the regulation of numerous target enzymes (e.g., Ca^{2+} channels and Na^+ channels) in addition to the ATPase can be coordinated.

Studying Cellular Processes Controlled by Phosphorylation–Dephosphorylation Requires a Set of Criteria

Major goals of signal-transduction research are to delineate pathways by which signals such as neurotransmitters transduce their signals, usually across the plasma membrane, and to determine how the transduced signal is transmitted to the ultimate cellular components that are to be modified by the extracellular signal. Many signaling components are yet to be discovered; in other circumstances, which of the known pathways are utilized by a given physiological stimulus is unclear. For the transmission of the signal, the question is often, "Which kinase(s) and which phosphatase(s) are responsible for the phosphorylation?" For the sake of brevity, a number of criteria for testing whether a particular kinase is responsible for mediating some physiological effect are listed in Table 10.6, and the necessary reagents for such an analysis are given in Tables 10.7 and 10.8. Similar criteria can be set up for identifying the relevant phosphatase.

Summary

A cell's morphology is determined by protein constituents. Its function is regulated by the phosphorylation or dephosphorylation of the proteins. Phosphorylation modifies the function of regulatory proteins subsequent to their genetic expression. The activities of the protein kinases and protein phosphatases are typically regulated by second messengers and extracellular ligands. Kinases and phosphatases integrate and encode stimulation of a large group of cellular receptors. The number of possible effects is almost limitless and enables the tuning of cellular processes over a broad time scale. The kinases that regulate phosphorylation can exhibit conformational changes that potentiate the activity of the kinase. This may be one of the key elements in molecular memory and neuronal plasticity. Most of the effects of Ca^{2+} in cells are mediated by calmodulin, which in turn mediates changes in protein phosphorylation–dephosphorylation. The phosphoinositol signaling system is mediated through protein kinase C, which modulates many cellular processes from exocytosis to gene expression. All three classes of enzymes discussed have been described as cognitive kinases because they are capable of sustaining their activated states after their second-messenger stimuli have returned to basal levels. PKA has been implicated in learning and memory in *Aplysia* and in hippocampus, where it is involved in long-term potentiation. Protein phosphatases play an equally important role

TABLE 10.6 Criteria for Identifying the Protein Kinase(s) That Mediates Effects of a Stimulus

1. The second messengers of the kinase should be increased by the physiological stimulus (if the kinase is activated in a conventional manner).
2. The kinase is activated by the physiological stimulus and by an increase in its second messenger *in situ*.
3. Pharmacological agents that increase kinase activity or introduction of an activated kinase into cells should lead to phosphorylation of the target substrate and elicit its physiological effects.
4. Genetic manipulations that increase expression of the kinase or introduce a recombinant kinase into cells should lead to phosphorylation of the target substrate and elicit its physiological effects.
5. Selective inhibition of the kinase or a block of its activation should inhibit the phosphorylation and the physiological effects of cell stimulation.
6. Genetic disruption of kinase expression should block the phosphorylation and its effects in response to cell stimulation.
7. Phosphorylation of the target substrate by the kinase *in vitro* produces the same change in function that is seen *in situ*.
8. The site(s) of phosphorylation of the target substrate by the kinase *in vitro* overlaps with the site(s) modified *in situ*.

TABLE 10.7 Tools and Strategies for Increasing Kinase Activity

Microinjection of constitutively active kinase	PKA: Purified C subunit CaM kinase II: Autothiophosphorylated kinase or catalytic fragment made by proteolytic removal of its autoinhibitory domain PKC: Catalytic fragment made by proteolytic removal of its autoinhibitory domain
Transfection of cDNA encoding a constitutively active kinase	PKA: Normal C subunit construct CaM kinase II: Construct in which the autoinhibitory domain is disrupted by substituting aspartic acid for Thr-286 to simulate autophosphorylation or by truncating the domain PKC: Construct lacking the pseudosubstrate sequence
Increase second-messenger or pharmacological analog	PKA: Cell-permeable cAMP analogs (cAMP, 8-Br-cAMP, Sp-cAMPS) CaM kinase II: Increase intracellular Ca^{2+} by depolarization or with ionophore, introduce excess calmodulin PKC: Brief addition of cell-permeable DAG analog (e.g., TPA or DiC8)
Microinjection of reagents that stabilize the activated conformation	PKA: Not available CaM kinase II: Not available PKC: Pseudo-RACK peptide that simulates stabilization of active PKC by endogenous RACKs

TABLE 10.8 Tools and Strategies for Decreasing Kinase Activity

Microinjection of inhibitory peptide or protein	PKA: Excess regulatory subunit or PKI CaM kinase II: e.g., autocamtide-3I or CaMK(273-302) PKC: e.g., PKC(19-36)
Transfection of cDNA for inhibitory peptide or protein	PKA: cyclic AMP-unresponsive R subunit, PKI CaM kinase II: Autoinhibitory domain PKC: Minigene encoding PKC(19-36)
Transfection of a dominant negative mutant that complexes with its substrates or disrupts its targeting	PKA: Not available CaM kinase II: An inactive construct that coassembles and reroutes endogenous kinase away from its normal target PKC: An inactive construct that competes for binding to its RACKs.
Addition of pharmacological inhibitors	PKA: Rp-cAMPS (a cell-permeable antagonist) CaM kinase II: e.g., KN62, which blocks activation by calmodulin PKC: e.g., chelerythrine or calphostin C
Microinjection of antibody to the kinase	
Microinjection of anchoring displacing peptide	PKA: AKAP-binding peptide, e.g., Ht31 CaM kinase II: Not available PKC: RACK-binding peptide, e.g., Peptide I
Stimulate proteolytic degradation of kinase	PKA: Not available CaM kinase II: Not available PKC: Downregulation by chronic exposure to DAG analog (e.g., TPA)
Elimination of endogenous kinase by targeted gene knockout or antisense	

in neuronal signaling by dephosphorylating proteins. Cross talk between protein kinases and protein phosphatases is key to their ability to integrate inputs into neurons. A major effort of signal transduction research is to delineate the pathways through which the neurotransmitters' signals across the plasma membrane are transmitted to the ultimate cellular components to be modified.

THE REGULATION OF TRANSCRIPTION

The signal transduction systems described so far regulate the function of cellular proteins once expressed; another critical level of control exerted by these systems is their ability to regulate the synthesis of cellular proteins by regulating the expression of genes. For all living cells, regulation of gene expression by extracellular signals is a fundamental mechanism of development, homeostasis, and adaptation to the environment. Protein phosphorylation and regulation of gene expression by extracellular signals are the most important mechanisms underlying the remarkable degree of plasticity exhibited by neurons. Alterations in gene expression underlie many forms of long-term changes in neural functioning, with a time course that ranges from hours to many years. Indeed, much evidence suggests that formation of long-term memories in many neural systems requires changes in gene expression and new protein synthesis. In the remainder of this chapter, we will focus on general principles of gene regulation by extracellular signaling leading to intracellular signaling and specific examples that illustrate these principles particularly well.

Interactions of DNA Sequences with Regulatory Proteins (Transcription Factors) Control Both Basal and Extracellular-Signal-Regulated Transcription

As a stable, unreactive, linear polymer, the double helix of DNA is an ideal molecule for the storage of information; when transiently unwound, it can be readily replicated or serve as a template for the synthesis of other macromolecules: enzymes processing down its length can add a succession of nucleotides complementary to those in the template strand. However, its chemical simplicity and relatively rigid helical structure limit its functions in the cell to information storage and transfer. The information contained within DNA must therefore be expressed through other molecules: RNA and proteins. The human genome contains approximately 100,000 genes that encode structural RNAs or protein-coding messenger RNAs (mRNAs). Within genes, a fundamental distinction can be made between DNA sequences that code for RNAs—and, in the case of protein-coding genes, mRNAs that will eventually be translated—and DNA sequences that exert control functions. Certain control sequences determine the beginnings and ends of segments of DNA that can be transcribed into RNA. Other closely linked DNA sequences determine whether a potentially transcribed segment is actually transcribed in a particular cell and, if so, under what circumstances. Regulated gene expression conferred by the nucleotide sequence of the DNA itself is called *cis*-regulation because the control regions are physically linked on the DNA to the regions that can potentially be transcribed. The *cis*-regulatory sequences function by serving as high-affinity binding sites for regulatory proteins called transcription factors (or *trans*-acting factors because they may be encoded anywhere in the genome rather than on the same stretch of DNA that they regulate).

The process by which information contained in the DNA is read to yield RNA is **transcription.** For the purposes of analysis, the transcription of DNA into RNA is often divided into three steps: initiation of RNA synthesis, RNA chain elongation, and chain termination. Biologically significant regulation may occur at any of these steps; however, it is at the step of **transcription initiation** that extracellular signals, such as neurotransmitters, hormones, drugs, and growth factors, exert their most significant control over the processes that gate the flow of information out of the genome.

Transcription initiation requires two critical processes: (1) positioning of the appropriate RNA polymerase—the enzyme that synthesizes RNA from a DNA template—at the correct start site of the gene to be transcribed and (2) controlling the efficiency of initiations to produce the appropriate transcriptional rate for the circumstances of the cell.[90] The *cis*-regulatory elements that set the transcription start sites of genes are called the basal, or core, promoter. Other *cis*-regulatory elements tether additional activator and repressor proteins to the DNA to regulate the transcriptional rate.

The Core Promoter

In eukaryotic cells, transcription is carried out by three distinct RNA polymerases—RNA polymerases I, II, and III. Each of these polymerases interacts with distinct classes of genes, each of which contains a spe-

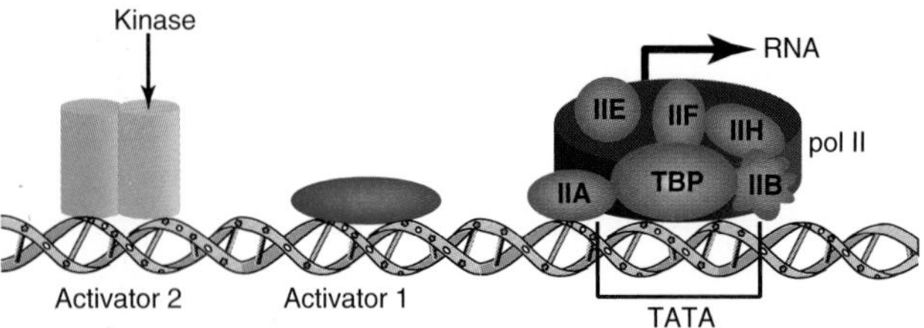

FIGURE 10.19 Schematic of a generalized polymerase II promoter, showing three separate *cis*-regulatory elements along a stretch of DNA. These elements are two hypothetical activator protein-binding sites and the TATA element. The TATA element is shown binding the TATA-binding protein (TBP). Multiple general transcription factors (IIA, IIB, etc.) and RNA polymerase II (pol II) associate with TBP. Each transcription factor comprises multiple individual proteins complexed together. This basal transcription apparatus recruits RNA polymerase II into the complex and also forms the substrate for interactions with the activator proteins binding to the activator elements shown. Activator 2 is shown to be a substrate for a protein kinase.

cific type of promoter element. Polymerase I (pol I) promoters are utilized by genes that encode large ribosonal RNAs (rRNAs). Polymerase II (pol II) promoters are utilized by genes that are transcribed to yield mRNAs and hence proteins. Pol II promoters are also used by a subset of the genes that encode the small nuclear RNAs (snRNAs) that form parts of the machinery for RNA splicing. Polymerase III (pol III) promoters are utilized by genes that encode other small RNAs, including the remainder of the snRNAs, small rRNAs, and transfer RNAs (tRNAs).

No RNA polymerase recognizes DNA regulatory sequences or binds directly; rather the polymerases are recruited to the DNA by other proteins. The promoters for each of the three polymerases contain a distinct core promoter element on which a basal transcription complex is assembled. The basal promoters of RNA polymerase I, II, and III genes bind a variety of different basal transcription factors (Fig. 10.19). Because a focus of this chapter is the regulated expression of protein-encoding genes, only transcription by RNA polymerase II will be described.

The core promoter of most of the genes transcribed by pol II is sequence rich in the nucleotides adenine (A) and thymine (T) located between 25 and 30 bases upstream of the transcription start site. This sequence is called the TATA element or TATA box. When the TATA element is mutated, transcription initiation may not occur or may be inaccurate. In addition to setting the start site of transcription, the TATA box sets the orientation of the basal transcription complex and therefore the direction in which pol II will synthesize the RNA. Certain pol II promoters, most commonly those controlling "housekeeping genes," lack a TATA box; in such cases, other specialized guanosine–cytosine (GC)-rich nucleotide sequences stand in for the TATA box.

The basal transcription complex assembled at the TATA element is sufficient to set the start site and direction of transcription and to carry out very low levels of transcription. The protein that binds the TATA box and initiates the construction of the basal transcription apparatus is called the TATA-binding protein (TBP). In humans, TBP, multiple TAFs (TBP-associated proteins), and multiple additional general transcription factors assemble with pol II to form the basal transcription complex.[91] Each of the transcription factors represented in Fig. 10.19 was originally identified as a chromatographic fraction derived from cell nuclei and is actually a mixture of multiple proteins. Thus, TBP, together with the TAFs, was originally identified as a fraction called TFIID; TFII identifys general transcription factors associated with pol II, and the final letter designates the fraction. Although it plays somewhat different roles in RNA polymerase I, II, and III promoters, TBP plays a critical role in all eukaryotic transcription and is one of the more highly conserved proteins throughout evolution.

Sequence-Specific Transcription Factors

The basal transcription apparatus is not adequate to initiate more than low levels of transcription. To achieve significant levels of transcription, this multiprotein assembly requires help from transcriptional activators that recognize and bind *cis*-regulatory elements found elsewhere within the gene. Because they are tethered to DNA by specific *cis*-regulatory recognition sequences, such proteins have been described as sequence-specific transcription factors.

Functional *cis*-regulatory elements are generally found within several hundred base pairs of the start site of the gene to which they are linked, but they can occasionally be found many thousands of base pairs away either upstream or downstream of the start site. The *cis*-regulatory elements that exert control near the core promoter itself have been called "promoter elements" and those that act at a distance have been called "enhancer elements," but the distinction between promoter and enhancer elements is artificial from a mechanistic point of view. Both are generally composed of small "modular" DNA sequences (generally 7–12 base pairs in length), each of which is a specific binding site for one or more transcription factors. Each gene has a particular combination of *cis*-regulatory elements, the nature, number, and spatial arrangement of which determine the gene's unique pattern of expression, including the cell types in which it is expressed, the times during development in which it is expressed, and the level at which it is expressed in adults both basally and in response to physiological signals.

The most important experimental approach to testing the function of putative *cis*-regulatory elements is to introduce the regulatory sequences of a gene into eukaryotic cells in culture in both their natural (wild type) and mutated forms. The introduction of recombinant DNA into eukaryotic cells is called **transfection.** In investigations of the function of *cis*-regulatory sequences, the most common strategy is to fuse the entire regulatory region of the gene to a "reporter gene," a stretch of DNA that encodes a protein that can be assayed simply and quantitatively and that ideally has no background expression in the cells being used for the experiment. Commonly used reporter genes encode such proteins as firefly luciferase, *Escherichia coli* β-galactosidase, or bacterial chloramphenicol acetyltransferase. The level of expression of the reporter gene is measured after transfection into an appropriate cell type, first when driven by the wild-type control sequences and then after mutations (either deletions, insertions, or base substitutions) in the sequences of interest. If the mutation destroys the binding site for a positively acting transcription factor, the level of expression will decrease; if a new or stronger binding site is formed, expression may increase. The general approach of mutagenesis and transfection is used not only to study gene regulation but also to dissect the functional domains of proteins. In the latter case, a reporter gene is not used; instead, the coding region of the gene under study is expressed with and without mutations, and the consequences of the mutations for the function of the protein (rather than simply the level of expression) are examined.

Sequence-specific transcription factors commonly comprise several physically distinct functional domains (Fig. 10.20). In particular, such transcription factors frequently contain (1) a domain that recognizes and binds a specific nucleotide sequence (i.e., a *cis*-regulatory element), (2) a transcription activation domain that interacts with general transcription factors to form an active transcription complex, and (3) a multimerization domain that permits the formation of homo- and heteromultimers with other transcription factors.[90] The modular nature of transcription factors was first established in experiments in which the DNA-binding domain of one protein was fused to the transcriptional activation domain of another, resulting in a perfectly functional, albeit artificial, transcriptional activator.

Many DNA-binding domains contain stretches of basic amino acid residues. Activation domains are more variable. Three major types of activation domains have been identified: acidic, proline rich, and glutamine rich. The mechanisms by which these different types of domains interact with the basal transcription apparatus or with adapter proteins that mediate the interaction with the basal transcription apparatus are not yet understood. Indeed, researchers are not certain that, within these types of domains, the acidic or glutamine residues interact directly with their targets. Bulky hydrophobic amino acids interspersed within these motifs also may play important roles in activation.

Many transcription factors are active only as dimers or higher-order complexes. Multimerization domains are diverse and include so-called leucine zippers, (which are described in the next section), Src homology SH2 domains, and certain α-helical motifs. Within active transcription-factor dimers, whether homodimers or heterodimers, both partners commonly contribute jointly to both the DNA-binding domain and the activation domain.

Dimerization can be a mechanism of either positive or negative control of transcription. This mechanism is illustrated by certain interactions within the helix–loop–helix (HLH) family of transcription factors, so named because an HLH transcription factor contains two conserved amphipathic α helices connected by an unconserved loop of variable length. These proteins dimerize through their α-helical domains; dimerization is necessary for HLH proteins to bind DNA and activate transcription. When the muscle-specific HLH protein MyoD is dimerized with the ubiquitous HLH

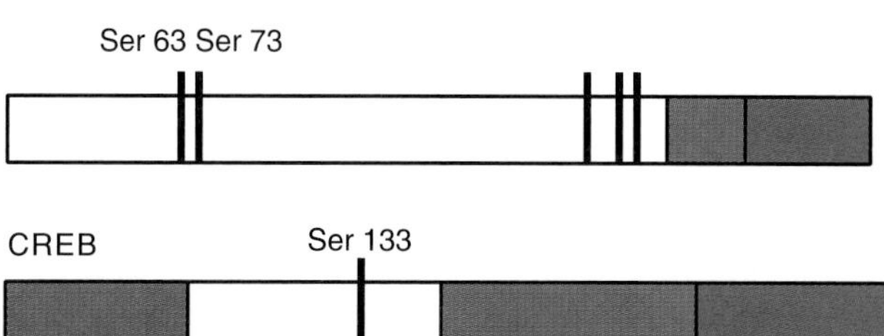

FIGURE 10.20 The modular structure of sequence-specific transcription factors. CREB is a member of the basic leucine zipper (bZIP) superfamily. The bZIP region (green) contains both a basic DNA-binding domain and a leucine zipper dimerization domain. bZIP proteins can bind DNA effectively only when dimerized with an appropriate partner. CREB contains two glutamine-rich domains (purple) that take part in transactivation. Serine-133 must be phosphorylated for CREB to be a transcriptional activator. Serine-133 can be phosphorylated by the cAMP-dependent protein kinase, Ca^{2+}–calmodulin-dependent protein kinase II, and probably other protein kinases.

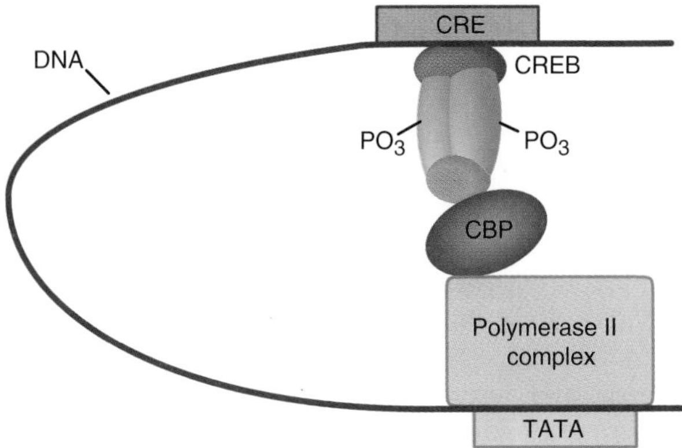

FIGURE 10.21. Looping of DNA permits activator (or repressor) proteins binding at a distance to interact with the basal transcription apparatus. The basal transcription apparatus is shown as a single box (pol II complex) bound at the TATA element. The activator protein (CREB) is shown as having been phosphorylated. On phosphorylation, many activators, such as CREB, are able to recruit adaptor proteins that mediate between the activator and the basal transcription apparatus. An adaptor protein that binds phosphorylated CREB is called CREB-binding protein (CBP).

protein E12/E47, it activates a wide variety of genes within muscle cells associated with the differentiated state of muscle. In proliferating myoblasts, however, these same muscle genes are not transcribed despite the presence of high levels of MyoD and E12/E47, because a negatively acting dimerization partner of MyoD, called Id, is expressed at high levels. Id lacks the basic DNA-binding domain that is found just N-terminal to the first α helix within HLH proteins that are transcriptional activators. MyoD-Id dimers cannot bind DNA and therefore cannot activate transcription. In other cases of negative regulation, the dimer of an activator and its negative regulator can bind DNA, but the negative regulator lacks an activation domain, thus disrupting the formation of the mature transcription complex. Overall, the ability of transcription factors to form heterodimers and other multimers increases the diversity of transcription-factor complexes that can form in cells and, as a result, increases the types of specific regulatory information that can be exerted on gene expression.

Sequence-specific transcriptional activator and repressor proteins may produce an active transcription complex by contacting one or more proteins within the basal transcription complex. Frequently, however, they do not interact with the basal transcription apparatus directly but through the mediation of adapter proteins[92,93] (Fig. 10.21). In either of these scenarios, transcription factors that bind at a distance from the core promoter can interact with the basal transcription apparatus because the DNA forms loops that bring distant regions in contact with each other.

A Significant Consequence of Intracellular Signaling Is the Regulation of Transcription

Extracellular signals play a major role in the regulation of gene expression during development. Many activator proteins can participate in the assembly of the mature transcription apparatus only after an extracellular-signal-directed change in subcellular localization (e.g., from the cytoplasm to the nucleus) or a posttranslational modification, most commonly phosphorylation. Such alterations in location or conformation permit information from the environment to regulate gene expression. Extracellular signals are required for the processes of development because the genome itself does not contain enough information to produce a mature organism.

All diploid cells within an organism, starting with the fertilized one-cell embryo, contain a complete copy of the organism's genome (albeit with some rearrangements taking place in mature T and B lymphocytes). Differential expression of this common genome is required for the formation of distinct cell types during development, including the differentiation of hundreds of distinct types of neurons found in the brain (see Chapter 3). The mechanisms by which these differentiated cells form are highly dependent on intercellular signaling. Much work in this area has been done in *Drosophila* and *Xenopus,* organisms in which viable embryos can be well studied in isolation.

In certain cases, restriction of the expression of a gene to specific cell types depends on the presence of critical activator proteins only in those cell types. For example, the pituitary hormones—growth hormone and prolactin—are expressed only in pituitary lactotrophs and somatotrophs because their required positive activator, Pit 1, is expressed only in those two cell types in the mature organism.[94] In other cases, genes contain *cis*-regulatory elements that bind transcriptional repressor proteins; the presence of the repressor proteins in a particular cell type blocks expression of those genes in that cell type.[95]

The sequential expression, during development, of hierarchies of activator and repressor proteins depends initially on the asymmetric distribution of critical signaling molecules within the embryo, leading to differential gene expression within embryonic cells. As cells gain individual identities during development, cell–cell interactions mediated by contact or by the elaboration of intercellular autocrine, paracrine, or longer-range signaling continue the process of specifying the complement of genes expressed in target cells. Genes that are silent during particular phases of development may become unavailable for subsequent activation because they become wrapped in inactive chromatin structures. The mechanisms by which a subset of genes is permanently silenced in some cells and rendered potentially active in others are not well understood.

Transcriptional Regulation by Extracellular Signals

Most and possibly all protein-encoding genes contain *cis*-regulatory sequences that permit the genes to which they are linked to be activated or repressed by physiological signals; such sequences are sometimes called **response elements**. Response elements work by binding transcription factors that are activated or inhibited by specific physiological signals, such as phosphorylation.

Extracellular signals can activate transcription factors through a variety of different general mechanisms, but each requires a translocation step by which the signal is transmitted from the cell membrane to the nucleus. Some transcription factors are themselves translocated to the nucleus. For example, the transcription factor NF-κB is retained in the cytoplasm by its binding protein IκB; this interaction masks the NF-κB nuclear localization signal. Signal-regulated phosphorylation of IκB by protein kinase C and other protein kinases leads to dissociation of NF-κB, permitting it to enter the nucleus; IκB may then be proteolyzed within the cytoplasm. Other transcription factors must be phosphorylated or dephosphorylated to bind DNA. For example, in many cytokine-signaling pathways, tyrosine phosphorylation at the membrane of transcription factors known as signal transducers and activators of transcription (STATs) permits multimerization, which in turn permits both nuclear translocation and construction of an effective DNA-binding site within the multimer. Yet other transcription factors are already bound to their cognate *cis*-regulatory elements within the nucleus under basal conditions and become able to activate transcription after phosphorylation. The transcription factor CREB, for example, is constitutively bound to cAMP response elements (CREs) found within many genes. The critical nuclear translocation step in CREB activation involves not the transcription factor itself, but the catalytic subunit of protein kinase A, which, upon entering the nucleus, can phosphorylate CREB. Phosphorylation of CREB converts it into its active state by permitting it to interact with the adapter protein CBP, which can then contact the basal transcription apparatus (see Fig. 10.21).

Role of cAMP and Ca^{2+} in the Activation Pathways of Transcription

As described earlier, the cAMP second-messenger pathway is among the best characterized intracellular signaling pathways; a major feature of signaling by this pathway is the regulation of a large number of genes. cAMP response elements have been identified in many genes expressed in the nervous system, including those encoding somatostatin, proenkephalin, vasoactive intestinal polypeptide, tyrosine hydroxylase, and the transcription factor c-Fos. CREs were historically among the first response elements to be characterized, with the use of methods such as deletion and base substitution followed by transfection into cultured cells. An idealized consensus sequence can be derived by comparing response element sequences that have been investigated by mutagenesis within many genes. For CREs, the consensus nucleotide sequence is TGACGTCA, with the nucleotides CGTCA absolutely required. Indeed, mutations that altered the CGCTA core of a CRE rendered it incapable of conferring cAMP responsiveness on a gene. We now know that this occurred because the element could no longer bind CREB.

The consensus CRE sequence illustrates a common feature of many transcription-factor-binding sites; it is a palindrome. Examination of the sequence TGACGTCA readily reveals that the sequences on the two complementary strands, which run in opposite directions, are identical (Fig. 10.22). Many *cis*-regulatory elements are perfect or approximate palindromes because many transcription factors bind DNA as dimers, in which each member of the dimer recognizes one of the "half sites." CREB binds to CREs as a homodimer, with a higher affinity for perfectly palindromic than for asymmetric CREs.

Cyclic AMP response element (CRE)

5' TGACGTCA 3'

3' ACTGCAGT 5'

AP-1 Element

5' TGACTCA 3'

3' ACTGAGT 5'

FIGURE 10.22. The palindromic structure of consensus CRE and activator protein 1 (AP-1) elements. Palindromes or near palindromes are common features of *cis*-regulatory elements that bind transcription factors as dimers. For CREs, perfect palindromes, such as the sequence shown, which was first identified within the somatostatin promoter, are the strongest binding sites for CREB homodimers. Slightly asymmetric CREs, such as the sequence TGCGTCA found within the proenkephalin promoter, bind CREB homodimers with slightly lower affinity. CREB binding under most circumstances appears to require an intact CGTCA motif. Some variant CRE sequences may bias a *cis*- regulatory element to the binding of heterodimers. The AP-1 sequence is palindromic, as it flanks a core C or G. Most AP-1 proteins bind this sequence as heterodimers.

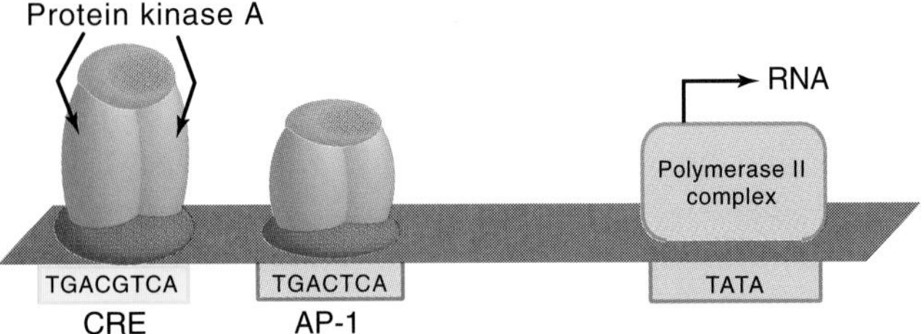

FIGURE 10.23 A generalized promoter containing CRE and AP-1 sites. In the hypothetical gene shown, a CREB family heterodimer is bound to a consensus CRE sequence and a Fos-Jun heterodimer is bound to a consensus AP-1 site. Many neural genes contain both CREs and AP-1 sites, including the tyrosine hydroxylase gene. Such genes could be activated by multiple signaling pathways, including the cAMP-dependent protein kinase (protein kinase A) and protein kinase C.

When bound to a CRE, CREB activates transcription when it is phosphorylated on its Ser-133. It does so, as described earlier, because phosphorylated CREB, but not unphosphorylated CREB, can recruit the adapter protein, CBP, into the transcription complex. CBP, in turn, interacts with the basal transcription complex. CBP is itself a phosphoprotein, but the significance of CBP phosphorylation is not yet understood.

The regulation of CREB activation by phosphorylation illustrates several general principles, including the requirement for nuclear translocation of protein kinases in cases where transcription factors are already found in the nucleus under basal conditions and the role of phosphorylation in regulating protein–protein interactions. An additional important principle illustrated by CREB is the convergence of signaling pathways. CREB is phosphorylated on Ser-133 by the free catalytic subunit of the cAMP-dependent protein kinase (Figs. 10.23 and 10.24). However, CREB Ser-133 can also be phosphorylated by Ca^{2+}–calmodulin-dependent protein kinases types II and IV[96] and by RSK2, a kinase activated in growth-factor pathways including Ras and MAP kinase.[97] When each individual signal is relatively weak, convergence may be a critical mechanism resulting in specificity of gene regulation, with some genes being activated only when multiple pathways are stimulated. Some genes that contain CREs are known to be induced in more than additive fashion by the interaction of cAMP and Ca^{2+}, but how convergent phosphorylation on the same serine might produce synergy is not yet clear. Synergy is more readily understood in cases in which a particular protein is modified at two different sites, causing interacting conformational changes. In addition to Ser-133, CREB contains sites for phosphorylation by a variety of protein kinases, including glycogene synthase kinase 3 (GSK3), but the biological effects of phosphorylating these additional serines are not yet well understood. These additional phosphorylation events may fine-tune the regulation of CREB-mediated transcription.

The convergent activation of a single transcription factor by multiple signaling pathways is particularly important in the nervous system, because convergent activation is an important candidate mechanism for long-term memory. Associative memory depends on the temporally closely coordinated arrival of two different signals that must then be integrated within target cells and circuits. The attractiveness of hippocampal long-term potentiation as a candidate mechanism for certain types of long-term memory is based in part on the need for simultaneous activation of two different inputs for its initiation (see Chapter 55). Invertebrate models, such as *Aplysia* and *Drosophila,* provide evidence that at least some forms of long-term memory

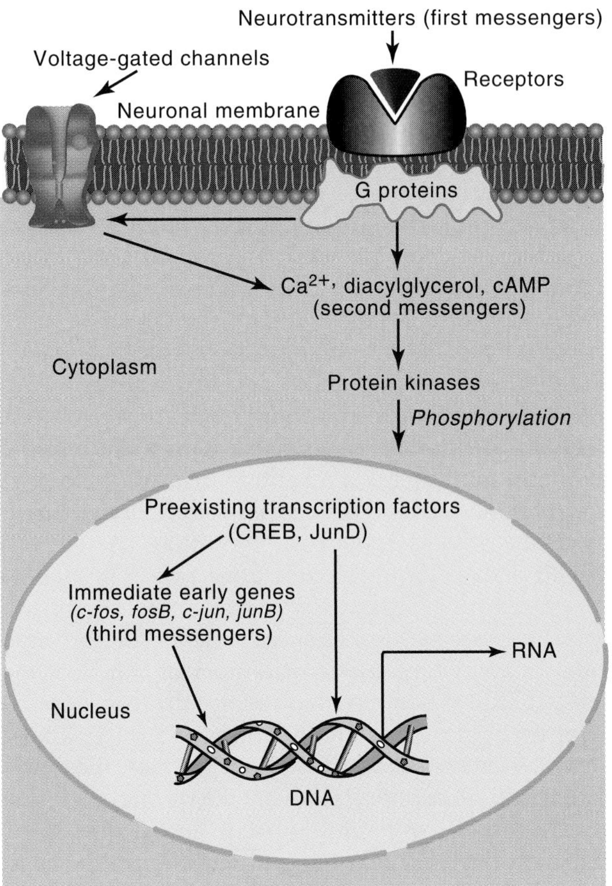

FIGURE 10.24 Signal transduction to the nucleus. In this schematic, activation of a neurotransmitter receptor activates cellular signals (G proteins and second-messenger systems). These signals, in turn, regulate the activation of protein kinases, which translocate to the nucleus. Within the nucleus, protein kinases can activate genes regulated by constitutively synthesized transcription factors. A subset of these genes encodes additional transcription factors (third messengers), which can then activate multiple downstream genes.

require new gene expression. Specific evidence implicates CREB in memory formation.[98] In *Drosophila,* CREB was inactivated by a dominant negative transgene, and, in mice, CREB was inactivated by homologous recombination (one minor isoform of CREB was preserved in these mice; when it too is knocked out, the mutation is lethal to the embryo). Both manipulations yielded organisms with deficits in long-term memory.[99,100] These results must be considered preliminary, however; inactivation of even a subset of the isoforms of an important transcription factor, such as CREB in the mouse brain, may produce subtle developmental abnormalities not readily detected by light microscopic examination. Such abnormalities could interfere in multiple indirect ways with long-term memory. Despite these experimental problems, which will soon be dealt with by means of improved targeting technologies for gene inactivation, the implication of CREB's involvement in memory is quite exciting, especially because CREB is at the intersection of two major neural signaling pathways, the cAMP and Ca^{2+} pathways, both of which are known to be involved in memory. The mechanisms underlying the many forms of plasticity of which the nervous system is capable are likely to be quite complex, requiring a multitude of different target genes and many different types of regulation. Nevertheless, the control of transcription factor CREB provides a good model for investigating molecular mechanisms that could underlie important long-term alterations in neural signaling.

CREB illustrates yet another important principle of transcriptional regulation: CREB is a member of a family of related proteins. Many transcription factors are members of families; this permits complex forms of positive and negative regulation, as described earlier for the HLH protein MyoD. CREB is closely related to other proteins called activating transcription factors (ATFs) and CRE modulators (CREMs), which result from alternative splicing of a single CREM gene. All of these proteins bind CREs as dimers; many can dimerize with CREB itself. ATF-1 appears to be very similar to CREB; it can be activated by both the cAMP and Ca^{2+} pathways. Many of the other ATF proteins and CREM isoforms can activate transcription; however, certain CREMs may act to repress it. These CREM isoforms lack the glutamine-rich transcriptional activation domain of CREB–ATF family members that are activators of transcription. Thus CREB–CREM homodimers may bind DNA but fail to activate transcription. Like CREB, many of the ATF proteins are constitutively synthesized, but ATF 3 and certain CREM isoforms are inducible in response to environmental stimuli. The new synthesis of transcription factors is yet another mechanism of gene regulation.

The dimerization domain used by the CREB–ATF proteins and several other families of transcription factors is called a leucine zipper. This domain was first identified in transcription factor C/EBP and is also utilized by the AP-1 family of transcription factors. The so-called leucine zipper actually forms a coiled coil. The dimerization motif is an α helix in which every seventh residue is a leucine; based on the periodicity of α helices, the leucines line up along one face of the helix two turns apart. The aligned leucines of the two dimerization partners interact hydrophobically and stabilize the dimer. In CREB, C/EBP, and the AP-1 family of proteins, the leucine zipper is at the carboxy terminus of the protein. Just upstream of the leucine zipper is a region of highly basic amino acid residues that forms the DNA-binding domain. Dimerization by means of the leucine zipper domain juxtaposes the adjacent basic regions of each of the partners; these juxtaposed basic regions undergo a conformational change when they bind DNA. The interaction of these proteins with DNA has been described as a "scissors grip." This combination of motifs is why this superfamily of proteins is referred to as the basic leucine zipper proteins (bZIPs).

AP-1 Transcription Factors

In addition to the CREB–ATF family, activator protein 1 (AP-1) is another family of bZIP transcription factors that play a central role in the regulation of neural gene expression by extracellular signals. The name AP-1 was originally applied to a transcriptional activity that was subsequently found to comprise multiple proteins that bind as heterodimers (and a few as homodimers) to the DNA sequence TGACTCA, the AP-1 sequence. As shown in Fig. 10.22, the consensus AP-1 sequence is a heptamer that forms a palindrome flanking a central C or G. The AP-1 sequence differs from the CRE sequence by only a single base. Yet this one-base difference strongly biases protein binding away from CREB (which requires an intact CGTCA motif) to the AP-1 family of proteins and means that, in most circumstances, this sequence will not confer cAMP responsiveness on a gene. Instead AP-1 sequences confer responsiveness to the protein kinase C pathway; thus the AP-1 sequence is sometimes described as a TAP-response element (TRE) because the phorbol ester 12-*O*-tetradecanoylphorbol 13-acetate (TPA), which activates protein kinase C, can induce gene expression through AP-1 proteins.

The transcription-factor-encoding genes *c-fos* and *c-jun* were first studied not in their cellular forms but in the form of viral oncogenes that could produce neoplastic transformation of cultured cells. The *fos* and *jun* oncogenes were first isolated as the retroviral-transforming genes of the FBJ murine osteosarcoma virus and the avian sarcoma virus 17, respectively. As with many retroviral-transforming genes, both were derived by mutation of normal cellular homologs (c-*fos* and c-*jun*) that could function as components of growth-factor-signaling pathways potentially involved in cell proliferation. The normal cellular counterparts of retroviral-transforming genes are often called cellular proto-oncogenes.

The AP-1 proteins generally bind DNA as heterodimers composed of one member each of two different families of related bZIP proteins, the Fos family and the Jun family. The known members of the Fos family are c-Fos, Fra-1 (Fos-related antigen-1), Fra-2, and FosB, although there is evidence that additional Fras are likely to exist. The known members of the Jun family are c-Jun, JunB, and JunD. Heterodimers form between proteins of the Fos family and proteins of the Jun family by means of the leucine zipper. Unlike the Fos proteins, c-Jun and JunD, but not JunB, can form homodimers that bind to AP-1 sites, albeit with far lower affinity than Fos–Jun heterodimers. The potential complexity of transcriptional regulation is greater still because some AP-1 proteins can heterodimerize through the leucine zipper with members of the CREB–ATF family, for example, ATF2 with c-Jun. AP-1 proteins can also form higher-order complexes with unrelated families of transcription factors. AP-1 proteins can complex with and thus apparently inhibit the transcriptional activity of steroid hormone receptors. AP-1 proteins also form a complex with unrelated transcription factors containing the Rel DNA-binding and dimerization domain to form the nuclear factor of activated T cells (NF-AT). NF-AT takes part in the transduction of T-cell-receptor activation into activation of the interleukin-2 gene. However, this complex transcription factor clearly has other biological functions and is found in the nervous system.

Among the known Fos and Jun proteins, only JunD is expressed constitutively at high levels in many cell types. The other AP-1 proteins tend to be expressed at low or even undetectable levels under basal conditions but, with stimulation, may be induced to high levels of expression. Thus, unlike genes that are regulated by constitutively expressed transcription factors such as CREB, genes that are regulated by c-Fos–c-Jun heterodimers require new transcription and translation of their required regulatory factors.

Cellular Immediate-Early Genes

Genes that are transcriptionally activated by synaptic activity, drugs, and growth factors have often been classified roughly into two groups. Genes, such as the c-*fos* gene itself, that are activated rapidly (within minutes), transiently, and without requiring new protein synthesis are often described as cellular immediate-early genes (IEGs). Genes that are induced or repressed more slowly (within hours) and are dependent on new protein synthesis have been described as late-response genes. The term IEG was initially applied to describe viral genes that are activated "immediately" upon infection of eukaryotic cells by utilization of preexisting host-cell transcription factors. Viral immediate-early genes generally encode transcription factors needed to activate viral "late" gene expression. This terminology has been extended to cellular (i.e., nonviral) genes with varying success. The terminology is problematic because many cellular genes are induced independent of protein synthesis, but with a time-course intermediate between "classical" IEGs and late-response genes. In fact, some genes may be regulated with different time courses or requirements for protein synthesis in response to different extracellular signals. Moreover, many cellular genes regulated as IEGs encode proteins that are not transcription factors. Despite these caveats, the concept of IEG-encoded transcription factors in the nervous system is a useful heuristic. Because of their rapid induction from low basal levels in response to neuronal depolarization (the critical signal being Ca^{2+} entry) and second-messenger and growth-factor pathways, several IEGs have been used as cellular markers of neural activation, permitting novel approaches to functional neuroanatomy (Box 10.3).

The protein products of those cellular IEGs that function as transcription factors bind to *cis*-regulatory elements contained within a subset of late-response genes to activate or repress them. As illustrated in Fig. 10.24, IEGs such as c-*fos* have therefore been termed third messengers in signal transduction cascades, with neurotransmitters designated as intercellular first messengers, and small intracellular molecules, such as cAMP and Ca^{2+}, as second messengers. However, IEGs are not always a necessary step in extracellular-signal-regulated expression of genes having roles in the differentiated function of neurons. In fact, many such genes, including many genes encoding neuropeptides such as proenkephalin[104] and prodynorphin[105] and some genes encoding neurotrophic factors, are activated in response to neuronal depolarization or cAMP by phosphorylation of the constitutively expressed transcription factor CREB rather than by IEG third messengers. In sum, neural genes that are regulated by extracellular signals are activated or repressed with varying time courses by reversible phosphorylation of constitutively synthesized transcription factors and by newly synthesized transcription factors, some of which are regulated as IEGs.

BOX 10.3

USE OF IMMEDIATE-EARLY GENE INDUCTION AS ANATOMIC MARKERS OF NEURONAL ACTIVATION

Because c-*fos* and several other cellular IEGs, including c-*jun*, *junB*, and *zif/268* (*egr-1*), are strongly and rapidly induced in response to a variety of neural stimuli, they have become the most widely used markers in functional neuroanatomy. For example, under unstimulated conditions, c-*fos* mRNA and c-Fos protein are nearly undetectable in many cell types. However, neural stimuli that induce cAMP, Ca^{2+}, protein kinase C, Ras/MAP kinase, or Jak/STAT pathways (see Fig. 10.27) produce a rapid and powerful induction of c-*fos* gene expression. The lack of background expression and high levels of induction contribute to the sensitivity of this approach. Immunohistochemical detection of c-Fos and other IEG-encoded proteins and, more recently, *in situ* hybridization for their mRNAs have become standard tools for mapping cells and circuits activated by neurotransmitters, drugs, growth factors, cytokines, and injury. This approach has been facilitated by the wide availability of antisera recognizing c-Fos and similarly regulated proteins.

The major problems with the use of IEGs to map cellular activation are the lack of response of most IEGs to inhibitory neurotransmission, the observation that not all cell types express c-*fos* (although essentially all cells express one IEG or another), and, given the sensitivity of the technique, the possibility of inducing c-*fos* or other IEGs even by nonspecific stresses. Despite these drawbacks, the sensitivity, cellular resolution, and utility, with respect to diverse stimuli, of c-Fos immunohistochemistry and other IEG mapping techniques have led to their having been applied to a large number of paradigms, including many investigations relevant to psychiatry. For example, IEGs have been used to map pathways activated by sensory stimuli, such as nociceptive stimuli (Fig. 10.25). They have also been used to map the cellular targets of pharmacologic agents. For example, IEG mapping has been used to study differences in the target cells of D_2 dopamine receptor antagonist antipsychotic drugs such as haloperidol and atypical antipsychotic drugs such as clozapine. Haloperidol was shown to induce expression of c-*fos* mRNA[101] and c-Fos-like immunoreactivity[101–103] in the caudate putamen as well as in the limbic regions of the rat striatum, such as the nucleus accumbens.[101,102] In contrast, clozapine was shown to include c-Fos protein only in the nucleus accumbens, but not in the caudate putamen.[101,103] Experiments such as these demonstrate that, though both typical and atypical antipsychotic drugs affect the terminal fields of mesolimbic dopamine projections, only the typical drugs affect the terminal fields of the nigrostriatal pathway. Such findings help explain the lack of extrapyramidal side effects seen with clozapinelike drugs and suggest a potentially useful screen for the likelihood that a given drug will cause extrapyramidal symptoms referable to the caudate putamen.

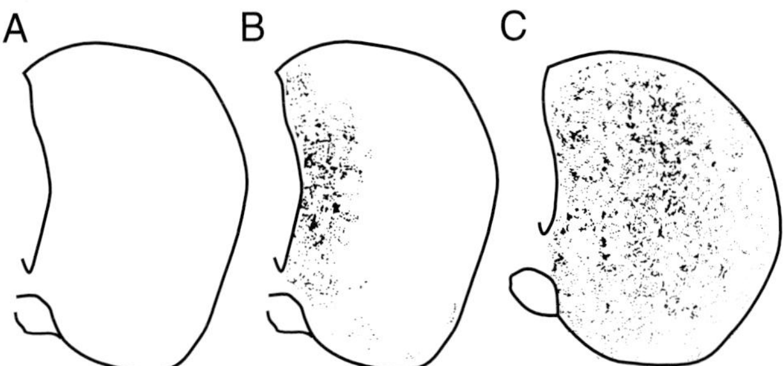

FIGURE 10.25 Fos mapping has been used to study patterns of cellular activation in the striatum in response to cocaine and amphetamine. Illustrated below is a camera lucida drawing of the rat striatum prior to stimulation (A) and then after low (B) and high (C) doses of amphetamine. Each stipple represents a Fos-positive nucleus as determined by immunohistochemistry with a monoclonal antibody against c-Fos.

Altering the Composition of Transcription Complexes

Subsequent to the acute stimulation of cells—and depending on the precise stimulus—different proteins of the Fos and Jun families are induced with varying time courses of expression, which leads to a succession of different AP-1 protein complexes. Thus, for example, c-Fos is induced more rapidly than Fras or FosB and is degraded more rapidly. JunB can be induced rapidly by cAMP, but c-Jun generally requires the activation of additional signaling pathways to be induced above its basal levels. The resulting complexes can provide great specificity to the regulation of target genes. Experimentally, the procession of different Fos and Jun family members induced over time can be documented by protein immunoblots. The changing composition of AP-1 complexes that can bind to DNA can be analyzed by means of a technique called electrophoretic mobility shift assays (EMSA) using antisera specific for the different transcription factors. EMSA, which has proved extremely important in the study of transcription factor–DNA interactions generally, is a simple method of detecting high-affinity binding of proteins to DNA (Fig. 10.26).

Under resting conditions within most neuronal cell types, c-*fos* mRNA and protein are barely detectable; c-*fos* gene expression can be induced dramatically in response to a variety of stimuli. For example, many early experiments showed the induction of high levels of c-*fos* mRNA within 30 min and high levels of c-Fos protein within 2 h in brain regions such as the hippocampus, subsequent to the induction of a generalized seizure. Similarly, administration of cocaine or amphetamine causes a marked induction of c-*fos* gene expresison in the rat striatum. In either of these stimulus paradigms, *fras* also are induced, but with a longer temporal latency than c-*fos;* their peak levels of expression lag behind that of c-*fos* by approximately 1 h. With repeated stimulation, the c-*fos* gene becomes refractory to further activation (i.e., its expression is desensitized); however, certain *fras* and *fosB* gene products continue to be expressed. In sum, in the early time periods after acute induction of a seizure, administration of cocaine, or other stimuli, the predominant Fos family member found within AP-1 complexes is c-Fos itself. With chronic stimulation, c-Fos is no longer detectable within AP-1 complexes, and the predominant Fos family members within these complexes are low-molecular-weight Fras, which appear to be truncated products of the *fosB* gene. Although the precise biological significance of these changes in the composition of AP-1 complexes over time is not yet known, these changes are thought to produce precisely varying patterns of expression of AP-1-regulated genes, permitting neu-

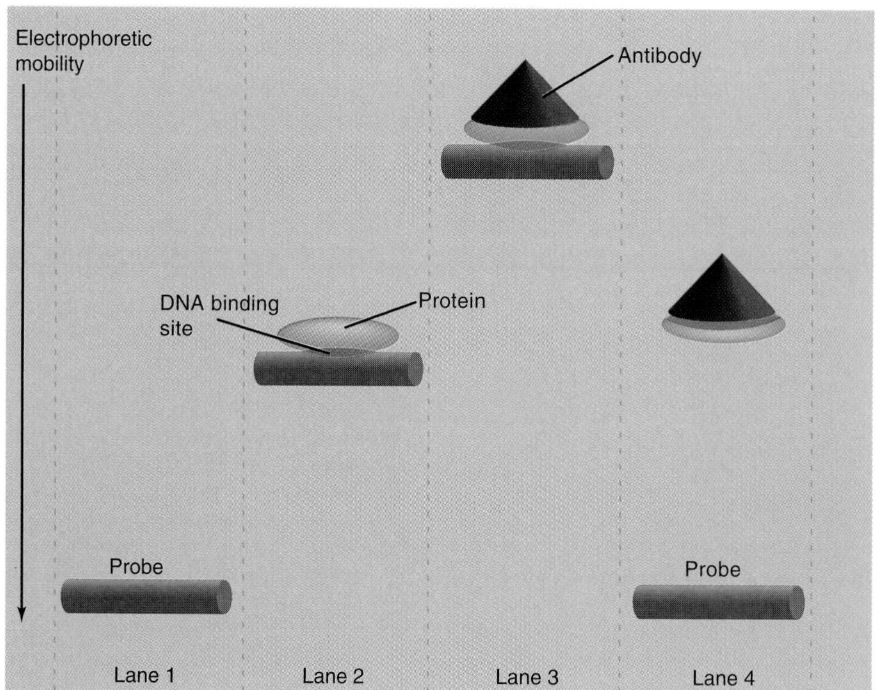

FIGURE 10.26 Schematic depiction of an electrophoretic mobility shift assay. The first lane shows the migration of an unbound radiolabeled oligonucleotide (free probe) on a nondenaturing gel. Experimentally, the position of the probe would be visualized by autoradiography. The second lane shows that with protein binding, and therefore increased molecular weight, the oligonucleotide migrates more slowly; therefore, the band detected by autoradiography is shifted upward. In the presence of an antibody that recognizes the transcription factor that binds the oligonucleotide probe, the complex is even larger, resulting in a greater upward band shift (or supershift), as shown in the third lane. Alternatively, if the antibody recognizes the binding domain of the protein, it may disrupt complex formation, as shown in the last lane.

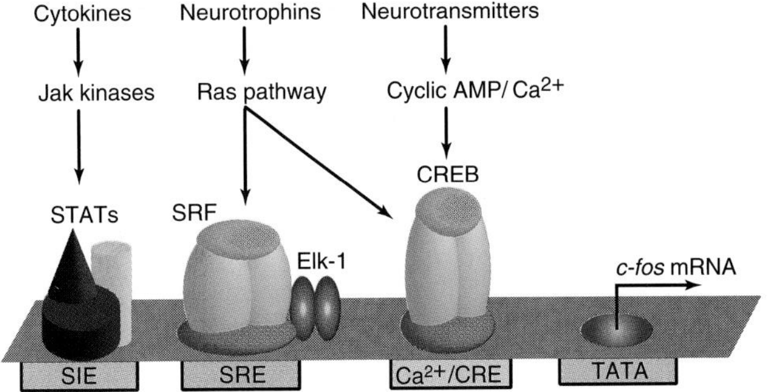

FIGURE 10.27 The regulatory region of the c-*fos* gene, showing only three of the known transcription-factor-binding sites within the c-*fos* gene: (1) a CRE, which binds CREB; (2) a serum response element (SRE), which binds serum response factor (SRF) and the ternary complex factor Elk-1; and (3) a SIS inducible element (SIE), which binds STAT proteins. Proteins binding at each of these sites are constitutively present in cells and are activated by phosphorylation. CREB is activated by the cAMP-dependent protein kinase and Ca^{2+}-dependent protein kinases, Elk-I is activated by the MAP kinases ERK1–ERK2, and the STAT proteins by the Janus (Jak) kinases. Thus activation of c-*fos* by multiple pathways depends only on signal-regulated phosphorylation rather than on new protein synthesis.

rons to adapt to the pattern of stimulation to which they are being subjected.

Activation of the c-fos Gene

The c-*fos* gene is activated rapidly by neurotransmitters or drugs that stimulate the cAMP pathway or Ca^{2+} entry. Both pathways produce phosphorylation of transcription factor CREB.[96] The c-*fos* gene contains three binding sites for CREB, the best studied of which is shown in Fig. 10.27. The c-*fos* gene can also be induced by the Ras / MAP kinase pathway, which is activated by a number of growth factors. For example, neurotrophins, such as nerve growth factor (NGF), bind a family of receptor tyrosine kinases (Trks); NGF interacts with Trk A, which activates Ras. Ras then acts through a cascade of protein kinases including Raf and the cytoplasmic MAP kinase kinases (MAPKKs) MEK1 / MEK2, which phosphorylate the MAP kinases ERK1 / ERK2. These kinases translocate into the nucleus, where they can activate RSK2 to phosphorylate CREB, but they can also apparently directly phosphorylate other transcription factors such as the ternary complex factor Elk-1. Elk-1 binds along with the serum response factor (SRF) to the serum response element (SRE) within the c-*fos* gene and many other growth-factor-inducible genes (Fig. 10.27). Cross talk between neurotransmitter and growth-factor-signaling pathways has been documented with increasing frequency and likely plays an important role in the precise tuning of neural plasticity to diverse environmental stimuli.

Regulation of c-Jun

Expression of most of the proteins of the Fos and Jun families that constitute transcription factor AP-1 and the binding of AP-1 proteins to DNA is regulated by extracellular signals. However, both Fos and Jun family members are phosphoproteins themselves and AP-1-mediated transcription requires not only the new synthesis of AP-1 proteins but also the phosphorylation of proteins within AP-1 complexes. Phosphorylation of c-Jun on Ser-63 and Ser-73 within its N-terminal activation domain has been shown to markedly enhance its ability to activate transcription without affecting its ability to form dimers or bind DNA.[106] Other phosphorylation sites within c-Jun regulate its ability to bind DNA.

Phosphorylation and activation of c-Jun can result from the action of Jun N-terminal kinase (JNK), also termed stress-activated protein kinase (SAPK) because it was initially shown to be activated by cellular stressors such as ultraviolet radiation, heat shock, and hyperosmolar conditions.[102,106,107] SAPK–JNK is a member of the mitogen-activated protein kinase (MAPK) family of protein kinases whose mammalian members include the ERKs, p38, and SAPK–JNK. In addition to cellular stressors, the inflammatory cytokines interleukin-1β (IL-1β) and tumor necrosis factor α (TNFα) have been shown to activate both SAPK–JNK and p38. SAPK–JNK has also been shown to be activated by neurotransmitters, including glutamate. Thus, AP-1-mediated transcription within the nervous system requires multiple steps beginning with the activation of genes encoding AP-1 proteins.

Cytokines as Inducers of Gene Expression in the Nervous System

With regard to function, the boundary between trophic, or growth, factors and cytokines in the nervous system has become increasingly arbitrary. However, cell-signaling mechanisms offer a useful means of distinction. Growth factors, such as the neurotrophins (e.g., nerve growth factor, brain-derived neurotrophic factor, and neurotrophin 3), epidermal growth factor (EGF), and fibroblast growth factor (FGF), act through receptor protein tyrosine kinases, whereas the cytokines, such as leukemia inhibitory factor (LIF), ciliary neurotrophic factor (CNTF), and interleukin-6 (IL-6), act through nonreceptor protein tyrosine kinases.

LIF, CNTF, and IL-6 subserve a wide array of overlapping functions inside and outside the nervous system, including hematopoietic and immunologic functions outside the nervous system and regulation of neuronal survival, differentiation, and in certain circumstances, plasticity within the nervous system.

These peptides have marked homologies of their tertiary structures rather than their primary sequences, which presumably permits them to interact with related receptor complexes that contain a common signal-transducing subunit, gp130.

The receptors for these cytokines consist of a signal-transducing β component, which includes gp130 and, in some cases, additional subunits. As is typical of cytokine receptors, the cytoplasmic tails of the signal-transducing β components of the IL-6, LIF, and CNTF receptors lack kinase domains. Rather, the cytoplasmic domains interact with nonreceptor protein tyrosine kinases (PTKs) of the Janus kinase (Jak) family, which include Jak1, Jak2, and Tyk2. Some cytokine receptors, such as the prolactin receptor, which interacts exclusively with Jak2, can interact only with a single Jak PTK. In contrast, the IL-6, LIF, and CNTF receptors can interact with multiple Jak PTKs, including Jak1, Jak2, and Tyk2. Presumably, the dimerization of receptors on ligand binding permits Jak-family PTKs to cross-phosphorylate each other.

Signal transduction to the nucleus includes tyrosine phosphorylation by the Jak PTKs of one or more of the STAT proteins mentioned earlier. The first STAT family members were identified as proteins binding to interferon-regulated genes but have subsequently been found to take part in the activity of multiple cytokines. Upon phosphorylation, STAT proteins form dimers through the association of SH2 domains, an important type of protein interaction domain described earlier. Dimerization is thought to trigger translocation to the nucleus, where STATS bind their cognate cytokine response elements. Different STATs become activated by different cytokine receptors, not because of differential use of Jak PTKs but because of specific coupling of certain STATs to certain receptors. Thus, for example, the IL-6 receptor preferentially activates STAT1 and STAT3; the CNTF receptor preferentially activates STAT3.

The c-*fos* gene, for example, contains an element called the SIS-inducible element (SIE), which binds STAT proteins (Fig. 10.27); thus, c-*fos* gene expression can be induced by cytokines. Cytokine response elements have now been identified within many neural genes, including vasoactive intestinal polypeptide and several other neuropeptide genes.

Steroid Hormone Receptors

The differentiation of many cells types in the brain is established by exposure to steroids. For example, exposure to estrogen or testosterone during critical developmental periods results in sexually dimorphic development of certain nuclei. The steroid hormones, including the glucocorticoids, sex steroids, mineralocorticoids, retinoids, thyroid hormone, and vitamin D, are small lipid-soluble ligands that can diffuse across cell membranes. They act on their receptors within the cell cytoplasm in marked distinction to the other types of intercellular signals described herein. Another unique feature of the steroid family is that their receptors are transcription factors. Like other factors described in this chapter, the steroid hormone receptors are modular in nature. Each has a transcriptional-activation domain at its amino terminus, a DNA-binding domain, and a hormone-binding domain at its carboxy terminus. The DNA-binding domains recognize different types of steroid hormone response elements within the regulatory regions of genes. The DNA-binding domains of the steroid hormone receptors are described as zinc finger domains, a cysteine-rich motif that contains a zinc ion. This motif is utilized by many other transcription factors.

After having been bound by hormone, activated steroid hormone receptors translocate into the nucleus, where they bind to their cognate response elements. Such binding then increases or decreases the rate at which these target genes are transcribed, depending on the precise nature and DNA sequence context of the element.

Summary

The formation of long-term memories requires changes in gene expression and new protein synthesis. Control sequences on DNA determine which segments of DNA can be transcribed into RNA. It is at transcription initiation that extracellular signals such as neurotransmitters, hormones, drugs, and growth factors exert their most significant control. The transcription itself is carried out by RNA polymerases. The transcription is mediated by transcription factors that recruit the polymerases to the DNA. Using mutagenesis and transfection, one can study gene regulation but also dissect the functional domains of the proteins being expressed. Extracellular signals are required for the processes of development because the genome itself does not contain enough information to produce a mature organism. For example, the critical nuclear translocation step in the activation of transcription factor CREB involves the catalytic subunit of PKA, which can phosphorylate CREB on entering the nucleus. In addition, increasing evidence indicates that at least some forms of long-term memory require new gene expression.

The genes that encode the transcription factors themselves may respond quickly or slowly. These genes have been coined third messengers in signal transduction cascades. Cross talk between neurotransmitter and growth factor signaling pathways is likely to play an important role in the precise tuning of neuronal plasticity to diverse environmental stimuli.

The active, mature transcription complex is a remarkable architectural assembly of proteins assembled at the core promoter—in most cases, at a sequence called the TATA box. In addition to pol II, this complex includes TBP and a large number of associated general transcription factors, sequence-specific transcription factors, and intervening adapters. TBP, the central protein in the formation of this complex architectural array, is one of the more highly conserved proteins in evolution. A wide variety of transcription factors bound to *cis*-regulatory elements elsewhere in the gene, but permitted to interact by the looping of DNA, join in the formation of the active transcription complex. This remarkable mechanism permits cells to exert exquisite control of the genes being transcribed in a variety of situations—for example, to govern appropriate entry or exit from the cell cycle, to maintain appropriate cellular identity, and to respond appropriately to extracellular signals.

Transcription can be regulated by many different extracellular signals modulated by a large array of signaling pathways (many including reversible phosphorylation) and a complex array of transcription factors. Most of these factors are members of families and regulate transcription only as multimers. Given this complexity, the potential for very precise regulation is clear, but the mechanisms by which such precision is achieved are not fully understood. In this chapter, regulation has been illustrated by only a few of the families of transcription factors. Those chosen appear to play important roles in the nervous system and illustrate many of the basic principles of gene regulation.

References

1. Hille, B. (1992). G protein-coupled mechanisms and nervous signaling. *Neuron* **9:** 187–195.
2. Bourne, H. R., Sanders, D. A., and McCormick, F. (1990). The GTPase superfamily: A conserved switch for diverse cell functions. *Nature* **348:** 125–132.
3. Stryer, L., and Bourne, H. R. (1986). G proteins: A family of signal transducers. *Annu. Rev. Cell. Biol.* **2:** 391–419.
4. Neer, E. J. (1995). Heterotrimeric G proteins: organizers of transmembrane signals. *Cell* **80:** 249–257.
5. Cassel, D., and Selinger, Z. (1978). Mechanism of adenylate cyclase activation through the β-adrenergic receptor: catecholamine-induced displacement of bound GDP by GTP. *Proc. Natl. Acad. Sci. USA* **75:** 1455–4159.
6. Northup, J. K., Smigel, M. D., Sternweis, P. C., and Gilman, A. G. (1983). The subunits of the stimulatory regulatory component of adenylate cyclase. Resolution of the 45,000-dalton a subunit. *J. Biol. Chem.* **258:** 11369–11376.
7. Logothetis, D. E., Kurachi, Y., Galper, J., Neer, E. J., and Clapham, D. E. (1987). The $\beta\gamma$ subunits of GTP-binding proteins activate the muscarinic K^+ channel in heart. *Nature* **325:** 321–326.
8. Huang, C.-L., Slesinger, P. A., Casey, P. J., Jan, Y. N., and Jan, L. Y. (1995). Evidence that direct binding of $G_{\beta\gamma}$ to the GIRK1G protein-gated inwardly rectifying K^+ channel is important for channel activation. *Neuron* **15:** 1133–1143.
9. Clapham, D. E., and Neer, E. J. (1993). New roles for G-protein $\beta\gamma$-dimers in transmembrane signalling. *Nature* **365:** 403–406.
10. Simon, M. I., Strathmann, M. P., and Gautam, N. (1991). Diversity of G proteins in signal transduction. *Science* **252:** 802–808.
11. Sondek, J., Bohm, A., Lambright, D. G., Hamm, H. E., and Sigler, P. B. (1996). Crystal structure of a G protein $\beta\gamma$ dimer at 2.1 Å resolution. *Nature* **379:** 369–374.
12. Wall, M. A., Coleman, D. E., Lee, E., Iniguez-Lluhi, J. A., Posner, B. A., Gilman, A. G., and Sprang, S. R. (1996). The structure of the G protein heterotrimer $G_{i\alpha1}\beta_1\gamma_2$. *Cell* **83:** 1047–1058.
13. Conklin, R. B., Farfel, Z., Lustig, K. D., Julius, D., and Bourne, H. R. (1993). Substitution of three amino acids switches receptor specificity of $G_q\alpha$ to that of $G_i\alpha$. *Nature* **369:** 274–276.
14. Coleman, D. E., Berghuis, A. M., Lee, E., Linder, M. E., Gilman, A. G., and Sprang, S. R. (1994). Structures of active conformations of $G_{i\alpha1}$ and the mechanism of GTP hydrolysis. *Science* **265:** 1405–1412.
15. Sondek, J., Lambright, D. G., Noel, J. P., Hamm, H. E., and Sigler, P. B. (1994). GTPase mechanism of G proteins from the 1.7 Å crystal structure of transducin α-GDP-ALF_4^-. *Nature* **372:** 276–279.
16. Ross, E. M. (1989). Signal sorting and amplification through G protein-coupled receptors. *Neuron* **3:** 141–152.
17. Taussig, R., and Gilman, A. G. (1995). Mammalian membrane-bound adenylyl cyclases. *J Biol Chem* **270:** 1–4.
18. Krupinski, J., Coussen, F., Bakalyar, H. A., Tang, W.-J., Feinstein, P. G., Orth, K., Slaughter, C., Reed, R. R., and Gilman, A. G. (1989). Adenylyl cyclase amino acid sequence: possible channel- or transporter-like structure. *Science* **244:** 1558–1564.
19. Tang, W.-J., and Gilman, A. G. (1991). Type-specific regulation of adenylyl cyclase by G protein $\beta\gamma$ subunits. *Science* **254:** 1500–1503.
20. Bourne, H. R., and Nicoll, R. (1993). Molecular machines integrate coincident synaptic signals. *Cell* **72:** 65–75.
21. Wayman, G. A., Impey, S., Wu, Z., Kindsvogel, W., Prichard, L., and Storm, D. R. (1994). Synergistic activation of the type I adenylyl cyclase by Ca^{2+} and G_s-coupled receptors in vivo. *J. Biol. Chem.* **269:** 25400–25405.
22. Federman, A. D., Conklin, B. R., Schrader, K. A., Reed, R. R., and Bourne, H. R. (1992). Hormonal stimulation of adenylyl cyclase through G_i-protein $\beta\gamma$ subunits. *Nature* **356:** 159–161.
23. Divecha, N., and Irvine, R. F. (1995). Phospholipid signaling. *Cell* **80:** 269–278.
24. Berridge, M. J. (1993). Inositol trisphosphate and calcium signalling. *Nature* **361:** 315–325.
25. Clapham, D. E. (1995). Calcium signaling. *Cell* **80:** 259–268.
26. Braun, A. P., and Schulman, H. (1995). The multifunctional calcium/calmodulin-dependent protein kinase: From form to function. *Annu. Rev. Physiol.* **57:** 417–445.
27. Takai, Y., Kishimoto, A., Kikkawa, U., Mori, T., and Nishizuka, Y. (1979). Unsaturated diacylglycerol as a possible messenger for the activation of calcium-activated, phospholipid-dependent protein kinase system. *Biochem. Biophys. Res. Commun.* **91:** 1218–1224.
28. Tanaka, C., and Nishizuka, Y. (1994). The protein kinase C family for neuronal signaling. *Annu. Rev. Neurosci.* **17:** 551–567.
29. Hokin, L. E., and Hokin, M. R. (1955). Effects of acetylcholine on the turnover of phosphoryl units in individual phospholipids of

pancreas slices and brain cortex slices. *Biochim. Biophys. Acta* **18:** 102–110.
30. Nishizuka, Y. (1995). Protein kinase C and lipid signaling for sustained cellular responses. *FASEB J.* **9:** 484–496.
31. Streb, H., Irvine, R. F., Berridge, M. J., and Schulz, I. (1983). Release of Ca^{2+} from a nonmitochondrial intracellular store in pancreatic acinar cells by inositol-1,4,5-trisphosphate. *Nature* **306:** 67–69.
32. Tsien, R. W., and Tsien, R. Y. (1990). Calcium channels, stores, and oscillations. *Annu. Rev. Cell. Biol.* **6:** 715–760.
33. Carafoli, E., and Klee, C. (1998). *Calcium as a Cellular Regulator.* Oxford University Press, New York.
34. Niemeyer, B. A., Suzuki, E., Scott, K., Jalink, K., and Zuker, C. S. (1996). The Drosophila light-activated conductance is composed of the two channels TRP and TRPL. *Cell* **85:** 651–659.
35. Minta, A., and Tsien, R. Y. (1989). Fluorescent indicators for cytosolic calcium based on rhodamine and fluorescein chromophores. *J. Biol. Chem.* **264:** 8171–8178.
36. Allbritton, N. L., Meyer, T., and Stryer, L. (1992). Range of messenger action of calcium ion and inositol 1,4,5-trisphosphate. *Science* **258:** 1812–1815.
37. Cohen, P., and Klee, C. B. (1988). *Calmodulin,* Vol. 5, *Molecular Aspects of Cellular Regulation.* Elsevier, Amsterdam.
38. Ikura, M., Clore, G. M., Fronenborn, A. M., Zhu, G., Klee, C. B., and Bax, A. (1992). Solution structure of a calmodulin-target peptide complex by multidimensional NMR. *Science* **256:** 632–638.
39. Schmidt, H. H. H. W., and Walter, U. (1994). NO at work. *Cell* **78:** 919–925.
40. Furchgott, R. F., and Zawadski, J. V. (1980). The obligatory role of the endothelial cells in the relaxation of arterial smooth muscle by acetylcholine. *Nature* **288:** 373–376.
41. Schuman, E. M., and Madison, D. V. (1994). Locally distributed synaptic potentiation in the hippocampus. *Science* **263:** 532–536.
42. Garbers, D. L., and Lowe, D. G. (1994). Guanylyl cyclase receptors. *J. Biol. Chem.* **269:** 30741–30744.
43. Stryer, L. Visual excitation and recovery. *J. Biol. Chem.* **266:** 10711–10714.
44. Wickman, K. D., Iñiguez-Lluhi, J. A., Davenport, P. A., Taussig, R., Krapivinsky, G. B., Linder, M. E., Gilman, A. G., and Clapham, D. E. (1994). Recombinant G-protein $\beta\gamma$-subunits activate the muscarinic-gated atrial potassium channel. *Nature* **368:** 255–257.
45. Delcour, A. H., and Tsien, R. W. (1993). Altered prevalence of gating modes in neurotransmitter inhibition of N-type calcium channels. *Science* **259:** 980–984.
46. Kleuss, C., Scherübl, H., Hescheler, J., Schultz, G., and Wittig, B. (1992). Different β-subunits determine G-protein interaction with transmembrane receptors. *Nature* **358:** 424–426.
47. Kleuss, C., Scherübl, H., Hescheler, J., Schultz, G., and Wittig, B. (1993). Selectivity in signal transduction determined by γ subunits of heterotrimeric G proteins. *Science* **259:** 832–834.
48. Rosenmund, C., Carr, D. W., Bergeson, S. E., Nilaver, G., Scott, J. D., and Westbrook, G. L. (1994). Anchoring of protein kinase A is required for modulation of AMPA/kainate receptors on hippocampal neurons. *Nature* **368:** 853–856.
49. Greengard, P., Snyder, G., Fisone, G., and Aperia, A. (1996). Interactions of signal transduction pathways in the nervous system. In *Challenges and Perspectives in Neuroscience* (D. Ottoson, ed.), pp. 3–26. Pergamon, London.
49a. Ferrell, J. E., Jr. and Machledes, G. M. (1998). The biochemical basis of an all-or-none cell fate switch in *Xenopus* oocytes. *Science* **280:** 895–898.
50. Hunter, T. (1995). Protein kinases and phosphatases: The yin and yang of protein phosphorylation and signaling. *Cell* **80:** 225–236.
51. Nairn, A. C., Hemmings, H. C., Jr., and Greengard, P. (1985). Protein kinases in the brain. *Annu. Rev. Biochem.* **54:** 931–976.
52. Scott, J. D. (1991). Cyclic nucleotide-dependent protein kinases. *Pharmac. Ther.* **50:** 123–145.
53. Hanks, S. K., and Hunter, T. (1995). Protein kinases 6. The eukaryotic protein kinase superfamily: kinase (catalytic) domain structure and classification. *FASEB J.* **9:** 576–596.
54. Kennelly, P. J., and Krebs, E. G. (1991). Consensus sequences as substrate specificity determinants for protein kinases and protein phosphatases. *J. Biol. Chem.* **266:** 15555–15558.
55. Walsh, D. A., and Patten, S. M. V. (1994). Multiple pathway signal transduction by the cAMP-dependent protein kinase. *FASEB J.* **8:** 1227–1236.
56. Kemp, B. E., Faux, M. C., Means, A. R., House, C., Tiganis, T., Hu, S.-H., and Mitchelhill, K. I. (1994). Structural aspects: Pseudosubstrate and substrate interactions. In *Protein Kinases* (J. R. Woodgett, ed.), pp. 30–67.
57. Su, Y., Dostmann, W. R., Herberg, F. W., Durick, K., Xuong, N. H., Ten Eyck, L., Taylor, S. S., and Varughese, K. I. (1995). Regulatory subunit of protein kinase A: Structure of deletion mutant with cAMP binding domains. *Science* **269:** 807–813.
58. Dell'Acqua, M. L., and Scott, J. D. (1997). Protein kinase A anchoring. *J. Biol. Chem.* **272:** 12881–12884.
59. Schulman, H., and Braun, A. (1998). Ca^{2+}/calmodulin-dependent protein kinases. In *Calcium as a Cellular Regulator* (E. Carafoli and C. Klee, eds.) Oxford University Press, New York.
60. Saitoh, T., and Schwartz, J. H. (1985). Phosphorylation-dependent subcellular translocation of a Ca^{2+}/calmodulin-dependent protein kinase produces an autonomous enzyme in *Aplysia* neurons. *J. Cell Biol.* **100:** 835–842.
61. Miller, S. G., and Kennedy, M. B. (1986). Regulation of brain type II Ca^{2+}/calmodulin-dependent protein kinase by autophosphorylation: A Ca^{2+}-triggered switch. *Cell* **44:** 861–870.
62. Hanson, P. I., Kapiloff, M. S., Lou, L. L., Rosenfeld, M. G., and Schulman, H. (1989). Expression of a multifunctional Ca^{2+}/calmodulin-dependent protein kinase and mutational analysis of its autoregulation. *Neuron* **3:** 59–70.
63. Meyer, T., Hanson, P. I., Stryer, L., and Schulman, H. (1992). Calmodulin trapping by calcium-calmodulin-dependent protein kinase. *Science* **256:** 1199–1201.
64. Lisman, J. (1994). The CaM kinase II hypothesis for the storage of synaptic memory. *Trends Neurosci.* **17:** 406–412.
65. Newton, A. C. (1995). Protein kinase C: Structure, function, and regulation. *J. Biol. Chem.* **270:** 28495–28498.
66. Kraft, A. S., and Anderson, W. B. (1983). Phorbol esters increase the amount of Ca^{2+} phospholipid-dependent protein kinase associated with plasma membrane. *Nature* **301:** 621–623.
67. Zhang, G., Kazanietz, M. G., Blumberg, P. M., and Hurley, J. H. (1995). Crystal structure of the cys2 activator-binding domain of protein kinase C delta in complex with phorbol ester. *Cell* **81:** 917–924.
68. Ron, D., Chen, C. H., Caldwell, J., Jamieson, L., Orr, E., and Mochly-Rosen, D. (1994). Cloning of an intracellular receptor for protein kinase C: a homolog of the beta subunit of G proteins. *Proc. Natl. Acad. Sci. USA* **91:** 839–843.
69. Muramatsu, M., Kaibuchi, K., and Arai, K. (1989). A protein kinase C cDNA without the regulatory domain is active after transfection in vivo in the absence of phorbol ester. *Mol. Cell. Biol.* **9:** 831–836.
70. Mochly-Rosen, D., and Gordon, A. S. (1998). Anchoring proteins for protein kinase C: a means for isozyme selectivity. *FASEB J.* **12:** 35–42.

71. Klauck, T. M., Faux, M. C., Labudda, K., Langeberg, L. K., Jaken, S., and Scott, J. D. (1996). Coordination of three signaling enzymes by AKAP79, a mammalian scaffold protein. *Science* **271:** 1589–1592.
72. Bacskai, B. J., Hochner, B., Mahaut-Smith, M., Adams, S. R., Kaang, B. K., Kandel, E. R., and Tsien, R. Y. (1993). Spatially resolved dynamics of cAMP and protein kinase A subunits in Aplysia sensory neurons. *Science* **260:** 222–226.
73. Wen, W., Meinkoth, J. L., Tsien, R. Y., and Taylor, S. S. (1995). Identification of a signal for rapid export of proteins from the nucleus. *Cell* 82:463–473.
74. Schwartz, J. H. (1993). Cognitive kinases. *Proc. Natl. Acad. Sci. USA* **90:** 8310–8313.
75. Chain, D. G., Hegde, A. N., Yamamoto, N., Liu-Marsh, B., and Schwartz, J. H. (1995). Persistent activation of cAMP-dependent protein kinase by regulated proteolysis suggests a neuron-specific function of the ubiquitin system in *Aplysia. J. Neurosci.* **15:** 7592–7603.
76. Kaang, B. K., Kandel, E. R., and Grant, S. G. (1993). Activation of cAMP-responsive genes by stimuli that produce long-term facilitation in Aplysia sensory neurons. *Neuron* **10:** 427–435.
77. Huang, Y. Y., Li, X. C., and Kandel, E. R. (1994). cAMP contributes to mossy fiber LTP by initiating both a covalently mediated early phase and macromolecular synthesis-dependent late phase. *Cell* **79:** 69–79.
78. Wu., Z. L., Thomas, S. A., Villacres, E. C., Xia, Z., Simmons, M. L., Chavkin, C., Palmiter, R. D., and Storm, D. R. (1995). Altered behavior and long-term protentiation in type I adenylyl cyclase mutant mice. *Proc. Natl. Acad. Sci. USA* **92:** 220–224.
79. Hanson, P. I., and Schulman, H. (1992). Neuronal Ca^{2+}/calmodulin-dependent protein kinases. *Annu. Rev. Biochem.* **61:** 559–601.
80. Hanson, P. I., Meyer, T., Stryer, L., and Schulman, H. (1994). Dual role of calmodulin in autophosphorylation of multifunctional CaM kinase may underlie decoding of calcium signals. *Neuron* **12:** 943–956.
80a. De Koninck, P., and Schulman, H. (1998). Sensitivity of Ca^{2+}/calmodulin-dependent protein kinase II to the frequency of Ca^{2+} oscillations. *Science* **279:** 227–230.
81. Silva, A. J., Stevens, C. F., Tonegawa, S., and Wang, Y. (1992). Deficient hippocampal long-term potentiation in α-calcium-calmodulin kinase II mutant mice. *Science* **257:** 201–206.
82. Mayford, M., Wang, J., Kandel, E. R., and O'Dell, T. J. (1995). CaMKII regulates the frequency response function of hippocampal synapses for the production of both LTD and LTP. *Cell* **81:** 891–904.
83. Sacktor, T. C., Osten, P., Valsamis, H., Jiang, X., Naik, M. U., and Sublette, E. (1993). Persistent activation of the ζ isoform of protein kinase C in the maintenance of long-term potentiation. *Proc. Natl. Acad. Sci. USA* **90:** 8342–8346.
84. Shenolikar, S. (1994). Protein serine/threonine phosphatases—new avenues for cell regulation. *Annu. Rev. Cell. Biol.* **10:** 55–86.
85. Hubbard, M. J., and Cohen, P. (1993). On target with a new mechanism for the regulation of protein phosphorylation. *Trends Biochem. Sci.* **18:** 172–177.
86. Hemmings, H. C., Jr., Greengard, P., Tung, H. Y., and Cohen, P. (1984). DARPP-32, a dopamine-regulated neuronal phosphoprotein, is a potent inhibitor of protein phosphatase-1. *Nature* **310:** 503–505.
87. Goldberg, J., Huang, H., Kwon, Y., Greengard, P., Nairn, A. C., and Kuriyan, J. (1995). Three-dimensional structure of the catalytic subunit of protein serine/threonine phosphatase-1. *Nature* **376:** 745–753.
88. Griffith, J. P., Kim, J. L., Kim, E. E., Sintchak, M. D., Thomson, J. A., Fitzgibbon, M. J., Fleming, M. A., Caron, P. R., Hsiao, K., and Navia, M. A. (1995). X-ray structure of calcineurin inhibited by the immunophilin-immunosuppressant FKBP12-FK506 complex. *Cell* **82:** 507–522.
89. Cohen, P. (1992). Signal integration at the level of protein kinases, protein phosphatases and their substrates. *Trends Biochem. Sci.* **17:** 408–413.
90. Tjian, R., and Maniatis, T. (1994). Transcription activation: a complex puzzle with few easy pieces. *Cell* **77:** 5–8.
91. Goodrich, J. A., Cutler, G., and Tjian, R. (1996). Contacts in contex: promoter specificity and macromolecular interactions in transcription. *Cell* **84:** 825–830.
92. Kwok, R. P., Lundblad, J. R., Chrivia, J. C., Richards, J. P., Bachinger, H. P., Brennan, R. G., Roberts, S. G., Green, M. R., and Goodman, R. H. (1994). Nuclear protein CBP is a coactivator for the transcription factor CREB. *Nature* **370:** 223–226.
93. Arias, J., Alberts, A. S., Brindle, P., Claret, F. X., Smeal, T., Karin, M., Feramisco, J., and Montminy, M. (1994). Activation of cAMP and mitogen responsive genes relies on a common nuclear factor. *Nature* **370:** 226–229.
94. Nelson, C., Albert, V. R., Elsholtz, H. P., Lu, L. I. W., and Rosenfeld, M. G. (1988). Activation of Cell-specific expression of rat growth hormone and prolactin genes by a common transcription factor. *Science* **239:** 1400–1405.
95. Chong, J. A., Tapia-Ramirez, J., Kim, S., Toledo-Aral, J. J., Zheng, Y., Boutros, M. C., Altshuller, Y. M., Frohman, M. A., Kraner, S. D., and Mandel, G. (1995). REST: A mammalian silencer protein that restricts sodium channel gene expression to neurons. *Cell* **80:** 949–957.
96. Sheng, M., McFadden, G., and Greenberg, M. E. (1990). Membrane depolarization and calcium induce c-fos transcription via phosphorylation of transcription factor CREB. *Neuron* **4:** 571–582.
97. Xing, J, Ginty, D. D., and Greenberg, M. E. (1996). Coupling of the RAS-MAPK pathway to gene activation by RSK2, a growth factor-regulated CREB kinase. *Science* 959–963.
98. Carew, T. J. (1996). Molecular enhancement of memory formation. *Neuron* **16:** 5–8.
99. Yin, J. C. P., Wallach, J. S., Vecchio, M. D., Wilder, E. L., Zhou, H., Quinn, W. G., and Tully, T. (1994). Induction of a dominant negative CREB transgene specifically blocks long-term memory in *Drosophila. Cell* **79:** 49–58.
100. Bourtchuladze, R., Frenguelli, B., Blendy, J., Cioffi, D., Schutz, G., and Silva, A. J. (1994). Deficient long-term memory in mice with a targeted mutation of the cAMP-responsive element-binding protein. *Cell* **79:** 59–68.
101. Nguyen, T. V., Kosofsky, B., Birnbaum, R., Cohen, B. M., and Hyman, S. E. (1992). Differential expression of c-fos and zif268 in rat striatum after haloperidol, clozapine and amphetamine. *Proc. Natl. Acad. Sci. USA* **89:** 4270–4274.
102. Dragunow, M., Robertson, G. S., Faull, R. L., Robertson, H. A., and Jansen, K. (1990). D2 dopamine receptor antagonists induce fos and related proteins in rat striatal neurons. *Neuroscience* **37:** 287–294.
103. Robertson, G. S., Vincent, S. R., and Fibiger, H. C. (1992). D1 and D2 dopamine receptors differentially regulate c-fos expression in striatonigral and striatopallidal neurons. *Neuroscience* **49:** 285–296.
104. Konradi, C., Kobierski, L. A., Nguyen, T. V., Heckers, S. H., and Hyman, S. E. (1993). The cAMP-response-element-binding protein interacts, but Fos protein does not interact, with the

proenkephalin enhancer in rat striatum. *Proc. Natl. Acad. Sci. USA* **90:** 7005–7009.

105. Cole, R. L., Konradi, C., Douglass, J., and Hyman, S. E. (1995). Neuronal adaptation to amphetamine and dopamine: molecular mechanisms of prodynorphin gene regulation in rat striatum. *Neuron* **14:** 813–823.

106. Dérijard, B., Hibi, M., Wu, I-H., Barrett, T., Su, B., Deng, T., Karin, M., and Davis, R. J. (1994). JNK1: a protein kinase stimulated by UV light and Ha-Ras that binds and phosphorylates the c-Jun activation domain. *Cell* **76:** 1025–1037.

107. Kyriakis, J. M., Banerjee, P., Nikolakaki, E., Dal, T., Ruble, E. A., Ahmad, M. F., Avruch, J., and Woodgett, J. R. (1994). The stress-activated protein kinase subfamily of c-Jun kinases. *Nature* **369:** 156–160.

CHAPTER

11

Cell–Cell Communication via Gap Junctions

David C. Spray, Eliana Scemes, and Renato Rozental

Pharmacological experiments carried out by Bernard, Elliot, Loewi, and others (see Ref. 1 and Chapter 8) so severely challenged the electrical theory of synaptic transmission that, until the 1950s, all direct communication between neurons was viewed as chemically mediated. However, this dogma was changed by the demonstrations by Harry Grundfest's group[2] and by Edward Furshpan and David Potter[3] that transmission between segments of cord giant fibers in crustaceans and at the giant cord–motor synapse of the crayfish was electrically mediated. In this chapter we will focus on **electrical transmission** between neurons via **gap junctions,** contrasting that mode of communication with chemical transmission.

GAP JUNCTIONS: ANOTHER FORM OF COMMUNICATION

The electrical intracellular transmission observed by Grundfest and by Furshpan and Potter was initially termed "ephaptic" (not occurring at real synapses), a term that had been used more than a century before to describe electrical interactions between nerves placed in contact (for an extensive discussion of ephapses, see Grundfest[2]). However, because the giant fiber segments forming the nerve cord did indeed meet the synaptic criterion of anatomical discontinuity,[4] and the giant fiber–giant motor synapse exhibited the additional requirement of polarized transmission, these electrotonic synapses were a legitimate synaptic mechanism whereby nerve cells communicate with one another. Subsequently, neurons in many other arthropods, in mollusks, and even in vertebrates have been shown to be electrically coupled.[5,6]

Furshpan and Potter's experiments[3] showed that depolarizing current injected into the prefiber crosses the junctional membrane to depolarize the postfiber (Fig. 11.1). However, when the postfiber is depolarized, the electrotonic potential spread to the prefiber is small; conversely, hyperpolarization spreads well from postsynaptic to presynaptic cells, whereas antidromic depolarization is largely prevented. This junction thus exhibits rectification, with conductance in the orthodronic direction about 20 times as great as that in the opposite direction, so that action potential propagation toward the periphery is vastly favored over centrifugal conduction.

Electrical transmission in vertebrate brain was demonstrated in 1959 by Michael Bennett, Stanley Crain, and Harry Grundfest,[7] who showed that the synchronous activity of the supramedullary neurons of the puffer, a teleost fish, was due to electrical coupling. This demonstration was soon followed by numerous examples of coupling between neurons in the medullary and spinal electromotor relay nuclei of gymnotid fish and between neurons in the supramedullary and oculomotor nuclei of teleost fish, clearly establishing that electrical synaptic connections are commonly found in synchronously active neuronal populations.[8–11] Although the idea of electrical transmission in mammalian cardiac and smooth muscles became well established in the 1960s,[12] the existence of electrical synapses in mammalian brain finally was demonstrated unequivocally by Rodolfo Llinas and Henri Korn and colleagues in the early 1970s.[13–16] Electrotonic synapses between mammalian neurons have now been described virtually throughout the brain, including the sensory neocortex, olfactory bulb, cerebellar cortex, inferior olive, mesencephalic fifth nucleus, vestibular system, hypothalamus, and dendate gyrus[3,5,11,13,14,16–21]

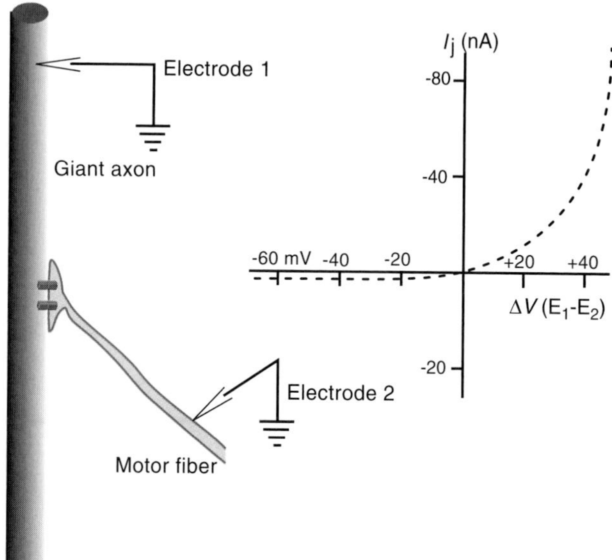

FIGURE 11.1 Anatomy and function of the rectifying electrotonic synapse between the giant axon and motor fiber mediating the escape tail flip in crayfish. Impulses normally flow from the head (not illustrated) down the giant axon in the nerve and across the electrotonic synapse to the giant motor fiber innervating the tail. The graph to the right illustrates the current (I–voltage (V) relation of this synapse when Electrode 1 polarizes the giant fiber and Electrode 2 records the current. The I–V relation strongly rectifies, so that positive (depolarizing) voltages spread well to the postsynaptic fiber, whereas negative (hyperpolarizing) voltages are strongly attenuated. For voltages applied at Electrode 2 and currents recorded at Electrode 1, the I–V relation is a mirror image across the I_j axis.

and in the retina (between cone, horizontal, bipolar, amacrine, and possibly even ganglion cells[22–24]). Because electrical synapses provide a pathway for diffusion of small tracer molecules (as described in more detail later in this chapter), intraneuronal injection of fluorescent or immunoreactive probes has now revealed that in certain brain regions and at certain developmental stages neurons do form syncytial cytoplasmic connections,[17,25] in contrast to the view of individuality that was provided by the Golgi method.

As presented in Chapters 7 and 8, the components of chemical synapses are more complicated than those of electrical synapses: not only do various gene families encode channel-forming proteins in postsynaptic membranes, but numerous other proteins take part in various aspects of the presynaptic release of vesicles containing neurotransmitters, in the binding of vesicles to the presynaptic release site, and in holding the postsynaptic receptors in arrays proximal to sites of neurotransmitter release.

When compared to the multiple steps involved in chemical neurotransmission, transmission at electrical synapses is much simpler. Driven by their electrochemical gradients, ions flow from a stimulated presynaptic cell through gap-junction channels that connect the cytoplasmic compartment of one cell with that of another, thereby changing the resting potential of the electrically coupled postsynaptic cell (Fig. 11.2). An aggregate of junctional channels is referred to as a **gap junction,** the site of the electrical synapse (Fig. 11.3).

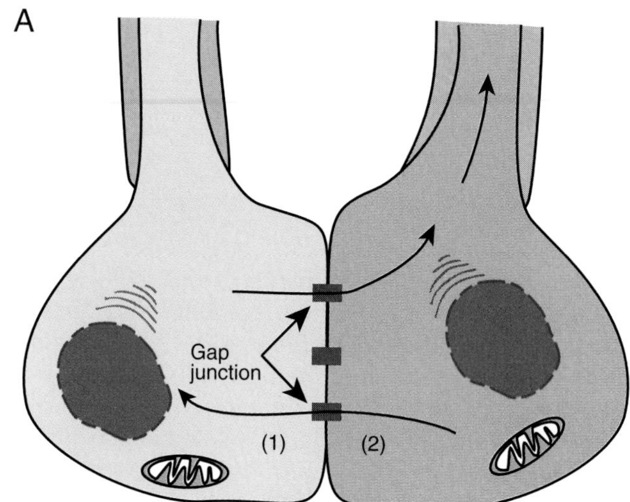

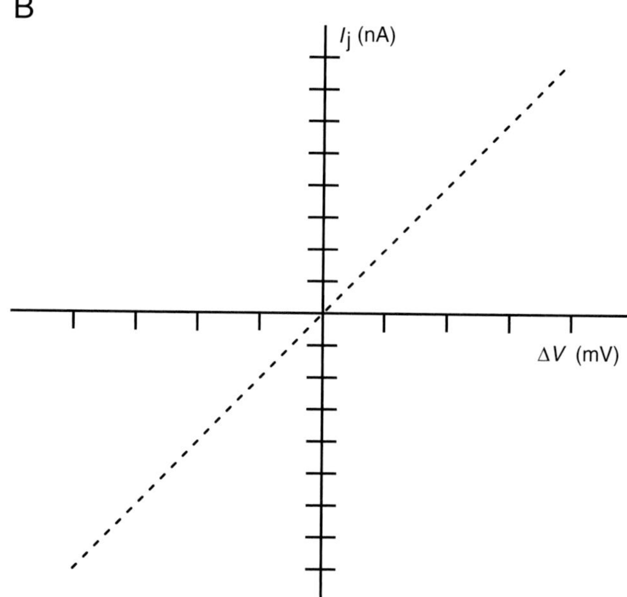

FIGURE 11.2 Bidirectional electrotonic transmission. (A) Under dual whole-cell voltage-clamp conditions, a voltage command pulse is applied to one cell (E_1 or E_2), creating transjunctional voltage ($\Delta V = E_1 - E_2$) while junctional current (I_j) that flows through gap-junction channels is measured in the other cell, whose membrane potential is maintained constant. (B) Junctional current (I_j) vs transjunctional voltage (ΔV) relation for an electrotonic synapse in which coupling is ohmic. In contrast to the rectification shown in Fig. 11.1, transmission at this electrotonic synapse is bidirectional.

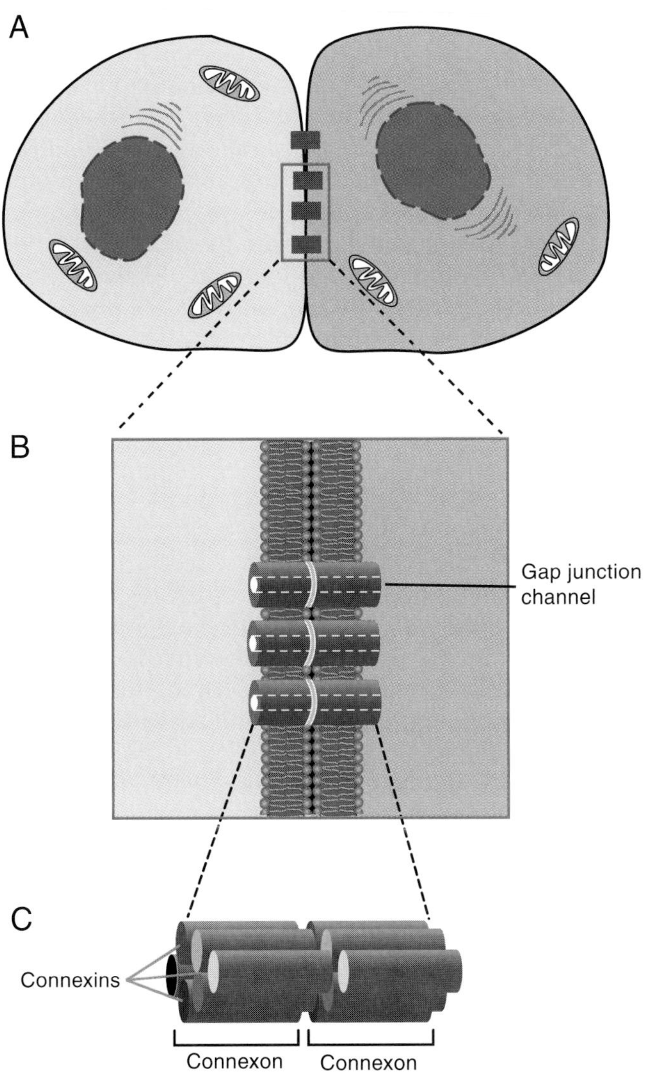

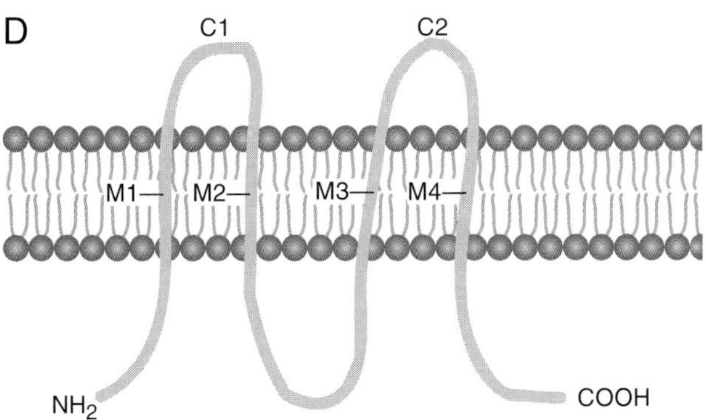

FIGURE 11.3 Diagrammatic structure of electrotonic synapses. (A) Two apposed cells linked by a junctional plaque composed of numerous gap-junction channels. (B) Three gap-junction channels in a junctional plaque. Each cell provides a hemichannel or connexon that is linked to its partner by protein domains extending across the extracellular gap. (C) The gap-junction channel is formed by two hemichannels (connexons); each connexon is formed by six identical subunits of proteins called connexins surrounding the central pore through which ions flow. (D) Membrane topology of a connexin protein showing the two extracellular loops (C1, C2), four intramembranous segments (M1, M2, M3, M4), and cytosolic carboxyl and amino terminals (COOH, NH_2).

Under most conditions, the electrical equivalent current elements describing gap-junction channels are purely resistive (although ionic driving force does dissipate under steady-state conditions owing to limited cell volume, which acts as a capacitative element).

At sites of gap-junctional contact, appositional membranes of contiguous cells tend to be planar; thus, gap junctions viewed in grazing thin section or in freeze–fracture replicas generally appear as plaques between cells (schematized in Figs. 11.3A and 11.3B). Gap-junction plaques can be quite large (as much as several micrometers across in liver, ventricular myocytes, and astroglia) or quite small (probably as small as a single channel or only a few gap-junction channels between neurons). Each gap-junction channel is made of two mirror-image, symmetric components (one contributed by each cell) called **connexons** or **hemichannels,** and each connexon in turn comprises six homologous subunits, the **connexin** molecules (Fig. 11.3C). Connexin proteins (more than a dozen of which already have been cloned and sequenced in rodents and many of which have human homologs) are encoded by a gene family with a common gene structure (a single intron separating a small upstream exon from an exon containing the entire connexin coding sequence) and common membrane topology (Fig. 11.3D).[26] In the human and mouse genomes, these single-copy genes map to at least four chromosomes, including chromosome X (see Table 11.1).[27–34]

Connexin family members are quite homologous, with about 50% sequence identity at the amino acid level, and display a diverse pattern of tissue distribution.[35,36] Each connexin molecule crosses the membrane four times (segments M1, M2, M3, and M4 in Fig. 11.3D), and both its amino and carboxy termini are on the cytoplasmic side of the membrane. Extracellular loops (C1 and C2) are structurally conserved, with three cysteine residues in each loop identically positioned in all 13 connexins (Fig. 11.3D).[26,37] Presumably, this conservative motif accounts for the high-affinity interactions between many (but not all) different connexin molecules when connexons are paired end to end.[38,39] The part of the connexin molecule between segments M2 and M3 forms a loop or hinge region in the cytoplasm whose length (long or short) separates the different connexins into α (group II) and β (group I)

TABLE 11.1 Chromosomal Locations of Mouse and Human Connexin Genes

Gene[a]	Human	Mouse	Ref.
Group I (β connexins)			
Cx26	13q11	14	Carrasquillo *et al.*[27] Haefliger *et al.*[28]
Cx30.3	1[b]	4	Hennemann *et al.*[29]
Cx31	1[b]	4	
Cx31.1	1[b]	4	Hennemann *et al.*[29]
Cx32	Xq13.1	X	Reaume *et al.*[30]
Group II (α connexins)			
Cx33	Probably X	X	Schwarz *et al.*[31]
Cx37	1p35.1	4	VanCamp *et al.*[32]
Cx40	1	3	
Cx43[b]	6q21–q23.2	10	Corcos *et al.*[33]
Cx45	1[b]	4	
Cx46	13	14	Haefliger *et al.*[28]
Cx50	1[b]	3	Kerscher *et al.*[34]

Note. This table shows the distribution of connexin genes in the mouse and human genomes. Although connexin genes are found on numerous chromosomes, some of the genes are clustered, notably on human chromosomes 1, 13, and X.

[a] Connexin genes are named according to the molecular weights predicted for the proteins encoded by their cDNA sequences.

[b] Implied by synteny with mouse chromosomes.

subfamilies (see Fig. 11.3).[26,37] The third transmembrane domain is the most amphipathic (with charged amino acid residues at every third or fourth position in a predominantly hydrophobic sequence), and six of these M3 regions may provide the hydrophilic face lining the lumen of the channel, although other domains may also contribute.[40]

Chemical and Electrical Synapses Differ in Functional Characteristics

The major functional characteristics of chemical transmission that distinguish chemical from electrotonic synapses[11] include transmission that is usually only in one direction; a delay (0.2–0.5 ms) between the pre- and postsynaptic signals necessary for transmitter release, intercellular diffusion, ligand binding, and postsynaptic channel opening; inhibitory action; and fatigue or facilitation in response to repeated stimuli. However, there are exceptions to each of these generalizations.

Directionality

Although chemical synaptic transmission is generally unidirectional and electrotonic transmission is generally bidirectional, electrotonic transmission strongly rectifies in some cases, such as the rectifying junction in crayfish[3] and in hatchetfish pectoral fin motor neurons.[41] Conversely, in the nerve net of the syphozoan jellyfish *Cyanea,* chemical transmission is bidirectional: neurotransmitter vesicles are present on both pre- and postsynaptic sides of apposed membranes, and transmission can be evoked by stimulation of either post- or presynaptic elements.[42,43] Nevertheless, the bidirectionality of most electrotonic synapses is an ideal property for the synchronization of activity, providing a mechanism by which depolarization (or hyperpolarization) can be effectively and reciprocally spread throughout the neural network.

Speed

The importance of transmission speed in "escape" or "startle" responses is obvious, with shorter reaction times exerting evolutionary pressure to select for more successful survival. Electrotonic transmission characterizes stereotypic escape behaviors of invertebrates and lower vertebrates, which are mediated by the first gap junctions to be identified with structural and electrophysiological techniques (the crayfish nerve cord and the Mauthner cells of goldfish brain[4,44]). In addition to the crayfish tail flip escape response, teleost fish brains contain a medullary Mauthner cell, where electrotonic synapses provide rapid transmission for escape from predators.[45,46] In teleosts, the rapid predator evasion is mediated by a neuronal circuit involving both chemical and electrotonic synapses. Mauthner fibers are involved in the control of the large pectoral adductor muscles, the activation of which causes the fish to jump upward. These fibers also control the axial musculature that mediates a tail flip to both sides.

The escape response circuit of certain teleost fish can be described by the following sequence of events (Fig. 11.4): peripheral sensory receptors ("hair cells") chemically activate processes of vestibular neurons in the 8th nerve, whose central projections electrotonically excite the Mauthner fibers. The Mauthner fibers make electrical synapses with the giant fibers, which then electrically excite the motor neurons, finally stimulating the muscles through chemical neuromuscular junctions.

Synaptic Inhibition

Chemical synapses can be either excitatory or inhibitory, depending on whether the net flow of ions resulting from ligand-gated opening of postsynaptic channels is depolarizing or hyperpolarizing. Thus, if the channels opened by neurotransmitter are primarily K^+ selective, the postsynaptic cell will hyperpolarize

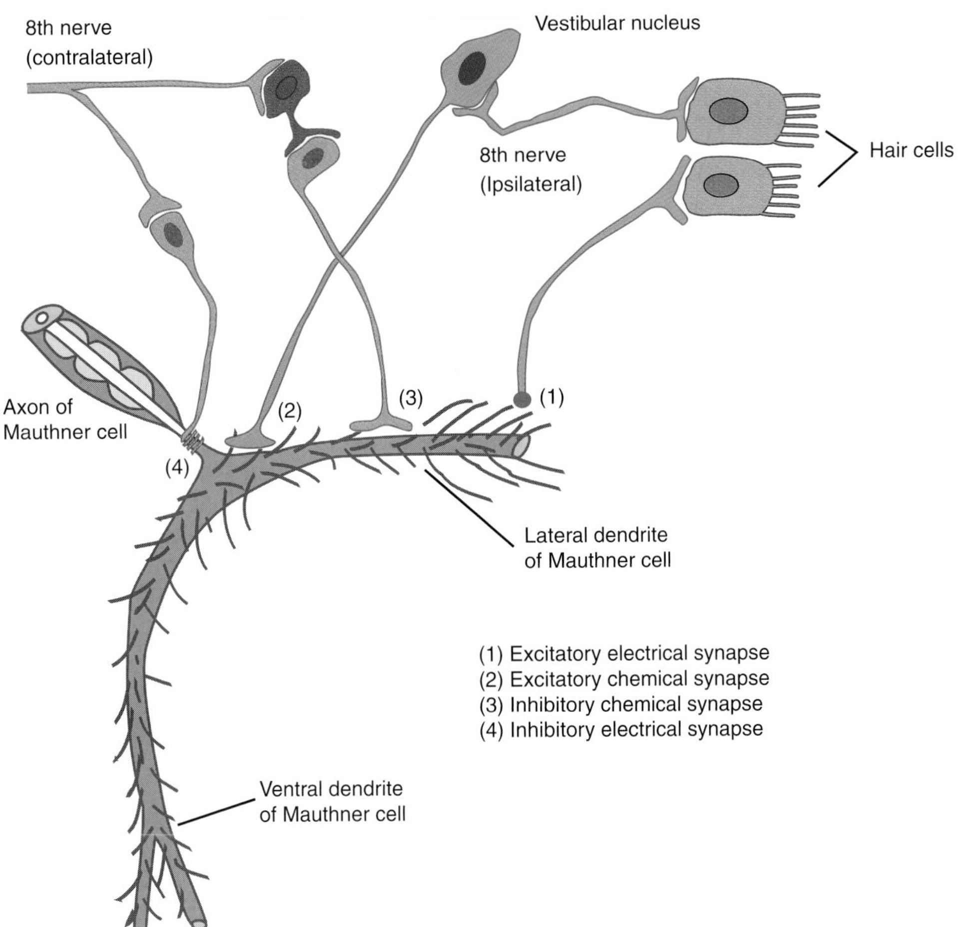

FIGURE 11.4 The Mauthner cell synapses involved in the escape response in teleost fish. From the hair cells that sense the approach of predators, the ipsilateral 8th nerve forms direct electrical excitatory synapses onto the lateral dendrite of the Mauthner cell and indirect (through the vestibular nucleus) excitatory chemical synapses onto the cell body. The contralateral 8th nerve makes two inhibitory synapses to the Mauthner cell, one chemical on the lateral dendrite and one electrical onto the cell body, both of which serve to prevent inappropriate "escape" toward the predator.

owing to K^+efflux, whereas if channels are nonselective to cations or primarily selective to Na^+, the cell will depolarize owing to Na^+ influx.

Electrotonic synapses are usually excitatory, with the depolarizing phase of the action potential giving rise to brief electrotonic postsynaptic potentials (electrotonic PSPs or "fast prepotentials") if coupling strength is low or to synchronized activity if coupling strength is high. However, electrotonic synapses can also inhibit, through electrotonic spread of hyperpolarizing chemical PSPs as well as transmission of the hyperpolarizing phase of the action potential. Such inhibitory action of contralateral 8th-nerve electrical synapse plays an important role in the escape behavior of teleost fish[47] (Fig. 11.4), so that motor neuron activation propels the animal away from the predator. In addition, the interplay between chemical and electrotonic PSPs can provide flexibility in the output from coupled neurons.

Fatigue, Facilitation, and Modulation

Plasticity is the most fascinating aspect of chemical neurotransmission, allowing the establishment and storage of memory traces. Both pre- and postsynaptic structures appear to be endowed with mechanisms by which the amplitude of the postsynaptic event can be strengthened or depressed, depending on coincidence with the activity of other synapses or with the activity pattern within the same terminal.

Although the structural simplicity of electrotonic synapses limits the degree of plasticity of their transmission, the strength of coupling can be altered by changing the junctional conductance itself, the conductance of an adjacent nonjunctional membrane, or the shape or duration of the presynaptic impulse. Junctional conductance depends on the number and type of gap-junction proteins expressed between cells, as well as the probability of these channels being open (gating, the subject of the next section). Because the turnover of gap-junction proteins is extraordinarily rapid (half-lives from synthesis to degradation may be 3 h or less for the connexins thus far assessed), transcriptional and posttranscriptional controls can in principle provide flexibility in coupling strength over this time frame. Moreover, because channels formed of different connexins exhibit different unitary conductances, sensitivity to gating stimuli, phosphorylation properties, and affinities to one another, modulation of the relative expression levels of different connexins may be an important factor in such processes as neuronal differentiation.

As mentioned earlier, the interplay between chemical and electrotonic postsynaptic potentials provides considerable flexibility in coupling strength, as illustrated by the neural circuit responsible for the ingestive phase of feeding in the opisthobranch mollusk *Navanax* (Fig. 11.5A). In this organism, coupled expansion motor neurons (Fig. 11.5B) mediate synchronized pharyngeal expansion and then become uncoupled. This uncoupling is due to shunting of chemical synaptic inputs (Fig. 11.5C) and allows the neurons to fire individually so that the pharynx can expand regionally for the peristaltic movement of the prey into the esophagus.[48,49] Because chemical synapses are generally near electrical synapses in the vertebrate nervous system, such a mechanism may commonly modulate coupling strength, as in the mammalian inferior olivary nucleus.[16,50] Interactions between expansion and circumferential motor neurons (Fig. 11.5B) are also important for peristalsis, as illustrated in Fig. 11.5D. In this case, coupling to an inhibitory interneuron reverses the sign of coupling, enabling activity in one group of motor neurons to either excite or inhibit the other, depending on the degree of activity in the populations.[51]

Another way in which the interplay between chemical and electrotonic synapses may confer plasticity is seen in cases in which coupling synchronizes chemical synaptic inputs. In the establishment of retinal–tectal connections, for example, graded strength of ganglion-cell coupling across the retina may lead to additional synchronous inputs by adjacent ganglion cells onto postsynaptic cells, thus specifically strengthening chemical synaptic connections onto appropriate targets in the optic tectum.[52–54]

Plasticity at electrotonic synapses also arises from changes in form of the presynaptic impulse, due to the time required to charge the postsynaptic membrane. Such effects may be especially significant when the postsynaptic time constant is long and the initially brief presynaptic impulse becomes prolonged by tetanic stimulation or other manipulations.[55]

Electrical Synapses Do Some Things That Chemical Synapses Cannot

Electrotonic synapses exert their postsynaptic effects through the passage of electrical current between cells. Although this current is predominantly carried by K^+ ions, owing to the high intracellular abundance and junctional permeability of this ion, the gap junctions that underlie electrotonic synapses are not nearly as selective as nonjunctional K^+ channels. Gap-junction channels are permeant to molecules whose molecular mass is as much as ~1000 Da, including the second-messenger molecules Ca^{2+}, 3′:5′-cyclic adenosine monophosphate (cAMP), and inositol 1,4,5-triphosphate (IP_3).[56] Diffusion of these molecules between coupled cells may therefore mean that levels of these second messengers are co-regulated in pre- and postsynaptic elements. Among the expected consequences of such exchange at synaptic regions having both chemical and electrotonic components is modulation of presynaptic neurotransmitter release by changes in levels of second-messenger molecules in postsynaptic cells.[57]

Gap junctions between glial cells provide a pathway for long-range metabolite delivery[58] and second-messenger signaling throughout the brain.[36,59,60] Propagation of Ca^{2+} waves through astrocyte gap junctions in response to glutamate application or mechanical stimulation has been observed both in culture and in hypothalamic slices[59,61,62] (Fig. 11.6). In most cases, this propagation is partially or completely blocked by gap-junction inhibitors, indicating that conducting gap-junction channels are required, and the Ca^{2+} waves most probably consist of intracellular release of Ca^{2+} that is triggered by Ca^{2+} and/or IP_3 diffusing across the junctional membrane.[59,63,64]

With regard to the various functions that have been proposed for gap junctions between astrocytes (dissipation of K^+ ions, regulation of cell volume, control of cell proliferation),[65–68] the spread of intercellular Ca^{2+} waves has been hypothesized to provide a mechanism by which cooperative cell activity is coordinated.[69]

The studies demonstrating that both induced and spontaneous Ca^{2+} waves spread for long distances through the astrocytic network have allowed speculation that gap-junction-mediated interactions among glia may play an active role in neuromodulation. However, calcium ion waves can also spread between cells through a paracrine route, in which extracellular aden-

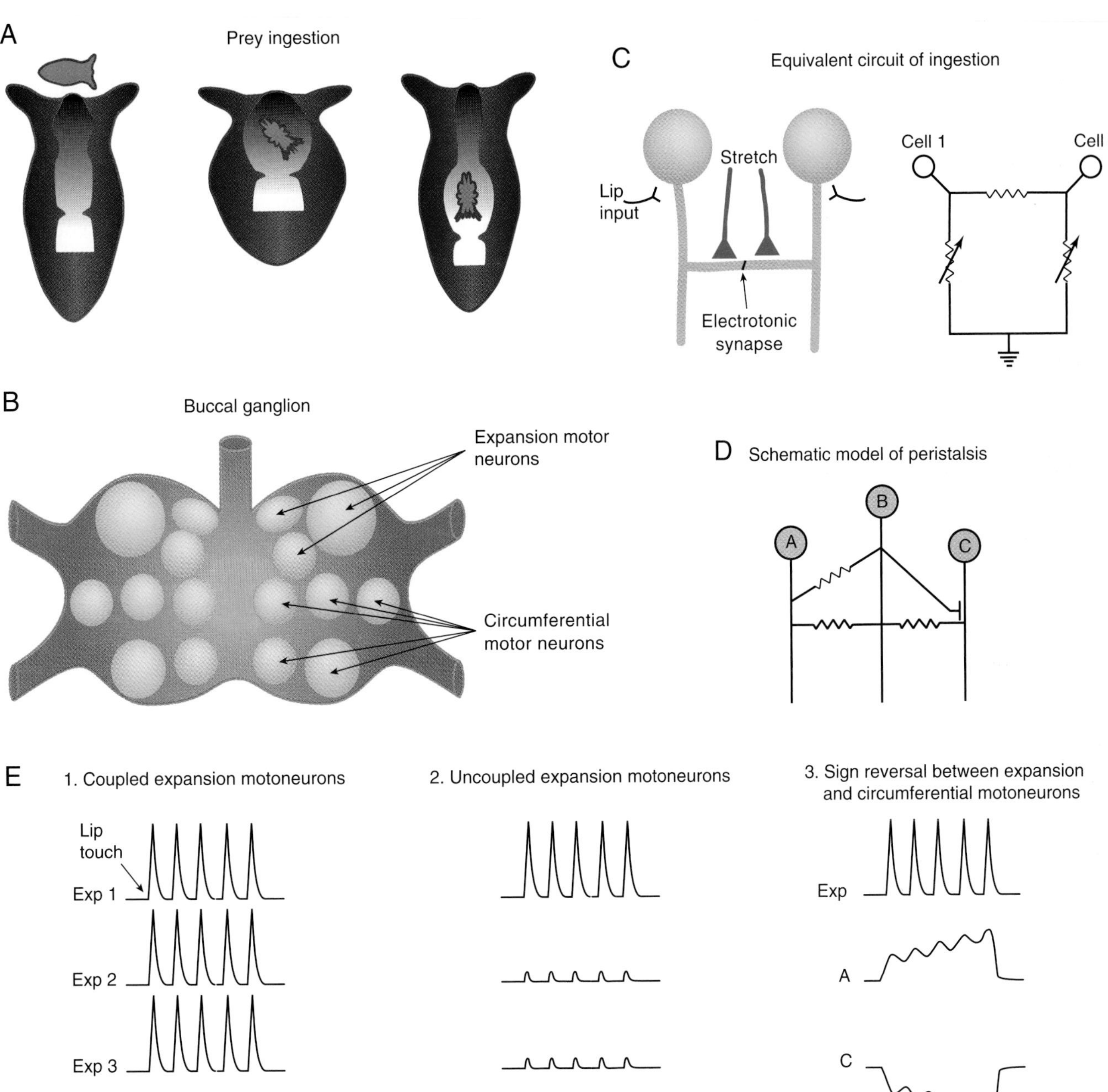

FIGURE 11.5 Neural circuitry responsible for prey ingestion and swallowing in the mollusk *Navanax*. (A) Prey is engulfed by rapid expansion of the buccal cavity, owing to simultaneous contraction of radial musculature innervated by coupled expansion motor neurons. Prey is then swallowed by regional pharyngeal expansion, together with peristaltic pharyngeal constriction by circumferential muscular bands innervated by weakly coupled circumferential motor neurons. (B) Buccal ganglion of *Navanax*, illustrating the positions of expansion and circumferential neurons mediating ingestion and swallowing. (C) Schematic diagram and equivalent electrical circuit describing behavior of expansion motor neurons. Initial pharyngeal expansion is due to activation of the coupled expansion motor neurons from olfactory and mechanoreceptors on the animal's lips. Thereafter, chemical synaptic input from pharyngeal stretch receptors provides a nonjunctional conductance increase, shunting the electrotonic current and uncoupling the cells to allow regional expansion. (D) Schematic diagram of circumferential motor neuron electrical connections to one another (A, C) and to an inhibitory interneuron (B). (E) Changes in coupling that occur between motor neurons during prey ingestion and swallowing. 1. Electrically coupled expansion motor neurons (Exp1, Exp2, Exp3) fire in synchrony when prey is contacted. 2. Inhibitory synapses from pharyngeal stretch receptors shunt current, reducing coupling strength. 3. Expansion motor neuron (Exp) produces electronic psps in circumferential motor neuron A, which results in inhibition of motor neuron C through a coupled interneuron.

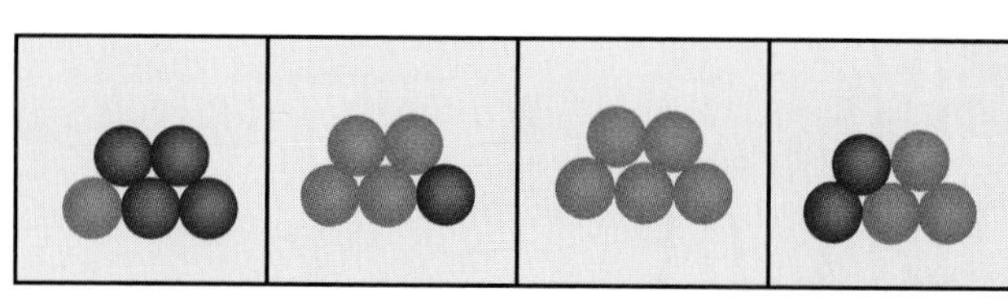

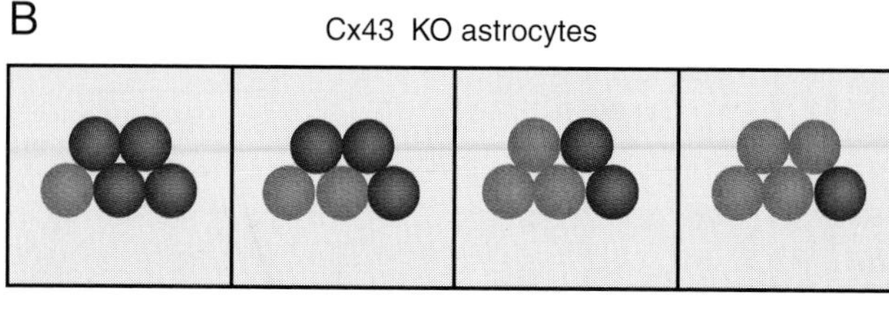

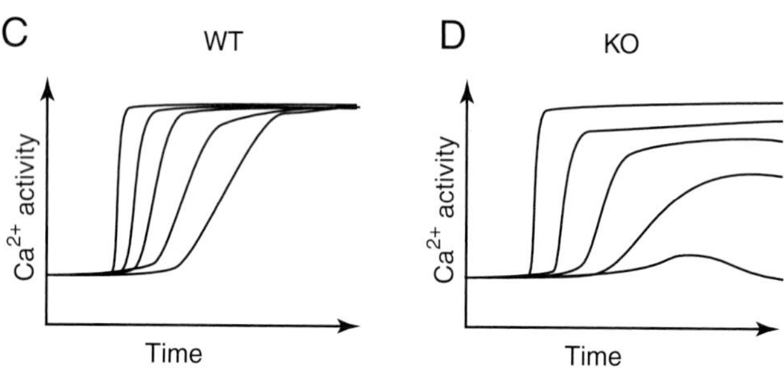

FIGURE 11.6 Intracellular Ca^{2+} waves between astrocytes from (A) wild-type (WT) and (B) Cx43-deficient (KO) mice. In astrocytes from wild-type mice, mechanical, electrical, or pharmacological stimulation can induce a rise in intracellular Ca^{2+} that spreads from cell to cell (high Ca^{2+} activity is represented by red) with a conduction velocity of about 10–20 $\mu m\ s^{-1}$ (illustrated in frames at 2-s intervals in A and plotted schematically in C). In astrocytes from Cx43-deficient (KO) mice, spread is slower and to fewer cells (illustrated in frames at 2-s intervals in B and plotted in D).

osine triphosphate (ATP) or glutamate released from injured or excited cells activates purinergic P_2 or glutamatergic receptors, leading to propagated changes in intracellular Ca^{2+} over long distances and even across regions of cell separation.[61,64,70]

Summary

Cells within the nervous system interact with other neural cells through long-range and local signaling mechanisms. True synapses between neurons are of two types—electrical and chemical—and both consist of membrane specializations between discrete cells that can be unidirectional and functionally flexible. Electrical synapses (which are formed of gap-junction channels) are also found between glia, providing an intimate pathway for potentially long-range exchange of signaling molecules, nutrients, and osmolytes.

BIOPHYSICAL AND PHARMACOLOGICAL PROPERTIES OF GAP JUNCTIONS IN THE NERVOUS SYSTEM

Of the 13 rodent connexins so far identified, at least 8 (Cx26, Cx32, Cx33, Cx37, Cx40, Cx43, Cx45, Cx46) are expressed to varying degrees in the nervous system.[36] Functional studies in diverse cell types and in various exogenous expression systems have revealed that gap-junction channels formed by different connexins are regulated differently, both at the single-channel level (gating controls such as voltage sensitivity and variations in unitary conductance[71]) and at the level of synthesis (expression, altered to differing extents for different connexins by various hormones, extracellular matrix, and cell cycle conditions[37]). Similarly to the K^+ channel family, gap-junction channels have an array of diverse properties. Some gap-junction channels are more sensitive to certain gating stimuli than others; some display a degree of ionic selectivity; and whereas some pair promiscuously with other connexins (to form heterotypic channels), others are quite selective in their interaction (homotypic channels). Such differences are important from the standpoint of the physiological roles of gap junctions in different cell types, as well as in the establishment of communication compartments within the nervous system.

Gap Junctions Are Gated by Transjunctional Voltage

Voltage-clamp studies on cell pairs have revealed that like other ionic channels in the cell membrane, individual gap-junction channels open and close in discrete steplike transitions between states (Fig. 11.7A). The average time that mammalian gap-junction channels are open is sensitive to voltage. Unlike other voltage-dependent channels, gap junctions are primarily sensitive to voltage differences between the coupled cells (**transjunctional voltage**) but much less to the cells' membrane potentials themselves.[72] When either cell of a pair is depolarized or hyperpolarized (i.e., when the transjunctional potential is increased), the time during which the channel is open is reduced. However, even when junctional channels are closed by voltage, for most types of gap-junction channels, the remaining or residual conductance can be as high as 40% of maximal conductance (e.g., in Cx43) or as low as zero (Cx46). This residual conductance is believed to be due to conformational changes in gap-junction channels, in which transjunctional voltage shifts most junction channels from a main-state to a substate behavior.[73] After subtraction of the residual conductance from the total junctional conductance, the voltage-sensitive decline in open time for potentials of either polarity is well fit by two Boltzmann equations, with parameters that are generally symmetric about the zero transjunctional voltage axis. Each connexin has a distinct voltage sensitivity (Fig. 11.7B). For example, Cx43 channels are insensitive to transjunctional voltages below 50 mV, whereas the open time of Cx46 channels is dramatically reduced by transjunctional voltages as low as 10–15 mV. Differences in voltage sensitivity may reflect functional advantages for expression of certain connexins in certain tissues. For example, a highly voltage-sensitive gap-junction channel would be of limited utility in cardiac tissues, where action potential plateaus can create large and long-lasting transjunctional voltage gradients, but could be useful in generating compartment boundaries during embryonic morphogenesis.

Junctional Channels Are Also Gated by Other Factors

Very high (micromolar to millimolar) intracellular Ca^{2+} levels may close some gap-junction channels, either directly through cell acidification or indirectly through generation of phospholipases or through lipid peroxidation and consequent elevations in phospholipid metabolites such as arachidonic acid.[71] Moderate acidification to levels shown to be reached during ischemic episodes has been shown to block gap-junction channels.[74] Some connexins are apparently more sensitive to acidification than others (e.g., Cx43 is more sensitive than Cx32), providing the possibility that un-

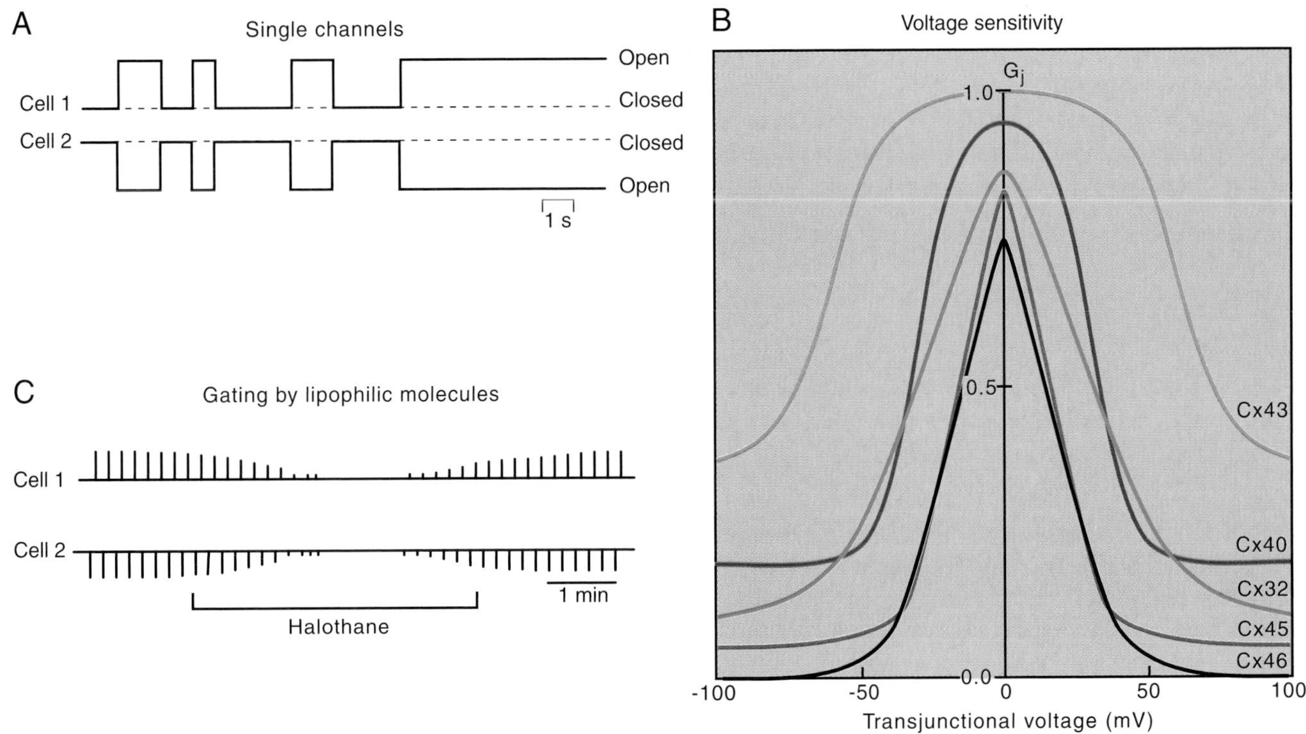

FIGURE 11.7 Gating of gap-junction channels. (A) When each cell of a coupled pair is voltage-clamped and a transjunctional voltage maintained, current flows between the cells through gap-junction channels. When few channels are open, single-channel currents can be resolved as simultaneous steplike transitions of opposite sign recorded in each cell's current trace. The probability of gap-junction channels being open is determined by the transjunctional voltage (V_j: B) and by various other factors (C). (B) Voltage sensitivity of junctional conductance (G_j) is a connexin-specific property. All mammalian gap-junction channels are maximally open at $V_j = 0$ mV and close when one cell is either depolarized or hyperpolarized relative to its partner. Note that Cx43 gap-junction channels are not very sensitive to V_j below $\pm$ 50 mV, whereas Cx32 channels are more voltage sensitive and Cx46 channels close in response to even small imposed V_j values. (C) Sensitivity of junctional conductance to the volatile anesthetic halothane. In this illustration, hyperpolarizing pulses are applied to cell 2 at a rate of 5 per minute, eliciting outward currents in cell 1. Application of halothane at anesthetic doses reduces junctional current to zero; when halothane is removed, passage of junctional currents is quickly restored.

der ischemic conditions coupling within certain cellular compartments might be selectively affected.

The most effective way to block gap-junction channels experimentally is to treat cells with a lipophilic agent such as heptanol, octanol, halothane (illustrated in Fig. 11.7C), or arachidonic, glyccyrhetinic, or oleic acid.[71,75] Although the mechanism of action of these compounds is unknown, they may disrupt gap-junction function by intercalating into the membrane surrounding the connexon or within hydrophobic connexin domains. Because structurally similar blocking compounds are generated through lipid peroxidation and by phospholipases activated under ischemic conditions, this mechanism may be the ultimate cause of the observed cell uncoupling in acute pathological conditions.

Most connexins (with the exception of Cx26) are phosphoproteins and are thus sensitive to the action of protein kinases and phosphatases.[76] The serine phosphorylation of specific residues within the carboxyl tail of gap-junction proteins by cAMP-dependent protein kinase and protein kinase C has been demonstrated for Cx32 and Cx43. Phosphorylation of connexin molecules affects the conductance and open time of the channels. For Cx43, serine phosphorylation is correlated with decreased unitary conductance[77]; for Cx32, it appears to increase the time that the channel is open.[76] In contrast, phosphorylation of a specific tyrosine residue uncouples cells that are connected by Cx43.[78]

Gap-Junction Channels Formed of Different Connexins Show Differences in Unitary Conductances and Ionic Selectivities

Gap-junction channels allow the intercellular passage of molecules ranging widely in size. The highly charged anionic fluorescent dye Lucifer Yellow, designed by Walter Stewart to detect gap-junctional communication,[79] has been used extensively as a diagnostic test for the presence of functional gap junctions between cells. The number of cells that are fluorescent after Lucifer Yellow has been injected into one cell gives a so-called dye-coupling measurement used to quantify coupling strength. A comparison of the extent of dye coupling by using dyes with different charges indicates ionic selectivity of gap-junction channels.[80,81]

Interestingly, studies in retina and central neurons have shown that the spread of injected neurobiotin (a positively charged molecule that is smaller than Lucifer Yellow) through coupled cellular networks is much more extensive than that of Lucifer Yellow.[17,23] Such results may indicate both that some gap junctions are more permeable to cations than anions (cationic selectivity) and that the channels may differ in pore size.

In fact, gap-junction channels have a range of ionic selectivities.[71,80,81] Perfusion of coupled cells with similar-sized compounds has shown that Cx32 favors the permeation of anions over cations, in a ratio of at least 2:1, whereas Cx43 is about equally anion and cation permeant and Cx45 is more permeant to cations than anions ($P_{anion}:P_{cation} \sim 1:5$). When unitary conductances of channels formed of different connexins are measured using internal solutions containing 150 m*M* KCl or CsCl, the most selective connexins may have higher or lower conductances (250 pS for Cx37, 30 pS for Cx45) than the less selective connexins (60–100 pS for Cx43).

Connexons Have Selective Affinities for One Another

Because gap junctions are formed by the pairing of two connexins, the unusual term **selective affinity** can be used to describe the functional relevance of heterologous channels formed by connexons made of different connexin proteins. As mentioned earlier, the two extracellular loops (C1 and C2 in Fig. 11.3D) of each connexin join the connexons tightly together to form a gap-junction channel. As would be expected from the high degree of amino acid homology among these extracellular loops of all connexins, a large number of functional heterologous channels have been observed.[42,43] However, connexons formed of some connexins pair avidly with others (e.g., Cx45 with Cx43), whereas other heterologous pairings (e.g., Cx40 or Cx32 with Cx43) produce nonfunctional channels. In addition, Cx33 appears to form functional channels neither with itself nor with other connexins.[82] Such differential selective affinity presumably plays a role in separating cells of the nervous system into functionally discrete compartments.[35]

Summary

Gap-junction channels make up electrical synapses between neurons and form direct pathways for diffusional exchange of metabolites and ions among glia. Gap-junction channels formed by different connexins have different unitary conductances and selective permeabilities and are differentially sensitive to transjunctional voltage and intracellular pH. Lipophilic agents provide the possibility of reducing junctional conductance experimentally, although none of these treatments is without effects on other channels. Gap-junction connexons formed of one connexin type may or may not pair with hemichannels formed of another connexin, providing the possibility for the existence of compartmental boundaries created by connexin expression patterns in different cell types.

ROLE OF GAP JUNCTIONS IN FUNCTIONS OF NERVOUS TISSUE

Cells constituting the nervous system are specialized for different roles (such as impulse transmission in the case of neurons or for metabolic support as in astrocytes) and form functional compartments within the tissue. The strength of intercellular communication within each compartment and the types of connexins expressed vary according to cell type (Fig. 11.8):[35,36] communication extends across some of these compartmental boundaries as well. Between neurons, chemical transmission is generally the major mechanism by which cells interact. Gap junctions between glial cells are common, providing direct pathways for intercellular communication of second messengers, metabolites, and ions. Moreover, gap junctions between some populations of neurons have been identified, as has chemical responsiveness in glia.

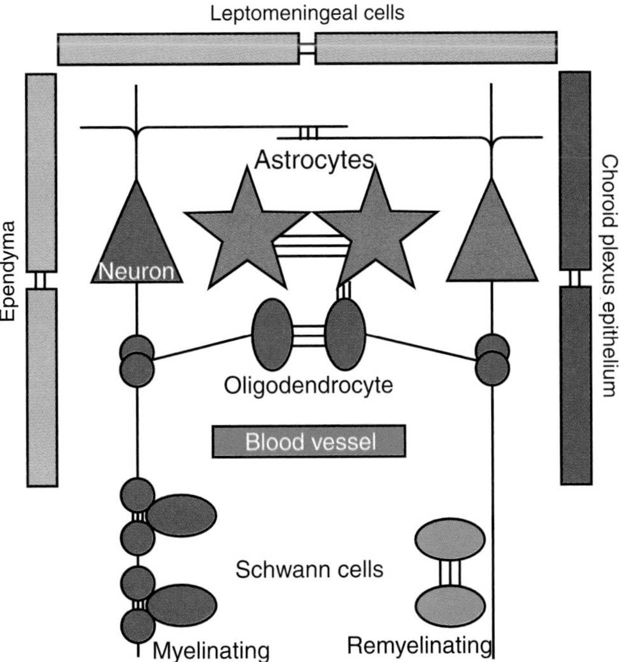

FIGURE 11.8 Communication compartments in the nervous system. This diagram depicts coupling between astrocytes, between oligodendrocytes, between some neurons, and also between ependymal, leptomeningeal, and vascular endothelial and choroid plexus cells. Gap junctions are also present between cytoplasmic processes of individual myelinating Schwann cells and between proliferating Schwann cells. Cell types are color-coded to correspond to major connexin types expressed in each population. Red represents Cx43; orange, the coexpression of Cx43 and Cx26; dark blue, Cx32; light blue, Cx46; and green, the coexpression of Cx37, Cx40, and Cx43.

Gap Junctions Connect Neuronal Cell Populations

Electrophysiological studies demonstrating electrical transmission in numerous nuclei of the vertebrate brain and the optimization of neural function attributed to this coupling have been summarized in detailed reviews by Michael Bennett[5,10,11] and Rodolfo Llinas.[15,16] The synchronization of activity of presynaptic sensory neurons by such electrotonic coupling may be important in optimizing reflex activity, as in the stretch reflex involving the mesencephalic 5th nucleus.[83] Moreover, even weak electrotonic interaction may be important in generating rhythmic levels of increased or decreased excitability of neuronal populations, as in the inferior olivary nucleus,[16] or in strengthening synaptic connections during development (see below). The high speed of electrotonic synaptic transmission may optimize the performance of certain behaviors, as in "escape" or "startle" responses discussed earlier in this chapter, and rapid electrotonic transmission in Dieter's neurons could be critical for quick adjustments in balance in mammals.[14,83] Finally, the interplay between chemical and electrical synaptic events can enhance contrast detection, as in sensory cortex and olfactory bulb,[84] and in the cerebellum, where coupling between stellate and basket cell populations synchronizes the inhibition of Purkinje cells.[21] Such sharpening of contrast provided by electrical and chemical synapses is especially prominent in the retina, where horizontal cell coupling provides surround effects.[23,24]

The identification of the connexins forming neuronal gap junctions has been elusive. Connexin32 appears to be one connexin type forming neuronal gap junctions, as evidenced by immunostaining in certain neuronal populations of the brainstem, in cerebral cortical layers, in the basal ganglia, and in substantia nigra.[85] Interestingly, Cx32 staining has not been demonstrated between hippocampal pyramidal cells, which have been shown to be electrically coupled, raising the possibility that the gap junctions there are too small to be detected by this technique or that additional connexin types might contribute to neuronal gap junctions. In fact, Cx26, Cx32, Cx33, Cx37, Cx40, and Cx43 are all present in certain neuronal populations *in vivo* at certain developmental stages or *in vitro* under certain conditions,[36] and other, neuron-specific connexins may yet be discovered.

Expression of connexins is developmentally regulated in the brain. Numerous studies have demonstrated that the incidence of interneuronal coupling (and, by inference, the expression of gap-junction proteins) dramatically decreases during the processes of brain embryogenesis and neuronal maturation.[3,30,89,94,95] In addition, during both early and late stages of neural differentiation, expression shifts from one type of connexin to another. For instance, Cx26 is highly expressed in fetal compared with adult brain, whereas Cx32 shows developmentally regulated increases in abundance that reach maximal levels only after birth.[85] Because these changes in coupling strength and patterns of connexin expression coincide with the progressive differentiation and commitment of cells and of cell groups to the neuronal lineage, the early presence of gap junctions may hypothetically enable signaling molecules to diffuse among the cells, retarding neuronal differentiation.

Tissue culture preparations from embryonic neural tissue have allowed the manipulation of individual cells and evaluation of changes in junctional distribution and expression during maturation.[86] Such studies have clarified the relations between sequential changes in phenotypes of neural cells, revealing that the extent of coupling mediated by Cx43 (which is abundant in neural precursor populations) declines, whereas other gap-junction proteins appear. For instance, Cx43 continues to be expressed in cells destined for the astrocytic lineage, but is progressively reduced in cells acquiring neuronal phenotypes[87] (Table 11.2)

Even after neuronal circuits are formed, however, coupling among neurons persists to varying degrees in different brain regions. In regions such as the neocortex, coupling is gradually restricted during early neonatal life, as the necessity for synchrony in the establishment of projections onto adjacent cells declines.[17,25,54] In this way, the individual identity of neurons within functional subcircuits is optimized.

Interestingly, the persistent expression of gap junctions during development may have deleterious consequences. For example, the incidence of seizure activity that is more common in young children than later in development correlates well with the decline in coupling that is observed among neurons.[96] Thus, the incidence of neuronal dye-coupling in cultured fetal brain cells is similar to that observed during early postnatal (3–16 months) human neocortical maturation, and both of these percentages contrast with the low incidence of coupling in human neocortical tissue from older children (7- to 14-year-olds).[90]

Gap Junctions Connect Glial Cells

The brain can be envisioned as being separated into volumes that are filled with intracellular, extracellular, and cerebrospinal fluids (Fig. 11.9). The intracellular volume of the brain is primarily glial, consisting of communication compartments formed by distinct cell types (ependymal, ependymoglial, astrocytes, oligodendrocytes, leptomeningeal cells). Cells within each compartment that are well coupled to one another (homologous coupling) can be considered a **functional**

TABLE 11.2 Timeline of Neuronal Differentiation

Least differentiated→→Most differentiated

Phenotypic marker	Untreated neuroblasts	IL7 singly	bFGF (IL7 + TGFα)	Murine primary neurons	Human primary neurons
Appearance	Round	Extended neurites	Simple networks	Complex networks	Complex network
Neurofilament protein	NF-66	NFH-P	NFH-P	NFH-P	NF-66/NFH-P
Dye-coupling	93%	80%	30%	9%	35%
Unitary junctional conductance	~60 pS	~ 60 pS/200 pS	~ 60 pS	?	?
Connexin type	43	33, 40, 43	33, 43	?-*but not Cx43*	?
Excitability	0	10%	20%	100%	100%
Tetrodotoxin sensitivity	Inexcitable	Resistant	Sensitive	Sensitive	Sensitive
Ligand-gated responses	(−)	(−/+)	(+)	(+++)	(+++)

Note. This table summarizes phenotypic changes observed in cultured neuroblasts during progressive neuronal maturation in the presence of cytokines and compares these changes to the properties of murine and fetal neurons. Excitability of cells was determined under voltage- or current-clamp conditions, excitable cells were either insensitive or sensitive to 1 μM tetrodotoxin (TTX),[86] and ligand-gated responses were evaluated by exposure to glutamate, GABA, glycine, and acetylcholine. For each experimental condition, the most mature neurofilament protein expressed is listed: nestin, NF-66 (low-molecular-weight neurofilament protein), and NFH-P (high-molecular-weight neurofilament protein) to GABA ($\leq$100 μM). The connexin types expressed in these cultures were identified by RT-PCR analysis. (Data from Chiu *et al.*[88] and Rozental and Spray[89].)

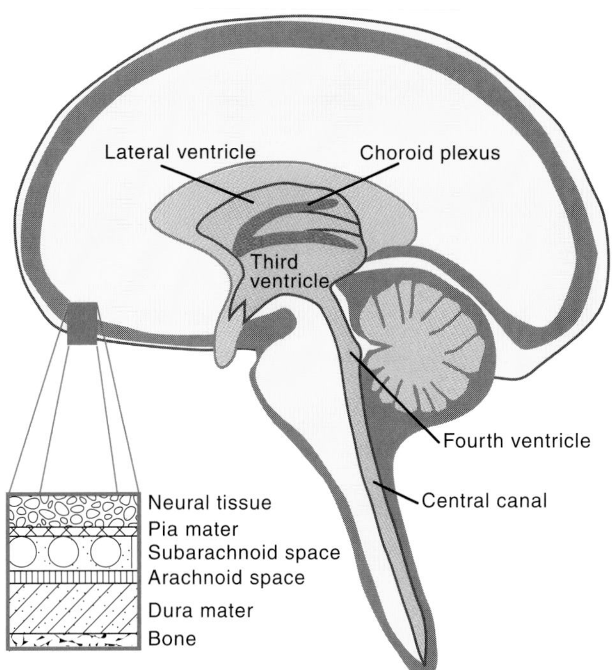

FIGURE 11.9 The compartments of the nervous system are encased in a rigid structure (bone indicated in the inset), imposing limits on volume changes. Between the mass of the brain and the skull are two layers of connective tissue, the pia mater and the dura mater, which is attached to the bone. The pia mater forms a trabecular meshwork providing fluid space on the surface on the brain (subarachnoid spaces). The cerebrospinal fluid (CSF) around the brain surface communicates with the CSF within the cavities of the brain (ventricles) and spinal canal.

syncytium. In addition to this communication within a compartment, certain cell types can interact with one another across compartmental boundaries (heterologous coupling). Within each glial compartment, the role of gap-junction channels is to allow the exchange of second-messenger molecules and to permit the sharing of cellular metabolites and other regulatory molecules.[35,91]

Each specific cell type in the brain expresses a specific set of connexins, and expression patterns thus coincide with tissue compartmentalization (Fig. 11.9).[40] In adult brains the predominant connexin is Cx43, which is abundant in astrocytes and is also expressed in leptomeninges, endothelial cells, and ependyma. The second type of macroglia, the oligodendrocytes (and their peripheral counterparts, the Schwann cells), appear to express a different gap junction protein, Cx32, although to a lower extent *in situ* than the level of Cx43 expression exhibited by astrocytes. In addition to these two proteins, Cx26 is found at modest levels in the adult brain, where it is confined to leptomeninges, ependyma and pinealocytes.

Astrocytes

Astrocytes express Cx43 and are well coupled *in vivo* and under culture conditions.[92,93] However, the strength of coupling and degree of Cx43 expression between astrocytes vary depending on brain regions, being higher in the hypothalamus than in the striatum.[94,95] Differences may also occur according to the astrocytic cell types.

Studies using genetically engineered Cx43 knockout mice[30] reveal that astrocytes also express minor amounts of other connexins, including Cx45, Cx46, and Cx40.[36] As previously stated, the voltage sensitivity of Cx43 is weak. The junctional conductance can be increased by agents that activate cAMP-dependent protein kinase or kinase C, presumably through phosphorylation of the Cx43 molecule. Additionally, astrocytic gap junctions can be closed by products of phospholipase C that are generated under ischemic conditions,[36] by canabinoid metabolites,[96] and by the sleep-inducing molecule oleamide.[97] However, the issue of whether gap-junction channels totally underlie phenomena such as spreading depression (see the section on neuropathologies later in this chapter), spread of Ca^{2+} waves, and actions of kinases and phospholipases on astrocytic communication remains to be explored fully.

Oligodendrocytes and Schwann Cells

Myelinating cells of both the CNS (the oligodendrocytes) and the periphery (the Schwann cells) express gap-junction channels that may have a role in the coordination of the processes of myelination or demyelination, as well as in the metabolic maintenance of the inner, most adaxonal, portions of the cells.

In Schwann cells, Cx32 immunoreactivity is confined to the Schmidt–Lanterman incisures and the paranodal parts of the nodes of Ranvier.[98,99] These reflexive junctional contacts in myelinating cells may promote nutrient exchange between the soma and the cytoplasmic processes that would otherwise be isolated by the myelin lamellae.

Accumulating data indicate that expression of another gap-junction protein, Cx46, is induced in Schwann cells in response to cell injury.[100] During the bursts of Schwann cell proliferation in regenerating nerve, there is upregulation of Cx46, which is believed to form gap-junction channels between dividing Schwann cells and to play a role in remyelination. Cx43 and its mRNA are also detected in both myelinating and proliferating Schwann cells, although its role in these cells is as yet undetermined.[101]

Cx32 provides intercellular coupling between oligodendrocytes. Unexpectedly, this coupling is weaker, with regard to the spread of Lucifer Yellow, than that observed between the less-anion-selective Cx43 of astrocytes. This difference is due in part to the higher junctional conductances that are measured electrophysiologically in astrocytes, and it may be due to the expression of additional populations of Lucifer Yellow-impermeant gap-junction channels between the oligodendrocytes.[102]

Leptomeningeal Cells

In culture, leptomeningeal cells are coupled even more strongly than astrocytes, they do not show prominent voltage dependence, and they display at least two types of junctional single-channel currents, which is consistent with their expression of two junctional proteins, Cx43 and Cx26.[103] Junctional conductance between leptomeningeal cells is doubled within 5 min after the addition of membrane-permeant cAMP or the adenylate cyclase activator forskolin and is strongly inhibited by the addition of the kinase C-activating phorbol esters. Junctional responses to both sorts of stimuli are accompanied by rapid morphological changes from flattened to rounder morphology, but the degree to which these changes contribute to the effects of these agents on junctional conductance is unknown. Leptomeningeal cell coupling presumably plays a role in volume regulation in the meningeal cell layer and in maintaining ionic balance between brain and nonneural tissue.

Ependymoglia

A striking feature of ependymoglial cells is their cilia, which project into the cerebrospinal fluid[104] (Fig. 11.10). The cilia beat in a coordinated manner, tending to sweep foreign particles in the same direction as that of the bulk flow of CSF, the cerebrospinal fluid. Such coordinated activity of ciliated cells in mammalian trachea and molluskan gills is attributed to the presence of gap junctions between the cells.[69] Freeze–fracture studies reveal abundant gap junctions and orthogonal arrays of particles between neighboring ependymal cells and occasionally between ependymal cells and astrocytes. Immunohistochemical studies of gap-junction proteins reveal the presence of Cx26 and Cx43 in mature ependymal cells.[85] The gap junctions allow transfer of tracer substances and electrical current between these cells, which probably serves to integrate cell function not only between ependymal cells but also possibly between ependymoglia and astrocytes.

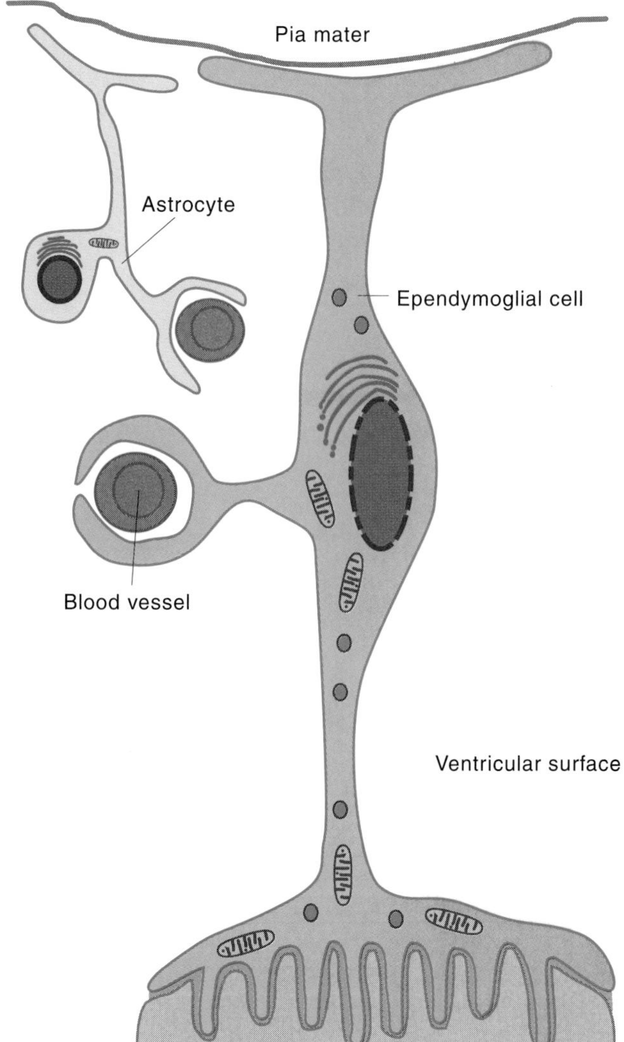

FIGURE 11.10 The ependymoglial cell. The ependyma is a single-layered, ciliated epithelium that covers the surface of the ventricular system of the brain and central canal of the spinal cord. Ependymoglial cells are polarized, having luminal, lateral, and basal sides. Highly specialized ependymal cells cover the choroid plexus and the circumventricular organs. In certain regions of the CNS, a substantial but unknown number of ependymal cells maintain basal processes of varying lengths. When these basal processes establish direct contact with the pia mater, such ependymoglial cells resemble in form the radial glia of the developing CNS. The pial end feet of these cells together with the end feet of central astroglial cells participate in the formation of the blood–brain barrier. The ependymoglial basal processes, in passing through neural tissue, usually extend appendages or side arms that may end in contact with neuronal cell bodies, dendritic, axonal, and synaptic processes, and the walls of the blood vessels.

The Astrocytic Compartment Is a Functional Syncytium

The astrocyte syncytium extends to the circulation in the CNS capillaries and to the cerebrospinal fluid. Astrocytes buffer the accumulation of extracellular K^+ resulting from neuronal activity, and gap junctions in this system most likely provide a direct pathway to K^+ disposal into the perivascular compartments.[65] An equally plausible notion is that coupling between astrocytes creates a large volume that could act as a buffer sink.[105]

To better comprehend the role of the astrocytic syncytium, let us briefly consider the blood–brain barrier. The way in which the brain maintains the constancy of its environment depends in part on isolation of brain tissue by the blood–brain barrier, the cells of which can exclude certain molecules because they are joined by tight junctions of high electrical resistance (on the order of thousands of ohms per square centimeter). This exclusion ability prevents the transcellular movement of molecules and even ions. However, active ion-exchange processes within these specialized cells are primarily responsible for maintenance of the brain microenvironment.

The stability of the brain water content is determined by the coupled transport of water and electrolytes across the blood–brain barrier, by the pressure-dependent bulk flow between the interstitial space and the cerebral spinal fluid, by the exchange between the interstitial space and the intercellular compartment, and by the ways in which the balance between these exchanges are affected by extracellular osmotic perturbation.[106] More is known about the contribution of extracellular than is known about that of intracellular compartments with regard to adjustments regulating brain volume (= water content) *in vivo*; however, *in vitro* studies reveal that the cells themselves possess volume regulatory mechanisms enabling them to respond to conditions that produce osmotic imbalance.[107] Ultimately, maintenance of brain volume depends on coordinated regulation of intracellular and extracellular compartments. The increase in gap-junctional coupling and in the velocity of calcium waves spreading between astrocytes exposed to hypoosmotic shocks[108] suggests that the astroglial synctium greatly contributes to such a role.

A variety of pathological situations, such as brain tumors, bacterial meningitis, and brain edema, disrupt the blood–brain barrier. The cytotoxic effects of edema include intracellular swelling of neurons, glia, and endothelial cells, with a concomitant reduction in brain extracellular space.[109] **Cytotoxic edema** develops in hypoxia from asphyxia or global cerebral ischemia after cardiac arrest due to failure of the ATP-dependent Na^+–K^+ pump, allowing Na^+, and therefore water, to accumulate within cells.[110] Another cause of cytotoxic edema is water intoxication, a consequence of acute systemic hypoosmolality due to excessive ingestion of water or administration of intravenous fluids. Acute hyponatremia, induced, for example, by inappropriate secretion of antidiuretic hormone or atrial natriuretic hormone, also can cause swelling and brain edema.

Extracellular space constitutes about 27% of brain volume.[112,116] Under numerous physiological and pathological conditions, this extracellular volume is reduced. For example, under anoxia and membrane depolarization elicited by elevation of extracellular K^+ concentration or by repeated electrical pulses, the observed cell swelling may substantially reduce the size of the extracellular compartment, severely affecting neuronal and glial functions.[109]

Changes in extracellular space in the brain are secondary to volume changes within the cellular elements (Fig. 11.11). Glutamate, a ubiquitous excitatory neurotransmitter in the mammalian nervous central system (see Chapter 8), shrinks the extracellular compartment. Both high K^+ and glutamate elicit cortical spreading depression (the tie-in with gap junctions is discussed in more detail later in this chapter). This phenomenon consists of a wavelike progression of neuronal hyperexcitability across the cortical surface, followed by a period of unresponsiveness. During spreading depression, the extracellular compartment is substantially reduced (to half its volume), as revealed by electron microscopy, ionic activity, and electrical impedance measurements.[111] For example, in response to repetitive stimulation of the cat motor sensory cortex, the extracellular compartment shrinks by about 50% in regions where the stimulus-induced release of K^+ is maximal, whereas within the honeybee retina, extracellular space can be reduced by at least one-third during light stimulation.[112,113] Interestingly, activity-dependent shrinkage coincides temporally with the differentiation of glial cells during development, indicating that movements of electrolyte and water into glial cells may be responsible for shrinkage of the extracellular compartment.[114]

Summary

The nervous system is divided into compartments of cells that are specialized for different functions. Communication within compartments is strong for leptomeningeal cells, astroglia, and ependymal cells and is weaker for neurons and oligodendroglia. Coupling among glial cells helps the brain cope with volume changes resulting from hypoosmotic and hyperosmotic shocks and following K^+ and glutamate release from neurons. Myelinating Schwann cells are not appreciably coupled to one another, although Cx32 gap-junction proteins appear to form reflexive junctional channels between cytoplasmic processes at internodes and Schmidt–Lantermann incisures; coupling between proliferating Schwann cells due to expression of another gap-junction protein after injury may promote remyelination. Neuronal precursor cells are well coupled, and decline in connexin expression is correlated

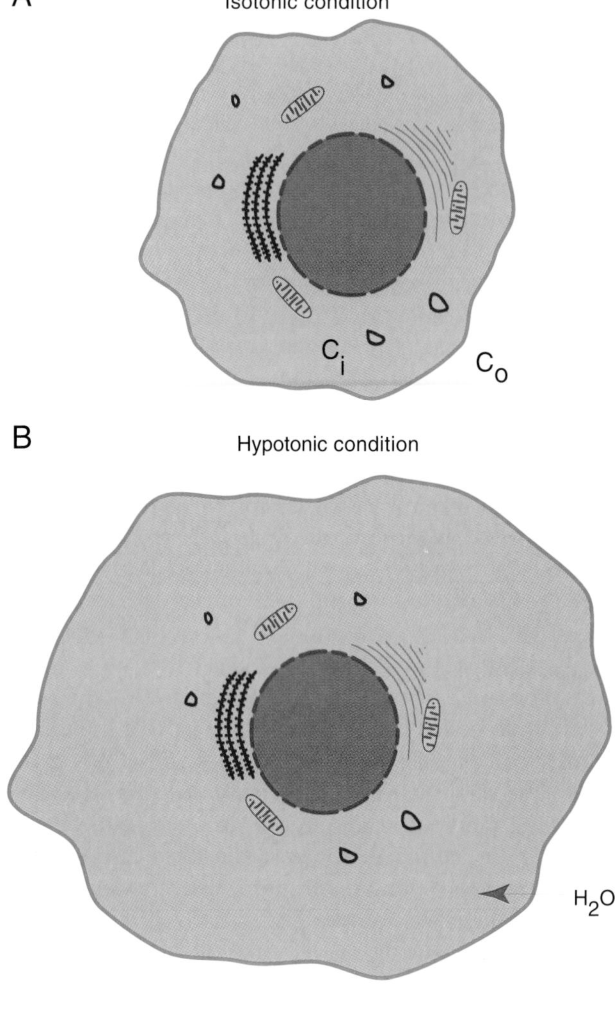

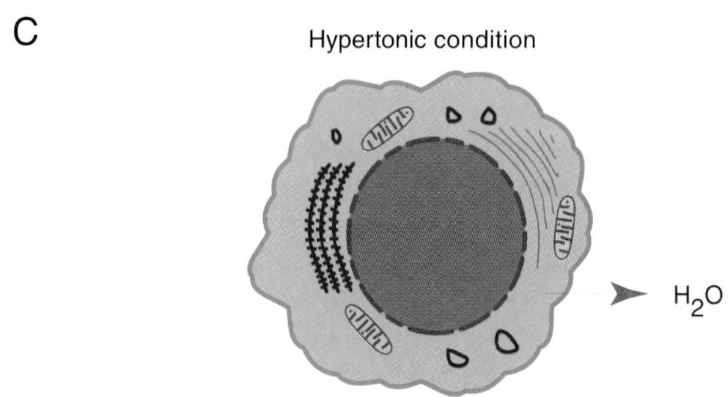

FIGURE 11.11 Cell volume changes. (A) Under conditions in which extra- and intracellular osmotic concentrations are the same ($C_o = C_i$), the osmotic pressure in both compartments is the same ($\pi_0 = \pi_i$). Therefore, such isotonic conditions are characterized by $\Delta\pi = 0$ and by a steady-state cell volume given by

$$V = (A/S_0) \times (1 - l/\rho),$$

where A is concentration of the impermeant solute, S_o is that of the permeant solute, l is the partition coefficient, and ρ represents activity of the metabolic pump. (B) Under hypotonic conditions ($C_0 < C_i$), water chemical potential increases in the external compartment, leading to a positive osmotic pressure gradient ($\Delta\pi > 0$); the influx of water (arrow) causes cell swelling. (C) Under hypertonic conditions ($C_0 > C_i$), the osmotic pressure gradient is negative ($\Delta\pi < 0$), leading to an efflux of water from the cell and consequent cell shrinkage.

with neuronal differentiation. Coupling between cells of different compartments in the nervous system appears to be quite limited. Although astroglia may be connected to oligodendrocytes, creating a "pan-glial syncytium,"[115,116] connections between glia and neurons do not appear to be present in the adult brain. Separation of neural communication compartments is generally predicted by whether the types of connexin molecules expressed by each cellular population can functionally pair with the other cells' connexins. Nevertheless, the role that matrix and cell adhesion molecules play in establishing and maintaining such compartmental boundaries remains to be determined.

GAP-JUNCTION-RELATED NEUROPATHOLOGIES

Most of our understanding of the physiology and molecular biology of gap junctions in brain has been obtained from studies of neural cells in culture or of channels formed by the gap-junction proteins expressed in exogenous systems such as *Xenopus* oocytes or transfected mammalian cells. However, alterations in gap-junction expression, distribution, and function have been found in a number of naturally occurring or induced somatic disease states, and a peripheral neuropathy (X-linked Charcot–Marie–Tooth disease) has been found to be a gap-junction genetic disease specifically affecting Schwann cells in the peripheral nervous system. In this section, we consider various pathological conditions in the brain that may result from aberrant gap-junction expression or function.[117] How do these alterations in junctional communication affect nervous system function? What are the underlying mechanisms of these dysfunctional states?

Neuronal Hyperexcitability and Hypoexcitability Underlie Epilepsy and Spreading Depression and May Involve Changes in Cell Coupling

Abnormal electrical activity is the hallmark of nervous system dysfunction. Paroxysmal neuronal excitability, as occurs in epilepsy, might arise from strengthened electrical coupling between neurons, thereby synchronizing activity patterns. Because astrocytes located at epileptic foci lose expression of inwardly rectifying K^+ currents,[118] neuronal hyperexcitability may result from the increased extracellular K^+ concentration[119] caused by glial inability to buffer extracellular K^+. Alternatively, reduced coupling between glial cells could be involved in such enhanced neuronal hyperexcitability due to the impaired ability of uncoupled glia to efficiently remove excess extracellular K^+ (see the preceding section); in these circumstances, neurons would be constantly depolarized.

That electrical coupling is strengthened between hyperexcitable neurons and that electrotonic connections may contribute to the positive feedback that synchronizes neuronal firing in tissues prone to epileptogenesis are proposals made more than a decade ago.[120,121] More recent studies show that spontaneous synchronized activity of neurons (the so-called "field bursting") continues to occur and is even enhanced under these conditions.[122] Moreover, this synchrony (and the occurrence of electrotonic PSPs) is blocked when *in vitro* preparations are treated with gap-junction-uncoupling agents such as weak acids (which lower intracellular pH), halothane, and octanol.[123]

A comparison of Cx43 mRNA levels in cerebral cortical samples from epileptic cortices gives further evidence that coupling strength may increase in hyperexcitable brain regions; Cx43 expression is markedly increased in epileptic foci compared with nonepileptic controls.[124,125] Because Cx43 in the brain is localized predominantly in astrocytes and possibly also in some neurons, this finding indicates that glial or neuronal gap-junction expression, or both, may be altered in epileptogenic foci. Furthermore, some anti-epileptic drugs block gap-junction channels, and preliminary evidence supports the notion that astrocytes cultured from hyperexcitable regions of human brain are coupled more strongly than those in normal regions, a property that persists for weeks in tissue culture.[126]

Spreading depression (SD) consists of a number of different reactions to local stimulation of the gray matter. This phenomenon, first defined by Leão in 1914, was developed further by his collaborator, Hiss Martins-Ferreira.[127]

Leão's SD, when occurring in the cerebral cortex, is accompanied by intense metabolic changes that lead to cellular dysfunctions.[128] The slow negative potential, changes in electrical impedance, the existence of a refractory period in a range of minutes, the increase in $[K]_o$, and variations in tissue volume during the reaction are the most common events observed during SD. These reactions have also been observed in the hippocampus, olfactory bulb, striatum, spinal cord, superior colliculus, and cerebellum.[127–131] Moreover, spreading depression is now considered a widespread and general phenomenon of the nervous system that may be involved in several disease states such as seizure discharges, migraine headaches, and cerebral ischemia.

Retinal tissue has been widely used in studies aimed at understanding the phenomenon of spreading depression.[132] In this tissue, the SD reaction can be observed repeatedly over a period of several hours by visual observations of an enlarging milky circle starting from the point of focal stimulation (illustrated in Fig. 11.12). Because the rate of propagation of this wave of depression (20–50 $\mu m\ s^{-1}$) is so similar to that measured for Ca^{2+} waves among glial cells both in tissue culture (see Fig. 11.6) and in brain slice preparations, and because the phenomenon is blocked by gap-junction inhibitors,[133–135] it has been suggested that spreading depression results from the propagation of Ca^{2+} waves through gap junctions between the cells. Whether the aura associated with migraine headaches is due to gap-junction-mediated spreading depression and whether gap-junction blockade might reduce damage due to ischemic insults[136] are intriguing ideas that are currently being investigated.

CMTX Is Linked to Connexin32 Mutations

Charcot–Marie–Tooth (CMT) disease affects conduction in both motor and sensory axons. It is the most common hereditary peripheral neuropathy, occurring in the population with an incidence of about 1 in 2000 individuals. Three genetic loci and alterations in their encoded gene products are now believed to be responsible for the three major demyelinating forms of this disease. The most prevalent of these disorders, CMT1A, is mapped to duplications or missense mutations in human chromosome 17 (17p11.2–p12) and involves the myelin protein PMP22; CMT1B maps to human chromosome 1 and appears to involve missense mutations in the myelin constituent P_0, while the CMTX form is linked to mutations within the Cx32 locus of chromosome X.[98,137] Reports on the X-linked form of the disease thus far have identified a total of more than 100 families in which sequencing of the coding region of the Cx32 gap-junction gene revealed more than 130 different mutations.[99,138] Most of these mutations involve single base substitutions leading to single amino acid alterations; others result in formation of premature stop codons at various points in the sequence, produce frameshift leading to premature translational termination, or result in the elimination of one or more amino acid residues (Fig. 11.13). Most of these mutations occur in regions of the molecule believed to line the pore (M3, the third membrane-

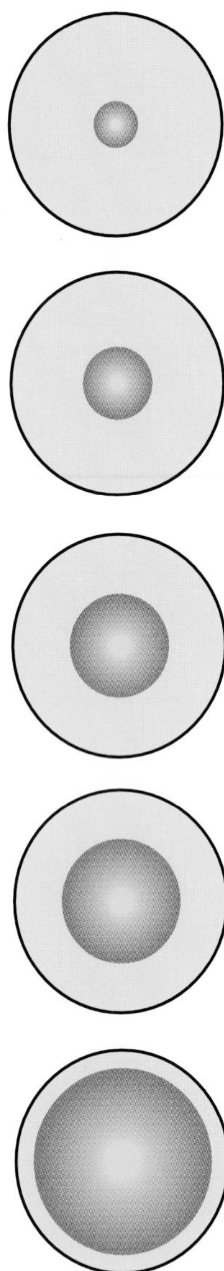

FIGURE 11.12 The chick eyecup model of spreading depression. Mechanical, electrical, or pharmacological focal stimulation of the chick eyecup results in radially propagating change in opacity with a conduction velocity of about 10–50 μm s^{-1}. As this change sweeps across the eyecup, illustrated by an orange wavefront, the tissue is refractory to further stimulation, a phenomenon termed spreading depression.

spanning domain of Cx32), to mate connexon subunits across extracellular space (C1, C2, the two extracellular loops), or to terminate the molecule proximal to its phosphorylation sites. Coding-region mutations are absent in some families, in which cases defects of expression may arise from derangement of Cx32 gene regulatory elements.

The phenotype resulting from mutations of Cx32 is limited to peripheral nerves, which is surprising because Cx32 is a major component of gap junctions of diverse tissues, including liver, exocrine pancreas, and epithelium of the gastrointestinal tract. Moreover, although Cx32 appears to be a major component of gap junctions in oligodendrocytes and in at least some neurons in the CNS, no impairment of brain function has yet been demonstrated in CMTX patients. Because most tissues express other connexins in addition to Cx32, these other connexins may compensate functionally. Alternatively, the mutations of the Cx32 gene may result in specific loss of function in the peripheral myelin sheath because of this tissue's unique structural organization or metabolic requirements, or both.

As noted above, the role ascribed to Cx32 gap-junction channels in myelinating Schwann cells has been to form reflexive gap junctions between cytoplasmic loops at nodes of Ranvier and Schmitt–Lantermann incisures.[98,99,138] These channels would thus short-circuit an otherwise very long and tortuous pathway for nutrient and metabolite exchange between the nucleus and the adaxonal Schwann cell cytoplasm. The coding-region mutations in Cx32 seen in CMTX pedigrees could interfere with Schwann cell function through altered expression or trafficking to the membrane,[139] alterations in channel permeability,[140–142] or negative-dominant effects on other connexins.[141,142] Conduction slowing and demyelination seen progressively in CMTX patients are also observed in Cx32 null mice,[143] strongly indicating that the loss of functional Cx32 channels is responsible for the disease. See Box 11.1 and Table 11.3.

Gap Junctions May Play Roles in Tumorigenesis and Provide a Therapeutic Strategy

Along with the first description of gap-junction-mediated intercellular coupling came the hypothesis that intercellular communication may affect the growth rate of embryonic cells[144] and that reduced gap-junction expression or function could lead to the loss of growth control in tumors.[145] Although most studies of this correlation between coupling strength (or junctional expression) and growth rate have been performed on cells derived from tumors (such as hepatomas) of the digestive system, glial tumors offer an opportunity to extend this analysis to cells of the brain. Most nervous system tumors are of astrocytic origin (astrocytomas) and can be graded according to their severity and growth characteristics from the least invasive (type I) to the most malignant (type IV). Tumors developing from oligodendrocytes (oligodendrogliomas), although less common, are quite severe. These two glial populations express different connexins (Cx43 in astrocytes, Cx32 in oligodendrocytes); thus, the question arises whether the expression of either the type or the abundance of connexins correlates with severity of malignancy. Preliminary studies indicate that connexin type is not altered in tumors, with astrocytomas and oligodendrogliomas expressing the same Cx43 and Cx32, respectively.[117] Moreover, the abundance of Cx43 is not correlated with the severity of the astrocytoma, high levels being expressed even in the most severe pathology.

Thus, the escape of glial tumor cells from growth control regulation does not appear to result from the absence of gap-junction communication. Moreover, most recent studies on tumor cells transfected with connexin cDNA sequences indicate that growth arrest is not restored in culture.[146–148] However, growth of these cells as tumors in nude mice is retarded compared to growth of communication-deficient cell lines, and both spontaneous and carcinogen-induced hepatomas are reported to be more common in Cx32 null mice than in wild-type siblings.[149] Ironically, the presence of gap junctions between tumor cells is responsible for a phenomenon known as "bystander cell killing," which is the basis for a therapeutic strategy (Fig. 11.14) currently undergoing clinical trials.[150] Cells transduced with viral thymidine kinase are rendered sensitive to the chemotherapeutic drug acyclovir, which is metabolized by viral thymidine kinase to a phosphorylated low-molecular-weight cytotoxin that intercalates into the DNA, causing apoptotic cell death. The phosphory-

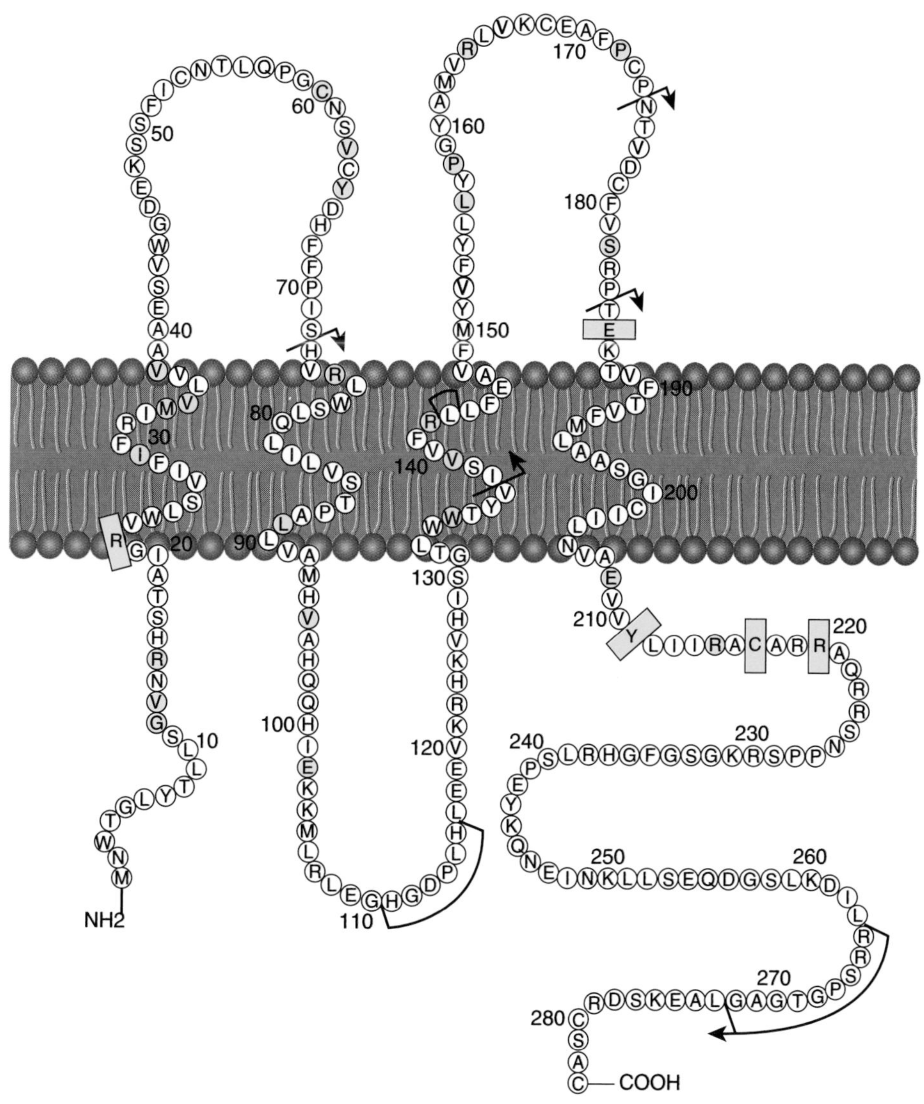

FIGURE 11.13 Examples of the diversity of coding-region mutations in human Cx32 associated with the X-linked form of Charcot–Marie–Tooth disease. Each ball in the chain represents an amino acid residue, indicated by a letter identifying the amino acid present in the wild-type sequence. Different symbols represent different sorts of mutations: Missense mutations are indicated by yellow circles, nonsense mutations by yellow bars, frameshift mutations by arrows, and deletions by brackets. From Deschenes *et al.*[138]

BOX 11.1

NEW MODELS FOR EXPLORING GAP-JUNCTION ROLES IN BRAIN FUNCTION

Owing to technical advances in molecular biology, the functional role of specific cellular components and products can be examined using transgenic animals in which genes are targeted to specific tissues or removed from them. Since 1981, transgenic models have progressively but dramatically contributed to biomedical research. Clearly, gene knockout and delivery technologies enable the evaluation of the role of specific genes in cellular commitment, differentiation, function, and dysfunction. Unequivocally, such studies allow the reevaluation of several strategies for treating a diversity of diseases and provide the basis for gene therapy. Recent examples include transgenic animal models for kidney diseases, hypertension, tumorigenesis, lipoprotein and cholesterol distribution, and skeletal muscle disease.

Similarly, antisense strategies (i.e., endogenous gene suppression by either antisense or sense transcripts) have generated new clinical perspectives allowing specific gene regulation *in vivo.* For example, reduced expression of the Na^{+}–Ca^{2+} exchanger by antisense oligonucleotides alters $[Ca^{2+}]_i$ regulation, leading to an enhanced spontaneous beating rate of cardiac myocytes and shortening the duration of the cardiac cycle in developing cells.[151] In the brain, inhibition of the interaction of G protein with Ca^{2+} channels in neurons has been shown to limit the efficacy of specific agonists.[152] Molecular biology has had a significant role in defining the genes encoding the connexin family of gap-junction proteins and their chromosomal locations (Table 11.1), providing primary sequence and mutational manipulations for evaluating gating properties and structure–function relations in exogenous expression systems and allowing targeted over- or underexpression of specific junctional proteins in transgenic animals.

The most exciting experimentally engineered preparations at present are the recent generation and cultivation of populations of mice in which genes encoding seven of the connexins have been deleted (Table 11.3).[153–166] Initial examination of these animals and studies of human genetic diseases involving the connexins reveal interesting phenotypes. Cx26 knockout mice die *in utero*, presumably because of unsuccessful placental formation, a process in which Cx26 expression appears to play a key role. In humans, however, dysfunctional Cx26 is associated with hereditary nonsyndromic deafness and perhaps skin disorders. Cx32 knockout mice exhibit impaired peripheral nerve conduction, decreased hepatic glucogenesis in response to sympathetic nerve stimulation, and increased susceptibility to hepatic tumors. Humans with Cx32 mutations (Fig. 11.13) exhibit extreme abnormalities in myelinating Schwann cells and in nerve conduction in CMTX disease. Cx37 knockout mice exhibit decreased fertility, presumably due to loss of nutritive support between oocytes and nurse cells in the Graafian follicles; Cx40 knockout mice exhibit slowed atrioventricular conduction, attributable to reduced coupling in the cardiac conduction system. Cx43 knockout mice die as a consequence of pulmonary atresia and right ventricular hypertrophy soon after birth, cardiac contractions are less rhythmic, lenses are cataractous, and spread of astrocyte Ca^{2+} waves is affected (Fig. 11.6), but effects on other aspects of brain function are unknown.

TABLE 11.3 Consequences of Connexin Deletion or Dysfunction in Genetically Altered Mice and in Human Hereditary Diseases

Connexin	KO mouse phenotype	Human genetic disease
Cx26	Dies *in utero*[153]	Hearing loss[29,154], Skin disease[155]
Cx32	Liver tumors[149] Liver dysfunction[156] Slowed nerve conduction[143]	CMTX[98]
Cx37	Decreased fecundity[157]	
Cx40	Slowed AV conduction[30,158]	
Cx43	Cardiac abnormalities[159] Slowed, asynchronous conduction[159] Lens structural abnormalities[160]	Visceroatrial-heterotaxia[161–163]
Cx46	Nuclear cataracts[164]	
Cx50	Micro-ophthalmia[165] Nuclear cataracts[165]	Nuclear cataracts[166]

In mice lacking Cx46 or Cx50, both of which are major components of gap junctions between lens fiber cells, the primary defect appears to be nuclear cataracts and microophthalmia; a rare familial human cataract maps to the region of the Cx50 gene locus.

Physiologists are now challenged to determine whether specific, disease-related phenotypes correspond to or overlap with the pathological conditions that have been correlated with changes in gap-junction expression and function and to use these deficiencies to more fully explore the roles that gap junctions play in normal brain function.

Despite the fact that these preparations are sources of insight into disease mechanisms, it remains to be seen whether novel therapeutic strategies will immediately emerge. In cases such as acute ischemia, in which functional deficiency would be expected to derive from gating abnormalities, reversal of the deficiency may be made straightforward by altering cytoplasmic constituents. In cases where wild-type connexin expression is altered or in conditions such as CMTX, where mutations may result in dysfunctional channels, successful targeted gene therapy may conceivably overcome the block. However, regardless of whether these strategies are therapeutically useful, their application in attempting to correct these pathological conditions should certainly enhance our understanding of the role of gap junctions in the diverse functions of nervous tissue.

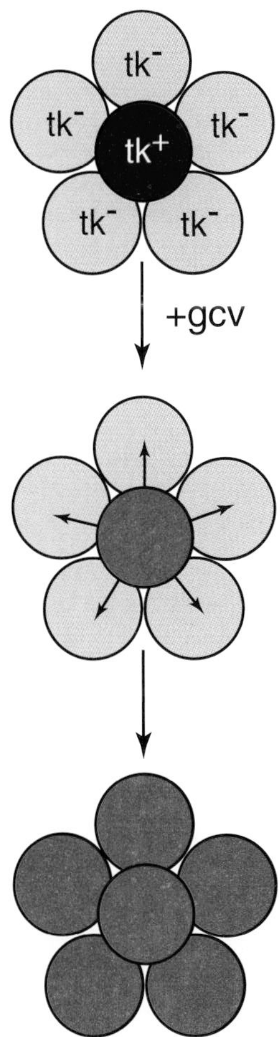

FIGURE 11.14 Gap-junction-mediated cell killing through the bystander effect. Cells transfected with Herpes thymidine kinase (tk^+, dark blue) die apoptotically (turn red in this figure) when they are exposed to the anticancer drug acyclivor (gcv). When tk^+ cells are cocultured with untransfected cells (tk^-) (light blue) to which they make gap-junctional contact, the tk^- "bystanders" are also killed (turning red). This bystander effect also occurs in tumors, allowing the possibility of gap-junction-mediated tumor therapy.

lated acyclovir is presumably gap junction permeant, thereby killing cells that are coupled to the viral thymidine kinase transfectants, both in culture and in tumors *in vivo*.[147,167–170]

Brain Lesions Affect Intercellular Coupling

In cardiac muscle, both acute and chronic infarctions lead first to loss of gap junctions and, after a period of days, to reexpression and reorganization of these channels.[171] Glial gap-junction expression may be similarly responsive to such insult. For example, lesion of the facial nerve results in rapidly increased Cx43 expression by astrocytes in the ipsilateral facial nucleus.[172] Furthermore, traumatic injury to the spinal cord leads to both loss of Cx43 immunoreactivity in the center of the spinal cord and increased immunostaining in outer regions.[173] Finally, subsequent to a local stab wound of the visual cortex, regional loss of dye coupling between astrocytes has been observed to persist for as long as 4 weeks after wounding.[123]

Mechanisms responsible for over- or underexpression of glial gap junctions may include changes in the composition of the extracellular matrix or in membrane-bound ligands (i.e., integrins and cell adhesion molecules), changes that are consistent with proteoglycan-stimulated connexin biosynthesis or proteoglycan-induced alterations in neuronal excitability due to elaboration of recurrent electrotonic interactions. Alternatively, such changes may be mediated by transcriptional control related to the cell cycle.

Protozoan Infections Affect Coupling between CNS Cell Populations

Protozoan parasites associated with brain infection in immunosuppressed persons include *Trypanosoma cruzi* (which causes American trypanosomiasis, or Chagas disease, the prevalent cause of cardiomyopathy in

South America) and *Toxoplasma gondii* (which causes toxoplasmosis, an opportunistic infection contributing to death from HIV infection). *T. cruzi* infection leads to disorganization of gap junctions and severe reductions in intercellular communication in cultured cardiac myocytes.[174] In astrocytes, both *T. gondii* and *T. cruzi* infections are associated with the loss of coupling and reduced expression of Cx43-containing junctional plaques.[175] In leptomeningeal cells, both protozoans reduce the coupling and the organized expression of both Cx26 and Cx43. Thus, the effects on junctional disruption are generalized with regard to both type of host cell and type of connexin interconnecting the cell populations. Because the changes in connexin distribution occur in parasitized cells without changes in connexin abundance (at either protein or mRNA levels), a trafficking disorder appears responsible for the loss of coupling between parasitized cells. Whatever the mechanism, parasite-induced loss of intercellular communication would be expected to affect astrocyte functions dramatically, disturbing K^+ balance and interfering with propagation of Ca^{2+} waves between these glial cells.

Summary

Gap junctions in nervous tissue synchronize neuronal activity, provide pathways for second messenger and metabolite exchange, and may modulate cell growth, differentiation, and organization. Abnormal gap-junction expression or function is associated with both genetic and somatic disease states, presumably contributing to the pathology through the loss of the important intercellular pathway provided by these channels. As considered in Box 11.1, mice in which connexins are deleted by molecular genetic manipulation provide model systems in which the roles of specific gap-junction types can be explored in detail and in which the contribution of functionally ablated gap junctions to different pathological situations can be directly assessed.

References

1. Brazier, M. A. B. (1959). The historical development of neurophysiology. In *Handbook of Physiology* (J. Field, ed.), Sect. 1, Vol. 1, pp. 1–58. Am. Physiol. Soc., Washington, DC.
2. Grundfest, H. (1959). Synaptic and ephaptic transmission. In *Handbook of Physiology* (J. Field, ed.), Sect. 1, Vol. 1, pp. 147–197. Am. Physiol. Soc., Washington, DC.
3. Furshpan, E. J., and Potter, D. D. (1959). Transmission at the giant motor synapses of the crayfish. *J. Physiol. (London)*, **145:** 289–325.
4. Robertson, J. D. (1961). Ultrastructure of excitable membranes and the crayfish median-giant synapse. *Ann. N.Y. Acad. Sci.* **94:** 339–389.
5. Bennett, M. V. L. (1977). Electrical transmission: A functional analysis and comparison to chemical transmission. In *Handbook of Physiology* (E. R. Kandel, ed.), Sect. 1, Vol. 1, *I*, pp. 357–416. Am. Physiol. Soc., Washington, DC.
6. Bennett, M. V. L., Spray, D. C., and Harris, A. L. (1981). Electrical coupling in development. *Am. Zool.* **21:** 413–427.
7. Bennett, M. V. L., Crain, S. M., and Grundfest, H. (1959). Electrophysiology of supramedullary neurons in Spheroides maculatus. I. Orthogromic and antidromic responses. *J. Gen. Physiol.* **43:** 159–188.
8. Bennett, M. V. L., Nakajima. Y., and Pappas, G. D. (1967). Physiology and ultrastructure of electrotonic junctions. I. Supramedullary neurons. *J. Neurophysiol.* **30:** 161–179.
9. Bennett, M. V. L., Nakajima, Y., and Pappas, G. D. (1967). Physiology and ultrastructure of electrotonic junctions. III. Giant electromotor neurons of *Malapterurus electricus*. *J. Neurophysiol.* **30:** 209–235.
10. Bennett, M. V. L. (1996). Gap junctions as electrical synapses. In *Gap Junctions in the Nervous System* (D. C. Spray and R. Dermietzel, eds.), pp. 61–74. R. G. Landes, Austin, TX.
11. Bennett, M. V. L. (1997). Gap junctions as electrical synapses. *J. Neurocytol.* **26:** 349–366.
12. Spray, D. C., Rook, M., Moreno, A. P., Saez, J. C., Christ, G., Campos de Carvalho, A. C., and Fishman, G. I. (1994). Cardiovascular gap junctions: Gating properties, function and dysfunction. In *Ion Channels in the Cardiovascular System: Function and Dysfunction* (P. M. Spooner, A. M. Brown, W. A. Catterall, G. J. Kaczorowski, and H. C. Strauss, eds.), pp. 185–217. Futura Publ. Co., Mt. Kisco, NY.
13. Baker, R., and Llinas, R. (1971). Electrotonic coupling between neurons in the rat mesencephalic nucleus. *J. Physiol. (London)* **212:** 45–63.
14. Korn, H., Sotelo, C., and Crepel, F. (1973). Electrotonic coupling between neurons in the rat lateral vestibular nucleus. *Exp. Brain Res.* **16:** 225–275.
15. Llinas, R. (1975). Electrical synaptic transmission in the mammalian central nervous system. In *Golgi Centennial Symposium: Perspectives in Neurobiology* (M. Santini, ed.), pp. 379–386. Raven Press, New York.
16. Llinas, R. (1985). Electrotonic transmission in the mammalian central nervous sytem. In *Gap Junctions* (M. V. L. Bennett and D. C. Spray, eds.), pp. 337–353. Cold Spring Harbor, Lab., Cold Spring Harbor, NY.
17. Peinado, A., Yuste, R., and Katz, L. C. (1993). Extensive dye coupling between rat neocortical neurons during the period of circuit formation. *Neuron* **10:** 103–114.
18. Llinas, R., Baker, R., and Sotelo, C. (1974). Electrotonic coupling between neurons in cat inferior olive. *J. Neurophysiol.* **37:** 560–571.
19. Dudek, F. E., Andrew, R. D., MacVicar, B. A., and Hatton, G. I. (1982). Intracellular electrophysiology of mammalian peptidergic neurons in rat hypothalamic slices. *Fed. Proc., Fed. Am. Soc. Exp. Biol.* **41**(13): 2953–2958.
20. MacVicar, B. A., and Dudek, F. E. (1982). Electrotonic coupling between granule cells of rat dentate gyrus: physiological and anatomical evidence. *J. Neurophysiol.* **47**(4): 579–592.
21. Welsh, J. P., and Llinas, R. (1997). Some organizing principles for the control of movement based on olivocerebellar physiology. *Prog. Brain Res.* **114:** 449–461.
22. Penn, A. A., Wong, R. O., and Shatz, C. J. (1994). Neuronal coupling in the developing mammalian retina. *J. Neurosci.* **14**(6): 3805–3815.
23. Vaney, D. I. (1996). Cell coupling in the retina. In *Gap Junctions*

in the Nervous System (D. C. Spray and R. Dermietzel, eds.), pp. 79–102. R. G. Landes, Austin, TX.

24. Weiler, R. (1996). The modulation of gap junction permeability in the retina. In *Gap Junctions in the Nervous System* (D. C. Spray and R. Dermietzel, eds.), pp. 103–122. R. G. Landes, Austin, TX.
25. Lo Turco, J. J., and Kriegstein, A. R. (1991). Clusters of coupled neuroblasts in embryonic neocortex. *Science* **252:** 563–566.
26. Kumar, N. M., and Gilula, N. B. (1996). The gap junction channel. *Cell (Cambridge, Mass.)* **84:** 381–388.
27. Carrasquillo, M. M., Zlotogora, J., Barges, S., and Chakravarti, A. (1997). Two different connexin26 mutations in an inbred kindred segregating non-syndromic recessive deafness: Implications for genetic studies in isolated populations. *Hum. Mol. Genet.* **6:** 2163–2172.
28. Haefliger, J. A., Bruzzone, R., Jenkins, N. A., Gilbert, D. J., Copeland, N. G., and Paul, D. L. (1992). Four novel members of the connexin family of gap junction proteins. Molecular cloning, expression, and chromosome mapping. *Biol. Chem.* **25:** 2057–2064.
29. Hennemann, H., Dahl, E., White, J. B., Schwarz, H. J., Lalley, P. A., Chang, S., Nicholson, B. J., and Willecke, K. (1992). Two gap junction genes, Connexin 31.1 and 30.3, are closely linked on mouse chromosome 4 and preferentially expressed in skin. *J. Biol. Chem.* **267:** 17225–17233.
30. Réaume, A. G., deSousa, P. A., Kulkarni, S., Langille, B. L., Zhu, D., Davies, T. C., Juneja, S. C., Kidder, G. M., and Rossant, J. (1995). Cardiac malformation in neonatal mice lacking connexin43. *Science* **267:** 1831–1834.
31. Schwarz, H. J., Chang, Y. S., Lalley, P. A., and Willecke, K. (1994). Chromosomal assignments of mouse genes for connexin50 and connexin33 by somatic cell hybridization. *Somatic Cell Mol. Genet.* **20:** 243–247.
32. Van Camp, G., Coucke, P., Speleman, F., Van Roy, N., Beyer, E. C., Oostra, B. A., and Willems, P. J. (1995). The gene for human gap junction protein connexin37 (GJA4) maps chromosome 1p35.1, in the vicinity of D1S195. *Genomics* **30:** 402–403.
33. Corcos, I. A., Meese, E. U., and Loch-Caruson, R. (1993). Human connexin43 gene locus, GJA1, sublocalized to band 6q21→q.23.2. *Cytogenet. Cell Genet.* **64:** 31–32.
34. Kerscher, S., Church, R. L., Boyd, Y., and Lyon, M. F. (1995). Mapping of four mouse genes encoding eye lens-specific structural, gap junction, and integral membrane proteins: Crybal (crystallin beta A3/A1). Crybb2 (crystallin beta B2), Gja8 (MP70), and Lim2 (MP19). *Genomics* **29:** 445–450.
35. Dermietzel, R., and Spray, D. C. (1993). Gap junctions in the brain: Where, what type, how many and why. *Trends Neurosci.* **16:** 186–192.
36. Dermietzel, R., and Spray, D. C. (1998). From neuro-glue ("Nervenkitt") to glia: A prologue. *Glia* **24:** 1–7.
37. Bennett, M. V. L., Barrio, L., Bargiello, T. A., Spray, D. C., Hertzberg, E. L., and Saez, J. C. (1991). Gap junctions: New tools, new answers, new questions. *Neuron* **6:** 305–320.
38. White, T. W., Paul, D. L., Goodenough, D. A., and Bruzzone, R. (1995). Functional analysis of selective interactions among rodent connexins. *Mol. Biol. Cell* **6:** 459–470.
39. Elfgang, C., Eckert, R., Lichtenberg-Frate, H., Butterweck, A., Traub, O., Klein, R. A., Hülser, D. F., and Willecke, K. (1995). Specific permeability and selective formation of gap junction channels in connexin-transfected HeLa cells, *J. Cell Biol.* **129:** 805–817.
40. Zhou, X. W., Pfahnl, A., Werner, R., Hudder, A., Llanes, A., Luebke, A. and Dahl, G. (1997). Identification of a pore lining segment in gap junction hemichannels. *Biophys. J.* **72**(5): 1946–1953.
41. Auerbach, A. A., and Bennett, M. V. L. (1969). A rectifying synapse in the central nervous system of a vertebrate. *J. Gen. Physiol.* **53:** 211–237.
42. Anderson, P. A. (1985). Physiology of a bidirectional, excitatory, chemical synapse. *J. Neurophysiol.* **53:** 821–835.
43. Anderson, P. A., and Grunert, U. (1988). Three-dimensional structure of bidirectional, excitatory chemical synapses in the jellyfish *Cyanea capillata*. *Synapse* **2:** 606–613.
44. Robertson, J. D. (1963). The occurrence of a subunit pattern in the unit membranes of club endings in Mauthner cell synapses in goldfish brains. *J. Cell Biol.* **19:** 201–221.
45. Korn, H., and Faber, D. S. (1975). An electrically mediated inhibition in goldfish medulla. *J. Neurophysiol.* **38:** 452–471.
46. Korn, H., and Faber, D. S. (1996). Escape behavior—brainstem and spinal cord circuitry and function. *Curr. Opin. Neurobiol.* **6:** 826–832.
47. Furukawa, T., and Furshpan, E. J. (1963). Two inhibitory mechanisms in the Mauthner neurons of goldfish. *J. Neurophysiol.* **26:** 140–176.
48. Spira, M. E., and Bennett, M. V. L. (1972). Synaptic control of electrotonic coupling between neurons. *Brain Res.* **37:** 294–300.
49. Spira, M. E., Spray, D. C., and Bennett, M. V. (1980). Synaptic organization of expansion motoneurons of Navanax inermis. *Brain Res.* **195:** 241–269.
50. Sotelo, C., Gotow, T., and Wassef, M. (1968). Localization of glutamic-acid-decarboxylase-immunoreactive axon terminals in the inferior olive of the rat, with special emphasis on anatomical relations between GABAergic synapses and dendrodendritic gap junctions. *J. Comp. Neurol.* **252**: 32–50.
51. Spira, M. E., Spray, D. C., and Bennett, M. V. L. (1976). Electrotonic coupling: Effective sign reversal by inhibitory neurons. *Science* **194:** 1065–1067.
52. Katz, L. C. (1993). Coordinate activity in retinal and cortical development. *Curr. Opin. Neurobiol.* **3**(1): 93–99.
53. Shatz, C. J. (1994). Viktor Hamburger Award review. Role for spontaneous neural activity in the patterning of connections between retina and LGN during visual system development. *J. Dev. Neurosci.* **12**(6): 531–546.
54. Kandler, K., and Katz, L. C. (1995). Neuronal coupling and uncoupling in the developing nervous system. *Curr. Opin. Neurobiol.* **5**(1): 98–105.
55. Pereda, A. E., and Faber, D. S. (1996). Activity-dependent short-term enhancement of intercellular coupling. *J. Neurosci.* **16:** 983–992.
56. Saez, J. C., Connor, J. A., Spray, D. C., and Bennett, M. V. (1989). Hepatocyte gap junctions are permeable to the second messenger, inositol, 1,4,5-trisphosphate, and to calcium ions. *Proc. Natl. Acad. Sci. U.S.A.* **86:** 2708–2712.
57. Pereda, A. E., Bell, T. D., and Faber, D. S. (1995). Retrograde synaptic communication via gap junctions coupling auditory afferents to the Mauthner Cell. *J. Neurosci.* **15:** 5943–5955.
58. Giaume, C., Tabernero, A., and Medina, J. M. (1997). Metabolic trafficking through astrocytic gap junctions. *Glia* **21**(1): 114–123.
59. Charles, A. (1998). Intercellular calcium waves in glia. *Glia* **24(1):** 39–49.
60. Giaume, C., and Venance, L. (1998). Intercellular calcium signaling and gap junction communication in astrocytes. *Glia* **24(1):** 50–64.
61. Enkvist, M. O., and McCarthy, K. D. (1992). Activation of protein kinase C blocks astroglial gap junction communication and inhibits the spread of calcium waves. *Neurochemistry* **59:** 519–526.
62. Cornell-Bell, A. H., Finkbeiner, S. M., Cooper, M. S., and Smith,

S. J. (1991). Glutamate induces calcium waves in cultured astrocytes: Long-range glial signaling. *Science* **247:** 470–473.
63. Sanderson, M. J. (1995). Intercellular calcium waves mediated by inositol trisphosphate. In *Calcium Waves, Gradients and Oscillations* (G. R. Bock and K. Akrill, eds.), pp. 175–194. Wiley, Chichester.
64. Scemes, E., Dermietzel R., and Spray, D. C. (1998). Calcium waves between astrocytes from Cx43 knockout mice. *Glia* **24(1):** 65–73.
65. Kuffler, S. W., and Nicholls, J. G. (1966). The physiology of neuroglial cells. *Ergeb Physiol.* **57:** 1–90.
66. Naus, C. C. G., Becherger, J. F., and Bond, S. L. (1996). Effect of gap junctional communication on glioma cell function. In *Gap Junctions in the Nervous System* (D. C. Spray and R. Dermietzel, eds.), pp. 193–202. R. G. Landes, Austin, TX.
67. Kimelberg, H. K., and Kettenmann, H. (1990). Swelling-induced changes in electrophysiological properties of cultured astrocytes and oligodendrocytes. I. Effects on membrane potential, input impedance and cell-cell coupling. *Brain Res.* **529:** 255–261.
68. Bender, A. S., Neary, J. T., and Norenberg, M. D. (1993). Role of phosphoinositide hydrolysis in astrocyte volume regulation. *Neurochemistry* **6:** 1506–1514.
69. Sanderson, M. J. (1996). Intercellular waves of communication. *News Physiol. Sci.* **11:** 262–269.
70. Hassinger, T. D., Guthrie, P. B., Atkinson, P. B., Bennett, M. V., and Kater, S. B. (1996). An extracellular signaling component in propagation of astrocytic calcium waves. *Proc. Natl. Acad. Sci. U.S.A.* **93:** 13268–13273.
71. Spray, D. C. (1994). Physiological and pharmacological regulation of gap junction channels. In *Molecular Mechanisms of Epithelial Cell Junctions: From Development to Disease* (S. Citi, ed.), pp. 195–215. R. G. Landes, Austin, TX.
72. Spray, D. C., Harris, A. L., and Bennett, M. V. L. (1981). Equilibrium properties of a voltage-dependent junctional conductance. *J. Gen. Physiol.* **77:** 77–93.
73. Moreno, A. P., Rook, M. B., Fishman, G. I., and Spray, D. C. (1994). Gap junction channels: distinct voltage-sensitive and -insensitive conductance states. *Biophys. J.* **67:** 113–119.
74. Spray, D. C., and Scemes, E. (1998). Effects of pH (and Ca) on gap junction channels. In *pH and Brain Function* (K. Kaila and B. R. Ransom, eds.), John Wiley & Sons, NY.
75. Mantz, J., Cordier, J., and Giaume, C. (1993). Effects of general anesthetics on intercellular communications mediated by gap junctions between astrocytes in primary culture. *Anesthesiology* **78**(5): 892–901.
76. Saez, J. C., Berthoud, V. M., Moreno, A. P., and Spray, D. C. (1993). Gap junctions. Multiplicity of controls in differentiated and undifferentiated cells and possible functional implications. *Adv. Second Messenger Phosphoprotein Res.* **27:** 163–198.
77. Moreno, A. P., Saez, J. C., Fishman, G. I., and Spray, D. C. (1994). Human connexin43 gap junction channels. Regulation of unitary conductances by phosphorylation. *Circ. Res.* **74:** 1050–1057.
78. Swenson, K. I., Piwnica-Worms, H., McNamee, H., and Paul, D. L. (1990). Tyrosine phosphorylation of the gap junction protein connexin43 is required for the pp60v-src-induced inhibition of communication. *Cell Regul.* **1:** 989–1002.
79. Stewart, W. W. (1981). Lucifer dyes—highly fluorescent dyes for biological tracing. *Nature (London)* **292:** 17–21.
80. Veenstra, R. D., Wang, H. Z., Beyer. E. C., and Brink, P. R. (1994). Selective dye and ionic permeability of gap junction channels formed by connexin45. *Circ. Res.* **75:** 483–490.
81. Veenstra, R. D., Wang, H. Z., Beblo, D. A., Chilton, M. G., Harris, A. L., Beyer, E. C., and Brink, P. R. (1995). Selectivity of connexin-specific gap junctions does not correlate with channel conductance. *Circ. Res.* **77:** 1156–1165.
82. Chang, M., Werner, R., and Dahl, G. (1996). A role for an inhibitory connexin in testis? *Dev. Biol.* **175:** 50–56.
83. Hinricksen, C. F. L., and Larramendi, M. H. (1968). Synapses and cluster formation of the mouse mesencephalic fifth nucleus. *Brain Res.* **7:** 296–299.
84. Rall, W., Shepherd, G. M., Reese, T. S., and Brightman, M. W. (1966). Dendrodendritic synaptic pathway for inhibition in the olfactory bulb. *Exp. Neurol.* **14:** 44–56.
85. Dermietzel, R., Traub, O., Hwang, T. K., Beyer, E., Bennett, M. V., Spray, D. C., and Willecke, K. (1989). Differential expression of three gap junction proteins in developing and mature brain tissues. *Proc. Natl. Acad. Sci. U.S.A.* **86:** 10148–10152.
86. Mehler, M. F., Rozental, R., Doudgherty, M., Spray, D. C., and Kessler, J. A. (1993). Cytokine regulation of neuronal differentiation in immortalized hippocampal progenitor cells. *Nature (London)* **362:** 62–65.
87. Rozental, R., Morales, M., Urban, M., Mehler, M. F., Kremer, M., Kessler, J. A., Dermietzel, R., and Spray, D. C. (1998). Changes in the properties of gap junctions during neuronal differentiation of hippocampal progenitor cells. *J. Neurosci.* **18:** 1753–1762.
88. Chiu, F.-C., Rozental, R., Bassallo, C., Lyman, W. D., and Spray, D. C. (1994). Human fetal neurons in culture: Intercellular communication and voltage- and ligand-gated responses. *J. Neurosci. Res.* **38:** 687–697.
89. Rozental, R., and Spray, D. C. (1996). Temporal expression of gap junctions during neuronal ontogeny. In *Gap Junctions in the Nervous System* (D.C. Spray and R. Dermietzel, eds.), pp. 261–273. R. G. Landes, Austin, TX.
90. Cepeda, C., Walsh, J. P., Peacock, W., Buchwald, N. A., and Levine, M. S. (1993). Dye-coupling in human neocortical tissue resected from children with intractable epilespy. *Cereb. Cortex* **3:** 95–107.
91. Giaume, C., and McCarthy, K. D. (1996). Control of junctional communication in astrocytic networks. *Trends Neurosci.* **19:** 319–325.
92. Dermietzel, R., Hertzberg, E. L., Kessler, J. A., and Spray, D. C. (1991). Gap junctions between cultured astrocytes: Immunocytochemical, molecular, and electrophysiological analysis. *J. Neurosci.* **11:** 1421–1432.
93. Giaume, C., Fromaget, C., el Aoumari, A., Cordier, J., Glowinski, J., and Gros, D. (1991). Gap junctions in cultured astrocytes: Single-channel currents and characterization of channel-forming protein. *Neuron* **6:** 133–143.
94. Batter, D. K., Corpina, R. A., Roy, C., Spray, D. C., Hertzberg, E. L., and Kessler, J. A. (1992). Heterogeneity in gap junction expression in astrocytes cultured from different brain regions. *Glia* **6:** 213–221.
95. Lee, S. H., Kim, W. T., Cornell-Bell, A. H., and Sontheimer. H. (1994). Astrocytes exhibit regional specificity in gap-junction coupling. *Glia* **11**(4): 315–325.
96. Venance, L., Piomelli, D., Glowinski, J., and Giaume, C. (1995). Inhibition by anandamide of gap junctions and intercellular calcium signalling in striatal astrocytes. *Nature (London)* **376:** 590–594.
97. Guan, X., Cravatt, B. F., Ehring, G. R., Hall, J. E., Boger, D. L., Lerner, R. A., and Gilula, N. B. (1997). The sleep-inducing lipid oleamide deconvolutes gap junction communication and calcium wave transmission in glial cells. *J. Cell Biol.* **29:** 1785–1792.
98. Bergoffen, J., Scherer, S. S., Wang, S., Scott, M. O., Bone, L. J., Paul, D. L., Chen, K., Lensch, M. W., Chance, P., and Fischbeck,

K. (1993). Connexin mutations in X-linked Charcot-Marie-Tooth disease. *Science* **262:** 2039–2042.

99. Scherer, S. S., Xu, Y. T., Nelles, E., Fischbeck, K., Willecke, K., and Bone, J. (1998). Connexin32-null mice develop demyelinating peripheral neuropathy. *Glia* **24:** 8–20.

100. Chandross, K. J., Kessler, J. A., Cohen, R. I., Simburger, E., Spray, D. C., Bieri, P., and Dermietzel, R. (1996). Altered connexin expression after peripheral nerve injury. *Mol. Cell. Neurosci.* **7:** 501–518.

101. Zhao, S. M., and Spray, D. C. (1998). Localization of Cx26, Cx32 and Cx43 in myelinating Schwann cells of mouse sciatic nerve during postnatal development. In *Gap Junctions* (R. Werner, ed.), IOS Press, New York pp. 198–202.

102. Dermietzel, R., Farooq, M., Kessler, J. A., Althaus, H., Hertzberg, E. L., and Spray, D. C. (1997). Oligodendrocytes express gap junction proteins connexin32 and connexin45. *Glia* **20:** 101–114.

103. Spray, D. C., Moreno, A. P., Kessler, J. A., and Dermietzel, R. (1991). Characterization of gap junctions between cultured leptomeningeal cells. *Brain Res.* **24:** 1–14.

104. Del Bigio, M. R. (1994). The Ependyma: A protective barrier between brain and cerebrospinal fluid. *Glia* **14:** 1–13.

105. Ransom, B. R. (1996). Do glial gap junctions play a role in extracellular homeostatis? In *Gap Junctions in the Nervous System* (D. C. Spray and R. Dermietzel, eds.), pp. 161–173. R. G. Landes, Austin, TX.

106. Van Harreveld, A. (1966). *Brain Tissue Electrolytes,* pp. 95–126. Butterworth, London.

107. Kimelberg, H. K. (1991). Swelling and volume control in brain astroglial cells. *Comp. Environ Phys.* **9:** 81–117.

108. Scemes, E., and Spray, D. C. (1998). Increased intercellular communication in mouse astrocytes exposed to hyposmotic shocks. *Glia* **24(1):** 74–84.

109. Kimelberg, H. K. (1995). Brain edema. In *Neuroglia* (H. Kettenmann and B. R. Ransom, eds.), pp. 919–935. Oxford University Press, New York.

110. Rapoport, S. I. (1979). Role of cerebrovascular permeability, brain compliance and brain hydraulic conductivity in vasogenic brain edema. In *Neural Trauma* (A. J. Popp, R. S. Bourke, L. R. Nelson, and H. K. Kimelberg, eds.), pp. 51–62. Raven Press, New York.

111. Van Harreveld, A., and Khattab, F. (1967). Changes in cortical extracellular space during spreading depression investigated with the electron microscope. *J. Neurophysiol.* **30:** 911–929.

112. Dietzel, L., Heinemann, V., Hofmeier, G., and Lux, H. (1980). Transient changes in the size of the extracellular space in the sensoirmotor cortex of cells in relation to stimulus-induced changes in potassium concentrations. *Exp. Brain Res.* **40:** 432–439.

113. Orkand, R., Dietzel, I., and Coles, J. (1984). Light-induced changes in extracellular volume in the retina of the drone, *Apis mellihera. Neurosci. Lett.* **45:** 273–278.

114. Bourke, R., and Nelson, K. (1972). Further studies on the K^+-dependent swelling of primate cerebral cortex in vivo: The enzymatic basis of the K^+-dependent transport of chloride. *J. Neurochem.* **19:** 663–685.

115. Rash, J. E., Duffy, H. S., Dudek, F. E., Bilhartz, B. L., Whalen, L. R., and Yasumura, T. (1997). Grid-mapped freeze-fracture analysis of gap junctions in gray and white matter of adult rat central nervous system, with evidence for a "pan-glial syncytium" that is not coupled to neurons. *J. Comp. Neurol.* **388:** 1–28.

116. Mugnaini, E. (1986). Cell junctions of astrocytes, ependyma, and related cells in the mammalian central nervous system, with emphasis, on the hypothesis of a generalized functional syncytium of supporting cells. In *Astrocytes* (S. Fedoroff and A. Vernadakis, eds.), Vol. I., pp. 329–371. Academic Press, New York.

117. Spray, D. C., and Dermietzel, R. (1995). X-linked dominant Charcot-Marie-Tooth disease and their potential gap-junction diseases of the nervous system. *Trends Neurosci* **18:** 256–262.

118. Bordy, A., and Sontheimer, H. (1998). Properties of human glial cells associated with epileptic seizure foci. *Epilepsy Res.* (in press).

119. Janigro, D., Gasporini, S., D'Ambrosio, R., McKhann, G., and DiFrancesco, D. (1997). Reduction of K^+ uptake in glial prevents long-term depression maintenance and causes epileptiform activity. *J. Neurosci.* **17:** 2813–2824.

120. Taylor, C. P., and Dudek, F. E. (1982). Synchronous neural afterdischarges in rat hippocampal slices without active chemical synapses. *Science* **218:** 810–812.

121. Dudek, E. E., Snow, R. W., and Taylor, C. P. (1986). Role of electrical interactions in synchronication of epileptiform bursts. *Adv. Neurol.* **44:** 593–617.

122. Jeffreys, J. G. R. (1995). Nonsynaptic modulation of neuronal activity in the brain: Electric currents and extracellular ions. *Physiol. Rev.* **75:** 689–723.

123. Perez-Velazquez, J. L., Valiante, T. A., and Carlen, P. L. (1994). Modulation of gap junctional mechanisms during calcium-free induced field burst activity: A possible role for electrotonic coupling in epileptogenesis. *J. Neurosci.* **14:** 4308–4317.

124. Naus, C. C., Bechberger, J. F., and Paul, D. L. (1991). Gap junction gene expression in human seizure disorder. *Exp. Neurol.* **111**(2): 198–203.

125. Elisevich, K., Rempel, S. A., Smith, B. J., and Edvardsen, K. (1997). Hippocampal connexin43 expression in human complex partial seizure disorder. *Exp. Neurol.* **45**(1): 154–164.

126. Lee, S. H., Magge, S., Spencer, D. D., Sontheimer, H., and Cornell-Bell. A. H. (1995). Human epileptic astrocytes exhibit increased gap junction coupling. *Glia* **15**(2): 195–202.

127. Leão, A. A. P. (1987). Spreading depression. In *Encyclopedia of Neuroscience* (G. Adelman, ed.), pp. 1137–1138. Birkhauser, Stuttgart.

128. do Carmo, R. J., Somjen, G. G. (1994). Spreading depression of Leao: 50 years since a seminal discovery. *J. Neurophysiol.* **72**(1): 1–2.

129. McLachlan, R. S., and Girvin, J. P. (1994). Spreading depression of Leao in rodent and human cortex. *Brain Res.* **12**(1): 133–136.

130. Herreras, O., Largo, C., Ibarz, J. M., Somjen, G. G., and Martin del Rio, R. (1994). Role of neuronal synchronizing mechanisms in the propagation of spreading depression in the in vivo hippocampus. *J. Neurosci.* **14**(11, Pt 2): 7087–7098.

131. Streit, D. S., Ferreira Filho, C. R., and Martins-Ferreira, H. (1995). Spreading depression in isolated spinal cord. *J. Neurophysiol.* **74**(2): 888–890.

132. Martins-Ferreira, H. (1993). Propagation of spreading depression in isolated retina. In *Migraine: Basic Mechanisms and Treatment* (A. Lehmenkuller, K. H. Grotemeyer, and F. Tegmeier, eds.), pp. 533–546. Urban & Schwarzenberg, München-Wien-Baltimore.

133. Largo, C., Tombaugh, G. C., Aitken, P. G., Herreras, O., and Somjen, G. G. (1997). Heptanol but not fluoroacetate prevents the propagation of spreading depression in rat hippocampal slices. *J. Neurophysiol.* **77**(1): 9–16.

134. Martins-Ferreira, H., and Ribeiro, L. J. (1995). Biphasic effects of gap junctional uncoupling agents on the propagation of retinal spreading depression. *Braz. J. Med. Biol. Res.* **28**(9): 991–994.

135. Nedergaard, M., Cooper, A. J. L., and Goldman, S. A. (1995).

Gap junctions are required for the propagation of spreading depression. *J. Neurobiol.* **28:** 433–444.
136. Rawanduzy, A., Hansen, A., Hansen, T. W., and Nedergaard, M. E. (1997). Effective reduction of infarct volume by gap junction blockade in a rodent model of stroke. *J. Neurosurg.* **87**(6): 916–920.
137. Ouvrier, R. (1996). Correlation between the histopathologic, genotypic and phenotypic features of hereditary peripheral neuropathies in childhood. *J. Child Neurol.* **11:** 133–146.
138. Deschenes, S. M., Bone, L. J., Fischbeck, K. H. and Scherer, S. S. (1996). Connexin32 and X-linked Charcot–Marie–Tooth disease. In *Gap Junctions in the Nervous System* (D. C. Spray and R. Dermietzel, eds.), pp. 213–227. R. G. Landes Co., Austin, TX.
139. Deschenes, S. M., Walcott, J. L., Wexler, T. L., Scherer, S. S., and Fischbeck, K. H. (1997). Altered trafficking of mutant connexin32. *J. Neurosci.* **17:** 9077–9084.
140. Oh, S., Ri, Y., Bennett, M. V., Trexler, E. B., Verselis, V. K., and Bargiello, T. A. (1997). Changes in permeability caused by connexin32 mutations underlie X-linked Charcot-Marie-Tooth disease. *Neuron* **19:** 927–938.
141. Omori, Y., Mesnil, M., and Yamasaki, H. (1996). Connexin 32 mutations from X-linked Charcot-Marie-Tooth disease patients: Functional defects and dominant negative effects. *Mol. Biol. Cell* **7:** 907–916.
142. Bruzzone, R., White, T. W., Scherer, S. S., Fishbeck, K. H., and Paul, D. L. (1994). Null mutations of connexin32 in patients with X-linked Charcot-Marie-Tooth disease. *Neuron* **13:** 1253–1260.
143. Anzini, P., Neuberg, D. H., Schachner, M., Nelles, E., Willecke, K., Zielasek, J., Toyka, K. V., Suter, U., and Martini, R. (1997). Structural abnormalities and deficient maintenance of peripheral nerve myelin in mice lacking the gap junction protein connexin32. *J. Neurosci.* **17:** 4545–4551.
144. Furshpan, E. J., and Potter, D. D. (1968). Low-resistance junctions between cells in embryos and tissue culture. *Curr. Top. Dev. Biol.* **3:** 95–127.
145. Loewenstein, W. R. (1979). Junctional intercellular communication and the control of growth. *Biochim. Biophys. Acta* **560:** 1–65.
146. Eghbali, B., Kessler, J. A., Reid, L. M., Roy, C., and Spray, D. C. (1991). Involvement of gap junctions in tumorigenesis: Transfection of tumor cells with connexin32 cDNA retards growth in vivo. *Proc. Natl. Acad. Sci. U.S.A.* **88:** 10701–10705.
147. Elshami, A. A., Saavedra, A., Zhang, H., Kucharczuk, J. C., Spray, D. C., Fishman, G. I., Amin, K. M., Kaiser, L. R., and Albelda, S. M. (1996). Gap junctions play a role in the 'bystander effect' of the herpes simplex virus thymidine kinase/ganciclovir system in vitro. *Gene Ther.* **3:** 85–92.
148. Bond, S. L., Bechberger, J. F., Khoo, N. K., and Naus, C. C. (1994). Transfection of C6 glioma cells with connexin32: The effects of expression of a nonendogenous gap junction protein. *Cell Growth Differ.* **5:** 179–186.
149. Temme, A., Buchmann, A., Gabriel, H. D., Nelles, E., Schwarz, M., and Willecke, K. (1997). High incidence of spontaneous and chemically induced liver tumors in mice deficient for connexin32. *Curr. Biol.* **7:** 713–716.
150. Shinoura, N., Chen, I., Wani, M. A., Kim, Y. G., Larson, J. J., Warnick, R. E., Simon, M., Menon, A. G., Bi, W. L., and Stambrook, P. J. (1996). Protein and messenger RNA expression of connexin43 in astrocytomas: implications in brain tumor gene therapy. *J. Neurosurg.* **84:** 839–845.
151. Takahashi, K., Bland, K. S., Islam, S., and Michaelis, M. L. (1995). Effects of antisense oligonucleotides to the cardiac Na^+/Ca^{2+} exchanger on cultured cardiac myocytes. *Biochem. Biophys. Res. Commun.* **212:** 524–530.
152. Campbell, V., Berrow, N. S., Fitzgerald, E. M., Brickley, K., and Dolphin, A. C. (1995). Inhibition of interaction of G protein G (o) with calcium channel beta-subunit in rat neurones. *J. Physiol. (London)* **485:** 365–372.
153. Willecke, K., Buchmann, A., Bützler, C., Gabriel, H.-D., Hagendorff, A., Jung, D., Kirchhoff, S., Krüger, O., Nelles, E., Schwarz, M., Temme, A., Traub, O., and Winterhager, E. (1998). Biological functions of gap junctions revealed by targeted inactivation of mouse connexin32, -26 and -43 genes. In *Gap Junctions* (R. Werner, ed.), pp. 304–308. IOS Press, Amsterdam.
154. Kelsell, D. P., Dunlop, J., Stevens, H. P., Lench, N. J., Liang, J. N., Parry, G., Mueller, R. F., and Leigh, I. M. (1997). Connexin26 mutations in hereditary non-syndromic sensorineural deafness. *Nature (London)* **387:** 80–83.
155. Richard, G., Lin, J. P., Smith, L., Whyte, Y. M., Itin, P., Wollina, U., Epstein, E., Jr., Hohl, D., Giroux, J. M., Charnas, L., Bale, S. J., and DiGiovanna, J. J. (1997). Linkage studies in erythrokeratodermias: Fine mapping, genetic heterogeneity and analysis of candidate genes. *J. Invest. Dermatol.* **109:** 666–671.
156. Nelles, E., Butzler, C., Jung, D., Temme, A., Gabriel, H.-D., Dahl, U., Traub, O., Stumpel, F., Jungermann, K., Zielasek, J., Toyka, K. V., Dermietzel, R., and Willecke, K. (1996). Defective propagation of signals generated by sympathetic nerve stimulation in the liver of connexin32-deficient mice. *Proc. Natl. Acad. Sci. U.S.A.* **93:** 9565–9570.
157. Simon, A. M., Goodenough, D. A., Li, E., and Paul, D. L. (1997). Female infertility in mice lacking connexin 37. *Nature (London)* **385:** 525–529.
158. Goodenough, D. A., Simon, A. M., and Paul, D. L. (1997). Cardiac conduction abnormalities in mice lacking connexin40. *Mol. Biol. Cell* **8:** 124a.
159. Guerrero, P. A., Schuessler, R. B., Davis, L. M., Beyer, E. C., Johnson, C. M., Yamada, K. A., and Saffitz, J. E. (1997). Slow ventricular conduction in mice heterozygous for a connexin43 null mutation. *J. Clin. Invest.* **15:** 1991–1998.
160. Gao, Y., and Spray, D. C. (1998). Gap junction expression in lens and cornea of wildtype (WT) and Cx43 deficient (KO) mice: Cataractous changes in lens but no striking defect in cornea. In *Gap Junctions* (R. Werner, ed.), ISO Press, pp. 314–318. Amsterdam.
161. Britz-Cunningham, S. H., Shah, M. M., Zuppan, C. W., and Fletcher, W. H. (1995). Mutations of the connexin43 gap-junction gene in patients with heart malformations and defects of laterality. *N. Engl. J. Med.* **332:** 1323–1329.
162. Penman-Splitt, M., Tsai, M. Y., Burn, J., and Goodship, J. A. (1997). Absence of mutations in the regulatory domain of the gap junction protein connexin43 in patients with visceroatrial heterotaxy. *Heart* **77:** 369–370.
163. Gebbia, M., Towbin, J. A., and Casey, B. (1996). Failure to detect connexin43 mutations in 38 cases of sporadic and familial heterotaxy. *Circulation* **94:** 1909–1912.
164. Gong, X., Li, E., Klier, G., Huang, Q., Wu, Y., Lei, H., Kumar, N. M., Horwitz, H., and Gilula, N. B. (1997). Disruption of α_3 connexin gene leads to proteolysis and cataractogenesis in mice. *Cell (Cambridge, Mass.)* **91:** 833–843.
165. White T. W., Goodenough, D. A., and Paul, D. L. (1997). Ocular abnormalities in connexin50 knockout mice. *Mol. Biol. Cell* **8:** 93a.
166. Mackay, D., Ionides, A., Berry, V., Moore, A., Bhattacharya, S., and Shiels, A. (1997). A new locus for dominant "zonular pulverulent" cataract on chromosome 13. *Am. J. Hum. Genet.* **60:** 1474–1478.
167. Dilber, M. S., Abedi, M. R., Christensson, B., Bjorkstrand, B., Kidder, G. M., Naus, C. C., Gahrton, G., and Smith, C. I. (1997). Gap junctions promote the bystander effect of herpes simplex virus thymidine kinase in vivo. *Cancer Res.* **57:** 1523–1528.

168. Fick, J., Barker, F. G., 2nd, Dazin, P., Westphale, E. M., Beyer, E. C., and Israel, M. A. (1995). The extent of heterocellular communication mediated by gap junctions is predictive of bystander tumor cytotoxicity in vitro. *Proc. Natl. Acad. Sci. U.S.A.* **92:** 11071–11075.
169. Mesnil, M., Piccoli, C., Tiraby, G., Willecke, K., and Yamasaki, H. (1996). Bystander killing of cancer cells by herpes simplex virus thymidine kinase gene is mediated by connexins. *Proc. Natl. Acad. Sci. U.S.A.* **93:** 1831–1835.
170. Vrionis, F. D., Wu, J. K., Qi, P., Waltzman, M., Cherington, V., and Spray, D. C. (1997). The bystander effect exerted by tumor cells expressing the herpes simplex virus thymidine kinase (HSVtk) gene is dependent on connexin expression and cell communication. *Gene Ther.* **6:** 577–585.
171. Saffitz, J. E. (1997). Gap junctions: Functional effects of molecular structure and tissue distribution. *Adv. Exp. Med. Biol.* **430:** 291–301.
172. Laskawi, R., Rohlmann, A., Landgrebe, M., and Wolff, J. R. (1997). Rapid astroglial reactions in the motor cortex of adult rats following peripheral facial nerve lesions. *Eur. Arch. Otorhinolaryngol.* **254:** 81–85.
173. Thériault, E., Frankenstein, U. N., Hertzberg, E. L., and Nagy, J. I. (1997). Connexin43 and astrocytic gap junctions in the rat spinal cord after acute compression injury. *J. Comp. Neurol.* **382:** 199–214.
174. Campos de Carvalho, A. C., Tanowitz, H. B., Wittner, M., Dermietzel, R., Roy, C., Hertzberg, E. L., and Spray, D. C. (1993). Gap junction distribution is altered between cardiac myocytes infected with *Trypanosoma cruzi. Circ. Res.* **70:** 733–742.
175. Campos de Carvalho, A. C., Roy, C., Hertzberg, E. L., Tanowitz, H. B., Kessler, J. A., Weiss, L. M., Wittner, M., Dermietzel, R., Gao, Y., and Spray, D. C. (1998). Gap junction disappearance in astrocytes and leptomeningeal cells as a consequence of protozoan infection. *Brain Res.* **790:** 304–314.

CHAPTER

12

Postsynaptic Potentials and Synaptic Integration

John H. Byrne

The study of synaptic transmission in the central nervous system provides an opportunity to learn more about the diversity and richness of mechanisms underlying this process and to learn how some of the fundamental signaling properties of the nervous system, such as action potentials and synaptic potentials, work together to process information and generate behavior.

Postsynaptic potentials (PSPs) in the CNS can be divided into two broad classes on the basis of mechanisms and, generally, duration of these potentials. One class is based on the *direct* binding of a transmitter molecule(s) with a receptor–channel complex; these receptors are **ionotropic.** The structure of these receptors is discussed in detail in Chapter 9. The resulting PSPs are generally short lasting and hence are sometimes called fast PSPs; they have also been referred to as "classical" because they were the first synaptic potentials to be recorded in the CNS.[1,2] The duration of a typical fast PSP is about 20 ms.

The other class of PSPs is based on the *indirect* effect of transmitter molecule(s) binding with a receptor. The receptors that produce these PSPs are **metabotropic.** As discussed in Chapter 9, the receptors activate G proteins that affect the channel either directly or through additional steps in which the level of a second messenger is altered. The responses mediated by metabotropic receptors can be long-lasting and are therefore called slow PSPs. The mechanisms for fast PSPs mediated by ionotropic receptors are considered first.

IONOTROPIC RECEPTORS: MEDIATORS OF FAST EXCITATORY AND INHIBITORY SYNAPTIC POTENTIALS

The Stretch Reflex Is a Useful Means of Examining the Properties and Functional Consequences of Ionotropic PSPs

The stretch reflex, one of the simpler behaviors mediated by the central nervous system, is a useful example with which to examine the properties and functional consequences of ionotropic PSPs. The tap of a neurologist's hammer to a ligament elicits a reflex extension of the leg, as illustrated in Fig. 12.1. The brief stretch of the ligament is transmitted to the extensor muscle and is detected by specific receptors in the muscle and ligament (Chapter 30). Action potentials initiated in the stretch receptors are propagated to the spinal cord by afferent fibers (Chapter 31). The receptors are specialized regions of sensory neurons with somata located in the dorsal root ganglia just outside the spinal column. The axons of the afferents enter the spinal cord and make excitatory synaptic connections with at least two types of postsynaptic neurons. First, a synaptic connection is made to the extensor motor neuron. As the result of its synaptic activation, the motor neuron fires action potentials that propagate out of the spinal cord and ultimately invade the terminal regions of the motor axon at neuromuscular junctions. There, acetylcholine (ACh) is released, nicotinic ACh receptors are activated, an end-plate potential (EPP) is

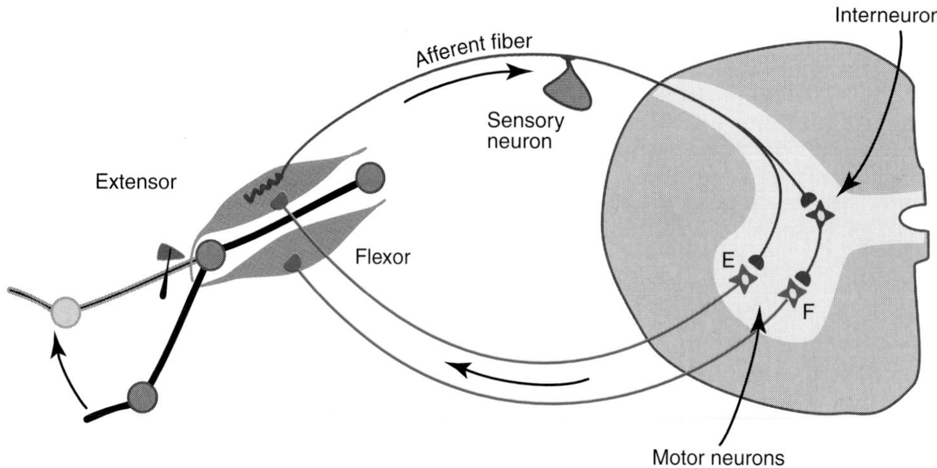

FIGURE 12.1 Features of the vertebrate stretch reflex. Stretch of an extensor muscle leads to the initiation of action potentials in the afferent terminals of specialized stretch receptors. The action potentials propagate to the spinal cord through afferent fibers (sensory neurons). The afferents make excitatory connections with extensor motor neurons (E). Action potentials initiated in the extensor motor neuron propagate to the periphery and lead to the activation and subsequent contraction of the extensor muscle. The afferent fibers also activate interneurons that inhibit the flexor motor neurons (F).

produced, an action potential is initiated in the muscle cell, and the muscle cell is contracted, producing the reflex extension of the leg. Second, a synaptic connection is made to another group of neurons called **interneurons** (nerve cells interposed between one type of neuron and another). The particular interneurons activated by the afferents are **inhibitory interneurons,** because activation of these interneurons leads to the release of a chemical transmitter substance that inhibits the flexion motor neuron. This inhibition tends to prevent an uncoordinated (improper) movement (i.e., flexion) from occurring. The reflex system illustrated in Fig. 12.1 is also known as the **monosynaptic stretch reflex** because this reflex is mediated by a single ("mono") excitatory synapse in the central nervous system. Spinal reflexes are described in greater detail in Chapter 31.

Figure 12.2 illustrates procedures that can be used to experimentally examine some of the components of synaptic transmission in the reflex pathway for the stretch reflex. Intracellular recordings are made from one of the sensory neurons, the extensor and flexor motor neurons, and an inhibitory interneuron. Normally, the sensory neuron is activated by stretch to the muscle, but this step can be bypassed by simply injecting a pulse of depolarizing current of sufficient magnitude into the sensory neuron to elicit an action potential. The action potential in the sensory neuron leads to a potential change in the motor neuron known as an **excitatory postsynaptic potential** (EPSP; Fig. 12.2).

Mechanisms responsible for fast EPSPs mediated by ionotropic receptors in the CNS are fairly well known. Moreover, the ionic mechanisms for EPSPs in the CNS are essentially identical with the ionic mechanisms at the skeletal neuromuscular junction. Specifically, the transmitter substance released from the presynaptic terminal (Chapters 7 and 11) diffuses across the synaptic cleft, binds to specific receptor sites on the postsynaptic membrane (Chapters 8 and 10), and leads to a simultaneous increase in permeability to Na^+ and K^+, which makes the membrane potential move *toward* a value of about 0 mV. However, the processes of synaptic transmission at the sensory neuron–motor neuron synapse and the motor neuron–skeletal muscle synapse differ in two fundamental ways: (1) in the transmitter used and (2) in the amplitude of the PSP. The transmitter substance at the neuromuscular junction is ACh, whereas that released by the sensory neurons is an amino acid, probably glutamate (see Chapter 8). Indeed, glutamate is the most common transmitter that mediates excitatory actions in the CNS. The amplitude of the postsynaptic potential at the neuromuscular junction is about 50 mV; consequently, each PSP depolarizes the postsynaptic cell beyond threshold, so there is a one-to-one relation between an action potential in the spinal motor neuron and an action potential in the skeletal muscle cell. Indeed, the EPP must depolarize the muscle cell by only about 30 mV to initiate an action potential, allowing a safety factor of about 20 mV. In contrast, the EPSP in a spinal motor neuron produced by an action potential in an afferent fiber has an amplitude of only about 1 mV. The mechanisms by which these small PSPs can trigger an action potential in the postsynaptic neuron are discussed in a later section of this chapter and in Chapter 13.

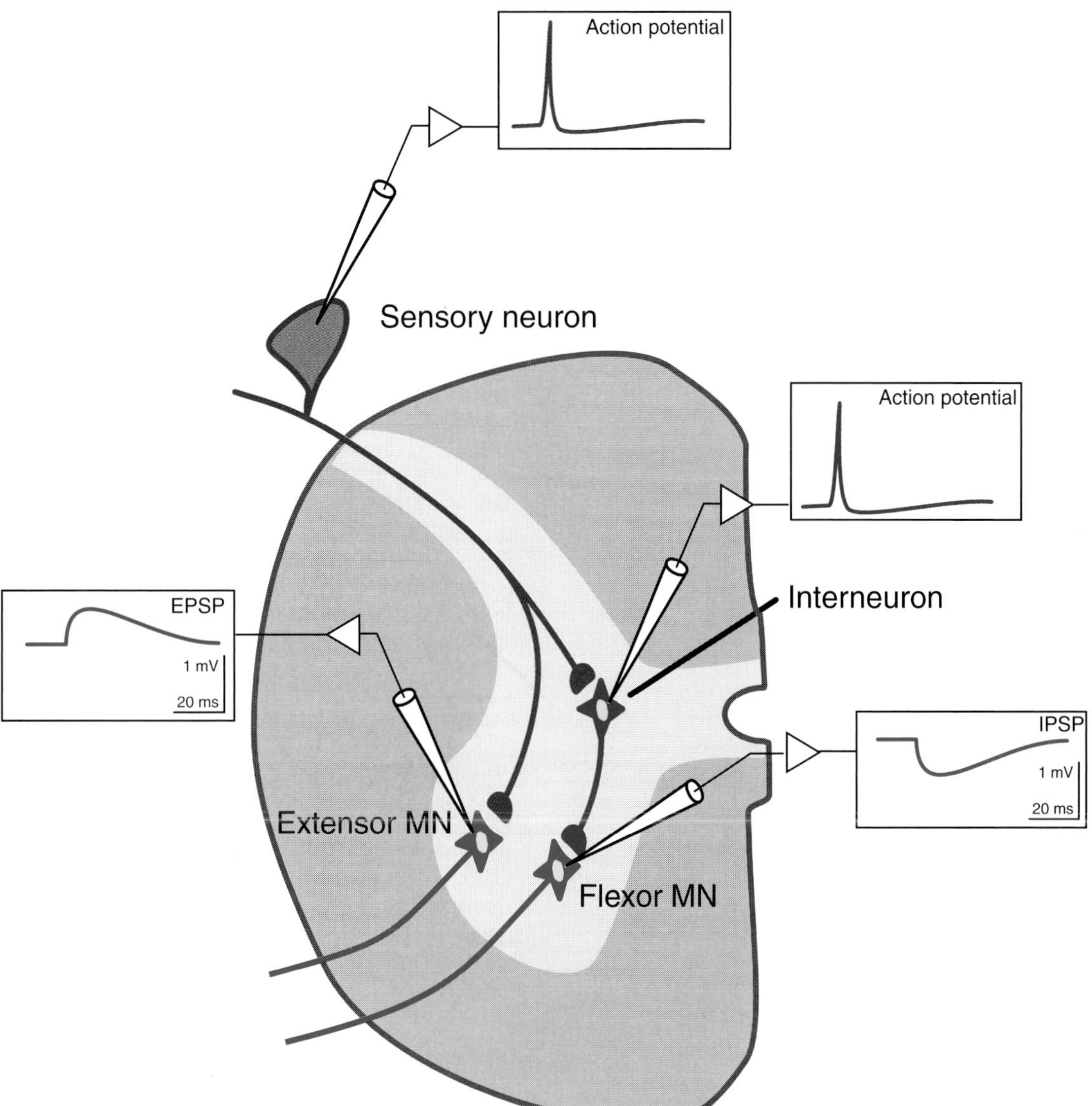

FIGURE 12.2 Excitatory (EPSP) and inhibitory (IPSP) postsynaptic potentials in spinal motor neurons. Idealized intracellular recordings from a sensory neuron, interneuron, and extensor and flexor motor neurons (MNs). An action potential in the sensory neuron produces a depolarizing response (an EPSP) in the extensor motor neuron. An action potential in the interneuron produces a hyperpolarizing response (an IPSP) in the flexor motor neuron.

Macroscopic Properties of PSPs Are Determined by the Nature of the Gating and Ion-Permeation Properties of Single Channels

Patch-Clamp Techniques

Patch-clamp techniques,[3] with which current flowing through single isolated receptors can be measured directly, can be sources of insight into both the ionic mechanisms and the molecular properties of PSPs mediated by ionotropic receptors. This approach was pioneered by Erwin Neher and Bert Sakman in the 1970s and led to their being awarded the Nobel Prize in Physiology or Medicine in 1991.

Figure 12.3A illustrates an idealized experimental arrangement of an "outside-out" patch recording of a single ionotropic receptor. The patch pipette contains a solution with an ionic composition similar to that of the cytoplasm, whereas the solution exposed to the outer surface of the membrane has a composition similar to that of normal extracellular fluid. The electrical potential across the patch, and hence the transmembrane potential (V_m), is controlled by the patch-clamp amplifier. The extracellular (outside) fluid is considered "ground." Transmitter can be delivered by applying pressure to a miniature pipette filled with an agonist (in this case, ACh), and the current (I_m) flowing across the patch of membrane is measured by the

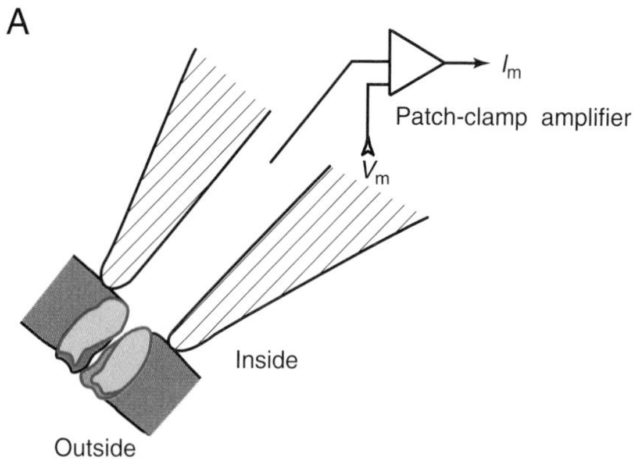

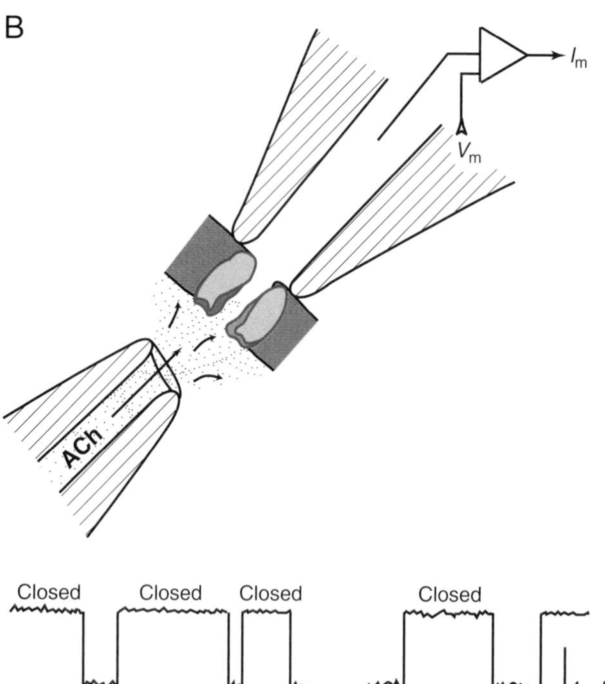

FIGURE 12.3 Single-channel recording of ionotropic receptors and their properties. (A) Experimental arrangement for studying properties of ionotropic receptors. (B) Idealized single-channel currents in response to application of ACh.

patch-clamp amplifier (Fig. 12.3B). Pressure in the pipette that contains ACh can be continuous, allowing a constant stream of ACh to contact the membrane, or can be applied as a short pulse to allow a precisely timed and discrete amount of ACh to contact the membrane. The types of recordings obtained from such an experiment are illustrated in the traces in Fig. 12.3. In the absence of ACh, no current flows through the channel (Fig. 12.3A). When ACh is continuously applied, current flows across the membrane (through the channel), but remarkably, the current does not flow continuously; instead, small steplike changes in current are observed (Fig. 12.3B). These changes represent the probabilistic (random) opening and closing of the channel.

Channel Openings and Closings

As a result of the type of patch-recording techniques heretofore described, three general conclusions about the properties of ligand-gated channels can be drawn. First, ACh, as well as other transmitters that activate ionotropic receptors, causes the opening of individual ionic channels (for a channel to open, usually two molecules of transmitter must bind to the receptor). Second, when a ligand-gated channel opens, it does so in an all-or-none fashion. Increasing the concentration of transmitter in the ejection microelectrode does not increase the permeability (conductance) of the channel; it increases its probability (P) of being open. Third, the ionic current flowing through a single channel in its open state is extremely small (e.g., 10^{-12} A); as a result, the current flowing through any single channel makes only a small contribution to the normal postsynaptic potential. Physiologically, when a larger region of the postsynaptic membrane, and thus more than one channel, is exposed to released transmitter, the net conductance of the membrane increases owing to the increased probability that a larger population of channels will be open at the same time. The normal PSP, measured with standard intracellular recording techniques (see, e.g., Fig. 12.2), is then proportional to the sum of the currents that flow through these many individual open channels. The properties of voltage-sensitive channels (see Chapter 6) are similar in that they, too, open in all-or-none fashion, and, as a result, the net effect on the cell is due to the summation of the currents flowing through many individual open ion channels. The two types of channels differ, however, in that one is opened by a chemical agent, whereas the other is opened by changes in membrane potential.

Statistical Analysis of Channel Gating and the Kinetics of the PSP

The experiment illustrated in Fig. 12.3B was performed with continuous exposure to ACh. Under such conditions, the channels open and close repeatedly. When ACh is applied by a brief pressure pulse to more accurately mimic the transient release from the presynaptic terminal, the transmitter diffuses away before it can cause a second opening of the channel. A set of data similar to that shown in Fig. 12.4A would be obtained if an ensemble of these openings were collected and aligned with the start of each open-

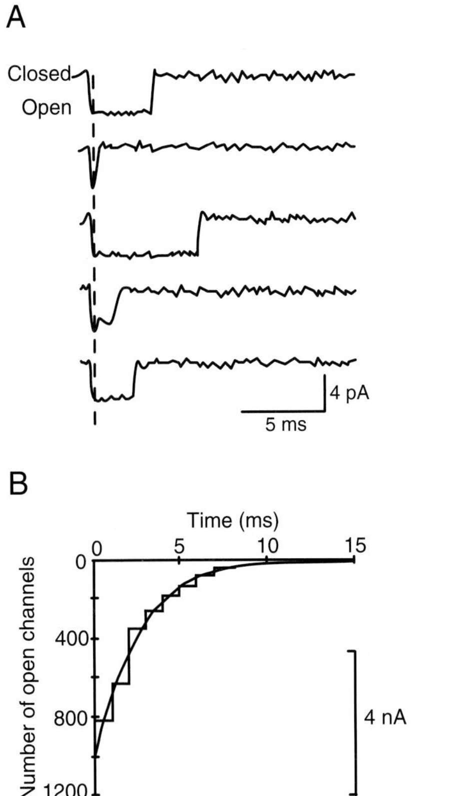

FIGURE 12.4 Determination of the shape of the postsynaptic response from the single-channel currents. (A) Each trace represents the response of a single channel to a repetitively applied puff of transmitter. The traces are aligned with the beginning of the channel opening (dashed line). (B) The addition of 1000 of the individual responses. If a current equal to 4 pA were generated by the opening of a single channel, then a 4-nA current would be generated by 1000 channels opening at the same time. The data are fitted with an exponential function having a time constant equal to $1/\alpha$ [see Eq. (9)]. Reprinted with permission from Sakmann.[9] Copyright 1992 American Association for the Advancement of Science.

ing. Each individual trace represents the response to each successive "puff" of ACh. Note that, among the responses, the duration of the opening of the channel varies considerably—from very short (less than 1 ms) to more than 5 ms. Moreover, channel openings are independent events. The duration of any one channel opening does not have any relation to the duration of a previous opening. Figure 12.4B illustrates a plot that is obtained by adding 1000 of these individual responses. Such an addition roughly simulates the conditions under which transmitter released from a presynaptic terminal leads to the near simultaneous activation of many single channels in the postsynaptic membrane. (Note that the addition of 1000 channels would produce a synaptic current equal to about 4 nA.) This simulation is valid given the assumption that the statistical properties of a single channel over time are the same as the statistical properties of the ensemble at one instant of time (i.e., an ergotic process). The ensemble average can be fit with an exponential function with a decay time constant of 2.7 ms. An additional observation (explored in the next section) is that the value of the time constant is equal to the mean duration of the channel openings. The curve in Fig. 12.4B is an indication of the probability that a channel will remain open for various times, with a high probability for short times and a low probability for long times.

The ensemble average of the single-channel currents (Fig. 12.4B) roughly accounts for the time course of the EPSP. However, note that the time course of the aggregate synaptic *current* can be somewhat faster than that of the excitatory postsynaptic *potential* in Fig. 12.2. This difference is due to the charging of the membrane capacitance by a rapidly changing synaptic current. Because the single-channel currents were recorded with the membrane voltage-clamped, the capacitive current [$I_c = C_m{}^*(dV/dt)$] is zero. In contrast, for the recording of the postsynaptic potential in Fig. 12.2, the membrane was not voltage-clamped, and therefore as the voltage changes (dV/dt), some of the synaptic current charges the membrane capacitance [see Eq. (17)].

Analytical expressions that describe the shape of the ensemble average of the open lifetimes and the mean open lifetime can be derived by considering that single-channel opening and closing is a stochastic process.[4–9] Relations are formalized to describe the likelihood (probability) of a channel being in a certain state. Consider the following two-state reaction scheme:

$$C \underset{\alpha}{\overset{\beta}{\rightleftharpoons}} O$$

In this scheme, α represents the rate constant for channel closing and β the rate constant for channel opening. The scheme can be simplified further if we consider a case in which the channel has been opened by the agonist and the agonist is removed instantaneously. A channel so opened (at time 0) will then close after a certain random time (Fig. 12.4). We first formulate an analytical expression that describes the probability that the channel is open (o) at some time (i.e., time t), given that it was open at time 0. This expression is referred to as $P_{o/o}(t)$. To formulate an analytical expression for $P_{o/o}(t)$, first consider the probability that a channel will be *closed* (c) at time $t + \Delta t$, given that it was open at time t, in the limit that Δt is so small that we can ignore multiple events such as an opening followed by a closing. This term, which is referred to as $P_{c/o}(\Delta t)$, will equal $\alpha\Delta t$ (the product of the reverse rate constant and the time interval). Therefore, the probability [$P_{o/o}(\Delta t)$] that a channel will be *open* at time $t + \Delta t$, given that it was open at time t, will equal $1 - \alpha\, \Delta t$ (i.e., 1 minus the probability that it will be closed at $t + \Delta t$). Finally, the probability that the channel will be open at time t *and* will be open at time $t + \Delta t$ can be described by

$$P_{o/o}(t + \Delta t) = P_{o/o}(t)\, P_{o/o}(\Delta t). \quad (1)$$

By substituting and factoring, we obtain

$$P_{o/o}(t + \Delta t) = P_{o/o}(t)\,(1 - \alpha \Delta t) \quad (2)$$

$$P_{o/o}(t + \Delta t) = P_{o/o}(t) - \alpha \Delta t\, P_{o/o}(t) \quad (3)$$

$$\frac{P_{o/o}(t + \Delta t) - P_{o/o}(t)}{\Delta t} = -\alpha P_{o/o}(t). \quad (4)$$

Note that, as $\Delta t \to 0$, the left-hand term defines the derivative. Thus,

$$\frac{dP_{o/o}(t)}{dt} = -\alpha P_{o/o}(t). \quad (5)$$

This differential equation is satisfied by an exponential function. Consequently,

$$P_{o/o}(t) = e^{-\alpha t} \quad (6)$$

We can now determine the probability $[P_{c/o}(t)]$ that the channel is closed at time t, given that it was open at time 0. This will simply be $1 - P_{o/o}(t)$. Therefore,

$$P_{c/o}(t) = 1 - e^{-\alpha t}. \quad (7)$$

The function $P_{c/o}(t)$ represents the cumulative distribution function (or simply the distribution function) for the channel (i.e., the probability that a channel will be closed by time t). This quantity is called the cumulative distribution because it is equal to the sum, or integral, over the probabilities that the channel closes at each of the preceding times. Distribution functions satisfy the relationship

$$0 \leq P(t) \leq 1. \quad (8)$$

Note that, for Eq. (7), at $t = 0$ the probability of a channel being closed is 0 and, at $t = \infty$, the probability of a channel being closed is 1. To obtain an equation for the probability that a channel closing occurs in exactly some period $t + \Delta t$ as Δt approaches 0, we need to determine the probability density function $[p(t)]$, which is defined as the first derivative of the cumulative distribution function.[10] Thus, the probability density function is

$$p(t) = \alpha e^{-\alpha t}. \quad (9)$$

Note that the distribution of open lifetimes illustrated in Fig. 12.4B corresponds well to that predicted by Eq. (9). With an analytical expression for the probability density function in hand, we can now determine another important property of channels—the mean open lifetime. The mean open lifetime can be obtained by taking the average of the probability density function (i.e., the expected value). Operationally, we multiply t and $p(t)$ and integrate between time 0 and ∞. Thus,

$$\text{mean open time} = \int_0^\infty t\,\alpha\, e^{-\alpha t}\, dt = \frac{1}{\alpha}. \quad (10)$$

Note that the mean open time is the time constant of the cumulative distribution function [Eq. (7)] and the probability density function [Eq. (9)] of the channel.

Gating Properties of Ligand-Gated Channels

Although statistical analysis can be a valuable source of insight into the statistical nature of the gating process and the molecular determinants of the macroscopic postsynaptic potential, the description in the preceding section is a simplification of the actual processes. Specifically, a more complete description must include the kinetics of receptor binding and unbinding and the determinants of the channel opening, as well as the fact that channels display rapid transitions between open and closed states during a single agonist receptor occupancy. Thus, the open states illustrated in Figs. 12.3B and 12.4A represent the period of a *burst* of extremely rapid openings and closings. If the bursts of rapid channel openings and closings are thought of, and behave functionally, as a single continuous channel closure, the formalism developed in the preceding section is a reasonable approximation for many ligand-gated channels. Nevertheless, a more complex reaction scheme is necessary to quantitatively explain the available data. Such a scheme would include the following states,

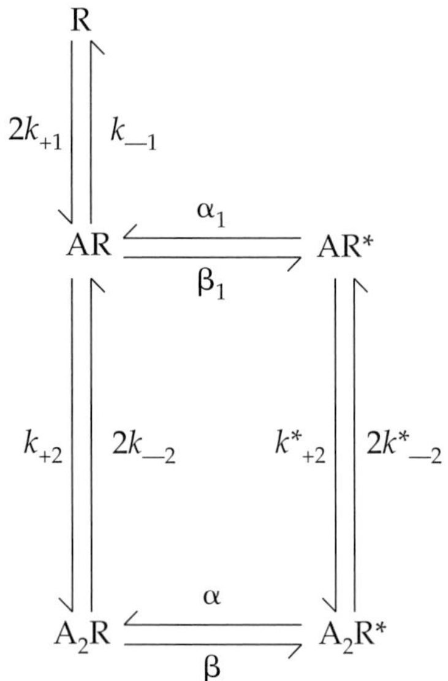

where R represents the receptor, A the agonist, and the α's, β's, and k's the forward and reverse rate constants for the various reactions. A_2R^* represents a channel opened as a result of the binding of two agonist molecules. The asterisk indicates an open channel.[7,9] (Note that the lower part of the reaction scheme is equivalent to the one developed earlier, i.e., $C \underset{\alpha}{\overset{\beta}{\rightleftharpoons}} O$.) With the use of probability theory, equations describing the transitions between the states can be determined. The approach is identical to that used in the simplified two-state scheme. However, the mathematics and analytical expressions are more complex because of the interactions among transitions and the multiple dimensionality of the variables.[4–6] For some receptors, additional states must be represented. For example, as described in Chapter 9, some ligand-gated channels exhibit a process of desensitization in which continued exposure to a ligand results in channel closure.

The Null (Reversal) Potential and Slope of I–V Relations

What ions are responsible for the synaptic current that produces the EPSP? Early studies of the ionic mechanisms underlying the EPSP at the skeletal neuromuscular junction yielded important information. Specifically, voltage-clamp and ion-substitution experiments indicated that the binding of transmitter to receptors on the postsynaptic membrane led to a simultaneous increase in Na^+ and K^+ permeability that depolarized the cell toward a value of about 0 mV.[11,12] These findings are applicable to the EPSP in a spinal motor neuron produced by an action potential in an afferent fiber and have been confirmed and extended at the single-channel level.

Figure 12.5 illustrates the type of experiment in which the analysis of single-channel currents can be a source of insight into the ionic mechanisms of EPSPs. Transmitter is delivered to the patch while the membrane potential is systematically varied (Fig. 12.5A). In the upper trace, the patch potential is −40 mV. The ejection of transmitter produces a sequence of channel openings and closings, the amplitudes of which are constant for each opening (i.e., about 4 pA). Now consider the case in which the transmitter is applied when the potential across the patch is −20 mV. The frequency of the responses, as well as the mean open lifetimes, is about the same as when the potential was at −40 mV, but now the amplitude of the single-channel currents is decreased uniformly. Even more interesting, when the patch is artificially depolarized to a value of about 0 mV, an identical puff of transmitter produces no current in the patch. If the patch potential is depolarized to a value of about +20 mV and the puff again delivered, openings are again observed, but the flow of current through the channel is reversed in sign; a series of

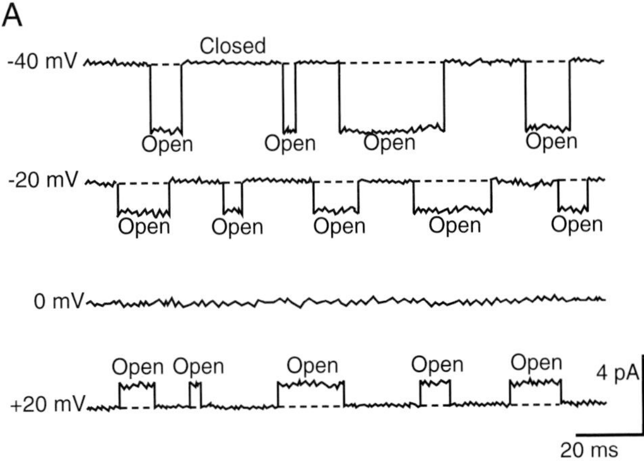

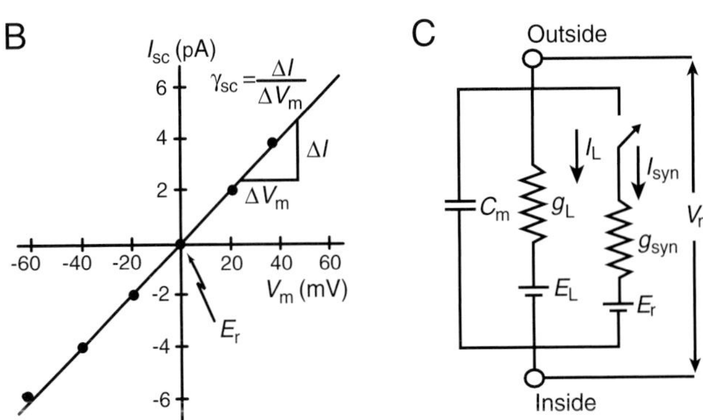

FIGURE 12.5 Voltage dependence of the current flowing through single channels. (A) Idealized recording of an ionotropic receptor in the continuous presence of agonist. (B) *I–V* relation of the channel in A. (C) Equivalent electrical circuit of a membrane containing that channel. Abbreviations: γ_{SC}, single-channel conductance; I_L, leakage current; I_{SC}, single-channel current; g_L, leakage conductance; g_{syn}, macroscopic synaptic conductance; E_L, leakage battery; E_r, reversal potential.

upward deflections indicates outward single-channel currents. In summary, there are downward deflections (inward currents) when the membrane potential is at −40 mV, no deflections (currents) when the membrane is at 0 mV, and upward deflections (outward currents) when the membrane potential is moved to +20 mV.

The simple explanation for these results is that no matter what the membrane potential, the effect of the transmitter binding with receptors is to produce a permeability change that tends to move the membrane potential toward 0 mV. If the membrane potential is more negative than 0 mV, an inward current is recorded. If the membrane potential is more positive than 0 mV, an outward current is recorded. If the membrane potential is at 0 mV, there is no deflection because the membrane potential is already at 0 mV. At 0 mV, the channels are opening and closing as they always do in response to the agonist, but there is no net movement of ions through them. This 0-mV level is known as the **synaptic null potential** or **reversal potential,** because it is the potential at which the sign of the synaptic current reverses. The fact that the experimentally determined reversal potential equals the calculated value obtained by using the Goldman–Hodgkin–Katz (GHK) equation (Chapter 6) provides strong support for the theory that the EPSP is due to the opening of channels that have equal permeabilities to Na^+ and K^+. Ion-substitution experiments also confirm this theory. Thus, when the concentration of Na^+ or K^+ in the extracellular fluid is altered, the value of the reversal potential shifts in a way predicted by the GHK equation. (Some other cations, such as Ca^{2+}, also permeate these channels, but their permeability is low compared with that of Na^+ and K^+.)

Different families of ionotropic receptors have different reversal potentials because each has unique ion selectivity. In addition, it should now be clear that the sign of the synaptic action (excitatory or inhibitory) depends on the value of the reversal potential relative to the resting potential. If the reversal potential of an ionotropic receptor channel is more positive than the resting potential, opening of that channel will lead to a depolarization (i.e., an EPSP). In contrast, if the reversal potential of an ionotropic receptor channel is more negative than the potential, opening of that channel will lead to a hyperpolarization, that is, an **inhibitory postsynaptic potential** (IPSP), which is the topic of a later section in this chapter.

Plotting the average peak value of the single-channel currents (I_{sc}) versus the membrane potential (transpatch potential) at which they are recorded (Fig. 12.5B) can be a source of quantitative insight into the properties of the ionotropic receptor channel. Note that the current–voltage (I–V) relation is linear; it has a slope, the value of which is the single-channel conductance, and an intercept at 0 mV. This linear relation can be put in the form of Ohm's law ($I = G^*\Delta V$). Thus,

$$I_{sc} = \gamma_{sc} * (V_m - E_r), \qquad (11)$$

where γ_{sc} is the single-channel conductance and E_r is the reversal potential (here, 0 mV).

Summation of Single-Channel Currents

We now know that the sign of a synaptic action can be predicted by knowledge of the relation between the resting potential (V_m) and the reversal potential (E_r), but how can the precise amplitude be determined? The answer to this question lies in understanding the relation between the synaptic conductance and the extra synaptic conductances. These interactions can be rather complex (see Chapter 15), but some initial understanding can be obtained by analyzing an electrical equivalent circuit for these two major conductance branches. We first need to move from a consideration of single-channel conductances and currents to that of macroscopic conductances and currents. The postsynaptic membrane contains thousands of any one type of ionotropic receptor, and each of these receptors could be activated by transmitter released by a single action potential in a presynaptic neuron. Because conductances in parallel add, the total conductance change produced by their simultaneous activation would be

$$g_{syn} = \gamma_{sc} * P * N, \qquad (12)$$

where γ_{sc}, as before, is the single-channel conductance, P is the probability of opening of a single channel (controlled by the ligand), and N is the total number of ligand-gated channels in the postsynaptic membrane. The macroscopic postsynaptic current produced by the transmitter released by a single presynaptic action potential can then be described by

$$I_{syn} = g_{syn} * (V_m - E_r). \qquad (13)$$

Equation (13) can be represented physically by a voltage (V_m) measured across a circuit consisting of a resistor (g_{syn}) in series with a battery (E_r). An equivalent circuit of a membrane containing such a conductance is illustrated in Fig. 12.5C. Also included in this circuit is a membrane capacitance (C_m), a resistor representing the leakage conductance (g_L), and a battery (E_L) representing the leakage potential. (Voltage-dependent Na^+, Ca^{2+}, and K^+ channels that contribute to the generation of the action potential have been omitted for simplification.)

The simple circuit allows the simulation and further analysis of the genesis of the PSP. Closure of the switch simulates the opening of the channels by transmitter released from some presynaptic neuron [i.e., a change in P of Eq. (12) from 0 to 1]. When the switch is open (i.e., no agonist is present and the ligand-gated channels are closed), the membrane potential (V_m) is equal to the value of the leakage battery (E_L). Closure of the switch (i.e., the agonist opens the channels) tends to polarize the membrane potential toward the value of the battery (E_r) in series with the synaptic conductance. Although the effect of the channel openings is to depolarize the postsynaptic cell *toward* E_r (0 mV), this value is never achieved, because the ligand-gated receptors are only a small fraction of the ion channels in the membrane. Other channels (such as the leakage channels, which are not affected by the transmitters) tend to hold the membrane potential at E_L and prevent the membrane potential from reaching the 0-mV level. In terms of the equivalent electrical circuit (Fig. 12.5C), g_L is much greater than g_{syn}.

An analytical expression that can be a source of insight into the production of an EPSP by the engagement of a synaptic conductance can be derived by examining the current flowing in each of the two conductance branches of the circuit in Fig. 12.5C. As previously shown [Eq. (13)], the current flowing in the branch representing the synaptic conductance is equal to

$$I_{syn} = g_{syn} * (V_m - E_r).$$

Similarly, the current flowing through the leakage conductance is equal to

$$I_L = g_L * (V_m - E_L). \tag{14}$$

By conservation of current, the two currents must be equal and opposite. Therefore,

$$g_{syn} * (V_m - E_r) = -g_L * (V_m - E_L).$$

Rearranging and solving for V_m, we obtain

$$V_m = \frac{g_{syn} E_r + g_L E_L}{g_{syn} + g_L}. \tag{15}$$

Note that when the synaptic channels are closed (i.e., switch open), g_{syn} is 0 and

$$V_m = E_L.$$

Now consider the case of the ligand-gated channels being opened by release of transmitter from a presynaptic neuron (i.e., switch closed) and a neuron with $g_L = 10$ nS, $E_L = -60$ mV, $g_{syn} = 0.2$ nS, and $E_r = 0$ mV. Then

$$V_m = \frac{(0.2 \times 10^{-9} * 0) + (10 \times 10^{-9} * -60)}{10.2 \times 10^{-9}}$$

$$= -59 \text{ mV}$$

Thus, as a result of the closure of the switch, the membrane potential has changed from its initial value of −60 mV to a new value of −59 mV; that is, an EPSP of 1 mV has been generated.

The preceding analysis ignored the membrane capacitance (C_m), the charging of which makes the synaptic potential slower than the synaptic current. Thus, a more complete analytical description of the postsynaptic factors underlying the generation of a PSP must account for the fact that some of the synaptic current will flow into the capacitative branch of the circuit. Again, by conservation of current, the sum of the currents in the three branches must equal 0. Therefore,

$$0 = C_m \frac{dV_m}{dt} + I_L + I_{syn}, \tag{16}$$

$$0 = C_m \frac{dV_m}{dt} + g_L * (V_m - E_L) + g_{syn}(t) * (V_m - E_r), \tag{17}$$

where C_m (dV_m/dt) is the capacitative current.

By solving for V_m and integrating the differential equation, we can determine the magnitude and time course of a PSP. An accurate description of the kinetics of the PSP requires that the simple switch closure (all-or-none engagement of the synaptic conductance) be replaced with an expression [$g_{syn}(t)$] that describes the dynamics of the change in synaptic conductance with time. Equation (9), which describes the dynamics of channel closure, could be used as an approximation of these effects, but a more accurate simulation requires an expression that also describes the kinetics of channel opening [which in Eq. (9) is assumed to be instantaneous].[13]

Nonlinear I–V Relations of Some Ionotropic Receptors

For many PSPs mediated by ionotropic receptors, the current–voltage relation of the synaptic current is linear or approximately linear (Fig. 12.5B). Such ohmic relations are typical of nicotinic ACh channels and non-NMDA (*N*-methyl-D-aspartate) glutamate channels (as well as many receptors mediating IPSPs). The linear *I–V* relation is indicative of a channel whose conductance is not affected by the potential across the membrane. Such linearity should be contrasted with the steep voltage dependency of the conductance of channels underlying the initiation and repolarization of action potentials (Chapter 6).

NMDA glutamate channels are a class of ionotropic receptors that have nonlinear current–voltage relations. At negative potentials, the channel conductance is low even when glutamate is bound to the receptor. As the membrane is depolarized, the conductance increases and the current flowing through the channel increases, resulting in the *I–V* relation illustrated in Fig. 12.6A. This nonlinearity is represented by an arrow through the resistor representing this synaptic conductance in the equivalent circuit of Fig. 12.6B. The nonlinear *I–V* relation of the NMDA receptor can be explained by a voltage-dependent block of the channel

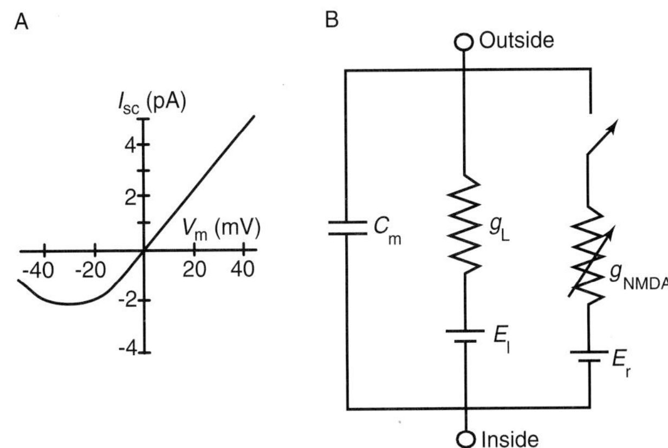

FIGURE 12.6 (A) *I–V* relation of the NMDA receptor. (B) Equivalent electrical circuit of a membrane containing NMDA receptors.

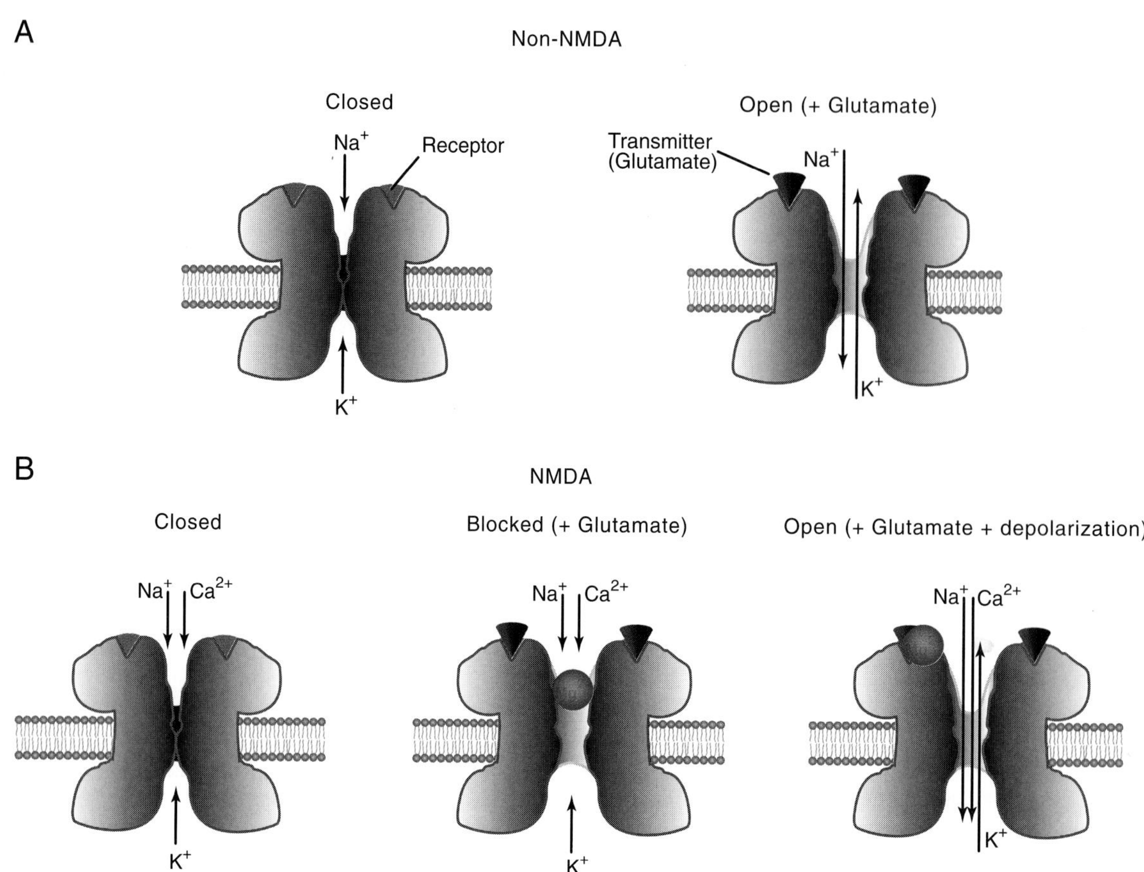

FIGURE 12.7 Features of non-NMDA and NMDA glutamate receptors. (A) Non-NMDA receptors: (left) in the absence of agonist, the channel is closed; (right) glutamate binding leads to channel opening and an increase in Na^+ and K^+ permeability. (B) NMDA receptors: (left) in the absence of agonist, the channel is closed; (middle) the presence of agonist leads to a conformational change and channel opening, but no ionic flux occurs, because the pore of the channel is blocked by Mg^{2+}; (right) in the presence of depolarization, the Mg^{2+} block is removed and the agonist-induced opening of the channel leads to changes in ion flux (including Ca^{2+} influx into the cell).

by Mg^{2+} (Fig. 12.7). At normal values of the resting potential, the pore of the channel is blocked by Mg^{2+}. Thus, even when glutamate binds to the receptor (Fig. 12.7B), the blocked channel prevents ionic flow (and an EPSP). The block can be relieved by depolarization, which presumably displaces the Mg^{2+} from the pore (Fig. 12.7B). When the pore is unblocked, cations (i.e., Na^+, K^+, and Ca^{2+}) can readily flow through the channel, and this flux is manifested in the linear part of the *I–V* relation (Fig. 12.6A). Non-NMDA channels (Fig. 12.7A) are not blocked by Mg^{2+} and have linear *I–V* relations (Fig. 12.5B).

Inhibitory Postsynaptic Potentials Decrease the Probability of Cell Firing

Some synaptic events *decrease* the probability of generating action potentials in the postsynaptic cell. Potentials associated with these actions are called inhibitory postsynaptic potentials. Consider the inhibitory interneuron illustrated in Fig. 12.2. Normally, this interneuron is activated by summating EPSPs from converging afferent fibers. These EPSPs summate in space and time such that the membrane potential of the interneuron reaches threshold and fires an action potential. This step can be bypassed by artificially depolarizing the interneuron to initiate an action potential. The consequences of that action potential from the point of view of the flexor motor neuron are illustrated in Fig. 12.2. The action potential in the interneuron produces a transient increase in the membrane potential of the motor neuron. This transient hyperpolarization (the IPSP) looks very much like the EPSP, but it is reversed in sign.

What are the ionic mechanisms for these fast IPSPs and what is the transmitter substance? Because the membrane potential of the flexor motor neuron is about −65 mV, one might expect an increase in the conductance to some ion (or ions) with an equilibrium potential (reversal potential) more negative than −65 mV. One possibility is K^+. Indeed, the K^+ equilibrium potential in spinal motor neurons is about −80 mV; thus, a transmitter substance that produced a selective increase in K^+ conductance would lead to an IPSP. The K^+-conductance increase would move the membrane potential from −65 mV toward the K^+ equilibrium potential of −80 mV. Although an increase in K^+ conductance mediates IPSPs at some inhibitory synapses, it does not at the synapse between the inhibitory interneuron and the spinal motor neuron. At this particular synapse, the IPSP seems to be due to a selective increase in Cl^- conductance. The equilibrium potential for Cl^- in spinal motor neurons is about −70 mV. Thus, the transmitter substance released by the inhibitory neuron diffuses across the cleft and interacts with receptor sites on the postsynaptic membrane. These receptors are normally closed, but when opened they become selectively permeable to Cl^-. As a result of the increase in Cl^- conductance, the membrane potential moves from a resting value of −65 mV toward the Cl^- equilibrium potential of −70 mV.

As in the sensory neuron–spinal motor neuron synapse, the transmitter substance released by the inhibitory interneuron in the spinal cord is an amino acid, but in this case the transmitter is glycine. Indeed, glycine is frequently used in the central nervous system as an inhibitory transmitter. Although glycine was originally thought to be localized to the spinal cord, it is also found in other regions of the nervous system. The most common transmitter associated with inhibitory actions in many areas of the brain is γ-aminobutyric acid (GABA; see Chapter 8).

Ionotropic receptors that lead to the generation of IPSPs and ionotropic receptors that lead to the generation of EPSPs have biophysical features in common. Indeed, the analyses of the preceding section are generally applicable. A quantitative understanding of the effects of the opening of glycine or GABA receptors can be obtained by using the electrical equivalent circuit of Fig. 12.5C and Eq. (15), with the values of g_{syn} and E_r appropriate for the respective ionotropic receptor. Interactions between excitatory and inhibitory conductances can be modeled by adding additional branches to the equivalent circuit (see Fig. 12.13D and Chapter 15).

Some PSPs Have More Than One Component

The transmitter released from a presynaptic terminal diffuses across the synaptic cleft, where it binds to ionotropic receptors. In many cases, the postsynaptic receptors are homogeneous. In other cases, the same

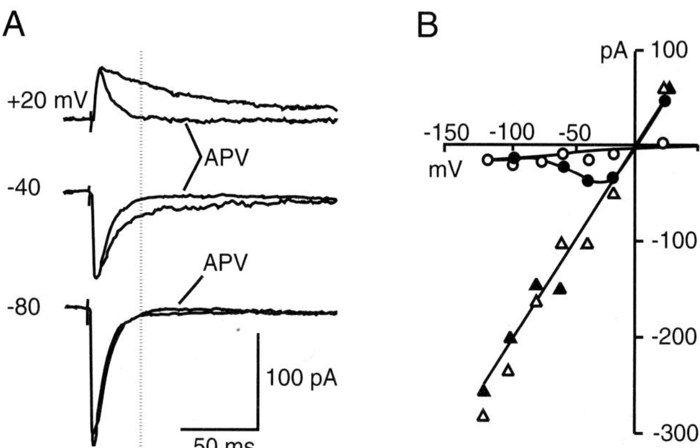

FIGURE 12.8 Dual-component glutamatergic EPSP. (A) The excitatory postsynaptic current was recorded before and during the application of APV at the indicated membrane potentials. (B) Peak current–voltage relations are shown before (solid triangles) and during (open triangles) the application of APV. The current–voltage relations measured 25 ms after the peak of the EPSC [dotted line in (A)] before (solid circles) and during (open circles) application of APV are also shown. Reprinted with permission from Hestrin *et al.*[14]

transmitter activates more than one type of receptor. A major example of this type of heterogeneous postsynaptic action is the simultaneous activation by glutamate of NMDA and non-NMDA receptors on the same postsynaptic cell. Figure 12.8 illustrates such a dual-component glutamatergic EPSP in the CA1 region of the hippocampus. The cell is voltage-clamped at various fixed holding potentials, and the macroscopic synaptic currents produced by activation of the presynaptic neurons are recorded. The experiment is performed in the presence and absence of the agent 2-amino-5-phosphonovalerate (APV), which is a specific blocker of NMDA receptors. When the cell is held at a potential of +20 or −40 mV, APV leads to a dramatic reduction of the late, but not the early, phase of the excitatory postsynaptic current (EPSC). In contrast, when the potential is held at −80 mV, the EPSC is unaffected by APV. These results indicate that the PSP consists of two components: (1) an early non-NMDA component and (2) a late NMDA component. In addition, the results indicate that the conductance of the non-NMDA component is linear, whereas the conductance of the NMDA component is nonlinear. The *I–V* relations of the early (peak) and late (at approximately 25 ms) components of the EPSC are plotted in Fig. 12.8B.[14] Note the similarity in form of these plots of macroscopic currents to the plots of single-channel currents in Figs. 12.5B and 12.6A.

Dual-component PSPs need not be combinations of excitatory actions. For example, a presynaptic cholinergic neuron in the mollusk *Aplysia* produces a diphasic excitatory–inhibitory (*E–I*) response in its postsynaptic

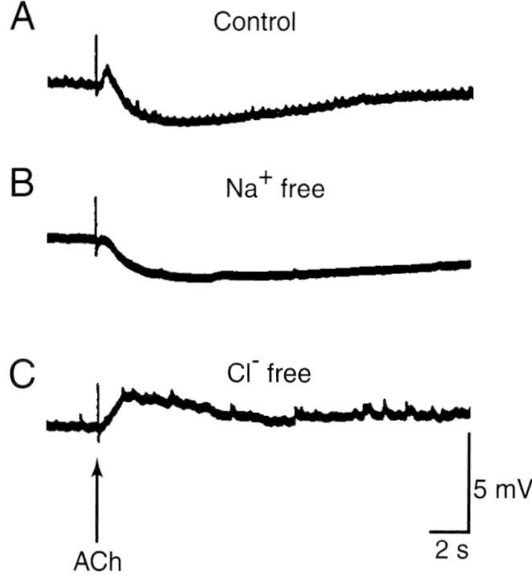

FIGURE 12.9 Dual-component cholinergic excitatory–inhibitory response. (A) Control in normal saline. Ejection of ACh produces a rapid depolarization followed by a slower hyperpolarization. (B) In Na^+-free saline, ACh produces a purely hyperpolarizing response, indicating that the depolarizing component in normal saline includes an increase in g_{Na}. (C) In Cl^--free saline, ACh produces a purely depolarizing response, indicating that the hyperpolarizing component in normal saline includes an increase in g_{Cl}. Reprinted with permission from Blankenship *et al.*[15].

follower cell. The response can be simulated by local discrete application of ACh to the postsynaptic cell (Fig. 12.9).[15] The ionic mechanisms underlying this synaptic action were investigated in ion-substitution experiments, which revealed that the dual response is due to an early Na^+-dependent component followed by a slower Cl^--dependent component. Molecular mechanisms underlying such slow synaptic potentials are discussed next.

Summary

Synaptic potentials mediated by ionotropic receptors are the fundamental means by which information is rapidly transmitted between neurons. Transmitters cause channels to open in an all-or-none fashion, and the currents through these individual channels summate to produce the macrosynaptic postsynaptic potential. The sign of the postsynaptic potential is determined by the relationship between the membrane potential of the postsynaptic neuron and the ion selectivity of the ionotropic receptor.

METABOTROPIC RECEPTORS: MEDIATORS OF SLOW SYNAPTIC POTENTIALS

A common feature of the types of synaptic actions heretofore described is the direct binding of the transmitter with the receptor–channel complex. An entirely separate class of synaptic actions has as its basis the indirect coupling of the receptor with the channel. So far, two types of coupling mechanisms have been identified: (1) coupling of the receptor and channel through an intermediate regulatory protein, such as a G protein; and (2) coupling through a diffusible second-messenger system. Because the coupling through a diffusible second-messenger system is the most common mechanism, it is the focus of this section.

A comparison of the features of direct, fast ionotropic-mediated and indirect, slow metabotropic-mediated synaptic potentials is shown in Fig. 12.10. Slow synaptic potentials are not observed at every postsynaptic neuron, but Fig. 12.10A illustrates an idealized case in which a postsynaptic neuron receives two inputs, one of which produces a conventional fast EPSP and the other of which produces a slow EPSP. An

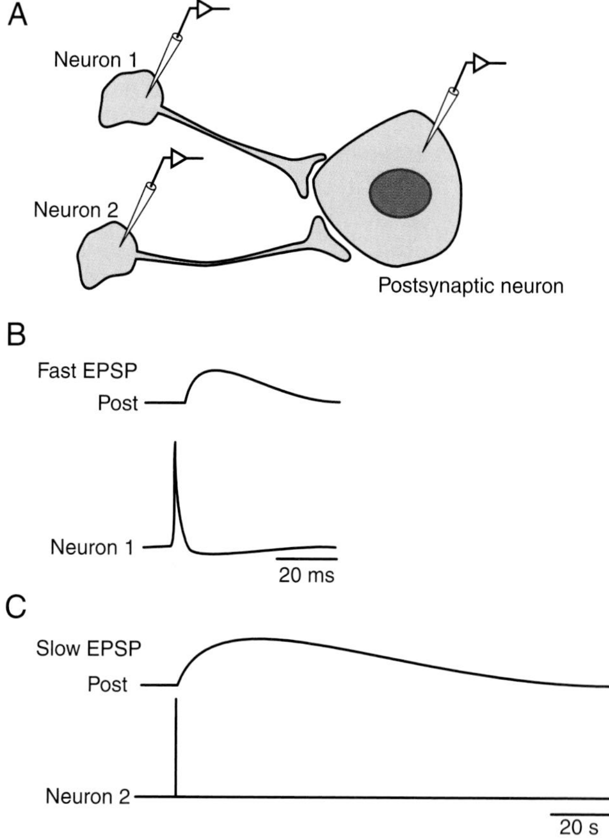

FIGURE 12.10 Fast and slow synaptic potentials. (A) Idealized experiment in which two neurons (1 and 2) make synaptic connections with a common postsynaptic follower cell (Post). (B) An action potential in neuron 1 leads to a conventional fast EPSP with a duration of about 30 ms. (C) An action potential in neuron 2 also produces an EPSP in the postsynaptic cell, but the duration of this slow EPSP is more than three orders of magnitude greater than that of the EPSP produced by neuron 1. Note the change in the calibration bar.

action potential in neuron 1 leads to an EPSP in the postsynaptic cell with a duration of about 30 ms (Fig. 12.10B). This type of potential might be produced in a spinal motor neuron by an action potential in an afferent fiber. Neuron 2 also produces a postsynaptic potential (Fig. 12.10C), but its duration (note the calibration bar) is more than three orders of magnitude greater than that of the EPSP produced by neuron 1.

How can a change in the postsynaptic potential of a neuron persist for many minutes as a result of a single action potential in the presynaptic neuron? Possibilities include a prolonged presence of the transmitter due to continuous release, to slow degradation, or to slow re-uptake of the transmitter, but the mechanism here involves a transmitter-induced change in the metabolism of the postsynaptic cell. Figure 12.11 compares the general mechanisms for fast and slow synaptic potentials. Fast synaptic potentials are produced when a transmitter substance binds to a channel and produces a conformational change in the channel, causing it to become permeable to one or more ions (both Na^+ and K^+ in Fig. 12.11A). The increase in permeability leads to a depolarization associated with the EPSP. The duration of the synaptic event critically depends on the amount of time during which the transmitter substance remains bound to the receptors. Acetylcholine, glutamate, and glycine remain bound only for a very short period. These transmitters are removed by diffusion, enzymatic breakdown, or re-uptake into the presynaptic cell. Therefore, the duration of the synaptic potential is directly related to the lifetimes of the opened channels, and these lifetimes are relatively short (see Fig. 12.4B).

One mechanism for a slow synaptic potential is shown in Fig. 12.11B. In contrast with the fast PSP for which the receptors are actually part of the ion-channel complex, the channels that produce the slow synaptic potentials are not directly coupled to the transmitter receptors. Rather, the receptors are physically separated and exert their actions indirectly through changes in metabolism of specific second-messenger systems. Figure 12.11B illustrates one type of response in *Aplysia*, for which the cAMP–protein kinase A system is the mediator, but other slow PSPs use other second-messenger–kinase systems (e.g., the protein kinase C system). In the cAMP-dependent slow synaptic responses in *Aplysia*, transmitter binding to membrane receptors activates G proteins and stimulates an increase in the synthesis of cAMP. Cyclic AMP then leads to the activation of cAMP-dependent protein kinase (protein kinase A, PKA), which phosphorylates a channel protein or protein associated with the channel.[16] A conformational change in the channel is produced, leading to a change in ionic conductance. Thus, in contrast with a direct conformational change produced by the binding of a transmitter to the receptor–channel complex, in this case, a conformational change is produced by protein phosphorylation. Indeed, phosphorylation-dependent channel regulation is a fairly general feature of slow PSPs. However, channel regulation by second messengers is not exclusively produced by phosphorylation. In one family of ion channels, the channels are gated or regulated directly by cyclic nucleotides. These cyclic-nucleotide-gated channels require cAMP or cGMP to open but have other features in common with members of the superfamily of voltage-gated ion channels.[17,18]

Another interesting feature of slow synaptic responses is that they are sometimes associated with decreases rather than increases in membrane conductance. For example, the particular channel illustrated in Fig. 12.11B is selectively permeable to K^+ and is normally open. As a result of the activation of the second messenger, the channel closes and becomes less permeable to K^+. The resultant depolarization may seem paradoxical, but recall that the membrane potential is due to a balance between the resting K^+ and Na^+ permeability. The K^+ permeability tends to move the membrane potential toward the K^+ equilibrium potential (−80 mV), whereas the Na^+ permeability tends to move the membrane potential toward the Na^+ equilibrium potential (+55 mV). Normally, the K^+ permeability predominates, and the resting membrane potential is close to, but not equal to, the K^+ equilibrium potential. If K^+ permeability is decreased because some of the channels close, the membrane potential will be biased toward the Na^+ equilibrium potential and the cell will depolarize.

At least one reason for the long duration of slow PSPs is that second-messenger systems are slow (from seconds to minutes). Take the cAMP cascade as an example. Cyclic AMP takes some time to be synthesized, but, more importantly, after synthesis, cAMP levels can remain elevated for a relatively long period (minutes). The duration of the elevation of cAMP depends on the actions of cAMP–phosphodiesterase, which breaks down cAMP. However, duration of an effect could outlast the duration of the change in the second messenger because of persistent phosphorylation of the substrate protein(s). Phosphate groups are removed from the substrate proteins by protein phosphatases. Thus, the net duration of a response initiated by a metabotropic receptor depends on the actions of not only the synthetic and phosphorylation processes but also the degradative and dephosphorylation processes.

The activation of a second messenger by a transmitter can have a localized effect on the membrane poten-

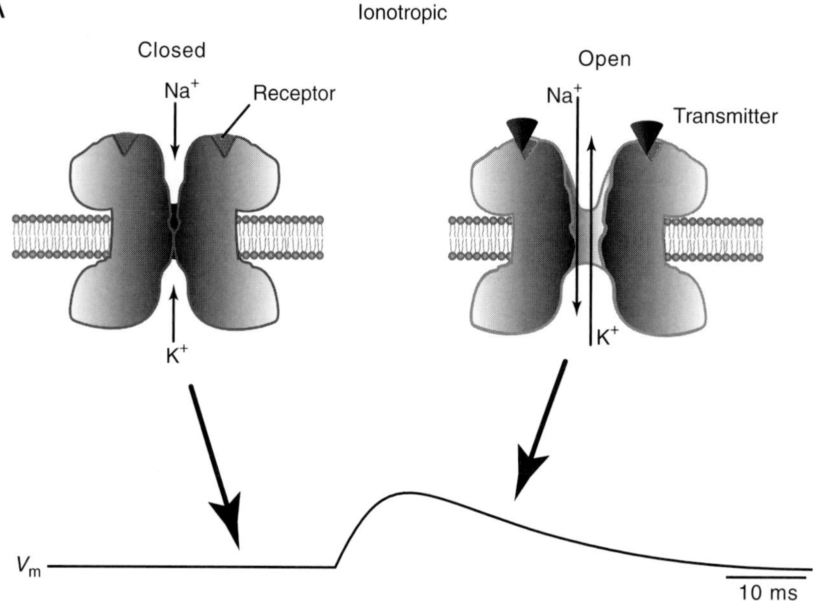

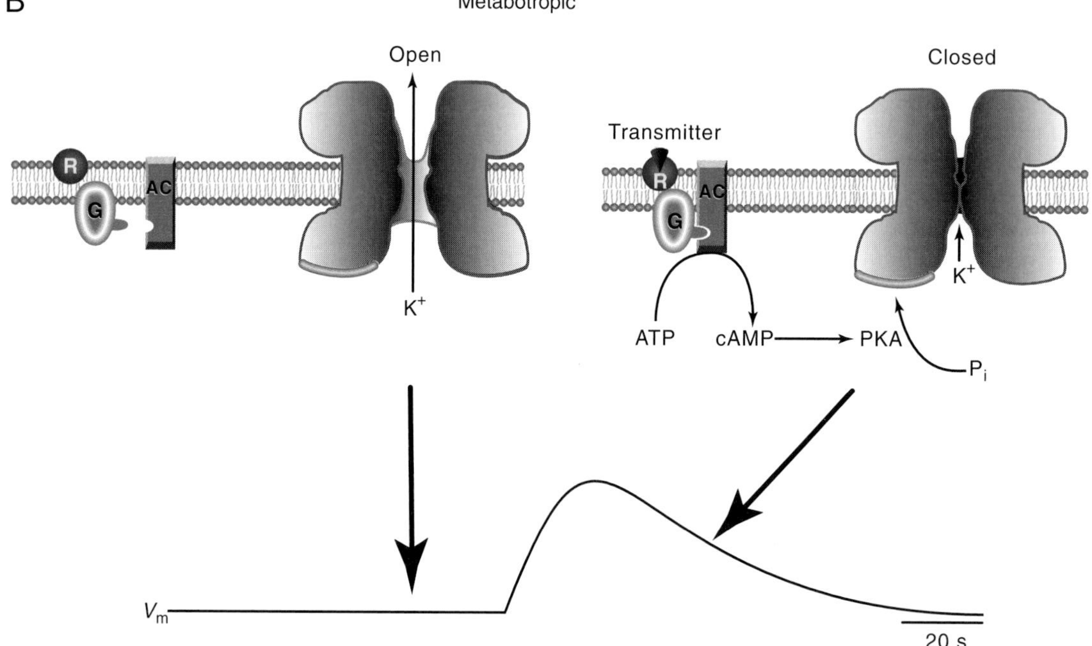

FIGURE 12.11 Ionotropic and metabotropic receptors and mechanisms of fast and slow EPSPs. (A, left) Fast EPSPs are produced by the binding of transmitter to specialized receptors that are directly associated with an ion channel (i.e., a ligand-gated channel). When the receptors are unbound, the channel is closed. (A, right) Binding of the transmitter to the receptor produces a conformational change in the channel protein such that the channel opens. In this example, the channel opening is associated with a selective increase in the permeability to Na^+ and K^+. The increase in permeability results in the EPSP shown in the trace. (B, left) Unlike fast EPSPs that are due to the binding of a transmitter with a receptor–channel complex, slow EPSPs are due to the activation of receptors (metabotropic) that are not directly coupled to the channel. Rather, the coupling takes place through the activation of one of several second-messenger cascades, in this example, the cAMP cascade. A channel that has a selective permeability to K^+ is normally open. (B, right) Binding of the transmitter to the receptor (R) leads to the activation of a G protein (G) and adenylyl cyclase (AC). The synthesis of cAMP is increased, cAMP-dependent protein kinase (protein kinase A, PKA) is activated, and a channel protein is phosphorylated. The phosphorylation leads to closing of the channel and the subsequent depolarization associated with the slow EPSP shown in the trace. The response decays owing to both the breakdown of cAMP by cAMP-dependent phosphodiesterase and the removal of phosphate from channel proteins by protein phosphatases (not shown).

tial through phosphorylation of membrane channels near the site of a metabotropic receptor. The effects can be more widespread and even longer lasting than depicted in Fig. 12.11B. For example, second messengers and protein kinases can diffuse and affect more-distant membrane channels. Moreover, a long-term effect can be induced in the cell by altering gene expression. For example, protein kinase A can diffuse to the nucleus, where it can activate proteins that regulate gene expression. Detailed descriptions of second messengers and their actions are given in Chapter 10.

Summary

In contrast to the rapid responses mediated by ionotropic receptors, responses mediated by metabotropic receptors are generally relatively slow to develop and persistent. These properties arise because metabotropic responses can involve the activation of second-messenger systems. By producing slow changes in the resting potential, metabotropic receptors provide long-term modulation of the effectiveness of responses generated by ionotropic receptors. Moreover, these receptors, through the engagement of second-messenger systems, provide a vehicle by which a presynaptic cell can not only alter the membrane potential but also produce widespread changes in the biochemical state of a postsynaptic cell.

INTEGRATION OF SYNAPTIC POTENTIALS

The small amplitude of the EPSP in spinal motor neurons (and other cells in the CNS) poses an interesting question. Specifically, how can an EPSP with an amplitude of only 1 mV drive the membrane potential of the motor neuron (i.e., the postsynaptic neuron) to threshold and fire the spike in the motor neuron that is necessary to produce the contraction of the muscle? The answer to this question lies in the principles of temporal and spatial summation.

When the ligament is stretched (Fig. 12.1), many stretch receptors are activated. Indeed, the greater the stretch, the greater the probability of activating a larger number of the stretch receptors; this process is referred to as **recruitment.** However, recruitment is not the complete story. The principle of frequency coding in the nervous system specifies that the greater the intensity of a stimulus, the greater the number of action potentials per unit time (frequency) elicited in a sensory neuron. This principle applies to stretch receptors as well. Thus, the greater the stretch, the greater the number of action potentials elicited in the stretch receptor in a given interval and therefore the greater the number of EPSPs produced in the motor neuron from that train of action potentials in the sensory cell. Consequently, the effects of activating multiple stretch receptors add together (**spatial summation**), as do the effects of multiple EPSPs elicited by activation of a single stretch receptor (**temporal summation**). Both of these processes act in concert to depolarize the motor neuron sufficiently to elicit one or more action potentials, which then propagate to the periphery and produce the reflex.

Temporal Summation Allows Integration of Successive PSPs

Temporal summation can be illustrated by firing action potentials in a presynaptic neuron and monitoring the resultant EPSPs. For example, in Figs. 12.12A and 12.12B, a single action potential in sensory neuron 1 produces a 1-mV EPSP in the motor neuron. Two action potentials in quick succession produce two EPSPs, but note that the second EPSP occurs during the falling phase of the first, and the depolarization associated with the second EPSP adds to the depolarization produced by the first. Thus, two action potentials produce a summated potential that is about 2 mV in amplitude. Three action potentials in quick succession would produce a summated potential of about 3 mV. In principle, 30 action potentials in quick succession would produce a potential of about 30 mV and easily drive the cell to threshold. This summation is strictly a passive property of the cell. No special ionic conductance mechanisms are necessary. Specifically, the postsynaptic conductance change [g_{syn} in Eq. (13)] produced by the second of two successive action potentials adds to that produced by the first. In addition, the postsynaptic membrane has a capacitance and can store charge. Thus, the membrane temporarily stores the charge of the first EPSP, and the charge from the second EPSP is added to that of the first. However, the "time window" for this process of temporal summation very much depends on the duration of the postsynaptic potential, and temporal summation is possible only if the presynaptic action potentials (and hence postsynaptic potentials) are close in time to each other. The time frame depends on the duration of changes in the synaptic conductance and the time constant (Chapter 5). Temporal summation, however, is rarely observed to be linear as in the preceding examples, even when the postsynaptic conductance change [g_{syn} in Eq. (13)] produced by the second of two successive action potentials is identical with that produced by the first (i.e., no presynaptic facilitation or depression), the synaptic current is slightly less because the

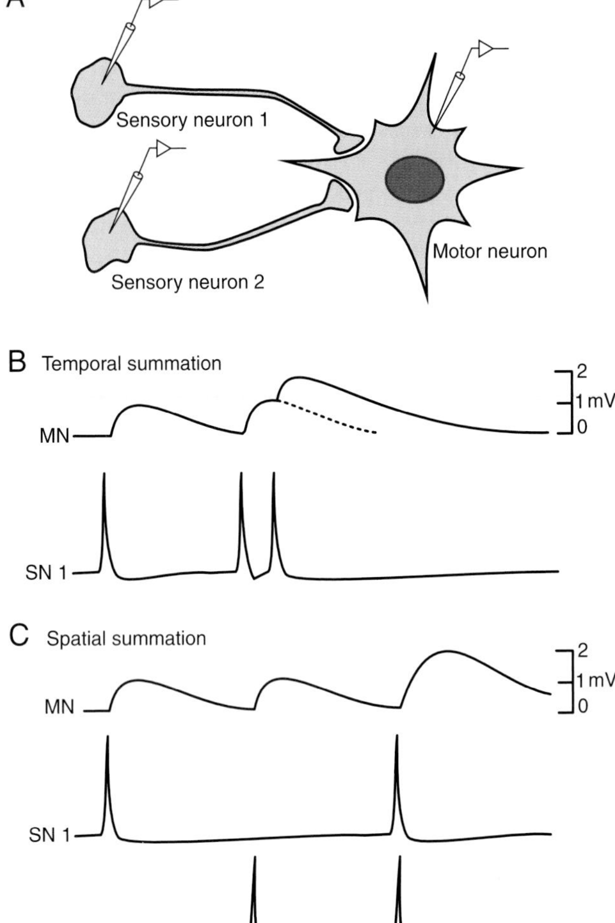

FIGURE 12.12 Temporal and spatial summation. (A) Intracellular recordings are made from two idealized sensory neurons (SN1 and SN2) and a motor neuron (MN). (B) Temporal summation: A single action potential in SN1 produces a 1-mV EPSP in the MN. Two action potentials in quick succession produce a dual-component EPSP, the amplitude of which is approximately 2 mV. (C) Spatial summation: Alternative firing of single action potentials in SN1 and SN2 produce 1-mV EPSPs in the MN. Simultaneous action potentials in SN1 and SN2 produce a summated EPSP, the amplitude of which is about 2 mV.

first PSP reduces the driving force ($V_m - E_r$) for the second. Interested readers should try some numerical examples.

Spatial Summation Allows Integration of PSPs from Different Parts of a Neuron

Spatial summation (Fig. 12.12C) requires a consideration of more than one input to a postsynaptic neuron. An action potential in sensory neuron 1 produces a 1-mV EPSP, just as it did in Fig. 12.12B. Similarly, an action potential in a second sensory neuron by itself also produces a 1-mV EPSP. Now, consider the consequences of action potentials elicited simultaneously in sensory neurons 1 and 2. The net EPSP is equal to the summation of the amplitudes of the individual EPSPs. Here, the EPSP from sensory neuron 1 is 1 mV, the EPSP from sensory neuron 2 is 1 mV, and the summated EPSP is approximately 2 mV (Fig. 12.12C). Thus, spatial summation is a mechanism by which synaptic potentials generated at different sites can summate. Spatial summation in nerve cells is influenced by the space constant—the ability of a potential change produced in one region of a cell to spread passively to other regions of a cell (see Chapter 5).

Summary

Whether a neuron fires in response to synaptic input depends, at least in part, on how many action potentials are produced in any one presynaptic excitatory pathway and on how many individual convergent excitatory input pathways are activated. The summation of EPSPs in time and space is only part of the process, however. The final behavior of the cell is also due to the summation of inhibitory synaptic inputs in time and space, as well as to the properties of the voltage-dependent currents (Fig. 12.13) in the soma and along the dendrites.[19,20] For example, voltage-dependent conductances such as the A-type K^+ conductance have a low threshold for activation and can thus oppose the effectiveness of an EPSP to trigger a spike. Low-threshold Na^+ and Ca^{2+} channels can boost an EPSP. Finally, we need to consider that the spatial distribution of the various voltage-dependent channels, ligand-gated receptors, and metabotropic receptors is not uniform. Thus, each segment of the neuronal membrane can

FIGURE 12.13 Modeling the integrative properties of a neuron. (A) Partial geometry of a neuron in the CNS revealing the cell body and pattern of dendritic branching. (B) The neuron modeled as a sphere connected to a series of cylinders, each of which represents the specific electrical properties of a dendritic segment. (C) Segments linked with resistors representing the intracellular resistance between segments, with each segment represented by the parallel combination of the membrane capacitance and the total membrane conductance. Reprinted with permission from Koch and Segev.[19] Copyright 1989 MIT Press. (D) Electrical circuit equivalent of the membrane of a segment of a neuron. In (D), the segment has a membrane potential V and a membrane capacitance C_m. Currents arise from three sources: (1) m voltage-dependent conductances (g_{vd_1}–g_{vd_m}), (2) n conductances due to electrical synapses (g_{es_1}–g_{es_n}), and (3) n times o time-dependent conductances due to chemical synapses with each of the n presynaptic neurons ($g_{cs_{1,1}}$–$g_{cs_{n,o}}$). E_{vd} and E_{cs} are constants and represent the values of the equilibrium potential for currents due to voltage-dependent conductances and chemical synapses, respectively. V_1–V_n represent the value of the membrane potential of the coupled cells. Reprinted with permission from Ziv *et al.*[20]

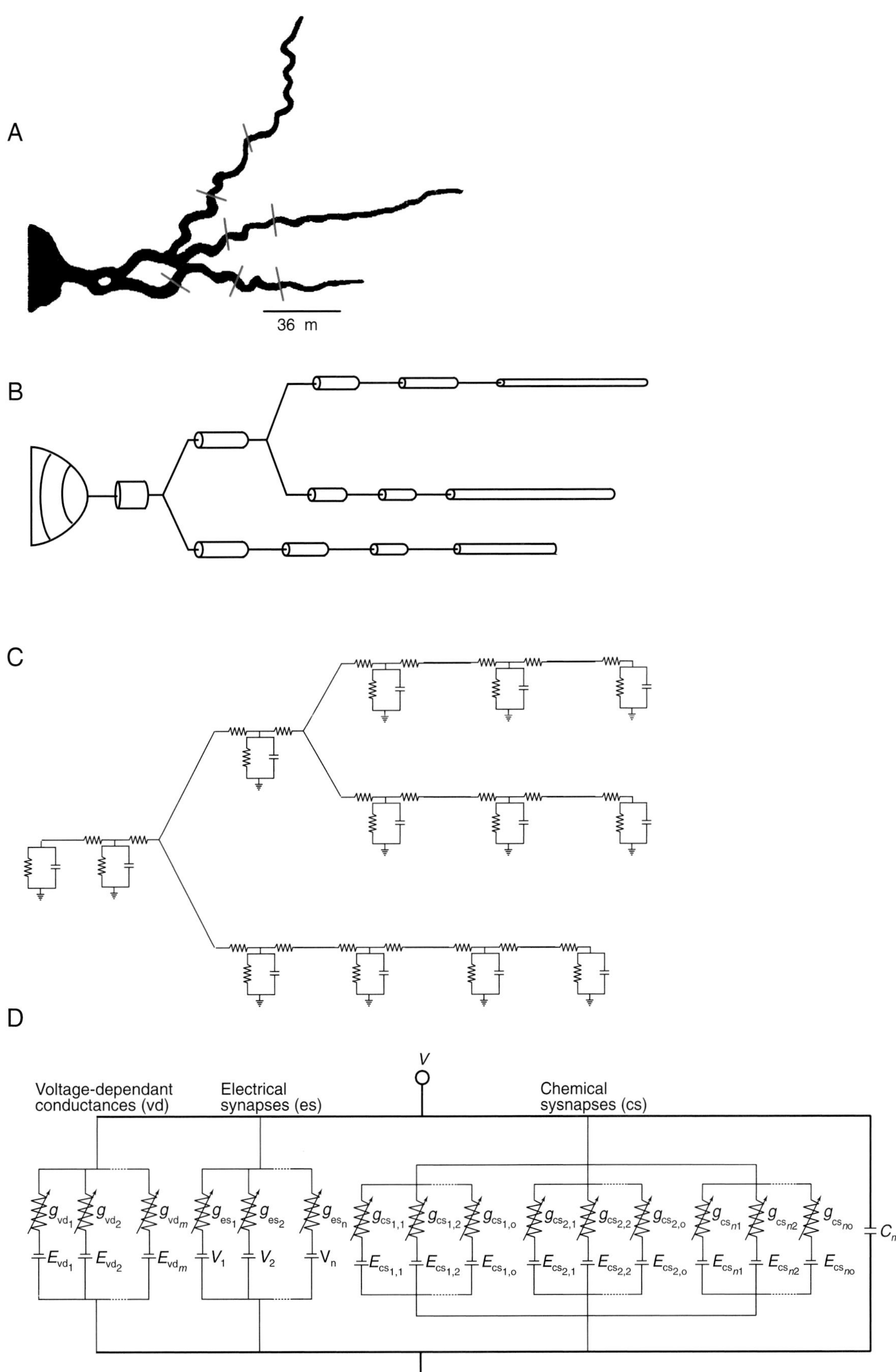
A
36 m
B
C
D
V
Voltage-dependant conductances (vd)
Electrical synapses (es)
Chemical sysnapses (cs)
g_{vd_1}
g_{vd_2}
g_{vd_m}
g_{es_1}
g_{es_2}
g_{es_n}
$g_{cs_{1,1}}$
$g_{cs_{1,2}}$
$g_{cs_{1,o}}$
$g_{cs_{2,1}}$
$g_{cs_{2,2}}$
$g_{cs_{2,o}}$
$g_{cs_{n1}}$
$g_{cs_{n2}}$
$g_{cs_{no}}$
C_m
E_{vd_1}
E_{vd_2}
E_{vd_m}
V_1
V_2
V_n
$E_{cs_{1,1}}$
$E_{cs_{1,2}}$
$E_{cs_{1,o}}$
$E_{cs_{2,1}}$
$E_{cs_{2,2}}$
$E_{cs_{2,o}}$
$E_{cs_{n1}}$
$E_{cs_{n2}}$
$E_{cs_{no}}$

perform selective integrative functions. Clearly, this system has an enormous capacity for the local processing of information and for performing logical operations. The flow of information in dendrites and the local processing of neuronal signals are discussed in Chapters 13 and 15.

References

General

Barnard, E. A. (1992). Receptor classes and the transmitter-gated channels. *Trends Biochem. Sci.* **17:** 368.

Burke, R. E. and Rudomin, P. (1977). Spatial neurons and synapses. In *Handbook of Physiology* (E. R. Kandel, ed.), Sect. 1, Vol. 1, Part 2, pp. 877–944. American Physiological Society, Bethesda, MD.

Krogsgaard-Larsen, P., and Hansen, J. J., eds. (1992). *Excitatory Amino Acid Receptors*. Ellis Horwood, New York.

Shepherd, G. M., ed. (1990). *The Synaptic Organization of the Brain*, 3rd ed., Chapters 1–4, 13. Oxford University Press, New York.

Cited

1. Eccles, J. C. (1964). *The Physiology of Synapses*. Springer-Verlag, New York.
2. Spencer, W. A. (1977). The physiology of supraspinal neurons in mammals. In *Handbook of Physiology* (E. R. Kandel, Ed.), Sect. 1, pp. 969–1022. Vol. 1, Part 2, American Physiological Society, Bethesda, MD.
3. Hamill, O. P., Marty, A., Neher, E., Sakmann, B., and Sigworth, J. (1981). Improved patch-clamp techniques for high-resolution current recording from cells and cell-free membrane patches. *Pflügers Arch.* **391:** 85–100.
4. Colquhoun, D., and Hawkes, A. G. (1977). Relaxation and fluctuations of membrane currents that flow through drug-operated channels. *Proc. R. Soc. London, Ser. B* **199:** 231–262.
5. Colquhoun, D., and Hawkes, A. G. (1981). On the stochastic properties of single ion channels. *Proc. R. Soc. London, Ser. B* **211:** 205–235.
6. Colquhoun, D., and Hawkes, A. G. (1982). On the stochastic properties of bursts of single ion channel openings and of clusters of bursts. *Proc. R. Soc. London, Ser. B* **300:** 1–59.
7. Colquhoun, D., and Sakmann, B. (1981). Fluctuations in the microsecond time range of the current through single acetylcholine receptor ion channels. *Nature (London)* **294:** 464–466.
8. Johnston, D., and Wu, S. M.-S. (1995). *Foundations of Cellular Neurophysiology*. MIT Press, Cambridge, MA.
9. Sakmann, B. (1992). Elementary steps in synaptic transmission revealed by currents through single ion channels. *Science* **256:** 503–512.
10. Papoulis, A. (1965). *Probability, Random Variables, and Stochastic Processes*. McGraw-Hill, New York.
11. Takeuchi, A. and Takeuchi, N. (1960). On the permeability of end-plate membrane during the action of transmitter. *J. Physiol. (London)* **154:** 52–67.
12. Fatt, P. and Katz, B. (1951). An analysis of the end-plate potential recorded with an intra-cellular electrode. *J. Physiol. (London)* **115:** 320–370.
13. Magleby, K. L., and Stevens, C. F. (1972). A quantitative description of end-plate currents. *J. Physiol. (London)* **223:** 173–197.
14. Hestrin, S., Nicoll, R. A., Perkel, D. J., and Sah, P. (1990). Analysis of excitatory synaptic action in pyramidal cells using whole-cell recording from rat hippocampal slices. *J. Physiol. (London)* **422:** 203–225.
15. Blankenship, J. E., Wachtel, H., and Kandel, E. R. (1971). Ionic mechanisms of excitatory, inhibitory and dual synaptic actions mediated by an identified interneuron in abdominal ganglion of *Aplysia*. *J. Neurophysiol.* **34:** 76–92.
16. Siegelbaum, S. A., Camardo, J. S., and Kandel, E. R. (1982). Serotonin and cyclic AMP close single K^+ channels in *Aplysia* sensory neurones. *Nature (London)* **299:** 413–417.
17. Kaupp, U. B. (1995). Family of cyclic nucleotide gated ion channels. *Curr. Opin. Neurobiol.* **5:** 434–442.
18. Zimmermann, A. L. (1995). Cyclic nucleotide gated channels. *Curr. Opin. Neurobiol.* **5:** 296–303.
19. Koch, C. and Segev, I. (1989). *Methods in Neuronal Modeling*. MIT Press, Cambridge, MA.
20. Ziv, I., Baxter, D. A., and Byrne, J. H. (1994). Simulator for neural networks and action potentials: Description and application. *J. Neurophysiol.* **71:** 294–308.

C H A P T E R

13

Information Processing in Dendrites

Gordon M. Shepherd

In Chapter 5, we introduced the concept of the neuron as a functional unit that processes neural information through four basic operations: (1) reception of inputs, (2) integration of inputs with intrinsic activity, (3) impulse encoding, and (4) synaptic output. To understand the basic mechanisms underlying each of these operations, we studied passive current spread within the neuron (Chapter 5), the wide range of synaptic and second-messenger properties (Chapters 6–9), and the multiplicity of membrane channels (Chapters 10–12).

We are now in a position to ask how these operations are integrated within the neuron to carry out information processing. A key role in integration is played by the branching dendritic trees that characterize many neurons. A question often asked is: What do dendrites do? In this chapter, we consider the evidence that is accumulating to answer that question. First, we show that this evidence has emerged in relation to four types of information flow within a dendritic tree: (1) information transfer from dendrites to the axon hillock, (2) local integrative sites within the tree, (3) information flow from the axon hillock back into the dendrites, and (4) multiple active dendritic sites for initiating information flow. The importance of active properties of dendrites was recognized early, but only in recent years has direct evidence for the location and function of voltage-gated conductances become available. These conductances confer non-linear properties that can perform a range of functions, from boosting synaptic responses in a graded fashion, through thresholding operations at local dendritic sites, to propagating all-or-nothing action potentials similar to those in axons in anterograde or retrograde directions within the dendritic tree. These properties are currently receiving intense interest. It is too early to provide a comprehensive conceptual framework for their significance, but it is clear that they add new levels of complexity to our understanding of information processing in the neuron in all four of the types mentioned above.

Next, we consider some of the best examples of information processing in dendrites. A problem for neuroscientists in tackling this question is that often the focus is too narrow—on only one or two neuron types. Purkinje cells in the cerebellum and pyramidal neurons in the cerebral cortex attract the most attention because of their relevance to the functions of those important regions. However, information processing in those regions is not as well understood as it is in many other regions where the properties of dendrites have been correlated with specific functions. In addition, neurons that function without axons or impulses, in both vertebrates and invertebrates, have provided clear models for what dendrites do, and yet they are often ignored in discussions of dendritic properties. We therefore begin by considering some examples of this class.

Building on this foundation, we consider the evidence for dendritic processing in neurons that give rise to axons. We consider how information is processed through different combinations of synaptic and intrinsic membrane properties in their dendrites. We focus on mitral cells, Purkinje cells, and pyramidal neurons and assess the progress that is being made in understanding "what their dendrites do." We close with a special consideration of dendritic spines, the smallest functional compartments in the neuron, and the contributions that they make to the information processing capacity of the neuron.

TYPES OF INFORMATION FLOW WITHIN A DENDRITIC TREE

Information in neurons can take many forms. It can involve the actions of external signal molecules, such as neurotransmitters and hormones, on membrane receptors or internal cytoplasmic or nuclear receptors; the actions of second and third messengers on effector molecules within the neuron; the movement of substances within the soma, axon, or dendrites by diffusion or by active transport; or the generation, passive spread, or active propagation of electrical signals along the cell membrane. In general, all of these forms involve reception of a signal and transmission of the signal from one part of the neuron to another, eventually bringing about an action on another neuron, neighboring or distant. Here, we focus on the transmission of signals from one part of a neuron to another, building on the principles of electrotonic signal spread discussed in Chapter 5 and adding the complexities of nonlinear interactions between synaptic and membrane conductances and active properties due to voltage-gated membrane conductances. We begin by considering the main types of information transfer within complex dendritic trees.

Information Flows from Dendrites to the Axon Hillock

Camillo Golgi[1] was the first to stain neuronal dendrites and axon collaterals in their entirety (1886). As is well known,[2] he believed that information processing is carried out through networks formed by the axon collaterals, whereas the dendrites provide only nutritive support to the neuron. Santiago Ramón y Cajal,[3] in his first studies with the Golgi stain, concluded that the dendrites participate directly in neural transmission, basing his initial interpretation on the anatomical arrangements of neurons in the cerebellar cortex and the olfactory bulb. In the olfactory bulb, for example, he saw clearly that the incoming olfactory nerve fibers end on the distal dendritic tufts of mitral cells; therefore, the only pathway for activation of the mitral cell axons is by transmission through the mitral cell dendrite to the cell body and axon hillock.

This deduction not only provided circumstantial proof of the role of the dendrites in neural functions, but also led to a generalization that all neurons have a similar functional organization, which proceeds in a linear sequence from the dendrites through the axon. This idea was put forth about 1890, when Ramón y Cajal in Spain and Arthur van Gehuchten in Belgium began anatomical studies to deal with the dazzling variety of neuron shapes.[2,4–6] To make sense of this variety, they inferred that all neurons function in essentially the same manner. As Ramón y Cajal expressed it,[2,3]

> The transmission of neuronal electrical activity takes place from the dendrites and cell body toward the axon. Therefore every neuron has a *receptive component*, the cell body and dendrites; a *transmission component*, the axon; and an *effector component*, the varicose terminal arborization of the axon (italics added).

This was called the **law of dynamic polarization** (see Fig. 13.1). Its merit was that it provided a simple rule by which all neurons would operate as equivalent functional units. Ramón y Cajal and van Gehuchten soon realized that some neurons, such as dorsal root ganglion cells and superior colliculus cells, were difficult to include under this simple rule and attempted to refine the theory to take these cells into account.[2] However, to most workers, the rule seemed almost self-evident and was widely adopted.

Dendrites Disappear (but Rise Again)

During the first part of the 20th century, work on dendrites waned, partly through loss of interest in applying the Golgi stain to the anatomical analysis of different neurons and partly because of the growing

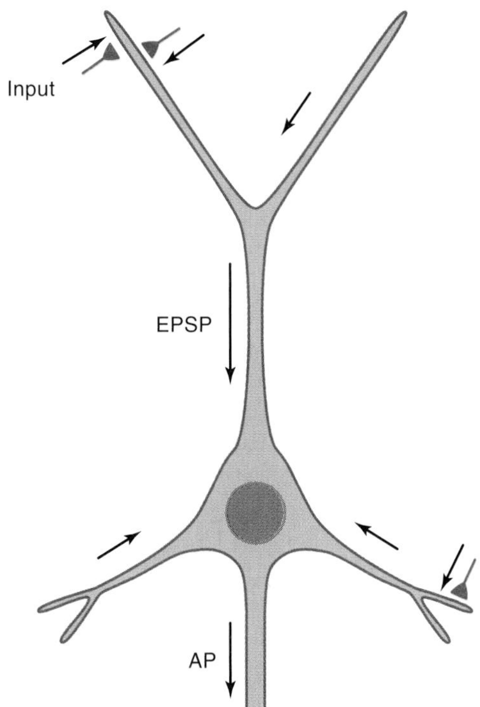

FIGURE 13.1 Development of concepts of the functional organization of the neuron: Ramón y Cajal and van Gehuchten's law of dynamic polarization.

interest of neurophysiologists in analyzing chains of neurons connected by axons. For this purpose, the soma–dendritic part of the neuron was reduced to a simple node, the axon to a simple wire, and the axonal terminals to simple connectors. With the use of this node-and-wire convention, reflex pathways and ascending and descending neural systems were depicted as simple loops or chains of nodes.

This reduction of the soma–dendritic part of the neuron to a single node, representing only the cell body, eliminated the dendrites from having a significant role in neuronal functions as effectively as did Golgi's postulate. Thus, Lorente de Nó's well-known chapter on the organization of the cerebral cortex for Fulton's *Physiology of the Nervous System*[7] showed Golgi-stained cortical neurons in all their dendritic glory, but reduced them to nodes and wires in representations of cortical reverberating circuits. Warren McCulloch and Walter Pitts, in their pioneering paper in 1943[8] on cortical circuits as logic gates, similarly depicted neurons as single summing nodes. And, when the first intracellular recordings become available,[9] the fact that they were obtained from the cell body led naturally to the assumption that the physiology of the neuron was dominated by synaptic inputs on the soma and proximal dendrites.[10] From that time on, a commonly held view of the functional organization of the neuron was that the rapid input–output functions of the neuron are governed by synaptic inputs on the soma and proximal dendrites and that distal dendrites can mediate only weak and slow background modulation of these functions. However, as we saw in Chapter 5, dendrites were put back in the picture by the work of Wilfrid Rall on dendritic electrotonus. In addition, a number of physiological studies, significant at the time but since then largely ignored, supported the importance of dendrites. Much of this chapter focuses on the accumulating evidence that the entire dendritic tree participates in the processing of information by the neuron.

Information Can Be Integrated at Local Sites in Complex Dendrites

Modern anatomical studies have indeed confirmed that in most neurons, input synapses are located over the cell body and dendritic tree, and output synapses are located on the axon terminals.[11] Electrophysiological studies have shown that, in neurons with long axons, synaptic potentials spread through the dendrites to the region of the cell body and axon hillock and into the axonal initial segment, where they generate impulses that propagate through the axon to the axon terminals to activate synapses onto the next target cell. Thus, the overall flow of activity is from dendrites to axon, as deduced by the classical anatomists (see Fig. 13.1).

However, modern studies have also provided a wealth of evidence that within this simple framework is the capacity for much more complex types of information processing. Some axons may have synaptic inputs as well as outputs, and some dendrites may have synaptic outputs as well as inputs. Some axons may mediate mainly passive spread of electric potential. Some neurons do not have axons, and some neurons do not generate propagating impulses. Most dendrites are now believed to have active membrane conductances mediating a variety of functions. It has thus become apparent that any given site within the neuron can have any combination of functional properties—passive or voltage-sensitive channels, synaptic input or output, and activity dependence or independence.[4,12] These combinations of properties endow any local site with the capacity to process local information or to take part in interactions with other neurons or glia. In addition, in many cases, local sites form virtual compartments that may function to a certain extent independently of the rest of the neuron.

The evidence thus suggests that neurons are much more complex functional units than previously thought. To subsume this complexity, a **law of local dendritic integration** would state that

> The soma and dendrites constitute an extremely adaptable cellular substrate that carries out basic functions of information generation, reception, integration, and output by forming multiple processing units at several levels of organization, with multiple actions overlapping in time.

A representation of the neuron combining the forward flow of information from dendrites to axon with the capacities for integration at many local sites is depicted in Fig. 13.2.

Action Potentials Backpropagate into Dendrites and Synapses

In addition to the overall flow of information from dendrites to axons and the local input–output processing of information, a third type of information processing deals with retrograde flow. One type of retrograde flow is the backward spread of the action potential from its site of initiation in the axon hillock into the soma and dendrites. This type was first recognized in the 1950s and has recently become the subject of intense investigation. Another type of retrograde signaling takes place at synapses, where a postsynaptic process is believed to send retrograde signals to presynaptic processes through a variety of biochemical

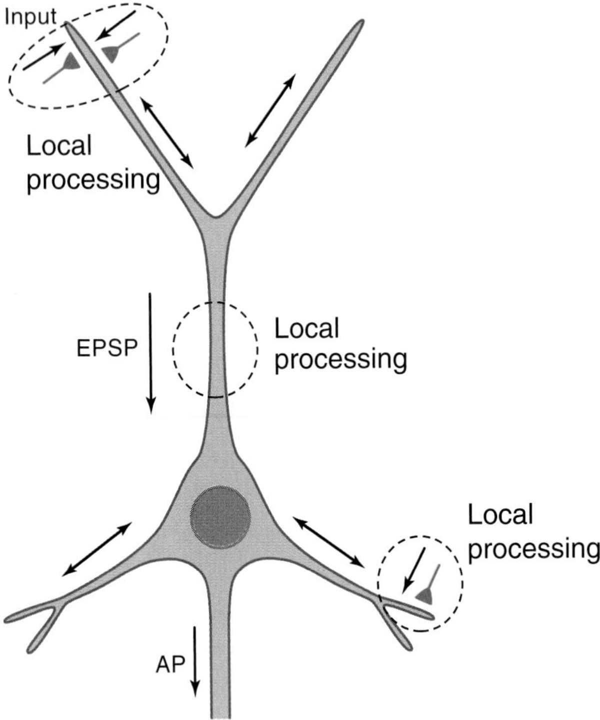

FIGURE 13.2 Development of concepts of the functional organization of the neuron: Expanded concept incorporating local integrative activity.

cues that operate during development and in relation to activity-dependent processes. Although retrograde flow has received less attention than the other two types of information processing, we may formulate a tentative **law of retrograde information flow** along the following lines:

> Accompanying the forward flow of information and the integrative activity at local sites, a retrograde flow of information signals the output state; this signaling occurs at all levels of organization, from the most local, involving individual biochemical and electrical processes, through individual synaptic and active sites in a dendritic tree, to the most global, involving the impulse output from the axon hillock with spread back into the dendritic tree.

Incorporation of this third type of information flow into the functional model of the neuron is shown in Fig. 13.3.

A fourth type of information flow in dendrites involves initiation of action potentials in distal dendrites and forward propagation of these impulses to the soma and axon hillock. From one point of view, this can be considered confirmation of the classical view of dynamic polarization of the neuron, as discussed above, in which impulses travel from their site of generation in response to synaptic inputs to the soma and out from the axon. However, recent evidence indicates that the situation is much more complicated than this. The view that is emerging may be summarized in a tentative **law of dynamic control of impulse initiation** sites as follows:

> There may be one or more sites capable of action potential generation in a dendritic tree. Whether these actually serve as sites of action potential initiation (before the impulse in the axon hillock) in response to a given input depends on a variety of factors, such as the intensity of excitatory input and the location and intensity of concomitant inhibitory input. These dendritic action potentials extend the dynamic operating range of the neuron and can contribute to a variety of local integrative functions underlying synaptic plasticity as well.

This fourth type of information flow is depicted in Fig. 13.4.

Much of current neuroscience is concerned with determining the functional properties of the soma–dendritic domains of complex neurons, as well as their roles in information processing, and how the activities

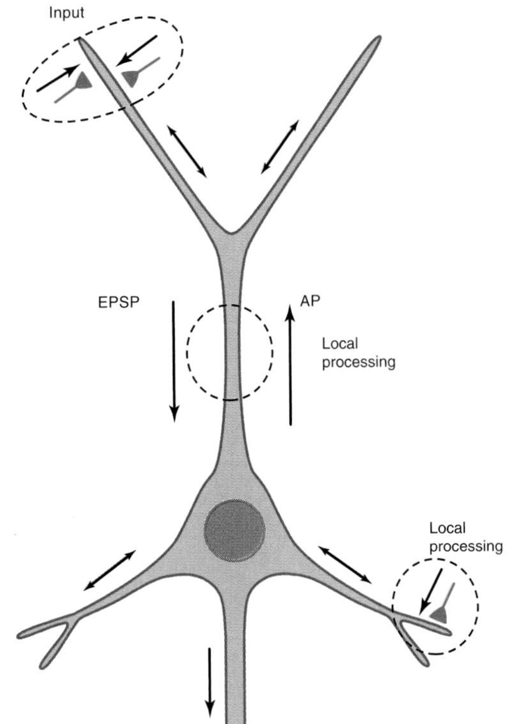

FIGURE 13.3 Development of concepts of the functional organization of the neuron: Expanded concept incorporating action potential backpropagation.

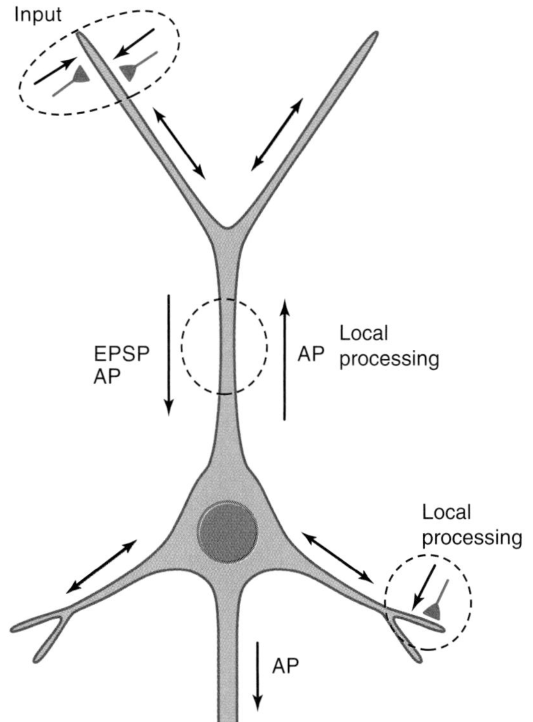

FIGURE 13.4 Development of concepts of the functional organization of the neuron: Expanded concept incorporating forward action potential propagation. Abbreviations: EPSP, excitatory postsynaptic potential; AP, action potential.

of these domains contribute to the neural basis of behavior. We first focus on some of the best-known examples that illustrate the basic functional properties of the dendrites and then consider the functional significance of the backpropagating impulse.

Summary

The direction of information flow is dependent on several factors. One is the extent and complexity of branching patterns of the dendrites. Another is the distribution of excitatory and inhibitory synapses on this branching pattern and their interactions according to the laws of electrotonic cable properties (Chapter 5). Another is the distribution of voltage-gated membrane conductances within this branching pattern. Finally, there is the interaction of these voltage-gated properties with the synaptic and cable properties to generate either local active integrative sites or action potential propagation in either a retrograde or anterograde direction with regard to the final site of impulse generation at the axon hillock. The dynamic interactions that take place among all these factors determine the nature of the integration of signals and the direction of flow of information at any given instant and in the overall processing of information by a given neuron.

DENDRITIC OPERATIONS IN THE ABSENCE OF AXONS AND IMPULSES

A common belief, stemming from the law of dynamic polarization, is that all neurons function by converting synaptic inputs into impulse discharges in their axons. However, many neurons carry out their input–output functions without the need to generate impulses. In these neurons, electrotonic spread of synaptic potentials is sufficient, governed by the rules for passive spread of activity that were discussed in Chapter 5. Some of the earliest and best examples of neurons operating in this mode were found in the vertebrate retina and olfactory bulb, as well as in the nonspiking neurons of invertebrates. Here we focus on specific properties of these neurons that clearly illustrate principles of information processing having general applicability to complex dendrites throughout the nervous system.

Membrane Conductances Interact in Photoreceptors

In the peripheral retina, photoreceptor cells, horizontal cells, and bipolar cells normally respond to light stimulation with only slow potentials, graded in amplitude with the level of stimulation, as first shown by the pioneering studies of Frank Werblin and John Dowling in 1968.[13] In the photoreceptors, these graded potentials can spread to the synaptic terminals because of the relatively short electrotonic length of the photoreceptor processes. The photoreceptor also illustrates the important principle that an impulse is not needed for neurotransmitter release; graded potentials are sufficient.

The normal graded response to light of the photoreceptor[14] is due to modulation by cGMP of the dark current mediated by cyclic-nucleotide-gated channels.[15] The finding of a graded potential response in a neuron commonly implies the lack of voltage-gated channels, but, as the refrain goes in *Porgy and Bess*, "it ain't necessarily so." When an isolated retina is bathed in the K^+ conductance blocker tetraethylammonium (TEA), the photoreceptors generate an all-or-nothing action potential during the depolarization after the cessation of a light pulse (Fig. 13.5)[16]; this impulse is removed by further exposure to the Ca^{2+} conductance blocker $CoCl_2$. This indicates that the photoreceptor

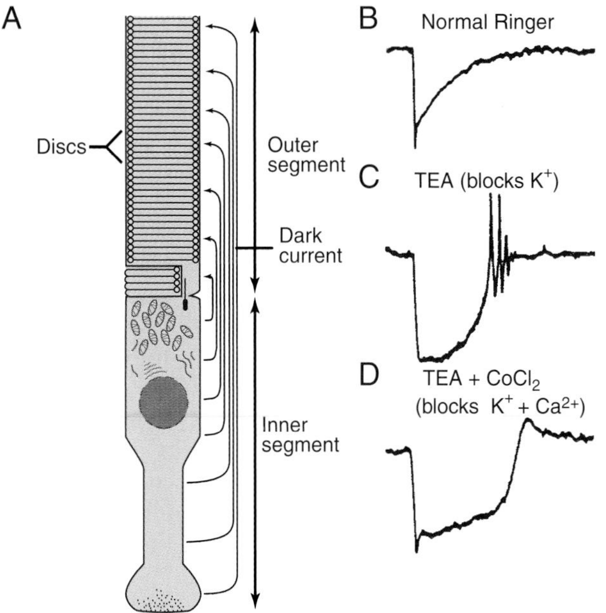

FIGURE 13.5 Graded passive responses may conceal active membrane properties: (A) Diagram of a vertebrate rod photoreceptor, showing generation of the standing current in the dark; (B) response to light when the rod is bathed in normal Ringer solution; (C) impulses at off response when TEA is added to the bath to block K^+ conductances; (D) blockade of Ca^{2+} by cobalt chloride in the bath blocks the impulses. (A) from Fain in Roberts and Bush[17]; (B–D) from Fain *et al.*[16]

cell membrane contains voltage-gated Ca^{2+} channels, which are normally short-circuited by K^+ channels. The voltage-gated channels may serve to boost the graded potentials under some operating conditions; such boosting functions have been observed for other types of sensory neurons without impulses.[17]

The first important principle from this example is that voltage-gated channels appear to be much more widely distributed than previously thought; indeed, it is a useful working rule to assume that they may be ubiquitous in nerve membranes. The second is that K^+ channels have important roles in controlling the functions of active channels in somata and dendrites. Thus, the expression of active-channel properties depends on interactions with other channels, which in turn depend on the densities of the different channel types and the electrotonic properties that govern the interactions between them and with other parts of the neuron. These principles underlie many of the functional properties of dendrites.

Horizontal Cells Exemplify Network Formation and Compartmentalization

Two aspects of the horizontal cell are relevant to the theme of the complex neuron: (1) the formation of gap junction networks and (2) compartmentalization.

Gap Junction Networks

Subpopulations of horizontal cells in some species are extensively interconnected by gap junctions, forming virtual electrical syncytia.[18] These syncytia play an important role in facilitating the lateral spread of responses to generate the receptive-field properties of ganglion cells. But, by lowering the input resistance of cells and increasing the conductance load, gap junctions reduce the amplitude of individual responses at a given site in a neuron. This smooths the responses to individual photoreceptor inputs, thus reducing noise and increasing the signal-to-noise ratio when correlated photoreceptor inputs are activated by visual scenes.[19,20] Gap junctions between dendrites may play similar roles elsewhere in the nervous system.

Separation of Axonal and Dendritic Compartments

In primates, one subpopulation of horizontal cells is characterized by a cell body with bushy dendrites, giving rise to a thin axon that terminates in an axon terminal tree with extensive branches[21] (Fig. 13.6). In this cell type, the dendrites receive synaptic connections mainly from cone receptors, whereas the axon terminals receive connections mainly from rod receptors; this difference has been documented by physiological recordings.[25] Thus, in this cell, the axon not only does not generate an impulse, but actually functions to separate the axon terminals from the dendrites, with the result that the two carry out their input–output functions as separate compartments. It is as if this horizontal cell consists of two neurons instead of one. This subpopulation of horizontal cells clearly exemplifies the principle of functional compartmentation within a neuron in the processing of distinct types of information.

Tight Electronic Coupling Occurs within Bipolar Cells

Bipolar cells provide the pathway between photoreceptors and ganglion cells, but how is effective linkage between the photoreceptor input and the synaptic output accomplished in the absence of impulses? The answer requires an estimate of the electrotonic length (L) of the bipolar cell. The combined length of the dendrite and the axon is only approximately 100 μm, and the diameters of these processes are approximately 1 μm. For the usual values of the specific membrane resistance (R_m) and internal resistance (R_i) (Chapter 5), the characteristic length (λ) may be calculated to be at most a few tenths. The spread of synaptic potentials from

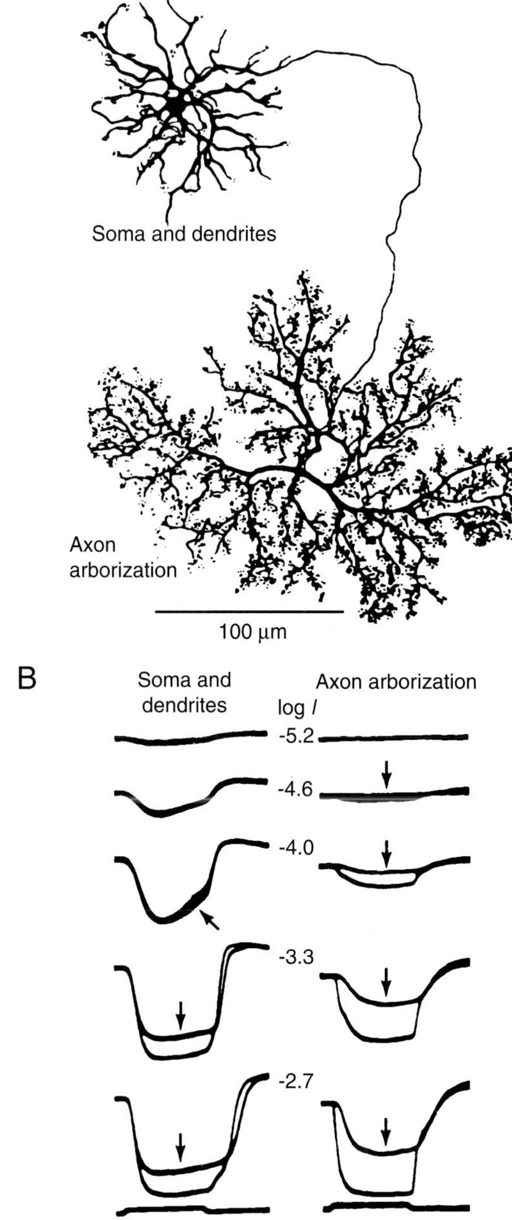

FIGURE 13.6 A neuron may show extreme structural and functional compartmentalization of its axonal and dendritic regions, as in this example of the horizontal cell of the cat retina. (A) The Type B horizontal cell has a cell body and dendritic tree (top) and a long thin axon that gives rise to a large terminal arborization (bottom). (B) Intracellular recordings were made both from the axonal termination and from the soma and in response to two different wavelengths of light (superimposed traces) at increasing light intensity (log *I*). Down to log $I = -4.0$, the soma plus dendrites show wavelength discrimination, but the axonal arborization does not, because the soma and dendrites receive cone inputs, whereas the axonal arborization receives primarily rod inputs. At higher intensities, there is a spread of responses between the compartments through the thin axon. From Nelson *et al.*[22]

their site of input from the photoreceptors to the site of output onto ganglion cell and amacrine cell dendrites is therefore presumably very effective; thus, over this short distance, impulse generation is not necessary for the conversion of the synaptic input into a synaptic output. See Chapter 5 for a review of the principles underlying this passive spread.

The principles applying to tight electrotonic linkage also apply to the spread of synaptic potentials in the other direction, from the reciprocal synaptic input in the axon terminals from the amacrine-cell dendrites back to the dendritic terminals that receive the photoreceptor input.[23] This backspreading synaptic potential carries information about the output state of the axon terminal to the site of photoreceptor input. In this way, a backspreading synaptic potential can implement a retrograde signal that is in a graded, passive form, rather than the backpropagating impulse in cells with axons. A general principle derived from these considerations is that in a segment of dendrite with both input and output synapses, the coupling between the integrative states of the input and output sites is tight.

Reciprocal Synapses Mediate Input–Output Functions of Amacrine Cells

Some cells lack axons; their ability to function as neurons was therefore originally in doubt. Amacrine cells are a classical example of this type. The puzzle was resolved by the finding that amacrine-cell dendrites have output as well as input synapses.[23] Reciprocal pairs connect the distal amacrine dendrites with the terminals of bipolar cells. In addition, several amacrine-cell processes may be interdigitated between bipolar terminals and ganglion cells. Thus, amacrine-cell dendrites have input synapses from bipolar cells and output synapses onto bipolar cells, other amacrines, and ganglion cells. Through the spread of activity in the amacrine-cell dendrites, these synaptic connections enable long-distance lateral interactions, important in shaping receptive-field properties of the ganglion cells; the lateral spread may be boosted by dendritic spikes.

In addition to these long-distance interactions, the reciprocal and serial synaptic interactions may be mediated by local graded synaptic potentials. In the starburst amacrine cell, the distal dendrites have both input and output synapses, whereas the proximal dendrites have only input synapses (Fig. 13.7). The distal dendrites can function as input–output compartments, the size of which varies with membrane resistance (R_m).[24] When the effective R_m is small, the compartments are relatively restricted and a compartment may have input–output operations that are relatively isolated from the rest of the cell.

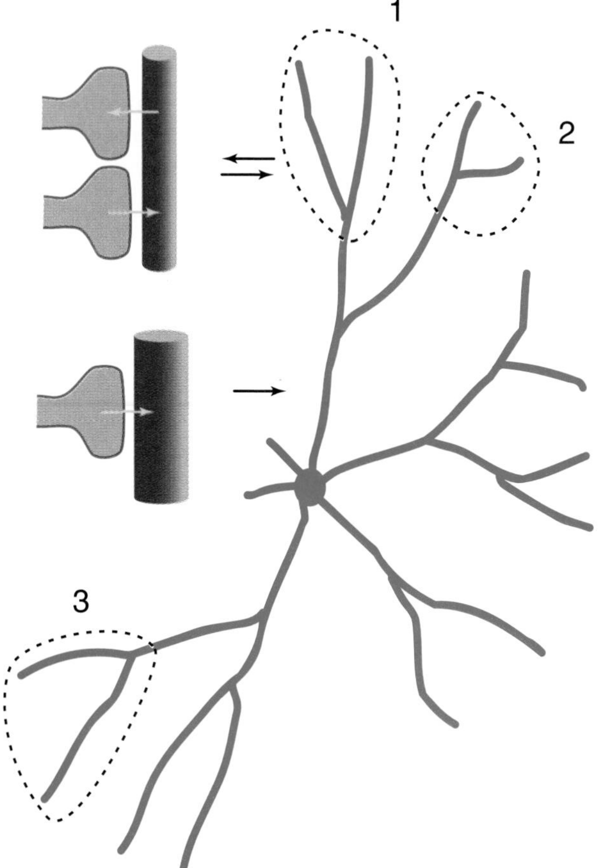

FIGURE 13.7 Functional compartmentalization may exist within a dendritic tree, as in this example of the starburst amacrine cell of the retina. Distal dendrites are both presynaptic and postsynaptic; populations of pre- and postsynaptic synapses form input–output functional subunits (1–3), depending on the spread of EPSPs controlled by the membrane resistance. Proximal dendrites are only postsynaptic. Adapted from Koch *et al.*[24]

Olfactory Granule-Cell Spines Function as Local Input–Output Compartments

The olfactory granule cell is another example of an axonless cell, with a peripheral dendritic tree covered with spines and several central dendrites. Several key functions have been identified in its dendrites. Physiological studies first indicated that the peripheral dendrites have inhibitory synaptic actions on mitral and tufted cell dendrites.[25,26] A computational model of mitral- and granule-cell interactions suggested that the peripheral dendrite is activated by excitatory synaptic input from the mitral-cell dendrites; electron microscopic analysis then demonstrated the reciprocal dendrodendritic synapses mediating these interactions.[27,28] These synaptic arrangements provide for self- and lateral inhibition of the mitral cells (Figs. 13.8A and 13.8B). This model has been subjected to numerous tests (Fig. 13.8C).[29,30] The tight organization of these local connections has made this a prototype of a synaptic microcircuit.[31]

These synaptic arrangements and interactions have enlarged our view of dendritic functions beyond the classical model in several ways. First, although impulses can be recorded in the region of the granule-cell body, the synaptic outputs from the dendritic spines do not appear to depend on impulse activity.[30] Thus, like the amacrine cell, the granule cell mediates synaptic output without the need of either an axon or impulses. The defining characteristic of a neuron therefore appears to be not an axon or the generation of impulses, but rather synaptic outputs.

Second, dendrites can be presynaptic as well as postsynaptic. The synapses are similar to Type I and Type II synapses elsewhere in the nervous system; thus, it is not the special properties of the synapses that differ from the classical model, but rather their arrangement. These synaptic arrangements and interactions showed that the law of dynamic polarization does not apply to the synaptic interactions mediated by local sites within a neuron. They provide evidence for the law of local dendritic integration stated earlier.

Third, the granule-cell spine acts as a local input–output compartment, operating to some extent independent of neighboring spines and, particularly, of distant spines in a granule-cell dendritic tree. As in the amacrine cell, the degree of localness varies with the effective R_m.[32] This compartmentalization has important functional consequences. Different dendritic compartments can interact differently with their respective targets, in contrast with axonal output, which is the same to all targets (though it may be modulated by various factors).

A particularly clear example of how the local compartmentation of these interactions can have functional importance is provided by studies of the role of the dendrodendritic synapses in the accessory olfactory bulb in olfactory memory. A female mouse learns and remembers the odor of the familiar male who impregnates her; if, within a few days, the pregnant mouse is exposed to the odor of a strange male, the fetus is aborted (the so-called Bruce effect).[33] An exploration of the neural mechanism for this odor memory revealed that the mitral cell activated by the familiar male odor releases glutamate from its secondary dendrites, which activates the mGluR2 receptor on the granule cells contacted by the mitral cell and reduces reciprocal inhibitory transmission from those granule cells[34] (Fig. 13.9). The enhanced responsiveness of these synapses, but not of the granule-cell synapses on surrounding

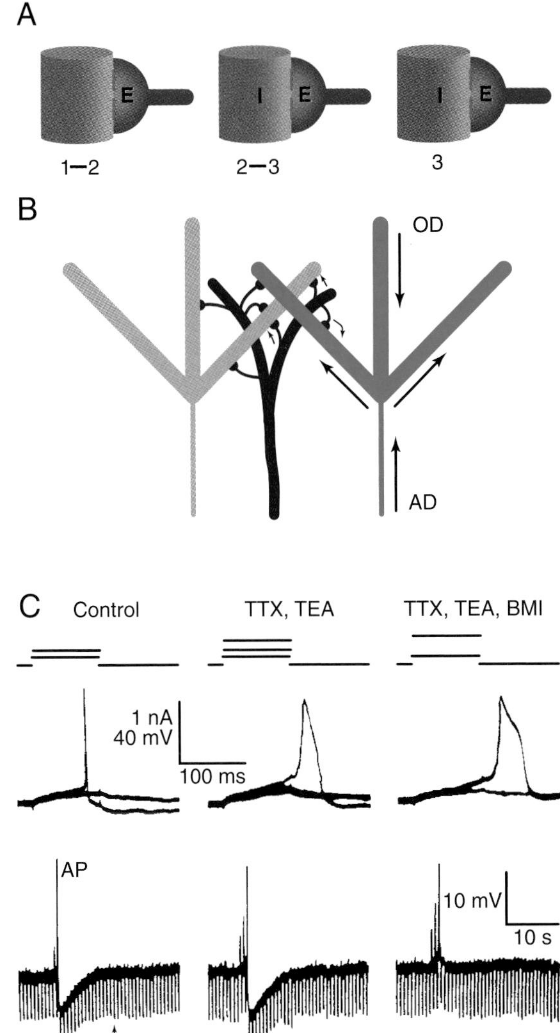

FIGURE 13.8 Dendritic spines form functional units, as in this example of dendrodendritic synapses in the olfactory bulb. (A) Model showing depolarization by backspreading impulse in time period 1–2, activating excitatory output from mitral-cell dendrite, and setting up an EPSP (E) in a granule-cell spine. During time period 2–3, the granule-spine EPSP activates a reciprocal inhibitory synapse, setting up an inhibitory postsynaptic potential, or IPSP (I) in the mitral-cell dendrite. This is long-lasting into time period 3. (B) Diagram showing how either orthodromic (OD) or antidromic (AD) activation of the mitral cell sets up a backspreading or backpropagating impulse into the secondary dendrites, activating both feedback and lateral inhibition of the mitral cells through the dendrodendritic pathway. (C) Experimental demonstration of the dendrodendritic pathway. (Left) In an intracellular recording from a mitral cell in an isolated turtle olfactory bulb bathed in control Ringer solution, injected depolarizing current elicits an impulse [fast trace and action potential (AP) in slow trace below] followed by a long-lasting hyperpolarizing IPSP; downward deflections are reduced during the IPSP, indicating an increase in membrane conductance during the IPSP. (Middle) Depolarizing current elicits a lower amplitude and slower impulse when the preparation is bathed in TTX (which blocks the Na component of the impulse) and TEA (which blocks K^+ conductances that would shunt the remaining Ca^{2+} component; see Fig. 13.5. The IPSP persists, activated by the Ca^{2+} impulse (bottom trace). (Right) Addition of bicuculline (BMI) to the bath blocks the IPSP (bottom trace), presumably by blocking the granule-to-mitral reciprocal synapse. (A, B) From Rall and Shepherd[28]; (C) adapted from Jahr and Nicoll.[30]

less-active mitral cells, represents the memory of the odor that activated this cell. This effect can be reproduced by infusions of a specific mGluR2 agonist, DCG-IV, into the accessory olfactory bulb of the female mouse, coupled with exposure to a pheromone of a male mouse; a reduction of reciprocal inhibition from granule cells to mitral cells, through mGluR2 activation, mimics the memory formation that occurs during mating.[35]

Much effort is currently being invested in analyzing long-term potentiation/long-term depression (LTP/LTD) as the synaptic basis of memory (see Chapters 55 and 56). However, these studies of dendrodendritic interactions constitute the best evidence in a mammalian system of a link between a specific set of learned behaviors and changes in the efficacy of an identified synapse.[36] This activity-dependent memory mechanism occurs at an inhibitory synapse, in contrast with LTP/LTD, which is commonly believed to be mainly at excitatory synapses.

Nonspiking Neurons Are Common in Invertebrates

Most of the types of local dendritic organization seen in vertebrates, including dendrodendritic synapses, neurons without axons, and nonimpulse input–output operations, are also found in many parts of invertebrate nervous systems.[17] We consider two well-studied examples.

Local and Distributed Reciprocal Synapses in the Lobster Stomatogastric Ganglion

Local synaptic interconnections similar to those in the retina and olfactory bulb have been identified in several regions of the invertebrate neuropil. One of the first examples discovered was in the stomatogastric ganglion of the lobster.[37] Neurons were recorded intracellularly and stained with Procion yellow. Serial electron micrographic reconstructions showed the synaptic relations between stained varicosities in the neurites and their neighbors. In many cases, a varicosity could be seen to be not only presynaptic to a neighboring varicosity, but also postsynaptic to that same process (Fig. 13.10). It was concluded that synaptic inputs and outputs are distributed over the entire dendritic arbori-

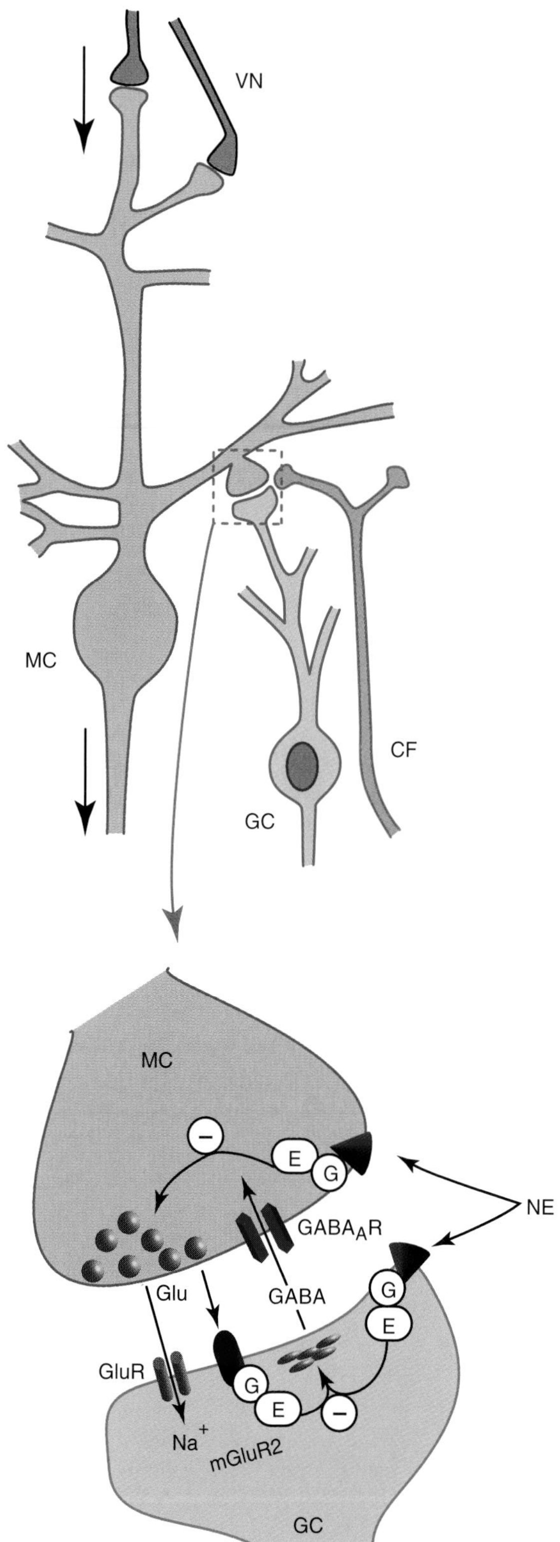

FIGURE 13.9 Spine units can support learning mechanisms, as in this example of the compartment formed by the granule-cell spine in the accessory olfactory bulb, which is believed to mediate olfactory memory for the odor of a familiar male. Abbreviations: VN, vomeronasal nerve; MC, mitral cell; GC, granule cell; CF, centrifugal fiber; NE, norepinephrine; E, effector; G, G protein. Adapted from Kaba *et al.*[35]

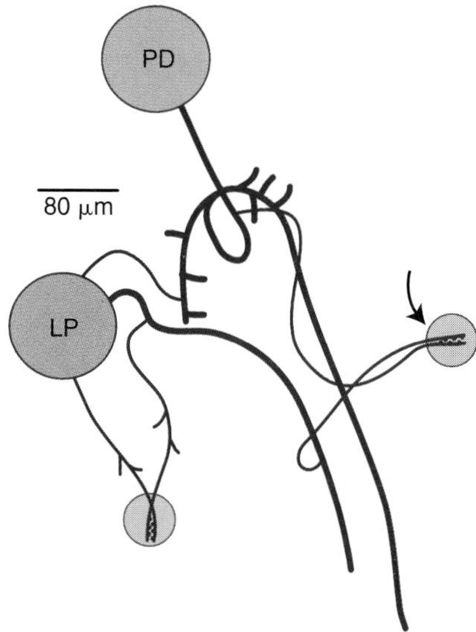

FIGURE 13.10 Local functional subunits are widely found within the neuropil of invertebrate ganglia. This shows the formation of local synaptic input–output subunits in the neurites of neurons in the stomatogastric ganglion of the lobster. Reconstructions of pyloric dilator (PD) and lateral pyloric (LP) neurons are shown. From Selverston *et al.*[37])

zation. Polarization was not from one part of the tree to another. The "bifunctional" varicosities appeared to act as local input–output units, similar to the manner described earlier, in which granule-cell spines appear to operate. The entire set of these local input–output units, distributed throughout the dendritic tree, mediates the generation and coordination of oscillatory activity characteristic of the stomatogastric ganglion in controlling the rhythmic movements of the stomach.

Sensorimotor Integration through Nonspiking Neurons in the Control of Movement

In insects, a class of non-impulse-generating (nonspiking) neuron processes tactile stimuli that control leg movements.[38] Tactile information from a leg is conveyed to the metathoracic ganglion, where connections are made to two types of interneurons, spiking and nonspiking. In both types, the cell body has a single process that gives rise to a richly ramified tree of fine branches, as shown in Fig. 13.11A (the branches are equivalent to dendrites, but are often referred to as neurites in the invertebrate literature). The spiking interneurons receive direct excitatory connections that preserve the spatial organization of the input from the leg. They make inhibitory (presumably GABAergic) connections onto each other and onto the nonspiking interneurons (Fig. 13.11B), which in turn make inhibitory connections onto each other and inhibitory (Fig.

13.11C)[38] or excitatory connections onto the motor neurons.

Intracellular recordings from the nonspiking neurons show that all their responses consist of graded synaptic potentials. A given nonspiking interneuron receives convergent connections from several spiking interneurons. Input and output synapses are intermingled in their branches, suggesting that local sites act as semi-independent input–output compartments, similar to the spines and distal dendritic branches of vertebrate neurons discussed earlier. Within the network of inhibitory connections between nonspiking

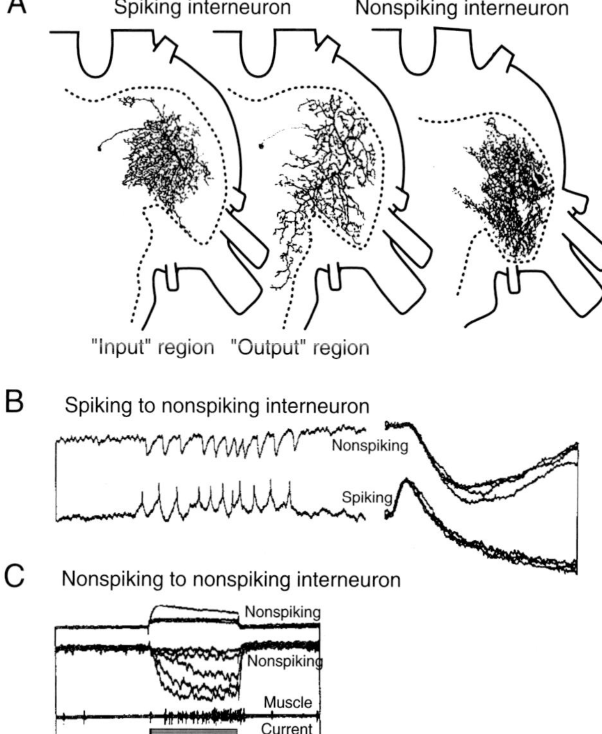

FIGURE 13.11 Spiking and nonspiking interneurons form a complex network mediating sensory–motor coordination of the locust leg. (A) Local interneurons within the right metathoracic ganglion of the locust, anterior above, stained with cobalt: (left) the neuritic tree of a spiking interneuron is divided into an input region (receiving input from the ventral femur) and an output region (providing output to motor neurons supplying the femur); (right) the neuritic tree of a nonspiking interneuron whose output controls motor neurons that move the femorotibial joint. (B) Functional analysis of the interactions between spiking and nonspiking interneurons, with the use of double intracellular recordings. Touching hairs on the dorsal femur elicits EPSPs and spikes in a spiking interneuron, which appear to set up an IPSP in a nonspiking interneuron. (C) Injection of depolarizing current into a nonspiking interneuron causes a graded inhibition of another nonspiking interneuron; this inhibition is associated with increased firing in a leg muscle. Nonspiking interneurons may be either excitatory or inhibitory to motor neurons. From Burrows.[38]

interneurons, the amplitude of a postsynaptic response encodes the amplitude of the synaptic potentials in the presynaptic process rather than impulse frequency. Because of their finely graded nature, these local interactions enable the exquisite targeting of input to precisely the correct set of motor neurons to elicit leg movement in response to local sensory stimulation of the leg. In this control, the contribution of any one compartment is always in the context of the activity of the others. In this way, a given neuron contributes many simultaneous, parallel, and contextually dependent computations to the overall reflex control of the limb. The operating principle of parallel local input–output units appears to be similar to that of the lobster stomatogastric ganglion.

In overall perspective, this sensory–motor reflex pathway can be seen to include complex nonspiking neurons operating in accord with principles similar to those that apply in the vertebrate retina. Spatially specific information is fed forward through the nonspiking interneuronal network, which operates through multiple local input–output units functioning mainly by means of graded inhibitory interactions. This organization is not unlike the network of graded feed-forward and lateral antagonistic interactions that characterize the processing of spatially specific information in the retina, described earlier. The output then goes to motor neurons, where it is encoded into impulse trains to the muscles, similar to the impulse output from ganglion cells to the brain.

Summary

"What do dendrites do?" The answer is often, "Still mysterious." However, experiments on neurons that carry out input–output operations in the absence of axons and impulses provide surprisingly clear evidence. As we have seen, horizontal-cell dendrites process one type of information differently from axon terminals. Bipolar cells provide transmission lines from photoreceptors to ganglion cells, modulated at the input end by horizontal cells and at the output end by amacrine cells. Amacrine-cell dendrites mediate center-surround antagonism by their interactions with bipolar and ganglion cells. The spine compartments of olfactory granule cells have multiple functions that provide feedback inhibition in sensory feature extraction, generation of oscillatory potentials, and a mechanism for modulation that underlies olfactory memory. These types of synaptic organization have their counterparts in the invertebrate neuropil. Nonspiking neurons in invertebrates provide distributed systems of local input–output units, acting in parallel, that mediate a variety of functions, including rhythmic control of the lobster stomach and finely graded sensory–motor coordination of insect leg movements.

Given this evidence, let us next consider what dendrites do when their parent cell bodies are connected to axons.

DENDRITIC INTEGRATION IN RELATION TO AXONAL OUTPUT

Since Golgi's time,[1] neurons with axons have been classified into two types: (1) long-axon cells, which function as the output neuron of a region; and (2) short-axon cells, which function as interneurons within a region. Long-axon cells tend to be larger and have therefore been more accessible to experimental analysis. Indeed, virtually everything that we know about the functional relations between dendrites and axons has been obtained from studies of long-axon cells. By the same token, much of what we think we understand about that relation in short-axon cells is only by inference.

By starting as we have with anaxonal cells, we are immediately able to recognize that critical constraints on the nature of dendritic processing are present in a cell with an axon that are not present in an anaxonal cell (Fig. 13.12). The first obvious constraint is the presence of the axon. If a neuron has an axon, it usually has only one. This near-universal developmental rule is remarkable and still little understood; it is currently being analyzed in neuronal cultures.[39] The rule means that for dendritic integration to lead to output from the neuron to distant targets, all of the activity within the dendrites must eventually be funneled into the origin of the axon in the single axon hillock. Therefore the flow of information in dendrites has an overall orientation, just as surmised by the classical neuroanatomists. Another constraint, and virtually a universal rule, is that the main function of the axon in long-axon cells is to support the generation of impulses in the axon hillock–initial segment region that propagate through the axon to the axon terminals (as well as spreading back into the dendrites). By definition, impulses have thresholds for generation; thus, the critical functional constraint is that the results of dendritic integration affect the output through the axon only by initiating or modulating impulse generation in the axon hillock. Thus a considerable amount of subthreshold activity in the dendrites can affect the integrative states of the dendrites but not directly or immediately affect the output of the neuron. Such subthreshold activity underlies action potential initiation in the dendrites themselves.

We turn now to the functional adaptations that allow branching dendrites to process information within these constraints.

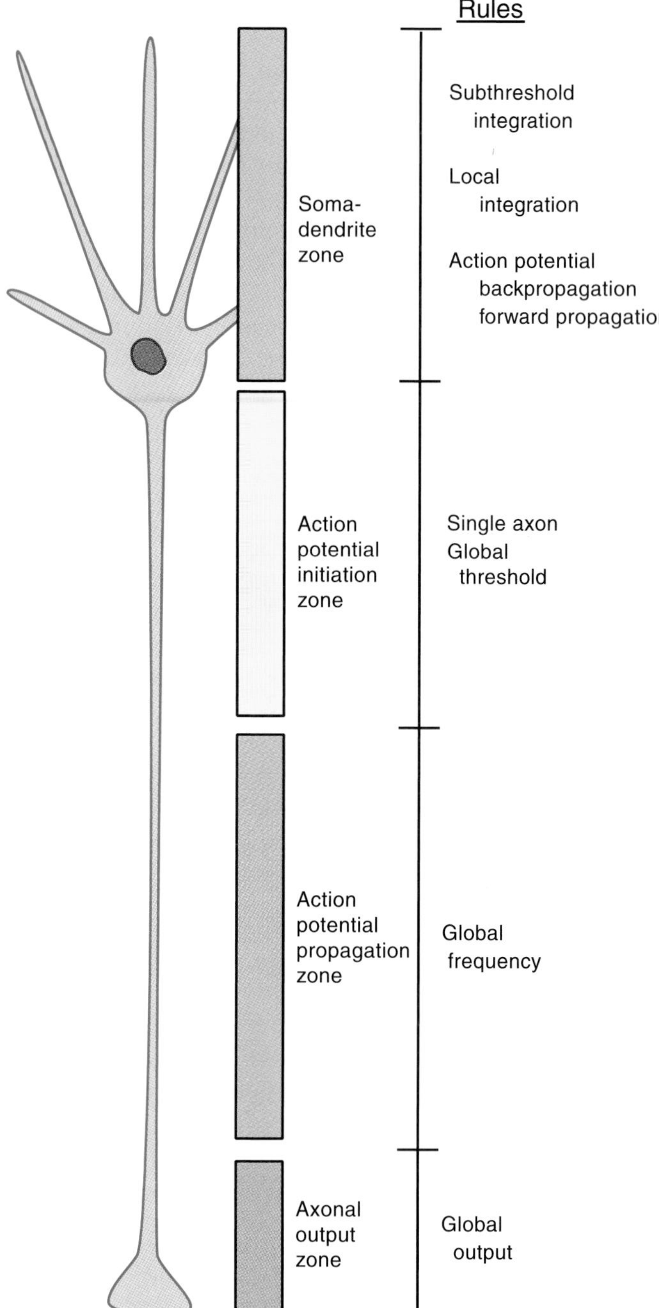

FIGURE 13.12 The presence of a single axon forces several organizational rules onto a neuron. See text for details.

Distal Dendrites Can Be Closely Linked to Axonal Output

What is the contribution of distal dendrites to the functions of axonal cells? As mentioned earlier, the common perception is that distal dendrites are too distant from the site of axonal origin and impulse generation to have more than a slow and weak background modulation of impulse output. However, in many cases, specific inputs are located preferentially on distal dendrites. Such is true of the mitral and tufted cells in the olfactory bulb, where the input from the olfactory nerves ends on the most distal dendritic branches in the glomeruli; in mitral cells this may be 400–500 μm or more from the cell body.[40] Such is also true of their targets, the pyramidal neurons of the olfactory cortex, where the input terminates on the spines of the most distal dendrites in layer I.[41] These examples prove beyond any doubt, just as Ramón y Cajal inferred, that distal dendrites can in fact mediate rapid processing of specific information, even at the weakest levels of detection.

In many other neurons, a given type of input terminates over much or all of the dendritic tree, including the distal branches; such is the case, for example, for climbing fiber and parallel fiber inputs to the cerebellar Purkinje cells.[42] The relative significance of the more distal inputs is not so apparent; nevertheless, it is clear that judgment on whether a distal input mediates rapid specific information or slow and weak background information should be withheld pending experimental evidence.

Research is beginning to define the functional properties that must underlie effective transmission from distal dendritic responses to axonal output. The first such property is the amplitude of the conductance generated by the synapse itself (Fig. 13.13A). In motor neurons, the conductances of the most distal excitatory synapses may be many times the amplitude of proximal synapses.[43,44] This would account for the fact that the peak unitary synaptic response recorded at the soma varies in time course according to synaptic location but has a constant amplitude of approximately 100 μV (Fig. 13.13A).

A second key property is the specific membrane

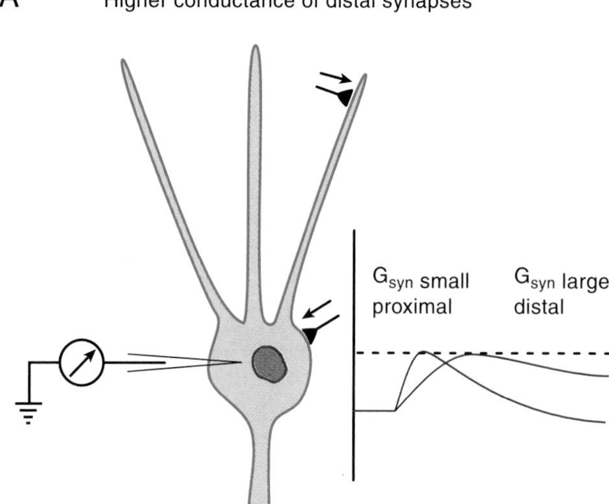

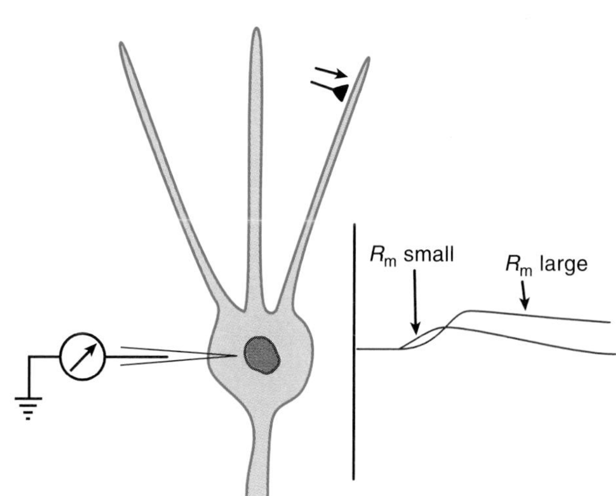

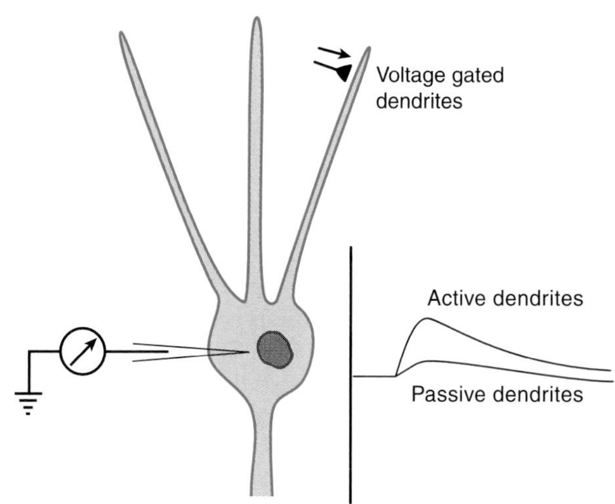

FIGURE 13.13 Mechanisms by which the synaptic responses in distal dendrites can have an enhanced affect in controlling impulse output from the axon–hillock–initial segment region. (A) Schematized neuron with patch recording from the soma. The soma response to a distal input can be equivalent in amplitude to the response to a soma input if the distal synapses have larger conductances (the response will be slower because of the electrotonic delay in the intervening dendrites). (B) The soma response to a distal input is enhanced in amplitude if the membrane resistance of the dendrites is increased (the response is slowed by the larger time constant). (C) The soma response to a distal input is enhanced by the presence of voltage-gated channels in the dendrites, which boost the passive synaptic potential.

resistance (R_m) of the dendritic membrane. Traditionally, the argument against the distal dendrites having a direct effect on axonal output has been made on electrotonic grounds: if R_m is relatively low, then the characteristic length of the dendrites will be relatively short, the electrotonic length will be correspondingly long, and synaptic potentials will therefore decrement sharply in spreading toward the axon hillock. However, as discussed in Chapter 5, even early intracellular recordings indicated that R_m is sufficiently high that the electrotonic lengths of most dendrites are in the range of 1–2,[45] and recent patch recordings suggest much higher R_m values, indicating electrotonic lengths less than 1. Thus, a relatively high R_m seems adequate for close electrotonic linkage, at least in the steady state (Fig. 13.13B).

For transient responses, the electrotonic linkage becomes longer because of the capacitance of the membrane, and it is made worse by a higher R_m, which increases the membrane time constant and thereby slows the spread of a passive potential (see Chapter 5). How does the cell overcome this disadvantage? Active properties implemented by voltage-gated channels can do this in several ways (Fig. 13.13C).

The Axon Hillock–Initial Segment Is a Key Encoding Site in Cells with Axons

In cells with long axons, activity in the dendrites eventually leads to activation and modulation of impulse output in the axon. The impulse in the axon depends on I_{Na} and I_K, in the classical Hodgkin–Huxley formulation. A key question is the precise site of origin of this impulse.

The first intracellular recordings from motor neurons[46] suggested that the impulse arises in the soma region, as mentioned earlier. In these classical experiments, the antidromic impulse showed an inflection on its rising phase, which was attributed to its encountering a lower safety factor in propagating from the smaller-diameter axon into the larger-diameter cell body. This same inflection was also seen in the impulse when it was generated in response to intracellular current injection and even to an EPSP generated in the dendrites (Fig. 13.14).[10] Fuortes and colleagues[47] were the first to deduce, in 1957, that the EPSP spreads from the dendrites through the soma to the region of the axon hillock and the initial axon segment. They therefore suggested that the impulse has two components: (1) an A component that is normally associated with the axon hillock and initial segment and (2) a B component that is normally associated with the cell body. The site of impulse initiation can shift under different membrane potentials, so they preferred the noncommittal terms "A" and "B" for the impulse components

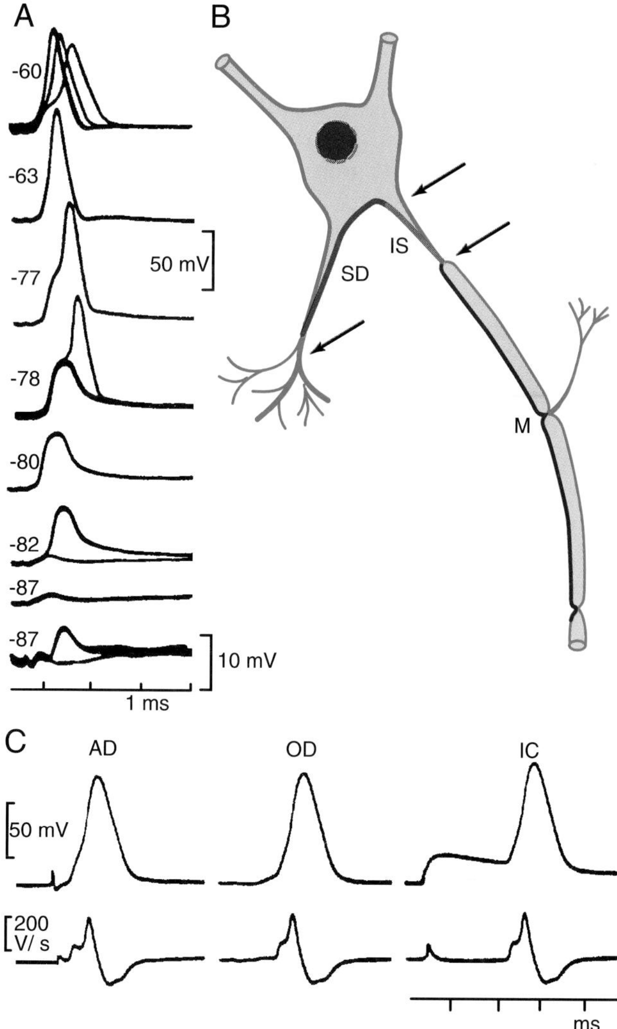

FIGURE 13.14 Classical evidence for the site of impulse initiation. Intracellular recordings were from the cell body of the motor neuron of an anesthetized cat. (A) Differential blockade of an antidromic impulse by adjusting the membrane potential by holding currents. The recordings reveal the sequence of impulse invasion in the myelinated axon (recordings at −87 mV, two amplifications), initial segment of the axon (first component of the impulse beginning at −82 mV), and soma-dendritic region (large component beginning at −78 mV). (B) Sites of the three regions of impulse generation (M, myelinated axon; IS, initial segment; SD, soma and dendrites); arrows show probable sites of impulse blockade in (A). (C) Comparison of intracellular recordings of impulses generated antidromically (AD), synaptically (orthodromically, OD), and by direct current injection (IC). Lower traces indicate electrical differentiation of these recordings, showing the separation of the impulse into the same two components and indicating that sequence of impulse generation from the initial segment into the soma-dendritic region is the same in all cases. From Eccles.[10]

as recorded from the cell body. In contrast, Eccles[10] referred to the initial component as the initial-segment (IS) component and to the second component as the soma–dendritic (SD) component.

Apart from the motor neuron, the best early model

for intracellular analysis of neuronal mechanisms was the crayfish stretch receptor, described by Carlos Eyzaguirre and Stephen Kuffler in 1955.[48] Intracellular recordings from the cell body showed that stretch causes a depolarizing receptor potential equivalent to an EPSP, which spreads through the cell to initiate an action potential. In the early work, it was assumed that this impulse arose at or near the cell body. In 1958, Edwards and Ottoson[49] tested this postulate by recording the local extracellular current along the surface of the cell to locate precisely the site of inward current associated with impulse initiation. Surprisingly, this site turned out to be far out on the axon, some 200 μm from the cell body (Fig. 13.15). This result showed without any doubt that potentials generated in the distal dendrites can spread all the way through the dendrites and soma well out into the initial segment of the axon to initiate impulses. It further showed that the impulse recorded at the cell body is the backward spreading impulse from the initiation site. Edwards and Ottoson's study was important in establishing the basic model of impulse initiation in the neuron.

The fact that an EPSP spreads across the soma to initiate an impulse in the axon hillock–initial segment region was somewhat counterintuitive, because it required that the soma–dendritic membrane have sufficient Na channels to generate the backward-spreading B spike but insufficient channels to respond first to the forward-spreading EPSP. The active response of the soma–dendritic membrane was therefore the subject of early investigation. In the absence of direct dendritic recordings, local field potentials were plotted around single activated motor neurons; evidence that an antidromic impulse spreads into the dendrites was obtained, but it was difficult to conclude whether this spread was by active or passive means.[50]

These classical studies, showing impulse initiation in the axon hillock–initial segment with backspread into the soma–dendritic region, provided a model that was quite persuasive. The stretch receptor model and

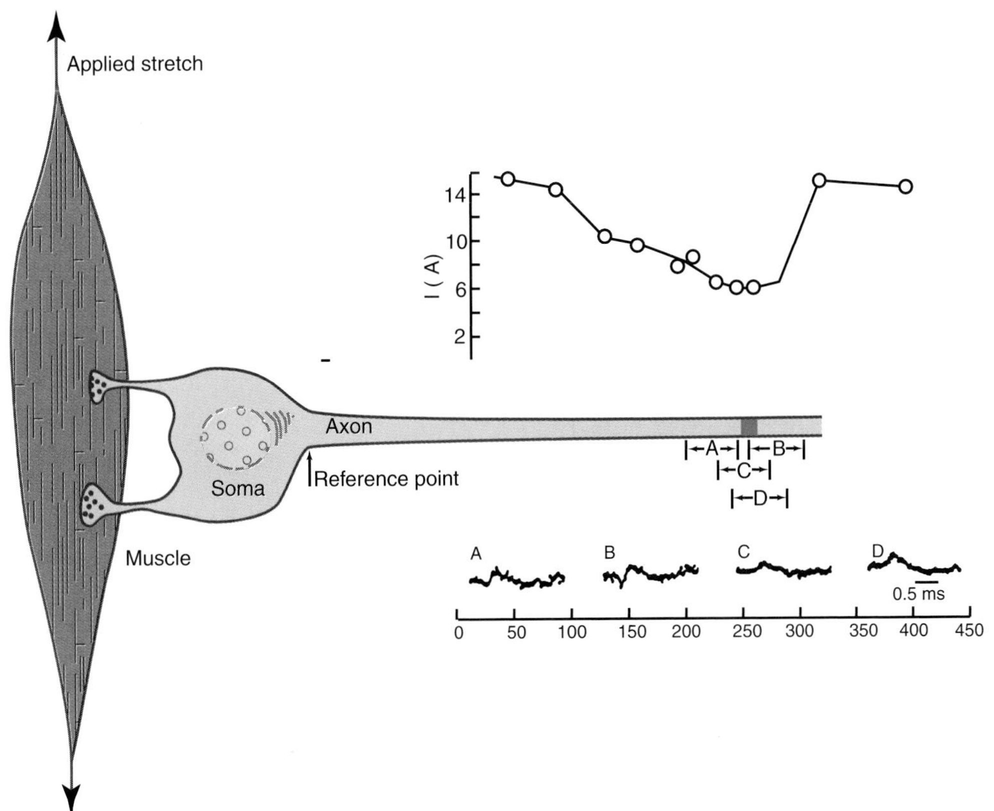

FIGURE 13.15 Classical demonstration of the site of impulse initiation in the stretch receptor cell of the crayfish. Moderate stretch of the receptor muscle generated a receptor potential that spread from the dendrites across the cell body into the axon. Paired electrodes recorded the longitudinal extracellular currents at positions A–D, showing the site of the trigger zone (green region). The excitability curve (shown at the top), obtained by passing current between the electrodes and finding the current (*I*) intensity needed to evoke an impulse response, also shows the trigger zone to be several hundred micrometers out on the axon. From Ringham.[53]

the motor-neuron model were soon taken for granted, so much so that they were rarely described explicitly in most basic textbooks. Further testing was obviously needed, but had to await the development of methods for recording from cell bodies and dendrites in tissue slices. In CA1 hippocampal pyramidal neurons, weak synaptic potentials elicited impulses near the cell body,[51] but this site shifted to the proximal dendrites with stronger synaptic excitation.[52] This confirmed the suggestion of Fuortes and his colleagues that the site of impulse initiation can shift under different stimulus conditions and was consistent with the stretch receptor, where larger receptor potentials shift the initiation site closer to the cell body.[53]

Analysis of impulse initiation has been carried to a more definitive level of detail by combining dual patch recordings from somatic and dendritic sites with direct observation, by using confocal, infrared, or two-photon microscopy.[54] Experiments in cortical pyramidal neurons have shown that, in response to current injected into the soma, the action potential arises first at the soma; this sequence is the same for current injected into the dendrite and for the response to an EPSP in the dendrites (Fig. 13.16). These results, as far as they go (see below), are thus an elegant confirmation of the classical studies.

Voltage-Gated Channels Take Part in Dendritic Integration

Detailed analysis of active dendritic properties began with the studies of cerebellar Purkinje cells in the 1970s.[61–64] Since then, studies of active dendritic properties have proliferated, particularly after the introduction of the patch recording method. Studies of several types of neurons provide important models for the possible functional roles of active dendritic properties in the processing of synaptic inputs. Because of the small size and complicated geometry of most dendrites, their study has been at the forefront of the development of patch recording and microscopic imaging techniques.[8]

Purkinje Cells

The cerebellar Purkinje cell has the most elaborate dendritic tree in the nervous system, with more than 100,000 dendritic spines receiving synaptic inputs from parallel fibers and mossy fibers. The contribution of active dendritic properties in processing this tremendous barrage of inputs is therefore the focus of a great deal of interest.

The basic distribution of active properties in the Purkinje cell was indicated by the pioneering experiments of Llinás and Sugimori[62–64] in tissue slices (Fig.

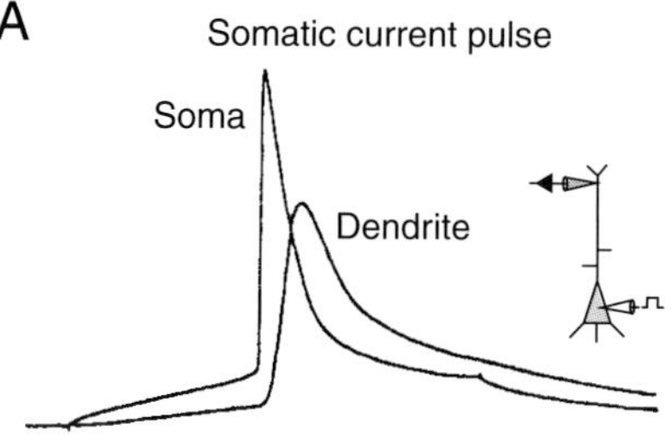

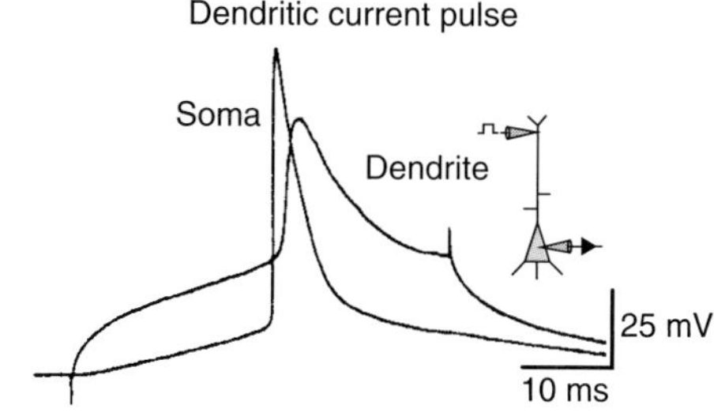

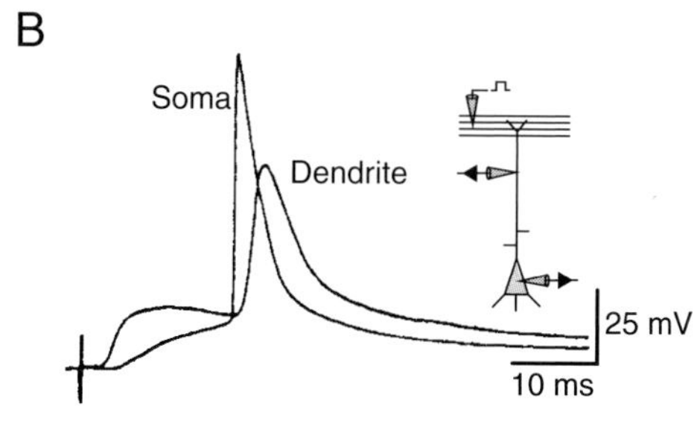

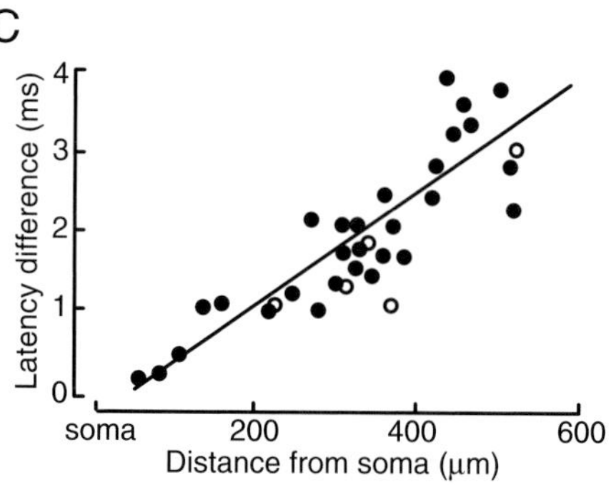

FIGURE 13.16 Direct demonstration of impulse-initiation zone and backpropagation into dendrites, using dual patch recordings from soma and dendrites of a layer V pyramidal neuron in a slice preparation of the rat neocortex. (A) Depolarizing current injection in either the soma or the dendrites elicits an impulse first in the soma. (B) The same result is obtained with synaptic activation of layer I input to distal dendrites. Note the close similarity of these results to the earlier findings in the motor neuron (Fig. 13.14). (C) The increase in latency of the impulse as it propagates into the dendrites is similar after both somatic (solid circles) and distal dendritic (open circles) activation. From Stuart and Sakmann.[54]

BOX 13.1

ACTIVE DENDRITIC PROPERTIES: A BRIEF HISTORY

The idea that dendrites support impulse activity is an old one. It was inherent in Ramón y Cajal's concept that the dendrites take part in neural transmission; the arrows that Ramón y Cajal placed beside dendrites and axons signified impulse flow, because, apart from the passive spread of electrotonic potentials, that was the only kind of nerve activity known. This implication continued in the diagrams of Rafael Lorente de Nó for the activity in cortical neurons.[55] Theories were elaborated in which collisions between impulses in dendrites could account for inhibition (e.g., "Wedensky inhibition" in Katz[56]). The concept that neurons have central excitatory and inhibitory synaptic "states," generated by synaptic activity, was introduced by Sherrington in 1932,[57] but experimental evidence for the excitatory and inhibitory postsynaptic potentials in dendrites awaited the first intracellular recordings from spinal motor neurons by Eccles and his collaborators in 1952.[9]

The discovery of synaptic potentials raised the question of how they are linked to impulse generation. In Eccles' early recordings, the EPSPs, when of sufficient amplitude, gave rise at their peaks to an impulse in the cell body, which propagated out the axon. Eccles concluded that synaptic potentials were generated close to the site of recording, at the soma or proximal dendrites. The analytical and computational methods developed by Wilfrid Rall in the late 1950s and early 1960s made it possible to show that synapses over the whole dendritic tree are linked by electrotonic current spread to the soma and axon hillock (Chapter 5). There was also keen awareness of the possibility that this electrotonic linkage might be augmented by active dendritic properties. Single unit recording studies did provide evidence of active dendritic properties.[58]

Further evidence came in the 1950s from another line of study on "decremental conduction" in dendrites. In this work, potentials recorded in the cortex displayed the properties neither of propagating all-or-nothing impulses nor of stationary synaptic potentials. Therefore these potentials were inferred to represent weakly regenerative activity that could serve to enhance the spread of synaptic activity through the dendritic tree.[59] A limitation of these studies was that they were based on recordings of extracellular field potentials, which do not directly represent membrane potentials. The interpretation of these potentials therefore remained speculative.

The first intracellular recordings of active properties of dendrites were obtained in 1958 by Eccles himself, from motor neurons undergoing chromatolytic degeneration after amputation of their axons.[60] In these recordings, small spikes could be seen riding on EPSPs, and these spikes were thought to be due to impulse "booster" sites in the dendrites. Similar activity was seen in the first intracellular recordings from hippocampal pyramidal neurons.[61] These "fast prepotentials" appeared to intervene between the EPSP in the dendrite and the impulse initiation in the soma–axon hillock region (Fig. 13.7). These active sites were suggested to be at branch points in the apical dendrite, where they would serve to boost the EPSPs generated by more distal dendritic inputs. This boosting property has provided an important model for the possible significance of active dendritic properties.

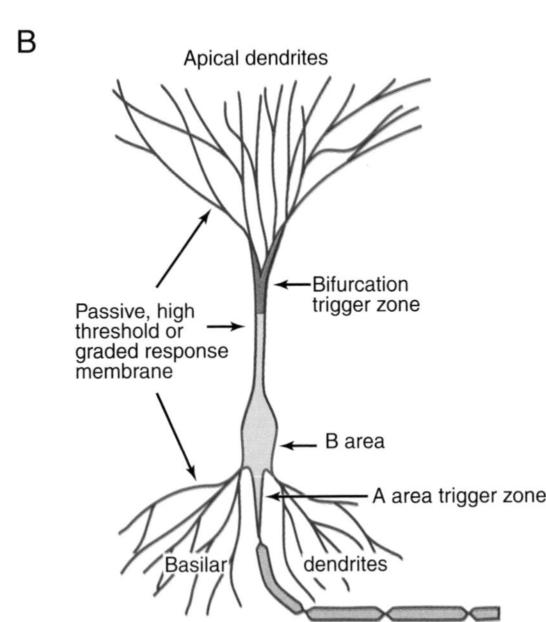

FIGURE 13.17 Early evidence for active dendritic properties in normal adult neurons. (A) Intracellular recordings from the soma of a hippocampal pyramidal neuron in an anesthetized cat; the large spontaneous action potentials are preceded by a small "fast prepotential" (small arrows), which occasionally occurs in isolation (large arrow). (B) Conceptual schema of how a "trigger zone" at bifurcating dendritic branches could give rise to the fast prepotential and boost the distal dendritic response. From Spencer and Kandel.[61]

13.18). The output impulse is generated in the cell body and axon hillock mainly by fast Na^+ and delayed K^+ channels; there is also a Ca^{2+} component. This impulse correspondingly has its highest amplitude in the cell body and decreases by electrotonic decay in the dendrites. In contrast, the recordings in the dendrites are dominated by slower spike potentials that are Ca dependent, owing to a P-type Ca^{2+} conductance. These spikes are generated from a plateau potential due to a persistent Na_p current (see Chapter 6). Correlated with this electrophysiological evidence are Ca accumulations in both soma and dendrites, seen by using calcium imaging.[65,66]

The possible functions of voltage-gated channels in Purkinje cell dendrites are still a matter of speculation[6] but may be best understood at this stage in relation to the two distinct operating modes of the Purkinje cell in relation to climbing fiber and mossy fiber inputs. Climbing fibers mediate strong depolarizing EPSPs throughout most of the dendrites that appear to give rise to synchronous Ca^{2+} dendritic spikes throughout the dendritic tree, which then spread to the soma to elicit the bursting "complex spike" in the axon hillock.[62] In contrast, parallel fibers are active in small groups, giving rise to smaller populations of individual EPSPs possibly targeted to particular dendritic regions. In this mode, subthreshold amplification through active dendritic properties may enhance the effect of a particular set of input fibers in controlling or modulating the frequency of Purkinje cell impulse output in the axon hillock.

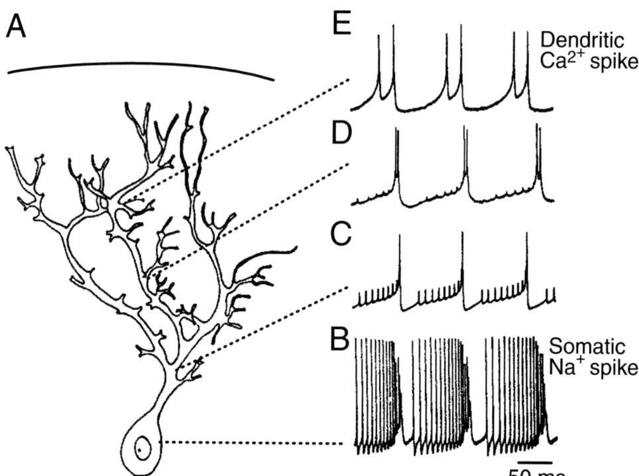

FIGURE 13.18 A classical demonstration of the difference between soma and dendritic action potentials. (A) Drawing of a Purkinje cell in the cerebellar slice. (B) Intracellular recordings from the soma, showing fast Na^+ spikes. (C–E) Intracellular recordings from progressively more distant dendritic sites; the fast soma spikes become small, owing to electrotonic decrement, and are replaced by large-amplitude dendritic Ca^{2+} spikes. Spread of these spikes to the soma causes an inactivating burst that interrupts the soma discharge. Adapted from Llinás and Sugimori.[64]

Pyramidal Neurons

Active properties of the apical dendrite of hippocampal pyramidal neurons have been amply documented by patch recordings.[67] In contrast with the Purkinje cell, both fast Na^+ and Ca^{2+} conductances are present throughout the dendritic tree of the pyramidal neuron. Dye-imaging studies have shown the presence of Ca^{2+} channels in the dendrites, as well as a close correlation in the time course of Ca^{2+} signals and electrophysiological responses.[68,69] Both Na^+ and Ca^{2+} channels have been demonstrated in recordings from membrane patches of apical dendrites,[70,71] as has the participation of regenerative Ca^{2+} conductances in the dendritic response to excitatory synaptic input.[67] Activation of the low-threshold Na^+ channels is believed to play an important role in triggering the higher-threshold Ca^{2+} channels. Similar results have been obtained in studies of pyramidal neurons of the cerebral cortex.[71–74]

The output pattern of a neuron depends not only on its dendritic properties but also on their interaction with the soma. The emerging picture of the generation of a burst response in a CA3 pyramidal neuron may be summarized as follows[6] (see Fig. 13.19). Synaptic inputs lead to EPSPs that spread through the dendrite, activating fast Na^+ and then high-threshold (HT) Ca^{2+} channels that give a subthreshold boost to the EPSP. The enhanced EPSP spreads to the soma–axon hillock, triggering a Na^+ impulse. This Na^+ impulse not only propagates into the axon but also backpropagates into the dendrites, eliciting a slower all-or-nothing Ca^{2+} impulse (backpropagation is further considered later in this chapter). This large-amplitude, slow depolarization then spreads through the dendrites and back to the soma, triggering a train of action potentials that form a burst response. This sequence emphasizes not only the importance of the interplay between the different types of channels, but also the critical role of the compartmentation of the neuron into dendritic and somatic compartments so that they can interact in controlling the intensity and time course of the impulse output.

Does the specific form of the input–output transformation depend on a specific distribution of active channels in the dendritic tree or can the channels be distributed uniformly throughout the tree? On the one hand, we have evidence that Na^+ and Ca^{2+} channels are distributed widely in pyramidal neuron dendrites, and, in computational simulations, that grouping channels in different distributions has little effect on the input–

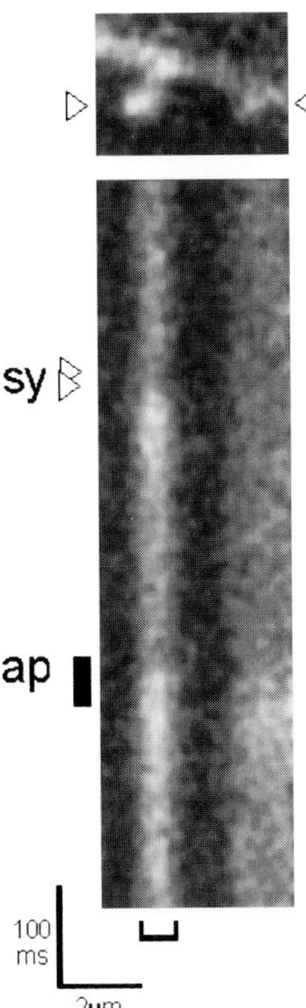

FIGURE 13.19 Calcium transients can be imaged in single dendritic spines in a rat hippocampal slice. Two nearby spines (arrowheads) on the apical dendrite of a CA1 pyramidal neuron are imaged with the fluorescent dye calcium green-1. Successive line scans through the spines show that weak synaptic stimulation (SY) activated only the left spine, whereas action potential (AP) backpropagation activated both spines. The signals were reversibly abolished by the voltage-sensitive calcium channel blocker Ni^{2+} but not by glutamate receptor blockers. The results show that spines contain voltage-gated Ca^{2+} channels, act as Ca^{2+} compartments, are invaded by action potentials, and can function as coincidence detectors. See text for details. From Yuste and Denk.[5]

output functions of a neuron. On the other hand, we have evidence that subthreshold amplification by voltage-gated channels may tend to occur in the more proximal dendrites of some neurons.[5] In addition, the dendritic trees of some neurons are clearly divided into different anatomical and functional subdivisions as discussed in the next section.

Medium Spiny Cell

A third instructive example of the role of active dendritic properties is found in the medium spiny cell of the neostriatum.[75] (Figs. 13.20A and 13.20B). The passive electrotonic properties of this cell are described in Chapter 5 (see Fig. 5.12). Inputs to a given neuron from the cortex are widely distributed, meaning that a given neuron must summate a significant number of synaptic inputs before generating an impulse response. Under background conditions, individual responses in the spines are filtered out by the large capacitance of the spiny dendrite, so individual EPSPs recorded at the soma are small. With specific input, the larger summated EPSPs depolarize the dendritic membrane strongly. The dendritic membrane contains inwardly rectifying channels (Fig. 13.20C), which reduce their conductance upon depolarization and thereby increase the effective membrane resistance and shorten the electrotonic length of the dendritic tree. The large depolarization also activates HT Ca^{2+} channels, which contribute to the large-amplitude, slow depolarizations. These combined effects change the neuron from a state in which it is insensitive to small noisy inputs into a state in which it gives a large response to a specific input and is maximally sensitive to additional inputs. Through this voltage-gated mechanism a neuron can enhance the effectiveness of distal dendritic inputs, not by boosting inward Na^+ and K^+ currents, but by reducing outward shunting K^+ currents.

Dendritic Trees May Be Functionally Compartmentalized

The complex properties of dendrites indicate that the input–output operations of many neurons cannot be represented by a single summing node. Compartmentation is an important contributor to complexity, as illustrated by the mitral cell and the inferior olive cell.

Mitral Cell

The distal tuft of the primary dendrite of the mitral cell is specialized for reception of the sensory input from the olfactory receptor cell axons and for the initial processing of that input through dendrodendritic synapses with periglomerular short-axon cells. These terminals make glutamatergic synapses onto the dendritic branches within a glomerulus.[76] The branches have glutamatergic outputs and receive both GABAergic and DAergic inputs.[77] In contrast, the proximal part of the primary dendrite is concerned almost exclusively with transmission of the EPSP response in the tuft to the soma–axon hillock.[80,81] Action potential propagation in the primary dendrite is discussed further below. Finally, as discussed previously, the secondary dendrites of the mitral cell are concerned exclusively with the reciprocal dendrodendritic interactions with the granule cells that mediate self- and lateral inhibition (see Figs. 13.8 and 13.9).[27–30, 78] These dendrodendritic inter-

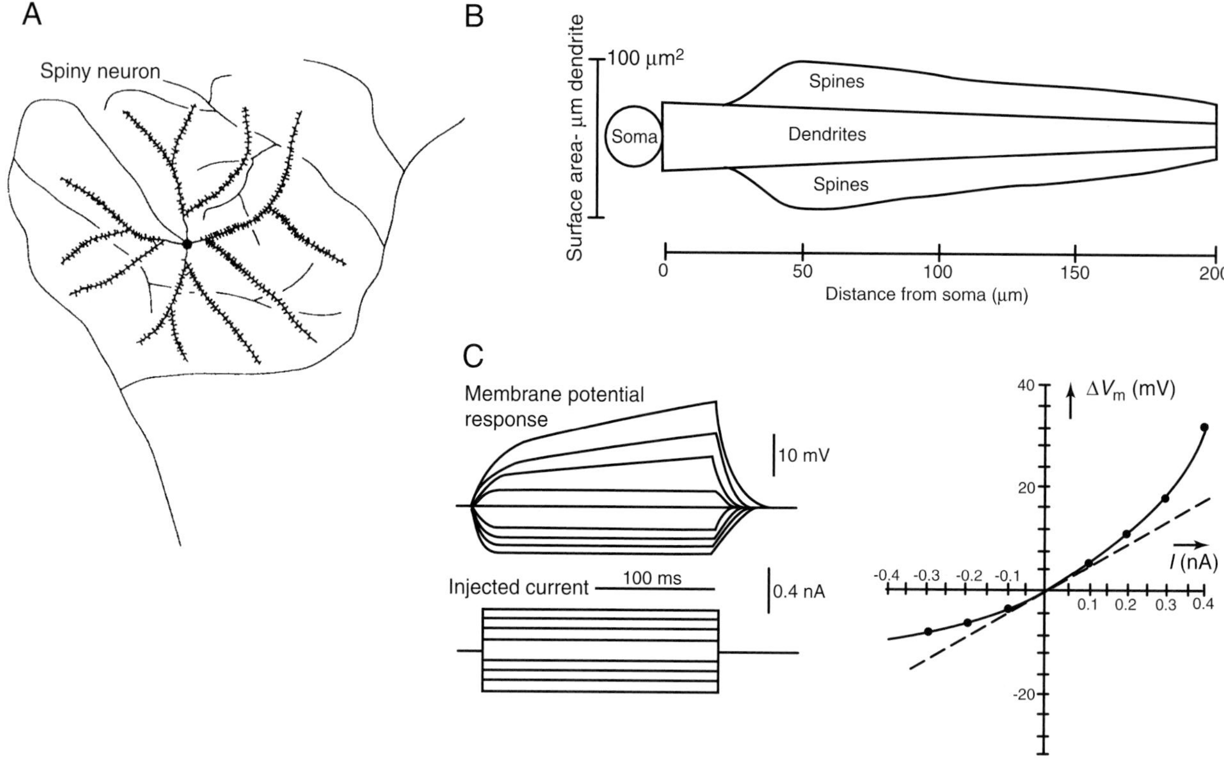

FIGURE 13.20 Dendritic spines and dendritic membrane properties interact to control neuronal excitability. (A) Diagram of a medium spiny neuron in the caudate nucleus; (B) plot of surface areas of different compartments, showing large increase in surface area due to spines; (C) intracellular patch-clamp analysis of medium spiny neuron, showing inward rectification of the membrane that controls the response of the dendrites to excitatory synaptic inputs (cf. Chapter 5, Fig. 5.12). From Wilson.[75]

actions are activated by the retrograde spread of the impulse from the soma–axon hillock region.

Thus, the dendritic tree of the mitral cell is divided into three compartments, each distinct in anatomical structure and functional properties from the other two dendritic compartments and from the soma compartment. This compartmentation is critical for the essential operations of the mitral cell: forward transmission of sensory information through EPSPs, backspread of the impulse to activate the dendrodendritic synapses, forward spread of dendritic impulses to extend the operating range of the mitral cell, self- and lateral inhibition for abstraction of sensory determinants underlying odor discrimination, storing of olfactory memory, and shaping of the temporal characteristics of the output by generating oscillatory activity.

Inferior Olive Cell

Cells in the inferior olive provide the climbing fiber input to the cerebellar Purkinje cells. Two mechanisms governing their output illustrate special aspects of somatic and dendritic compartmentation. First, the dendrites are interconnected through electrical synapses between their spines, thus forming a dendritic network reminiscent of the horizontal-cell network in the retina. The electrical coupling between cells is modulated by the activity of chemical synapses onto the dendrites.[79] Second, the inferior olive cells clearly exemplify the interactions between dendritic and somatic compartments that generate oscillatory behavior. The sequence parallels that already described for pyramidal neurons. Synaptic excitation depolarizes the cell, leading to a somatic Na^+ action potential, which backspreads into the dendrites to trigger a dendritic $I_{Ca,HT}$. This activates in turn $I_{K,Ca}$ in the dendrites, which hyperpolarizes the dendrite. This current spreads to the soma, deinactivating a somatic $I_{Ca,LT}$, which triggers a second somatic Na^+ action potential, and the process repeats itself. Thus, the separation of different types of conductances into the soma and dendrite compartments introduces delayed interactions that underlie the generation of oscillatory output. The resulting intense burst of impulses in the axon becomes the climbing fiber input that is matched to the generation of a burst response in the cerebellar Purkinje cell, as described earlier. Thus, the special properties of dendritic compartments are matched not only to those of their own cell but also to the properties of their target cells.

Retrograde Impulse Spread into Dendrites Can Have Several Important Functions

From the initiation zone, an impulse propagates into the axon to reach the axon terminals and bring about transmitter release onto target neurons. What is the function of the impulse spreading back into the soma and dendrites? The classical models in the motor neuron and stretch receptor cell assumed primarily passive spread, without specifying the possible function of the decrementing depolarizing wave spreading outward in the dendrites.

The first specific evidence for the function of a backward spreading dendritic action potential was provided by the computational model of the olfactory mitral cell. The mitral-to-granule dendrodendritic synapses are triggered by the impulse spreading from the soma into the secondary dendrites, as mentioned earlier (Fig. 13.8). Because of the delay in activating the reciprocal inhibitory synapses from the granule cells, self-inhibition of the mitral cell occurs in the wake of the passing impulse; the two do not collide. The mechanism functions similarly when both active impulse backpropagation and passive impulse spread into the dendrites, as tested in computer simulations.[28] Thus, the function of the retrograde impulse in the mitral cell model can be clearly stated: it is to activate self- and lateral inhibition of the mitral cells. The functional operations of this inhibition also can be specified: (1) center-surround antagonism underlying the discrimination of different odor molecules,[78] (2) storing of olfactory memories, and (3) generation of oscillating activity in mitral- and granule-cell populations.[28,80]

Current studies of other types of neurons are providing new evidence for critical functions of retrograde impulses. In several types of pyramidal neurons, active dendritic properties appear to boost the retrograde impulse, so that the depolarization reaches significant levels throughout the dendritic tree. One possible function is that the Na^+ and K^+ conductance increases associated with active propagation wipe out the existing membrane potential, resetting the membrane potential for new inputs. A second possible function is that the impulse depolarization is coincident with the synaptic responses that triggered the impulse. Because the impulse in the dendritic branches would reach into the spines (because of the electrotonic factors discussed in Chapter 5), the impulse depolarization would summate with the depolarization of the spine synapses, which would enable the spines to function as coincidence detectors and implement Hebb-like changes in synaptic plasticity. This postulate is currently being tested by electrophysiological recordings[81] and Ca imaging.[5] There is evidence that activity-dependent changes of dendritic synaptic potency are not seen with passive retrograde depolarization but require actively propagating retrograde impulses.[81]

A third possible function is that trains of impulses generated at the soma–axon hillock can invade the dendrites to varying extents. The proximal dendrites appear to be invaded throughout a high-frequency burst, whereas the distal dendrites appear to be invaded only by the early impulses.[68,74,81,82] Activation of Ca^{2+}-activated K^+ conductances by the early may effectively switch off the distal dendritic compartment. A fourth possibility is that the retrograde impulse may contribute to the activation of neurotransmitter release from the dendrites. Dynorphin released by synaptically stimulated dentate granule cells can affect the presynaptic terminals.[83]

Multiple Impulse Initiation Sites Are under Dynamic Control

We have seen that in the classical model of the neuron with a long axon, the site of action potential initiation in response to an excitatory synaptic input anywhere in the dendritic tree appears to be at the axon hillock–initial segment region. This model actually allowed for significant flexibility, with the site of action potential initiation shifting along the initial segment toward the axon hillock[53] and even from the axon hillock–cell body region into the proximal dendrites[51,84] with stronger excitatory input. Finally, we have seen that there is ample evidence for active properties of distal dendrites that boost their responses to excitatory synaptic inputs, as well as boost the backpropagation of action potentials from the cell body.

It remains to consider whether the active properties of dendrites can give rise to full dendritic action potentials that propagate toward the cell body and precede the action potential in the soma–axon hillock–initial segment region, thereby requiring revision of the classical model. Evidence for this began with extracellular recordings of a "population spike" that appears to propagate along the apical dendrites toward the cell body in hippocampal pyramidal cells.[50] Current source density calculations also provided evidence for this in cortical pyramidal neurons.[85] And the somatic recordings of fast prepotentials arising in dendrites have implied dendritic action potentials preceding axon hillock action potentials.[61] However, because of the indirect nature of this evidence, it has been argued[88] that

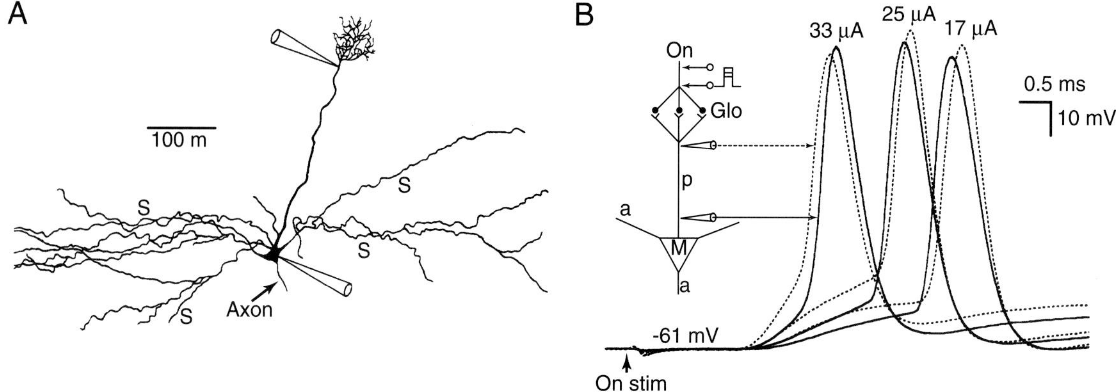

FIGURE 13.21 Shift of action potential initiation site between soma and distal dendrite. (A) A mitral cell in a slice preparation from the rat olfactory bulb stained with biocytin, showing placement of dual patch recording electrodes, one on the soma and one at the distal end of the primary dendrite 300 μm from the soma near the distal dendritic tuft in the glomerulus. (B) In another cell, an electrode site near the soma is paired with a distal dendritic site. With weak shocks to the olfactory nerves (17 μA) the soma action potential arises first; as the shocks are strengthened to 33 μA, the action potential initiation shifts to the distal dendrite recording site. From Chen *et al.*[87]

these active properties of distal dendrites can boost dendritic synaptic responses but may be too slow to lead to action potential initiation and forward propagation.

The clearest evidence to date has been obtained from the olfactory mitral cell. With the use of dual patch recordings under infrared microscopical observation, the site of impulse initiation has been tested, first with excitatory inputs to the distal dendrite (see Fig. 13.21A).[87] At weak levels of electrical shocks to the olfactory nerves, the site of impulse initiation is at or near the soma, in confirmation of the classical model (17 μA in Fig. 13.21B). This shows that despite its long length, the primary dendrite is not an impediment to the transfer of the EPSP carrying specific sensory information from the distal dendrite to the site of impulse initiation near the soma. It adds another nail to the coffin of the common misconception that, in neurons with axons, specific inputs must be targeted near the axon hillock and that distal dendrites can mediate only slow background modulation of that site.

As the level of distal excitatory input is increased, the dual recordings show clearly that the impulse initiation site is not fixed; instead, the site shifts gradually from the soma to the distal dendrite (see 25 and 33 μA in Fig. 13.21B). Similar results are obtained with depolarizing current injected into the distal dendrite through the patch electrode. This provides unambiguous evidence that the site of impulse initiation is not fixed in the mitral cell, but varies with the level of distal excitatory input. The action potential is due to tetrodotoxin-sensitive Na channels, which are distributed along the extent of the primary dendrite.[88] Experiments are in progress to determine whether the impulse arises initially within the terminal dendritic tuft or in the primary dendrite near the tuft.

The effect of synaptic inhibition on the site of impulse initiation can also be tested because the dendrodendritic inhibition of the mitral cells by the granule cells is especially concentrated on the separate compartment formed by the secondary dendrites (see Fig. 13.8). At low to intermediate levels of distal excitatory input, activation of the inhibition in this compartment shifts the site of impulse initiation from the soma to the distal dendrite. This adds to previous evidence that inhibition can control the extent of backpropagation of an impulse in some cells[89] by showing that it can also shift impulse propagation from backward to forward.

These studies indicate that the site of impulse initiation and the direction of impulse propagation in a dendritic tree are determined by the dynamic interaction between excitatory and inhibitory synaptic inputs. The logic of this arrangement is still under study. One interpretation is that the shift of impulse initiation to the distal site provides the means for a cell to overcome inhibition directed to the soma and thereby give the cell an extended operating range. In addition, even though impulse output may be blocked at the soma, the distal impulse can continue to evoke Ca^{2+} influx that can mediate local processes such as release of dendritic transmitters or gaseous messengers and synaptic plasticity.[89]

Dendritic Spines Are Multifunctional Microintegrative Units

An additional level of complexity is found in neurons that have spiny dendrites. Spines were introduced and discussed in Chapter 5, where it was explained that they form electrical and biochemical microcompartments that, even under the assumption of passive cable properties, have a number of important properties. These include, because of their small size, the development in response to brief synaptic conductance changes of rapid large amplitude synaptic potentials and large changes in concentrations of ions and second messengers. In addition, because of the impedance mismatch, there are pronounced asymmetries in interactions with the parent dendrite.

The very small size of dendritic spines has made it difficult to study them directly. However, it has become obvious that the possible contributions of spines to the integrative life of the complex neuron go far beyond these initial properties. In a few cell types, such as the olfactory granule cell (see above), it has been possible to make direct inferences. Spines have been implicated in cognitive functions from observations of dramatic changes in spine morphology in relation to different types of mental retardation and different hormonal exposures. It was previously suggested that activity-dependent changes in spine morphology could be a mechanism contributing to learning and memory (because they contain actin filaments, they might even twitch!) Computational models have been very useful in testing these hypotheses, as well as suggesting other possible functions, such as the dynamic changes of electrotonic structure in medium spiny cells of the basal ganglia (see above). With the development of more powerful light microscopical methods, such as two-photon laser confocal microscopy, it has become possible to image Ca^{2+} fluxes in individual spines in relation to synaptic inputs and neuronal activity. The concomitant evidence for active properties of dendrites has suggested that these may extend to the spines themselves. Thus, spines may be devices for nonlinear thresholding operations, either through voltage-gated ion channels or thorugh voltage-dependent synaptic properties such as *N*-methyl-D-aspartate receptors. On the other hand, spines may function as compartments to isolate changes at the synapse, such as excess Ca^{2+} that would be harmful to the rest of the neuron.

The range of functions that have been hypothesized for spines is partly a reflection of how little direct evidence we have of specific properties of spines. It also indicates that the answer to the question "What is the function of the dendritic spine?" is unlikely to be only one function but rather a range of functions that is tuned in a given neuron to the specific operations of that neuron. Thus, the spine is increasingly regarded as a microcompartment that integrates a range of functions.[90–94] With regard to the complex functions of dendrites, this means that a spiny dendritic tree is covered with a large population of microintegrative units. The effect of any given one of these units on the action potential output of the neuron should therefore not be assessed with regard only to the far-off cell body and axon hillock, but rather with regard first to its effect on its neighboring microintegrative units. From this perspective, if a spine can affect its neighbor, and that spine its neighbor, a dendritic tree becomes a cascade of decision points, with multiple cascades operating over multiple overlapping time scales.

Summary

Dendritic trees provide a remarkably flexible substrate for passive and active properties to generate a wide variety of types of information processing. A variety of specific types of input–output functional operations have been identified in neurons that lack axons, clearly demonstrating that dendrites are well suited for information-processing tasks. To understand these possibilities in neurons with axons we have focused on four basic modes of information flow in dendrites and have attempted to illustrate them with examples drawn from a variety of neuron types. First is an overall functional polarization from distal dendrites to axon hillock (Ramón y Cajal and van Gehuchten's law of dynamic polarization), such as the spread of excitatory synaptic potentials to the axon hillock region that is found in most neurons with axons. Second are functional operations carried out locally in different parts of a dendritic tree (law of local dendritic integration), exemplified by booster sites at dendritic branch points and synaptic outputs from dendritic branches and spines. Third is backpropagation of the action potential from the axon hillock and soma into the dendrites (law of retrograde information flow), which plays an essential role in activating dendritic output synapses when they are present and may play a critical role in contributing to plasticity of synapses in response to subsequent inputs. Fourth is forward action potential propagation (law of forward information flow) from multiple dendritic sites, which increases the operational range of the neuron and may also contribute to plasticity of local dendritic synapses.

References

1. Golgi, C. (1886). *Sulla Fina Anatomia degli Organi Centrali del Sistema Nervoso.* Hoepli, Milan.

2. Shepherd, G. M. (1991). *Foundations of the Neuron Doctrine.* Oxford University Press, New York.
3. Ramón y Cajal, S. (1894). *Les nouvelles ideés sur la structure du système nerveux chez l'homme et chez les vertébrés (New Ideas on the Structure of the Nervous System of Man and the Vertebrates* (N. Swanson and L. W. Swanson, transl.). MIT Press, Cambridge, MA / Paris, Reinwald.
4. Shepherd, G. M. (1972). The neuron doctrine: A revision of functional concepts. *Yale J. Biol. Med.* **45:** 584–599.
5. Yuste, R., and Denk, W. (1995). Dendritic spines as basic functional units of neuronal integration in dendrites. *Nature (London)* **375:** 682–684.
6. Yuste, R., and Tank, D. W. (1996). Dendritic integration in mammalian neurons, a century after Cajál. *Neuron* **16:** 701–716.
7. Fulton, J. F. (1938). *Physiology of the Nervous System.* Oxford University Press, London.
8. McCulloch, W. S., and Pitts, W. H. (1943). A logical calculus of the ideas immanent in nervous activity. *Bull. Math. Biophys.* **5:** 115–133.
9. Brock, L. G., Coombs, J. S., and Eccles, J. C. (1952). The recording of potentials from motorneurons with an intracellular electrode. *J. Physiol. (London)* **117:** 431–460.
10. Eccles, J. C. (1957). *The Physiology of Nerve Cells.* Johns Hopkins University Press, Baltimore.
11. Peters, A., Palay, S. F., and Webster, H. de F. (1991). *The Fine Structure of the Nervous System.* Oxford University Press, New York.
12. Bodian, D. (1972). Synaptic diversity and characterization by electron microscopy. In *Structure and Function of Synapses* (G. D. Pappas and D. P. Purpura, eds.), pp. 45–66. Raven Press, New York.
13. Werblin, F. S., and Dowling, J. E. (1968). Organization of the retina of the mudpuppy. *Necturus maaculosus. J. Neurophysiol.* **32,** 339–355.
14. Tomita, T. (1965). Electrophysiological study of the mechanisms subserving color thalamic nuclei. *Cold Spring Harbor Symp. Quant. Biol.* **30:** 559–566.
15. Fesenko, E. E., Kolesnikov, S. S., and Lyubarsky, A. L. (1985). Induction by cyclic GMP of cationic conductance in plasma membrane of retinal rod outer segment. *Nature (London)* 310–313.
16. Fain, G. L., Gerschenfeld, H. M., and Quandt, F. N. (1980). Calcium spike in toad rods. *J. Physiol. (London)* 495–514.
17. Roberts, A., and Bush, M. H. (1981). *Neurones Without Impulses: Their Significance for Vertebrate and Invertebrate Nervous Systems.* Cambridge University Press, Cambridge, UK.
18. Borst, A., and Egelhaaf, M. (1994). Dendritic processing of synaptic information by sensory interneurons. *Trends Neurosci.* **17:** 257–263.
19. Laughlin, S. (1981). Neural principles in the visual system. In *Handbook of Sensory Physiology* (H. Autrum, ed.), Vol. 7, Part 6B, pp. 133–280. Springer-Verlag, Berlin.
20. Sterling, P. (1998). Retina. In *The Synaptic Organization of the Brain* (G. M. Shepherd, ed.), fourth ed., pp. 205–253. Oxford University Press, New York.
21. Boycott, B. B., Dowling, J. E., Fisher, S. K., Kolb, H., and Laties, A. M. (1975). Interplexiform cells of the mammalian retina and their comparison with catecholamine-containing retinal cells. *Proc. R. Soc. London, Ser. B* **191:** 353–368.
22. Nelson, R., Lutzow, A. V., Kolb, H., and Gouras, P. (1975). Horizontal cells in cat retina with independent dendritic systems. *Science* **189,** 137–139.
23. Dowling, J. E., and Boycott, B. B. (1966). Organization of the primate retina: Electron microscopy. *Proc. R. Soc. London, Ser. B.* **166:** 80–111.
24. Koch, C., Poggio, T., and Torre, V. (1982). Retinal ganglion cells: A functional interpretation of dendritic morphology. *Philos. Trans. R. Soc. London, Ser. B* **298:** 227–263.
25. Phillips, C. G., Powel, T. P. S., and Shepherd, G. M. (1963). Responses of mitral cells to stimulation of the lateral olfactory tract in the rabbit. *J. Physiol. (London)* **168,** 65–88.
26. Shepherd, G. M. (1963). Responses of mitral cells to olfactory nerve volleys in the rabbit. *J. Physiol. (London)* **168,** 89–100.
27. Rall, W., Shepherd, G. M., Reese, T. S., and Brightman, M. W. (1966). Dendrodendritic synaptic pathway for inhibition in the olfactory bulb. *Exp. Neurol.* **14:** 44–56.
28. Rall, W., and Shepherd, G. M. (1968). Theoretical reconstruction of field potentials and dendrodendritic synaptic interactions in olfactory bulb. *J. Neurophysiol.* **31:** 884–915.
29. Mori, K, Nowycky M. C., and Shepherd, G. M. (1981). Analysis of synaptic potentials in mitral cells in the isolated turtle olfactory bulb. *J. Physiol. (London)* **314:** 281–294.
30. Jahr, C. E., and Nicoll, R. A. (1982). An intracellular analysis of dendrodendritic inhibition in the turtle in vitro olfactory bulb. *J. Physiol. (London)* **326:** 213–234.
31. Shepherd, G. M. (1978). Microcircuits in the nervous system. *Sci. Am.* **238:** 93–103.
32. Woolf, T. B., Shepherd, G. M., and Greer, C. A. (1991). Local information processing in dendritic trees: Subsets of spines in granule cells of the mammalian olfactory bulb. *J. Neurosci.* **11:** 1837–1854.
33. Bruce, H. M. (1959). An exteroceptive block to pregnancy in the mouse. *Nature (London)* 105.
34. Hayashi, Y., Momiyama, A., Takahashi, T., Ohishi, H., Ogawa-Meguro, R., Shigemoto, R., Mizuno, N., and Nakanishi, S. (1993). Role of a metabotropic glutamate receptor in synaptic modulation in the accessory olfactory bulb. *Nature (London)* **336:** 687–690.
35. Kaba, H., Hayashi, Y., Higuchi, T., and Nakanishi, S. (1994). Induction of an olfactory memory by the activation of a metabotropic glutamate receptor. *Science* **265:** 262–264.
36. Marty, A., and Llano, I. (1995). Modulation of inhibitory synapses in the mammalian brain. *Curr. Opin. Neurobiol.* **5:** 335–341.
37. Selverston, A. I., Russell, D. F., and Miller, J. P. (1976). The stomatogastric nervous system: Structure and function of a small neural network. *Prog. Neurobiol.* **37,** 215–289.
38. Burrows, M. (1992). Local circuits for the control of leg movements in an insect. *Trends Neurosci.* **15:** 226–232.
39. Craig, A. M., and Banker, G. (1994). Neuronal polarity. *Annu. Rev. Neurosci.* **17:** 267–310.
40. Mori, K. (1987). Membrane and synaptic properties of identified neurons in the olfactory bulb. *Prog. Neurobiol.* **29:** 274–320.
41. Haberly, L. B. (1998). Olfactory cortex. In *The Synaptic Organization of the Brain* (G. M. Shepherd, ed.), fourth ed. Oxford University Press, New York.
42. Llinás, R. R., and Walton, K. D. (1990). Cerebellum. In *The Synaptic Organization of the Brain* (G. M. Shepherd, ed.). pp. 377–416. Oxford University Press, New York.
43. Redman, S. J., and Walmsley, B. (1983). Amplitude fluctuations in synaptic potentials evoked in cat spinal motoneurons at identified group Ia synapses. *J. Physiol. (London)* **343,** 135–145.
44. Redman, S. J., and Walmsley, B. (1983). The time course of synaptic potentials evoked in cat spinal motoneurons at identified group Ia synapses. *J. Physiol. (London)* **343,** 117–133.
45. Rall, W. (1977). Core conductor theory and cable properties of neurons. In *The Nervous System: Cellular Biology of Neurons* (E. R. Kandel, ed.). Am. Physiol. Soc., Bethesda, MD.
46. Eccles, J. C. (1953). *The Neurophysiological: Basis of Mind.* Clarendon Press, Oxford.

47. Fuortes, M. G. F., Frank, K., and Becker, M. C. (1957). Steps in the production of motor neuron spikes. *J. Gen. Physiol.* **40:** 735–752.
48. Eyzaguirre, C., and Kuffler, S. W. (1955). Processes of excitation in the dendrites and in the soma of single isolated sensory nerve cells of the lobster and crayfish. *J. Gen. Physiol.* **39:** 87–119.
49. Edwards, C., and Ottoson, D. (1958). The site of impulse initiation in a nerve cell of a crustacean stretch receptor. *J. Physiol. (London)* **143:** 138–148.
50. Anderson, P. (1960). Interhippocampal impulses: II. Apical dendritic activation of CA1 neurons. *Acta Physiol. Scand.* **48:** 178–208.
51. Richardson, T. L., Turner, R. W., and Miller, J. J. (1987). Action-potential discharge in hippocampal CA1 pyramidal neurons. *J. Neurophysiol.* **58,** 981–996.
52. Turner, R. W., Meyers, E. R., Richardson, D. L., and Barker, J. L. (1991). The site for initiation of action potential discharge over the somatosensory axis of rat hippocampal CA1 pyramidal neurons. *J. Neurosci.* **11,** 2270–2280.
53. Ringham, G. L. (1971). Origin of nerve impulse in slowly adapting stretch receptor of crayfish. *J. Neurophysiol.* **33:** 773–786.
54. Stuart, G. J., and Sakmann, B. (1994). Active propagation of somatic action potentials into neocortical pyramidal cell dendrites. *Nature (London)* **367:** 69–72.
55. Lorente de Nó, R. (1938). The cerebral cortex: Architecture, intracortical connections and motor projections. In *Physiology of the Nervous System* (J. F. Fulton, ed.), pp. 291–339. Oxford University Press, London.
56. Katz, B. (1962). The transmission of impulses from nerve to muscle, and the subcellular unit of synaptic action. *Proc. R. Soc. London* 455–477.
57. Creed, R. S., Denny-Brown, D., Eccles, J. C., Liddell, E. G. T., and Sherrington, C. S. (1932). *Reflex Activity of the Spinal Cord.* Oxford University Press, London.
58. Fatt, P. (1957). Sequence of events in synaptic activation of a motoneurone. *J. Neurophysiol.* **20,** 61–80.
59. Bishop, G. H. (1956). Natural history of the nerve impulse. *Physiol. Rev.* **36:** 376–399.
60. Eccles, J. C., Libet, B., and Young, R. R. (1958). The behaviour of chromatolysed motoneurons studied by intracellular recording. *J. Physiol. (London)* **143:** 11–40.
61. Spencer, W. A., and Kandel, E. R. (1961). Electrophysiology of hippocampal neurons: IV. Fast potentials. *J. Neurophysiol.* 272–285.
62. Llinás, R., and Nicholson, C. (1971). Electrophysiological properties of dendrites and somata in alligator Purkinje cells. *J. Neurophysiol.* **34:** 532–551.
63. Llinás, R. R., and Hess, R. (1976). Tetrodotoxin-resistant dendritic spikes in avian Purkinje cells. *Soc. Neurosci. Abstr.*, p. 112.
64. Llinás, R., and Sugimori, M. (1980). Electrophysiological properties of in vitro Purkinje cell dendrites in mammalian cerebellar slices. *J. Physiol. (London)* **305,** 197–213.
65. Ross, W. N., and Werman, R. (1987). Mapping calcium transients in the dendrites of Purkinje cells from guinea-pig cerebellum in vitro. *J. Physiol. (London)* **389:** 319–336.
66. Tank, D. W., Sugimori, M., Connor, J. A., and Llinás, R. R. (1988). Spatially resolved calcium dynamics of mammalian Purkinje cells in cerebellar slice. *Science* **242:** 773–777.
67. Magee, J. C., Christofi, G., Miyakawa, H., Christie, B., Lasser-Ross, N., and Johnston, D. (1995). Subthreshold synaptic activation of voltage-gated Ca^{++} channels mediates a localized Ca^{++} influx into the dendrites of hippocampal pyramidal neurons. *J. Neurophysiol.* **74:** 1335–1342.
68. Regehr, W. G., Connor, J. A., and Tank, D. W. (1989). Optical imaging of calcium accumulation in hippocampal pyramidal cells during synaptic activation. *Nature (London)* 533–536.
69. Jaffe, D. B., Johnston, D., Lasser-Ross, N., Lisman, J. E., Miyakawa, H., and Ross, W. N. (1992). The spread of Na spikes determines the pattern of dendritic Ca entry into hippocampal neurons. *Nature (London)* **357,** 244–246.
70. Magee, J. C., and Johnston, D. (1995). Characterization of single voltage-gated Na^{+} and Ca^{++} channels in apical dendrites of rat CA1 pyramidal neurons. *J. Physiol. (London)* **487:** 67–90.
71. Magee, J. C., and Johnston, D. (1995). Synaptic activation of voltage-gated channels in the dendrites of hippocampal pyramidal neurons. *Science* **268:** 301–304.
72. Huguenard, J. R., Hamill, O. P., and Prince, D. A. (1989). Sodium channels in dendrites of rat cortical pyramidal neurons. *Proc. Natl. Acad. Sci. U.S.A.* **86,** 2473–2477.
73. Markram, H., and Sakmann, B. (1994). Calcium transients in apical dendrites evoked by single sub-threshold excitatory post-synaptic potentials via low voltage-activated calcium channels. *Proc. Natl. Acad. Sci. U.S.A.* **91,** 5207–5211.
74. Yuste, R., Gutnick, M. J., Saar, D., Delaney, K. D., and Tank, D. W. (1994). Calcium accumulations in dendrites from neocortical neurons: An apical band and evidence for functional compartments. *Neuron* **13,** 23–43.
75. Wilson, C. (1998). Basal ganglia. In *The Synaptic Organization of the Brain* (G. Shepherd, ed.), fourth ed., pp. 329–375. Oxford University Press, New York.
76. Berkowicz, D. A., Trombley, P. Q., and Shepherd, G. M. (1994). Evidence for glutamate as the olfactory receptor cell neurotransmitter. *J. Neurophysiol.* **71:** 2557–2561.
77. Halasz, N., Ljungdahl, A., Hokfelt, T., Johannsson, O., Goldstein, M., Park, D., and Biberfeld, P. (1977). Transmitter histochemistry of the rat olfactory bulb. I. Immunohistochemical localization of monoamine-synthesizing enzymes. *Brain Res.* **126,** 455–474.
78. Yokoi, M., Mori, K., and Nakanishi, S. (1995). Refinement of odor molecule tuning by dendrodendritic synaptic inhibition in the olfactory bulb. *Proc. Natl. Acad. Sci. U.S.A.* **92:** 3371–3375.
79. Llinás, R., Baker, R., and Sotelo, C. (1974). Electronic coupling between neurons in the cat inferior olive. *J. Neurophysiol.* **37,** 560–571.
80. Freeman, W. J. (1974). Relation of glomerular neuronal activity to glomerular transmission attenuation. *Brain Res.* **65:** 91–107.
81. Spruston, N., Schiller, Y., Stuart, G., and Sakmann, B. (1995). Activity-dependent action potential invasion and calcium influx into hippocampal CA1 dendrites. *Science* **268:** 297–300.
82. Callaway, J. C., and Ross, W. N. (1995). Frequency-dependent propagation of sodium action potentials in dendrites of hippocampal CA1 pyramidal neurons. *J. Neurophysiol.* **74:** 1395–1403.
83. Simmons, M. L., Terman, G. W., Gibbs, S. M., and Chavkin, C. (1995). L-type calcium channels mediate dynorphin neuropeptide release from dendrites but not axons of hippocampal granule cells. *Neuron* **14:** 1265–1272.
84. Spruston, N., Jaffe, D. B., and Johnston, D. (1994). Dendritic attenuation of synaptic potentials and current: The role of passive membrane properties. *Trends Neurosci.* **17:** 161–166.
85. Herreras, O. (1990). Propagating dendritic action potential mediates synaptic transmission in CA1 pyramidal cells in situ. *J. Neurophysiol.* **64:** 1429–1441.
86. Stuart, G., Spruston, N., Sakmann, B., and Hausser, M. (1997). Action potential initiation and backpropagation in neurons of the mammalian central nervous system. *Trends in Neurosci.* **20:** 125–131.
87. Chen, W. R., Midtgaard, J., and Shepherd, G. M. (1997). Forward and backward propagation of dendritic impulses and their synaptic control in mitral cells. *Science* **278:** 463–467.

88. Bischofberger, J., and Jonas, P. (1997). Action potential propagation into the presynaptic dendrites of rat mitral cells. *J. Physiol. (London)* **504:** 359–365.
89. Tsubokawa, H., and Ross, W. (1966). IPSPs modulate spike backpropagation and associated $[Ca^{2+}]$i changes in dendrites of hippocampal pyramidal neurons. *J. Neurophysiol.* **76:** 2896–2906.
90. Shepherd, G. M. (1974). *The Synaptic Organization of the Brain.* Oxford University Press, New York.
91. Zador, A., and Koch, C. (1994). Linearized models of calcium dynamics: Formal equivalence to the cable equation. *J. Neurosci.* **14:** 4705–4715.
92. Harris, K. M., and Kater, S. B. (1994). Dendritic spines: Cellular specializations imparting both stability and flexibility to synaptic function. *Annu. Rev. Neurosci.* **17:** 341–371.
93. Yuste, R., and Tank, D. (1996). Dendritic integration in mammalian neurons, a century after Cajál. *Neuron* **13:** 23–43.
94. Shepherd, G. M. (1996). The dendritic spine: A multifunctional integrative unit. *J. Neurophysiol.* **75:** 2197–2210.

CHAPTER

14

Brain Energy Metabolism

Pierre J. Magistretti

All the processes described in this textbook require energy. Ample clinical evidence indicates that the brain is exquisitely sensitive to perturbations of energy metabolism. In this chapter, we cover the topics of energy delivery, production, and utilization by the brain. Careful consideration of the basic mechanisms of brain energy metabolism is an essential prerequisite to a full understanding of the physiology and pathophysiology of brain function. We review the features of brain energy metabolism at the global, regional, and cellular levels, and at the cellular level, extensively describe recent advances in the understanding of neuron–glial metabolic exchanges. A particular focus is the cellular and molecular mechanisms that tightly couple neuronal activity to energy consumption. This tight coupling is at the basis of functional brain-imaging techniques, such as positron emission tomography and functional magnetic resonance imaging.

ENERGY METABOLISM OF THE BRAIN AS A WHOLE ORGAN

Glucose Is the Main Energy Substrate for the Brain

The human brain constitutes only 2% of the body weight, yet the energy-consuming processes that ensure proper brain function account for approximately 25% of total body glucose utilization. With a few exceptions that will be reviewed later, glucose is the obligatory energy substrate of the brain.[1-3] In any tissue, glucose can follow various metabolic pathways; in the brain, glucose is almost entirely oxidized to CO_2 and water through its sequential processing by glycolysis (Fig. 14.1), the tricarboxylic acid (TCA) cycle (Fig. 14.2), and the associated oxidative phosphorylation, which yield, on a molar basis, 38 ATP per glucose. Indeed, the oxygen consumption of the brain, which accounts for almost 20% of the oxygen consumption of the whole organism, is 160 μmol per 100 g of brain weight per minute and roughly corresponds to the value determined for CO_2 production. This O_2/CO_2 relation corresponds to what is known in metabolic physiology as a respiratory quotient of nearly 1 and demonstrates that carbohydrates, and glucose in particular, are the exclusive substrates for oxidative metabolism. This rather detailed information of whole-brain energy metabolism was obtained by using an experimental approach in which the concentration of a given substrate in the arterial blood entering the brain through the carotid artery is compared with that present in the venous blood draining the brain through the jugular vein.[1,2] If the substrate is utilized by the brain, the **arteriovenous** (A-V) **difference** is positive; in certain cases, the A-V difference may be negative, indicating that metabolic pathways resulting in the production of the substrate predominate. In addition, when the rate of cerebral blood flow (CBF) is known, the steady-state rate of utilization of the substrate can be determined per unit time and normalized per unit brain weight according to the following relation: CMR = CBF (A-V), where CMR is the cerebral metabolic rate of a given substrate. This approach was pioneered by Seymour Kety and C. F. Schmidt in the late 1940s and further developed in the 1950s and 1960s.[2,4] In normal adults, CBF is approximately 57 ml per 100 g of brain weight per minute, and the calculated glucose utilization by the brain is 31 μmol per 100 g of brain weight per minute, as determined with the A-V difference method.[2,4] This value is slightly higher than that predicted from the rate of oxygen consumption of the

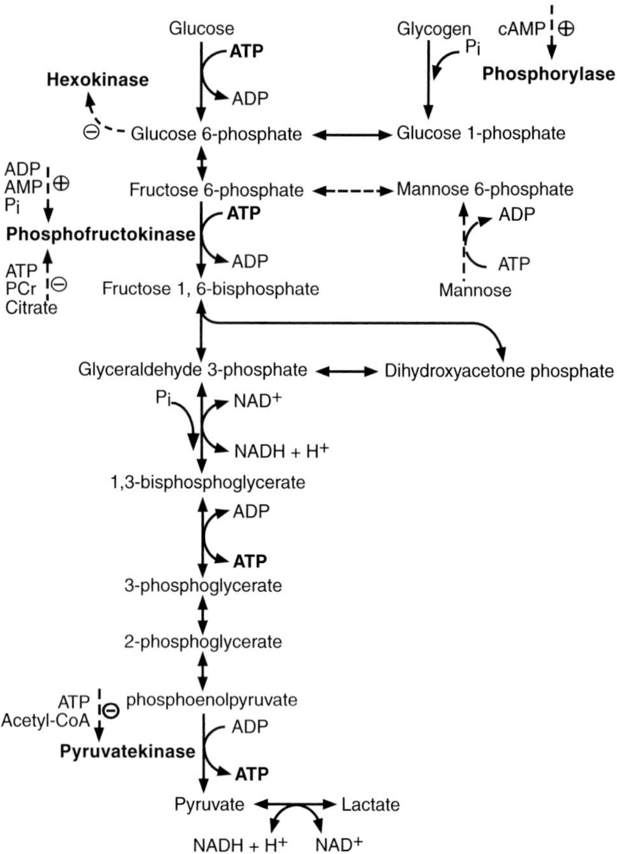

FIGURE 14.1 Glycolysis (Embden–Meyerhof pathway). Glucose phosphorylation is regulated by hexokinase, an enzyme inhibited by glucose 6-phosphate. Glucose must be phosphorylated to glucose 6-phosphate to enter glycolysis or to be stored as glycogen. Two other important steps in the regulation of glycolysis are catalyzed by phosphofructokinase and pyruvate kinase. Their activity is controlled by the levels of high-energy phosphates as well as of citrate and acetyl-CoA. Pyruvate, through lactate dehydrogenase, is in dynamic equilibrium with lactate. This reaction is essential to regenerate NAD^+ residues necessary to sustain glycolysis downstream of glyceraldehyde 3-phosphate. PCr, phosphocreatine.

brain. Thus, in an organ such as the brain with a respiratory quotient of 1, the stoichiometry would predict that 6 μmol of oxygen is needed to fully oxidize 1 μmol of the six-carbon molecule of glucose; given an oxygen consumption rate of 160 μmol per 100 g of brain weight per minute, the predicted glucose utilization would be 26 μmol per 100 g of brain weight per minute (160 : 6), yet the actual measured rate is 31 μmol. What then is the fate of the excess 4.4 μmol? First, glucose metabolism may proceed, to a very limited extent, only through glycolysis, resulting in the production of lactate without oxygen consumption (see Fig. 14.1); glucose can also be incorporated into glycogen (Fig. 14.1). Second, glucose is an essential constituent of macromolecules such as glycolipids and glycoproteins present in neural cells. Finally, glucose enters the metabolic pathways that result in the synthesis of three key neurotransmitters of the brain: glutamate, GABA, and acetylcholine (see Chapter 8).

Ketone Bodies Become Adequate Energy Substrates for the Brain in Particular Circumstances

In particular circumstances, substrates other than glucose can be utilized by the brain. For example, breast-fed neonates have the capacity to utilize the ketone bodies acetoacetate (AcAc) and D-3-hydroxybutyrate (3-HB), in addition to glucose, as energy substrates for the brain.[5,6] This capacity is an interesting example of a developmentally regulated adaptive mechanism, because maternal milk is highly enriched in lipids, resulting in a lipid-to-carbohydrate ratio

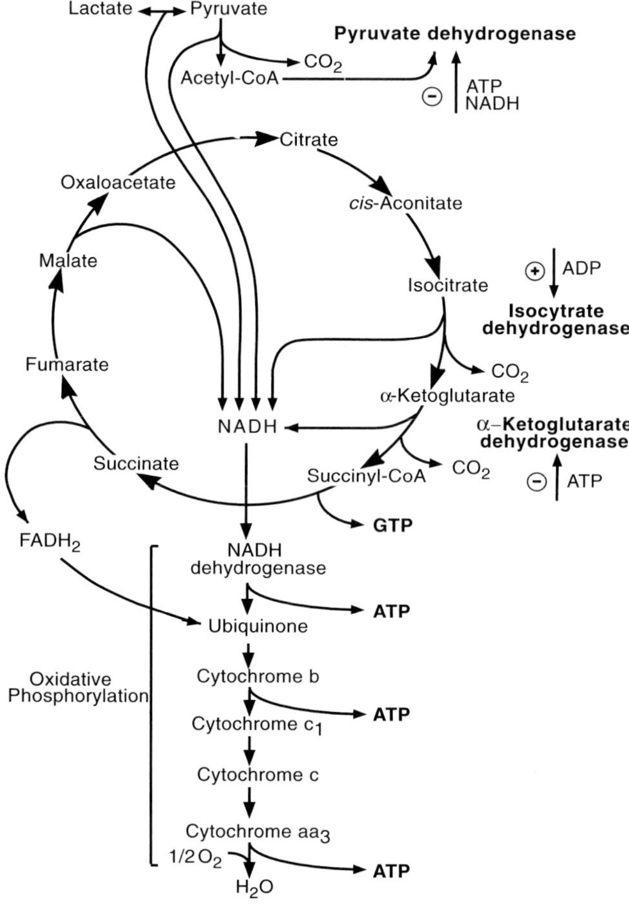

FIGURE 14.2 Tricarboxylic acid cycle (Krebs' cycle) and oxidative phosphorylation. Pyruvate entry into the cycle is controlled by pyruvate dehydrogenase activity that is inhibited by ATP and NADH. Two other regulatory steps in the cycle are controlled by isocitrate and α-ketoglutarate dehydrogenases, whose activity is controlled by the levels of high-energy phosphates.

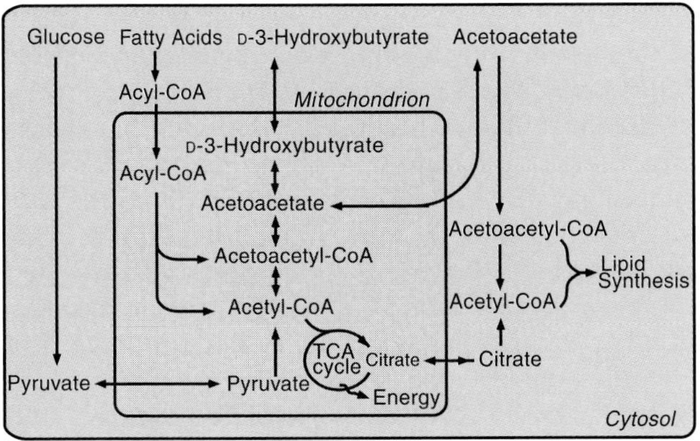

FIGURE 14.3 Relation between lipid metabolism and the TCA cycle. Under particular dietary conditions, such as lactation in newborns or fasting in adults, the ketone bodies acetoacetate and D-3-hydroxybutyrate and circulating fatty acids can provide substrates to the TCA cycle after conversion into acetyl-CoA. Carbon atoms for lipid synthesis can be provided by glucose through citrate produced in the TCA cycle, a particularly relevant process for the developing brain.

much higher than that present in postweaning nutrients.[7] Indeed, lipids account for approximately 55% of the total calories contained in human milk, in contrast with 30–35% for a balanced postweaning diet.[7] In addition to the ketone bodies AcAc and 3-HB, other products of lipid metabolism relevant to brain metabolic processes are free fatty acids. Acetoacetate, 3-HB, and free fatty acids can all be processed to acetyl-CoA, thus providing ATP through the TCA cycle (Fig. 14.3). We will see later that brain energy metabolism is highly compartmentalized, with certain metabolic pathways specifically localized in a given cell type. It is therefore not surprising that, whereas ketone bodies can be oxidized by neurons, oligodendrocytes, and astrocytes,[8] the β-oxidation of free fatty acids is localized exclusively in astrocytes.[9] Another consideration regarding the lipid-rich diet provided during the suckling period relates to its contribution to the process of myelination.[10] The question is whether the polar lipids and cholesterol that make up myelin are derived from dietary sources or are synthesized within the brain. There is evidence that brain lipids can be synthesized from blood-borne precursors such as ketone bodies.[11] In addition, when suckling rats are fed a diet low in ketones, carbon atoms for lipogenesis can also be provided by glucose.[12] Compared with energy supply, lipogenesis is quantitatively a minor (less than 10%) pathway for circulating ketone bodies and glucose, even during brain development.[13] To summarize, ketone bodies and AcAc are adequate energy substrates as well as precursors for lipogenesis during the suckling period; however, the developing brain appears to be metabolically quite flexible because glucose, in addition to its energetic function, can be metabolized to generate substrates for lipid synthesis.

Starvation and diabetes are two situations in which the availability of glucose to tissues is inadequate and in which plasma ketone bodies are elevated because of enhanced lipid catabolism. Under these conditions, the adaptive mechanisms described for breast-fed neonates become operative in the brain, allowing it to utilize AcAc or 3-HB as energy substrates.[14]

Mannose, Lactate, and Pyruvate Serve as Instructive Cases

A number of metabolic intermediates have been tested as alternative substrates to glucose for brain energy metabolism. Among the numerous molecules tested, mannose is the only one that can sustain normal brain function in the absence of glucose.[15] Mannose readily crosses the blood–brain barrier and, in two enzymatic steps, is converted into fructose 6-phosphate, an intermediate of the glycolytic pathway (see Fig. 14.1). However, mannose is not normally present in the blood, and therefore is not considered a physiological substrate for brain energy metabolism.

Lactate and pyruvate can be sources of insight into the intrinsic properties of isolated brain tissue versus those of the brain as an organ receiving substrates from the circulation. Lactate and pyruvate can adequately sustain the synaptic activity of isolated brain samples, usually thin slices, maintained *in vitro* in a physiological medium lacking glucose[16,17]; *in vivo*, because of their limited permeability across the blood–brain barrier, circulating lactate or pyruvate cannot substitute for glucose to adequately maintain brain function. Indeed, the rates of uptake into the brain parenchyma for lactate and pyruvate are 35 and 15 nmol per gram of tissue per minute, respectively, compared with 700 nmol per gram of tissue per minute for glucose.[18] However, as we will see later, if formed within the brain parenchyma from glucose that has crossed the blood–brain barrier, lactate and pyruvate may in fact become the preferential energy substrates for activated neurons.

Summary

Glucose is the obligatory energy substrate for brain, and it is almost entirely oxidized to CO_2 and H_2O. This simple statement summarizes, with few exceptions, over four decades of careful studies of brain energy metabolism at the organ and regional levels. Under ketogenic conditions, such as starvation and diabetes and during breast-feeding, ketone bodies may provide an adequate energy source for the brain. Lactate and pyruvate, formed from glucose within the brain parenchyma, are adequate energy substrates as well.

TIGHT COUPLING OF NEURONAL ACTIVITY, BLOOD FLOW, AND ENERGY METABOLISM

A striking characteristic of the brain is its high degree of structural and functional specialization. Thus, when we move an arm, motor areas and their related pathways are selectively activated (see Chapter 30); intuitively, one can predict that as "brain work" increases locally (e.g., in motor areas), the energy requirements of the activated regions will increase in a temporally and spatially coordinated manner. Because energy substrates are provided through the circulation, blood flow should increase in the modality-specific activated area. More than a century ago, the British neurophysiologist C. Sherrington showed, in experimental animals, increases in blood flow localized to the parietal cortex in response to sensory stimulation.[19] He postulated that "the brain possesses intrinsic mechanisms by which its vascular supply can be varied locally in correspondence with local variations of functional activity." With remarkable insight, he also proposed that "chemical products of cerebral metabolism" produced in the course of neuronal activation could provide the mechanism to couple activity with increased blood flow.[19]

Which Mechanisms Couple Neuronal Activity to Blood Flow?

Since Sherrington's seminal work, the search for the identification of chemical mediators that can couple neuronal activity with local increases in blood flow has been intense. These signals can be broadly grouped into two categories: (1) molecules or ions that transiently accumulate in the extracellular space after neuronal activity and (2) specific neurotransmitters that mediate the coupling in anticipation or at least in parallel with local activation (neurogenic mechanisms). The increases in extracellular K^+, adenosine, and lactate and the related changes in pH are all a consequence of increased neuronal activity, and all have been considered mediators of neurovascular coupling because of their vasoactive effects.[20] However, the spatial and temporal resolution achieved by these mediators may not be sufficient to entirely account for the activity-dependent coupling between neuronal activity and blood flow. Indeed, these vasoactive agents are formed with a certain delay (seconds) after initiation of neuronal activity and can diffuse at considerable distance. In this respect, neurogenic mechanisms appear to be better fitted. Brain microvessels are richly innervated by neuronal fibers. These fibers may have an extrinsic origin (e.g., in the autonomic ganglia) or be part of neuronal circuits intrinsic to the brain, such as local interneurons or long projections that originate in the brainstem (e.g., those containing monoaminergic neurotransmitters).[21–23] In addition, functional receptors coupled to signal transduction pathways have been identified for several neurotransmitters on intraparenchymal microvessels.[24] The neurotransmitters with potential roles in coupling neuronal activity with blood flow include the amines noradrenaline, serotonin, and acetylcholine and the peptides vasoactive intestinal peptide, neuropeptide Y (NPY), calcitonin gene-related peptide (CGRP), and substance P (SP). The neurogenic mode of neurovascular coupling implies that vasoactive neurotransmitters are released from perivascular fibers as excitatory afferent volleys activate a discrete and functionally defined brain volume.

A recent and very attractive addition to the list of potential mediators for coupling neuronal activity to blood flow is nitric oxide (NO). Indeed, NO is an ideal candidate; it is formed locally by neurons and glial cells under the action of a variety of neurotransmitters likely to be released by depolarized afferents to an activated brain area.[25] Nitric oxide is a diffusible and potent vasodilator whose short half-life spatially and temporally restricts its domain of action. However, in several experimental models in which the activity of NO synthase, the enzyme responsible for NO synthesis, was inhibited, a certain degree of coupling was still observed, indicating that NO is probably only one of the regulators of local blood flow acting in synergy with others.[26]

In summary, several products of activity-dependent neuronal and glial metabolism such as lactate, H^+, adenosine, and K^+ have vasoactive effects and are therefore putative mediators of coupling, although the kinetics and spatial resolution of this mode do not account for all the observed phenomena. As attractive as it is, an exclusively neurogenic mode of coupling neuronal activity to blood flow is unlikely and, moreover, still awaits firm functional confirmation *in vivo.* Nitric oxide is undoubtedly a key element in coupling, particularly in view of the fact that glutamate, the principal excitatory neurotransmitter, triggers a receptor-mediated NO formation in neurons and glia[27]; this is consistent with the view that whenever a functionally defined brain area is activated and glutamate is released by the depolarized afferents, NO may be formed, thus providing a direct mechanism contributing to the coupling between activity and local increases in blood flow.

Through the activity-linked increase in blood flow, more substrates—namely, glucose and oxygen—necessary to meet the additional energy demands are delivered to the activated area per unit time. The cellular and molecular mechanisms involved in oxygen consumption and glucose utilization are treated in a later section.

Blood Flow and Energy Metabolism Can Be Visualized in Humans

Modern functional brain-imaging techniques enable the *in vivo* monitoring of human blood flow and the two indices of energy metabolism—namely, glucose utilization and oxygen consumption (Box 14.1).[28] For instance, with the use of positron emission tomography (PET) and appropriate positron-emitting isotopes such as ^{18}F and ^{15}O, basal rates as well as activity-related changes in local blood flow or oxygen consumption can be studied by using ^{15}O-labeled water or ^{15}O, respectively.[29,30] Local rates of glucose utilization (also defined as local cerebral metabolic rates for glucose, or LCMRglu) can be determined with ^{18}F-labeled 2-deoxyglucose (2-DG).[31,32] The use of 2-DG as a marker of LCMRglu was pioneered by Louis Sokoloff and his associates at the National Institutes of Health, first in laboratory animals.[33,34] The method is based on the fact that 2-DG crosses the blood–brain barrier, is taken up by brain cells, and is phosphorylated by hexokinase with kinetics similar to that for glucose; however, un-

BOX 14.1

PET AND fMRI

We have seen that neuronal activity is tightly coupled to blood flow and metabolism. With the advent of sophisticated imaging procedures such as positron emission tomography (PET) and functional magnetic resonance imaging (fMRI), it is now possible to detect the signals generated by the metabolic processes associated with neuronal activity, thus providing a unique opportunity to see the "brain at work." Indeed, local changes in blood flow, glucose utilization, and oxygen consumption can be noninvasively monitored under basal and activated conditions in human subjects. How is this possible?

For PET, a solution containing slightly radioactive molecules is injected into the circulation, and its sites of brain uptake can be visualized. The molecule is radioactively labeled with an unstable radionuclide possessing an excess number of protons; as a consequence of normal radioactive decay, the excess proton is converted into a neutron. In this process, a positron (a positively charged electron) is emitted and collides with an electron, releasing energy in the form of two photons with opposite trajectories. The photons are sensed by specialized detectors placed around the head; when two photons simultaneously reach two detectors positioned at 180° of each other, the origin of the positron–electron collision can be localized with a resolution of 5 to 10 mm. Commonly used positron-emitting radionuclides are oxygen-15 (^{15}O), carbon-11 (^{11}C), and fluorine-18 (^{18}F). Blood flow is monitored with ^{15}O-labeled water and glucose utilization with ^{18}F-2-deoxyglucose. Oxygen consumption is visualized directly with ^{15}O. With the use of sophisticated algorithms to process the data, the localization of activity to specific brain areas during a given task (sensory, motor, cognitive) can be achieved. Thus, the activity of neuronal ensembles, and of the associated glia, coupled to increased blood flow and glucose utilization results in a localized signal due to the augmented concentration of ^{15}O-labeled water (monitoring blood flow) and ^{18}F-2-deoxyglucose (assessing glucose utilization) in the activated area (see Fig. 14.5).

PET is one of the ways in which brain work can be visualized. An increasingly popular technique, fMRI relies on the magnetic signals detected in an activated brain region in relation to its degree of oxygenation. Depending on the degree to which it is saturated by oxygen, hemoglobin (by acting as a paramagnetic contrast agent) can alter the magnetic signal detected in a tissue exposed to the magnetic fields used for structural MRI.[28] In other words, different MRI signals can be obtained depending on the oxyhemoglobin/deoxyhemoglobin ratio in a given brain area. Local activation of a brain area results in increased blood flow (see Fig. 14.5). Although the precise mechanisms are still being discussed, it is currently thought that this phenomenon, by leading to a localized enrichment in oxyhemoglobin, alters the oxyhemoglobin/deoxyhemoglobin ratio, providing the signal for fMRI. Functional MRI is a remarkably convenient and powerful technique: the signal acquisition time is extremely rapid (on the order of seconds) and the resolution equals that of PET (i.e., a few millimeters). In addition, fMRI is totally noninvasive and can thus be frequently repeated on the same subject, who can then serve as its own control.

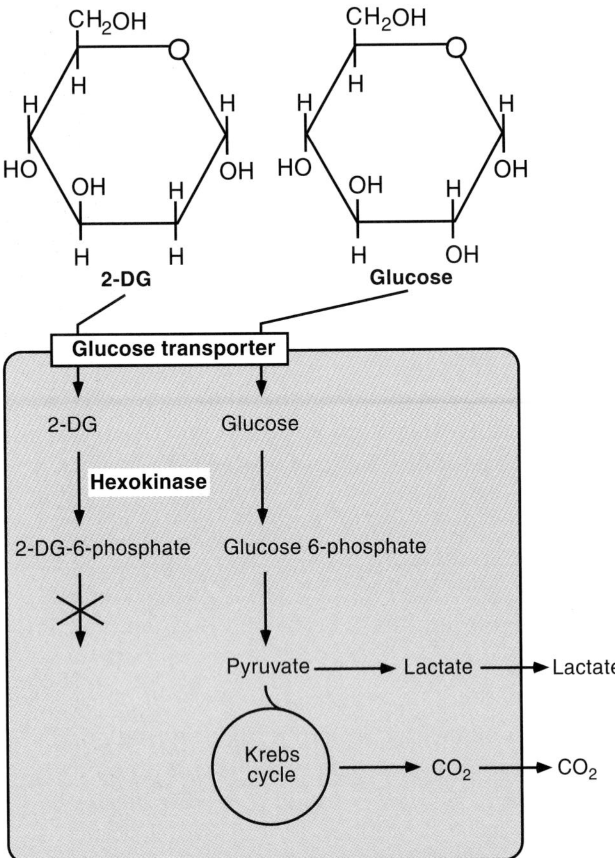

FIGURE 14.4 Structure and metabolism of glucose and 2-deoxyglucose. 2-Deoxyglucose (2-DG) is transported into cells through glucose transporters and phosphorylated by hexokinase to glucose 6-phosphate without significant further processing or dephosphorylation back to glucose. Therefore, when radioactively labeled, 2-DG used in tracer concentrations is a valuable marker of glucose uptake and phosphorylation, which directly indicates glucose utilization.

like glucose 6-phosphate, 2-deoxyglucose 6-phosphate cannot be metabolized further and therefore accumulates intracellularly (Fig. 14.4).

For studies in laboratory animals, tracer amounts of radioactive 2-DG are injected intravenously; the animal is subjected to the behavioral paradigms of interest and sacrificed at the end of the experiment. Serial thin sections of the brain are prepared and processed for autoradiography. This autoradiographic method provides, after appropriate corrections, an accurate measurement of LCMRglu with a spatial resolution of approximately 50–100 μm.[33] Using this method, researchers have determined LCMRglu in virtually all structurally and functionally defined brain structures in various physiological and pathological states, including sleep, seizures, and dehydration, and after a variety of pharmacological treatments.[35–37] Furthermore, glucose utilization increases in the pertinent brain areas during motor tasks[38] or activation of pathways subserving specific modalities, such as visual, auditory, olfactory, or somatosensory stimulation.[34,39–41] For example, in mice, sustained stimulation of the whiskers results in marked increases in LCMRglu in discrete areas of the primary sensory cortex called the **barrel fields,** where each whisker is represented with an extreme degree of topographical specificity[42] (see Chapter 26). Basal glucose utilization of the gray matter as determined by 2-DG autoradiography varies, depending on the brain structure, between 50 and 150 μmol per 100 g of wet weight per minute in the rat.[33]

A Transient Uncoupling between Oxygen Consumption and Glucose Utilization Occurs during Activation

In humans, LCMRglu determined by PET with the use of ^{18}F-2-DG is approximately 50% lower than that in rodents,[43] and physiological activation of specific modalities increases LCMRglu in discrete areas of the brain that can be visualized with a spatial resolution of a few millimeters.[44,45] For example, visual stimulations presented to subjects as checkerboard patterns reversing at frequencies ranging from 2 to 10 Hz selectively increase LCMRglu in the primary visual cortex and a few connected cortical areas.[46] With the use of this stimulation paradigm, the combined PET analysis of local cerebral blood flow (LCBF) and local oxygen consumption (LCMRO$_2$), in addition to LCMRglu, has revealed a unique and unexpected feature of human brain energy metabolism regulation (Fig. 14.5). The canonical view was that the three metabolic parameters were tightly coupled, implying that, if, for example, CBF increased locally during physiological activation, LCMRglu and LCMRO$_2$ would increase in parallel. In what is now referred to as the phenomenon of ''uncoupling,'' physiological stimulation of the visual system increases LCBF and LCMRglu (both by 30–40%) in the primary visual cortex without a commensurate increase in LCMRO$_2$ (which increases only 6%),[47,48] indicating that the additional glucose utilized during neuronal activation can be processed through glycolysis rather than through the tricarboxylic acid (TCA) cycle and oxidative phosphorylation (see Fig. 14.5). The phenomenon of uncoupling has been confirmed in other cortical areas, although its magnitude differs depending on the modality that is being tested.[49] A glance at the metabolic pathways reveals that if glucose does not enter the TCA cycle to be oxidized, then lactate will be produced (see Figs. 14.1 and 14.2). Lactate, like several other metabolically relevant molecules, can be determined with the technique of magnetic resonance imaging (MRI) spectroscopy for ^{1}H, which provides a means of unequivocally identifying in living tissues the presence of molecules that bear the naturally occurring

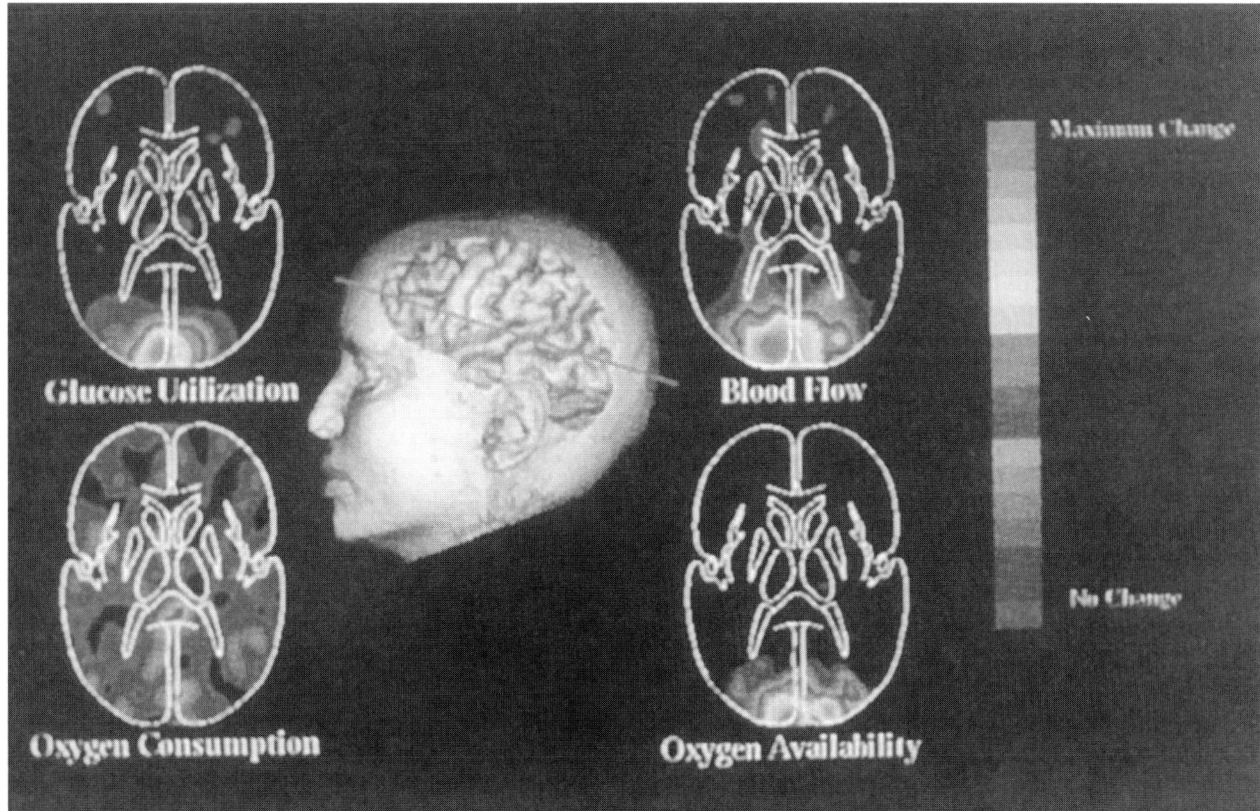

FIGURE 14.5 Series of PET scans illustrating glucose utilization, blood flow, and oxygen consumption during visual stimulation in the human cortex. In this particular study, the increase in blood flow and glucose utilization exceeded the increase in oxygen consumption. For these PET acquisitions, blood flow was monitored with ^{15}O-labeled water and glucose utilization with ^{18}F-2-deoxyglucose. Oxygen consumption was visualized directly with ^{15}O. Color code: Red corresponds to highest increases over the nonactivated state; purple indicates no change. Illustration kindly provided by Dr. Marcus E. Raichle, Washington University.

isotope ^{1}H. Consistent with the prediction that if during activation glucose is predominantly processed glycolytically, then lactate should be produced locally in the activated region, a *transient* increase in the lactate signal is detected with ^{1}H MRI spectroscopy in the human primary visual cortex during appropriate visual stimulation.[50,51] These observations further support the view that to face the local increases in energy demands linked to neuronal activation, the brain *transiently* resorts to glycolysis rather than oxidative phosphorylation. (See pp. 403–405 for cellular and molecular mechanisms.)

Summary

Studies at the whole-organ level, based on the A-V differences of metabolic substrates, have revealed a great deal about the global energy metabolism of the brain. They have indicated that, under normal conditions, glucose is virtually the sole energy substrate for the brain and that it is entirely oxidized. New techniques that allow imaging of the three fundamental parameters of brain energy metabolism—namely, blood flow, oxygen consumption, and glucose utilization—provide a more refined level of spatial resolution and demonstrate two basic principles: (1) brain energy metabolism is regionally heterogeneous and is tightly coupled to the functional activation of specific neuronal pathways and (2) although blood flow, oxygen consumption, and glucose utilization are tightly correlated under basal conditions, during local activation, the brain transiently resorts, within the activated domains, to glycolysis to meet the increased energy demands.

ENERGY-PRODUCING AND ENERGY-CONSUMING PROCESSES IN THE BRAIN

What are the cellular and molecular mechanisms that underlie the regulation of brain energy metabolism revealed by the foregoing studies at the global and regional levels? In particular, what are the metabolic events taking place in the cell types that make up the brain parenchyma? How is it possible to reconcile whole-organ studies indicating complete oxidation of glucose with *transient* activation-induced glycolysis at the regional level? These and other related questions will be addressed here and in the next sections.

Glucose Metabolism Produces Energy

Before we move on to an analysis of the cell-specific mechanisms of brain energy metabolism, it seems appropriate to briefly review some basic aspects of the brain's energy balance. Because glucose, in normal circumstances, is the main energy substrate of the brain, the overview will be restricted to its metabolic pathways. Glucose metabolism in the brain is similar to that in other tissues and includes three principal metabolic pathways: glycolysis, the tricarboxylic acid cycle, and the pentose phosphate pathway. Because of the global similarities with other tissues, these pathways are simply summarized in Figs. 14.1, 14.2, and 14.6, and only a few aspects specific to the nervous tissue will be discussed.

Glycolysis

Glycolysis (Embden–Meyerhof pathway) is the metabolism of glucose to pyruvate (see Fig. 14.1). It results in the net production of only two molecules of ATP per glucose molecule; indeed, four ATPs are formed in the processing of glucose to pyruvate, whereas two ATPs are consumed to phosphorylate glucose to glucose 6-phosphate and fructose 6-phosphate to fructose 1,6-bisphosphate, respectively (see Fig. 14.1). Under anaerobic conditions, pyruvate is converted into lactate, allowing the regeneration of nicotinamide adenine dinucleotide (NAD^+), which is essential to maintain a continued glycolytic flux. Indeed, if NAD^+ were not regenerated, glycolysis could not proceed beyond glyceraldehyde 3-phosphate (see Fig. 14.1). Another situation in which the end product of glycolysis is lactate rather than pyruvate is when oxygen consumption does not match glucose utilization, implying that the rate of pyruvate production through glycolysis exceeds pyruvate oxidation by the TCA cycle (see Fig. 14.2). This condition has been well described in skeletal muscle during intense exercise and appears to share similarities with the transient uncoupling observed between glucose utilization and oxygen consumption that has been described in the human cerebral cortex during activation with the use of PET.[47,48]

The Tricarboxylic Acid Cycle

Under aerobic conditions, pyruvate is oxidatively decarboxylated to yield acetyl-CoA, in a reaction catalyzed by the enzyme **pyruvate dehydrogenase** (PDH). Acetyl-coenzyme A condenses with oxaloacetate to produce citrate (see Fig. 14.2). This is the first step of the **tricarboxylic acid cycle,** in which three pairs of electrons are transferred from NAD^+ to NADH—and one pair from flavin adenine dinucleotide (FAD) to its reduced form ($FADH_2$)—through four oxidation–reduction steps (see Fig. 14.2). NADH and $FADH_2$ transfer their electrons to molecular O_2 through the mitochondrial electron-transfer chain to produce ATP in the process of oxidative phosphorylation. Thus, under aerobic conditions (i.e., when glucose is fully oxidized through the TCA cycle to CO_2 and H_2O), NAD^+ is regenerated, and glycolysis proceeds to pyruvate, not lactate. However, as soon as a mismatch, even a transient one, occurs between glucose utilization and oxygen consumption, lactate is produced. As discussed earlier, such a transient production of lactate appears to occur in the human brain during activation. Experiments performed in freely moving rats also have demonstrated a transient increase in lactate content in the extracellular space of discrete brain regions during physiological sensory stimulation.[52,53] In these experiments, lactate was determined in the extracellular fluid collected by microdialysis.

The Pentose Phosphate Pathway

Although glycolysis, the TCA cycle, and oxidative phosphorylation are coordinated pathways that produce ATP, using glucose as a fuel, ATP is not the only form of metabolic energy. Indeed, for several biosynthetic reactions in which the precursors are in a more oxidated state than the products, metabolic energy in the form of reducing power is needed in addition to ATP. This is the case for the reductive synthesis of free fatty acids from acetyl-CoA, which are components of myelin and of other structural elements of neural cells, such as the plasma membrane.[54] In cells of the brain, as in other organs, the reducing power is provided by the reduced form of nicotinamide adenine dinucleotide phosphate (NADPH). The processing of glucose through the **pentose phosphate pathway** produces NADPH. The first reaction in the pentose phosphate pathway is the conversion of glucose 6-phosphate into ribulose 5-phosphate (Fig. 14.6). This dehydrogenation, in which two molecules of NADPH are generated per molecule of glucose 6-phosphate, is the rate-limiting step of the pentose phosphate pathway. The NADP/NADPH ratio is the single most important factor regulating the entry of glucose 6-phosphate into the pentose phosphate pathway. Thus, if a high reducing power is needed, NADPH levels decrease and the pentose phosphate pathway is activated to generate new reducing equivalents. In addition to reductive biosyn-

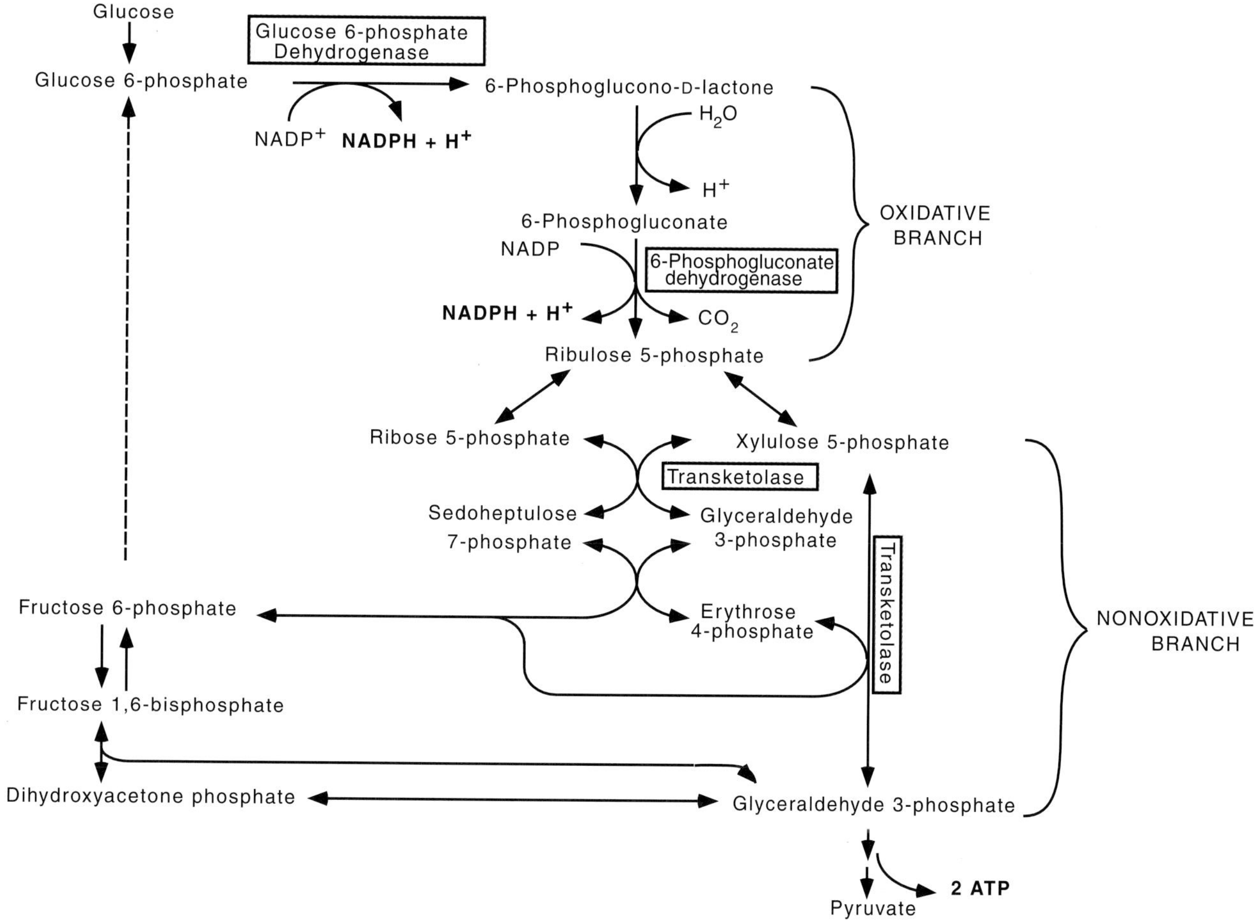

FIGURE 14.6 The pentose phosphate pathway. In the oxidative branch of the pentose phosphate pathway, two NADPH are generated per glucose 6-phosphate. The first, rate-limiting, reaction of the pathway is catalyzed by glucose-6-phosphate dehydrogenase; the second NADPH is generated through the oxidative decarboxylation of 6-phosphogluconate, a reaction catalyzed by glucose-6-phosphogluconate dehydrogenase. The nonoxidative branch of the pentose phosphate pathway provides a reversible link with glycolysis, by regenerating the two glycolytic intermediates glyceraldehyde 3-phosphate and fructose 6-phosphate. This regeneration is achieved through three sequential reactions. In the first, catalyzed by transketolase, xylulose 5-phosphate and ribose 5-phosphate (which originate from ribulose 5-phosphate, the end product of the oxidative branch) yield glyceraldehyde 3-phosphate and sedoheptulose 7-phosphate. Under the action of transaldolase, these two intermediates yield fructose 6-phosphate and erythrose 4-phosphate. This latter intermediate combines with glyceraldehyde 3-phosphate, in a reaction catalyzed by transketolase, to yield fructose 6-phosphate and glyceraldehyde 3-phosphate. Thus, through the nonoxidative branch of the pentose phosphate pathway, two hexoses (fructose 6-phosphate) and one triose (glyceraldehyde 3-phosphate) of the glycolytic pathway are regenerated from three pentoses (ribulose 5-phosphate).

thesis, NADPH is needed for the scavenging of **reactive oxygen species** (ROS). The superoxide anion, hydrogen peroxide, and the hydroxy radical are three ROS, generated by the transfer of single electrons to molecular oxygen as by-products of certain physiological cellular processes.[55] Examples of such processes are the electron-transfer chain associated with oxidative phosphorylation and the activities of monoamine oxidase, tyrosine hydroxylase, nitric oxide synthase, and the eicosanoid-forming enzymes lipoxygenases and cyclooxygenases.[56–59] Reactive oxygen species are highly damaging to cells because they can cause DNA disruptions and mutations, as well as activation of enzymatic cascades including proteases and lipases that can eventually lead to cell death.[60,61] Although multiple factors, including aging, can lead to oxidative stress through the formation of ROS, excess activation of ionotropic glutamate receptors (see Chapter 9) also plays a prominent role.[62]

Scavenging of ROS is ensured by the sequential action of **superoxide dismutase** (SOD) and **glutathione peroxidase**[63,64] (Fig. 14.7). Thus, two superoxide anions

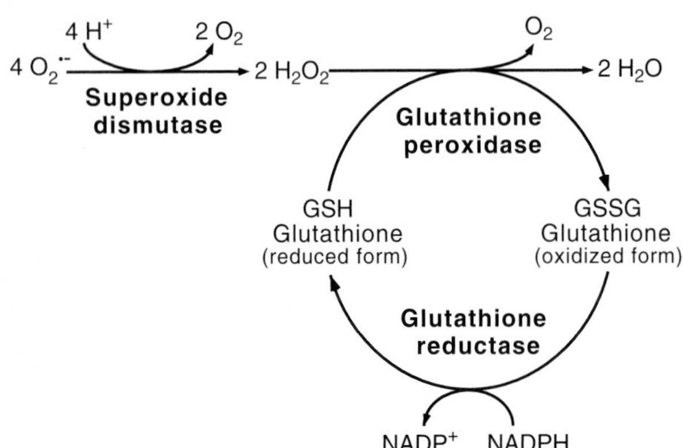

FIGURE 14.7 Enzymatic reactions for scavenging reactive oxygen species (ROS). The toxic superoxide anion ($O_2^{\cdot -}$) formed by a variety of physiological reactions, including oxidative phosphorylation, is scavenged by superoxide dismutase, which converts the superoxide anion into hydrogen peroxide (H_2O_2) and molecular oxygen. Glutathione peroxidase converts the still toxic hydrogen peroxide into water; reduced glutathione (GSH) is required for this reaction, in which it is converted into its oxidized form (GSSG). GSH is regenerated through the action of glutathione reductase, a reaction requiring NADPH.

formed by the aforementioned cellular processes are converted by SOD into H_2O_2, still a ROS. Glutathione peroxidase converts H_2O_2 into H_2O and O_2 at the expense of reduced glutathione, which is regenerated by glutathione reductase in the presence of NADPH. In addition to the scavenging mechanisms for ROS, the pentose phosphate pathway is also tightly connected to glycolysis through two enzymes, **transketolase** and **transaldolase,** which recycle ribulose 5-phosphate to fructose 6-phosphate and glyceraldehyde 3-phosphate, two intermediates of glycolysis (see Fig. 14.6).

The Wernicke–Korsakoff Syndrome: A Neuropsychiatric Disorder Due to a Dysfunction of Energy Metabolism

A well-characterized neuropsychiatric disorder, the Wernicke–Korsakoff syndrome, is caused by transketolase hypoactivity.[65] The Wernicke–Korsakoff syndrome is characterized by a severe impairment of memory and of other cognitive processes accompanied by balance and gait dysfunction and by paralysis of oculomotor muscles. The syndrome is due to a lack of thiamine (vitamin B1) in the diet; it affects only susceptible persons who are also alcoholics or chronically undernourished. Thiamine pyrophosphate is a thiamine-containing cofactor essential for the activity of transketolase. In patients with the Wernicke–Korsakoff syndrome, thiamine pyrophosphate binds 10 times less avidly to transketolase compared with the enzyme of normal persons.[65] This enzymatic dysfunction renders patients with the Wernicke–Korsakoff syndrome much more vulnerable to thiamine deficiency. This syndrome illustrates how an anomaly in a discrete metabolic pathway of energy metabolism may result in severe alterations in behavior and motor function.

The Processes Linked to Neuronal Function Consume Energy

The main energy-consuming process of the brain is the maintenance of ionic gradients across the plasma membrane, a condition that is crucial for excitability. Maintenance of these gradients is achieved predominantly through the activity of ionic pumps fueled by ATP, particularly **Na^+,K^+-ATPase,** localized in neurons as well as in other cell types such as glia. Activity of these pumps accounts for approximately 50% of basal glucose oxidation in the nervous system.[66–68] An important notion to assimilate is the fact that the propagation of action potentials per se does not consume energy[69]; it is driven by the electrochemical gradients existing across neuronal membranes, mainly for Na^+ and K^+ (see Chapter 6). Indeed, entry of Na^+ through voltage-sensitive Na^+ channels generating an action potential (or through ionotropic receptors generating an excitatory postsynaptic potential) may have, depending on the diameter of the process (axon, dendrite), a variable effect on intracellular neuronal Na^+ concentration.

Why is this the case? As described in Chapter 6, the establishment of a membrane potential is due to the uneven distribution of charges across the plasma membrane. This charge distribution is restricted to a thin (~1 nm) layer on each side of the membrane. A voltage difference of 100 mV across the membrane (remember that the amplitude of an action potential is 100–150 mV and that of an EPSP is 5–10 mV) is generated by the movement of 1 femtocoulomb (fC) of charges across 1 μm^2 of membrane. For univalent ions such as Na^+, a charge of 1 C is carried by 6×10^{18} ions, meaning that 1 fC is carried by 6×10^3 Na^+ ions. A volume of about 3 μm^3 of cytoplasm (corresponding roughly to a 1-μm segment of an axon with a 1-μm section) contains about 10^8 Na^+ ions. At elevated firing rates, the sustained influx of Na^+ in a restricted volume may result in a transient, localized increase in Na^+ concentration. In addition, because depolarizing events such as action potentials and EPSPs occur continuously, the tonic activity of the neuronal Na^+,K^+-ATPase is essential to prevent the dissipation of the Na^+ gradient, particularly at sites such as the nodes of Ranvier (see Chapter 6), where the density of voltage-sensitive Na^+ channels is high. An analogy can be made with a battery, in which energy is needed to charge it (i.e., reestablishing the ionic gradients after neuronal activity), but current can be generated (i.e., the generation of action potentials) once it has been charged.

Maintenance of the electrochemical gradient for Na^+ is also important to ensure the efficacy of excitatory synaptic transmission. As discussed later in this chapter, synaptically released glutamate is rapidly removed from the synaptic cleft via a Na^+-dependent transporter localized on astrocytic processes ensheathing the synapse. Activation of the astrocytic Na^+,K^+-ATPase by the Na^+-driven uptake of glutamate constitutes an energy-consuming process tightly linked to synaptic activity.

In addition to the maintenance of ionic gradients that are disrupted during activity, other energy-consuming processes exist in neurons. Thus, the permanent synthesis of molecules needed for communications, such as neurotransmitters, or for general cellular purposes consumes energy.[70,71] Axonal transport of molecules synthesized in the nucleus to their final destination along the axon or at the axon terminal is yet another process fueled by cellular energy metabolism.[72]

Summary

Exactly as in other tissues, the metabolism of glucose, the main energy substrate of the brain, produces two forms of energy: ATP and NADPH. Glycolysis and the TCA cycle produce ATP, whereas energy in the form of reducing equivalents stored in the NADPH molecule is predominantly produced through the pentose phosphate pathway. Maintenance of the electrochemical gradients, particularly for Na^+ and K^+, needed for electrical signaling via the action potential and for chemical signaling through synaptic transmission, is the main energy-consuming process of neural cells.

BRAIN ENERGY METABOLISM AT THE CELLULAR LEVEL

Glia and Vascular Endothelial Cells, in Addition to Neurons, Contribute to Brain Energy Metabolism

Neurons exist in a variety of sizes and shapes and express a large spectrum of firing properties (see Chapter 6). These differences are likely to imply specific energy demands; for example, large pyramidal cells in the primary motor cortex, which must maintain energy-consuming processes such as ion pumping over a large membrane surface or axonal transport along several centimeters, have considerably larger energy requirements than do local interneurons. However, it is now clear that the other cell types of the nervous system—namely, glia and vascular endothelial cells—not only consume energy but also play a crucial role in the flux of energy substrates to neurons. The arguments for such an active role for nonneuronal cells—in particular, glia—are both quantitative and qualitative. Glial cells make up approximately half of the brain volume.[73,74] However, because their volume per cell is smaller, an even more striking figure is the ratio between the number of astrocytes, one of the predominant glial cell types (see Chapter 3), and neurons, which can be as high as 10 : 1, depending on the regions, developmental ages, or species. Indeed, the astrocyte-to-neuron ratio increases with the size of the brain and is thus high in humans.[75] It is therefore clear that glucose reaching the brain parenchyma provides energy substrates to a variety of cell types, only some of which are neurons.

Even more compelling for the realization of the key role that astrocytes play in providing energy substrates to active neurons are the cytological relations that exist between brain capillaries, astrocytes, and neurons. These relations, which are illustrated in Fig. 14.8, are as follows. First, through specialized processes, called endfeet, astrocytes surround brain capillaries.[76] This implies that astrocytes form the first cellular barrier that glucose entering the brain parenchyma encounters and makes them a likely site of prevalent glucose uptake and energy substrate distribution. More than a century ago, the Italian histologist Camillo Golgi and his pupil Luigi Sala sketched such a principle.[77] A lucid formulation of it was presented by the British neuropathologist W. L. Andriezen in an article describing the features of the perivascular glia[78]: "The development of a felted sheath of neuroglia fibers in the ground-substance immediately surrounding the blood vessels of the Brain seems therefore . . . to allow the free passage of lymph and metabolic products which enter into the fluid and general metabolism of the nerve cells." In addition to perivascular endfeet, astrocytes bear processes that ensheathe synaptic contacts.[76] Astrocytes also express receptors and uptake sites with which neurotransmitters released during synaptic activity can interact[79] (Chapter 8). These features endow astrocytes with an exquisite sensitivity to detect increases in synaptic activity. In summary, because of the foregoing structural and functional characteristics, astrocytes are ideally suited to couple local changes in neuronal activity with coordinated adaptations in energy metabolism (see Fig. 14.8).

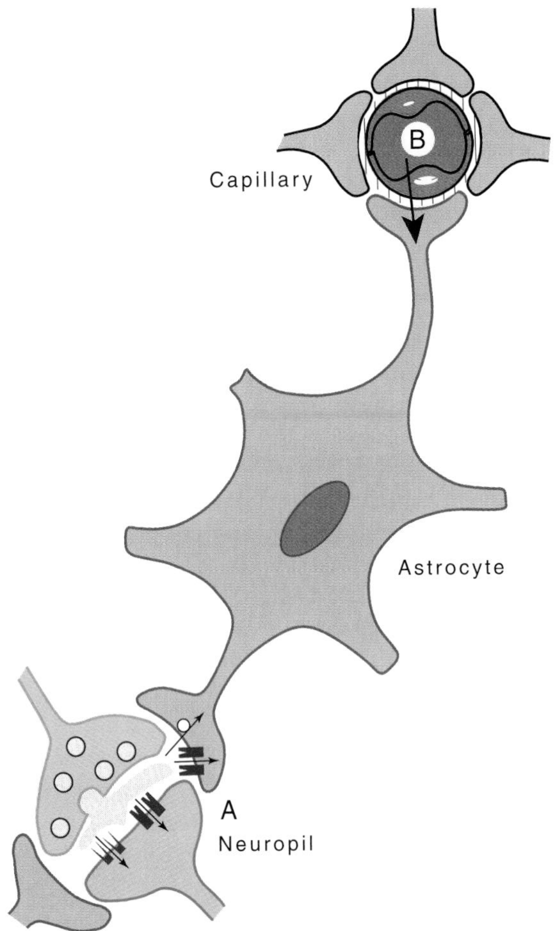

FIGURE 14.8 Schematic representation of the cytological relations existing between intraparenchymal capillaries, astrocytes, and the neuropil. Astrocyte processes surround capillaries (endfeet) and ensheathe synapses; in addition, receptors and uptake sites for neurotransmitters are present on astrocytes. These features make astrocytes ideally suited to sense synaptic activity (A) and to couple it with uptake and metabolism of energy substrates originating from the circulation (B).

A Tightly Regulated Glucose Metabolism Occurs in All Cell Types of the Brain, Neuronal and Nonneuronal

Given the high degree of cellular heterogeneity of the brain, understanding the relative role played by each cell type in the flux of energy substrates has largely depended on the availability of purified preparations such as primary cultures enriched in neurons, astrocytes, or vascular endothelial cells. Such preparations have some drawbacks, because they may not necessarily express all the properties of the cells *in situ*. In addition, one of the parameters of energy metabolism *in vivo*—namely, blood flow—cannot be examined in cultures. Despite these limitations, *in vitro* studies in primary cultures have proved very useful in identifying the cellular sites of glucose uptake and its subsequent metabolic fate—in particular, glycolysis and oxidative phosphorylation—thus providing illuminating correlations of two parameters of brain energy metabolism that are monitored *in vivo*: (1) glucose utilization and (2) oxygen consumption.

Glucose Transporters in the Brain

Glucose is a highly hydrophilic molecule that enters cells through a facilitated transport mediated by specific transporters. Six genes, encoding glucose transporter proteins, and one pseudogene have been identified and cloned so far; these are designated *GLUT1* to *GLUT7*.[80] Glucose transporters belong to a family rather homologous to glycosylated membrane proteins with 12 transmembrane-spanning domains, and both the amino and the carboxyl terminals are exposed to the cytoplasmic surface of the membrane. In the brain, three transporters are predominantly expressed in a cell-specific manner. They are GLUT1, 3, and 5.[81]

Two forms of GLUT1 with molecular masses of 55 and 45 kDa, respectively, are detected in the brain, depending on their degree of glycosylation.[82,83] The 55-kDa form of GLUT1 is essentially localized in brain microvessels, choroid plexus, and ependymal cells. In microvessels, the distribution of GLUT1 is asymmetric, with a higher density on the ablumenal (parenchymal) side than on the vascular side.[81] An intracellular pool of GLUT1 also has been identified in vascular endothelial cells.[81] In the brain *in situ*, the 45-kDa form of GLUT1 is localized predominantly in astrocytes.[84] Under culture conditions, all neural cells, including neurons and other glial cells, express GLUT1; however, this phenomenon appears to be due to the capacity of GLUT1 to be induced by cellular stress.[81]

The glucose transporter specific to neurons is GLUT3.[85] Its cellular distribution appears to predominate in the cell bodies rather than in the axon terminal compartment.

GLUT5 is localized to microglial cells, the resident macrophages of the brain, taking part in the immune and inflammatory responses of the nervous system.[81] In peripheral tissues, particularly in the small intestine (from which it was cloned), GLUT5 functions as a transporter for fructose, whose concentrations are very low in the brain.[81] In the nervous system, therefore, GLUT5 may have diverse transport functions.

Another glucose transporter, GLUT2, has been localized selectively in astrocytes of discrete brain areas, such as certain hypothalamic and brainstem nuclei, which participate in the regulation of feeding behavior and in the central control of insulin release.[86] The insulin-sensitive glucose transporter GLUT4 has been localized in brain vascular endothelium.[81]

It is clear that glucose uptake into the brain parenchyma is a highly specified process regulated in a cell-specific manner by glucose transporter subtypes. Figure 14.9 summarizes this process: Glucose enters the brain through 55-kDa GLUT1 transporters localized on endothelial cells of the blood–brain barrier. Uptake into astrocytes is mediated by 45-kDa GLUT1 transporters, whereas GLUT3 transporters mediate this process in neurons. GLUT2 transporters on astrocytes may "sense" glucose, a function of this glucose transporter subtype in pancreatic β cells.[86] Finally, GLUT5 mediates the uptake of an unidentified substrate into microglial cells.

Cell-Specific Glucose Uptake and Metabolism

As we have seen, glucose utilization can be assessed with radioactively labeled 2-DG. To determine the cellular site of basal and activity-related glucose utilization, this technique has been applied to homogeneous cultures of astrocytes or neurons. For quantitative purposes and to allow comparisons with *in vivo* studies, these *in vitro* experiments, in which radioactive 2-DG is used as a tracer, must be conducted in a medium containing a concentration of glucose near that measured *in vivo* in the extracellular space of the brain, for which values ranging between 0.5 and 2.0 m*M* have been reported.[87,88] The basal rate of glucose utilization is higher in astrocytes than in neurons, with values of about 20 and 6 nmol per milligram of protein per minute, respectively.[89] These values are of the same order as those determined *in vivo* for cortical gray matter (10–20 nmol mg^{-1} min^{-1}), with the 2-DG autoradiographic technique.[33] In view of this difference and of the quantitative preponderance of astrocytes compared with neurons in the gray matter, these data reveal a significant contribution by astrocytes to basal glucose utilization as determined by 2-DG autoradiography or PET *in vivo* (see Fig. 14.5).

The contribution of astrocytes to glucose utilization during activation is even more striking. *In vitro*, activation can be mimicked by exposure of the cells to glutamate, the principal excitatory neurotransmitter (Chapter 8), because, during activation of a given cortical area, the concentration of glutamate in the extracellular

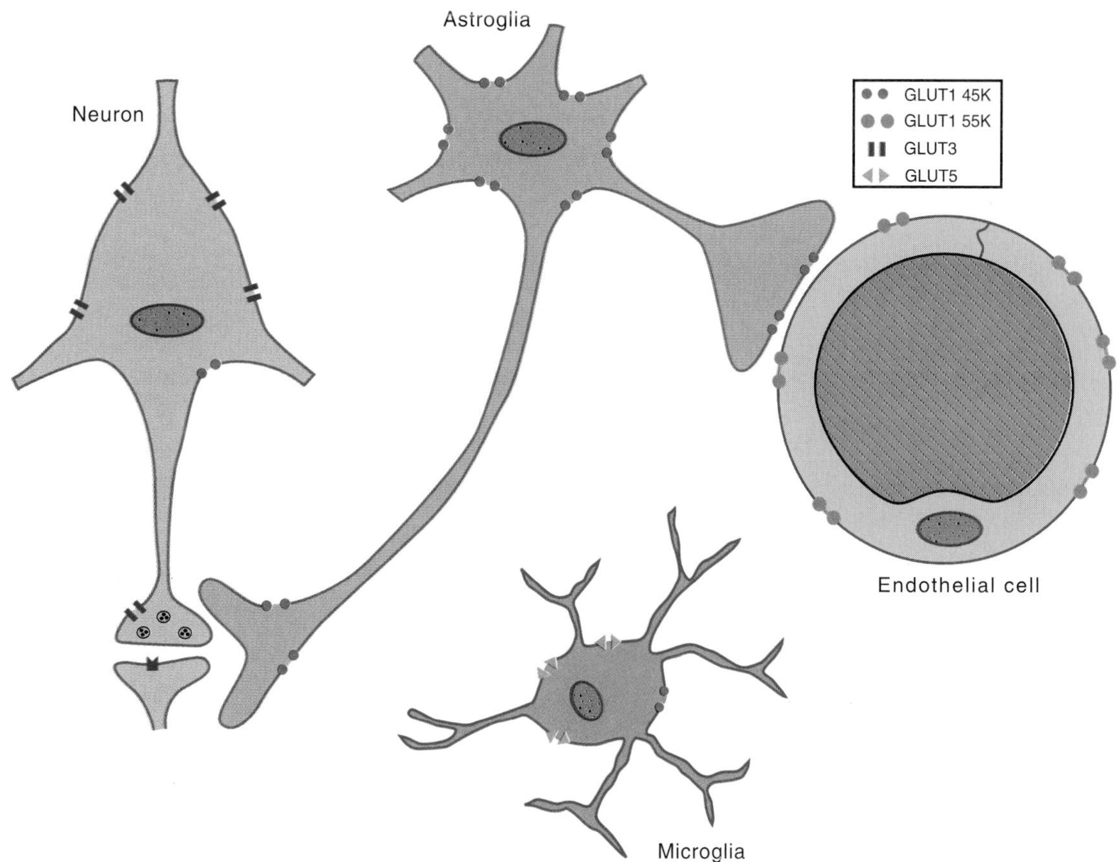

FIGURE 14.9 Cellular distribution of the principal glucose transporters in the nervous system.

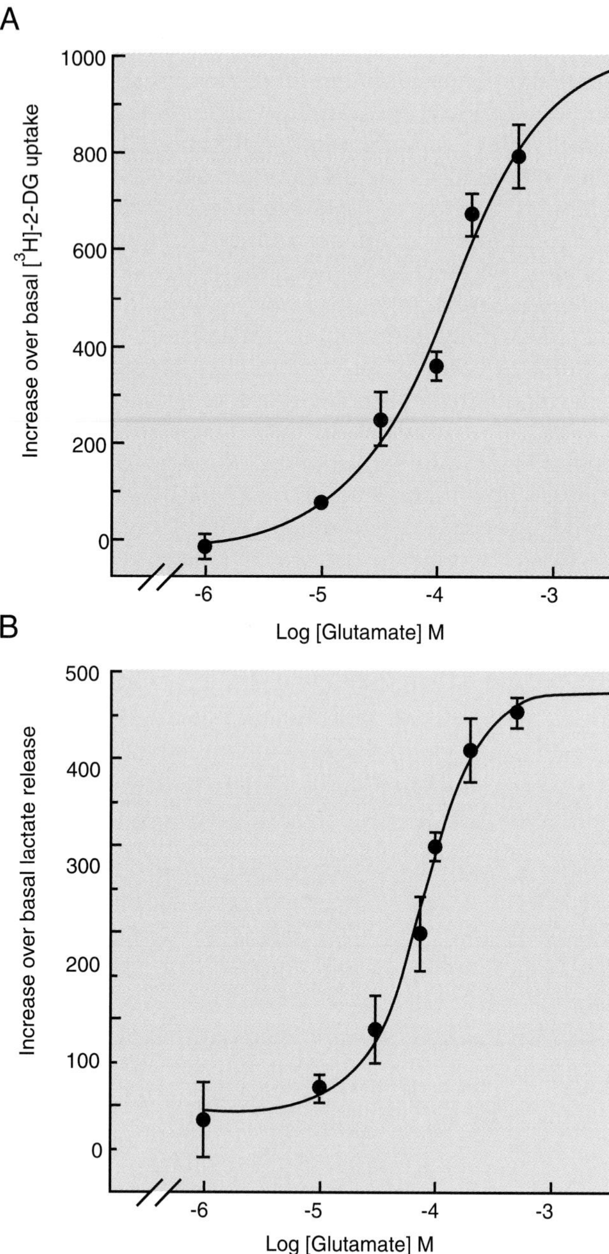

FIGURE 14.10 Stimulation by glutamate of glycolysis in astrocytes. Glutamate stimulates glucose uptake and phosphorylation (A) and lactate production (B) in astrocytes. This effect is concentration dependent with an EC_{50} of ≈60 μM.

space increases considerably owing to its release from the axon terminals of activated pathways.[90] As shown in Fig. 14.10A, L-glutamate stimulates 2-DG uptake and phosphorylation by astrocytes in a concentration-dependent manner, with an EC_{50} of 60 to 80 μM.[91,92] Unlike other actions of glutamate, stimulation of glucose utilization in astrocytes is mediated not by specific glutamate receptors but by glutamate transporters.[91,92] Indeed, in addition to the maintenance of extracellular K^+ homeostasis, one of the well-established functions of astrocytes is to ensure the reuptake of certain neurotransmitters, in particular, that of glutamate at excitatory synapses.[93] At least three glutamate transporter subtypes have been cloned in various species, including humans.[94,95] The GLT-1 subtype is exclusively localized in astrocytes, whereas the EAAC1 subtype is exclusively neuronal; GLAST, the third subtype, is expressed both in glia and in neurons, with a predominant distribution in astrocytes. The density of GLT-1 and GLAST is particularly high on astrocytes that surround nerve terminals and dendritic spines, consistent with the prominent role of these transporters in the reuptake of synaptically released glutamate.[96,97] The driving force for glutamate uptake through the specific transporters is the transmembrane Na^+ gradient; indeed, glutamate is cotransported with Na^+ in a ratio of one glutamate for every two or three Na^+ ions.[94,95] The selective loss of GLT-1, the astrocyte-selective glutamate transporter, has been demonstrated in the motor cortex and spinal cord of patients who died of amyotrophic lateral sclerosis, a neurodegenerative disease affecting motor neurons.[98]

Glutamate-Stimulated Uptake of Glucose by Astrocytes Is a Source of Insight into the Cellular Bases of ^{18}F-2-DG PET *in Vivo*

The glutamate-stimulated uptake of glucose by astrocytes is a source of insight into the cellular bases of the activation-induced local increase in glucose utilization visualized with ^{18}F-2-DG PET *in vivo*. As we have seen, focal physiological activation of specific brain areas is accompanied by increases in glucose utilization (see Fig. 14.5); because glutamate is released from excitatory synapses when neuronal pathways subserving specific modalities are activated, the stimulation by glutamate of glucose utilization in astrocytes provides a direct mechanism for coupling neuronal activity to glucose utilization in the brain (Fig. 14.11). The intracellular molecular mechanism of this coupling requires Na^+,K^+-ATPase, because ouabain completely inhibits the glutamate-evoked 2-DG uptake by astrocytes.[91] The astrocytic Na^+,K^+-ATPase responds predominantly to increases in intracellular Na^+ (Na_i^+) for which it shows a K_m of about 10 mM.[99,100] In astrocytes, the Na_i^+ concentration ranges between 10 and 20 mM,[93] and so Na^+,K^+-ATPase is set to be readily activated when Na_i^+ rises concomitantly with glutamate uptake.[101] Experiments in which Na_i^+ was increased artificially by using the ionophore monensin confirmed that, under these conditions, 2-DG uptake into astrocytes is markedly stimulated.[102] These observations indicate that a major determinant of glucose utilization is the activity of Na^+,K^+-ATPase.[103] In this context, we should note that, *in vivo*, the main mechanism that accounts for the activation-induced 2-DG uptake is the activity of Na^+,K^+-ATPase.

It is important here to briefly consider the relative participation of the neuronal and astrocytic Na^+,K^+-ATPases in glucose utilization. When glutamate is released from depolarized neuronal terminals, it is taken up predominantly into astrocytes. The stoichiometry of glutamate reuptake being one molecule of glutamate cotransported with two or three Na^+ ions, the increase in intracellular *astrocytic* Na^+ *concentration* associated with glutamate reuptake massively activates the pump. Thus, although the tonic activity of the Na^+,K^+-ATPase is needed to maintain the transmembrane neuronal and glial ionic gradients and accounts for *basal* glucose utilization, on a short-term temporal scale (from milliseconds to seconds), when glutamate is released from depolarized axon terminals of modality-specific afferents, the *astrocytic* Na^+,K^+*-ATPase* is briskly activated, owing to the massive increase (by at least 10 m*M*) in intracellular Na^+ associated with glutamate reuptake, providing the signal for the *activation-dependent* glucose utilization.

How does the activation of the Na^+,K^+-ATPase cause increased glucose utilization? The mechanism was explained by pioneering studies on erythrocytes by Joseph Hoffmann and his colleagues at Yale University,[104] which have been confirmed in a number of other cell systems including brain[105,106] and vascular smooth muscle.[107] The increase in pump activity consumes ATP, which is a negative modulator of phosphofructokinase, the principal rate-limiting enzyme of glycolysis (see Fig. 14.1). Thus, when ATP concentration is low, phosphofructokinase activity is stimulated, resulting in increased glucose utilization. The activity of hexokinase, the enzyme responsible for glucose and 2-DG phosphorylation (see Fig. 14.4), also is increased under these conditions. This explains why the increase in glucose utilization, associated with the stimulation of Na^+,K^+-ATPase, can be monitored with 2-DG, which is not processed beyond the hexokinase step.

A compartmentalization of glucose uptake during activation has also been unequivocably found by Marco Tsacopoulos and his colleagues in the honeybee drone retina.[108] In this highly organized, crystal-like, nervous tissue preparation, photoreceptor cells form rosette-like structures that are surrounded by glial cells. In addition, mitochondria are exclusively present in the photoreceptor neurons. Light activation reveals an increase in radioactive 2-DG uptake in the glial cells surrounding the rosettes but not in the photoreceptor neurons.[108] An increase in O_2 consumption is nevertheless measured in photoreceptor neurons.[109] After activation of photoreceptors by light, glucose is probably taken up predominantly by glial cells, which then release a metabolic substrate to be oxidized by photoreceptor neurons.

In summary, as indicated in the operational model described in Fig. 14.11, upon activation of a particular brain area, glutamate released from excitatory terminals is taken up by a Na^+-dependent transporter located on astrocytes. The ensuing local increase in intracellular Na^+ concentration activates the Na^+,K^+-ATPase, which in turn stimulates glucose uptake by astrocytes. This model delineates a simple mechanism for coupling synaptic activity to glucose utilization; in addition, it is consistent with the notion that the signals detected during physiological activation in humans with ^{18}F-2-DG PET and autoradiography in laboratory animals may predominantly reflect uptake of the tracer into astrocytes. This conclusion does not question the validity of the 2-DG-based techniques; rather, it provides a cellular and molecular basis for these functional brain-imaging techniques.

Lactate Released by Astrocytes May Be a Metabolic Substrate for Neurons

The fact that the increase in glucose uptake during activation can be ascribed predominantly, if not exclusively, to astrocytes indicates that energy substrates must be released by astrocytes to meet the energy demands of neurons. As indicated earlier, lactate and pyruvate are adequate substrates for brain tissue *in vitro*.[16,17] In fact, synaptic activity can be maintained *in vitro* in cerebral cortical slices with only lactate or pyruvate as a substrate.[16,17] Lactate is quantitatively the main metabolic intermediate released by cultured astrocytes at a rate of 15 to 30 nmol per milligram of protein per minute.[110] Other, quantitatively less important intermediates released by astrocytes are pyruvate (approximately 10 times less than lactate) and α-ketoglutarate, citrate, and malate, which are released in marginal amounts.[111] For lactate (or pyruvate) to be an adequate metabolic substrate for neurons, particularly during activation, two additional conditions must be fulfilled: (1) that indeed during activation lactate release by astrocytes increases and (2) lactate uptake by neurons must be demonstrated. Both mechanisms have been demonstrated. Mimicking activation *in vitro* by exposing cultured astrocytes to glutamate results in a marked release of lactate and, to a lesser degree, pyruvate[91] (see Fig. 14.10B). This glutamate-evoked lactate release shows the same pharmacology and time course as does the glutamate-evoked glucose utilization and indicates that glutamate stimulates the processing of glucose through glycolysis. As noted earlier, *in vivo* ^{1}H MRI studies in humans that show a *transient* lactate peak in the primary visual cortex during physiological stimulation are consistent with the notion of activation-induced glycolysis.[50,51] In addition, lactate levels in the rat somatosensory cortex transiently increase subsequent to forepaw stimulation.[52,53] Finally, evidence obtained in purified neuronal cultures indicates the presence of a saturable and specific transport system for lactate in neurons.[112]

Thus, a metabolic compartmentation whereby glucose taken up by astrocytes and metabolized glycolytically to lactate is then released in the extracellular space to be utilized by neurons is consistent with biochemical and electrophysiological observations.[89,113] This array of *in vitro* and *in vivo* experimental evidence is summarized in the model of cell-specific metabolic regulation illustrated in Fig. 14.11.

Studies of the well-compartmentalized honeybee drone retina and of isolated preparations of guinea pig retina containing photoreceptors attached to Müller (glial) cells corroborate the existence of such metabolic fluxes between glia and neurons.[114,115] In addition to the

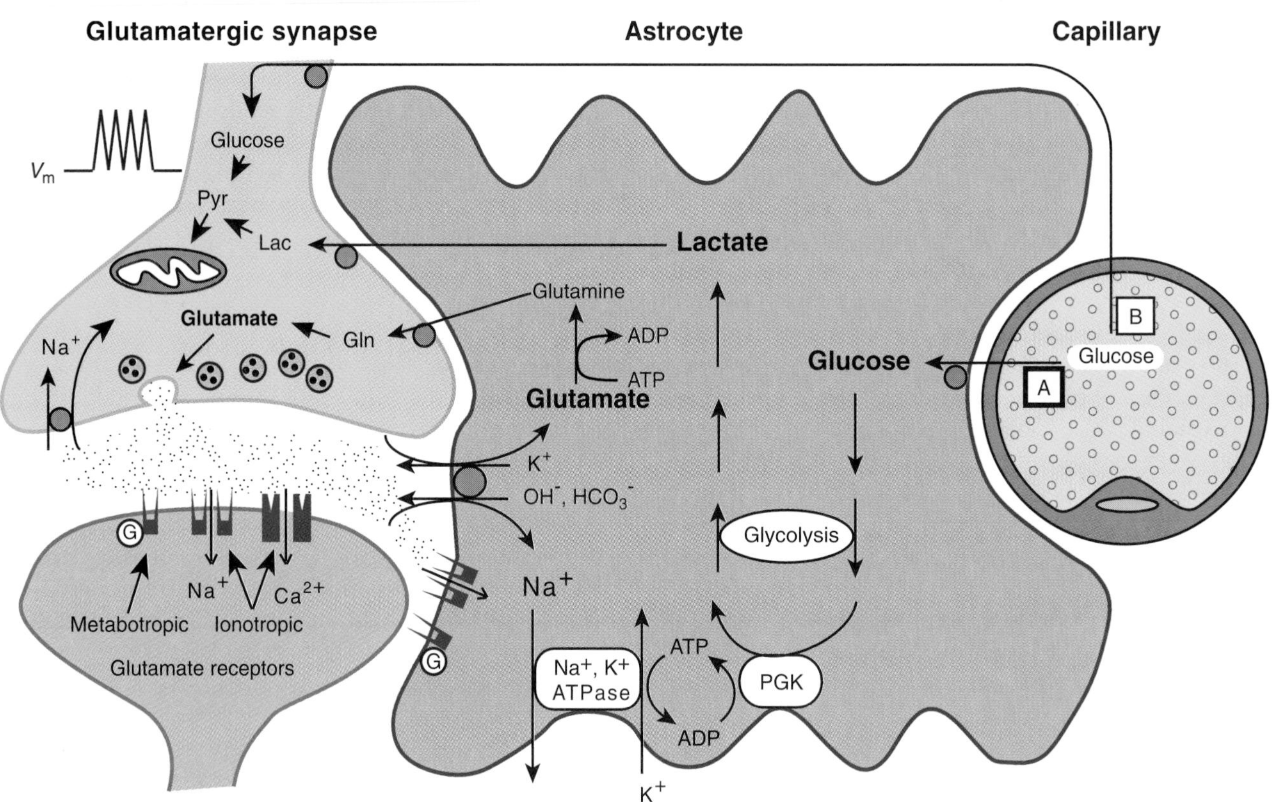

FIGURE 14.11 Schematic representation of the mechanism for glutamate-induced glycolysis in astrocytes during physiological activation. At glutamatergic synapses, presynaptically released glutamate depolarizes postsynaptic neurons by acting at specific receptor subtypes. The action of glutamate is terminated by an efficient glutamate uptake system located primarily in astrocytes. Glutamate is cotransported with Na^+, resulting in an increase in the intra-astrocytic concentration of Na^+, leading to an activation of the astrocyte Na^+,K^+-ATPase. Activation of the Na^+,K^+-ATPase stimulates glycolysis (i.e., glucose utilization and lactate production). The stoichiometry of this process is such that for one glutamate molecule taken up by two to three Na^+ ions, one glucose molecule enters astrocytes, two ATP molecules are produced through glycolysis, and two lactate molecules are released. Within the astrocyte, one ATP fuels one "turn of the pump," while the other provides the energy needed to convert glutamate to glutamine by glutamine synthase (see Fig. 14.13). Lactate, once released by astrocytes, can be taken up by neurons and serve as an adequate energy substrate. (For graphic clarity only, lactate uptake into presynaptic terminals is indicated. However, this process could also take place at the postsynaptic neuron.) In accord with recent evidence, glutamate receptors are also shown on astrocytes. This model, which summarizes *in vitro* experimental evidence indicating glutamate-induced glycolysis, is taken to show cellular and molecular events occurring during *activation* of a given cortical area (arrow labeled A, activation). Direct glucose uptake into neurons under basal conditions is also shown (arrow labeled B, basal conditions). Abbreviations: Pyr, pyruvate; Lac, lactate; Gln, glutamine; G, G protein. Modified from 91.

glial localization of glucose uptake during activation, glycolytic products have been shown to be released. In particular, during activation, glial cells in the honeybee drone retina release alanine produced from pyruvate by transamination; the released alanine is taken up by photoreceptor neurons and, after reconversion into pyruvate, can enter the TCA cycle to yield ATP through oxidative phosphorylation (see Fig. 14.2).[114] In the guinea pig retina, lactate, formed glycolytically from glucose, is released by the Müller cells to fuel photoreceptor neurons.[116]

Although plasma lactate cannot fully substitute for glucose as a metabolic substrate for the brain, because of its limited permeability across the blood–brain barrier[18] lactate formed within the brain parenchyma (e.g., through glutamate-activated glycolysis in astrocytes) can fulfill the energetic needs of neurons. Lactate, after conversion into pyruvate by a reaction catalyzed by **lactate dehydrogenase** (LDH), can provide, on a molar basis, 18 ATP through oxidative phosphorylation. Conversion of lactate into pyruvate does not require ATP, and, in this regard, lactate is energetically more favorable than the first, obligatory step of glycolysis, in which glucose is phosphorylated to glucose 6-phosphate at the expense of one molecule of ATP (see Fig. 14.1).

Glycogen, the Storage Form of Glucose, Is Localized in Astrocytes

Glycogen is the single largest energy reserve of the brain[117]; it is mainly localized in astrocytes, although ependymal and choroid plexus cells, as well as certain large neurons in the brainstem, contain glycogen.[118,119] When compared to the contents in liver and muscle, the glycogen content of the brain is exceedingly small, about 100 and 10 times inferior, respectively. Thus, the brain can hardly be considered a glycogen storage organ, and here the function of glycogen should be viewed as that of providing a metabolic buffer during physiological activity.

Glycogen Metabolism Is Coupled to Neuronal Activity

Glycogen turnover in the brain is extremely rapid,[120] and glycogen levels are finely coordinated with synaptic activity.[121] For example, during general anesthesia, a condition in which synaptic activity is markedly attenuated, glycogen levels rise sharply.[122] Interestingly, however, the glycogen content of cultures containing exclusively astrocytes is not increased by general anesthetics[123]; this observation indicates that the *in vivo* action of general anesthetics on astrocyte glycogen is due to the inhibition of neuronal activity, stressing the existence of a tight coupling between synaptic activity and astrocyte glycogen. Accordingly, reactive astrocytes, which develop in areas where neuronal activity is decreased or absent as a consequence of injury, contain high amounts of glycogen.[124,125]

In addition to glycogen, glucose is incorporated into other macromolecules such as proteins (glycoproteins) and lipids (glycolipids) at rates specific for the turnover of each macromolecule, which can span from a few minutes to a few days.

Certain Neurotransmitters Regulate Glycogen Metabolism in Astrocytes

Glycogen levels in astrocytes are tightly regulated by various neurotransmitters. Several monoamine neurotransmitters—namely, noradrenaline, serotonin, and histamine—are glycogenolytic in the brain, in addition to certain peptides, such as vasoactive intestinal peptide (VIP) and pituitary adenylate cyclase activating peptide (PACAP), and adenosine and ATP.[121,126,127] The effects of all these neurotransmitters are mediated by their cogent specific receptors coupled to second-messenger pathways that are under the control of adenylate cyclase or phospholipase C.[128] The initial rate of glycogenolysis activated by VIP and noradrenaline is between 5 and 10 nmol per milligram of protein per minute,[128] a value that is remarkably close to glucose utilization of the gray matter, as determined by the 2-DG autoradiographic method.[33] This correlation indicates that the glycosyl units mobilized in response to the glycogenolytic neurotransmitters can provide quantitatively adequate substrates for the energy demands of the brain parenchyma. At present, whether the glycosyl units mobilized through glycogenolysis are used by astrocytes to meet their energy demands during activation or are metabolized to a substrate such as lactate, which is then released for the use of neurons, is not clear. It appears, however, that glucose is not released by astrocytes after glycogenolysis, supporting the view that the activity of glucose-6-phosphatase (see Fig. 14.1) in astrocytes is very low.[129] *In vitro* evidence suggests that lactate may be the metabolic intermediate produced through glycogenolysis and exported from astrocytes.[129]

These observations show that neuronal signals (e.g., certain neurotransmitters) can exert receptor-mediated metabolic effects on astrocytes in a manner similar to peripheral hormones on their target cells. However, the action of this type of neurotransmitter is temporally specified and spatially restricted to activated areas. Indeed, brain glycogenolysis visualized by autoradiography in laboratory animals has also been demonstrated *in vivo* after physiological activation of a modality-specific pathway.[130] Repeated stimulation of whiskers resulted in a marked decrease in the density of glycogen-associated autoradiographic grains in the somatosensory cortex of rats (barrel fields), as well as in the relevant thalamic nuclei.[130] These observations indicate that the physiological activation of specific neuronal circuits results in the mobilization of glial glycogen stores.

Summary

Under basal conditions, glucose uptake and metabolism occur in every brain cell type. Glucose uptake is mediated by specific transporters that are distributed in a cell-specific manner. Astrocytes play a critical role in the utilization of glucose coupled to excitatory synaptic transmission. The molecular mechanisms of this coupling are stoichiometrically directed: for each synaptically released glutamate molecule taken up with two to three Na^+ ions by an astrocyte, one glucose molecule enters the same astrocyte, two ATP molecules are produced through glycolysis, and two lactate molecules are released and consumed by neurons to yield 18 ATPs through oxidative phosphorylation. Neuronal signals, for example, certain neurotransmitters, can exert receptor-mediated glycogenolysis in astrocytes in a manner similar to peripheral hormones on their target cells. However, this type of effect by neurotransmitters is temporally specified and spatially restricted within activated areas, possibly to provide additional energy substrates in register with local increases in neuronal activity.

GLUTAMATE AND NITROGEN METABOLISM: A COORDINATED SHUTTLE BETWEEN ASTROCYTES AND NEURONS

As we have seen, synaptically released glutamate is rapidly removed from the extracellular space by a transporter-mediated reuptake system that is particularly efficient in astrocytes.[93] This mechanism contributes in a crucial manner to the fidelity of glutamate-mediated neurotransmission. Indeed, glutamate levels in the extracellular space are low (<3 μM), allowing for optimal glutamate-mediated signaling after depolarization while preventing overactivation of glutamate receptors, which could eventually result in excitotoxic neuronal damage.[131]

One may wonder how astrocytes dispose of the glutamate that they take up, because, unlike carbohydrates or lipids, amino acids cannot be stored. The predominant pathway in peripheral tissues for disposing of amino acids is the transfer of their α-amino group to a corresponding α-keto acid; this reaction is catalyzed by aminotransferases (Fig. 14.12). In astrocytes, the α-amino group of glutamate can be transferred to oxaloacetate to yield α-ketoglutarate (α-KG) and aspartate in a reaction catalyzed by **aspartate amino transferase** (AAT).[132] The α-KG generated is an intermediate of the TCA cycle and is therefore further oxidized.[133] Another transamination reaction catalyzed by **alanine amino transferase** (ALAT) transfers the α-amino group of glutamate to pyruvate, resulting in the formation of alanine and α-KG.[134]

Two other pathways exist in astrocytes to metabolize glutamate. First, glutamate can be directly converted into α-KG through an NAD-requiring oxidative deamination catalyzed by **glutamate dehydrogenase** (GDH)[132,134] (see Fig. 14.12). Glutamate, by indirectly (through AAT or ALAT) or directly (through GDH) entering the TCA cycle, is an energy substrate for astrocytes.[133] Second, the quantitatively predominant metabolic pathway of glutamate in astrocytes is its amidation to glutamine, an ATP-requiring reaction in which an ammonium ion is fixed on glutamate (see Fig. 14.12).[135] This reaction is catalyzed by **glutamine synthase** (GS), an enzyme almost exclusively localized in astrocytes,[136] and provides an efficient means of disposing not only of glutamate but also of ammonium. Glutamine is released by astrocytes and taken up by neurons, where it is hydrolyzed back to glutamate by the phosphate-dependent mitochondrial enzyme **glutaminase.**[137] This metabolic pathway, often referred to as the **glutamate–glutamine shuttle,** is a clear example

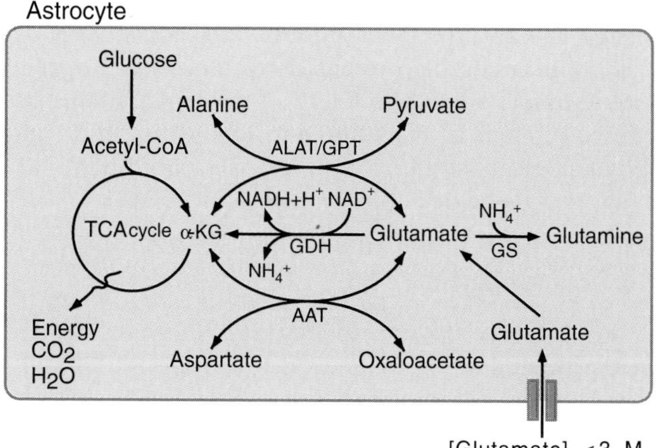

FIGURE 14.12 Metabolic fate of glutamate taken up by astrocytes. Abbreviations: ALAT, alanine aminotransferase; GDH, glutamate dehydrogenase; GS, glutamine synthase; AAT, aspartate aminotransferase; GPT, glutamate dehydrogenase; α-KG, α-ketoglutarate.

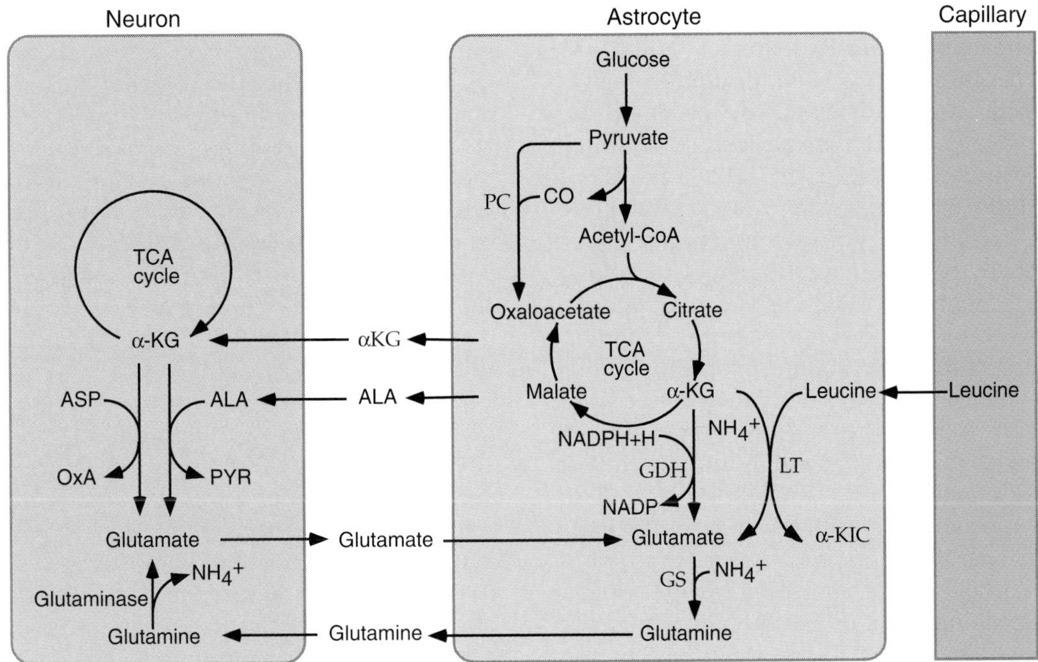

FIGURE 14.13 Metabolic intermediates are released by astrocytes to regenerate the glutamate neurotransmitter pool in neurons. Glutamine, formed from glutamate in a reaction catalyzed by glutamine synthase (GS), is released by astrocytes and taken up by neurons, which convert it into glutamate under the action of glutaminase. GS is an enzyme selectively localized in astrocytes. This metabolic cycle is referred to as the glutamate–glutamine shuttle. Other, quantitatively less important sources of neuronal glutamate are alanine and α-ketoglutarate (α-KG). In astrocytes, glutamate is synthesized *de novo* from α-KG in a reaction catalyzed by glutamate dehydrogenase (GDH). The carbon backbone of glutamate is exported by astrocytes after conversion into glutamine under the action of GS; the conversion of leucine into α-ketoisocaproate (α-KIC), catalyzed by leucine transaminase (LT), provides the amino group for the synthesis of glutamine from glutamate. The carbons "lost" from the TCA cycle as α-KG is converted into glutamate are replenished by oxaloacetate (OxA) formed from pyruvate in a reaction catalyzed by pyruvate carboxylase, another astrocyte-specific enzyme.

of cooperation between astrocytes and neurons (Fig. 14.13). It allows the removal of potentially toxic excess glutamate from the extracellular space, while returning to the neuron a synaptically inert (glutamine does not affect neurotransmission) precursor with which to regenerate the neuronal pool of glutamate.

However, not all glutamate is regenerated through the glutamate–glutamine shuttle, because some of the glutamate released by neurons enters at the α-KG, the TCA cycle in astrocytes; therefore, *de novo* synthesis is required to maintain the neuronal glutamate pool. Glutamate can be synthesized through NADPH-dependent reductive amination of α-KG catalyzed by GDH (note that here the cofactor is NADPH, whereas, for the opposite reaction also catalyzed by GDH, the oxidant is NAD; see Figs. 14.12 and 14.13).[138,139] For the synthesis of glutamate, glucose provides the carbon backbone as α-KG through the TCA cycle, whereas an exogenous source of nitrogen is necessary (see Fig. 14.13). Convincing evidence, obtained by using ^{15}N-labeled amino acids whose metabolic fate was determined by gas chromatography and mass spectrometry, indicates that plasma leucine provides the nitrogen required for net glutamate synthesis from α-KG.[140] Thus, leucine taken up from the circulation at astrocytic end feet[141] provides the amino group to α-KG in a reaction catalyzed by **leucine transaminase** (LT), resulting in the formation of glutamate and α-ketoisocaproate (α-KIC) (see Fig. 14.13). Because this reaction takes place in astrocytes, to replenish the neuronal glutamate pool, the astrocytes export glutamate as glutamine.

Another potential pathway described by Arne Schousboe and colleagues exists for the *de novo* synthesis of glutamate in neurons from substrates provided by astrocytes. With the use of uniformly labeled ^{13}C compounds in combination with magnetic resonance spectroscopy, astrocytes have been shown to release significant amounts of alanine and α-KG.[111] Both metabolic intermediates are taken up by neurons and can be converted into glutamate and pyruvate in a transamination reaction catalyzed by ALAT (see Fig. 14.12). In this case, as for the glutamate–glutamine shuttle

(Fig. 14.13), astrocytes provide the substrate(s) necessary for glutamate synthesis in neurons.

Note that because α-KG is used for glutamate synthesis, metabolic intermediates downstream of α-KG must be available to maintain a sustained flux through the TCA cycle in astrocytes (see Fig. 14.13). This need is met by the activity of the enzyme **pyruvate carboxylase** (PC), which fixes CO_2 on pyruvate to generate oxaloacetate, which, by condensing with acetyl-CoA, maintains the flux through the TCA cycle. The carboxylation of pyruvate to oxaloacetate is referred to as an **anaplerotic** (Greek for "fill up") **reaction.** Interestingly, like glutamine synthase, PC is selectively localized in astrocytes.[142] The fact that these two enzymes are localized in astrocytes in conjunction with the existence of a glutamate–glutamine shuttle stresses that astrocytes are essential for maintaining the neuronal glutamate pool used for neurotransmission (see Fig. 14.13).

As noted earlier, the metabolic intermediate α-KG lies at the branching point of glucose and glutamate metabolism (see Fig. 14.12). Any change in the activities of the enzymes that convert α-KG into glutamate or into succinyl-CoA, the next intermediate in the TCA cycle, may affect the efficacy of the TCA cycle or glutamate levels. Interestingly, a marked decrease in the activity of ***α-ketoglutarate dehydrogenase*** (α-KGDH), the enzyme catalyzing the conversion of α-KG into succinyl-CoA, was found in a very high proportion of postmortem brains from patients with Alzheimer disease[143]; in addition, a similar decrease in α-KGDH activity has been demonstrated in the fibroblasts of patients affected by the familial form of Alzheimer disease.[144]

Summary

A key function of astrocytes is to remove synaptically released glutamate. A large proportion of glutamate is transformed to glutamine through an energy-requiring process that also allows for the detoxification of ammonium. Glutamine released by astrocytes regenerates the neuronal glutamate pool. Some of the

BOX 14.2

HEPATIC ENCEPHALOPATHY IS A DISORDER OF ASTROCYTE FUNCTION RESULTING IN A NEUROPSYCHIATRIC SYNDROME

Hepatic encephalopathy is observed in patients with severe liver failure. The disease can be in one of two forms: an acute form, called fulminant hepatic failure, and (2) a chronic form, portosystemic encephalopathy.[145] The neuropsychiatric symptoms of fulminant hepatic failure are delirium, coma, and seizures associated with acute toxic or viral hepatic failure. Patients having portosystemic encephalopathy may present personality changes, episodic confusion, or stupor, and, in the most severe cases, coma. The current view on the pathophysiology of hepatic encephalopathy is that, owing to liver failure, "toxic" substances that affect brain function accumulate in the circulation.[146] One of the substances thought to be responsible for the neuropsychiatric "toxicity" is ammonia. The neuropathological findings are rather striking: astrocytes are the brain cells that appear principally affected. In the acute form, astrocyte swelling is prominent and likely to be the cause of the observed acute brain edema. In portosystemic encephalopathy, astrocytes adopt morphological features characteristic of what is defined as an Alzheimer type II astrocyte: in these cells, the nucleus is pale and enlarged, chromatin is marginated, and a prominent nucleolus is often observed. Lipofuscin deposits may be present, and the amount of the astrocyte-specific protein glial fibrillary acidic protein (see Chapter 4) is decreased. Neurons appear structurally normal. All the foregoing histopathological changes have been reproduced *in vitro* by acutely or chronically applying ammonium chloride to primary astrocyte cultures.[146] As mentioned earlier, detoxification of ammonium is an ATP-requiring, astrocyte-specific reaction catalyzed by glutamine synthase (see Fig. 14.12). It is therefore not surprising that excess ammonia perturbs energy metabolism; indeed, ammonia stimulates glycolysis[147] whereas it inhibits TCA-cycle activity.[148] In addition, ammonia markedly decreases the glycogen content of astrocytes.

In summary, while the precise pathophysiological mechanisms of the neuropsychiatric syndrome in hepatic encephalopathy are still unknown, this clinical condition provides a striking illustration of the fundamental importance of neuron–astrocyte metabolic interactions, because structural and functional alterations apparently restricted to astrocytes result in severe behavioral perturbations.

glutamate is also regenerated through the fixation of the amino group of leucine onto the TCA intermediate α-KG, providing another indication of the tight link existing between glutamate and nitrogen metabolism and of the crucial function that astrocytes play in maintaining the neuronal glutamate pool at levels that ensure the maintenance of synaptic transmission.

THE ASTROCYTE–NEURON METABOLIC UNIT

From a strictly energetic viewpoint, the brain can be seen as an almost exclusive glucose-processing machine producing H_2O and CO_2. However, the metabolism of glucose in the brain is temporally, spatially, and functionally specified. Thus, glucose metabolism increases with exquisite spatiotemporal precision in register with neuronal activity. The site of this increase is not the neuronal cell body; rather, it is the neuropil, where presynaptic terminals, postsynaptic elements, and astrocytes ensheathing synaptic contacts are localized.[149] This cytological relation between astrocytes and neurons is also manifested by a functional metabolic partnership: in response to a neuronal signal (glutamate), astrocytes release a glucose-derived metabolic substrate for neurons (lactate). Glucose also provides the carbon backbone for regeneration of the neuronal pool of glutamate. This process results from a close astrocyte–neuron cooperation. Indeed, the selective localization of pyruvate carboxylase in astrocytes, indicating the need to replenish the TCA cycle with carbon backbones, strongly suggests that glucose-derived metabolic intermediates are used for glutamate (and other amino acid) synthesis. This view is supported by tracer studies, indicating the labeling of glutamate from radioactive glucose.[150] The newly synthesized glutamate is not provided as such by astrocytes to neurons; rather, it is converted into glutamine by glutamine synthase, another enzyme selectively localized in astrocytes. Glutamate, taken up by astrocytes during synaptic activity, undergoes the same metabolic process, also being released as glutamine (the glutamate–glutamine shuttle).

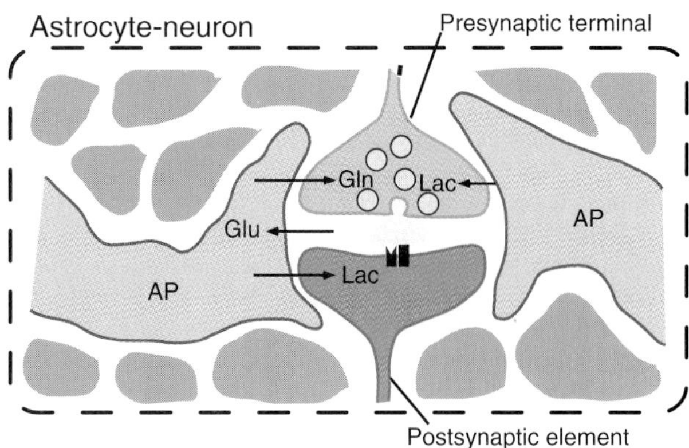

FIGURE 14.14 The astrocyte–neuron metabolic unit. Glutamatergic terminals and the astrocytic processes that surround them can be viewed as a highly specialized metabolic unit in which the activation signal (glutamate) is furnished by the neuron to the astrocyte, whereas the astrocyte provides the precursor needed to maintain the neurotransmitter pool (glutamine), as well as the energy substrate (lactate). AP, astrocyte process.

Summary

In conclusion, the axon terminal of glutamatergic neurons, which are the main communication lines in the nervous system, and the astrocytic processes that surround them should be viewed as a *metabolic unit*, in which the neuron furnishes the activation signal (glutamate) to the astrocyte and the astrocyte provides not only the precursor needed to maintain the neurotransmitter pool (glutamine) but also the energy substrate (lactate) (Fig. 14.14). The efficacy of the predominant excitatory synapse in the brain, the glutamatergic synapse, cannot be maintained without a close astrocyte–neuron interaction.

References

1. Kety, S. S. (1957). The general metabolism of the brain in vivo. In *The Metabolism of the Nervous System* (D. Richter, ed.), pp. 221–237. Pergamon Press, London.
2. Sokoloff, L. (1960). The metabolism of the central nervous system in vivo. In *Handbook of Physiology* (J. Field, H. W. Magoun, and V. E. Hall, eds.), Sect. 1, Vol. II, pp. 1843–1864. Am. Physiol. Soc., Washington, DC.
3. Edvinsson, L., MacKenzie, E. T., and McCulloch, J. (1993). *Cerebral Blood Flow and Metabolism*, pp. 161–168. Raven Press, New York.
4. Kety, S. S., and Schmidt, C. F. (1948). The nitrous oxide method for the quantitative determination of cerebral blood flow in man: Theory, procedure, and normal values. *J. Clin. Invest.* **27:** 476–483.
5. Krebs, H. A., Williamson, D. H., Bates, M. W., Page, M. A., and Hawkins, R. A. (1971). The role of ketone bodies in caloric homeostasis. *Adv. Enzyme Regul.* **9:** 387–409.
6. Girard, J., Ferré, P., Pégorier, J.-P., and Duée, P. H. (1992). Adaptations of glucose and fatty acid metabolism during the perinatal period and suckling-weaning transition. *Physiol. Rev.* **72:** 507–562.
7. Smith, S., and Abraham, S. (1975). The composition and biosynthesis of milk fat. *Adv. Lipid Res.* **13:** 195–239.
8. Edmond, J. (1992). Energy metabolism in developing brain cells. *Can. J. Physiol. Pharmacol.* **70:** S118–S129.
9. Auestad, N., Korsak, R. A., Morrow, J. W., and Edmond, F. (1991). Fatty acid oxidation and ketogenesis by astrocytes in primary culture. *J. Neurochem.* **56:** 1376–1386.
10. Cuzner, M. L., and Davison, A. N. (1968). The lipid composition of rat brain myelin and subcellular fractions during development. *Biochem. J.* **106:** 29–34.

11. Nehlig, A., and Pereira de Vasconcelos, A. (1993). Glucose and ketone body utilization by the brain of neonatal rats. *Prog. Neurobiol.* **40:** 163–221.
12. Auestad, N., Fisher, R., Chiappelli, F., Korsak, R. A., and Edmond, J. (1990). Growth and development of brain of artificially reared hypoketonemic rat pups. *Proc. Soc. Exp. Biol. Med.* **195:** 335–344.
13. Cremer, J. E., and Heath, D. F. (1974). The estimation of rates of utilization of glucose and ketone bodies in the brain of the suckling rat using compartmental analysis of isotopic data. *Biochem. J.* **142:** 527–544.
14. Owen, O. E., Morgan, A. P., Kemp, H. G., Sullivan, J. M., Herrera, M. G., and Cahill, G. F. J. (1967). Brain metabolism during fasting. *J. Clin. Invest.* **46:** 1589–1595.
15. Sloviter, H. A., and Kamimoto, T. (1970). The isolated, perfused rat brain preparation metabolizes mannose but not maltose. *J. Neurochem.* **17:** 1109–1111.
16. McIlwain, H., and Bachelard, H. S. (1985). In *Biochemistry and the Central Nervous System*, Vol. 5, pp. 54–83. Churchill-Livingstone, Edinburgh and London.
17. Schurr, A., West, C. A., and Rigor, B. M. (1988). Lactate-supported synaptic function in the rat hippocampal slice preparation. *Science* **240:** 1326–1328.
18. Pardridge, W. M., and Oldendorf, W. H. (1977). Transport of metabolic substrates through the blood-brain barrier. *J. Neurochem.* **28:** 5–12.
19. Roy, C. S., and Sherrington, C. S. (1890). On the regulation of the blood supply of the brain. *J. Physiol.* (*London*) **11:** 85–108.
20. Villringer, A., and Dirnagl, U. (1995). Coupling of brain activity and cerebral blood flow: basis of functional neuroimaging. *Cerebrovasc. Brain Metab. Rev.* **7:** 240–276.
21. Chédotal, A., Umbriaco, D., Descarries, L., Hartman, B. K., and Hamel, E. (1994). Light and electron microscopic immunocytochemical analysis of the neurovascular relationships of choline acetyltransferase and vasoactive intestinal polypeptide nerve terminals in the rat cerebral cortex. *J. Comp. Neurol.* **343:** 57–71.
22. Reinhard, J. F., Jr., Liebmann, J. E., Schlosberg, A. J., and Moskowitz, M. A. (1979). Serotonin neurons project to small blood vessels in the brain. *Science* **206:** 85–87.
23. Swanson, L. W., Connelly, M. A., and Hartman, B. K. (1977). Ultrastructural evidence for central monoaminergic innervation of blood vessels in the paraventricular nucleus of the hypothalamus. *Brain Res.* **136:** 166–173.
24. Owman, C., and Hardebo, J. E. (1986). *Neural Regulation of Brain Circulation.* Elsevier, Amsterdam.
25. Iadecola, C. (1992). Does nitric oxide mediate the increases in cerebral blood flow elicited by hypercapnia? *Proc. Natl. Acad. Sci. U.S.A.* **89:** 3913–3916.
26. Iadecola, C., Pelligrino, D. A., Moskowitz, M. A., and Lassen, N. A. (1994). Nitric oxide synthase inhibition and cerebrovascular regulation. *J. Cereb. Blood Flow Metab.* **14:** 175–192.
27. Zhang, J., and Snyder, S. H. (1995). Nitric oxide in the nervous system. *Annu. Rev. Pharmacol. Toxicol.* **35:** 213–233.
28. Ogawa, S., Tank, D. W., Menon, R., Ellermann, J. M., Kim, S.-G., Merkle, H., and Ugurbil, K. (1992). Intrinsic signal changes accompanying sensory stimulation: Functional brain mapping with magnetic resonance imaging. *Proc. Natl. Acad. Sci. U.S.A.* **89:** 5951–5955.
29. Frackowiak, R. S. J., Lenzi, G. L., Jones, T., and Heather, J. D. (1980). Quantitative measurement of regional cerebral blood flow and oxygen metabolism in man using ^{15}O and positron emission tomography: Theory, procedure and normal values. *J. Comput. Assist. Tomogr.* **4:** 727–736.
30. Raichle, M. E., Martin, W. R. W., Herscovitch, P., Mintun, M. A., and Markham, J. (1983). Brain blood flow measured with intravenous $H_2{}^{15}O$. II. Implementation and validation. *J. Nucl. Med.* **24:** 790–798.
31. Phelps, M. E., Huang, S. C., Hoffman, E. J., Selin, C., Sokoloff, L., and Kuhl, D. E. (1979). Tomographic measurement of local cerebral glucose metabolic rate in humans with (F-18)2-fluoro-2-deoxy-D-glucose: Validation of method. *Ann. Neurol.* **6:** 371–388.
32. Reivich, M., Kuhl, D., Wolf, A., Greenberg, J., Phelps, M., Ido, T., and Cassella, V. (1979). The ^{18}F-fluoro-deoxyglucose method for the measurement of local cerebral glucose utilization in man. *Circ. Res.* **44:** 127–137.
33. Sokoloff, L., Reivich, M., Kennedy, C., Des Rosiers, M. H., Patlak, C. S., Pettigrew, K. D., Sakurada, O., and Shinohara, M. (1977). The [^{14}C]deoxyglucose method for the measurement of local cerebral glucose utilization: Theory, procedure, and normal values in the conscious and anesthetized albino rat. *J. Neurochem.* **28:** 897–916.
34. Sokoloff, L., Kennedy, C., and Smith, C. B. (1989). The [^{14}C]deoxyglucose method for measurement of local cerebral glucose utilization. In *Neuromethods* (A. A. Boulton, G. B. Baker, and R. F. Butterworth, eds.), Vol. II, pp. 155–193. Humana Press, Clifton, NJ.
35. Lothman, E. W., Hatlelid, J. M., and Zorumskij, C. F. (1985). Functional mapping of limbic seizures originating in the hippocampus: A combined 2-deoxyglucose and electrophysiological study. *Brain Res.* **360:** 92–100.
36. Ramm, P., and Frost, B. J. (1986). Cerebral and local cerebral metabolism in the cat during slow wave and REM sleep. *Brain Res.* **365:** 112–124.
37. Schwartz, W. J., Smith, C. B., Davidsen, L., Savaki, H., Sokoloff, L., Mata, M., Fink, D. J., and Gainer, H. (1979). Metabolic mapping of functional activity in the hypothalamo-neurohypophyseal system of the rat. *Science* **205:** 723–725.
38. Roland, P. E. (1985). Cortical organization of voluntary behavior in man. *Hum. Neurobiol.* **4:** 155–167.
39. Ginsberg, M. D., Dietrich, W. D., and Busto, R. (1987). Coupled forebrain increases of local cerebral glucose utilization and blood flow during physiologic stimulation of a somatosensory pathway in the rat: Demonstration by double-label autoradiography. *Neurology* **37:** 11–19.
40. Kennedy, C., Des Rosiers, M. H., Sakurada, O., Shinohara, M., Reivich, M., Jehle, J. W., and Sokoloff, L. (1976). Metabolic mapping of the primary visual system of the monkey by means of the autoradiographic [^{14}C]deoxyglucose technique. *Proc. Natl. Acad. Sci. U.S.A.* **73:** 4230–4234.
41. Sharp, F. R., Kauer, J. S., and Shepherd, G. M. (1975). Local sites of activity-related glucose metabolism in rat olfactory bulb during olfactory stimulation. *Brain Res.* **98:** 596–600.
42. Melzer, P., Van der Loos, H., Dörfl, J., Welker, E., Robert, P., Emery, D., and Berrini, J. C. (1985). A magnetic device to stimulate selected whiskers of freely moving or restrained small rodents: Its application in a deoxyglucose study. *Brain Res.* **348:** 229–240.
43. Hatazawa, J., Ito, M., Matsuzawa, T., Ido, T., and Watanuki, S. (1988). Measurement of the ratio of cerebral oxygen consumption to glucose utilization by positron emission tomography: Its consistency with the values determined by the Kety-Schmidt method in normal volunteers. *J. Cereb. Blood Flow Metab.* **8:** 426–432.
44. Roland, P. E. (1993). *Brain Activation.* Wiley-Liss, New York.
45. Raichle, M. E. (1994). Visualizing the mind. *Sci. Am.* **270:** 36–42.
46. Phelps, M. E., Mazziotta, J. C., Kuhl, D. E., Nuwer, M., Packwood, J., Metter, J., and Engel, J. (1981). Tomographic mapping

of human cerebral metabolism: visual stimulation and deprivation. *Neurology* **31:** 517–529.
47. Fox, P. T., and Raichle, M. E. (1986). Focal physiological uncoupling of cerebral blood flow and oxidative metabolism during somatosensory stimulation in human subjects. *Proc. Natl. Acad. Sci. U.S.A.* **83:** 1140–1144.
48. Fox, P. T., Raichle, M. E., Mintun, M. A., and Dence, C. (1988). Nonoxidative glucose consumption during focal physiologic neural activity. *Science* **241:** 462–464.
49. Roland, P. E., Eriksson, L., Stone-Elander, S., and Widen, L. (1987). Does mental activity change the oxidative metabolism of the brain? *J. Neurol. Sci.* **7:** 2373–2389.
50. Prichard, J., Rothman, D., Novotny, E., Petroff, O., Kuwabara, T., Avison, M., Howseman, A., Hanstock, C., and Shulman, R. (1991). Lactate rise detected by ^{1}H NMR in human visual cortex during physiologic stimulation. *Proc. Natl. Acad. Sci. U.S.A.* **88:** 5829–5831.
51. Petroff, O. A. C., Novotny, E. J., Avison, M., Rothman, D. L., Alger, J. R., Ogino, T., Shulman, G. I., and Prichard, J. W. (1992). Cerebral lactate turnover after electroshock: In vivo measurements by ^{1}H/^{13}C magnetic resonance spectroscopy. *J. Cereb. Blood Flow Metab.* **12:** 1022–1029.
52. Fellows, L. K., Boutelle, M. G., and Fillenz, M. (1993). Physiological stimulation increases nonoxidative glucose metabolism in the brain of the freely moving rat. *J. Neurochem.* **60:** 1258–1263.
53. Schasfoort, E. M. C., DeBruin, L. A., and Korf, J. (1988). Mild stress stimulates rat hippocampal glucose utilization transiently via NMDA receptors, as assessed by lactography. *Brain Res.* **475:** 58–63.
54. Ledeen, R. W. (1992). Enzymes and receptors of myelin. In *Myelin: Biology and Chemistry* (R. E. Martenson, ed.), pp. 531–570. CRC Press, Boca Raton, FL.
55. Halliwell, B. (1992). Reactive oxygen species and the central nervous system. *J. Neurochem.* **59:** 1609–1623.
56. Pou, S., Pou, W. S., Bredt, D. S., Snyder, S. H., and Rosen, G. M. (1992). Generation of superoxide by purified brain nitric oxide synthase. *J. Biol. Chem.* **267:** 24173–24176.
57. Boveris, A., and Chance, B. (1973). The mitochondrial generation of hydrogen peroxide. *Biochem. J.* **134:** 707–716.
58. Chan, P. H., and Fishman, R. A. (1980). Transient formation of superoxide radicals in polyunsaturated fatty acid-induced brain swelling. *J. Neurochem.* **35:** 1004–1007.
59. Cross, A. R., and Jones, O. T. S. (1991). Enzymatic mechanisms of superoxide production. *Biochim. Biophys. Acta* **1057:** 281–298.
60. Coyle, J., and Puttfarcken, P. (1993). Oxidative stress, glutamate, and neurodegenerative disorders. *Science* **262:** 689–695.
61. Greenlund, L. J. S., Deckwreth, T. L., and Johnson, E. M., Jr. (1995). Superoxide dismutase delays neuronal apoptosis: A role for reactive oxygen species in programmed neuronal death. *Neuron* **14:** 303–315.
62. Lafon-Cazal, M., Pietri, S., Culcasi, M., and Bockaert, J. (1993). NMDA-dependent superoxide production and neurotoxicity. *Nature (London)* **364:** 535–537.
63. Beal, M. F. (1995). Mitochondria and oxidative stress. In *Mitochondrial Dysfunction and Oxidative Damage in Neurodegenerative Diseases* (M. F. Beal, ed.), pp. 7–18. Springer-Verlag, New York.
64. Ben-Yoseph, O., Boxer, P. A., and Ross, B. D. (1994). Oxidative stress in the central nervous system: Monitoring the metabolic response using the pentose phosphate pathway. *Dev. Neurosci.* **16:** 328–336.
65. Blass, J. P., and Gibson, G. E. (1977). Deleterious aberrations of a thiamine-requiring enzyme in four patients with Wernicke-Korsakoff syndrome. *N. Engl. J. Med.* **297:** 1367–1370.
66. Astrup, J., Moller Sorensen, P., and Rahbeck Sorensen, H. (1981). Inhibition of cerebral oxygen and glucose consumption in the dog by hypothermia, pentobarbital, and lidocaine. *Anesthesiology* **55:** 263–268.
67. Erecinska, M., and Dagani, F. (1990). Relationships between the neuronal sodium/potassium pump and energy metabolism—effects of K^+, Na^+, and adenosine triphosphate in isolated brain synaptosomes. *J. Gen. Physiol.* **95:** 591–616.
68. Mata, M., Fink, D. J., Gainer, H., Smith, C. B., Davidsen, L., Savaki, H., Schwartz, W. J., and Sokoloff, L. (1980). Activity-dependent energy metabolism in rat posterior pituitary primarily reflects sodium pump activity. *J. Neurochem.* **34:** 213–215.
69. Sokoloff, L. (1991). Relationship between functional activity and energy metabolism in the nervous system: Whether, where and why? In *Brain Work and Mental Activity* (N. A. Lassen, D. H. Ingvar, M. E. Raichle, and L. Friberg, eds.), pp. 52–64. Munksgaard, Copenhagen.
70. Bachelard, H. S. (1975). Energy utilized by neurotransmitters. In *Brain Work* (D. H. Ingvar and N. A. Lassen, eds.), pp. 79–81. Munksgaard, Copenhagen.
71. Tucek, S., and Cheng, S. H. (1974). Provenance of the acetyl group of acetylcholine and compartmentation of acetyl-CoA and Krebs cycle intermediates in the brain in vivo. *J. Neurochem.* **22:** 893–914.
72. Ochs, S., and Ranish, N. (1970). Metabolic dependence of fast axoplasmic transport in nerve. *Science* **167:** 878–879.
73. Kimelberg, H. K., and Norenberg, M. D. (1989). Astrocytes. *Sci. Am.* **260:** 44–52.
74. O'Kusky, J., and Colonnier, M. (1982). A laminar analysis of the number of neurons, glia and synapses in the visual cortex (area 17) of the adult macaque monkey. *J. Comp. Neurol.* **210:** 278–290.
75. Tower, D. B., and Young, O. M. (1973). The activities of butyrylcholinesterase and carbonic anhydrase, the rate of anaerobic glycolysis, and the question of a constant density of glial cells in cerebral cortices of various mammalian species from mouse to whale. *J. Neurochem.* **20:** 269–278.
76. Peters, A., Palay, S. L., and Webster, de F. H. (1991). *The Fine Structure of the Nervous System: Neurons and Their Supporting Cells.* Saunders, Philadelphia.
77. Sala, L. (1891). Zur feineren Anatomie des grossen Seepferdefusses. *Z. Wiss. Zool.* **52:** 18–45.
78. Andriezen, W. L. (1893). On a system of fibre-like cells surrounding the blood vessels of the brain of man and mammals, and its physiological significance. *Int. Monatsschr. Anat. Physiol.* **10:** 532–540.
79. Barres, B. A. (1991). New roles for glia. *J. Neurosci.* **11:** 3685–3694.
80. Gould, G. W., and Holman, G. D. (1993). The glucose transporter family: Structure, function and tissue-specific expression. *Neurosci. Lett.* **97:** 209–214.
81. Maher, F., Vannucci, S. J., and Simpson, I. A. (1994). Glucose transporter proteins in brain. *FASEB J.* **8:** 1003–1011.
82. Birnbaum, M. J., Haspel, H. C., and Rosen, O. M. (1986). Cloning and characterization of a cDNA encoding the rat brain glucose transporter protein. *Proc. Natl. Acad. Sci. U.S.A.* **83:** 5784–5788.
83. Kasaniki, M. A., Cairns, M. T., Davies, A., Gardiner, R. M., and Baldwin, S. A. (1987). Identification and characterization of the glucose transport protein of the bovine blood-brain barrier. *Biochem. J.* **247:** 101–108.
84. Morgello, S., Uson, R. R., Schwartz, E. J., and Haber, R. S. (1995). The human blood-brain barrier glucose transporter (GLUT1) is a glucose transporter of gray matter astrocytes. *Glia* **14:** 43–54.
85. Bondy, C. A., Lee, W.-H., and Zhou, J. (1992). Ontogeny and cellular distribution of brain glucose transporter gene expression. *Mol. Cell. Neurosci.* **3:** 305–314.

86. Leloup, C., Arluison, M., Lepetit, N., Cartier, N., Marfaing-Jallat, P., Ferré, P., and Pénicaud, L. (1994). Glucose transporter (GLUT2): Expression in specific brain nuclei. *Brain Res.* **638:** 221–226.

87. Silver, I. A., and Erecinska, M. (1994). Extracellular glucose concentration in mammalian brain: Continuous monitoring of changes during increased neuronal activity and upon limitation in oxygen supply in normo-, hypo-, and hyperglycemic animals. *J. Neurol. Sci.* **14:** 5068–5076.

88. Fellows, L. K., Boutelle, M. G., and Fillenz, M. (1992). Extracellular brain glucose levels reflect local neuronal activity: A microdialysis study in awake, freely moving rats. *J. Neurochem.* **59:** 2141–2147.

89. Magistretti, P. J., and Pellerin, L. (1996). Cellular bases of brain energy metabolism and their relevance to functional brain imaging: Evidence for a prominent role of astrocytes. *Cereb. Cortex* **6:** 50–61.

90. Fonnum, F. (1984). Glutamate: A neurotransmitter in mammalian brain. *J. Neurochem.* **42:** 1–11.

91. Pellerin, L., and Magistretti, P. J. (1994). Glutamate uptake into astrocytes stimulates aerobic glycolysis: A mechanism coupling neuronal activity to glucose utilization. *Proc. Natl. Acad. Sci. U.S.A.* **91:** 10625–10629.

92. Takahashi, S., Driscoll, B. F., Law, M. J., and Sokoloff, L. (1995). Role of sodium and potassium ions in regulation of glucose metabolism in cultured astroglia. *Proc. Natl. Acad. Sci. U.S.A.* **92:** 4616–4620.

93. Kimelberg, H. K., Jalonen, T., and Walz, W. (1993). Regulation of brain microenvironment: Transmitters and ions. In *Astrocytes: Pharmacology and Function* (S. Murphy, ed.), pp. 193–228. Academic Press, San Diego, CA.

94. Kanai, Y., Smith, C. P., and Hediger, M. A. (1994). A new family of neurotransmitter transporters: The high-affinity glutamate transporters. *FASEB J.* **8:** 1450–1459.

95. Kanner, B. I. (1993). Glutamate transporters from brain: A novel neurotransmitter transporter family. *FEBS Lett.* **325:** *95–99.*

96. Rothstein, J. D., Martin, L., Levey, A. I., Dykes-Hoberg, M., Jin, L., Wu, D., Nash, N., and Kunci, R. W. (1994). Localization of neuronal and glial glutamate transporters. *Neuron* **13:** 713–725.

97. Chaudhry, F. A., Lehre, K. P., van Lookeren Campagne, M., Ottersen, O. P., Danbolt, N. C., and Storm-Mathisen, J. (1995). Glutamate transporters in glial plasma membranes: Highly differentiated localizations revealed by quantitative ultrastructural immunocytochemistry. *Neuron* **15:** 711–720.

98. Rothstein, J. D., Van Kammen, M., Levey, A. I., Martin, L. J., and Kunci, R. W. (1995). Selective loss of glial glutamate transporter GLT-1 in amyotrophic lateral sclerosis. *Ann. Neurol.* **38:** 73–84.

99. Kimelberg, H. K., Biddlecome, S., Narumi, S., and Bourke, R. S. (1978). ATPase and carbonic anhydrase activities of bulk-isolated neuron, glia and synaptosome fractions from rat brain. *Brain Res.* **141:** 305–323.

100. Erecinska, M. (1989). Stimulation of the Na^+/K^+ pump activity during electrogenic uptake of acidic amino acid transmitters by rat brain synaptosomes. *J. Neurochem.* **52:** 135–139.

101. Bowman, C. L., and Kimelberg, H. K. (1984). Excitatory amino acids directly depolarize rat brain astrocytes in primary culture. *Nature (London)* **311:** 656–659.

102. Yarowsky, P. J., Boyne, A. F., Wierville, R., and Brookes, N. (1986). Effect on monensin on deoxyglucose uptake in cultured astrocytes: Energy metabolism is coupled to sodium entry. *J. Neurosci.* **6:** 859–866.

103. Brookes, N., and Yarowsky, P. J. (1985). Determinants of deoxyglucose in cultured astrocytes: The role of sodium pump. *J. Neurochem.* **44:** 473–479.

104. Proverbio, F., and Hoffman, J. F. (1977). Membrane compartmentalized ATP and its preferential use by the Na^+-K^+ ATPase of human red cell ghosts. *J. Gen. Physiol.* **69:** 605–632.

105. Raffin, C. H., Rosenthal, M., Busto, R., and Sick, T. J. (1992). Glycolysis, oxidative metabolism and brain potassium ion clearance. *J. Cereb. Blood Flow Metab.* **12:** 34–42.

106. Lipton, P., and Robacker, K. (1983). Glycolysis and brain function: $[K+]o$ stimulation of protein synthesis and K^+ uptake require glycolysis. *Fed. Proc. Fed. Am. Soc. Exp. Biol.* **42:** 2875–2880.

107. Paul, R. J., Hardin, D. C., Raeymaekers, L., Wuytack, F., and Casteels, R. (1979). Vascular smooth muscle: Aerobic glycolysis linked to sodium and potassium transport processes. *Science* **206:** 1414–1416.

108. Tsacopoulos, M., Evêquoz-Mercier, V., Perrottet, P., and Buchner, E. (1988). Honeybee retinal glial cells transform glucose and supply the neurons with metabolic substrates. *Proc. Natl. Acad. Sci. U.S.A.* **85:** 8727–8731.

109. Tsacopoulos, M., and Poitry, S. (1982). Kinetics of oxygen consumption after a single flash of light in photoreceptors of the drone (*Apis mellifera*). *J. Gen. Physiol.* **80:** 19–55.

110. Walz, W., and Muckerji, S. (1988). Lactate release from cultured astrocytes and neurons: A comparison. *Glia* **1:** 366–370.

111. Westergaard, N., Sonnewald, U., and Schousboe, A. (1995). Metabolic trafficking between neurons and astrocytes: The glutamate/glutamine cycle revisited. *Dev. Neurosci.* **17:** 203–211.

112. Dringen, R., Wiesinger, H., and Hamprecht, B. (1993). Uptake of L-lactate by cultured rat brain neurons. *Neurosci. Lett.* **163:** 5–7.

113. Tsacopoulos, M., and Magistretti, P. J. (1996). Metabolic coupling between glia and neurons. *J. Neurosci.* **16:** 877–885.

114. Tsacopoulos, M., Veuthey, A.-L., Saravelos, S. G., Perrottet, P., and Tsoupras, G. (1994). Glial cells transform glucose to alanine, which fuels the neurons in the honeybee retina. *J. Neurosci.* **14:** 1339–1351.

115. Poitry-Yamate, C. L., and Tsacopoulos, M. (1992). Glucose metabolism in freshly isolated Müller glial cells from a mammalian retina. *J. Comp. Neurol.* **320:** 257–266.

116. Poitry-Yamate, C. L., Poitry, S., and Tsacopoulos, M. (1995). Lactate released by Müller glial cells is metabolized by photoreceptors from mammalian retina. *J. Neurosci.* **15:** 5179–5191.

117. Lajtha, A. L., Maker, H., and Clarke, D. D. (1981). Metabolism and transport of carbohydrates and amino acids. In *Basic Neurochemistry* (G. J. Siegel, R. W. Albers, R. W. Agranoff, and R. Katzman, eds.), pp. 329–353. Little, Brown, Boston.

118. Sotelo, C., and Palay, S. L. (1968). The fine structure of the lateral vestibular nucleus in the rat. I. Neurons and neuroglial cells. *J. Cell Biol.* **36:** 151–179.

119. Vaughn, J. E., and Grieshaber, J. A. (1972). An electron microscopic investigation of glycogen and mitochondria in developing and adult rat spinal motor neuropil. *J. Neurocytol.* **1:** 397–412.

120. Watanabe, H., and Passonneau, J. V. (1973). Factors affecting the turnover of cerebral glycogen and limit dextrin in vivo. *J. Neurochem.* **20:** 1543–1554.

121. Magistretti, P. J., Sorg, O., and Martin, J. L. (1993). Regulation of glycogen metabolism in astrocytes: Physiological, pharmacological, and pathological aspects. In *Astrocytes: Pharmacology and Function* (S. Murphy, ed.), pp. 243–265. Academic Press, San Diego, CA.

122. Phelps, C. H. (1972). Barbiturate-induced glycogen accumula-

tion in brain. An electron microscopic study. *Brain Res.* **39:** 225–234.

123. Swanson, R. A., Yu, A. C. H., Sharp, F. R., and Chan, P. H. (1989). Regulation of glycogen content in primary astrocyte culture: Effect of glucose analogues, phenobarbital, and methionine sulfoxime. *J. Neurochem.* **52:** 1359–1365.
124. Watanabe, H., and Passonneau, J. V. (1974). The effect of trauma on cerebral glycogen and related metabolites and enzymes. *Brain Res.* **66:** 147–159.
125. Shimizu, N., and Hamuro, Y. (1958). Deposition of glycogen and changes in some enzymes in brain wounds. *Nature (London)* **181:** 781–782.
126. Magistretti, P. J., Morrison, J. H., Shoemaker, W. J., Sapin, V., and Bloom, F. E. (1981). Vasoactive intestinal polypeptide induces glycogenolysis in mouse cortical slices: A possible regulatory mechanism for the local control of energy metabolism. *Proc. Natl. Acad. Sci. U.S.A.* **78:** 6535–6539.
127. Magistretti, P. J., Hof, P. R., and Martin, J. L. (1986). Adenosine stimulates glycogenolysis in mouse cerebral cortex: A possible coupling mechanism between neuronal activity and energy metabolism. *J. Neurosci.* **6:** 2558–2562.
128. Sorg, O., and Magistretti, P. J. (1991). Characterization of the glycogenolysis elicited by vasoactive intestinal peptide, noradrenaline and adenosine in primary cultures of mouse cerebral cortical astrocytes. *Brain Res.* **563:** 227–233.
129. Dringen, R., Gebhardt, R., and Hamprecht, B. (1993). Glycogen in astrocytes: Possible function as lactate supply for neighboring cells. *Brain Res.* **623:** 208–214.
130. Swanson, R. A., Morton, M. M., Sagar, S. M., and Sharp, F. R. (1992). Sensory stimulation induces local cerebral glycogenolysis: Demonstration by autoradiography. *Neuroscience* **51:** 451–461.
131. Attwell, D., Sarantis, M., Szatkowski, M., Barbour, B., and Brew, H. (1991). Patch-clamp studies of electrogenic glutamate uptake: Ionic dependence, modulation and failure in anoxia. In *Excitatory Amino Acids and Synaptic Transmission* (H. Wheal and A. Thomson, eds.), pp. 223–237. Academic Press, San Diego, CA.
132. Yudkoff, M., Nissim, I., Hummeler, K., Medow, M., and Pleasure, D. (1986). Utilization of [^{15}N]glutamate by cultured astrocytes. *Biochem. J.* **234:** 185–192.
133. Sonnewald, U., Westergaard, N., Petersen, S. B., Unsgard, G., and Schousboe, A. (1993). Metabolism of [U-^{13}C]glutamate in astrocytes studied by ^{13}C NMR spectroscopy: Incorporation of more label into lactate than into glutamine demonstrates the importance of the TCA cycle. *J. Neurochem.* **61:** 1179–1182.
134. Farinelli, S. E., and Nicklas, W. J. (1992). Glutamate metabolism in rat cortical astrocyte cultures. *J. Neurochem.* **58:** 1905–1915.
135. Van den Berg, C. J., and Garfinkel, D. (1971). A simulation study of brain compartments. Metabolism of glutamate and related substances in mouse brain. *Biochem. J.* **123:** 211–218.
136. Noremberg, M. D., and Martinez-Hernandez, A. (1979). Fine structural localization of glutamine synthetase in astrocytes of rat brain. *Brain Res.* **161:** 303–310.
137. Yudkoff, M., Zaleska, M. M., Nissim, I., Nelson, D., and Erecinska, M. (1989). Neuronal glutamine utilization: pathways of nitrogen transfer studied with [^{15}N]glutamine. *J. Neurochem.* **53:** 632–640.
138. Erecinska, M., and Silver, I. A. (1990). Metabolism and role of glutamate in mammalian brain. *Prog. Neurobiol.* **35:** 245–296.
139. Yudkoff, M., Nissim, I., Nelson, D., Lin, Z.-P., and Erecinska, M. (1991). The glutamate dehydrogenase reaction as a source of glutamic acid in synaptosomes. *J. Neurochem.* **57:** 153–160.
140. Yudkoff, M., Daikhin, Y., Lin, Z.-P., Nissim, I., Stern, J., and Pleasure, D. (1994). Inter-relationships of leucine and glutamate metabolism in cultured astrocytes. *J. Neurochem.* **62:** 1953–1964.
141. Cangiano, C., Cardelli-Cangiano, P., James, J., Rossi Fanelli, F., Patrizi, M. A., Brackett, K. A., Strom, R., and Fischer, J. E. (1983). Brain microvessels take up large neutral amino acids in exchange for glutamine. *J. Biol. Chem.* **258:** 8949–8954.
142. Shank, R. P., Bennet, G. S., Freytag, S. O., and Campbell, G. L. (1985). Pyruvate carboxylase: An astrocyte-specific enzyme implicated in the replenishment of amino acid neurotransmitter pools. *Brain Res.* **329:** 364–367.
143. Blass, J. P., and Gibson, G. E. (1991). The role of oxidative abnormalities in the pathophysiology of Alzheimer's disease. *Rev. Neurol.* **147:** 513–525.
144. Sheu, K. F., Cooper, A. J., Koike, M., Lindsay, J. G., and Blass, J. P. (1994). Abnormality of the alpha-ketoglutarate dehydrogenase complex in fibroblasts from familial Alzheimer's disease. *Ann. Neurol.* **35:** 312–318.
145. Plum, F., and Hindfeld, B. (1976). Handbook of clinical neurology. In *Handbook of Clinical Neurology* (P. J. Vinken and G. W. Bruyn, eds.), Vol. 27, pp. 349–377. North-Holland, Amsterdam.
146. Noremberg, M. D., Neary, J. T., Bender, A. S., and Dombro, R. S. (1992). Hepatic encephalopathy: A disorder in glial-neuronal communication. *Prog. Brain Res.* **94:** 261–269.
147. McKhann, G. M., and Tower, D. B. (1961). Ammonia toxicity and cerebral oxidative metabolism. *Am. J. Physiol.* **200:** 420–424.
148. Muntz, J. A., and Hurwitz, J. (1951). The effect of ammonia ions upon isolated reactions of the glycolytic scheme. *Arch. Biochem. Biophys.* **32:** 137–149.
149. Kadekaro, M., Crane, A. M., and Sokoloff, L. (1985). Differential effects of electrical stimulation of sciatic nerve on metabolic activity in spinal cord and dorsal root ganglion in the rat. *Proc. Natl. Acad. Sci. U.S.A.* **82:** 6010–6013.
150. Zielke, R. H., Tildon, T. J., Baab, P. J., and Hopkins, I. B. (1989). Synthesis of glutamate and glutamine in dibutyryl cyclic AMP-treated astrocytes. *Neurosci. Lett.* **97:** 209–214.

SECTION III

NERVOUS SYSTEM DEVELOPMENT

CHAPTER

15

Neural Induction and Pattern Formation

Christopher Kintner and Andrew Lumsden

In this chapter, we discuss the early stages in the development of the vertebrate nervous system, focusing on three key events that occur when the anlage of the nervous system first emerges in early embryonic development. The first of these events is **neural induction,** a process that specifies a region of embryonic ectoderm that will form the **neural plate** on the dorsal surface of the embryo. The second event involves **neurulation,** a morphogenetic process during which the neural plate forms the neural tube, thus giving the nervous system its final position and shape within the dorsal axis of the embryo. Finally, the most complex event occurring during the early formation of the nervous system is **neural patterning.** Neural patterning involves a series of inductive interactions by which the neural tube is divided into distinct regions that form the different areas of the vertebrate nervous system. Neural patterning begins with the establishment of polarity along the anteroposterior and dorsoventral axes and progresses to finer levels of patterning within the neural tube, such as segmentation.

EMBRYONIC ORIGINS OF THE NERVOUS SYSTEM

The vertebrate nervous system is derived from a portion of the embryo called the **ectoderm.** The ectoderm, the endoderm, and the mesoderm represent the three major regions, or germ layers, of the blastula-stage embryo that form during early cleavage stages, as shown in Fig. 15.1. During gastrulation, the embryo is converted into a three-layer structure as the endodermal and mesodermal tissues invaginate inward and the ectoderm covers the surface. When gastrulation is complete, the different germ layers begin to form the anlagen for the different organs that constitute the vertebrate body plan.

The anlage of the nervous system is first apparent when a portion of the ectoderm on the dorsal side of the embryo thickens to form the neural plate, which subsequently forms a neural tube and gives rise to the CNS. The ectoderm outside the neural plate is fated to differentiate into skin. Tissues such as the olfactory and auditory sensory epithelia, as well as some peripheral ganglia, are derived from placodal structures that form adjacent to the neural plate. Finally, the edges of the neural plate become the neural folds, which give rise to the neural crest, the progenitor cells for the PNS. Thus, during this early phase, the ectoderm is divided into different regions, each fated to form neural, epidermal, or placodal tissues.

Neural Tissue Is Induced by the Organizer

The division of the ectoderm into different fates requires inductive interactions between the ectoderm and other regions of the embryo. **Neural induction** was discovered in the 1930s by Hilde Mangold and Hans Spemann, during experiments with amphibian embryos in which they grafted pieces of tissue from one blastula-stage embryo to another.[1] At the blastula stage, the amphibian embryo is divided into the three germ layers along its animal/vegetal axis: the ectoderm occupies the animal pole, the mesoderm is in the middle, and the endoderm occupies the vegetal pole (Fig. 15.1). In addition, at the blastula stage, the prospective dorsal side of the embryo is conveniently marked by a site, called the **blastopore lip,** where the endoderm and mesoderm first invaginate at the start of gastrulation. When Mangold and Spemann transplanted a small piece of tissue including the dorsal

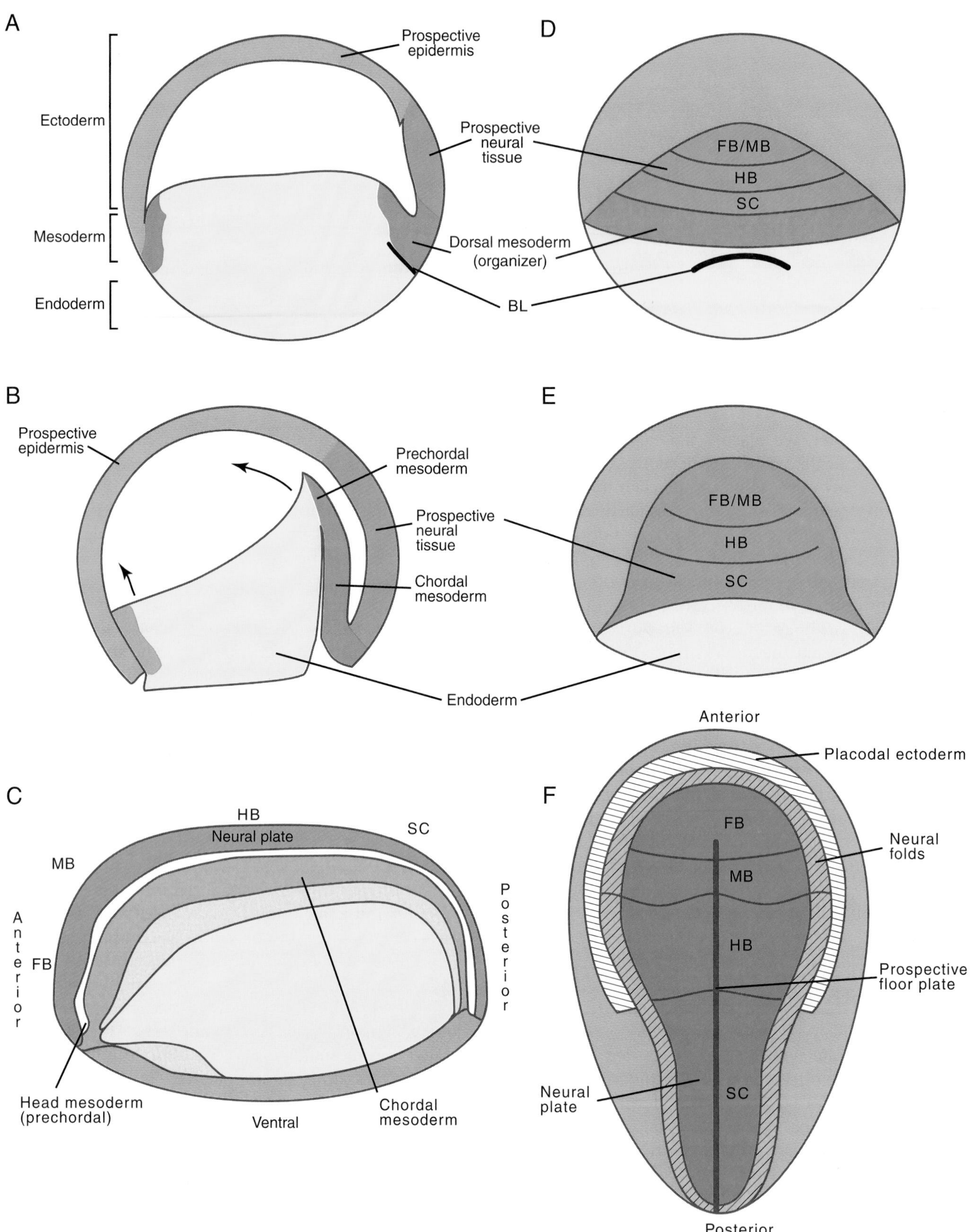
A
Ectoderm
Mesoderm
Endoderm
Prospective epidermis
Prospective neural tissue
Dorsal mesoderm (organizer)
BL
D
FB/MB
HB
SC
B
Prospective epidermis
Prechordal mesoderm
Prospective neural tissue
Chordal mesoderm
Endoderm
E
FB/MB
HB
SC
C
HB
Neural plate
SC
MB
Anterior
FB
Posterior
Head mesoderm (prechordal)
Ventral
Chordal mesoderm
Anterior
Placodal ectoderm
F
FB
MB
HB
SC
Neural folds
Prospective floor plate
Neural plate
Posterior

blastopore lip (DBL) from one blastula-stage embryo to the ventral side of another, the host embryo responded to the grafted tissue by forming a complete secondary dorsal axis (Fig. 15.2). Importantly, the only tissues in the second dorsal axis that were formed from the transplanted DBL tissue were those that would be normally derived from dorsal mesoderm, such as the notochord. The other tissues in the secondary dorsal axis were not derived from the transplant but from the host embryo. In particular, the secondary dorsal axis contained neural tissue that was derived from the ventral ectoderm of the host embryo, a region that would have differentiated into skin in the absence of a graft. This experiment provided the first evidence that dorsal ectoderm is specified to form neural rather than epidermal tissue in response to inductive signals from the organizer. Following Mangold and Spemann's lead, other researchers found that transplanting tissue that forms at the anterior end of the primitive streak in chick or mammalian embryos, called **Hensen's node,** also duplicates the dorsal axis and induces a secondary nervous system.[2] Thus, all vertebrate embryos appear to contain a region, called **Spemann's organizer,** that initiates the formation of neural tissue by inducing dorsal ectoderm to form a neurogenic epithelium rather than undergoing epidermal differentiation.

The organizer transplantation experiment also gave the first indication that signals from tissue in the DBL or Hensen's node were responsible for inducing different regions of the vertebrate nervous system.[3,4] In organizer transplantation experiments in which the timing of the graft was varied, organizer grafts from younger embryos induced head structures that contained neural tissue from the rostral portions of the neuraxis; conversely, those from older embryos induced tail structures that contained neural tissue from only the caudal portions of the neuraxis. These observations indicated that the organizer consists of two parts—a head organizer and a tail organizer—each of which appears to be a source of signals that not only induce ectoderm to form neural rather than epidermal tissue but also determine what region of neural tissue will form. The role of the organizer tissue in regionalization of the nervous system is discussed further below.

FIGURE 15.1 Early neural development in a vertebrate embryo. (A, B, and C) Side views of the rearrangement of tissues during gastrulation in a typical amphibian embryo. (A) Diagram of a blastula stage, in which the embryo consists of a ball of cells with a cavity in the top called the blastocoel. At this stage the embryo can be divided into three parts along the animal (top) to vegetal (bottom) axis. Ectoderm (red) is an epithelial sheet covering the blastocoel. Mesoderm (blue) occupies the middle regions, and endoderm (yellow) lies at the bottom. The embryo also has dorsal and ventral sides, with the former marked by the first site of invagination at the start of gastrulation, the blastopore lip (BL). The area above the BL is fated to give rise to dorsal mesoderm and is the site of Spemann's organizer. The ectoderm closest to the BL is fated to give rise to neural tissue, and that further away on the ventral side will give rise to epidermis. (B) An embryo in midgastrulation, showing the involution of the dorsal mesoderm (organizer tissue) underneath the region of ectoderm that will form neural tissue. The prechordal, or head, mesoderm involutes first and comes to lie underneath the prospective forebrain (FB), while the posterior or chordal mesoderm that forms the notochord comes to lie underneath more caudal regions of the prospective neural tissue that will form midbrain (MB), hindbrain (HB), and spinal cord (SC). (C) An embryo that has completed gastrulation, in which the three germ layers have arrived at their final positions. Head mesoderm lies underneath the anterior neural plate, while chordal mesoderm underlies the posterior neural plate. (D, E, and F) The same stages as shown in A, B, and C, respectively, but viewed from the dorsal side of the embryo. (D) The prospective dorsal side of the blastula-stage embryo including the fate map of the ectoderm that forms neural tissue. Note how the area of ectoderm that will form neural tissue lies adjacent to the organizer region and wraps around the embryo prior to the movements of gastrulation and neurulation that narrow the region of ectoderm that forms neural tissue. By midgastrulation (E), the dorsal mesoderm (organizer tissue) has invaginated inside, underneath the prospective neural region. Both the dorsal ectoderm and the underlying dorsal mesoderm undergo the convergent-extension movements that greatly narrow this region of the embryo and extend it along the anterior–posterior axis. (F) Dorsal view of the embryo after gastrulation has completed. Note that the prospective neural region of the ectoderm has converged and extended even more while giving rise to the keyhole-shaped neural plate. Neural crest will arise from the edges of the neural plate that form structures called the neural folds. Placodal tissues will arise from ectoderm that lies around the edges of the anterior neural plate.

The Search for the Elusive Neural Inducer Has a Long History

The transplantation experiments of Mangold and Spemann described earlier suggested that ectoderm is induced to form neural tissue by a factor produced by the organizer. In subsequent years, the identification of the neural inducer has been the focus of several generations of scientists, thus representing one of the holy grails in developmental neurobiology. This search has also had important historical significance, because many of the techniques now used to study cytokines in neurobiology have their origins in the early attempts to identify neural inducers. For example, in the late 1920s, Holtfreter described methods for culturing amphibian embryos in which the ectoderm is removed from blastula-stage embryos and maintained *in vitro* in a medium composed of simple salt solutions.[5] One important application of these early tissue culture techniques was in assays for neural inducers; isolated ectoderm grown in culture differentiates into epidermal tissue but forms neural tissue when exposed to neural-inducing signals, such as a piece of organizer tissue.

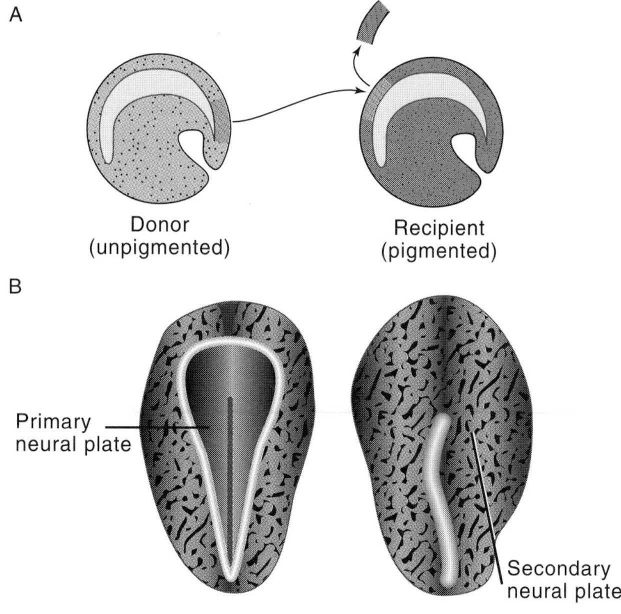

FIGURE 15.2 Organizer transplant experiment. (A) The method used by Mangold and Spemann in the organizer transplant experiment. A region of the embryo just above the blastopore lip was excised from a donor embryo and transplanted to the ventral side of a host. In the original experiment, the donor tissue was unpigmented and the host pigmented. (B) As a result of the graft, the host embryo develops with a secondary dorsal axis that is first made evident by a second neural plate. Note that the secondary axis has the same orientation as the primary axis. (C) A section through a host embryo with two dorsal axes, showing that the secondary dorsal axis contains all the same tissues as the primary dorsal axis, including a nervous system. Importantly, however, the only tissue in the secondary dorsal axis derived from the transplanted tissue is mesodermal in origin: primarily the notochord, and a portion of the somitic mesoderm. Thus, the other tissues in the secondary axis, including the nervous system, are derived from the host embryo. This result strongly suggested that the transplanted organizer tissue had induced the adjacent ectoderm on the ventral side of the host embryo to form neural tissue, implying that a similar induction occurs between the organizer and the ectoderm on the dorsal side of a normal embryo.

With this assay available, the search for neural inducers became an active area of research in the 1940s and 1950s. Unfortunately, the search for a true neural inducer proved to be more problematic than expected. Early attempts to purify inducers biochemically were frustrated because ectoderm could be neuralized when exposed to a wide variety of differentiated tissues, tissue extracts, and various purified molecules. These inducers were eventually termed **artificial inducers** or **activators** because many of them were clearly not physiological and there was no obvious way to determine which molecule was normally responsible for neural induction. Perhaps the most important concept to emerge from these early experiments, however, was that neural inducers are probably not instructional but permissive in their action.[6] In other words, ectoderm appears to be preprogrammed to form neural tissue and needs very little impetus to do so. The ease with which ectoderm could be neuralized by so many different molecules cast a long shadow over the field of neural induction and greatly slowed the search for molecules produced by organizer tissue that normally act to neuralize the ectoderm during neural induction.

Several important findings in the 1990s revitalized the field of neural induction. First, the choice of experimental animal is an important factor.[7] Ectoderm from *Xenopus laevis*, the frog now used in most laboratories, is much less susceptible to the effects of artificial inducers than the species of amphibian used previously. Another factor that has contributed to recent progress is the introduction of techniques used to identify genes that are expressed only by organizer tissue. A bona fide neural inducer not only should induce neural tissue in ectoderm culture experiments but also should be expressed by the organizer. Whether a potential neural inducer meets this criterion can now be tested using *in situ* hybridization techniques. A third factor that underlies recent progress is the ability to generate synthetic messenger RNAs from cloned genes *in vitro* and then introduce these RNAs into *Xenopus* embryos to test the biological effects of their encoded products. This technique has been modified for use in so-called expression cloning, in which the ability of random cloned genes to induce neural tissue can be tested.

BOX 15.1

TRANSGENIC MICE AND ENGINEERED MUTATIONS

Rapid and complementary advances in the fields of molecular biology and experimental embryology have combined to offer neuroscience researchers unprecedented power to manipulate the mammalian genome. The technologies used for these manipulations have been worked out primarily in the laboratory mouse and fall into two basic classes: those used for transgenic mice and embryonic stem cell chimeric mice.

Transgenic mice are created by the injection of a cloned DNA fragment into the male pronucleus of a recently fertilized mouse embryo. The fragment will integrate into the host genome and be passed through subsequent mitoses to all of the cells of the adult, including the gametes. The integrated DNA fragment, now known as a "transgene," is usually engineered to contain a promoter and associated regulatory sequences, a structural gene, and a 3′ polyadenylation signal. Transgenes add to the genome. As a genetic element, the chromosomal site of integration is random, and there is no wild-type allele on the sister chromosome. As an expressed locus, the transgene message is made over and above the endogenous gene expression pattern. This technique can be used as both an analytical and an experimental tool. Used as an analytical tool, the potency of a certain genetic element to direct cell- or tissue-specific gene expression can be determined by using the element to regulate marker genes such as β-galactosidase or green fluorescent protein. The genetic elements that regulate the temporal and spatial expression pattern of the *Hox* genes in hindbrain, tyrosine hydroxylase in adrenergic neurons, and L7 in Purkinje cells have all been explored by this means. Used as an experimental tool, transgenes can exploit a genetic element with known specificity to deliver a gene product to an ectopic cell site or developmental time. Thus, the PDGF promoter has been used to drive the expression of human β-amyloid precursor protein, the L7 promoter has been used to deliver diphtheria toxin to differentiating Purkinje cells, and the β-actin promoter has been used to deliver *Hox-A1* to inappropriate sites in the developing embryo.

Embryonic stem cells (ES cells) are stable cell lines derived from the inner cell mass of the preimplantation embryo. They are totipotent, which means that if they are introduced into a host embryo, they can contribute to all cell types in the resulting chimera (including the gametes). The use of homologous recombination in ES cells allows changes to be engineered in specific genetic loci in culture. By using the modified cells to create chimeras, changes can be introduced into the mouse germline and propagated as new mutations. The mutations can be insertions, deletions, modifications, or any combination of the three. When the engineered insertion/deletion disables the normal allele, the resulting mutation is often referred to by the slang term "knockout." These techniques alter the genome. As a genetic element, the engineered locus replaces a specific gene locus, and there is a normal wild-type allele on the sister chromosome. Used in this way, a knockout mutation can be used to model an inherited disease. Lesch–Nyhan (HPRT-null), ataxia–telangectasia (ATM-null), and fragile-X mental retardation syndrome (FMR1-null) have all been modeled in this way. As an expressed locus, the knockout transcript is made instead of the wild-type gene product. This technique can thus be used to create a modified locus such that the targeted gene is mutated rather than destroyed. In the same way an endogenous transcript of one gene can be replaced with that of a different one. Thus, sequences encoding *Engrailed-2* have been inserted into the *Engrailed-1* locus in such a way that the *Engrailed-1* transcript is lost (a null mutation) and *Engrailed-2* is made in its place.

These are only some of the ways in which the powerful new technologies of transgenic and knockout mice are providing genetic tools of unprecedented power for use in neuroscience research.

Karl Herrup

Armed with these techniques, investigators have identified several factors, some of which are expressed in organizer tissue, that can induce ectoderm from *Xenopus* embryos to form neural tissue. Whether these factors are responsible for neural induction or whether they simply mimic the effects of the true neural inducers is still not known. Nevertheless, the properties of these factors have provided an entirely new picture of neural induction and may also explain the early phenomenology observed with artificial inducers.

The TGF-β–like Polypeptide Growth Factors Play a Role in Many Tissue Interactions

Embryological studies by Nieuwkoop in the 1960s showed that the organizer, which induces neural tissue and which gives rise to mesodermal tissues, is itself induced by an inductive tissue interaction occurring in very early embryos.[8] Indeed, Nieuwkoop showed that isolated ectoderm exposed to the appropriate inducing signals not only could be induced to be neural but also could be induced to form organizer tissue and give rise to mesoderm. As with neural induction, early attempts to identify the mesodermal inducers using biochemical approaches were unsuccessful. In the 1980s, however, a number of investigators found that ectoderm could be induced to form mesoderm with **polypeptide growth factors** (PGFs), some of which belong to a large family of molecules whose structures are related to transforming growth factor-β (TGF-β).[9] The TGF-β–like PGFs include such molecules as activin and inhibin, which were originally identified as hormonal regulators of the reproductive system, and the bone morphogenetic proteins (BMPs), which were identified as inducers of chrondrogenesis. The TGF-β–like PGFs have diverse biological activities that are mediated through a large family of related receptors. These receptors are heterodimeric, containing type I and type II subunits, both of which contain cytoplasmic domains with serine/threonine kinase activity. Dimerization of two receptor subunits after binding of a TGF-β–like PGF is thought to result in auto-crossphosphorylation and the activation of downstream intracellular signaling cascades.

The TGF-β–like PGFs and their receptors have been firmly established as potential mediators of the many tissue interactions that control cell fate during embryonic development. Demonstration of the role of the TGF-β–like PGFs in neural induction began with observations that activin is a potent inducer of mesodermal tissue in isolated ectoderm from *Xenopus* embryos.[10] To determine whether mesodermal tissues are normally induced by activin, Melton and his colleagues used truncated receptors to block signaling through the activin receptor in embryos.[11] The rationale behind this approach was that a truncated receptor lacking the intracellular kinase not only would be nonfunctional but also would act as a "poisonous" receptor subunit when it formed a complex with other receptor subunits. By forming nonfunctional complexes, the truncated receptors would act as a dominant-negative mutant and therefore block activin signaling. Indeed, when the truncated type II activin receptor is expressed in *Xenopus* embryos, mesodermal induction is blocked, and the embryo develops without any axial structures. The key finding however, came when the truncated, type II activin receptor was expressed in isolated ectoderm. The ectoderm expressing the truncated receptor formed neural tissue instead of differentiating into epidermis, thus behaving as if it had been treated with a neural inducer.[12] This experiment suggested for the first time that neural inducers might block the activity of molecules, such as activin, that cause the ectoderm to form epidermal tissue. In this new view, ectoderm is epidermalized by an endogenously produced factor, suggesting that ectoderm needs an active mechanism to become epidermal rather than neural. Thus, any treatment that disrupted this active mechanism would reveal the ability of ectoderm to become neural, perhaps explaining why neural tissue is so readily induced by artificial inducers, many of which appear to be cytotoxic.

Although the experiments with the truncated activin receptor changed the prevailing view of neural inducers, they were misleading in terms of the specific role of activin in the process of neural induction. It is now known that the inhibitory effects produced by the truncated type II activin receptor in these experiments were not confined to activin signaling. Most if not all of TGF-β–like PGF receptors are inhibited when they form nonspecific dimers with the truncated type II activin receptor. Thus, if ectoderm requires a TGF-β–like PGF to become epidermis, as suggested by the effects of the truncated receptor, which PGF is it? The likely answer to this question came from experiments using dissociated ectodermal cells. As a tissue, isolated ectoderm forms epidermis in culture. When the ectoderm is dissociated into single cells, however, the dissociated cells become neural, presumably because the concentration of any endogenously produced epidermalizing factor becomes too dilute under these conditions.[13] Dissociated ectodermal cells can be induced to become epidermal—and thus not neural—by treatment with two other TGF-β–like PGFs, called BMP-2 and BMP-4. The potential role of these molecules as epidermal inducers is supported by the fact that during gastrulation, BMP-2 and BMP-4 are first expressed within the ectoderm that gives rise to epidermis. In addition, expression of dominant-negative mutants that block the function of these molecules also neuralizes the ectoderm.[14] Thus, these observations suggest that the ectoderm produces BMPs, which causes it to become epidermal, and that neural inducers block the effects of BMPs to induce neural tissue.

The truncated receptor experiments and those with BMPs suggested that neural inducers produced by the organizer act by inhibiting the signaling by these TGF-β–like PGFs. However, these neural inducers are not likely to be truncated receptors, but molecules that are secreted by the organizer and act extracellularly to inhibit BMP signaling. Several molecules may function in this way. One candidate is a small protein called follistatin, which was originally identified as an inhibitor of activin.[15] A second candidate is *noggin*, which was isolated using expression cloning.[16] A third candidate is *chordin*, a gene expressed by organizer tissue (Fig. 15.3).[17] When any of these three molecules are expressed in isolated ectoderm, they block the formation of epidermis and induce the formation of neural tissue. All three molecules are also expressed by organizer tissue. Finally, all three molecules appear to bind to the BMPs and competitively inhibit ligand–receptor interactions. Whether any or all of these three inhibitors are essential for neural induction *in vivo* is not known. One critical test will come from gene knockout studies in mice, in which the gene encoding each of these potential neural inducers is disrupted by homologous recombination in embryonic stem cells (Box 15.1). For example, mice whose *follistatin* gene has been disrupted by gene targeting are born with normal nervous systems, suggesting that follistatin is not essential for neural induction. Similar analyses of mutant mice for *noggin* and *chordin* are in progress. It may be, however, that the loss of any single inducer has no effect because of functional redundancy and that neural induction is blocked only when all three genes are absent.

We should emphasize that noggin, chordin, and follistatin induce neural tissue that lacks many of the regional characteristics found in neural tissue induced by organizer tissues. The neural tissue induced by these inducers can be characterized as forebrainlike based on the expression of regional gene markers such as those discussed further below. In fact, the structure of the neural tissue that forms in response to these inducers is primitive; most of the regional characteristics associated with a mature nervous system do not appear. The type of forebrainlike neural tissue obtained with these neural inducers appears to be identical to that obtained in early experiments with artificial inducers referred to as activators.[8] Thus, the inhibition of BMP signaling may be a mechanism that allows ectoderm to undergo neural rather than epidermal differentiation, while other molecules produced by the organizer are required for inducing different areas of the nervous system via different mechanisms.

A

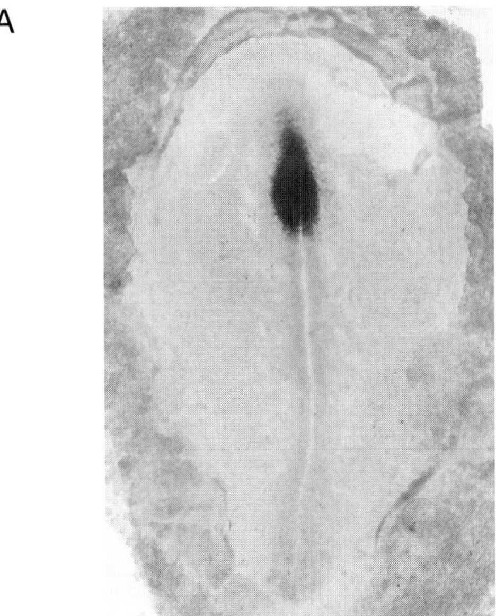

B

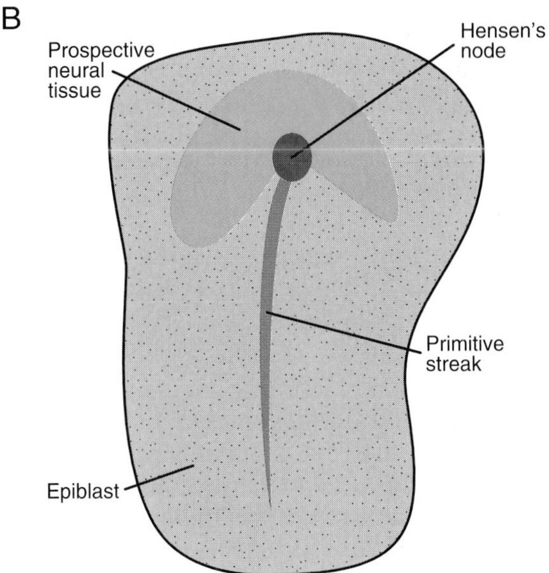

FIGURE 15.3 (A) Whole mount *in situ* hybridization showing the expression of chick *chordin* RNA. *Chordin* encodes a small secreted protein that acts as a neural inducer when expressed in frog ectoderm.[17] The expression of RNA encoding the chick homolog of *chordin* was determined by whole mount *in situ* hybridization on a stage 4 chick embryo. At this stage, Hensen's node (the organizer) has formed at the anterior end of the primitive streak, and the portion of the epiblast around the node is fated to form neural tissue as shown in panel B. The region of the epiblast that forms neural tissue has not yet undergone convergent extension and thus can be considered to be equivalent in developmental stage to dorsal ectoderm in amphibian embryo at midgastrulation as shown in Fig. 15.1E. Both Hensen's node and the anterior end of the primitive streak express high amounts of *chordin* RNA as revealed by the purple reaction product, suggesting that *chordin* is produced by these tissues and could be involved in neural induction. Photo compliments of Dr. Anne Bang.

Summary

In vertebrate embryos, the nervous system first arises from a region of ectoderm that is induced to form a neuroepithelium rather than differentiating into epidermis. Classical transplantation studies have shown that ectoderm forms neural tissue in response to signals from the organizer. More recent studies have shown that ectoderm undergoes epidermal differentiation in response to endogenously produced, BMP-like molecules and that neural inducers act by inhibiting the activity of these epidermalizing signals. Current candidates for neural inducers include the molecules follistatin, noggin, and chordin; however, whether these molecules contribute to neural induction is still not known.

EARLY NEURAL MORPHOGENESIS

Changes in tissue morphology occur relatively early during formation of the vertebrate nervous system. At the cellular level, the ectoderm loses the morphology associated with a simple embryonic epithelium and take on the morphology of the pseudostratified **neuroepithelium** of the neural plate and tube. During this process, the apical/basal polarity of the epithelium is maintained. At a tissue level, the neuroepithelium of the neural plate undergoes complex morphogenetic movements to form the neural tube, pinches off from the surrounding ectoderm, and segregates into the embryo as a separate tissue anlage. On a smaller scale, but with similar morphogenetic movements, the anlagen for the sense organs delaminate from the ectoderm around the neural plate, following inductive interactions between particular regions of the invaginating neuroepithelium and adjacent, overlying nonneural ectoderm. These placodal structures include the otocyst, which forms the ear; the lens of the eye; the olfactory placodes, which form the nose; and neurons that contribute to the cranial ganglia. Thus, the morphological processes that underlie the formation of the neural tube and placodal tissues have a number of features in common, but how these processes are mediated at the molecular and cellular levels remains poorly understood.

Neurulation Plays a Fundamental Role in the Establishment of Neural Tissue

In higher vertebrates, neurulation can be divided into two phases that differ in their morphological movements: a primary phase, which forms the brain and spinal cord; and a secondary phase, which occurs in more caudal regions of the spinal cord. During primary neurulation (Fig. 15.4), the neural plate buckles at the midline, and the edges of the neural plate elevate and fuse at the dorsal midline to form the tube. Primary neurulation is probably driven by complex tissue mechanics that result from coordinated changes in cell shape and cell movements within subregions of the neuroepithelium, as well as changes in cell behavior outside the neural plate.[18] Within the neural plate, neuroepithelial cells along the dorsal midline of the neural plate become wedge-shaped, forming a furrow that acts as a hinge around which the plate bends. This median hinge point, which becomes the floor plate of the neural tube, probably contributes to the buckling of the neural plate but is apparently not necessary for neurulation to take place. The shape of the neural plate changes dramatically as the cells within it undergo an active rearrangement process, called **convergent extension.**[19] The extensive cell intercalation during convergent extension greatly narrows the neural plate along its medial–lateral axis and extends the plate along the rostral–caudal axis of the embryo. The movements of convergent extension, coupled with the bending of the neural plate at flexure points and cell intercalation in the surrounding ectoderm, cause the neural folds to fuse at the dorsal midline, thus creating the tube that separates from the nonneural ectoderm.

The morphogenetic movements that occur during neurulation also appear to be important in setting up the different regions of the neuraxis. For instance, the neural tube is wider at its rostral end, where the brain forms, than at the caudal end, which forms the spinal cord. This difference in shape arises, in part, because the movements of convergent extension, which narrow the neural plate, are much more pronounced in posterior parts of the neural plate, presumably as a result of early patterning events along the rostral–caudal axis. In addition, the neuroepithelium in some regions of the tube undergoes significant changes in shape and cell movement to establish a region that will form a particular portion of the nervous system. One of the more impressive examples of these more specialized regionalized movements occurs as a prerequisite to the formation of the eye (Fig. 15.5). Eye formation is first evident morphologically during neurulation, when the neuroepithelium at the level of the prospective diencephalon evaginates outward to form the bilaterally paired eye vesicles. At the point where the neural tube and eye vesicle join, the neuroepithelium eventually pinches together to form the optic stalk. At the same time, the eye vesicle forms a cup and divides further into an inner layer, which gives rise to the retina, and an outer layer, which will form the pigmented epithelium. Thus, the formation of the eye initially requires a specialized series of morphogenetic processes that shape the neuroepithelium into a structure appropriate for the differentiation of the neuroepithelium into different parts of the eye.

Morphogenesis Requires Differential Cell Adhesion

Differential cell adhesion is a property of embryonic tissues that contributes to morphogenetic processes during early neural development. The role of differential cell adhesion was first demonstrated by

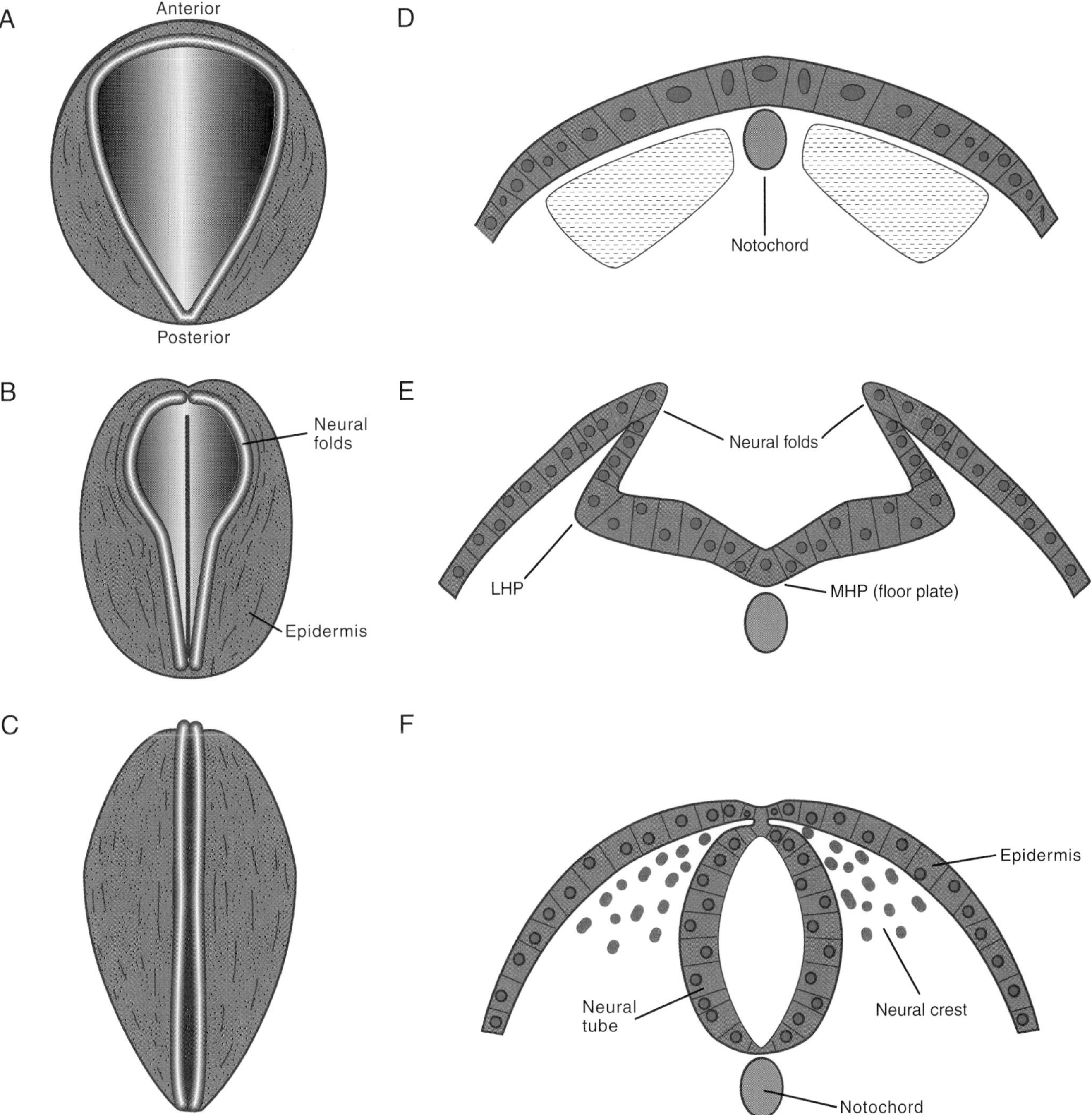

FIGURE 15.4 Neurulation. (A, B, C) Dorsal view of a frog embryo showing the morphological changes that occur during primary neurulation, starting when the neural plate first forms after gastrulation is complete (A) and proceeding through neural tube closure in B and C. (D, E, F) Cross-sectional views of the ectoderm from embryos at the corresponding stages in A, B, and C. When the neural plate first forms (D), the cells columnarize by lengthening along their apical/basal axis, and narrowing circumferentially. This change in cell shape contributes somewhat to the narrowing of the neural plate along its medial–lateral axis. However, more of the narrowing is due to cell rearrangements in which cells intercalate along the mediate–lateral axis, thus both narrowing the neural plate and extending it along the A/P axis as shown in A and B. As the plate begins to roll into a tube (E), several changes in cell behavior can be detected in subdomains of the neural plate. The cells at the midline, which forms the floor plate at later stages, shorten and constrict apically, thus producing a hinge point around which the neural plate can buckle (medial hinge point, MHP). Similar wedging of cells also occurs in the lateral walls of the neural plate as the neural folds elevate toward each other (lateral hinge point, LHP). As the tube forms and segregates into the embryo (F), neural crest cells emigrate from the dorsal aspect of the neural tube.

A

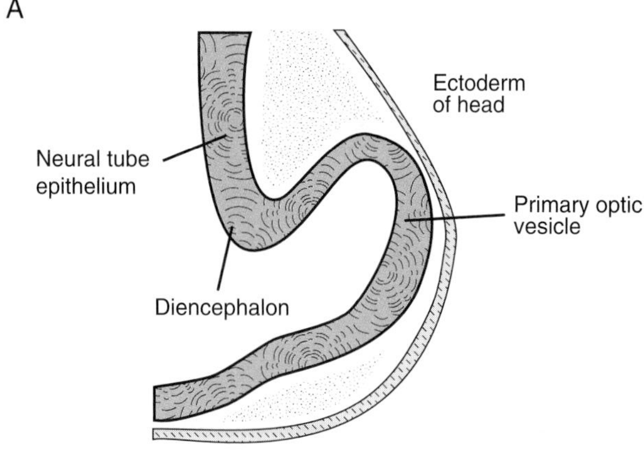

B

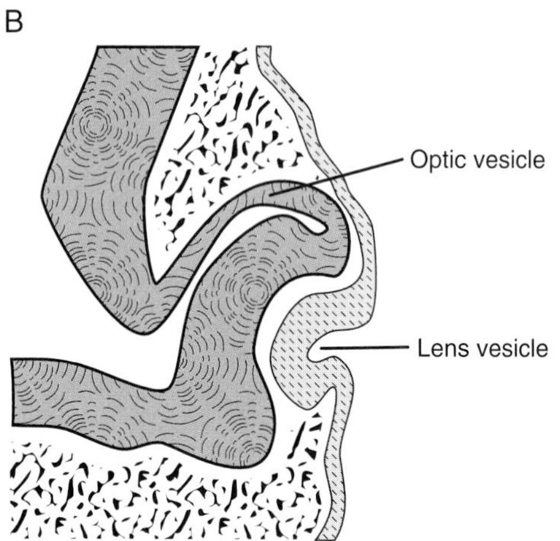

C

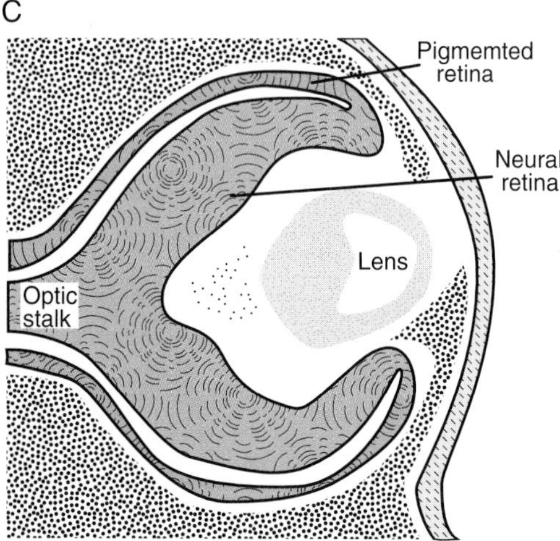

FIGURE 15.5 Formation of the eye rudiment. Different steps of early eye formation are diagrammed, with only one side of the embryo shown. (A) The formation of the eye begins with a bilateral evagination of the neural tube epithelium at the level of the diencephalon to form the primary optic vesicles. (B) The eye cup contacts the adjacent surface ectoderm and induces the formation of the lens, which segregrates as a placodal structure. (C) The optic vesicle forms a cup, with the inner surface fated to form the neural retina, while the outer surface will form the pigmented epithelium. The region between the cup and the neural tube will form the optic stalk.

cell aggregation assays in which the epidermis and neural tube were isolated from early amphibian embryos and dissociated into single cells, and the two populations of cells were mixed in explant culture.[20] Over time in culture, the two cell populations sorted out and self-organized into the appropriate tissue structures. That is, the epidermal cells covered the outside of the explant and re-formed an epidermis with the correct apical–basal polarity, while the neural cells reformed a neural tube with the correct polarity inside the explant. This experiment revealed that epidermal cells and neural tube cells bear molecules on their surfaces through which they recognize and differentially adhere to each other. Presumably, the differential expression of these adhesion molecules in presumptive neural or epidermal cells during neural induction could contribute to the segregation of ectoderm into neural and epidermal tissues.

Differential cell adhesion also appears to play an important role during the first steps in the formation of the neural crest. Neural crest cells arise early on from the neuroepithelium of the neural folds during neurulation, and later on from the dorsal aspects of the neural tube (see Chapter 16). To leave the neuroepithelium, neural crest cells must lose their epithelial characteristics and take on the properties of a migratory mesenchymal cell. The epithelial–mesenchymal transition is thought to require major restructuring of cell–cell contacts and, in particular, downregulation in the expression of molecules that serve an adhesive function in epithelial cells.

The Cadherins Are a Family of Cell Adhesion Molecules

Cadherins, a family of cell surface glycoproteins, appear to play a role in differential cell adhesion. The extracellular domain of a typical cadherin contains a homotypic binding site that mediates the interaction of adjacent cells expressing the same cadherin type. The cadherin intracellular domain binds to cytoplasmic components, thereby linking the cadherins to the actin-based cytoskeletal network. By binding on both sides of the membrane, the cadherins could be the transmembrane linkage in the adherens junction, an important means of contact between epithelial cells. Through the formation of adherens junctions and by interacting with the force-generating, actin-based cytoskeletal network, the cadherins are perfectly placed to regulate cell contacts in neural tissue undergoing such morphogenetic processes as cell delamination, boundary formation, cell rearrangements, and motility over cell surfaces.[21]

Different members of the cadherin family are expressed in different epithelial tissues. A classic example is the differential expression of N-cadherin and E-cadherin when the ectoderm forms epidermal and neural tissue. Thus, E-cadherin is expressed on the portion of ectoderm that forms epidermis but not the neural tube, whereas N-cadherin shows the opposite pattern of expression. Cells expressing E- or N-cadherin will sort into separate populations in *in vitro* aggregation assays.[22] Moreover, disrupting the expression of either cadherin produces neural tube defects.[23] Thus, the cadherins may be the molecular bases of the differential adhesion of embryonic cells that was originally observed in cell aggregation assays.

Emigration of neural crest cells from the neural tube may also depend on modulation of cell adhesion by downregulation of cadherin expression. N-cadherin is expressed on cells of the neural tube but is absent at the dorsal aspect of the neural tube, where the neural crest arises. Migrating neural crest cells do not express N-cadherin; they express other members of the cadherin family and then upregulate the expression of N-cadherin when they stop migrating and differentiate. Thus, during their generation, migration, and differentiation, neural crest cells alter between a stationary epithelial state and a migratory mesenchymal state. The transition between these states may depend on the expression of different cadherins, as well as other molecules involved in cell–cell and cell–matrix interactions.

Summary

The formation of the vertebrate nervous system begins with a series of striking changes in tissue morphology as the ectoderm forms the neural plate and tube. Neural tube formation involves the complex morphogenetic process of neurulation, which requires changes in cell shape and division together with coordinated changes in cell migration and rearrangement. Changes in cell adhesion, through the expression of such molecules as the cadherins, are important both in the segregation of the ectoderm into neural and nonneural tissues and in the formation of the neural crest by promoting an epithelial-to-mesenchymal transition.

NEURAL PATTERNING

The neural plate is a morphologically and cytologically homogeneous sheet of epithelial cells that emerges from competent ectoderm as a consequence of inductive signaling. As the neural plate rolls up and closes into a tube, a series of constrictions appear in its wall, subdividing the rostral end of the neuraxis into a series of expanded vesicles representing the anlagen of fore-, mid-, and hindbrain (Fig. 15.6). Further subdivision immediately ensues, generating a series of segmentlike swellings or **neuromeres** in the brain region. Caudal to the hindbrain, the tube forms a long and uniformly narrow cylinder that is the precursor of the spinal cord. These early morphological features of the neural tube dictate the overall plan of the CNS and predict its later regional specializations. The neuroepithelium then commences to produce a huge diversity of region-specific cell types, each having a distinctive identity in terms of morphology, axonal trajectory, synaptic specificity, and neurotransmitter content and sensitivities. Perhaps most striking, individual neurons or groups of similar neurons appear at predictable times and at precise positions within the various regions of the neural tube. Correct specification of this intricate spatial ordering (pattern) of cells is crucial to later events in CNS development, when the different cell types establish complex arrays of interconnections that constitute functional networks. How the different regions of the CNS, and the individual

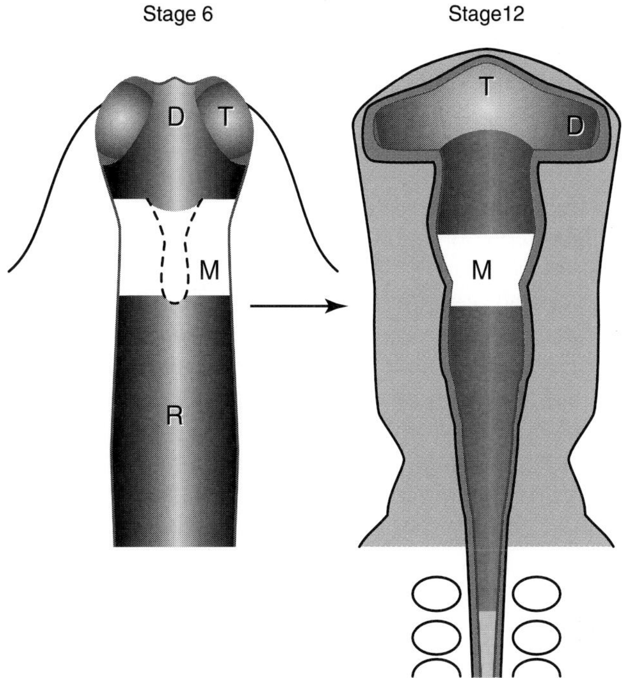

FIGURE 15.6 Early, coarse-grained restrictions to regional identity along the A/P axis at the neural plate stage (chick embryo at stage 6) predict the morphological subdivisions of the closed neural tube at stage 12. T, telencephalon; D, diencephalon; M, mesencephalon; R, rhombencephalon.

cell types they each contain, are assigned their identity in early development remains an outstanding problem in neurobiology.

The overwhelming complexity of the CNS would seem to present a daunting prospect for the analysis of pattern-forming mechanisms, but the questions are the same whatever the system: How do cells sense their position, how is their positional value encoded, and how is this information then interpreted into cell-type-specific differentiation? Until recently, studies of the earliest developmental stages were hampered severely by the inability to detect a nascent pattern. The discovery of a multitude of molecular markers that reveal subregions of the neuroepithelium, or cell types that are formed only in specific regions, has made it possible to visualize emergent heterogeneity in what was previously seen only as a "white sheet" of cells.

The Nervous System Is Organized along Two Principal Axes and a Minor Axis

From its inception at neural induction, the nervous system is organized along two principal axes: the anteroposterior (rostrocaudal) axis **(neuraxis),** which corresponds with the main body axis, and the mediolateral axis. Closure of the neural plate into a tube deflects the latter from mediolateral to dorsoventral. The third axis, which lies between the ventricular and pial surfaces (inside-outside),[24] contributes less to the early pattern and is described in Chapter 16. The radial organization of the tube is largely uniform throughout the tube (with the principal exception of the cerebral and cerebellar cortices), and though specific clusters of neurons form nuclei at different radial positions in most brain regions, this pattern emerges only later in development. In contrast, both the anteroposterior and dorsoventral axes are distinctly nonuniform. Different neuronal types appear at different positions in these two dimensions as if reading their specific grid references on a map. Indeed, the concept of a simple Cartesian coordinate system of positional information is a useful framework in which to describe and investigate neural pattern: according to this scheme,[25] uncommitted neuroepithelial precursor cells measure their position with respect to both anteroposterior and dorsoventral axes and then differentiate accordingly.

Formation of the Early Neuraxis Involves Establishment of Polarity

The initial establishment of polarity along the neuraxis appears to be intimately coupled to the establishment of main body axis during early embryonic development. Although axis determination in the vertebrate embryo remains poorly understood, it may have conceptual similarities to the strategies used for axis determination in the *Drosophila* embryo, for which genetic studies have produced a detailed understanding. In *Drosophila,* anteroposterior (A/P) polarity is first established by a gradient of positional information produced by the maternal morphogen bicoid emanating from the anterior pole of the egg. The gradient of the bicoid transcription factor initiates a cascade of transcription factor activation, which progressively subdivides the body axis further into smaller segmental units. As these repeat units are established, the genes of the *Antennapedia/Bithorax* homeotic complex (*HOM-C*) act in a well-ordered manner to define unique segment identities. Similarly, the formation of the body axis in vertebrates is likely to begin with the imposition of a crude polarity along the A/P axis, which is then refined at later stages into smaller and smaller units of tissue organization. As described earlier, the initial establishment of A/P polarity in the vertebrate system is likely to occur during neural induction via the interactions between the organizer (the dorsal blastopore lip of amphibian embryos or Hensen's node in amniote embryos) and the ectoderm. The details of how the organizer tissues establish the initial A/P polarity of the nervous system are still unknown, but several models are under investigation.

During gastrulation, the organizer tissues come to underlie the neural plate and form different tissues along the A/P axis of the embryo (Fig. 15.7A). The tissue in the tail organizer comes to lie underneath the caudal portion of the neural plate, where it differentiates into a thin rodlike structure called the **notochord.** The region of dorsal mesoderm containing the notochord is referred to as **chordal mesoderm,** and it underlies the portion of the neural plate that will eventually form the midbrain, hindbrain, and spinal cord. The tissue in the head organizer comes to lie rostral to the notochord during gastrulation, where it differentiates into **prechordal mesoderm** and underlies the rostral portion of the neural plate that gives rise to the forebrain. Thus, apposition of chordal mesoderm with posterior neural plate and prechordal mesoderm with anterior neural plate could allow **vertical** (or radial) interactions that establish the initial A/P polarity along the neuraxis. The einsteck experiments of Otto Mangold,[26] in which strips of different mesoderm along the A/P axis were inserted into the blastocoel (Fig. 15.7C), provided the principal support for this mode of neural patterning and led to the view that qualitatively different neural inducers are present in different regions of the dorsal mesoderm.

While Mangold's experiments indicated that vertical interactions between the underlying mesoderm and dorsal ectoderm could impose A/P patterning, Spemann argued that the same A/P polarity could be imposed via a **planar interaction** between the organizer tissue and the adjacent dorsal ectoderm (Fig. 15.7B).[1] The main difference between planar and vertical signaling is one of timing. Planar signaling is more likely to be effective at early gastrula stages when the prospective neural plate still abuts the organizer tissue on the blastula fate map. At this early stage, inducing signals from both the tail and the head organizer regions need only to transmit over a short distance within the plane of the ectoderm to induce neural tissue and impose A/P patterning. In contrast, by late gastrula stages, the shortest distance between the organizer tissue and the dorsal ectoderm is by a vertical interaction.

In the 1930s, Holtfreter addressed the mechanism of signaling during neural induction by analyzing amphibian embryos that were forced to exogastrulate, so that dorsal mesoderm did not come to lie beneath the dorsal ectoderm as it would normally do during gastrulation (Fig. 15.7).[27] Holtfreter found that exogastrulae lacked neural tissue, and he concluded that planar signaling did not occur. More recently, this issue has been reexamined using regional neural markers (e.g., En-2, *Krox-20,* and *Hoxb-9*) in both exogastrulae[28] and a particular type of explant, called the Keller sandwich,[19] in which organizer tissue is prevented from invaginating beneath the dorsal ectoderm. In both exogastrulae and Keller sandwiches, neural markers are expressed at appropriate axial positions in the ectoderm, provided that neural tissue remains in contact at its posterior margin with the organizer region.[29] Whether the signaling is planar or vertical, the induction and initial A/P polarity of the neural plate probably first occurs at extremely early stages of gastrulation. These early interactions are probably not sufficient for complete A/P patterning because when only planar signaling occurs, the pattern of anterior neural tissue is deficient. Forebrain and eye induction may therefore require vertical signals from the earliest involuting mesoderm that forms the prechordal plate.

Two types of signals are thought to impose A/P polarity on neural plate ectoderm. As described earlier, isolated ectoderm could be induced to form neural tissue by treatment with a class of artificial inducers called activators.[30] Both the activators and neural inducers such as chordin, noggin, and follistatin induce neural tissue that appears to be forebrainlike in character, based on the fact that it expresses gene markers that are normally found only in the anterior neural plate.[15-17] These three proteins antagonize the actions of members of the TGF-β family of signaling molecules—suggesting that the induction of anterior neural plate differentiation involves the inhibition of TGF-β–like signals that repress neural development. The type of neural tissue induced by activators was proposed to be the ground state, which could be induced to be more posterior by treatment with a second signal. Since these second agents were incapable of neuralizing the ectoderm on their own, they were referred to as **transforming signals.** The ratio of activating and transforming signals impinging on different regions of the neural plate was thought to account for the different regions along the A/P axis.[30] The activation–transformation model remains the most viable hypothesis for the generation of A/P polarity along the neuraxis. A number of molecules, including basic fibroblast growth factor (bFGF), members of the Wnt family of signaling molecules, and retinoic acid, can posteriorize neural tissue that has been induced by activators, even though these agents have little neuralizing capability on their own.[31-33] At present, however, the number and types of activating and transforming signals required for generating the full spectrum of neural tissue along the A/P axis are not known.

Summary

The neural plate is subdivided very early along the A/P axis into a prechordal plate, which will give rise to the forebrain, and the epichordal plate, which will give rise to the midbrain, hindbrain, and spinal cord. This initial subdivision is likely to arise during neural induction via signals of posterior origin that pass in planar fashion into the ectoderm or vertically from the underlying mesoderm. The combined action of neural inducers confers a crude A/P polarity on the neural plate, which becomes refined during subsequent stages. Neural inducers that act to neuralize the ectoderm appear to induce prechordal neural plate, while additional transforming signals are required for the induction of the chordal neural plate. The mechanism by which early polarity along the A/P axis of the neural plate is established, however, is for the most part unknown.

REGIONALIZATION OF THE NERVOUS SYSTEM

Following the establishment of polarity along the A/P axis in the form of the prechordal and chordal regions of the neural plate, subsequent patterning events then subdivide the neural plate and tube along the A/P axis into smaller organizational units. Subdivision of the main body axis by segmentation (metamerism) is a developmental theme found in many animal phyla. **Segmentation** involves the allocation of defined

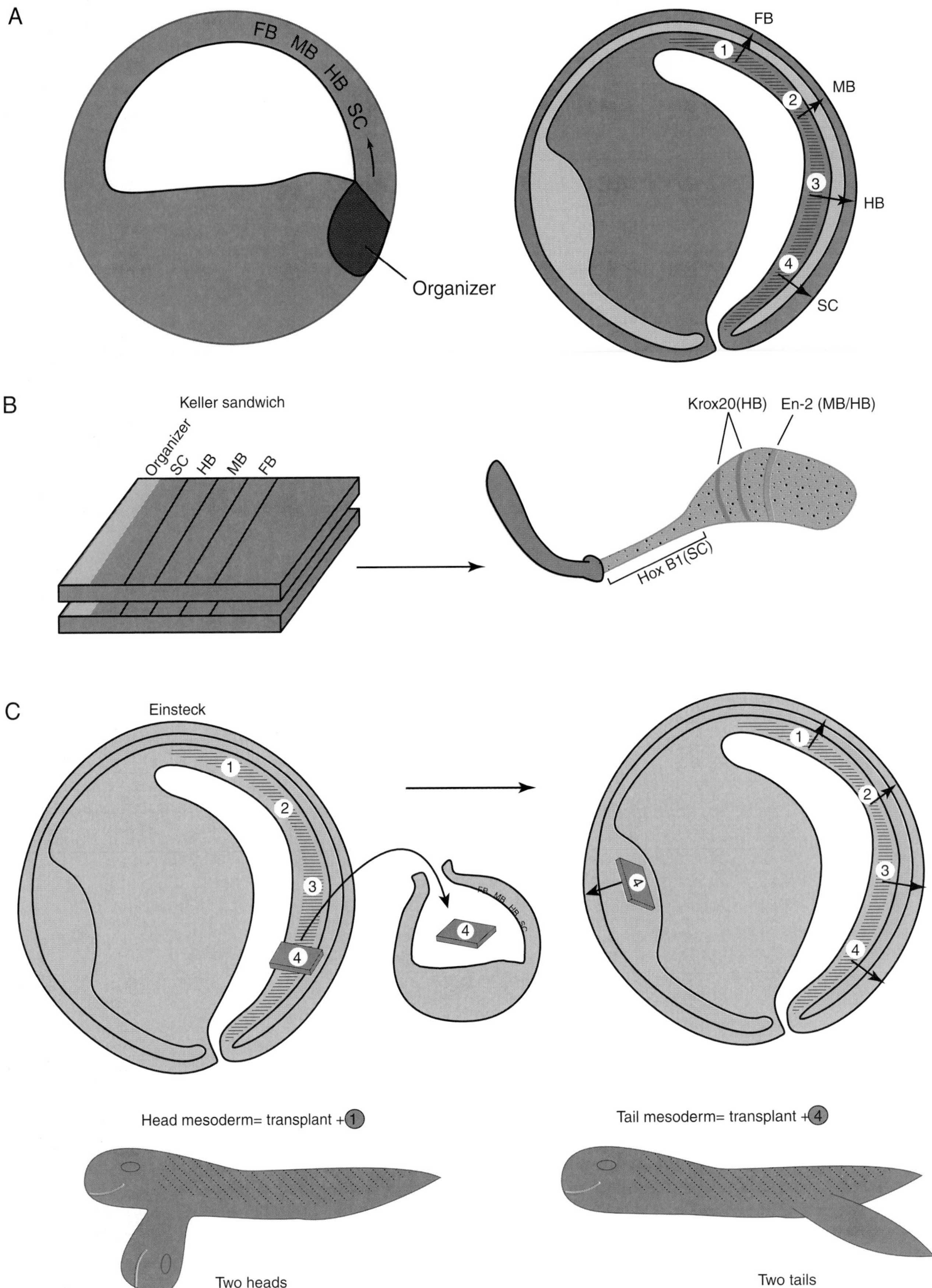
A
FB
MB
HB
SC
Organizer
FB
MB
HB
SC
1
2
3
4
B
Keller sandwich
Organizer
SC
HB
MB
FB
Krox20(HB)
En-2 (MB/HB)
Hox B1(SC)
C
Einsteck
1
2
3
4
FB
MB
HB
SC
Head mesoderm= transplant + 1
Tail mesoderm= transplant + 4
Two heads
Two tails

sets of precursor cells into an axially repeated set of similar modules, such that developmental fields remain small and specializations of cell type and pattern can be generated as local variations on the repetitive theme. In a segmented system, precise boundaries can be set for both cellular assemblies and realms of gene action.[34] It has long been recognized that the mesoderm of the vertebrate embryo is segmented—into two rows of somites, whose skeletal and muscular derivatives retain an obviously segmented arrangement in the adult—but only recently has segmentation been shown to also play a part in CNS development.

The Neuraxis Is Segmented

Certain regions of the cranial neural tube, the hindbrain and diencephalon, are patently subdivided into a series of segmentlike structures, **neuromeres,** first described by Ernst von Baer in 1828. Despite their long pedigree, the significance of neuromeres has remained elusive, mainly because evidence of a repeat pattern of embryonic cytoarchitecture has been lacking but also because no clear trace of segmental beginnings remains in the adult brain. Recent studies, however, have conclusively shown that the **rhombomeres,** a series of eight subdivisions that partition the hindbrain neuroepithelium, are true metameric units that play a crucial role in patterning this brain region.[35,36] Thus, the earliest neurons are laid out in stripes that match the morphological repeat pattern, with neuronal differentiation and axonogenesis starting with the confines of alternate, even-numbered rhombomeres, and only appearing later in the odd-numbered rhomobomeres—a "two-segment repeat" pattern that involves all of the early forming neuronal systems.[37] The branchial motor nerves emerge from the hindbrain through focal exit points in the lateral wall of even-numbered rhombomeres and grow toward the branchiomeric muscles of the jaws and pharynx: these nerves extend from neurons contained precisely within two adjacent rhombomeres (Fig. 15.8A). The rhombomere-specific pattern of efferent neurons is superimposed on a reiterated pattern of reticular cells. Most rhombomeres are similar to each other in that they each initially contain the same set of eight reticular cell types (Fig. 15.8B), as defined by axonal pathway choice.[38] Later in development, these segmental origins become obscured as specific reticular cell types become more abundant in some rhombomeres and reduced in number in others. In addition, the motor nuclei and other rhomobomerically derived cell groups condense and migrate bodily to new positions (Fig. 15.8C). Segmentation is a developmental mechanism for specifying the pattern of developing structures, not necessarily for deploying those structures in the adult.

The neuronal cytoarchitecture of the early hindbrain suggests that rhombomeres are true segments or **developmental compartments.** Lineage tracing studies in the chick revealed that before rhombomeres form, clonal descendants of single marked cells are dispersed widely within the epithelium, mixed with unmarked cells. When the precursor cell is marked after the rhombomeres appear, however, the clone always remains within a single rhombomere, confined at its boundaries.[39,40] Later, young neurons may escape the restriction to mixing, presumably having acquired positional specification.

What Cellular Mechanism Is Responsible for Segregating Cells into Compartments?

One possible mechanism whereby cells become segregated into compartments may be through rhombomere boundaries enforcing the separation by forming a mechanical barrier to cell dispersal. Numerous molecular specializations that could confer this role are acquired by boundaries later in development (Fig. 15.9), including the expression of chondroitin sulfate proteoglycan, a zinc finger gene (*plzf*), and the interme-

FIGURE 15.7 Planar versus vertical interactions during neural induction. (A) Two models for how the dorsal ectoderm and organizer tissues interact during neural induction. In the model on the left, signals generated by the organizer pass in a planar fashion into the ectoderm, as proposed by Spemann. Note from the fate map (Fig. 15.1) that the prospective neural area of the ectoderm closely apposes the organizer region; thus, the signals need not pass over large distances to affect the neural region. In the model diagrammed on the right, the organizer tissue interacts with the overlying ectoderm during gastrulation, as proposed by Mangold. (B) The contribution of planar signaling to neural induction can be tested experimentally using an explant called a Keller sandwich. A Keller sandwich is made by excising the organizer tissue with adjacent dorsal ectoderm from two embryos and placing them together with the insides facing each other as shown on the left. In this configuration, the explant remains flat, so that the mesoderm and neural tissue converge and extend in opposite directions as diagrammed on the right. Even though the only contact between the organizer tissue and ectoderm is that across the boundary they share at blastula stages, the neural tissue that forms in a Keller sandwich is properly patterned along the A/P axis. HoxB1, Krox-20, and En-2 are markers of the spinal cord, hindbrain, and the midbrain/hindbrain boundary, respectively. (C) The contribution of vertical signaling to neural induction can be tested experimentally by einsteck experiments. A piece of dorsal mesoderm is dissected out from gastrulae and transplanted into the blastocoel of a host embryo as shown on the left. When the host embryo gastrulates, the transplanted tissue is pressed up against the ventral ectoderm. When this experiment is performed with prechordal (head) mesoderm (labeled ①), the explant induces a secondary head, containing a brain. Conversely when this experiment is performed with posterior mesoderm (labeled ④), the explant induces a tail containing a spinal cord.

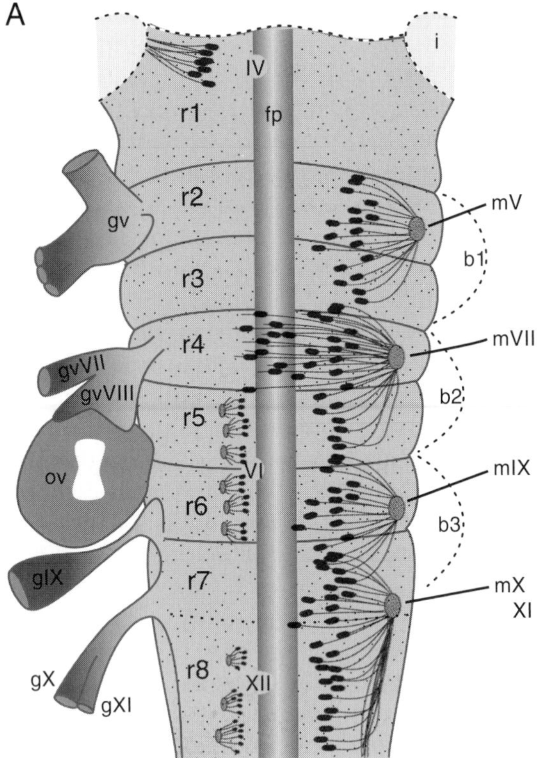

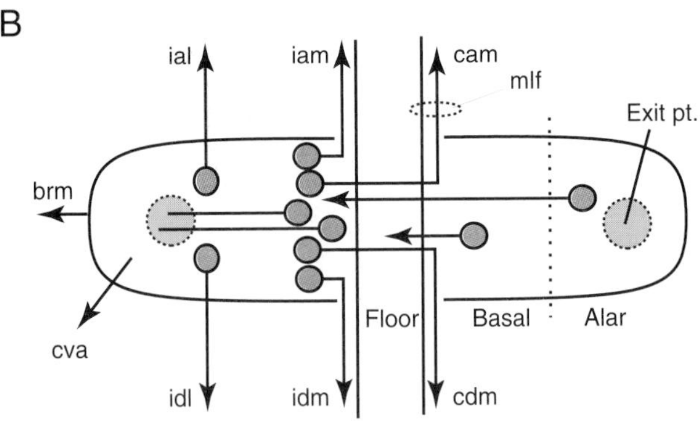

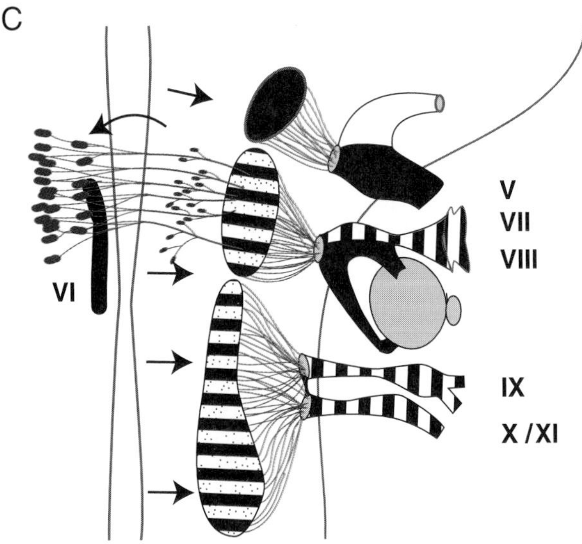

diate filament protein vimentin. From the earliest appearance of neurons, the rhombomere boundaries also become selective conduits for axon growth.[37] But none of these specializations appears early enough in development to be implicated in lineage restriction. An alternative possibility is that cells in one rhombomere are in a state different from that of the cells in neighboring rhombomeres. The expression of cell surface molecules would favor cohesion between the cells of one rhombomere but reduce adhesion with their neighbors. The boundaries (or interfaces) between rhombomeres might thus reflect a tendency of adjacent rhombomeres to separate from one another. Heterotopic grafting experiments using the chick–quail technique (see Chapter 16), together with *in vitro* cell aggregation experiments with vital dye-labeled cells, support the idea that rhombomeres partition from each other according to an adhesion differential—obeying a two-segment repeat rule.[36] Thus, cells from even-numbered rhombomeres mix with cells from other evens, and cells from odd-numbered rhombomeres mix with other odds, but odd cells separate away from even cells when mixed together in cultured aggregates.

The formation of rhombomeres is likely to be an intrinsic property of the neural tube. If the head mesoderm is extirpated during gastrulation in the chick

FIGURE 15.8 Diagram showing the distribution of some neuronal cell types in the chick hindbrain. (A) Stages 17–20. On the right side of the figure are shown the branchiomotor neurons, forming in rhombomeres r2 + r3 (Vth nerve, trigeminal), r4 + r5 (VIIth nerve, facial), and r6 + r7 (IXth nerve, glossopharyngeal). Also shown are the contralaterally migrating efferent neurons of the VIIIth nerve (vestibuloacoustic), which are in the floor plate (fp) at r4 level at stages 19–20. On the left side are the somatic motor neurons, forming in r1 (IVth nerve, trochlear), r5 + r6 (VIth nerve, abducens), and r8 (XIIth nerve, hypoglossal). Cranial nerve entry/exit points and sensory ganglia associated with r2 (trigeminal), r4 (geniculate, vestibuloacoustic), r6 (superior), and r7 (jugular) are shown, as is the otic vesicle (ov). Modified from Ref. 37. (B) Each rhombomere at stages 17–20 also contains cells of each of six classes of reticular neuron (ial, iam, cam, idl, idm, cdm) that are defined by their axon trajectory: basal plate cell types project either ipsilaterally (i..) or contralaterally (c..), where their axons either ascend (.a.) or descend (.d.) in the medial longitudinal fasciculus (..m), at the border between the basal and floor plates. More laterally located cells in the alar plate have projections that either ascend or descend in the lateral longitudinal tract (..l). Data from Ref. 38. Each rhombomere also contains branchiomotor neurons (brm) and uncharacterized basal plate and alar plate commissural neurons. Even-numbered rhombomeres contain an efferent nerve exit point, whereas r4 (shown) also contains contralaterally migrating vestibuloacoustic neurons (cva). (C) Later in development, at stages 26–30, the branchiomotor neurons have completed their laterally directed migration (short arrows) and have condensed as defined nuclei close to their exit points. Similarly, the contralateral vestibuloacoustic neurons have completed their migration across the midline (curved arrow) and have formed a grouping in r4 and r5. See Ref. 25.

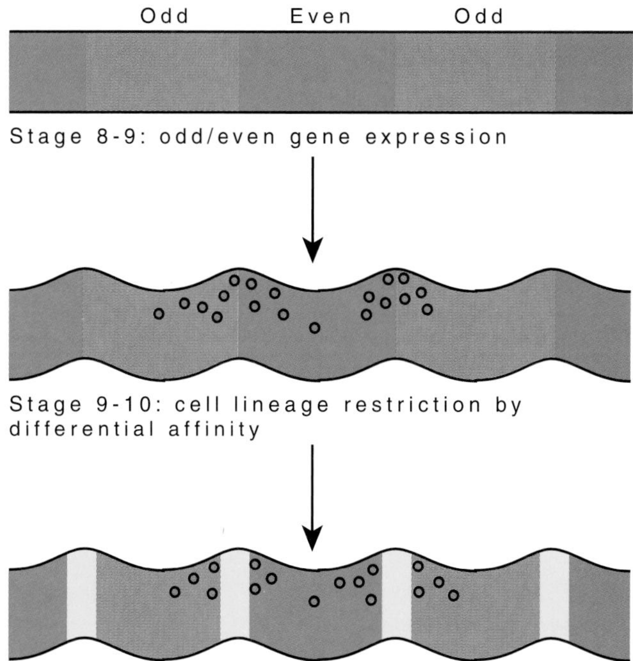

FIGURE 15.9 Diagram showing stages in the formation of compartmental organization of rhombomeres. At stages 8–9, genes such as *Krox-20, Sek-1* (blue), and *Elf-2* (green) are expressed in alternate stripes that correspond with presumptive rhombomeres. At stages 9–10, there is restriction on the movement of mitotic precursor cells across the interfaces between newly formed rhombomeres, which are now visible macroscopically by the sinuous deflection of the neuroepithelium on the ventricular–pial axis. The containment of cells may reflect the acquisition of differences in the adhesive properties in adjacent rhombomeres. At stage 13 onward, the interfaces between rhombomeres acquire molecular and morphological specializations that mark them as distinct boundaries (yellow).

embryo so that the head develops as an ectodermal sac devoid of mesoderm, it contains a near-normal-looking neural tube in which rhombomeres are morphologically well defined and exhibit the cellular and molecular patterns of the normal embryo.[41] This experiment, together with the normal segmental expression patterns of genes in Keller explants (Fig. 15.7B), suggests that the hindbrain is segmented by a mechanism intrinsic to the neural epithelium.

Studies in mouse and chick embryos provide evidence that segmentation also operates in the forebrain.[42,43] Six or seven morphological neuromeres can be seen in the forebrain (Fig. 15.10), but their significance remains unclear. Repeat patterns of cellular organization or gene expression—repetition (or metamerism) is the essence of segmentation—have not been described for this brain region. What has been documented, however, is the expression of developmental control genes in a patchwork quilt of small domains, subdividing the diencephalon and telencephalon into a number of transverse and longitudinal domains. This pattern could reflect the complex and early regionalization of the forebrain. Cell lineage tracing experiments have failed to identify any strict compartmental boundaries in the telencephalon comparable to those shown for the rhombencephalon. Instead, a prominent longitudinal boundary is formed between the dorsal (presumptive cortex) and ventral (presumptive striatum) regions.[44] When cells from these regions are mixed together *in vitro*, they segregate from each other according to an adhesion differential.[45]

Regions of the Developing CNS Are Defined by Gene Expression

Central to the illumination of CNS pattern formation is the discovery that **developmental control genes** related to genes with a known patterning role in the *Drosophila* embryo are expressed in spatially restricted domains of the neural plate and tube. These genes fall into two main categories: those encoding transcription factors and those encoding cell-surface or secreted signaling molecules.

Segmentation of the vertebrate hindbrain bears more than a passing resemblance to segmentation in the fly embryo, in which a hierarchy of gap genes, pair

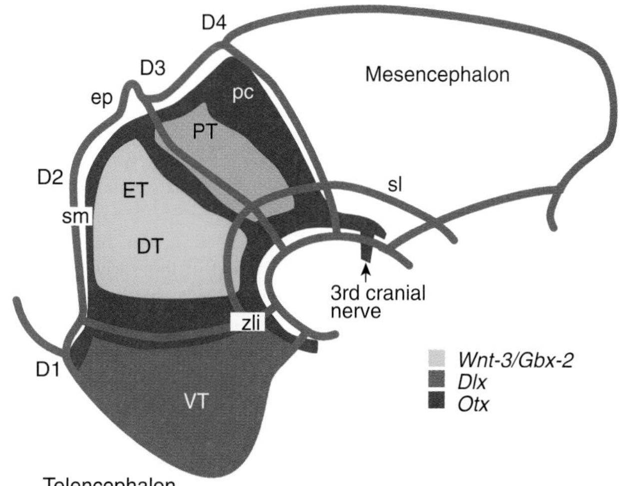

FIGURE 15.10 Diagrammatic representation of the expression domains of *Otx-1* and *Otx-2, Wnt-3, Gbx-2,* and *Dlx* genes in the mouse embryo diencephalon. Coincident with borders of gene expression domains are divisions between major subregions of the future thalamus: VT, ventral thalamus; DT, dorsal thalamus; ET, epithalamus; PT, pretectum. Prominent early axon tracts form at the midbrain/pretectal boundary (posterior commissure, pc), and at the dorsal thalamus/ventral thalamus boundary (zona limitans intrathalamica, zli). Embryonic subdivision of the diencephalon into four neuromeres (D1–D4) has been proposed on the basis of these domains.[42,43] sl, sulcus limitans; sm, stria medullaris. Adapted from Ref. 104.

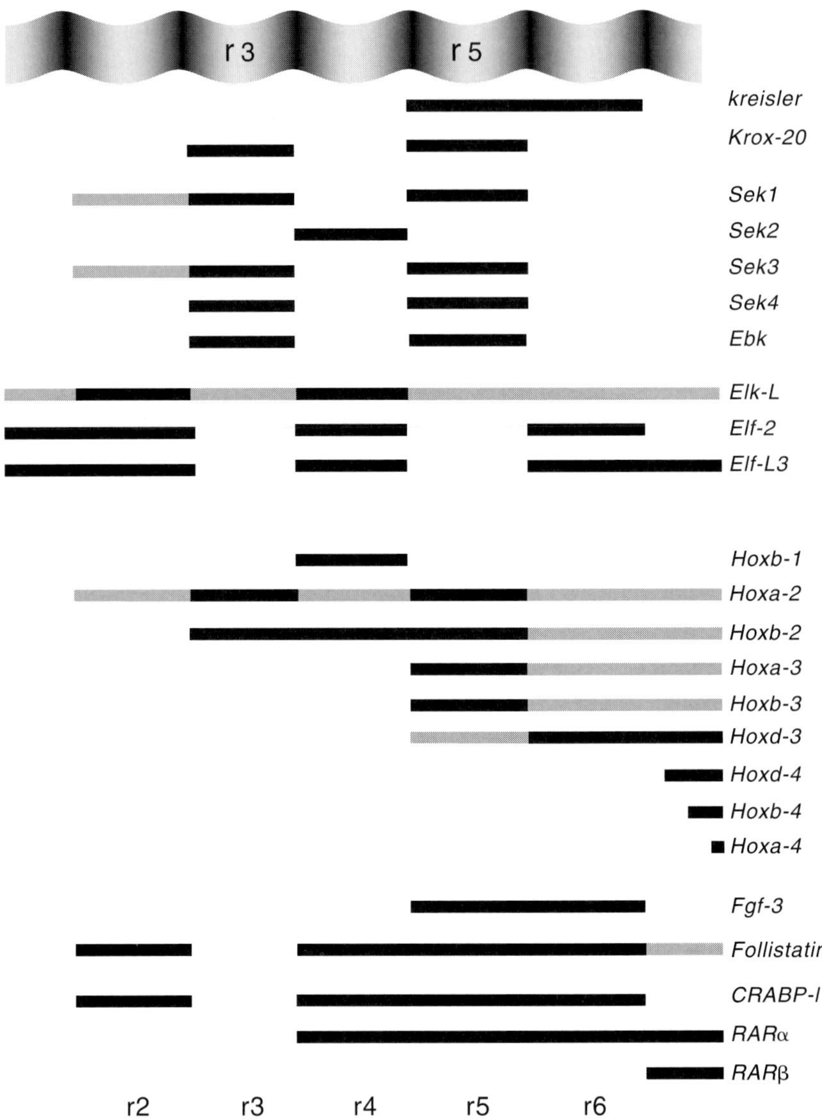

FIGURE 15.11 Diagram showing the expression domains of several classes of genes that are expressed in the early hindbrain and have rhombomere boundary restricted expression. For details, see text. Adapted from Ref. 36.

rule genes, and segment polarity genes partitions the axis into parasegments, individual anterior and posterior compartments, and finally segments. Odd/even pairs of rhombomeres (e.g., r3/r4) may correspond to parasegments, whereas even/odd pairs (r4/r5) may correspond to segments. Are there parallels with *Drosophila* at the molecular level—in the mechanisms that give rise to the segmental organization of the hindbrain? Although many *Drosophila* segmentation genes have vertebrate homologs, these are generally not expressed in a segmental manner in the hindbrain. This is not altogether surprising because segmentation in arthropods and vertebrates is convergent.[46] These two animal groups, representative of protostome and deuterostome organizations, respectively, diverged from a common unsegmented ancestor in which the homeotic genes specified position along the long axis without the constraint of compartmentalization. Thus, genes involved in the segmentation process in flies would not necessarily have the same role in vertebrates.

A number of candidate **segmentation genes** could function in the regulatory network that controls hindbrain segmentation (Fig. 15.11). Notable among these are *Krox-20* and members of the Eph-related tyrosine kinases and their ligands. *Krox-20* encodes a zinc finger transcription factor that is expressed in two sharp stripes in the neural plate that later become r3 and r5.[47] Targeted disruption of *Krox-20* results in the elimination of these rhombomeres and the fusion of r2/r4/r6 into a single composite region.[48] This phenotype has similarities to that of pair rule mutants in flies, suggesting that *Krox-20* may be responsible for generating periodicity along the axis from nonperiodic cues established by upstream genes. In close parallel with fly development, *Krox-20* exerts downstream control on *Hox* genes.[36]

A second category of genes with a possible role in hindbrain segmentation comprises genes that encode molecules involved in cell interaction. These include certain members of the Eph family of receptor tyrosine kinases—transmembrane proteins that contain both immunoglobulin and fibronectin repeat domains associated with cell–cell recognition and/or adhesion events—and their transmembrane or GPI-anchored ligands. The Eph receptors, Sek1 and Sek4, for example, are expressed in r3 and r5,[49] whereas a ligand for Sek4 (Elf2) is expressed through alternate rhombomeres (r2, r4, and r6).[50] These patterns suggest a function in cell–cell recognition between adjacent rhombomeres that perhaps reinforces compartmentation and may also result in the formation of specialized boundary cells (Fig. 15.9). Indeed, perturbing Sek1 function in zebrafish by overexpressing a dominant-negative mutant form of the receptor leads to the absence of sharp inter-rhombomere boundaries.[51]

A third class of segmentation gene is represented by the *kreisler* gene, first identified as an X-ray-induced recessive mutation in mice and subsequently as a chemically induced mutation (*valentino*) in zebrafish. In homozygous *kreisler* mice, gross malformation of the inner ear is related to abnormalities in the adjacent hindbrain region of the embryo. The neural tube posterior to the r3/r4 boundary appears unsegmented, a defect attributable to the loss of r5 and r6 as identifiable territories.[52,53] Their place is taken by a region that fails to form boundaries with either r4 or r7 and that might represent a persisting "parasegmental" progenitor region that lacks the identity and adhesive properties of either rhombomere. The *kreisler* mutation involves a b-Zip member of the c-*maf* proto-oncogene family,[54] expressed in r5 and r6, that may act via the regulation of *Krox-20* and *Hox* genes. In the $kr^{-/-}$ embryo, the r5 stripe of *Krox-20* is absent, and the expression domains of both *Hoxa-4* and *Hoxd-4* extend further rostrally than normal.[52,53] Thus, the c-*maf* genes may participate in establishing the initial parasegmental (two-compartment) subdivision of the hindbrain; if so, it would be expected that as yet unidentified family members are expressed with two-compartment periodicity in more rostral regions of the hindbrain.

The emergence of regional pattern along the A/P axis appears to depend on the expression of position-specifying genes. Perhaps the single most important discovery in recent years has been that a complex of genes specifying positional values along the main body axis of the fly embryo is conserved in vertebrates. The **homeotic selector** genes within this complex (HOM-C) are the master control genes that coordinate the development of structures appropriate to axial position in the epidermal segments of the fly. Consistent with their serving a similar function in vertebrates, the homologs of these genes, the **Hox family** of homeobox genes, retain a clustered chromosomal organization in which the relative position of a gene in the cluster reflects its boundary of expression along the A/P axis (the **principle of colinearity**). Duplications during evolution of the vertebrate genome have increased the number of *Hox* genes, and mammals may have up to four copies of genes that are represented singly in *Drosophila*. Divergence between these paralogous genes increase the resolution of pattern control. *Hox* genes are expressed in overlapping, or nested, domains along the axis of the early embryo; those at the 3′ ends of the clusters are expressed most anteriorly, in the hindbrain, where a striking correspondence exists between their rostral expression boundaries and the interfaces between rhombomeres[55] (Fig. 15.11).[56,57]

The overlapping distribution of *Hox* gene transcripts in the hindbrain region suggests that their proteins may act in a combinatorial manner to set the positional value of individual rhombomeres and thereby control their identity and phenotypic specializations. Accumulating evidence supports this view. Loss-of-function mutations of rostrally expressed *Hox* genes in mice may result in malformations that are consistent with transformation of regional identity. In the *Hoxb-1* knockout mouse, for example, r4 (where the gene is normally expressed at high level) loses its r4-specific characters and takes on those of r2, r6, and other rhombomeres where the gene is not normally expressed.[58] Knockouts of other *Hox* genes, however, have less easily interpreted phenotypes.[59,60]

The genes in HOM-C are expressed in specific regions of the fly CNS that correspond, in A/P position, to equivalent regions of the vertebrate CNS.[61] Although this may imply that the nervous systems are in some way related, this is clearly not the case. Rather, it illustrates the remarkable conservation of genes that encode positional values along the A/P axis—independent of the specific structure that forms at any particular value.

Hox genes are not expressed rostral to the hindbrain, but more anterior levels of the neuraxis display spatially restricted expression of other transcriptional control genes whose homeoboxes are divergent from the *Hox* (*Antennapedia*) type. These genes are also highly conserved between flies and vertebrates. Two homologs of the *Drosophila* segmentation gene *engrailed* (*En*) are expressed before any signs of region-specific development in overlapping broad domains spanning the

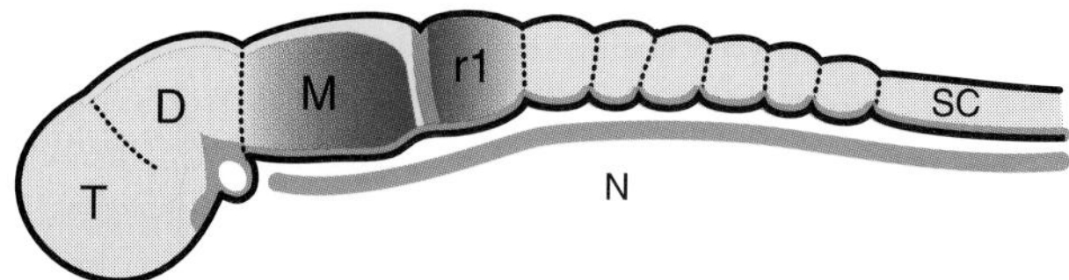

FIGURE 15.12 Diagram of an early neural tube stage embryo showing the expression domains of *Sonic hedgehog* (red), *engrailed* (blue), *Wnt-1* (yellow), and *Fgf8* (green). *Fgf8* expression is in a ring that precisely circumscribes the constriction (isthmus) between midbrain (M) and hindbrain. *Engrailed* genes are expressed in a gradient that peaks at the isthmus and decreases both anteriorly, in the midbrain, and posteriorly, in rhombomere 1 (r1). T, telencephalon; D, diencephalon; SC, spinal cord; N, notochord. Data from Refs. 56 and 57.

hindbrain–midbrain junction, the region that later forms the cerebellum and the caudal part of the optic tectum (Fig. 15.12). Gene ablation experiments in mice by Alex Joyner have shown that the *En-1* and *En-2* genes are crucially involved in the morphogenetic specification of the region.[62] The entire domain of *En* expression is deleted in *En-1* knockout mice, while *En-2* null mutants display much less severe abnormalities in development of the cerebellum. *En* expression in chick embryos appears to regulate the rostrocaudal polarity of the tectum and therefore of retinotectal projections.[63,64] When *En-1* is misexpressed in rostral tectum using retroviral vectors, this region acquires the cellular and molecular characteristics of caudal tectum.[65]

Homologs of the gap genes *orthodenticle* (*otd*) and *empty spiracles* (*ems*), which function as homeotic selectors in the specification of particular head segments and brain neuromeres in *Drosophila,* have been cloned from mice and chicks and found to be expressed in overlapping domains that encompass the entire rostral extremity of the mouse neuraxis with the exception of the ventral forebrain.[66] As with the *Hox* genes, the nested expression of *Emx-1* < (within) *Emx-2* < *Otx-1* < *Otx-2* suggests that their proteins may be employed in a combinatorial manner to specify the identity of mesencephalic, telencephalic, and dorsal diencephalic regions. To date, only the *Otx-2* knockout has been reported,[67] and it results in a phenotype that betrays little of the gene's function—the entire head rostral to r3 is deleted. Because *Otx-2* is also expressed in the notochord and the prechordal plate—mesodermal tissues that have been implicated in patterning the neurectoderm—it is unclear whether *Otx-2* is involved intrinsically in rostral brain specification or whether it acts indirectly, through the head mesoderm.

Fate maps of both amphibian[68] and chick[69] embryos show that the ventral diencephalon, the principal region excluded from *Emx* and *Otx* expression and fated to form the hypothalamus and hypophysis, develops at the rostral extremity of the neural plate (Fig. 15.13). The telencephalon, initially posterior and lateral to the terminal region, gains its frontal position later in development through a combination of pronounced overgrowth of the anterolateral rim of the neural plate and the cephalic flexure at midbrain level. Specification of the ventral diencephalon may be under the control of another family of homeobox genes, *Dlx*, which is related to the *Drosophila* gene *distal-less* (*dll*). *Dlx* is expressed at the rostral tip of the amphibian neural plate; in the mouse, four *Dlx* genes are expressed in hypothalamic and striatal regions of the ventral forebrain (Fig. 15.10).[70]

Hensen's Node and the Isthmus Are Signaling Regions

The expression of *Hox* genes is directed to specific domains at specific levels on the A/P axis. Examples where rhombomere-specific control elements have been identified include *Hoxb-1* and *Hoxb-2*. If *Hox* genes encode positional values along the A/P axis, what positional signaling mechanism is responsible for activating their specific regional control elements at appropriate levels of the axis? A strong candidate for this role is a gradient of **retinoic acid** (RA).

Hensen's node is a rich source of retinoids,[71] and like bicoid in *Drosophila,* node-derived RA may act as a morphogen conferring positional information on cells at different A/P positions by differentially regulating *Hox* expression. First, RA is a biologically active derivative of vitamin A, a deficiency of which leads to embryopathies, as does an excess of exogenous RA. In both cases, the defects are particularly severe in the hindbrain and branchial arch region; excess RA, for example, causes a dose-dependent anterior-to-posterior transformation of cell fate[31,72] in which the hindbrain is expanded at the expense of the forebrain and midbrain. Second, this change in cell fate is associated with changes in *Hox* gene expression patterns in a manner consistent with the principle of colinearity. There is a direct correspondence between the location of a *Hox* gene in the cluster and its responsiveness to RA—3′ genes respond more rapidly and at a lower RA concentration than 5′ genes.[73] The changes in expression are followed by stable changes in morphology, including the ordered transformation of anterior rhombomere cell types to those of a more posterior type,[74,75] suggesting that an RA signal normally regulates the pattern of *Hox* expression. Third, RA exerts its effects on development by controlling target gene transcription via multiple types of RA receptors (RARs and RXRs), members of the nuclear receptor superfamily.[76] RA-bound receptors are transcription factors that bind as homo- or heterodimers (RAR–RXR) to RA re-

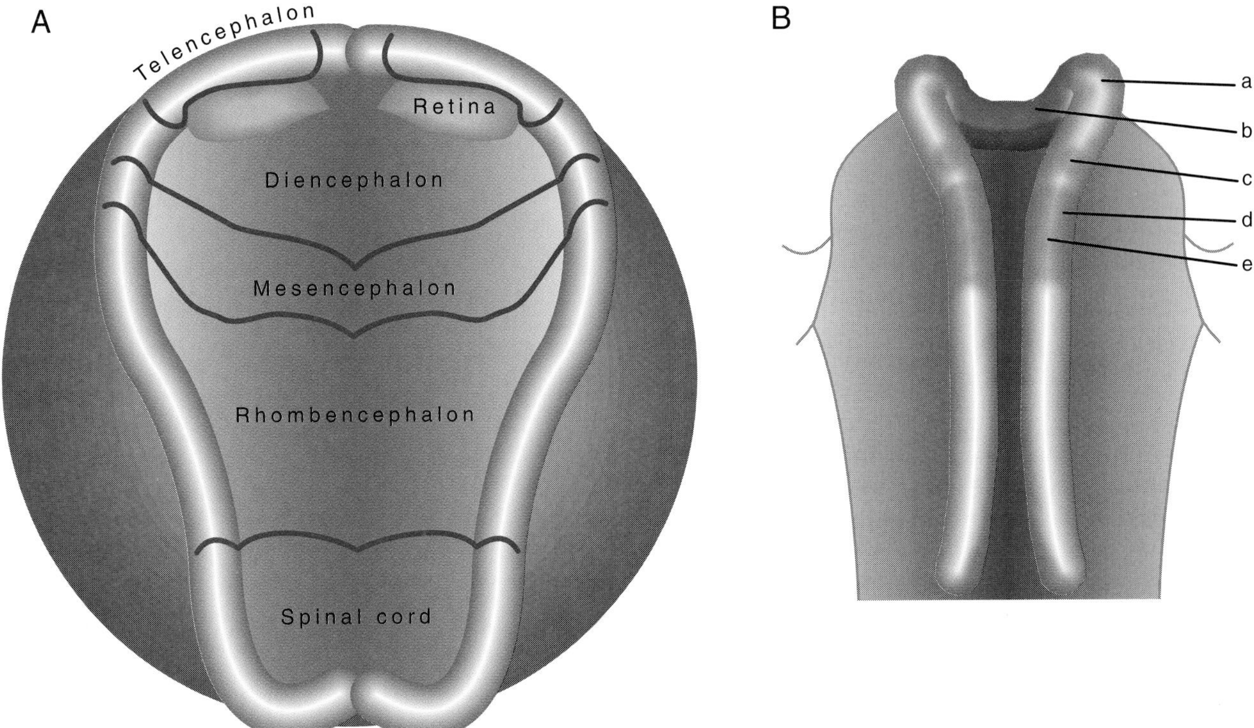

FIGURE 15.13 Fate map of the amphibian (A) and chick (B) neural plates. In both species, the most rostral midline region of the neural plate gives rise to the infundibulum and hypothalamus, which are diencephalic structures. The telencephalon derives from more posterior and lateral (later dorsal) regions of the neural plate. As the neural tube forms, a pronounced D/V flexure at the level of the midbrain (cephalic flexure) moves the telencephalon to its later, terminal position. (a) Presumptive area of the nasal ectoderm. (b) Anterior neural ridge containing the hypophyseal placode. (c) Region containing the presumptive olfactory placode. (d) Presumptive territory of the upper beak. (e) Presumptive diencephalon. After Refs. 68, 69.

sponse elements (RAREs and RXREs) in the promoters of target genes. The promoters of at least some of the *Hox* genes contain RAREs, which are required for gene activation.[77,78] RA may thus directly control the expression of *Hox* genes. Because Hensen's node is the only rich source of RA in the gastrula-stage embryo, a posterior-to-anterior gradient of RA may be responsible for establishing the nested expression of these genes along the A/P axis.

Regional specification of the posterior midbrain and cerebellum may be coordinated by the midbrain–hindbrain boundary, or **isthmus region.** Hindbrain development is characterized by *Hox* gene expression that extends up to the r1/r2 boundary. No *Hox* genes are expressed in r1, a region that, together with the posterior midbrain, forms the cerebellum. The unitary fate of these adjacent regions is reflected at the molecular level and by aspects of their developmental potential. The *engrailed* homologs, *En-1* and *En-2*, and the *Drosophila paired* homologs, *Pax-2*, *Pax-5*, and *Pax-8*, are expressed in this domain,[79] and targeted disruption of the *En* genes (see above) has demonstrated that both are required for normal cerebellar development. Heterotopic grafts of the isthmic region locally induce En expression in the host and change the fate of the host neuroepithelium such that it ultimately forms tectal structures (in caudal diencephalon or rostral mesencephalon) or cerebellar structures (in caudal rhombencephalon).[57] These data provide compelling evidence that a signal emanating from the isthmus is involved in local A/P patterning.

Two secreted signaling proteins are candidates for this organizing activity: *Wnt-1*, which is expressed in a dorsoventrally oriented ring in the posterior midbrain just anterior to the isthmus (Fig. 15.12), and other *Wnt* genes, which are expressed uniquely in the posterior midbrain. Targeted mutation of the *Wnt-1* gene in mice results in defects in both the midbrain and the rostral hindbrain.[57] A second candidate secreted factor, FGF8, is expressed immediately posterior to the *Wnt-1* domain (Fig. 15.12) and has midbrain-inducing and polarizing abilities.[56] When a bead coated with recombinant FGF8 is implanted in the posterior diencephalon of chick embryos, expression of the isthmic/caudal mesencephalic markers *Fgf8*, *Wnt-1*, and *En-2* is induced in the surrounding cells. The posterior diencephalon of treated embryos later acquires the phenotypic character of a complete ectopic midbrain, whose A/P polarity is reversed with respect to that of the normal host midbrain. Thus, neuroectodermal *Fgf8* expression, which is normally restricted to a circumferential ring that precisely delineates the isthmic constriction, may be sufficient to establish both midbrain pattern and its polarity. Whether *En-1* is also regulated by FGF8 remains unclear.

An Anteroposterior Pattern Is Present in the Spinal Cord and Nerves

The spinal nerves that form a ladderlike array on either side of the spinal cord are an obvious manifestation of segmentation. But here, in contrast to the intrinsic patterning mechanism that operates in the hindbrain, the segmentation process is under the direct control of the paraxial mesoderm. As shown by the pioneering experiments of Roger Keynes and Claudio Stern,[80] the segmental pattern of dorsal root ganglia and ventral root nerves is imposed by a serially reiterated asymmetry in the sclerotomal component of the somites (Fig. 15.14). Neural crest cells collect preferentially within the rostral sclerotome of each somite, which is also permissive for axon growth, whereas the caudal sclerotome of each somite excludes both neural crest cells and motor axons through expression of glycoproteins that inhibit cell migration and cause the collapse of growth cones.[81] Subdivision of the paraxial mesoderm into anteroposteriorly polarized somites thus ensures a positional correspondence between the segmented dermomyotome on the one hand and its sensorimotor innervation on the other. Despite extensive searches, no segmental patterns of neuronal differentiation or clear evidence of cell lineage restriction along the A/P axis of the spinal cord has been found in higher vertebrates.

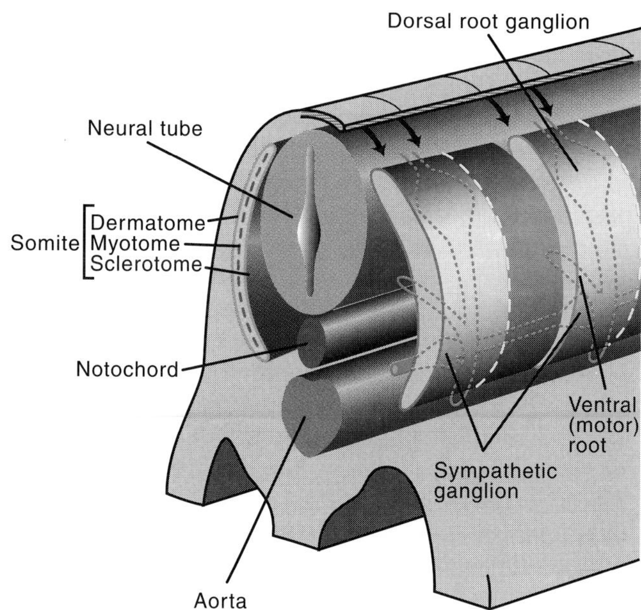

FIGURE 15.14 The principal pathways of motor axon growth and neural crest migration in the trunk region of the chick embryo. By the stage at which these constituents of the peripheral nervous system start to appear, the somites have dispersed into their three components: dermatome (presumptive dermis), myotome (presumptive skeletal muscle), and sclerotome (presumptive vertebrae). The sclerotome is divided into anterior (light gray) and posterior (dark gray) halves, which are distinct from each other according to morphological and molecular criteria. All components of the peripheral nervous system (ventral nerve roots, dorsal root ganglia, sympathetic chain ganglia) are confined to the anterior half sclerotome of each somite, which is permissive for the migration of neural crest cells (arrows) and the ingrowth of motor neuron growth cones. After Ref. 80.

Although it lacks segmentation and has a superficial uniformity of organization along the A/P axis, the developing spinal cord manifests distinct A/P variations in cellular subtype composition, particularly with respect to the motor neurons that are arranged in discontinuous longitudinal columns (Fig. 15.15). Thus, the neurons that form the lateral motor columns at limb (brachial and lumbar) levels are distinct from those that form at cervical and thoracic levels, both in the identity of their peripheral targets and in the expression of different combinations of LIM-homeobox genes. The expression of a specific combination of LIM-homeobox genes is believed to confer motor neuron subtype identity and targeting specificity.[82] Furthermore, genes that lie 5′ in the *Hox* clusters have sharp boundaries of expression along the spinal region of the neuraxis, suggesting, by analogy with the hindbrain, that they underlie regional diversity, for example, between brachial and thoracic regions. Transposition of the prospective brachial and thoracic regions leads to a change in *Hox* coding, a change in LIM-homeobox gene coding, respecification of motor neuron subtypes, and adoption of a normal columnar organization in accord with their new positions.[83] The most likely source of molecular signals that effect the acquisition of this regional identity is the mesoderm that flanks the neural tube. The paraxial mesoderm is also implicated in the specification of primary motor neurons of the zebrafish.[83] Transplantation of single cells to new A/P positions with respect to the adjacent somite results in respecification of both the LIM code of the motor neuron and its subsequent axon trajectory and target specificity.

Cranial Sensory Ganglia Show Segmentation

The cranial mesoderm of the avian embryo is not organized into segmental blocks; yet there is obvious

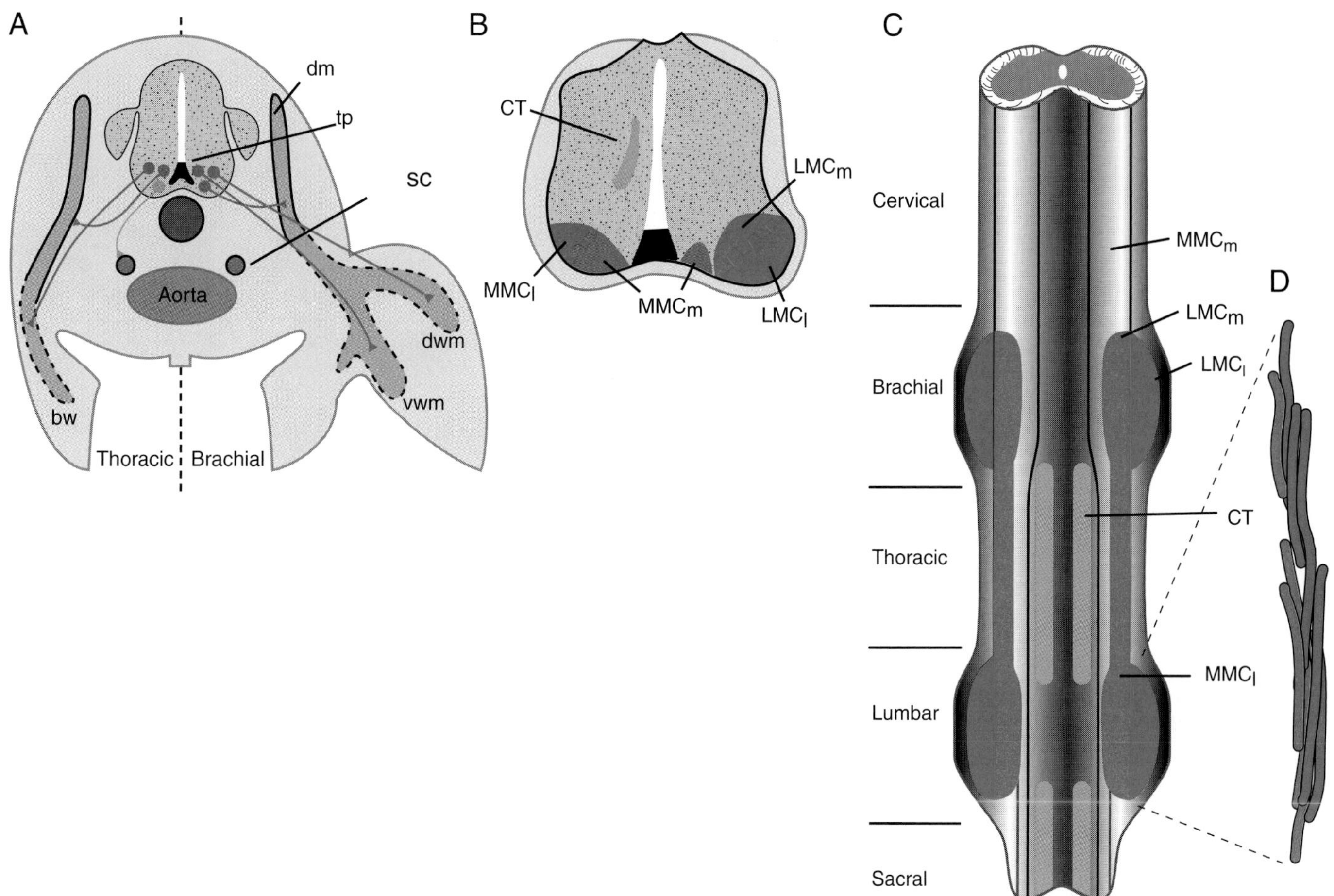

FIGURE 15.15 LIM code in spinal motor neurons. (A) A diagrammatic cross section of an E3.5 chick embryo at thoracic (left half) and brachial (right half) levels of the axis, showing LIM-homeobox gene expression in relation to early motor axonal trajectories. Motor neuron subtypes in the single ventrolateral motor column of the spinal cord are intermixed but have distinct pathways in the periphery: neurons of the medial motor column (MMC_m, blue) coexpress Isl-1, Isl-2, and Lim-3 and grow toward the dorsal dermomyotome (dm). Neurons of the lateral medial motor column (MMC_l, red, left) coexpress Isl-1 and Isl-2 and grow into the ventral body wall muscles (bw). Neurons of the medial lateral motor column (LMC_m, red, right) also coexpress Isl-1 and Isl-2 and grow into the ventral premuscle mass of the wing (vwm). Neurons of the lateral lateral motor column (LMC_l, green) coexpress Isl-2 and Lim-1 and grow into the dorsal premuscle mass (dwm). LMC_m and LMC_l axons diverge from a common path at the base of the wing. Preganglionic sympathetic neurons of the column of Terni (CT, orange, left side) express Isl-1 and grow into the prevertebral sympathetic chain (SC). (B) By E8, the five subtypes of motor neuron distinguished by their individual LIM-homeobox gene codes have segregated into columns that occupy distinct positions on the transverse axis. At the thoracic level (left half), two medial motor columns can be distinguished (MMC_m and MMC_l) together with the preganglionic visceral motor column of Terni (CT). At the brachial level (right half), there is an expansive lateral motor column (LMC_m and LMC_l,) but there is no MMC_l or CT. (C) Diagrammatic representation of the chick embryo spinal cord on E5–8, showing the A/P organization of motor columns. The axis is subdivided into five regions according to the presence or absence of five subtypes of motor neuron: MMC_m, MMC_l, LMC_m, and LMC_l neurons innervate voluntary muscles in the neck and trunk (MMC) or limbs (LMC); CT (orange) innervate neurons of the autonomic nervous system. (D) Motor neuron pools in the lumbar LMC. Laterally located pools (green) each innervate a muscle derived from the dorsal premuscle mass of the hind limb, whereas medially located pools (red) innervate ventral muscles. The lumbar LMC extends over eight spinal cord segments, and individual pools are between 1 and 4 spinal segments in length. Note the considerable rostrocaudal overlap between pools. Data from Ref. 82.

segmentation of the cranial sensory ganglia, the cephalic equivalent of dorsal root ganglia. Segmentation of the cranial peripheral nervous system is achieved without the repetitive alternation of permissive and inhibitory properties in the paraxial mesoderm that characterizes the segmentation of spinal nerves. In the head, ectodermal placodes contribute neurons to certain sensory ganglia, whereas the neural crest contributes both neurons and glial cells. The cranial neural crest also contributes to the parasympathetic autonomic ganglia and to the bulk of skeletal and connective tissues; it also has an important role in patterning the mesoderm-derived muscle cells. Some remarkable experiments by Drew Noden have shown that the ultimate pattern of these cranial elements appears to be already established in the neural tube, where the neural crest is morphogenetically specified before migrating ventrally into the branchial arches.[84]

The *Hox* genes, expressed in the premigratory neural crest populations as in their parent rhombomeres, may also confer identity on neural crest cells, which would then migrate from the neural tube in an orderly and predictable way, carrying preassigned positional information into the appropriate arch. The combinatorial expression of *Hox* genes, a **Hox code,** could control the morphogenetic program for patterning the branchial arches.[85] Consistent with this idea, rhombencephalic crest cells emigrate from discrete segmental levels of the avian hindbrain (Fig. 15.16A); the crest cells from r1 and r2 migrate into the first (mandibular) arch, from r4 into the second (hyoid) arch, and from r6 and r7 into the third arch, whereas the premigratory crest is massively depleted in the intervening rhombomeres, r3 and r5, by programmed cell death (apoptosis).[86] Neural crest cells in r3 and r5 die when in contact with even-numbered rhombomeres but survive when separated from them, either by grafting or by explanting in culture. Even-numbered rhombomeres cause cell death by inducing high levels of *Bmp4* expression, followed by expression of the homeobox gene *Msx-2* in the neural crest primordium of r3 and r5 (Fig. 15.16B). Since BMP4 effects the depletion of the neural crest from isolated r3 and r5 but not from r4 or from the neural tube at spinal cord levels, intrinsic A/P differences exist in the response properties of neural cells in odd versus even rhombomeres. Separation of the migrating crest cells into discrete nonmixing streams may be important in maintaining the fidelity of the branchial prepattern during its transfer into the periphery. The reduction of crest emigration from r3 and r5 suggests a surprisingly simple mechanism for keeping the neural crest cells from different rhombomeres apart during their migration. Furthermore, the cranial sensory ganglia that develop from late-migrating crest cells collecting in the dorsal region of the migration streams would necessarily lie in register both with appropriate A/P levels of the hindbrain and with their innervation territories. The influence of even-numbered rhombomeres on the fate of neural crest cells in adjacent odd-numbered rhombomeres provides a secondary mechanism for establishing positional differences. This effect extends more widely than the effect of neural crest production: r2 and r4 are responsible for maintaining the expression of *Krox-20* and for repression of the activin/BMP-binding protein, follistatin, in r3.[86]

Dorsoventral Patterning Is Evident in the Chordal Neural Tube

The nervous system exhibits a characteristic dorsoventral zonation, particularly prominent in the hindbrain and spinal cord, where different cell types differentiate according to position. Specialized glia—**floor plate cells**—form in a narrow strip at the ventral midline, motor neurons develop in the ventral third of the neuroepithelium on either side of the floor plate, relay neurons in the middle third, and smaller interneurons in the dorsal third. The most dorsal region, represented early on by the neural folds that mark the transition between cells with neural and epidermal fates, produces the migratory neural crest cells that give rise to the glia and the majority of neurons in the peripheral nervous system. Later, after the neural crest has departed, the dorsal midline is formed by a nonneurogenic roof plate (Fig. 15.17A).[87,88]

Over the past few years a wealth of data from both genetic and tissue recombination and transplantation experiments have demonstrated that the notochord, a mesodermal skeletal structure that occupies the midline of the embryo and directly underlies the neuroectoderm, is a signaling center for patterning the ventral region of the overlying (chordal) neural tube. Grafting experiments on avian embryos have shown that both floor plate and motor neuron differentiation depend on notochord signals. Early removal of the notochord results in a normal-sized spinal cord in which both of these ventral cell types are absent; dorsal cell types and dorsal-specific cell-surface antigens appear in their place, suggesting that multipotent precursors have switched fate in the notochord's absence[88,89] (Fig. 15.17B). Similarly, implanting a supernumerary notochord alongside and in contact with the lateral or dorsal neural tube results in the formation of an additional group of floor plate cells at the point of contact and flanking clusters of motor neurons. Again, it appears that cells originally fated to form dorsal interneurons switch fates to become ventral cell types in the noto-

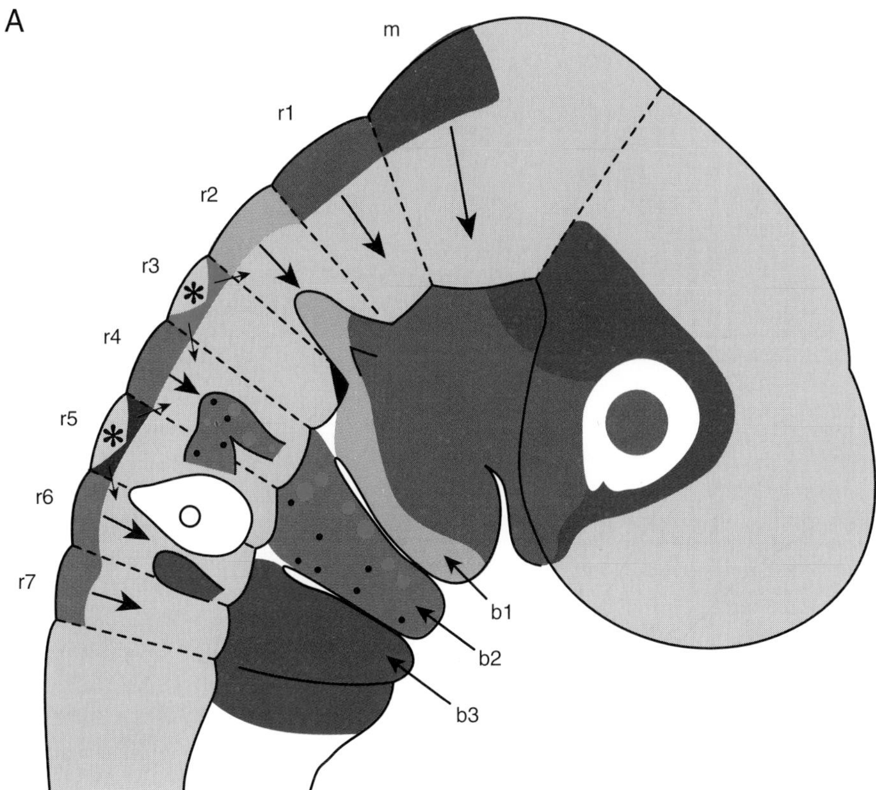

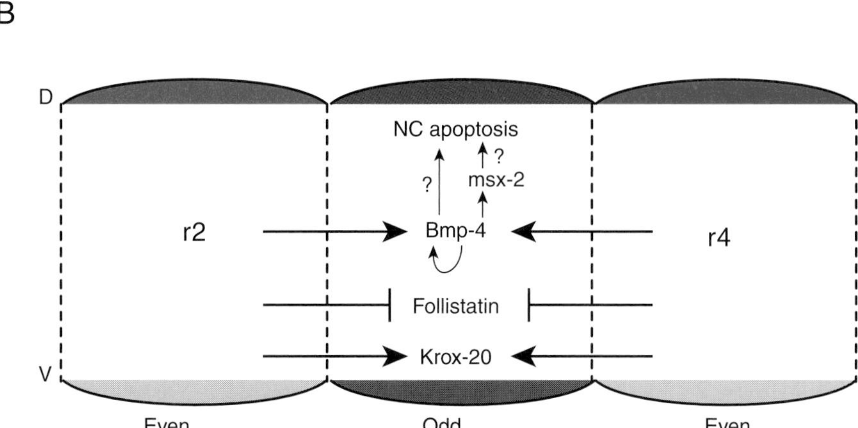

FIGURE 15.16 (A) Axial levels of origin and migration territories of neural crest cells in the hindbrain and midbrain region at stage 15 in the chick. The branchial arches (b1–b3) are populated by cells that migrate ventrally, preserving their axial order of origin, from all A/P levels except rhombomeres 3 and 5. Here the neural crest progenitor cells are almost completely eliminated by apoptosis (programmed cell death). Surviving r3 and r5 crest cells are detectable in the cranial ganglia (aqua dots) and, later, in the branchial skeleton. The spatial separation of discrete streams of cells that enter each branchial arch (from m/r1, r2, r4, and r6, respectively) may provide a mechanism for preserving patterning information already conferred on the premigratory neural crest. (B) Interactions between two even-numbered rhombomeres (r2 and r4) and their neighbor, r3. Neural crest cells in dorsal (D) r3 die following their induced expression of Bmp-4 and Msx-2. Further interactions involve the maintenance of Krox-20 expression and the silencing of follistatin, an activin-binding protein.

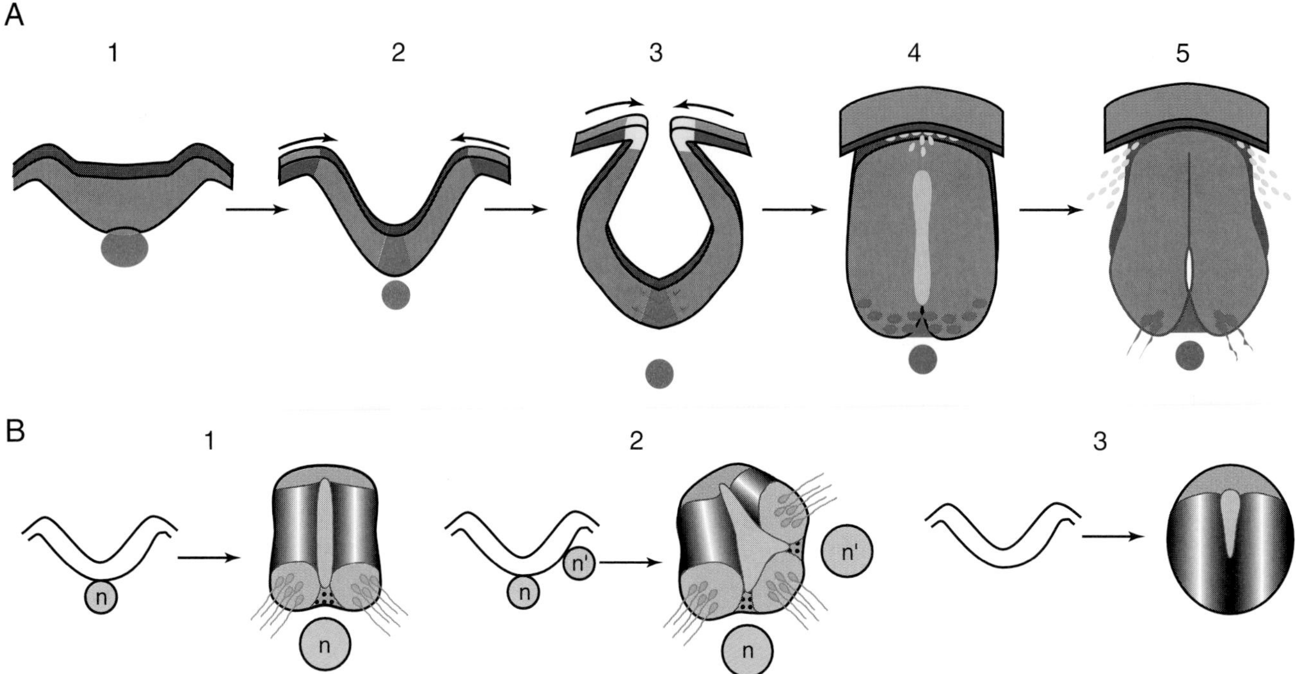

FIGURE 15.17 (A) Stages in the formation of the D/V pattern in the spinal cord and hindbrain, seen in transverse section. (1) The notochord underlies the neural plate and expresses *Shh* (red). (2) Notochord-derived SHH induces the differentiation of the floor plate, which also expresses *Shh*. *Bmp-7* (blue) is expressed in epidermal ectoderm adjoining the neural plate. (3) As the neural plate closes, *Slug* (yellow), an early marker for neural crest, is expressed at the junction between neural and epidermal ectoderm. (4) At the early neural tube stage, *Isl-1*–expressing cells (green) appear close to the floor plate, and neural crest cells (yellow) leave the dorsal tube and midline ectoderm through breaks in the basal lamina. (5) Finally, motor neurons (green) differentiate in the ventral cord. (B) Cross sections through the developing chick spinal cord at stage 10 (left) and stage 24 (right) showing the effect of adding or removing notochord. (1) During normal development, the floor plate (stippled) develops above the notochord (n), and motor neurons (red) differentiate in the adjacent ventrolateral region of the neural tube. AC4 antigen and Pax-6 are expressed in more dorsal regions (gray). (2) Grafting a donor notochord (n′) alongside the closing neural tube results in the formation of an additional floor plate and a third column of motor neurons. AC4 and Pax-6 expression retreats from the transformed region. (3) Removing the notochord from beneath the neural plate results in the permanent absence of both floor plate and motor neurons in the region of the extirpation. AC4 and Pax-6 expression extends through the ventral region of the cord. Data from Refs. 87 and 88.

chord's presence. The notochord can also induce both floor plate cells and motor neurons in midlateral neural plate explants *in vitro*, indicating that an inductive signal from the notochord is sufficient to initiate the development of these two ventral cell types, even in heterotypic tissue. These experiments show not only the power of the midline signal to influence fate choice but also the multipotent competence of responding neural tube cells. While floor plate induction seems to require intimate contact, motor neuron induction can be achieved at a distance—suggesting that a diffusible molecule is involved. At a slightly later developmental stage, the floor plate itself acquires the same inductive capabilities; it can also induce motor neurons and it will homeogenetically induce itself.[88]

Although motor neuron induction and floor plate induction appear to require different signals, the one diffusible and the other contact-dependent, a single molecule can account for both processes. The gene *Sonic hedgehog* (*Shh*) displays the appropriate expression dynamics, being expressed first in the notochord and then the floor plate. When misexpressed in dorsal regions of the neural tube, *Shh* can also elicit ectopic floor plate and motor neuron differentiation.[83] The choice of cell fate by progenitor cells in neural plate explants appears to be influenced by the concentration of Sonic hedgehog (SHH) protein to which they are exposed: the concentration threshold of SHH for motor neuron induction is about five times lower than that required for floor plate differentiation.[90] Biochemical studies of the SHH protein have revealed a mechanism whereby cells at different dorsoventral (D/V) positions could be exposed to different concentrations (Fig. 15.18). The SHH precursor protein synthesized by the notochord is autoproteolytically cleaved to generate an active N-terminal product (SHH-N), the majority of which is retained on the cell surface, and a C-terminal product, which is involved in the cleavage process and in coupling the N-terminal peptide to the cell surface but which has no inductive activity.[83] Midventral neural plate cells that are contacted by the notochord are thus likely to be exposed to a high local concentration of SHH-N, exceeding the threshold for floor plate induction, whereas the low levels of SHH-N that can diffuse from the notochord are sufficient to induce motor neuron differentiation (Fig. 15.18). Activity-blocking antibodies to SHH abolish the notochord-mediated induction of ventral cell types, showing that SHH is necessary as well as sufficient for establishing the ventral polarity of the neural tube.[83]

The ability of midline signals to influence the development of the ventral region of the neural tube is not restricted to the spinal cord; they are also influential in both the hindbrain and the midbrain. In addition to inducing motor neurons and the floor plate at these more anterior levels of the neuraxis, midline signals are involved in the development of region-specific neuronal subpopulations. Serotonergic neurons of the hindbrain raphe nucleus[88] and dopaminergic neurons of the midbrain substantia nigra[91,92] both develop close to the floor plate and can be induced to form in competent neural plate tissue by contact with notochord grafts or floor plate explants. The interpretation of the midline signal is determined by the responding tissue; thus, serotonergic neurons can be induced in ectopic regions of the anterior hindbrain by notochord from more posterior axial levels,[88] and, similarly, the induction of dopaminergic neurons in midbrain neuroepithelium can be triggered by the floor plate from different axial levels.[91,92] These experiments demonstrate that the same inductive signals are produced all along the axis by the midline tissues and that the specific outcome depends on the A/P position of the responding tissue (Fig. 15.19). Thus, recombinant SHH induces dopaminergic neurons only in explants of midbrain neuroepithelium. Furthermore, when SHH signaling is antagonized by an increase in activity of cAMP-dependent protein kinase A, the induction of dopaminergic neurons by the floor plate is blocked.[91,92]

Target genes activated in neural plate cells as a direct response to SHH signaling include the winged helix transcription factor HNF3β—a marker of floor plate differentiation—and the homeobox gene *Nkx-2.2*—a marker of ventrolateral neural tube cells. SHH signaling also represses the expression of two other homeobox genes, *Msx-1* and *Pax-3,* suggesting that the inactivation of certain transcriptional control genes is an essential step in the determination of ventral fate. Indeed, the misexpression of *Pax-3* in the ventral neural tube of transgenic mice appears to inhibit floor plate and motor neuron differentiation.[93]

The first molecular marker of motor neuron differentiation is the expression of the LIM-homeobox gene *Isl-1,*[94] which is expressed by prospective motor neurons after their final mitosis. Rather than playing a role in determining motor neuron fate, *Isl-1* may function in the developmental progression of these cells. That *Isl-1* is required for this process has been shown by targeted mutation in mice and antisense oligonucleotide treatment of chick neural tube explants, both of which result in presumptive motor neurons undergoing programmed cell death.[95] Also absent in the *Isl-1* knockout mice is a small population of ventrolateral interneurons that express the homeobox gene *En-1* and that differentiate shortly after the motor neurons. Because these cells do not themselves express *Isl-1,* their

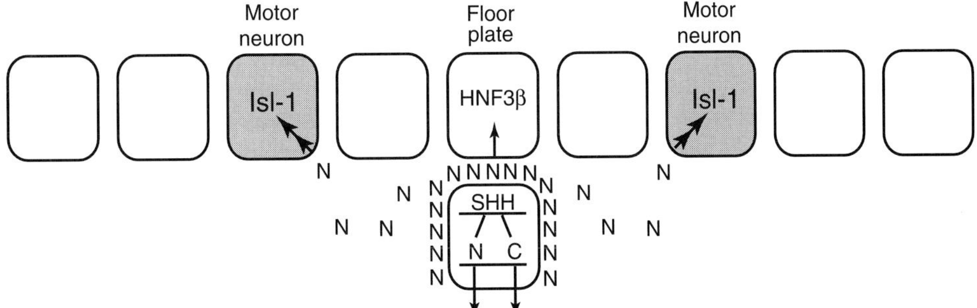

FIGURE 15.18 A possible pathway by which SHH signaling from the notochord and floor plate could induce motor neuron differentiation. A high concentration of secreted N-terminal cleavage product (SHH-N) is retained at the notochord surface, which is in contact with the basal surface of the midline cells of the neural plate. This concentration is sufficient to induce HNF3β expression and floor plate differentiation. A small amount of SHH-N (N) diffuses away from the notochord and (later) the floor plate, sufficient to meet the threshold required for motor neuron induction at a certain distance but below the threshold for floor plate induction. Modified from Ref. 83.

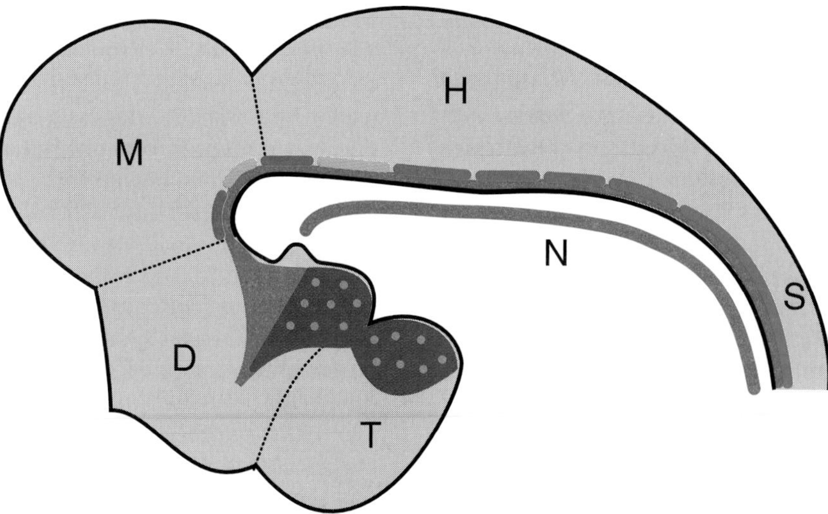

FIGURE 15.19 Stage in the formation of the anterior CNS pattern, seen in lateral view. A uniform D/V signal (SHH, red) elicits different responses at different A/P levels of the axis, showing prior A/P regionally specified competence. The notochord (N) underlies spinal cord (S), hindbrain (H), midbrain (M), and diencephalon (D), where its tip lies close to the infundibulum, and telencephalon (T). *Shh* (red) is expressed by both notochord and midventral neural tube cells, including those at forebrain levels. At midbrain and hindbrain levels, *Isl-1*-positive motor neurons (green), serotonergic neurons (orange), and dopaminergic neurons (orange) differentiate adjacent to the *Shh*-expressing ventral midline cells. In the forebrain, the expanded domain of *Shh* expression is also associated with *Isl-1*-expressing cells (blue).

formation seems to depend on unknown cell–cell signals emanating from young motor neurons. The existence of serial inductive interactions extending up the D/V axis of the neural tube may provide a reliable and precise mechanism for generating the large number of different interneuron cell types that it finally contains.

In notochordless animals, dorsal antigen markers are expressed in the ventral spinal cord, showing that cell pattern in the dorsal half of the spinal cord is unaffected by early notochord removal and also suggesting that dorsal may be a default state for the entire neural plate.[88] However, dorsal cell types such as neural crest, roof plate, and sensory relay neurons do not develop by default; rather, they are induced by an interaction between the lateral neuroectoderm and the epidermal ectoderm with which it is initially contiguous.[96] The latter is the source of a contact-dependent signal that induces the differentiation of both roof plate cells and neural crest cells and is likely to be transmitted in planar fashion at the open neural plate stage, when the neural and epidermal ectoderm have an edge contact with each other (Fig. 15.17A). This dorsalizing signal appears to be mediated by members of the BMP family of TGF-β-like signaling molecules, in particular BMP4 and BMP7. Both BMP4 and BMP7 are expressed in the dorsal epidermal ectoderm and both recombinant proteins mimic the ability of epidermal ectoderm to induce roof plate and neural crest cells. Later, as the rising neural folds bring the epidermal ectoderm into vertical contact with the dorsal surface of the closing neural tube, both these BMPs and other TGF-β–like proteins, BMP5 and DSL-1, are expressed in the dorsal neural tube itself—suggesting the operation of a homeogenetic induction process analogous to the expression of SHH by the floor plate after induction by notochord-derived SHH. In both cases, the induction of expression of signal molecules in the neural epithelium attends the physical separation of the neural tube from the initial source of the inductive signal. Unlike in the ventral neural tube, however, the differentiation of distinct dorsal cell types does not appear to depend on varying concentrations of inducer. Rather, the same concentration of BMP produces a number of different cell types.[83] Although the question of how these distinct cell types are generated is unresolved, one possibility suggested by the sequential appearance of these cell types is that the time at which naive cells are exposed to BMPs could influence their fate.

A number of developmental control genes containing the *Drosophila* paired-type box and expressed in sharply defined dorsoventral domains in the neural tube have been cloned. *Pax-3*, for example, is expressed in the dorsal (alar) half of the neural tube, whereas *Pax-6* is expressed in the dorsal two-thirds of the tube, excluding the most dorsal cells. Homozygous *Pax-3* null mutants (the *Splotch* mouse) have spina bifida and lack dorsal root ganglia and other neural crest derivatives.[97] *Pax-6* null mutants (*small eye*) lack eyes and olfactory epithelium.[97] These phenotypes are spectacular, and, perhaps because of their prominence, neither mutant has yet been analyzed for more subtle changes in regionalization of the D/V axis of the spinal cord. Both genes are expressed during the period when the neural tube is labile to midline signals; both are profoundly affected by notochord removal or addition, with altered domains of expression that presage the repatterning of cell types that later arise from such manipulations.[87] The possibility remains, therefore, that *Pax* genes may encode positional value on the D/V axis in much the same way as *Hox* genes do on the A/P axis—but here, the nature of the positional signal that could direct *Pax* gene expression is known.

Anteroposterior and Dorsoventral Patterning Mechanisms Are Related

The early inductive interactions that establish D/V cell fate appear to be conserved in the spinal cord and hindbrain. However, at a constant D/V position, marked differences exist in the identity of neural cell types at different A/P positions. Thus, for example, dopaminergic neurons develop in the posterior ventral midbrain, oculomotor neurons develop in the anterior ventral midbrain, and serotonergic neurons develop in the anterior ventral hindbrain. In all cases, these distinct cell types appear in response to identical notochord–SHH signaling. How can a single molecule, SHH, exert such widespread control of such diverse cell pattern on the A/P axis? The specific consequence of its action must depend on the responding tissue. SHH must be a general, permissive signal that is interpreted in a specific way by an individual competence of the induced tissue, its patterning activities working within the context of previously established A/P positional cues and previously specified A/P regional identity. That this is indeed the case has been demonstrated experimentally in the hindbrain of the chick embryo.[25] As described above, each metameric unit of the hindbrain (rhombomeres) has a unique identity. In particular, r4 is marked by the high level expression of *Hoxb-1* and at a later stage by the emergence of a unique cell group adjacent to the floor plate—the contralateral vestibuloacoustic (CVA) efferent neurons. When r4 is transplanted to a more rostral position (in place of r2), it maintains *Hoxb-1* expression, and the CVA neurons are produced. Furthermore, the CVA neurons are produced by dorsal r4 tissue when it is placed close to the ventral midline in this ectopic A/P location—the r4-specific ventral cell types are formed irrespective of the dorsoventral level of origin of the graft. Cells are apparently first assigned their A/P identity, but their ultimate choice of fate must await a later midline signal. The multipotency of precursor cells is restricted first to a repertoire appropriate to A/P position (regional identity), leaving them in a state of competence to respond to ventral midline signals that only later determine specific cell identity appropriate to D/V position (Fig. 15.20).

Dorsoventral Patterning Is Evident in the Prechordal Neural Tube

The extent of motor neurons along the A/P axis corresponds with that of their inducing tissues. Both have an anterior limit close to the midbrain–forebrain junction. Thus, the forebrain (telencephalon and diencephalon) is devoid of motor neurons and, in all regions but its most posterior, has no floor plate nor is underlain by notochord. The absence of these midline structures therefore raises the question of how the bilateral organization of the forebrain and the differentiation of its ventral cell types are controlled. Even in this terminal expansion of the CNS, however, a common mechanism appears to be used for ventral patterning.[98] SHH is expressed along the ventral midline of the forebrain, extending into bilateral wings in the diencephalon (Fig. 15.19), and ventral forebrain cells express *Isl-1*, an early marker of motor neuron specification in the more caudal regions of the CNS. Expression of *Isl-1* in the forebrain suggests, however, that it is a general marker of ventral character rather than a specific marker of motor neurons. Forebrain explants that are cultured away from ventral midline tissue do not develop *Isl-1*-expressing cells, but they will do so when cocultured with COS cells that have been transfected with *Shh*.[98] The *Isl-1*-positive cells induced by this treatment are forebrain-specific, in that they express *Nkx-2.1* and do not express any of the markers that are indicative of motor neurons. Whereas SHH is expressed in the ventral regions of both the diencephalon and telencephalon, the diencephalic domain is influential in controlling cell patterning in the ventral forebrain as a whole. SHH is expressed in the ventral diencephalon considerably before the appearance of ISL-1^+ cells in either forebrain region, and the midline rostral diencephalic cells can induce *Isl-1* expression in telencephalic cells. By contrast, the onset of telencephalic expression is later in development, apparently after the induction of *Isl-1* cells in that region has occurred. It is possible

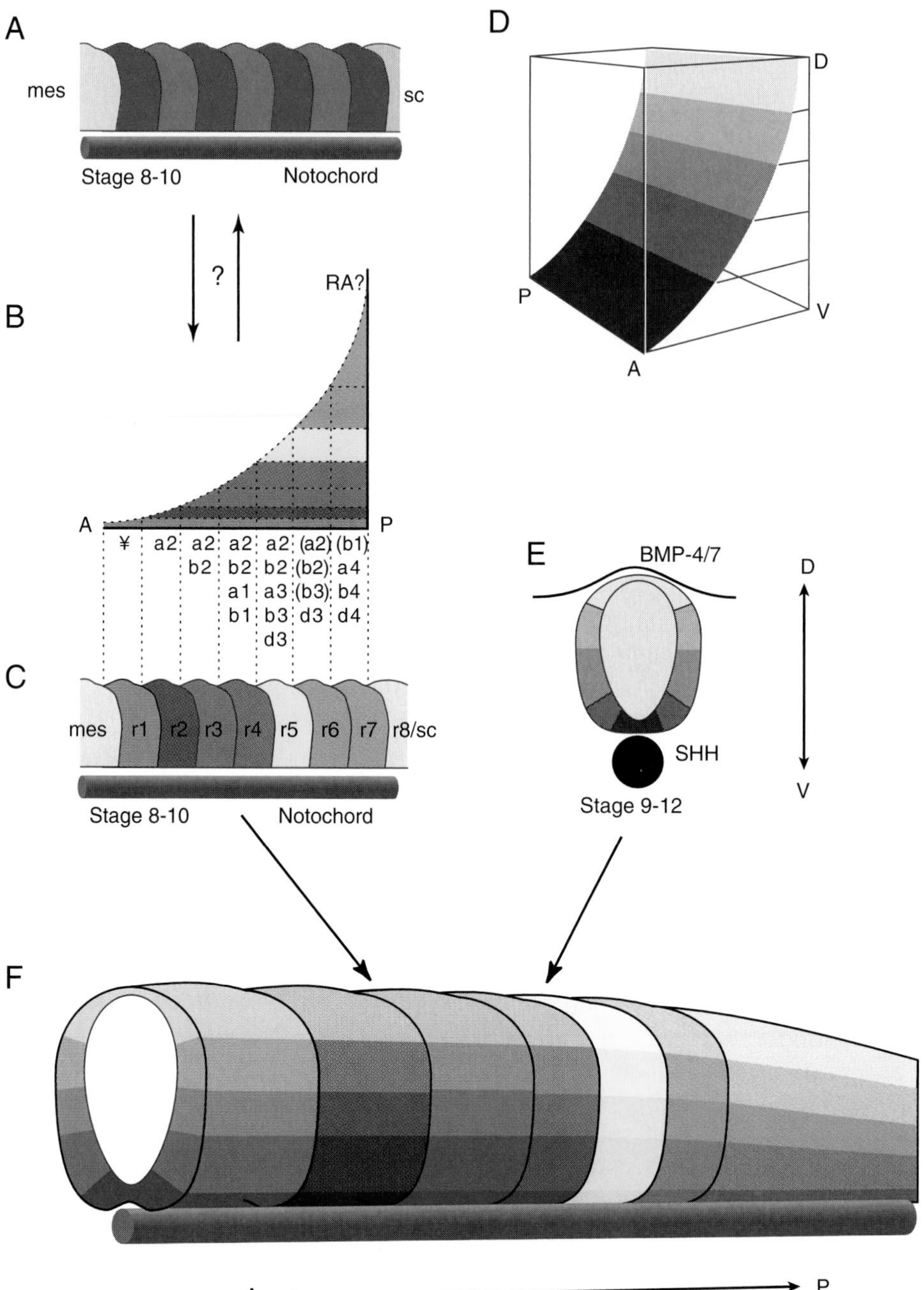

FIGURE 15.20 Conceptual scheme depicting a coordinate system of positional information in the hindbrain neural tube. In (A), the hindbrain has already acquired odd / even compartmentation. In (B, C), positional values along the A / P axis, represented by different combinations of *Hox* genes expressed by different rhombomeres, could be set up by a gradient signal of retinoids diffusing from a posterior source, possibly Hensen's node. The different A / P positional values of rhombomeres are represented by different colors, and there is as yet no D / V coordinate. This is established later (D, E), when each level of the A / P axis receives (presumably identical) signals from both the ventral pole (SHH, black) and the dorsal pole (BMP7, light gray). Finally, in (F), each rhombomere has both an A / P positional value (color) and a set of D / V positional values (intensity of color). mes, mesencephalon; sc, spinal cord. Based on data from Ref. 25.

that planar SHH signaling extends anteriorly from the diencephalon into the telencephalon.

Genetic studies in zebrafish have also identified the ventral midline of the diencephalon as a controlling region for patterning the anterior end of the nervous system. This midline territory is deleted in the *cyclops* mutant, whose phenotype most obviously involves fusion of the eyes around the anterior pole of the embryo. Molecular analysis of the early cyclops phenotype has revealed that there is no SHH expression in ventral midline structures of these embryos, presenting the possibility that the normal expression of SHH has consequences that extend beyond patterning the ventral neural tube. In homozygous *cyclops* embryos, the optic stalk, a region that normally expresses *Pax-2,* is diminished, whereas the retina, which normally expresses *Pax-6,* extends throughout the optic territory so that the eyes are fused not by optic stalk tissue but by the retina. That SHH has a role in patterning the eye was demonstrated in ectopic overexpression studies by *Shh* mRNA injection into the one-cell stage embryo.[99,100] These embryos have phenotypes that are reciprocal to those seen in cyclops: the domain of *Pax-2* expression is extended and encroaches into the territory that would normally be *Pax-6* positive, and, at the cellular level, the overexpressing embryos have an enlarged optic stalk and a reduced retina. Although the consequences of interfering with SHH signaling have yet to be analyzed in respect of eye development, these studies indicate that SHH is responsible for patterning not only the ventral forebrain but also the optic territories.

The *Pax-6* gene encodes a transcription factor that is expressed in the developing neural tube and the optic vesicle. Later, as the eye develops, transcripts appear in the lens, retina, and cornea.[101] A fundamental role in eye development is indicated by both the conservation of this expression pattern in all vertebrate embryos and the absence of eyes in mice homozygous for a mutant *Pax-6* allele (the small eye mutation is named after the heterozygous phenotype of these animals). *Pax-6* may thus lie at the head of a genetic cascade that controls development of the visual apparatus. The *Drosophila* homolog of *Pax-6* is encoded by *eyeless,* a gene that is expressed transiently during early stages of eye disc development and that is required for eye development.[102] *Eyeless* mutants have small or absent eyes, whereas overexpression of *eyeless* leads to the formation of eyes by other imaginal discs, including those of wing, leg, and antenna.[103] Although the discovery of homologous genes in related developmental pathways in flies and vertebrates is no longer greeted with surprise, what is extraordinary about this gene conservation is that vertebrate and insect eyes bear no structural similarities to each other and they function in quite different ways; they have classically been regarded as analogous rather than homologous structures. The vertebrate eye has a lens that forms an entire image on the retina, whereas the insect eye is compound, and an image is formed, pixel fashion, from a large number of separate ommatidia. Thus, the discovery of a homologous master gene suggests persuasively that the eyes of flies and vertebrates have a common developmental origin—perhaps in the establishment of an eye field.

Summary

Neural-inducing factors and modifiers produced during gastrulation have a basic role in establishing an initial crude A/P regional identity in the neural plate that emerges from the dorsal surface of the embryo at the end of this period. The nature of this earlier patterning information remains unclear, but (endo)-mesoderm-derived factors have been implicated in conferring forebrain identity and establishing an axial signaling center at the midbrain/hindbrain boundary. Posteriorly, node-derived neuralizing factors and retinoids have been implicated as positional signals that may posteriorize an initially anterior neural specification state; the *Hox* genes seem to mediate the assign-

CASE 3: A POLITICAL POWDER KEG

Ed Levine works for a federal agency that funds neuroscience research. One of the applications assigned for review by his division is from a senior investigator who proposes to test the hypothesis that there is a genetic basis for violent behavior. The review panel that examined the application for technical merit gave it an outstanding score: The proposal is well-written and the experiments are carefully designed. However, despite the fact that it was rated so highly, Dr. Levine is unsure what action he should recommend regarding the funding of this proposal. He believes that the resulting data could have serious social implications that may be politically unpopular. What should Dr. Levine do?

See Appendix for discussion questions.

ment of positional values in response to these factors. This coarse-grained pattern is subsequently reinforced and refined by both intrinsic (hindbrain) and extrinsic (spinal cord) signaling systems that result in a precise regional variation in cell identity. Although we tend to think of these as separate events, a constraint perhaps imposed by the use of different model systems, neuraxial patterning is a continuous process that extends over a protracted period of development and involves a continuity of signaling systems (e.g., retinoic acid). We tend also to think of pattern being acquired separately on the A/P and D/V axes, whereas it is clear that cell specification on the D/V axis must incorporate existing A/P positional values.

References

1. Spemann, H. (1938). *Embryonic Development and Induction.* Hafner, New York.
2. Waddington, C. H., and Schmidt, C. A. (1933). Induction by heteroplastic grafts of the primitive streak in birds. *Wilhelm Roux' Arch. Entwicklungs mech. Org.* **128:** 522–563.
3. Kintner, C. R., and Dodd, J. (1991). Hensen's node induces neural tissue in *Xenopus* ectoderm. Implications for the action of the organizer in neural induction. *Development* **113:** 1495–1505.
4. Spemann, H. (1931). Über den Anteil von Implantat und Wirtskeim and der Orientierung und Beschaffenheit der induzierten Embryonalanlage. *Wilhelm Roux' Arch. Entwicklungs mech. Org.* **123:** 389–517.
5. Holtfreter, J. (1931). Über die Aufzucht isolierter Teile des Amphibienkeimes. II. *Wilhelm Roux' Arch. Entwicklungs mech. Org.* **124:** 404–466.
6. Holtfreter, J. (1947). Neural induction in explants which have passed through a sublethal cytolysis. *J. Exp. Zool.* **106:** 197–222.
7. Harland, R. M. (1994). Neural induction in *Xenopus. Curr. Opin. Genet. Dev.* **4:** 543–549.
8. Nieuwkoop, P. D. (1973). The "organization center" of the amphibian embryo, its origin, spatial organization and morphogenetic action. *Adv. Morphog.* **10:** 1–39.
9. Smith, J. C., Cooke, J., Green, J. B., Howes, G., and Symes, K. (1989). Inducing factors and the control of mesodermal pattern in *Xenopus laevis. Development* (*Cambridge, UK*) *Suppl.* **107:** 149–159.
10. Smith, J. C., Price, B. M., Van Nimmen, K., and Huylebroeck, D. (1990). Identification of a potent *Xenopus* mesoderm-inducing factor as a homologue of activin A. *Nature* (*London*) **345:** 729–731.
11. Hemmati-Brivanlou, A., and Melton, D. A. (1992). A truncated activin receptor inhibits mesoderm induction and formation of axial structures in *Xenopus* embryos. *Nature* (*London*) **359:** 609–614.
12. Hemmati-Brivanlou, A., and Melton, D. A. (1994). Inhibition of activin receptors signaling promotes neuralization in *Xenopus. Cell* (*Cambridge, Mass.*) **77:** 273–282.
13. Grunz, H., and Tacke, L. (1989). Neural differentiation of *Xenopus laevis* ectoderm takes place after disaggregation and delayed reaggregation without inducer. *Cell Differ. Dev.* **28:** 211–217.
14. Hawley, S. H., Wünnenberg Stapleton, K., Hashimoto, C., Laurent, M. N., Watabe, T., Blumberg, B. W., and Cho, K. W. (1995). Disruption of BMP signals in embryonic *Xenopus* ectoderm leads to direct neural induction. *Genes Dev.* **9:** 2923–2935.
15. Hemmati-Brivanlou, A., and Melton, D. A. (1994). Follistatin, an antagonist of activin, is expressed in the Spemann organizer and displays direct neuralizing activity. *Cell* (*Cambridge, Mass.*) **77:** 283–296.
16. Lamb, T. M., Knecht, A. K., Smith, W. C., Stachel, S. E., Economides, A. N., Stahl, N., Yancopolous, G. D., and Harland, R. M. (1993). Neural induction by the secreted polypeptide noggin. *Science* **262:** 713–718.
17. Sasai, Y., Lu, B., Steinbeisser, H., and De Robertis, E. M. (1995). Regulation of neural induction by the Chd and Bmp-4 antagonistic patterning signals in *Xenopus. Nature* (*London*) **376:** 333–336.
18. Schoenwolf, G. C. (1994). Formation and patterning of the avian neuraxis: One dozen hypotheses. *Ciba Found. Symp.* **181:** 25–38.
19. Keller, R., Shih, J., and Sater, A. (1992). The cellular basis of the convergence and extension of the *Xenopus* neural plate. *Dev. Dyn.* **193:** 199–217.
20. Townes, P. L., and Holtfreter, J. (1955). Directed movements and selective adhesion of embryonic amphibian cells. *J. Exp. Zool.* **128:** 53–120.
21. Gumbiner, B. M. (1996). Cell adhesion: The molecular basis of tissue architecture and morphogenesis. *Cell* (*Cambridge, Mass.*) **84:** 345–357.
22. Miyatani, S., Shimamura, K., Hatta, M., Nagafuchi, A., Nose, A., Matsunaga, M., Hatta, K., and Takeichi, M. (1989). Neural cadherin: Role in selective cell–cell adhesion. *Science* **245:** 631–635.
23. Fujimori, T., Miyatani, S., and Takeichi, M. (1990). Ectopic expression of N-cadherin perturbs histogenesis in *Xenopus* embryos. *Development* (*Cambridge, UK*) **110:** 97–104.
24. Sauer, F. C. (1936). The interkinetic migration of embryonic epithelial nuclei *J. Morphol.* **60:** 1–11.
25. Simon, H., Hornbruch, A., and Lumsden, A. (1995). Independent assignment of antero-posterior and dorso-ventral positional values in the developing chick hindbrain. *Curr. Biol.* **5:** 205–214.
26. Mangold, O. (1933). Über die Induktionsfähigkeit der vershiendenen Bezirke der Neurula bon Urodelen. *Naturwissenschaften* **21:** 761–766.
27. Holtfreter, J. (1933). Die totale Exogastrulation, eine Selbstablosung des Ektoderms von entomesoderm. *Wilhelm Roux' Arch. Entwiklungs mech. Org.* **129:** 669–793.
28. Ruiz i Altaba, A. (1990). Neural expression of the *Xenopus* homeobox gene Xhox3: Evidence for a patterning neural signal that spreads through the ectoderm. *Development* (*Cambridge, UK*) **108:** 595–604.
29. Doniach, T., Phillips, C. R., and Gerhart, J. C. (1992). Planar induction of anteroposterior pattern in the developing central nervous system of *Xenopus laevis. Science* **257:** 542–545.
30. Saxén, L. (1989). Neural induction. *Int. J. Dev. Biol.* **33:** 21–48.
31. Blumberg, B., Bolado, J., Moreno, T., Kintner, C., Evans, R., and Papalopulu, N. (1997). An essential role for retinoid signaling in anteroposterior neural patterning. *Development* (*Cambridge, UK*) **124:** 373–379.
32. Kroll, K. L., and Amaya, E. (1996). Transgenic *Xenopus* embryos from sperm nuclear transplantations reveal FGF signaling requirements during gastrulation. *Development* (*Cambridge, UK*) **122:** 3173–3183.
33. Papalopulu, N., and Kintner, C. (1996). A posteriorising factor, retinoic acid, reveals that anteroposterior patterning controls the timing of neuronal differentiation in *Xenopus* neuroectoderm. *Development* (*Cambridge, UK*) **122:** 3409–3418.
34. Lawrence, P. A., and Struhl, G. (1996). Morphogens, compartments, and pattern: Lessons from *Drosophila? Cell* (*Cambridge, Mass.*) **85:** 951–961.

35. Lumsden, A. (1990). The cellular basis of segmentation in the developing hindbrain. *Trends Neurosci.* **13:** 329–335.
36. Lumsden, A., and Krumlauf, R. (1996). Patterning the vertebrate neuraxis. *Science* **274:** 1109–1115.
37. Lumsden, A., and Keynes, R. (1989). Segmental patterns of neuronal development in the chick hindbrain. *Nature* (*London*) **337:** 424–428.
38. Clarke, J. D., and Lumsden, A. (1993). Segmental repetition of neuronal phenotype sets in the chick embryo hindbrain. *Development* (*Cambridge, UK*) **118:** 151–162.
39. Fraser, S., Keynes, R., and Lumsden, A. (1990). Segmentation in the chick embryo hindbrain is defined by cell lineage restrictions. *Nature* (*London*) **344:** 431–435.
40. Wingate, R., and Lumsden, A. (1996). Persistence of rhombomeric organisation in the postsegmental avian hindbrain. *Development* (*Cambridge, UK*) **122:** 2143–2152.
41. Hornbruch, A., and Lumsden, A. Unpublished work.
42. Figdor, M. C., and Stern, C. D. (1993). Segmental organisation of embryonic diencephalon. *Nature* (*London*) **363:** 630–634.
43. Rubenstein, J. L. R., Martinez, S., Shimamura, K., and Puelles, L. (1994). The embryonic vertebrate forebrain: The prosomeric model. *Science* **266:** 578–580.
44. Fishell, G., Mason, C. A., and Hatten, M. E. (1993). Dispersion of neural progenitors within the germinal zones of the forebrain. *Nature* (*London*) **362:** 636–638.
45. Götz, M., Wizenmann, A., Lumsden, A., and Price, J. (1996). Selective adhesion of cells from different telencephalic regions. *Neuron* **16:** 551–564.
46. Newman, S. A. (1993). Is segmentation generic? *BioEssays* **15:** 277–283.
47. Wilkinson, D. G., Bhatt, S., Chavrier, P., Bravo, R., and Charnay, P. (1989). Segment-specific expression of a zinc-finger gene in the developing nervous system of the mouse. *Nature* (*London*) **337:** 461–465.
48. Schneider-Maunoury, S., Topilko, P., Seitanidou, T., Levi, G., Cohen-Tannoudji, M., Pournin, S., Babinet, C., and Charnay, P. (1993). Disruption of *Krox*-20 results in alteration of rhombomeres 3 and 5 in the developing hindbrain. *Cell* (*Cambridge, Mass.*) **75:** 1199–1214.
49. Becker, N., Seitanidou, T., Murphy, P., Mattei, M.-G., Topilko, P., Nieto, M. A., Wilkinson, D. G., Charnay, P., and Gilardo-Hebenstreit, P. (1994). Several receptor tyrosine kinase genes of the *Eph* family are segmentally expressed in the developing hindbrain. *Mech. Dev.* **47:** 3–17.
50. Bergeman, A. D., Cheng, H. J., Brambilla, R., Klein, R., and Flanagan, J. G. (1995). Elf-2, a new member of the Eph ligand family, is segmentally expressed in mouse embryos in the region of the hindbrain and newly formed somites. *Mol. Cell. Biol.* **15:** 4921–4929.
51. Xu, Q., Alldus, G., Holder, N., and Wilkinson, D. G. (1995). Expression of truncated Sek-1 receptor tyrosine kinase disrupts the segmental restriction of gene expression in the *Xenopus* and zebrafish hindbrain. *Development* (*Cambridge, UK*) **121:** 4005–4016.
52. Frohman, M. A., Martin, G. R., Cordes, S., Halamek, L. P., and Barsh, G. S. (1993). Altered rhombomere-specific gene expression and hyoid bone differentiation in the mouse segmentation mutant kreisler (kr). *Development* (*Cambridge, UK*) **117:** 925–936.
53. McKay, I. J., Muchamore, I., Krumaluf, R., Maden, M., Lumsden, A., and Lewis, J. (1994). The *kreisler* mouse: A hindbrain segmentation mutant that lacks two rhombomeres. *Development* (*Cambridge, UK*) **120:** 2199–2211.
54. Cordes, S. P., and Barsh, G. S. (1994). The mouse segmentation gene kr encodes a novel basic domain-leucine zipper transcription factor. *Cell* (*Cambridge, Mass.*) **79:** 1025–1034.
55. Krumlauf, R. (1994). Hox genes in vertebrate development. *Cell* (*Cambridge, Mass.*) **78:** 191–201.
56. Crossley, P. H., Martinez, S., and Martin, G. R. (1996). Midbrain development induced by FGF8 in the chick embryo. *Nature* (*London*) **380:** 66–68.
57. Joyner, A. L. (1996). Engrailed, wnt and pax genes regulate midbrain–hindbrain development. *Trends Genet.* **12:** 15–20.
58. Studer, M. Unpublished data.
59. Lufkin, T., Dierich, A., LeMeur, M., Mark, M., and Chambon, P. (1991). Disruption of the Hox-1.6 homeobox gene results in defects in a region corresponding to its rostral domain of expression. *Cell* (*Cambridge, Mass.*) **66:** 1105–1119.
60. Mark, M., Lufkin, T., Vonesch, J. L., Ruberte, E., Olivo, J. C., Dolle, P., Gorry, P., Lumsden, A., and Chambon, P. (1993). Two rhombomeres are altered in Hoxa-1 mutant mice. *Development* (*Cambridge, UK*) **119:** 319–338.
61. Thor, S. (1995). The genetics of brain development: Conserved programs in flies and mice. *Neuron* **15:** 975–977.
62. Wurst, W., Auerbach, A. B., and Joyner, A. L. (1994). Multiple developmental defects in *Engrailed*-1 mutant mice: An early mid-hindbrain deletion and patterning defects in forelimbs and sternum. *Development* (*Cambridge, UK*) **120:** 2065–2075.
63. Alvarado-Mallart, R. M. (1993). Fate and potentialities of the avian mesencephalic/metencephalic neuroepithelium. *J. Neurobiol.* **24:** 1341–1355.
64. Itasaki, N., Ichijo, H., Hama, C., Matsuno, T., and Nakamura, H. (1991). Establishment of rostrocaudal polarity in tectal primordium: Engrailed expression and subsequent tectal polarity. *Development* (*Cambridge, UK*) **113:** 1133–1144.
65. Logan, C., Wizenmann, A., Drescher, U., Monschau, B., Bonhoeffer, F., and Lumsden, A. (1996). Rostral optic tectum adopts a caudal phenotype following ectopic engrailed expression. *Curr. Biol.* **6:** 1006–1014.
66. Simeone, A., Acampora, D., Gulisano, M., Stornaiuolo, A., and Boncinelli, E. (1992). Nested expression domains of four homeobox genes in developing rostral brain. *Nature* (*London*) **358:** 687–690.
67. Acampora, D., Mazan, S., Lallemand, Y., Avantaggiato, V., Maury, M., Simeone, A., and Brulet, P. (1995). Forebrain and midbrain regions are deleted in Otx2-/- mutants due to a defective anterior neuroectoderm specification during gastrulation. *Development* (*Cambridge, UK*) **121:** 3279–3290.
68. Eagleston, G. W., and Harris, W. A. (1990). Mapping of the presumptive brain region in the neural plate of *Xenopus laevis. J. Neurobiol.* **21:** 427–440.
69. LeDouarin, N. (1986). Cephalic placodes and neurogenesis. *Trends Neurosci.* **9:** 175–180.
70. Bulfone, A., Puelles, L., Porteus, M. H., Frohman, M. A., Martin, G. R., and Rubenstein, J. L. R. (1993). Spatially restricted expression of *Dlx-1, Dlx-2* (*Tes-1*), *GBx-2* and *Wnt-3* in the embryonic day 12.5 mouse forebrain defines potential transverse and longitudinal segmental boundaries. *J. Neurosci.* **13:** 3155–3172.
71. Chen, Y. P., Huang, L., Russo, A. F., and Solursh, M. (1992). Retinoic acid is enriched in Hensen's node and is developmentally regulated in the early chick embryo. *Proc. Natl. Acad. Sci. U.S.A.* **89:** 10056–10059.
72. Durston, A. J., Timmermans, J. P., Hage, W. J., Hendriks, H. F., de Vries, N. J., Heideveld, M., and Nieuwkoop, P. D. (1989). Retinoic acid causes an anteroposterior transformation in the developing central nervous system. *Nature* (*London*) **340:** 140–144.
73. Simeone, A., Acampora, D., Nigro, V., Faiella, A., D'Esposito,

M., Stornaiuolo, A., Mavilio, F., and Boncinelli, E. (1991). Differential regulation by retinoic acid of the homeobox genes of the four HOX loci in human embryonal carcinoma cells. *Mech. Dev.* **33:** 215–228.

74. Hill, J., Clarke, J. D. W., Vargesson, N., Jowett, T., and Holder, N. (1995). Exogenous retinoic acid causes specific alterations in the development of the midbrain and hindbrain of the zebrafish embryo including positional respecification of the Mauthner neuron. *Mech. Dev.* **50:** 3–16.
75. Marshall, H., Nonchev, S., Sham, M.-H., Muchamore, I., Lumsden, A., and Krumlauf, R. (1992). Retinoic acid alters hindbrain *Hox* code and induces transformation of rhombomeres 2/3 into a 4/5 identity. *Nature (London)* **360:** 737–741.
76. Mangelsdorf, D. J., and Evans, R. M. (1995). The RXR heterodimers and ophan receptors. *Cell (Cambridge, Mass.)* **83:** 841–850.
77. Marshall, H., Studer, M., Popperl, H., Aparicio, S., Kuroiwa, A., Brenner, S., and Krumlauf, R. (1994). A conserved retinoic acid response element required for early expression of the homeobox gene Hoxb-1. *Nature (London)* **370:** 567–571.
78. Studer, M., Popperl, H., Marshall, H., Kuroiwa, A., and Krumlauf, R. (1994). Role of a conserved retinoic acid response element in rhombomere restriction of Hoxb-1. *Science* **265:** 1728–1732.
79. Song, D.-L., Chalepakis, G., Gruss, P., and Joyner, A. L. (1996). Two Pax-binding sites are required for early embryonic brain expression of an *Engrailed*-2 transgene. *Development (Cambridge, UK)* **122:** 627–635.
80. Keynes, R., and Stern, C. (1984). Segmentation in the vertebrate nervous system. *Nature (London)* **310:** 786–789.
81. Davies, J., Cook, G., Stern, C. D., and Keynes, R. J. (1990). Isolation from chick somites of a glycoprotein that causes collapse of dorsal root ganglion growth cones. *Neuron* **4:** 11–20.
82. Tsuchida, T., Ensini, M., Morton, S. B., Baldassare, M., Edlund, T., Jessell, T. M., and Pfaff, S. L. (1994). Topographic organisation of embryonic motor neurons defined by expression of LIM homeobox genes. *Cell (Cambridge, Mass.)* **79:** 957–970.
83. Jessell, T. M., and Lumsden, A. (1997). Inductive signals and the assignment of cell fate in the spinal cord and hindbrain: An axial coordinate system for neural patterning. In *Molecular and Cellular Approaches to Development*, (W. M. Cowan, T. M. Jessell, and S. L. Zipursky, eds.), pp. 290–333. Oxford University Press, Oxford.
84. Noden, D. (1988). Interactions and fates of avian craniofacial mesenchyme. *Development (Cambridge, UK)* **103:** 121–140.
85. Hunt, P., Gulisano, M., Cook, M., Sham, M.-H., Faiella, A., Wilkinson, D., Boncinelli, E., and Krumlauf, R. (1991). A distinct *Hox* code for the branchial region of the vertebrate head. *Nature (London)* **353:** 861–864.
86. Lumsden, A., and Graham, A. (1996). Death in the neural crest: Implications for pattern formation. *Semin. Cell Dev. Biol.* **7:** 169–174.
87. Goulding, M. D., Lumsden, A., and Gruss, P. (1993). Signals from the notochord and floor plate regulate the region-specific expression of two Pax genes in the developing spinal cord. *Development (Cambridge, UK)* **117:** 1011–1016.
88. Yamada, T., Placzek, M., Tanaka, H., Dodd, J., and Jessell, T. M. (1991). Control of cell pattern in the developing nervous system: Polarizing activity of the floor plate and notochord. *Cell (Cambridge, Mass.)* **64:** 635–647.
89. Van Straaten, H. W. M., Hekking, J. W. M., Wiertz-Hoessels, F., Thors, F., and Drukker, J. (1988). Effect of the notochord on the differentiation of a floor plate area in the neural tube of the chick embryo. *Anat. Embryol.* **177:** 317–324.
90. Roelink, H., Porter, J. A., Chiang, C., Tanabe, Y., Chang, D. T., Beachy, P. A., and Jessell, T. M. (1995). Floor plate and motor neuron induction by different concentrations of the amino-terminal cleavage product of sonic hedgehog autoproteolysis. *Cell (Cambridge, Mass.)* **81:** 445–455.
91. Hynes, M., Porter, J., Chiang, C., Chang, D., Tessier-Lavigne, M., Beachy, P., and Rosenthal, A. (1995). Induction of midbrain dopaminergic neurons by sonic hedgehog. *Neuron* **15:** 1–20.
92. Hynes, M., Poulsen, K., Tessier-Lavigne, M., and Rosenthal, A. (1995). Control of neuronal diversity by the floor plate: Contact-mediated induction of midbrain dopaminergic neurons. *Cell (Cambridge, Mass.)* **80:** 95–101.
93. Tremblay, P., Pituello, F., and Gruss, P. (1996). Inhibition of floor plate differentiation by Pax3: Evidence from ectopic expression in transgenic mice. *Development (Cambridge, UK)* **122:** 2555–2567.
94. Ericson, J., Thor, S., Edlund, T., Jessell, T. M., and Yamada, T. (1992). Early stages of motor neuron differentiation revealed by expression of homeobox gene Islet-1. *Science* **256:** 1555–1560.
95. Pfaff, S. L., Mendelsohn, M., Stewart, C. L., Edlund, T., and Jessell, T. M. (1996). Requirement for LIM homeobox gene Is11 in motor neuron generation reveals a motor neuron-dependent step in interneuron differentiation. *Cell (Cambridge, Mass.)* **84:** 1–20.
96. Liem, K. F., Tremml, G., Roelink, H., and Jessell, T. M. (1995). Dorsal differentiation of neural plate cells induced by BMP-mediated signals from epidermal ectoderm. *Cell (Cambridge, Mass.)* **82:** 969–979.
97. Chalepakis, G., Stoykova, A., Wijnholds, J., Tremblay, P., and Gruss, P. (1993). Pax gene regulators in the developing nervous system. *J. Neurobiol.* **24:** 1367–1384.
98. Ericson, J., Muhr, J., Placzek, M., Lints, T., Jessell, T. M., and Edlund, T. (1995). Sonic hedgehog induces the differentiation of ventral forebrain neurons: A common signal for ventral patterning within the neural tube. *Cell (Cambridge, Mass.)* **81:** 747–756.
99. Ekker, S. C., Ungar, A. R., Greenstein, P., von Kessler, D. P., Porter, J. A., Moon, R. T., and Beachy, P. A. (1995). Patterning activities of vertebrate hedgehog proteins in the developing eye and brain. *Curr. Biol.* **5:** 944–955.
100. Macdonald, R., Barth, K. A., Xu, Q., Holder, N., Mikkola, I., and Wilson, S. W. (1995). Midline signalling is required for Pax gene regulation and patterning of the eyes. *Development (Cambridge, UK)* **121:** 3267–3278.
101. Macdonald, R., and Wilson, S. W. (1996). Pax proteins and eye development. *Curr. Opin. Neurobiol.* **6:** 49–56.
102. Quiring, R., Walldorf, U., Kloter, U., and Gehring, W. J. (1994). *Small eye* results from mutations in a paired-like homeobox-containing gene. *Nature (London)* **354:** 522–525.
103. Halder, G., Callaerts, P., and Gehring, W. J. (1995). Induction of ectopic eyes by targeted expression of the *eyeless* gene in *Drosophila*. *Science* **267:** 1788–1792.
104. Boncinelli, E. (1994). Early CNS development: Distal-less related genes and forebrain development. *Curr. Opin. Neurobiol.* **4:** 29–36.

CHAPTER

16

Neurogenesis and Migration

Mary E. Hatten and Nathaniel Heintz

One of the more remarkable features of the developing nervous system is the wide-ranging migration by precursor cells. These movements are orchestrated to promote the differentiation of an astonishing array of phenotypes and to arrange young neurons into the most complex biological structure known, the vertebrate brain. In humans, more than a hundred billion cells, including hundreds of different types of neurons, utilize directed cell migrations to aid in the assembly of neural networks that comprise some 10^{14} synaptic contacts. This complexity of cellular structure and synaptic connections is achieved by the construction of a novel cellular organization—most notably the laminar arrangement of neurons in higher cortical regions. Thus, central questions concerning the nervous system are: Why is cellular migration pervasive in the formation of these structures? How is the movement of cells across long distances achieved? In this chapter, we compare the cellular and molecular strategies used to generate the peripheral and central nervous systems, focusing on the role of directed cell migrations in the execution of specific programs of neuronal differentiation.

DEVELOPMENT OF THE PERIPHERAL NERVOUS SYSTEM

Neural Crest Cells Migrate Over Long Distances and Adopt a Variety of Fates

The **neural crest** is a transitory, embryonic structure that generates a population of proliferating cells that migrate away from the closing neural tube to populate the periphery. Although many cells within this population will acquire a neuronal fate and form the peripheral nervous system (PNS), others will give rise to a wide variety of structures ranging from the melanocytes of the skin to the craniofacial skeleton. In vertebrate embryos, cells of the neural crest population form within the dorsal aspect of the neuroepithelium. In the chick, emerging neural crest cells express a number of specific transcriptional regulatory proteins under the inductive influence of the overlying ectoderm.[1–3] Shortly after fusion of the neural folds, the neural crest cell population separates from the neural plate, and streams of dividing crest cells begin their journey through the embryo. An important regulatory element in the specification of the fate of individual cells in the crest population is the migratory pathway taken by the cells, as this pathway controls the availability of inducing factors for particular cell fates.

Mapping the fates of neural crest cell populations was greatly facilitated by Nicole le Douarin's development of a system for marking cells within the population and following them from their sites of origin along the axis of the neural tube to distal sites throughout the developing embryo.[4] This method consists of constructing embryos that are **chimeras**—or mixtures—of chick and quail cells by grafting portions of the quail neuraxis into chicks at the times when neural crest populations arise at various locales (Fig. 16.1).[5] The use of the chick–quail marking system made it possible to demonstrate that neural crest cell populations originating in different axial levels follow different migratory pathways and give rise to different progeny once they reach their destinations.[5] These experiments revealed that crest cells assume different fates in different locales

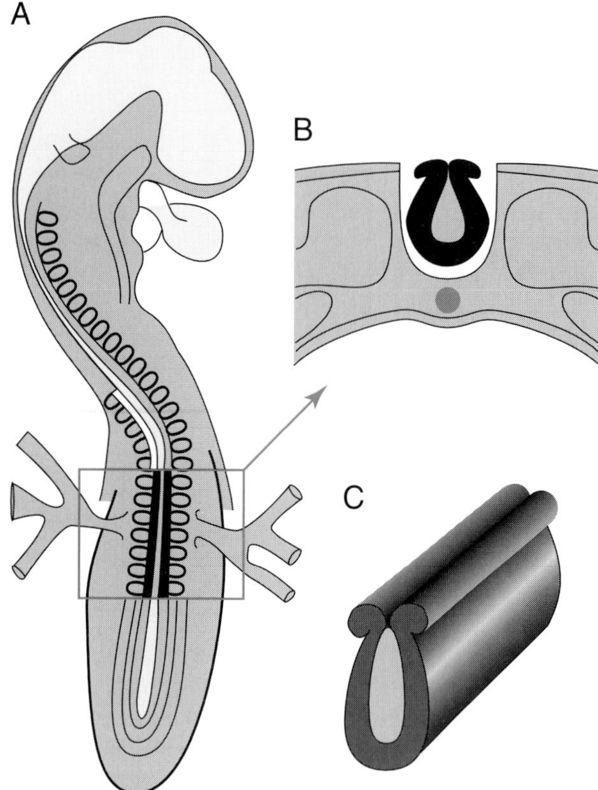

FIGURE 16.1 Procedures for grafting a fragment of the neural primordium from a quail donor into a chick host, as used by LeDouarin and her colleagues. (A) Dorsal view of an avian embryo (anterior is at the top). The neural folds are shown in black in the boxed region; this structure was removed and transplanted into a host embryo. (B) Cross section through the embryo in the regions shown in the box in (A). The neural tube is shown in black. (C) Representation of a region of neural tissue to be grafted into a host embryo. From LeDouarin.[5]

within the developing PNS. See Box 16.1 for a description of this and other cell marking techniques

To illustrate how migration may contribute to neural crest cell specification, it is helpful to summarize the pathways of migration and fates of cells that arrive in particular spatial domains in the embryo. We can accomplish this by tracing the movements of cells emanating from various levels of the neural tube by vital dye labeling[6] or retroviral marking methods,[7] and deciphering programs of differentiation taken by specific classes of cells using the expression of specific genes as markers for specific classes of neurons in the PNS.

The Cranial Pathways

The craniofacial neural crest population has a remarkably complex pattern of migration and cell fates that has only begun to be decoded. In the head region of the embryo, the PNS is a mixture of cells that arise in **placodes,** described in Chapter 15, and the neural crest cell population from the cranial region. The migration of the neural crest cell populations commences shortly after the neural folds fuse at the midline, when streams of labeled cells can be seen moving away under the cranial ectoderm toward the periphery. Neural crest cells from the most anterior portion, the forebrain, migrate ventrally in a continuous stream, passing through the mesenchyme between the developing eye and the diencephalon. Neural crest cells at the level of the midbrain take a ventrolateral route, coursing through the mesenchyme at the lateral surface of the mesencephalon and ectoderm. Cells in the dorsal aspect of the developing hindbrain generate neural crest populations, undergoing individuation and migration in three streams of cells that follow the segmental pat-

BOX 16.1

LABELING EMBRYONIC CELLS AND THEIR PROGENY

To study the movements and fates of specific cells over time, researchers usually must label the cells in some way that distinguishes them from their neighbors. In the earliest fate-mapping studies, cells were labeled by external application of either vital dyes or colored powders. These methods provided valuable information about the movements of large populations of cells, but were compromised by the tendency of the labels to either diffuse away or detach from the cells to which they were initially applied. More accurate marking was obtained with the [^{3}H]thymidine-labeling method, first developed in the late 1950s by Richard Sidman to study neural crest cell migration.[1] In this method, the tissue piece or cells of interest are removed from a donor animal, incubated with [^{3}H]thymidine, which becomes incorporated into cell nuclei during DNA synthesis, and transplanted into a host animal from which the equivalent endogenous cell population has usually been removed. The transplanted cells could be distinguished from those of the host by autoradiography. Although the thymidine label is nondiffusible, it has the disadvantage of becoming diluted over time as the labeled cells divide. In addition, autoradiographic processing is very time consuming. Additional sensitivity and much greater ease of use can be obtained with fluorescent dyes, of which the lipophilic dye DiI has proven by far the most popular because of the intensity of its fluorescence.[2,3] However, even the DiI signal becomes diluted to undetectable levels in rapidly dividing cell populations.

To follow cells through unlimited cell divisions, researchers turned to interspecific chimeras, in which the cell population of interest is removed from a donor animal and transplanted into a host of a different species. This method is applicable in cases where (1) the cells of the donor species have features that distinguish them from the cells of the host and (2) the donor and host species are sufficiently similar to permit relatively normal development of the donor tissue within the host. The most commonly used interspecific chimeras have employed either unpigmented and pigmented species of amphibians or quail and chick embryos. The quail / chick chimera system, developed by Nicole Le Douarin,[4] takes advantage of a heterochromatin marker found in the nuclei of quail cells but absent from chick cells. The quail / chick chimera system proved key to the accurate delineation of the migratory pathways and developmental potentials of neural crest cells and has more recently been extended to studies of CNS development as well. Moreover, the use of chimeras is no longer confined to avian and amphibian embryos: in the past 10 years, species-specific antibodies and cDNA probes that permit transplantation between many of the standard experimental species have been developed.

Researchers encounter a special challenge when trying to examine the fates of single cells rather than cell populations. Some organisms, such as *Caenorhabditis elegans* and zebrafish, are sufficiently translucent that each of their cells can be identified under Nomarski optics and followed with time-lapse photography. In most organisms, however, the cells must be labeled in some way. Two methods for doing this have so far been developed. In the first method, individual cells are intracellularly microinjected with a dye, usually fluorescent.[5,6] Because the dyes that are used cannot diffuse out of the cell or pass through gap junctions, only the injected cell and its progeny are labeled. The limitation of this method, as with all dye-labeling methods, is dilution of the dye with cell division. This problem led to the development of a second method, the retroviral labeling method, by which cells can be labeled permanently and heritably.[7] In this method, cells are infected with a retrovirus carrying a reporter gene, such as β-galactosidase, the expression of which can be detected histochemically (Fig. 16.11). The gene is incorporated into the cell's DNA and is subsequently expressed in both the infected cell and its progeny. The retrovirus is administered by injection into the region of interest. The concentrations used are low enough that only a few cells within the exposed population are infected, and the distance between infected cells is greater than the distance across which progeny of any one cell (i.e., a clone) would be expected to disperse. Hard data supporting assumptions about the spatial dispersion of cells within a clone may be lacking; hence, the major drawback to the retroviral labeling technique is lack of complete certainty about the clonal nature of a group of labelled cells. For further discussion of this problem, see Refs. 8 and 9. The retroviral labeling technique has proven especially useful for analyses of cell lineages within the cerebral cortex.

Gabrielle G. LeBlanc

References

1. Weston, J. A. (1963). A radioautographic analysis of the migration and localization of trunk neural crest cells in the chick. *Dev. Biol.* **6:** 279–310.
2. Honig, M. G., and Hume, R. I. (1986). Fluorescent carbocyanine dyes allow living neurons of identified origin to be studied in long-term cultures. *J. Cell Biol.* **103:** 171–187.
3. O'Rourke, N. A., Dailey, M. E., Smith, S. J., and McConnell, S. K. (1992). Diverse migratory pathways in the developing cerebral cortex. *Science* **258:** 299–302.
4. LeDouarin, N. M. (1982). *The Neural Crest.* Cambridge University Press, Cambridge.
5. Jacobson, M., and Hirose, G. (1981). Clonal organization of the central nervous system of the frog. II. Clones stemming from individual blastomeres of the 32- and 64-cell stages. *J. Neurosci.* **1:** 271–284.
6. Bronner-Fraser, M., and Fraser, S. E. (1988). Cell lineage analysis reveals multipotency of some avian neural crest cells. *Nature* **335:** 161–164.
7. Walsh, C., and Cepko, C. (1988). Clonally related cortical cells show several migration patterns. *Science* **241:** 1342–1345.
8. Luskin, M. B., Parnavelas, J. G., and Barfield, J. A. (1993). Neurons, astrocytes, and oligodendrocytes of the rat cerebral cortex originate from separate progenitor cells: an ultrastructural analysis of clonally related cells. *J. Neurosci.* **13:** 1730–1750.
9. Walsh, C., and Cepko, C. L. (1992). Widespread dispersion of neuronal clones across functional regions of the cerebral cortex. *Science* **255:** 434–440.

terning of the hindbrain. All three of these streams move ventrolaterally, beneath the ectoderm, from the dorsal portion of the tube into the distal portion of the branchial arches.

By labeling embryos at different stages of development with vital dyes, researchers mapped[8] the migratory range of the streams of neural crest cells, drawing the general conclusion that cells are generated in a ventral-to-dorsal order (Fig. 16.2A). Thus, in the head, migratory cells generated early form the most ventral structures, and cells generated later form dorsal structures. The process of neural crest cell migration is very rapid, with the time span between the earliest and the latest cells in the cranial neural crest cell population of the mouse being a brief 9–12 h.

The Trunk Pathways

In the trunk region, crest cells give rise to critical PNS structures, including the chain of sympathetic ganglia stretching down the trunk region and the dorsal root ganglia. In addition to these neuronal classes, the crest generates **Schwann cells**—PNS glia that ensheathe or myelinate PNS axons—and nonneural cells, particularly melanocytes. Neuronal precursor cells within the crest population arise in a stream of cells that migrate over a ventral route[9] through the somites, giving rise to the **dorsal root ganglia** (sensory neurons), the **sympathetic ganglia** (autonomic nervous system), and the **adrenal chromaffin cells** (Figs. 16.3 and 16.4). In contrast, precursors of the melanocytes of the skin follow a dorsal route under the overlying ectoderm. Thus, the phenotypic specification of precursor cells within the neural crest population is correlated with the migratory pathways of the cells.

The Enteric Nervous System

Neural crest cells from anterior (vagal) and posterior (sacral) regions migrate into the gut, where they form the enteric nervous system. Within the gut, the earliest-generated crest cells move as a wave from anterior to posterior to populate the bowel. Both retroviral marking methods and neurogenetic approaches have been used to examine the role of the migratory pathway in the differentiation of enteric neural crest cells.[10] Interspecies chimeras between chick and mouse demonstrated that failure of crest migration in the aganglionic bowel of *lethal spotted* mutant mice relates to a defect in mesenchymal components. These experiments provide support for the idea that normal mesenchymal development is required to support neural crest cell colonization by the vagal and sacral crest populations. Surprisingly, the genes identified as giving rise to inherited aganglionic syndromes in mice and humans encode endothelins and endothelin receptors, whose role in determining mesenchymal development and/or neuronal responses to the extracellular matrix (ECM) remains to be defined.

Migratory Pathways Are Linked to Phenotypic Specification

To test the role of migratory pathways in the phenotypic specification of neural crest cells, portions of the neuraxis have been grafted to different levels of the spinal cord and the cells allowed to undergo migration and development in a new location. Surprisingly, transplanted cells differentiated according to their new migratory pathway, not according to their site of origin along the neuraxis.[11] Whether the instructive cues arise along the pathway or from the destination determined by the migratory pathway has not yet been determined in most cases. One exception to this is sympatho-adrenal precursors that colonize the adrenal gland. In response to glucocorticoids, these cells become endocrine chromaffin cells, whereas those that will form ganglia become neurons[12] (see Chapter 17). Thus, the range of potential fates that may be adopted by migrating crest cells is much greater than the set of fates actually expressed by any given set of cells as they settle and differentiate within their final positions.

Results of studies on heterotypic and heterochronic transplants in the neural crest system allow us to draw a number of general conclusions about how the time of origin of the cells, pathways of migration, and final site contribute to cell fate specification. The first general conclusion is that the neural crest population contains multipotential cells.[8,13]

The capacity of cells to give rise to appropriate derivatives depends on the time of grafting. If the crest population is transplanted early, prior to migration, a number of cells can alter their fates. At progressively

FIGURE 16.2 (A) Labeling of neural tube and neural crest cells with the lipophilic tracers. On the left is a chick embryo viewed shortly after unilateral ablation of roughly half of the neural tube in the midbrain, including the neural crest. DiO (green) was injected focally into the residual neural tube in this region. DiI (red-orange) was injected into the bordering intact neural folds of the neighboring hindbrain. On the right is a view of the embryo 36 h later, when cells that originated in the neural tube (green) have dispersed to form neural crest cells in the midbrain. The undisturbed neural crest cells of the hindbrain (red-orange) have migrated laterally into the second branchial arch, as expected for their normal development. Only a few have moved rostrally into the region of the ablated midbrain. This experiment reveals the normal migratory pathways for cephalic crest cells and the potential for the neural tube to regenerate neural crest cells following ablation. (B) The origins and distributions of cephalic neural crest cells in chick–quail transplantation experiments. Grafts were obtained from a variety of levels and stages. The prosencephalon (Pros.), mesencephalon (Mes.), and anterior and posterior rhombencephalon (ant. Rhomb. and Post. Rhomb.) were removed from quail embryos (shown) and transplanted isotopically and isochronically into host chick embryos. S4, S6, S8, and S10 indicate the stage at which the graft was removed, defined by the number of somite pairs that were present (e.g., S4 = 4 somite pair stage). (C) The final destinations of neural crest cells derived from each of the different grafts at stage 20 in the host chick embryo are indicated in pink or red stripping. (1) Positions of cells derived from and transplanted into the prosencephalon. (2) Mesencephalon. (3) Rhombencephalon. (4) An overview of the derivatives of the entire cephalic neural crest. From Nicole LeDouarin.[5]

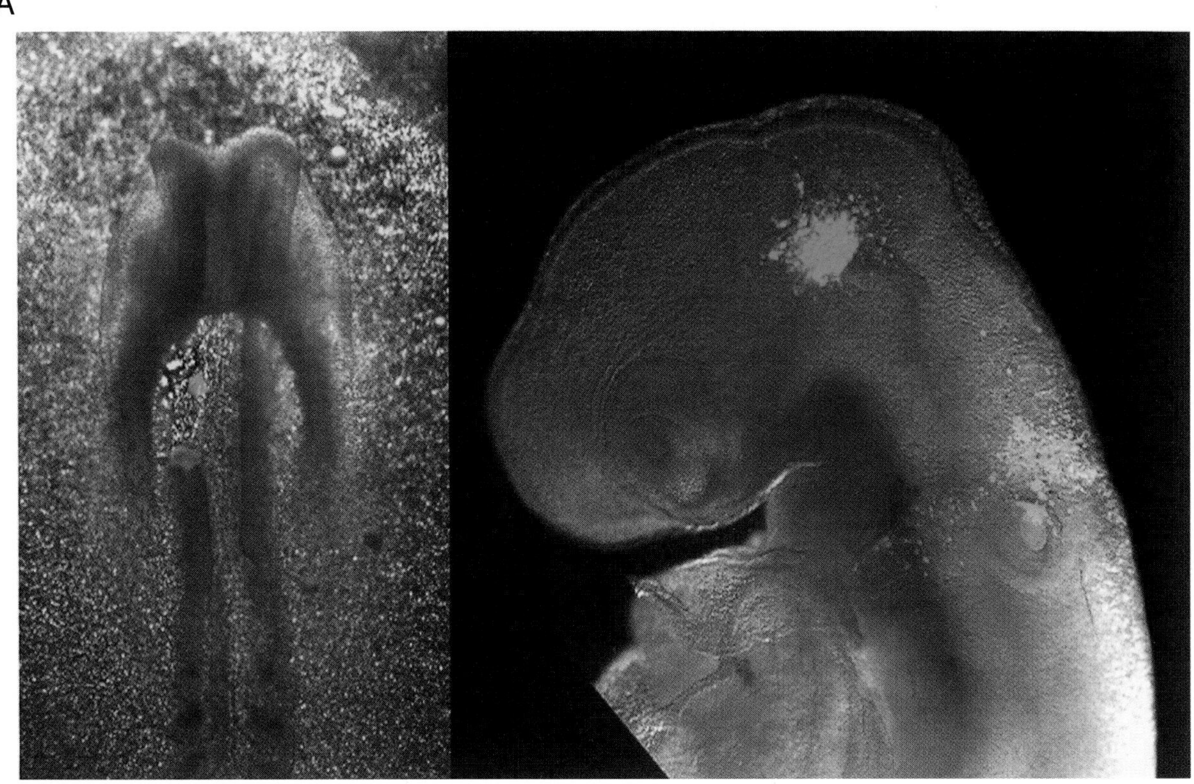
A

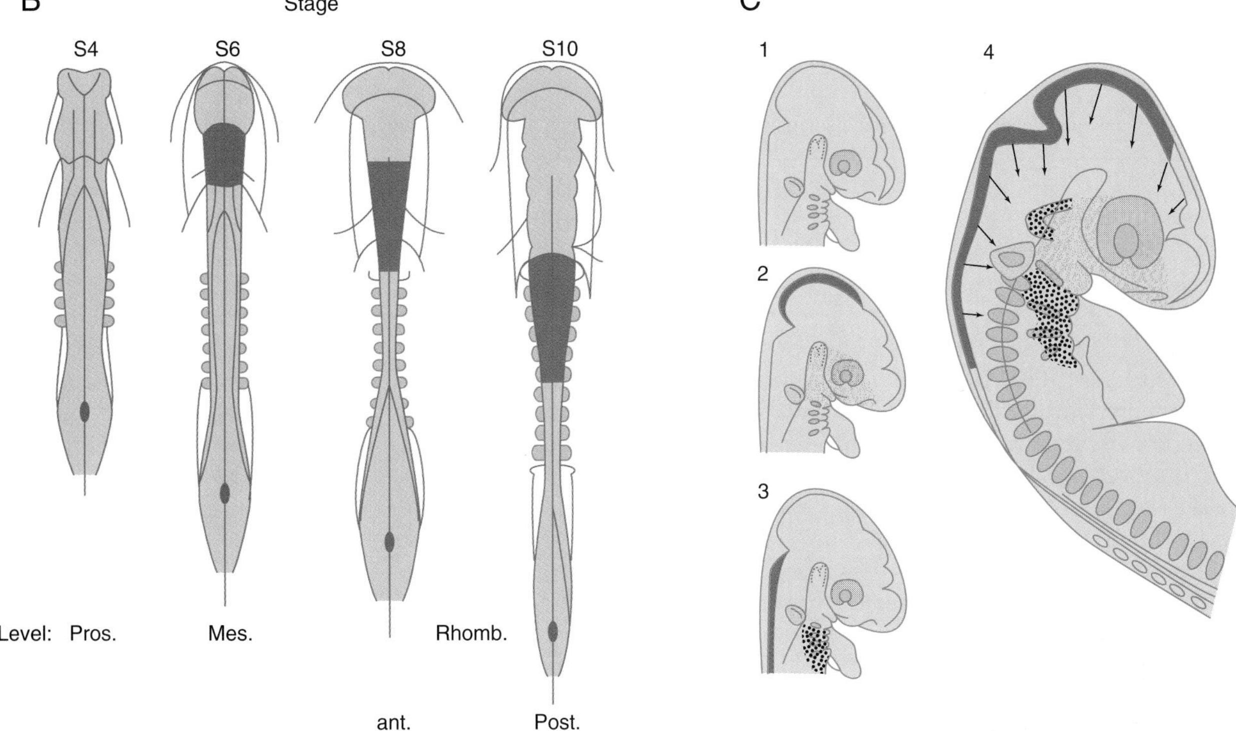
B
Stage
S4
S6
S8
S10
Level: Pros.
Mes.
Rhomb.
ant.
Post.
C
1
2
3
4

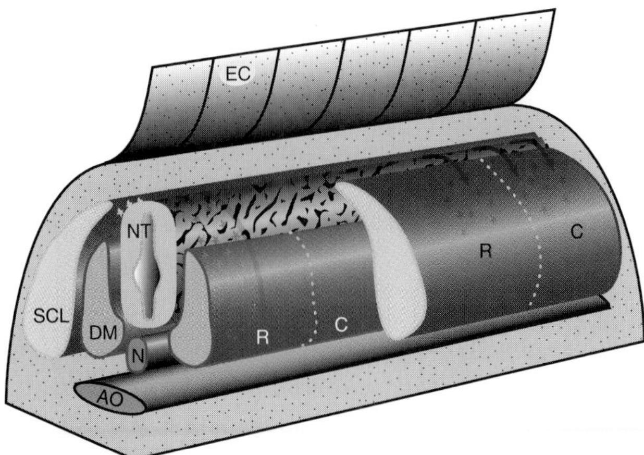

FIGURE 16.3 The two major migratory pathways of neural crest cells in the trunk region of the body. Crest cells (green) migrate ventrally (yellow arrow) through the rostral (R) region of somite's dermatome (DM) and avoid the caudal (C) region. These cells give rise to neurons of the dorsal root and sympathetic ganglia, Schwann cells, and adrenal chromaffin cells. Crest cells also migrate along a dorsal route (pink arrows) between the epidermis or ectoderm (EC) and the sclerotome (SCL) to form melanocytes. Abbreviations: NT, neural tube; N, notochord; AO, aorta.

later times, transplanted cells do not colonize targets appropriate to their new sites, i.e., they do not assume new phenotypes. Thus, the time at which precursor cells emigrate from the neural folds helps determine the range of cell types that they can become. This finding suggested a second general conclusion about neural crest cell development: that the cell population undergoes a progressive change in the range of fates that the cells can assume, with later cells having a more restricted developmental potential.[14]

Both Permissive and Repulsive Cues Guide Neural Crest Cell Migration

Unlike cells of the central nervous system, cells in the neural crest use a fibroblast-like mode of locomotion, general to metazoan cells. Neural crest cell motility is promoted by integrins, a class of cell-surface adhesion receptors that bind to ECM components. Fibronectin and laminin are the most prominent ECM components along crest migratory pathways.[15] Scanning electron microscopy has revealed that neural crest cells migrate through cell-free zones, rich in collagen fibrils typical of ECM.[16] Perturbation experiments using antibodies raised against integrins (the receptors for fibronectin and laminin) provide evidence for ECM as a substrate for crest cell migration. Thus, a common feature of crest cell migration is the utilization of mesenchymal-derived ECM for cell movements. Using this mode of movement, proliferating crest cells move through tissue at speeds between 10 and 50 μm h^{-1}.

Since cells transplanted from one region of the neuroaxis to another can move freely out into the extracellular space surrounding the neural tube, the ECM appears to provide a permissive rather than an instructive substrate for migration.[16] *In vitro* assays suggest that crest cells undergo a "random walk" along ECM substrates.[17] Cells are apparently held to their migratory paths *in vivo* by inhibitory signals in neighboring tissues. Transplantation studies suggest that the perinotochordal region is an inhibitory structure, barring crest cells from taking ventromedial routes through the embryo. Another example of inhibition is found in the trunk region at the level of the somites, where crest cells migrate only through the rostral portion of the sclerotomes.[18–20] Thus, crest cells are routed through

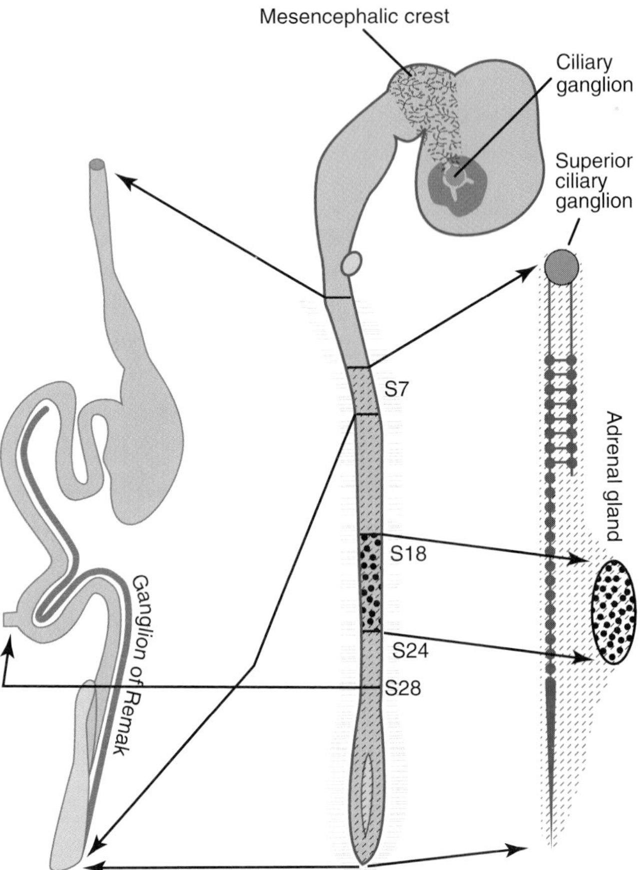

FIGURE 16.4 Neural crest cells at different levels along the anterior–posterior axis give rise to distinct autonomic and adrenomedullary derivatives in avian embryos. In the cephalic region (center), mesencephalic crest cells populate the ciliary ganglion. The ganglia of the sympathetic chain (right), including the superior ciliary ganglion, are formed from spinal neural crest cells originating caudal to somite 5. Cells of the adrenal medulla (right) originate exclusively from crest cells between somites 18 and 24. Vagal neural crest cells generated between somites 1 and 7 form enteric ganglia (left), while cells of the ganglion of Remak (left) are derived from the lumbosacral neural crest posterior to somite 28. Drawing provided by Dr. M. Bronner-Fraser.

permissive corridors of ECM by repulsive substrates in neighboring structures. As the postmigratory cells settle into their destinations, they begin to express adhesion molecules of the immunoglobulin G and cadherin superfamilies, and the cells aggregate into ganglia, where they undergo terminal neuronal and glial differentiation.[15]

Precursors of the peripheral nervous system thus begin a program of neurogenesis within the neural folds, with individual cells generating as many as 20,000 derivatives during subsequent migration along ventrolateral pathways of the ECM.[14] Streams of migratory cells pour through the developing embryo, with individual precursor cells within these populations undergoing either continued proliferation or entry into specific programs of differentiation according to (1) the time of origin of the precursors, (2) the sequence of factors encountered by each cell in its journey through the spatial program of cues, and (3) locally induced programs of phenotypic specification.[8,12,14,21]

Summary

Neural crest cells migrate over long distances throughout the body to form diverse cell types, including neurons, glia, melanocytes, and cells of the adrenal gland. The migratory pathways of neural crest cells vary along the anterior–posterior body axis, and the local environments through which cells migrate and eventually differentiate play an important role in phenotype specification. The migration of neural crest cells is guided by both positive (attractive or permissive) and inhibitory (repulsive) cues that are found in the extracellular matrix.

DEVELOPMENT OF THE CNS

In the developing central nervous system (CNS), as seen for the PNS, neurons are generated at sites far from the position they will occupy in the adult nervous system. Unlike that of the neural crest population, the development of the CNS builds from a basic columnar organization of the cells, an organization that favors the radial migration of the cells. The rich diversity of cells that appear in the vertebrate brain and the development of their patterns of connectivity were studied in brilliant detail by the Spanish neuropathologist Ramón y Cajal, with precise information on the development and anatomy of fiber tracts and circuitry emerging later (see Box 2.2). By examining embryos of different vertebrate species and using modifications of the Golgi staining methods, Cajal[22] was able to discern the key features of neural development and to chronicle the growth and connectivity of the major classes of nerve cells. In studies of cortical development, he proposed that the laminar structure of higher vertebrates was essential to the formation of complex circuits.

Deciphering the detailed patterns of neurogenesis and migration in the mammalian brain depended critically on Richard Sidman's development of an autoradiographic method for labeling cells in the developing brain.[23–26] By injecting radiolabeled thymidine at embryonic stages of development and imaging the cells that were labeled in that stage in the adult, Sidman was able to define the sites of origin of the cells in the embryo and to chart their migratory paths during brain development. Pulse labeling with radioactive thymidine, which is incorporated into DNA during replication,[23–25] provides a key tool for marking the "birthdate" or time of last division of any given precursor cell in the developing brain. Whereas cells that continue to divide after that time dilute the radioactive label, cells that exit the cell cycle after this division retain strong thymidine labeling. The movements of precursor cells away from CNS germinal zones lead to the formation of three general classes of structures: (1) layered structures with predominantly radial migration patterns, including the cerebral cortex, the hippocampal formation, and the cerebellar cortex; (2) layered structures formed by mixed radial and tangential migration, including the retina and spinal cord; and (3) nonlayered structures, including the brainstem, mesencephalon, and diencephalon.

Precursor Cells Proliferate in the Developing Brain

The key features of neurogenesis in the developing brain derive from the geometry of the system: the arrangement of progenitors in a pseudostratified neuroepithelium in the neural tube. The identity of the cells within this epithelium was the subject of intense debate for more than a century. One early theory, put forward by Wilhelm His[27] in the 1880s, was that the two classes of cells in brain—neurons and glia—arise from committed precursor cells in the neuroepithelium. He reasoned that the cells residing at the ventricular surface of the tube, which he termed germinal cells, would give rise to neurons, and the overlying "spongioblasts" would give rise to glial cells. He based his model on his newly developed technique of serial sectioning, which gave the first detailed view of the cellular structure of the neuroepithelium. In 1897, A. Schaper[28] put forward a different view, unpopular at the time but soon recognized as more plausible, that the neuroepithelium consisted of uncommitted or "indifferent" cells as he termed them, that would give rise to both neurons and glia.

To resolve the character of the cells in the "neurospongium" matrix, Ramón y Cajal[22] developed methods for fixing tissues of the early embryo. Toward that end, he used barbiturates as fixatives and then dipped the embryos into photographic reagents to provide a reduced silver solution. His methods resolved cells with different morphological features, which he envisioned as representing a series of developmental stages—germinal, apolar, bipolar, and then multipolar cells. Thus, the differences in the morphological appearance of cells in the neuroepithelium, interpreted by Wilhelm His to reflect different classes of cells, related to the facts that mitotic cells (germinal cells) were located along the ventricular surface, and interphase cells extend a bipolar process across the epithelium.

The mitotic activity of cells in the early neuroepithelium was confirmed by Fred and Mary Sauer, who showed that cells in different positions within the **ventricular zone** contain different amounts of DNA and that cells at the ventricular surface had completed DNA replication and were proceeding through mitosis.[29,30] Striking views of the pseudostratified character of the columnar neuroepithelium emerged from scanning electron microscopy of the embryonic brain in cross section. The walls of the three emerging vesicles of the brain can be seen as a thin, single epithelium[31–33] (Fig. 16.5). Reconstructions of serial electron micrographs have captured static views of the to-and-fro movements of the nuclei within cells in various phases of the cell cycle, movements that Ramón y Cajal postulated from the shape of the cells and that Sauer showed from their DNA content. In the very early embryo (E8–9 in the mouse), the wall of the emerging brain is one cell deep, with cells in interphase extending their processes across the thin wall of the epithelium. As the progenitor cells enter mitosis, they retract their processes, falling to the ventricular surface during mitosis. The changing shapes of the cells and the apparent movement of the nucleus within the cells, as they un-

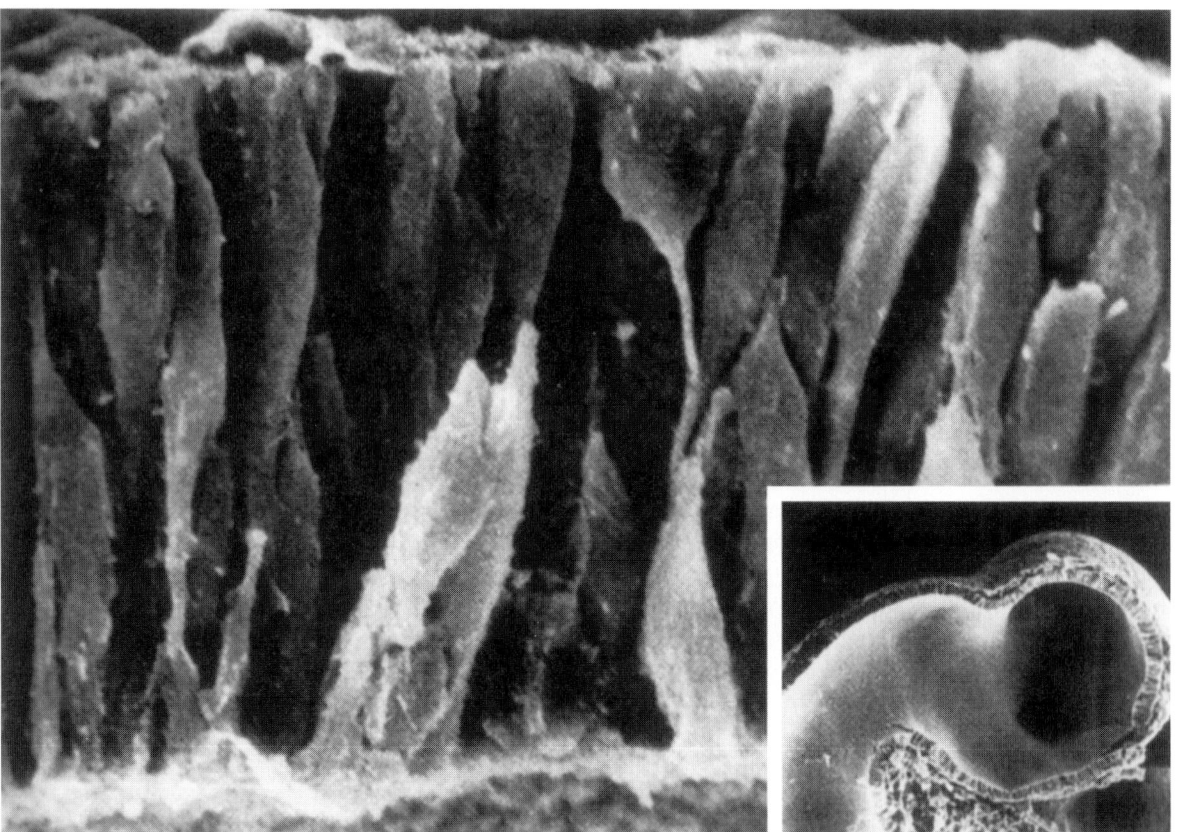

FIGURE 16.5 The ventricular zone forms a pseudostratified columnar neuroepithelium. Here neural progenitor cells have been visualized in the cerebral vesicle of a hamster embryo using scanning electron microscopy. Neuroepithelial cells are elongated bipolar cells that, at this early stage of development (E9.25), span the entire wall of the cerebrum. Some of the cells at the ventricular surface (bottom) appear spherical; these cells have retracted their cytoplasmic processes and are presumably rounding up in preparation for mitosis. Other rounded cells at the external surface (top) may be young neurons beginning to differentiate. The inset shows a low-power view of the hamster cerebral vesicle, corresponding roughly to that of a human embryo at the end of the first month of gestation. From Sidman and Rakic.[26]

dergo morphological changes during the phases of the cell cycle, orchestrate the dynamics termed interkinetic movements.[34]

Within the ventricular zone, one of the first cells to express markers of differentiation is a specialized form of glial cell, called the **radial glial cell**. This cell, recognized by its expression of the RC2 antigen, extends long processes perpendicular to the ventricular surface toward the overlying cerebral wall. Immature radial glial cells continue to grow as the laminae develop, generating processes that span the wall of the thickening brain vesicle. As development proceeds, the length of the radial glial processes is remarkable, extending many millimeters across the radial dimension in primates.[35–38] As discussed later in this chapter, these radial processes presage the basic columnar plan of development, providing a scaffold "in plane" with the layer of dividing cells for young neurons to migrate away from the primary germinal matrix. This general scheme of migration sustains the earlier patterning of gene expression seen to set forth regional domains described in Chapter 15 and sets the stage for the wide ranging cell migrations seen during the brain histogenesis.

Cells Move within the Primary Proliferative Matrix

The geometry of the emerging nervous system, with cells arranged in a tubular neuroepithelium, is unique. As cells enter programs of neuronal differentiation, they form layers above the germinal zone by directed migrations. A key factor in deciphering the patterning of progenitors in these early stages of histogenesis is whether precursors retain a position on a "protomap" such that subsequent migration in the radial plane causes clones of cells to cluster into radial arrays, or whether the cells intermingle with their neighbors, relying on stochastic mechanisms for induction of specific phenotypes. Whereas in the radial plan, cells are held in a "prefixed" columnar position, experiments using retroviral markers to identify clonally related cells in the developing brain showed widespread tangential dispersion of cells within the developing cerebral cortex.[39–41] Direct observation of dye-labeled cells in whole mount preparations of embryonic cortical tissue reveals extensive movements within the ventricular zones of the murine forebrain. While some clonally related cells remain in tight clusters, other cells rapidly disperse, moving in random walks at speeds of 10–100 μm h^{-1}. Thus, current models of cortical development indicate that some, but not all, clonally related cells undergo dispersion during brain development.[40,42,43]

The Basic Embryonic Zones Are the Building Blocks of the Mature Cerebral Cortex

As rapid cell division thickens the proliferative zone, the emerging cortical structure progresses from a simple neuroepithelial sheet into a complex multilaminar structure (Fig. 16.6). The first step in this process involves the creation of the **marginal zone**, a cell-sparse zone from which nuclei are excluded during interkinetic movements in the epithelium.[44] Shortly thereafter, the first neurons to be generated exit the ventricular zone and form a single layer called the **preplate**. Together with axons growing into the cortex, the axons of preplate neurons form the **intermediate zone**, which separates the ventricular zone from the preplate. Collectively, these axons pioneer the connections in both directions between the cortex and the thalamus. The neuroepithelium thus progresses from a single layer of mitotically active ventricular cells to a more complex structure that contains three layers: the ventricular zone containing proliferating cells, the intermediate zone containing axons and migrating neurons, and the preplate containing postmitotic neuronal precursors that will be subdivided later into the subplate and the marginal zone.[44,45] As the pace of neuronal production continues, the ventricular zone begins to produce neurons destined for the different layers of the cortex. These cells migrate through the intermediate zone and form the **cortical plate**, a structure that splits the embryonic preplate into two domains: the marginal zone, or future layer 1; and the **subplate**, a transient population of neurons that largely disappears by programmed cell death (see Chapter 20 for a description of programmed cell death) early in postnatal life. Finally, during the middle and latter stages of neurogenesis, a second zone of mitotically active cells forms between the ventricular and the intermediate zones; this region is called the **subventricular zone** (not shown in Fig. 16.6). With the exception of the cortical plate, these embryonic cellular zones are unique to the developing brain and have no direct counterparts in the adult structure. All become so altered as development progresses that they are unrecognizable in the mature nervous system.

The importance of these rudimentary embryonic layers as building blocks for the subsequent laminar architecture of the cortex is illustrated in cases of cortical malformations arising from neurogenetic disorders. In such cases, disturbances in these apparently simple early events of cortical development reverberate spatially through a wide area. Although migration has been studied in detail, relatively little is known about the mechanisms that halt the migration of postmitotic neurons and induce them to form layers. Studies on the *reeler* neurological mutant mouse, an animal with

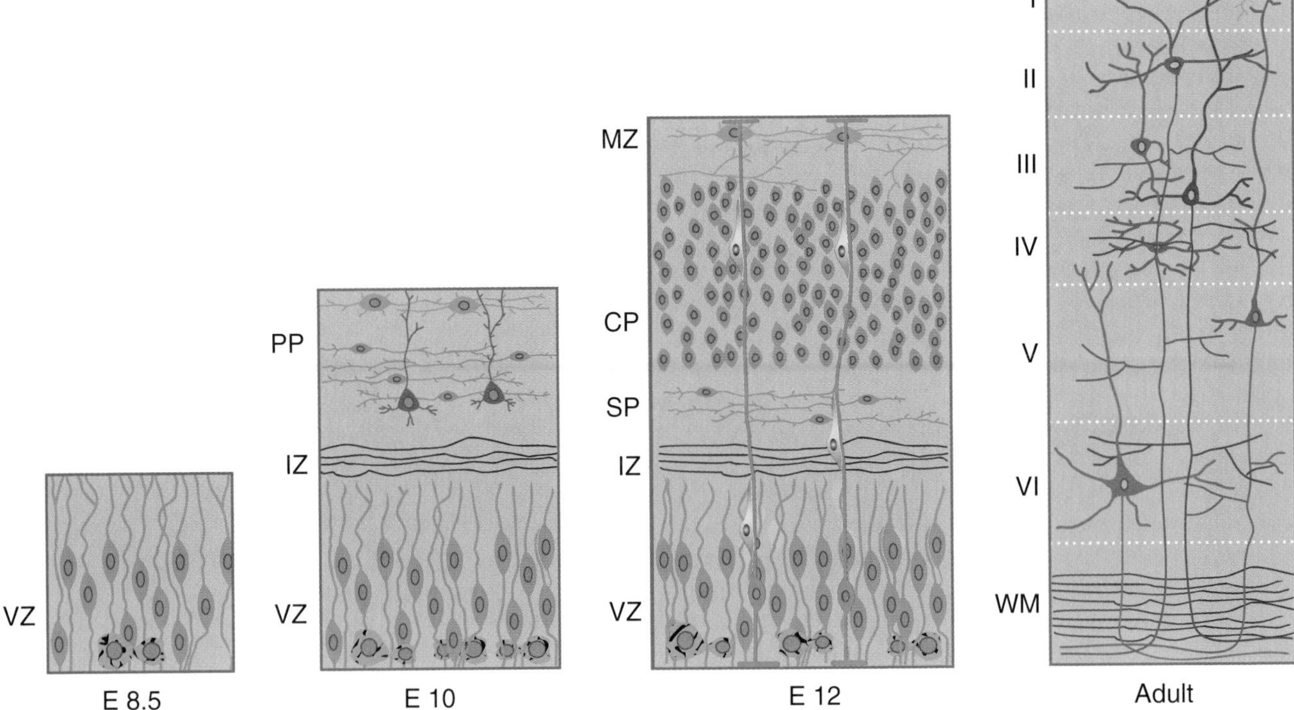

FIGURE 16.6 Development of the cerebral cortex. The ventricular zone (VZ) contains the progenitors of neurons and glia. The first neurons to be generated establish the preplate (PP); their axons, as well as ingrowing axons from the thalamus, establish the intermediate zone (IZ). The subsequently generated neurons of cortical layers II–VI establish the cortical plate (CP), which splits the preplate into the marginal zone (MZ), or future layer I, and the subplate (SP), a transient population of neurons. After the completion of neuronal migration and differentiation, six cortical layers are visible overlying the white matter (WM), and the subplate has largely disappeared.

inherited defects in the formation of the embryonic layers,[46–48] indicate that the mutated gene encodes an ECM-related protein, called reelin.[49,50] The absence of reelin in Cajal–Retzius cells within the marginal zone may interfere with the division of the preplate into the subplate and the marginal zone. Because this subdivision[44] provides the framework for the patterning of cortical laminae, subsequent migratory events are disturbed. The identification of reelin as the target of this spontaneous mutation and the presence of reelin protein in the ECM suggest that ECM molecules function in the arrest of radial migration and formation of neural laminae.

Secondary Germinal Matrices Form in the Subventricular Zone

During primary neurogenesis and migration, the principal output neurons of the forebrain, midbrain, and cerebellar cortex are generated and assembled into laminar arrays. During the later phases of cortical neurogenesis, secondary germinal zones form in the overlying subventricular zone, which overlies the ventricular zone. These specialized secondary germinal matrices have apparently arisen in higher vertebrates to generate extremely abundant neuronal cell populations late during development of the CNS (see Llinas and Hillman[51] for a discussion of the evolution of the cerebellum). In the mouse, secondary neurogenesis continues into the second postnatal week, with low levels of neurogenesis persisting in the subventricular zone of the forebrain into adulthood. In humans, secondary neurogenesis continues in early childhood, through the second year of life. During this period, neurogenesis in the subventricular zone of the forebrain and in the external germinal layer of the cerebellum supply their corresponding brain structures with extremely large numbers of neurons—generally small interneurons such as granule cells of the cerebellar cortex and hippocampal formation.

As seen for primary neurogenesis, proliferation of precursors in secondary neurogenesis occurs in compact zones. In the forebrain, the subventricular zone is situated just above the collapsing ventricular zone, where it gives rise to neurons that migrate into the olfactory bulb, to cortical glial cells,[52] and to the granule cell population of the hippocampal formation. Although the subventricular zone generates some small interneurons, in the cerebellar cortex the vast granule cell population arises from a unique program of neurogenesis and migration that emanates from the rhombic lip. Cells generated in this later phase of neurogenesis include the granule neurons that form the internal granule cell layer of the cerebellum.[26,53,54] Neurons derived from the subventricular zone and external germinal layer intercalate into an existing embryonic framework, consisting of cell layers generated from the primary germinal matrix, to complete the adult brain structure.

Migration of Precursors over the Rhombic Lip

Precursors of the cerebellar granule cell undergo a unique developmental scheme (Fig. 16.7F). Proliferating in the rhombic lip at the edge of the neuroepithel-

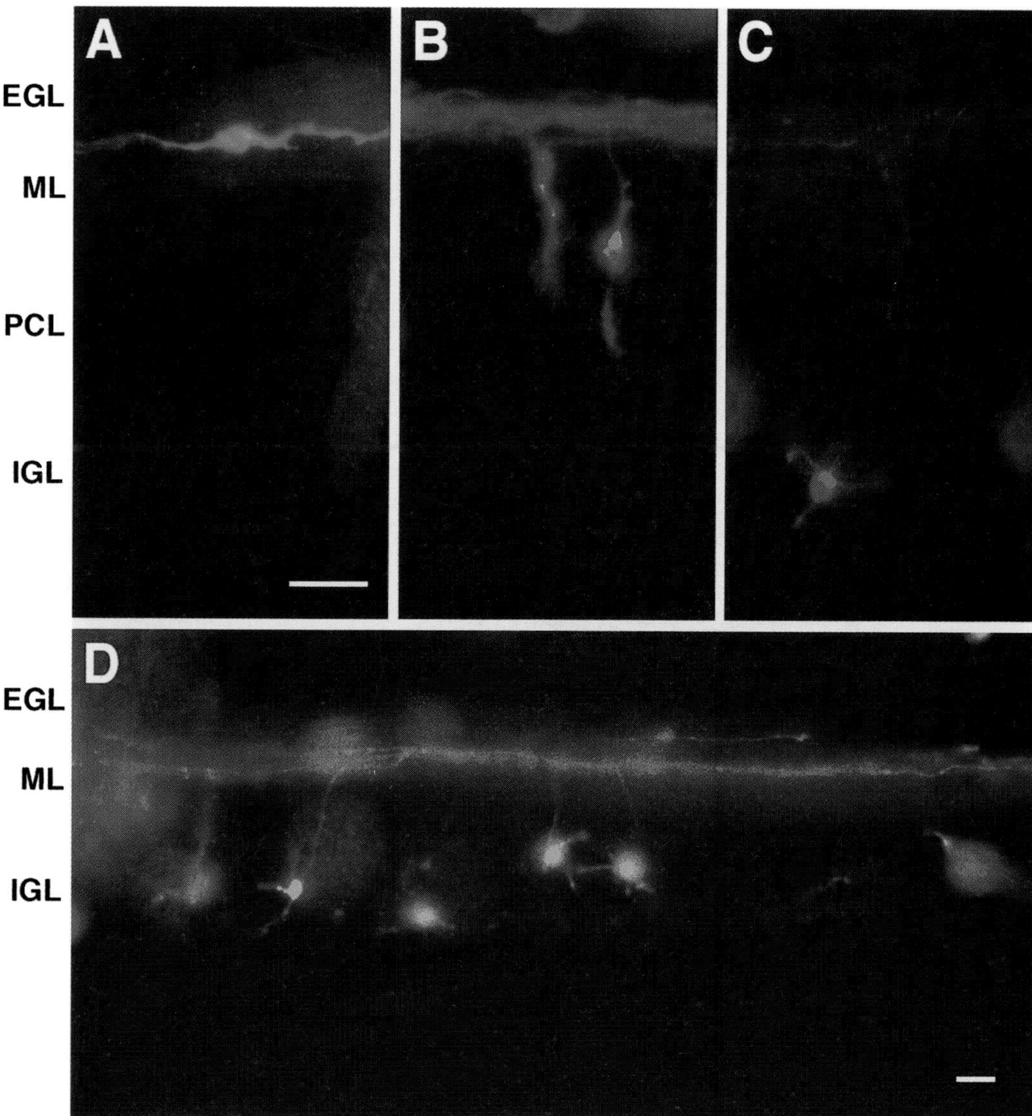

FIGURE 16.7 (A–D) When EGL cells are transplanted into the EGL of a P6 mouse cerebellum, they differentiate exclusively into granule cells. The EGL cells were labeled with a fluorescent marker prior to transplantation. Abbreviations: EGL, external granular layer; ML, molecular layer; PCL, Purkinje cell layer; IGL, internal granular layer. Scale bar, 15 μm. (A) 2 days after transplantation: labeled cells extend parallel fibers. (B) 3–4 days after transplantation: labeled cells begin to migrate inward through the molecular layer. (C) 6 days after transplantation: labeled cells have reached the IGL, where they exhibit the T shape characteristic of a mature granule neuron. Cells in the IGL extend several short dendritic processes. (D) Low-power view of labeled granule neurons that have completed their migration into and differentiation within the IGL. (*Continues*)

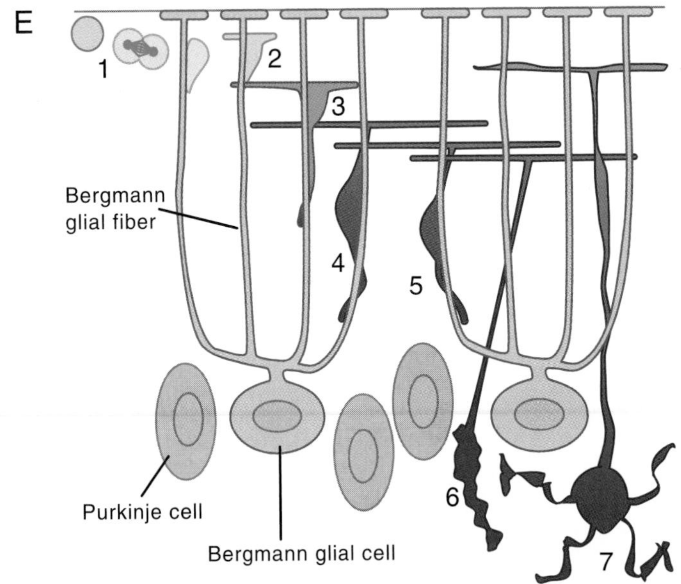

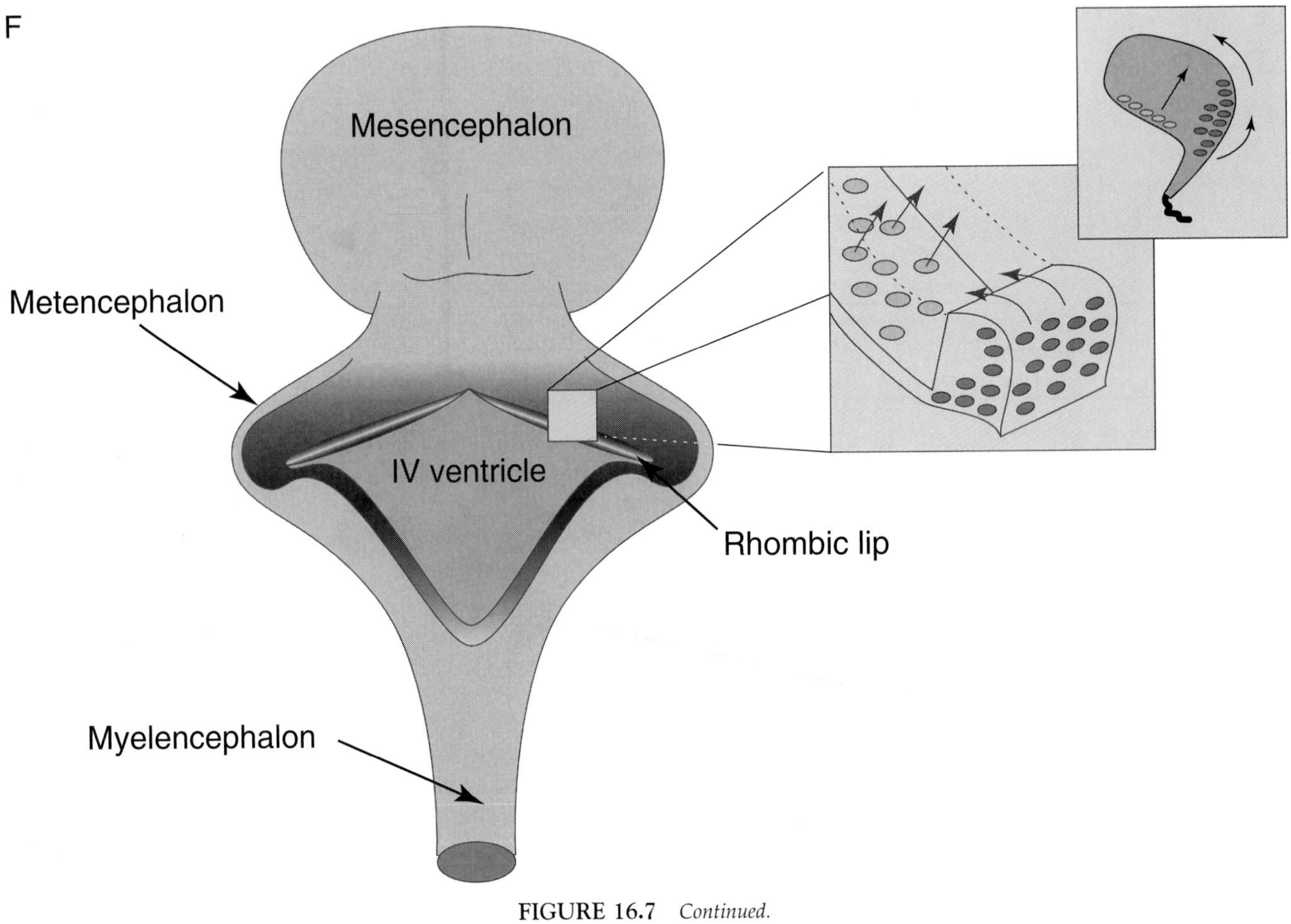

FIGURE 16.7 *Continued.*

ium, where there is no overlying cellular structure, these dividing precursor cells stream rostrally across the lip, onto the surface of the developing cerebellum, where they establish a displaced germinal zone—the external germinal layer.[55]

Continued migration of cells from the rhombic lip generates a displaced zone of precursors that spread rostromedially across the roof of the cerebellar primordium.[22,53,56] By E16 in the mouse, the external germinal layer covers the surface of the cerebellum at a cell depth of one to two cells. After birth, rapid proliferation in the external germinal layer expands the zone from a single cell layer to a layer eight cells in thickness. Precursor cell proliferation continues until about P15 in the mouse, when the zone disappears due to the inward migration of postmitotic cells to form the internal granular layer (Figs. 16.7A–16.7E). Whereas Purkinje cells, the principal target neurons of the granule cell, undergo a short period of proliferation within the ventricular zone of the cerebellar anlage, at approximately E11–E14 in the mouse, the prolonged period of clonal expansion of precursor cells within the secondary germinal zone, from E13 until P15, generates a huge population of cells. In adulthood, granule neurons outnumber Purkinje cells by 250 : 1 in the mouse, a figure that rises to approximately 400 : 1 in humans.

FIGURE 16.7 (E) Summary of the migration of EGL cells into the IGL, where they complete their differentiation into granule neurons: (1) Precursor cells undergo cell division, generating a young postmitotic neuron. (2) The neuron begins to extend two long axons called parallel fibers parallel to the cerebellar surface. (3) The T-shaped granule neuron attaches to a Bergmann glial fiber and translocates its cell body inward. (4–5) Continued migration is accompanied by the further elaboration of the parallel fibers. (6) Upon entering the IGL, a dense cell layer just below the layer of Purkinje neurons and cell bodies of Bergmann glia, the granule cell detaches from the glial highway. (7) The cell completes its differentiation by extending short dendrites that receive synaptic inputs from ingrowing afferent axons. Drawing provided by Dr. C. A. Mason. (F) Formation of the cerebellar anlage in mouse. The cerebellar primordium arises just anterior to the IVth ventricle (darkly shaded area), a mouthlike opening formed by a gap in the neural tube in the region of the pontine flexure. Within the roof of the IVth ventricle, a period of rapid proliferation starting at about E13–14 results in a thickening of this tissue. The middle box shows a three-dimensional enlargement of the roof of the ventricle, including the region known as the rhombic lip (which lies at the edge of the opening). The precursors of granule neurons (blue) arise from the rhombic lip; at and after E14, they migrate to cover the surface of the cerebellar anlage (curved arrows; hatched lines denote surface), forming the external granular layer (EGL). Here they undergo clonal expansion until the early postnatal period, when differentiation begins. By contrast, precursors of Purkinje neurons (gray) arise in the ventricular zone. These cells exit the cell cycle at about E14, then migrate radially upward through the wall of the anlage (straight arrows) before differentiating. The box on the right shows a transverse section through the cerebellar primordium, representing the movement of rhombic lip cells into the EGL (curved arrows), and the radial migration of Purkinje cells from the ventricular zone (straight arrows). The choroid plexus (black) extends from the edge of the rhombic lip. Drawing from Dr. M. E. Hatten.

For progenitors in secondary germinal matrices, the relationship between the cell cycle and cell specification is quite different from that for other neuronal classes. Although the mechanisms responsible for the continued proliferation of these specialized neuronal precursors for long periods during development have not been discovered, it is becoming evident that these cell populations share many common features. In particular, they express several interesting regulatory molecules that are not expressed in neuronal precursors dividing in primary germinal zones. For example, a zinc finger transcription factor called RU49 is present in each of these cell lineages from their creation during early embryogenesis throughout development and in the mature neuronal populations.[57] Furthermore, two neuron-specific variants of important cell cycle regulatory molecules, an alternatively spliced version of cyclin D2 (MN20) and a novel regulatory subunit of protein phosphatase 2a (PP2ABB), are present at high levels in these secondary matrices.[58,59] While no information is yet available concerning the specific roles of these molecules in the generation and maintenance of these cell populations, the fact that these cells are marked by specific regulatory molecules argues that they share a developmental pathway that is genetically distinct.[60]

Development of the Cerebellar Granule Cell

Among cells that are generated in displaced germinal zones, the **cerebellar granule cell** is one of the more amenable classes of CNS neurons for developmental studies. As cells in the external germinal layer proliferate, some cells begin to exit the cycle and undergo differentiation, as evidenced by the formation of axons called parallel fibers (see Figs. 16.7A–16.7E). Molecular biological studies indicate that the subdivision of the external germinal layer into a superficial zone of dividing cells and an inner zone of differentiating cells is accompanied by the expression of genes that are differentially regulated at the transcriptional level during cerebellar development (see Fig. 16.8). Localization of these genes by *in situ* hybridization reveals that granule neuron development can be divided into at least four discrete stages—neurogenesis, initiation of neuronal differentiation, axon outgrowth and migration, and formation of synaptic connections.[55]

Migration of Cells from the Cortical Subventricular Zone to the Olfactory Bulb

Whereas external germinal layer cells spread across the roof of the ventricle, forming a germinal layer that

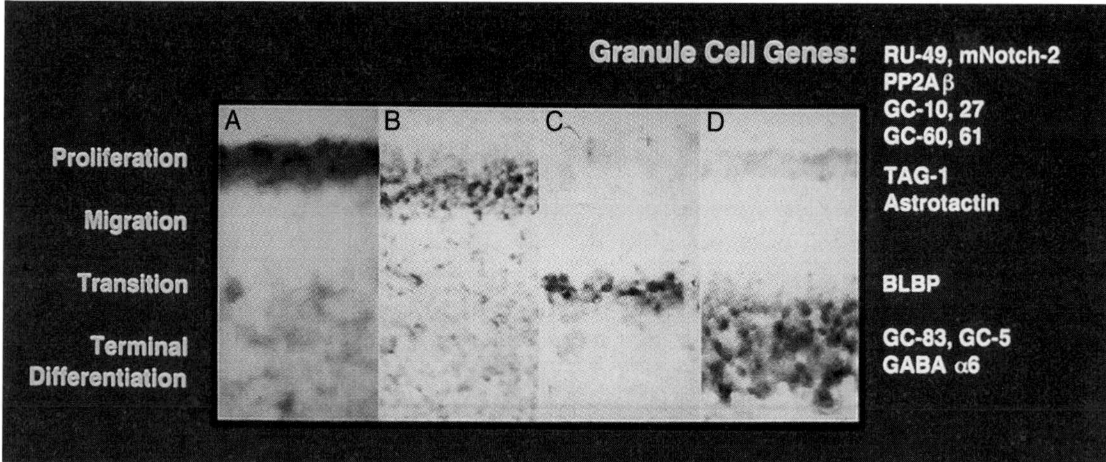

FIGURE 16.8 The pattern of gene expression in granule cells changes during the four stages of granule cell maturation: proliferation, migration, transition, and terminal differentiation. This figure shows examples of four such genes, revealed by *in situ* hybridization. (A) GC10 mRNA is expressed by proliferating granule cell precursors only in the outer region of the EGL. (B) Postmitotic and migrating granule cells in the inner region of the EGL and in the molecular layer express TAG-1 mRNA. (C) In a region just below the cell bodies of Purkinje cells termed the "transition zone," granule cells express GC44 mRNA. (D) Granule cells in the IGL express the α_6 subunit of the $GABA_A$ receptor as they undergo terminal differentiation. At the far right are examples of other genes expressed by granule cells at these different stages of development. The position of the gene name reflects the temporal and spatial pattern of expression. From Kuhar *et al.*[58]

will give rise to only one class of neuron, cells of the subventricular zone migrate into a number of brain regions, forming multiple classes of neurons and glia. Progenitors within the forebrain subventricular zone cells can undergo migration from the lateral ventricle, where they originate, into both the overlying cortex and the far distant olfactory bulb. Retroviral marking methods have demonstrated multiple classes of olfactory neurons that derive from the population of cortical subventricular zone cells fated to migrate to the olfactory bulb. Moreover, the subventricular zone continues to provide cells into adulthood, apparently as a response to the loss of neurons in the olfactory bulb.[62] In the subventricular zone of the subcortical region, an even more diverse population of cells is generated and, as described later in this chapter, undergoes migration into both neighboring areas and distant areas, including the thalamus.[26] Like other secondary germinal zones discussed in this chapter, the subventricular zone of the lateral ganglionic eminence supports proliferation well into the postnatal era.

Just as reported for cells in the primary germinal matrix and in the external germinal layer of the cerebellar cortex, subventricular zone cells undergo extensive intermixing in the tangential plane.[61] Within the forebrain subventricular zone, tangential migrations are extensive, with cells moving from the forebrain into the olfactory system and into the diencephalon.[54,62,63] Targeted mutational analysis indicates a functional role for polysialated forms of the neural cell adhesion molecule[64] (NCAM) in cell migration from the subventricular zone to the olfactory bulb. These neurons move along the interwoven bundles of neighboring processes in chains of migrating cells.[65] Thus, cells from secondary germinal zones—the subventricular zone of the forebrain and the external germinal layer of the cerebellar cortex—traverse remarkably long migratory routes.

Young Neurons Migrate away from Primary Proliferative Zones

Radial Migrations along Glial Fibers

As mentioned earlier, radial glial cells are among the first cells to differentiate within the thickening cerebral wall. The radial glia span the neural tube, providing cellular "spokes" that extend outward along the radial plane of the neuroaxis.[36,37] Neuroanatomical studies, including three-dimensional reconstructions of electron microscopic views, showed that postmitotic neurons are closely apposed to the radial glial fibers, leading Pasko Rakic to propose that this system provides a primary substrate for migration in neocortex[66–68] (Fig. 16.9). In this model, young neurons are thought to use the glial fibers as a substrate for the journey out to the emerging cortical layers, a distance of some 3000 μm in primates.

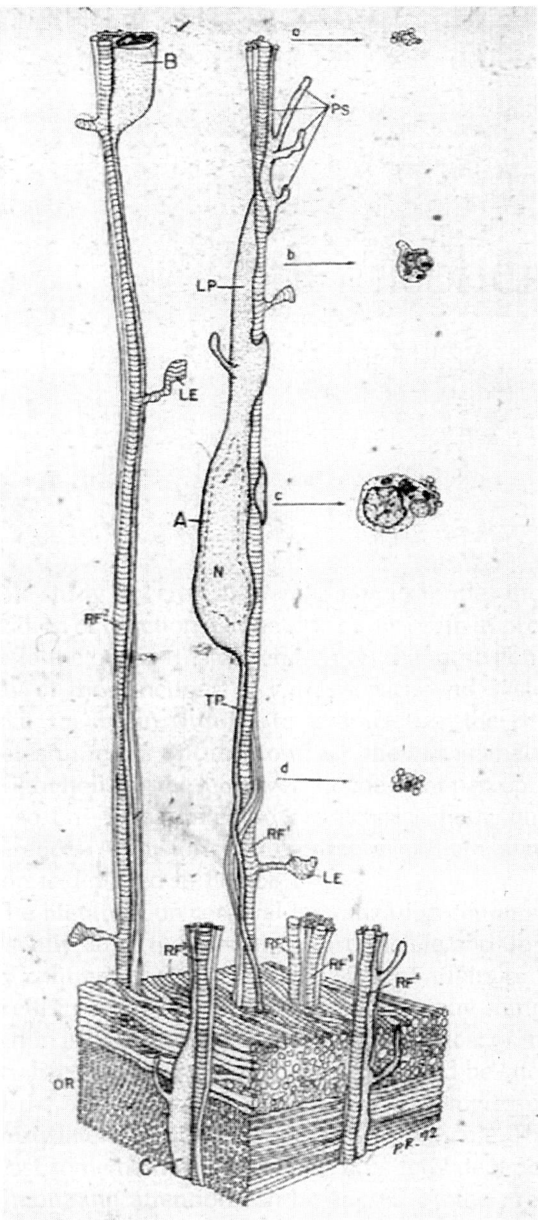

FIGURE 16.9 Serial section electron microscopy was used to create three-dimensional reconstructions of three migrating neurons (A–C) in the developing cerebral cortex. Migrating neurons in the intermediate zone are intimately apposed to radial glial fibers (striped vertical shafts, RF1–6), which extend short lamellate expansions (LE) at a right angle to their main axis. The lower part of the diagram depicts the numerous parallel axons of the optic radiations (OR). These axons have been deleted from the upper portion of the figure to reveal the radial glial fibers. The nuclei (N) of migrating neurons are elongated, and their leading processes (LP) are thicker and richer in organelles than are their trailing processes (TP). Each leading process extends several pseudopodial endings (PS), which are thought to explore the territory through which the neuron is migrating. Several cross sections through a migrating neuron are shown in (a–d), revealing that the migrating cell partially encircles the shaft of the radial glial fiber, and that these intimate contacts are continuous throughout the length of the cell. From Sidman and Rakic.[26]

A role for radial glia in directed migration along the radial plane of the neuroaxis was confirmed by studies in the developing hippocampus, where neurons followed the undulating pathways of the radial fibers to form the neural layers.[69] These studies suggested that young neurons retract the processes seen within the pseudostratified epithelium and undergo directed individual cell movement to assume their laminar positions. As discussed later, this mode of migration is a cardinal feature of the developing cortex, where the distance between the ventricular zone and the surface of the brain is too great to make interkinetic movement of cell nuclei an effective means of long-distance cell locomotion.

To examine the dynamics of neuronal migration along glial fibers, Hatten and colleagues used video-enhanced differential contrast microscopy to obtain a detailed view of the morphology and behavior of migrating cerebellar neurons.[70] The cytological features of living, migrating granule neurons *in vitro* were remarkably similar to those described by Rakic for cells that had been assumed to be migrating *in vivo*. Migrating neurons possessed a highly extended bipolar shape (Fig. 16.10), forming a close apposition with the glial process along the length of the neuronal cell soma and extending a leading process in the direction of migration.[70–72] Thus, the mode of migration of cells *in vitro* closely parallels that seen *in vivo* (Fig. 16.7).

Video observations were extended by correlating the behavior of migrating neurons with their cytology, as viewed in the electron microscope. Specialized migration junctions—called interstitial junctions—are present in migrating cells beneath the neuronal cell soma at the site of apposition with the glial fiber.[73] These junctions consist of a widening of the intercellular space, and filamentous material is present in this space; some of these filaments are contiguous with submembrane cytoskeletal elements. The interstitial junctions form only in cells that are moving along a glial process. In contrast, in resting cells, *puncta adherentia* or attachment junctions occur where the neuron apposes the glial fiber, and unlike the migration junction, these small focal densities lack any obvious connections to the cytoskeleton of the apposing cells.

An important stage of granule cell development involves the control of cell positioning via migration along the glial fiber system. Antibody perturbation studies of granule neuron migration *in vitro* demonstrated that the neural glycoprotein **astrotactin** provides a neural receptor system for migration along glial fibers. The recent molecular cloning of the major component of the astrotactin activity indicates that the gene encodes a protein that contains EGF repeats and fibronectin type III domains.[74] cDNAs for astrotactin

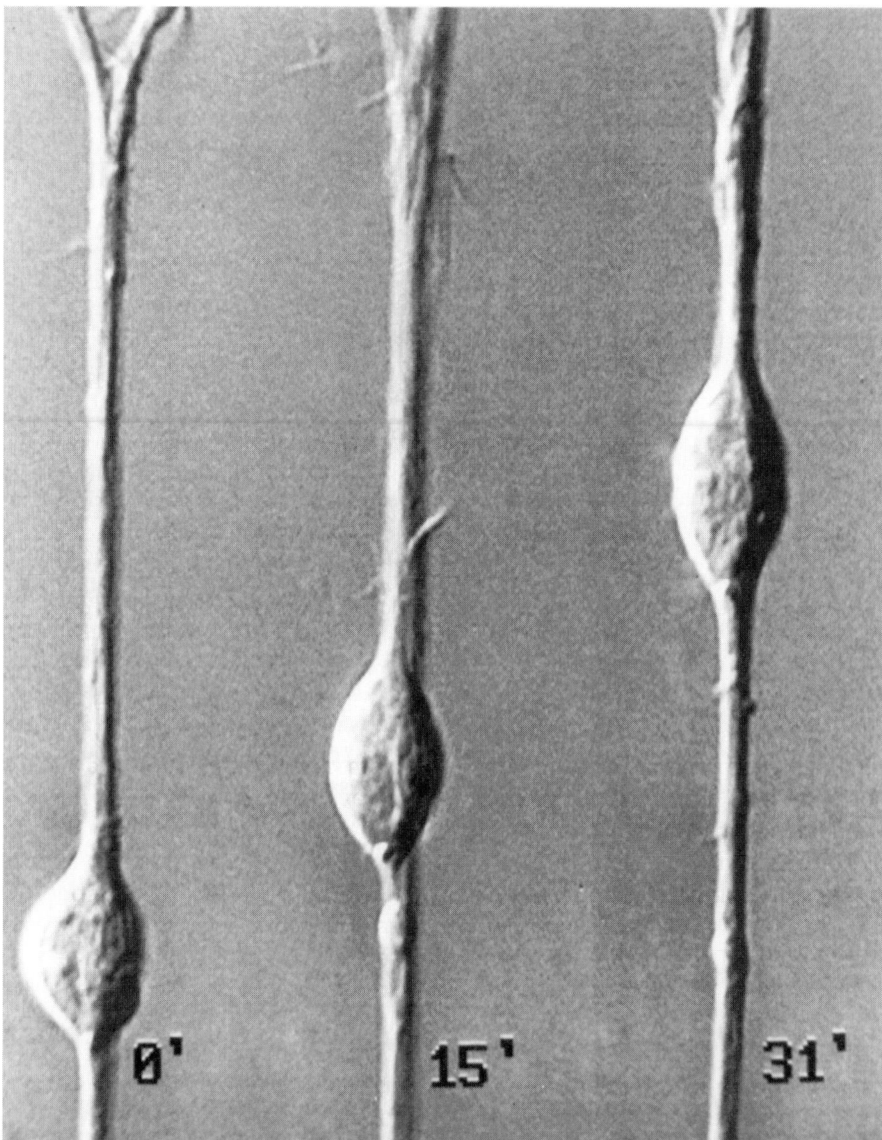

FIGURE 16.10 Hippocampal neurons migrating *in vitro* along the processes of astroglial cells from the cerebellum. Neurons are capable of migrating along a variety of radial glial fibers, even those derived from heterotypic regions. In both heterotypic and homotypic cocultures of neurons and glia, time-lapse imaging reveals that the elongated migrating neurons form close associations with glial processes as they crawl along them. The leading processes of migrating cells are highly active, extending numerous lamellipodia and filopodia. In contrast to the filopodia of axonal growth cones (see Chapter 18), filopodia extending from leading processes are short (1–5 μm in length). Time elapsed (minutes) in real time. Photo provided by Dr. M. E. Hatten.

encode a brain-specific transcript that is developmentally regulated, showing high levels of expression in the developing brain and low levels in the adult brain. Astrotactin appears to provide a neuronal ligand for migration along glial fibers, but the glial component of this receptor ligand system remains unidentified. Recent studies[75] have provided candidates for neuron–glial junctional domain proteins that appear to play a role in mediating migration.

Nonradial Patterns of Migration

Although the glial fiber system is thought to provide the primary guidance system for radial migrations in developing neocortex, some neurons undergo **tangential migration** across the plane of the glial fiber system, possibly along the tracts of neurites within the intermediate zone.[76] Although the radial plane and radial glial scaffold accommodate the bulk of the migrating neurons in developing ferret brain, a subpopulation of the cells moves tangentially within the intermediate zone. At present, it is not clear whether these cells represent a particular class of neurons or whether all cells stray across the glial scaffold at some point during their migration.

Some cells migrating along the glial fiber system also move tangential to the radial plane of the neuraxis. This class of tangential dispersion arises from two features of the glial scaffold: (1) radial glial fibers are not strictly radial in all areas of developing cortex, and (2) radial glial fibers branch in the superficial aspect of the developing cortical plate.[36] Labeling of neurons, in combination with RC2 labeling of glial fibers, indicates that most labeled, migrating neurons are aligned closely with glial fibers, despite variations in the trajectories of the glial fibers themselves.[77] The radial glial fiber system may thus provide the primary guidance system for CNS migrations through the thickening cortical plate. Regional variations in the patterning of glial fascicles are present, however, and migrating neurons may deviate from the radial plane of the neuraxis as they maintain their alignment with the radial glial system.

Cell Migration Patterns Reflect Neuronal Fate Specification

Three cortical regions of the brain provide paradigms for the formation of laminar structures: the cortex, the hippocampus, and the cerebellum. Of these, the cerebellum and the hippocampus are simpler structures, having only two neuronal layers, each with one principal class of neuron. The cortex is more complex, with six layers of cells containing multiple neuron types. Although the details of the development of these three regions differ, three basic steps underlie their formation: precursor proliferation in a germinal zone, radial migration of postmitotic cells away from the germinal zone to form displaced neuronal layers, and the establishment of synaptic circuits among differentiating neurons.

A key question in understanding the role of glial fibers in migration is whether the glial fiber system provides an instructive scaffold, directing young neurons to specific locations or whether glial fibers provide a permissive substrate for cell movements directed by genes expressed in the neuron. Mosaic cultures of neurons and glia from several different cortical regions, cerebellum, and hippocampus indicated that neurons from one region migrate freely on glia from another region.[78] These results suggested that the glial fiber system provides a permissive rather than an instructive pathway for CNS neuronal migration.

Methods for marking cells undergoing cell division and cells entering specific differentiation pathways have made it possible to decipher the pattern in which different neuronal populations are generated in the embryonic brain. The tritiated thymidine labeling method described earlier showed that the layers of neurons in the cerebral cortex are generated in an "inside-out" pattern; that is, later generations of postmitotic neurons migrate out beyond earlier generated cells to form successive layers. Thus, within the ventricular zone, specific neuronal cell populations arise in sequence. As neurons emigrate out from the germinal layer along the radial fibers, they begin their complex differentiation programs.[26,44]

Two general models for the sequential birth of neuronal cell types from the ventricular zone have been proposed. The first model posits that a given precursor cell population possesses an internal clock; these cells can measure either time or the number of cell divisions that have passed since the formation of the ventricular zone. According to this internal timing mechanism, the proliferating precursors then switch their developmental fate to generate each successive individual neuronal population. A second model posits that cell fates are not determined by the history of individual precursor neurons, but each cell class is generated in response to "community" cues that change with time during development of the ventricular zone. In this model, one can easily envisage that particular neuronal cell populations are still generated in a required sequence, simply by proposing that each newly generated cell population provides information to the precursors to change the fate of the succeeding cell types.

Before discussing this further, we should emphasize that studies on several CNS cell populations have provided evidence that local signals function to control CNS precursor cell proliferation. *In vitro* assays with purified external germinal layer precursors of the cerebellar cortex show that reaggregation of isolated cells, in the absence of growth factors, is sufficient to stimulate and sustain cell division beyond the time expected *in situ*. The finding that local environmental cues control cerebellar granule cell division[79] is supported by *in vitro* studies on neurogenesis of cortical precursor cells,[80–82] thereby showing that local interactions influence entry into neuronal lineages. Also, *in vivo* transplantation experiments show that the penultimate cell cycle influences the commitment of cortical precursor cells to a particular laminar fate in the developing cortex.[83] All of these findings are consistent with the location of neuronal precursor cell proliferation within compact ventricular zones in the developing mammalian brain—zones where close cell appositions are maintained.

To address the acquisition of laminar fate by cortical neurons, heterochronic cell transplantation experiments were performed in the developing ferret brain.[84] If an internal timing mechanism exists, precursor cells isolated at one time in embryonic development should "remember" their identity after being transplanted to a host brain of a different age, and they should continue to generate cells appropriate for the donor cell type in the host.[83] In contrast, if dynamic cues specify cell types in the developing ventricular zone, then the transplanted cells should switch their identity to generate cell types appropriate to the development stage of the host. The results of the transplantation studies showed that progenitor cells from very young embryos could switch their laminar fate to that of the host tissue when the cells were transplanted. Thus, an internal timing mechanism cannot fully explain the sequential generation of specific neuronal cell types within the ventricular zone. Furthermore, progenitor cells transplanted late in the penultimate cell cycle retain the fate of the donor tissue, showing that extrinsic cues act to specify cell fates at roughly the time a young neuron is born. From these experiments, we can conclude that laminar fates within the cortical ventricular zone are specified during the last cell cycle, and cues that change over time during formation of the cortical layers can provide critical information to determine cell fates. Transplantation experiments have also provided evidence, however, that the rules for fate determination change over the course of development. When progenitors from older embryos (during the final stages of neurogenesis) are transplanted into younger host brains, the transplanted cells adopt only the fates typical of their donor origin.[84] Older progenitor cells have thus lost the "competence" to produce early-generated phenotypes. These results suggest that fate specification involves a complex interaction between extrinsic signals and the intrinsic properties of progenitor cells that change over time.

The molecular identity of cues regulating cell fate in the ventricular matrix has not yet been determined. A particularly attractive model is that each cell type generated provides to the ventricular zone critical information, which changes the fate of dividing precursors and results in generation of the next cell type. For example, the first neurons to arise from the ventricular zone and persist in the adult cerebral cortex are layer VI pyramidal cells. According to this simple model, generation of these cells would require the prior differentiation of previous transient neuronal cell populations, which constitute a temporary structure called the subplate, and the differentiation of layer VI neurons would in turn be required to specify the fate of layer V neurons. Thus, the information available to ventricular precursors to determine cell fates is in dynamic flux, depending on the local information available to the dividing precursors.

Researchers[85] have addressed the more general issue of how migratory paths affect the identity of clonally related cells in the developing chick optic tectum. Although descendants of a single progenitor begin their migrations in the same area of the ventricular zone, subgroups of the progeny diverge, follow distinct migratory pathways (radial migration along the glial pathway and tangential migration in the intermediate zone), and acquire distinct neuronal phenotypes. Thus, precursor cells in the ventricular zone may be multipotential, with diverse migration routes away from these germinal zones spatially restricting particular neuronal phenotypes. Specification could occur early, with migratory routes restricting different neuronal phenotypes, or partially specified cells could randomly follow one or the other migratory pathway, with diverse epigenetic cues present along the two pathways inducing different neuronal phenotypes.

Molecular markers are used to examine pathways of migration, especially pathways of cells that will give rise to specific sets of precursor cells. Although markers have been developed for select cell populations, they do not reveal whether such cells travel alone or in cohorts with other sets of precursor cells that influence their differentiation. Moreover, the technical problems faced in tracing cells—sectioning the embryonic brain, detecting labeled cells, and reconstructing the spatial distribution of the entire population—are formidable. Within the context of neurogenesis, the cell numbers are large, and it may not be possible to detect misrouted cells. Further, if misrouted cells undergo programmed cell death in the absence of factors and connections needed to maintain their survival, they would not be detected with current cell tracing methodologies.

Multiple Modes of Migration Generate Other Laminar Structures: Retina and Spinal Cord

Although the general scheme of proliferation portrayed for the cortical ventricular zone is maintained throughout the developing CNS, the retina and spinal cord do not use the entire program of migration-based laminar formation seen for cortex, hippocampus, and cerebellum. In the retina, clonally related cells are derived from multipotent precursor cells that disperse in radial arrays.[7] Young neurons in the retina apparently migrate by an accentuation of the interkinetic, to-and-fro movements of the nuclei within cells in various phases of the cell cycle. These movements are also seen in the early phases of cortical development, prior to the formation of the four embryonic layers. One class of retinal cell, the amacrine cells, does appear to undergo somewhat longer range tangential migrations, up to several cell lengths. Such cells apparently migrate without an underlying cellular substrate. Radial glia, so prominent in layered cortical regions, do not develop in the retina.

The spinal cord extends the range of cell movements seen in the retina to combine interkinetic displacements, formation of a mantle layer, and limited radial migration along glial fibers, followed by extensive tangential migration along axon tracts (Fig. 16.11).[86] Retroviral marking methods (Box 16.2) have revealed extensive intermixing of precursor cells within the germinal zone of the spinal cord.[86] The extent of precursor cell movement apparently becomes progressively restricted during cord development. An interesting feature of spinal cord development is the movement of cells along the rostrocaudal axis of the posterior portion of the CNS.

The Brainstem and Diencephalon Are Nonlayered Structures

Development of the brainstem proceeds along the general program of organization used in cortical regions of brain. Proliferation of precursor cells in the pseudostratified neuroepithelium is followed by interkinetic dispersion toward the periphery and formation of marginal and intermediate zones. A special feature of the developing brainstem is the population of precursor cells that emerges from a prominent longitudinal bulge, located along the lateral edges, named the rhombic lip by His[27] a century ago. As seen for the external germinal layer of the cerebellum, cells in the medullary and pontine region of the fourth ventricle pour over the surface of the developing brainstem, generating a migratory stream from the external surface of the medulla and forming the inferior olivary structures.[26,87] The migratory stream across the surface of the brainstem is a transient embryonic structure, called the corpus pontobulbare. Two key distinctions between the external germinal layer of the cerebellum and the migratory stream seen across the brainstem are that the migrating neurons of the brainstem are postmitotic and that they turn inward to form the olivary nucleus by migrating along axons, not glial cells.

Within the developing diencephalon, a similar program is seen—proliferation within the ventricular zone, followed by formation of a mantle zone by postmitotic cell populations. Whereas cells in the cortex undergo directed migration along glial fibers to form laminae, cells in the diencephalon gradually accumulate and aggregate into ganglion-like structures (nuclei) or sheets. Multipotent precursor cells undergo widespread dispersion across bulges termed neuromeres, thought to be counterparts of the rhombomeres of the hindbrain as described in Chapter 15. Thus, a very different—and as yet elusive—mode of cell assembly occurs in subcortical regions of the brain. One finding of possible relevance in the formation of nuclei or condensed groups of cells is the expression of the cadherins in nonlaminar areas of the brain. Postmitotic neurons undergoing assembly in the diencephalon in developing chick brain express the cell adhesion molecule R-cadherin.[88] In this respect, cell assembly in the diencephalon proceeds according to strategies described earlier in the formation of PNS ganglia.

Studies of the human thalamus provided the first insights into another major pattern of cell migration in nonlaminar structures.[26] Although it is not accessible for experimental manipulation, the human brain offers extended developmental epochs and relatively larger cell populations, which facilitate cell tracking. In the forebrain, thalamic migrations provide several parallels to those in the brainstem. Whereas proliferation in the ventricular zone generates early cell populations in the ventral aspect of the forebrain, later migration from the lateral **ganglionic eminence,** a structure analogous to the rhombic lip of the fourth ventricle, generates a late population of cells in the thalamus. The ganglionic eminence is composed of subventricular zone cells that continue rapid proliferation until well after birth. At that time, many cells migrate to adjacent ventral structures, including the caudate putamen and the amygdala. In addition, a large population of these cells undergoes a long-distance migration through the internal capsule to the thalamus (Fig. 16.12).[26] Thus, the ganglionic eminence of the forebrain supplies a large number of postmitotic precursor cells that migrate rostrally along an axon tract, rather than radially through the thickness of the diencephalic wall.

Neurons Expressing GnRH Migrate from the Olfactory Pit into the CNS

Although it was long assumed that all CNS cells originate within the wall of the developing neural tube, recent experiments demonstrate that one population of neurons in the hypothalamus originates outside the brain vesicles, entering the brain through a highly unusual migratory pathway.[89,90] This group of cells, **the gonadotropin-releasing hormone** (GnRH), express a key hormone neuroendocrine system for both the maturation of the reproductive system and its maintenance in the adult. Experiments to trace the origin of these cells within the region of the diencephalic neuroepithelium that gives rise to the adult hypothalamus unexpectedly revealed that these neurons first appear in

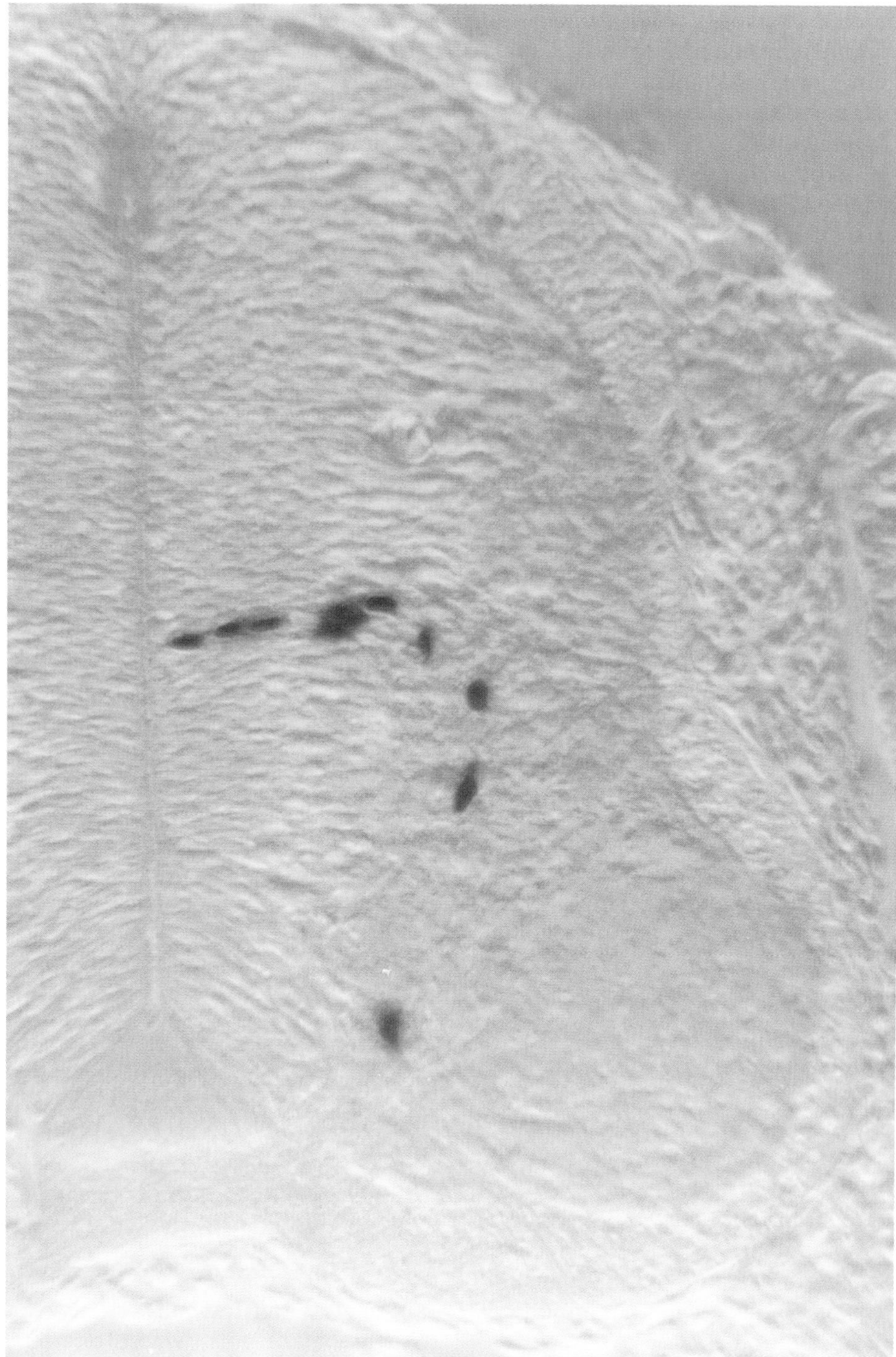

FIGURE 16.11 Lineage analysis using retroviral vectors in the embryonic chick spinal cord reveals both radial and tangential pathways for neuronal migration. A recombinant retrovirus was used to infect progenitor cells of the spinal cord with a harmless bacterial marker gene that encodes the enzyme β-galactosidase. Expression of this enzyme by the progeny of the infected cell can be detected by a histochemical reaction that turns the cell blue. The clonal progeny of spinal progenitor cells initially migrate radially out of the ventricular zone. In many clones, however, some young neurons then turn orthogonally to migrate tangentially within the intermediate zone. These neurons appeared to employ circumferentially oriented axons to guide their tangential movements. From Leber and Sanes.[86]

BOX 16.2

VIRAL VECTORS AND GENE THERAPY

Viruses cause a range of animal diseases, and it is somewhat ironic that these infectious agents, which consist only of nucleic acid (DNA or RNA) and protein, can be used as therapeutic gene delivery systems.[1] Novel genes intended to correct an inherent genetic flaw can be introduced into weakened forms of viruses—termed viral vectors—and used in gene therapy. In some ways, this approach of using modified viruses to correct molecular defects is analogous to the use of the fabled Trojan horse, which was used as a decoy to sneak Greek soldiers into the ancient city of Troy.

Gene therapy can be accomplished in two major ways. The first is called *ex vivo* gene therapy, in which the cells are removed from an individual, grown in tissue culture, and modified following treatment with a viral vector. The modified cells are then introduced by injection back into the host individual. The second method involves *in vivo* gene therapy, in which viral vectors are injected into specific sites in the brain of the host, enter local neurons or glial cells, and then selectively destroy or transform them. Both types of gene therapy may have important clinical applications.

Viruses are natural vehicles for gene transfer, because they are intracellular parasites that exist to shuttle their own genetic material into host cells, which then permit replication of the viral genome and production of new virions. This process often results in toxicity or death of the host cell due to production of viral proteins. In an attempt to limit the damage, the immune system often responds to the viral proteins with a strong inflammatory response that can also cause profound local tissue damage. Thus, viral vectors have been designed to capitalize on the high efficiency of transfer of genetic material by viruses while attempting to limit the toxicity caused by viral replication, spread of infection, and/or viral proteins.

A variety of viruses have been used in neurobiology, and each affords certain advantages and disadvantages depending on its application. One type of virus, the retrovirus, contains a RNA genome, which after entering the host cell must be converted into a complementary DNA (cDNA) copy by the viral enzyme reverse transcriptase. This process requires a sufficient pool of DNA precursors, which are usually present only in actively dividing cells. Efficient expression also requires mitosis-dependent integration of the cDNA into the host chromosome. Therefore, these viruses have been used in applications where the goal is to direct gene transfer into dividing cells. For example, retroviruses have been used in research studies dealing with development of the CNS in which a marker gene (e.g., the *lacZ* gene from *Escherichia coli* that codes for the enzyme β-galatosidase) is transferred into dividing neuronal precursors, and the fate of these cells can be traced into adulthood. A second application has been to introduce genes into dividing cells in tissue culture, prior to brain tissue transplantation experiments in animal models of neurological disorders such as Parkinson and Alzheimer diseases. The third application has been their use in treating brain tumors in humans. Because brain tumors contain actively dividing cells thriving in a background of nondividing neurons and glia, a logical choice for treatment is the use of genetically engineered forms of retroviruses that carry therapeutic or potentially toxic genes that could be used to selectively infect and subsequently destroy the tumor cells. Clinical trials have suggested that this strategy is promising. However, the slow rate of division of most brain tumor cells has led to the use of other vectors based on adeno- and herpesviruses, which infect nondividing cells. Another retroviral vector system has been developed using a nonreplicating form of human immunodeficiency virus (HIV)—a lentivirus in the same general virus family as the one that causes AIDS.[2] This virus integrates its genome into nondividing cells without expression of HIV proteins and been shown to efficiently and safely transfer genes into neurons of the mammalian brain *in vivo*, suggesting the possibility that certain retroviral vectors may be useful in neurobiology.

Viruses containing DNA genomes (e.g., adenoviruses and herpesviruses) are particularly useful agents for gene transfer into either neurons or glial cells of the adult brain, because they do not require cell division for efficient uptake and expression of their genetic material. Two general classes of vectors have been created on the basis of these viruses: recombinant vectors and defective vectors. Recombinant vectors contain deletions of one or more genes that promote viral replication or cause cellular toxicity, and the gene of interest is inserted into the mutated viral chromosome. These vehicles are easily grown in very large amounts, and the genomes can be manipulated so that the viruses will replicate only under certain conditions. Even when viral replication is completely eliminated, however, genes that may promote cellular toxicity often remain. Defective vectors contain a gene of interest attached to recognition signals that permit replication and packaging of the DNA into a viral coat. No viral genes are present, and the necessary viral proteins are provided either by a "helper" virus or by a cell line that constitutively expresses such genes. The packaged vector is thus incapable of replication, and no viral proteins are ever expressed in target cells. The major advantage of this class of vectors is that all elements responsible for viral toxicity have been eliminated. These vehicles are technically very difficult to synthesize, however, and great effort is required to grow titers similar to those easily obtained with recombinant vectors. Furthermore, the potentially toxic "helper" virus must be completely eliminated, and in some systems, this is not yet practical.

Recombinant vectors developed from adenoviruses (AD) and herpes simplex viruses (HSV) are the most common vehicles used for gene transfer in neurobiology. AD contains a 35-kilobase (kb) genome with a capsid, whereas HSV is far larger with a 150-kb genome and a second protein-studded membrane around the capsid called an envelope. Both vectors almost invariably contain deletions in a key immediate-early gene, which results in a lack of expression of numerous genes essential for replication and packaging. AD recombinants are simpler to construct and deletion of multiple genes is easier compared with HSV, largely owing to factors related to the smaller size and fewer number of genes present in the AD genome. Such vectors have been used for a variety of applications in the adult brain in the laboratory setting, ranging from the destruction of brain tumors, promoting neuronal regeneration, to altering glial cell responses following trauma.

A variety of recombinant herpesviruses have been used for other types of experimental studies, including those studies using viruses as transneuronal tracers to define brain circuits in laboratory animals. For example, weakened strains of HSV or a related pig herpes virus (pseudorabies virus) can be microinjected into a specific peripheral site (e.g., visceral organ or muscle) or the brain itself, and after several days, an infection spreads in a hierarchial manner within the chain of neurons that regulate this target. The wave of infection can be detected in first-, second-, and often third-order neurons of a neural network by histochemical methods. This approach has been used to define the chemical organization of many of the CNS circuits involved in control of visceral functions.[3]

Recombinant HSV vectors with deletions in certain DNA-synthetic enzymes (such as thymidine kinase or ribonucleotide reductase) have also been used as potential treatments for brain tumors. These genes are only necessary to promote DNA synthesis in nondividing cells, but they are dispensable in actively dividing cells. These vectors replicate in and destroy dividing tumor cells (which contain adequate DNA precursors) while sparing normal, nondividing brain cells. This approach has shown promise in preclinical studies in rodent and primate brain tumors and may be useful for treatment of human patients.

Defective HSV and adeno-associated virus vectors are the major types of defective DNA viral vectors used in neurobiology. Defective HSV vectors contain an HSV origin of DNA replication and packaging signal, which permits packaging into an HSV coat, but the vector contains no viral genes. As a result, no toxic or immunogenic viral proteins are produced in the target cells. Another advantage of this system is that many copies of the viral gene are packaged into a single viral particle, thereby amplifying expression of the gene of interest. To package the DNA of a defective HSV, HSV proteins are required, and these are usually provided by a helper virus. The helper virus cannot be entirely eliminated from the vector stock. Thus, when defective HSV viruses are used, a potential toxicity may remain due to residual helper viruses. However, a multiple-plasmid system has been used to express necessary HSV proteins without creating any helper virus, so improvements in this technology may make it safe to use defective HSV vectors in a clinical setting.

Adeno-associated virus (AAV) vectors have received increased interest because the problems related to helper virus toxicity can be avoided. AAV is a parvovirus that requires co-infection of a cell by adenovirus (or herpesvirus) to efficiently replicate and package new AAV virions. A multiple-plasmid system has been used in which the AAV vector (containing only AAV packaging/replication signals and a gene of interest) is transfected with a second plasmid containing all AAV genes without the replication/packaging sequences. This "helper" plasmid permits vector packaging, but no helper virus is produced. Co-infection by adenovirus (or introduction of a plasmid containing adenovirus genes) then efficiently produces the packaged vector. Because any contaminating adenovirus can easily be removed, the AAV system is completely defective and free of any helper virus contamination. Disadvantages of this system include its small size (only 5 kb of foreign DNA can be packaged) and the technical difficulty in producing large amounts of high-titer virus stocks. Both AAV and defective HSV systems have been used for a variety of basic and clinical neuroscience applications, including *in vivo* promoter analysis, study of genes influencing neuronal regeneration, and gene therapy in animal models of Parkinson and Alzheimer diseases, epilepsy, and stroke. These viral systems have been shown to be safe and effective in a variety of circumstances, and clinical trials using AAV and possibly defective HSV are likely in the near future.

In summary, viral vectors offer unique molecular tools with which to alter CNS diseases as well as to study basic cellular functions of both neurons and glial cells. By carefully tailoring the type of genetic messsage and packaging system used, researchers may now be able to create viral vectors for amelioriation of certain human diseases.

Michael G. Kaplitt and Arthur D. Loewy

References

1. Kaplitt, M. G., and Loewy, A. D. (1995). *Viral vectors: Tools for the study and genetic manipulation of the nervous system.* Academic Press, San Diego.
2. Naldini, L., Blömer, U., Gallay, P. Ory, D., Mulligan, R., Gage, F. H., Verma, I. M., and Trono, D. (1996). In vivo gene delivery and stable transduction of nondividing cells by a lentiviral vector. *Science* **272:** 263–267.
3. Jansen, A. S. P., Nguyen, X. V., Karpitskiy, V., Mettenleiter, T. C., and Loewy, A. D. (1995.) Central command neurons of the sympathetic nervous system: Basis of the fight-or-flight response. *Science* **270:** 644–646.

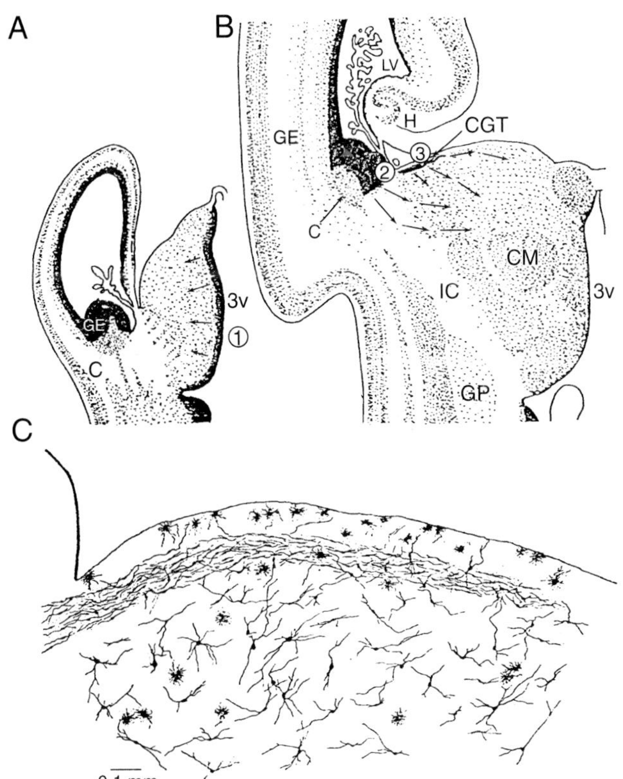

FIGURE 16.12 Pathways for neuronal migration in the posterior region of the human thalamus. (A and B) Drawings of horizontal sections through the thalamus and adjacent structures. (A) In a 10-week fetus, ventricular cells (position 1) near the IIIrd ventricle (3V) generate neurons that migrate inward to populate the thalamus (arrows). The ventricular zone serves as the major source of thalamic neurons during early stages of development. (B) In a 24-week fetus, cells that originate in the ganglionic eminence (GE) migrate across the posterior thalamic peduncle and internal capsule to reach the lateral thalamus (position 2). Another migratory path (position 3) is found posterolaterally: here cells migrate through the corpus gangliothalamicum (CGT) into the thalamus. This second stage of migration occurs at a time when the ventricular zone of the IIIrd ventricle has been depleted, yet the lateral and dorsal regions of thalamus are acquiring large numbers of new neurons. (C) Golgi-filled cells in the posterior region of the lateral thalamus, adjacent to the ganglionic eminence. Many cells have a bipolar migratory morphology, with increasingly complex shapes apparent in deeper regions of the thalamus. Abbreviations: C, caudate nucleus; IC, internal capsule; GP, globus pallidus; CM, nucleus centrum mediatum; LV, lateral ventricle; H, hippocampus. From Sidman and Rakic.[26]

the olfactory pit, a placodal derivative that gives rise to the nasal epithelium. Combined use of the thymidine-labeling methods, *in situ* hybridization of GnRH mRNA, and immunocytochemical localization of cells expressing the GnRH protein proved that the 800 or so GnRH neurons of the murine hypothalamus originate in the vomeronasal area of the olfactory system. As the precursor cells exit the cycle and initiate expression of GnRH, they migrate 1–3 mm through the nasal septum and into the forebrain. The pathway of their migration follows the axon tract of the vomeronasal–nervus terminalis neurons, cells that express pheromone receptors, a novel class of protein kinase receptors thought to play a signaling role in neuroendocrine function.[91] Kallman syndrome in humans disrupts the development and/or migration of these neurons (Box 16.3).

Molecular Subroutines Underlie Cell Specification and Differentiation

Histogenesis in the developing brain is responsive to environmental cues and local cell–cell interactions that are most easily interpreted as epigenetic mechanisms for neural development.[91] This is discussed in detail in Chapter 17. A general principle derived from genetic and experimental neuroanatomical studies is that *histogenesis in the developing CNS is controlled by spatially and temporally dynamic epigenetic cues that pro-*

gram specific stages in neuronal or glial differentiation. Such cues, their transducing mechanisms, and the resultant pleiotrophic functions elicited by their actions constitute a molecular subroutine of neural differentiation. As an example, the molecular subroutine for glial-guided migration might consist of (1) a signal generated by interactions between a differentiating neuron and radial glia, (2) transduction of that signal to the

BOX 16.3

KALLMANN SYNDROME

Although many somatic and developmental abnormalities (hearing loss, cleft lip and palate, renal aplasia, and various neurological deficits) may be present in Kallmann syndrome, the principle features are anosmia (the inability to smell) and infertility (hypogonadism and sterile gonads). A dysfunction involving smell and reproduction was originally described in 1856 by Maestre de San Juan,[1] and Kallmann *et al.* reported the first familial cases in 1944.[2] The symptoms associated with Kallmann syndrome remained unexplained, however, until researchers demonstrated that two key players in the dysfunction share a common developmental origin—the olfactory placode.[3–5] These key players are:

1. *Olfactory receptor neurons*—primary sensory neurons for the sense of smell. Cell somata are located in the nasal epithelium, and axons terminate in glomeruli in the olfactory bulb.
2. *Gonadotropin-releasing hormone* (GnRH) neurons—neuroendocrine cells required for reproductive maturation and competence. The cell somata are located in the forebrain, and axons terminate in the median eminence of the hypothalamus.

During normal prenatal development, the olfactory receptor neurons and pheromone receptor neurons, primary sensory neurons for olfactory stimuli related to social and/or reproductive behavior, remain in the nasal cavity while their axons traverse the nasal septum to the developing brain. When they reach the brain, olfactory receptor axons induce formation of the olfactory bulb, the region in the telencephalon containing mitral cells, secondary neurons for relay of olfaction, which together with olfactory receptor axons form the functional olfactory unit—the glomeruli while, the axons, pheromone receptor neuron grows caudally into the developing accessory olfactory nucleus. In contrast to olfactory and pheromone receptor neurons, GnRH neurons reside in the brain after birth. To attain their adultlike distribution, during normal development, GnRH neurons leave the nasal cavity and migrate into the developing telencephalon, following a route across the nasal septum similar to that taken by olfactory and pheromone receptor neuron axons. However, as axons from the olfactory receptor neurons head rostrally into the developing olfactory bulb, GnRH neurons turn caudally, perhaps in association with pheromone receptor neuron axons, toward the developing diencephalon. Figure 6.13 summarizes these events.

In Kallmann syndrome, the development of these systems is perturbed; both GnRH neurons and olfactory and pheromone receptor neurons axons migrate to the base of the cribiform plate but halt outside the brain, as seen in a fetus prenatally diagnosed with Kallmann syndrome.[6] Kallmann syndrome is a rare disorder. The most frequent mode of transmission is X-linked, although autosomal recessive and autosomal dominant transmissions have been reported. The rarity of the syndrome is directly related to reproductive dysfunction of affected individuals, which results in deletion of the mutant gene(s) from the populations.

The cloning of the KAL gene, the deduced amino acid sequence of which suggested an extracellular matrix component (secreted protein) with antiprotease and/or cell adhesion functions,[7,8] heightened anticipation that a candidate molecule guiding olfactory and pheromone receptor axons and GnRH neurons through nasal regions had been found. Unexpectedly, the KAL gene was expressed in brain by cells of the olfactory bulb[9] but not in cells in nasal regions, that is, in neither migrating neurons (GnRH cells) nor neurons in the nasal epithelium. Interestingly, the KAL gene has not been identified in rodents. However, based on its spatiotemporal expression pattern in humans and chickens, KAL is no longer a viable candidate for a guidance molecule directly involved in the migrational events observed in nasal regions. KAL is now proposed to have a role in the events regulating contact and maintenance of olfactory receptor axons within the olfactory bulb. How the KAL protein affects movement of GnRH neurons into the brain remains a mystery, but the current hypothesis suggests that the anosmia (due to hypoplasia or aplasia of the olfactory bulb) observed in Kallmann syndrome results from a CNS olfactory target cell defect. Effective treatment for reproductive dysfunction is available for patients with Kallmann syndrome, but early diagnosis is important; without treatment, pubertal onset does

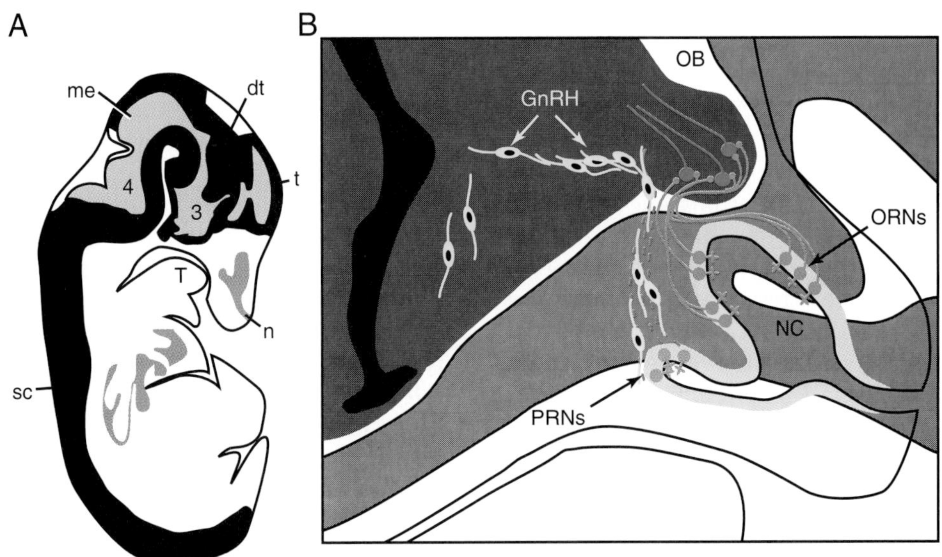

FIGURE 16.13 Development of the olfactory region. (A) Diagram of an E12.5–E13.0 staged mouse embryo. The developing brain is indicated by dark stippling and the ventricular regions by light stippling. n, nose; t, telencephalon; dt, dorsal thalamus; me, mesencephalon; sc, spinal cord; T, tongue; 3, third ventricle; 4, fourth ventricle. (B) Diagram of the nose–brain region and a schematic of the relationship between neurons in the olfactory epithelium (Olfactory and pheromone receptor neurons: ORNs and PRNs), GnRH neurons, and the developing olfactory bulb (OB). Axons of the ORNs enter the OB and contact mitral cells (known to express KAL protein in humans and chickens) while axons from PRNs enter the olfactory accessory bulb. Unlike ORNs and PRNs, GnRH neurons actually leave the nasal region and migrate into the developing brain. Large arrow, region where GnRH neurons cross into forebrain.

not occur. Substitution hormone therapy is necessary to induce secondary sex characteristics, and treatment with GnRH often restores fertility.

Susan Wray

References

1. Maestre de San Juan, A. (1856). Falta total de los nervios olfactorios con anosmia en un individuo en quien exista una atrofia congenita de los testiculos y miembro viril (II). *El Siglo Medico* **131:** 211.
2. Kallmann, F. J., Schoenfeld, W. A., and Barrera, S. E. (1944). The genetic aspects of primary eunuchoidism. *Am. J. Ment. Defic.* **48:** 203–236.
3. Schwanzel-Fukuda, M., and Pfaff, D. W. (1989). Origin of luteinizing hormone releasing hormone neurons. *Nature* 338–340.
4. Wray, S., Nieburgs, A., and Elkabes, S. (1989). Spatiotemporal cell expression of luteinizing hormone releasing hormone in the prenatal mouse: Evidence for an embryonic origin in the olfactory pit. *Dev. Brain Res.* **46:** 309–318.
5. Wray, S., Grant, P., and Gainer, H. (1989). Evidence that cells expressing luteinizing hormone releasing hormone mRNA in the mouse are derived from progenitor cells in the olfactory placode. *Proc. Natl. Acad. Sci. U.S.A.* **86:** 8132–8136.
6. Schwanzel-Fukuda, M., Bick, D., and Pfaff, D. W. (1989). Luteinizing hormone releasing hormone (LHRH)-expressing cells do not migrate in an inherited hypogonadal (Kallmann) syndrome. *Mol. Brain Res.* **6:** 311–326.
7. Franco, B., Guiolo, S., Pragliola, A., Incerti, B., Bardoni, B., Tonlorenzi, R., Carrozzo, R., Maestrini, E., Pieretti, M., Taillon-Miler, P., Brown, C. J., Willard, H. F., Lawrence, C., Persico, M. G., Camerino, G., and Ballabio, A. (1991). A gene deleted in Kallmann's syndrome shares homology with neural cell adhesion and axonal path-finding molecules. *Nature* **353:** 529–536.
8. Legouis, R., Hardelin, J-P., Levilliers, J., Claverie, J-M., Compain, S., Wunderle, V., Millasseau, P., Le Paslier, D., Cohen, D., Caterina, D., Bougueleret, L., Delemarre-Van de Waal, H., Lutfalla, G., Weissenbach, J., and Petit, C. (1991). The candidate gene for the X-linked Kallmann syndrome encodes a protein related to adhesion molecules. *Cell* **67:** 423–435.
9. Rugarli, E. I., Lutz, B., Kuranti, S. C., Wawersik, S., Borsani, G., Ballabio, A., and Eichele, G. (1993). Expression pattern of the Kallmann syndrome gene in the olfactory system suggests a role in neuronal targeting. *Nature Genet.* **4:** 19–26.

nucleus, (3) production of proteins important for the mechanics of neuronal migration or the maintenance of glial function, (4) reception of a "stop" signal on arrival in the appropriate laminar position, and (5) cessation of the synthesis of proteins specific to glial-guided migration.

Three important points concerning the nature of epigenetic regulation and the functions of subroutines deserve further consideration. First, differentiation of a particular cell type likely results from cascades of several epigenetic subroutines. Thus, activation of a molecular subroutine can activate downstream genes that are also transcriptional regulatory factors. Second, although these subprograms are shared across cell types in the CNS, local signals in different environments may induce their expression in different orders. Third, the order of subroutines can, in turn, serve to organize the program for differentiation of a particular class of neurons. The timing of cell migration and axon outgrowth among cerebellar precursor cells is an example. Whereas precursors of the Purkinje neuron, like neural precursors in the developing neocortex, migrate just after exit from the cell cycle and form axonal connections relatively late in their program of differentiation, granule cell precursors extend axons just after exit from the cell cycle and migrate along Bergmann glia later in development. Thus, the temporospatial ordering of local cues for specific molecular subroutines can generate multiple programs for neuronal differentiation.

Given the existence of developmental cues that change in time and space throughout the developing nervous system, cell migration appears to be an integral part of neuronal differentiation. The changing patterns of gene expression during cerebellar granule cell migration provide a pertinent illustration of this concept. In the postnatal cerebellum, granule cells at all stages of their differentiation program are evident at a single time. At each stage of differentiation, the developing granule cell is found in a different laminar position. Thus, rapidly dividing granule cell precursors in the external germinal layer are subject to proliferative signals. On the other hand, granule cells that have finished their migratory route are receiving entirely different information that allows them to incorporate into the internal granule layer, extend dendrites, and make synapses with their mossy fiber afferents. In this way, several different molecular subroutines can take place at a single developmental time.

Finally, in some instances, cell migration provides a mechanism for establishing the final connectivity of a neuronal circuit. A case in point is again the cerebellar granule cell. These cells possess an extended T-shaped axon. The cross of the T is composed of a fiber that extends for long distances parallel to the surface of the cerebellum. A descending portion that comprises the vertical axis of the T extends from the parallel fiber to the granule cell body in the internal granule cell layer. Unlike many neurons, which first migrate to the appropriate position in the developing brain and then extend an axon that grows toward its target, cerebellar granule cells produce their axon as they migrate through the developing cerebellum on Bergmann glial guides. In this case, therefore, axonogenesis and glial-guided migration occur concurrently, resulting in the final structure of the granule cell T-shaped axon and its proper integration into cerebellar circuitry. Several other neuronal cell types also appear to grow their axons during glial-guided migration in the developing brain. In these cases, migration provides a topological solution to establishing correct connectivity by guiding the migration of the neuronal cell body rather than the directions of the growing axons.

Summary

The development of the vertebrate nervous system relies on a series of cell movements and migrations to produce complex multilayered and nuclear structures. In the CNS, neural progenitor cells undergo characteristic to-and-fro intracellular movements during the cell cycle within primary germinal matrices, and progenitors undertake long-distance migrations through the secondary matrices of the cerebellum and telencephalon. As young neurons exit from the cell cycle, they typically move away from their site of generation to their final destinations within the brain and spinal cord. Radial migrations are guided by the elongated processes of radial glial cells, and tangentially migrating cells may travel along axons or even upon one another. In both the CNS and the PNS, these migratory processes propel cells through microenvironments that alter patterns of gene expression, directing cell differentiation and controlling the timing of maturation of cells. Now that the pathways of migration and the general role of migration in pacing the tempo of neurogenesis and differentiation have been established, it should be possible to identify the signals that control these processes. Resolution of these epigenetic signals will, in turn, reveal the mystery of how the billions of young precursor cells in both the brain and the body utilize migration and programs of cell assembly to direct their development.

References

1. Selleck, M., and Bronner-Fraser, M. (1995). Origins of the avian neural crest: The role of neural plate-epidermal interactions. *Development (Cambridge, UK)* **121:** 525–538.

2. Liem, K. F., Jr., Tremml, G., Roelink, H., and Jessell, T. M. (1995). Dorsal differentiation of neural plate cells induced by BMP-mediated signals from epidermal ectoderm. *Cell (Cambridge, Mass.)* **82:** 969–979.
3. Tanabe, Y., and Jessell, T. M. (1996). Diversity and pattern in the developing spinal cord. *Science* **274:** 1115–1121.
4. LeDouarin, N. (1969). Particularités du noyau interphasique chez la caille japonaise *Coturnix coturnix japonica.* Utilisation de ces particularités comme 'marquage biologique' dans les récherches sur les interactions tissulaires et les migrations cellulaires au cours de l'ontogénèse. *Bull. Biol. Fr. Belg.* **103:** 435–452.
5. LeDouarin, N. M. (1982). *The Neural Crest.* Cambridge University Press, Cambridge, UK.
6. Bronner-Fraser, M., and Cohen, A. M. (1980). Analysis of the neural crest ventral pathway using injected tracer cells. *Dev. Biol.* **77:** 130–141.
7. Turner, D. L., and Cepko, C. L. (1987). A common progenitor for neurons and glia persists in rat retina late in development. *Nature (London)* **328:** 131–136.
8. Bronner-Fraser, M., and Fraser, S. E. (1988). Cell lineage analysis reveals multipotency of some avian neural crest cells. *Nature (London)* **335:** 161–164; (1989). Developmental potential of avian trunk neural crest cells *in situ. Neuron* **3:** 755–766.
9. Serbedzija, G. N., Bronner-Fraser, M., and Fraser, S. E. (1989). A vital dye analysis of the timing and pathways of avian trunk neural crest cell migration. *Development (Cambridge, UK)* **106:** 809–816.
10. Gershon, M. D., Chalazonitis, A., and Rothman, T. P. (1993). From neural crest to bowel: Development of the enteric nervous system. *J. Neurobiol.* **24:** 199–214.
11. LeDouarin, N. M., Renaud, D., Teillet, M.-A., and LeDouarin, G. H. (1975). Cholinergic differentiation of presumptive adrenergic neuroblasts in interspecific chimeras after heterotopic transplantation. *Proc. Natl. Acad. Sci. U.S.A.* **72:** 728–732.
12. Anderson, D. J., and Axel, R. (1986). A bipotential neuroendocrine precursor whose choice of cell fate is determined by NGF and glucocorticoids. *Cell (Cambridge, Mass.)* **47:** 1079–1090.
13. Sieber-Blum, M., and Sieber, F. (1984). Heterogeneity among early quail neural crest cells. *Dev. Brain Res.* **14:** 241–246.
14. Anderson, D. J. (1989). The neural crest lineage problem: Neuropoiesis? *Neuron* **3:** 1–12.
15. Perris, R., Paulsson, M., and Bronner-Fraser, M. (1989). Molecular mechanisms of avian neural crest cell migration on fibronectin and laminin. *Dev. Biol.* **136:** 222–238.
16. Erickson, C. A., Tosney, K. W., and Weston, J. A. (1980). Analysis of migrating behavior of neural crest and fibroblastic cells in embryonic tissues. *Dev. Biol.* **77:** 142–156.
17. Newgreen, D., and Thiery, J. P. (1980). Fibronectin in early avian embryos: Synthesis and distribution along the migration pathways of neural crest cells. *Cell Tissue Res.* **211:** 269–291.
18. Bronner-Fraser, M. (1986). Analysis of the early stages of trunk neural crest migration in avian embryos using monoclonal antibody HNK-1. *Dev. Biol.* **115:** 444–455.
19. Teillet, M.-A., Kalcheim, C., LeDouarin, N. M. (1987). Formation of the dorsal root ganglia in the avian embryo: Segmental origin and migratory behavior of neural crest progenitor cells. *Dev. Biol.* **120:** 329–347.
20. Loring, J. F., and Erickson, C. A. (1987). Neural crest migratory pathways in the trunk of the chick embryo. *Dev. Biol.* **121:** 220–236.
21. Shah, N. M., Groves, A. K., and Anderson, D. J. (1996). Alternative neural crest cell fates are instructively promoted by TGFβ superfamily members. *Cell (Cambridge, Mass.)* **85:** 331–343.
22. Ramón y Cajal, S. (1911/1995). *Histology of the Nervous System of Man and Vertebrates* (N. Swanson and L. W. Swanson, transl.), Vols. 1 and 2, Oxford University Press, New York.
23. Sidman, R. L., Miale, I. L., and Feder, N. (1959). Cell proliferation and migration in the primitive ependymal zone: An autoradiographic study of histogenesis in the nervous system. *Exp. Neurol.* **1:** 322–333.
24. Fugita, S. (1964). Analysis of neuron differentiation in the central nervous system by tritiated thymidine autoradiography. *J. Comp. Neurol.* **122:** 311–328.
25. Sidman, R. L. (1970). Autoradiographic methods and principles for study of the nervous system with thymidine-H^3. In *Contemporary Research Techniques of Neuroanatomy* (W. J. Nauta and S. O. E. Ebbesson, eds.), pp. 252–274. Springer, New York.
26. Sidman, R. L., and Rakic, P. (1973). Neuronal migration with special reference to developing human brain: A review. *Brain Res.* **62:** 1–35.
27. His, W. (1889). Die Neuroblasten und deren Entstehung im embryonalen Marke. *Abh. Math.-Phys. Kl. K. Saechs. Ges. Wiss.* **15:** 313–372.
28. Schaper, A. (1897). The earliest differentiation in the central nervous system of vertebrates. *Science* **5:** 430–431.
29. Sauer, F. C. (1935). Mitosis in the neural tube. *J. Comp. Neurol.* **62:** 377–405.
30. Sauer, M. E., and Chittenden, A. (1959). Deoxyribonucleic acid content of cell nuclei in the neural tube of the chick embryo: Evidence for intermitotic migration of the nuclei. *Exp. Cell Res.* **16:** 1–6.
31. Hinds, J. W., and Ruffett, T. L. (1971). Cell proliferation in the neural tube: An electron microscopic and Golgi analysis in the mouse cerebral vesicle. *Z. Zellforsch. Mikrosk. Anat.* **115:** 226–264.
32. Hinds, J. W., and Hinds, P. L. (1974). Early ganglion cell differentiation in the mouse retina: An electron microscopic analysis utilizing serial sections. *Dev. Biol.* **37:** 381–416.
33. Berry, M., and Rogers, A. W. (1965). The migration of neuroblasts in the developing cerebral cortex. *J. Anat.* **99:** 691–709.
34. Seymour, R. M., and Berry, M. (1975). Scanning and transmission electron microscope studies of interkinetic nuclear migration in the cerebral vesicles of the rat. *J. Comp. Neurol.* **160:** 105–126.
35. Schmechel, D. E., and Rakic, P. (1979). A Golgi study of radial glial cells in developing monkey telencephalon: Morphogenesis and transformation into astrocytes. *Anat. Embryol.* **156:** 115–152.
36. Misson, J.-P., Edwards, M. A., Yamamoto, M., and Caviness, V. S. (1988). Identification of radial glial cells within the developing murine central nervous system: Studies based upon a new immunohistochemical marker. *Dev. Brain Res.* **44:** 95–108.
37. Voigt, T. (1989). Development of glial cells in the cerebral wall of ferrets: Direct tracing of their transformation from radial glia into astrocytes. *J. Comp. Neurol.* **289:** 74–88.
38. Hunter, K. E., and Hatten, M. E. (1995). Radial glial cell transformation is bidirectional: Regulation by a diffusible factor in embryonic forebrain. *Proc. Natl. Acad. Sci. U.S.A.* **92:** 2061–2065.
39. Walsh, C., and Cepko, C. L. (1988). Clonally related cortical cells show several migration patterns. *Science* **241:** 1342–1345.
40. Walsh, C., and Cepko, C. L. (1992). Widespread dispersion of neuronal clones across functional regions of the cerebral cortex. *Science* **255:** 434–440.
41. Walsh, C., and Cepko, C. L. (1993). Clonal dispersion of neural progenitors within the germinal zones of the forebrain. *Nature (London)* **362:** 636–638.
42. Fishell, G., Mason, C. A., and Hatten, M. E. (1993). Dispersion of neural progenitors within the germinal zones of the forebrain. *Nature (London)* **362:** 636–638.
43. Tan, S. S., and Breen, S. (1993). Radial mosaicism and tangential cell dispersion both contribute to mouse neocortical development. *Nature (London)* **362:** 638–640.

44. Marin-Padilla, M. (1978). Dual origin of the mammalian neocortex and evolution of the cortical plate. *Anat. Embryol.* **152:** 109–126.
45. Boulder Committee (1970). Embryonic vertebrate central nervous system: Revised terminology. *Anat. Rec.* **166:** 257–262.
46. Caviness, V. S., and Sidman, R. L. (1973). Time of origin and corresponding cell classes in the cerebral cortex of normal and reeler mutant mice: An autoradiographic analysis. *J. Comp. Neurol.* **148:** 141–152.
47. Pinto-Lord, C. M., Evrard, P., and Caviness, V. S. (1982). Obstructed neuronal migration along radial glial fibers in the neocortex of the reeler mouse: A Golgi-EM analysis. *Dev. Brain Res.* **4:** 379–393.
48. Miao, G. G., Smeyne, R. J., D'Arcangelo, G., Copeland, N. G., Jenkins, N. A., Morgan, J. I., and Curran, T. (1994). Isolation of an allele of reeler by insertional mutagenesis. *Proc. Natl. Acad. Sci. U.S.A.* **91:** 11050–11054.
49. Ogawa, M., Miyata, T., Nakajima, K., Yagyu, K., Seike, M., Ikenaka, K., Yamamoto, H., and Mikoshiba, K. (1995). The reeler gene-associated antigen on Cajal-Retzius neurons is a crucial molecule for laminar organization of cortical neurons. *Neuron* **14:** 899–912.
50. D'Arcangelo, G., Miao, G., Chen, S.-C., Soares, H., Morgan, J. I., and Curran, T. (1995). A protein related to the extracellular matrix proteins deleted in the mouse mutant reeler. *Nature (London)* **374:** 719–723.
51. Llinas, R., and Hillman, D. E. (1969). Physiological and morphological organization of the cerebellar circuits in various vertebrates. In *Neurobiology of Cerebellar Evolution and Development* (R. Llinas, ed.), pp. 43–73. AMA-ERF Institute for Biomedical Research, Chicago.
52. Levison, S. W., and Goldman, J. E. (1993). Both oligodendrocytes and astrocytes develop from progenitors in the subventricular zone of postnatal rat brain. *Neuron* **10:** 201–212.
53. Miale, I., and Sidman, R. L. (1961). An autoradiographic analysis of histogenesis in the mouse cerebellum. *Exp. Neurol.* **4:** 277–296.
54. Altman, J. (1969). Autoradiographic and histological studies of postnatal neurogenesis. IV. Cell proliferation and migration in the anterior forebrain with special reference to persisting neurogenesis in the olfactory bulb. *J. Comp. Neurol.* **136:** 433–458.
55. Hatten, M. E., and Heintz, N. (1995). Mechanisms of neural patterning and specification in the developing cerebellum. *Annu. Rev. Neurosci.* **18:** 385–408.
56. Altman, J., and Bayer, S. (1985). Embryonic development of the rat cerebellum. I. Delineation of the cerebellar primordium and early cell movement. *J. Comp. Neurol.* **231:** 1–26.
57. Yang, X. W., Zhong, R., and Heintz, N. (1996). Granule cell specification in the developing mouse brain as defined by expression of the zinc finger transcription factor RU49. *Development (Cambridge, UK)* **122:** 555–566.
58. Kuhar, S. G., Feng, L., Vidan, S., Ross, M. E., Hatten, M. E., and Heintz, N. (1993). Changing patterns of gene expression define four stages of cerebellar granule neuron differentiation. *Development (Cambridge, UK)* **117:** 97–104.
59. Ross, M. E., Carter, M. L., and Lee, J. H. (1996). MN20, a D2 cyclin, is transiently expressed in selected neural populations during embryogenesis. *J. Neurosci.* **16:** 210–219.
60. Hatten, M. E., Alder, A. J., Zimmerman, K., and Heintz, N. (1997). Genes involved in cerebellar cell specification and differentiation. *Curr. Opin. Neurobiol.* **7:** 40–47.
61. Ryder, E. F., and Cepko, C. L. (1994). Migration patterns of clonally related granule cells and their progenitors in the developing chick cerebellum. *Neuron* **12:** 1011–1029.
62. Lois, C., and Alvarez-Buylla, A. (1994). Long-distance neuronal migration in the adult mammalian brain. *Science* **264:** 1145–1148.
63. Menezes, J. R., and Luskin, M. B. (1994). Expression of neuron-specific tubulin defines a novel population in the proliferative layers of the developing telencephalon. *J. Neurosci.* **14:** 5399–5416.
64. Hu, H., Tomasiewicz, I. T., Magnuson, T., and Rutishauser, U. (1996). Role of polysialic acid in migration of olfactory bulb interneuron precursors in the subventricular zone. *Neuron* **16:** 735–743.
65. Lois, C., Garcia-Verdugo, J. M., and Alvarez-Buylla, A. (1996). Chain migration of neuronal precursors. *Science* **271:** 978–981.
66. Rakic, P. (1971). Neuron–glia relationship during granule cell migration in developing cerebellar cortex: A Golgi and electron microscopic study in Macaques rhesus. *J. Comp. Neurol.* **141:** 283–312.
67. Rakic, P. (1972). Mode of cell migration to the superficial layers of foetal monkey neocortex. *J. Comp. Neurol.* **145:** 61–83.
68. Rakic, P., Stensaas, L. J., Sayre, E. P., and Sidman, R. L. (1974). Computer-aided three-dimensional reconstruction and quantitative analysis of cells from serial electron microscopic montages of fetal monkey brain. *Nature (London)* **250:** 31–34.
69. Nowakowski, R., and Rakic, P. (1979). The mode of migration of neurons to the hippocampus: A Golgi and electron microscopic analysis in fetal rhesus monkeys. *J. Neurocytol.* **8:** 697–718.
70. Edmondson, J. C., and Hatten, M. E. (1987). Glial-guided granule neuron migration *in vitro:* A high-resolution time-lapse video microscopic study. *J. Neurosci.* **7:** 1928–1934.
71. Hatten, M. E., and Mason, C. A. (1990). Mechanisms of glial-guided neuronal migration in vivo and in vitro. *Experientia* **46:** 907–916.
72. Hatten, M. E. (1990). Riding the glial monorail: A common mechanism for glial-guided neuronal migration in different regions of the developing mammalian brain. *Trends Neurosci.* **13:** 179–184.
73. Gregory, W. A., Edmondson, J. C., Hatten, M. E., and Mason, C. A. (1988). Cytology and neuron–glia apposition of migrating cerebellar granule cells *in vitro. J. Neurosci.* **8:** 1728–1738.
74. Zheng, C., Heintz, N., and Hatten, M. E. (1996). CNS gene encoding astrotactin, which supports neuronal migration along glial fibers. *Science* **272:** 417–419.
75. Anton, E. S., Cameron, R. S., and Rakic, P. (1996). Role of neuron-glial junctional domain proteins in the maintenance and termination of neuronal migration across the embryonic cerebral wall. *J. Neurosci.* **16:** 2283–2293.
76. O'Rourke, N., Dailey, M. E., Smith, S. J., and McConnell, S. K. (1992). Diverse migratory pathways in developing cerebral cortex. *Science* **258:** 299–302.
77. Misson, J.-P., Austin, C. P., Takahashi, T., Cepko, C. L., and Caviness, V. S., Jr. (1991). The alignment of migrating neural cells in relation to the murine neopallial radial glial fiber system. *Cereb. Cortex* **1:** 221–229.
78. Gasser, U. E., and Hatten, M. E. (1990). CNS neurons migrate on astroglial fibers from heterotypic brain regions in vitro. *Proc. Natl. Acad. Sci. U.S.A.* **87:** 4543–4547.
79. Gao, W.-Q., Heintz, N., and Hatten, M. E. (1991). Granule cell neurogenesis is regulated by cell–cell interactions. *Neuron* **6:** 705–715.
80. Temple, S. (1994). A self-renewing multipotential stem cell in embryonic rat cerebral cortex. *Nature (London)* **372:** 263–266.
81. Temple, S., and Davis, A. A. (1994). Isolated rat cortical progenitor cells are maintained in division *in vitro* by membrane-associated factors. *Development (Cambridge, UK)* **120:** 999–1008.
82. Qian, X., Davis, A. A., Goderie, S. K., and Temple, S. (1997). FGF2 concentration regulates the generation of neurons and glia from multipotent cortical stem cells. *Neuron* **18:** 81–93.
83. McConnell, S. K., and Kaznowski, C. E. (1991). Cell cycle dependence of laminar determination in developing neocortex. *Science* **254:** 282–285.

84. Frantz, G. D., and McConnell, S. K. (1996). Restriction of late cerebral cortical progenitors to an upper-layer fate. *Neuron* **17:** 55–61.
85. Gray, G. E., and Sanes, J. R. (1992). Migratory paths and phenotypic choices of clonally related cells in the avian optic tectum. *Neuron* **6:** 211–225.
86. Leber, S. M., and Sanes, J. R. (1995). Migratory pathways of neurons and glia in the embryonic chick spinal cord. *J. Neurosci.* **15:** 1236–1248.
87. Taber-Pierce, E. (1966). Histogenesis of the nuclei griseum pontis, corporis pontobulbaris and reticularis tegmenti pontis (Bechterew) in the mouse: An autoradiographic study. *J. Comp. Neurol.* **126:** 219–240.
88. Ganzler, S. I., and Redies, C. (1995). R-cadherin expression during nucleus formation in chicken forebrain. *J. Neurosci.* **15:** 57–72.
89. Wray, S., Grant, P., and Gainer, H. (1989). Evidence that cells expressing luteinizing hormone-releasing hormone mRNA in mouse are derived from progenitor cells in the olfactory placode. *Proc. Natl. Acad. Sci. U.S.A.* **86:** 8132–8136.
90. Schwanzel–Fukada, M. (1992). Biology of normal luteinizing hormone-releasing hormone neurons during and after their migration from olfactory placodes. *Endocr. Rev.* **13:** 623–634.
91. Sidman, R. L.(1968). Development of interneuronal connections in brains of mutant mice. In *Physiological and Biochemical Aspects of Nervous Integration* (F. D. Carlson, ed.), pp. 163–193. Prentice-Hall, Englewood Cliffs, NJ.

CHAPTER

17

Cellular Determination

William A. Harris and Volker Hartenstein

During development, neural cells express many different anatomical, physiological, and biochemical characteristics or "phenes." Some of these characteristics are transient; others are permanent. These traits represent the **phenotype**, or identity, of each individual neural cell. The terms phenotype, identity, and fate are often used interchangeably; however, **fate** refers strictly to the future phenotype of an as yet undifferentiated neural precursor.

Neurons express an enormous variety of different phenotypes. Differences between neurons can be dramatic. For example, retinal photoreceptors and cerebellar Purkinje cells have completely different shapes, connectivities, and physiological characteristics. In other neurons, phenotypic differences can be more subtle; for example, various pyramidal cells of the cerebral cortex may differ only with regard to their axonal projections to different subcortical targets. The distribution of neurons expressing particular, different phenotypes is not random, but follows a highly reproducible pattern in a given species. In other words, neurons located at a given position within the nervous system usually express the same phenotype. In vertebrates, this statement is true at the level of populations of neurons (e.g., cells of layer III of cortical area 17 are glutaminergic pyramidal cells projecting to cortical areas 18 and 19). It is true even at the level of individual, uniquely identifiable cells in many invertebrate organisms (e.g., the deep optic neuropile of the brain of the fruit fly *Drosophila melanogaster* has one large neuron—the giant fiber neuron—which in all individuals has the same set of afferent inputs, physiology, and connectivity to thoracic motor neurons and interneurons).[1] Observations like these raise the question of how neuronal fate is controlled during development. Experimental studies carried out over the Past few decades have made substantial progress in answering this question.[2] In this chapter, we summarize some of the main insights we have gained into the mechanisms that control neuronal fate.

NEURONAL PHENOTYPES AND DETERMINANTS

When investigating mechanisms controlling the fate of a cell, we look for activities associated with molecules, cells, or larger populations of cells that induce changes in the development of the cell. For example, precursors derived from the neural crest take on the fate of adrenal chromaffin cells when grown in the presence of glucocorticoid hormone. This fact clearly indicates that this hormone can influence the fate of these crest cells, which otherwise give rise to sympathetic neurons. Glucocorticoid hormone constitutes a "cue" specifying adrenal fate.

Generally speaking, there are two different realms in which cell fate controlling cues can act (Fig. 17.1):

1. The environment into which the neuron is born and gradually differentiates provides **extrinsic cues** in the form of diffusible molecules, cell-membrane-attached factors, and extracellular-matrix-bound signal molecules.

2. The neuron itself, before the onset of differentiation, expresses or inherits from its precursor **intrinsic cues**. Many intrinsic cues that have been investigated molecularly turn out to be transcriptional activators or repressors (Fig. 17.1).

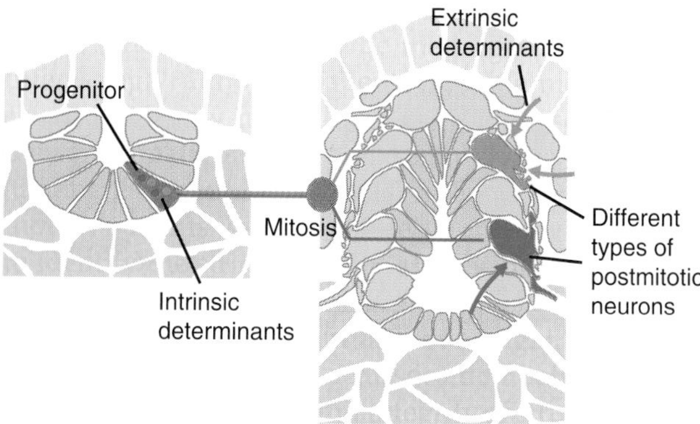

FIGURE 17.1 Neural fate is controlled by intrinsic determinants expressed in neural progenitors (left) and extrinsic determinants derived from the microenvironment of the postmitotic neurons (right).

Extrinsic Cues Activate Signal Transduction Cascades and Control Differential Gene Expression in the Recipient Cell

Signal molecules can be secreted from remote cells (hormones, growth factors), in which case one speaks of **endocrine signaling**. In other cases, signal molecules can be secreted from, or presented on the membrane of, neighboring cells—a mechanism called **paracrine signaling**. Signal molecules activate specific receptors, usually membrane-associated proteins, which then initiate a signal transduction cascade in the responding cell. Activated receptors may themselves possess enzymatic activity. The tyrosine kinase and serine–threonine kinase receptors are members of an important family of receptors in this category. Activated receptors may also interact with other membrane-bound or cytosolic proteins, which in turn have enzymatic activity. The signal transduction cascades activated by the receptors involve a variety of different effector or second-messenger systems, which act on **transcription factors**, proteins that bind to the regulatory sites of specific genes and thereby increase or decrease the expression of these genes. Increased or decreased gene expression controls structural and physiological changes, which directly impose particular cellular phenotypes. A typical signal transduction cascade involved in neuronal fate specification in *Drosophila* is shown in Fig. 17.18E. See Chapter 10 for a more detailed discussion of intracellular signaling.

Intrinsic Cues Are Cytoplasmic or Nuclear Proteins Inherited from Progenitor Cells or Present in the Newborn Cells

Many types of neurons, particularly in invertebrates, are formed in a lineage-dependent mechanism from progenitor cells called neuroblasts. It is thought that intrinsic factors expressed at various stages during progenitor cell proliferation play a dominant role in specifying the different fates of these cells. A large number of genes give rise to specific expression patterns in subsets of neuroblasts and their progeny. Among these genes are many that encode transcription factors—molecules of a type one might expect as intrinsic cues of cell fate. Genetic studies in *Drosophila* and *Caenorhabditis elegans* have confirmed that at least some of these molecules do indeed play a role in cell fate determination in the central nervous system (CNS).

Cells Make a Transition from Competent Precursors to Committed Sublineages and Mature Cells

This chapter draws on experiments performed on a number of different organisms, from nematodes to mammals, that illustrate the steps in the transformation of an uncommitted ectodermal cell of the early embryo into a differentiated neuron with its specific projection and neurochemistry (Fig. 17.2). The experiments show that cell fate is not a single entity, but consists of a multitude of potentially independent traits that may be determined at different times and by different cues. We describe numerous studies in which the alteration of one given developmental cue (such as the absence

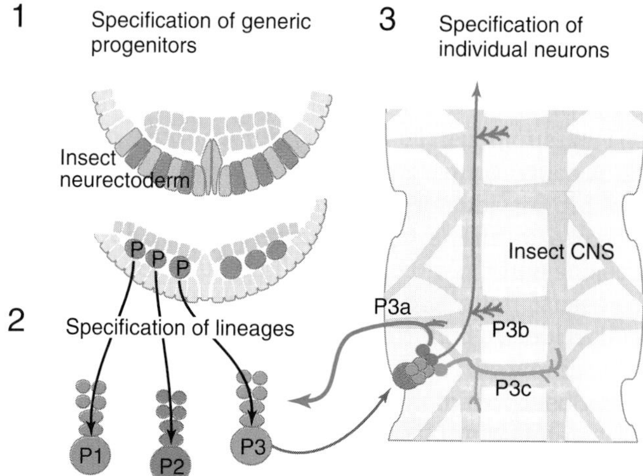

FIGURE 17.2 Stepwise commitment of neural cells. Neural development begins with the determination of generic neural progenitors (step 1, exemplified by neuroblasts (P) segregating from neurectoderm). In a second step, these cells become committed as different stem cells (P1–P3), each producing a specific lineage. Note that steps 1 and 2 are not necessarily temporally separate from each other. In step 3, the fate of individual neurons is specified. Three hypothetical neurons (P3a–P3c, all part of the P3 lineage), which develop as a motor neuron (P3a), an intersegmental interneuron (P3b), and a local interneuron (P3c), are shown.

of a particular gene) may change one aspect of the phenotype of a particular neuron, but leave other aspects of its fate unaltered. A temporally extended interplay of external and internal cues acts on cell fate. For example, external cues influence an insect neurectodermal cell's "decision" to become a neural progenitor (neuroblast). The intrinsic "program" that is then set up in each neuroblast has an impact on the phenotypes of the progeny of that cell. Later in development, extrinsic cues, such as trophic factors provided by the innervated target, again act on the immature neuron and guide its proper differentiation. In different parts of the nervous system of any organism, different combinations of intrinsic and extrinsic cues act together. Deleting a regulatory gene that is expressed in several different neurons may cause dramatic phenotypic defects in one of these neurons, yet leave the other neurons unchanged. This implies that this particular gene acts by itself as a crucial intrinsic cue in the first neuron, whereas in the other neurons it may form part of a larger regulatory complex in which other elements can substitute. It is therefore difficult to generalize the conclusion of experimental results obtained on one particular system; each part of the nervous system deserves separate analysis.

In this chapter, we first describe the formation of neural progenitor cells in the central and peripheral nervous systems and the function of the proneural genes—transcription factors that work to establish a neuron's fate. We also describe how negative regulators, encoded by the neurogenic paracrine pathway of genes, inhibit uncommitted cells from assuming a neuroblast identity, thus regulating the number of cells with neural fates. In the next section, we follow individual neural progenitors through several rounds of mitosis and progressive determination, thus moving from a "generic" neural progenitor through its specific lineage commitment and the further specification of sublineages, including the key decision to become neural or glial. This process involves the interaction of a variety of local signaling molecules and inherited determinants. In the final part of this chapter, we trace this process to the level of single cells, where determinative events at the end of this process, including a cell's interactions with its neighbors and target, establish the final identity and mature phenotype of a neuron.

Summary

An enormous variety of neural phenotypes are generated during development. Cells may acquire their specific fates by interactions with extrinsic signals that are provided by other cells. Extrinsic cues generally act on receptors that initiate signal transduction cascades in the responding cell. Ultimately, these cues affect gene transcription, which underlies structural and physiological changes. Alternatively, intrinsic cues may determine cell fates. These cues are cytoplasmic or nuclear proteins that are often inherited from a progenitor in a lineage-dependent manner. Cells and lineages undergo transitions during development from competent precursors, to committed sublineages, and finally to maturity and differentiation. Both extrinsic and intrinsic cues shape these transitions, as development involves a dramatic interplay between these factors.

ACQUISITION OF NEURAL COMPETENCY

The Nervous System Is Derived from Neurectoderm

Formation of the Central Nervous System

The progenitors of the nervous system arise from specialized regions of the ectoderm called the **neurectoderm** (Fig. 17.3). In vertebrates (left side of Fig. 17.3), the entire dorsal part of the ectoderm forms the neurectoderm, which invaginates to become the elongated, dorsally located neural tube from which the brain and spinal cord develop (see Chapter 15). In many invertebrate groups, in particular arthropods (right side of Fig. 17.3), a ventrally located strip of ectoderm gives rise to the ventral chain of segmental ganglia (which functionally can be compared to the vertebrate spinal cord), and an anterior–lateral patch of ectoderm forms the brain. The dorsal ectoderm does not give rise to the CNS, only to the epidermis (epidermal ectoderm). In invertebrates, the central nervous system's progenitors (neuroblasts) separate from the neurectoderm and move inside the embryo as individual cells, whereas neighboring cells that stay behind in the neurectoderm form epidermal progenitors.

After segregation from the ectoderm, neural progenitors start to proliferate (Fig. 17.3). In insects and many other invertebrate groups, the mode of proliferation is peculiar: Each mother neuroblast divides unequally into one large and one small daughter cell. The large cell (still called a neuroblast) continues to divide unequally for a variable number of generations. The small cell, called a **ganglion mother cell**, typically divides equally one more time. Both its daughter cells differentiate into neurons. Often, ganglion mother cells and immature neurons form a stack on top of the neuroblast from which they originated. In this manner, the progeny (lineage) of a neuroblast remain spatially close together. Postmitotic neurons do not generally migrate;

therefore, the position of a neuron depends mainly on the position of the neuroblast and the time at which the neuron was born. Each differentiating neuron sends out a single process in the direction opposite of the neuroblasts. Thereby, a two-layered cortex–neuropile architecture typical of the mature ganglion is generated.

In vertebrates, neural progenitors form a continuous epithelium lining the lumen of the neural tube. They divide symmetrically in the plane of this epithelium. After variable periods of time, neuroblasts spin off postmitotic daughters. The generation of a postmitotic neuron in the cortical neuroepithelium is often associated with vertical rather than horizontal cleavages. The cell that remains next to the ventricle continues to divide as a blast cell, while the postmitotic daughter

BOX 17.1

EXPERIMENTAL STUDIES OF NEURAL DETERMINATION

A cell's fate may be determined long before it is born. It may inherit its destiny from its ancestors. Alternatively, when a cell leaves the mitotic cycle, it may still have myriad potentials and settle on a fate only through a series of subsequent choices. It may even switch fates or remain uncommitted. Different cells achieve their destinies by different means. These various possibilities are resolved by the experimental analysis of cell fate determination. Such studies are challenged by the fact that the moment in ontogeny when a cell's fate is determined usually precedes the expression of any obvious marker of cell fate by hours or even days. So how does one know where and when a particular cell's fate is specified?

Transplantation

Transplantation is a classical technique used in experimental embryology for determining whether a cell's fate has been fixed or is still flexible. A cell or group of cells fated to become a particular cell type in a donor animal is transplanted to another part of a host animal. If the normal fate of the cell is unaltered by such procedures, then the conclusion is that the cell's fate is already determined. If, however, the cell takes up a new fate consistent with its new position in the host, then it is obvious that the cell's fate was still flexible. The power of transplantation is that the transplanted cell is placed in a supportive environment for growth and is challenged to assume a new fate. Transplantation is also effective for investigating extrinsic or inductive cues. It was by such transplantation experiments that the organizer was first discovered.[3] If a group of cells is producing a signal that affects the fate of its neighbors, then transplanting that group into a field of competent pluripotent cells will make the new neighbors switch their fates. Such an experiment reveals the transplanted cell as the source of an important fate-determining signal.

In animals such as frogs, genes can be easily misexpressed, and then tissue misexpressing a particular gene can be transplanted or combined with nonexpressing pluripotent tissue. By combining a molecular strategy with embryology, experimenters can explore whether particular gene products are likely to be important signaling molecules or involved in autonomously fixing fates. Transplants between normal and mutant or transgenic animals can serve a similar end.

Genetic Approaches

There are mutations in several experimental organisms in which certain cell types do not develop. With a mutant, genetic approaches can show where and when the normal gene product must function. An obvious experimental question is whether the gene acts intrinsically or extrinsically to control the fate of the cells missing in the mutant. This can best be approached by making mosaic animals—animals that are part mutant and part normal. It is important to tag the mutant cells so that they can be identified by an independent marker. Then, if only mutant cells, even when completely surrounded by normal cells, express the mutant phenotype, the conclusion is that the mutant gene acts intrinsically and is autonomous. Examples of autonomously acting genes include receptors that bind to cell-fate-inducing ligands. If, however, normal cells express the mutant phenotype in mosaic animals, then the gene product must act extrinsically or nonautonomously. Such a gene product could be a secreted signaling molecule. In the case of a nonautonomous cell-fate mutant, it is often possible by careful analysis to localize the exact cells responsible by correlating the mutant phenotype with the genotype of different populations of cells. Thus, for example, if cell A never gets its fate when cell B is mutant but cell A always gets its normal fate when cell B is normal, the conclusion is clear—cell B uses the gene in question to control the fate of cell A.

Whether a particular gene is autonomously or nonautonomously involved in cell fate can often be discovered by examination of expression patterns using a histological technique such as *in situ* hybridization, enhancer trap, or immunohistochemistry. If the gene of interest is expressed only in cells whose fate is affected by mutations at that locus, then nonautonomous or extrinsic influence of that gene is unlikely. If the gene is usually expressed primarily in the neighbors of the phenotypically affected cell, this is an indication for a nonautonomous function. A similar but more invasive genetic strategy involves the misexpression of certain candidate genes. Techniques for misexpressing a normal, overactive, or dominantly interfering form of genes in particular tissues or cells at particular stages of development are available. One can, for example, drive a gene for a putative signal not normally expressed in cell A and see if that has any effect on cell B. Or one can drive a gene for a mutant form of a receptor that blocks normal receptor function to test whether this receptor is normally used by this cell in fate determination.

Cell Culture and Organ Culture

The question of cell fate can also be approached in systems and animals where the genes involved are not defined by available mutants and where there is no genetic handle on the phenotype. One way to discover when a cell's fate is determined is to remove it from its surroundings at different points in its history and place it in tissue culture, isolated from other cells. If such isolated cells, taken at a certain developmental stage, consistently have the capacity to show a particular neural fate, then these cells must have made a commitment to become that type of neuron at some earlier time. If cells are isolated during an earlier phase of development and do not take on their normal fated phenotype in culture, then these cells are not determined during this phase.

The culture approach has been used with great success to identify diffusible extracellular factors that influence cell fate. Growth factors or media conditioned by a particular tissue or cell type may influence the determination of neural precursors *in vitro*. Powerful molecular biochemical strategies can then be used to identify the active factors.

Cell Ablation

Cell ablation is useful for determining equivalence and/or primary versus secondary fate (a question that transplant studies seldom address perfectly). Under equivalence, a cluster of cells is ready to take on a particular limited fate, so that when a particular cell that is differentiating into that fate is eliminated, its equivalent neighbor will take its place.[4] Usually only one cell takes this fate, and in doing so sends out an inhibitory signal to its neighbors preventing them from also taking on this fate. The fate that all the cells of the equivalence group are ready to assume is called the primary fate.[5] Mutations in this inhibitory signaling cascade usually lead to all the cells of the equivalence group taking on the primary fate. In such an equivalence group, there may be a further cascade, such that cells taking a secondary fate inhibit their equivalent neighbors, which then may take the third available fate and so on. Cell ablation can be accomplished with a laser, with a microelectrode, or more recently by genetic methods whereby a toxic gene product is misexpressed in particular cells.

migrates toward the outer surface of the neural tube. Here the young neurons form dendrites and axons, which collect in bundles in the developing white matter. At this stage, the nervous system has reached a configuration of three layers: the ventricular zone, the intermediate zone, and the mantle layer.

Formation of the Peripheral Nervous System

The sensory part of the peripheral nervous system of anthropods and other invertebrates is formed by multiple small organs, called **sensilla**, which are scattered at more or less regular intervals over the entire body surface. Sensillum cells are born during several rounds of mitosis of **sensory organ progenitors** (SOPs) (Fig. 17.3), which appear in the epidermal layer at various developmental stages (usually later than the progenitors of the CNS). The peripheral nervous system of vertebrates consists of sensory neurons, most of which derive from the neural crest (Fig. 17.3)—an elongated population of cells located on either side of the neural plate along its lateral border. During neurulation, these cells are not incorporated into the neural tube; instead, they form a solid column of cells dorsal to the neural tube. Some components of the cranial peripheral nervous system derive from ectodermal placodes located on either side of the neural plate.

The Proneural/Neurogenic Network of Genes Was Discovered in Insects

The neurectoderm of insects and most other invertebrates is a mixed population of cells. Some of these cells become neuroblasts and SOPs, whereas others stay at the surface of the embryo and develop as epider-

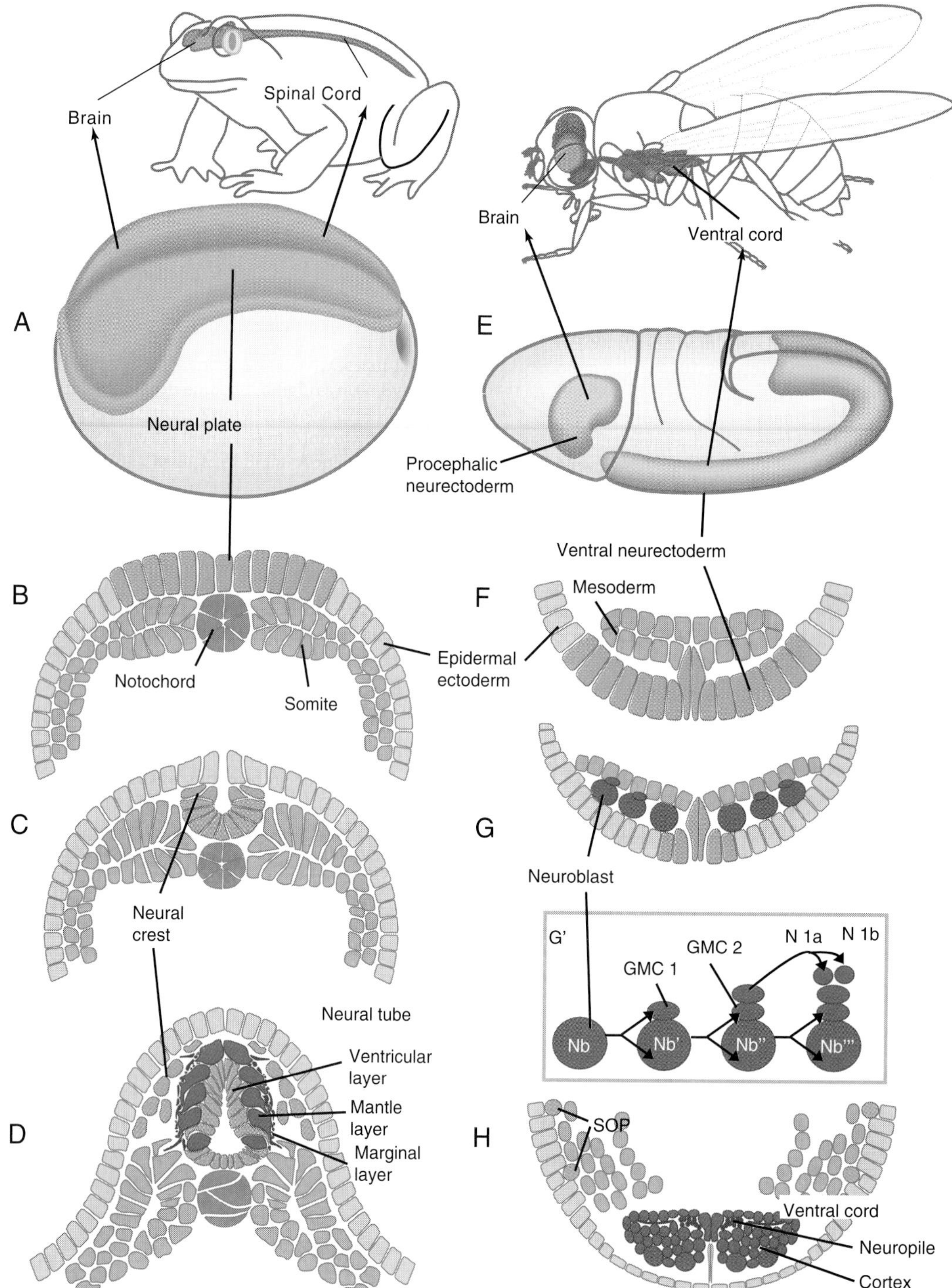

FIGURE 17.3 Synopsis of early neural development in amphibians (A–D) and insects (E–H). (A and E) Dorsolateral views of embryos at the onset of neurulation. The neurectoderm is shaded light blue. (B and F) Schematic cross sections of the embryos shown above. (C and G) Cross sections at a later stage, when neurulation is well under way. In vertebrates, the neural plate folds in to become the neural tube. Cells at the junction between the neural tube and the epidermal ectoderm (green) form the neural crest, which gives rise to the peripheral and autonomic nervous systems. In insects, individual neural progenitors (neuroblasts; purple) delaminate from the ventral neurectoderm. They divide in a stem cell mode (G′), producing stacks of daughter cells called ganglion mother cells (GMC). Each ganglion mother cell divides into two neurons (e.g., N1a, N1b). (D and H) Cross sections of late embryos in which some neurons (red) have differentiated. In vertebrates, these neurons delaminate from the neuroepithelium and form the so-called mantle layer. Neurites gather at the outside of the neural tube (marginal layer). In insects, neuronal cell bodies form an outer layer (cortex); neurites gather in the center, forming the neuropile. Progenitors of the peripheral nervous system (sensory organ progenitors or SOPs; green) segregate from different locations in the epidermis.

mal progenitors. Cell–cell interactions that take place within the neurectoderm define the number and pattern of neuroblasts and SOPs. Experimental and genetic studies suggest a two-step mechanism for this process (Fig. 17.4). First, discrete groups of neurectodermal cells are made competent to become neuroblasts. These groups of cells, called **proneural clusters**, represent equivalence groups in which all cells initiate a neural fate. In *Drosophila*, a group of genes—called **proneural genes**—expressed in the proneural clusters seem to be involved in making ectoderm cells competent to become neural progenitors.[6–8]

In a second step, cells of the proneural cluster interact to sort out which of them will become neurons and which will fall back to become epidermoblasts. In particular, nascent neuroblasts send out inhibitory signals to their neighbors, inhibiting these cells from becoming neuroblasts. The best evidence for this kind of inhibitory cell–cell interaction within the neurectoderm comes from experiments done in grasshopper embryos.[5] Here, due to their large size, neuroblasts can be followed individually during and after their segregation. Each neuroblast originates from a unique, well-defined position of the neurectoderm. Shortly after the neuroblasts have segregated, they are ablated by a laser microbeam. The ablated neuroblasts are replaced by other, nearby cells of the neurectoderm, which would otherwise have developed into epidermal cells, and not neuroblasts. Genetic studies in *Drosophila* led to the discovery of a group of genes, called **neurogenic genes**, that mediate the inhibitory cell–cell interaction within the neurectoderm.

Proneural Genes

The proneural genes identified so far encode DNA-binding proteins of the basic helix–loop–helix (bHLH) family. Four of these genes, *ac*, *sc*, *l'sc*, and *ase*, form a complex called the *achaete–scute* complex (*AS-C*).[9,10] Other proneural genes are *daughterless* (*da*) and *atonal* (*ato*). In all cases, the loss of proneural gene function leads to a reduction or total loss of neuroblasts and/or SOPs. Typically, cells deprived of proneural gene function do not form neural progenitors and develop as epidermoblasts instead. In other cases, neural progenitors may start to form, but abort their neural development and undergo apoptosis. Obviously, the (unknown) target genes controlled by the proneural genes are required for cells to initiate some crucial aspect of neural morphogenesis and/or differentiation.

An important question is how the pattern of expression of the proneural genes, and thereby the pattern of proneural clusters, is regulated. Several genes expressed in regular geometric patterns in the early blastula have been defined. In the anterior–posterior axis, *gap* genes and *pair rule* genes are expressed in stripes of varying widths and positions. These genes encode transcription factors that define domains of expression of proneural genes in a combinatorial mode[11] (Fig. 17.4). Deletion of a given *pair rule* gene results in the absence of proneural gene expression in those domains in which that particular *pair rule* gene is normally expressed. Similarly, genes encoding transcription factors are expressed in distinct dorsoventral domains that define proneural gene expression along this axis.[12]

Neurogenic Genes

The activity of proneural genes in the neurectoderm would lead to a large fraction of this layer forming the nervous system. This is prevented by the function of neurogenic genes that encode a cell communication mechanism used by the ectoderm cells to restrict the number of neural progenitors. Loss of function of all of the neurogenic genes results in a higher number of neural progenitors, at the expense of epidermoblasts (Fig. 17.5). The neurogenic genes *Notch* (*N*), *big brain* (*bib*), and *Delta* (*Dl*) encode membrane proteins. The other neurogenic loci, *mastermind* (*mam*), *neuralized* (*neu*), and *Enhancer of split* complex [*E*(*spl*)-C], code for nuclear proteins.[7] There is now ample evidence that several of the different transcripts of the *E*(*spl*) complex encode DNA-binding transcription factors. These may act to control the expression of other neurogenic genes, as well as the proneural genes.

Proneural/Neurogenic Gene Interaction

The proneural genes are expressed in various combinations in all cells of a given proneural cluster (Fig. 17.4). Genes activated by proneural gene products are other proneural genes (e.g., *ac* upregulates its own expression and is also transactivated by *sc*), as well as the neurogenic genes *Dl* and *E*(*spl*)-*C*. Thus, the same group of genes that triggers neural development in a group of cells also turns on an inhibitory function that blocks neural development (in all but a few cells). The function of proneural-gene-encoded transcription factors is modulated by other nuclear proteins that complex with the proneural bHLH proteins. For example, the HLH protein *emc* dimerizes with *ac* and sequesters it in a complex that is unable to bind DNA, thereby suppressing proneural gene function.[13] Other nuclear factors, such as *daughterless* (*da*)[14] and *ventral nerve cord defective* (*vnd*), activate the expression of the *AS-C* genes.[15]

The activation of *Dl*, initially in all cells of the proneural cluster, initiates the inhibitory process leading to the restriction of proneural gene expression and neural competence to a single cell, which will then segregate as a neural progenitor. *Dl* encodes a mem-

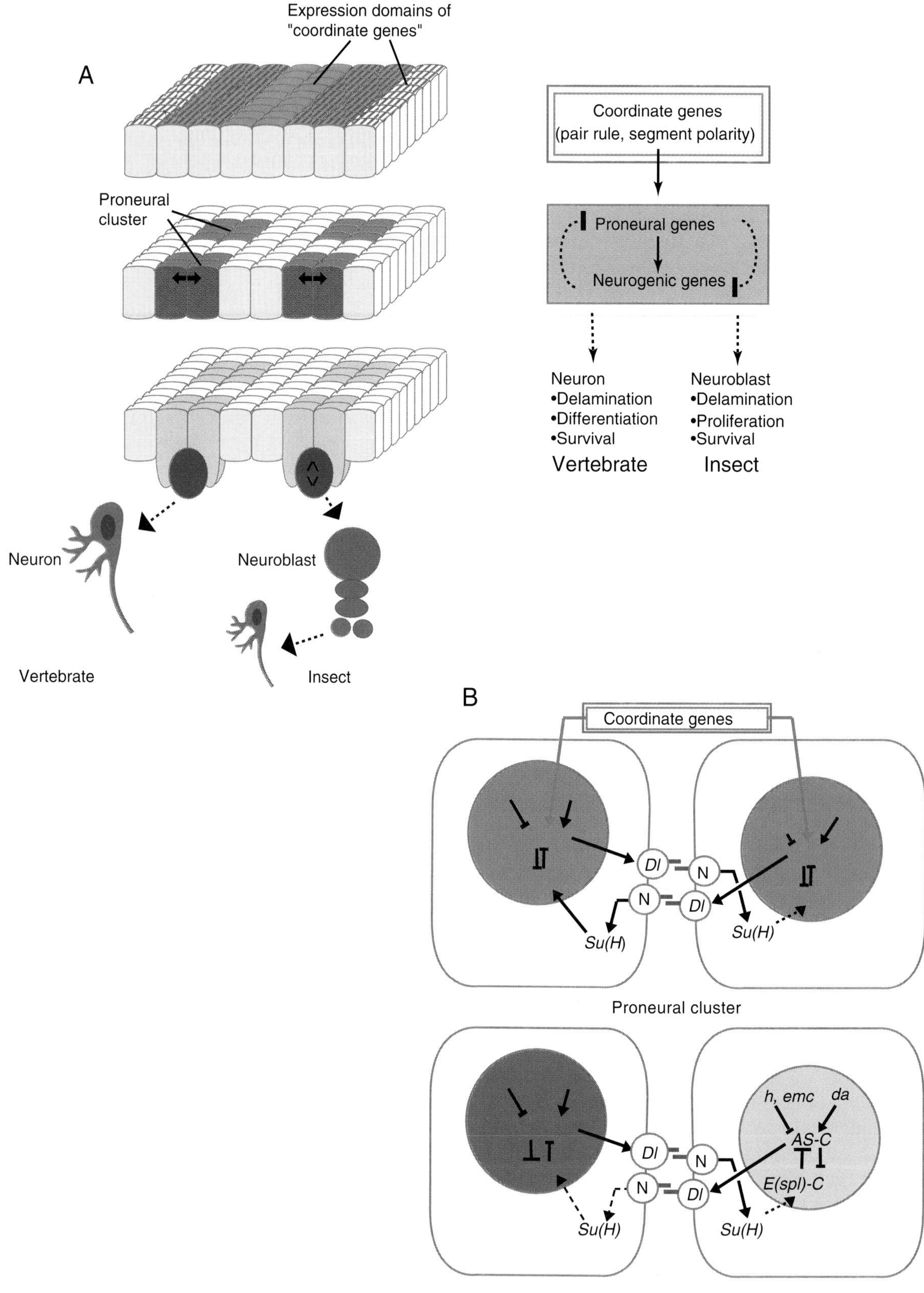
A
Expression domains of "coordinate genes"
Proneural cluster
Neuron
Neuroblast
Vertebrate
Insect
Coordinate genes (pair rule, segment polarity)
Proneural genes
Neurogenic genes
Neuron
•Delamination
•Differentiation
•Survival
Vertebrate
Neuroblast
•Delamination
•Proliferation
•Survival
Insect
B
Coordinate genes
Dl
N
Su(H)
Proneural cluster
h, emc
da
AS-C
E(spl)-C
Epidermal progenitor
Neural progenitor

brane molecule characterized by a stretch of epidermal growth factor (EGF)-like repeats in its extracellular domain. This protein serves as a "signal" that acts on a receptor-molecule encoded by the *N* gene. The N protein (which is similar to Dl in its possession of multiple EGF-like repeats) is expressed on all cells of the proneural cluster. Binding of *Dl* activates *N* and sets in motion a signal transduction cascade that is only partially understood. One factor involved is a DNA-binding protein encoded by the neurogenic gene *Suppressor of Hairless, Su(H)*.[16,17] In the absence of a *Dl* signal, this protein is sequestered in the cytoplasm, a process in which the product of the *deltex* (*dx*) gene is involved. Activation of N leads to the translocation of *Su(H)* to the nucleus, where it activates other genes, among them the neurogenic *E(spl)-C* and, possibly, other nuclear neurogenic genes (*mam, neu*). *E(spl)-C* proteins are bHLH transcription factors which, among other unknown targets, repress the proneural genes (Fig. 17.4).

FIGURE 17.4 Function of proneural and neurogenic genes in neural development. (A) The sequence of events that lead to the segregation of individual neural progenitors (in insects) or neurons (in vertebrates). First, proneural genes are turned on in discrete neurectodermal cell populations, called proneural clusters (purple). In *Drosophila*, a number of genes, among them *gap* and *pair rule* genes (called "coordinate genes" in the diagram), have been identified. They are expressed in distinct patterns before proneural genes come on and are likely candidates to control the expression of the proneural genes. Proneural genes in turn trigger several different events in the proneural clusters. One outcome of their expression is a cell–cell interaction process, mediated by the neurogenic genes, that selects a single cell from each proneural cluster (in the typical case). Only this cell continues along the neural pathway and segregates from the neurectoderm as a neuroblast (intense purple), which divides and produces a neural lineage (red); the remaining cells remain within the neurectoderm. In vertebrates, the entire neurectoderm (i.e., the neural plate/neural tube) is formed by neural progenitors. Here, the proneural/neurogenic gene network seems to select cells that become postmitotic and differentiate as neurons from other (neural progenitor!) cells, which remain in the neuroepithelium and continue to proliferate. (B) Interaction between proneural and neurogenic genes in the *Drosophila* neurectoderm. Two cells of a proneural cluster in which "coordinate genes" have turned on proneural genes of the *AS-C* are shown. Expression of these genes is modulated by other, more widely expressed transcription factors (encoded by *h, emc, da*). Genes of the *AS-C* turn on the expression of the signal molecule *Dl*. *Dl* activates the receptor *N* in the neighboring cell; this leads to translocation of the Su(H) protein (a transcription factor) into the nucleus, where it upregulates expression of the *E(spl)-C*. *E(spl)-C*, by turning on an unknown group of genes, initiates (or maintains) the development of an epithelial cell; at the same time, it directly inhibits the *AS-C*, which initiates differentiation as a neuron or neural progenitor. Imbalances introduced by an unknown mechanism into the levels of *As-C* or *E(spl)-C* expression, respectively, are rapidly amplified (lower half of B) and lead to the segregation of a single neural cell (high level of *AS-C*) from other cells that stay epithelial (high level of *E(spl)-C*).

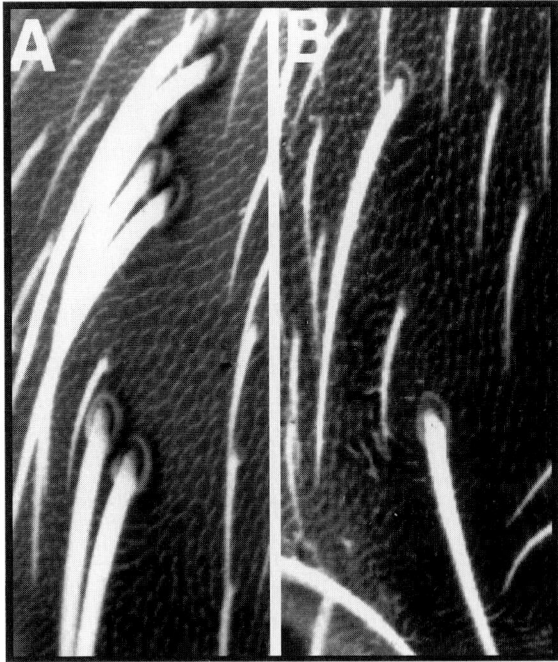

FIGURE 17.5 Extra bristles in a *bearded* mutant arise from inhibition of *Notch* signaling. (A) When *Notch* signaling is compromised in the *Drosophila* thorax as in the *bearded* mutant, too many sensory organ precursors develop and clusters of bristles arise instead of singles as in (B), a wild-type fly. Provided by J. Posakony.

If every cell in the proneural cluster behaved in exactly the same way regarding the activation of this gene network, no neural progenitors would be formed. Thus, following a short burst of expression, proneural genes would turn themselves off (or keep their expression at a uniformly low level) by activating *E(spl)-C* directly and via the *Dl/N* pathway. Fluctuations in the level of gene expression may lead to a slightly higher level of proneural genes in one cell, or a few cells, of the proneural cluster. This cell has an advantage over its neighbors because it expresses more *Dl* signal and thereby suppresses proneural genes in the neighboring cells. This kind of dynamic can be directly observed in assays of proneural gene expression by *in situ* hybridization. Initially, the expression level is uniformly high in all cells of the proneural cluster. Subsequently, expression increases in one cell, which at that point already starts to delaminate (Fig. 17.6).[18] At the same time, the neighboring cells that will become epidermoblasts decrease proneural gene expression.

Proneural and Neurogenic Genes Play Important Roles in Vertebrates

Homologs of both proneural and neurogenic genes have been identified in several vertebrate species.[19] All

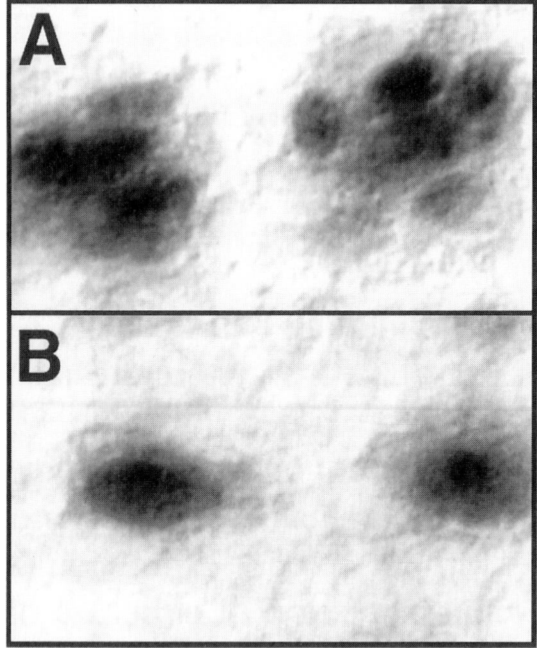

FIGURE 17.6 Refinement of achaete expression. (A) The *achaete* gene is expressed in proneural clusters in the neurogenic region of a normal *Drosophila* embryo. (B) Over time, *achaete* expression becomes confined to a single neuroblast. Adapted from Doe.[18]

of these genes are expressed in the neural primordium (neural tube or neural crest), in addition to several other embryonic tissues. Furthermore, loss and gain of function of these genes lead to severe abnormalities in early neural development, indicating that their role in vertebrate neurogenesis is as crucial as it is in *Drosophila*. A comparative look at the sequence of morphogenetic events that lead up to the segregation of neural cells in vertebrates and invertebrates will help to elucidate this function.

In both groups of animals, a dichotomy of two different cell types takes place in the neurectoderm. From an epithelial matrix, individual cells are singled out to leave the matrix, thereby losing their epithelial character (Figs. 17.3, 17.4). The time when this dichotomy occurs is different in vertebrates and invertebrates. In vertebrates, the dichotomy takes place in the neural tube when postmitotic neurons are separated from other neuroepithelial cells that continue dividing. In invertebrates, the dichotomy takes place at an earlier stage, when neural progenitors are singled out from the surrounding epithelial cells that will go on as epidermal progenitors.

Among the proneural genes, three *AS-C* homologs (*ASH* genes) have been identified. *ASH* genes show a temporally and spatially restricted distribution, predominantly in the nervous system. *MASH-1* in mouse, *XASH-1* and -3 in *Xenopus*, and *ZASH-1* in zebrafish are expressed in a complex pattern in the proliferating neuroepithelium of the brain and spinal cord.[20–23] As observed for the *Drosophila* proneural genes, expression of their homologs in vertebrates is transient and disappears in differentiated neural cells.

Experimental studies using **transgenic animals**, in which genes have been mutated by homologous recombination (gene knockouts), as well as injection of active or inactive forms of the message, suggest that the proneural genes in vertebrates are required for the determination of certain populations of neural cells. In *Xenopus*, injection of active *XASH-3* mRNA into blastomeres leads to an increased number of neural progenitor cells in the neural tube, at the expense of neural crest and epidermal cells.[21] Knockout of *MASH-1* in mice leads to the absence of two populations of neural cells: the olfactory sensory neurons in the nasal epithelium and the peripheral neurons of the autonomic nervous system.[24] The defect in the olfactory system occurs at the level of the neural progenitors. In the neural-crest-derived autonomic neurons, progenitor cells appear normally and form peripheral ganglia, but fail to differentiate into neurons. On the other hand, no defects are observed in the CNS, which also expresses *MASH-1*. A related gene, called *neuroD*, appears to act at a later stage than the *ASH* genes, directly causing the differentiation of neurons. When *neuroD* is expressed in ventral ectodermal cells, it drives them to assume neural characteristics much as the promuscle gene *myoD* converts fibroblasts into muscle cells[25] (Fig. 17.7).

Homologs of the neurogenic genes *N*, *E(spl)-C*, and *Dl* have been identified in vertebrates. There appear to be at least three copies of the *N* gene with partially overlapping expression patterns in a multitude of different embryonic tissues.[26,27] The most detailed results are available for *Notch-1*, which, in the nervous system, is expressed in the proliferating neuroepithelium; outside the nervous system, it is expressed preferentially in epithelia (somites, gut, lung, kidney, epidermis).

Experimental studies show that the neurogenic genes in vertebrates promote an epithelial phenotype and inhibit the formation of postmitotic neurons. The most revealing insight has been gained by experiments in *Xenopus*, where active forms of *Notch-1* or *Delta-1* mRNAs were injected into early blastomeres. This treatment resulted in decreased formation of the so-called primary neurons. Normally, these neurons segregate from the neural plate prior to its invagination and differentiate during embryogenesis. In animals injected with active *N* or *Dl*, primary neurons are reduced and all neurectodermal cells express an epithelial phenotype.[28,29] At least in the case of active *N* injections, the resulting neural tube appeared enlarged and disor-

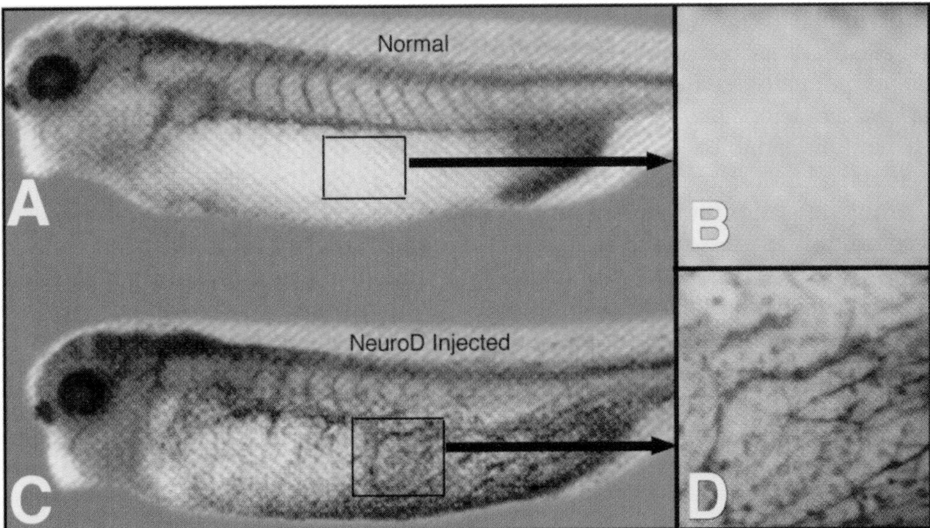

FIGURE 17.7 *NeuroD* turns epidermal cells into neurons. (A) A normal *Xenopus* embryo, stained for the neural marker NCAM, shows no staining in the epidermis enlarged in (B). In (C) a *neuroD*-injected embryo has NCAM staining cells in the ventral epidermis (D) with neuronal-like morphology. Adapted from Lee *et al.*[25]

ganized, possibly as a result of the increased number of proliferating neuroepithelial cells. A similar phenotype has been described in transgenic mice expressing a truncated form of the *int-3* gene, which is homologous to the activated *N* mutant. In these animals, numerous epithelial tissues (e.g., mammary gland, salivary gland, lacrimal gland) were hyperplastic and appeared undifferentiated. Lack of *Dl* function (obtained by injecting a dominant negative *Dl* deletion construct) has an effect opposite from that of overexpression of active *Dl*, that is, increased formation of primary neurons.

Summary

In both vertebrate and invertebrate animals, the nervous system is derived largely from cells in the neurectoderm. Experiments on invertebrates have provided detailed information about how neural progenitors are specified and distinguished from other cells that are competent to generate neurons. These equivalent groups of cells are called proneural clusters; their competence to form neuroblasts is conferred by the expression of proneural genes, which generally encode transcription factors. From each equivalence group emerges a single neuroblast; this cell then inhibits its neighbors from also becoming neural progenitors. The genes that are involved in this process are known as neurogenic genes, and they encode a wide variety of proteins that are involved in lateral signaling and signal transduction. Although the emergence of neural progenitors in vertebrates is by quite distinct cellular mechanisms, it appears that the functions of both the proneural and neurogenic genes are highly conserved throughout the animal kingdom. Homologs of both classes of genes play important roles in vertebrate neurogenesis.

SPECIFICATION OF NEURAL LINEAGES

Many Genes Are Involved in the Transition from a Generic Neuroblast to a Specific Lineage in the Fly Peripheral Nervous System

In the introduction to this chapter, the idea of a "generic" neural progenitor as opposed to a "lineage-committed" neural progenitor was introduced. A generic neural progenitor is a neuroblast or SOP that has segregated from the neurectoderm and thereby committed itself to a neural pathway, but it is not yet specified with respect to the progeny it will produce. A **lineage-committed neural progenitor** is a cell that has acquired the cues that determine its later progeny. The question is whether these two events—the specification of generic progenitors (from nonneural cells) and the specification of lineage-committed progenitors—occur at different times or are simultaneous. Another question is whether the proneural/neurogenic genes, which in the previous section were portrayed as determinants of generic neural progenitors, are involved in specifying lineage commitment of a neuroblast or SOP. Such a function was proposed for the proneural genes in 1987. Thus, given the highly complex, partially overlapping pattern of expression of the *AS-C* genes in different proneural clusters, researchers speculated that a combinatorial code of proneural genes specifies the lineage commitment of the neural progenitor formed by a given proneural cluster.[30–32] This hypothesis regarding the proneural *AS-C* genes has been shown to be wrong by experiments in which individual *AS-C* genes with specific expression patterns in different SOPs were deleted or exchanged, with no detectable effect on the identity of the resulting sensilla. For example, *l'sc* is normally not expressed in larval SOP; however, in SOPs giving rise to a set of sensilla called macrochaetes it completely substituted for the genes *ac* and *sc*, which are normally expressed in these SOPs.[33] Consequently, position-specific cues other than the proneural genes must control the lineage commitment of a given SOP or neuroblast. What then are these cues, and when do they act on the developing neural progenitor?

The same early expressed patterning genes that control expression of the proneural genes are generally assumed to regulate other genes, expressed concomitantly with the proneural genes, which supply the neural progenitor *in statu nascendi* with intrinsic cues committing it to a particular lineage. One example is the gene *wingless* (*wg*), which encodes a secreted protein acting on a number of different cell types in both *Drosophila* and vertebrate development. In *Drosophila*, *wg* acts during a short time window, before and during neuroblast segregation, on a subset of proneural clusters.[34] In the absence of *wg* function in this time window, the proneural clusters involved either do not produce any neuroblast or produce one with altered lineage. This finding vividly demonstrates the complicated entanglement of factors, such as *wg*, that seemingly control generic commitment and lineage-specific commitment of a neurectodermal cell at the same time.

Cascades of Gene Expression Are Involved in the Determination of Sensillum Lineages and Sublineages

A system well suited to the study of lineage commitment of individual neural progenitors is the sensilla in *Drosophila*. Sensilla are built of a small number of uniquely identifiable cells that form a clone; that is, the cells all derive from one cell called the sensillum precursor or mother cell (SOP).[10] Most *Drosophila* sensilla fall into three classes (Fig. 17.8): (i) External mechanosensilla are formed by one neuron surrounded by three accessory cells. (ii) Chemoreceptors and hygroreceptors, similar to mechanoreceptors in the composition of accessory cells, are sensilla innervated by several (often physiologically different) neurons. Kinship relationships among cells in these sensilla seem to be similar to those within mechanosensilla, except that the cell that differentiates as a neuron in mechanosensilla undergoes more divisions to generate multiple neurons. (iii) Chordotonal organs are also formed by one neuron and three accessory cells. These structures are sunk beneath the epidermis. They insert at the epidermis at two points and are stimulated by stretching (analogous to tendon receptors or muscle spindles in vertebrates).

Substantial progress has been made in identifying the molecules involved in sensillum cell fate determination. Four steps lead to the determination of individual sensillum cells (Fig. 17.8):

1. Generic SOPs are singled out from the neurectoderm by a mechanism very similar to that controlling the determination of neuroblasts. Thus, the expression of proneural genes of the *AS-C* class defines proneural clusters in the ectoderm that are competent to form SOPs. At the same time, proneural genes activate inhibitory cell–cell interactions, mediated by the neurogenic genes, which single out one SOP and prompt all other cells of the proneural cluster to abort neural development.
2. SOPs are specified to produce different sensillum types. Several putative transcription factors involved in this process—among them *cut* (*ct*), *pox-neuro* (*poxn*), and *atonal* (*ato*)—have been identified. The homeobox-containing gene *ct* is expressed in precursors of external sensilla (mechanosensilla and multiply innervated sensilla). If *ct* is absent, external sensilla do not develop and chordotonal organs appear instead.[35–37] The gene *poxn* is expressed in precursors of multiply innervated sensilla; in the absence of *poxn*, multiply innervated sensilla are "transformed" into singly innervated mechanoreceptors.[38–40] Overexpression of these two genes in ectopic SOPs leads to the opposite transformation. The *poxn* gene can act over an extended period of time from SOP to postmitotic sensillum cells. Thus, for example, when *poxn*, controlled by a heat-shock promoter, is turned on ectopically in the neurons of a mechanosensillum, these cells are transformed with respect to their morphology and axonal projection into cells typical of chemosensilla.

As stated earlier, the proneural genes of the *AS-C* probably do not specify the identity (the lineage commitment) of a given neural progenitor. On the other hand, other bHLH genes, among them *ato*, are definitely important for particular neural fates. The gene

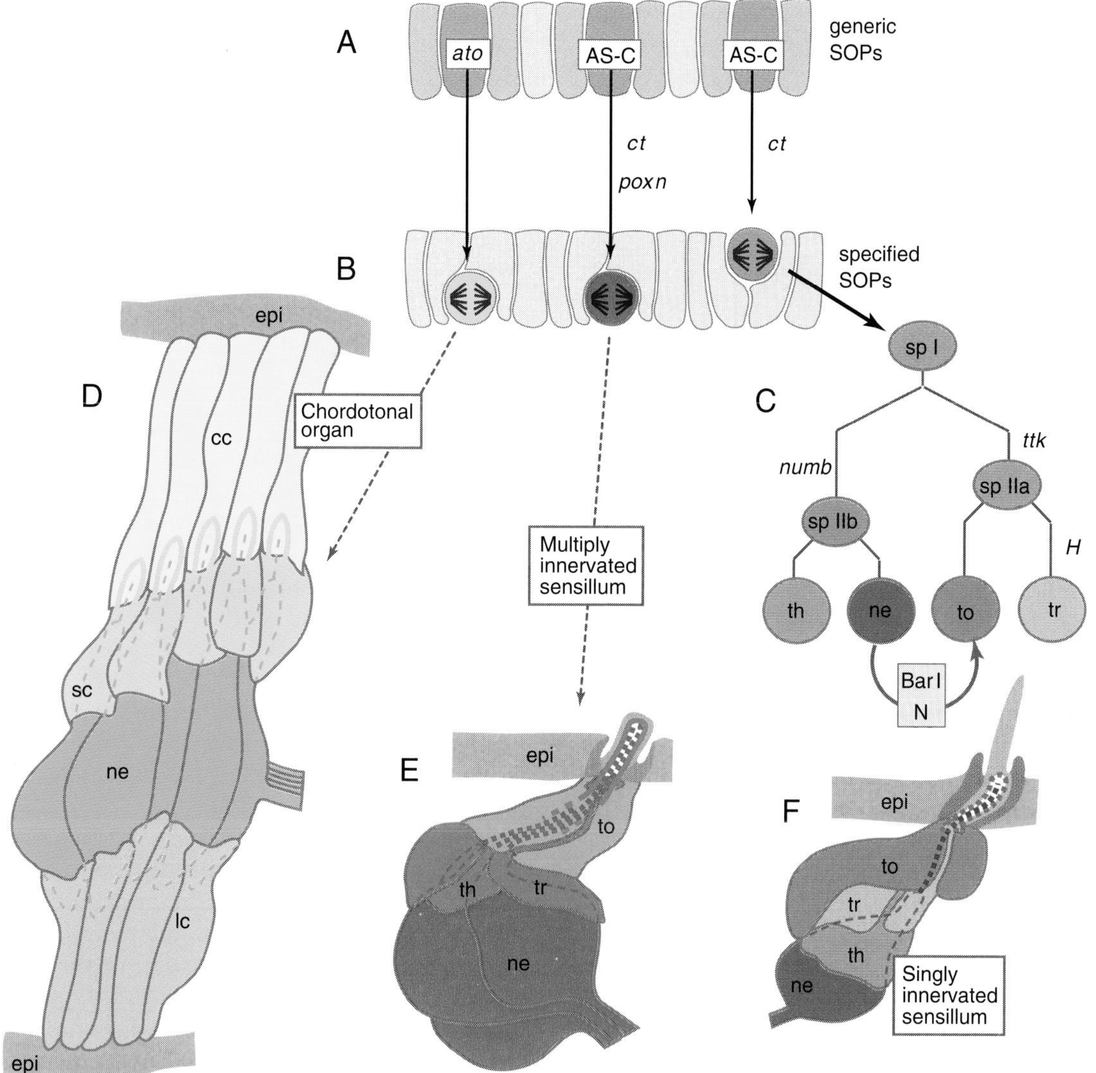

FIGURE 17.8 Determination of sensillum cell fate in *Drosophila.* In a first step involving the proneural and neurogenic genes, generic precursors of sensilla (sp I; light purple) are selected from the ectoderm (A). Progenitors of chordotonal organs require the proneural gene *atonal* (*ato*). Expression of other sensillum-type specific transcription factors (B) specifies different SOP types. For example, the gene *pox-neuro* (*poxn*) is required for the development of multiply innervated sensilla (which are typically chemoreceptors); *cut* (*ct*) is required for all classes of external sensilla, as opposed to chordotonal organs. SOPs undergo a fixed program of cell divisions (shown in (C) for singly innervated sensilla) and produce clones of cells that take on the different sensillum cell fates. The arrangement and shape of differentiated sensillum cells are shown for chordotonal organs (D), multiply innervated sensilla (E), and singly innervated sensilla (F). All sensilla have bipolar neurons (ne; shown in orange for chordotonal organ, turquoise for multiply innervated sensilla, purple for singly innervated sensilla) and accessory cells (shades of yellow for chordotonal organ, green for multiply innervated sensilla, blue for singly innervated sensilla). In external sensilla, three accessory cells (th, thecogen cell; to, tormogen cell; tr, trichogen cell) form sheaths around the dendrites and produce the stimulus-receiving apparatus. In chordotonal organs, accessory cells form a ligament that attaches the neurons at two distant points of the epidermis (epi; cc, cap cell; lc, ligament cell; sc, scolopale cell). (C) Genes required for specific sublineages of SOPs of external sensilla. *numb* is required for the secondary SOP sp IIb, which gives rise to neuron and thecogen cells; *tramtrack* (*ttk*) is needed for sp IIa, which forms tormogen and trichogen cells; *Hairless* (*H*) is required for the trichogen cell fate. In addition to these intrinsic determinants of sensillum cell fate, cell–cell interactions among postmitotic cells, involving the neurogenic genes (e.g., *N*) and other genes (e.g., *BarI*), are involved in controlling sensillum cell fate.

ato is expressed and required in the proneural clusters giving rise to chordotonal organs, as well as the developing larval and adult eye.[41,42] Loss of *ato* function results in the absence of these cell types; ectopic expression of *ato* in other SOPs induces them to produce chordotonal organs.

3. SOPs undergo a number of divisions that produce the set of sensillum cells in an invariant pattern. Although morphologically identical, the early postmitotic sensillum cells are inherently different from one another as a result of a number of intrinsic cues expressed in the SOP and its progeny during SOP division (see above). The primary SOPs of the mechanosensilla (called sp I) divide into two inherently different secondary SOPs, sp IIa and sp IIb (Fig. 17.8C). The sp IIa cell is characterized by a shorter cell cycle and always produces the outer two accessory (tormogen and trichogen) cells; sp IIb divides later than its sibling and forms a neuron and a thecogen cell. Several genes, among them *numb*[43,44] and *tramtrack* (*ttk*)[45] have been identified. They are reciprocally involved in controlling the fate of sp IIa versus sp IIb (Fig. 17.8). *numb* encodes a membrane-bound protein that starts to appear in the primary precursor but is asymmetrically distributed to only one of its daughters (presumably sp IIb) (Fig. 17.9). In the absence of *numb*, no neurons or thecogen cells appear; instead, in many sensilla, supernumerary tormogen and trichogen cells are formed. This phenotype indicates that the secondary precursor sp II may have been transformed into a sp IIa cell, which gives rise to tormogen and trichogen cells. Mutations in *ttk* lead to the opposite phenotype.

4. Cell–cell interactions that are mediated by the neurogenic genes take place between the SOP progeny (e.g., the sp IIa/IIb cells in mechanosensilla; see Fig. 17.8), as well as between postmitotic sensillum cells. For example, if *Notch* function is reduced transiently shortly after the sensillum cells are born, all of these cells convert into neurons.[46] Another gene required for interactions among sensillum cells is *Bar*, a putative transcription factor expressed in sensory neurons.[47,48] Absence of *Bar* function leads to changes in trichogen cell differentiation, indicating that the neuron must exert an influence on this cell. Therefore, cell–cell interactions, in conjunction with intrinsic cues inherited from the SOP, determine the differentiative fate of the sensillum cells.

Neural Lineages in the CNS Are Determined by Both Intrinsic and Extrinsic Factors

A good example of how components of the egg cytoplasm can be distributed to different cells and thus influence their determination is found in the origins of the leech CNS. The fertilized leech egg initially divides three times to produce eight cells. Four of these are large cells called macromeres A, B, C, and D (Fig. 17.10A). Only macromere D gives rise to the ectoderm and mesoderm and ultimately to the segmented mesoderm.

The fate of D is intrisically specified by inheritance of **teloplasm**, a cytosolic component of the egg that is enriched in ribosomes and RNA. The teloplasm can be moved to other macromeres by centrifugation, transforming their fate to an N type.[49]

The D cell divides to produce a cell called DM, which gives rise to mesoderm, and another cell called DNOPQ, which gives rise to the neural ectoderm and epidermis (Fig. 17.10B). Ablation of the DM teloblast eliminates all mesodermal precursors, yet the nervous system develops normally, showing that the DNOPQ has intrinsic ectodermal fate. This separation of fates appears to be determined by the separate inheritance of animal versus vegetal teloplasm; when the animal teloplasm is lost from DNOPQ, it transforms to the fate of DM. Its original fate can be restored by the addition of more teloplasm at the animal pole. Ectoder-

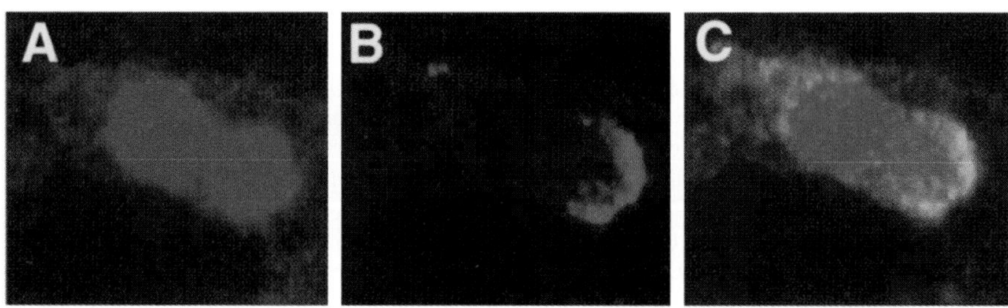

FIGURE 17.9 The gene *numb* is inherited asymmetrically. (A) A dividing pair of daughters of an SOP stained with an antisense probe to the proneural gene *asense* (red). (B) Only one of the daughters inherits the numb protein (green), which is localized to one side of the dividing pair. (C) Double labeling shows that the numb protein is inherited by only one of the daughters. Adapted from Rhyu *et al.*[44]

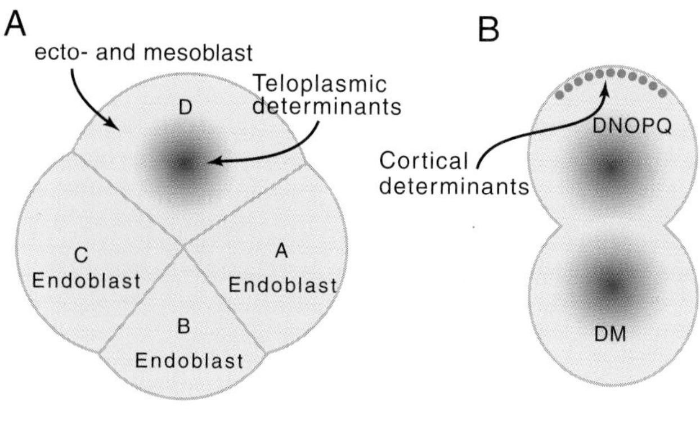

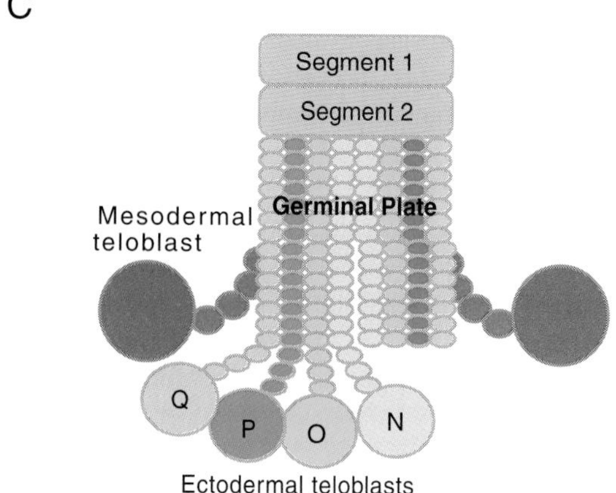

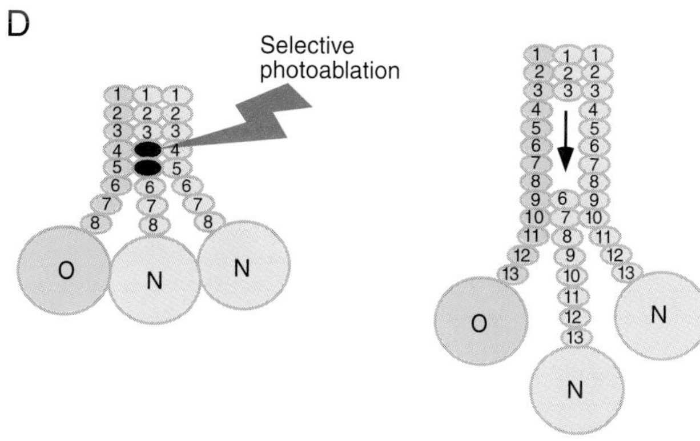

FIGURE 17.10 Early development of the leech nervous system. (A) In the four-cell embryo, macromere D inherits teloplasm (purple), which specifies it as the blast cell that will give rise to the ectoderm and mesoderm. (B) Macromere D divides asymmetrically with respect to a membrane-attached cortical determinant (red), thereby separating the fates of the ectodermal teloblasts (which are descended from the cell called DNOPQ) from the mesodermal teloblast DM. (C) The ectodermal teloblasts (called cells N, O, P, and Q), produce parallel bandlets of cells that coalesce in the forming germinal plate into the segmental ganglia of the nervous system. (D) An "ablation slippage" study, in which the registration of bandlet cells to one another is misaligned by photoablating some anterior daughters (cells 4 and 5, marked in black). This causes cells 1, 2, and 3 in the central bandlet to slip forward into a new segment. The neurons produced by the misaligned bandlet cells develop fates appropriate for their intrinsic (original) segmental origin rather than the segment they eventually come to occupy. An exception to this general rule is that when neurons from more anterior segments are displaced into more posterior regions, they develop the peptidergic phenotype typical of posterior segments.

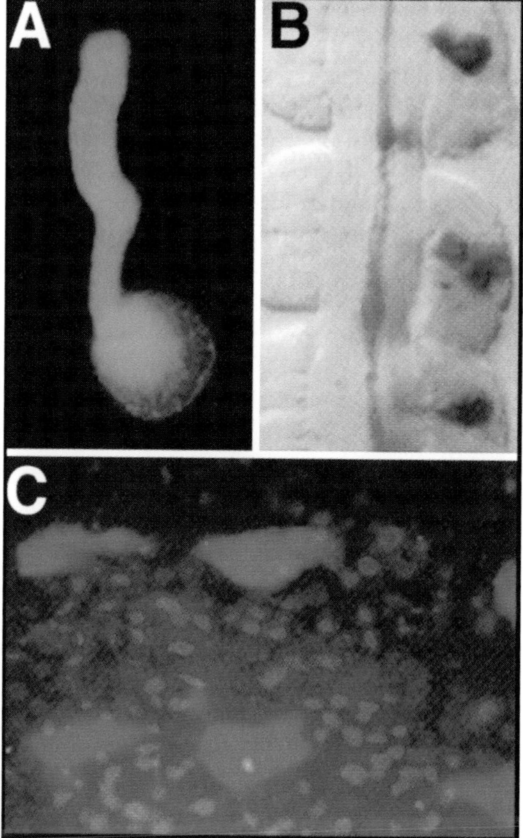

FIGURE 17.11 Neuronal genesis in a leech. (A) A single teloblast is injected with a fluorescent dye. One day later, all the bandlet cells that it generated are seen to form a column that combines with other bandlet cells to generate the germinal plate. (B) Mature progeny of the M teloblast contribute a repeating cluster of four neuronal cells and a stream of midline muscle cells. (C) Red cells are neuroblast and glioblast daughters of bandlet cells. These blast cells are migrating to the right, where they will be incorporated into the ganglia of the developing CNS. Adapted from Shankland and Martindale.[51]

malizing factors on the animal cortex of the DNOPQ cell interact with teloplasm to produce ectodermal fates (Fig. 17.10B).

DNOPQ divides twice to produce the NOP and Q teloblasts. These teloblasts give rise by asymmetrical divisions to linear columns of neighboring bandlets of blast cells, which fuse together at the midline to form the germinal plate[50] (Figs. 17.10C and 17.11).[51] Injection of a tracer into NOP or Q shows that each of these teloblasts generates blast cells of different segments. Segmentally homologous blast cells have stereotyped division patterns, giving rise to homologous sets of identifiable neurons repeated in each segmental ganglion. This pattern is strongly suggestive of intrinsic programs of neurogenesis (Fig. 17.10D). It is, however, interesting that different daughters of the same teloblast show some subtle segmental differences. Thus, a peptidergic neuron produced from the N teloblast forms in every segment, but retains this transmitter only in some of the most anterior ganglia. When the N-derived blast cells on one side are shifted so that the blast cells giving rise to one of these anterior ganglia are displaced and thereby contribute to a more posterior ganglion, the fate of the peptidergic cell follows. These events show the amazing lineage determination built into each blast cell.[52]

Transcription Factors Are Determinants of CNS Lineage Identity in C. *elegans* and *Drosophila*

The nervous system of *C. elegans*, although highly determinative, is generated in a piecemeal fashion. Given neural elements may come from a variety of different lineages. For example, some of the motor neurons of *C. elegans* arise during embrogenesis from 3 separate precursors, while the rest arise postembryonically from 13 different precursors. Because *C. elegans* is a powerful genetic organism, most of our knowledge concerning the generation of different cell types comes from mutants that interfere with cellular determination. Many of the mutations that affect CNS lineages are in genes that code for transcription factors.

One family of transcription factors is called the "POU" family (named after its charter members, *Pit-1*, *Oct-2*, and *unc-86*); POU proteins contain a DNA-binding domain, including a homeodomain, that is characteristic of this family. The nematode POU domain gene *unc-86* is expressed transiently in many neural precursors, as well as in several immature neurons.[53] A well-studied example is the lineage produced by a neuroblast called "QL." In the wild type, QL divides into two daughter cells, Ql.a and Ql.p (Fig. 17.12A). Both of these cells continue dividing, giving rise to different progeny. Ql.p produces two sensory neurons (called PVM and SDQ); Ql.a. produces one central neuron (called PQR) and one cell that undergoes programmed cell death. The *unc-86* gene is turned

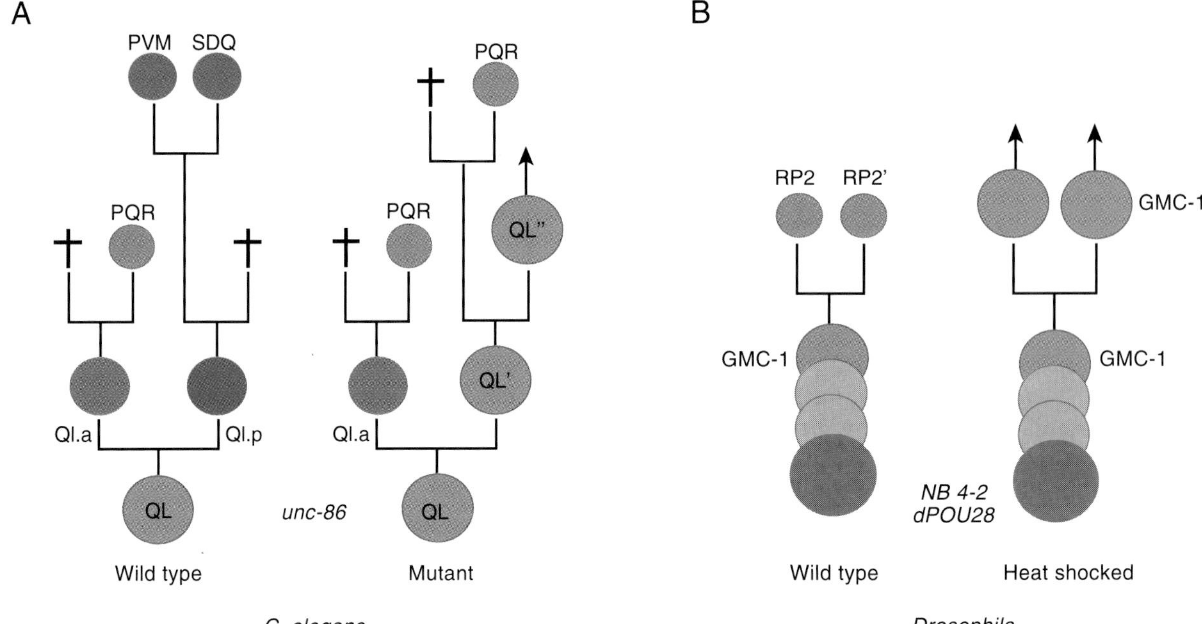

FIGURE 17.12 Control of CNS lineages by POU transcription factors. (A) *unc-86*, which encodes a *C. elegans* POU protein, is expressed in the neural progenitor cell QL. Ql.p and its sibling, Ql.a, derive from the QL cell. In normal development in wild-type animals (left), Ql.a after one division gives rise to a neuron (PQR) and a cell that undergoes programmed cell death (cross); Ql.p divides twice and produces two neurons (PVM, SDQ) and one cell that dies. In *unc-86* loss-of-function mutations (right), Ql.p behaves like its mother, QL. (B) The *Drosophila* dPOU28 protein is expressed in a number of ganglion mother cells, among them GMC-1, which is formed by the 4–2 neuroblast. In wild-type flies (left), this GMC produces two identified motor neurons (RP2 and its sibling). If *dPOU28* is expressed under heat-shock control in these neurons (right), they behave like ganglion mother cells and continue to divide.

on only in the Ql.p daughter cell and its progeny. A loss of function mutation in *unc-86* results in the "transformation" of Ql.p, the cell in which it is normally expressed, into a stem cell that behaves like the mother cell of Ql.a and Ql.p. Thus, instead of producing the neurons PVM and SDQ, the cell continues to divide in the pattern of its mother cell, the Q neuroblast.[54]

Present in *Drosophila* is a homolog of *unc-86* (called *dPOU28*), which is also expressed in a subset of neural cells, more specifically ganglion mother cells (GMCs). Its function seems closely related to its function in *C. elegans*.[55,56] In one particular lineage, *dPOU28* is expressed in the first GMC (GMC-1) of the neuroblast 4–2 lineage (Fig. 17.12B). In wild-type flies, GMC-1 produces two identified neurons, RP2 and its sibling, which discontinue *dPOU28* expression. When *dPOU28* is expressed by heat-shock control in the postmitotic neurons, they adopt the fate of their GMC-1 mother cell and divide.

A large number of other transcription factors expressed in neuroblasts and/or ganglion mother cells of the *Drosophila* CNS have been identified. In several cases, mutant phenotypic analysis, based on the expression of neuron-specific molecular markers, has shown that absence or overexpression of these genes leads to alterations of whole groups of clonally related cells. An example shown in Fig. 17.13 is the control of neuroblast lineage fate by the homeobox gene *gooseberry* (*gsb*).[57,58] In normal development, *gsb* is expressed in a complete row of neuroblasts, which includes the neuroblast 5-2. The lineage produced by 5-2 consists of at least 10 neurons with different phenotypes. In contrast, neuroblast MP2, which normally does not express *gsb*, exhibits a quite unusual lineage formed by 2 neurons, MP2d and MP2v. When *gsb* is expressed ectopically in MP2, its lineage is converted into a neuroblast lineage.

Neuronal and Glial Lineages Are Produced from Common Progenitors during Development

The nervous system is composed of two classes of cells: neurons and glial cells. Both can be further subdivided into a multitude of different subtypes of cells. Although very different in structural and functional properties, neurons and glia are generally produced by the same progenitors. Thus, in both vertebrates and invertebrates, the application of lineage tracers to individual progenitors has yielded clones that contain both neurons and glia. How is the separation of neuronal and glial cell types controlled? Some insight into the molecular mechanism controlling cell diversification has been gained from studies on the peripheral nervous system (PNS) in vertebrates and the central nervous system in *Drosophila.*

Vertebrates

Both the PNS and the CNS are composed of neurons and glial cells. Experiments using lineage tracers indicate that many progenitors of the neural tube and neural crest are not yet committed to either of these fates. Thus, extracting crest progenitors when the ganglia are already starting to form and culturing them *in vitro* can still yield neuronal and glial progeny from a single progenitor.

A variety of intrinsic programs and cellular interactions contribute to the diversification of glial cell types in the mammalian CNS.[59] The optic nerve, in addition to containing the axons of retinal ganglion cells, has three types of glia: Type 1 astrocytes, which make contact with blood vessels; Type 2 astrocytes, which make contact with nodes of Ranvier; and oligodendrocytes, which myelinate axons (Fig. 17.14A). Experiments using an array of antibodies to glial cells that proliferate and differentiate in culture have shown that oligodendrocytes and Type 2 astrocytes develop from a common stem cell called the O-2A progenitor (Fig. 17.14B). Type 1 astrocytes, however, derive from a distinct progenitor. In the rat optic nerve, O-2A cells proliferate during embryogenesis, and after the animal is born they begin to spin off differentiated oligodendrocytes. When the same cells are cultured in a serum-free medium, they invariably stop dividing immediately and become oligodendrocytes. When O-2As are cultured in the same medium in the presence of Type 1 astrocytes, however, they continue to divide before differentiating as they do *in vivo.* Platelet-derived growth factor (PDGF) and neurotophin 3 (NT-3)[60] are critical factors secreted by Type 1 astrocytes that allow the O-2As to continue dividing. Interestingly, in the presence of PDGF, the O-2A progenitors appear to rely on an intrinsic clock to time their differentiation; once enough PDGF is present, the O-2As differentiate after a given number of cell divisions. One possibility is that cell division dilutes a factor that allows O-2As to be responsive to PDGF. How do Type 2 astrocytes get made? When O-2A progenitors are cultured in the presence of fetal calf serum (FCS) instead of serum-free medium, they become Type 2 astrocytes. Ciliary neurotrophic factor (CNTF) presumably released from the cells in the optic nerve can cause O-2As to differentiate into Type 2 astrocytes, at least transiently. CNTF is also important for the survival of the oligodendrocytes, where as yet undetermined factors are responsible for the continued differentiation of the Type 2 astrocytes (Fig. 17.14B).

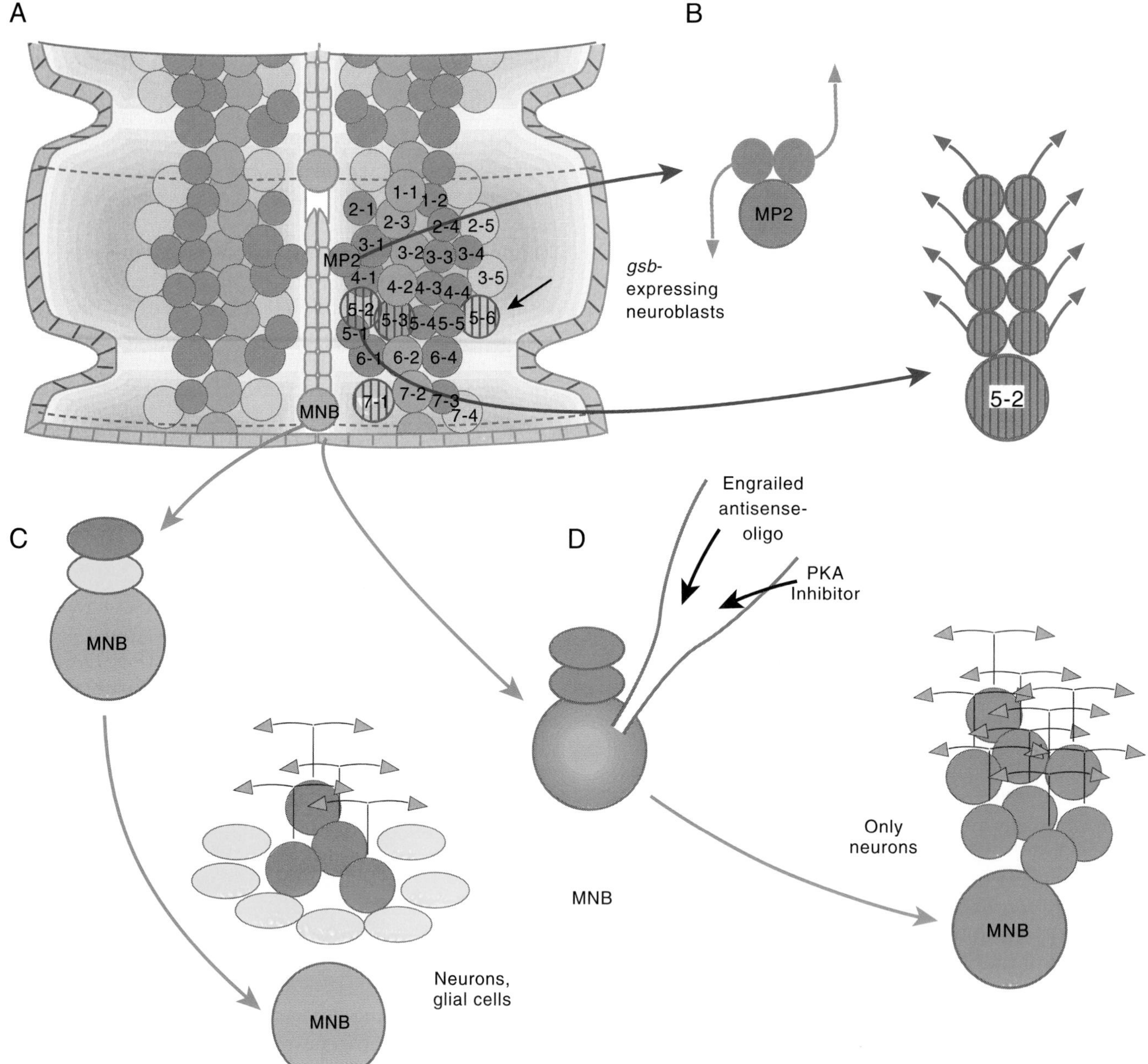

FIGURE 17.13 Specification of neuronal and glial lineages in the insect CNS. (A) A schematized neuroblast map of *Drosophila*. All neuroblasts of one hemisegment are numbered (nomenclature according to Doe[18]). Different shades of blue indicate affiliation of neuroblasts to different subpopulations, distinguished by their time of birth. Red hatching indicates a row of neuroblasts expressing the *gooseberry* (*gsb*) gene. (B) Two lineages, MP2 with two neurons and 5-2 with more than 10 neurons, are shown. Normally, only the 5-2 lineage expresses *gsb*. Ectopic expression of *gsb* in MP2 leads to the conversion of this lineage into a 5-3 lineage. (C) The MNB neuroblasts, which exist in all insects, produce both glial cells (yellow) and neurons (red). The *engrailed* (*en*) gene, which encodes a homeodomain transcription factor, is required for the glial sublineage. When *en* function is reduced by injecting antisense oligonucleotides, MNB forms only neurons (D). The same result is achieved by injecting protein kinase A (PKA) inhibitors into MNB, indicating that cAMP signaling is involved in specifying the glial sublineage.

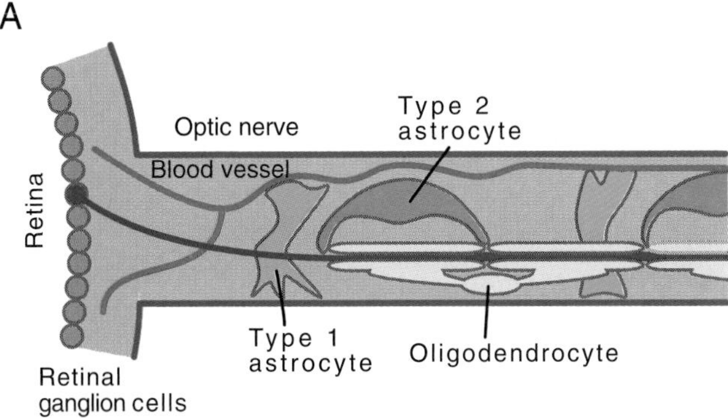

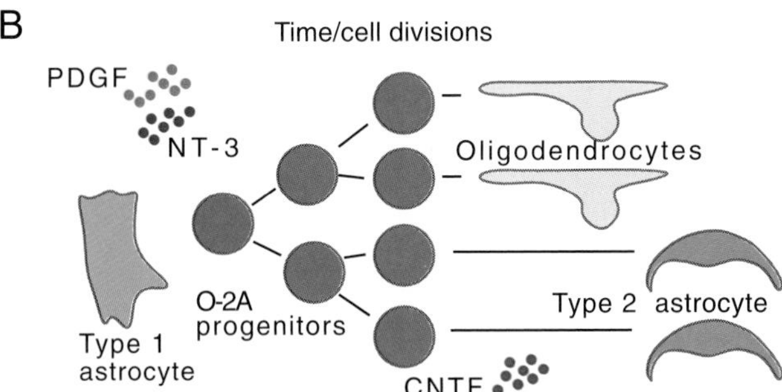

FIGURE 17.14 Glial cell diversity within the vertebrate CNS. (A) The optic nerve contains three types of glia: Type 1 astrocytes, which contact blood vessels; Type 2 astrocytes, which contact nodes of Ranvier; and oligodendrocytes, which make myelin. (B) Type 1 astrocytes release NT-3 and PDGF, which cause O-2A progenitor cells to proliferate. After a certain amount of proliferation, O-2A cells spontaneously differentiate into oligodendrocytes; yet if CNTF is present, as it is to a certain extent in the developing optic nerve, O-2As differentiate into Type 2 astrocytes.

In the peripheral nervous system, glial growth factor (GGF) influences the fate of the progeny of cultured neural-crest-derived progenitors (Fig. 17.15).[61,62] GGF2 is a member of the epidermal growth factor / transforming growth factor α (TGFα) family of ligands. A number of different names for these molecules exist in the literature, among which are heregulins, neuregulins, ARIA, and Neu differentiation factor. GGF2 is produced by neurons, and increases acetylcholine receptor expression in muscle cells (Chapter 19) and increases cell divison of peripheral glial cells (Schwann cells). Receptors to which GGF binds have been identified as belonging to the receptor tyrosine kinase superfamily (c-Neu / Her2 / p185erbB2). GGF2 is expressed in neural crest cells once they have migrated peripherally and coalesced into distinct ganglionic masses. Specifically, GGF2 is expressed in cells that have already started to express a neuronal phenotype, and not in glial cells. The GGF receptor is already expressed by migrating neural crest cells. *In vitro*, GGF2 suppresses neuronal differentiation. In the absence of GGF2, the majority of clones obtained from cultured neural crest cells contain both neurons and glial cells. If GGF2 is applied, most clones develop as pure glial cell clones, as assayed by the absence of neural specific markers such as *MASH-1*. Because the overall number of clones remains unchanged, GGF2 probably does not affect cell division in this system, but suppresses the expression of a neuronal phenotype. Thus, all cells become glial cells.

Transcription Factors Specifying Glial Cell Fate in the Insect Nervous System

The median neuroblast (MNB) of *Drosophila* and grasshopper has been thoroughly studied (Fig. 17.13C). Each segmental ganglion possesses one MNB, which gives rise to uniquely identifiable neurons and glial cells along the midline. During the proliferation period of MNB, three phases can be distinguished. During the first phase, this cell produces exclusively neurons; during the second, glial cells; during the third, neurons again. The switch to produce glial cells requires the expression of an identified transcription factor, *engrailed* (*en*), which belongs to the homeodomain-containing (HOM) class of DNA-binding proteins. The expression of *en* can be inhibited by injecting into the MNB antisense oligodeoxynucleotides (ODN), which bind to the corresponding DNA sequence and suppress its transcription. Following ODN injection, the glial cell progeny of the MNB fail to develop. Instead, supernumerary neurons of the same type normally produced by the MNB appear (Figs. 17.13D and 17.16). This result indicates that *en* controls genes that initiate glial development in the neural progenitor in which they are expressed.

The *pointed* (*pnt*) gene encodes a transcription factor of the Ets family. Like *engrailed*, *pnt* is expressed in neural precursors at the midline of the nervous system. These cells normally give rise to both neurons and glial cells. In loss-of-function mutations of *pnt*, most neurons and glial cells of the midline are missing.[63] Conversely, when active *pnt* is overexpressed in other neuroblasts that normally produce only neurons, these precursors give rise to glial cells. *Glial cells missing* (*gcm*) is another gene that encodes a nuclear protein expressed in nearly all glial cells.[64] When *gcm* is mutant, these glial cells fail to form and are transformed into neurons. Moreover, when *gcm* is misexpressed in presumptive neurons, it changes their fate so that they become glial cells. Thus, *gcm* acts as a neural–glial switch similar to the action of *en* in the MNB.

Some insight into the signaling cascade that influences the neuron versus glial cell switch has been gained for the grasshopper MNB.[65] Protein kinase A (PKA) is part of the cAMP signaling pathway. Experi-

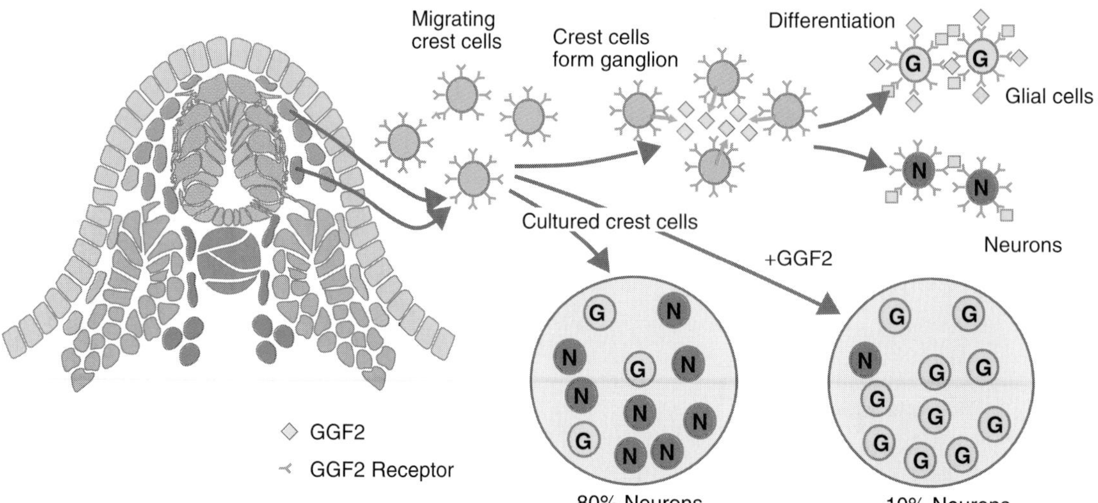

FIGURE 17.15 Function of glial growth factor (GGF) 2 in specifying glial versus neuronal cells in the neural crest. (A) Cross section of an embryo in which migrating neural crest cells (green) are indicated. These cells follow two different pathways: a dorsal one (light green), giving rise to melanocytes; and a ventral one (dark green), leading to the formation of sensory and autonomic ganglia. If placed in culture (B), the majority of neural crest cells differentiate as neurons (red). Adding GGF2 to the culture (C) reverses the ratio of neurons to glial cells in favor of the latter, indicating that GGF2, in this system, promotes glia and suppresses neural development. *In vivo* studies showed that migrating crest cells express the GGF2 receptor early on followed by their expression of GGF2. These findings imply a mechanism by which fluctuations of GGF2 in the local environment of neural crest cells will lead to the segregation of glial cells and neurons from an initially homogeneous cell population. Thus, cells that receive a higher concentration of GGF2 are more likely to become glial, and vice versa.

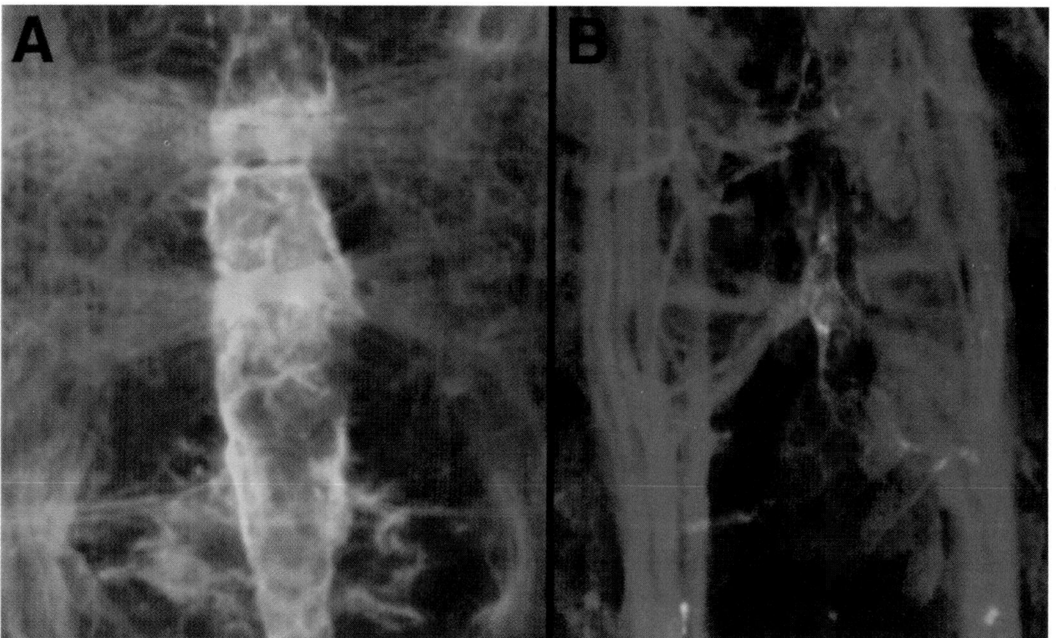

FIGURE 17.16 The progeny of MNB in the grasshopper. (A) The normal product of MNB's divisions is a grapelike bunch of nerve-cell bodies hanging from a stem of axons (both in red) almost invisible within their sheath of green glial cells. (B) If the *engrailed* gene is sabotaged by injecting antisense, the glial cells never appear, but are replaced by extra nerve cells. Provided by Kai Zinn.

mentally changing the level of activated PKA in the MNB, by injecting activators or inhibitors of this enzyme, influences the glial cell-to-neuron ratio. For example, if PKA is inhibited shortly before the onset of the third proliferatory phase, which normally gives rise to neurons, the formation of neurons is blocked; instead, glial cells continue to form. This raises the possibility that external stimuli impinge on the proliferating MNB and restrict the number of glial cell progeny by activating the cAMP pathway.

Summary

The emergence of a neuroblast or a neural precursor is accompanied by processes that confer an identity to each cell. The precursor's identity influences or determines the fates of its progeny. In many invertebrates, early expressed patterning genes (and their targets) are expressed concomitantly with the proneural genes, supplying neural progenitors with intrinsic cues that commit them to specific lineages. The fates of their progeny are then influenced by cell–cell interactions and by the differential inheritance of intrinsic determinants. Examples of cytoplasmic factors that influence cell fates include the Numb protein in *Drosophila* and the animal versus vegetal teloplasm of developing cells in the leech. Transcription factors also influence lineage identity; null mutations in genes encoding transcription factors and the ectopic expression of these genes can result in cell fate transformations. In vertebrates, the processes that determine neuronal and glial lineages are thought to be complex and involve a variety of intrinsic programs and cellular interactions. Several different growth factors act on progenitors to trigger the production of distinct types of glia. In invertebrates, the expression of nuclear proteins such as gcm can cause cells to switch from neuronal to glial fates.

DETERMINING THE FATE OF INDIVIDUAL NEURONS

Once cells have become postmitotic, both the factors they have inherited from their progenitors and the cues that they encounter in their environment influence their particular fate. As cells assume their final phenotypes, they are influenced by local diffusible cues and cues presented on the membranes of neighboring cells. A good example of the diffusible cues can be seen in the sympathoadrenal progenitors that become either chromaffin cells or sympathetic neurons, depending on the growth factors to which they are exposed. The *Drosophila* retina, which incorporates postmitotic cells into a growing crystalline lattice, shows clearly how interactions between neighboring cells determine neural fate. In any portion of the nervous system, the environment in which a cell differentiates changes over time. Thus, birthdate may also play a key role in the fate of neurons. The projection of axons to particular targets is a very important aspect of a neuron's final differentiation. Experiments on the vertebrate spinal cord show that positional information is used to influence this aspect of a neuron's phenotype. Finally, target-derived factors can influence the morphology, transmitter phenotype, and survival of neurons.

In the Vertebrate PNS, Sympathoadrenal Progenitors Can Produce Multiple Types of Neurons

The neural crest was discussed earlier as a model system for studying the influence of extrinsic cues on neuronal differentiation. The neural crest gives rise to a large variety of cell types, among them sensory neurons and glial cells (Schwann cells) of the peripheral nervous system, adrenergic and cholinergic neurons of the autonomic nervous system, and the endocrine chromaffin cells of the adrenal medulla. As described in Chapter 16, experiments in which crest cells have been transplanted to different regions of the body axis indicate that precursors are multipotent when they start migrating out from the crest; they acquire instructions to differentiate as distinct cell types during their migration or when they arrive at their final destination.[66] Furthermore, according to a widely accepted model, the commitment to a particular fate is a multistep process.[67,68]

First, the initially totipotent neural crest cells segregate into several classes of more specialized progenitors. Each of these progenitor classes is still not committed to a single fate (e.g., the sympathoadrenal (SA) progenitors, which are discussed in more detail below can give rise to adrenergic and cholinergic neurons, as well as to endocrine cells); however, they have lost their totipency; that is, they can no longer give rise to all neural crest derivatives. The specification of different progenitor classes takes place during the migration of neural crest cells. Although the mechanism is unknown, a stochastic mechanism has been proposed.

The second step is the commitment of cells within one of the progenitor classes to one particular fate. Extrinsic cues that play an important role during the specification of individual cell types are growth factors. These secreted peptides have an effect on proliferation, differentiation, and survival of neural precursors in culture. Growth factors derived from many different tissues, as well as their receptors, have been identified.

In several cases evidence suggests that they also play a role *in vivo* in neural differentiation.

The SA progenitors, which can be isolated from the adrenal gland primordium of embryonic mammals and raised in culture, can give rise (among other cells) to two very different types of cells: adrenergic sympathetic neurons and endocrine chromaffin cells (Fig. 17.17A). These cell types differ morphologically (sympathetic neurons have long axonal processes; chromaffin cells do not) and biochemically (for example, sympathetic neurons express the neural-specific genes *GAP-43* and *peripherin*; chromaffin cells express the enzyme PNMT). Prior to differentiation, all SA progenitors express markers for both cell types at the same time. In culture, SA progenitors exposed to glucocorticoid hormone, which normally is produced in the adrenal gland, develop as chromaffin cells. Exposed to nerve growth factor (NGF) and fibroblast growth factor (FGF), these progenitors develop as sympathetic neurons.

Glucocorticoid Function

Glucocorticoids are steroid hormones that act on cytoplasmic receptors. After binding to the hormone (ligand), the receptor–ligand complex is transported to the nucleus, where it directly acts as a transcription factor: It binds to DNA and activates and / or represses certain genes. In the case of the SA progenitor, glucocorticoids sequentially evoke two different responses (Fig. 17.17B): First, they inhibit neuronal differentiation by suppressing the transcription of neuron-specific genes (*peripherin, GAP-43*); second, they activate transcription of chromaffin cell-specific genes (e.g., *PNMT*). The effect of the hormone-activated glucocorticoid receptor on these genes, at least in the case of *PNMT*, seems to be a direct one: Binding sites for the glucocorticoid receptor have been identified in the regulatory region of the *PNMT* gene.

bFGF/NGF Function

The expression of a neuronal phenotype by SA progenitors depends on the sequential action of the growth factors bFGF and NGF (Fig. 17.17C). SA progenitors plated on a suitable laminin-containing substrate in the absence of any growth factor form short, neuron-like processes. These processes are much more extensive when FGF is added to the medium, whereas NGF has no effect. The amount of process formation also depends on cell density: SA progenitors grown at high density develop more processes than those grown at low density. This difference can be explained as a so-called autocrine effect.

SA progenitors that initiate neuronal development produce bFGF, the secretion of which further increases neuronal development. Initially, SA progenitors are unresponsive to NGF. This experimental finding is supported by the fact that the SA progenitors do not express the gene(s) encoding the NGF receptor. One of the effects of FGF is to induce the NGF receptor gene, thereby making the cell responsive to NGF.

Cell–Cell Signaling Determines Fate in the Insect Compound Eye

The insect compound eye is composed of a large number of identical photoreceptive units, called **ommatidia** (Fig. 17.18).[69] *Drosophila*, for example, possesses approximately 800 such units in each eye. Each ommatidium contains several different types of photoreceptors and accessory cells. Photoreceptors are specialized sensory neurons. Their apical membrane (called rhabdomere) is folded into many regularly spaced microvilli, which contain the photopigment rhodopsin. There are eight photoreceptors in each ommatidium; six of them (R1–R6) form a trapezoidal array of rhabdomeres, and two (R7, R8) are located in the center. Among the accessory cells are **cone cells**, which form the lens of each ommatidium, and pigment cells, which surround the photoreceptors and optically shield the ommatidia from one another.

The eye, like most other external parts of the adult fly, develops from a so-called **imaginal disc**, the eye-antenna disc. Imaginal discs arise as invaginations of the embryonic epidermis. They do not participate structurally or functionally in the larval body; instead, they form epithelial sacs which grow by cell division. During the pupal stage, the larval body wall degenerates and is replaced by the imaginal discs. The eye-antenna disc gives rise not only to the eye but also to the head capsule and the antenna.

Experimental results have shown that the cells of the ommatidia are not clonally related. Instead, after the eye imaginal disc cells have proliferated, all cells are still uncommitted to their differentiative fate. This situation is quite different from what was said earlier about the sensilla, whose cells are typically produced in a fixed lineage from intrinsically specified SOPs. By contrast, in the eye, cell–cell interactions between the postmitotic photoreceptors and accessory cells are solely responsible for specifying cell fate. It is crucial that ommatidial cells do not appear all at once, but follow a precise, reproducible temporal sequence (Fig. 17.18B). Thus, during late larval life, a wave of differentiation passes over the eye disc in a posterior-to-anterior direction. The wave front—the position at which ommatidial differentiation begins—is morphologically visible as the so-called morphogenetic furrow (MF) (a narrow groove formed by apical constriction

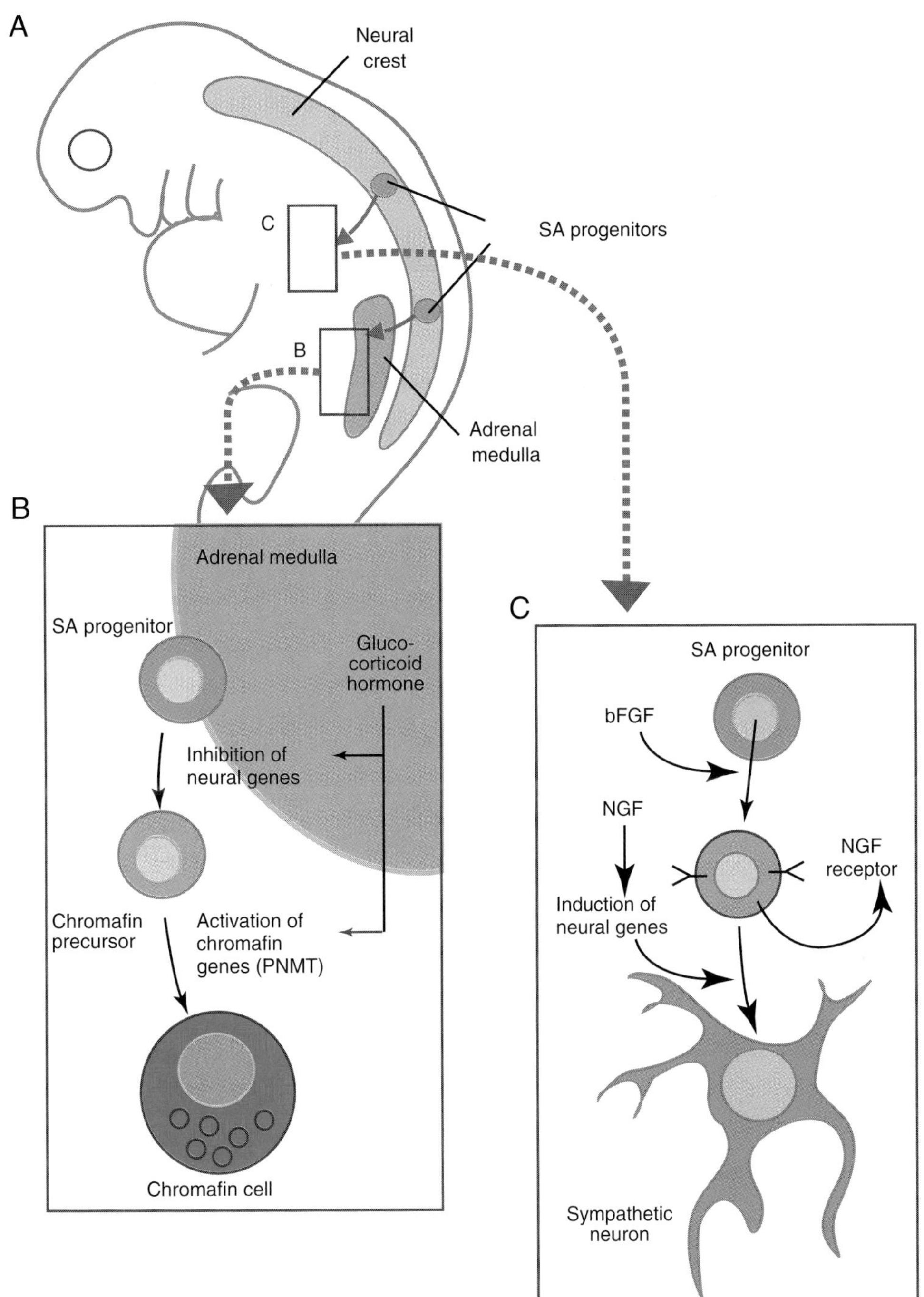

FIGURE 17.17 Cell fate determination of the SA progenitor in vertebrates. SA progenitors represent a subpopulation of neural crest cells (A), which, depending on the environmental conditions, develop as either chromaffin cells (B) or sympathetic neurons (C). Glucocorticoids (B) sequentially evoke two different responses. First, they inhibit neuronal differentiation by suppressing the transcription of neuron-specific genes (*peripherin*, *GAP-43*); second, they activate transcription of chromaffin cell-specific genes (e.g., *PNMT*). The effect of the hormone-activated glucocorticoid receptor on these genes, at least in the case of *PNMT*, seems to be a direct one. Binding sites for glucocorticoid receptor have been identified in the regulatory region of the *PNMT* gene (C). The expression of a neuronal phenotype by SA progenitors depends on the sequential action of bFGF and NGF.

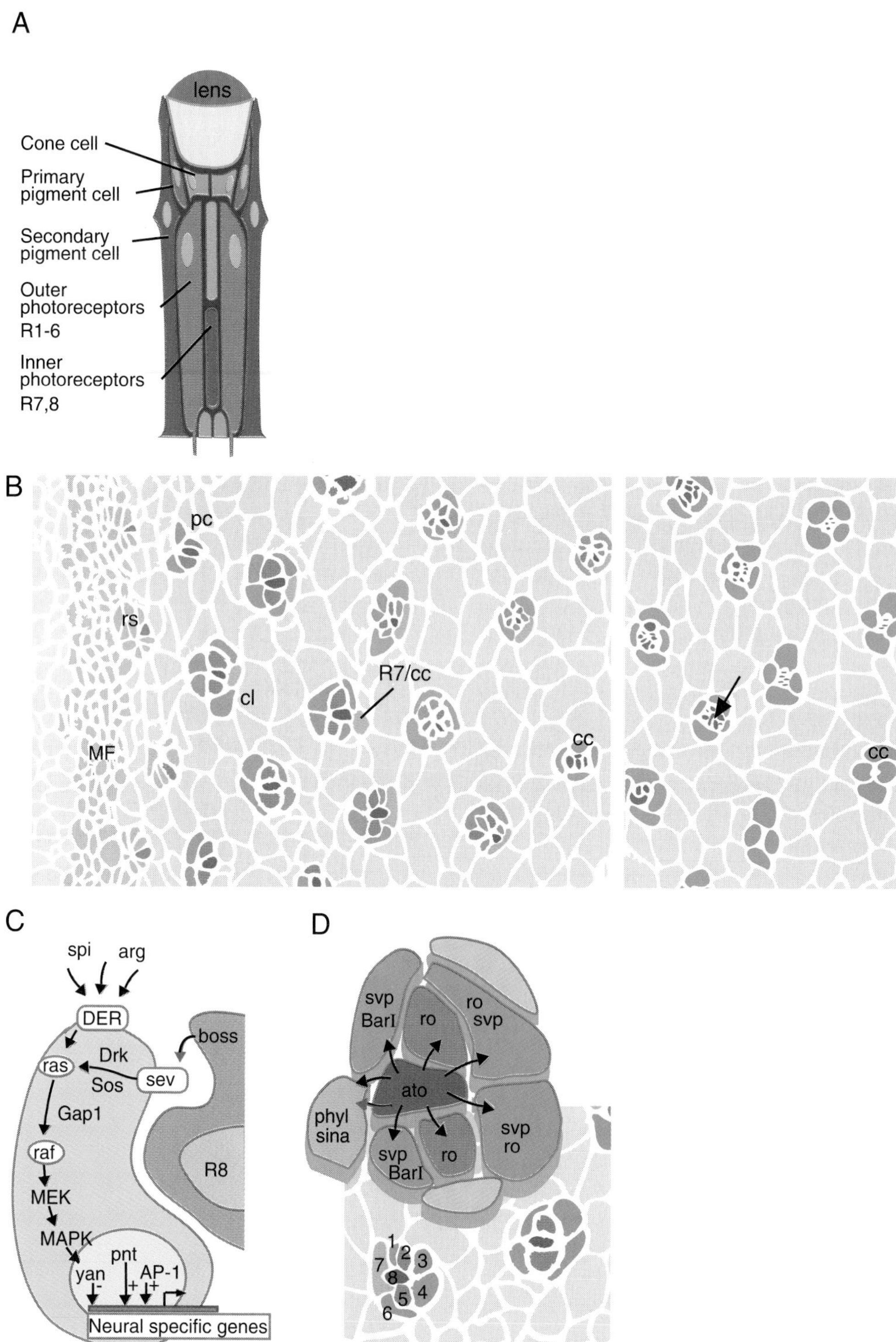

FIGURE 17.18 Determination of photoreceptor cell fate in the *Drosophila* compound eye. (A) A longitudinal view of the cells that constitute each ommatidium, depicting cell types in different colors. The cone cell at the top of each ommatidium forms a lens. Primary and secondary pigment cells surround and optically insulate the photoreceptor cells R1–R8. (B) The sequence of ommatidial development is revealed in a surface view of the eye imaginal disc at a stage when photoreceptor clusters are assembled. Gray profiles indicate the apical surfaces of undifferentiated cells; colored profiles demarcate different types of photoreceptors and cone cells. To the extreme left, all cells are undifferentiated. In the next phase, eye disc cells become more closely packed and constricted at their apical pole, thereby forming the morphogenetic furrow (MF; note small surface area of cells in MF, compared to cells in front or behind the MF). As they leave the furrow, cells form more or less regularly spaced rosettes (rs; light purple). Within each rosette, a single cell becomes singled out as the photoreceptor R8 (dark purple). Shortly thereafter it becomes clear that four other photoreceptors (R2, R5: lilac; R3, R4: blue) have joined R8. Together, these five cells form the so-called precluster (pc). Three more photoreceptors (R1, R6: blue; R7: orange) join the preclusters, leading to complete photorecep-

of the eye disc cells). As they leave the furrow, cells of the eye disc form an intricate pattern of "rosettes," foreshadowing the regular ommatidial pattern. Soon afterward, one cell that will become the R8 photoreceptor is singled out in each rosette. Thus, the rosettes might be considered morphological manifestations of proneural clusters. Both proneural and neurogenic genes play roles in the determination and spacing of R8 photoreceptors. The proneural gene *atonal* is expressed in the MF and subsequently concentrated in the rosettes and in R8.[42,70] How *atonal* expression is regulated is currently unknown. The genes *emc* and *h* seem to act as negative regulators of *ato* (similar to their function in SOP specification).[71] Loss of *atonal* function results in the absence of R8 photoreceptors. *Notch* and *Delta* mediate cell–cell interaction within the rosettes; loss of either gene results in all rosette cells becoming R8. Another gene, *scabrous* (*sca*), is involved in proper spacing of R8 cells.

R8 cells act as organizers of ommatidium assembly. The first cells that join each R8 cell shortly after its determination are R2, R3, R4, and R5. Together with R8 they make up what has been called an ommatidial "precluster" (Fig. 17.18B). The next cells to join the ommatidial clusters are R1, R6, R7, and four cone cells—nonneuronal cells that will form the lens. R1–R6, called the outer photoreceptors, are arranged in a ring like pattern. They surround R8 and R7, which form the inner photoreceptors. At this time, the photoreceptors segregate from the surface and come to lie beneath the four cone cells. The ommatidia are completed during the first day of the pupal stage (not shown in Fig. 17.18B). Thus, cells surrounding the cone cell–photoreceptor cluster become arranged in two regular layers of pigment cells, which optically shield neighboring ommatidia from each other (Fig. 17.18A).

The inductive mechanism that, starting with R8, leads to the successive determination of the different photoreceptors is known in some detail.[72] Conceptually, two mechanisms may be distinguished. First, all future photoreceptors receive a signal in the form of the Spitz (Spi) protein (a member of the TGFα family of proteins) to become "generic" neuronal cells.[73,74] Spi is secreted by R8 and other photoreceptors. In the cells surrounding R8 it activates the DER receptor (*Drosophila* EGF receptor), which in turn triggers a signal transduction cascade involving the Ras pathway. Many components of this pathway, which is conserved to a high degree in all animals, have been identified in *Drosophila* photoreceptor cells, in particular the R7 cell (Fig. 17.18C). At the end of the Ras pathway are several transcription factors, among them those encoded by the *yan* and *pointed* genes, which activate an (unknown) program of genes required for photoreceptor differentiation. It is important to note that the Ras pathway in itself does not seem to convey any photoreceptor specificity. Thus, reduction in Ras signaling leads to variable reduction in all photoreceptors; overactivity (achieved, for example, by Spitz overexpression) converts cells of the eye disc that normally would not have developed as photoreceptors into such cells. The action of Spitz as the photoreceptor-promoting signal is modulated by other genes, among them *argos* (*arg*), *rhomboid*, and *Star*.[75–77]

A second signaling mechanism conveys specific fates on the different photoreceptors. This mechanism emanates from R8, which signals to the cells of the precluster, R2–R5, as well as the later-forming photoreceptors R1, R6, and R7. Except for the R8–R7 interaction, little is known about the signal molecules, their receptors, and the signal transduction cascades specifying photoreceptor fate. However, a group of transcription factors is required in particular subsets of photoreceptors (Fig. 17.18D).[78] In the absence of any of these molecules, the corresponding set of photoreceptors is missing. Overexpression of these molecules, in some cases, leads to the conversion of other cell types into the corresponding photoreceptors. In this manner, the homeobox gene *BarI*[47,48] and *rough* (*ro*) are required in R1/R6 and R2–R5, respectively; *seven-up* (*svp*), a member of the nuclear receptor family of genes, is required for the outer photoreceptors R1/6 and

tor clusters (cl). This step is followed by the appearance of four cone cells (cc; green), which surround the photoreceptors in a circular fashion. On the right side, photoreceptors can be seen to segregate from the surface. Their apical membranes become increasingly smaller (arrow), and finally they disappear altogether. (C–D) Summary of the function of several genes during photoreceptor development. (C) The determination and spacing of R8 cells are controlled by Spitz (Spi) from R8 (followed by other photoreceptors). In cells surrounding R8, Spi protein interacts with DER, the *Drosophila* epidermal growth factor receptor homolog. Activation of DER stimulates the Ras signaling pathway (symbolized by black arrows). This inductive signaling is required for the aquisition of a "generic" neural phenotype by all photoreceptor cells. The Ras pathway can also be stimulated by the interaction of the sevenless (sev) receptor with its ligand, bride of sevenless (boss). See text for further details. (D) In conjunction with other, less well understood signaling events, photoreceptors are induced to express specific transcription factors, which are required for their respective fates. At the bottom left of this panel is a key showing the position of each photoreceptor; R8 is in the center of the cluster. The larger figure at the top shows the pattern of transcription factor expression seen in each: *seven-up* (*svp*) is expressed in R1, R6, R3, and R4; *rough* (*ro*) is expressed in R2, R3, R4, and R5; *BarI* is expressed in R1 and R6; and *seven in absentia* (*sina*) and *phyllopod* (*phyl*) are expressed only in R7. In R7, Ras signaling is triggered via the sev receptor by the boss protein, which is presented on the R8 membrane (purple arrow).

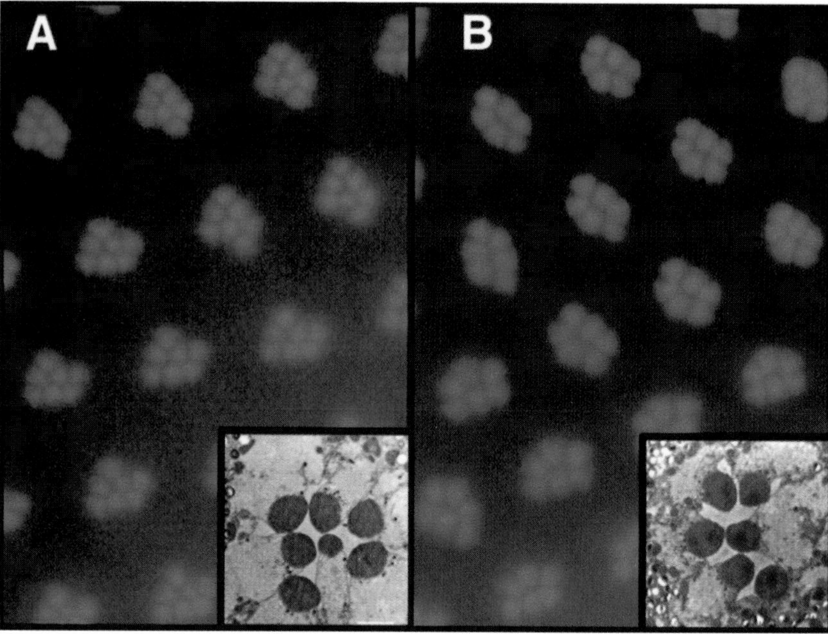

FIGURE 17.19 Photoreceptors in the eye of normal and *sevenless* mutants. (A) If a light is shined from the back of a fly's head and focused on the facets of the eye, individual photoreceptors can be seen because of their ability to pipe light. The wild-type animal has the normal pattern of seven photoreceptors visible in each facet. The small one in the center is photoreceptor 7. (B) The same technique used in a *sevenless* mutant shows only six large photoreceptors in each facet. Number 7 is missing. Insets show electron micrographs through single facets. Adapted from Harris *et al.*[83]

R3/4.[79,80] The transcription factors *seven in absentia* (*sina*) and *phyllopod* (*phyl*)[78] are expressed and required in R7 (Fig. 17.18D). One signaling mechanism initiates the development of "generic" photoreceptors; another provides each photoreceptor with a specific fate. How the two interact is unknown. With *svp*, the two mechanisms may act sequentially. Activation of the Ras pathway—prompting a cell to become a generic photoreceptor—is a prerequisite for *svp* to function.[80] Another unsolved question is how the photoreceptor-specific transcription factors are activated in the correct cells. One gene, *lozenge* (*lz*), is involved in this process.[81] Thus, *lz* is required to activate *BarI* in R1/R6 and to inhibit *svp* in R7, thereby "allowing" for the differentiation of this cell as an inner photoreceptor. Absence of *lz*, similar to misexpression of *svp* in the presumptive R7, results in the development of this cell as an outer photoreceptor (R1–R6).

Signaling has been studied in the most detail for photoreceptor R7, which is the last neuronal cell to join the photoreceptor cluster.[82] In R7, the Ras pathway leading to neuronal determination is activated (possibly beside the DER) by another receptor tyrosine kinase, *sevenless* (*sev*) (Fig. 17.18C, Fig. 17.19).[83] A signaling molecule, encoded by the *bride of sevenless* (*boss*) gene, is expressed specifically by R8 and reacts with *sev* present on the membrane of the presumptive R7. *Boss–sev* interaction triggers the Ras pathway, leading to the activation of *pnt* and *AP-1*, as well as the inhibition of the negative regulator of R7 differentiation, *yan*. Loss of any member of this signaling pathway results in the transformation of R7 into a cone cell.

In conclusion, we are just beginning to understand photoreceptor determination in the *Drosophila* eye in terms of the pattern of intrinsically expressed transcriptional regulators and receptor–ligand interactions shown by a given cell. It may soon become feasible to causally relate these molecular patterns to the exact position and time at which a given photoreceptor is born.

Neuronal Fates in the Vertebrate Spinal Cord Are Induced through Cell–Cell Interactions

The early differentiating neurons of the spinal cord include the primary motor neurons, which send out axons to the forming skeletal muscle. Transplantation experiments show that the floor plate of the embryonic spinal cord emits a signal that specifies the fate of neighboring ventral neurons—in particular motor neurons (Figs. 17.20A and 17.20B).[84] Recent experiments have shown that the vertebrate *Sonic hedgehog* gene encodes two peptides that are secreted from the notochord and floor plate. *In vitro*, one of these peptides (19K) is able to induce the expression of motor neuron-specific biochemical markers (e.g., the transcription factor Islet-1) in early neural tube explants.[85,86] Conversely, antibodies against the 19K peptide can block the development of motor neurons in explants pretreated with notochord cells, which by themselves induce motor neuron characteristics. The *Isl-1* gene is critical for the autonomous differentiation of motor neurons, for motor neurons do not differentiate in *Isl-1* knockout mice. A secondary consequence of lack of motor neuron differentiation is the absence of a class of ventral interneurons that express *engrailed*. This suggests that cell fate in the vertebrate neural cord involves a series of inductive interactions (Fig. 17.20C).

In the chick, specific muscles of the limb are innervated by motor neurons from different positions along the anterior–posterior axis of the spinal cord. When a length of the embryonic spinal cord of the chick is rotated, the motor neurons still establish connections to their normal target muscles, although axons now have to navigate along novel pathways. This establishes that the position of the cell body along the anterior–posterior axis is an important determinant in the specification of a motor neuron's target choice.[87] In zebrafish, this issue has been approached on a single-cell level, since each spinal segment has just three primary motor neurons: RoP, MiP, and CaP (for rostral, middle, and caudal primary) (Fig. 17.20D). Each sends an axon out the spinal cord to the same choice point. But then the CaP grows down to innervate the ventral muscle, RoP continues out to the lateral muscle, and MiP grows up to the dorsal muscle.[88] When these motor neurons were transplanted to different positions at the time of axonogenesis, each maintained its original projection pattern (Fig. 17.20E). Thus, at that time these cells are committed to a particular fate and differentiate autonomously. When these cells were transplanted several hours earlier, however, a different result was obtained (Fig. 17.20F). Thus, a very young CaP can develop RoP axonal characteristics and innervate more lateral muscle if transplanted to the RoP position soon after its birth.[89] These results suggest that the position of their soma along the rostrocaudal axis of the segment specifies the axonal projection of the different primary neurons.

One possible molecular determinant of the projection of these motor neurons is the pattern of LIM transcription factors they express.[90] Each motor neuron expresses a unique combination of these transcription factors. Transplantation experiments demonstrate that when primary motor neurons change their projection pattern, they initiate a new program of LIM homeobox gene expression (Fig. 17.21). However, whether the pattern of LIM expression controls target choice and, if so, the intermediate molecular steps that link transcription factors in these neurons to particular pathway choices of their axons remain to be determined.

The connection between an intrinsic transcriptional determinant and innervation pattern has also been shown in *C. elegans*.[92] The *C. elegans* ventral nerve cord, which is analogous to the vertebrate spinal cord, possesses a number of motor neurons—called VAs and VBs—that receive input from defined sets of interneurons. One VA and one VB form a pair. In the wild type, VA motor neurons receive input from a set of interneurons called AVA, AVD, and AVE; VB receives input from interneurons AVB and PVC. A homeobox gene, *unc-4*, controls the input. If expression of *unc-4* is turned off (using a temperature-sensitive allele) late in embryogenesis, when the input to VAs and VBs is formed, both VA and VB will be innervated by the interneurons AVB and PVC. This defect is not accompanied by any other structural abnormality, indicating that *unc-4* specifically controls synaptic input to the motor neurons (Fig. 17.22).

Both Extrinsic and Intrinsic Cues Change over Time

External cues change with time. One of the best examples of this comes from the mammalian cortex. The cells of the cerebral cortex are generated in an inside-out manner, with the cells of layer 6, the deepest layer, being born first (at E29 in the ferret); the cells of layer 5 are born next; and the last cells born are those nearest the surface, layer 1.[93] The cells are born in the ventricular zone and migrate to the cortical plate along radial glia. Cells born at P1 are fated for layers 2/3 and must migrate through layers 6, 5, and 4, which have already formed (Figs. 17.23A, 17.23B). In principle, cortical cells could be determined with respect to layer as they are generated, or they might obtain their fate from the position they migrate into. To test these possibilities, cells generated at E29 (labeled with [^{3}H]thymidine) from the cortical germinal epithelium of a ferret were transplanted into older P1 hosts.[94] Although in a normal environment their time of birth would have fated them for layer 6, some of the transplanted cells switch their fates and end up in layers 2/3 (Fig. 17.23C). Thus, some cortical neurons were committed to a deep-layer fate even before they began to migrate out of the ventricular zone. On the other hand, some neurons were clearly multipotent and their fate was influenced by the older environment. But why weren't all the cells behaving similarly? Perhaps neurons that had just finished mitosis were committed,

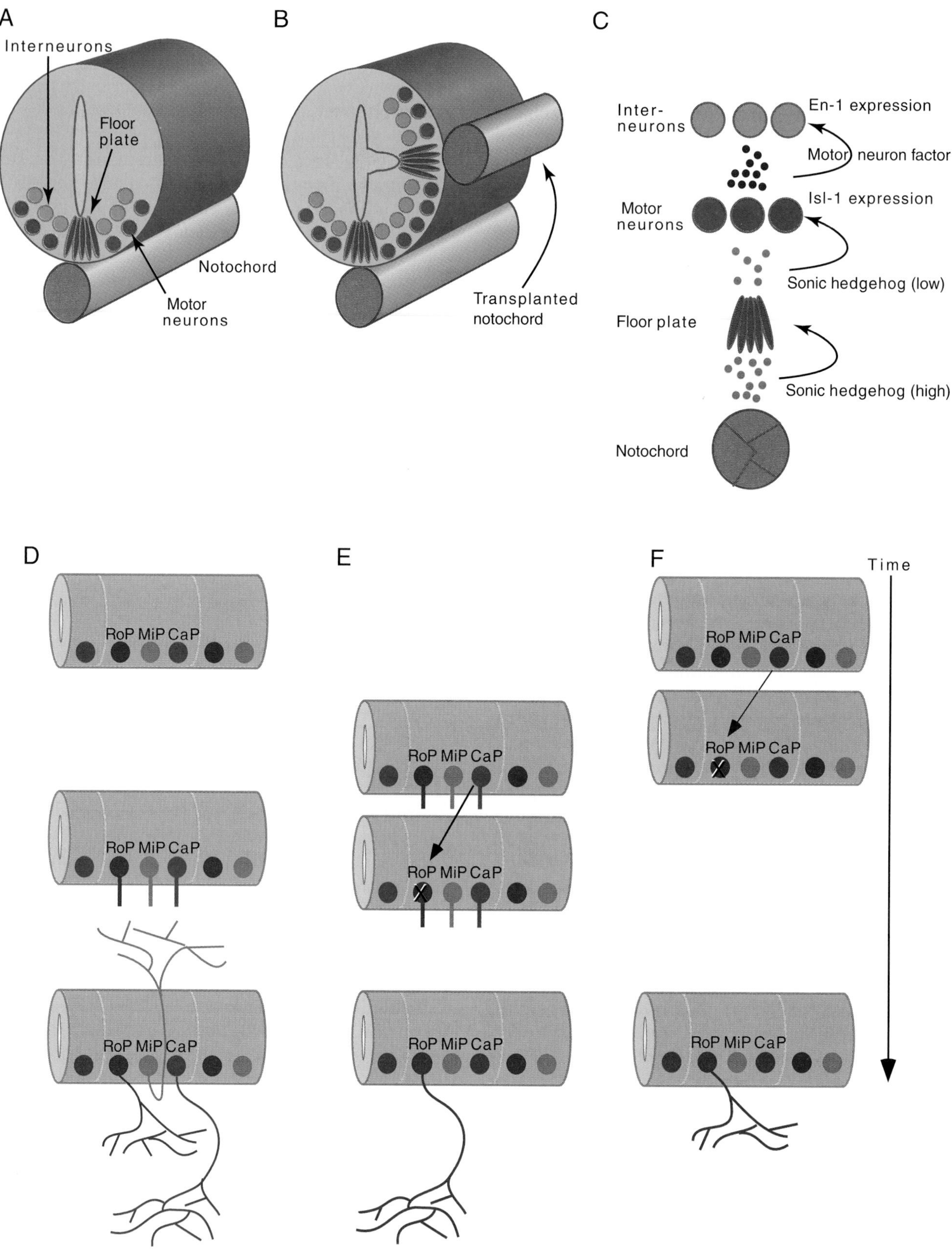
A
Interneurons
Floor plate
Notochord
Motor neurons
B
Transplanted notochord
C
Inter-neurons
En-1 expression
Motor neuron factor
Motor neurons
Isl-1 expression
Sonic hedgehog (low)
Floor plate
Sonic hedgehog (high)
Notochord
D
RoP MiP CaP
RoP MiP CaP
RoP MiP CaP
E
RoP MiP CaP
RoP MiP CaP
RoP MiP CaP
F
Time
RoP MiP CaP
RoP MiP CaP
RoP MiP CaP

but the precursor cells with another round of cell division to go were multipotent. To answer this question, E29 pulse [^{3}H]thymidine-labeled cells either were left in the donor to complete a round of division before transplantation or were transplanted immediately after labeling.[95] The results were clear. Cells allowed to complete their final division in the donor retained a deep-layer fate, while precursor cells transplanted to an older host to complete their final division switched to a layer 2/3 fate. When the transplanted cells were sorted according to the phase of the cell cycle, by the time DNA synthesis was completed and before mitosis was over, the precursor cell had already made a commitment to generate a daughter committed to a particular cell layer (Fig. 17.23C). Thus, cell fate, according to layer, is decided by precursor cells in the environment of the germinal zone, and not in the cortical plate.[96] This same environment must change with time in a way that influences cellular fate. When older precursor cells were transplanted into younger brains, these cells, though influenced by their environment, lost the potential to differentiate as deep-layer cells. These results show that the pluripotency of cortical precursors is restricted over time, perhaps by environmental factors controlling intrinsic competence, or by an intrinsic clock (Fig. 17.23D).

The vertebrate retina develops from a population of pluripotent neuroepithelial progenitors, which produce a diversity of neurons and glia[97,98] (Fig. 17.24). Neuronal genesis and determination in the retina follow a temporal but lineage-independent order.[99,100] Thus, at any given time during retinogenesis, only a few fates are available to differentiating cells. Cells born early in mammals generally have fates as retinal

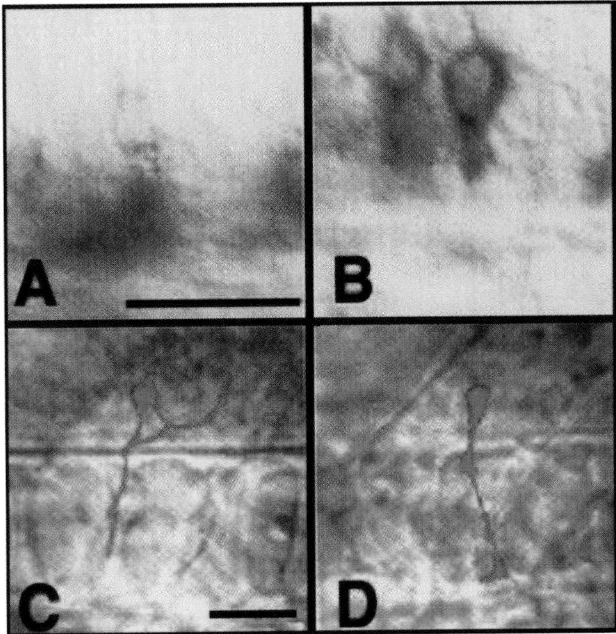

FIGURE 17.21 *Islet-2* gene expression in transplanted primary motor neurons. (A, C) Cell transplanted from the MiP to the CaP position near the time of axonogenesis and probed for *Islet-2* expression after axon formation. This cell retained an MiP-like projection pattern (C) and did not express *Islet-2* (A). (B, D) Cell transplanted from the MiP to the CaP position 2–3 h before axonogenesis and probed for *Islet-2* expression after axon formation. This cell developed a CaP-like expression pattern (D) and began to express *Islet-2* (B). Scale, 25 mm. Adapted from Appel *et al.*[91]

ganglion cells. Horizontal cells and cones are also born early. Amacrine cells are followed by rods, bipolars, and Müller cells. This progressive change is supported by dissociation experiments in which cells are plated into culture at low density at various stages of development.[101] It is possible to force cells to be born early, because isolation inhibits mitotic activity. Thus, if mitotic cells are isolated when retinal ganglion cells are born, they tend to turn into ganglion cells in culture. If mitotic cells are isolated at later stages, they become rod photoreceptors in culture.

These results are consistent with the intrinsic progression of cell fates, which may operate via a clock mechanism, such that cells generated early become RGCs and later ones become rods. In heterochronic experiments, retinal cells, at the stage when RGCs are being born, were labeled with a birth-dating marker, dissociated, mixed into an aggregate, and cultured *in vitro*. The labeled cells differentiated into RGCs, showing that the exact position of the cells within the retinal primordium is not critical for this differentiation. However, if the early born cells were mixed with an excess of retinal cells several days older (i.e., when photoreceptors were being generated), the labeled cells gener-

←

FIGURE 17.20 Motor neuron differentiation. (A) The normal arrangement of cell types in the ventral spinal cord. The notochord is directly under the floor plate. Next to the floor plate are the motor neurons and next to the motor neurons are the *engrailed* positive interneurons. (B) When a notochord is transplanted to the side of a forming neural tube, a series of inductions occurs, giving rise to a new floor plate and extra sets of motor neurons and ventral interneurons. (C) The notochord secretes *Sonic hedgehog*, which at high levels induces ventral neural tube cells to become floor plate. The floor plate then becomes itself a source of *Sonic hedgehog*, which at low concentrations induces ventral neural tube cells to express *Islet-1* and become motor neurons. Motor neurons then secrete other factors, which causes the next most distant cells to become *engrailed*-expressing ventral interneurons. (D) The zebrafish spinal cord, showing the development of the three primary motor neurons RoP, MiP, and CaP and their specific projection patterns. In (E) a CaP is transplanted to the RoP position at the time of axonogenesis and retains its intrinsic projection pattern. In (F) the transplantation is done a few hours before axonogenesis, and now the CaP cell, influenced by its local environment, acquires a RoP-like projection pattern.

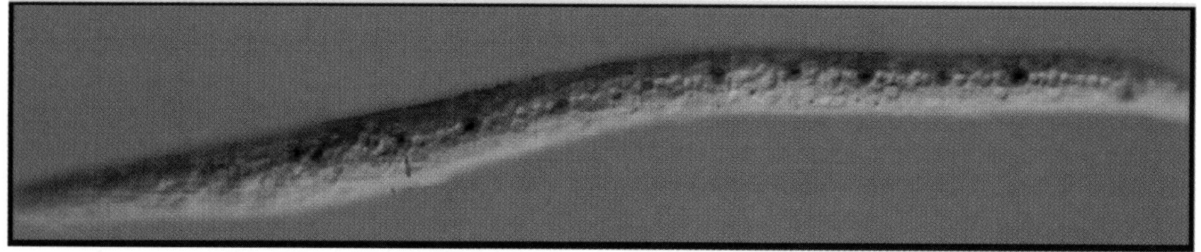

FIGURE 17.22 The gene *unc-4* is expressed in VA motor neurons. View of late larval nematode transformed with galactosidase gene under the control of an *unc-4* promoter. All the VA motor neurons that express *unc-4* are stained blue. Adapted from Miller and Niemeyer.[92]

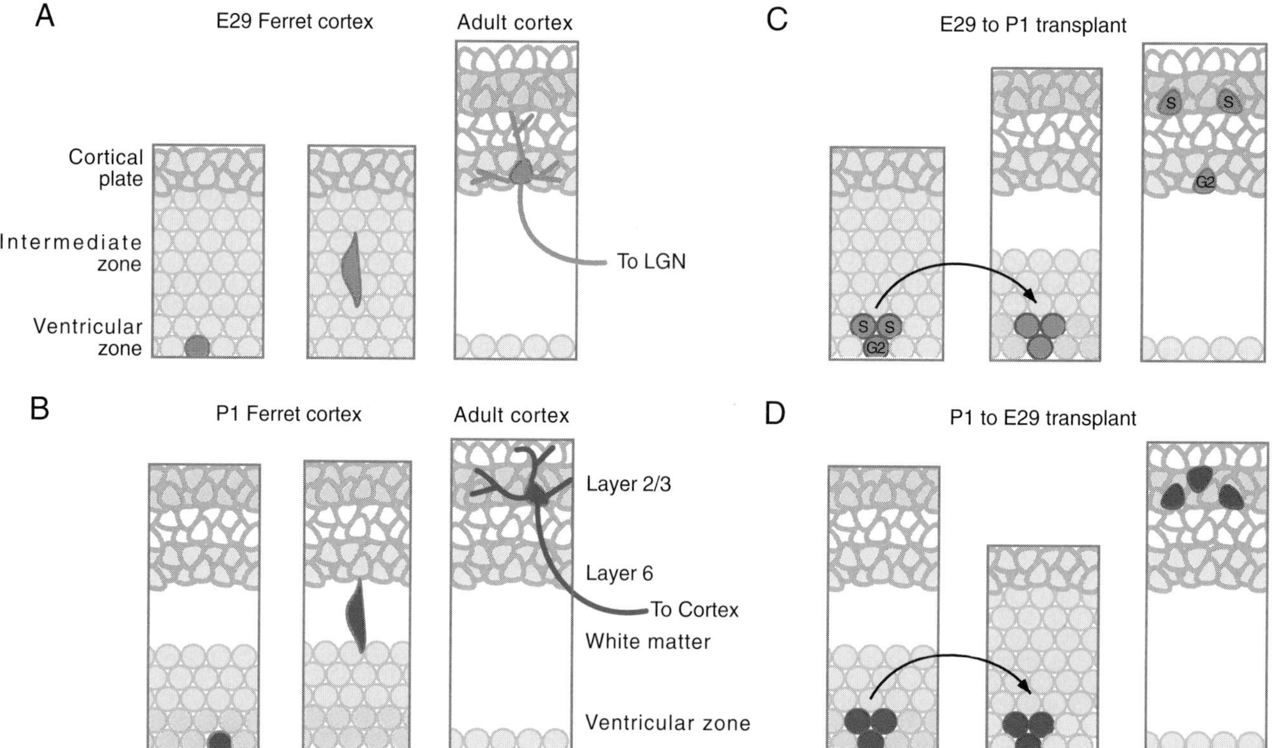

FIGURE 17.23 Laminar fate determination in the cerebral cortex. (A) At E29, cells in the ventricular zone of the ferret cortex progress through the cell cycle and generate young neurons (left). The neurons migrate outward to establish the cortical plate, which will ultimately form the layered adult cerebral cortex (right). The "birthdays" of cortical neurons have been marked by pulses of [^{3}H]-thymidine. Neurons generated on E29 in ferret differentiate into pyramidal neurons in layer 6, many of which send axons to the thalamus. (B) Cells generated postnatally in the ferret are destined for the upper layers. (Left) Progenitor cells in the ventricular zone generate young neurons that migrate outward through the intermediate zone and past the deep layers of the cortical plate. Neurons generated on P1 ultimately migrate into layer 2/3, where they differentiate as pyramidal cells that send axons to other cortical targets (right). (C) Heterochronic (young to old) transplants of presumptive deep-layer progenitors in an older cortical environment. The results depend on when during the cell cycle the cells were transplanted. When E29 progenitors are moved into an older (P1) environment during S-phase (cells marked S), their daughters are plastic and adopt the fates of neighboring cells in the ventricular zone. Cells transplanted at G2 (cell marked G2) are already specified to form layer 6 cells and stop migrating when they reach the deep layers. (D) Heterochronic (old to young) transplants of presumptive upper-layer progenitors from P1 ferrets into a younger cortical environment (E29). Older progenitor cells seem to be incapable of responding to the younger environment, as though they had already progressed past all possible earlier fates and could not look back. They migrate through the younger cortex and do not stop until the upper layers are generated, at which point they finally differentiate.

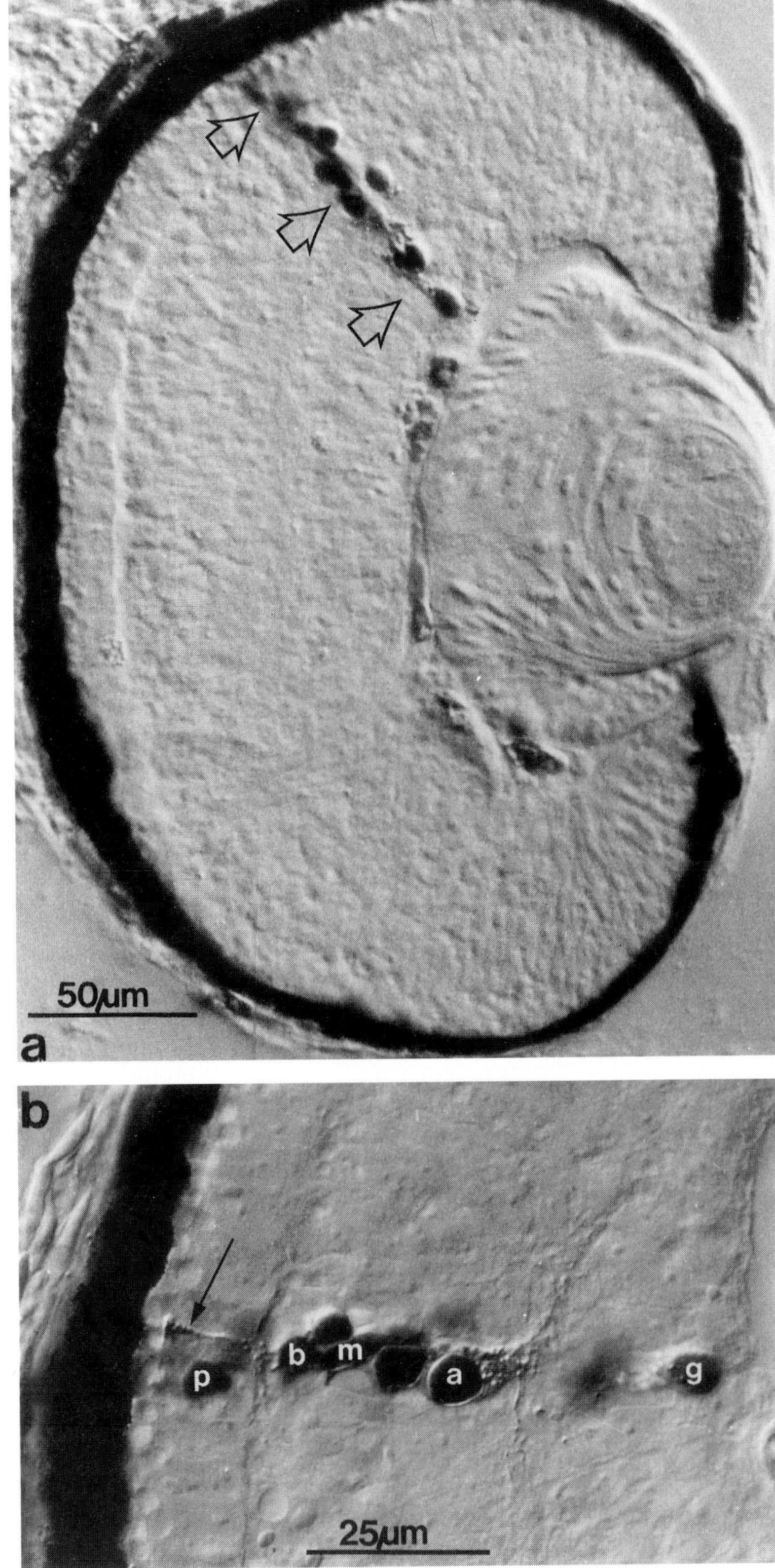

FIGURE 17.24 Clone of cells in the *Xenopus* retina. (a) The daughters of a single retina progenitor injected with horseradish peroxidase are seen to form a column that spans the retinal layers and contribute many distinct cell types (b) p, photoreceptor; b, bipolar cell; m, Müller cell; a, amacrine cell; and g, ganglion cell. From Holt *et al.*[98]

ally became photoreceptors.[102,103] This work showed that the same cells have the capacity to differentiate into different cell types, depending largely on when they are born, and thus the state of the germinal epithelium at that time.

It is not clear which molecular signals the retina uses to induce different fates at successive stages of development, but evidence suggests that through local factors and cell–cell interactions the earlier generated cell types may negatively regulate their own numbers while inducing subsequent cell types.[104–106] In the constantly changing environment of the developing retina, progenitor cells must be able to respond differentially to these cues in order to produce the variety of mature cell types in the correct proportions.[100,107]

Differences in response may be achieved by mechanisms affecting the competence of cells to respond to external signals at a particular place or time. Vertebrate homologs of the *Drosophila* neurogenic genes in the retina appear to control the timing of differentiation and thus regulate how many cells adopt early versus later fates.[108–110] Retinal cells can be made to differentiate earlier or later than normal by manipulating the levels of *Notch* and *Delta* signaling; this in turn causes cells to assume fates that appear appropriate for the time at which they differentiate (Fig. 17.25). Thus, mechanisms regulating the competence of cells to respond to changing inductive cues can dramatically influence cell fate choice and the proportions of cells choosing different fates.

Target Tissues Regulate Cell Fate

A neuron's fate may be completely determined in many respects at the time it is born or shortly thereafter. For some neurons, however, the final fate choice comes only after the cell has established contact with its synaptic targets, showing that decisions about cell fate can stretch from early embryogenesis to the final phases of differentiation. In many neurons, a final fate choice is between survival and death, and this decision is often strongly influenced by trophic factors produced by the target. Target-dependent neuronal cell death is discussed in Chapter 20. In this chapter, we present examples of other dramatic decisions influenced by the target.

The Retzius Neuron of the Leech

The Retzius neuron of the leech is a serotonergic interneuron involved in swimming and other behavior.[111] The Retzius cell comes from the N teloblast, and ablation of one particular blast cell derived from the N-teloblast on one side of the embryo leads to the loss of the Retzius cell on that side. Although these findings suggest that Retzius cell fate is highly determined and lineage dependent, the story is a bit more complicated. Retzius neurons in each of the leech's midbody segments start life identically by making serotonin, and sending projections laterally into the body wall and longitudinally along the interganglionic connectives. At Embryonic Day 10, however, Retzius neurons in

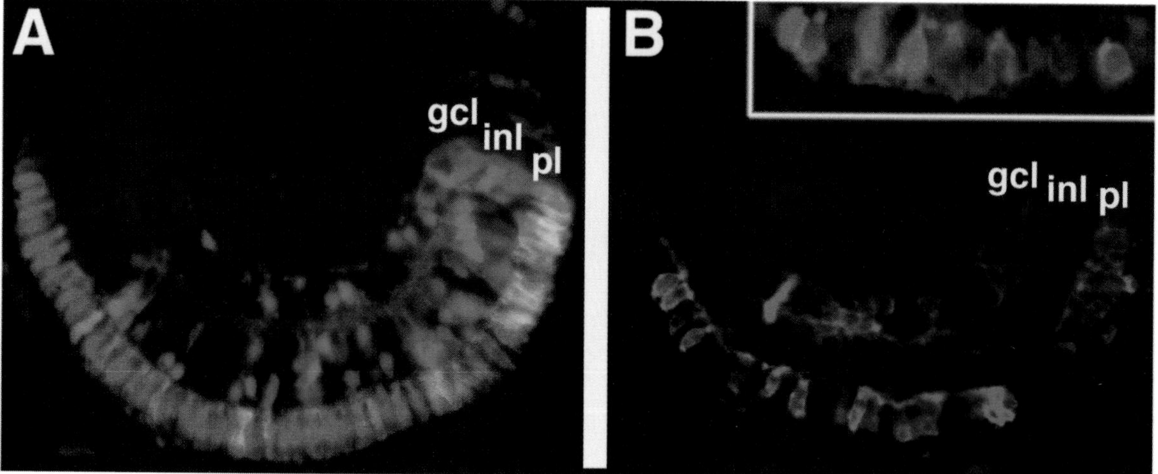

FIGURE 17.25 The effect of *Delta* on cell type in the retina. (A) In a normal animal in which a single blastomere is injected with cDNA coding for a green fluorescent protein, cells in all retinal layers are labeled. Some of the photoreceptors of the injected blastomere are cone cells (red). (B) When the blastomere is injected with *Delta* (green), almost all of the retinal descendents are in two layers, the ganglion cell layer (gcl) or the photoreceptor layer (pl); the inner nuclear layer (inl) is almost empty of *Delta*-positive cells and almost all the *Delta*-positive photoreceptors are double labeled with a cone marker (inset). Shown by R. Dorsky.

ganglia 5 and 6 (otherwise known as the sex ganglia because of their relationship to the gonads) start to develop very differently from the Retzius neurons in all the other ganglia. Instead of continuing their growth laterally into the body wall, the growth cones of these processes change directions and head toward the midline genital tissues that they innervate. The interganglionic connectives retract, and the cells change their physiological responsiveness to neurotransmitters, rearrange their central connectivity within the ganglion, and remain smaller than the Retzius neurons in other segments. Interaction of the Retzius cell axons with the reproductive tissue appears to control the fate choice—as transplantation and embryonic mesodermal bandlet slippage experiments have shown. If moved into a nonsex segment early enough, gonadal tissue—but not body wall tissue from segments 5 and 6—causes the Retzius cells of that segment to innervate the transplanted reproductive tissue and transform physiologically and anatomically into Retzius neurons typical of the sex ganglia. Similarly, ablation of the reproductive tissue in segments 5 and 6 causes transformation of the Retzius cells in the sex ganglia toward those of the standard midbody ganglia. Contact with the reproductive tissue is critical for the transformation, because in ablation or transplantation experiments only the Retzius neurons that successfully make contact with the reproductive tissue show the sex ganglion Retzius cell characteristics.

Transmitter Choice by Sympathetic Neurons

All neural crest cells that become sympathetic neurons start life producing the neurotransmitter noradrenalin (Fig. 17.26). They receive the signal to be adrenergic as they migrate; by the time these neurons coalesce into ganglia, they are all adrenergic.[112,113] Many of these neurons send out axons to smooth muscle targets; these sympathetic neurons remain adrenergic throughout life. A few sympathetic neurons, however—for example, those that innervate sweat glands—switch their neurotransmitter phenotype late in development and become cholinergic (Fig. 17.26A).[114] Neurotransmitter choice in these cells is a late aspect of cell fate that is regulated by the target. Sweat gland innervation starts off adrenergic, and all the enzymes and transmitter machinery for noradrenalin are found in the sympathetic neurons that first innervate the sweat glands. During the second postnatal week in the rat, these neurons begin to turn off tyrosine hydroxylase and other adrenergic enzymes and begin to make choline acetyltransferase, the synthetic enzyme for ACh production. Ablating the early adrenergic fibers with the neurotoxin 6-hydroxydopamine also abolishes the later cholinergic innervation, showing

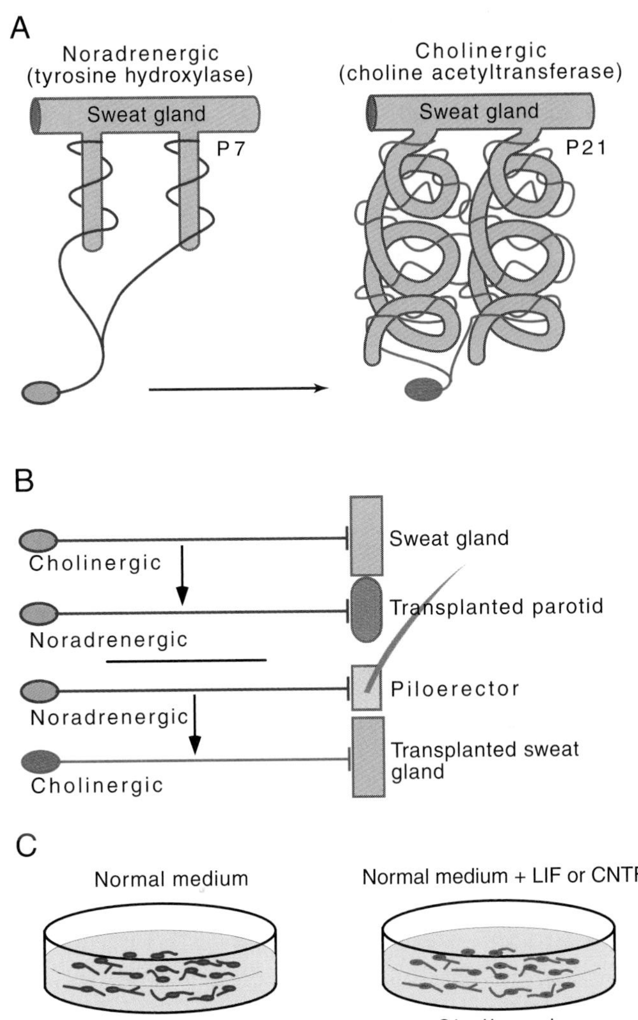

FIGURE 17.26 Transmitter switching by target-derived factors. (A) All sympathetic neurons appear to start differentiation as noradrenergic neurons. Some of these neurons—in this case in a rat—innervate the sweat glands. Noradrenergic sympathetic neurons that innervate the sweat gland invariably switch their transmitter phenotype as the sweat gland matures. These neurons stop making tyrosine hydroxylase and start making choline acetyltransferase. (B) Switching *in vivo* can be effected by transplanting different end organs to the same sympathetic neurons. Thus the adrenergic to cholinergic switch can be prevented by replacing sweat gland-rich targets like the foot pad with a piece of parotid gland, usually the recipient of adrenergic innervation. Conversely, an adrenergic-to-cholinergic switch can be accomplished by transplanting foot pad tissue onto hairy skin, which is usually innervated by adrenergic sympathetic neurons. (C) Factors such as LIF and CNTF, found in target tissues like heart muscle and food pad, can influence neurotransmitter choice in cultured sympathetic neurons causing cells that would differentiate as adrenergic neurons to become cholinergic.

that the two transmitters come from the same fibers that switch transmitter phenotype from adrenergic to cholinergic, rather than from distinct populations of innervating fibers arriving at different times.[115] Evidence for the role of the sweat glands themselves in inducing the switch in phenotypes comes from transplant and explant experiments (Fig. 17.26B). Coculturing young sympathetic neurons with either sweat gland tissue or pineal gland (a common adrenergic target) caused the neurons to become either cholinergic or adrenergic, respectively. Transplanting foot pad tissue, rich in sweat glands, to areas of the body that usually receive adrenergic sympathetic innervation, such as the hairy skin of the thorax, leads to the induction of cholinergic function in the sympathetic axons that innervate the transplanted glands. Similarly, replacing the footpad tissue with parotid gland, noradrenergic target, causes the population of sympathetic neurons that usually switch their transmitter to remain noradrenergic. Factors that are capable of causing an adrenergic-to-cholinergic switch in phenotype have been purified from culture media[116,117] (Fig. 17.26C). But the actual factor that operates in the sweat glands to produce this effect has not yet been definitively identified. Nevertheless, these experiments, and others like them in other systems, make it clear that targets can retrogradely determine the transmitter type of the innervating neurons.

Summary

Young neurons encounter a variety of influences that influence their differentiated fates. Both extrinsic and intrinsic cues can change over time as the animal develops. Extrinsic signals are presented on the surfaces of neighboring cells or are secreted into the environment, where they can act locally or diffuse over long distances. Diffusible factors play an important role in specifying the fates of sympathoadrenal progenitors. In the adrenal gland, glucocorticoids inhibit the differentiation of sympathoadrenal cells into neurons and activate the transcription of genes expressed by chromaffin cells. Sympathoadrenal progenitors that are exposed to the growth factors bFGF and NGF, in contrast, develop into neurons. Membrane-bound cues affect the development of specific photoreceptor fates in the *Drosophila* eye, in which the classic and best-understood interaction is that between the boss ligand, presented by the R8 cell, and the Sev receptor on R7. Activation of Sev stimulates the Ras signaling pathway and the transcription of genes required for R7 development. Fate specification in the vertebrate spinal cord, cerebral cortex, and retina involves a complex interplay between intrinsic determinants and induction. Cell fates can remain malleable even after neurons have extended axons to long-distance targets. Interactions between axons and targets can alter a neuron's neurochemical phenotype, physiology, and anatomy by initiating the transmission of retrograde signals back to the neuronal cell body.

The production of diverse neuronal and glial phenotypes is accomplished by an elaborate interplay between intrinsic cues and extrinsic signals. Intrinsic determinants include cytoplasmic factors that are inherited from a cell's ancestor and nuclear proteins that act cell-autonomously by regulating gene expression. Cells also receive instructions from neighboring cells that influence their fates. Whether diffusible or membrane bound, extrinsic signals act via receptors on the responding cell to initiate signal transduction cascades and alter the expression of genes important for cell fate. Substantial progress has been made in identifying the genes and proteins that are required for normal cell fate determination. Many of these molecular mechanisms are highly conserved between invertebrates and vertebrates.

References

1. Koto, M., Tanouye, M. A., Ferrus, A., Thomas, J. B., and Wyman, R. J. (1981). The morphology of the cervical giant fiber neuron of *Drosophila*. *Brain Res.* **221:** 213–217.
2. Shankland, M., and Macagno, E. R., eds. (1992). *Determinants of Neuronal Identity.* Academic Press, San Diego, CA.
3. Spemann, H. (1938). *Embryonic Development and Induction.* Hafner, New York.
4. Kimble, J. (1981). Alterations in cell lineage following laser ablation of cells in the somatic gonad in *Caenorhabditis elegans*. *Dev. Biol.* **87:** 286–300.
5. Doe, C. Q., and Goodman, C. S. (1985). Early events in insect neurogenesis. II. The role of cell interactions and cell lineage in the determination of neuronal precursor cells. *Dev. Biol.* **111:** 206–219.
6. Ghysen, A., and Dambly-Chaudière, C. (1989). Genesis of the *Drosophila* peripheral nervous system. *Trends Genet.* **5:** 251–255.
7. Campos-Ortega, J. A. (1993). Early neurogenesis in *Drosophila melanogaster*. In *The Development of* Drosophila (M. Bate and A. Martinez-Arias, eds.), pp. 1091–1130. Cold Spring Harbor Press, Cold Spring Harbor, NY.
8. Skeath, J. B. (1995). Tag team specification of a neural precursor in the *Drosophila* embryonic central nervous system. *BioEssays* **17:** 829–831.
9. Campuzano, S., and Modolell, J. (1992). Patterning of the *Drosophila* nervous system: The achaete-scute gene complex. *Trends Genet.* **8:** 202–208.
10. Ghysen, A., Dambly-Chaudière, C., Jan, L. Y., and Jan, Y. N. (1993). Cell interactions and gene interactions in peripheral neurogenesis. *Genes Dev.* **7:** 723–733.
11. Skeath, J. B., and Carroll, S. B. (1992). Regulation of proneural gene expression and cell fate during neuroblast segregation in the *Drosophila* embryo. *Development (Cambridge, UK)* **114:** 936–946.
12. Gonzalez-Crespo, S., and Levine, M. (1993). Interactions between dorsal and helix-loop-helix proteins initiate the differentiation of the embryonic mesoderm and neuroectoderm in *Drosophila*. *Genes Dev.* **7:** 1703–1713.
13. Van Doren, M., Powell, P. A., Pasternak, D., Singson, A., and Posakony, J. W. (1992). Spatial regulation of proneural gene

activity: Auto- and cross-activation of achaete is antagonized by extramacrochaetae. *Genes Dev.* **6:** 2592–2605.

14. Caudy, M., Vässin, H., Brand, M., Tuma, R., Jan, L. Y., and Jan, Y. N. (1988). Daughterless, a *Drosophila* gene essential for both neurogenesis and sex determination, has sequence similarity to myc and the achaete-scute complex. *Cell (Cambridge, Mass.)* **55:** 1061–1067.
15. Skeath, J. B., Panganiban, G. F., and Carroll, S. B. (1994). The ventral nervous system defective gene controls proneural gene expression at two distinct steps during neuroblast formation in *Drosophila. Development (Cambridge, UK)* **120:** 1517–1524.
16. Matsuno, K., Diederich, R. J., Go, M. J., Blaumueller, C. M., and Artavanis-Tsakonas, S. (1995). Deltex acts as a positive regulator of Notch signaling through interactions with the Notch ankyrin repeats. *Development (Cambridge, UK)* **121:** 2633–2644.
17. Fortini, M. E., and Artavanis-Tsakonas, S. (1994). The suppressor of hairless protein participates in notch receptor signaling. *Cell (Cambridge, Mass.)* **79:** 273–282.
18. Doe, C. Q. (1992). The generation of neuronal diversity in the *Drosophila* embryonic nervous system. In *Determinants of Neuronal Identity* (M. Shankland and E. R. Macagno, eds.), pp. 119–154. Academic Press, San Diego, CA.
19. Ferreiro, B., and Harris, W. A. (1994). Neurogenesis in *Xenopus:* A molecular genetic perspective. *Adv. Genet.* **31:** 29–78.
20. Allende, M. L., and Weinberg, E. S. (1994). The expression pattern of two zebrafish achaete-scute homolog (ash) genes is altered in the embryonic brain of the cyclops mutant. *Dev. Biol.* **166:** 509–530.
21. Ferreiro, B., Kintner, C., Zimmerman, K., Anderson, D., and Harris, W. A. (1994). XASH genes promote neurogenesis in *Xenopus* embryos.
22. Zimmerman, K., Shih, J., Bars, J., Collazo, A., and Anderson, D. J. (1993). XASH-3, a novel *Xenopus* achaete-scute homolog, provides an early marker of planar neural induction and position along the mediolateral axis of the neural plate. *Development (Cambridge, UK)* **119:** 221–232.
23. Guillemot, F., and Joyner, A. L. (1993). Dynamic expression of the murine Achaete-Scute homologue Mash-1 in the developing nervous system. *Mech. Dev.* **42:** 171–185.
24. Guillemot, F., Lo, L. C., Johnson, J. E., Auerbach, A., Anderson, D. J., and Joyner, A. L. (1993). Mammalian achaete-scute homolog 1 is required for the early development of olfactory and autonomic neurons. *Cell (Cambridge, Mass.)* **75:** 463–476.
25. Lee, J. E., Hollenberg, S. M., Snider, L., Turner, D. L., Lipnick, N., and Weintraub, H. (1995). Conversion of *Xenopus* ectoderm into neurons by NeuroD, a basic helix-loop-helix protein. *Science* **268:** 836–844.
26. Lardelli, M., and Lendahl, U. (1993). Motch A and motch B—two mouse Notch homologues coexpressed in a wide variety of tissues. *Exp. Cell Res.* **204:** 364–372.
27. Weinmaster, G., Roberts, V. J., and Lemke, G. (1992). Notch2: A second mammalian Notch gene. *Development (Cambridge, UK)* **116:** 931–941.
28. Coffman, C. R., Skoglund, P., Harris, W. A., and Kintner, C. R. (1993). Expression of an extracellular deletion of Xotch diverts cell fate in Xenopus embryos. *Cell (Cambridge, Mass.)* **73:** 659–671.
29. Chitnis, A., Henrique, D., Lewis, J., Ish-Horowicz, D., and Kintner, C. (1995). Primary neurogenesis in *Xenopus* embryos regulated by a homologue of the *Drosophila* neurogenic gene Delta. *Nature (London)* **375:** 761–766.
30. Cabrera, C. V., Martinez-Arias, A., and Bate, M. (1987). The expression of three members of the achaete-scute gene complex correlates with neuroblast segregation in *Drosophila. Cell (Cambridge, Mass.)* **50:** 425–433.
31. Martìn Bermudo, M. D., Martìnez, C., Rodrìguez, A., and Jimènez, F. (1991). Distribution and function of the lethal of scute gene product during early neurogenesis in *Drosophila. Development (Cambridge, UK)* **113:** 445–454.
32. Romani, S., Campuzano, S., and Modolell, J. (1987). The achaete-scute complex is expressed in neurogenic regions of *Drosophila* embryos. *EMBO J.* **6:** 2085–2092.
33. Hinz, U., Giebel, B., and Campos-Ortega, J. A. (1994). The basic-helix-loop-helix domain of *Drosophila* lethal of scute protein is sufficient for proneural function and activates neurogenic genes. *Cell (Cambridge, Mass.)* **76:** 77–87.
34. Chu-LaGraff, Q., and Doe, C. Q. (1993). Neuroblast specification and formation regulated by wingless in the Drosophial CNS. *Science* **261:** 1594–1597.
35. Bodmer, R., Barbel, S., Sheperd, S., Jack, J. W., Jan, L. Y., and Jan, Y. N. (1987). Transformation of sensory organs by mutations of the cut locus of *D. melanogaster. Cell (Cambridge, Mass.)* **51:** 293–307.
36. Blochlinger, K., Bodmer, R., Jack, J., Jan, L. Y., and Jan, Y. N. (1988). Primary structure and expression of a product from cut, a locus involved in specifying sensory organ identity in *Drosophila. Nature (London)* **333:** 629–635.
37. Merritt, D. J., Hawken, A., and Whitington, P. M. (1993). The role of the cut gene in the specification of central projections by sensory axons in *Drosophila. Neuron* **10:** 741–752.
38. Dambly-Chaudière, C., Jamet, E., Burri, M., Bopp, D., Basler, K., Hafen, E., Dumont, N., Spielmann, P., Ghysen, A., and Noll, M. (1992). The paired box gene pox neuro: A determinant of poly-innervated sense organs in *Drosophila. Cell (Cambridge, Mass.)* **69:** 159–172.
39. Nottebohm, E., Dambly-Chaudière, C., and Ghysen, A. (1992). Connectivity of chemosensory neurons is controlled by the gene poxn in *Drosophila. Nature (London)* **359:** 829–832.
40. Nottebohm, E., Usui, A., Therianos, S., Kimura, K., Dambly-Chaudière, C., and Ghysen, A. (1994). The gene poxn controls different steps of the formation of chemosensory organs in *Drosophila. Neuron* **12:** 25–34.
41. Jarman, A. P., Grau, Y., Jan, L. Y., and Jan, Y. N. (1993). Atonal is a proneural gene that directs chordotonal organ formation in the *Drosophila* peripheral nervous system. *Cell (Cambridge, Mass.)* **73:** 1307–1321.
42. Jarman, A. P., Grell, E. H., Ackerman, L., Jan, L. Y., and Jan, Y. N. (1994). Atonal is the proneural gene for *Drosophila* photoreceptors. *Nature (London)* **369:** 398–400.
43. Uemura, T., Shepherd, S., Ackerman, L., Jan, L. Y., and Jan, Y. N. (1989). Numb, a gene required in determination of cell fate during sensory organ formation in *Drosophila* embryos. *Cell (Cambridge, Mass.)* **58:** 349–360.
44. Rhyu, M. S., Jan, L. Y., and Jan, Y. N. (1994). Asymmetric distribution of numb protein during division of the sensory organ precursor cell confers distinct fates to daughter cells. *Cell (Cambridge, Mass.)* **76:** 477–491.
45. Guo, M., Bier, E., Jan, L. Y., and Jan, Y. N. (1995). Tramtrack acts downstream of numb to specify distinct daughter cell fates during asymmetric cell divisions in the *Drosophila* PNS. *Neuron* **14:** 913–925.
46. Hartenstein, V., and Posakony, J. W. (1990). A dual function of the Notch gene in *Drosophila* sensillum development. *Dev. Biol.* **142:** 13–30.
47. Higashijima, S., Kojima, T., Michiue, T., Ishimaru, S., Emori, Y., and Saigo, K. (1992). Dual Bar homeo box genes of *Drosophila*

required in two photoreceptor cells, R1 and R6, and primary pigment cells for normal eye development. *Genes Dev.* **6:** 50–60.

48. Higashijima, S., Michiue, T., Emori, Y., and Saigo, K. (1992). Subtype determination of *Drosophila* embryonic external sensory organs by redundant homeobox genes BarH1 and BarH2. *Genes Dev.* **6:** 1005–1018.
49. Nelson, B. H., and Weisblat, D. A. (1992). Cytoplasmic and cortical determinants interact to specify ectoderm and mesoderm in the leech embryo. *Development (Cambridge, UK)* **115:** 103–115.
50. Weisblat, D. A., and Shankland, M. (1985). Cell lineage and segmentation in the leech. *Philos. Trans. R. Soc. London, Ser. B* **312:** 39–56.
51. Shankland, M., and Martindale, M. Q. (1992). Segmental differentiation of lineally homologous neurons in the central nervous system of the leech. In *Determinants of Neuronal Identity* (M. Shankland, and E. R. Macagno, eds.), pp. 45–77. Academic Press, San Diego, CA.
52. Martindale, M. Q., and Shankland, M. (1990). Segmental founder cells of the leech embryo have intrinsic segmental identity. *Nature (London)* **347:** 672–674.
53. Finney, M., Ruvkun, G., and Horvitz, H. R. (1988). The *C. elegans* cell lineage and differentiation gene unc-86 encodes a protein with a homeodomain and extended similarity to transcription factors. *Cell (Cambridge, Mass.)* **55:** 757–769.
54. Chalfie, M., and Au, M. (1989). Genetic control of differentiation of the *caenorhabditis elegans* touch receptor neurons. *Science* **243:** 1027–1033.
55. Yang, X., Yeo, S., Dick, T., and Chia, W. (1993). The role of a *Drosophila* POU homeo domain gene in the specification of neural precursor cell identity in the developing embryonic central nervous system. *Genes Dev.* **7:** 504–516.
56. Yeo, S. L., Lloyd, A., Kozak, K., Dinh, A., Dick, T., Yang, X., Sakonju, S., and Chia, W. (1995). On the functional overlap between two *Drosophila* POU homeodomain genes and the cell fate specification of a CNS neural precursor. *Genes Dev.* **9:** 1223–1236.
57. Buenzow, D. E., and Holmgren, R. (1995). Expression of the *Drosophila* gooseberry locus defines a subset of neuroblast lineages in the central nervous system. *Dev. Biol.* **170:** 338–349.
58. Skeath, J. B., Zhang, Y., Holmgren, R., Carroll, S. B., and Doe, C. Q. (1995). Specification of neuroblast identity in the *Drosophila* embryonic central nervous system by gooseberry-distal. *Nature (London)* **376:** 427–430.
59. Raff, M. C. (1989). Glial cell diversification in the rate optic nerve. *Science* **243:** 1450–1455.
60. Barres, B. A., Raff, M. C., Gaese, F., Bartke, I., Dechant, G, and Barde, Y. A. (1994). A crucial role for neurotrophin-3 in oligodendrocyte development. *Nature (London)* **367:** 371–375.
61. Shah, N. M., Marchionni, M. A., Isaacs, I., Stroobant, P., and Anderson, D. J. (1994). Glial growth factor restricts mammalian neural crest stem cells to a glial fate. *Cell (Cambridge, Mass.)* **77:** 349–360.
62. Stemple, D. L., and Anderson, D. J. (1992). Isolation of a stem cell for neurons and glia from the mammalian neural crest. *Cell (Cambridge, Mass.)* **71:** 973–985.
63. Klaes, A., Menne, T., Stollewerk, A., Scholz, H., and Klämbt, C. (1994). The Ets transcription factors encoded by the *Drosophila* gene pointed direct glial cell differentiation in the embryonic CNS. *Cell (Cambridge, Mass.)* **78:** 149–160.
64. Jones, B. W., Fetter, R. D., Tear, G., and Goodman, C. S. (1995). Glial cells missing: A genetic switch that controls glial versus neuronal fate. *Cell (Cambridge, Mass.)* **82:** 1013–1023.
65. Condron, B. G., and Zinn, K. (1995). Activation of cAMP-dependent protein kinase triggers a glial-to-neuronal cell-fate switch in an insect neuroblast lineage. *Curr. Biol.* **5:** 51–61.
66. LeDourain, N. M. (1982). *The Neural Crest.* Cambridge University Press, New York.
67. Anderson, D. J. (1993). Molecular control of cell fate in the neural crest: The sympathoadrenal lineage. *Annu. Rev. Neurosci.* **16:** 129–158.
68. Stemple, D. L., and Anderson, D. J. (1993). Lineage diversification of the neural crest: In vitro investigations. *Dev. Biol.* **159:** 12–23.
69. Wolff, T., and Ready, D. F. (1993). Pattern formation in the *Drosophila* retina. In *The development of* Drosophila melanogaster (M. Bate and A. Martinez-Arias, eds.), pp. 1277–1326. Cold Spring Harbor Lab. Press, Cold Spring Harbor, NY.
70. Jarman, A. P., Sun, Y., Jan, L. Y., and Jan, Y. N. (1995). Role of the proneural gene, atonal, in formation of *Drosophila* chordotonal organs and photoreceptors. *Development (Cambridge, UK)* **121:** 2019–2030.
71. Brown, N. L., Sattler, C. A., Paddock, S. W., and Carroll, S. B. (1995). Hairy and emc negatively regulate morphogenetic furrow progression in the *Drosophila* eye. *Cell (Cambridge, Mass.)* **80:** 879–887.
72. Dickson, B., and Hafen, E. (1993). Genetic dissection of eye development in *Drosophila.* In *The Development of* Drosophila melanogaster (M. Bate and A. Martinez-Arias, eds.), pp. 1327–1362. Cold Spring Harbor Lab. Press, Cold Spring Harbor, NY.
73. Tio, M., Ma, C., and Moses, K. (1994). Spitz, a *Drosophila* homolog of transforming growth factor-alpha, is required in the founding photoreceptor cells of the compound eye facets. *Mech. Dev.* **48:** 13–23.
74. Freeman, M. (1994). The spitz gene is required for photoreceptor determination in the *Drosophila* eye where it interacts with the EGF receptor. *Mech. Dev.* **48:** 25–33.
75. Freeman, M., Kimmel, B. E., and Rubin, G. M. (1992). Identifying targets of the rough homeobox gene of *Drosophila*: Evidence that rhomboid functions in eye development. *Development (Cambridge, UK)* **116:** 335–346.
76. Freeman, M., Klämbt, C., Goodman, C. S., and Rubin, G. M. (1992). The argos gene encodes a diffusible factor that regulates cell fate decisions in the *Drosophila* eye. *Cell (Cambridge, Mass.)* **69:** 963–975.
77. Kolodkin, A. L., Pickup, A. T., Lin, D. M., Goodman, C. S., and Banerjee, U. (1994). Characterization of Star and its interactions with sevenless and EGF receptor during photoreceptor cell development in *Drosophila. Development (Cambridge, UK)* **120:** 1731–1745.
78. Dickson, B. J., Domínguez, M., van der Straten, A., and Hafen, E. (1995). Control of *Drosophila* photoreceptor cell fates by phyllopod, a novel nuclear protein acting downstream of the Raf kinase. *Cell (Cambridge, Mass.)* **80:** 453–462.
79. Begemann, G., Michon, A. M., van der Voorn, L., Wepf, R., and Mlodzik, M. (1995). The *Drosophila* orphan nuclear receptor seven-up requires the Ras pathway for its function in photoreceptor determination. *Development (Cambridge, UK)* **121:** 225–235.
80. Kramer, S., West, S. R., and Hiromi, Y. (1995). Cell fate control in the *Drosophila* retina by the orphan receptor seven-up: Its role in the decisions mediated by the ras signaling pathway. *Development (Cambridge, UK)* **121:** 1361–1372.
81. Daga, A., Karlovich, C. A., Dumstrei, K., and Banejee, U. (1996). Patterning of cells in the *Drosophila* eye by Lozenge, which shares homologous domains with AML1. *Genes Dev.* **10,** 1194–1205.

82. Zipursky, S. L., and Rubin, G. M. (1994). Determination of neuronal cell fate: Lessons from the R7 neuron of *Drosophila. Annu. Rev. Neurosci.* **17:** 373–397.
83. Harris, W. A., Stark, W. S., and Walker, J. A. (1976). Genetic dissection of the photoreceptor system in the compound eye of *Drosophila melanogaster. J. Physiol. (London)* **256:** 415–439.
84. Yamada, T., Pfaff, S. L., Edlund, T., and Jessell, T. M. (1993). Control of cell pattern in the neural tube: Motor neuron induction by diffusible factors from notochord and floor plate. *Cell (Cambridge, Mass.)* **73:** 673–686.
85. Marti, E., Bumcrot, D. A., Takada, R., and McMahon, A. P. (1995). Requirement of 19K form of sonic hedgehog for induction of distinct ventral cell types in CNS explants. *Nature (London)* **375:** 322–325.
86. Roelink, H., Porter, J. A., Chiang, C., Tanabe, Y., Chang, D. T., Beachy, P. A., and Jessell, T. M. (1995). Floor plate and motor neuron induction by different concentrations of the amino-terminal cleavage product of sonic hedgehog autoproteolysis. *Cell (Cambridge, Mass.)* **81:** 445–455.
87. Lance-Jones, C., and Landmesser, L. (1980). Motoneurone projection patterns in chick hind limb following partial reversals of the spinal cord. *J. Physiol. (London)* **302:** 581–602.
88. Eisen, J. S., Myers, P. Z., and Westerfield, M. (1986). Pathway selection by growth cones of identified motoneurons in live zebrafish embryos. *Nature (London)* **320:** 269–271.
89. Eisen, J. (1991). Determination of primary motor neuron identity in developing zebrafish embryos. *Science* **252:** 569–572.
90. Lumsden A. (1995). Neural development. A "LIM code" for motor neurons? *Curr. Biol.* **5:** 491–495.
91. Appel B., Korzh, V., Glasgow, E., Thor, S., Edlund, T., Dawid, I. B., and Eisen, J. S. (1995). Motoneuron fate specification revealed by patterned LIM homeobox gene expression in embryonic zebrafish. *Development (Cambridge, UK)* **121:** 4117–4125.
92. Miller, D. M., 3rd, and Niemeyer, C. J. (1995). Expression of the unc-4 homeoprotein in *Caenorhabditis elegans* motor neurons specifies presynaptic input. *Development (Cambridge, UK)* **121:** 2877–2886.
93. Angevine, J. B., Jr., and Sidman, R. L. (1961). Autoradiographic study of cell migration during histogenesis of cerebral cortex in the mouse. *Nature (London)* **192:** 766–768.
94. McConnell, S. K. (1988). Fates of visual cortical neurons in the ferret after isochronic and heterochronic transplantation. *J. Neurosci.* **8:** 945–974.
95. McConnell, S. K., and Kaznowski, C. E. (1991). Cell cycle dependence of laminar determination in developing neocortex. *Science* **254:** 282–285.
96. McConnell, S. K. (1995). Constructing the cerebral cortex: Neurogenesis and fate determination. *Neuron* **15:** 761–768.
97. Turner, D. L., and Cepko, C. L. (1987). A common progenitor for neurons and glia persists in rat retina late in development. *Nature (London)* **328:** 131–136.
98. Holt, C. E., Bertsch, T. W., Ellis, H. M., and Harris, W. A. (1988). Cellular determination in the Xenopus retina is independent of lineage and birth date. *Neuron* **1:** 15–26.
99. Sidman, R. L. (1961). Histogenesis of the mouse retina studied with [3H]thymidine. In *The Structure of the Eye* (G. Smelser, ed.), pp. 487–506. Academic Press, New York.
100. Cepko, C. L., Austin, C. P., Yang, X., Alexiades, M., and Ezzeddine, D. (1996). Cell fate determination in the vertebrate retina. *Proc. Natl. Acad. Sci. U.S.A.* **93:** 589–595.
101. Reh, T. A., and Klavjin, I. J. (1989). Age of differentiation determines rat retinal germinal cell phenotype: Induction of differentiation by dissociation. *J. Neurosci.* **9:** 4179–4189.
102. Reh, T. A. (1992). Cellular interactions determine neuronal phenotypes in rodent retinal cultures. *J. Neurobiol.* **23:** 1067–1083.
103. Watanabe, T., and Raff, M. C. (1990). Rod photoreceptor development in vitro: Intrinsic properties of proliferating neuroepithelial cells change as development proceeds in the rat retina. *Neuron* **4:** 461–467.
104. Anchan, R. M., and Reh, T. A. (1995). Transforming growth factor-beta-3 is mitogenic for rat retinal progenitor cells in vitro. *J. Neurobiol.* **28:** 133–145.
105. Kelley, M. W., Turner, J. K., and Reh, T. A. (1994). Retinoic acid promotes differentiation of photoreceptors in vitro. *Development (Cambridge, UK)* **120:** 2091–2102.
106. Lillien, L. (1995). Changes in retinal cell fate induced by overexpression of EGF receptor. *Nature (London)* **377:** 158–162.
107. Adler, R. (1993). Determination of cellular types in the retina. *Invest. Ophthalmol. Visual Sci.* **34:** 1677–1682.
108. Dorsky, R. I., Rapaport, D. H., and Harris, W. A. (1995). Xotch inhibits cell differentiation in the *Xenopus* retina. *Neuron* **14:** 487–496.
109. Dorsky, R. I., Chang, W. S., Rapaport, D. H., and Harris, W. A. (1997). Regulation of neuronal diversity in the *Xenopus* retina by Delta signalling. *Nature (London)* **385:** 67–70.
110. Austin, C. P., Feldman, D. E., Ida, J. J., and Cepko, C. L. (1995). Vertebrate retinal ganglion cells are selected from competent progenitors by the action of Notch. *Development (Cambridge, UK)* **121:** 3637–3650.
111. French, K. A., and Kristan, W. B., Jr. (1992). Intrinsic and extrinsic factors influencing the development of Retzius neurons in the leech nervous system. In *Determinants of Neuronal Identity* (M. Shankland and E. R. Macagno, eds.), pp. 97–117. Academic Press, San Diego, CA.
112. Teillet, M. A., Cochard, P., and LeDourain, N. M. (1978). Relative roles of the mesenchymal tissues and of the complex neural tube-notochord on the expression of adrenergic metabolism in neural crest cells. *Zoon* **6:** 115–122.
113. Howard, M. J., and Bronner-Fraser, M. (1985). The influence of neural tube derived factors on the differentiation of neural crest cells in vitro I. Histochemical study on the appearance of adrenergic cells. *J. Neurosci.* **5:** 3302–3309.
114. Landis, S. C., Schwab, M., and Siegal, R. E. (1988). Evidence for neurotransmitter plasticity in vivo. II. Immunocytochemical studies of rat sweat gland innervation. *Dev. Biol.* **126:** 129–138.
115. Landis, S. C. (1992). Cellular and molecular mechanisms determining neurotransmitter phenotypes in sympathetic neurons. In *Determinants of Neuronal Identity* (M. Shankland and E. R. Macagno, eds.), pp. 497–523. Academic Press, San Diego, CA.
116. Fukada, K. (1985). Purification and partial characterization of a cholinergic differentiation factor. *Proc. Natl. Acad. Sci. U.S.A.* **82:** 8795–8799.
117. Yamamori, T., Fukada, K., Aebersold, R., Korsching, S., Fann, M. J., and Patterson, P. H. (1989). The cholinergic neuronal differentiation factor from heart cells is identical to leulemia inhibitory factor. *Science* **246:** 1412–1416.

CHAPTER

18

Growth Cones and Axon Pathfinding

Jonathan A. Raper and Marc Tessier-Lavigne

Approximately 100 years ago, Ramón y Cajal described for the first time the growing tips of nerve cell axons. He named them **growth cones** and, in an unparalleled feat of scientific conjecture based on morphological observations of fixed material, described their behavior:

> From the functional point of view, one might say that the growth cone is like a club or battering ram endowed with exquisite chemical sensitivity, rapid ameboid movements, and a certain motive force allowing it to circumvent obstacles in its path, thus coursing between various cells until reaching its destination.[1]

Decades later, Harrison developed the technique of growing living tissue in culture and demonstrated the truth of Cajal's description of a highly motile, ameboid specialization at the tips of growing axons.[2] Shortly after, Speidel took advantage of the thinness and transparency of tadpole fins to examine living growth cones extending *in situ*.[3] Viewed in real time, their shape changes very slowly, at a rate just detectable by an observer. But viewed with modern time-lapse techniques, the dynamism of their ever-changing morphology as they crawl forward is striking. The pioneering studies of Cajal, Harrison, and Speidel identified the growth cone as the key decision-making component in the elaboration of axonal pathways and inspired subsequent studies of the cell biology and behavior of growth cones *in vivo* and *in vitro*.

STRUCTURE OF THE GROWTH CONE

An axon extending in tissue culture is flattened at its distal tip into a thin fan-shaped sheet with many long, very thin spikes radiating forward (Fig. 18.1).[4] This distal tip is termed the growth cone. The fan-shaped sheets are called **lamellipodia,** and the spikes are called **filopodia** or microspikes. Some growth cones growing *in situ* have a similar appearance, particularly when extending on basement membranes or cell surfaces (Fig. 18.2). It is not unusual, however, to observe spindle-shaped growth cones with tufts of forward-directed filopodia within axon bundles. It has been suggested that more complex growth cone shapes are characteristic of slowly extending growth cones choosing between possible routes of extension, whereas simpler morphologies are characteristic of rapidly extending growth cones coursing along permissive tracts.[5]

The fan-shaped growth cone can be further subdivided into distal and proximal regions that are easily distinguishable by their outward appearance and internal structure.[6] The distal region includes the filopodia and the outer rim of the lamellipodia (Fig. 18.3).[7] It is extremely thin. When examined with the electron microscope, it is found to be filled with fibrillar **actin** (F-actin) and few organelles. The proximal region of the growth cone is considerably thicker and is packed with mitochondria, endosomes, and stacks of multilaminated membrane-bound vesicles. Coated pits and clear vesicles are found in both the distal and proximal regions. The large number of mitochondria in the proximal region help to provide the considerable energy consumed by the growth cone's constant movement. The stacks of membrane presumably provide an inventory of new membrane that will be added to the cell surface as the growth cone advances.[8] The coated pits and endosomes suggest considerable recycling of membrane already incorporated into the surface. Polyribosomes that appear to incorporate tritiated amino acids into polypeptides have been seen in some growth

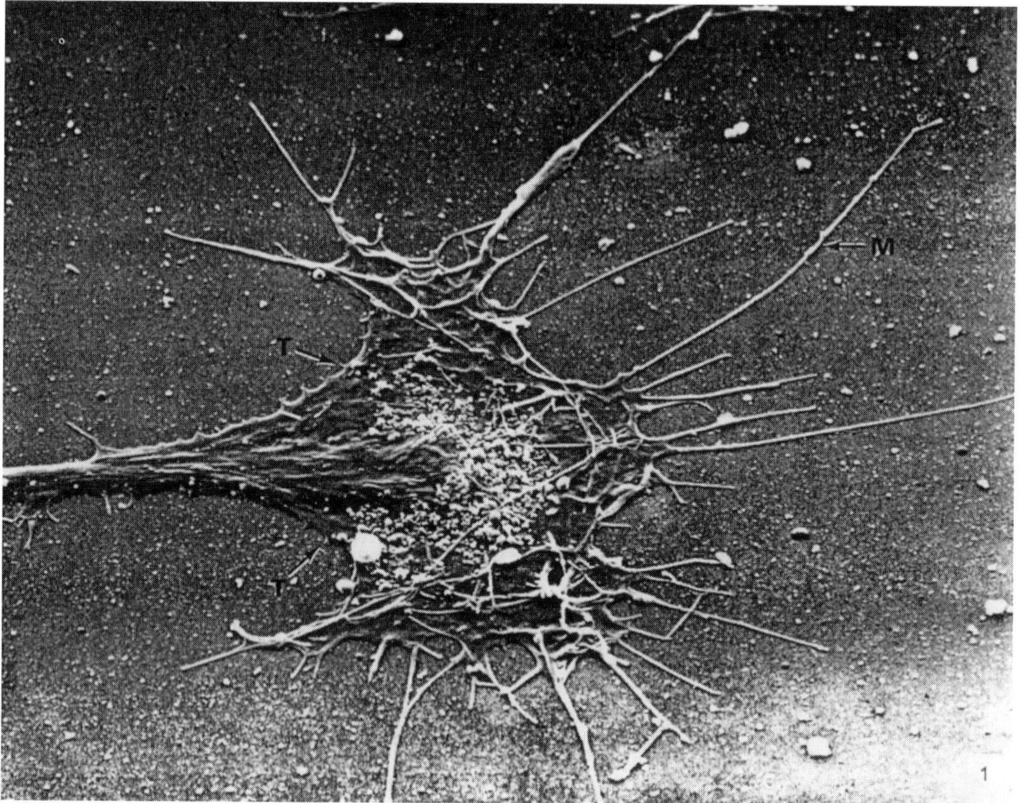

FIGURE 18.1 Scanning electron micrograph of a growth cone in culture. Growth cones extending on a flat surface in culture are typically very thin, with broad lamellae and numerous filopodia. From Wessells and Nuttall.[4]

cones, raising the possibility that the local synthesis of proteins may sometimes help to supply the growth cones' needs.[9] However, most of the proteins and organelles required for the production of the extending axon are supplied by the cell body. Membrane-bound vesicles, their contents, and associated cell surface and transmembrane proteins are delivered to the growth cone by fast axonal transport, whereas structural and soluble cytoplasmic proteins are delivered by slow axonal transport.

It is likely that the external structure of the growth cone is determined by the arrangement of various internal cytoskeletal components. The most important fibrillar structures within the axon are microfilamentous actin, **microtubules,** and **neurofilaments.** Neurofilaments generally extend only as far as the end of the axon and do not penetrate very far into the lamellae of growth cones. Microtubules extend further, filling the lamellae and occasionally entering one or two filopodia. The microtubules are polarized and arranged so that their "plus" ends (the ends at which tubulin polymerizes most rapidly) point toward the leading edge of the growth cone. One function of microtubules is to provide a highway for the fast axonal transport of material to the leading edge of the growth cone. Predominating in the distal region of the growth cone is an unusually dense concentration of polymerized actin filaments.[10] In the filopodia, these are tightly bundled together and oriented with their barbed (fast-

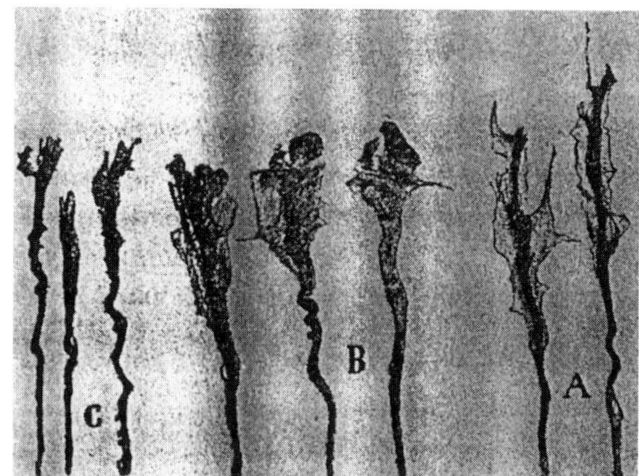

FIGURE 18.2 Growth cones are highly variable in morphology. Growth cones *in vivo* have a wide variety of shapes. This variability is partially due to the seemingly chaotic generation and withdrawal of individual lamellae and filopodia over time and partially due to the variety of surfaces over which growth cones crawl. From Ramón y Cajal.[1]

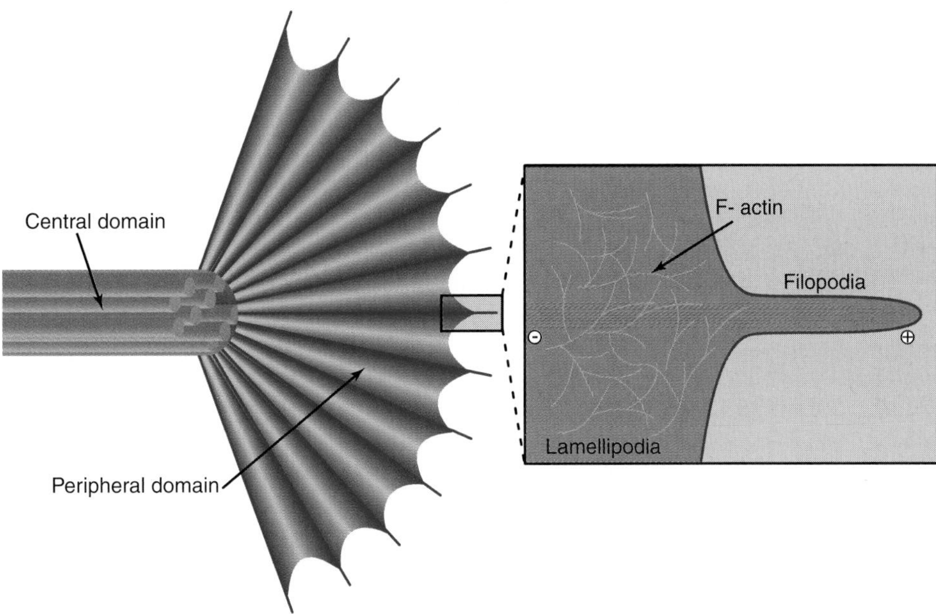

FIGURE 18.3 The distributions of microtubules and fibrillar actin in a growth cone. Microtubules are an important component of the axon. They splay out within the proximal portion of the growth cone. All of their growing ends are pointed toward the leading edge. Actin is highly concentrated in the filopodia and leading edge. Within filopodia, actin fibrils are oriented with their growing tips pointed distally. The same is true of many fibrils within lamellae, although many additional fibrils are randomly oriented and form a dense meshwork. Modified from Lin *et al.*[7]

est growing) ends pointed toward the filopodium tip. Much of the fibrillar actin within distal lamellipodia is also oriented with the barbed ends oriented toward the leading edge, but a significant portion is more randomly oriented and forms a dense tangled meshwork. As discussed below, the dynamic changes in growth cone shape associated with the extension and withdrawal of distal processes are probably the direct result of the production, rearrangement, and destruction of this fibrillar actin meshwork.

Summary

Growth cones can have different morphological appearances that are likely to reflect the terrain through which they are growing. Each growth cone has a thin distal region with lamellipodia and / or filopodia and a thicker proximal region filled with organelles. Growth cone advance is dependent on materials synthesized in the cell body and transported down the axon.

MECHANISMS OF GROWTH CONE ADVANCE

The forward-crawling motion of a growth cone depends on its own intrinsic motile mechanism interacting with a permissive outside environment. The extension and withdrawal of the leading edge and of the filopodia are an intrinsic, autonomous property of a healthy growth cone. However, once the leading edge has extended, an appropriate substratum on which it can attach and become stabilized must be present. Once attached, an inherent traction-generating mechanism within the growth cone causes tension to develop. Unattached or poorly attached processes are thereby withdrawn, while tension exerted against attached processes may help to draw forward the body of the growth cone, or at least some components within it. The continuous repeated cycling of extension, attachment, and retraction of poorly attached processes generates net forward extension.

By what intrinsic mechanism is the leading edge advanced? Several theories have been proposed. One attractive hypothesis is that actin polymerization just behind the leading edge of the growth cone effectively pushes the edge forward.[11] In this scheme, actin is constantly polymerized at the leading edge of the growth cone while it is simultaneously depolymerized at an equal rate elsewhere (Fig. 18.4). The total amount of fibrillar actin remains approximately constant, but the most recently formed actin fibrils are just behind the leading edge. A second important component of this model is a continuous rearward flow of polymerized actin away from the leading edge toward the more proximal part of the growth cone. Actin monomers

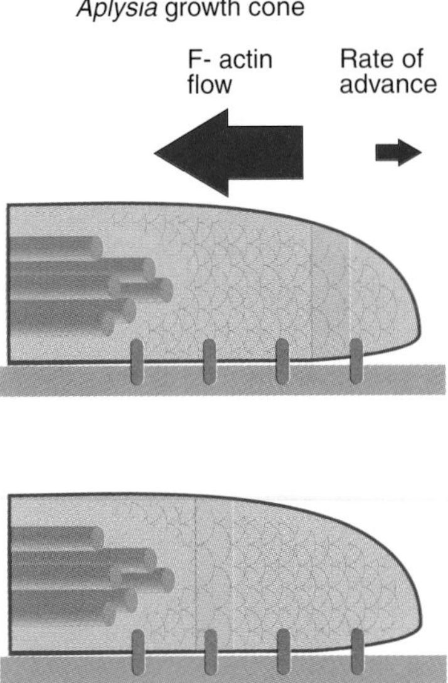

FIGURE 18.4 Linkage of the actin cytoskeleton to a permissive surface is required for forward advance. Actin is polymerized at the leading edge of the growth cone (right) and swept toward the rear. If the actin meshwork is not linked to cell surface receptors that bind permissive molecules on adjacent cell surfaces, the actin cycles from front to rear but does not advance the growth cone. If the actin meshwork is attached to these receptors, the meshwork remains in place and newly polymerized actin helps to advance the leading edge. Modified from Lin *et al.*[7]

generated by depolymerization in the body of the growth cone are then recycled to the front, polymerized again at the leading edge, and swept rearward, where they are depolymerized once again. This continuous cycling of actin monomer to the leading edge, along with the rearward flow of polymerized actin, generates a kind of **"caterpillar tread"** within the interior of the growth cone. If this caterpillar tread is linked to a permissive substratum through cell surface receptors, it advances the leading edge and withdraws the trailing edge.[7]

Advances in the leading edge must be fastened against the substratum to consolidate what would otherwise be only transient gains. This consolidation can occur only on a **permissive substratum.** Most proteins selected at random do not provide a substratum on which growth cones can advance. Particular representatives of several special families of proteins have been shown to provide permissive substrata for growth cone extension. Among the best studied of these are extracellular matrix molecules such as laminin-1 and fibronectin, as well as specialized cell surface molecules from either the immunoglobin superfamily or the cadherin family. These permissive substratum molecules are bound by specific cell surface molecules, which include members of the integrin, immunoglobin, and cadherin superfamilies. Interactions between these cell surface molecules and their partners on the substratum are discussed in detail later in this chapter.

Simple binding of the cell surface to the substratum is probably not sufficient by itself to promote vigorous outgrowth. The cell surface receptors that bind permissive substratum molecules must in turn be linked to the cellular cytoskeleton.[7] Indirect linkages between the cytoskeleton and members of the integrin, cadherin, and immunoglobin families have been described.[12,13] These linkages give the cytoskeleton traction on the substratum and hold it in place. With the F-actin fixed in place against the substratum, new actin polymerizing at the leading edge generates forward extension, while depolymerization at the rear of the growth cone shrinks proximal processes.

Observations of normal growth cones treated with drugs that specifically inhibit actin polymerization are consistent with this model of growth cone advance. For example, growth cones crawl forward very slowly on the nonphysiological cationic substratum polylysine, to which the cell surface adheres very strongly but to which the actin cytoskeleton is not linked through any known cell surface receptors. Fibrillar actin within these growth cones is seen to move continually rearward without being fastened against the substratum.[14] Consequently, a futile cycle of actin polymerization and rearward migration generates lit-

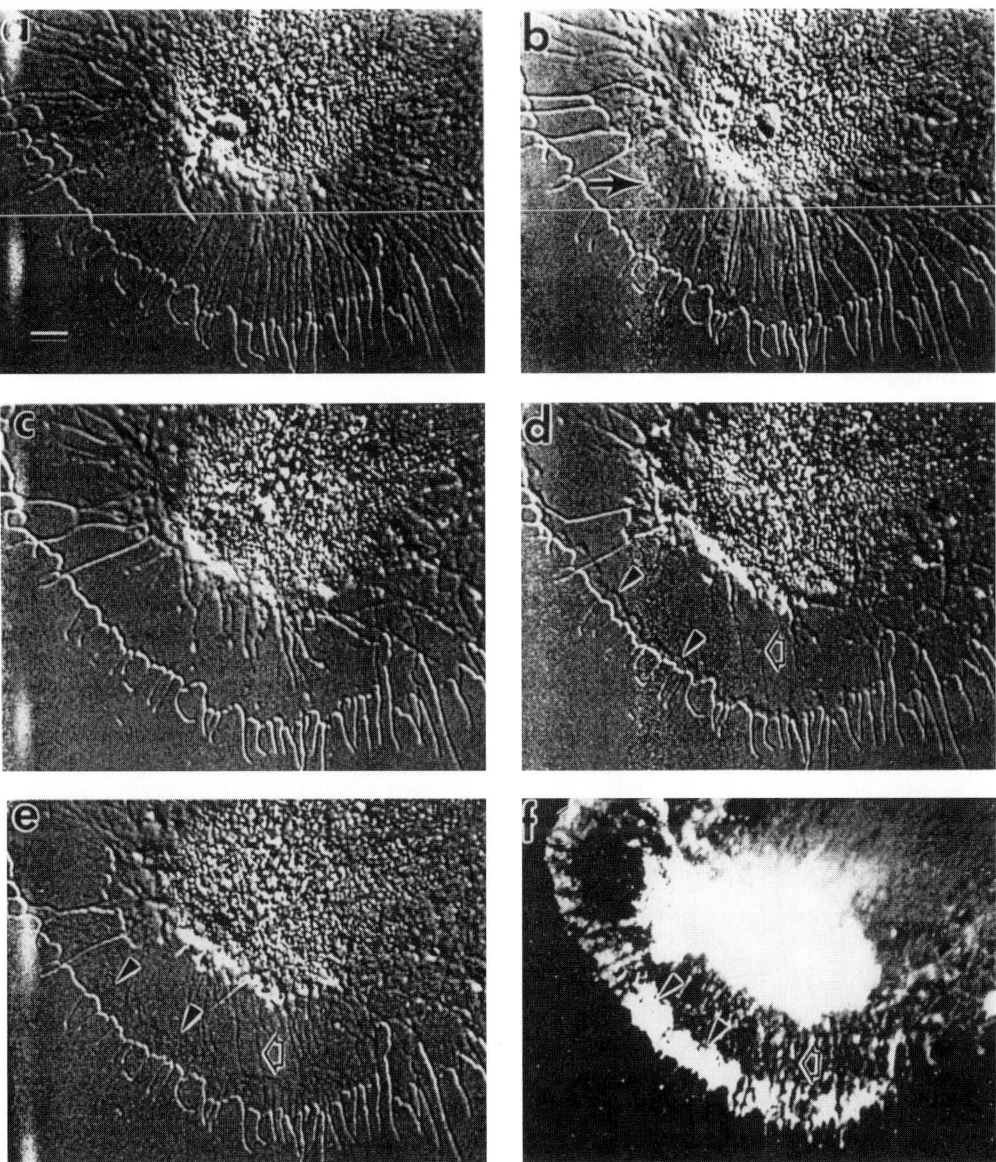

FIGURE 18.5 Actin polymerizes at the leading edge and is then translocated rearward. A growth cone on polylysine is well spread but does not advance forward (a). Fibrillar actin within the growth cone can be visualized with differential interference contrast optics. (b) The addition of a drug that halts actin polymerization, cytochalasin B, first leads to the loss of actin just behind the leading edge (the most distal form of F-actin is indicated by the arrow in (b)). An F-actin-free zone grows as the remaining F-actin is translocated toward the center of the growth cone (c). F-actin begins to polymerize at the leading edge when the cytochalasin B is removed (d, e). The distribution of F-actin in (e) is shown after it was decorated with fluorescently conjugated phalloidin (f). From Forscher and Smith.[14]

tle net advance of the leading edge. Treating growth cones with cytochalasins specifically blocks the polymerization of actin monomers at the leading edge. Lamellae that are very strongly attached to a nonphysiological polylysine substratum are emptied of fibrillar actin by the normal retrograde flow of actin fibrils and their subsequent depolymerization (Fig. 18.5). This loss is first apparent at the leading edge and then spreads rearward, consistent with the idea that actin polymerization is localized primarily to the leading edge. Lamellae attached less strongly to a physiological substratum such as laminin collapse inward on themselves and then advance very slowly as material is transported to the tip and microtubules continue to grow.[15,16] This collapse is presumably caused by the loss of the actin meshwork that, under physiological conditions, simultaneously provides a supporting scaffold for the membrane and drives normal motile behavior. Smaller concentrations of cytochalasins tend to inhibit filopodial formation more than lamellar production, suggesting that higher rates of actin polymerization may be required for efficient filopodial extension.[17]

Growth cones generate considerable **tension** as they advance.[18] This tension is presumably generated by the continuous retrograde flow of actin away from the leading edge toward the proximal region of the growth cone. This same retrograde movement of actin causes processes poorly attached to the substratum to shrink or withdraw. Recent evidence indicates that **myosin-based motors** drive retrograde actin flow.[19] These motors may cause opposing actin filaments to slide against themselves, contracting the randomly oriented actin meshwork and causing it to fall in on the center of the growth cone. Alternatively, myosin-based motors could be oriented on other structures within the growth cone such that they pull actin away from the leading edge. When retrograde movement of actin is impeded by a relatively strong attachment between the actin cytoskeleton and the surface substratum, new actin polymerization helps to advance the leading edge, and microtubules tend to advance forward. Strong attachment of individual filopodia to appropriate cellular targets induces additional localized actin accumulation in the contacting process, and these processes are preferentially invaded by microtubules.[20,21] Perhaps actin accumulates because it is too firmly attached to be withdrawn, and the resulting reduction in actin withdrawal allows microtubules to advance or helps to draw them forward. Filopodia may act as scouts for the less advanced portions of the growth cone, seizing hold of permissive substrata and reorienting subsequent process extension.

Although microtubules play an important role in growth cone extension, that role is not entirely understood. Tubulin must polymerize for growth cones to advance. Low concentrations of vinblastin or nocodazole, which inhibit tubulin polymerization within the growth cone, do not halt growth cone motility but do prevent net forward advance.[22,23] The actin-based motile machinery described above apparently cannot make a sustained advance without the supporting advance of microtubules from behind. In addition, microtubules within the axon provide the cytoskeletal substrate on which fast axonal transport depends. In intact neurons, normal sustained growth requires that new material be synthesized in the cell body and that fast axonal transport deliver this material to the extending growth cone.[24] It is important to point out, however, that the mechanism of growth cone motility itself is autonomous. A growth cone separated from the cell body by severing of its axon can remain motile for many hours or even days.[25]

Summary

Growth cones advance by adhesion of the leading edge to a permissive substrate. This causes actin polymerization at the leading edge. At the same time, actin depolymerization at the rear of the growth cone causes proximal processes to shrink. Growth cone collapse occurs when adhesion does not occur at the leading edge and actin polymerization is not initiated.

GROWTH CONE BEHAVIOR *IN VITRO*

Much of our understanding of growth cones is based on studies in tissue culture. Purified molecules can be tested for their ability to promote or inhibit growth cone extension. Drugs that affect specific cellular processes can be tested for their effects on locomotion. Time-lapse techniques can be used to visualize living growth cones at high magnification. The response of growth cones to individual cell surfaces or other environmental features can be studied in detail. The primary aim of such studies is to determine how growth cones work and how they respond to their surroundings. The experimental control offered by a tissue culture environment is a powerful tool for identifying potential guidance mechanisms and molecules that can control **growth cone trajectories.**

Growth cones have inherent capabilities and properties that limit what they can do in response to inhomogeneities in their environment. For example, it is very rare that a growth cone is seen to turn through an angle of more than 90°. Presumably, the inherent polarization of a growth cone makes it almost impossible for its trailing edge to be transformed into its leading edge. Another aspect of growth cone advance recognized as early as the pioneering work of Harrison is that growth cone trajectories can be strongly influenced by mechanical constraints in their environment. Growth cones need to have an appropriate surface on which to grow. Moreover, they have difficulty traversing discontinuities in a surface. For example, they are easily aligned along grooves or ridges in the substratum or even along the subtle alignment of fibrils in a collagen gel.[26,27]

Another inherent property of growth cones that may have a strong influence on their trajectories is the tension they generate. For example, if the trailing axon is lifted gently from the surface and deflected to the side,

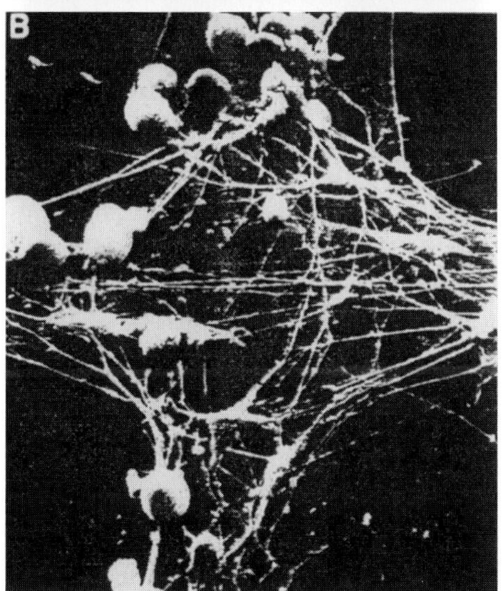

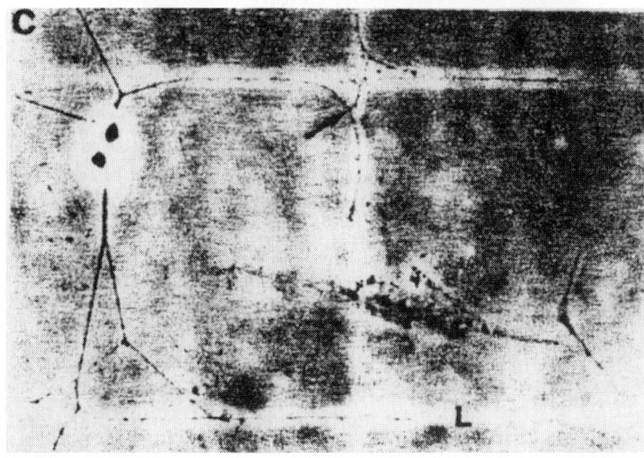

FIGURE 18.6 Growth cone trajectories on surfaces coated with molecules permissive for outgrowth. (IA) A low-power scanning electron micrograph of dissociated sensory cells cultured on a laminin-coated surface. The permissive activity of the laminin was inactivated by UV irradiation everywhere except in intersecting orthogonal lanes. Cells bind and grow axons only where there is active laminin present. (IB) A higher magnification view of the intersecting lanes. The large round profiles are neuron cell bodies and the fine processes are axons. (IC) Viewed with fluorescence microscopy, axons are shown to extend only where active laminin is detected by immunofluorescence (narrow bright orthogonal lanes). From Hammarback *et al.*[30]

the attached growth cone extends parallel to the new orientation of the deflected axon.[28] Conversely, relieving the tension on individual attached filopodia by severing them from the main body of the growth cone tends to bias extension of the growth cone toward the remaining attached filopodia.[4] These observations are consistent with the hypothesis that extension is biased in the direction of greatest tension. Thus, filopodia and lamellae that are most firmly attached to the substratum for the greatest length of time, against which the greatest tension accumulates, may serve as foci for enhanced extension. In addition to the mere stabilization of adherent processes, this effect could further amplify a preferred orientation toward, and extension on, permissive substrata. The subsequent preferential invasion of these processes by microtubules may further enhance localized extension and help to consolidate successful growth cone processes.[29]

Growth cone trajectories are easily confined to tracks of permissive molecules surrounded by a nonpermissive surface.[30] Growing axons are beautifully channeled between the nonpermissive borders surrounding a stripe of substratum-bound laminin (Fig. 18.6).[30,31] A growth cone on a permissive surface can be forced to turn through as much as a 90° angle when its leading edge confronts a nonpermissive border. In these instances, the growth cone can be seen to remain motile during turns, extending and retracting processes. Lamellipodia and filopodia extend over both nonpermissive and permissive regions of the surface, but accumulate and make net forward progress only on the permissive surface.

The extent to which growth cones can distinguish between two differentially permissive surfaces is less clear. Early studies of nonphysiological surfaces coated with nonphysiological and consequently weak promoters of outgrowth indicated that growth cones prefer surfaces to which they adhere more strongly.[32] More recent experiments with more physiologically permissive molecules suggest that growth cones do not prefer one permissive molecule over another and that this lack of preference occurs despite significant differences in adhesivity.[31] Similarly, growth cones extending across a shallow gradient of laminin are not biased toward higher laminin concentrations anywhere in the gradient, but fail to extend altogether in regions of the gradient where the concentration is too low to support outgrowth.[33] One interpretation of these results is that

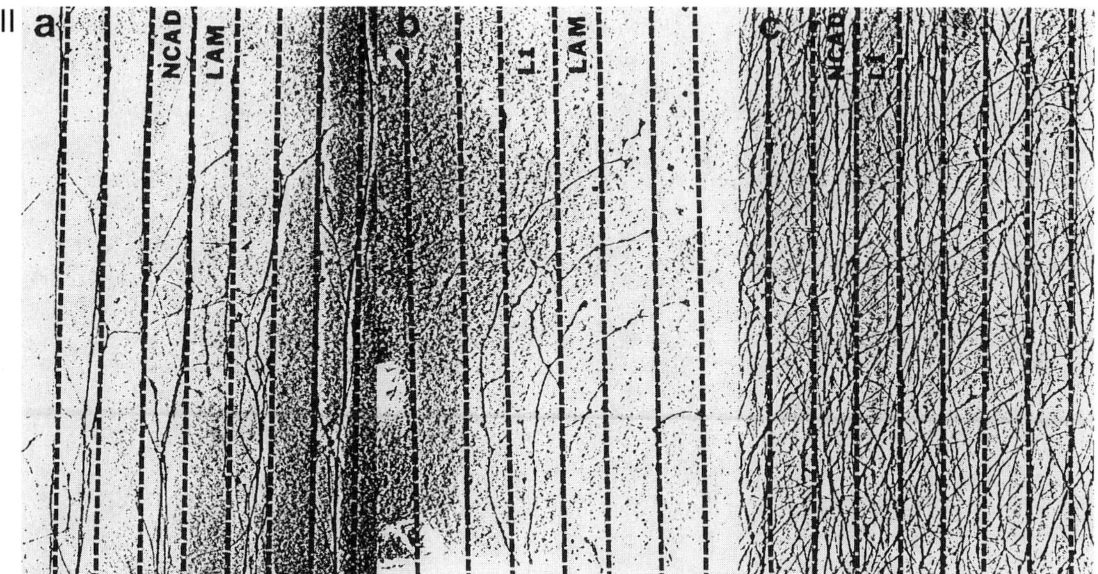

FIGURE 18.6 (*Continued*) (II) Retinal ganglion cell axons cross easily between surfaces coated with different physiological permissive molecules. (IIA) Neural cell adhesion molecule (N-CAM) and N-cadherin, (IIB) L1/Nr-CAM and laminin, and (IIC) L1-Nr-CAM and N-cadherin. Growth cones adhere much more tightly to L1-coated surfaces than to laminin- or N-cadherin–coated surfaces. From Lemmon *et al.*[31]

as long as a sufficient concentration of a permissive molecule is present, outgrowth can occur, but extension is not strongly biased toward still higher concentrations of a permissive molecule that exceed this threshold value.

Experiments in culture suggest that electrical fields can have a very powerful influence on growth cone trajectories.[29] The mechanism that steers growth cones in an electric field is unknown. One possibility is that some critical component within the growth cone accumulates to one side by electrophoresis and thereby biases the direction of extension. Another possibility is that voltage-induced ion flow through channels in the membrane affects the direction in which growth cones extend. For example, one such reasonable candidate ion is Ca^{2+}. Calcium ions, as might be expected from their importance in many biochemical processes, including the polymerization and depolymerization of actin and the activation of second-messenger pathways, can play an important role in the modulation of growth cone behavior.[35] Internal calcium ion concentrations that are either too high or too low inhibit growth cone motility. The entry of calcium ions from outside the growth cone through transmembrane channels or the induced release of calcium ions from internal stores can potentiate or inhibit the inherent motility of growth cones. If electrical fields can induce localized changes in calcium ion concentrations within a growth cone, and these localized perturbations affect the motile apparatus, they could initiate turns by making extension in one direction more effective than extension in another direction. Consistent with this hypothesis is the finding that localized changes in calcium ion concentration can be initiated by electric fields. Additionally, galvanotropism is reduced in low calcium ion media or in the presence of calcium ion channel blockers.[36] Localized changes in calcium ion concentrations induced by neurotransmitters or chemotactic factors could alter growth cone trajectories in a similar manner.[37]

Summary

Several factors that direct growth cones have been identified in cell culture studies. Mechanical constraints can block growth cone advance, as can the presence of a nonpermissive substrate. Surprisingly, once the threshold value for a permissive substrate is present, growth cones do not prefer higher concentrations of that factor.

MECHANISMS OF GROWTH CONE GUIDANCE

Growth cones crawl forward as they elaborate the axons trailing behind them, and their extension is controlled by cues in their outside environment that direct them toward their appropriate targets. Only by their stopping, starting, turning, and branching in the correct locations and directions can the basic wiring diagram of the developing nervous system be generated. How might **guidance cues** control growth cone trajectories?

For a single growth cone to change its direction in response to an outside cue, the cue must be inhomogeneously distributed in the outside environment, and the cue must have a localized effect on the growth cone. Filopodia radiating out from the growth cone are well situated to identify permissive substrata upon which additional growth can occur, or to report back to the growth cone the presence of attractants or repellents nearby. An attractant to the left of a growth cone, or a repellent to the right of a growth cone, must induce more net extension of filopodia and membrane addition or less net retraction from the left than from the right leading edge. The model of growth cone advance presented earlier, in which (1) the leading edge is pushed forward by the polymerization of actin, (2) cell surface receptors attach the newly advanced process to an appropriately permissive substratum, (3) the receptors are linked to fibrillar actin inside the growth cone, and (4) the actin is pulled toward the base of the growth cone, suggests several independent control points at which guidance cues may act.

First, the localized induction of actin polymerization by an attractant could cause the leading edge to advance more rapidly in the direction of highest attractant concentrations. In a complementary way, the leading edge should fail to advance or might even withdraw from repellents that locally inhibit actin polymerization at the leading edge. Second, the positioning of permissive substrata can determine which processes are stabilized and thereby direct net advance over time. Third, if a means exists by which guidance cues can locally modulate the linkage of cell surface receptors to the underlying actin meshwork, the cues could modulate the advance of the leading edge even on wholly permissive substrata. For example, attractants might induce a tighter linkage between the cytoskeleton and the substratum, while repellents might induce a weaker linkage. Finally, it is conceivable that the effectiveness of the motors that pull actin rearward could be locally modulated by guidance cues outside the growth cone. It is important to point out that three of these four putative guidance mechanisms require a specific receptor to be linked to an intracellular signaling system to activate the appropriate cellular responses. As a first step in characterizing the mechanisms mediating growth cone advance and guidance *in vivo*, it is important to identify the location and character of the cues that determine growth cone trajectories.

Summary

Guidance cues are likely to direct growth through altering the location or rate of actin polymerization. Such a mechanism requires the presence of receptors for such cues on the growth cone surface that are linked to intracellular signaling systems.

HIGHLY DIRECTED AXON MIGRATION *IN VIVO*

In vitro studies have provided considerable insight into the cell biology of growth cones, but these studies alone cannot reveal the strategies used by growth cones to reach their targets in developing organisms. Speidel's studies of growth cone migration in living tadpoles in the 1920s were not extended to other classes of axons until the 1980s, when novel techniques were developed to visualize growing axons in embryos *in vivo*. In the interim, several different theories were proposed to account for the ability of the nervous system to wire itself. One view, already implicit in Ramón y Cajal's writings[38] and reinforced by Speidel's observations, held that axonal growth was highly directed, with each class of axons navigating along a distinctive prescribed pathway to reach its target. Competing with this view was the idea that axonal growth involved a certain amount of random wandering of axons throughout the embryonic environment and that connections that were appropriate for proper functioning of the nervous system were somehow reinforced at the expense of inappropriate connections, for example, by retraction of inappropriately projecting axons. In the 1920s and 1930s, Paul Weiss vigorously proposed various mechanisms to explain the selective retention of appropriate connections.[39]

A number of experiments rapidly provided evidence against Weiss's ideas, which were all but refuted by the classic experiments of Sperry, started in the 1940s, which are discussed later in this chapter. Further, the application of axonal tracing techniques over the past two decades has made it possible to observe a variety of different classes of axons en route to their targets. These studies have shown that it is necessary to distinguish two phases in the establishment of connections.[40] When projecting to the vicinity of their target field, axons grow along very **stereotyped trajectories** and make very few, if any, errors of projection. The growth is highly directed, and in cases where a single axon navigates to an isolated target cell (as occurs in many places in invertebrate species), selection of the target cell is equally precise. A more complex process occurs, however, when many similar axons arrive at a target field containing numerous similar target cells, as in the case of a group of motor axons all innervating the many muscle fibers in a single muscle. In these cases, individual axons do arborize widely within the target field and initially contact many target cells, only later refining their pattern of connections in a process that depends on the precise patterns of electrical activity in the neurons and target cells. In the rest of this chapter, we focus on the first step in the formation of connections, the directed growth of axons to target fields. The selection of target cells and the role of electrical activity in this process are discussed in Chapter 19.

Summary

Two general notions have been proposed to explain how appropriate connections are established in the developing nervous system: axon growth could be highly directed or alternatively it could be less specific and inappropriate connections eliminated later. It is now clear that axons follow highly specific and stereotyped pathways to reach their target fields. Once in the target field, axons may arborize widely so that establishment of the final pattern of connections involves the selective expansion of correct connections and retraction of incorrect ones.

STEPWISE AXON MIGRATION *IN VIVO*

How do axons succeed in navigating through the embryonic environment to targets that in some cases can be many centimeters away? The trajectories of many axons appear to be broken up into short segments, each perhaps a few hundred micrometers long. The daunting task of reaching a distant target is then reduced to the simpler task of navigating each of these successive segments. This task is well illustrated by the central projections of sensory axons in the developing limb of the grasshopper. The pathway they follow can be divided into discrete segments, each bounded by a specific cell or group of cells that marks the end of one segment and the beginning of the next (Fig. 18.7).[41] Ablation of some of these cells with a laser microbeam results in profound misrouting of the axons when they reach the vacant site (Figs. 18.7B and 18.7C).[42] Evidence for the existence of such **guidepost cells** harboring important guidance information has been obtained in a variety of species, including vertebrates.[43]

Another important source of guidance information for developing axons is other axons. The wiring of the nervous system is a protracted process; in humans, axons extend to their targets in successive waves over a period of several months. The first **pioneer axons** that develop in an embryo navigate through an axon-free environment, but the bulk of axons project in an environment crisscrossed with a scaffold of earlier projecting axons. Many of the later developing axons use preexisting axon tracts as guides, growing along specific bundles of axons (or fascicles) for a portion of their trajectory and switching from one fascicle to another at specific junctures. In insects, in which this process of **selective fasciculation** has been observed in some detail, it is clear that individual axons actively seek out specific axons with which to fasciculate (bundle), ignoring the others in their vicinity.[44–46]

The growth of axons along preexisting axon tracts greatly simplifies the wiring of large nervous systems. For example, in mammals—including humans—an initial scaffold of axon tracts forms when the embryo is less than a centimeter long (Fig. 18.8).[47] As the embryo grows, these axons become stretched to many times their original length, a process that requires intercalation of additional membrane into the axons. Other axons can then extend considerable distances along these tracts and are themselves stretched further, providing additional tracts that can be used by even later developing axons. This is not to say that all late growth occurs along preexisting tracts. Many axons project over large distances through axon-free environments even at late stages.

A stepwise assembly process seems a sensible way to organize the complex task of wiring the nervous system, but it might also seem prone to a domino effect: misroute one axon early, and a cascade of errors might be expected! Two additional features appear to prevent such outcomes. First is the **redundancy** of the sources of **guidance information.** For axons navigating through an axon-free environment, guidance information in many cases is vested not in a single cell but in multiple cells; experimental ablation of any one cell individually causes only minor perturbations in guidance, whereas ablation of many cells produces more profound perturbations (an example is the zebrafish spinal cord).[48] Likewise, an axon growing along a specific axon fascicle is capable of correct navigation even if the fascicle is absent owing to an experimental perturbation.[49–51] A second feature that increases the fidelity of the wiring process is that cues capable of guiding a particular group of axons appear not to be confined only to the normal path that the axons follow, but are more widely distributed in the embryo. This has been demonstrated in experiments in which growing axons were displaced from their normal trajectory, yet the axons were able to correct their projections and find their way to their targets. One example of this was obtained in chick embryos in which small segments of spinal cord were rotated along the rostrocaudal axis.

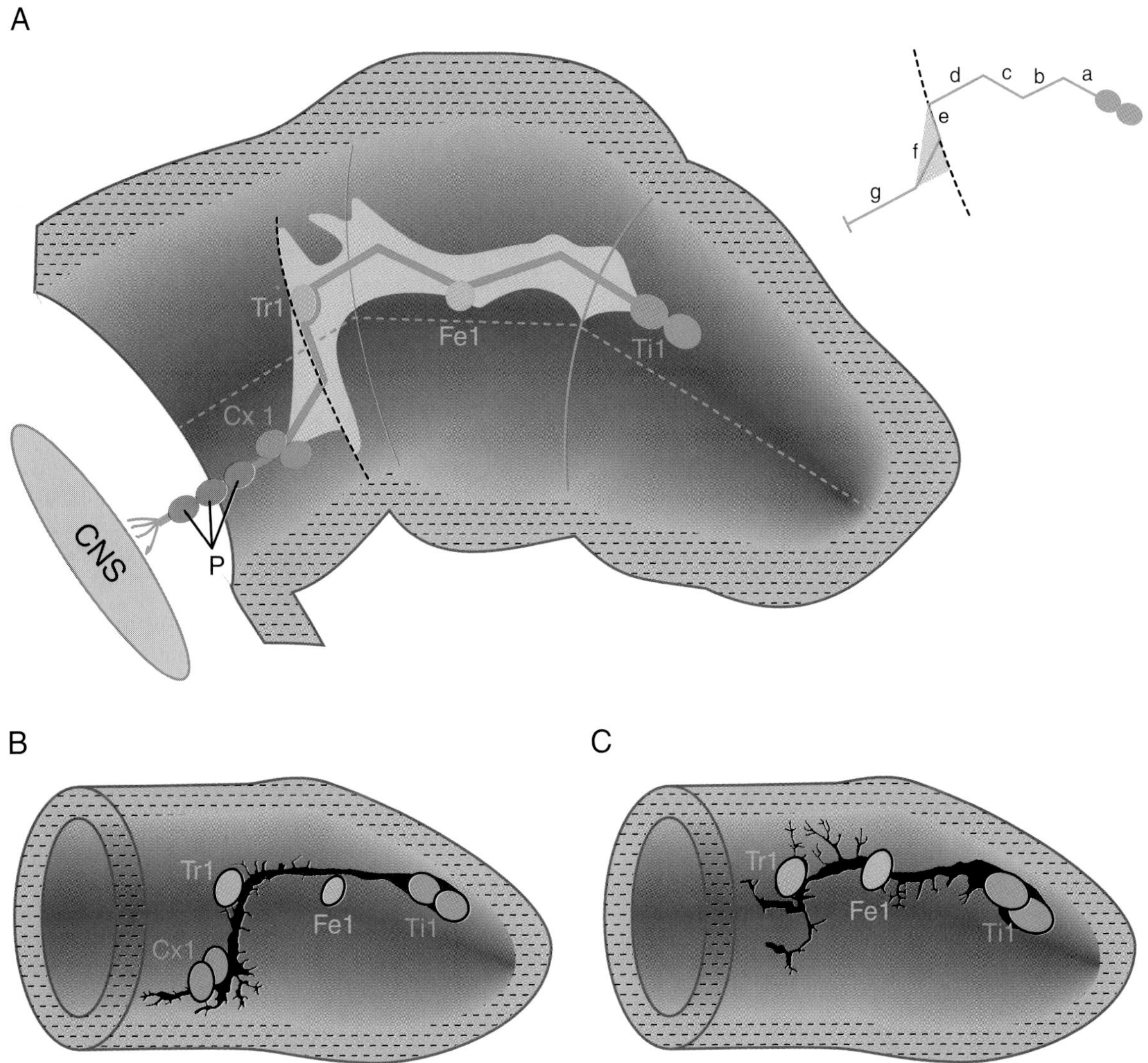

FIGURE 18.7 Stepwise guidance of axons in the grasshopper limb. (A) Summary drawing of a grasshopper limb showing the trajectory of the axons of the pair of Ti1 neurons, which take a characteristic trajectory to the central nervous system. The red line indicates the average trajectory of these axons, based on analysis of several thousand axons. The stippled area indicates the regions in which branches of Ti1 axons occur. The trajectory is broken into seven segments designated a–g, as shown in the diagram to the right of the drawing. Shaded regions in the diagram indicate the range of axon locations that are observed. Some of the segments end at a particular cellular landmark, such as segment b, which ends at the Fe1 neuron. Other segments end at stereotyped locations where there is no obvious landmark, such as segment a, which ends about 50 μm from the Ti1 cell bodies. Adapted from Caudy and Bentley.[41] (B, C) Segment f ends at the Cx1 cell, which is required for guidance, because axons fail to progress forward when the Cx1 cell is ablated (C). (B) Control trajectory. Adapted from Bentley and Caudy.[42]

In these embryos, motor axons approached the base of the hindlimb from inappropriate directions, yet were able to correct their trajectories to project to their appropriate muscle targets.[52] Another example was obtained in *Xenopus* tadpoles in which the eye primordium containing retinal ganglion cells was moved to a novel location in the brain. Despite entering the brain at a widely inappropriate site, the growing axons were able to make their way to their target, the optic tectum (Fig. 18.9).[53] These and other experiments have suggested that the embryo may contain a **coordinate system** that, in effect, enables growth cones to know where they are and to correct any navigational errors. However, the ability of the system to correct itself, though impres-

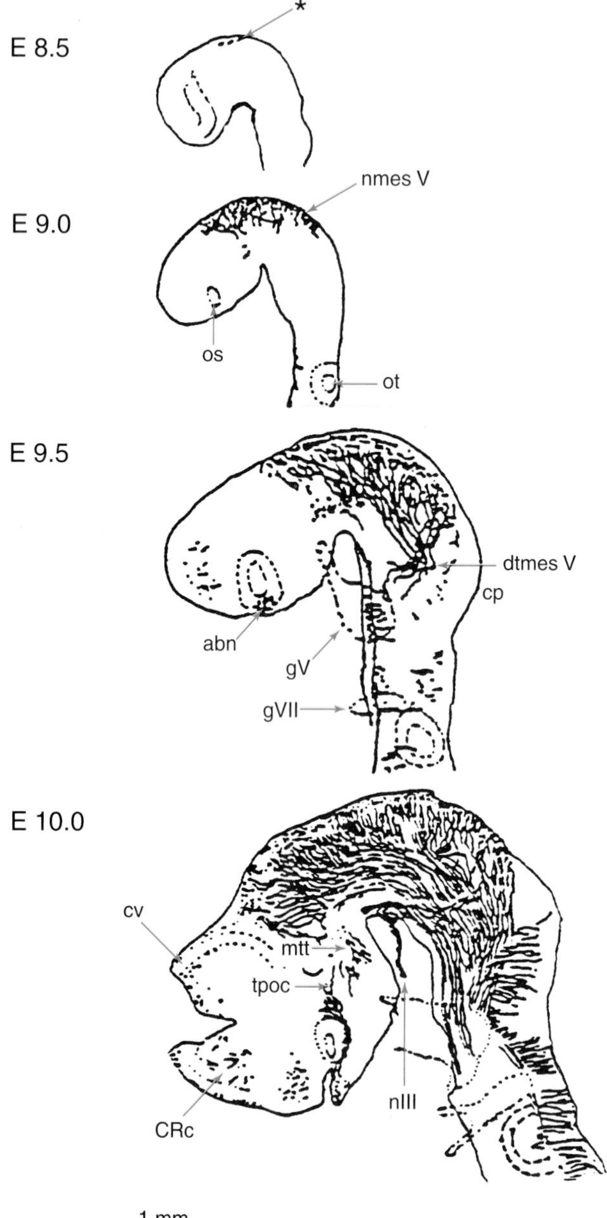

FIGURE 18.8 An initial scaffold of axons is established when embryos are relatively small. Camera lucida tracings of axonal projections in the forebrain and brainstem of a mouse embryo, which were visualized by whole-mount immunochemistry with an axonal marker between embryonic days 8.5 and 10.0 (E8.5–E10.0). The first axons at E9.0 navigate through an axon-free environment when the embryo is small, but soon axons are navigating through an expanding environment and encounter other axons that projected earlier. Adapted from Easter *et al.*[47]

sive, is limited; axons that are too widely displaced in these experiments do in fact become misrouted.

Summary

Many axons are guided to distant target fields in stepwise fashion. Guidance cues in particular segments

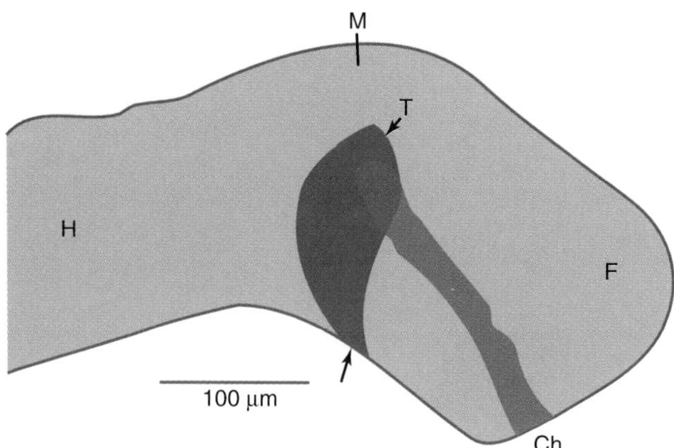

FIGURE 18.9 Homing of retinal axons to the tectum from ectopic locations in *Xenopus* embryos. One eye primordium of a tadpole, including epidermis and optic stalk, was carefully excised and transplanted to an excavation on the opposite side of the same tadpole, creating an embryo with two eyes on the same side of its head (a sort of "artificial flounder"). After the axons were allowed to grow to their targets, the axons of both the normal and the grafted eye were visualized by injecting horseradish peroxidase (HRP) into the eyes. The HRP was transported down the axons and could be reacted enzymatically to give a visible reaction product. Axons from the ectopic eye (blue) home from their entry point in the brain (arrow) to their normal target, the optic tectum primordium (T). For comparison, the normal projection of axons is illustrated by the superimposing on this diagram of the trajectory of the axons of the normal eye (red) from the optic chiasm (Ch) to the tectum (note that those axons projected on the contralateral side of the brain). F, forebrain; M, midbrain; H, hindbrain. Adapted from Harris.[53]

of their pathways can be provided by guidepost cells or by others axons. Mistakes in axon guidance are prevented by the presence of redundant cues and by a general coordinate system in the embryo.

GUIDANCE OF AXONS BY SHORT- AND LONG-RANGE CUES—ATTRACTIVE OR REPULSIVE

The appreciation that axonal trajectories are formed in small segments pushes the question back one step: How do axons navigate each small segment of their trajectory? Studies in the past decade have led to the view that axon guidance involves the coordinate action of four types of cues: **short-range** (or **local**) **cues** and **long-range cues**, each of which can be either **positive (attractive)** or **negative (repellent)** (Fig. 18.10). Researchers have also made some progress in recent years in identifying extracellular molecules that are good candidates for mediating these guidance effects. The same mechanisms that control axon growth during development are likely to be important to our understandings of why axons fail to regenerate after injury

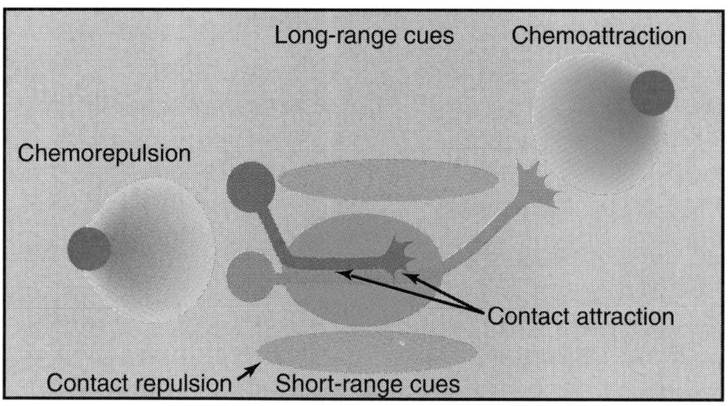

FIGURE 18.10 Axons are guided by the simultaneous and coordinate actions of four types of guidance mechanisms: contact attraction, chemoattraction, contact repulsion, and chemorepulsion. Individual growth cones might be "pushed" from behind by a chemorepellent, "pulled" from in front by a chemoattractant, and "hemmed in" by attractive and repulsive local cues (cell surface or extracellular matrix molecules). Push, pull, and hem: these forces act together to ensure accurate guidance. Adapted from Tessier-Lavigne and Goodman.[70]

in the adult mammalian nervous system and to our efforts to promote regrowth and repair (Box 18.1).

Local Cues Channel Axons along Corridors and Direct Complex Choices

We have already seen an example of the operation of local cues in the process of selective fasciculation of an axon with a preexisting axon tract. In this case, the growing axon is presumed to recognize a specific complement of molecules that are presented on the surface of axons in the tract and that direct fasciculation, in effect, channeling the axon along the tract. Channeling of axons along narrow corridors can also occur in an axon-free environment. Studies of this process have indicated that **axon channeling** may be directed both by positive (permissive) cues presented on the surface of cells that form the channel and by inhibitory (or repellent) cues presented by cells that surround the channel and prevent the axons from straying from the channel. This "hemming in" of axons by inhibitory cues is exemplified by the initial trajectory of spinal motor axons as they leave the spinal cord to project to muscle cells, which involves their growth through segmented blocks of an embryonic tissue called the **sclerotome** (the embryonic precursor to the vertebral column and ribs). The sclerotome in each segment is divided into anterior and posterior portions, and the motor axons project only through the anterior sclerotome in each segment, thus giving rise to the segmented pattern of spinal nerves observed in the adult (Figure 18.11). As described in Chapter 16, neural crest cell migration is also restricted to the anterior sclerotome. What directs growth through the anterior sclerotome? The major determinant appears to be an inhibitory factor on the surface of posterior sclerotome cells that bars motor axon entry. This inhibition was shown by embryological manipulations in developing chicken embryos, in which the sclerotome in one or more segments was replaced by several fragments either of anterior sclerotome or of posterior sclerotome isolated from donor embryos. Motor axons readily grew through the pieces of anterior sclerotome but were unable to enter the pieces of posterior sclerotome (Fig. 18.11).[54]

The inability of motor axons to enter the posterior sclerotome is due to the **contact inhibition** of their growth cones. As viewed in time-lapse video microscopy, the growth cones typically arrest on contact with cells of the posterior sclerotome. After a period of time, a new growth cone sprouts from the axon shaft just behind the original growth cone to lead the axon away from the sclerotome cell.[55] Different types of contact inhibition have been documented in cell culture experiments, including examples where the growth cones stop progressing forward without much change in morphology and, at the other extreme, cases where growth cones undergo a dramatic retraction termed **growth cone collapse** (Fig. 18.12).[56] An active area of research aims to understand whether different types of inhibition observed *in vitro* are specialized for different types of guidance *in vivo*.

Local cues serve not only to channel but also to direct more complex decisions at important choice points for the axons. For example, the axons of retinal ganglion cells from one eye all grow together to an important decision region, the optic chiasm, where some axons turn to stay ipsilaterally within the brain and others cross the chiasm to project contralaterally. The decision to cross or not to cross appears to be directed by local cues in the region of the chiasm.[57–59] However, our understanding of the chiasm, as of most complex decision points in the nervous system, is only fragmentary. The nature of the cues, positive or negative, and how they are arrayed in the decision region to produce their guidance effects remain unclear.

Long-Range Attractants and Repellents Also Shape Axonal Trajectories

Cell migration directed by diffusible chemoattractants and chemorepellents is well documented in the immune system and other nonneural tissues. It is therefore no surprise that similar **chemotropic** guidance mechanisms operate in the nervous system to guide developing axons.[60,61]

Chemoattraction of axons by diffusible factors secreted by cells that form the targets of developing ax-

BOX 18.1

REGENERATION OF LESIONED AXONS IN THE CENTRAL NERVOUS SYSTEM

When the major pathways of the mammalian CNS are formed and start to myelinate (during the last part of gestation in humans and the first postnatal days in rats), axon growth progressively ceases, and the expression of growth-associated genes and proteins is downregulated. Whereas lesions at perinatal ages can still induce some degree of regeneration, plasticity, and functional restoration, lesions at juvenile or adult ages often lead to severe and persistent functional deficits. Regeneration of lesioned axons and pathways does not occur (with very few, limited exceptions), and adaptive rearrangements of circuits are limited. A number of factors and mechanisms involved in this limitation of regeneration in the adult CNS have been found. Of specific importance is the reaction of the lesioned neurons, the role of growth-promoting and growth-inhibiting factors in CNS tissue, and the specific conditions present at the lesion site (scars, caverns).

Lesioned adult CNS neurons often react spontaneously to axotomy by upregulation of immediate-early genes and growth-associated proteins, including GAP-43. Spontaneous sprouting of new collaterals and terminal branches by lesioned axons has been demonstrated in various parts of the CNS. Often, however, these regenerative reactions of the neurons seem to be transitory; sprouts and sometimes also the axon stump are retracted, and the neuronal cell body often enters an atrophic state or, in a minority of cases including the retina, dies.

An experiment of crucial importance was the demonstration that adult, lesioned spinal cord or optic nerve axons are able to regenerate and elongate over long distances in transplants of peripheral nerves grafted into the CNS. Clearly, these peripheral nerves represent a growth-permissive or growth-promoting local microenvironment, radically different from that of the adult CNS. These regeneration-enhancing properties of the denervated peripheral nerves are probably of great biological significance for the repair of microlesions, as they may occur throughout life in peripheral nerves. Three factors are responsible for the crucial differences between the lesioned CNS and the PNS: (1) the upregulation of the synthesis of several neurotrophic factors and growth-promoting substrate molecules in peripheral nerves upon denervation, (2) the presence of potent neurite growth inhibitors in the adult CNS, and (3) a difference in the process of inflammation and tissue repair, which leads to formation of regeneration-promoting bridges in peripheral nerves and to caverns and impermeable scars in the CNS.

Introducing neurotrophic factors into the lesioned adult CNS can enhance the survival and growth response of lesioned neurons and locally enhance sprouting of axon stumps. Long-distance regeneration, however, has been very limited in previous observations. Nevertheless, growth-promoting molecules can clearly influence adult neurons and support or enhance their attempts for regeneration.

The neurite growth inhibitory property of the adult CNS, as detected by a variety of *in vitro* and biochemical assays, seems to be particularly concentrated in white matter. Candidate molecules include the ECM molecules tenascin-C and -R, the myelin-associated neurite growth inhibitors NI-35 and NI-220/250, the myelin-associated glycoprotein MAG, and chondroitin sulfate proteoglycans. The role of recently discovered growth cone repellent axonal guidance molecules (semaphorin family, Ephrins), some of which also occur in the adult CNS, is not clear. Although all these molecules show repulsive or growth-cone collapse-inducing activity *in vitro, in vivo* evidence for a role in inhibiting regeneration and axon growth is at present available only for NI-35/250. MAG knockout mice show enhanced regeneration in peripheral nerves, but not in the CNS. Tenascin knockouts have a normal CNS anatomy, and effects on regeneration have not been reported.

The first evidence for long-distance regeneration in the differentiated CNS was obtained in experimentally myelin-free spinal cords in rats or chicken. Subsequently, a monoclonal antibody (mAB IN-1) raised against the myelin-associated neurite growth inhibitory protein NI-250 (rat homolog of bovine and human NI-220) neutralizes NI-250 as well as NI-35 and greatly reduces the inhibitory property of CNS myelin and white matter. Application of this antibody in adult, spinal-cord-lesioned rats induced regeneration of a population of corticospinal fibers from midthoracic to lumbar and sacral levels. Arborizations of these fibers in gray matter could be seen, a finding consistent with the important functional improvement found in certain parameters of locomotion of reflexes. A similar enhancement of regeneration was observed in the optic nerve and the septo-hippocampal connection. Recent anatomical and functional studies also showed that the same antibody treatments enhance topographically specific sprouting of intact fiber systems in spinal cord and brainstem, a process that again is correlated with restorations of functions.

The caverns and scars formed in the spinal cord and, after large lesions, in the brain after macrophage removal of the tissue debris are obvious obstacles in the path of regenerating fibers. Indirect, descriptive evidence also points to additional inhibitory effects of the local scar tissue, probably with a major role of astrocytes. Neither the processes that lead to secondary tissue loss and inflammation nor the complex cellular interactions during scar formation are currently understood. The roles of potential inhibitory molecules of lesion scars remain to be demonstrated. Much work has been done, however, in trying to bridge these scars. Whereas embryonic tissue works well in newborn lesions (rat), successful bridging of adult lesions has been obtained mainly with Schwann cells, olfactory nerve ensheathing cells, and peripheral nerve grafts.

Combined approaches, in which stimulatory factors are applied together with reagents neutralizing the neurite growth inhibitory properties of CNS tissue and implants to bridge the lesion will probably aid in a future, regeneration-enhancing therapy of spinal cord or brain lesions.

Martin E. Schwab

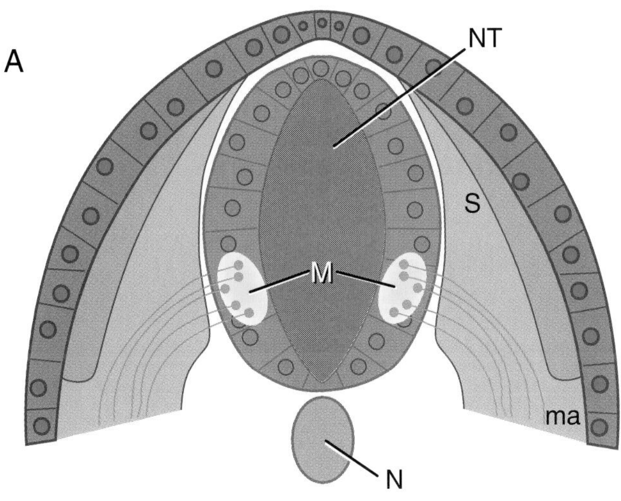

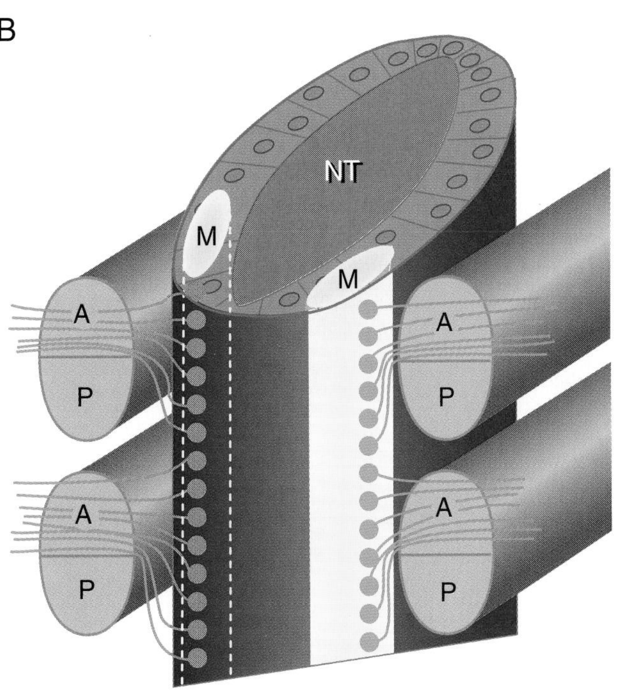

ons has been documented in both the peripheral and the central nervous system of vertebrates.[62,63] One example, to which we shall return later, is the guidance of spinal commissural axons along a dorsal-to-ventral trajectory to a specialized set of cells at the ventral midline of the spinal cord. These **floor plate cells** constitute an **intermediate target** for these axons. The existence of a floor-plate-derived chemoattractant for spinal commissural axons was demonstrated by culturing pieces of embryonic dorsal spinal cord, containing the cell bodies of commissural neurons, either alone or with pieces of floor plate.[64,65] These experiments showed that the floor plate secretes a diffusible factor(s) that can attract the axons of commissural neurons from a distance (Fig. 18.13).[66] The floor plate produces attractive effects over several hundred micrometers, a considerable distance on an embryonic scale (though not on the scale of the adult nervous system!). A similar range of action has been observed for other target-derived chemoattractants documented in other parts of the nervous system.[60]

The opposite process, long-range **chemorepulsion,** was discovered only recently, but has already been implicated in three different types of guidance events. The first event is perhaps best thought of as a "push from behind," in which a chemorepellent secreted by a group of cells located near neuronal cell bodies appears to ensure that axons head away from their cell bodies in the right direction. One example of this is the initial growth of olfactory tract axons *away* from the septum; cells in the septal region secrete a chemorepellent that seems to "push" these axons away (Fig. 18.14).[67] In a second type of repulsion, growing axons

FIGURE 18.11 Channeling of motor axons by repulsive cues in the posterior sclerotome. (A, B) The axons (orange) of motor neurons (M) that exit the ventral neural tube (NT) project through the sclerotome (S), as illustrated for a chick embryo. As seen in a ventral view (B), the axons grow through the anterior portion (A) of the sclerotome in each segment, avoiding the posterior sclerotome (P). Adapted from Keynes and Stern.[54]

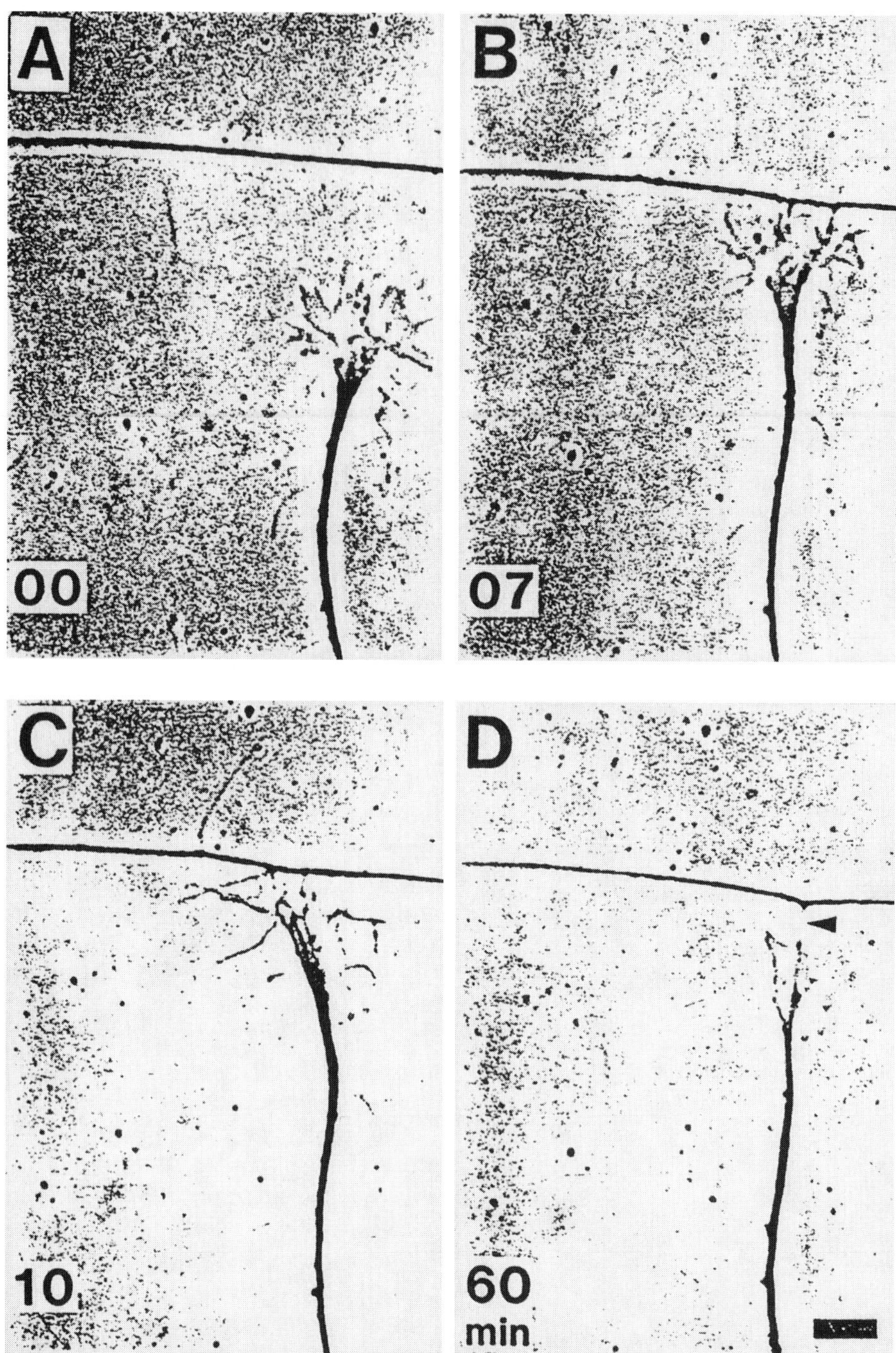

FIGURE 18.12 Collapse of a growth cone on contact with a heterologous axon, illustrated here for an encounter between the growth cone of a retinal axon and a sympathetic axon. A similar collapse is observed when the growth cones of sympathetic axons encounter retinal axons. No collapse is seen, however, when retinal growth cones contact other retinal axons or when sympathetic growth cones encounter other sympathetic axons. Time in minutes is shown in the lower left-hand corner. From Kapfhammer and Raper.[56]

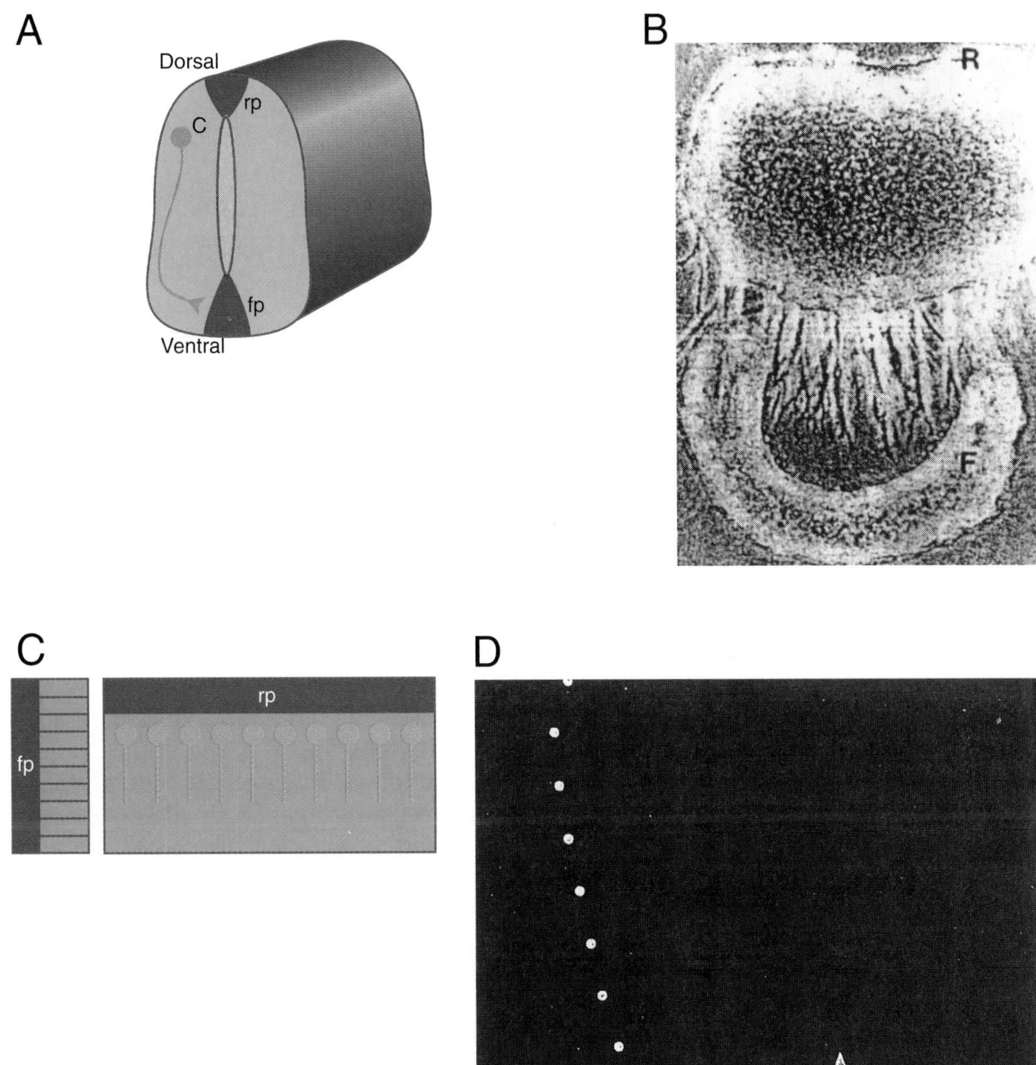

FIGURE 18.13 Chemoattraction of commissural axons by floor plate cells. (A) Schematic diagram of the trajectory of the commissural axons, which originate from cell bodies located in the dorsal spinal cord (C) and project along a dorsal-to-ventral trajectory, away from the roof plate (rp) toward floor plate (fp) cells at the ventral midline. Once they reach the ventral midline, the axons cross the floor plate then turn to project longitudinally along the midline (see Fig. 18.18). (B) When pieces of dorsal spinal cord (top) are cultured together with pieces of floor plate tissue (F, bottom) in a three-dimensional collagen matrix, profuse outgrowth of commissural axons toward the floor plate is observed. In control experiments, no outgrowth is observed from pieces of dorsal spinal cord cultured alone. Thus, floor plate cells secrete a diffusible factor(s) that can promote the apparently directed outgrowth of commissural axons. Adapted from Tessier-Lavigne *et al.*[64] (C, D) The floor plate can also cause turning of commissural axons, as shown in experiments in which pieces of dorsal spinal cord are cultured with a piece of floor plate placed to one side (diagram in C). This experiment takes advantage of the observation that in pieces of dorsal spinal cord cultured alone, commissural axons grow along a normal dorsal-to-ventral trajectory away from the roof plate (rp). When cultured with a piece of floor plate, however, commissural axons (visualized by immunohistochemistry) are deflected from this trajectory and turn toward the floor plate, as shown in D (white dots indicate the junction between floor plate and the piece of dorsal spinal cord). Adapted from (C) Placzek *et al.*[65] and (D) Kennedy *et al.*[66]

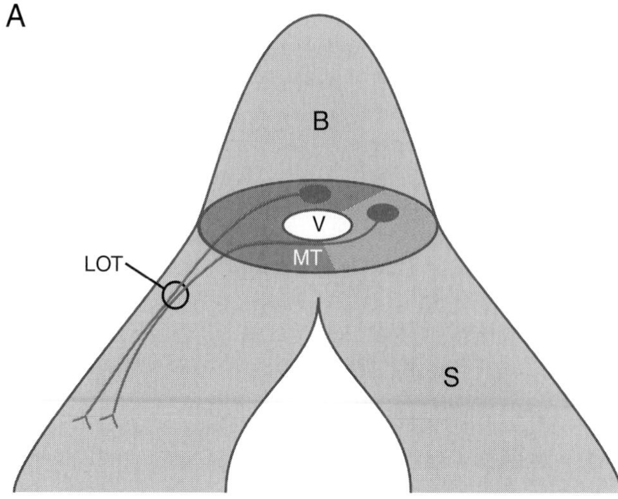

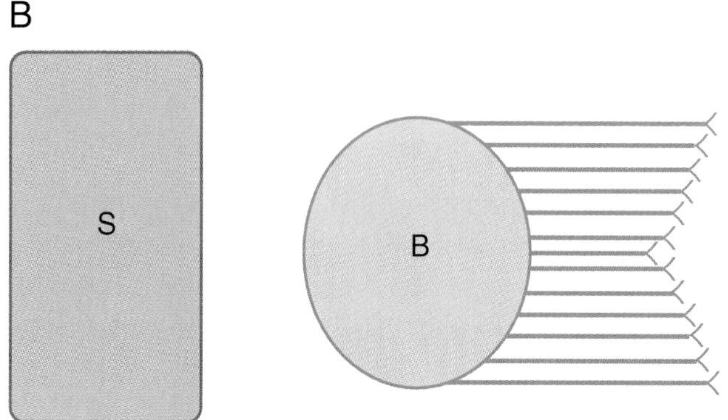

FIGURE 18.14 Chemorepulsion of olfactory bulb axons by septal tissues. (A) The axons of mitral and tufted cells (MT) of the olfactory bulb (B) project in a lateral direction away from the midline septum (S) to the lateral surface of the brain, where they form the lateral olfactory tract (LOT), (V, ventricle). (B) When pieces of olfactory bulb tissue containing the cell bodies of these neurons (B) are cultured in a collagen matrix with pieces of septal tissue (S), the axons of mitral and tufted cells are repelled from the septal tissue. Adapted from Pini.[67]

are deflected away from a particular region that they should avoid.[68] Finally, chemorepellents secreted by cells located beyond an axon's target may create an inhibitory barrier that prevents the axon from overshooting the proper target.[69]

Guidance Cues Act in Concert to Ensure Accurate Guidance

The operations of short- and long-range guidance mechanisms and of attraction and repulsion are not mutually exclusive. Rather, axons may generally be guided over each individual segment of their trajectories by several different types of mechanisms acting in concert to ensure reproducible and high-fidelity guidance. Many experiments have shown that axons may navigate short segments by using several and, in some cases, even all four types of cues: a repellent from behind the axons to "push," a corridor marked by a permissive local cue and bounded by an inhibitory local cue to "hem in" the growth, and an attractant at the end of the corridor to "pull".[70] Push, pull, and hem: these forces working together can ensure accurate guidance.

Summary

Four types of cues act in concert to guide axon growth *in vitro*. These include short- and long-range signals, which can be either attractive or repellent. Negative cues can serve to constrain or hem-in axon growth or stop it entirely. Positive cues serve to attract axons. Most guidance events appear to be directed by multiple cues acting in concert.

MOLECULAR MECHANISMS OF AXON GUIDANCE

As understanding of the cellular basis of accurate guidance has increased, attention has shifted to identifying the molecules that mediate these guidance effects. Here, knowledge is more fragmentary, although researchers may be on the verge of major breakthroughs in understanding. We now discuss a few of the most salient recent advances.

Cell-Surface and Extracellular Matrix Molecules Function as Local Guidance Cues

As mentioned earlier in this chapter, local guidance cues are produced by cells along the path that axons follow and are immobilized either on the surface of the cells or in the extracellular matrix that surrounds these cells. These cues are recognized by specific receptors on the surface of axons (and growth cones) that detect the cues and direct axonal responses to them.

Many **extracellular matrix (ECM) molecules** of diverse structures have been identified along axonal pathways, although evidence implicating them in axon guidance is largely indirect—based, for example, on the effects of these molecules on axon growth in simplified tissue culture experiments. One example, alluded to earlier, is provided by **laminin-1,** a member of a family of large (~1,000,000 Da) cruciform glycoproteins (Fig. 18.15).[71] When presented as a tissue-culture substrate, laminin-1 is a potent stimulator of extension of a variety of classes of axons.[71,72] Because it is expressed in several regions of the developing central

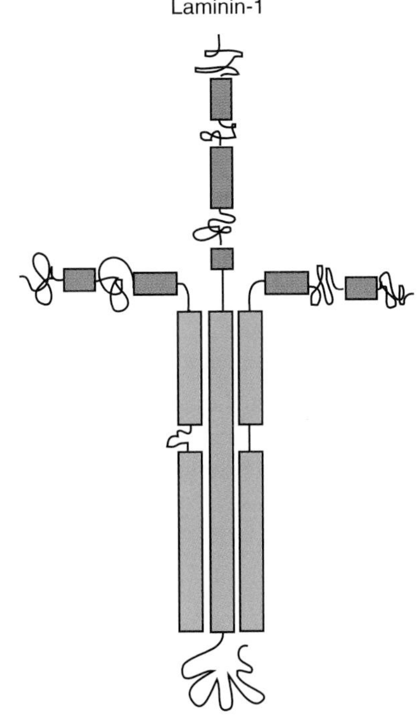

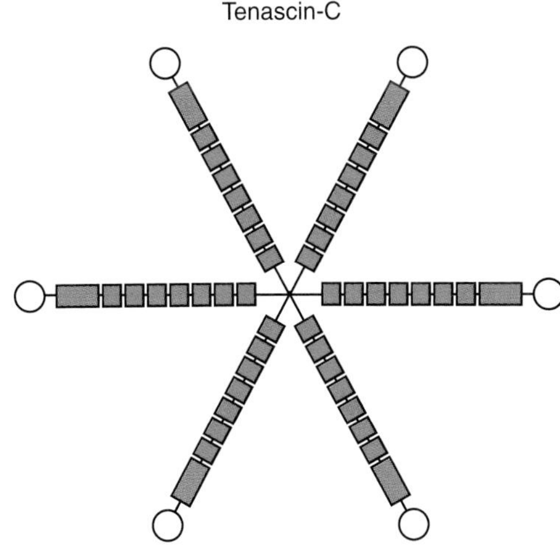

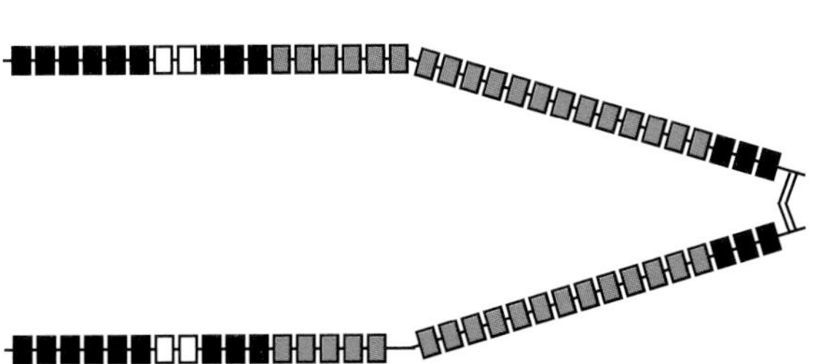

FIGURE 18.15 Examples of extracellular matrix molecules that modulate axon growth. Structures of three large molecules of the extracellular matrix that can either stimulate (laminin-1, tenascin-C, fibronectin) or inhibit (tenascin-C) the outgrowth of different classes of axons when presented as a substrate in tissue culture experiments. Tenascin-C is bifunctional, affecting different classes of axons in opposite ways. In these proteins repeated motifs include epidermal growth factor-like domains and fibronectin Type III domains. Adapted from Lander.[71]

and peripheral nervous system in "corridors" that mark the trajectory of several classes of axons, laminin-1 is strongly believed to be a positive corridor cue that contributes to channeling of some axons[73,74] as well as neural crest cells (Chapter 16). This hypothesis has not yet been directly tested for laminin-1 or for the many other ECM molecules, such as fibronectin or tenascin (Fig. 18.15), that can stimulate axonal growth and are thought to function as corridor cues. The major receptors on axons that mediate axonal responses to these ECM proteins are members of the **integrin** family, heterodimeric molecules comprising an α and a β chain.[75] There are now at least 15 known α chains and 8 known β chains. A large number of different combinations of individual α and β chains have been documented, each with its own set of binding specificities for different ECM molecules.[76]

Less is known about ECM molecules with inhibitory effects on axons. Some proteoglycans, large ECM molecules that possess highly sulfated sugar groups called glycosaminoglycans, are known to have inhibitory effects on axon extension *in vitro*.[77] Interestingly, some ECM molecules, such as tenascin, that have positive effects on some axons also have inhibitory effects on different classes of axons.[78,79] This illustrates a general principle that molecules involved in axon guidance may not necessarily be specialized for a particular purpose (e.g., attraction or repulsion) and instead may be multifunctional, producing different effects on different neurons. Many of the ECM proteins that have been characterized have distinct structural domains (Fig. 18.15), and there is evidence that different effects of these proteins on different cell types are in some cases mediated by distinct domains,[75,80] which may be recognized by distinct receptors on the different classes of responsive cells.

Cell-surface molecules presented by cells along axonal paths have also been implicated as local guidance cues. In particular, much evidence has indicated that various members of the **immunoglobulin gene (Ig) superfamily** (Fig. 18.16), cell-surface proteins whose extracellular portions comprise **immunoglobulin** domains and fibronectin Type III repeats—motifs first identified in antibody (immunoglobulin) molecules and in the ECM protein fibronectin, respectively[81]—provide guidance cues. Several members of this family are capable of binding to themselves (i.e., **homophilic**

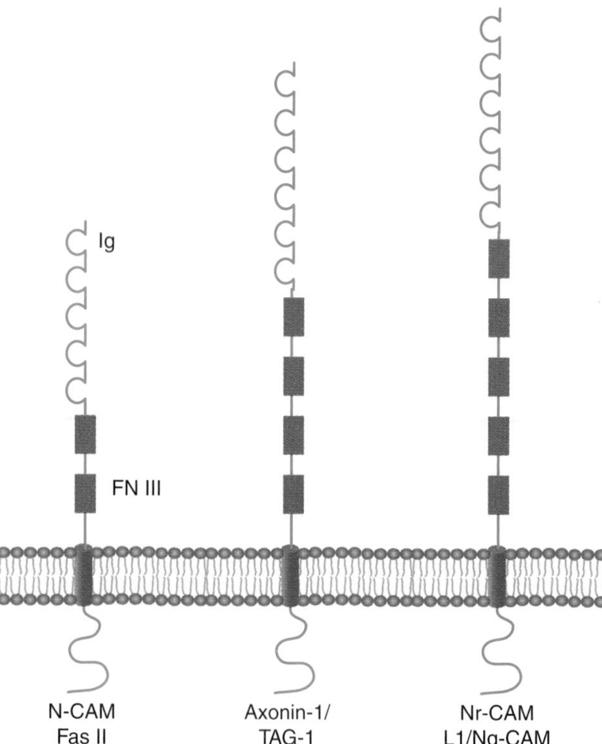

FIGURE 18.16 Examples of members of the immunoglobulin superfamily. These molecules are characterized by the presence of different numbers of immunoglobulin (Ig) domains and fibronectin Type III domains (FNIII) in their extracellular portions. They can be tethered to membranes either by a transmembrane domain or by a lipid anchor. The family is very large, but only those members discussed in the text are illustrated here. Adapted from Tessier-Lavigne and Goodman.[70]

binding) and of mediating adhesion between cells, so that they function as their own receptors. This homophilic binding is known to mediate some cases of axonal fasciculation. For example, in *Drosophila*, the axons of neurons dMP2, MP1, pCC, and vMP2 fasciculate with one another over a portion of their trajectories. This fasciculation is mediated by the homophilic Ig superfamily member fasciclin II, expressed on all of these axons; fasciculation is disrupted in mutant flies lacking fasciclin II (Fig. 18.17).[82] Some Ig superfamily members have also been implicated in other types of local guidance, in some cases through **heterophilic** interactions with distinct Ig superfamily members. For example, the spinal commissural axons discussed earlier express axonin-1, an Ig superfamily member that binds a distinct Ig superfamily member called Nr-CAM, which is present on the surface of floor plate cells. The interaction between axonin-1 and Nr-CAM is important in allowing commissural axons to grow across floor plate cells. Experimental perturbations of the interactions with antibodies or other function-blocking reagents in developing chicken embryos impair the ability of commissural axons to cross the floor plate (Fig. 18.18).[83] In addition to the positive effects of ligands like fasciclin II and Nr-CAM on axon growth, Ig superfamily members can also have inhibitory effects. In fact, some Ig superfamily members, like some ECM molecules, appear to have both growth stimulatory effects on some axons and growth inhibitory effects on other axons.[84,85] These effects are presumably dependent on the receptor and signal transduction apparatus present in the responding cell. Finally, surface molecules other than Ig superfamily members have also been implicated as local guidance cues. These molecules include the **cadherins**[86] and cell-surface members of the semaphorin family (discussed in the following section), although the roles of these molecules in guidance *in vivo* are still being defined.

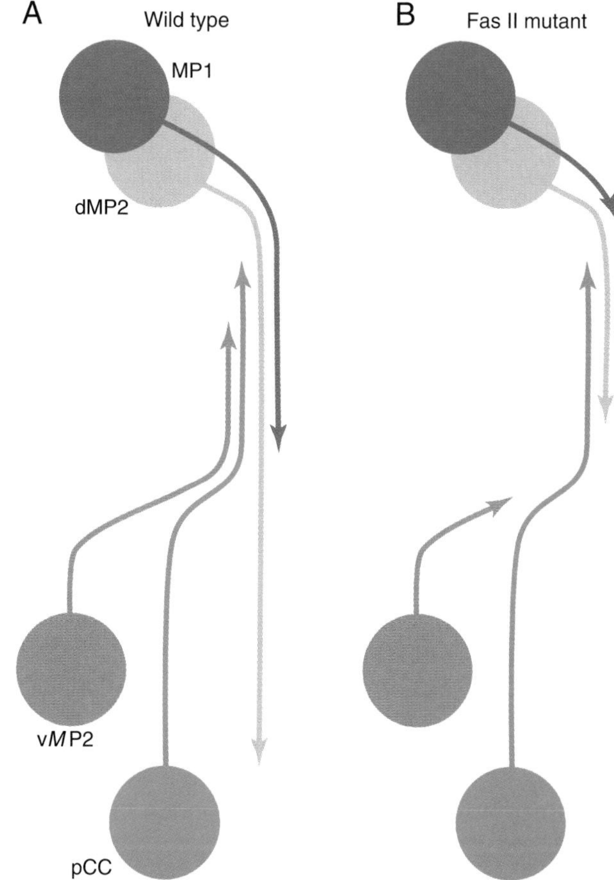

FIGURE 18.17 The Ig superfamily member fasciclin II (Fas II) mediates fasciculation of subsets of axons in *Drosophila*. Fasciclin II is a homophilic adhesion molecule. Axons of neurons MP1, dMP2, vMP2, and pCC express Fas II and course together and fasciculate for a portion of their trajectory in wild-type flies (A), but they fail to fasciculate in flies deficient in Fas II function (B). Adapted from Lin *et al.*[82]

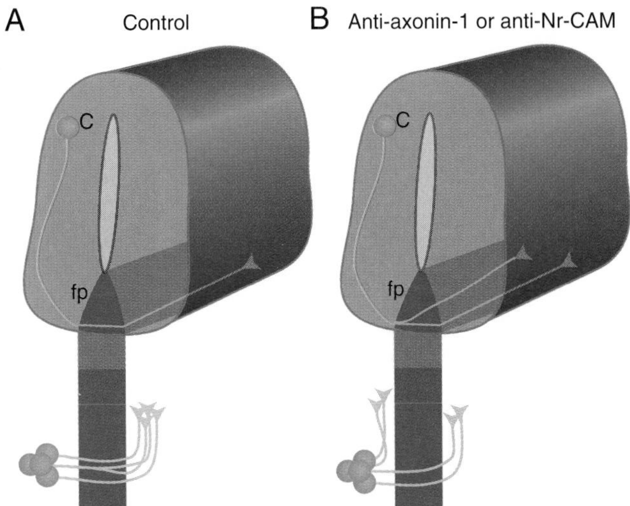

FIGURE 18.18 The Ig superfamily members axonin-1 and Nr-CAM are required for crossing of the floor plate by commissural axons in chick embryos. (A) Normal trajectory of commissural axons (see Fig. 18.13), which grow from their cell bodies of origin (C) in the dorsal spinal cord to the floor plate (fp) at the ventral midline. These axons cross the midline at the floor plate, then turn longitudinally to grow alongside the floor plate. The trajectory is viewed in transverse section in the upper portion of the drawing and in a ventral view in the lower portion. Commissural axons express axonin-1 on their surface, whereas floor plate cells express Nr-CAM. *In vitro,* axonin-1 can bind Nr-CAM. (B) When reagents that disrupt the axonin-1–Nr-CAM interaction (e.g., antibodies to either axonin-1 or Nr-CAM) are injected into the lumen of the neural tube of the chick embryo, commissural axon crossing of the floor plate is impaired, such that ~50% of axons turn to course alongside the floor plate without ever crossing. These and other results have suggested that the floor plate is relatively nonpermissive for commissural axon crossing in the absence of Nr-CAM, which normally facilitates crossing. Adapted from Stoeckli and Landmesser.[83]

Netrins and Semaphorins Can Function as Diffusible Attractants and Repellents

Two families of secreted factors, the netrins and semaphorins (Fig. 18.19),[87,88] have members that can mediate long-range attraction and repulsion of axons. The **netrins** were identified as proteins that can mimic the diffusible outgrowth-promoting activity of floor plate cells on commissural axons. Netrin-1 is produced by floor plate cells, contributes to the chemotropic activity of these cells, and is believed to be present in the spinal cord in a decreasing ventral-to-dorsal gradient that attracts commissural axons to the ventral midline of the spinal cord.[66,89] Remarkably, netrin-1 also appears to function as a long-range repellent, providing a push from behind for some axons that grow *away* from the floor plate.[90,91] Thus, netrin-1 appears to guide axons in both dorsal and ventral directions in the neural tube, thus illustrating that the bifunctionality of guidance cues, discussed above for local cues, extends to diffusible molecules as well. Strikingly, the netrins are vertebrate homologs of the UNC-6 protein of the nematode *Caenorhabditis elegans,* a protein involved in guiding axons along both dorsal and ventral circumferential trajectories.[92–94] Similarly, netrin homologs are expressed at the midline of the nervous system of *Drosophila melanogaster* and play a role in directing axons to the midline.[95,96] These findings vividly illustrate the remarkable conservation of axon guidance mechanisms during evolution.

Identification of the netrins as long-range cues illustrates another important principle. Although the netrins are capable of long-range attraction, they are closely related in structure to the archetypal nondiffusible ECM molecule laminin-1 (Fig. 18.19). The extent to which the netrins can diffuse in the embryo may be regulated,[87] so that in some circumstances they may function as local rather than long-range cues. Conversely, ECM molecules such as laminin-1, originally noted for their local actions, can in some cases diffuse long distances.[97] Thus, as in the distinction between attractive and repulsive cues, there may not be a hard and fast distinction between local and long-range cues.

The **semaphorins** are a large family of secreted and transmembrane proteins characterized by the presence in their extracellular portions of a "semaphorin" domain approximately 500 amino acids long (Fig. 18.19).[98–100] The first member of this family was identified in grasshoppers and implicated in axon guidance on the basis of antibody perturbation experiments.[101] The connection of the family to chemorepulsion was made with the purification of collapsin-1 (or Sema III), a secreted member of this family, as a protein that causes collapse of sensory growth cones in cell culture[102] and that has also been shown to function as a long-range chemorepellent for these axons.[88] The finding that another secreted member of the family in flies, Sema II, has inhibitory effects on axon terminals[103] has raised the possibility that members of the family might function quite generally as inhibitory guidance cues.

At present, it is unclear how widespread chemoattraction and chemorepulsion are in the developing nervous system. So far, apart from netrins and semaphorins, the only other chemotropic factor implicated in the guidance of developing axons is hepatocyte growth factor/scatter factor, a soluble ligand for the c-Met receptor tyrosine kinase, which has recently been implicated as a chemoattractant that plays a role in directing motor axon projections into the limb.[104]

Summary

The molecular basis of growth cone guidance is under investigation. Local guidance cues are provided

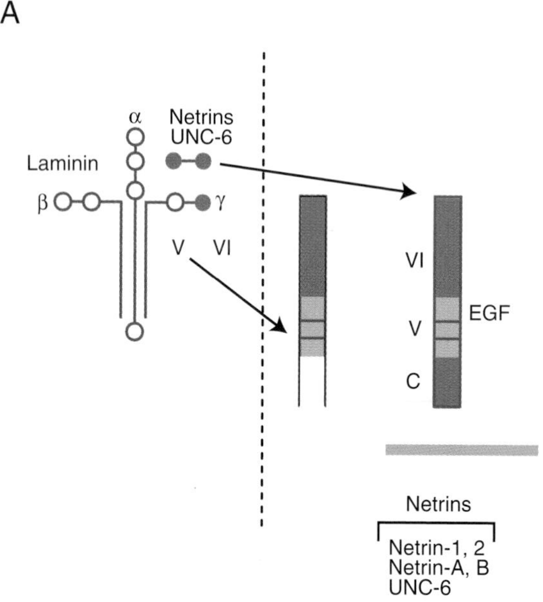
A
α
Netrins
UNC-6
Laminin
β
γ
V
VI
VI
EGF
V
C
Netrins
Netrin-1, 2
Netrin-A, B
UNC-6

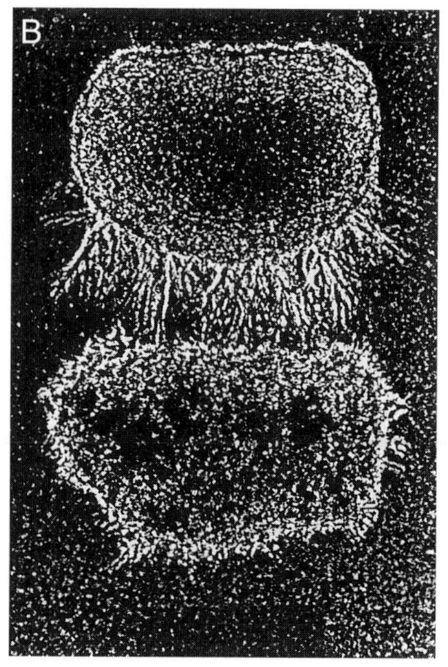
B

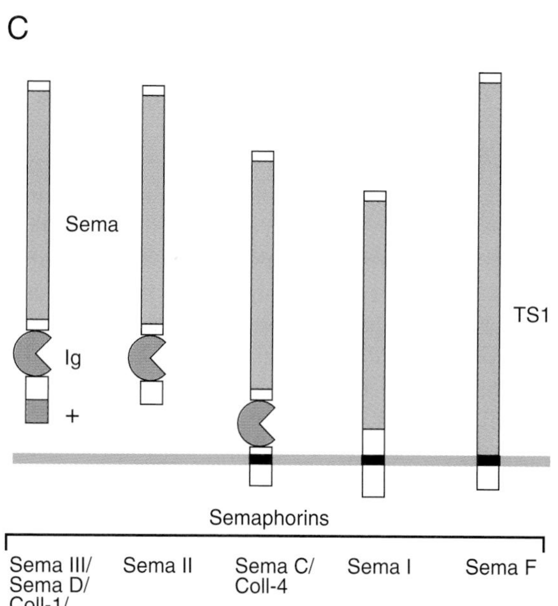
C
Sema
Ig
+
TS1
Semaphorins
Sema III/
Sema D/
Coll-1/
Sema II
Sema C/
Coll-4
Sema I
Sema F

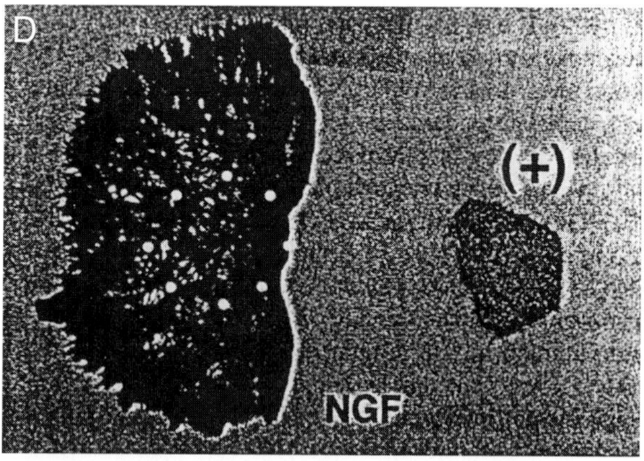
D
(+)
NGF

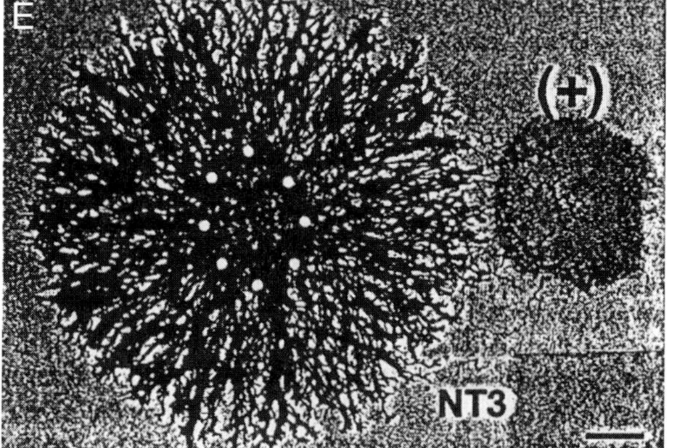
E
(+)
NT3

by extracellular matrix molecules such as laminin and by cell-surface molecules including members of the Ig super family. Long-range guidance cues are provided by at least two families of secreted molecules; the netrins and the semaphorins. In the case of both local and long-range guidance cues, specific molecules can function either as positive or negative regulators, depending on the neuron class and/or developmental stage.

CONTROL OF TOPOGRAPHIC PROJECTIONS BY GRADIENTS OF SIGNALING MOLECULES

Once axons reach their target fields, they must select appropriate target cells with which to form synaptic connections. A special challenge confronts populations of axons that form **topographic** projections (see Chapters 26–28), where the spatial order of the cells of origin is reflected in the order of their axon terminals, such that neighboring cells project to neighboring regions of the target to form a smooth and continuous map.

FIGURE 18.19 Netrins and semaphorins can function as diffusible attractants and repellents. (A) Structure of the netrins in relation to that of laminin-1. The amino-terminal two-thirds of the netrins is made up of domains VI and V, which are homologous to similar domains at the amino terminus of the γ chain of laminin-1. The carboxy-terminal third of the netrins, domain C, does not, however, share homology with laminin chains. Adapted from Tessier-Lavigne and Goodman.[70] (B) An aggregate of cells secreting recombinant netrin-1 protein (bottom in micrograph) elicits outgrowth of commissural axons from an explant of dorsal spinal cord (top tissue in micrograph), thus mimicking the effect of floor plate cells (Figure 18.13). Like floor plate cells, cells secreting netrin-1 protein can also turn commissural axons. Adapted from Kennedy *et al.*[66] and Serafini *et al.*[87] (C) Members of the semaphorin family fall into at least five different subfamilies, as illustrated here. They are all characterized by the presence of an ~500-amino-acid semaphorin domain (Sema), but some are soluble (illustrated here by Coll-1/Sema III and by Sema II), whereas others are tethered to membranes (illustrated by Sema C/Coll-4, Sema I, and Sema F). Members of different subfamilies possess additional structural motifs, including immunoglobulin (Ig) domains, basic domains (+), and thrombospondin Type 1 domains (TS1). Adapted from Tessier-Lavigne and Goodman.[70] (D, E). Coll-1/Sema III is a diffusible chemorepellent for subsets of sensory axons. Aggregates of cells secreting recombinant Coll-1/Sema III (right in each panel) and E14 rat dorsal root ganglia (outlined by dots) were cultured in collagen matrices in the presence of nerve growth factor (NGF) (D) or neurotrophin-3 (NT3) (E), to elicit outgrowth of different classes of sensory axons. At this stage of development, Coll-1/Sema III has a strong repellent effect on NGF-dependent axons (D) but not on NT3-dependent axons (E). This fits with the observation that NT3-dependent axons project into a region of high expression of Coll-1/Sema III, but NGF-dependent axons do not. Adapted from Messersmith *et al.*[88]

How do these topographic projections form? This question has been addressed most extensively in the developing retinotectal projection in lower vertebrates, where the precise map that is found in adults develops in several stages. Initially, a coarse map is formed, then becomes refined with the remodeling of axon terminal arbors. This refinement of projections is driven by mechanisms that are influenced by the relative patterns of electrical activity between neighboring cells (discussed in Chapters 19 and 22). However, a large body of literature developed over the past 50 years has shown that independent of electrical activity, the target presents guidance information to incoming axons that also helps direct them to their topographically correct locations on the tectum.

The nature of this guidance information was studied in some detail by Roger Sperry starting in the 1940s. Sperry designed a clever set of experiments to address earlier theories such as that of Weiss, which held that the specificity of neuronal connections in an adult organism resulted from the "functional molding" of circuits formed more or less at random; connections that were functionally appropriate were retained and others were eliminated. To test these theories, Sperry studied the regeneration of the **retinotectal projection** in newts and frogs; in these amphibians, unlike in mammals, cut retinal axons are capable of regenerating to re-form a functional pattern of connections with target cells in the tectum. Sperry simultaneously cut the optic nerve and rotated the eye in its orbit by 180°. He then allowed the retinal axons to regrow to the tectum. According to earlier theories, one might have expected the axons to make a novel pattern of connections that could generate appropriate behavioral responses to visual stimuli. Instead, Sperry[105] found that after regeneration the animals behaved as if their visual world had been rotated. For instance, when a fly was presented in the upper left-hand quadrant of the visual field of the rotated eye, the animal would respond by diving down to the right. Furthermore, this inappropriate response was retained throughout the animal's life, even after attempts to train the animals to compensate for the rotation. These findings suggested that the retinal axons had re-formed their original pattern of connections and provided rather decisive evidence against the idea that the adult pattern of connections arises from selective retention of functionally appropriate circuits.

Over the next 50 years, the specificity of the projections of retinal axons to tectal cells was investigated further by means of direct tracing of axonal projections, first in the regenerating retinotectal system and later during the initial projection of these axons in embryonic development. Experiments showed that regener-

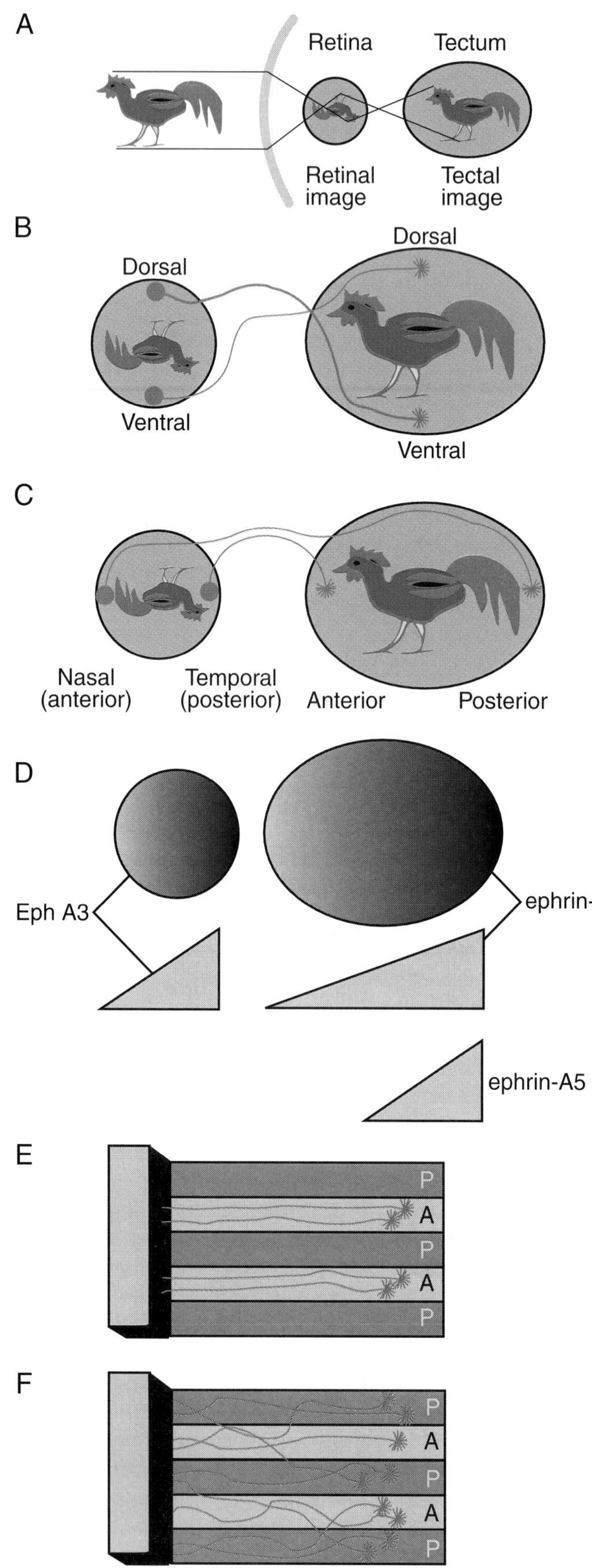

ating or developing retinal axons that are experimentally deflected to inappropriate regions of the tectum can reorient and home in on their topographically appropriate target region.[106,107] This evidence indicated that establishment of topographic projections involves the recognition of positional information on the tectum.

What is the nature of this **positional information?** Sperry[108] argued against the idea that each axon has a unique label that is complementary to another unique label on its appropriate target cell, both because of the implausibly large number of labels that would be required and because this model does not provide a mechanism for each axon to find its target, except by wandering aimlessly around the tectum. These considerations led him to propose that positional information might instead be encoded in the form of **gradients** of signaling molecules along both the anterior–posterior (A/P) and dorsoventral (D/V) axes of the target and that these gradients could be detected by complementary gradients of receptors on the axons. Positional information could thus be specified with a small number of molecules, and all axons could read positional information at every point on the tectum.

Evidence for the existence of gradients of signaling molecules on the tectum that influence retinal axon growth was first obtained through *in vitro* studies on projections along the A/P axis. Temporal retinal axons project to anterior tectum, whereas nasal retinal axons project to posterior tectum (Fig. 18.20).[109] When temporal retinal axons are confronted *in vitro* with a choice of live tectal cells from anterior or posterior tectum, they choose to grow on those from anterior tectum,

FIGURE 18.20 Topographic projections of retinal axons may be directed by gradients of repellent factors on the tectum. (A–C) The projection of retinal ganglion cells to the optic tectum is topographic. A map of the visual world on the tectum is inverted with respect to that on the retina (A), because axons from dorsal and ventral retinas project to ventral and dorsal tecta, respectively (B), whereas axons from nasal (anterior) and temporal (posterior) retinas project to posterior and anterior tecta, respectively (C). (D) The Eph family receptor tyrosine kinase EphA3 is expressed in a gradient in the retina. Two ligands for this receptor, ephrin-A2 and ephrin-A5 are expressed in overlapping countergradients in the tectum. (E, F) Temporal retinal ganglion cell axons show a preference for anterior over posterior tectal membranes in the "stripe assay." (E) When grown on carpets made of alternating 90-μm-wide stripes of anterior (A) and posterior (P) tectal membranes, axons projecting from pieces of temporal retina (left) grow exclusively on the anterior membranes. (F) In contrast, the axons do not show a preference for anterior membranes when posterior membranes are pretreated with heat or proteases, indicating that the preference is directed by a repellent in posterior membranes. ephrin-A2 and ephrin-A5 are candidate mediators of this repellent activity, since they are enriched in posterior membranes and can repel retinal axons. Adapted from Tessier-Lavigne[109] and Tessier-Lavigne and Goodman.[70]

their normal target.[110] A similar choice is made when the axons are confronted with membrane preparations from anterior or posterior tectum, in the so-called stripe assay (Fig. 18.20E).[111] This observation allowed researchers to determine whether the preference exhibited by temporal axons is due to attraction by the anterior tectal membranes or repulsion by the posterior tectal membranes. Because nonspecific treatment of posterior membranes with heat or protease abolished the preference, whereas similar treatment of anterior membranes did not (Fig. 18.20F), the preference was thought to be driven by a repellent activity in posterior membranes.[112] Recent studies have led to the identification of two related membrane-anchored proteins, ephrin-A5 and ephrin-A2, that are candidate repellents in posterior tectum. These proteins are ligands for receptor tyrosine kinases of the Eph subfamily,[109] some of which are expressed on retinal axons.[113] The ligands are present in overlapping anterior-to-posterior gradients in the tectum (Fig. 18.20D), and both can function to repel retinal axons.[114,115] We are still in the early stages of understanding the precise roles of these ligands in guiding retinal axons *in vivo* and of identifying the other factors that work with these ligands to guide retinal axons. Nevertheless, the finding of repellent ligands present in a graded distribution in the tectum provides direct support for Sperry's hypothesis that topographic projections may be directed by graded distributions of guidance cues.

Summary

The formation of topographic maps involves the establishment of an initial, coarse map that is subsequently refined. Analysis of the retinotectal system in amphibians, birds, and mammals suggests that the initial, coarse map is formed based on positional information present in the tectum. This information appears to be encoded in the form of gradients of signaling molecules along both the A/P and D/V axes of the target.

References

1. Ramón y Cajal, S. (1890). Sur l'origine et les ramifications des fibres nerveuses de la moelle embryonaire. *Anat. Anz.* **5:** 609–613. Extract from Ramón y Cajál, S., 1909. *Histology of the Nervous System,* (N. Swanson and L. W. Swanson transl.). Oxford University Press, Oxford, 1995.
2. Harrison, R. G. (1910). The outgrowth of the nerve fiber as a mode of protoplasmic movement. *J. Exp. Zool.* **9:** 787.
3. Speidel, C. C. (1933). Studies of living nerves: II. Activities of ameboid growth cones, sheath cells, and myelin segments, as revealed by prolonged observation of individual nerve fibers in frog tadpoles. *Am. J. Anat.* **52:** 1–79.
4. Wessells, N. K., and Nuttall, R. P. (1978). Normal branching, induced branching, and steering of cultured parasympathetic motor neurons. *Exp. Cell Res.* **115:** 111–122.
5. Bovolenta, P., and Mason, C. (1987). Growth cone morphology varies with position in the developing mouse visual pathway from retina to first targets. *J. Neurosci.* **7:** 1447–1460.
6. Cheng, T. P. O., and Reese, T. S. (1985). Polarized compartmentalization of organelles in growth cones from developing optic tectum. *J. Cell Biol.* **101:** 1473–1480.
7. Lin, C.-H., Thompson, C. A., and Forscher, P. (1994). Cytoskeletal reorganization underlying growth cone motility. *Curr. Opin. Neurobiol.* **4:** 640–647.
8. Dai, J., and Sheetz, M. P. (1995). Axon membrane flows from the growth cone to the cell body. *Cell* (*Cambridge, Mass.*) **83:** 693–701.
9. Davis, L., Dou, P., DeWit, M., and Kater, S. B. (1992). Protein synthesis within neuronal growth cones. *J. Neurosci.* **12:** 4867–4877.
10. Lewis, A. K., and Bridgman, P. C. (1992). Nerve growth cone lamellipodia contain two populations of actin filaments that differ in organization and polarity. *J. Cell Biol.* **119:** 1219–1243.
11. Condeelis, J. (1993). Life at the leading edge. *Annu. Rev. Cell Biol.* **9:** 411–444.
12. Gumbiner, B. M. (1993). Proteins associated with the cytoplasmic surface of adhesion molecules. *Neuron* **11:** 551–564.
13. Davis, J. Q., and Bennett, V. (1994). Ankyrin binding activity shared by the Neurofascin/L1/NrCAM family of nervous system cell adhesion molecules. *J. Biol. Chem.* **269:** 27163–27166.
14. Forscher, P., and Smith, S. J. (1988). Actions of cytochalasins on the organization of actin filaments and microtubules in a neuronal growth cone. *J. Cell Biol.* **107:** 1505–1516.
15. Fan, J., Mansfield, S. G., Redmond, T., Gordon-Weeks, P. R., and Raper, J. A. (1993). The organization of F-actin and microtubules in growth cones exposed to a brain-derived collapsing factor. *J. Cell Biol.* **121:** 867–878.
16. Marsh, L., and Letourneau, P. C. (1984). Growth of neurites without filopodial or lamellipodial activity in the presence of cytochalasin B. *J. Cell Biol.* **99**(6):2041–2047.
17. Chien, C. B., Rosenthal, D. E., Harris, W. A., and Holt, C. E. (1993). Navigational errors made by growth cones without filopodia in the embryonic *Xenopus* brain. *Neuron* **11**(2): 237–251.
18. Lamoureux, P., Buxbaum, R. E., and Heidemann, S. R. (1989). Direct evidence that growth cones pull. *Nature* (*London*) **340:** 159–162.
19. Lin, C. H., Espreafico, E. M., Mooseker, M. S., and Forscher, P. (1996). Myosin drives retrograde f-actin flow in neuronal growth cones. *Neuron* **16:** 769–782.
20. Sabry, J. H., O'Connor, T. P., Evans, L., Toroian-Raymond, A., Kirschner, M., and Bentley, D. (1991). Microtubule behaviour during guidance of pioneer growth cones in situ. *J. Cell Biol.* **115:** 381–395.
21. Lin, C. H., and Forscher, P. (1993). Cytoskeletal remodeling during growth cone–target interactions. *J. Cell Biol.* **121:** 1369–1383.
22. Tanaka, E., Ho, T., and Kirschner, M. W. (1995). The role of microtubule dynamics in growth cone motility and axonal growth. *J. Cell Biol.* **128:** 139–155.
23. Rochlin, M. W., Wickline, K. M., and Bridgman, P. C. (1996). Microtubule stability decreases axon elongation but not axoplasm production. *J. Neurosci.* **16:** 3236–3246.
24. Martenson, C., Stone, K., Reedy, M., and Sheetz, M. (1993). Fast axonal transport is required for growth cone advance. *Nature* (*London*) **366:** 66–69.

25. Shaw, G., and Bray, D. (1977). Movement and extension of isolated growth cones. *Exp. Cell Res.* **104:** 55–62.
26. Campenot, R. B. (1977). Local control of neurite outgrowth by nerve growth factor. *Proc. Natl. Acad. Sci. U.S.A.* **74:** 4516–4519.
27. Ebendal, T. (1976). The relative roles of contact inhibition and contact guidance in orientation of axons extending on aligned collagen fibrils *in vitro. Exp. Cell Res.* **98:** 159–169.
28. Bray, D. (1979). Mechanical tension produced by nerve cells in tissue culture. *J. Cell Sci.* **37:** 391–410.
29. Tanaka, E., and Sabry, J. (1995). Making the connection: Cytoskeletal rearrangements during growth cone guidance. *Cell* (*Cambridge, Mass.*) **83:** 171–176.
30. Hammarback, J. A., Palm, S. L., Furcht, L. T., and Letourneau, P. C. (1985). Guidance of neurite outgrowth by pathways of substratum-adsorbed laminin. *J. Neurosci. Res.* **13:** 213–220.
31. Lemmon, V., Burden, S. M., Payne, H. R., Elmslie, G. J., and Hlavin, M. L. (1992). Neurite growth on different substrates: Permissive versus instructive influences and the role of adhesive strength. *J. Neurosci.* **12:** 818–826.
32. Letourneau, P. C. (1975). Cell-to-substratum adhesion and guidance of axonal elongation. *Dev. Biol.* **44:** 92–101.
33. McKenna, M. P., and Raper, J. A. (1988). Growth cone behavior on gradients of substratum bound laminin. *Dev. Biol.* **130:** 232–236.
34. McCaig, C. D. (1986). Dynamic aspects of amphibian neurite growth and the effects of an applied electric field. *J. Physiol.* (*London*) **375:** 55–69.
35. Kater, S. B., and Mills, L. R. (1991). Regulation of growth cone behaviour by calcium. *J. Neurosci.* **11:** 891–899.
36. Bedlack, R. S., Jr., Wei, M., and Loew, L. M. (1992). Localized membrane depolarizations and localized calcium influx during electric field–guided neurite growth. *Neuron* **9:** 393–403.
37. Zheng, J. Q., Felder, M., Conner, J. A., and Poo, M. M. (1994). Turning of nerve growth cones induced by neurotransmitters. *Nature* (*London*) **368:** 140–144.
38. Ramón y Cajal, S. (1892). La rétine des vertebrés. *Cellule* **9:** 119–258.
39. Weiss, P. A. (1936). Selectivity controlling the central–peripheral relations in the nervous system. *Biol. Rev. Cambridge Philos. Soc.* **11:** 494–531.
40. Goodman, C. S., and Shatz, C. J. (1993). Developmental mechanisms that generate precise patterns of neuronal connectivity. *Cell* (*Cambridge, Mass.*) **72:** 77–98.
41. Caudy, M., and Bentley, D. (1986). Pioneer growth cone steering along a series of neuronal and non-neuronal cues of different affinities. *J. Neurosci.* **6:** 1781–1795.
42. Bentley, D., and Caudy, M. (1983). Pioneer axons lose directed growth after selective killing of guidepost cells. *Nature* (*London*) **304:** 62–65.
43. Palka, J., Whitlock, K. E., and Murray, M. A. (1992). Guidepost cells. *Curr. Opin. Neurobiol.* **2:** 48–54.
44. Raper, J. A., Bastiani, M., and Goodman, C. S. (1983). Pathfinding by neuronal growth cones in grasshopper embryos. II. Selective fasciculation onto specific axonal pathways. *J. Neurosci.* **3:** 31–41.
45. Raper, J. A., Bastiani, M. J., and Goodman, C. S. (1984). Pathfinding by neuronal growth cones in grasshopper embryos. IV. The effects of ablating the A and P axons upon the behavior of the G growth cone. *J. Neurosci.* **4:** 2329–2345.
46. Goodman, C. S., Bastiani, M. J., Doe, C. Q., du Lac, S., Helfand, S. L., Kuwada, J. Y., and Thomas, J. B. (1984). Cell recognition during neuronal development. *Science* **225:** 1271–1279.
47. Easter, S. S., Jr., Ross, L. S., and Frankfurter, A. (1993). Initial tract formation in the mouse brain. *J. Neurosci.* **13:** 285–299.
48. Greenspoon, S., Patel, C. K., Hashmi, S., Bernhardt, R. R., and Kuwada, J. Y. (1995). The notochord and floor plate guide growth cones in the zebrafish spinal cord. *J. Neurosci.* **15:** 5956–5965.
49. Keshishian, H., and Bentley, D. (1983). Embryogenesis of peripheral nerve pathways in grasshopper legs. III. Development without pioneer neurons. *Dev. Biol.* **96:** 116–124.
50. Chitnis, A. B., and Kuwada, J. Y. (1991). Elimination of a brain tract increases errors in pathfinding by follower growth cones in the zebrafish embryo. *Neuron* **7:** 277–285.
51. Lin, D. M., Auld, V. J., and Goodman, C. S. (1995). Targeted neuronal cell ablation in the *Drosophila* embryo: Pathfinding by follower growth cones in the absence of pioneers. *Neuron* **14:** 707–715.
52. Lance-Jones, C., and Landmesser, L. (1980). Motoneurone projection patterns in the chick hind limb following early partial reversals of the spinal cord. *J. Physiol.* (*London*) **302:** 581–602.
53. Harris, W. A. (1986). Homing behaviour of axons in the embryonic vertebrate brain. *Nature* (*London*) **320:** 266–269.
54. Keynes, R. J., and Stern, C. D. (1984). Segmentation in the vertebrate nervous system. *Nature* (*London*) **310:** 786–789.
55. Oakley, R. A., and Tosney, K. W. (1993). Contact-mediated mechanisms of motor axon segmentation. *J. Neurosci.* **13:** 3773–3792.
56. Kapfhammer, J. P., and Raper, J. A. (1987). Collapse of growth cone structure on contact with specific neurites in culture. *J. Neurosci.* **7:** 201–212.
57. Godement, P., Salaun, J., and Mason, C. A. (1990). Retinal axon pathfinding in the optic chiasm: Divergence of crossed and uncrossed fibers. *Neuron* **5:** 173–186.
58. Sretavan, D. W., and Reichardt, L. F. (1993). Time-lapse video analysis of retinal ganglion cell axon pathfinding at the mammalian optic chiasm: Growth cone guidance using intrinsic chiasm cues. *Neuron* **10:** 761–777.
59. Wizenmann, A., Thanos, S., von Boxberg, Y., and Bonhoeffer, F. (1993). Differential reaction of crossing and non-crossing rat retinal axons on cell membrane preparations from the chiasm midline: An in vitro study. *Development* (*Cambridge, UK*) **117:** 725–735.
60. Tessier-Lavigne, M., and Placzek, M. (1991). Target attraction: are developing axons guided by chemotropism? *Trends Neurosci.* **14:** 303–310.
61. Keynes, R., and Cook, G. M. (1995). Axon guidance molecules. *Cell* (*Cambridge, Mass.*) **83:** 161–169.
62. Lumsden, A. G., and Davies, A. M. (1983). Earliest sensory nerve fibers are guided to peripheral targets by attractants other than nerve growth factor. *Nature* (*London*) **306:** 786–788.
63. Heffner, C. D., Lumsden, A. G., and O'Leary, D. D. (1990). Target control of collateral extension and directional axon growth in the mammalian brain. *Science* **247:** 217–220.
64. Tessier-Lavigne, M., Placzek, M., Lumsden, A. G., Dodd, J., and Jessell, T. M. (1988). Chemotropic guidance of developing axons in the mammalian central nervous system. *Nature* (*London*) **336:** 775–778.
65. Placzek, M., Tessier-Lavigne, M., Jessell, T., and Dodd, J. (1990). Orientation of commissural axons in vitro in response to a floor plate–derived chemoattractant. *Development* (*Cambridge, UK*) **110:** 19–30.
66. Kennedy, T. E., Serafini, T., de la Torre, J. R., and Tessier-Lavigne, M. (1994). Netrins are diffusible chemotropic factors for commissural axons in the embryonic spinal cord. *Cell* (*Cambridge, Mass.*) **78:** 425–435.

67. Pini, A. (1993). Chemorepulsion of axons in the developing mammalian central nervous sysem. *Science* **261:** 95–98.
68. Tamada, A., Shirasaki, R., and Murakami, F. (1995). Floor plate chemoattracts crossed axons and chemorepels uncrossed axons in the vertebrate brain. *Neuron* **14:** 1083–1093.
69. Fitzgerald, M., Kwiat, G. C., Middleton, J., and Pini, A. (1993). Ventral spinal cord inhibition of neurite outgrowth from embryonic rat dorsal root ganglia. *Development* (*Cambridge, UK*) **117:** 1377–1384.
70. Tessier-Lavigne, M., and Goodman, C. S. (1996). The molecular biology of axon guidance. *Science* **274:** 1123–1133.
71. Lander, A. D. (1989). Understanding the molecules of neural cell contacts: Emerging patterns of structure and function. *Trends Neurosci.* **12:** 189–195.
72. Baron-Van Evercooren, A., Kleinman, H. K., Ohno, S., Marangos, P., Schwartz, J. P., and Dubois-Dalcq, M. E. (1982). Nerve growth factor, laminin, and fibronectin promote neurite growth in human fetal sensory ganglia cultures. *J. Neurosci. Res.* **8:** 179–193.
73. Rogers, S. L., Edson, K. J., Letourneau, P. C., and McLoon, S. C. (1986). Distribution of laminin in the developing peripheral nervous system of the chick. *Dev. Biol.* **113:** 429–435.
74. Edgar, D. (1991). The expression and distribution of laminin in the developing nervous system. *J. Cell Sci., Suppl.* **15:** 9–12.
75. Hynes, R. O., and Lander, A. D. (1992). Contact and adhesive specificities in the associations, migrations, and targeting of cells and axons. *Cell* (*Cambridge, Mass.*) **68:** 303–322.
76. Reichardt, L. F., and Tomaselli, K. J. (1991). Extracellular matrix molecules and their receptors: Functions in neural development. *Annu. Rev. Neurosci.* **14:** 531–570.
77. Snow, D. M., Lemmon, V., Carrino, D. A., Caplan, A. I., and Silver, J. (1990). Sulfated proteoglycans in astroglial barriers inhibit neurite outgrowth in vitro. *Exp. Neurol.* **109:** 111–130.
78. Wehrle, B., and Chiquet, M. (1990). Tenascin is accumulated along developing peripheral nerves and allows neurite outgrowth in vitro. *Development* (*Cambridge, UK*) **110:** 401–415.
79. Faissner, A., and Kruse, J. (1990). J1/tenascin is a repulsive substrate for central nervous system neurons. *Neuron* **5:** 627–637.
80. Gotz, B., Scholze, A., Clement, A., Joester, A., Schutte, K., Wigger, F., Frank, R., Spiess, E., Ekblom, P., and Faissner, A. (1996). Tenascin-C contains distinct adhesive, anti-adhesive, and neurite outgrowth promoting sites for neurons. *J. Cell Biol.* **132:** 681–699.
81. Brummendorf, T., and Rathjen, F. G. (1993). Axonal glycoproteins with immunoglobulin- and fibronectin type III-related domains in vertebrates: Structural features, binding activities, and signal transduction. *J. Neurochem.* **61:** 1207–1219.
82. Lin, D. M., Fetter, R. D., Kopczynski, C., Grenningloh, G., and Goodman, C. S. (1994). Genetic analysis of Fasciclin II in *Drosophila*: Defasciculation, refasciculation, and altered fasciculation. *Neuron* **13:** 1055–1069.
83. Stoeckli, E. T., and Landmesser, L. T. (1995). Axonin-1, Nr-CAM, and Ng-CAM play different roles in the in vivo guidance of chick commissural neurons. *Neuron* **14:** 1165–1179.
84. McKerracher, L., David, S., Jackson, D. L., Kottis, V., Dunn, R. J., and Braun, P. E. (1994). Identification of myelin-associated glycoprotein as a major myelin-derived inhibitor of neurite growth. *Neuron* **13:** 805–811.
85. Mukhopadhyay, G., Doherty, P., Walsh, F. S., Crocker, P. R., and Filbin, M. T. (1994). A novel role for myelin-associated glycoprotein as an inhibitor of axonal regeneration. *Neuron* **13:** 757–767.
86. Takeichi, M. (1995). Morphogenetic roles of classic cadherins. *Curr. Opin. Cell Biol.* **7:** 619–627.
87. Serafini, T., Kennedy, T. E., Galko, M. J., Mirzayan, C., Jessell, T. M., and Tessier-Lavigne, M. (1994). The netrins define a family of axon outgrowth-promoting proteins homologous to *C. elegans* UNC-6. *Cell* (*Cambridge, Mass.*) **78:** 409–424.
88. Messersmith, E. K., Leonardo, E. D., Shatz, C. J., Tessier-Lavigne, M., Goodman, C. S., and Kolodkin, A. L. (1995). Semaphorin III can function as a selective chemorepellent to pattern sensory projections in the spinal cord. *Neuron* **14:** 949–959.
89. Serafini, T., Colamarino, S. A., Leonardo, E. D., Wang, H., Beddington, R., Skarnes, W. H., and Tessier-Lavigne, M. (1996). Netrin-1 is required for commissural axon projections in the developing vertebrate nervous system. *Cell* (*Cambridge, Mass.*) **13:** 1001–1014.
90. Colamarino, S. A., and Tessier-Lavigne, M. (1995). The axonal chemoattractant netrin-1 is also a chemorepellent for trochlear motor axons. *Cell* (*Cambridge, Mass.*) **81:** 621–629.
91. Tucker, A., Varela-Echevarria, A., Puschel, A. W., and Guthrie, S. (1996). Motor axon subpopulations respond differentially to the chemorepellents netrin-1 and semaphorin D. *Neuron* **18:** 193–207.
92. Hedgecock, E. M., Culotti, J. G., and Hall, D. H. (1990). The unc-5, unc-6, and unc-40 genes guide circumferential migrations of pioneer axons and mesodermal cells on the epidermis in *C. elegans. Neuron* **4:** 61–85.
93. Ishii, N., Wadsworth, W. G., Stern, B. D., Culotti, J. G., and Hedgecock, E. M. (1992). UNC-6, a laminin-related protein, guides cell and pioneer axon migrations in *C. elegans. Neuron* **9:** 873–881.
94. Wadsworth, W. G., Bhatt, H., and Hedgecock, E. M. (1996). Neuroglia and pioneer neurons express UNC-6 to provide global and local netrin cues for guiding migrations in *C. elegans. Neuron* **16:** 35–46.
95. Mitchell, K. J., Doyle, J. L., Serafini, T., Kennedy, T. E., Tessier-Lavigne, M., Goodman, C. S., and Dickson, B. J. (1996). Genetic analysis of Netrin genes in *Drosophila*: Netrins guide CNS commissural axons and peripheral motor axons. *Neuron* **17:** 203–215.
96. Harris, R., Sabatelli, L. M., and Seeger, M. A. (1996). Guidance cues at the *Drosophila* CNS midline: Identification and characterization of two *Drosophila* Netrin/UNC-6 homologs. *Neuron* **17:** 217–228.
97. Kucherer-Ehret, A., Pottgiesser, J., Kreutzberg, G. W., Thoenen, H., and Edgar, D. (1990). Developmental loss of laminin from the interstitial extracellular matrix correlates with decreased laminin gene expression. *Development* (*Cambridge, UK*) **110:** 1285–1293.
98. Kolodkin, A. L., Matthes, D. J., and Goodman, C. S. (1993). The semaphorin genes encode a family of transmembrane and secreted growth cone guidance molecules. *Cell* (*Cambridge, Mass.*) **75:** 1389–1399.
99. Luo, Y., Shepherd, I., Li, J., Renzi, M. J., Chang, S., and Raper, J. A. (1995). A family of molecules related to collapsin in the embryonic chick nervous system. *Neuron* **14:** 1131–1140.
100. Püschel, A. W., Adams, R. H., and Betz, H. (1995). Murine semaphorin D/collapsin is a member of a diverse gene family and creates domains inhibitory for axonal extension. *Neuron* **14:** 941–948.
101. Kolodkin, A. L., Matthes, D. J., O'Connor, T. P., Patel, N. H., Admon, A., Bentley, D., and Goodman, C. S. (1992). Fasciclin IV: Sequence, expression, and function during growth cone guidance in the grasshopper embryo. *Neuron* **9:** 831–845.

102. Luo, Y., Raible, D., and Raper, J. A. (1993). Collapsin: A protein in brain that induces the collapse and paralysis of neuronal growth cones. *Cell (Cambridge, Mass.)* **75:** 217–227.

103. Matthes, D. J., Sink, H., Kolodkin, A. L., and Goodman, C. S. (1995). Semaphorin II can function as a selective inhibitor of specific synaptic arborizations. *Cell (Cambridge, Mass.)* **81:** 631–639.

104. Ebens, A., Brose, K., Hanson, M. G., Bladt, F., Birchmeier, C., Barres, B., and Tessier-Lavigne, M. (1996). Hepatocyte Growth Factor/Scatter Factor is an axonal chemoattractant and neurotrophic factor for spinal motor neurons. *Neuron* **17:** 1157–1172.

105. Sperry, R. W. (1943). Visuomotor coordination in the newt (*Triturus viridescens*) after regeneration of the optic nerve. *J. Comp. Neurol.* **79:** 33–35.

106. Thanos, S., and Bonhoeffer, F. (1986). Course corrections of deflected retinal axons on the tectum of the chick embryo. *Neurosci. Lett.* **72:** 31–36.

107. Holt, C. E., and Harris, W. A. (1993). Position, guidance, and mapping in the developing visual system. *J. Neurobiol.* **24:** 1400–1422.

108. Sperry, R. W. (1963). Chemoaffinity in the orderly growth of nerve fiber patterns and connections. *Proc. Natl. Acad. Sci. U.S.A.* **50:** 703–710.

109. Tessier-Lavigne, M. (1995). Eph receptor tyrosine kinases, axon repulsion, and the development of topographic maps. *Cell (Cambridge, Mass.)* **82:** 345–348.

110. Bonhoeffer, F., and Huf, J. (1982). In vitro experiments on axon guidance demonstrating an anterior-posterior gradient on the tectum. *EMBO J.* **1:** 427–431.

111. Walter, J., Kern-Veits, B., Huf, J., Stolze, B., and Bonhoeffer, F. (1987). Recognition of position-specific properties of tectal cell membranes by retinal axons in vitro. *Development (Cambridge, UK)* **101:** 685–696.

112. Walter, J., Henke-Fahle, S., and Bonhoeffer, F. (1987). Avoidance of posterior tectal membranes by temporal retinal axons. *Development (Cambridge, UK)* **101:** 909–913.

113. Cheng, H. J., Nakamoto, M., Bergemann, A. D., and Flanagan, J. G. (1995). Complementary gradients in expression and binding of ELF-1 and Mek4 in development of the topographic retinotectal projection map. *Cell (Cambridge, Mass.)* **82:** 371–381.

114. Drescher, U., Kremoser, C., Handwerker, C., Loschinger, J., Noda, M., and Bonhoeffer, F. (1995). In vitro guidance of retinal ganglion cell axons by RAGS, a 25 kDa tectal protein related to ligands for Eph receptor tyrosine kinases. *Cell (Cambridge, Mass.)* **82:** 359–370.

115. Nakamoto, M., Cheng, H.-J., Friedman, G. C., McLaughlin, T., Hansen, M. J., Yoon, C. H., O'Leary, D. D. M., and Flanagan, J. G. (1996). Topographically specific effects of ELF-1 on retinal axon guidance in vitro and retinal axon mapping in vivo. *Cell (Cambridge, Mass.)* **86:** 755–766.

C H A P T E R

19

Synapse Formation and Elimination

Jeff W. Lichtman, Steven J. Burden, Susan M. Culican, and Rachel O. L. Wong

The establishment and maintenance of synapses play central roles in the creation of functional neural circuits. Synapse formation follows the events that have been described in previous chapters: neuronal fate specification (Chapter 17) and axonal pathfinding and target selection (Chapter 18). The arrival of an axon at a target cell initiates a series of neurochemical and morphological events that create the structure known as the synapse (see also Chapters 7 and 9). The establishment of a synapse following the initial contact between a growing axon and its target cell involves an elaborate exchange of signals between neuron and target, in which each cell supports and induces the differentiation of its partner. In the first part of this chapter, we consider the cellular and molecular mechanisms by which synapses are established during development.

The formation of synapses, however, does not end the story of how the final pattern of synaptic connections is established. The developing nervous system overproduces connections in great excess during development; in some brain structures, roughly twice as many axonal connections are present early as will be maintained into adulthood. In the second half of this chapter, we discuss the elimination of synapses, a crucial step in the refinement of specific functional connections from an initially more diffuse pattern. Presynaptic axons compete with one another for postsynaptic targets, with the losers in the competition withdrawing their synapses and sometimes, but not always, even dying (see Chapter 20). Both the patterning and the efficacy of neural activity play essential roles in regulating this competition. It is thus through the combination of two developmental phenomena—the formation of synapses with appropriate target cells and the elimination of synapses that fail to be stabilized by appropriate patterns of neuronal activity—that the final and specific patterning of adult connections emerges during development.

SYNAPSE FORMATION

Although synapse formation is likely to be similar in the peripheral and central nervous systems, much of our understanding about the mechanisms of synapse formation arises from studies of the **neuromuscular junction,** the synapse formed between spinal motor neurons and their skeletal muscle cell targets in the body. Studies of neuromuscular synapse formation have benefited from: (1) the relative ease of experimentally manipulating developing or regenerating synapses *in vivo;* (2) the use of cell culture systems for both motor neurons and skeletal muscle cells; (3) the use of *Torpedo* electric organ, an abundant and homogeneous source of neuromuscular-like synapses; and (4) the use of transgenic and mutant mice for studying and altering gene expression.

Synapse Formation Follows Contact between Growth Cones of Developing Motor Neurons and Differentiating Muscle Fibers

Shortly after the initial contact between a growing motor axon and a differentiating myotube, signals are exchanged between nerve and muscle and initiate the formation and assembly of a highly differentiated presynaptic nerve terminal and the muscle's highly specialized postsynaptic apparatus. In vertebrates, there is no evidence to indicate that motor neurons prefer or select a predetermined site on the developing myotube; rather, synapses can form on most if not all of the myotube surface. Although functional synapses form within minutes after contact between developing motor nerves and myotubes, mature synapses are not evident, at least in mammals, until several weeks after the first contacts are made. Maturation requires further arborization of simple, poorly branched nerve terminals, withdrawal and editing of synaptic connections, changes in the efficiency of acetylcholine release, and modifications of the postsynaptic membrane.[1–3]

An adult myofiber, a syncitial cell containing several hundred to several thousand nuclei, is innervated by a single motor axon that terminates and arborizes over ~0.1% of the muscle fiber's cell surface.[3,4] The **acetylcholine receptor** (AChR) is localized to this small patch of the muscle fiber membrane (Fig. 19.1), and its localization to synaptic sites during development is a hallmark of the inductive events of synapse formation.

Complex Mechanisms Are Required to Assemble the Neuromuscular Synapse

Motor neuron nerve terminals are situated in shallow depressions of the muscle cell membrane, which is invaginated further into deep and regular folds, termed **postjunctional folds** (Fig. 19.1). AChRs and additional proteins are localized to the crests of these postjunctional folds, while other proteins, including sodium channels, are enriched in the troughs of the postjunctional folds. The nerve terminal is likewise spatially organized, and its substructural organization reflects that of the postsynaptic membrane. Synaptic vesicles are sparse in the region of the nerve terminal facing the Schwann cell and are abundant in the region of the nerve terminal facing the muscle fiber. Moreover, synaptic vesicles are clustered adjacent to a specialization of the presynaptic membrane, termed **active zones** (Fig. 19.2), which are the sites of synaptic vesicle fusion. The active zones are aligned precisely with the mouths of the postjunctional folds. This precise registration ensures that acetylcholine encounters a high concentration of AChRs within microseconds after release, thereby facilitating synaptic transmission. The alignment of structural specializations in both pre- and postsynaptic membranes suggests that spatially restricted signaling between pre- and postsynaptic cells is important for coordinating pre- and postsynaptic differentiation.[3]

The **synaptic basal lamina** in the cleft between the nerve terminal and muscle appears to be a repository for at least two different signaling molecules at developing and adult neuromuscular synapses. Whether these molecules must be associated with the basal lamina to signal or whether they can signal as membrane-associated or secreted molecules is not known. The precise arrangement of proteins in the postsynaptic membrane of the neuromuscular synapse, however, suggests that it may be important to restrict these signaling molecules to the synaptic site, and possibly even to subdomains within the synaptic site. Although membrane proteins, which are anchored to the cytoskeleton or to the extracellular matrix, have reduced lateral diffusion and could provide spatially restricted signaling, molecules in the basal lamina also do not diffuse laterally and are particularly well suited to providing spatially restricted signaling.

The Synaptic Basal Lamina Contains Signals for Synaptic Differentiation

The idea that signals for inducing both presynaptic and postsynaptic differentiation are contained in the synaptic basal lamina arose from studies of regenerating neuromuscular synapses.[5,6] Following damage to a motor axon, the distal portion of the motor axon (closest to the muscle) degenerates, and the proximal end regenerates and grows back into the muscle. The regenerated axon precisely reinnervates the original synaptic site and forms a synapse that is indistinguishable from the original synapse. The empty sheaths that had originally encircled the axons, formed by Schwann cells and their basal laminae, appear to provide a favorable substrate for motor axons and direct regenerating motor axons to original synaptic sites. Although motor axons precisely reinnervate original synaptic sites, both original and foreign motor neurons can accurately and functionally reinnervate original synaptic sites in denervated muscle.

Following damage to both motor axons and muscle, nerve terminals and muscle fibers degenerate and are phagocytized, but the basal lamina of the muscle fiber remains intact. Even in the absence of nerve terminals and muscle fibers, several structures—including the terminal Schwann cells and the basal laminae of the postjunctional folds—and acetylcholinesterase (AChE) remain at the original synaptic site and allow its identification. Axons eventually regenerate and grow toward muscle, and new myofibers regenerate within the basal lamina of the original myofiber. The regenerated motor axons form synapses with the regenerated myofibers precisely at the original synaptic site. Even when muscle fiber regeneration is prevented, regenerating motor axons will still form synapses at the original synaptic site when the basal lamina is intact. Furthermore, active zones will form in register with the basal lamina of the original postjunctional folds (Fig. 19.2). Thus, the

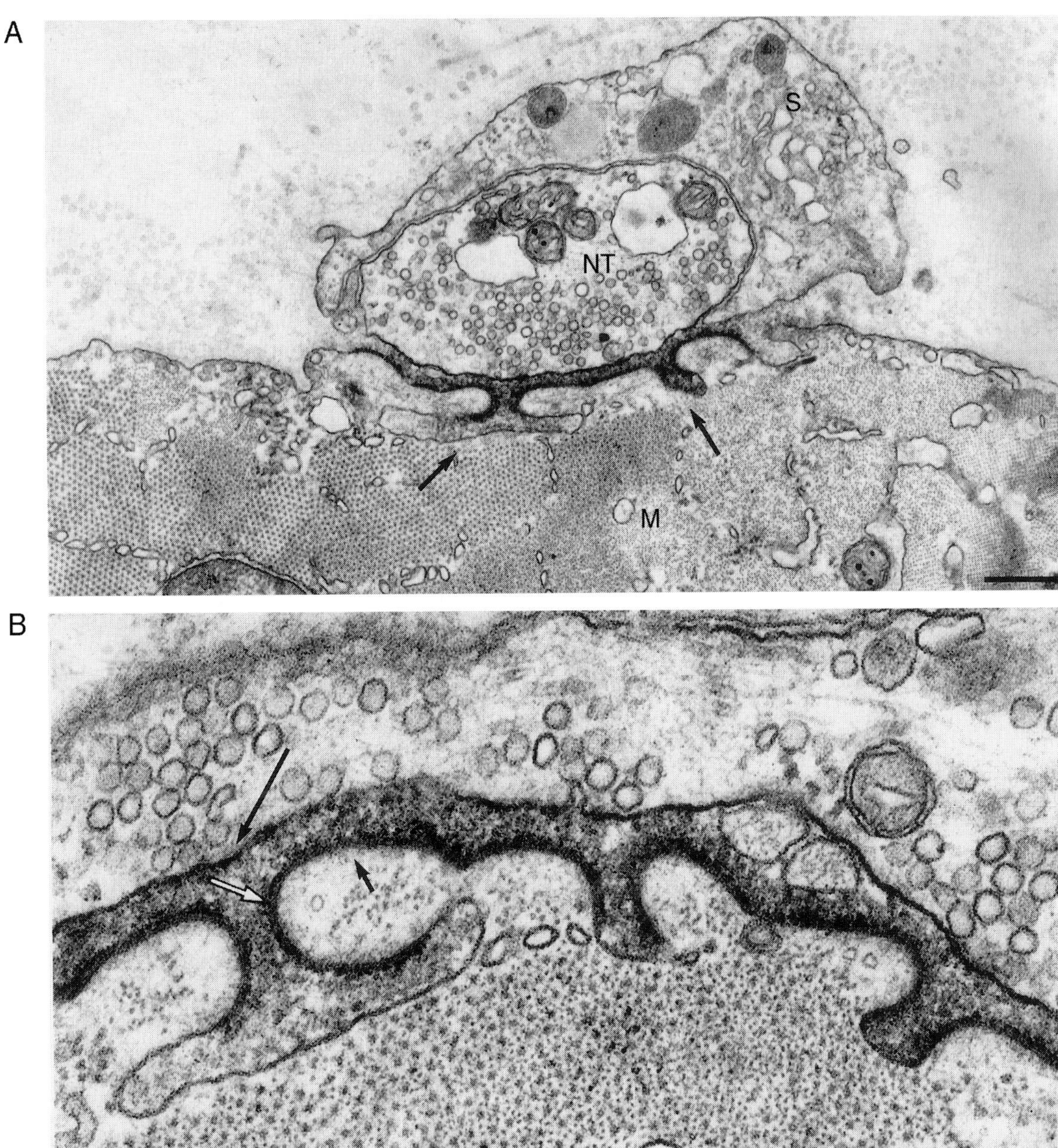

FIGURE 19.1 Pre- and postsynaptic membranes at the neuromuscular synapse are highly specialized. (A) An electron micrograph of a neuromuscular synapse shows that the nerve terminal (NT) is capped by a Schwann cell (S) and is situated in a shallow depression of the muscle cell (M) membrane, which is invaginated further into deep and regular folds, termed postjunctional folds (arrows). AChRs, labeled with α-bungarotoxin coupled to horseradish peroxidase, are concentrated at the synaptic site. (B) A higher magnification view shows that AChRs are concentrated at the crests and along the sides of the postjunctional folds (white arrow). Rapsyn, NRG receptors, and MuSK are also concentrated in the postsynaptic membrane, whereas agrin, NRG, acetylcholinesterase, S-laminin, and certain isoforms of collagen are localized to the synaptic basal lamina. The postjunctional folds of the myofiber are spaced at regular intervals and are situated directly across from active zones (long arrow) in which clusters of synaptic vesicles accumulate in the nerve terminal (arrows). From Burden *et al.*,[6] with permission.

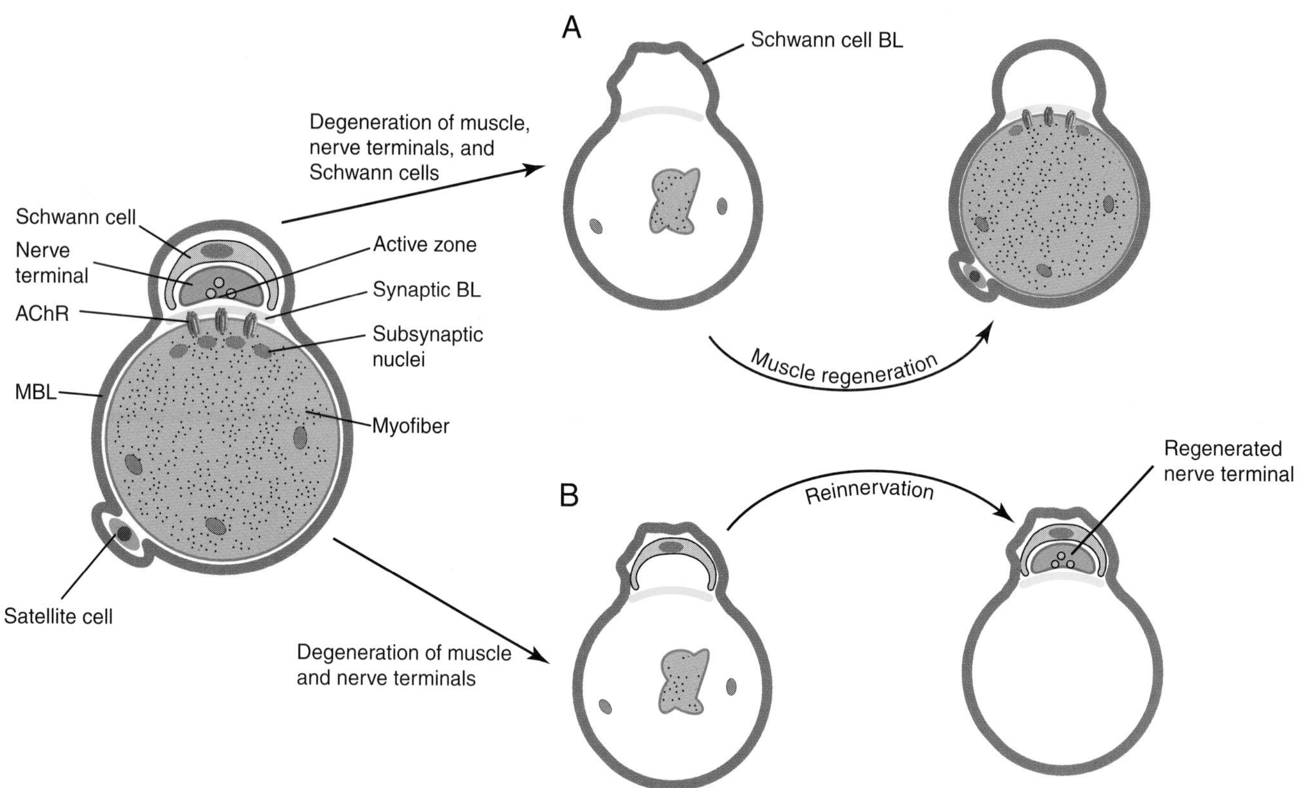

FIGURE 19.2 The synaptic basal lamina contains signals for presynaptic and postsynaptic differentiation. A cartoon illustrating a cross section of normal muscle containing a nerve terminal (NT), Schwann cell, and myofiber is shown to the far left. AChR genes are induced in synaptic nuclei (red), and AChRs (green) are concentrated at synaptic sites. Active zones and clusters of synaptic vesicles in the nerve terminal are aligned with postjunctional folds in the myofiber. Each myofiber is ensheathed by a basal lamina (MBL), which is specialized at the synaptic site (synaptic BL) and which remains intact following degeneration of the original myofiber. The MBL serves as a scaffold for regenerating myofibers, which form from the fusion of satellite cells that proliferate following damage to the original myofiber. (A) In this experiment, axons innervating the muscle were damaged and prevented from regenerating and the muscle was injured. New myofibers regenerate within the basal lamina of the original myofiber, in the absence of the nerve. AChRs cluster and AChR gene expression is reinduced at the original synaptic site, despite the absence of the nerve and other presynaptic cells such as the Schwann cells. This experiment shows that the synaptic basal lamina contains signals for clustering AChRs and for activating AChR genes in the synaptic nuclei of muscle cells. (B) In this experiment, both the motor axon and the muscle were damaged, but only the muscle fibers were prevented from regenerating. Axons regenerate to the original synaptic site, even in the absence of their muscle cell targets. They accumulate synaptic vesicles precisely across from the sites of the original postjunctional folds. This experiment shows that the synaptic basal lamina contains signals for inducing presynaptic differentiation.

presence of the myofiber is necessary neither for precise reinnervation nor for the morphological differentiation of regenerated nerve terminals. If regeneration of motor axons is prevented but myofibers are allowed to regenerate, AChRs accumulate and membrane folds form in the regenerated myofiber precisely at the original synaptic site on the basal lamina. Thus, in the absence of nerve terminals, myofibers, and terminal Schwann cells, information remains at the original synaptic site that is instructive for both presynaptic and postsynaptic differentiation. Because the synaptic basal lamina is the most prominent extracellular structure remaining at neuromuscular synapses following removal of all cells, these results indicate that the synaptic basal lamina contains signals that can induce differentiation of both nerve terminals and myofibers.

Agrin Induces Postsynaptic Differentiation

Because clustering of AChRs, unlike the formation of active zones, can be readily studied in cell culture, identifying the basal lamina signals that induce postsynaptic differentiation has been far simpler than identifying those that induce presynaptic differentiation. Extracellular matrix from *Torpedo* electric organ (see Box 19.1), a tissue that is homologous to muscle but more densely innervated, contains an activity that stimulates AChR clustering in cultured myotubes. The electric organ activity, termed **agrin,** is synthesized by motor neurons, transported in motor axons to synaptic sites, and deposited in the synaptic basal lamina.[7] Agrin also regulates the distribution of other synaptic proteins, including AChE, rapsyn, utrophin, and neuregulin (NRG) receptors, indicating that agrin has a central role in synaptic differentiation (Fig. 19.3).[8] cDNAs encoding agrin have been isolated from *Torpedo* electric lobe and from the central nervous system of higher vertebrates.[9,10] Agrin is an ~200-kDa protein containing multiple epidermal growth factor (EGF)-like signaling domains, two different laminin-like domains, and multiple follistatin-like repeats.[8] The four EGF-like domains and three laminin G domains are contained in the carboxyl-terminal region, which is sufficient for inducing AChR clusters in cultured myotubes[10–12]; sequences in the amino-terminal region are responsible for the association of agrin with the extracellular matrix.

Two lines of evidence indicate that local release of agrin by motor nerve terminals is necessary for clustering of AChRs at synaptic sites and for inducing postsynaptic differentiation. First, antibodies against agrin block AChR clustering at nerve–muscle synapses that form in cell culture,[13] and second, mice lacking agrin lack normal synapses (see below).

The agrin gene is expressed in a variety of cell types. Alternative splicing results in multiple agrin isoforms that differ in their AChR clustering efficiency.[11,12,14] The isoform that appears most active in clustering AChRs is expressed in motor neurons,[11] whereas other agrin isoforms are expressed in additional cell types, including skeletal muscle cells.[11] The active, neuronal-specific isoforms of agrin contain 8–19 amino acids at a splice site, referred to as the Z site in rat agrin and the B site in chick agrin.[11] Recent studies indicate that the B site, together with the last laminin G domain, is sufficient to cluster AChRs.[15]

Experiments with chimeric synapses between chick and rat indicate that blocking antibodies to nerve-derived but not to muscle-derived agrin inhibit AChR clustering.[13] Although muscle-derived agrin may have a role in synapse formation, these results demonstrate that muscle-derived agrin cannot substitute for nerve-derived agrin in clustering AChRs.

MuSK Is Required for Agrin-Mediated Signaling and Synapse Formation

The mechanism of agrin-mediated AChR clustering is not known, but a receptor tyrosine kinase (RTK) termed **muscle-specific kinase** (or MuSK) appears to be a critical component of the agrin receptor complex. MuSK is expressed in *Torpedo* electric organ and in skeletal muscle, where it is concentrated in the postsynaptic membrane.[16] Mutant mice in which either the

BOX 19.1

THE *Torpedo* ELECTRIC ORGAN

The majority of proteins localized to neuromuscular synapses were first identified in postsynaptic membranes isolated from the electric organ of the marine ray, *Torpedo.* The electric organ generates electrical discharges that enable the ray to navigate through its environment ("electrolocation") and to stun prey. The organ consists of a stack of thousands of thin, disklike cells called **electrocytes**. These cells begin their differentiation as skeletal muscle fibers, but then lose their contractile machinery. One side of each electrocyte receives synaptic input from cholinergic neurons so that nearly half of the cell's membrane is studded by nerve terminals. This extraordinarily dense innervation contrasts with that of a skeletal myofiber, in which only about 0.1% of the cell surface is occupied by nerve terminals. When the nerve innervating the electric organ is stimulated, the innervated face of the electrocyte depolarizes but the cell does not generate action potentials. Because the extracellular fluids on the two sides of the electrocyte are electrically isolated, the depolarization on one face of the cell generates a large electrical potential difference. The electrical potentials across each cell in the stacked electric organ add up, as in a battery, to create an electrical discharge of hundreds of volts, a voltage that is sufficient to stun prey.

Because the electric organ is specialized to receive a massive cholinergic input, the organ serves as a uniquely homogeneous and abundant source of pre- and postsynaptic membranes that are similar to those at neuromuscular synapses. The electric organ from a moderate-sized ray weighs several kilograms; thus, several milligrams of purified postsynaptic proteins may be obtained from a single electric organ. Indeed, this specialized tissue has been essential for the identification and purification of proteins such as the acetylcholine receptor, acetylcholinesterase, rapsyn, syntrophin, agrin, MuSK, and several synaptic vesicle proteins.

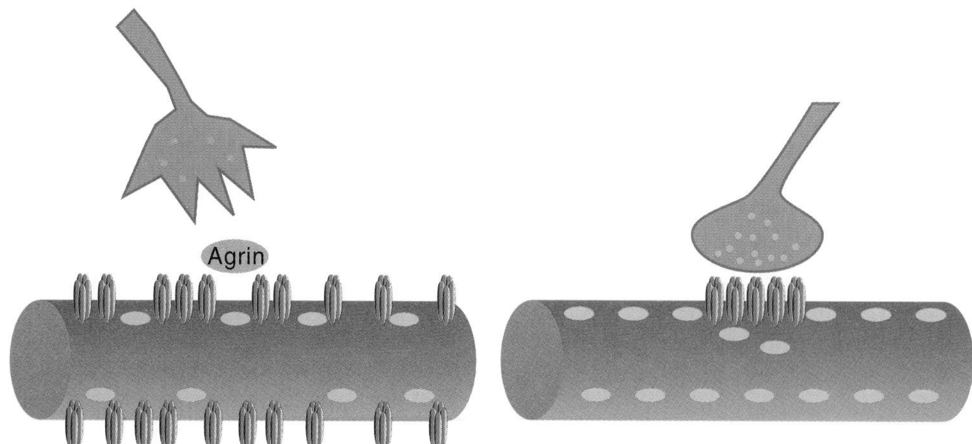

FIGURE 19.3 Agrin induces the redistribution of AChRs. (Left) Motor neurons synthesize and secrete agrin into the synaptic basal lamina. Before innervation, AChRs (green) are spread diffusely over the surface of the myotube. (Right) The release of agrin by the motor neuron results in the redistribution of previously unclustered AChRs to synaptic sites, immediately adjacent to the nerve terminal. Through the clustering of existing AChRs and the increased synthesis of new AChRs, the concentration of receptors at the synapse greatly exceeds that in extrasynaptic regions.

agrin gene or the *MuSK* gene has been disrupted genetically[17,18] lack normal neuromuscular synapses. Indeed, the similarity of the phenotypes of agrin and MuSK mutant mice is consistent with the idea that MuSK is a component of an agrin receptor complex. Both agrin and MuSK mutant mice are immobile, cannot breathe, and die shortly after birth. Muscle differentiation is normal in agrin and MuSK mutant mice, but the mutant muscle fibers lack all known features of postsynaptic differentiation. Muscle-derived proteins, including AChRs and AChE, which are concentrated at synapses in normal mice, are uniformly distributed in MuSK mutant myofibers. In addition, AChR genes, which are normally selectively transcribed in synaptic nuclei of normal muscle fibers (see below), are transcribed at similar rates in synaptic and nonsynaptic nuclei of muscle fibers from agrin and MuSK deficient mice.

Four lines of evidence indicate that MuSK is required for agrin-mediated signaling and is a component of the agrin receptor complex: (1) agrin can be chemically crosslinked to MuSK; (2) agrin induces rapid tyrosine phosphorylation of MuSK; (3) a recombinant, soluble extracellular fragment of MuSK inhibits agrin-induced AChR clustering in cultured muscle cells; (4) cultured MuSK mutant muscle cells, unlike normal muscle cells, do not cluster AChRs in response to agrin. MuSK alone, however, does not bind agrin, indicating that other activities or additional proteins are required for agrin-mediated signaling.[19]

Studies indicate that α-dystroglycan binds agrin,[20–23] raising the possibility that dystroglycan collaborates with MuSK to mediate agrin signaling. α-Dystroglycan is a peripheral membrane protein that binds laminin in the extracellular matrix and is covalently linked to β-dystroglycan, an integral membrane protein that associates with the intracellular cytoskeletal scaffold. Although antibodies to α-dystroglycan have been reported to perturb the formation of AChR clusters induced by agrin,[21,22] other studies have found the same antibodies to be ineffective in altering the response to agrin.[23] Moreover, the dystroglycan-binding sequences in agrin do not appear to be necessary for AChR clustering.[15] Thus, although α-dystroglycan may participate in agrin-mediated signaling, it may not have a role in initiating clustering but merely be one of many postsynaptic molecules that cluster in response to agrin.

Agrin and MuSK Are Required for Retrograde Signaling and Presynaptic Differentiation

Although pathfinding of motor axons to muscle is normal in mice lacking agrin or MuSK, agrin and MuSK mutant mice lack normal nerve terminals.[17,18] Branches of the main intramuscular nerve in the mutant mice neither establish normal contacts with the muscle nor form correctly positioned or specialized nerve terminals. These results suggest that motor axons in agrin or MuSK mutant mice are not provided with appropriate signals to prevent their wandering across the muscle. Because MuSK is expressed in skeletal muscle and not in motor neurons, the aberrant behavior of presynaptic terminals in MuSK mutant mice is probably due to indirect actions of the agrin–MuSK signaling system. These results raise the possibility that agrin released from nerve terminals causes the muscle cell, via MuSK activation, to reciprocally release a recognition signal back to the nerve, or to Schwann cells, to indicate that a functional contact has occurred. In response to this muscle-derived recognition or adhesion signal, the nerve undergoes presynaptic differentiation and stops growing. Alternatively, the lack of synaptic activity in MuSK mutant mice may result in aberrant retrograde signaling, causing exuberant growth of motor axons. In either case, these results demonstrate the importance of the reciprocal signaling relationship between nerve and muscle during development.

Rapsyn Is Required for Postsynaptic Differentiation and Is Downstream of Agrin and MuSK

The steps that follow MuSK activation and that lead to postsynaptic differentiation are not known. Agrin, however, causes tyrosine phosphorylation of the AChR β subunit[24] and other postsynaptic proteins, raising the possibility that tyrosine phosphorylation of synaptic proteins might be an important step in clustering AChRs and possibly other proteins at synapses.

It seems likely that a 43-kDa protein, termed **rapsyn,** has an important role in agrin-mediated signaling.[25] Rapsyn is a myristolated, peripheral membrane protein present at 1:1 stoichiometry with AChRs at synaptic sites[26,27] that may interact directly with AChRs and potentially other synaptic proteins.[28,29]

Agrin stimulates clustering of rapsyn in myotubes grown in cell culture, and clustering of rapsyn and AChRs appears to occur coincidentally at developing synapses.[30,31] Rapsyn is critical for synapse formation. Mice lacking rapsyn expression die within hours after birth and have difficulty moving and breathing.[32] Importantly, normal clustering of AChRs, neuregulin receptors, utrophin, and dystroglycan is lacking in rapsyn mutant mice. Nevertheless, AChR expression is enriched in the central region of the muscle, and synaptic basal lamina proteins—AChE and S-laminin—are localized, albeit at lower levels, at mutant synaptic sites. The persistence of synapse-specific gene expression (see below) in rapsyn mutant mice is likely to explain the enrichment of AChRs within the central region of rapsyn mutant muscle fibers. Synapse-specific transcription may also explain the localization of AChE and S-laminin to mutant synaptic sites, since AChE and S-laminin mRNAs, like AChR subunit mRNAs, are localized to normal synaptic sites. Because AChE and S-laminin are localized to the synaptic basal lamina, in contrast to the AChR, they are unlikely to readily diffuse from the site of their deposition. Forced expression of rapsyn in *Xenopus* oocytes or in a fibroblast/musclelike cell line results in clustering of rapsyn.[33,34] Moreover, clustering of rapsyn is necessary and sufficient for clustering AChRs in these cells.

Certain Genes Are Expressed Selectively in Synaptic Nuclei of Myofibers

Like AChR protein, the mRNAs encoding the different subunits (α, β, γ or ε, and δ) of the AChR are concentrated at synaptic sites.[35-37] Studies with transgenic mice that harbor gene fusions between regulatory regions of AChR subunit genes and reporter genes have shown that AChR genes are transcribed selectively in myofiber nuclei near the synaptic site.[38-40] Thus, localized transcription of AChR genes in synaptic nuclei is responsible, at least in part, for the accumulation of AChR mRNA at synaptic sites.

At present, only AChR subunit genes are known to be selectively transcribed in the synaptic nuclei of skeletal myofibers. Messenger RNAs encoding rapsyn, NCAM, MuSK, and the catalytic subunit of AChE, however, are also concentrated in the synaptic region of skeletal myofibers.[16,41] These results raise the possibility that these genes are transcribed preferentially in synaptic nuclei as well. Thus, synapse-specific transcription may be a common mechanism for localizing gene products to the neuromuscular synapse.

Neuregulin Activates Gene Expression in Synaptic Nuclei

Studies of regenerating muscle have shown that a signal for synapse-specific transcription is contained in the synaptic basal lamina.[42-43] Among the potential candidates for the transcriptional signal are the products of the **neuregulin** (NRG) gene.[44] The *NRG* gene encodes more than one dozen alternatively spliced products that have multiple activities. Although originally purified as a ligand that stimulates tyrosine phosphorylation of the *neu* oncogene, NRG was independently purified from the central nervous system as an activity, termed AChR-inducing activity (ARIA), that induces AChR synthesis[45] and from the pituitary as an activity, termed glial growth factor (GGF), that stimulates proliferation of Schwann cells.[46] NRG is concentrated at neuromuscular synapses and can activate AChR gene expression in muscle cells grown in cell culture.[47] Most NRG isoforms are transmembrane proteins, which may be active on the cell surface or processed, like EGF, to yield a soluble signaling fragment. NRG contains a single EGF-like domain, which alone is sufficient for cell signaling. Alternative splicing within the EGF-like domain yields two types of isoforms, α or β type, which differ in their affinities for the different NRG receptors (see below). Little is known about the role of alternative splicing in other domains of NRG.

Motor neurons synthesize NRG,[45,46] and NRG protein is detectable in motor axons,[47] indicating that some of the NRG protein at synaptic sites is synthesized by motor neurons. Skeletal myofibers, however, also synthesize NRG,[48] and some of the NRG at synaptic sites is synthesized by myofibers. Because neural forms of agrin can cause clustering of muscle NRG, agrin may have a role in localizing muscle NRG to synaptic sites, raising the possibility that synapse-specific gene expression may be initiated and maintained, at least in part, by an autocrine NRG / erbB signaling mechanism.

Two members of the EGF receptor family, ErbB3 and ErbB4, are receptors for NRG. Both ErbB3 and ErbB4 are concentrated in the postsynaptic membrane at neuromuscular synapses,[48,49] and the colocalization of NRG, ErbB3, and ErbB4 at synapses supports the idea that NRG is a signal that regulates synaptic differentiation (Fig. 19.4, Box 19.2). Nevertheless, whether NRG-mediated signaling is required for synapse-specific gene expression remains unclear. Mice lacking NRG, ErbB2, or ErbB4 die from a failure of heart development on embryonic day 10, which is 4 to 5 days prior to neuromuscular synapse formation.[50–52]

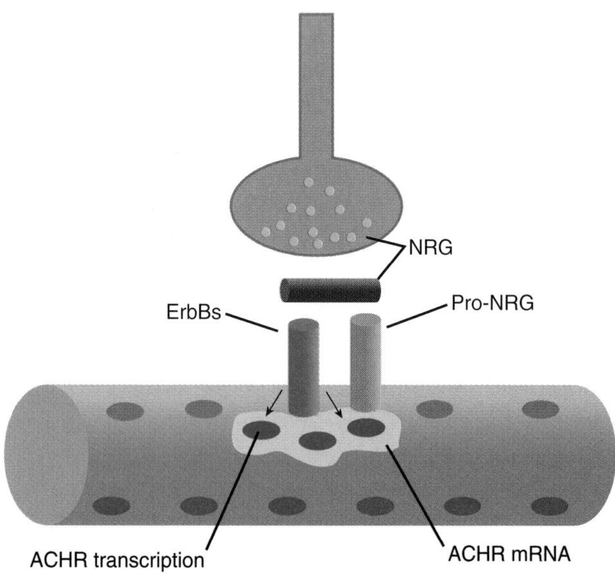

FIGURE 19.4 Synapse-specific gene expression. The cartoon illustrates a longitudinal view of a multinucleated myofiber innervated by a single nerve terminal. The diagram shows that AChR subunit genes are transcribed selectively in nuclei (dark blue) in the synaptic region of the myofiber, resulting in an accumulation of AChR mRNA (light blue) and AChR protein at synaptic sites. The nerve induces this spatially restricted pattern of transcription, and the extracellular signal that triggers synapse-specific gene expression is contained in the synaptic basal lamina. NRG (yellow), which is associated with the synaptic basal lamina, the nerve terminal, and the postsynaptic membrane, is the best candidate for the signal that induces synapse-specific transcription. NRG receptors, ErbB3 and ErbB4 (green), together with ErbB2, are concentrated in the postsynaptic membrane. This model proposes that NRG stimulates a signaling pathway (arrows) that induces AChR genes in nuclei near the activated NRG receptors.

Summary

Synapse formation is induced through a complex series of interactions between presynaptic neurons and their postsynaptic targets. The best understood example of synapse formation is the neuromuscular junction. Motor neurons synthesize and secrete a large protein called agrin into the extracellular matrix at synaptic sites. Both agrin and MuSK, a receptor tyrosine kinase present on muscle cells, are required for normal synapse formation at the neuromuscular junction. Agrin triggers the muscle cell to cluster its acetylcholine receptors at the synapse, a process in which the intracellular protein rapsyn plays a key role, and to begin the process of postsynaptic differentiation. In addition, the motor axon secretes neuregulin, which increases the expression of acetylcholine receptor expression by the muscle. The muscle cell in return sends signals back to the neuron that stabilize the presynaptic terminal and induce its differentiation. Less is known about the cellular and molecular mechanisms of synapse formation in the central nervous system, although it seems likely that similar strategies are employed.

AN OVERVIEW OF SYNAPSE ELIMINATION

The developmental processes responsible for creating the nervous system include not only mechanisms for establishing an enormous number of cellular and synaptic elements but also processes that remove many of those same elements. The phenomena of naturally occurring cell death, collateral withdrawal, and synapse elimination are some examples of how this retrenchment is achieved. Why the nervous system needs to eliminate already established neurons and dismantle their synaptic connections is not well understood. In engineering it has long been appreciated that one of the faster iterative algorithms for reaching a solution to a complex problem is a method of approximation that intentionally overshoots the mark and then regresses to narrow in on the true solution. It may be that getting the right numbers of neurons, axonal branches, and synapses is also more efficiently reached by a strategy that reaches the end point by regulation of both the processes of building and processes of taking away.

The elements that are removed during these developmental processes are not necessarily "erroneous" in a qualitative sense. Rather, the changes seem more related to adjustments in the *number* of cells or connections. For synapse elimination in particular, the reorganization seems to be related to fine-tuning the strength as well as the number of synaptic connections. As will be described in this section, these kinds of alterations may be achieved by "functional validation," in which some aspect of the early use of synaptic circuits guides the process. Because intrinsic mechanisms of wiring the nervous system are apparently quite good, it is not surprising that the use-dependent modifications in connectivity are often subtle. These subtleties are nevertheless critically important for creating a nervous system that is finely tuned for action in, and reception of, the world it will inhabit.

There Are Several Different Kinds of Synapse Elimination

Naturally occurring cell death, described in Chapter 20, contributes to the loss of synapses. An example of this kind of loss occurs in the embryonic chick ciliary ganglion.[62] During developmental stages 36–37, preganglionic cells undergo a period of cell death, which occurs after these cells have established functional synaptic connections with ciliary ganglion cells.[63] Consequently, when preganglionic cells die, some ganglion cells become transiently denervated, indicating that they had received input only from dying cells.

There is also evidence that neurons whose axons have been cut lose their presynaptic input as a consequence. This synapse stripping may be the result of an interruption in the supply of trophic factors (see Chapter 21). Although the loss of synapses in this situation is probably not due to activity-dependent competition, the underlying mechanisms may be related.[64] In this part of the chapter we will concentrate on the activity-dependent form of synapse elimination that occurs ordinarily in early postnatal life.

Why Does the Nervous System Undergo Synapse Elimination?

Synapse elimination during development seems to be most obvious in situations where there is a need to partition innervation among homogeneous populations of target cells. This situation arises with some frequency in the nervous systems of terrestrial vertebrates, where groups of neurons serve similar or even nearly identical functions. Take as an example the innervation of muscle fibers by motor neurons. In all terrestrial vertebrates (amphibians, reptiles, birds, and mammals), pools containing tens to hundreds of motor neurons innervate individual skeletal muscles, which are themselves composed of hundreds to thousands of nearly identical muscle fibers. This kind of redundancy is less common in invertebrates, where often a single identified motor neuron is responsible for innervating a particular muscle, which is also composed of only one or a few cells.

In skeletal muscles of the twitch variety (i.e., muscle fibers that respond to innervation with an all-or-nothing action-potential-based contraction), the majority of muscle fibers have a single neuromuscular junction located roughly in the middle of their length. This neuromuscular junction is typically innervated by only one motor axon (singly innervated). This raises a number of questions. What gives rise to the specificity? Why is it that only one of the many motor axons that project to the muscle will ultimately contact this fiber?

In both vertebrates and invertebrates, mechanisms such as axon pathfinding and selective synapse formation operate to allow particular neurons access to particular postsynaptic targets. Evidence for selectivity in motor axonal synapse formation in muscle has come from studies showing that some inputs are restricted in their choice of postsynaptic target cells. For example, there is evidence for both specificity in the choice of postsynaptic partners based on fiber type[65] and topographic matching of motor neuron position in the spinal cord and muscle fiber position.[66] However, several lines of evidence argue that the association of a motor axon with the particular muscle fibers it innervates cannot be fully explained by selective navigation of axons to the vicinity of some muscle fibers and not others, nor by mechanisms of selective synapse formation. In skeletal muscle, the spatial arrangement of connections between motor neurons and muscle fibers shows little evidence of any particular fine pattern, as might be expected if a motor unit's distribution resulted from a mechanism of specific pathfinding of the innervating axons. In mammals, for example, the distribution of muscle fibers in a motor neuron's motor unit has been seen in many muscles to be nearly random (see Chapter 30).Thus, neighboring muscle fibers are typically innervated by different motor axons, while each motor axon projects diffusely to large regions within a muscle, completely overlapping the projections of many other neurons. In addition, if some motor axons to a muscle are cut, the remaining axons can sprout to innervate the denervated muscle fibers, indicating that an axon *can* innervate other muscle fibers in the absence of other axons.[67] Furthermore, if motor nerves are diverted so that they project to a muscle they do not ordinarily innervate, the axons grow and easily establish synapses on the foreign muscle,[68] indicating that both axon navigation and synapse formation are quite permissive within a muscle. Thus, the fact that each skeletal muscle fiber has one neuromuscular junction and only one axon that innervates

BOX 19.2

SYNAPSE FORMATION IN THE CNS

A single neuron in the central nervous system (CNS) receives input from thousands of different synapses that use a variety of transmitters. Most synapses in the brain and spinal cord fall into one of two classes: (1) excitatory synapses that use the neurotransmitter glutamate and generally form on dendritic spines or (2) inhibitory synapses that secrete GABA and are found on dendritic shafts and cell bodies. A neuron could either localize all the potentially necessary signaling components to all postsynaptic sites or localize specific signaling components only to the synapses where they are required. Accumulating evidence points to the latter possibility.[53–55] Transmitter receptors do not indiscriminately localize to all postsynaptic sites made by a neuron; rather, glutamate receptors cluster selectively opposite glutamatergic terminals, and GABA receptors cluster selectively opposite GABAergic terminals[55] (Fig. 19.5, A–F). Additionally, different subtypes of glutamate receptor can selectively localize to different glutamatergic postsynaptic sites of a single neuron. Thus, there is considerable heterogeneity in the molecular composition of synapses in the CNS.

In the CNS, different sets of synapse organizing molecules may exist for each transmitter type. Rapsyn and MuSK have not been detected in the brain, and although agrin is widely expressed, tests for a potential role in interneuronal synapse formation have so far been negative. A combination of biochemical and molecular studies have identified a number of potential CNS receptor clustering molecules. **Gephyrin** is a peripheral membrane protein that binds to the inhibitory glycine receptor β subunit and to tubulin; it appears to provide an essential link between the glycine receptor and the postsynaptic cytoskeleton.[56] Although gephyrin is concentrated at GABAergic synapses, direct binding between gephyrin and GABA receptors has not been observed, leaving open the function of gephyrin at GABA synapses. Gephyrin is not present at glutamatergic synapses. Glutamate synapses contain several proteins with **PDZ domains,** novel domains that mediate protein–protein interaction either via binding of PDZ domains to specific C-terminal sequences or via PDZ domain–PDZ domain interactions[57] (Fig. 19.5G). The prototypic PDZ domain protein at glutamatergic synapses is PSD-95 / SAP90 and the related family members are chapsyn / PSD93 and SAP102. These proteins contain three PDZ domains: PDZ1 and 2 bind the C-termini of NMDAR2 glutamate receptor subunits as well as K^+ channels, and PDZ2 also binds the PDZ domain of nitric oxide synthase. Thus, PSD-95 family members may both crosslink receptors and serve as a scaffold for attaching downstream signal transducing molecules. Other families of divergent PDZ domain-containing proteins bind non-NMDA glutamate receptors, as exemplified by GRIP, a protein with seven PDZ domains, of which PDZ4 and 5 bind AMPA-selective glutamate receptor subunits.[58]

With the recent development of molecular probes and culture systems, the study of CNS synapse formation is advancing rapidly, but there are many open questions. What are the signals that induce synapse formation? Formation of postsynaptic sites is not dependent on neurotransmitter release,[55] an obvious potential mechanism. CNS synapses have a small synaptic cleft, about 15 nm, which does not contain a pronounced basal lamina, suggesting that direct contact between presynaptic and postsynaptic transmembrane proteins may be a major form of

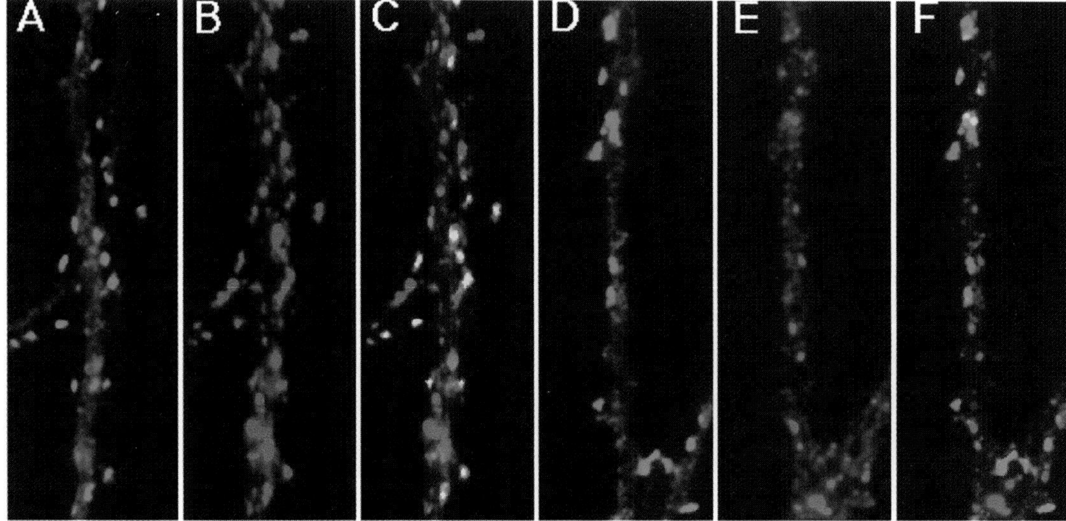

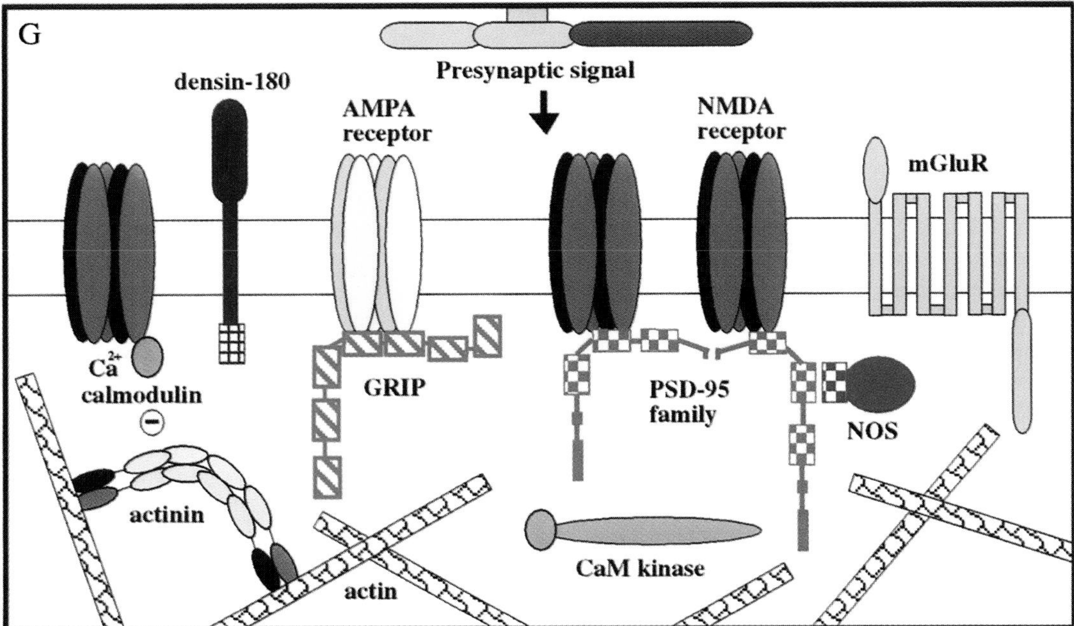

FIGURE 19.5 Synapse formation between CNS neurons. Synaptic proteins are clustered in cultured hippocampal neurons. (A–C) Hippocampal neurons were placed in culture and then labeled with antibodies that recognize (A) a subunit of the excitatory glutamate receptor called GluR1 (green), which is localized to the postsynaptic side of the synapse, and (B) a synaptic vesicle protein called synaptophysin (red), which marks the presynaptic terminal. (C) The overlay of the images shown in (A) and (B) reveals that the glutamate receptors cluster on dendritic spines where they are found apposed to a subset of presynaptic terminals, which appear as hot spots of synaptophysin immunoreactivity. The colocalization of both GluR1 and synaptophysin immunoreactivity appears as yellow. (D–F) Hippocampal neurons were placed in culture, and in this experiment the neurons were labeled with antibodies that recognize (D) the excitatory receptor subunit GluR1 (green) or (E) the $\beta 2/3$ subunit of an inhibitory receptor, the $GABA_A$ receptor (red). (F) In contrast to the colocalization of GluR1 and synaptophysin immunoreactivities, glutamate and GABA receptors cluster at distinctly nonoverlapping sites. GluR1 (green) is found primarily on dendritic spines, while the GABA receptor (red) is localized to dendritic shafts. Additional studies have revealed that glutamate receptors are clustered underneath synapses that secrete glutamate, while GABA receptors are concentrated at terminals that release GABA. (G) Model of the molecular composition of excitatory postsynaptic sites. Glutamate receptors are clustered at postsynaptic sites, with the ionotropic receptors (including AMPA and NMDA receptors) localized directly across from the presynaptic active zone and the metabotropic receptors (mGluRs) found at slightly more distal locations. The clustering of receptors at the synapse, as well as other aspects of synapse formation, is likely to be mediated in part by PDZ-containing proteins, PSD-95 and GRIP. PDZ domains (indicated as hatched or striped boxes) are protein–protein interaction domains that bind to specific sequences on the C-termini of other proteins or to other PDZ domains. Proteins with multiple PDZ domains (such as the PSD-95 family and GRIP) probably function both to crosslink receptors and to act as scaffolds for the clustering of other synaptic proteins (e.g., nitric oxide synthase, NOS). It is not known how PDZ proteins attach to the cytoskeleton. The attachment of NMDA receptors to the actin cytoskeleton may be mediated by α-actinin, which binds to NMDA receptors competitively with Ca^{2+}–calmodulin. Finally, transmembrane proteins such as densin-180 may function as signaling molecules to mediate communication across the synapse.

signaling. There are few candidate transsynaptic signaling molecules, although some promising ones include cadherins and the novel glutamate synapse transmembrane protein densin-180.[59] CNS synapses must also be able to undergo changes in strength in response to input, even in adulthood. A likely mechanism is to regulate the number as well as the efficacy of postsynaptic receptors. Potential molecular mechanisms for such regulation are an area of active study. For example, calcium entry through the NMDA receptor activates calmodulin, which both inhibits channel opening directly and competes with α-actinin for binding, thus perhaps inducing a longer term effect by releasing the NMDA receptor from the actin cytoskeleton.[61] The cellular interactions involved in CNS synapse development are perhaps even more difficult to study than uncovering the molecular constituents. The production and use of imaging tools such as specific fluorescent probes,[61] tagged antibodies, or green fluorescent protein fusions of synaptic proteins will be important in exploring the dynamic nature of CNS synapse development and plasticity.

it is probably not due to restrictions in axonal guidance or synaptogenesis.

Given that the processes of axon outgrowth and selectivity in the formation of synapses seem insufficient to account for the simple pattern of innervation observed in adult muscle, we must look elsewhere for the explanation. In this context, the fact that virtually all twitch skeletal muscles in terrestrial vertebrates *become* singly innervated, after a period in early life when they are contacted by more than one axon, takes on some significance. That multiple axons can and do make connections on a single muscle fiber means that single innervation requires the loss of previously established synapses. Thus, synapse elimination is apparently the means by which multiple innervation is removed from muscle fibers that require input from only one axon.

Why would it be advantageous for a postsynaptic cell to receive innervation from only one input when several are eager to do the job? A general answer cannot be given at present. In all known cases where one strong input is required to drive a postsynaptic cell, single innervation occurs as the result of a process of selection from multiple axons. The selection of only one input could be part of a process whereby homogeneous populations of pre- and postsynaptic cells are parsed out to make the final pattern of synaptic connections functionally more complex. For muscle in particular, the way that muscles are used requires the recruitment of firing of additional motor neurons to generate increasing tension. Neuromuscular junctions are designed to be faithful transmitters of presynaptic action potentials to postsynaptic action potentials so that a single axon causes the muscle fibers it innervates to contract. Because of this powerful connection, the presence of multiple axons innervating the same muscle fiber would be redundant. For such a system to give muscle contractions of varying strengths and without wasted synapses, two things are necessary: first, that an individual motor axon innervates only a subset of the fibers in a muscle; and second, that an individual muscle fiber is innervated by only one motor axon. This seems to be one functional reason that synapse elimination is useful in skeletal muscle. One can easily imagine analogous rationales in other parts of the nervous system where synapse elimination similarly partitions innervation among similar target cells.

What Does Synapse Elimination Do?

A more precise way to describe the quantitative changes in connectivity that occur during synapse elimination is to consider convergence and divergence in synaptic circuits. The degree of **convergence** on a target cell is defined as the number of inputs from different presynaptic cells that make synapses on a postsynaptic cell. During synapse formation, postsynaptic target cells may receive input from many presynaptic cells ("multiple innervation"). This extra innervation has been documented in a variety of parts of the CNS and PNS of developing animals. Although synapse elimination always results in a net decrease in the degree of convergence, the absolute number of inputs that are maintained varies.

This reduction in the degree of convergence on a postsynaptic cell may be achieved in two different ways. First, the number of axons that make synapses on particular targets can be decreasing secondarily as a result of cell death.[62,63] Second, the degree of **divergence,** or number of postsynaptic target cells on which a neuron forms synapses may be decreasing. In accord with this latter possibility, both anatomical and physiological evidence suggests that a loss of connections occurs within target fields while the number of innervating neurons remains constant.[69,71] Thus, axons must initially innervate more target cells than they will ultimately contact. The most direct evidence for decreased divergence during development comes from analyses of the number of muscle fibers a motor axon typically innervates as a function of age. In a variety of muscles the conclusion is the same: motor units decrease in size at exactly the time the muscle fibers are losing connections from some of the innervating axons,[65,69,72] proving that axons are relinquishing connections with some target cells while remaining connected with others (see Fig. 19.6A). Interestingly, this decrease in divergence and convergence is recapitulated in muscles in adult animals following reinnervation after nerve crush injury. When motor axons grow back to the muscle, the muscle fibers become transiently multiply innervated. After about 2 weeks, all but one of the axons contacting any individual muscle

FIGURE 19.6 Synapse elimination changes the amount of convergence and the amount of divergence in neuromuscular connections. (A) At birth, muscle fibers are innervated by multiple motor axons (MN, motor neuron). During the first few postnatal weeks, axonal convergence decreases as all but one input is eliminated from each muscle fiber. This occurs by branch removal rather than by motor neuron cell death. Thus, the elimination process also leads to a decrease in axonal divergence. (B) A decrease in both convergence and divergence is recapitulated during synapse elimination in adult muscle. After nerve damage (1), motor axons will grow back to the denervated muscle (2). During reinnervation, the axons will sprout and occupy many muscle fibers. Sometimes muscle fibers will become multiply innervated (3). About 3 weeks after reinnervation, synapse elimination occurs, largely restoring single innervation to each muscle fiber (4).

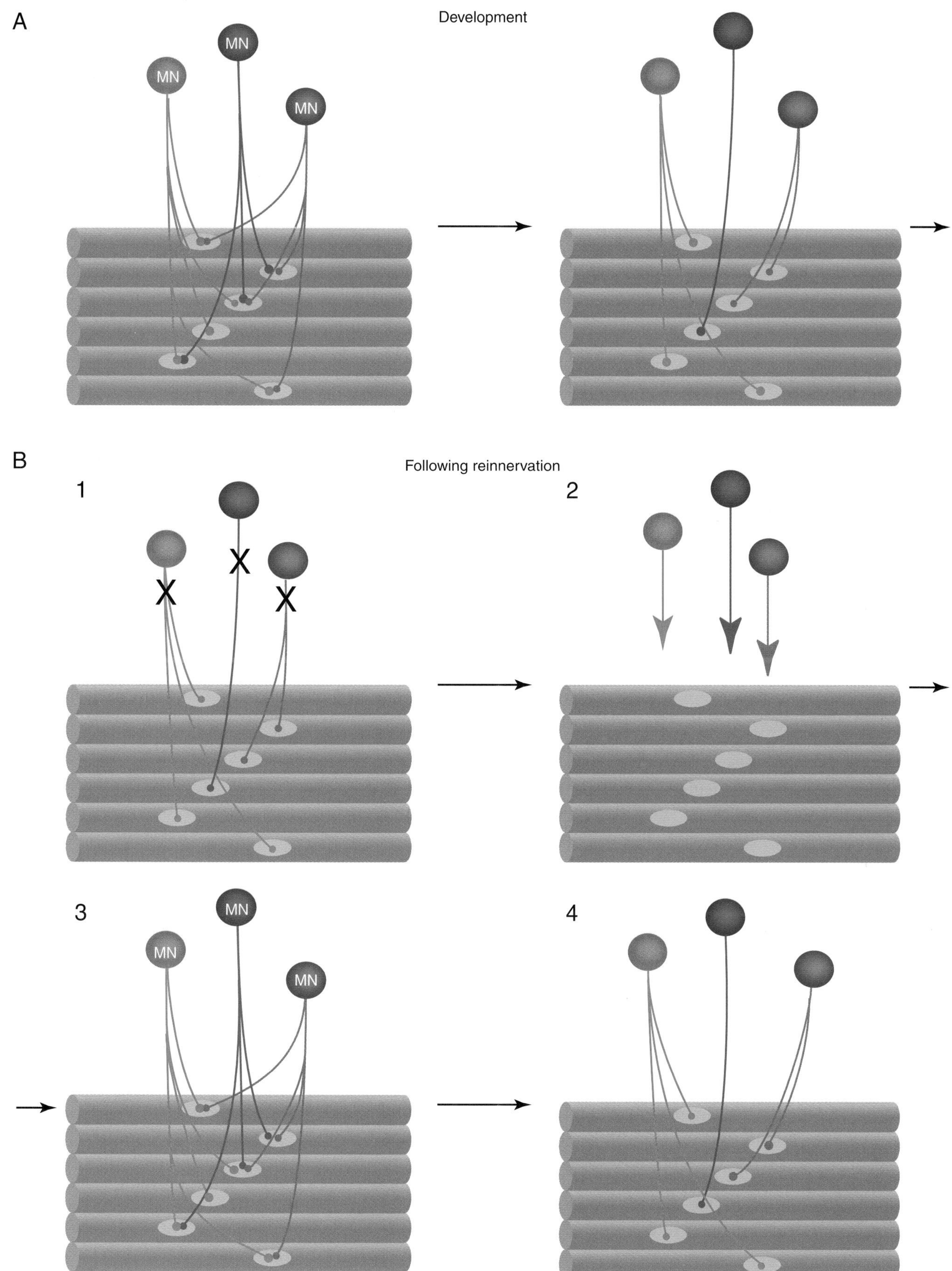

A
Development
MN
MN
MN
B
Following reinnervation
1
2
X
X
X
3
4
MN
MN
MN

fiber withdraws, leaving the muscle fiber singly innervated (see Fig. 19.6B).[73,74]

The term synapse elimination may give the mistaken impression that the total number of synapses on a postsynaptic cell decreases during the process. To see why this need not be the case, we need to distinguish the idea of a synapse from the term **input.** When individual axons or inputs innervate target cells, they may establish many synaptic release sites with the postsynaptic cell. The number of release sites is one determinant of the strength of the interconnection between the pre- and postsynaptic cells. As development proceeds, presynaptic cells strengthen connections by adding more terminal area on some postsynaptic cells,[75] and thus more release sites, and they weaken or even totally sever connections by removing synaptic sites on other postsynaptic targets. One example of contemporaneous addition and loss of synapses is in the simple parasympathetic autonomic ganglion, the submandibular ganglion, which is responsible for stimulation of salivation. At birth, submandibular ganglion cells in the rat are innervated by five or more axons. Over the first month of postnatal life, the number of axons decreases to one or two. Yet at the same time the total number of synapses on these target cells increases.[70] This must mean that the remaining inputs more than compensate for the loss of synaptic connections from the axons that are withdrawn by adding more synapses of their own. Thus, because the addition of synapses on some target cells is occurring while an axon loses its synaptic connections with other target cells, the process is to some degree a **redistribution of synapses** rather than a net loss. The functional effect of this redistribution is that axons begin with weak influence on many shared target cells and end with strong axonal control over a smaller number of postsynaptic targets.

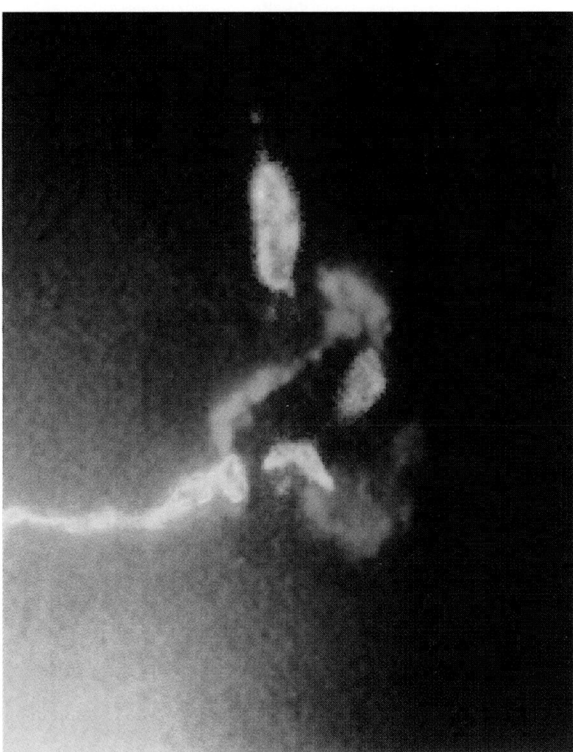

FIGURE 19.7 Synapses of multiple axons are interspersed at developing neuromuscular junctions. Shown is the distribution of boutons of two axons innervating a single muscle cell. The axons were separately labeled at birth by dye transfer with different colored lipophilic probes (diI in red, and diA in green). Analysis of such multiply innervated neuromuscular junctions showed that the terminal connections of each axon were randomly distributed and closely intermingled with the terminals of other axons within individual junctions. This close juxtaposition of synapses that will be maintained with synapses that will be eliminated means that synapse loss must be regulated in a highly local way. From Balice-Gordon *et al.*[88]

How Does Synapse Elimination Occur at the Neuromuscular Junction?

Anatomical studies of the transition from multiple to single innervation at the neuromuscular junction have provided substantial evidence that the loss of functional input is accompanied by physical removal of the losing nerve terminal. In general, axons appear to withdraw rather than degenerate during synapse elimination.[86,87] To convey the idea that the axon is withdrawing from the muscle fiber[84] the term "retraction bulb" has been used to describe the bulblike axonal endings found at junctions undergoing synapse elimination.

To determine how the competing inputs are spatially deployed, lipophilic dyes have been used to label the membranes of the competing axons with different colors. This approach provides a picture of the anatomical changes that occur at nerve terminals as an axon withdraws. These studies show that the terminals of the axons that multiply innervate a neuromuscular junction are interdigitated (Fig. 19.7): the synaptic endings of each axon are interspersed among the terminals of other axons confined to the same junction. Thus, the mechanism that leads to elimination must be a highly localized process. The loss of synapses appears to occur gradually (see Fig. 19.8), suggesting that each synaptic site is undergoing synapse elimination somewhat independently. After all of the terminals from one axon have retracted, the axon withdraws with a small bulb at its end. By this time, the axon appears quite thin compared to the axon remaining at the junction (Fig. 19.9). From a functional standpoint, an axon branch is still capable of releasing neurotransmitter in response to nerve stimulation even after some of its synapses have withdrawn.[75]

Although there is as yet no consensus on the full range of influences that regulate synapse elimination, most investigators would probably agree that **competition** between axons is a central driving force in the synapse loss. The term competition has multiple definitions,[89] but in all of the definitions what ultimately happens to one competitor (in this case, the fate of one axon) is influenced by the presence of other competitors (or other axons that innervate the same junction). Broadly speaking, competition occurs when individuals (i.e., competitors) vie to obtain something that, in the long run, cannot be shared or divvied up. Thus, at the neuromuscular junction the axons compete for the exclusive innervation of the muscle fiber.

The Synapse Elimination Cascade Occurs over Time

To study the changes that occur over the course of synapse elimination, it is useful to follow these events over time. Because the sequence of events is not occurring synchronously on all postsynaptic cells, methods that permit views of the same synaptic junction multiple times over many days were developed. This approach was used first to follow the loss of multiple innervation in adult animals after nerve regeneration.[74] Axonal sprouts multiply innervate many muscle fibers during the first several weeks following the nerve's return but eventually retract, leaving muscle fibers once again singly innervated.[73] Repeated imaging of the same neuromuscular junctions showed, surprisingly, that the site vacated by the losing input was not reoccupied by the remaining axon. Furthermore, vacated synaptic sites also underwent a postsynaptic change: sites that had lost nerve terminals had also lost all evidence of AChRs revealed by fluorescently tagged α-bungarotoxin labeling (see Fig. 19.10). Interestingly, the AChR disappearance began *before* the nerve terminals had withdrawn from the overlying sites. This morphological result is substantiated by electrophysiological findings showing that during synapse elimination following reinnervation in adult mus-

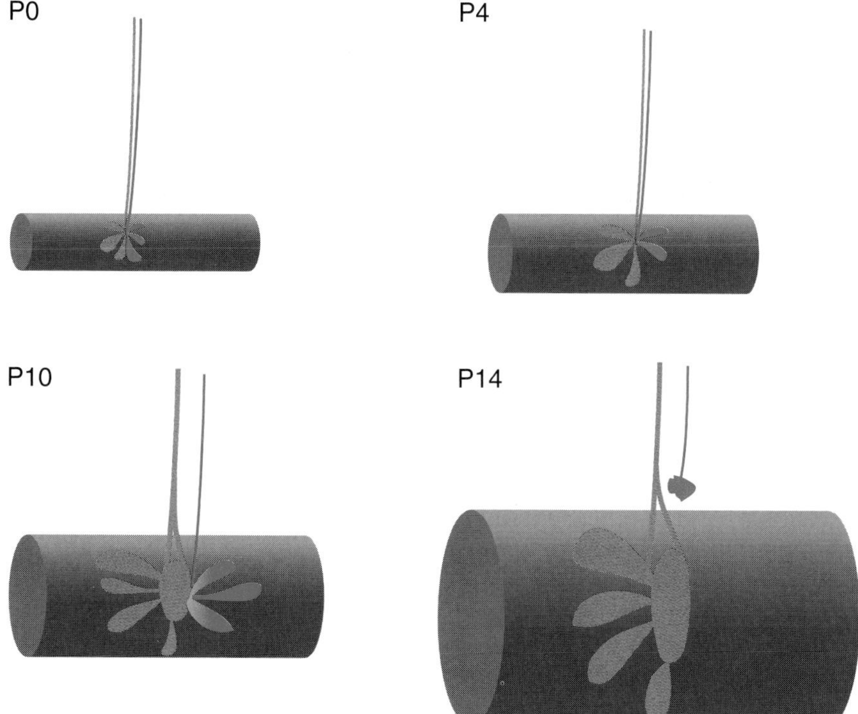

FIGURE 19.8 Synapse loss at the neuromuscular junction is a protracted process. In mice, for example, at birth (P0) two different axons that innervate a single muscle fiber typically occupy a similar amount of synaptic territory. At some point in the next 2 weeks the amount of synaptic territory occupied by the two inputs begins to diverge: one axon expands its synaptic connections and occupies more territory than it did at earlier stages (red axon), while the other loses synaptic sites due to synapse elimination (blue axon). Eventually, the synaptic areas occupied by the axons are vastly different. The axon destined to be eliminated has lost nearly all of its synapses. The caliber of the losing axon is reduced. Ultimately the nerve terminal retracts ("retraction bulb"; see also Fig. 19.9) from the synapse, leaving the muscle fiber singly innervated.

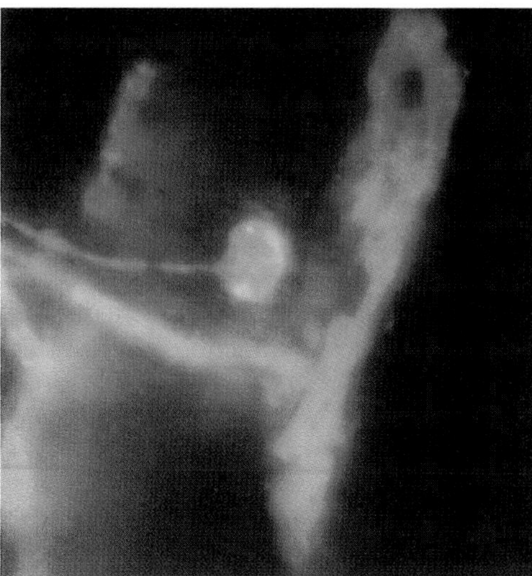

FIGURE 19.9 A retraction bulb is evident as one axon withdraws from a neuromuscular junction. Two axons innervating a single neuromuscular junction were labeled with two different lipophilic membrane dyes (diI in red, diA in green). After all of the synapses from one axon (green) have been eliminated, the axon is removed from the junction. The axon does not appear to be degenerating, but rather withdrawing into the parent axon. In addition, note the withered appearance of the axon itself, which is thin in comparison to the red axon, which maintains contact with the muscle fiber. From Balice-Gordon *et al.*[88]

cle (and during development) synaptic release comprising very weak quanta can be observed during stimulation of one of the axons multiply innervating a neuromuscular junction.[75,92] Together, these results make a strong case for the idea that the axon that will retract lingers for a while at sites that have begun to lose their complement of AChRs. This occupation is always temporary, however, because a few weeks after the regeneration of nerves is complete, no faint receptor regions remain and there is a perfect correspondence between the remaining axon and a uniformly dense, but remodeled, receptor pattern. This suggests that the low-density AChR sites observed at intermediate time points eventually go on to lose both their nerve terminals and the remainder of the AChRs. Thus, *in vivo* studies of synapse loss in adult muscle suggest that the postsynaptic membrane is permanently changed at sites of synapse loss.

Elimination of multiple innervation during normal development takes place in a similar fashion. AChRs are lost from the same synaptic sites from which nerve terminals had withdrawn. Furthermore, a decrease in AChR density is observed prior to the loss of the overlying nerve terminal. Thus, during synapse loss, both in adults following reinnervation and during development, the earliest evidence that a site will ultimately lose its synaptic connection is decreased AChR density, which is a postsynaptic alteration.[74,85] In this context, the weak synaptic events observed following reinnervation and during development[75] can be explained by the release of normal amounts of acetylcholine over postsynaptic sites that have already lost a significant number of AChRs.

The physiological and anatomical studies described above have led to the proposal that synapse loss occurs in a stepwise manner, beginning with the loss of postsynaptic reception to neurotransmitter and followed by the physical withdrawal of the overlying synaptic bouton. This process is repeated multiple times until an axon has lost all its connections with a target cell and then withdraws permanently. The onset of this stepwise loss appears to be slow, but once in motion it quickly (~1–2 days) leads to the complete detachment of an input.[75]

These observations on synapse elimination at regenerating and developing neuromuscular junctions raise the question, what is the nature of the competition between axon terminals? One of the simpler conceptions of synapse elimination has been that of a "direct" competition. In this scenario, each axon attempts to obtain exclusive control over something essential for synaptic maintenance. Many examples of direct competition exist in biology, such as competition for an ecological niche or the competition between populations of neurons for trophic factors vying for survival. Indeed, it has been proposed that synapse elimination is the result of competition between axons attempting to acquire the lion's share of a trophic factor (for synaptic maintenance) supplied by the target cell.[93] The increasing availability of putative candidate molecules has stimulated investigators to evaluate the roles of these molecules in synapse elimination, but these studies have been inconclusive.

An alternative possibility is that the competition is "indirect." In this case, the competitors would be unaffected by the competition and oblivious of the fact that they are even involved in a competition—until a decision is made at the end of the process. In such indirect competitions, a third party evaluates the competitors (e.g., a male bird showing its plumage or singing to court a female independent of other males doing the same thing). According to this scenario, the muscle could serve to select one axon over the others.

Because the competitive interaction in such indirect competition is mediated by a third party, evidence linking the actions of the competitors (e.g., presynaptic activity) and the ultimate result (e.g., single innervation) may not be obvious. This situation is quite different from direct competition, where the process (e.g., competing for a trophic factor) and the result (axonal

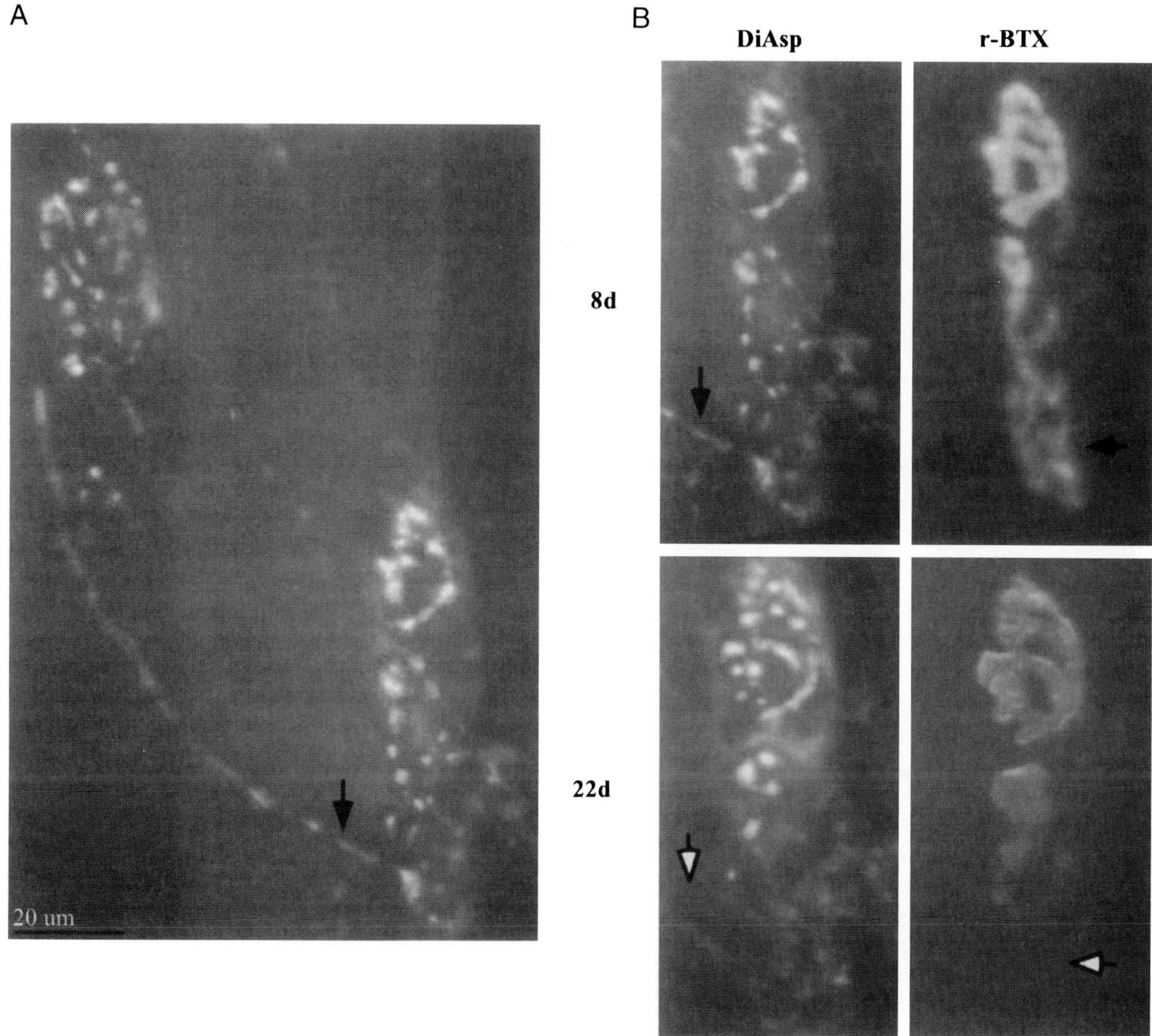

FIGURE 19.10 Synapse elimination at the neuromuscular junction involves the loss of both presynaptic and postsynaptic components. (A) Adult muscle fibers become multiply innervated after reinnervation following nerve crush. This panel shows two neuromuscular junctions on neighboring muscle fibers, 8 days after nerve crush. The nerve terminals have been stained with a vital dye (4-di-2-asp) to view them *in vivo*. The junction on the lower right is innervated by two inputs: one approaches from the right and innervates the top portion of the junction, and another is a sprout (arrowheads) from the adjacent junction on the left that innervates the bottom of this junction. (B) The same junction (lower right in A) seen at 8 days and 22 days after nerve crush. In these panels the nerve terminals are stained with a vital dye (DiAsp) (left), and the postsynaptic AChRs are stained with rhodamine-conjugated α-BGT (right). At 22 days, it is apparent that the sprout at the bottom of the junction has withdrawn and the postsynaptic AChRs under its terminals have disappeared (compare black and white arrowheads). Interestingly, the remaining axon did not sprout to occupy the vacated site. This suggests that the previous synaptic site is no longer capable of sustaining nerve terminals. Modified from Culican, S. M., Nelson, C. C., and Lichtman, J. W. (1998). Multiple postsynaptic markers lost at sites undergoing synapse elimination at the mouse neuromuscular junction. *J. Neurosci.* **(18)**13: 4953–4965.

withdrawal due to lack of trophic factor) are connected in a more straightforward way. Thus, in synapse elimination an axon may not have any competitive strategy to become the dominant innervation of a target cell; rather its normal behavior leads to that outcome because the muscle fiber has a **choosing strategy.** The findings that changes are detected early in the postsynaptic membrane when axon terminals are still present are consistent with the notion of indirect competition. Thus, synapse elimination may be instigated by a retrograde message.

It is unclear what mediates the association between the postsynaptic muscle and the victor neuron terminal. One simple, although far from certain, hypothesis is that the receptor per se plays this role, in addition to its role in neurotransmission. For example, in the disease myasthenia gravis, an autoimmune disorder in which antibodies to the acetylcholine receptor lead to dangerously low numbers of receptors, nerve terminals are lost from the sites where receptors have been eliminated.[97,98] Transgenic mice that lack either agrin,[10] which is responsible for receptor clustering at the neuromuscular junction, or MuSK,[9] which is likely a part of the agrin receptor in muscle,[11] show not only poor receptor localization in the postsynaptic membrane but also loss of normal nerve terminals. An alternative explanation is that another molecule(s), such as an adhesive protein, is responsible for nerve terminal maintenance and is regulated in parallel with AChRs. Evidence for this kind of mechanism includes the finding that a number of postsynaptic markers (including rapsyn, phosphotyrosine residues, and utrophin) are lost in addition to the AChR at sites of synapse elimination at the neuromuscular junction.[98a] All of these lines of evidence, however, argue that the maintenance of a nerve terminal depends in some important way on the integrity of the postsynaptic specialization.

The noncompetitive synapse loss that occurs on the dendrites and cell bodies of neurons whose own connections with their targets have been severed by axotomy (Fig. 19.11)[94–96] seems to take place by a similar mechanism. In particular, the presynaptic withdrawal in this experimental situation also occurs *after* a decrease in the density of neurotransmitter receptors in

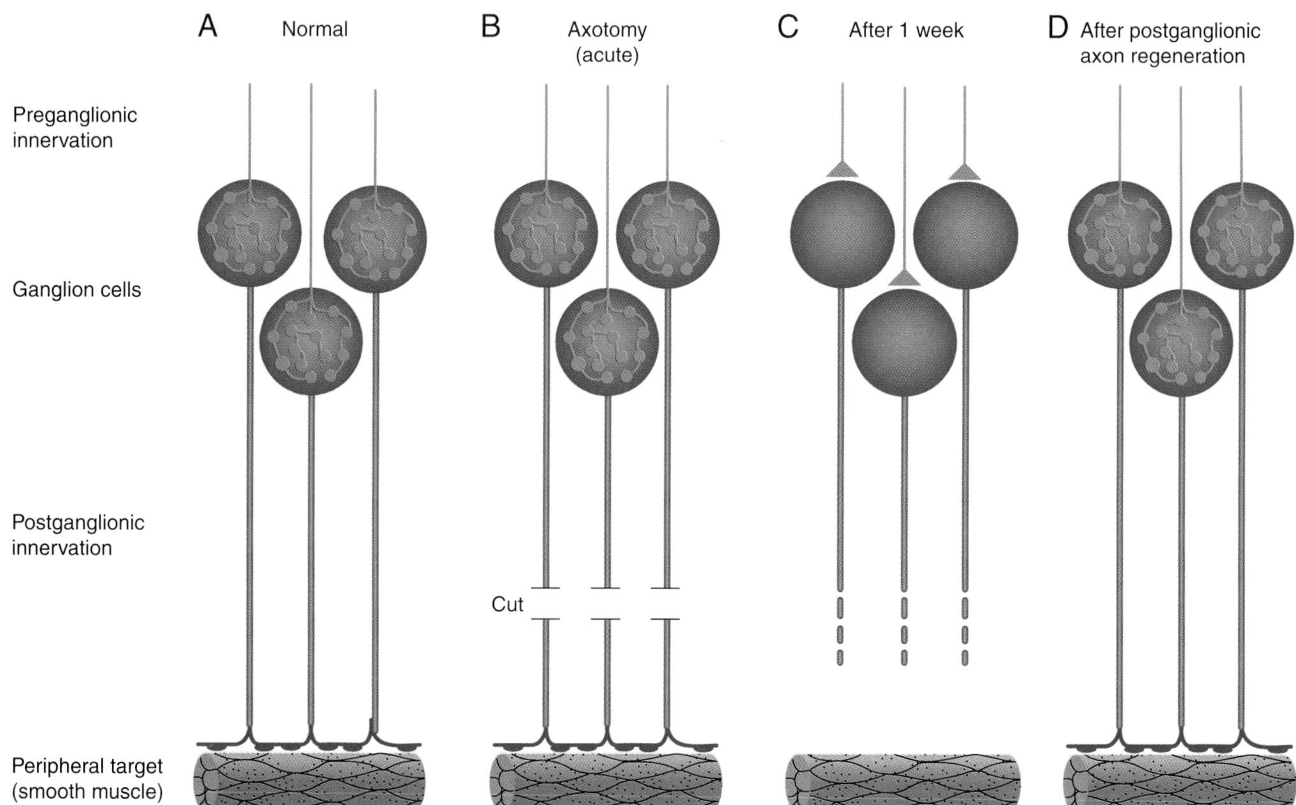

FIGURE 19.11 Presynaptic axons withdraw from target neurons after the target cells have had their axons severed (axotomy). For example, sympathetic ganglion cells send axons throughout the body to innervate cellular target (A). When the connection between ganglion cells and their peripheral targets is disrupted by axotomy (B), loss of preganglionic input to the ganglion cells is observed (C). By 1 week after axotomy, the innervation of ganglion cells is substantially reduced. The loss of synaptic connections is reversible; once ganglion cell axons reinnervate their peripheral targets, preganglionic synapses are reestablished (D). These results show that changes in postsynaptic cells can lead to the withdrawal of presynaptic nerve terminals. Other experiments with autonomic ganglia[165] show that changes in postsynaptic receptor density precede the synapse loss. After Purves.[95]

the postsynaptic membrane.[94] Thus, in two situations where synapses are permanently lost—competitive synapse elimination and synapse elimination following axotomy—the postsynaptic cell appears to undergo changes first.

The Postsynaptic Cell Acts as an Intermediary through Neurotransmitter Receptor Activation

That the postsynaptic cell can selectively disassemble receptors from beneath the terminals of one axon while maintaining the intermixed synaptic specializations associated with another axon raises an intriguing question. How can a muscle fiber discriminate between the sites occupied by different axons converging at the same junction? One likely difference between the inputs is their activity patterns. Motor axons are recruited in a fixed order to cause progressively larger contractions in a muscle (see Chapter 30). Thus, it is unlikely that the sites associated with the two different inputs at a neuromuscular junction would be synchronously active. To test whether a muscle fiber could distinguish between differentially active receptor regions at a neuromuscular junction based on the timing of their activation, small regions of singly innervated junctions were silenced by focal application of α-bungarotoxin, which blocks neuromuscular activity (see Box 19.3) in living mice.[61] The results showed that small inactivated regions were eliminated (receptor disappearance followed by axon withdrawal). Interestingly, when larger areas were silenced, these regions were not eliminated. These results suggest that neuromuscular transmission at unblocked sites was the stimulus for the elimination of the blocked sites. That is, neural activity at the majority of receptor sites selectively destabilized and ultimately caused the elimination of the silent regions. Such a destabilizing effect of activity implies that several signals in muscle fibers mediate the effect of activity.[99] For example, receptor activation by neurotransmitter elicits two opposite types of signals. One signal protects the activated receptors from the deleterious effects of activity, whereas the other signal has a destabilizing effect (due to activity) on receptors generally. Thus, when all synapses are synchronously active (as occurs at singly innervated junctions), all receptor regions are protected from the destabilizing effects of the activity. Similarly, when all or most of the synapses are silent (such as occurs during denervation), there are no destabilizing effects, and synapses are maintained in an enduring way. However, when some, but not all, synapses are strongly active, a signal leads to the destabilization of the inactive regions both pre- and postsynaptically (Fig. 19.13).

Summary

The process of synapse elimination refines an initially diffuse pattern of connections into an adult pattern, in which synapses specifically interconnect appropriate presynaptic and postsynaptic partners. Each muscle cell is innervated initially by several motor axons; during development all but one axon's inputs are eliminated. Synapse elimination at the neuromuscular junction occurs in a stepwise manner. At each site, both the postsynaptic junction loses its acetylcholine receptors, becoming unresponsive to neurotransmitter, and the presynaptic terminal atrophies and physically withdraws. Once all sites are removed, the axon branch to the muscle atrophies and is permanently removed from the muscle fiber. Synapse loss is initiated by an activity-dependent competition between motor axons, in which inactive inputs are selectively eliminated and more active inputs are stabilized. Synchronous activity among all of the terminals of one axon protects them from destabilization, resulting in the endurance of the large number of synaptic sites associated with one axon.

SYNAPSE ELIMINATION IN THE DEVELOPING VISUAL SYSTEM

Competition for postsynaptic targets leading to the elimination of erroneous connections is also a common means by which many diverse patterns of connectivity in the CNS are established during development. The most extensively studied example of competition in the CNS is the development of the visual pathway. The role of the critical period in the development of this system is discussed in detail in Chapter 22. The classic work of Hubel and Wiesel in the 1960s has provided important insights into how distinct patterns of visual connections are shaped during development. In young animals, neurons of layer IV in the visual cortex can be activated by inputs driven from both the left and the right eye—that is, they are binocularly driven. Subsequently, however, inputs driven by each eye are withdrawn from different cortical neurons, causing some cortical neurons to be strongly dominated by the right eye and others dominated by the left eye. The cortical neurons that are activated by each eye are grouped together in a striking pattern of alternating stripes known as ocular dominance columns (Fig. 19.14).[100,101] This pattern of innervation can be demonstrated either electrophysiologically[102] or anatomically by injecting into one eye a radioactive tracer that is anterogradely transported to the cortex.[103]

The emergence of ocular dominance columns re-

BOX 19.3

α-BUNGAROTOXIN

A number of different dyes, stains, and markers are useful in revealing synaptic structure and function. Some of the more powerful have been borrowed from nature. Many toxins and poisons bind to specific proteins. One example is the snake toxin α-bungarotoxin (α-btx). This toxin is a constituent of the venom of a cobralike snake of the species *Bungarus*. The lethality of α-btx is the consequence of its ability to bind to the α subunits of nicotinic AChRs in skeletal muscle cells of vertebrates (with the one notable exception: snake AChRs do not bind to α-btx). Because α-btx is an irreversible competitive antagonist of the AChR, its binding thus paralyzes and suffocates the prey.

Researchers have taken advantage of this snake toxin to study many aspects of the AChR. For example, α-btx was used to purify AChRs from *Torpedo* membranes. Furthermore, the toxin can be conjugated to radioactive markers or to fluorescent molecules (A) that can be seen in the microscope to stain receptors on muscle cells to determine their distribution, stability, and motility in the membrane. Because the toxin binds essentially irreversibly to the receptor in the muscle fiber membrane, receptors can be labeled once and then their behavior followed over time. (B) This approach has provided substantial evidence about the stability of synaptic regions on muscle fibers, the lifetime of receptors in the membrane at the junctional sites, and how AChRs move within the plane of the membrane. For studies of synapse elimination in particular, the toxin has also been used to selectively inactivate some regions of a synapse by "puffing" it locally over a small region of a junction.[61]

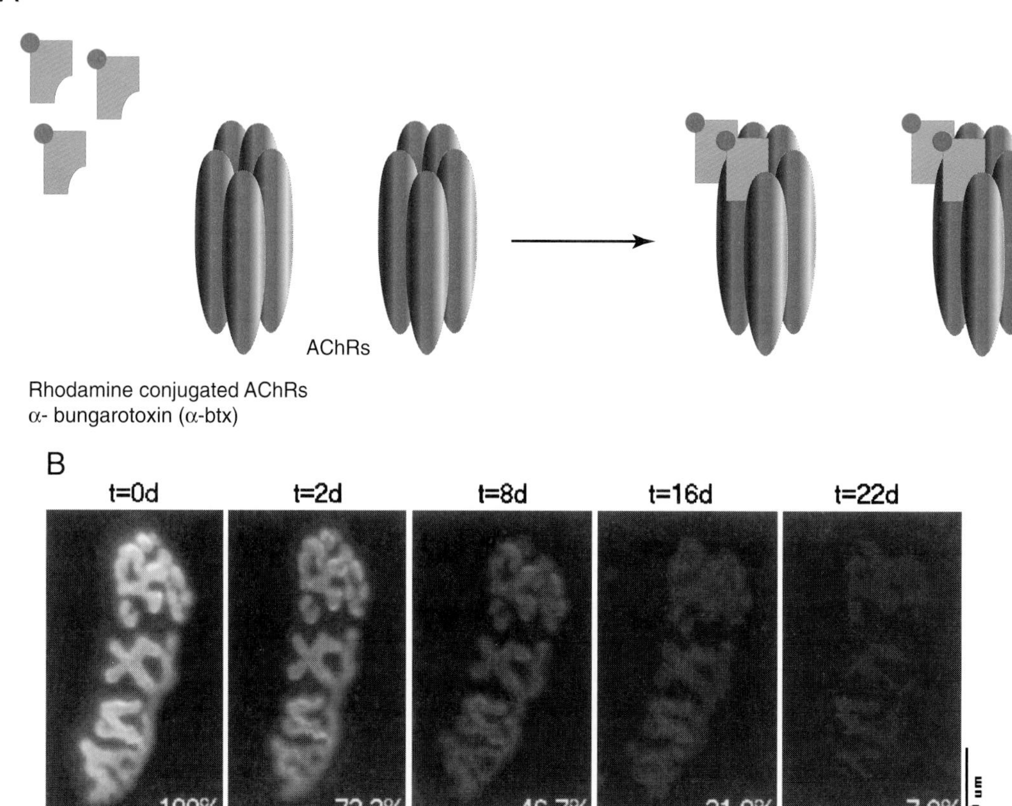

FIGURE 19.12 (A) α-Btx binds essentially irreversibly to the α subunit of muscle nicotinic AChRs. In these experiments, α-btx was labeled with the fluorescent dye rhodamine, indicated by the red circle. α-btx-labeled AChRs followed over time. (B) The AChRs in this junction were labeled once with α-btx prior to the first view (t = 0 day). The junction was imaged and the animal allowed to recover. The same junction was then relocated four more times over a 3-week period. The receptors that are apparent at 22 days are receptors that were labeled 3 weeks earlier but still remain in the membrane. Modified from Turney, S. G., Culican, S. M., and Lichtman, J. W. (1996). A quantitative fluorescence-imaging technique for studying acetylcholine receptor turnover at neuromuscular junctions in living animals. *J. Neurosci. Methods* **64:** 199–208.

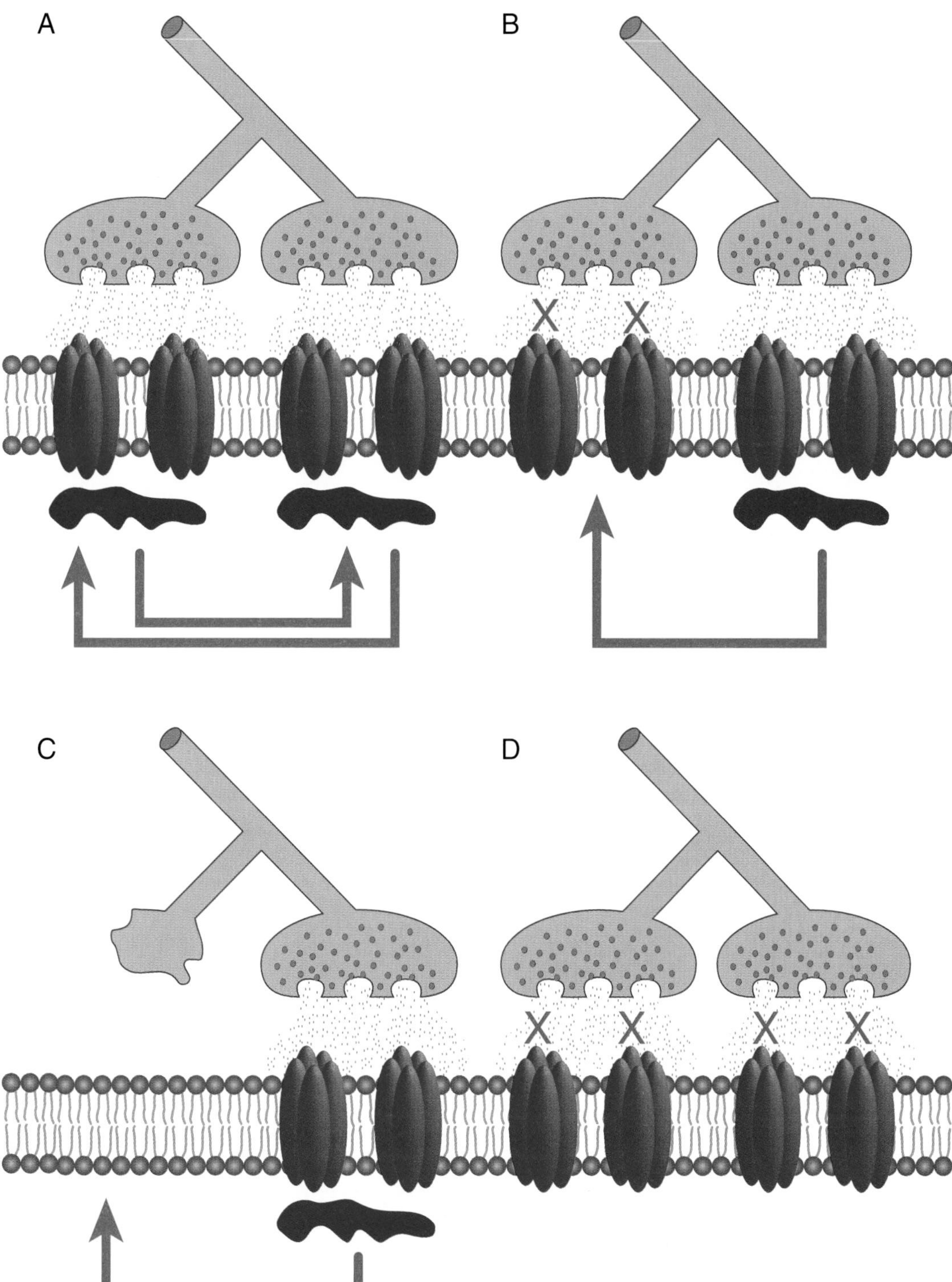

FIGURE 19.13 Experimental evidence suggests that synapse elimination results from activity-mediated signals within a postsynaptic cell. (A) Postsynaptic receptor activation may elicit two opposing signals within a muscle fiber. One consequence of receptor activation is a "punishment" signal (red arrows) that causes the loss of receptors from the postsynaptic membrane. Receptor activation may also generate a "protective" signal (blue clouds) that prohibits the punishment signals from destabilizing the postsynaptic apparatus at sites of receptor activation. When all the receptors are activated synchronously, there is no loss of receptors from the synapse (owing to the blue clouds). (B) When two inputs are differentially activated, the active receptors are protected, and the inactive ones (×) are not. (C) This leads to the loss of the inactive (unprotected) receptors from the membrane and a subsequent withdrawal of the overlying nerve terminal. (D) However, when all the receptors are silent, there is no punishment signal (red arrows) and thus no synapse loss. From Jennings.[99]

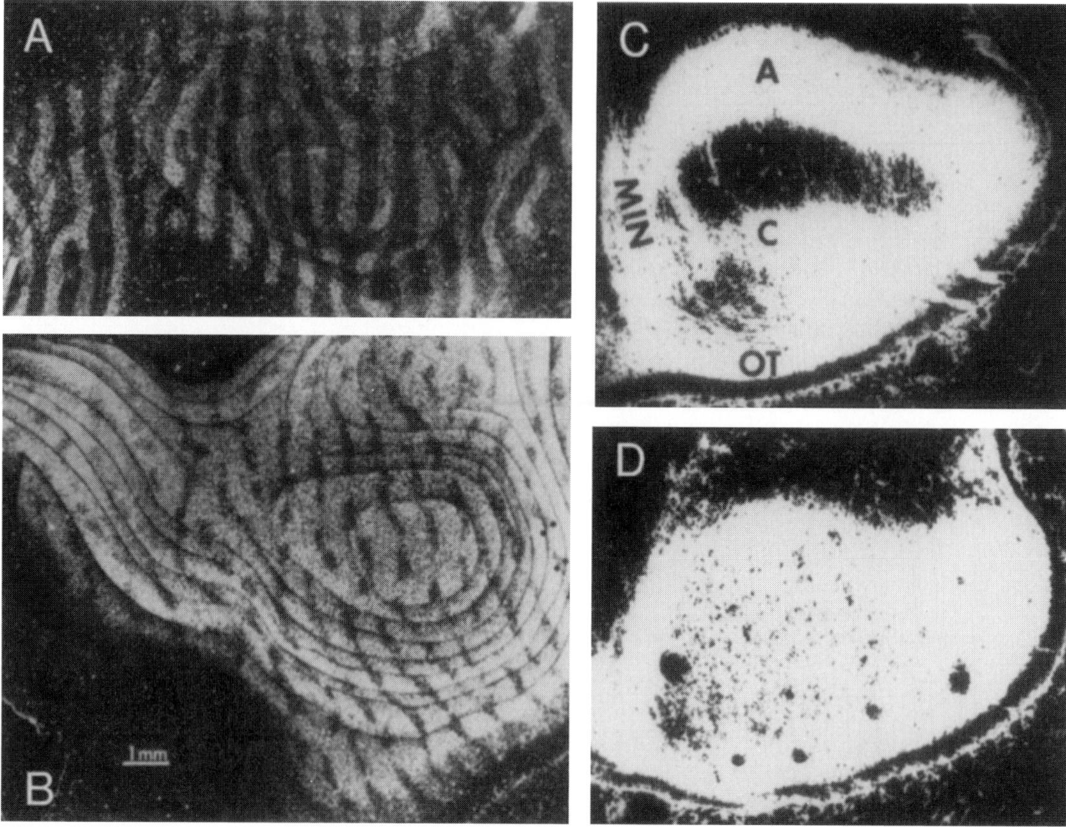

FIGURE 19.14 (A) Ocular dominance columns of the neonatal monkey primary visual cortex, at the level of layer IVC, revealed by injecting [^{3}H]proline into the vitreous of one eye. The light stripes represent the anterogradely transported label from the injected eye. The dark regions are occupied by axons driven by the other eye. (B) Monocular deprivation by lid suture of one eye (in this case, from 2 weeks after birth, for 18 months) results in the shrinkage of the columns representing the deprived eye and an expansion of the columns of the nondeprived eye (Hubel et al.[103]). (C) Injection of another tracer, horseradish peroxidase (light regions) into one eye reveals the layer pattern of axonal terminals of ganglion cells in the dorsal lateral geniculate nucleus of the cat, shown here for an animal at embryonic day 56 (about a week before birth). OT, optic tract; MIN, medial interlaminar nucleus; A and C, layers A and C of the geniculate receive inputs from the contralateral eye. (D) Chronic infusion of tetrodotoxin, TTX, into the brain between embryonic days 42 and 56 prevented the formation of the eye-specific layers. Shatz and Stryker.[101]

flects the anatomical remodeling that takes place at the level of individual axonal arbors. Thalamocortical axons projecting to layer IV are initially evenly distributed within this layer, but over the course of development, they end up with a patchy distribution, with arbors becoming restricted to one or more eye-specific columns. Thus, the change in the width of ocular dominance columns is mediated by a change in the relative amount of synapse elimination from the inputs of each eye. This should not be taken to mean that the total number of synapses is decreasing during this period. Just as in the PNS, the remaining axons elaborate many new connections that more than compensate numerically for the loss of connections from the withdrawing axons (Fig. 19.15). In other words, the process of ocular dominance column formation is one in which individual arbors lose, but also gain, synaptic space in the target. The critical distinction is thus related to where connections are added and lost. The elimination restricts the neuronal population that serves each eye while the addition strengthens the connections that remain.

Separation of the inputs from the two eyes occurs twice in the visual system. During the prenatal period, eye input to the dorsal lateral geniculate nucleus of mammals segregates into layers, rather than into columns. In embryonic cats, the axonal terminals of ganglion cells from the two eyes overlap extensively within the LGN, before gradually segregating to form the characteristic eye-specific layers by birth. As in the cortex, this refinement process involves both the retraction of axonal side branches in inappropriate re-

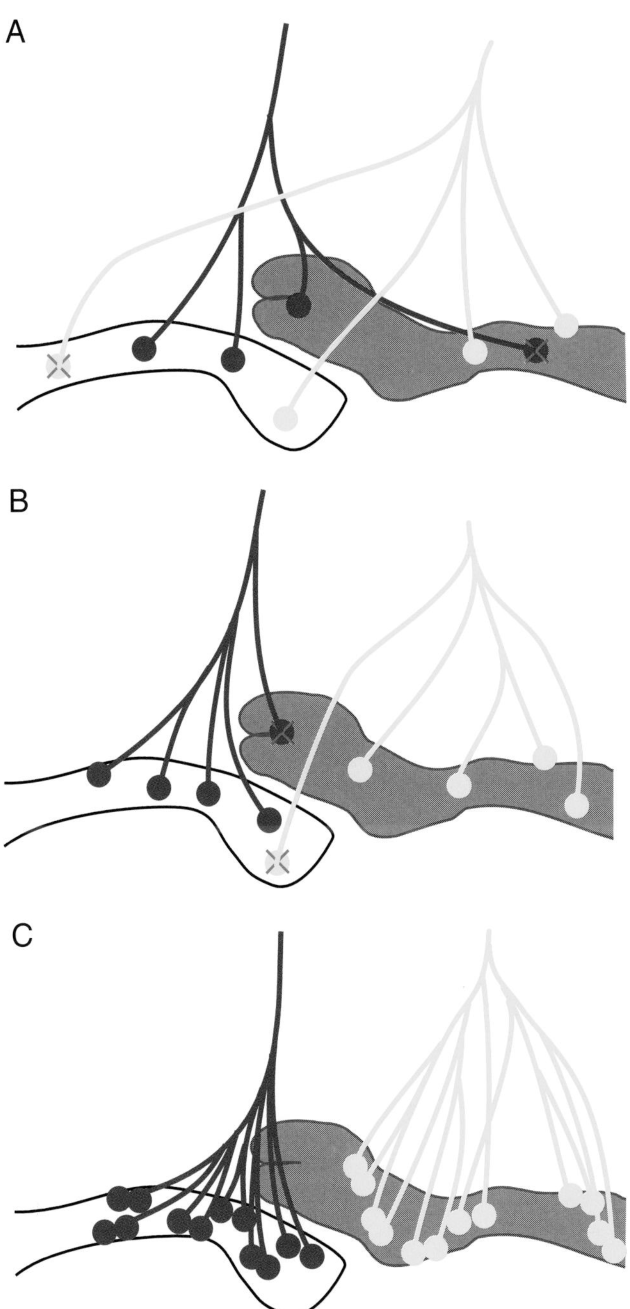

FIGURE 19.15 Synapse elimination in the developing visual system. Early in development, inputs from the left (purple) and right (yellow) eyes converge onto the same target cell dendrites. At this stage (A), each input makes a few synaptic contacts with both the dendrites that ultimately belong to the left ocular dominance column (white) and right ocular dominance columns (gray). As development proceeds (B and C), the inputs driven by the two eyes become segregated so that dendrites associated with each ocular dominance column are monocularly driven. This segregation process involves the elimination of synapses from the withdrawing inputs and the addition of synapses from the remaining inputs.

gions of the geniculate nucleus and the elaboration of processes within the correct eye layer. Physiological studies lend support to anatomical observations that geniculate neurons are binocularly driven initially, but maintain the input from only one eye at maturity.[104] Thus, like the formation of ocular dominance columns, the emergence of eye-specific layers in the LGN also takes place by means of the elimination of inappropriate connections (reviewed in Shatz[105]). Although elimination of connections results in the selection of input from one eye onto a geniculate neuron, addition of synapses from the remaining terminal may also take place.

Retinotopic Maps Are Refined by Synapse Elimination

The refinement of connectivity patterns by synapse loss in the visual system is not confined only to the separation of eye input but may also occur in the formation of retinotopic maps. These maps convey positional information concerning the image that is relayed in a topographical manner to visual centers in the brain. Retinotopic maps are found in the optic tecta of fish, amphibians, and chick and its analog, the superior colliculus, in mammals, as well as in the LGN and visual cortex of mammals. Evidence indicates that synapse elimination sharpens the relatively coarse retinotopic maps formed naturally during development (or, in fish and amphibians, during regeneration). The mechanisms responsible for the formation of the initial map are discussed in Chapter 18. In the lower vertebrates, however, a fairly precise map is laid down at the earliest stages when retinal axons first invade their targets, so that this refinement is minor. In chick and rodents, however, a significant degree of axonal remodeling takes place before a fine-grain map is apparent. This is not surprising because in lower vertebrates, the problem of making a fine-grain retinotopic map is complicated by the continual addition of ganglion cells at the periphery of the retina and by the continual growth of the tectum to accommodate newly arriving retinal axons. In contrast, in the chick and rodent, much of map formation occurs when the available target space is already defined. (See Roskies *et al.*[106] for review on map formation in the different species.)

Synapse elimination in the context of map refinement is assumed to occur as aberrant branches of axonal terminals are removed. This process appears to be more extensive in the rodent than in the chick. This is perhaps to be expected, because in the chick, the axonal arbors of ganglion cells from the temporal retina are more or less restricted to the rostral half of the tectum when they invade this target. In contrast, nasal axons extend caudally, across the entire surface of the tectum. The behavior of temporal versus nasal axons in their pattern of innervation of the chick tectum involves molecular guidance cues that set up topographical specificity at the onset of map formation.[107] In the newborn rat, unlike in the chick, there is complete overlap of the axonal branches and arbors of temporal and nasal retinal axons in the superior colliculus. However, by the end of the second postnatal week, the axonal arbors of temporal ganglion cells are highly restricted to the rostral end of the colliculus, whereas the terminal arbors of nasal ganglion cells are tightly positioned at the caudal portion of this target.[108] On the structural level, at least, map refinement in the mammalian superior colliculus, like the formation of eye-specific layers in the lateral geniculate nucleus and ocular dominance columns in the cortex, involves both retraction of incorrectly placed arbors and elaboration of correctly positioned terminals.

How are exuberant branches removed during map refinement? One way, as mentioned earlier in the chapter, is the removal of incorrectly positioned arbors by cell death. Indeed, this mechanism contributes to map refinement in the rat superior colliculus.[109] Likewise, cell death may also contribute to the refinement of eye input in the cat geniculate nucleus because eye-specific layers are formed during the period of naturally occurring cell death in the ganglion cell population.[110] Although cell death appears to contribute to the removal of inaccurately placed processes, anatomical studies, particularly those in which the activity in the visual pathways is disturbed, suggest that branches within incorrect target regions retract. Unlike the formation of ocular dominance columns or eye-specific layers, whether this structural remodeling of the axonal arbors truly reflects the elimination of synaptic connections is not known because to date the patterns of connections at each stage of map formation have not been physiologically assessed.

Activity Is Required for Remodeling Visual Connections

One of the more influential experiments in the field of synaptic plasticity was the discovery by Hubel and Wiesel that axonal segregation that occurs normally in early postnatal life can be dramatically altered by modifying the relative activity impinging on the cortex from the two eyes.[111] When kittens were reared with one eye sutured closed, the ocular dominance columns subserving that eye were dramatically smaller than those associated with the open eye (see Fig. 19.14). The large size of the columns driven by the open eye is not the result of sprouting of axonal terminals into territory normally occupied by the sutured eye. Rather, the open eye remains connected to a greater proportion of the cells that it initially contacted, whereas the sutured eye loses a greater proportion of its initial connections.

The "shift" in eye preference does not appear to depend on patterned vision per se. If the nonoccluded eye is silenced totally with an intraocular injection of tetroclotoxin (TTX), the cortical response is shifted toward the sutured and spontaneously active eye.[112] Interestingly, when postsynaptic activation of cortical cells is prevented by chronic application of $GABA_A$ receptor agonists, cortical neurons develop a preference for inputs from the closed eye.[113] With monocular deprivation alone, the cortical territory occupied by inputs driven by the closed eye is reduced compared to the territory occupied by the open eye's inputs. When postsynaptic activity is blocked, axons responding to the deprived eye do not lose territory and the open eye's inputs fail to innervate cortical regions they would otherwise have occupied if the cortical cells were responsive.[114] These findings clearly demonstrate that postsynaptic activity is important, and furthermore, the more active input does not always win the competition if the postsynaptic cell is prevented from responding. The effect of activity blockade on the structure of geniculate arbors is rapid, occurring within a few days after the blockade.[115,116] Functional suppression of the deprived eye input is closely accompanied by a remodeling of the arbor structure (Fig. 19.16).[117]

The segregation of eye inputs in the LGN also requires activation of the postsynaptic neurons. Chronic infusion of TTX during prenatal life into the region of the LGN during the period of eye-specific segregation prevents the emergence of the eye-specific layers in cats[101,117] (Figs. 19.14, 19.16). In mammals such as the ferret, at maturity, each eye-specific layer is further divided into sublaminae which contain the axonal arbors of ganglion cells with receptive field centers that respond either to light "On" or to light "Off." Blocking postsynaptic activity in LGN neurons prevents these sublaminae from emerging during development.[118] Thus, like the peripheral nervous system, the structure and connectivity patterns of ganglion cell and geniculate neuron axons are highly sensitive to manipulations that affect synaptic interactions with their target.

Implicit in all these experiments is that the activity required for the segregation of visual inputs does not arise only from visual stimulation through photoreceptor activation. Although ocular dominance columns remain plastic for a time (the critical period) after birth, in monkeys at least, ocular dominance columns are apparent prior to birth and eye opening. Indeed, spontaneous activity is important for the formation of ocular

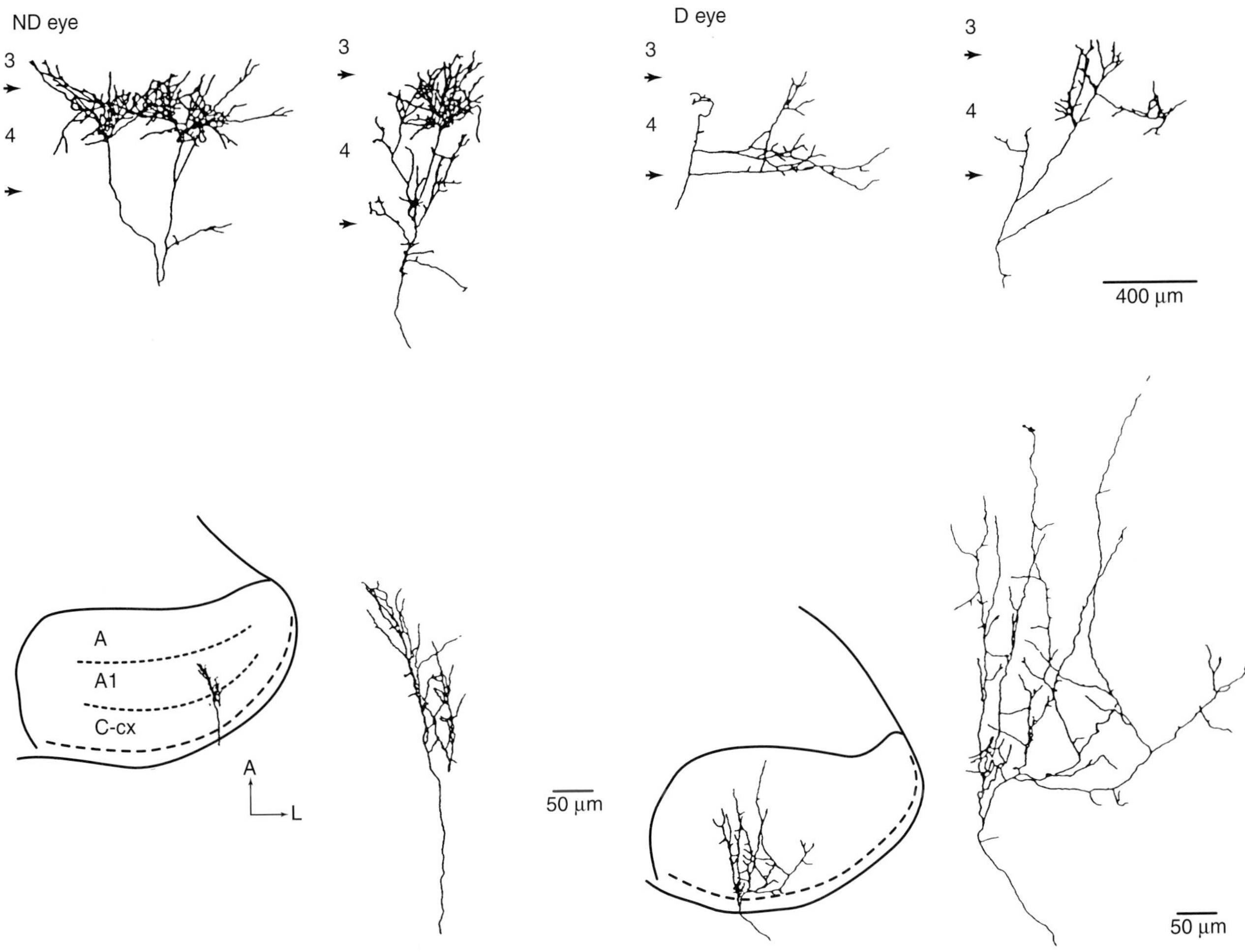

FIGURE 19.16 (Top) Coronal view of geniculocortical arbors in kittens with monocular lid suture for 33 days after birth. The terminal arbors representing the deprived eye (D eye) are dramatically reduced in complexity compared to those of the nondeprived eye (ND eye), which show a high degree of complexity and are clustered into "patches" (Antonini and Stryker.[115,116] (Bottom) The axonal terminals of ganglion cells fail to be confined to the appropriate region in the dorsal lateral geniculate nucleus (example of an ipsilateral arbor terminating in layer A1 of the normal animal) when activity is blocked by TTX during the normal period of eye-specific layer formation. Sretavan *et al.*[117] A, anterior; L, lateral; 3,4, cortical layers 3 and 4.

dominance columns. Ocular dominance columns do not form at all when postnatal kittens received injections of TTX into both eyes.[119] A role for spontaneous activity in guiding the development of retinogeniculate connections is also apparent, because in cats and monkeys, eye-specific segregation occurs well before birth. Furthermore, On and Off sublayers in the ferret geniculate nucleus appear before photoreceptors mature.[120] Taken together, these observations suggest that the immature retina may provide spontaneously generated signals that could be suitable for instructing the early segregation of visual inputs in the geniculate nucleus and cortex.

What is the nature of the instructions contained in the patterns of spontaneous activity? Activity per se is insufficient for synapse elimination in the visual system, and specific temporal patterns of activity are required.

Immature retinal ganglion cells can generate patterns of synchronous bursting activity. In the neonatal ferret retina the bursts of neighboring ganglion cells are correlated by propagating retinal waves which have no preferred direction of propagation and occur periodically, once every 15 s to 1 min (Fig. 19.17).[121–123] The retinal waves contain temporal and spatial cues that could guide the activity-dependent refinement of retinogeniculate connections. For example, because waves are generated independently in each retina, activities

A

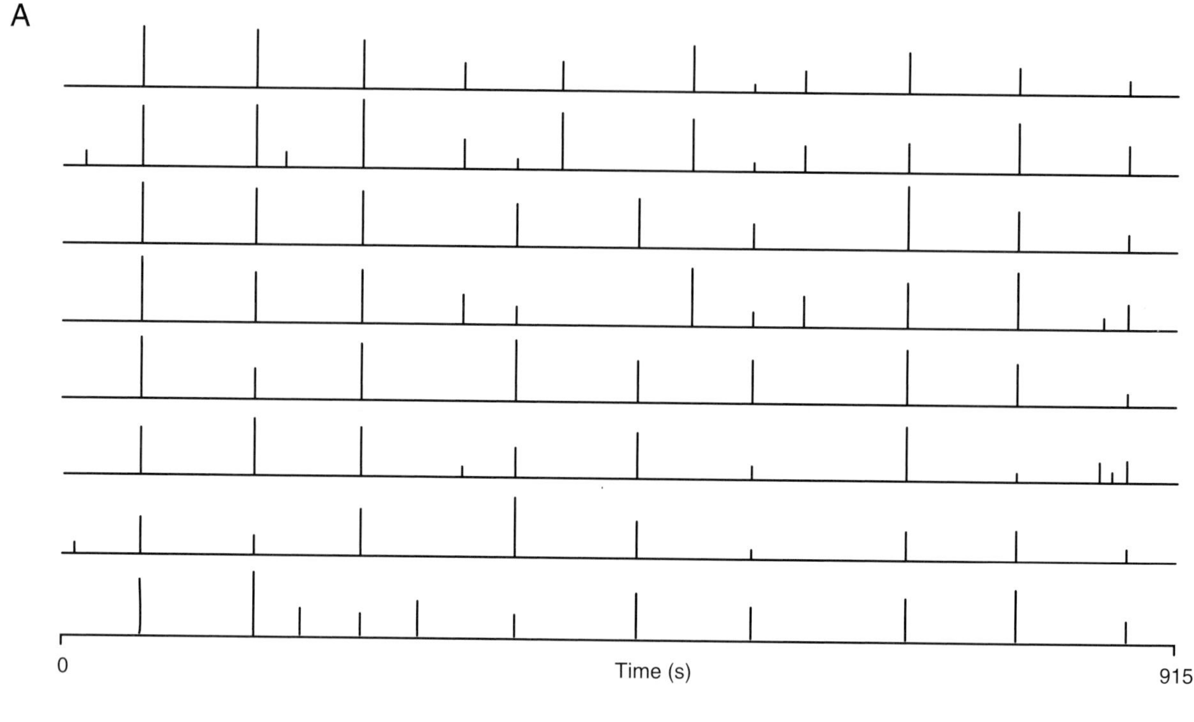

B

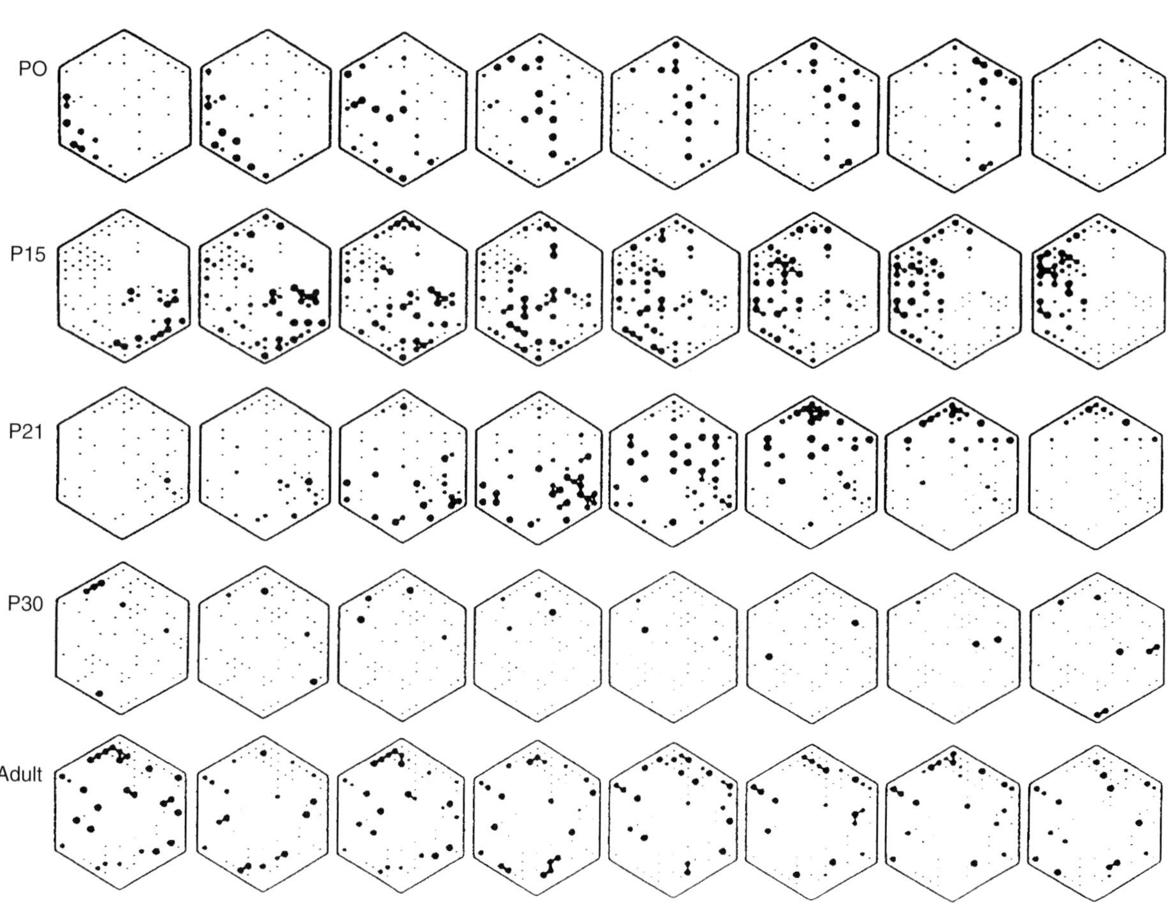

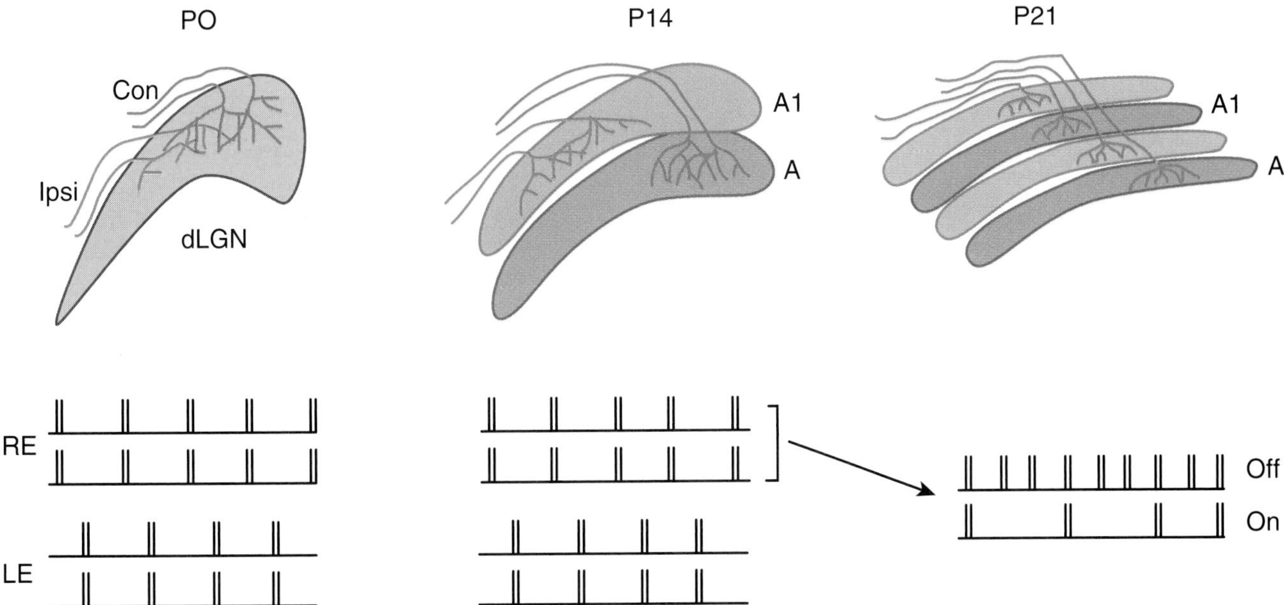

FIGURE 19.18 *Diagrammatic* representation of the segregation of retinal axonal arbors in the geniculate nucleus of ferrets during neonatal development. The correlated bursting activity within a retina contains temporal cues that appear suitable for instructing the refinement of retinogeniculate connections. Asynchronous activity between the right (RE) and left (LE) eyes could lead to the segregation of eye input and eventually the emergence of eye-specific layers by the first postnatal week. As each eye-specific layer becomes further divided into the On and Off sublaminae (between second and third postnatal weeks), On and Off cells exhibit different bursting rates, reducing the degree to which their activity is correlated. Con, contralateral axons; Ipsi, ipsilateral axons; A1 and A, layers A1 and A of the geniculate nucleus. P = postnatal day.

from the two eyes are unlikely to be coincident. Asynchrony between the inputs of the two eyes could account for the segregation of inputs into different eye-specific layers in the LGN and ultimately into different ocular dominance columns. Moreover, because the waves ensure that nearby retinal ganglion cells are better synchronized than more distant cells, geniculate neurons are able to gauge neighbor relationships in the retina by their sequential activation. This feature could be useful for the refinement of the retinotopic map. The retinal waves also may provide the means by which the terminals of On and Off ganglion cells segregate in the LGN[124] (Fig. 19.18). Whether retinal waves drive these developmental processes *in vivo* remains to be tested by altering, rather than abolishing, the activity patterns of the ganglion cells.

FIGURE 19.17 (A) Recordings from a large population of ganglion cells in the neonatal ferret retina using a multielectrode array reveal the presence of correlated spontaneous bursting activity, which occurs semiperiodically. Each set of vertical deflections represents a spike histogram, and each horizontal trace is a recording from one cell. (B) Reconstruction of the activity at the estimated positions of the cells indicates that the activity spreads like a wave across the recorded region. The size of the spot is proportional to the spike rate at that instance in time. These retinal "waves" are generated in the absence of visual stimulation and are present from birth (P0) until shortly before eye opening (P30). The outline of the array is indicated by the hexagons, and for each age, the activity is displayed at consecutive half-second intervals within a burst. Wong *et al.*[123]

We should emphasize here that the wave activity does not provide any cues that specify which layer in the LGN should subserve the left or right eye. All this pattern of activity can deliver is an "imbalance" of activity between competing inputs and a means by which the geniculate neuron can recognize whether it is being driven by the same or a different source. Ultimately, which input is retained and which is lost requires other mechanisms, which may or may not involve activity.

How Are Synaptic Connections Altered in the Developing Visual System?

In general, there are a number of ways by which the overall synaptic input is altered during competition for targets. First, existing connectivity can be changed by mechanisms that alter the number of contacts via elimination or synaptogenesis. Second, existing synapses can change their strength or efficacy via the mechanisms of long-term potentiation (LTP) or long-term depression (LTD). Both these possibilities have experimental support, and segregation of visual inputs probably occurs by a combination of these mechanisms.

Evidence also indicates that changes in synaptic efficacy may be the forerunner to elimination or may occur in parallel to synapse loss serving to strengthen (or weaken) competing inputs. For example, synaptic enhancement involving LTP-like modifications and NMDA receptors may play a role in segregation. LTP occurs in primary visual cortex,[125] it is easier to elicit in younger animals than in adults,[126] and the period during which it can be elicited is prolonged by rearing animals in the dark.[127] Experiments that disrupt LTP in developing visual cortex by infusing the NMDA receptor blocker APV, however, have yielded results that are difficult to interpret. In particular, although segregation into ocular dominance columns was disrupted,[128] APV apparently blocked all neural activity behaving much like TTX. The blockade of NMDA receptors in visual targets also prevents the refinement of the retinotopic map in frogs[129] and the formation of On and Off sublaminae in the ferret LGN.[118] In all these cases, however, whether the disruption of normal segregation events is the result of decreased LTP or decreased activity in general remains unclear.[130]

How does activity affect arbor size and distribution and, presumably, patterns of inputs? Accumulating evidence shows that neurons not only require specific growth factors for survival as described in Chapters 20 and 21 but also depend on the same factors for their maintenance. Interest in the role of neurotrophic molecules in synaptic competition has been sparked by the discovery of the developmental expression of neurotrophins and their receptors in the developing brain.[93,130] Nerve growth factor (NGF) has been implicated in the normal segregation of ocular dominance columns in visual cortex of rats, whereas NT-4 and BDNF are thought to play a role in synaptic rearrangement in visual cortex of cats. These trophic molecules appear to act both pre- and postsynaptically. Application of BDNF on cortical layer IV cells in culture promotes dendritic growth,[131] whereas continuous infusion of NT-4 and BDNF in the visual cortex prevents the formation of ocular dominance columns. Presumably the geniculate arbors either fail to refine or grow excessively.[132] The activity of neurons appears to be correlated with their response to trophic molecules. Although none of the present experiments conclusively demonstrates that neurotrophins are directly involved in synapse elimination at the cortex, the current findings do suggest that these molecules can be intimately involved in the establishment of synaptic connections in the developing visual system.

Does Activity-Driven Synapse Elimination Occur Everywhere in the Developing CNS?

Although activity-driven mechanisms seem to operate to eliminate inappropriate synaptic inputs in the developing visual system, they are not required for the formation of *all* visual connections. For example, within the developing neocortex, although the tangentially oriented connectivity between pyramidal cells in layers II/III requires refinement, their radial projections are precise from the onset of development.[133,134] Likewise, the spatial organization of orientation preference maps in the cortex of higher mammals is laid down without the need for visually driven activity,[135,136] even though orientation tuning of individual cortical neurons is affected by visual experience and spontaneous retinal activity.

A notable example outside the visual system in which precise distribution of inputs appears to form in the absence of activity is the unique spatial pattern of connectivity found in the rodent somatosensory system. The whiskers or vibrissae of rodents are innervated by separate vibrissal nerves, which are activated by movement of the whiskers. The vibrissal fibers terminate principally in two regions of the brainstem, the trigeminal nucleus and nucleus oralis, which send projections in turn to the ventroposterior thalamus and to region S1 of the somatosensory cortex. The arrangement of the whiskers on the face is reflected topographically in a distribution of discrete functional units, called barrels, in S1 (Fig. 19.19).[138,139] Such distinct arrangements of connections have encouraged neurobiologists to examine how this pattern forms and to draw similarities with the development of ocular dominance columns.

Experiments that manipulate activity in the somatosensory system, however, have produced unexpected and conflicting results. Early experiments in which activity was blocked by chronic infusion of TTX to the infraorbital nerve or to S1, or the application of NMDA receptor antagonists to S1, did not prevent the emergence or arrangement of the barrels during development.[138] However, in mice lacking the NR1 subunit of the NMDA receptor, barrelettes are absent in the trigeminal nucleus.[140] Pharmacological blockade of the NMDA receptor from birth, by contrast, did not prevent barrellete formation.[141] These results may conflict because barrellete formation is slowed in NR-1 knockout mice (because they die shortly after birth, it is not possible to test this hypothesis), or the pharmacological blockade from birth occurred too late, as barrelletes are normally present by this age.

When barrel formation is assessed by examining the distribution of cortical cells or the afferent arbor

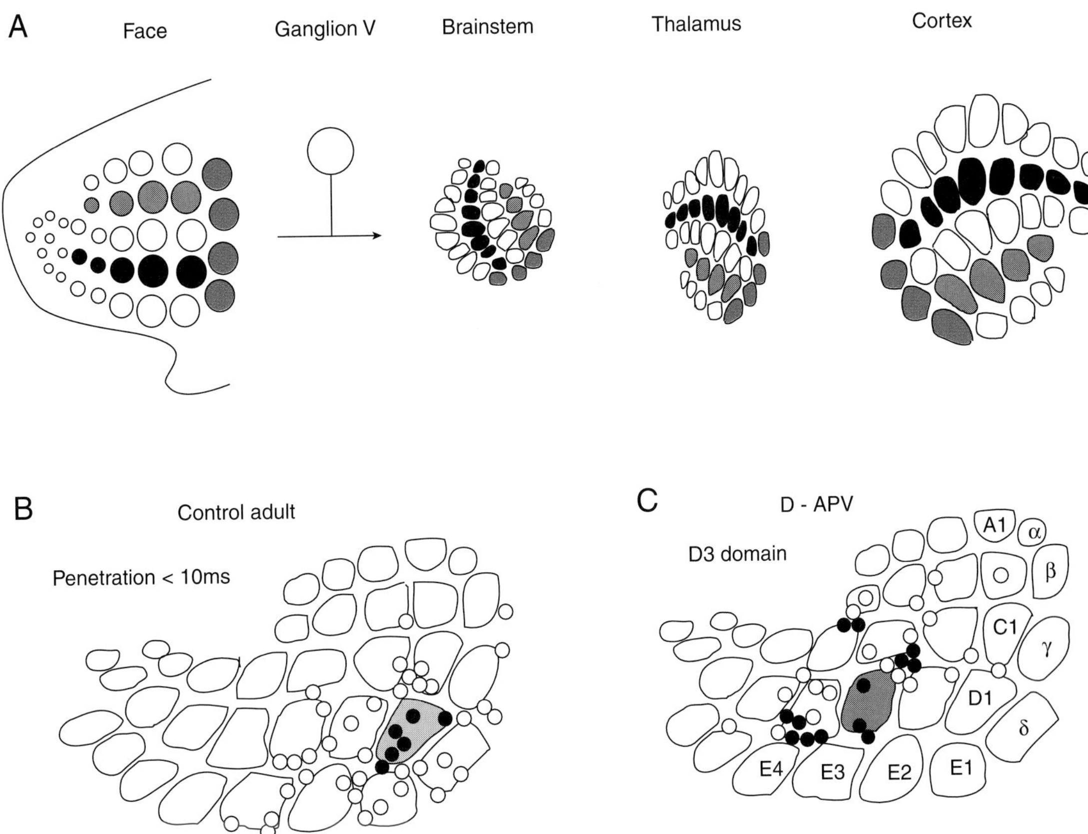

FIGURE 19.19 (A) Patterns of functional units in the somatosensory system of rodents. Each mystacial vibrassa on the face is represented in a one-to-one functional relationship with groups of target neurons along the somatosensory system, ultimately representing barrels in the S1 region of the cortex.[138] (B) Blockade of postsynaptic activity by the NMDA receptor antagonist D-APV during neonatal development does not prevent the emergence of barrels in S1. However, although the anatomical arrangement appears unaffected by this treatment, physiological analysis indicates otherwise. Short latency responses (direct monosynaptic excitation from thalamic afferents) of layer IV neurons in S1 to vibrassae stimulation are normally confined to the appropriate barrel (see control adult). However, in D-APV-treated cortex (C), short latency responses (black dots) are found not only within but also outside the boundaries of the appropriate barrel.[139]

structures by anatomical means, the results suggest that activity plays no role in the development of this topographical arrangement. However, more recent studies using physiological approaches indicate that activity is necessary. When cortical cells in S1 were chronically blocked with glutamate receptor antagonists, the anatomical arrangement of barrels as revealed by cytochrome oxidase staining remained unchanged.[139] Normally, short-latency responses for each vibrissa are confined within a single barrel, but in treated animals, these responses were detected in surrounding barrels as well.[139]

Is Synapse Rearrangement Strictly a Developmental Phenomenon?

Synapse elimination is generally thought to be a developmental phenomenon, occurring mostly during a discrete period of time. In the developing visual system, the period during which synaptic rearrangement, including synapse elimination, occurs is referred to as the **critical period.** For example, the effects of monocular deprivation can be partially reversed if the period of deprivation does not exceed the critical period.[100] Beyond the critical period, ocular dominance columns can no longer be adjusted even when one eye is no longer used for decades.

What signifies the end of the critical period? One possibility is that the end is related to a change in the milieu of developmental signals that control synaptic plasticity. An example of this could be the developmental regulation of the expression patterns of trophic factors or their receptors in the CNS.[93,130] In many cases, however, the disappearance or downregulation of trophic factors and their receptors does not coincide with the end of the critical period. A second possibility is that at the end of the critical period, synaptic competition no longer can occur because the inputs of the competitors have segregated, and the remaining inputs are all synchronously (or mostly synchronously) active. If this scenario occurs, then desynchronization of preserved inputs should result in further synaptic remodeling. This remodeling could be manifest as loss of some of the desynchronized connections, or strengthening of other connections, but not addition of new connections. Evidence to support this mechanism comes from experiments in both the PNS and the CNS. At the adult neuromuscular junction, blockade of postsynaptic AChRs in part of a junction results in synapse elimination in the inactive region.[61] In the CNS, focal binocular retinal lesions lead to the loss of visually driven activity in cortical cells subserving that part of the visual field. However, these cortical cells eventually become visually active, with receptive fields that are expanded and located in regions bordering the retinal scotoma. This rearrangement in receptive field organization has been explained by the strengthening of normally silent projections from adjacent retinal regions through elaboration of new synapses.[142,143,144]

Even though competition can reemerge under conditions in which the activity of existing inputs becomes asynchronous, the system must ultimately reach a state in which no more competition can occur because all possible competitors have been eliminated. Memory formation requires plasticity, but memory storage requires stability in the face of ongoing experience. This apparent dichotomy is mechanistically consistent with experience-induced loss of synaptic connections. In this view, the formation of memories requires that a subset of connections is selected while others are eliminated, and that once connections are eliminated, those inputs can no longer influence the circuits that have been established. Thus, new experiences are unable to overwrite the memories already laid down. Because losses induced during synapse elimination are permanent and activity mediated, such losses could potentially be a way in which alterations in the brain synaptic circuitry could occur and be maintained indefinitely.

Summary

In the visual system, the pattern of action potential activity plays a key role in the refinement of the topographic pattern of axonal connections, the creation of eye-specific layers in the lateral geniculate nucleus, and the generation of ocular dominance columns in the visual cortex. In each case, synaptic refinement involves both the retraction of incorrectly placed axon arbors and synapses and the further elaboration of correctly positioned terminals. Visual experience affects axonal development by affecting the pattern of action potentials originating in the two eyes. During fetal development, prior to visual experience, spontaneous waves of action potentials create distinct patterns of activity in the two eyes; the waves may be used during development to refine visual connections in the LGN. NMDA receptors and/or neurotrophins may be important in this process. Examples of activity-dependent competition are found throughout the central nervous system.

References

1. Frank, E., and Fischbach, G. D. (1979). Early events in neuromuscular junction formation in vitro. Induction of acetylcholine receptor clusters in the postsynaptic membrane and morphology of newly formed nerve-muscle synapses. *J. Cell Biol.* **83:** 143–158.
2. Kullberg, R., Lentz, T., and Cohen, M. W. (1977). Development of myotomal neuromuscular junction in *Xenopus laevis:* An electrophysiological and fine structural study. *Dev. Biol.* **60:** 101–129.
3. Hall, Z. W., and Sanes, J. R. (1993). Synaptic structure and development: The neuromuscular junction. *Cell/Neuron* **72**(10)(Suppl.): 99–121.
4. Jennings, C. G. B., and Burden, S. J. (1993). Development of the neuromuscular synapse. *Curr. Opin. Neurobiol.* **3:** 75–81.
5. Sanes, J. R., Marshall, L. M., and McMahan, U. J. (1978). Reinnervation of muscle fiber basal lamina by after removal of myofibers. Differentiation of regenerating axons at original synaptic sites. *J. Cell Biol.* **78:** 176–198.
6. Burden, S. J., Sargent, P. B., and McMahan, U. J. (1979). Acetylcholine receptors in regenerating muscle accumulate at the original synaptic site in the absence of the nerve. *J. Cell Biol.* **82:** 412–425.
7. McMahan, U. J. (1990). The agrin hypothesis. *Cold Spring Harbor Symp. Quant. Biol.* **55:** 407–418.
8. Bowe, M. A., and Fallon, J. R. (1995). The role of agrin in synapse formation. *Annu. Rev. Neurosci.* **18:** 443–462.
9. Rupp, F., Payan, D. G., Magill-Solc, C., Cowan, D. M., and Scheller, R. H. (1991). Structure and expression of a rat agrin. *Neuron* **6:** 811–823.
10. Tsim, K. W. K., Ruegg, M. A., Escher, G., Kröger, S., and McMahan, U. J. (1992). cDNA that encodes active agrin. *Neuron* **8:** 677–689.
11. Ruegg, M. A., Tsim, K. W. K., Horton, S. E., Kröger, S., Escher, G., Gensch, E. M., and McMahan, U. J. (1992). The agrin gene codes for a family of basal lamina proteins that differ in function and distribution. *Neuron* **8:** 691–699.
12. Ferns, M., Hoch, W., Campanelli, J. T., Rupp, F., Hall, Z. W., and Scheller, R. H. (1992). RNA splicing regulates agrin-mediated acetylcholine receptor clustering activity on cultured myotubes. *Neuron* **8:** 1079–1086.
13. Reist, N. E., Werle, M. J., and McMahan, U. J. (1992). Agrin released by motor neurons induces the aggregation of acetylcholine receptors at neuromuscular junctions. *Neuron* **8:** 865–868.
14. Ferns, M., Campanelli, J. T., Hoch, W., Scheller, R., and Hall, Z. W. (1993). The ability of agrin to cluster AChRs depends on alternative splicing and on cell surface proteoglycans. *Neuron* **11:** 491–502.
15. Gesemann, M., Denzer, A. J., and Ruegg, M. A. (1995). Acetyl-

choline receptor-aggregating activity of agrin isoforms and mapping of the active site. *J. Cell Biol.* **128:** 625–636.

16. Valenzuela, D. M., Stitt, T. N., DiStefano, P. S., Rojas, E., Mattsson, K., Compton, D. L., Lunøz, L., Park, J. S., Stark, J. L., Gies, D. R., Thomas, S., Copeland, N. G., Jenkins, N. A., Burden, S. J., Glass, D. J., and Yancopoulos, G. D. (1995). Identification of a receptor tyrosine kinase specific for the skeletal muscle lineage: Expression in embryonic muscle, at the neuromuscular junction and after injury. *Neuron* **15:** 573–584.
17. DeChiara, T. M., Bowen, D. C., Valenzuela, D. M., Simmons, M. V., Poueymirou, W. T., Thomas, S., Kinetz, E., Compton, D. L., Park, J. S., Smith, C., DiStefano, P. S., Glass, D. J., Burden, S. J., and Yancopoulos, G. D. (1996). The receptor tyrosine kinase, MuSK, is required for neuromuscular junction formation in vivo. *Cell (Cambridge, Mass.)* **85:** 501–512.
18. Gautam, M., Noakes, P. G., Moscoso, L., Rupp, F., Scheller, R. H., Merlie, J. P., and Sanes, J. R. (1996). Defective neuromuscular synaptogenesis in agrin-deficient mutant mice. *Cell (Cambridge, Mass.)* **85:** 525–535.
19. Glass, D. J., Bowen, D. C., Radziejewski, C., Bruno, J., Stitt, T. N., Ryan, T. E., Gies, D. R., Mattsson, K., Shah, S., Burden, S. J., Valenzuela, D. M., DeChiara, T. M., and Yancopoulos, G. D. (1996). Agrin acts via a MuSK receptor complex. *Cell (Cambridge, Mass.)* **85:** 513–523.
20. Bowe, M. A., Deyst, K. A., Deszyk, J. D., and Fallon, J. R. (1994). Identification and purification of an agrin receptor from Torpedo postsynaptic membranes: A heteromeric complex related to the dystroglycans. *Neuron* **12:** 1–20.
21. Campanelli, J. T., Roberds, S. L., Campbell, K. P., and Scheller, R. H. (1994). A role for dystrophin-associated glycoproteins and utrophin in agrin-induced AChR clustering. *Cell (Cambridge, Mass.)* **77:** 663–674.
22. Gee, S. H., Montanaro, F., Lindenbaum, M. H., and Carbonetto, S. (1994). Dystroglycan-α, a dystrophin-associated glycoprotein, is a functional agrin receptor. *Cell (Cambridge, Mass.)* **77:** 675–686.
23. Sugiyama, J., Bowen, D. C., and Hall, Z. W. (1994). Dystroglycan binds nerve and muscle agrin. *Neuron* **13:** 103–115.
24. Ferns, M., Deiner, M., and Hall, Z. W. (1996). Agrin-induced acetylcholine receptor clustering in mammalian muscle requires tyrosine phosphorylation. *J. Cell Biol.* **132:** 937–944.
25. Froehner, S. C. (1991). The submembrane machinery for nicotinic acetylcholine receptor clustering. *J. Cell Biol.* **114:** 1–7.
26. Froehner, S. C., Gulbrandsen, V., Hyman, C., Jeng, A. Y., Neubig, R. R., and Cohen, J. B. (1981). Immunofluorescence localization at the mammalian neuromuscular junction of the *Mr* 43,000 protein of Torpedo postsynaptic membranes. *Proc. Natl. Acad. Sci. U.S.A.* **78:** 5230–5234.
27. Burden, S. J., DePalma, R. L., and Gottesman, G. S. (1983). Crosslinking of proteins in acetylcholine receptor-rich membranes: Association between the β-subunit and the 43 kd subsynaptic protein. *Cell (Cambridge, Mass.)* **35:** 687–692.
28. Apel, E. D., Roberds, S. L., Campbell, K. P., and Merlie, J. P. (1995). Rapsyn may function as a link between the acetylcholine receptor and the agrin-binding dystrophin-associated glycoprotein complex. *Neuron* **15:** 115–126.
29. Froehner, S. C., Murnane, A. A., Tobler, M., Peng, H. B., and Sealock, R. (1987). A postsynaptic Mr 58,000 (58K) protein concentrated at acetylcholine receptor-rich sites in Torpedo electroplaques and skeletal muscle. *J. Cell Biol.* **104:** 1633–1646.
30. Burden, S. J. (1985). The subsynaptic 43-kDa protein is concentrated at developing nerve-muscle synapses in vitro. *Proc. Natl. Acad. Sci. U.S.A.* **82:** 8270–8273.
31. Noakes, P. G., Phillips, W. D., Hanley, T. A., Sanes, J. R., and Merlie, J. P. (1993). 43K protein and acetylcholine receptors colocalize during the initial stages of neuromuscular synapse formation in vivo. *Dev. Biol.* **155:** 275–280.
32. Gautam, M., Noakes, P. G., Mudd, J., Nichol, M., Chu, G. C., Sanes, J. R., and Merlie, J. P. (1995). Failure of postsynaptic specialization to develop at neuromuscular junctions of rapsyn-deficient mice. *Nature (London)* **377:** 232–236.
33. Froehner, S. C., Luetje, C. W., Scotland, P. B., and Patrick, J. (1990). The postsynaptic 43K protein clusters muscle nicotinic acetylcholine receptors in Xenopus oocytes. *Neuron* **5:** 403–410.
34. Phillips, W. D., Kopta, C., Blount, P., Gardner, P. D., Steinbach, J. H., and Merlie, J. P. (1991). ACh receptor-rich membrane domains organized in fibroblasts by recombinant 43-kilodalton protein. *Science* **251:** 568–570.
35. Burden, S. J. (1993). Synapse-specific gene expression. *Trends Genet.* **9:** 12–16.
36. Duclert, A., and Changeux, J.-P. (1995). Acetylcholine receptor gene expression at the developing neuromuscular junction. *Physiol. Rev.* **75:** 339–368.
37. Merlie, J. P., and Sanes, J. R. (1985). Concentration of acetylcholine receptor mRNA in synaptic regions of adult muscle fibers. *Nature (London)* **317:** 66–68.
38. Klarsfeld, A., Bessereau, J.-L., Salmon, A.-M., Triller, A., Babinet, C., and Changeux, J.-P. (1991). An acetylcholine receptor α-subunit promoter conferring preferential synaptic expression in muscle of transgenic mice. *EMBO J.* **10:** 625–632.
39. Sanes, J. R., Johnson, Y. R., Kotzbauer, P. T., Mudd, J., Hanley, T., Martinou, J. C., and Merlie, J. P. (1991). Selective expression of an acetylcholine receptor-lacZ transgene in synaptic nuclei of adult muscle fibers. *Development (Cambridge, UK)* **113:** 1181–1191.
40. Simon, A. M., Hoppe, P., and Burden, S. J. (1992). Spatial restriction of AChR gene expression to subsynaptic nuclei. *Development (Cambridge, UK)* **114:** 545–553.
41. Moscoso, L. M., Merlie, J. P., and Sanes, J. R. (1995). N-CAM, 43k-rapsyn, and s-laminin mRNAs are concentrated at synaptic sites in muscle fibers. *Mol. Cell. Neurosci.* **6:** 80–89.
42. Jo, S. A., and Burden, S. J. (1992). Synaptic basal lamina contains a signal for synapse-specific transcription. *Development (Cambridge, UK)* **115:** 673–680.
43. Goldman, D., Carlson, B. M., and Staple, J. (1991). Induction of adult-type nicotinic acetylcholine receptor gene expression in noninnervated regenerating muscle. *Neuron* **7:** 649–658.
44. Carraway, K. L., III, and Burden, S. J. (1995). Neuregulins and their receptors. *Curr. Opin. Neurobiol.* **5:** 606–612.
45. Falls, D. L., Rosen, K. M., Corfas, G., Lane, W. S., and Fischbach, G. D. (1993). ARIA, a protein that stimulates acetylcholine receptor synthesis, is a member of the neu ligand family. *Cell (Cambridge, Mass.)* **72:** 801–815.
46. Marchionni, M. A., Goodearl, A. D., Chen, M. S., Bermingham-McDonogh, O., Kirk, C., Hendricks, M., Danehy, F., Misumi, D., Sudhalter, J., Kobayashi, K. *et al.* (1993). Glial growth factors are alternatively spliced erbB2 ligands expressed in the nervous system. *Nature (London)* **362:** 312–18.
47. Jo, S. A., Zhu, X., Marchionni, M. A., and Burden, S. J. (1995). NRGs are concentrated at nerve-muscle synapses and activate ACH-receptor gene expression. *Nature (London)* **373:** 158–161.
48. Moscoso, L. M., Chu, G. C. Gautam, M., Noakes, P. G., Merlie, J. P., and Sanes, J. R. (1995). Synapse-associated expression of an acetylcholine receptor-inducing protein, ARIA/heregulin, and its putative receptors, ErbB2 and ErbB3, in developing mammalian muscle. *Dev. Biol.* **172:** 158–169.
49. Zhu, X., Lai, C., Thomas, S., and Burden, S. J. (1995). Neuregulin

receptors, erbB3 and erbB4, are localized at neuromuscular synapses. *EMBO J.* **14:** 5842–5848.
50. Meyer, D., and Birchmeier, C. (1995). Multiple essential functions of neuregulin in development. *Nature* (*London*) **378:** 386–390.
51. Gassmann, M., Casagranda, F., Orioli, D., Simon, H., Lai, C., Klein, R., and Lemke, G. (1995). Aberrant neural and cardiac development in mice lacking the ErbB4 neuregulin receptor. *Nature* (*London*) **378:** 390–394.
52. Lee, K. F., Simon, H., Chen, H., Bates, B., Hung, M. C., and Hauser, C. (1995). Requirement for neuregulin receptor erbB2 in neural and cardiac development. *Nature* (*London*) **378:** 394–398.
53. Kuhse, J., Betz, H., and Kirsch, J. (1995). The inhibitory glycine receptor: Architecture, synaptic localization and molecular pathology of a postsynaptic ion-channel complex. *Curr. Opin. Neurobiol.* **5:** 318–323.
54. Froechner, S. C. (1993). Regulation of ion channel distribution at synapses. *Annu. Rev. Neurosci.* **16:** 347–368.
55. Craig, A. M., Blackstone, C. D., Huganir, R. L., and Banker, G. (1994). Selective clustering of glutamate and γ-aminobutyric acid receptors opposite terminals releasing the corresponding neurotransmitters. *Proc. Natl. Acad. Sci. U.S.A.* **91:** 12373–12377.
56. Kuhse, J., Betz, H., and Kirsch, J. (1995). The inhibitory glycine receptor: Architecture, synaptic localization and molecular pathology of a postsynaptic ion-channel complex. *Curr. Opin. Neurobiol.* **5:** 318–368.
57. Sheng, M. (1996). PDZs and receptor/channel clustering: Rounding up the latest suspects. *Neuron* **17:** 575–578.
58. Dong, H., O'Brien, R. J., Fung, E. T., Lanahan, A. A., Worley, P. F., and Huganir, R. L. (1997). GRIP: A synaptic PDZ domain-containing protein that interacts with AMPA receptors. *Nature* (*London*) **386:** 279–284.
59. Apperson, M. L., Moon, I. S., and Kennedy, M. B. (1996). Characterization of densin-180, a new brain-specific synaptic protein of the O-sialoglycoprotein family. *J. Neurosci.* **16:** 6839–6852.
60. Wyszynski, M., Lin, J., Rao, A., Nigh, E., Beggs, A. H., Craig, A. M., and Sheng, M. (1997). Competitive binding of α-actinin and calmodulin to the NMDA receptor. *Nature* (*London*) **385:** 439–442.
61. Balice-Gordon, R. J., and Lichtman, J. W. (1994). Long-term synapse loss induced by focal blockade of postsynaptic receptors. *Nature* (*London*) **372:** 519–524.
62. Landmesser, L., and Pilar, G. (1974). Synaptic transmission and cell death during normal ganglionic development. *J. Physiol.* (*London*) **241:** 737–749.
63. Landmesser, L., and Pilar, G. (1976). Fate of ganglionic synapses and ganglion cell axons during normal and induced cell death. *J. Cell Biol.* **68:** 357–374.
64. Nguyen, Q., and Lichtman, J. W. (1996). Mechanism of synapse disassembly at the developing neuromuscular junction. *Curr. Opin. Neurobiol.* **6:** 104–112.
65. Thompson, W. J., Sutton, L. A., and Riley, D. A. (1984). Fibre type composition of single motor units during synapse elimination in neonatal rat soleus muscle. *Nature* (*London*) **309:** 709–711.
66. Laskowski, M. B., and Owens, J. L. (1994). Embryonic expression of motoneuron topography in the rat diaphragm muscle. *Dev. Biol.* **166:** 502–508.
67. Thompson, W., and Jansen, J. K. S. (1977). The extent of sprouting of remaining motor units in partly denervated immature and adult rat soleus muscle. *Neuroscience* **2:** 523–535.
68. Frank, E., Jansen, J. K. S., Lomo, T., and Westgaard, R. H. (1975). The interaction between foreign and original motor nerves innervating the soleus muscle of rats. *J. Physiol.* (*London*) **247:** 725–743.
69. Brown, M. C., Jansen, J. K. S., and VanEssen, D. (1976). Polyneuronal innervation of skeletal muscle in newborn rats and its elimination during maturation. *J. Physiol.* (*London*) **261:** 387–422.
70. Lichtman, J. W. (1977). The reorganization of synaptic connexions in the rat submandibular ganglion during post-natal development. *J. Physiol.* (*London*) **273:** 155–177.
71. Johnson, D. A., and Purves, D. (1981). Post-natal reduction of neural unit size in the rabbit ciliary ganglion. *J. Physiol.* (*London*) **318:** 143–159.
72. Betz, W. J., Caldwell, J. H., and Ribchester, R. R. (1979). The size of motor units during post-natal development of rat lumbrical muscle. *J. Physiol.* (*London*) **297:** 463–478.
73. MacArdle, J. J. (1975). Complex end-plate potentials at the regenerating neuromuscular junction of the rat. *Exp. Neurol.* **49:** 629–638.
74. Rich, M. M., and Lichtman, J. W. (1989). *In vivo* visualization of pre- and postsynaptic changes during synapse elimination in reinnervated mouse muscle. *J. Neurosci.* **9:** 1781–1805.
75. Colman, H. C., Nabekura, J., and Lichtman, J. W. (1997). Synaptic weakening precedes permanent loss of axonal connections in the mammalian nervous system. *Science* **275:** 356–361.
76. Gouze, J. L., Lasry, J. M., and Changeux, J.-P. (1983). Selective stabilization of muscle innervation during development: A mathematical model. *Biol. Cybernet.* **46:** 207–215.
77. Rasmussen, C. E., and Willshaw, D. J. (1993). Presynaptic and postsynaptic competition in models for the development of neuromuscular connections. *Biol. Cybernet.* **68:** 409–419.
78. Van Essen, D. C., Gordon, H., Soha, J. M., and Fraser, S. E. (1990). Synaptic dynamics at the neuromuscular junction: Mechanisms and models. *J. Neurosci.* **212:** 223–249.
79. Liu, Y., Fields, R. D., Fitzgerald, S., Festoff, B. W., and Nelson, P. G. (1994). Proteolytic activity, synapse elimination, and the Hebb synapse. *J. Neurobiol.* **25:** 325–335.
80. Thompson, W. (1983). Synapse elimination in neonatal rat muscle is sensitive to pattern of muscle use. *Nature* (*London*) **302:** 614–616.
81. Callaway, E. M., Soha, J. M., and VanEssen, D. C. (1987). Competition favoring inactive over active motor neurons during synapse elimination. *Nature* (*London*) **328:** 422–426.
82. Jordan, C. L. (1993). Ciliary neurotrophic factor delays synapse elimination in the rat levator ani muscle. *Soc. Neurosci. Abstr.* **19:** 1099.
83. English, A. W., and Schwartz, G. (1995). Both basic fibroblast growth factor and ciliary neurotrophic factor promote the retention of polyneuronal innervation of developing skeletal muscle fibers. *Dev. Biol.* **169:** 57–64.
84. Riley, D. A. (1981). Ultrastructural evidence for axon retraction during the spontaneous elimination of polyneuronal innervation of the rat soleus muscle. *J. Neurocytol.* **10:** 425–440.
85. Balice-Gordon, R. J., and Lichtman, J. W. (1993). In vivo observations of pre- and postsynaptic changes during the transition from multiple to single innervation at developing neuromuscular junctions. *J. Neurosci.* **13:** 834–855.
86. Bixby, J. L. (1981). Ultrastructural observations on synapse elimination in neonatal rabbit skeletal muscle. *J. Neurocytol.* **10:** 81–100.
87. Korneliussen, H., and Jansen, J. K. S. (1976). Morphological aspects of the elimination of polyneuronal innervation of skeletal muscle fibers in newborn rats. *J. Neurocytol.* **5:** 591–604.
88. Balice-Gordon, R. J., Chua, C. K., Nelson, C. C., and Lichtman, J. W. (1993). Gradual loss of synaptic cartels precedes axon withdrawal at developing neuromuscular junctions. *Neuron* **11:** 801–815.

89. Colman, H. C., and Lichtman, J. W. (1992). 'Cartellian' competition at the neuromuscular junction. *Trends Neurosci.* **15:** 197–199.
90. Kuffler, D., Thompson, W., and Jansen, J. K. S. (1977). The elimination of synapses in multiply-innervated skeletal muscle fibres of the rat: Dependence on distance between end-plates. *Brain Res.* **138:** 353–358.
91. Lichtman, J. W., and Wilkinson, R. S. (1987). Properties of motor units in the transversus abdominis muscle of the garter snake. *J. Physiol.* (*London*) **393:** 355–374.
92. Nabekura, J., and Lichtman, J. W. (1989). Progressive loss of synaptic efficacy during synapse elimination. *Soc. Neurosci. Abstr.* **15:** 165.
93. Snider, W. D., and Lichtman, J. W. (1996). Are neurotrophins synaptotrophins? *Mol. Cell. Neurosci.* **7:** 433–442.
94. Brenner, H. R., and Martin, A. R. (1976). Reduction in acetylcholine sensitivity of axotomized ganglion cells. *J. Physiol.* (*London*) **260:** 159–175.
95. Purves, D. (1988). *Body and Brain: A Trophic Theory of Neural Connections.* Harvard University Press, Cambridge, MA.
96. Wong, R. O. L. (1997). Patterns of correlated spontaneous bursting activity in the developing mammalian retina. *Cell Dev. Biol.* **8:** 5–12.
97. Engel, A. G., Tsujihata, M., Lindstrom, J. M., and Lennon, V. A. (1976). The motor end plate in myasthenia gravis and in experimental autoimmune myasthenia gravis. A quantitative ultrastructural study. *Ann. N.Y. Acad. Sci.* **274:** 60–79.
98. Rich, M. M., Colman, H., and Lichtman, J. W. (1994). In vivo imaging shows loss of synaptic sites from neuromuscular junctions in a model of myasthenia gravis. *Neurology* **44:** 2138–2145.
98a. Culican, S. M., Nelson, C. C., and Lichtman, J. W. (1998). Axon withdrawal during synapse elimination at the neuromuscular junction is accompanied by disassembly of the postsynaptic specialization and withdrawal of Schwann cell processes. *J. Neurosci.* **18:** 4953–4965.
99. Jennings, C. (1994). Death of a synapse. *Nature* (*News Views*) **372:** 498–499.
100. Wiesel, T. N. (1982). Postnatal development of the visual cortex and the influence of environment. *Nature* (*London*) **299:** 583–591.
101. Shatz, C. J., and Stryker, M. P. (1988). Prenatal tetrodotoxin infusion blocks segregation of retinogeniculate afferents. *Science* **242:** 87–89.
102. Hubel, D. H., and Wiesel, T. N. (1963). Receptive fields of cells in striate cortex of very young, visually inexperienced kittens. *J. Neurophysiol.* **26:** 994–1002.
103. Hubel, D. H., Wiesel, T. N., and LeVay, S. (1977). Plasticity of ocular dominance columns in the monkey striate cortex. *Philos. Trans. R. Soc. London* **278:** 377–409.
104. Shatz, C. J., and Kirkwood, P. A. (1984). Prenatal development of functional connections in the cat's retinogeniculate pathway. *J. Neurosci.* **4:** 1378–1397.
105. Shatz, C. J. (1990). Competitive interactions between retinal ganglion cells during prenatal development. *J. Neurobiol.* **21:** 197–211.
106. Roskies, A., Friedman, G. C., and O'Leary, D. D. M. (1995). Mechanisms and molecules controlling the development of retinal maps. *Perspect. Dev. Neurobiol.* **3:** 63–75.
107. Friedman, G. C., and O'Leary, D. D. M. (1996). Eph receptor tyrosine kinases and their ligands in neural development. *Curr. Opin. Neurobiol.* **6:** 127–133.
108. Simon, D. K., and O'Leary, D. D. M. (1992). Development of topographic order in the mammalian retinocollicular projection. *J. Neurosci.* **12:** 1212–1232.
109. O'Leary, D. D. M., Fawcett, J. W., and Cowan, W. M. (1986). Topographic targeting errors in the retinocollicular projection and their elimination by selective ganglion cell death. *J. Neurosci.* **6:** 3692–3705.
110. Wong, R. O. L., and Hughes, A. (1986). Role of cell death in the topogenesis of neuronal distributions in the developing cat retinal ganglion cell layer. *J. Comp. Neurol.* **262:** 496–511.
111. Wiesel, T. N., and Hubel, D. H. (1963). Single cell responses in striate cortex of kittens deprived of vision in one eye. *J. Neurophysiol.* **26:** 1003–1017.
112. Chapman, B., Jacobson, M. D., Reiter, H. O., and Stryker, M. P. (1986). Ocular dominance shift in kitten visual cortex caused by imbalance of retinal electrical activity. *Nature* (*London*) **324:** 154–156.
113. Reiter, H. O., and Stryker, M. P. (1988). Neural plasticity without postsynaptic action potentials: Less active inputs become dominant when kitten visual cortical cells are pharmacologically inhibited. *Proc. Natl. Acad. Sci. U.S.A.* **85:** 3623–3627.
114. Hata, Y., and Stryker, M. P. (1994). Control of thalamocortical afferent rearrangement by postsynaptic activity in developing visual cortex. *Science* **265:** 1732–1735.
115. Antonini, A., and Stryker, M. P. (1993). Development of individual geniculocortical arbors in cat striate cortex and effects of binocular impulse blockade. *J. Neurosci.* **13:** 3549–3573.
116. Antonini, A., and Stryker, M. P. (1993). Rapid remodeling of axonal arbors in the visual cortex. *Science* **260:** 1819–1821.
117. Sretavan, D. W., Shatz, C. J., and Stryker, M. P. (1988). Modification of retinal ganglion cell axon morphology by prenatal infusion of tetrodotoxin. *Nature* (*London*) **336:** 468–471.
118. Hahm, J.-O., Langdon, R. B., and Sur, M. (1991). Disruption of retinogeniculate afferent segregation by antagonists to NMDA receptors. *Nature* (*London*) **351:** 568–570.
119. Stryker, M. P., and Harris, W. (1986). Binocular impulse blockade prevents the formation of ocular dominance columns in cat visual cortex. *J. Neurosci.* **6:** 2117–2133.
120. Linden, C. D., Guillery, R. W., and Cucchiaro, J. (1981). The dorsal lateral geniculate nucleus of the normal ferret and its postnatal development. *J. Comp. Neurol.* **203:** 189–211.
121. Wong, R. O. L., Chernjavsky, A., Smith, S. A., and Shatz, C. J. (1995). Early functional neural networks in the developing retina. *Nature* (*London*) **374:** 716–718.
122. Feller, M. B., Wellis, D. P., Stellwagen, D., Werblin, F. S., and Shatz, C. J. (1996). Requirement for cholinergic synaptic transmission in the propagation of spontaneous retinal waves. *Science* **272:** 1182–1187.
123. Wong, R. O. L., Meister, M., and Shatz, C. J. (1993). Transient period of correlated bursting activity during development of the mammalian retina. *Neuron* **11:** 923–938.
124. Wong, R. O. L., and Oakley, D. M. (1996). Changing patterns of spontaneous bursting activity of On and Off retinal ganglion cells during development. *Neuron* **16:** 1087–1095.
125. Komatsu, Y., Fujii, K., Maeda, J., Sakaguchi, H., and Toyama, K. (1988). Long-term potentiation of synaptic transmission in kitten visual cortex. *J. Neurophysiol.* **59:** 124–141.
126. Kato, N., Artola, A., and Singer, W. (1991). Developmental changes in the susceptibility to long-term potentiation of neurones in rat visual cortex slices. *Dev. Brain Res.* **60:** 43–50.
127. Kirkwood, A., and Bear, M. F. (1994). Hebbian synapses in visual cortex. *J. Neurosci.* **14:** 1634–1645.
128. Bear, M. F., Kleinschmidt, A., Gu, Q. A., and Singer, W. (1990). Disruption of experience-dependent synaptic modifications in striate cortex by infusion of an NMDA receptor antagonist. *J. Neurosci.* **10:** 909–925.
129. Cline, H. T., and Constantine-Paton, M. (1989). NMDA receptor antagonists disrupt the retinotopic map. *Neuron* **3:** 413–426.

130. Katz, L. C., and Shatz, C. J. (1996). Synaptic activity and the construction of cortical circuits. *Science* **274:** 1133–1138.
131. McAllister, A. K., Lo, D. C., and Katz, L. C. (1995). Neurotrophins regulate dendritic growth in developing visual cortex. *Neuron* **15:** 791–803.
132. Cabelli, R. J., Hohn, A., and Shatz, C. J. (1995). Inhibition of ocular dominance column formation by infusion of NT-4/5 or BDNF. *Science* **267:** 1662–1666.
133. Callaway, E. M., and Katz, L. C. (1990). Emergence and refinement of clustered horizontal connections in cat striate cortex. *J. Neurosci.* **10:** 1134–1153.
134. Katz, L. C. (1990). Specificity in the development of vertical connections in cat striate cortex. *Eur. J. Neurosci.* **2:** 1–9.
135. Kim, D. S., and Bonhoeffer, T. (1994). Reverse occlusion leads to a precise restoration of orientation preference maps in visual cortex. *Nature (London)* **370:** 370–372.
136. Gödeke, I., and Bonhoeffer, T. (1996). Development of identical orientation maps for two eyes without common visual experience. *Nature (London)* **379:** 251–254.
137. Pettigrew, J. D. (1974). The effect of visual experience on the development of stimulus specificity by kitten cortical neurones. *J. Physiol. (London)* **237:** 49–74.
138. O'Leary, D. D. M., Ruff, N. L., and Duck, R. H. (1994). Development, critical period plasticity, and adult reorganizations of mammalian somatosensory systems. *Curr. Opin. Neurobiol.* **4:** 535–544.
139. Fox, K., Schalaggar, B. L., Glazweski, S., and O'Leary, D. D. M. (1996). Glutamate receptor blockade at cortical synapses disrupts development of thalamocortical and columnar organization in somatasensory cortex. *Proc. Natl. Acad. Sci. U.S.A.* **93:** 5584–5589.
140. Li, Y., Erzurumlu, R. S., Chen, C., Jhaceri, S., and Tonegawa, S. (1994). Whisker-related neuronal patterns fail to develop in the trigeminal brainstem nuclei of NMDAR1 knockout mice. *Cell (Cambridge, Mass.)* **76:** 427–437.
141. Henderson, T. A., Woolsey, T. A., and Jacquin, M. F. (1992). Infraorbital nerve blockade from birth does not disrupt central trigeminal pattern formation in the rat. *Dev. Brain Res.* **66:** 146–152.
142. Gilbert, C. D., and Wiesel, T. N. (1992). Receptive field dynamics in adult primary visual cortex. *Nature (London)* **356:** 150–152.
143. Darian-Smith, C., and Gilbert, C. D. (1994). Axonal sprouting accompanies functional reorganization in adult cat striate cortex. *Nature (London)* **368:** 737–740.
144. Das, A., and Gilbert, C. D. (1995). Long-range horizontal connections and their role in cortical reorganization revealed by optical recording of cat primary visual cortex. *Nature (London)* **375:** 780–784.

C H A P T E R

20

Programmed Cell Death

Ronald W. Oppenheim

The inclusion of chapters on cell death and trophic factors is now considered *de rigueur* in any comprehensive description of nervous system development. However, as we discuss below, this hasn't always been the case. Less than a generation ago the death of neurons during normal development was little appreciated, and the events leading to the discovery of the first neurotrophic agent, nerve growth factor (NGF), were just beginning.[1] Today, by contrast, both topics are in the forefront of research on neuronal development, and, in fact, from a historical perspective, the study of cell death and trophic factors is now undergoing a renaissance.[1a,1b,1c,21] One of the pioneers in this field, the American embryologist John Saunders, noted 30 years ago that one is uncomfortable with the notion that cell death has a place in embryonic development.[2] One of the hallmarks of embryonic development is the production of new cells and the acquisition of new cellular properties (phenotypes). Accordingly, in the past, the major focus of developmental neurobiologists has been the study of these progressive events, including proliferation and migration (Chapter 16), pathway formation (Chapter 18), synaptogenesis (Chapter 19), and phenotype determination (Chapters 15 and 17). In this context the concept of significant regressive events such as cell death occurring during development was considered counterintuitive, often relegated to a subordinate position, or even denied altogether.[1] Yet we now know that cell loss and other regressive events, including synapse elimination (Chapter 19), are the rule, not the exception. In virtually all developing tissues that have been examined, substantial cell loss occurs. Cell death has been suggested as a default pathway for all cells, and cells escape this fate only by receiving the appropriate survival (trophic) signals.[3] If this notion is correct, not only does cell death serve critically important functions, but fundamental issues concerning the evolution of cell death and how a balance between proliferation and death—or survival and death (and thus ultimately cell number)—is regulated need to be addressed.[4] Answers to these and other questions will, in turn, provide better understanding of why cells die (or fail to die) pathologically later in life and how one might counteract aberrant cell death in these situations.

Because neurons may die for a variety of reasons and in many different situations, it is important to describe the type of cell death observed most often in the developing nervous system. Although the loss of cells during normal development has been called many different things (including normal cell death, spontaneous cell death, naturally occurring cell death, or developmental cell death), we prefer the term **programmed cell death** or **PCD.** We define PCD as the spatially and temporally reproducible and species-specific loss of large numbers of individual cells during development. Accidental, injury-induced, pathological, and disease-related forms of cell death are not included. Because many, if not most, differentiated cells in adult vertebrates undergo continuous turnover by cell death and cell division (e.g., hepatocytes in liver, blood cells, gut epithelium, olfactory epithelium, skin), this form of cell loss is also probably a type of PCD. However, whether the mechanisms of cellular and molecular regulation of cell death during normal tissue turnover are the same as those involved in developmental cell death is not clear. Furthermore, much of cell death during development appears to serve distinct functions related to embryogenesis, rather than to tissue homeostasis. This definition of PCD also makes no a priori assumptions about either the morphological or biochemical pathways by which cells die or the stimuli that trigger cell death. The use of the word "programmed" refers to the reproducible, spatiotemporal occurrence of cell loss and is not meant to imply that the cell loss is genetically predetermined, inherited from precursor cells, or inevitable. In fact, PCD is clearly not predetermined in many cases, but instead is critically dependent on epigenetic signals arising from cellular interactions. Finally, as is discussed in more detail later, the term PCD is not synonymous with the term **apoptosis,** which refers to only one specific, albeit common, mode of cell death.

In the past 25 years, the investigation of cell death during development has become a major focus in neuroscience. The reasons for this intense interest are (1) the recognition that cell death plays an important role in nervous system development, (2) the increased understanding of the role of neurotrophic molecules and cell death genes in regulating survival, and (3) the hope that a better understanding of normal cell death will shed light on the causes and treatment of nervous system disease.

CELL DEATH AND THE NEUROTROPHIC HYPOTHESIS

The discovery and recognition of the significance of neuronal cell death during normal development, together with the early formulation of ideas about the regulation of cell death and the discovery of the first trophic factor, NGF, all occurred within a common conceptual framework: namely, the role of neuron–target interactions during development.[5–7] In retrospect, the discovery and recognition of normal cell death reflects the triumph of observation over conventional wisdom and the zeitgeist, whereas the discovery of NGF represents a colorful history marked by a rare combination of scientific reasoning, intuition, and good luck (see Table 20.1).[1,8,9] Although the decision about when a discovery occurred is often arbitrary, the consensus is that the trophic theory / cell death story began 60 years ago with the observations of Viktor Hamburger on the effects of early removal of the wing bud in the chick embryo on the later development of sensory and motor neurons in the spinal cord that innervate the limb.[10] Hamburger's observations confirmed earlier controversial studies claiming that in the absence of the limb, sensory ganglia and motor nuclei were greatly reduced in size. He postulated that peripheral target fields in the limb control the development of innervating centers (sensory ganglia and motor neurons) by signals that are transmitted retrogradely along axons from targets to nerve centers in the spinal cord. These signals were thought to act by *recruiting* or inducing undifferentiated precursor cells to develop into sensory or motor neurons (Fig. 20.1). Later studies by Hamburger supported this idea by showing that when the size of the peripheral field was increased by transplantation of a supernumerary wing bud, motor nuclei and sensory ganglia were enlarged or hypertrophied. Thus, as early as 1934 the stage was set for the search for hypothetical target-derived retrograde signals, a search that led to the discovery of NGF.

Although the **recruitment hypothesis** provided a simple and elegant means of accounting for the differences in size of nerve centers after the deletion or addition of wing buds, it was wrong.[1] As scientists develop hypotheses and theories to help them understand natural phenomena, errors such as this are commonplace. Nonetheless, one can sympathize with the lament of the 19th-century English philosopher of science Herbert Spencer, who once noted that "a tragedy is a good hypothesis killed by facts." The facts that "killed" the recruitment hypothesis were provided by another pioneer in the field of cell death and trophic factors, Rita Levi-Montalcini (see Box 20.1).[11]

Strikingly new ideas are seldom fully appreciated or accepted into the prevailing conceptual framework at the time they are first proposed. Neuronal cell death offers a prominent example. Over 60 years ago Ernst and Glucksmann first recognized that cell death is an integral part of normal embryonic development.[5] By 1949, Hamburger and Levi-Montalcini had provided further evidence for the significance of normal neuronal death and postulated that target-derived signals act to regulate the number of neurons that survive embryonic development. In subsequent studies, they and their colleagues identified a specific target-derived substance (NGF) that influenced the development of the same populations of neurons (sensory and sympathetic) that their earlier studies had suggested were regulated by target-derived signals (Fig. 20.2).

Only in 1960, however, when blocking antibodies to NGF became available and were shown to cause the almost total degeneration of sympathetic ganglia *in vivo* was NGF first considered to be an endogenous survival or maintenance factor for these neurons. Even then, it took another 20 years before the normal death of a proportion of developing sympathetic neurons was first described and shown to be regulated by NGF, and it was a few years later still before NGF was shown to be synthesized in limiting trace amounts by targets. Accordingly, not until three decades after the discov-

TABLE 20.1 Major Events in the Discovery and Characterization of NGF and Their Importance for Understanding Neuronal Cell Death[a]

1934	*Hamburger* discovered that removal of the limb bud in the chick embryo resulted in reduced numbers of sensory and motor neurons in the spinal cord and suggested that targets in the limb are the source of signals that control neuronal development and that travel retrogradely in axons to their respective centers.
1939	*Hamburger* discovered that transplantation of an additional supernumerary limb bud resulted in increased numbers of sensory and motor neurons in the spinal cord, providing additional evidence that targets are the source of signals that control neuronal development. He proposed that targets act on innervating neurons by providing signals that recruit undifferentiated cells to develop into sensory or motor neurons.
1942	*Levi-Montalcini and Levi* confirmed that early limb bud removal reduced the number of sensory and motor neurons but proposed that the hypothetical target-derived signals act to maintain the survival of differentiating neurons, not to recruit undifferentiated cells.
1948	*Bueker,* a former student of Hamburger, implanted different mouse tumors into the region of the chick hind limb as a source of rapidly growing homogeneous peripheral "target" tissue in an attempt to identify the cellular source of normal target-derived signals. One tumor, sarcoma 180, a cell line derived from connective tissue, was found to produce a modest (30%) but significant increase in the size of limb sensory ganglia. It was without effect on motor neurons. Bueker concluded that the tumor provided a periphery with specific histochemical properties favorable to sensory but not motor innervation.
1949	*Hamburger and Levi-Montalcini* repeated earlier limb removal experiments, and their results supported the previous interpretation of Levi-Montalcini and Levi. They also discovered that many sensory neurons undergo a period of normal or naturally occurring cell death. They proposed that the addition or removal of a limb bud acts to reduce or enhance the normal cell death process by perturbing target-derived signals that promote neuronal survival.
1951	*Levi-Montalcini and Hamburger* repeated the Bueker experiment using sarcoma 180 and discovered an even more striking effect of the tumor on both sensory and sympathetic ganglia but again no effect on motor neurons. They concluded that the tumor cells produce specific growth-promoting agents.
1953	*Levi-Montalcini and Hamburger* carried out additional transplantation experiments with sarcoma 180 and discovered that sympathetic and sensory ganglia remote from the tumor and not connected with it by nerve fibers were also greatly enlarged. This suggested the involvement of a diffusible factor. Transplantation of tumors onto the chorioallantois, which were therefore only in communication with the embryo via the circulation, was fully effective in causing hyperplasia of ganglia, confirming that the growth-promoting activity was indeed due to a diffusible agent.
1954	*Levi-Montalcini, Meyer, and Hamburger* developed an *in vitro* assay that used explanted sympathetic ganglia. Ganglia cocultured with fragments of tumor cells lacking any physical contacts between the two exhibited massive outgrowth of nerve fibers (Fig. 20.2). The extent and density of outgrowth provided a rapid quantitative bioassay for subsequent attempts to isolate and purify the tumor factor.
1956	*Cohen and Levi-Montalcini,* in an attempt to purify the agent found in mouse sarcoma 180, used snake venom as a rich source of phosphodiesterase for the separation of nuclei acid and protein fractions in the tumor material. To their great surprise, the tumor fractions containing the snake venom were several thousand-fold more potent than control tumor homogenates in promoting nerve growth *in vitro* and *in vivo.* Subsequent experiments showed that the activities in the tumor and snake venom were identical.
1960	*Cohen* examined the mammalian homolog of the snake venom gland—the salivary gland—and discovered that the salivary gland of male mice was an even richer source of the same growth-promoting activity found in the tumors and venom gland. When an antiserum to the mouse factor was injected into newborn mice, all sympathetic neurons were lost.
1969	*Bocchini and P. Angeletti* described a method for complete purification of biologically active NGF from mouse submaxillary glands. This activity is the β subunit of NGF and is also known as 2.5S NGF. It has been estimated that to purify NGF from target organs would have required a purification factor of 100 million, whereas a purification factor of 100–200 was sufficient to purify NGF from the mouse salivary gland.
1971	*R. Angeletti and Bradshaw* identified the amino acid sequence of 2.5S NGF purified from mouse submaxillary gland.
1983	*Korsching and Thoenen* developed a sensitive two-site immunoassay, allowing for the first time the detection of NGF in target organs. With this method it was possible to demonstrate a strong correlation between the density of sympathetic innervation and target levels of NGF, a finding consistent with the neurotrophic theory.

[a]The papers cited in this table can be found in Oppenheim[1,8] and Purves and Sanes.[9]

ery that a chemical substance in tumor cells dramatically affects the development of sensory and sympathetic neurons was it finally recognized that NGF was the hypothetical target-derived trophic signal first postulated by Hamburger and Levi-Montalcini in 1949 to be involved in regulating the number of surviving neurons in these populations during normal development.[8]

Today the validity of the neurotrophic theory for understanding cell death and survival stands as a

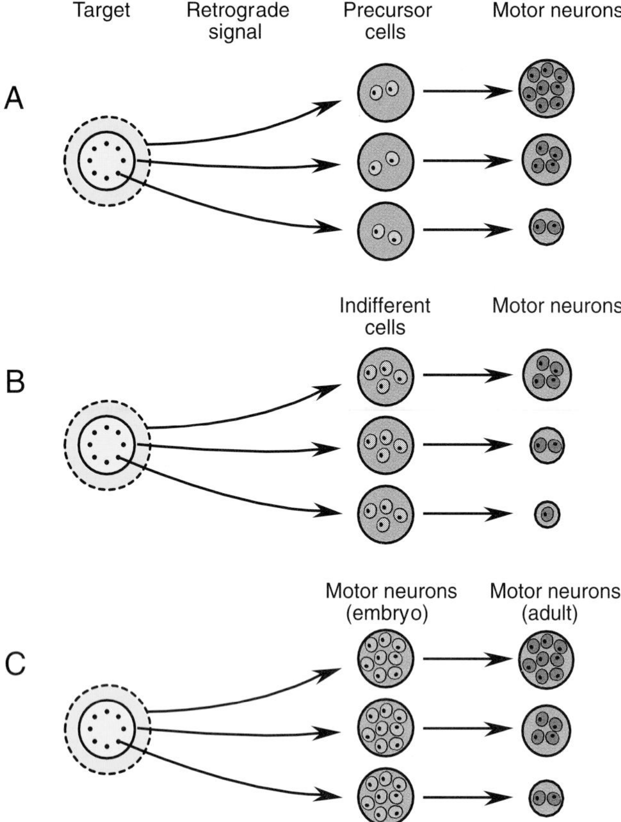

FIGURE 20.1 Neuron–target interactions involved in determining neuron number. There are three ways in which target size can influence the number of innervating neurons (motor neurons in this example). In all three models (A, B, C) the solid circle indicates normal target size, the smaller inner circle (dots) represents an experimentally reduced target, and the outer (dashed) circle represents an enlarged target. In model A, retrograde signals regulate the *proliferation* of motor neuron precursors. In model B, retrograde signals act to *recruit* unspecified postmitotic cells to differentiate into motor neurons. In model C, retrograde signals promote survival (i.e., prevent PCD) of postmitotic motor neurons.

crowning achievement of more than 60 years of observations and experiments by countless investigators. As discussed later (see Chapter 21), the theory continues to undergo elaboration and modification. However, a few central tenets derived from studies on the effects of NGF on sensory and sympathetic neurons are now firmly established. To summarize: (1) sensory and sympathetic neurons are overproduced during development and depend on NGF for their survival; (2) competition for NGF occurs when axons arrive at the relevant target tissues where NGF is synthesized and secreted in limiting amounts sufficient to support the survival of only a proportion of all of these neurons; (3) innervating neurons have specific high-affinity cell surface receptors for NGF that bind and internalize the protein; (4) the binding, internalization, and retrograde transport of NGF initiates intracellular signal cascades that mediate NGF's biological actions on survival and differentiation; (5) in the absence of NGF or its high-affinity receptor, innervating neurons die; and (6) treatment with exogenous NGF or endogenous overexpression of NGF rescues neurons that would normally die. At present, efforts to confirm the validity of these tenets for several other recently discovered neurotrophic factors are underway.

Summary

The modern study of neuronal cell death began with investigations of how synaptic targets of sensory and motor neurons regulate their development. Viktor Hamburger and Rita Levi-Montalcini, beginning in the 1930s, ultimately showed that targets promote the survival and maintenance of innervating neurons. This notion, in turn, provided a conceptual framework for the discovery of the first neurotrophic agent, nerve growth factor (NGF). From these beginnings the neurotrophic hypothesis was formulated: neurons compete for limiting amounts of target-derived survival promoting (trophic) agents during development.

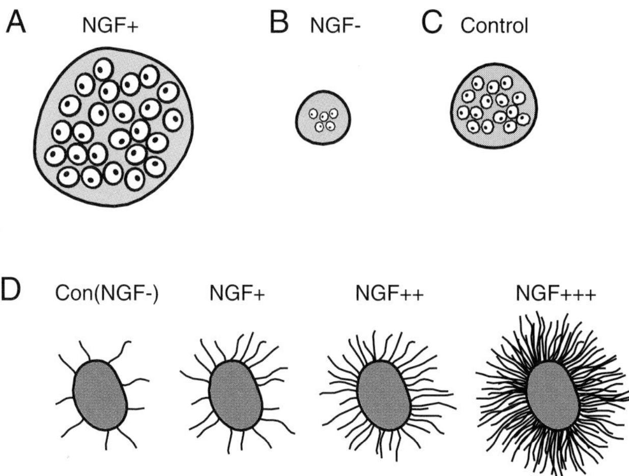

FIGURE 20.2 Effects of NGF and NGF deprivation on cell survival, cell size, and process outgrowth. Early studies characterizing the effects of NGF on sensory and sympathetic neurons showed that NGF can influence cell size, ganglion size, and ganglion cell number (A–C), as well as enhance the growth of neuronal processes in a dose-dependent manner (D). (A) Exogenous NGF was administered; (B) anti-NGF blocked the effects of endogenous NGF. (D) NGF− indicates the absence of added NGF in control explant cultures of ganglia, whereas +, ++, +++ indicate increasing amounts of exogenous NGF added to the cultures.

BOX 20.1

LEVI-MONTALCINI, HAMBURGER, AND THE NEUROTROPHIC HYPOTHESIS

In the early 1930s Rita Levi-Montalcini was a research associate working in the laboratory of the eminent neuroanatomist Guiseppe Levi in Turin, Italy. Viktor Hamburger sent a personal copy of his 1934 paper[10] on wing removal to his acquaintance Levi, who shared it with Levi-Montalcini. She was inspired by the results but was dubious about the validity of the recruitment hypothesis. Together with Levi, she reexamined the effects of limb bud removal on spinal ganglia in the chick embryo. By examining embryos at regular intervals after limb removal, she showed that neuron numbers develop normally up to a certain stage, after which a gradual neuron loss ensues—a finding incompatible with Hamburger's recruitment hypothesis, which predicted a deficit of neurons immediately after limb removal. Levi-Montalcini and Levi postulated that after the loss of peripheral targets, neurons develop normally but then later regress or degenerate. In other words, peripheral targets were apparently regulating the *survival* or *maintenance,* rather than the recruitment, proliferation, or differentiation of innervating populations of neurons. That targets might act to keep neurons alive was a novel perspective that ushered in a fundamentally new line of investigation of cell death and neurotrophic factors.

Although this important paper by Levi-Montalcini and Levi was published in 1942, Hamburger first saw it after World War II. Intrigued by the novel interpretation, in 1946 he invited Levi-Montalcini to join him in St. Louis to resolve their differences. She accepted and by 1947 they had begun experiments that resulted in their first joint publication in 1949.[11] This paper, which soon became a landmark in the history of this field, fully vindicated the original conclusion of Levi-Montalcini and Levi that regression and cell death, not the failure of recruitment, correctly explained the results of the limb removal experiments. More importantly, this same paper showed that many neurons normally die during development and that a major effect of altering target size is the perturbation of this normal regressive process. They proposed that both normal cell death and death following limb removal result from a lack of target-derived substances necessary for growth and survival. A year later, they used the term trophic or neurotrophic to designate these hypothetical signals or substances. In this context, "trophic" and "neurotrophic" refer to signals that mediate long-term dependencies between neurons and the cells they innervate (e.g., survival) and are distinct from "tropic" and "neurotropic," which refer to diffusible chemoattractant signals derived from target cells that guide or orient the migration of other cells or cell processes (e.g., axons) toward the target. By 1950, therefore, the basic tenets of what was subsequently called the **trophic theory** were established: developing neurons are overproduced and compete for limiting amounts of target-derived molecules that provide retrograde signal(s) for their survival. Despite this early conceptual breakthrough it would be more than 30 years before convincing evidence in support of all of the tenets of the trophic theory was available (see Chapter 21).

Historically, the prospect of large losses of cells during normal development was conceptually unpalatable to most biologists. Early in this century, German anatomists M. Ernst and A. Glucksmann and the French anatomist R. Collin described widespread cell death during embryonic development, including cell death in the nervous system, but their observations either went unrecognized or were ignored by other investigators of this period.[11] For this reason, the description of normal neuronal death and its proposed role in neuron–target interactions by Hamburger and Levi-Montalcini marked a watershed in the history of this field. Although it would be many more years before cell death was fully accepted as a fundamental process in nervous system development, after 1949 it was no longer possible to exclude it completely from consideration in discussions of the development of neuron–target interactions. Additionally, for the first time it also became possible to conceive of chemical substances (trophic factors) as the source of signals that regulate developmental events in the nervous system such as neuronal survival (see Chapter 21). Therefore, although Hamburger and Levi-Montalcini were not the first to observe normal cell death in the nervous system, they were the first to draw attention to its significance; they were the first to provide a plausible explanation for its occurrence; and they were the first to postulate a possible mechanism for its regulation. For these reasons, they deserve equal credit along with Collin, Ernst, and Glucksmann as pioneers in the history of this field.

PCD OF NEURONS IN INVERTEBRATE AND VERTEBRATE SPECIES

Although the loss of developing neurons has been reported in many vertebrate and invertebrate species, one cannot be certain that cell death is a universally conserved feature of all living animals. It appears that one of the driving forces in the evolution of programmed cell death was the necessity to selectively eliminate cells invaded by viruses or other pathogens. This process occurs in plants, prokaryotes, and eukaryotes.[12–15] Therefore, it seems reasonable to infer that PCD occurs in virtually all taxonomic groups. In contrast, the programmed death of developing cells in the nervous system could only occur once nervous systems evolved in multicellular organisms. Because a systematic study of the evolution of cell death in the nervous systems of multicellular organisms has not been undertaken, we do not know whether it occurs in coelenterates (e.g., hydra), in which the first primitive nervous systems have been identified. Nevertheless, the occurrence of cell death in unicellular organisms, and of neuronal cell death in many invertebrate species, including worms, flies, and grasshoppers,[16–18] is consistent with the idea that some developing neurons die in virtually all organisms with a distinct nervous system.

The available evidence suggests that neuron death involves virtually all regions and cell types in the nervous system. In fact, cell death in the nervous system has been found to occur almost everywhere that it has been looked for. Motor neurons, sensory neurons (and their peripheral receptors), autonomic neurons, and both long projection neurons and local circuit neurons in the brain and spinal cord all undergo restricted periods of PCD. Although the magnitude of neuronal cell death varies from population to population, as many as one-half or more of all cells in a population may die during development (Fig. 20.3). In some special cases, such as the loss of transient neuronal structures during insect and amphibian metamorphosis (e.g., the Rohon–Beard sensory neurons in frogs), most or all cells die. Cell death in the nervous system thus clearly occurs on a very large scale, indicating that it plays a fundamental and essential role in normal development. Despite the widespread occurrence of PCD, it does not occur in a few cell populations in the developing nervous system. In these cases, the number of postmitotic neurons remains stable. Two well-characterized examples are spinal interneurons and neurons in the medial and lateral pontine nuclei of the chick embryo.[19] All of the neurons in these populations are thought to survive because they possess collateral projections to multiple targets, thereby mitigating competition for limiting amounts of target-derived survival (trophic) agents.

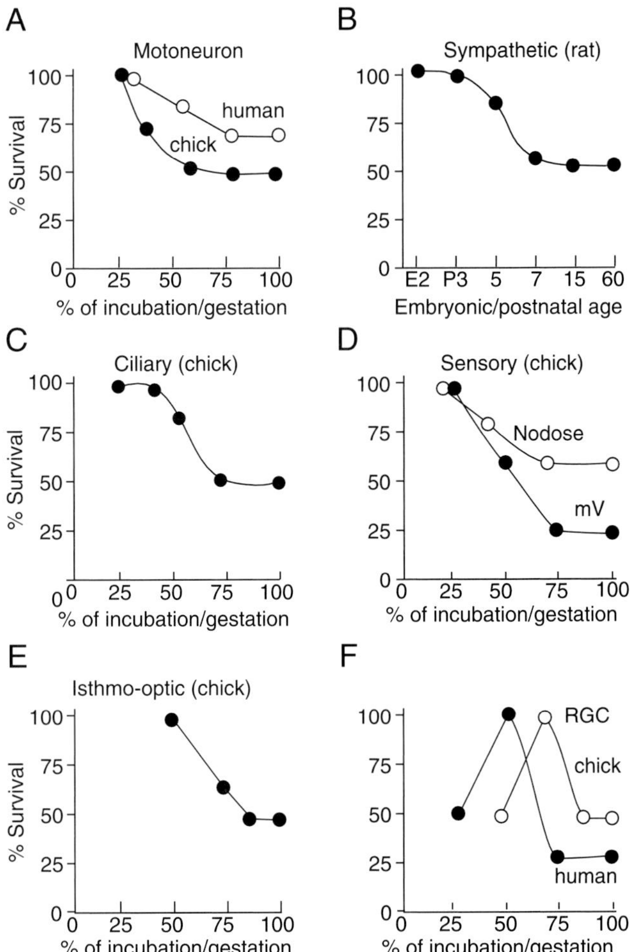

FIGURE 20.3 PCD in six different neuronal populations. The normal or natural PCD of a variety of central and peripheral neuronal populations in chick, rat, and human embryos. mV: mesencephalic nucleus of the fifth (trigeminal) nerve. RGC: retinal ganglion cells.

Studies of cell death in the nervous system have focused on the loss of developing postmitotic neurons as they form synaptic connections with targets and afferents (discussed later). However, extensive PCD also occurs during neurulation. Mitotically active cells, as well as postmitotic but undifferentiated neurons, in the early neural tube also undergo a period of PCD (Fig. 20.4). Accordingly, PCD in the nervous system is not limited to any particular stage of development. It can occur among dividing precursor populations as well as up to the time that synaptic connections are established.[21–23] The loss of cells at different developmental stages probably serves distinct functions and may be mediated by different mechanisms.

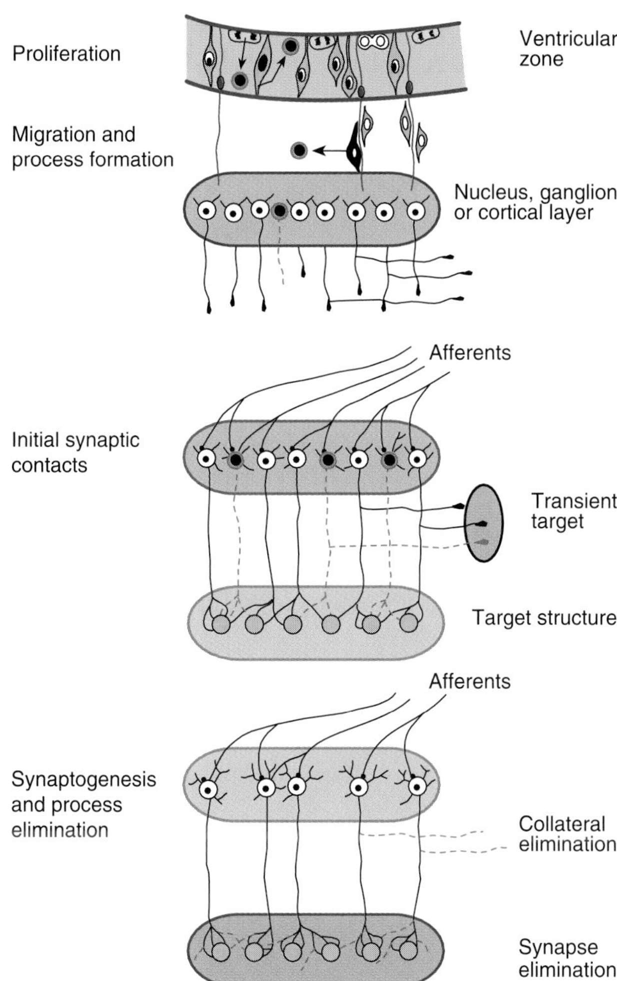

FIGURE 20.4 Stages of neural development where PCD occurs. Although PCD has been studied most intensively during the time when initial synaptic contacts are made, it can occur at all stages in nervous system development. Dying cells are readily identified in the neuroepithelium of the ventricular zone where neural precursors are dividing and giving rise to postmitotic neurons and glial cells. After undergoing a final division, postmitotic neurons migrate to the appropriate nucleus or cortical layer. PCD can occur during migration when neurons first extend axons or are making initial contacts with their target tissues. Once synaptic connections are well established, PCD is rare. Synaptic connections are refined by synapse elimination (Chapter 19). Round red cells with large dark nuclei represent cells undergoing PCD (modified from Cowan and O'Leary[20]).

PCD also occurs in central and peripheral glial cells. For example, myelin-forming oligodendrocytes in the optic nerve and Schwann cells in peripheral nerves undergo PCD.[24,25] Their loss is thought to reflect competition for axon-derived trophic signals, the end result of which is the survival of an appropriate number of glial cells for optimum myelination of axons (Fig. 20.5). Because glia have been studied much less extensively, it is not known whether the death of nonneuronal cells throughout the nervous system is as common as the death of neurons.

Summary

The programmed cell death (PCD) of neurons appears to occur in virtually all vertebrate and invertebrate species. More generally, PCD also occurs in many different cells and tissues of plants and unicellular and multicellular organisms and thus may have arisen early during evolution as a defense against viral infections. With few exceptions, PCD occurs in virtually all populations of developing neurons and can take place at all stages of development from the time of proliferation until the establishment of synaptic connections. Developing glial cells also exhibit PCD.

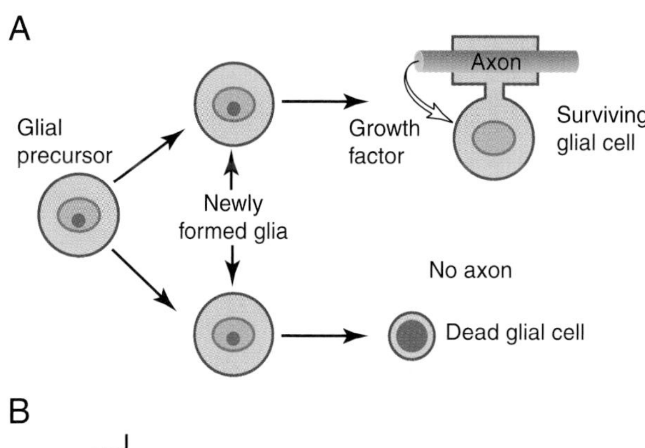

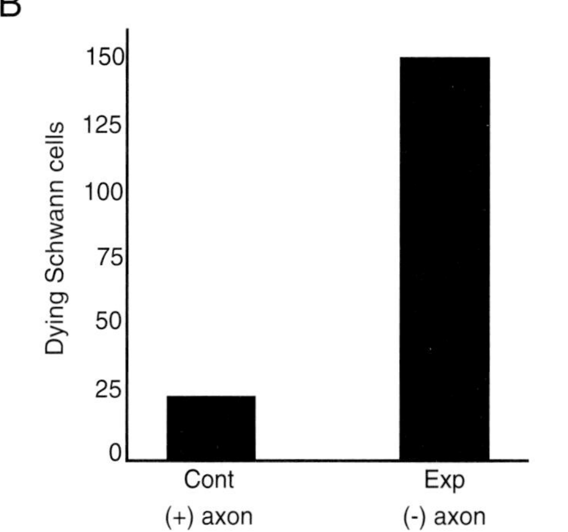

FIGURE 20.5 The PCD of glial cells is regulated by axonally derived signals. Glial cells that fail to compete successfully for these signals undergo PCD (A). (Modified from Barres *et al.*[25]) (B) The number of dying Schwann cells in the ventral root of the chick embryo is increased following the degeneration of motor neuron axons (modified from Ciutat *et al.*[24]). Cont (control) indicates the normal ventral root while Exp (experimental) indicates ventral roots that lack motor axons ((−) axon).

MODES OF CELL DEATH IN DEVELOPING NEURONS

The specific morphological appearance exhibited by degenerating neurons can provide insights into the cellular and molecular mechanisms by which the cells are destroyed. Historically, pathologists have been interested in this issue, and they focused on distinguishing different kinds of cell and tissue degeneration following disease, injury, and trauma.[28,29] Over 125 years ago, the term **necrosis** was coined to describe what today constitutes the major form of accidental or pathological degeneration. For example, the pathological death of neurons following injury usually involves degeneration of groups of contiguous cells in a region that initiates an inflammatory response that can easily be discerned in tissue sections (Fig. 20.6).[26] At about the same time that necrosis was described, however, another form of cell degeneration, **spontaneous cell death,** was observed in regressing ovarian follicles and mammary glands of normal adult mammals. In 1914, the German anatomist Ludwig Gräper summarized the available evidence on this new form of cell death now referred to as PCD and suggested that it was a mechanism to counterbalance mitosis in adult tissues in which turnover of cells normally occurs. PCD typically involves the sporadic loss of individual cells that degenerate by a different mode, **apoptosis,** which does not involve inflammation and can therefore be underestimated (Fig. 20.6). The steps in the cell-death cascade leading up to when signs of frank degeneration occur may take many hours or days. Once that point is reached, however, the degenerative process is rapid, with cells dying and being removed in minutes or a few hours. The loss of thousands of neurons over several days is the consequence of many rapid individual cell deaths that at any moment in time represent only

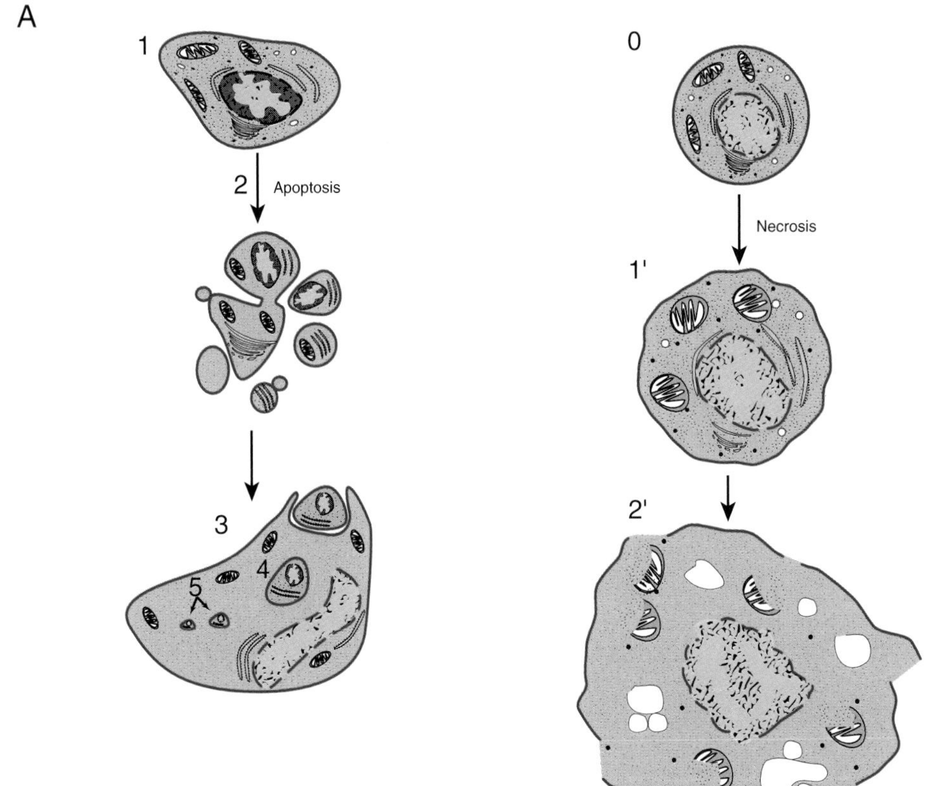

FIGURE 20.6 Apoptosis and necrosis (A) A healthy cell is depicted undergoing stages of apoptosis (1–5) or necrosis (1′, 2′) as observed with the electron microscope. Cell-membrane-bound apoptotic bodies (2) are engulfed and degraded by a macrophage (3–5). (A is modified from Schwartz and Osborne.[26]) In B and C, spinal motoneurons are shown from a control chick embryo (B) and following an excitotoxic (glutamate) lesion (C). In C all of the motor neurons are undergoing necrosis (compare with apoptotic motor neuron death in Figure 20.7). In D and E, examples of apoptotic (D) and necrotic (E) motor neurons are shown in the electron microscope.

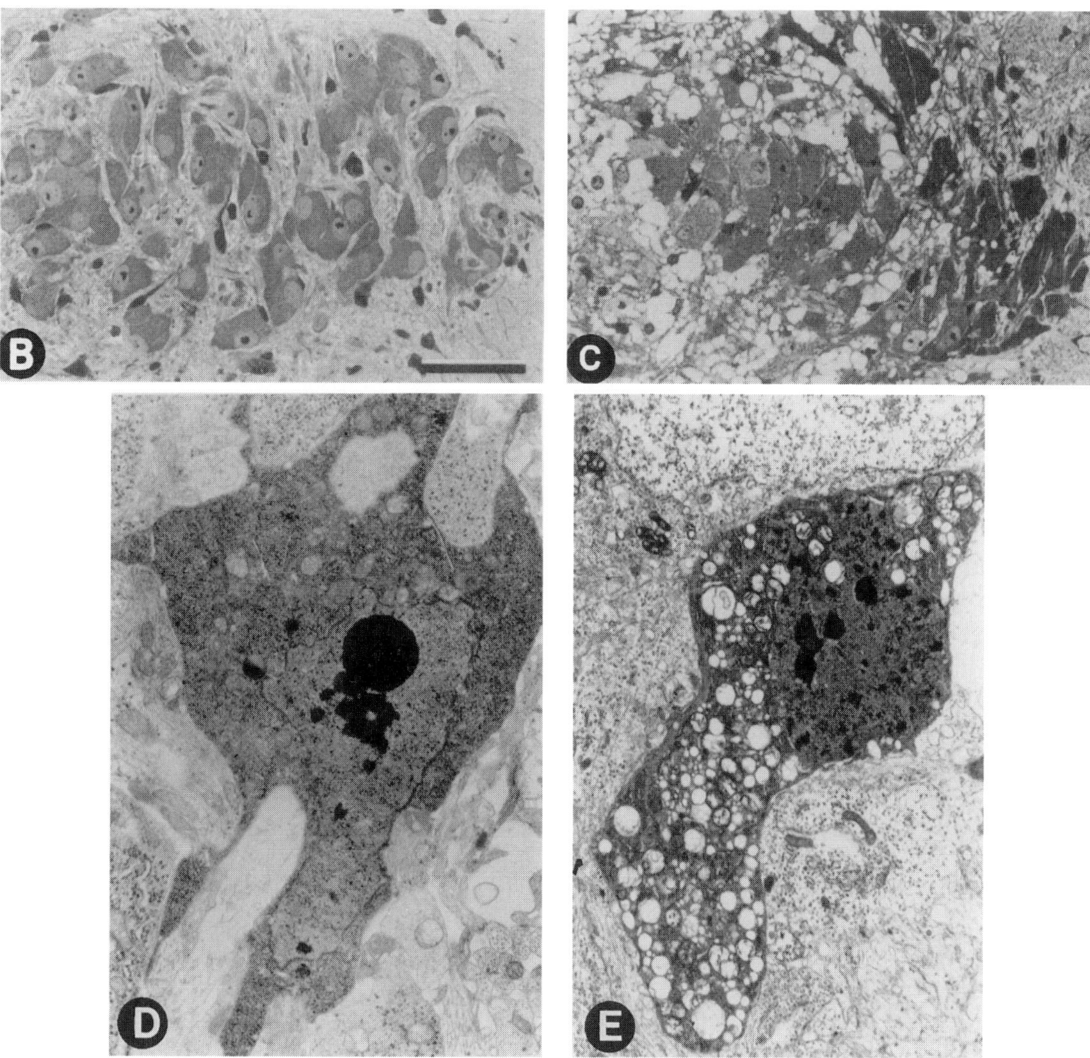

FIGURE 20.6 *(continued)*

a small minority (~1%) of the cells in the population. Therefore, the occurrence and magnitude of even massive cell death can (and often did) go unnoticed. To date, the most direct and commonly used method for estimating the number and timing of neurons that die *in vivo* during development is counting healthy neurons in serial histological sections through the entire neuronal population being studied[27] (Fig. 20.7).

Until quite recently, the pathways of cell degeneration in adult and developing tisues have been generally dichotomized into death by either apoptosis or necrosis, a distinction based initially on morphological differences and later on other apparent differences between the two.[30,31] *Apoptosis* is a Greek word indicating the seasonal, piecemeal dropping of leaves from a tree and has been used to describe all forms of spontaneous cell death that exhibit certain morphological characteristics. Cells dying by apoptosis shrink in size, the nuclear chromatin becomes pyknotic and condenses against the nuclear membrane, and cytoplasmic organelles remain intact. Eventually, the cytoplasm and nucleus break up into apoptotic bodies that are phagocytized by macrophages or by adjacent healthy cells (Fig. 20.6). *Necrosis,* by contrast, involves an initial swelling of the cell, only modest condensation of chromatin, cytoplasmic vacuolization, breakdown of organelles, and rupture of the cell membrane, allowing the release of cellular contents, followed by shrinkage and loss of nuclear chromatin (Fig. 20.6). Because necrotic cell death elicits an inflammatory response, macrophages derived from the immune system attack and phagocytize cellular debris. In contrast, cell death by apoptosis usually involves individual cells that are engulfed or phagocytized before they can release their cellular con-

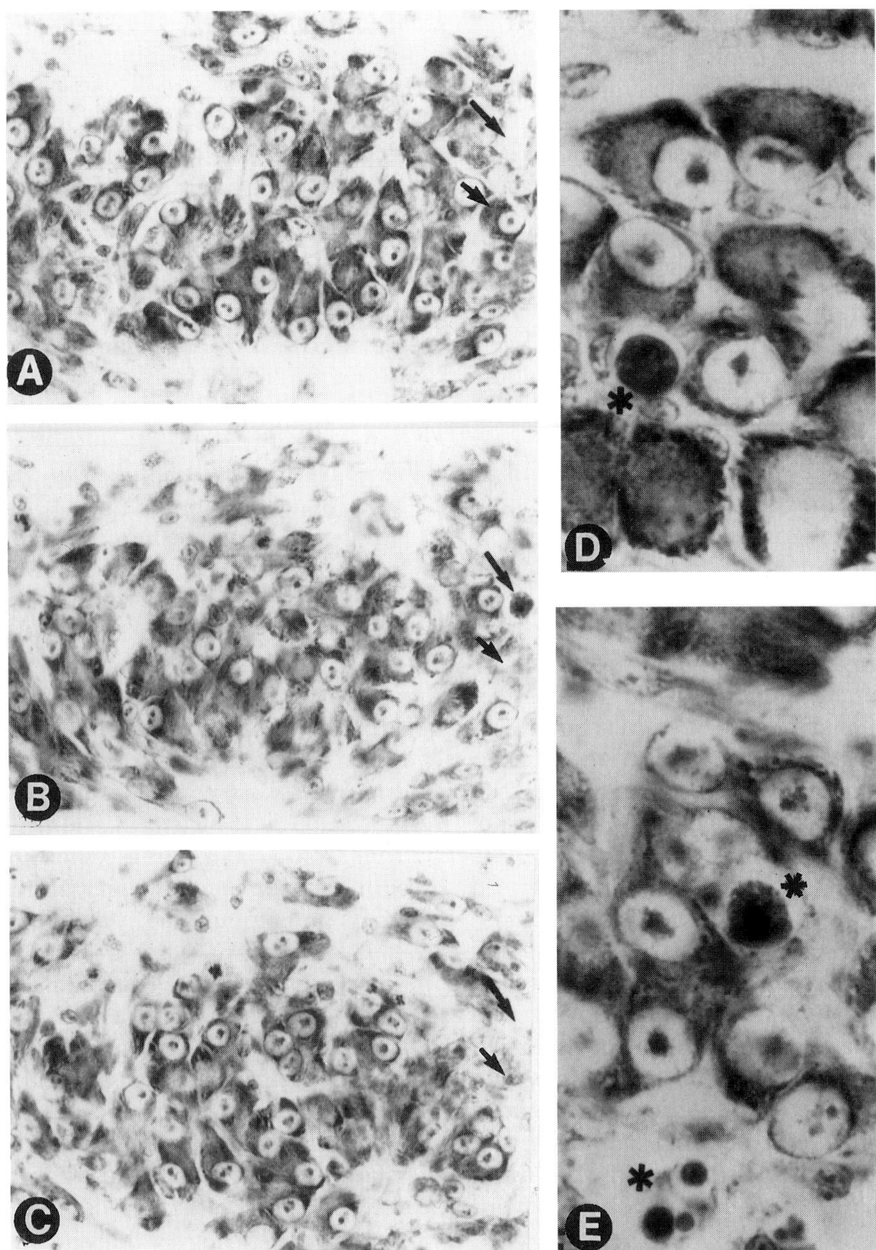

FIGURE 20.7 Examples of healthy and degenerating motor neurons in the spinal cord of the chick embryo. (A–C) Adjacent serial sections. Note that both healthy (short arrows) and dying (long arrows) cells appear in only one of the serial sections and therefore would not be counted twice in adjacent sections. Dying sensory (D) and motor (E) neurons are indicated by asterisks.

tents or induce an inflammatory response in adjacent tissue. In this case, phagocytosis can involve either typical macrophages or engulfment by adjacent cells that act transiently as nonprofessional macrophages (e.g., radial glial cells and Schwann cells). Phagocytes recognize dying cells by their expression of death-related cell surface signals.[32]

Another feature that distinguishes apoptotic and necrotic cell death is the occurrence of a specific form of chromosomal **DNA fragmentation** and degradation during the early stages of apoptosis.[26] DNA digestion occurs at internucleosomal sites, producing small, double-stranded fragments of DNA that migrate in a ladder pattern in multiples of 180–200 bp after electro-

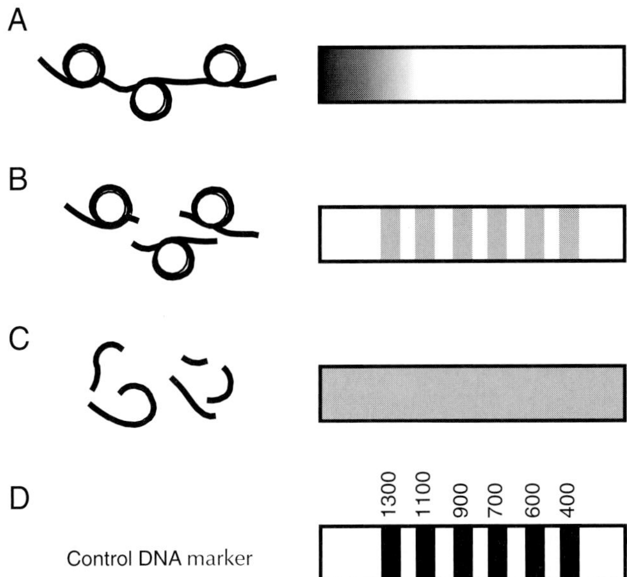

FIGURE 20.8 Schematic illustration of DNA isolated from control cells (A), apoptotic cells (B), and necrotic cells (C) and run on agarose gels. Only the DNA from apoptotic cells in which double-stranded DNA breaks occur between nucleosomes (left side) appears in a ladder pattern in multiples of ~200 bp on the gels.

phoresis in agarose gels (Fig. 20.8). In contrast, random, single-strand DNA breaks occur late in necrotic cell death and exhibit a different pattern on agarose gels (Fig. 20.8). DNA fragmentation can also be observed in tissue sections (Fig. 20.9).[33]

It is widely believed that apoptosis and necrosis reflect distinct cell death pathways that are triggered by different stimuli. However, our basic understanding of these pathways is limited, and caution should be exercised in drawing too fine a distinction between them.[34] For example, a variety of toxic and traumatic stimuli, such as CNS ischemia, previously thought to involve only necrotic cell death can also induce morphological signs of apoptosis and may be associated with changes in PCD-associated genes, such as members of the *bcl-2* gene family.[35,36] In some cases, the intensity of a stimulus may determine whether cell death is by apoptosis or necrosis.[37] In other cases, cells that undergo normal PCD and exhibit nuclear pyknosis may not display DNA laddering.

The PCD of developing vertebrate neurons provides a striking example of the problems encountered in attempting to rigidly classify the pathway of degeneration as being either necrotic or apoptotic.[38,38a] Developing neurons may adopt one of at least three different morphological modes during PCD: (1) apoptotic, (2) autophagic, and (3) cytoplasmic. Only the first fits the classic morphological definition of apoptosis. Whether the other forms undergo the typical degradation of DNA into double-stranded fragments of 180–200 bp is not known. The cytoplasmic type of PCD also has several features in common with necrotic cell death, including early breakdown of organelles and late lysis of the nucleus. Despite the occurrence of these different morphological types of death, it is clear that they all reflect PCD; they all involve the stereotypic loss of individual cells at specific times during development without triggering an inflammatory response.

Summary

Historically, degenerating cells have been categorized into two classes: death by apoptosis or death by necrosis. Although the situation is more complex than reflected by this simple dichotomy, in general apoptosis is more characteristic of PCD, whereas necrosis is more characteristic of cells that die following injury or trauma. A variety of morphological features have been used to distinguish between these two types of cell death, and the occurrence of a specific kind of DNA fragmentation in cells characterizing apoptosis has become a major criterion for categorization. The occurrence of certain features of apoptosis in neurons following injury has suggested that there may be some overlap in the mechanisms of cell death.

CELLULAR REGULATION OF PCD

Cell Death Can Be a Differentiated Fate

The process by which specialized cell types develop from a single cell (the fertilized egg) is called **differentiation.** The commitment to a particular differentiated fate occurs by a process of specification or determination. Differentiation involves overt changes in cellular biochemistry and morphology, whereas specification and determination involve the preceding covert commitment of cells to a particular fate (see Chapters 15 and 17). Because PCD is the normal differentiated or terminal fate of many developing cells, commitment to this fate can be studied in much the same way that the phenotypic fate of cells that survive in the embryo is studied.

Developmental biologists have identified two major ways in which the commitment of a cell to a particular differentiated phenotype occurs.[39] The first mechanism, **intrinsic** or **autonomous specification,** involves the segregation of critical cytoplasmic molecules dur-

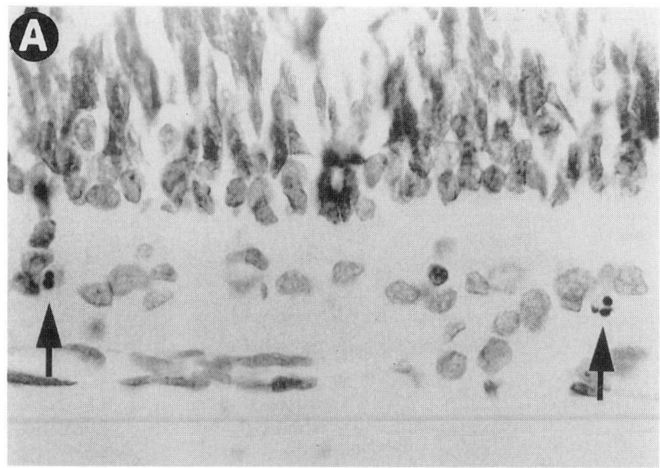

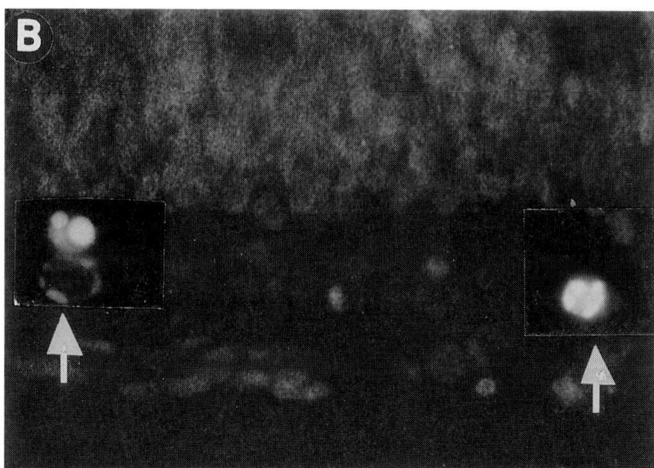

FIGURE 20.9 Degenerating neurons in neonatal rat retina (A, B) labeled by a method for detecting apoptotic DNA fragmentation in histological sections. (A) Nissl stain of pyknotic retinal ganglion cells (arrows). (B) The same section depicting DNA fragmentation of the pyknotic neurons shown in A. (A–B, modified from Rabacchi *et al.*[33])

ing embryonic cleavage. In this way each cell obtains a distinct set ("mosaic") of cytoplasmic determinative molecules that influence cell fate without reference to signals from neighboring cells. The second mechanism of commitment involves **extrinsic** signals from other cells and is called **conditional specification.** Initially, cells have the potential to follow more than one path of differentiation. As development proceeds, however, signals from other cells act to gradually limit and finally specify cell fate. Conditional specification gives rise to a pattern of differentiation known as regulative development. Although all organisms use a combination of autonomous and regulative developmental strategies, as a general rule most invertebrates predominantly exhibit mosaic development, whereas most vertebrates exhibit regulative development. Because PCD represents the normal differentiated fate of many developing cells, it is not surprising that much of the PCD in invertebrates is cell autonomous, whereas most PCD in vertebrates is regulated by cell–cell interactions and therefore is conditional.[16,21] Despite this difference, many of the genetic and molecular pathways for PCD are similar in invertebrates and vertebrates. Additionally, there are examples in invertebrate species in which cell–cell interactions are important for cell specification, including the determination of PCD.[18,40] For example, in insects, hormonal signals and afferent synaptic input specify the survival or death of developing neurons. In flies, survival of neurons in the visual system depends on cell–cell interactions; and in the moth *Manduca sexta*, the survival of some motor neurons is dependent on target-derived survival signals.

PCD Is Regulated by Interactions with Targets and Afferents

The PCD of vertebrate neurons and their precursors can occur at any stage of neuronal development from neurulation to the establishment of synaptic connections with targets and afferents and can involve mitotically active cells and migrating neurons, as well as immature postmitotic cells (see Fig. 20.4). However, the most common and best-studied type of neuronal PCD involves postmitotic, differentiating cells that die while establishing synaptic connections with other neurons and target cells. Because massive neuronal death and its regulation were first clearly recognized in studies of neuron–target interactions, the role of targets in controlling PCD has received the most attention. In addition, signals derived from afferent inputs as well as from nonneuronal cells (e.g., central and peripheral glia) are now being recognized as possible sources of trophic regulation of cell death and survival (Fig. 20.10).

Studies of the regulation of vertebrate neuronal PCD have shown that targets are critically involved in regulating how many cells in the innervating population survive or die.[21] Complete or partial deletion of targets reduces survival, whereas increases in the size or number of available targets result in increased survival (Fig. 20.11).[41] Although it has sometimes been assumed that the relationship between neuronal survival and the availability of targets is proportional and linear (this has been called size, or **systems matching**), some studies have, in fact, failed to confirm this kind of relationship.[42] One of the more intriguing of these studies is described in Box 20.2.[42–45] Before one can properly determine whether such failures require a reevaluation of the role of size matching in regulating cell numbers, however, one must know more precisely what factors neurons compete for in the target and whether these signals are altered following perturbations designed to increase or decrease target availability.[21] In the case of avian spinal motor neurons that innervate limb skeletal muscle, the number of neurons that survive the period of PCD bears a 1 : 1 relationship with the num-

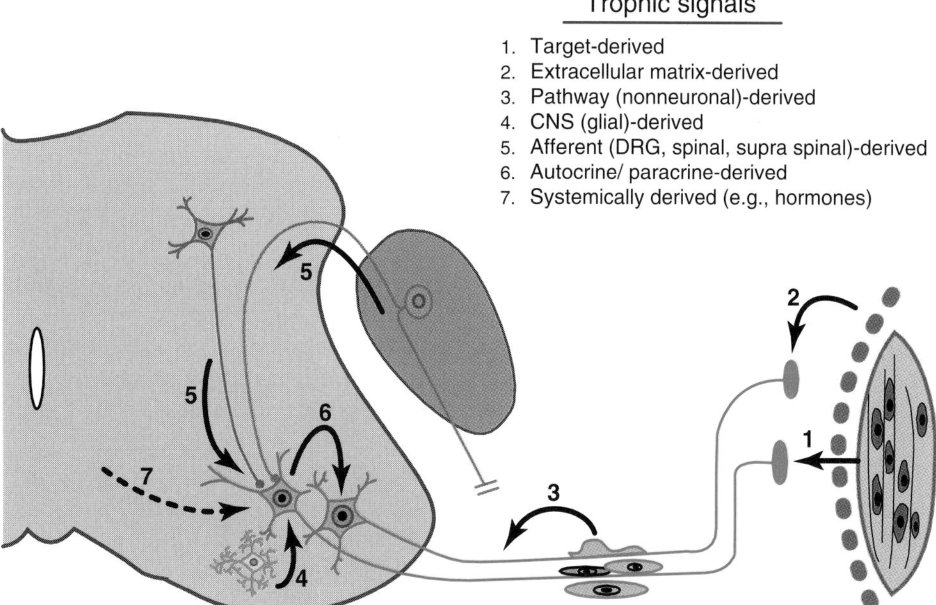

FIGURE 20.10 Schematic illustration of different sources of potential trophic signals acting on motor neurons in the spinal cord. Motor neurons (green cell bodies) can receive trophic support from a number of different sources. Axon terminals of the motor neurons have access to diffusible (1) or extracellular matrix-associated (2) trophic factors produced by muscle. Schwann cells (3) in the peripheral nerve or ventral root could provide trophic support. Glial cells (4) in the spinal cord, astrocytes, and/or oligodendrocytes could influence motor neuron survival. Motor neurons receive afferent input from several sources, including descending fibers, dorsal horn, and dorsal root axons (5), which could supply trophic support. Finally, motor neurons could influence the growth and survival of themselves and their neighbors (6) as well as from circulating hormones (7).

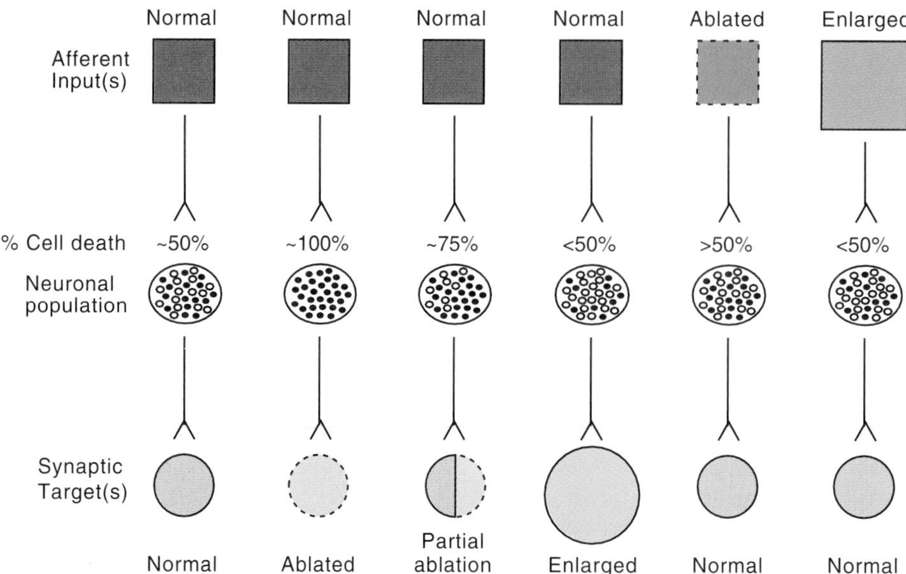

FIGURE 20.11 Schematic illustration of the regulation of neuronal survival by targets and afferents during development. Solid black circles in the middle row (neuronal population) represent dying neurons (modified from Cowan *et al.*[41]).

ber of primary myotubes present in individual muscle precursors during the period of cell death, rather than being correlated with the final number of myotubes or myofibers present after the cessation of cell death.[46] Accordingly, in this situation, motor neuron numbers, and therefore survival and death, are controlled by some factor (a neurotrophic agent?) that is limited by the number of primary myotubes available during the cell death period. However, in other cases, motor neuron survival could be related to different target-associated properties such as myotube type or size, the number and types of synaptic sites, postsynaptic receptors, nonmuscle mesenchyme or other cells associated with muscle, the molecular properties of the muscle cell membrane, or the extracellular matrix associated with muscle cells. In these cases, simple increases or decreases in target size that failed to change the availability of the critical target-associated signal would not be expected to alter neuronal survival.

Although the essential factor provided by targets that mediates neuronal survival is not known for many populations of neurons, extrapolation from what is known for sympathetic, sensory, and motor neurons suggests that specific target-derived neurotrophic factors are involved, as discussed in more detail in Chapter 21. For example, sympathetic neurons require target-derived NGF as a survival factor, whereas sensory neurons in peripheral ganglia require one or more of the neurotrophins, NGF, BDNF, NT-3, and NT-4/5.[47] Target-dependent motor neuron survival is mediated by muscle-derived proteins. Several candidate factors include BDNF, NT-4/5, IGF, and GDNF. PCD of CNS neurons in the avian isthmo-optic nucleus (ION) is controlled by many of the same mechanisms involved in the PCD of peripheral neurons, including a requirement for target-derived neurotrophic factors such as BDNF. As discussed previously, the survival of myelin-forming glial cells also involves a competition, in this case, for trophic signals derived from axons. In both neurons and glia, the final outcome of this competitive process is the survival of optimal numbers of cells for innervation (neurons) or myelination (glia).

Motor neurons (and some other neuronal populations as well, including retinal ganglion cells, ION cells, and ciliary neurons) have another interesting property: their target dependency appears to be regulated by physiological synaptic interactions with their targets.[48] Following the formation of synaptic contacts between motor neurons and target muscles, the initiation of synaptic transmission activates the muscle and results in embryo movements. Chronic blockade of this activity during the cell death period with specific drugs or toxins that cause paralysis prevents the death of all motor neurons. Although the cellular and molecular mechanisms that mediate this effect are not yet known, two major hypotheses have been proposed[49,50]: the **production hypothesis,** which predicts that the production of trophic factor by the target is inversely regulated by muscle activity; and the **access hypothesis,** which argues that sufficient trophic factor is initially produced by targets to maintain all motor neurons but that activity regulates access to this factor by modulating axonal branching and the formation of neuromuscular synapses, thus restricting uptake of trophic factor to synaptic terminals. Although not yet definitive, the available data tend to favor the access hypothesis. For example, evidence against the production hypothesis includes the observation that inactive muscles do not appear to "produce" more trophic factor. Support for the access hypothesis includes observations that activity blockade and other perturbations that alter axonal branching and synapse formation also result in changes in motor neuron survival. Regardless of which of these hypotheses is proven correct, neuronal activity at even early stages of embryogenesis makes fundamental contributions to nervous system development. The role of activity in later stages of development is discussed in Chapters 19 and 22.

PCD is modulated by perturbations of afferent inputs as well as of target interactions (Fig. 20.11). Four such cases that have been examined in considerable detail are spinal motor neurons, the ION, the avian ciliary ganglion, and optic tectal neurons that are innervated by retinal ganglion cells. In all four cases, surgical removal of afferent inputs prior to or during the period of PCD results in significant increases in cell death. Because similar changes in PCD also occur after the blockade of afferent synaptic activity, the functional input provided by afferents appears to be of fundamental importance in this situation. Functional afferent input may act to regulate the survival of postsynaptic neurons in a number of ways: (1) Depolarization by afferents can alter intracel-

BOX 20.2

PCD, SIZE-MATCHING, AND MONOPEDAL FROGS

As illustrated schematically in Fig. 20.11, most previous studies support an association between neuronal survival and some factor related to target size or availability. According to this scheme, neuronal targets are normally constrained in the number of innervating neurons they can support, such that any significant increase in the normal number of cells innervating the target at the beginning of the cell-death period should be eliminated. Surprisingly, one study designed to test this prediction in frog embryos failed to support the hypothesis. Removal of one limb bud together with perturbation of midline tissue barriers allows motor neurons from both sides of the spinal cord to innervate the remaining limb.[42,43] Whereas normally a single frog limb is innervated by approximately 1500 ipsilateral motor neurons at the end of the period of PCD, in the monopedal frogs a single limb is innervated by as many as 3000 motor neurons (ipsilateral plus contralateral), although on average there are about 2400 surviving motor neurons on the two sides (a 62% increase). Motor neurons on both sides established functional synaptic contacts with their appropriate muscles in the limb, and limb motility appeared normal. Motor unit size, however, is reduced, indicating that each motor neuron forms fewer synaptic contact with myofibers. Because the limb of monopedal frogs is able to support up to twice the normal number of innervating motor neurons, these results appear inconsistent with any simple version of the size-matching hypothesis. However, if the size of the target (e.g., the number of muscle cells) or the availability of the critical target-derived factor (e.g., a trophic agent) that promotes motor neuron survival is normally regulated by afferent signals associated with the number of innervating neurons, then these apparently negative results would still be consistent with size matching. Although there is, in fact, a 30% increase in the number of muscle fibers in the limb of monopedal frogs, this increase occurs at the end of the normal cell-death period and therefore is unlikely to be the major cause of the earlier increased survival of motor neurons. However, until other aspects of the target are examined (e.g., concentration or availability of trophic factor), it is not possible to conclude that the increase in motor neuron survival is independent of an increase in the availability of some critical factor in the target muscles of the monopedal frogs. In contrast to motor neurons, the number of sensory neurons in the DRG of monopedal frogs is similar to that seen in unamputated animals.[44] Similarly, the total number of neurons in the ipsilateral and contralateral avian ION that innervate one eye after unilateral eye removal is also similar to control values.[45] Accordingly, in these two situations, perturbations similar to those used to examine motor neuron survival in monopedal frogs provide strong support for the size-matching hypothesis. Although it is not possible to exclude an alternative to the size-matching hypothesis for explaining motor neuron survival in monopedal frogs, it seems more likely that once additional studies are carried out, some form of size matching will be shown to be involved.

lular calcium levels, which in turn can independently modulate survival.[51] (2) Afferent activity can regulate the expression of trophic factors and their receptors in postsynaptic cells. (3) The release of trophic factors from the terminals of afferent axons or adjacent glial cells may be regulated by activity.[52,53] At present, which, if any, of these mechanisms mediates the effects of afferent input on PCD is not known.

Because the PCD of many developing neurons is regulated by signals derived from both targets and afferents, an important question is how these two sources interact to control survival.[54] One possibility is that targets regulate the response of neurons to afferent input and that afferents regulate the response to target-derived signals. In this scheme, the relative influence of targets and afferents would have to be balanced in some way for optimal survival. Although targets and afferents appear to be the major source of signals regulating the survival of differentiating neurons, they are not likely to be the only source of such survival signals (Fig. 20.10). There are other possibilities: (1) Neurons themselves may produce neurotrophic factors that act by autocrine or paracrine pathways. (2) Glial cells synthesize trophic factors and, in some cases, may be the source of trophic survival signals for neurons. (3) The survival and differentiation of neurons in sexually dimorphic regions of the nervous system depend on hormonal signals from cells far removed from the neurons themselves. (4) Although it has yet to be demonstrated for neurons, the PCD of other kinds of cells is known to depend on signals associated with adhesive interactions between the cell and its extracellular matrix. (5) It also seems likely that the survival of neurons could be mediated by direct cell–cell contacts that do not involve classic trophic factors as mediators of the survival signal (e.g., modification of gap junctions and therefore the exchange of other signaling molecules).

Summary

During development, the fate of a cell, including PCD, can be determined by intrinsic cell-autonomous mechanisms or by extrinsic signals derived from cell–cell interactions. The survival of most developing neurons is likely to depend on a variety of signals, involving multiple trophic factors, derived from diverse sources, that serve to maintain survival and regulate differentiation in complex ways that reflect the specific requirements of neurons at each step in their development[55] (Fig. 20.10). Although developing neurons can undergo PCD at any stage of differentiation, the best-studied type of PCD occurs while neurons are establishing connections with targets and afferents. Targets and afferents provide critical survival-promoting signals that prevent PCD. One major class of such signals is neurotrophic molecules. Neurons are thought to compete for limiting amounts of these trophic agents. For some populations of neurons, synaptic transmission also plays a role in regulating survival.

MOLECULAR REGULATION OF PCD

Genetics Contributes to Identifying the Biochemical Mechanisms Responsible for PCD

The normal death of cells in the developing nervous system has been long thought to be regulated by competition for neurotrophic molecules (the **trophic theory;** see Chapter 21). Until quite recently, investigators agreed that the doomed neurons, lacking sufficient trophic factor to sustain normal metabolic events, passively degenerated by a process analogous to starvation. However, PCD of some nonneuronal cells was previously known to be an active, ATP-dependent process. For example, RNA or protein synthesis inhibitors prevent the programmed death of muscle cells in insects and amphibians and block the hormone-induced death of thymocytes in the immune system.[56] Additionally, genetic mutations in the nematode worm *Caenorhabditis elegans* that prevent PCD had also previously been described, thereby providing additional evidence that neuronal death is a genetically regulated process in which cells actively participate in their own demise.[57] Beginning in the late 1980s, these various lines of evidence forced a reappraisal of cell death in the nervous system and led to the demonstration that for many types of neurons, PCD is a metabolically active process and is regulated by the interaction of specific genetic programs that either inhibit or induce degeneration.[58,59] Neurotrophic survival molecules are thought to act as extracellular signals that inhibit either the expression or activity of proteins produced by **cell death** ("killer") **genes** or to induce the expression or activity of "protective" gene products that block the action of cell-death genes. Considerable progress has been made in identifying potential cell death–associated genes and their pathways of action.

Although genetic studies of cell death in *C. elegans* demonstrated that PCD is regulated by specific genes, the first indication that the PCD of developing vertebrate neurons may also be controlled by similar so-called "killer" or "death" genes appeared in 1988. Cultured neonatal rat sympathetic neurons, which normally require NGF for survival, survived following NGF removal if mRNA or protein synthesis inhibitors were added to the cultures.[60] Subsequently, other types of developing neurons were rescued by these drugs *in vitro* and *in vivo* after trophic factor deprivation. These findings were interpreted as evidence that neuronal PCD requires the *de novo* expression of genes and proteins that actively destroy the cell and that one important role of trophic factors is to suppress the activity of these genes. Not all types of PCD, however, are blocked by metabolic inhibitors, and in some cases these inhibitors can trigger PCD.[3,61]

Because the genetics, cellular anatomy, and cell lineages of *C. elegans* have been so well defined, and because much of its genome has now been sequenced, this organism is a particularly informative and powerful model for analyzing the molecular genetics of PCD.[57] Of the 1090 somatic cells generated, 131 undergo PCD, and most of these are neurons. In each individual, the same cells die at specific times in development and are then engulfed and degraded by neighboring cells. Despite the approximately 11 billion years that separates the appearance of worms and vertebrates, significant homology exists in the structure and function of specific cell-death genes between these two taxonomic groups. Two genes in *C. elegans* that are required for the PCD of all 131 somatic cells have been identified (Table 20.2). These are the cell death abnor-

TABLE 20.2 Some Known and Candidate Genes Associated with PCD

Gene	Known or suspected function
ced-3/ICE/caspase family	Induces cell death
ced-4	Induces cell death
ced-9	Prevents cell death
ced-1,2,5,6,7,8,10	Engulfment of dead or dying cells
ces-1,2	Determination of cell death fate
nuc-1	DNA degradation
Steroid (ecdysone) receptor	Ligand binding induces cell death
reaper	Induces cell death in *Drosophila*
hid	Induces cell death in *Drosophila*
grim	Induces cell death in *Drosophila*
Baculovirus p35	Prevents cell death by inhibiting ICE
CrmA	Prevents cell death by inhibiting ICE
nur77	Required for apoptosis of T cells
Fas/Apo-1 receptor	Ligand binding induces cell death
p75	Ligand binding induces cell death
TNFα	Induces cell death
Perforin/granzyme β	Induces death in cells infected with bacteria or viruses
p53	Required for the death of thymocytes
c-*myc*	Required for the death of immune cells
c-*fos*	Expressed in many types of cells undergoing PCD
c-*jun*	Expressed during cell death
$p21^{ras}$	Involved in trophic factor control of cell death
Transforming growth factor (TGF) β1	Induces cell death
Cyclin A	Involved in c-*myc*-induced cell death
Cyclin D1	Expressed during death of neurons
$p34^{cdc2}$	Expressed in some dying cells
Nuc-18	Endonuclease involved in DNA and fragmentation
bcl-2	Prevents cell death
bcl-x	Prevents cell death
Bax	Blocks the function of *bcl-2* and induces cell death
Bak	Promotes cell death
bad	Promotes cell death
Bl-1	Prevents cell death by interaction with *bcl-2* or *Bax*

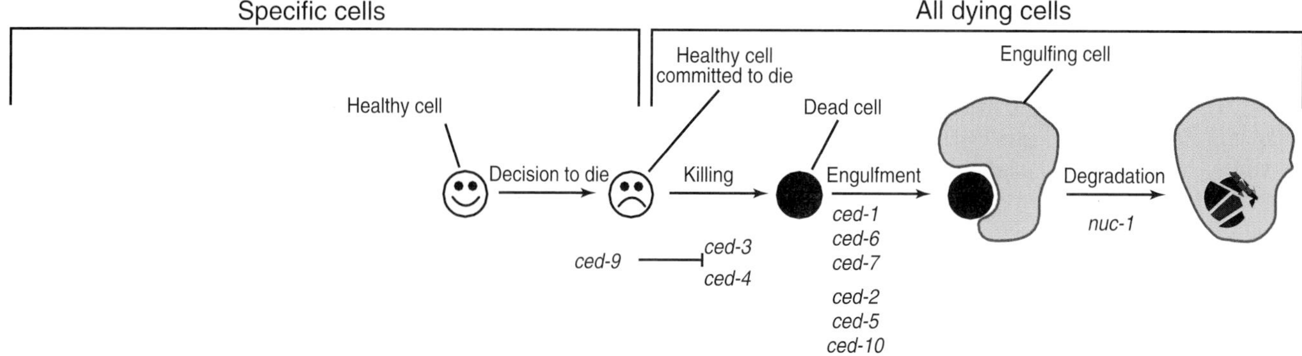

FIGURE 20.12 The genetic pathway for PCD in *C. elegans*.[57] See text for details.

mal (*ced*) genes, *ced-3* and *ced-4*. Loss-of-function mutations in either gene result in the survival of all cells that would undergo PCD. Thus, by initiating degeneration, *ced-3* and *ced-4* are positive regulators of cell death (pro-cell-death genes). By preventing degeneration, another gene, *ced-9*, acts as a negative regulator of cell death (cell-death-inhibitory gene). Gain-of-function mutations (abnormal activation) in *ced-9* block all cell deaths, whereas loss-of-function mutations (gene inactivation) cause increased cell death and, for that reason, are lethal in the embryo. The *ced-9* gene normally acts by inhibiting *ced-3* and *ced-4*, thereby protecting cells from the killing actions of these genes. In addition to *ced-3*, *ced-4*, and *ced-9*, several other genes identified in *C. elegans* constitute a genetic pathway that involves four separate steps (Fig. 20.12): (1) the determination or selection of which specific cells will die (e.g., *ces-1*, *ces-2*); (2) positive (*ced-3*, *ced-4*) and negative (*ced-9*) regulation of the *killing* process; (3) *engulfment* of dead cells (e.g., *ced-1*); and (4) *degradation* of the DNA of dead cells by nucleases (e.g., *nuc-1*).

The DNA sequences of *ced-3*, *ced-4*, and *ced-9* have now been determined. The sequence of *ced-4* is novel and until recently did not appear to be related to other known cell death genes. However, two related mammalian genes have recently been identified and named apoptosis protease-activating factors (*Apafs*) *1* and *2*.[62] *Apaf-2* is cytochrome *c*, a common mitochondrial protein that has recently been found to interact with the caspases and induce PCD (see below). *Apaf-1* shows a striking structural similarity to *ced-4* and includes a caspase-recruitment domain that may also bind directly to caspases. In the nematode, *ced-4* appears to promote autoprocessing of pro-*ced-3* and therefore is an essential component of the pro-apoptotic pathway in this species. In vertebrates, *Apaf-1* and *Apaf-2* act as cofactors necessary for binding to and activating caspases and inducing cell death. The *ced-3* gene has significant homology to a previously identified vertebrate gene, **interleukin-1β-converting enzyme (ICE).**[63] ICE is a cysteine protease that cleaves pro-interleukin-1β into the active form of the cytokine. Overproduction of ICE in cultured neurons causes cell death, whereas inhibitors of ICE and other cysteine proteases block PCD of neurons *in vitro* and *in vivo*.[63] Since the initial discovery of ICE, more than 10 family members have been identified, and this ICE/Ced-3 family of proteases has been renamed the **caspases.**[65] One of these found in the mouse (caspase-2) has 30% protein similarity with ICE and *ced-3;* when overexpressed in cultured neuroblastoma cells, it induces cell death. Of the various ICE family members, caspase-3 shares the closest homology with *ced-3*.[66] One substrate of caspase-3 is poly(ADP-ribose) polymerase (PARP), which is involved in DNA repair. Loss of normal PARP function after proteolytic action by caspase-3 is associated with the initiation of apoptosis in mammalian cells. Inhibition of caspase-3 by a specific tetrapeptide aldehyde blocks apoptosis, and caspase-3-deficient mice (produced by gene knockout) have reduced neuronal PCD.[67] It seems likely, therefore, that caspase-3 is a major ICE family member involved in PCD in vertebrates. Although *ced-3* and ICE family members represent evolutionarily conserved genes that are important in the basic killing process of PCD, the substrates of these enzymes and thus how they actually act to destroy neurons are not well understood. Because caspases normally reside in cells as inactive pro-enzymes, some family members probably transactivate other members, whereas others act on substrates whose breakdown is more directly involved in cell death (e.g., PARP).

The major gene for inhibiting PCD in the nematode, *ced-9*, is homologous to the mammalian gene *bcl-2* (for *B*-*c*ell *l*ymphoma-related gene).[68] Expression of the human *bcl-2* gene in *C. elegans* mimics the protective effects of *ced-9* on cell death in loss-of-function *ced-9* mutants. Overexpression of the human *bcl-2* gene in transgenic mice also rescues neurons from both normal PCD and injury-induced degeneration. Surprisingly, however, mutant mice with targeted disruption of *bcl-2* (gene knockout) appear normal at birth, indicating that other genes may also function to prevent or block vertebrate PCD. One such gene, *bcl-x*, another member of the *bcl-2* family, inhibits cell death after trophic factor deprivation *in vitro.* Mouse embryos lacking the *bcl-x* gene exhibit greatly increased PCD of immature postmitotic neurons.[69] Another *bcl-2* homolog, *Bax*, forms heterodimers with *bcl-2* and can act to accelerate apoptosis. Consequently, overexpression of *Bax* antagonizes the protective actions of *bcl-2* and results in enhanced cell death, whereas a targeted mutation of *Bax* protects many cells from PCD. Interestingly, *Bax* appears to be necessary for the normal death of many postmitotic neurons but not for the normal death of neuronal precursors still undergoing mitosis.[70] This again underscores the likelihood of diverse pathways for neuronal PCD. A striking observation in the *Bax*-deficient mice is that the neurons rescued from PCD are atrophic, indicating that survival but not growth is the major function of *Bax.* Another recently isolated novel gene, *Bax inhibitor-1* (*Bl-1*), which is unrelated to *bcl-2*, has been localized to intracellular membranes (e.g., the endoplasmic reticulum) and shown to inhibit cell death as effectively as *bcl-2*.[71] *Bl-1* is thought to act via interactions with either *Bax* or *bcl-2*, both of which have also been localized to intracellular membranes. The occurrence of complex interactions between genes such as *bcl-2* and *Bax*, *ced-3* and *ced-9*, and caspases, *Apafs*, *Bl-1*, and *bcl-2* may reflect common genetic pathways for the regulation of PCD (Fig. 20.13).

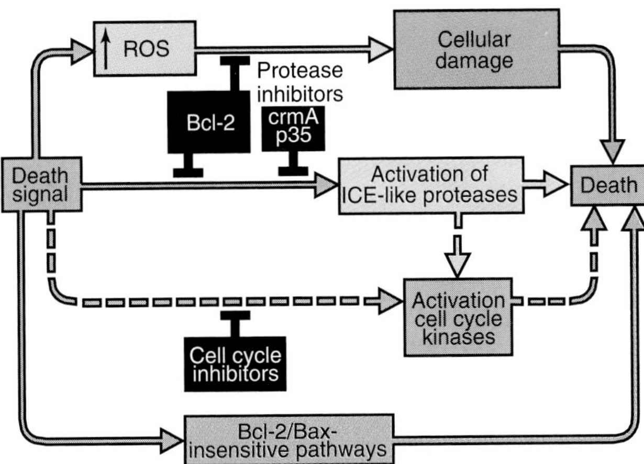

FIGURE 20.13 Some postulated pathways of gene activation involved in the cell death program of neurons and other cells (from Rubin *et al.*[59]). The agents in the filled-in boxes are able to block processes indicated by the arrows. This blockade is represented by the symbol T or ⊥.

The susceptibility to undergo PCD appears to be determined by the relative levels and interactions of proteins derived from these pro- and inhibitory cell-death genes.[72,73] Experimentally altering the balance of these proteins in neurons modulates their vulnerability to undergo PCD. At present, neither the biochemical mechanisms of the *bcl-2* or ICE families nor their specific biochemical interactions with other genes or substrates are very well understood. One of the apoptotic-inhibitory genes in the *bcl-2* family (*bcl-xl*) may act by regulating the permeability of intracellular membranes.[74]

As we discussed earlier, the evolution of PCD may have had its origins as a defense mechanism to selectively eliminate cells infected by viruses. Some viruses have, in turn, evolved a means to oppose such defenses by producing cell-death suppressors. The insect baculovirus gene p35 inhibits virus-induced apoptosis in insect cells and prevents PCD in *C. elegans*, *Drosophila*, and mammalian neurons.[75,76] p35 appears to act by inhibiting the activity of *ced-3* in *C. elegans* and of ICE-like cysteine proteases in vertebrates. Another viral gene, *CrmA*, is also a potent inhibitor of ICE and prevents cell death in cultured neurons deprived of trophic factor.[77]

Most of the genes and proteins that have been implicated in PCD act *within* target cells to induce or suppress degeneration. However, some gene products that induce cell death by acting as cell–cell signaling molecules have also been identified. Examples are certain members of the tumor necrosis receptor (TNF-R) superfamily (e.g., TNF-R1 and FAS/Apo-1), which induce cell death following ligand binding.[78] For some types of neurons, the low-affinity neurotrophin receptor p75 also appears to act in this way. For example, the early target-independent PCD of retinal ganglion cells is prevented when the interaction of endogenous NGF with this receptor is blocked.[79] This work is important in showing that cell–cell interactions in the nervous system involving trophic molecules may act as death-inducing signals as well as via their more common role as survival signals. Another example in which signaling molecules can induce cell death in target cells involves cytotoxic T cells.[61] Cytotoxic T cells kill other cells that have been infected with bacteria or viruses by releasing two types of cytolytic proteins. One of these proteins, perforin, produces holes in the cell membrane and the other, granzyme B (also known as fragmentin 2, proteinase-1, and RNKP-1), a serine protease, induces apoptosis. In view of the suspected role of cell cycle genes in some forms of PCD (discussed later), it is interesting that granzyme B also activates $P34^{cdc2}$, a serine–threonine kinase involved in the entry of a cell into mitosis. Additionally, granzyme B has the same substrate activity as ICE and has been shown to activate CPP32 (caspase-3). Cell death induced by ligand (TNF-α) binding to the FAS/apo-1 receptor is also mediated by a pathway that probably involves one or more members of the ICE family of proteases. The recently discovered *Drosophila* cell-death gene *reaper* (for the "grim reaper") is also reported to share structural similarity to the FAS/TNF receptor, and *Reaper* is thought to kill cells by a pathway involving ICE-like proteases.[76,80,81]

Like the role of the *ced-3* and *ced-4* genes in *C. elegans*, the *reaper* gene is necessary for all embryonic PCD in *Drosophila*. Two additional cell-death genes in *Drosophila* (*hid*, *h*ead *i*nvolution *d*efect, and *grim*) also appear to activate ICE family proteases and like *reaper* are both required for cell death in the fly.[82]

The explosion of interest in PCD over the past 10 years is in large measure due to our increased understanding of the genetic and molecular mechanisms involved and to the hope that with this increased knowledge it will be possible to prevent or correct perturbations in normal cell death and survival that may result in diseases such as cancer and neurodegeneration.

Mechanisms for PCD May Overlap with Processes That Control Cell Division

Studies of cell death in mitotically active cells have suggested that apoptosis may be a common outcome of perturbations of the cell cycle. Some shared structural features of cells undergoing mitosis and apoptosis include chromatin condensation and disassembly of the nuclear lamina. Several genes associated with the regulation of mitosis and the cell cycle have also been implicated in apoptosis. These include c-*myc*, c-*fos*, c-*jun*, cyclins, cyclin-dependent kinases, and the tumor suppressor genes p53 and *Rb-1*. The demonstration that these genes are involved in PCD in proliferating cells has led to the suggestion that cell death is somehow caused by unsuccessful passage through the cell cycle. One idea is that the cells may lack critical mitotic signals (e.g., growth factors) required for normal transition through the cell cycle, resulting in activation of an alternative, apoptotic, pathway.[83] Although this is an appealing idea with regard to actively proliferating cells, PCD of neurons typically involves postmitotic cells that have permanently withdrawn from the cell cycle. Despite their state of terminal differentiation, however, postmitotic neurons do, in fact, continue to express some genes and proteins associated with proliferation and cell-cycle events, and some of these may either increase or decrease expression coincident with the commitment to die after trophic factor deprivation.[84] For example, cultured rat sympathetic neurons deprived of NGF exhibit increases in c-*jun*, c-*fos*, cyclin D1, and c-*myb* and decreases in *fra-1*, *Rb*, and *bcl-2* at a time after NGF withdrawal that is consistent with their playing a critical role in PCD. Intracellular injection of either function-blocking antibodies specific for the c-*jun* family or of a c-*jun* dominant-negative mutant molecule protects NGF-deprived neurons from cell death.[85,86] Because each of the cell-cycle genes induced in neurons undergoing PCD is also induced in other nondeath situations, these genes are probably necessary but not sufficient for inducing cell death. These and other cell-cycle genes expressed during PCD may trigger postmitotic neurons to attempt to reenter the cell cycle, thereby producing conflicting growth signals that initiate cell death. Alternatively, the expression of these genes and their products in postmitotic neurons may directly mediate distinct functions other than those related to the cell cycle, such as PCD.

Is There a Final Common Pathway by Which Cells Are Destroyed during PCD?

Three possible biochemical mechanisms have been suggested as critical for the actual destruction of cells during PCD: (1) cytoplasmic proteases, (2) endonucleases that degrade DNA, and (3) oxidative stress. These are not necessarily mutually exclusive; they may act in concert by being part of a single signaling cascade or by dismantling a different part of the cell. Alternatively, each mechanism may act independently in different cell types or situations. The strongest evidence for the role of proteases in PCD is the fact that the ICE/*ced-3* family members (caspases) are cysteine proteases whose death-inducing activity in a variety of cell types, including neurons, can be blocked by specific cysteine protease inhibitors.[87] How these genes control PCD is unclear at present. They could activate substrate proteins essential for cell death, or they could cleave and degrade proteins that are crucial for survival.

As noted earlier, another protease, granzyme B, is part of the mechanism by which cytotoxic T cells kill cells infected with bacteria or viruses. The serine protease thrombin can also induce PCD in neurons, and this activity can be blocked by specific serine protease inhibitors such as protease nexin-1 and hirudin. The thiol protease calpain has also been implicated in some forms of apoptosis. Thus, proteases are a common feature of many forms of PCD. Although a few of the substrates degraded by proteases associated with PCD have been identified (e.g., poly(ADP-ribose) polymerase, lamin B1, topoisomerase, and β-actin), their role in cell death remains largely hypothetical.

Since the discovery in 1980 that apoptotic cell death

of thymocytes involves the degradation of DNA into a specific "ladder" pattern, many other cells undergoing apoptosis have also been found to exhibit a similar pattern of DNA breakdown. Because DNA fragmentation has been considered one of the earlier changes signifying an irreversible commitment to cell death, it has generally been thought to be involved in the induction of cell death rather than being the result of it. Although several candidate endonucleases have been identified,[85] until recently it has not been clear whether one or more of these are specific for and actually cause cell death. With regard to specificity, it has now been shown that a recently isolated novel endonuclease, named caspase-activated DNase (CAD), is specifically activated during apoptosis.[89] CAD is usually maintained in the cytoplasm in an inactive form by the action of a second protein called inhibitor of CAD (ICAD). ICAD releases CAD after caspase activation, allowing it to translocate to the nucleus and cleave DNA. However, CAD is not likely to be an early upstream inducer of PCD because there is, in fact, evidence that the nucleus may be dispensable for triggering apoptotic changes in the remainder of the cell. When cultured human fibroblasts are treated with cytochalasin B to disrupt actin filaments and then centrifuged, enucleated cells (cells, or so-called cytoplasts, that lack nuclei) are generated. When these cytoplasts are exposed to cell-death-inducing stimuli, they undergo apoptotic-like cytoplasmic changes and die by a process that can be prevented by *bcl-2*.[90] Although whether other types of cells can also undergo apoptosis in the absence of the nucleus remains to be seen, these findings suggest that the proteins necessary for PCD (the **death program** or machinery) are already present in the cytoplasm before the cells degenerate. Rather than acting as a trigger of cell death, DNA degradation may only represent another part of the cell that must be destroyed for completion of the cell-death program. Even when cell death is dependent on gene transcription (and therefore requires the presence of the nucleus), the proteins synthesized may not be the ones actually required for death, but instead may be activators of death proteins that are already present in the cytoplasm. Therefore, DNA fragmentation induced by specific nucleases, although a common feature of apoptosis, is probably not the initiator of most types of PCD and may, in fact, be only one of several essential manifestations of the death program.

The role of oxygen free radicals as direct agents in the destruction of cells during PCD has received considerable attention.[91] During aerobic metabolism, the **reactive oxygen species** (ROS) that are generated can interact with cellular macromolecules and cause damage (Chapter 14). To counter this potential for damage, cells have evolved an effective defense system in the form of antioxidants that scavenge or detoxify ROS. Cell survival therefore represents a balance between the levels of ROS and antioxidants. Extensive data indicate the involvement of ROS in the neuronal injury that occurs with stroke, ischemia, and chronic neurodegenerative disease. Perturbation of this balance may also contribute to the degenerative events seen in PCD: (1) PCD is often associated with increases in ROS (2). The addition of exogenous ROS or a reduction in antioxidants can induce apoptosis. (3) PCD can be prevented by treatment with antioxidants. (4) *bcl-2*, which acts as a negative regulator of PCD, may protect cells by decreasing the level of ROS.[92] (5) The PCD of NGF-deprived cultured sympathetic neurons is delayed by overexpression of antioxidant enzymes (superoxide dismutase) or by treatment with the antioxidant, *N*-acetylcysteine.[93,94] Interestingly, superoxide dismutase is effective in delaying PCD in this situation only when administered within the first 6–8 h after NGF deprivation, many hours prior to the irreversible commitment of these cells to PCD. This result indicates that a transient increase in ROS, which takes place shortly after NGF deprivation, may serve as a signal in the death pathway rather than as a toxic agent directly involved in cell destruction.

Although ROS may be sufficient to activate PCD, they may not be necessary for inducing normal cell death in some cell populations. For example, cells cultured under low oxygen (anaerobic) conditions in which ROS are not generated undergo PCD, and this death can be blocked by *bcl-2*.[95] Despite this uncertainty regarding its role in cell death, oxidative stress remains a promising candidate for a common cellular pathway of destruction in PCD.

At present, researchers are not certain whether any of the specific genes or pathways associated with the PCD of neurons or other cells reflect pathways that are common to all forms of PCD. However, a universal pathway for the entire genetic cascade leading to PCD appears unlikely. Although *ced-3* and *-4* in *C. elegans* and *reaper* in *Drosophila* participate in all (or most) forms of PCD in those organisms, no single gene that regulates all forms of neuronal death (with the possible exception of caspases) has yet been identified in vertebrates. Many genes induced in nonneuronal models of PCD are not induced in neurons (e.g., p53), some neurons express death-associated genes without undergoing PCD, and genes that regulate PCD in some types of neurons are ineffective in others (e.g., *Bax*, *bcl-2*). Given our present understanding of the complex genetic regulation of PCD, it is clear that specific genes play varying roles in the genetic hierarchies and cascades involved. The best understood cell death path-

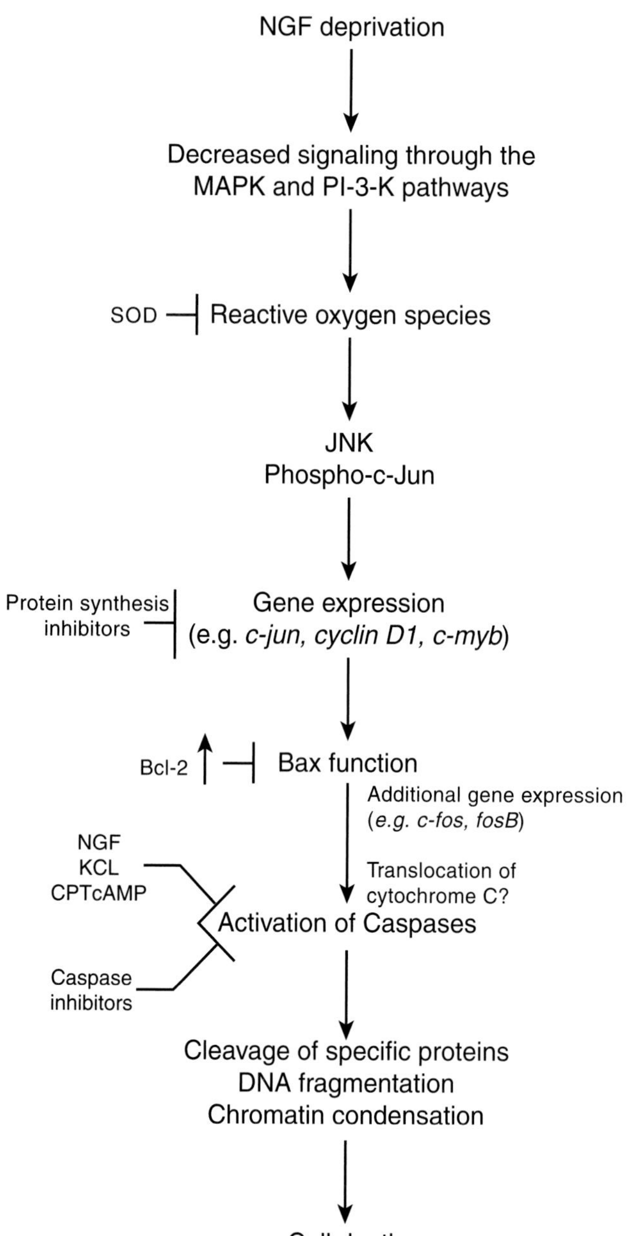

FIGURE 20.14 Temporal sequence of events during NGF-deprivation-induced sympathetic neuronal death. NGF removal activates the programmed cell death pathway and causes the apoptotic death of neurons within 24–48 h. The sequence of events is shown in a linear pathway for simplicity. Removal of NGF causes decreased signaling through the MAP kinase and the phosphatidylinositol 3-kinase (PI-3-K) pathways. One of the events that occur early after NGF deprivation is a transient increase in reactive oxygen species; these species appear to be important for mediating sympathetic neuronal death, as microinjection of superoxide dismutase delays neuronal apoptosis. Following that, the activity of *c-jun* N-terminal kinases (JNKs) and phosphorylation of *c-jun* protein are increased during sympathetic neuronal death. Because microinjection of either an anti-*c-jun* neutralizing antibody or a dominant negative *c-jun* construct prevents sympathetic neuronal apoptosis (see text), the function of *c-jun* protein appears to be important for mediating neuronal death. Sympathetic neuronal death is blocked by macromolecular synthesis inhibitors and, therefore, is thought to require the expression of certain death-promoting genes. *c-jun* may function by regulating the expression of such genes during sympathetic neuronal death. Expression of certain genes such as *c-jun*, *cyclin D1*, and *c-fos*, is increased during neuronal death. Although the expression of these genes is temporally correlated with the increase in *c-jun* phosphorylation, their importance in mediating cell death remains unclear. Concurrent with these changes is a marked decrease in metabolic functions as seen by decreases in RNA and protein synthesis. The role of these metabolic changes in cell death is also uncertain. Among the Bcl-2 family proteins, BAX is essential in mediating sympathetic neuronal death. Overexpression of Bcl-2 also retards apoptosis in these neurons. The final event in the neuronal cell death pathway appears to be the activation of caspases. Caspases are important mediators of sympathetic neuronal death, and their activation is regulated by the Bcl-2 family proteins by as yet unknown mechanisms. Activated caspases function by cleaving specific cellular proteins and irreversibly committing the neurons to undergo apoptosis. Modified from Deshmukh *et al.*[96]

way for vertebrate neurons involves developing sympathetic cells. Although still far from complete, many of the biochemical and molecular events associated with the temporal sequence of cell death following NGF deprivation *in vitro* have been elucidated (Fig. 20.14).[96] However, even here many unanswered questions remain, including the extent to which these events reflect normal PCD occurring *in vivo*.

Signal Transduction Events Precede and May Trigger PCD

Many genes that are associated with PCD have been identified. However, the sequence in which these are expressed and their place in the cascade of events between the initial signal specifying a fate of PCD and the actual destruction of the cell are perhaps the least well understood aspects of PCD. Although immediate-early genes (IEGs; Chapter 10) such as c-*fos*, c-*jun*, c-*myb*, and *erg-1* are expressed in neurons undergoing PCD, only c-*jun* appears to be necessary for the PCD of sympathetic neurons; Ca^{2+} ions also play a role in the early signaling events leading to survival and PCD in many cell types.[97] As with the IEGs, however, precisely how changes in Ca^{2+} are involved and where these changes occur in the signal transduction pathway are poorly defined.[98] Voltage-gated Ca^{2+} influx promotes neuronal survival *in vitro*, and this may be one means by which afferent synaptic transmission modulates neuronal survival. As discussed later, Ca^{2+} influx can activate $p21^{ras}$ (ras), a small guanine nucleotide-binding protein that functions in signal transduction cascades during development.

According to the neurotrophic hypothesis, developing neurons undergo PCD from a deficiency of trophic molecules required for their survival. Therefore, trophic molecules are considered essential for suppressing neuronal PCD, either by preventing the expression of genes required for initiating the cell-death cascade or by inducing the expression of protective genes. Either mechanism could act at the level of transcription or translation of gene products necessary for survival. Signal transduction during the PCD of neurons has been studied by examining the expression of putative signaling molecules following trophic factor deprivation.[85,99] Responses to members of the neurotrophin family of trophic molecules (i.e., NGF, BDNF, NT-4/5, NT-3) are mediated by trk receptor tyrosine kinases (see Chapter 21). High-affinity binding of neurotrophins to their specific trk receptor induces rapid protein phosphorylation and the activation of a complex cascade(s) of intracellular signals. Many of these signaling pathways are involved in non-survival-related events such as neurite outgrowth and neurotransmitter synthesis. Two pathways implicated in promoting survival are the ras and phosphatidylinositol 3-kinase (PI-3) signal transduction pathways.[97,100] Microinjection of anti-ras antibodies into peripheral neurons blocks the survival effects of NGF and results in PCD.[101] Targeted disruption of the gene encoding p120-ras-GAP, a negative regulator of ras, causes extensive PCD in the nervous system of embryonic mice.[102] The loss of ras expression in PC12 cells following NGF deprivation occurs at least 6 h before the cells become committed to PCD (i.e., the point at which 50% of the cells can no longer be rescued by reexposure to NGF). In contrast to ras, the PI-3 pathway of growth-factor-mediated survival appears to involve the serine–threonine kinase proto-oncogene *akt*.[103] IGF-1–induced survival of cerebellar neurons trigger *akt* expression, dominant-negative *akt* mutants increase apoptosis, and exogenous *akt* can rescue cerebellar neurons from trophic factor deprivation. The role of *akt* in cerebellar survival is mediated, at least in part, by inhibition of the pro-apoptotic gene *bad*. PI-3-induced phosphorylation of *bad* by *akt* dissociates *bad* and the anti-apoptotic gene *bcl-x*, allowing *bcl-x* to prevent cell death by blocking the release of cytochrome *c* from mitochondria. These data on ras and PI-3 suggest that signal transduction pathways for the survival and death of neurons differ depending on the type of cell and growth factor involved.

Summary

PCD is a metabolically active process that involves a specific genetic pathway(s) necessary for the cascade of events leading to degeneration. Several genes in the PCD pathway were first identified in *C. elegans* and homologs are found in vertebrates. Because genes and proteins involved in control of the cell cycle have been associated with PCD, cell death may be result from an aberrant attempt to reenter the cell cycle. Cytoplasmic proteases, endonucleases, and reactive oxygen species have all been proposed as elements of a final common-pathway for PCD.

At present, one of the least understood aspects of PCD is the signal transduction pathways(s) that ultimately result in cell degeneration. Because the survival of developing neurons is dependent on successful competition for trophic molecules, a widely used model for the investigation of PCD signaling pathways is trophic factor deprivation. Two important pathways identified by this strategy involve the ras guanine nucleotide-binding protein and PI-3/akt. Blocking these pathways inhibits the survival-promoting effects of NGF on sympathetic neurons (ras) and of IGF-1 on cerebellar neurons (PI-3/akt).

FUNCTIONS OF NEURONAL PCD

Why does cell death occur? This is a reasonable question to ask because the loss of large numbers of developing neurons is counterintuitive. Why should embryos invest precious resources in generating cells and tissues only to later cast many of these aside? A satisfactory answer to this apparent paradox requires an evolutionary perspective that addresses two central aspects of the problem: First, how did the biochemical machinery (the death program) needed to actively kill cells arise? Second, why, in many tissues, are more cells generated than are apparently needed? Because PCD acts to delete these excess cells, understanding the overproduction is critical to understanding cell death from an evolutionary perspective.

Because all animals are under considerable selective pressure to resist the cellular spread of viral infection, it is not surprising that several defense strategies have evolved to accomplish this.[12,15] One such defense is the activation of a cell-death (suicide) program in which the biochemical death pathway triggered by viral infection closely resembles that seen in PCD. This program effectively removes the infected cell and prevents the spread of the virus. Viruses, in turn, have evolved counterstrategies to block the activation of this suicide program. Selective pressures acting on both the virus and target cells may account for the evolution of the genetic and biochemical death program. An alternative model argues that PCD arose *pari passu* with the genetic and biochemical machinery regulating cell division. According to this view, uncoordinated (aberrant) activation of cell-cycle genes results in PCD as a means to eliminate the "defective" cells.

Understanding the evolution of the death program does not help answer the second question: Why is there often a massive overproduction of cells during development that are later eliminated by PCD? Two explanations have been offered. First, each case of PCD may have evolved to serve a distinct biological function. For example, in the case of spinal motor neurons, natural selection is thought to be responsible for both the overproduction and the subsequent death of neurons as means for creating an optimal (adaptive) level of muscle innervation (e.g., size matching). The second view is that the overproduction of neurons (or other cells) is an inevitable outcome of the kinetics of proliferation of precursor cells. Once excess cells are available, natural selection then acts via PCD to mediate a variety of different adaptive needs.[104] Elimination of the excess cells could be easily accomplished by coopting the cellular death machinery used to kill cells after viral infection. The major distinction between these two views is that in the first, the overproduction and later death or survival of the excess cells are believed to be directly selected for, whereas in the second, the overproduction and later death of cells are the inevitable and unselected outcome of proliferative mechanisms that alone are not able to precisely control the required final number of neurons. In the well-studied case of spinal motor neurons in the chick embryo, the pre-cell-death number of neurons varies little, indicating that proliferation is closely regulated. For example, at the end of the proliferative phase, there are about 24,000 (±2000) lumbar motor neurons, one-half of which subsequently undergo PCD (approximately 11,000–12,000 survive). Therefore, PCD is not needed to correct for imprecise, unregulated proliferation. Even though proliferation is tightly regulated, it may not by itself reliably generate optimum numbers of cells.[104] In reality, both of the proposed mechanisms may occur. For example, it seems highly likely that the creation of transient structures that function at one stage of development only to later regress and be discarded (e.g., the tail of tadpoles, larval muscles of insects, and transient neuronal structures such as the cortical subplate or sensory Rohon–Beard cells in frogs) reflects the direct selection via evolution of PCD as a means of regression. In contrast, the presence of increased numbers of neurons in limb versus those in nonlimb spinal segments of vertebrates may result from the unselected outcome of an overproduction of neurons at all spinal levels, followed by increased survival in limb compared to nonlimb regions. For chick spinal motor neurons, a combination of factors appears to contribute to final cell numbers. Prior to the onset of cell death, fewer motor neurons are present in nonlimb than in limb-innervating regions, whereas somewhat less cell loss occurs by PCD in the limb-innervating regions. Thus, regulation of final cell numbers can occur at both the production and the survival phases of development and thus involves a combination of proliferation and cell death.

Many circumstances in which the PCD of neurons is thought to mediate distinct adaptive functions are listed in Table 20.3. In many of these examples, the production of excess neurons provides a substrate on which PCD can act to regulate survival for a variety of adaptive needs. Although the biological functions attributed to PCD in these situations are quite plausible, few of them have been directly demonstrated to serve a specific adaptive role. As we identify new genes that regulate PCD, and as we gain a better understanding of how cellular and molecular signals control cell death and survival, we will be presented with increased opportunities for preventing PCD *in vivo* and for directly assessing whether its occurrence is selectively advantageous. For example, the creation of transgenic animals lacking or overexpressing specific cell-death-associated genes (e.g., *bcl-2*) is already providing considerable insight into this problem.

Summary

The biochemical and molecular pathways necessary for PCD may have evolved as a means to defend against viral infection. Once this cellular capacity arose, however, it is likely that it was coopted to serve a variety of other biological functions. In the nervous system, these functions include establishing optimal levels of connectivity between neuronal populations, eliminating aberrant connections, and serving transient functional needs of the embryo.

PCD, DEVELOPMENTAL DISORDERS, AND NEURODEGENERATION

The widespread occurrence of PCD during normal development indicates that cell loss, together with cell production (proliferation), is a fundamental mechanism for controlling final cell numbers in many tissues. The normal cessation of PCD in most tissues late in development (e.g., in the nervous system) and the homeostatic balance between proliferation and death in other adult tissues (e.g., skin) also underscore the importance of precisely regulating cell numbers even into adulthood. Dysregulation of normal PCD would be maladaptive and pathological.[105,106] For example, genetic or congenital neurological defects could be caused by perturbations of PCD. However, there is

TABLE 20.3 Some Possible Functions of PCD in the Nervous System

Category	Examples
1. Removal of cells that appear to have no function	The death of neurons in either males or females for creating sexually dimorphic structures
2. Removal of cells of an inappropriate phenotype	The death of neuronal precursors located in regions of the spinal cord, such as the roof or floor plate, that lack neurons in the adult
3. Pattern formation and morphogenesis	The death of neural crest cells in specific segments of the hindbrain
4. Systems matching	The creation of optimal levels of innervation between interconnected groups of neurons and between neurons and their nonneuronal targets
5. Error correction	The death of neurons with inappropriate synaptic connections or aberrant pathway projections
6. Guidance	The loss of neurons or glia that guide neuronal migration or axonal growth at specific stages of development
7. Transient function	The death of sensory, motor, and CNS neurons that serve a transient physiological/behavioral function during development (e.g., Rohon–Beard sensory neurons in tadpoles)
8. Removal of harmful cells	The death of cells having defective DNA or infected by viruses
9. A means of evolutionary change	Adaptive changes in the ontogenetic death and survival of cells in response to genetic mutations

relatively little solid evidence on this point. Although a number of genetic mutations in animals and humans involve significant alterations in neuron numbers, whether these always reflect the loss of control of PCD or also reflect other abnormalities that could influence final cell numbers is not known.

One genetic disease in humans in which PCD has been implicated is infantile spinal muscular atrophy (SMA). The most severe form of SMA (Type I SMA) is an autosomal recessive condition in which an excessive loss of spinal motor neurons during late prenatal and early postnatal life results in respiratory failure and death by 1 to 3 years of age. One gene involved in this disease has been mapped to chromosome 5 and shown to be homologous with a baculovirus gene product (p35) that acts in the same way as *bcl-2* to inhibit PCD in insects and vertebrate cells. The two first coding exons of the gene for this so-called "neuronal apoptosis inhibitory protein" (NAIP) are deleted in approximately 70% of Type I SMA patients.[107] A second gene involved in SMA has also been mapped to chromosome 5 and is mutated in 95% of *all* SMA patients (Types I–III). This gene (spinal motor neuron, SMN) normally interacts with *bcl-2* to exert synergistic effects on motor neuron survival. The specific mutations in SMN found in SMA patients inhibit this synergism and render the motor neurons more vulnerable to PCD.[108] This suggests that owing to mutations in one or both genes, the failure to inhibit normal PCD of motor neurons at the appropriate time in SMA patients may be responsible for the increased cell loss.

The idea that aberrant cell death in the nervous system may reflect a loss of normal control mechanisms for PCD is significant because the increased understanding of positive and negative genetic regulation of PCD may provide a potentially powerful and rational approach to the development of therapeutic treatment strategies. A hopeful sign in this regard comes from recent reports that neuronal death in Alzheimer, Parkinson, Huntington, Down syndrome, and ALS disease patients and in some forms of traumatic brain injury (e.g., ischemia, epilepsy) exhibits some characteristics of apoptosis, such as the stereotyped fragmentation of DNA and the expression of genes previously associated with developmental PCD (e.g., the *bcl-2* gene family).[109–114] Therefore, in addition to the important diverse roles of PCD during normal development (Table 20.3) and in adult tissue homeostasis, studies leading to better understanding of the cellular and molecular mechanisms of PCD may ultimately shed new light on the causes of a variety of neurological disorders that affect large numbers of the human population.

A number of major issues will need to be resolved before realistic therapeutic strategies involving the use of neurotrophic factors or interventions at the level of PCD genes can be considered. These issues include reliable modes of treatment, prevention of untoward side effects, and whether the rescue of neurons from cell death leads to long-term survival of functional cells. Although none of these issues has been satisfactorily addressed either for animal models or in human disease, the last problem, that of surviving functional neurons, has received some positive support from the study of fly mutants with a form of retinal degeneration equivalent to human cases of severe retinitis pigmentosa (RP), a leading cause of blindness involving cell death of photoreceptor cells. Overexpression of the anti-apoptotic gene p35—a caspase inhibitor—in the mutant flies prevents the apoptosis of photoreceptor cells, resulting in the retention of significant visual behavior and retinal function.[115] This success in preventing blindness in the fly provides hope and a rationale for the eventual use of cell death prevention strategies in the treatment of human disease.

Summary

Because PCD is primarily a developmental phenomenon, research has focused on the normal biology of cell death in the embryo, fetus, and newborn. However, with the growing recognition that pathological cell death may have certain biochemical and molecular features in common with PCD, hope is growing that better understanding of PCD may reveal potential therapeutic strategies for the treatment of neurodegenerative disease and neuronal loss following CNS trauma.

References

1. Oppenheim, R. W. (1981). Neuronal cell death and related regressive phenomena during neurogenesis: A selective historical review and progress report. In *Studies in Developmental Neurobiology: Essays in Honor of Viktor Hamburger* (W. M. Cowan, ed.), pp. 74–133. Oxford University Press, New York.

1a. Clarke, P. G. H., ed. (1994). Neuronal death in health and disease. *Seminars in Neurosci.* **6:** 281–347.

1b. Raff, M. C. (1992). Social controls on cell survival and cell death. *Nature* **356:** 397–400.

1c. Schwartz, L. M., Oppenheim, R. W., and Shatz, C. J., eds. (1992). Neuronal cell death. *J. Neurobiology* (Special Issue) **23:** 1111–1352.

2. Saunders, J. W. (1966). Death in embryonic systems. *Science* **154:** 604–612.

3. Raff, M. C., Barnes, B. C., Burne, J. F., Coles, H. S., Ishizaki, Y., and Jacobson, M. D. (1993). Programmed cell death and the control of cell survival: Lessons from the nervous system. *Science* **262:** 695–700.

4. Williams, R. W., and Herrup, K. (1988). The control of neuron number. *Annu. Rev. Neurosci.* **11:** 423–454.

5. Hamburger, V. (1992). History of the discovery of neuronal death in embryos. *J. Neurobiol.* **23:** 1116–1123.

6. Hamburger, V. (1993). The history of the discovery of the nerve growth factor. *J. Neurobiol.* **24:** 893–897.

7. Levi-Montalcini, R. (1987). The nerve growth factor 35 years later. *Science* **237:** 1154–1162.

8. Oppenheim, R. W. (1996). The concept of uptake and retrograde transport of neurotrophic molecules during development: History and present status. *Neurochem. Res.* **21:** 769–777.

9. Purves, D., and Sanes, J. R. (1987). The 1986 Nobel prize in Physiology or Medicine. *Trends Neurosci.* **10:** 231–235.

10. Hamburger, V. (1934). The effects of wing bud extirpation on the development of the central nervous system in chick embryos. *J. Exp. Zool.* **68:** 449–494.

11. Hamburger, V., and Levi-Montalcini, R. (1949). Proliferation, differentiation and degeneration in the spinal ganglia of the chick embryo under normal and experimental conditions. *J. Exp. Zool.* **111:** 457–502.

12. Vaux, D. L., Haecker, G., and Strasser, A. (1994). An evolutionary perspective on apoptosis. *Cell (Cambridge, Mass.)* **76:** 777–779.

13. Yarmolinsky, M. B. (1995). Programmed cell death in bacterial populations. *Science* **267:** 836–837.

14. Greenberg, J. T. (1996). Programmed cell death: A way of life for plants. *Proc. Natl. Acad. Sci. U.S.A.* **93:** 12094–12097.

15. Ameisen, J. C. (1996). The origin of programmed cell death. *Science* **272:** 1278–1279.

16. Ellis, R. E., Yuan, J., and Horvitz, H. R. (1991). Mechanisms and functions of cell death. *Annu. Rev. Cell Biol.* **7:** 663–698.

17. Truman, J. W., Thorn, R. S., and Robinow, S. (1992). Programmed neuronal death in insect development. *J. Neurobiol.* **23:** 1295–1311.

18. Stellar, H., and Grether, M. E. (1994). Programmed cell death in *Drosophila. Neuron* **13:** 1269–1274.

19. McKay, S. E., and Oppenheim, R. W. (1991). Lack of evidence for cell deaths among avian spinal cord interneurons during normal development and following removal of targets and afferents. *J. Neurobiol.* **22:** 721–733.

20. Cowan, W. M., and O'Leary, D. (1984). Cell death and process elimination: The role of regressive phenomena in the development of the vertebrate nervous system. *Medicine, Science and Society. Celebrating the Harvard Medical School Bicentennial.* Wiley, New York.

21. Oppenheim, R. W. (1991). Cell death during development of the nervous system. *Annu. Rev. Neurosci.* **14:** 453–501.

22. Homma, S., Yaginuma, H., and Oppenheim, R. W. (1994). Programmed cell death during the earliest stages of spinal cord development in the chick embryo: A possible means of early phenotypic selection. *J. Comp. Neurol.* **345:** 377–395.

23. Blaschke, A. J., Staley, K., and Chun, J. (1996). Widespread programmed cell death in proliferative and postmitotic regions of the fetal cerebral cortex. *Development (Cambridge, UK)* **122:** 1165–1174.

24. Ciutat, D., Calderó, J., Oppenheim, R. W., and Esquerda, J. E. (1996). Apoptosis in avian Schwann cells during normal development and following the loss of peripheral axons. *J. Neurosci.* **16:** 3979–3990.

25. Barres, B. A., Hurt, I. K., Coles, H. S. R., Burne, J., Voyvodic, J. T., Richardson, W. D., and Raff, M. C. (1992). Cell death and control of cell survival in the oligodendrocyte lineage. *Cell (Cambridge, Mass.)* **70:** 31–46.

26. Schwartz, L. M., and Osborne, B. A., eds. (1995). *Methods in Cell Biology,* Vol. 46. Academic Press, San Diego, CA.

27. Clarke, P. G. H., and Oppenheim, R. W. (1995). Neuronal death in vertebrate development: In vivo methods. *Methods Cell Biol.* **46:** 277–323.

28. Clarke, P. G. H., and Clarke, S. (1996). Nineteenth century research on naturally occurring cell death and related phenomena. *Anat. Embryol.* **193:** 81–99.

29. Manjo, G., and Joris, I. (1995). Apoptosis, oncosis and necrosis, an overview of cell death. *Am. J. Pathol.* **146:** 3–15.

30. Kerr, J. F. R., Wyllie, A. H., and Currie, A. R. (1972). Apoptosis: A basic biological phenomenon with wide-ranging implications in tissue kinetics. *B. J. Cancer* **26:** 239–257.

31. Kerr, J. F. R., Goble, G. C., Winterford, C. M., and Harmon,

B. V. (1995). Anatomical methods in cell death. *Methods Cell Biol.* **46:** 1–28.

32. Savill, J. S., Fadok, V., Henson, P., and Haslett, C. (1993). Phagocyte recognition of cells undergoing apoptosis. *Immunol. Today* **14:** 131–136.
33. Rabacchi, S. A., Bontanti, L., Liu, X., and Maffei, L. (1994). Apoptotic cell death induced by optic nerve lesion in the neonatal rat *J. Neurosci.* **14:** 5292–5301.
34. Choi, D. W. (1996). Ischemia-induced neuronal apoptosis. *Curr. Opin. Neurobiol.* **6:** 667–692.
35. Charriant-Morlangue, C., Aggoun-Zouaoui, D., Represa, A., and Ben-Ari, Y. (1996). Apoptotic features of selective neuronal death in ischemia, epilepsy and gp120 toxicity. *Trends Neurosci.* **19:**109–114.
36. Lawrence, M. S., Ho, D. Y., Sun, G. H., Steinberg, G. K., and Sapolsky, R. M. (1996). Overexpression of bcl-2 with herpes simplex virus vectors protects CNS neurons against neurological insults *in vitro* and *in vivo*. *J. Neurosci.* **16:** 486–496.
37. Bonfoco, E., Krainic, D., Ankarcrona, M., Nicotera, P., and Lipton, S. A. (1995). Apoptosis and necrosis: Two distinct events induced by mild and intense insults with *N*-methyl-D-aspartate or nitric oxide/superoxide in cortical cell cultures. *Proc. Natl. Acad. Sci. U.S.A.* **92:** 7162–7166.
38. Clarke, P. G. H. (1990). Developmental cell death: Morphological diversity and multiple mechanisms. *Anat. Embryol.* **181:** 195–213.

38a. Clarke, P. G. H. (1998). Apoptosis versus necrosis: How valid a dichotomy for neurons. In *Cell Death in Diseases of the Nervous System* (V. Koliatsos and R. Ratan, eds.), pp. 3–28. Humana Press, NJ.

39. Gilbert, S. F. (1994). *Developmental Biology.* Sinauer, Sunderland, MA.
40. Truman, J. W. (1984). Cell death in invertebrate nervous systems. *Annu. Rev. Neurosci.* **7:** 171–188.
41. Cowan, W. M., Fawcett, J. W., O'Leary D. D., and Stanfeld, B. B. (1984). Regressive events in neurogenesis. *Science* **225:** 1258–1265.
42. Lamb, A. H., Sheard, P. W., and Ferns, M. J. (1988). Meritocratic selection hypothesis in the control of motoneuron death during development. In *Developmental Neurobiology of the Frog* (E. D. Pollock and H. D. Bibb, eds.), pp. 53–76. Liss, New York.
43. Lamb, A. H. (1981). Selective bilateral motor innervation in *Xengrus* tadpoles with one hindlimb. *J. Embryol. Exp. Morph.* **65:** 149–163.
44. Lamb, A. H., Ferns, M. J., and Klose, K. (1989). Peripheral competition in the control of sensory neuron numbers in *Xenopus* frogs reared with a single bilaterally innervated hindlimb. *Dev. Brain Res.* **45:** 149–153.
45. O'Leary, D. D. M., and Cowan, W. M. (1984). Survival of isthmo-optic neurons after early removal of one eye. *Dev. Brain Res.* **12:** 293–310.
46. Tanaka, H., and Landmesser, L. T. (1986). Cell death of lumbosacral motoneurons in chick, quail and chick-quail chimera embryos: A test of the quantitative matching hypothesis of neuronal cell death. *J. Neurosci.* **6:** 2889–2899.
47. Snider, W. D. (1994). Functions of the neurotrophins during nervous system development: What the knockouts are teaching us. *Cell (Cambridge, Mass.)* **77:** 1–20.
48. Oppenheim, R. W. (1987). Muscle activity and motor neuron death in the spinal cord of the chick embryo. In *Selective Neuronal Death* (G. Bock and M. O'Connor, eds.), pp. 96–108. Wiley, New York.
49. Oppenheim, R. W. (1989). The neurotrophic theory and naturally occurring motoneuron death. *Trends Neurosci.* **12:** 252–255.
50. Landmesser, L. (1992). The relationship of intramuscular nerve branching and synaptogenesis to motoneuron survival. *J. Neurobiol.* **23:** 1131–1139.
51. Franklin, J. L., and Johnson, E. M. (1992). Suppression of programmed neuronal death by sustained elevation of cytoplasmic calcium. *Trends Neurosci.* **15:** 501–508.
52. von Bartheld, C. S., Byers, M. R., Williams, R., and Bothwell, M. (1996). Anterograde transport of neurotrophins and axodendritic transfer in the developing visual system. *Science* **379:** 830–833.
53. Yin, Q. W., Johnson, J., Prevette, D., and Oppenheim, R. W. (1994). Cell death of spinal motoneurons in the chick embryo following deafferentation: Rescue effects of tissue extracts, soluble proteins and neurotrophic agents. *J. Neurosci.* **14:** 7629–7640.
54. Cunningham, T. J. (1982). Naturally occurring death and its regulation by developing neural pathways. *Int. J. Cytol.* **74:** 163–186.
55. Korsching, S. (1993). The neurotrophic factor concept: A reexamination. *J. Neurosci.* **13:** 2739–2748.
56. Schwartz, L. M. (1992). Insect muscle as a model of programmed cell death. *J. Neurobiol.* **23:** 1312–1326.
57. Horvitz, H. R. (1994). The genetics of programmed cell death in the nematode *Caenorhabditis elegans.* Cold Spring Harbor Symp. Quant. Biol. **59:** 377–385.
58. Johnson, E. M., Jr., and Deckwerth, T. L. (1993). Molecular mechanisms of developmental neuronal death. *Annu. Rev. Neurosci.* **16:** 31–46.
59. Rubin, L. L., Gatchalian, C. L., Rimon, G., and Brooks, S. F. (1994). The molecular mechanisms of neuronal apoptosis. *Curr. Biol.* **4:** 696–702.
60. Martin, D. P., Martin, D. P., Schmidt, R. E., Distefano, P. S., Lowerhy, O. H., Cartere, J. G., and Johnson, E. M. (1988). Inhibitors of protein synthesis and RNA synthesis prevent neuronal death caused by NGF deprivation. *J. Cell Biol.* **106:** 829–844.
61. Osborne, B. A., and Schwartz, L. M. (1994). Essential genes that regulate apoptosis. *Trends Cell Biol.* **4:** 394–399.
62. Hengaartner, M. D. (1997). Apoptosis: ced-4 is a stranger no more. *Nature* **388:** 714–715.
63. Yuan, J., Shaham, S., Ledoux, S., Ellis, H. M., and Horvitz, H. R. (1993). The *C. elegans* cell death gene *ced-3* encodes a protein similar to mammalian interleukin-1B-converting enzyme. *Cell (Cambridge, Mass.)* **75:** 641–652.
64. Schwartz, L. M., and Milligan, C. E. (1996). Cold thoughts of death: The role of ICE proteases in neuronal cell death. *Trends Neurosci.* **19:** 555–562.
65. Alnemri, E. S., Livingston, D. J., Nicholson, D. W., Salvesen, G., Thornberry, N. S., Wong, W. W., and Yuan, J. (1996). Human ICE/CED-3 protease nomenclature. *Cell (Cambridge, Mass.)* **87:** 171.
66. Nicholson, D. W., Ali, A., Thornberry, N. A., Vaillancourt, J. P., Ding, C. K., Gallant, M., Garcan, Y., Griffin, P. R., Labelle, M., Lazebnik, Y. A., Munday, N. A., Raju, S. M., Smulson, M. E., Yamin, T.-T., Yu, V. L., and Miller, D. K. (1995). Identification and inhibition of the ICE/*ced-3* protease necessary for mammalian apoptosis. *Nature (London)* **376:** 37–43.
67. Kuida, K., Zheng, T. S., Na, S., Juan, C., Yang, D., Karasuyama, H., Rakic, P., and Flavell, R. A. (1996). Decreased apoptosis in the brain and premature lethality in CPP-32-deficient mice. *Nature (London)* **384:** 368–372.
68. Hengartner, M. O., and Horvitz, H. R. (1994). *C. elegans* cell survival gene *ced-9* encodes a functional homolog of the mammalian proto-oncogene *bcl-2*. *Cell (Cambridge, Mass.)* **6:** 665–676.
69. Motoyama, N., Wang, F., Roth, K. A., Sawa, H., Nakayama, K. I., Nakayama, K., Negishi, I., Senju, S., Zhang, Q., Fuji, S.,

and Loh, D. (1995). Massive death of immature hematopoietic cells and neurons in bcl-x-deficient mice. *Science* **267:** 1506–1510.

70. White, F. A., Keller-Peck, C. R., Knedson, C., Korsmeyer, J. J., and Snider, W. D. (1998). Widespread elimination of naturally occurring neuronal death in Bax-deficient mice. *J. Neurosci.* **15:** 1428–1439.
71. Shaham, S., Shuman, M. A., and Herskowitz, I. (1998). Death-defying yeast identify novel apoptosis genes. *Cell* **92:** 425–427.
72. Shaham, S., and Horvitz, H. R. (1996). Developing *Caenrhabditis elegans* neurons may contain both cell-death protective and killer activities. *Genes Dev.* **10:** 578–591.
73. Häcker, G., and Vaux, D. L. (1995). Apoptosis: A sticky business. *Curr. Biol.* **5:** 622–624.
74. Minn, A. J., Velez, P., Schendel, S. L., Liang, H., Muchmore, S. W., Fesik, S. W., Fill, M., and Thompson, C. B. (1997). Bcl-xl forms an ion channel in synthetic lipid membranes. *Nature* (*London*) **385:** 357.
75. Rabizadeh, S., LaCount, D. J., Friesen, P. D., and Bredesen, D. E. (1993). Expression of the baculovirus p35 gene inhibits mammalian neural cell death. *J. Neurochem.* **61:** 2318–2321.
76. Stellar, H. (1995). Mechanisms and genes of cellular suicide. *Science* **267:** 1445–1449.
77. Gagliardini, V., Ferrari, G., Yan, C. Y. I., and Greene, L. A. (1994). Prevention of vertebrate neuronal death by the crmA gene. *Science* **263:** 826–828.
78. Nagata, S., and Golstein, P. (1995). The *Fas* death factor. *Science* **267:** 1449–1456.
79. Frade, J. M., Rodriguez-Tebar, A., and Barde, Y.-A. (1996). Induction of cell death by endogenous nerve growth factor through its p75 receptor. *Nature* (*London*) **383:** 166–168.
80. Golstein, P., Marquet, D., and Depraetere, V. (1995). Fas bridging cell death and cytotoxicity. *Immunol. Rev.* **146:** 45–56.
81. White, K., Grether, M. E., Abrams, J. M., Young, L., Farrell, R., and Stellar, H. (1994). Genetic control of programmed cell death in *Drosophila. Science* **264:** 677–683.
82. Chen, P., Nordstrom, W., Gish, B., and Abrams, J. M. (1996). grim, a novel cell death gene in *Drosophila. Genes Dev.* **10:** 1773–1782.
83. Rubin, L. L., Philpott, L. K., and Brooks, S. F. (1993). The cell cycle and cell death. *Curr. Biol.* **3:** 391–394.
84. Freeman, R. S., Estus, S., Horigome, K., and Johnson, E. M. (1994). Analysis of cell-cycle related gene expression in postmitotic neurons: Selective induction of cyclin D1 during programmed cell death. *Neuron* **12:** 343–355.
85. Estus, S., Zaks, W. J., Freeman, R. S., Gurda, M., Bravo, R., and Johnson, E. M. (1994). Altered gene expression in neurons during programmed cell death: Identification of c-jun as necessary for neuronal apoptosis. *J. Cell Biol.* **127:** 1717–1727.
86. Ham, J., Babij, C., Whitfield, J., Pfarr, C. M., Lallemand, D., Yaniv, M., and Rubin, L. L. (1995). A c-Jun dominant negative mutant protects sympathetic neurons against programmed cell death. *Neuron* **14:** 927–939.
87. Martin, S. J., and Green, D. R. (1995). Protease activation during apoptosis: death by a thousand cuts. *Cell* (*Cambridge, Mass*) **82:** 349–352.
88. Bortner, C. D., Bortner, C. D., Olderburg, N. B. E., and Cidlowski, J. A. (1995). The role of DNA fragmentation in apoptosis. *Trends Cell Biol.* **5:** 21–26.
89. Wyllie, A. (1998). An endonuclease at last. *Nature* **391:** 20–21.
90. Jacobson, M. D., Burne, J. F., and Raff, M. C. (1994). Programmed cell death and bcl-2 protection in the absence of a nucleus. *EMBO J.* **13:** 1899–1910.
91. Buttke, T. M., and Sandstrom, P. A. (1994). Oxidative stress as a mediator of apoptosis. *Immunol. Today* **15:** 7–10.
92. Kane, D. J., Sarafian, T. A., Hahn, H., Gralla, E. B., Valentine, J. S., Ord, T., and Bredesen, D. E. (1993). Bcl-2 inhibition of neural death: Decreased generation of reactive oxygen species. *Science* **262:** 1274–1277.
93. Ferrari, G., Gagliardini, V., Fernandez, P.-A., Lee, R. K. K., Drexler, H. C. A., Rottello, R. J., Fishman, M. C., and Yuan, J. (1995). *N*-acetylcysteine prevents apoptotic death of neuronal cells. *J. Neurosci.* **15:** 2857–2866.
94. Greenlund, L. J. S., Deckwerth, T. L., and Johnson, E. M. (1995). Superoxide dismutase delays neuronal apoptosis: A role for reactive oxygen species in programmed neuronal death. *Neuron* **14:** 303–315.
95. Jacobson, M. D., and Raff, M. C. (1995). Programmed cell death and bcl-2 protection in very low oxygen. *Nature* (*London*) **374:** 814–816.
96. Deshmukh, M., Vasilakos, J., Deckwerth, T. L., Lampe, P. A., Shivers, B. D., and Johnson, E. M. (1996). Genetic and metabolic status of NGF-deprived sympathetic neurons saved by an inhibitor of ICE family proteases. *J. Cell Biol.* **135:** 1341–1354.
97. Finkbeiner, S., and Greenberg, M. E. (1996). Ca^{2+}-dependent routes to ras: Mechanisms for neuronal survival, differentiation and plasticity. *Neuron* **16:** 233–236.
98. McConkey, D. J., and Orrenius, S. (1994). Signal transduction pathways to apoptosis. *Trends Cell Biol.* **4:** 370–375.
99. Mesner, P. W., Epting, C. L., Hegarty, J. L., and Green, S. H. (1995). A timetable of events during programmed cell death induced by trophic factor withdrawal from neuronal PC12 cells. *J. Neurosci.* **15:** 7357–7366.
100. Ohmichi, M., Decker, S. J., and Saltiel, A. R. (1992). Activation of phosphatidylinositol-3 kinase by nerve growth factor involves direct coupling of the trk proto-oncogene with src homology 2 domains. *Neuron* **9:** 769–777.
101. Borasio, G. D., John, J., Wittinghofer, A., Barde, Y. A., Sendther, M., and Heumann, R. (1989). Ras p21 protein promotes survival and fiber outgrowth of cultured embryonic neurons. *Neuron* **2:** 1087–1096.
102. Henkemeyer, M., Rossi, D. J., Holmyard, D. P., Puri, M. C., Mbamalu, G., Harpal, K., Shih, T. S., Jacks, T., and Pawson, T. (1995). Vascular system defects and neuronal apoptosis in mice lacking ras GTPase-activating protein. *Nature* (*London*) **377:** 695–701.
103. Dudek, H., Datta, S. R., Franke, T. F., Birnbaum, M. J., Yao, R., Cooper, G. M., Segal, R. A., Kaplan, D. R., and Greenberg, M. E. (1997). Regulation of neuronal survival by the serine-threonine protein kinase akt. *Science* **275:** 661–665.
104. Hamburger, V., and Oppenheim, R. W. (1982). Naturally occurring neuronal death in vertebrates. *Neurosci. Commun.* **1:** 39–55.
105. Thompson, C. B. (1995). Apoptosis in the pathogenesis and treatment of disease. *Science* **267:** 1456–1462.
106. Tomei, L. D., and Cope, F. O., eds. (1994). *Apoptosis II: The Molecular Basis of Apoptosis in Disease.* Cold Spring Harbor Lab. Press, Cold Spring Harbor, NY.
107. Roy, N., Mahaderan, M. S., McLean, M., Suttler, G., Yaraghi, Z., Farahani, R., Baird, S., Besner-Johnson, A., Lefebvre, C., Kang, X., Salih, M., Arbry, H., Tamai, K., Guan, X., Ioannon, P., Crawford, T. O., deJong, P. J., Surh, L., Ikeda, J.-E., Korneluk, R. G., and MacKenzie, A. (1995). The gene for neuronal apoptosis inhibitory protein is partially deleted in individuals with spinal muscular atrophy. *Cell* (*Cambridge, Mass.*) **80:** 167–178.
108. Iwahashi, H., Eguchi, Y., Yasuhara, N., Hanafusa, T., Matsuzawa, Y., and Tsujimoto, Y. (1997). Synergistic and anti-apop-

totic activity between bcl-2 and SMN implicated in spinal muscular atrophy. *Nature* **390:** 413.

109. Brannon-Thomas, L., Gates, D. J., Richfield, E. K., O'Brien, T. F., Schweitzer, J. B., and Steindler, D. A. (1995). DNA end labeling (TUNEL) in Huntington's disease and other neuropathological conditions. *Exp. Neurol.* **133:** 265–272.
110. Portera-Cailliau, C., Hedreen, J. C., Price, D. L., and Koliatsos, V. E. (1995). Evidence for apoptotic cell death in Huntington disease and excitotoxic animal models. *J. Neurosci.* **15:** 3775–3787.
111. Smale, G., Nicols, N. R., Brady, D. R., Finch, C. I., and Horton, W. E. (1995). Evidence for apoptotic cell death in Alzheimer's disease. *Exp. Neurol.* **133:** 225–230.
112. Buscigilo, J., and Yankner, B. A. (1995). Apoptosis and increased generation of reactive oxygen species in Down's syndrome neurons *in vitro*. *Nature* **378:** 776–779.
113. Friedlander, R. M., Brown, R. H., Gagliardini, V., Wang, J., and Yuan, J. (1997). Inhibition of ICE slows ALS in mice. *Nature* **388:** 31.
114. Kosic, V., Jackson-Lewis, V., De Bilbao, F., Dubois-Dauphin, M., and Prezdborski, S. (1997). Bcl-2 prolongs life in a transgenic mouse model of familial ALS. *Science* **277:** 559–562.
115. Davidson, F. F., and Stellar, H. (1998). Blocking apoptosis prevents blindness in *Drosophila* retinal degeneration mutants. *Nature* **391:** 587–596.

General

Burek, M., and Oppenheim, R. W. (1997). Programmed cell death in the developing nervous system. *Brain Pathology* **6:** 427–446.

Coggeshall, R. E. (1992). A consideration of neuronal counting methods. *Trends Neurosci.* **15:** 9–13.

Koliatsos, V., and Ratan, R. (1998). *Cell Death in Diseases of the Nervous System.* Humana Press, Totowa, NJ.

Schwartz, L. M., Smith, S. W., Jones, M. E. E., and Osborne, B. A. (1993). Do all programmed cell deaths occur via apoptosis? *Proc. Natl. Acad. Sci. U.S.A.* **90:** 980–984.

CHAPTER

21

Neurotrophic Factors

James E. Johnson

In the vertebrate nervous system, a remarkably large number of neurons are normally lost during a period of developmentally programmed cell death (see Chapter 20). This process begins in virtually all neurons either during or following their final exit from mitosis. Mechanisms that suppress developmental cell death are required for the survival of most nerve cells. Survival factors prevent the completion of the default suicide program in selected neurons—about 50% of each neuron class. In vertebrates, the developmental period in which neurons undergo selection for survival or die coincides with the formation of synaptic connections with target tissues. In general, both the number and the size of the surviving neurons are proportional to the size of the target that they innervate. Neurons appear to compete for a limited supply of or access to survival factors provided by target tissues. The notion that the survival of developing neurons is dependent on competition for a limited supply of survival molecules provided by their targets has emerged as the **neurotrophic** (or *nerve feeding*) **theory.**[1] Neuron number is usually determined by birth (or hatching) in most species but the nervous system undergoes significant growth afterward to match increases in body size. Dramatic changes occur in the size of the cell body and the dendritic and axonal arbors. Adaptations in cell size and geometry are influenced by neurotrophic interactions between neurons and with their targets[1] as well as by neural activity.

If each of the many neuronal target tissues produced a unique survival factor to regulate the size and pattern of its innervation, then a very large number of molecules would be required to control these events in the central and peripheral nervous systems. Instead, a relatively limited number of proteins are used to regulate cell death for neurons in many different regions. These **neurotrophic factors** have evolved within several different gene families.[2–5] They are derived not only from target tissues but also from neighboring cells or from the neuron itself. Like neurotransmitters, neurotrophic factors act over relatively short distances as chemical messengers between cells and can cause rapid transient changes in synaptic activity as well as longer lasting changes in neurons. The period during development when neurons require trophic factor support varies. Some neurons normally switch their trophic dependencies from one factor to another during development.[6] The deletion of these factors or their receptors (as in transgenic mice with null mutations) results in the death of all dependent neurons.[7,8] The survival of most neurons appears to depend not on a single survival molecule but on multiple factors from the same related family or from multiple families that can be required sequentially or simultaneously.[7,9] In addition, some neurotrophic factors may serve as a reserve force of potential repair molecules that are readily available for a rapid response to injury in the mature nervous system.[10]

All neurotrophic factors that prevent neuronal death appear to have other important biological activities, including effects on development, maintenance, function, and plasticity of the nervous system (see Tables 21.1 and 21.2). Frequently, different populations of neurons respond to the same factor in distinct ways, and the same neuron may respond differently to the same factor at different developmental stages. Variations in neuronal responses to the same factor appear to depend not only on modifications of receptors but also on potential differences in downstream signaling pathways. In general, members of a particular neurotrophic factor family bind to one or more members of a related family of transmembrane receptors.[11,12] Neurotrophic

TABLE 21.1 The Neurotrophin Family and Its Receptors

Factor	Receptor: Full-length kinase-containing isoforms[a]	Receptor: Nonkinase forms[b]	Example of responsive neurons[c]
NGF	trkA ($trkA_{EI}$)	p75[d]	Cholinergic forebrain neurons Sympathetic ganglia DRG nociceptive
BDNF	trkB	$p75^{LNTR}$ $trkB_{T1}$ $trkB_{T2}$	Many CNS populations Vestibular ganglia Nodose ganglia DRG mechanoreceptors
NT-3	trkC ($trkC_{TK+14}$) ($trkC_{TK+25}$ $TrkC_{TK+39}$) trkB and trkA nonpreferred	$p75^{LNTR}$ $trkC_{TK-158}$ $trkC_{TK-143}$ $trkC_{TK-113}$ $trkC_{TK-108}$	Many CNS populations Choclear ganglia DRG proprioceptive
NT-4[e]	trkB	p75 $trkB_{T1}$ $trkB_{T2}$	Many CNS populations Nodose ganglia Petrosal ganglia
NT-6[f]	trkA	p75	

[a] $trkA_{EI}$ (extracellular 6-amino-acid insert) is expressed primarily in neurons, whereas trkA without the insert is expressed primarily on nonneuronal cells. Avian trkB receptors include five catalytic isoforms and four catalytic receptors with inserts or deletions. $trkC_{TK+}$ represent isoforms with kinase inserts of amino acid length indicated.

[b] Mammalian trkB noncatalytic receptors include two kinase-deleted isoforms (T1 is expressed at equivalent levels as catalytic trkB without tyrosine kinase but with 23 cytoplasmic amino acids, whereas T2 has only 21 cytoplasmic amino acids). Avian trkB isoforms include 5 kinase-deleted isoforms. $trkC_{TK-}$ represent isoforms with kinase deletions of amino acid length indicated.

[c] Only a few examples from a long list of responsive neurons. trkB and trkC (along with BDNF and NT-3) are more widespread than trkA or NGF in CNS.

[d] $p75^{LNTR}$ may associate with trkA to yield high-affinity binding. It can cause sphingomyelin hydrolysis, of Trk receptors in neurons and within internalization and retrograde transport of BDNF and NT-4.

[e] NT-4 is also called NT-4/5: cloned from frog and named NT-4 and cloned from mammals and named NT-5. The most variable neurotrophin family member.

[f] NT-6 found only in teleost fish. Receptor and biological properties are not fully characterized.

factor receptors are similar to receptors for growth factors present in other tissues. When the receptors bind their cognate neurotrophic factor, the intracellular messengers that are generated in turn activate a cascade of proto-oncogene signals involved in regulating cell proliferation in nonneuronal cells. The distinctive properties of neurotrophic factors in regulating neuronal cell death, rather than cell proliferation, reflect the intrinsic properties of differentiating neurons.

In this chapter, we will focus on the properties and functions of the best characterized family of neurotrophic factors, the neurotrophins, and their receptors. We will also provide brief summaries of several other families of neurotrophic factors.

THE NEUROTROPHIN FAMILY

Nerve Growth Factor Is the Prototype Target-Derived Neuronal Survival Factor

The neurotrophic theory of target-mediated neuronal survival was greatly strengthened by the fortuitous discovery and purification of **nerve growth factor** (NGF) by Rita Levi-Montalcini, Stan Cohen, and Vicktor Hamburger. The characterization of the functional role of NGF has become the model for defining target-derived neurotrophic factors. Analysis of the function(s) of a putative neurotrophic factor involves several steps. In general, the biological activities and target cell specificity are first investigated *in vitro* to determine whether the factor acts directly on the candidate target cell or whether its effects are mediated indirectly through other cell types. Analysis of the developmental time course of factor and receptor expression is needed to determine whether both are present in the correct time and place in the embryo for the factor to play a functional role in regulating responsive cells. Treatment of developing embryos with exogenous factor enables the investigator to determine whether endogenous levels are in limited supply. Finally, methods that deprive the developing embryo of endogenous factor or inhibit receptor function allow the investigator to determine whether the factor is essential for a particular developmental event. These methods include treatment with antibodies that block activity, treatment with receptor antagonists that block binding, and the generation of transgenic mice with null mutations of factors or their receptors.

In the case of NGF, sympathetic and sensory ganglia of either developing chicks or rodents treated with NGF *in vitro* produce a dense halo of axonal outgrowth[13] (Fig. 21.1).[14] In fact, this neurite outgrowth assay—not a survival assay—was used to purify NGF. NGF is required for the survival of dissociated sympathetic neurons when they are grown in the absence of nonneuronal cells, and therefore NGF acts directly on these neurons. Subpopulations of sensory neurons in the dorsal root ganglia are also dependent on NGF. When developing chick embryos are treated with NGF, sympathetic and sensory ganglia are significantly enlarged, and axon growth increases dramatically.[13] The ganglia contain many more neurons than normal because naturally occurring cell death has been prevented.[15] In addition, neuron cell bodies are larger, and rodent sympathetic neurons have more complex dendritic arbors.[1] These studies indicate that the supply of endogenous factor is rate limiting for the survival and growth of dependent populations. The most convincing evidence that NGF is required for neuron survival has been gained from NGF-deprivation experiments. When chick embryos are treated with NGF-blocking antisera, they lose nearly all their sympathetic neurons.[16] More recently, the null mutation of NGF or its catalytic receptor in transgenic mice has confirmed that sympathetic and a number of sensory neurons require NGF for survival (Fig. 21.2).[17,18]

If NGF is required for survival, then where and when is it made in the developing embryo? Because the amount of NGF produced by tissues *in vivo* is very low (about 1 ng / g tissue), a sensitive two-site immunoassay and molecular techniques for mRNA localization are required to quantify and localize NGF synthesis.

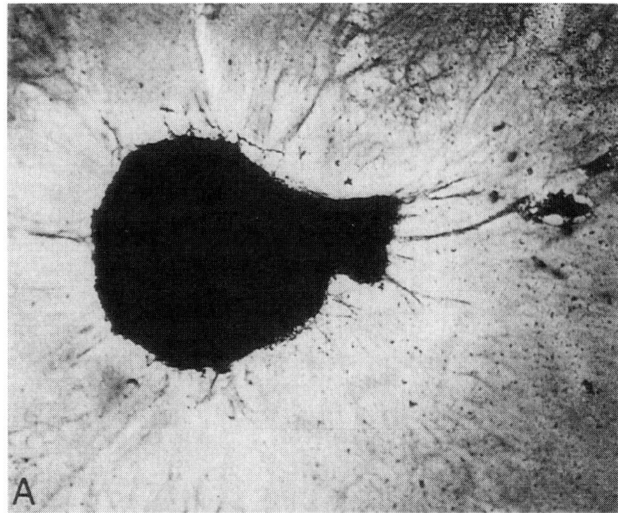

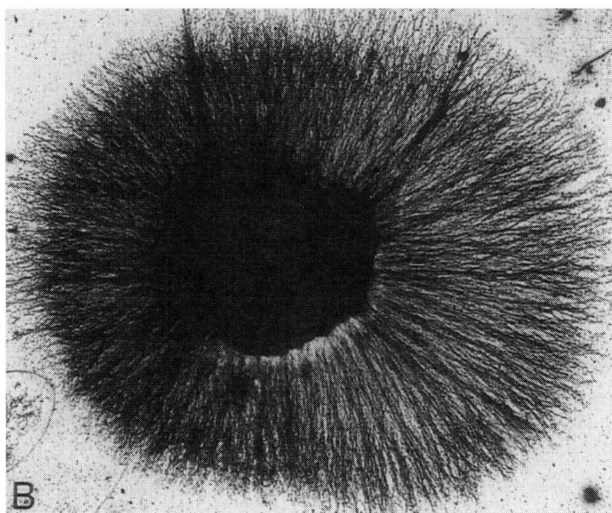

FIGURE 21.1 Response of isolated chick dorsal root ganglia to NGF treatment *in vitro*. Explanted ganglia or dissociated neurons are routinely used as a bioassay for neurotrophic activity. This ganglion explant assay was used to purify NGF. (A) control ganglion 24 h in culture without NGF and (B) particular ganglion 24 h after NGF treatment. Treatment with NGF causes the formation of a "halo" of axonal growth from sensory neurons in the ganglion (100 ng ml^{-1}). Why the factor was named is obvious. Reprinted with permission from Levi-Montalcini.[14] Copyright 1964 American Association for the Advancement of Science.

NGF is made in the targets of dependent cells at the time of innervation, consistent with its role as a target-derived survival factor. Further, the level of NGF synthesis is correlated with the density of target innervation. Finally, when the catalytic receptor for NGF, trkA, was identified, receptors were expressed in NGF-responsive neurons at the times and places appropriate for promoting neuron survival. These data strongly support the neurotrophic hypothesis that the quantity of factor made by target cells is rate limiting for the

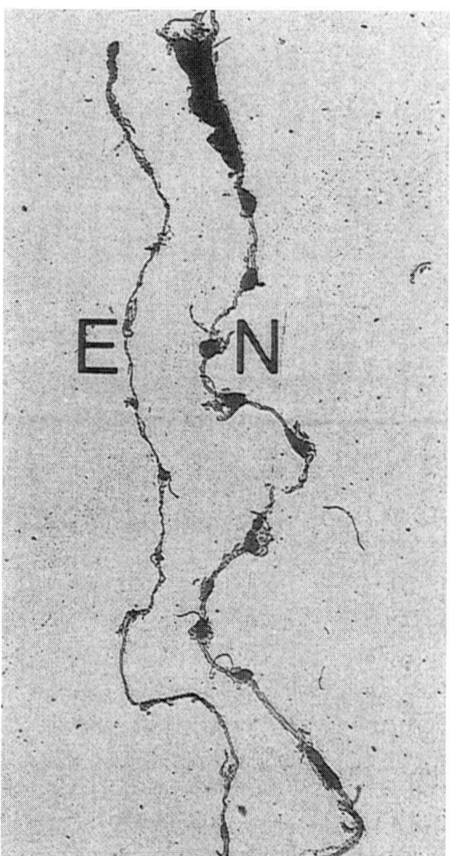

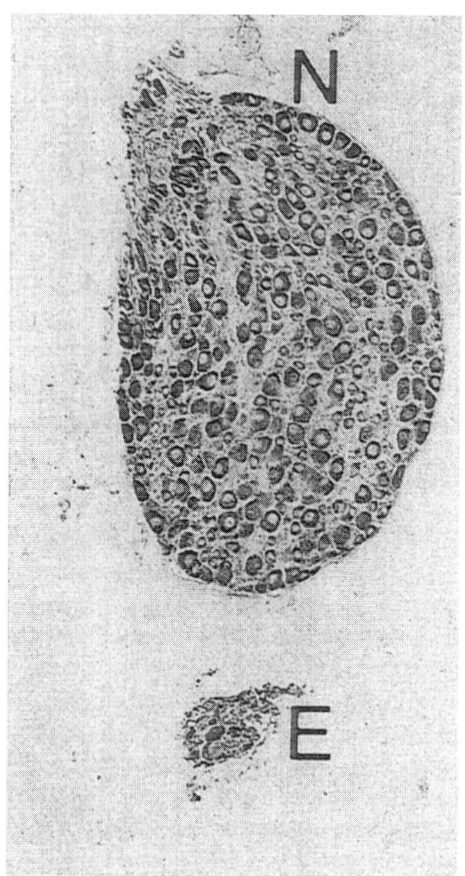

FIGURE 21.2 Immunosympathectomy. Antibodies that selectively block NGF activity were administered to newborn mice to deprive the developing animals of endogenous factor. Sympathetic ganglia were examined several weeks after the treatment (N, normal ganglia; E, ganglia deprived of NGF for 3–5 days). Note the almost complete disappearance of the sympathetic chain ganglia (left) and the loss of neurons in individual ganglia (right).

survival of the afferent population and determines the density of target innervation. The localization of NGF synthesis in sympathetic targets and the loss of these neurons with NGF deprivation firmly establish NGF as a prototype target-derived neurotrophic factor required for the survival of sympathetic neurons and a subset of sensory neurons.

The synthesis and release of NGF are controlled. Transcription of NGF mRNA is regulated during development and can be altered in mature animals by a number of environmental stimuli, including injury, hormone levels, and changes in neural activity.[5,19,20] NGF appears to be secreted from the cells that synthesize it by both constitutive and regulated release pathways.[21] Regulated secretion from neurons is activity-dependent and requires mobilization of intracellular Ca^{2+} stores.

NGF-responsive neurons possess both high-affinity ($K_D = 10^{-11}$) and low-affinity ($K_D = 10^{-9}$) NGF-binding sites. Receptor-bound NGF is internalized within membrane-bound vesicles and retrogradely transported to the neuronal cell body, where it is eventually degraded.[22] Both the receptor-binding event at the plasma membrane and retrograde axonal transport are required to prevent cell death. It is not clear, however, whether the retrograde transport of the internalized factor–receptor complex or of a second-messenger signaling molecule is required for survival (Fig. 21.3). One prediction of the neurotrophic hypothesis is that access to NGF in only the distant target region is adequate to support the survival of the cell body. In a multicompartment culture system developed to determine the long- and short-range effects of NGF treatment,[23] NGF can be applied only to axon terminals in three compartment chambers. Neuron cell bodies in the central chamber survived, indicating that NGF available only to axons can generate the signaling required for cell body survival. Axon branches were rapidly and selectively lost in chambers where NGF was withdrawn but were maintained and grew in chambers where NGF was added. Thus, NGF has impressive local effects on the maintenance and sprouting of axons.

NGF Is One Member of a Family of Structurally Related Factors

Only a few populations of neurons—including sympathetic and some sensory neurons—are NGF dependent. While some neurons in the basal forebrain are NGF responsive, no CNS neurons have been shown yet to require NGF for survival. Therefore, other survival factors must regulate neuron survival elsewhere in the nervous system. Extracts made from a number of tissues, as well as media containing proteins secreted by a variety of cultured cells, support the survival of many classes of neurons that are not NGF responsive. The existence of these non-NGF neurotrophic activities led to efforts to purify other survival factors during the 1960s, 1970s, and 1980s. Since neurotrophic factors are made in extremely low quantities, isolation of NGF-related molecules using conventional protein purification methods was difficult.

A significant breakthrough occurred with the purification of a second NGF-related neurotrophic factor in 1982.[24] Unlike NGF, which was purified several hundred-fold from an unusually rich source unrelated to the nervous system, **brain-derived neurotrophic factor** (BDNF) was purified several million-fold from adult pig brains. Each kilogram of starting material yielded only a microgram of factor. The molecular cloning and expression of BDNF opened the door for an exciting and accelerated period of research on NGF-related factors.[25] When the structures of BDNF and NGF were compared, they were found to be homodimers of small, very basic peptides with an amino acid homology of approximately 50%. Using PCR primers prepared from homologous domains to search for other related proteins, investigators rapidly identified additional neurotrophin family members.[4,5] Named NT-3 to NT-6 (neurotrophins 3 to 6), these additional factors were cloned and sequenced without prior protein purification.

Each neurotrophin family member is synthesized as an approximately 250-amino-acid precursor that is processed into roughly 120-amino-acid protomers. Homologous regions of the several family members are concentrated in six hydrophobic domains containing cysteine residues. The linkage formed by these regions creates a "cysteine knot" that ties the twin protomers together. The secreted dimer appears as a symmetrical twin with variable regions containing basic amino acid residues exposed on the surface (Fig. 21.4).[26] Because all family members share this core structure, they are remarkably similar, with three-dimensional symmetry around two axes (Fig. 21.4). The exposed regions that vary between family members are responsible for receptor-binding specificity.[27]

Summary

NGF is the prototype target-derived neurotrophic factor. Treatment of developing embryos with NGF

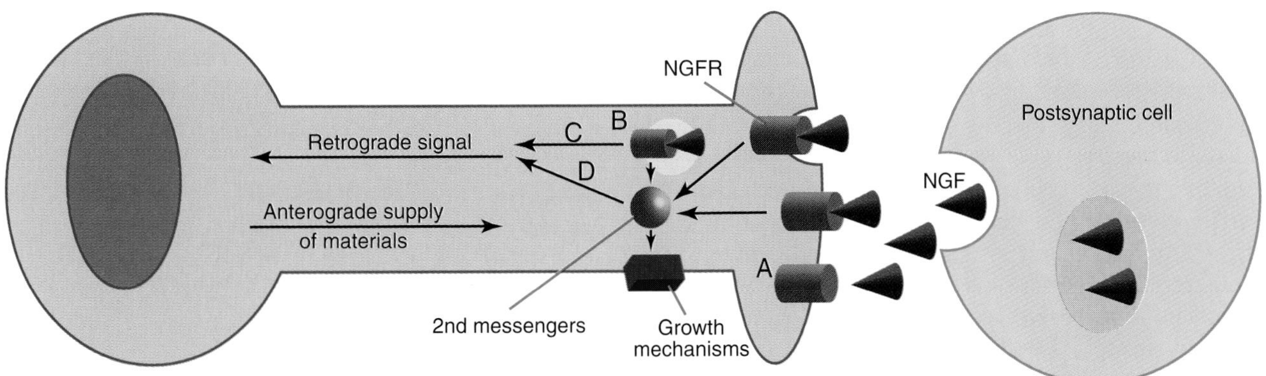

FIGURE 21.3 Models of NGF signaling and retrograde axonal transport. NGF is secreted by target postsynaptic cells. Once bound, the ligand–receptor complex is internalized in a vesicle inside the axon terminal. Signaling events after NGF is bound may include (A) rapid local signal transduction with or without receptor internalization, (B and C) receptor-mediated signaling from the internalized receptor–ligand complex in the axon terminal and during retrograde axonal transport, (D) the transport of second-messenger signals arising from the cascade of receptor transduction at the terminal. In addition to retrograde signaling, NGF can cause local changes in the rate and direction of axon growth.

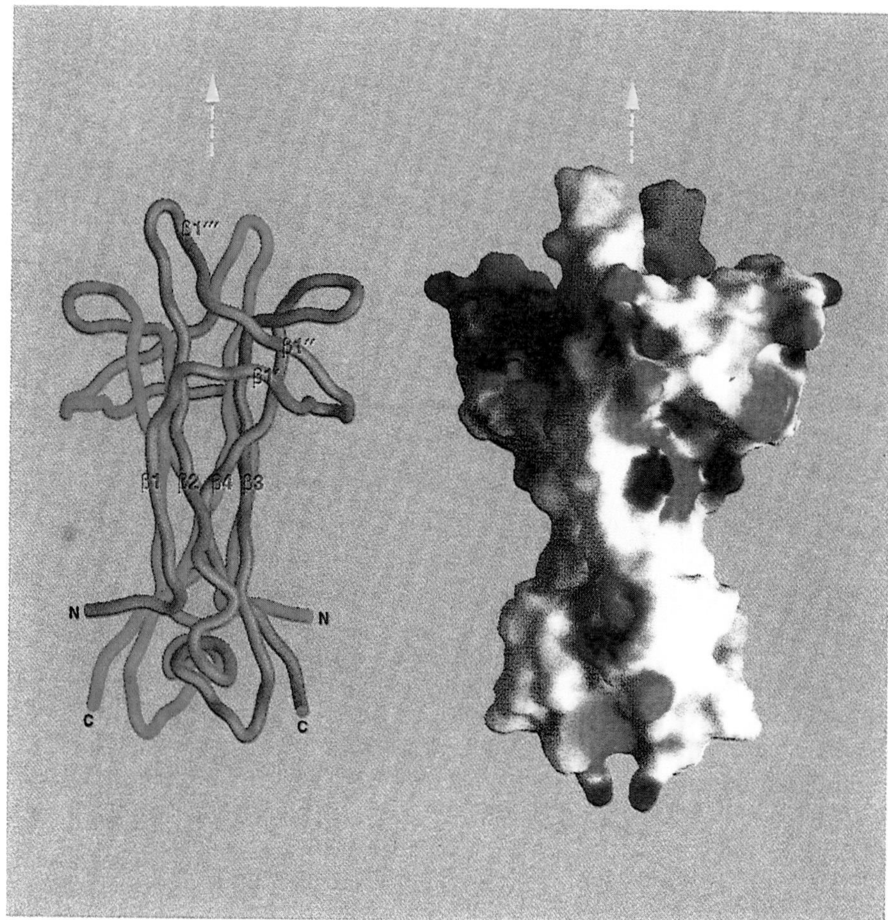

FIGURE 21.4 A three-dimensional model of the NGF homodimer (left) and an electrostatic surface model (right). Note the parallel arrangement of the subunits around a central axis (yellow arrows). Blue indicates a surface region with a positive electrostatic potential while red is negative and white more neutral. This symmetrical form allows the secreted ligand to bind and unite two receptor molecules in the plasma membrane of a responsive cell. From McDonald and Murray-Rust.[26] (Right) A surface electrostatic potential model for NGF.

dramatically alters the development of sympathetic and some sensory neurons by preventing normal cell death, increasing cell size and dendritic and axonal growth *in vitro*. The timing and distribution of the expression of NGF and its receptor match the developmental requirements for a target-derived neurotrophic factor. The physiological role of NGF in development is demonstrated by immunosympathectomy and transgenic experiments in which responsive neurons are lost in the absence of NGF or its receptor. The purification, molecular cloning, and expression of BDNF opened a floodgate of research on an NGF-related family of neurotrophic factors called neurotrophins. Each family member is a homodimer with a conserved region containing a cysteine knot in the core of the molecule. The secreted factor is a symmetrical twin with duplicate sites used for receptor binding.

NEUROTROPHIN RECEPTORS AND SIGNALING

There Are Two Classes of Neurotrophin Receptors

Binding studies suggested that NGF-responsive cells possessed two different receptors. NGF binds to a relatively small number of very high-affinity binding sites and a second set of about 10-fold more abundant, but lower affinity, binding sites at higher concentrations.[28] Cross-linking and purification studies suggested that the two sites had molecular weights of approximately 140 and 75 kDa, respectively. The **75-kDa protein** (p75) was purified and cloned first. It is a transmembrane glycoprotein with extracellular cysteine repeat motifs that share structural homology with the tumor necrosis factor receptor family.[29,30] The cytoplasmic domain of p75 lacks the kinase domain present in most growth factors for intracellular signal transduction, but as described below it can signal through ceramide pathways[12] (Fig. 21.5). When expressed in fibroblasts, this receptor has low-affinity (fast on and off) NGF-binding properties and therefore has also been called the **low-affinity NGF receptor** (LNGFR). Since other neurotrophin family members can also bind p75, it is more appropriately named the **low-affinity neurotrophin receptor** ($p75^{LNTR}$).

A major breakthrough in characterization of the NGF receptors came with the fortuitous discovery and cloning of an oncogene identified in a human colon cancer.[31,32] The sequence of this 140-kDa transmembrane protein contained a cytoplasmic kinase common to many growth factor receptors (Fig. 21.5). Because it did not have a known ligand, it was an "orphan" tyrosine kinase receptor. The corresponding proto-oncogene was named **trk** (pronounced "track"—for **tyrosine kinase-containing receptor**).[11] Surprisingly, trk expression was localized to the nervous system, in particular to NGF-responsive neurons. Expression of trk in a mouse fibroblast cell line or in frog oocytes conferred specific NGF binding and NGF-induced phosphorylation. NGF-signaling properties have been examined most extensively in the NGF-responsive pheochromocytoma (PC12) cell line, derived from adrenal medullary cells. Mutant PC12 cell lines that are unresponsive to NGF contain many $p75^{LNTR}$ receptors but lack trk. Transfection of these mutant cells with trk restores their biological responses to NGF. Combined with the localization of trk on NGF-responsive neurons, these studies indicated that trk alone is sufficient to bind NGF and mediate its biological activity.[33] The most convincing evidence for the necessity of trk comes from the analysis of transgenic mice lacking functional trk receptors.[34] As expected, these mice have a phenotype that is almost identical to that of transgenic animals that have a null mutation for NGF.

Low-stringency screening of cDNA libraries with trk proto-oncogene probes led to the discovery of other related neurotrophin receptors. The first 140-kDa re-

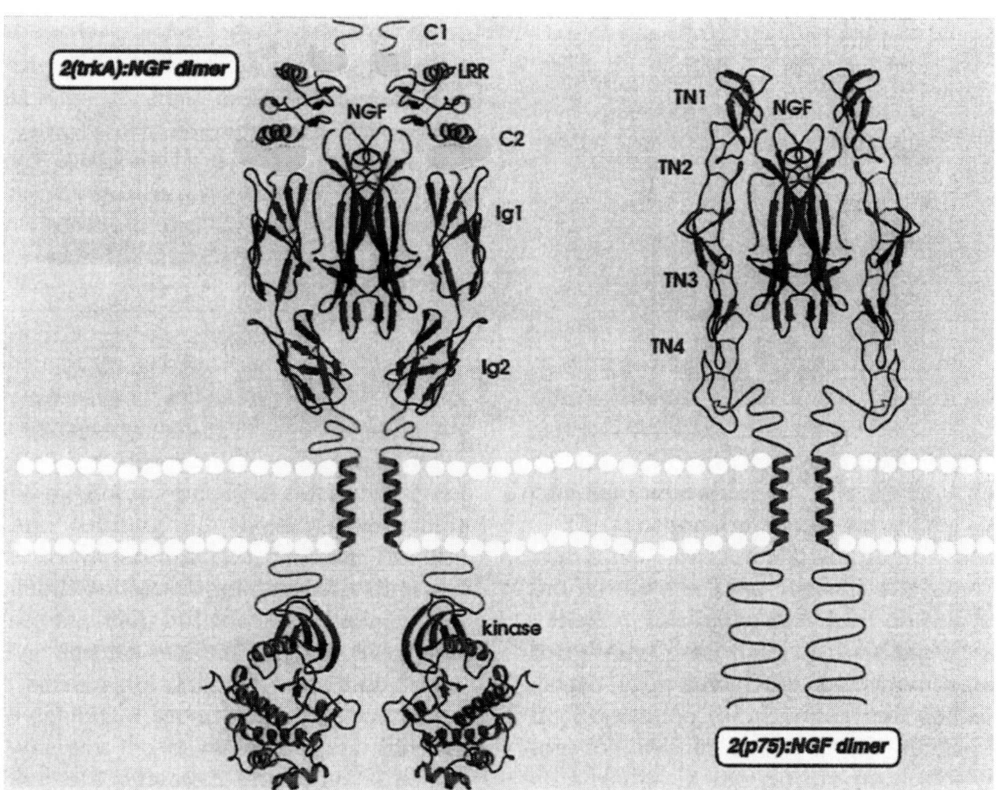

FIGURE 21.5 Models of the catalytic (full-length) trkA receptor for NGF and $p75^{LNTR}$. Note the absence of a cytosolic kinase domain in p75 and the ability of one ligand (NGF) to bring together two receptor molecules to initiate signaling. From McDonald and Rust.[26]

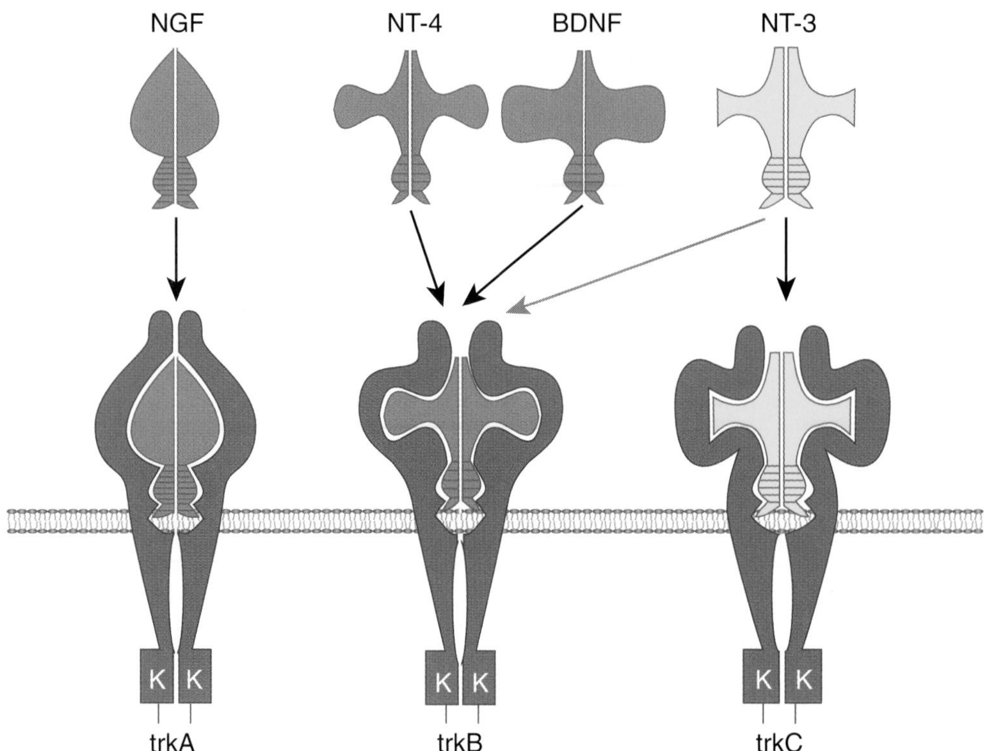

FIGURE 21.6 The ligand binding preferences of neurotrophins for each member of the trk receptor family. Not shown are the truncated (kinase deleted) isoforms of trkB and trkC. Other isoforms containing inserts and deletions also exist, providing a wide variety of receptors (see Table 21.1).

ceptor identified that binds NGF was called **trkA.** Two additional 145-kDa members of a related protein family are named **trkB** and **trkC.** The trkB receptor is specifically activated by low concentrations of BDNF or NT-4/5 and to a lesser extent by higher concentrations of NT-3. NT-3 activates the trkC receptor most effectively (Fig. 21.6). All trk receptors contain three leucine-rich motifs, two cysteine clusters, and two immunoglobulin-like motifs in the extracellular region, and a transmembrane domain and a tyrosine kinase domain in the cytosolic region. The unusual combination of extracellular motifs makes up the ligand-binding region and places this family in a novel class of tyrosine kinase receptors. The region of highest sequence homology among family members and other growth factor receptors is in the kinase domain.

Receptor isoforms resulting from splice variants of trk mRNA transcripts exist for each family member (Table 21.1). Some isoforms contain peptide inserts in the extracellular or cytoplasmic domain. In the case of trkA, the receptor containing an extracellular insert is found primarily in neurons. $trkC_{TK+}$ contains inserts in the cytoplasmic kinase region. Receptor inserts can alter receptor function.[35–37] Other trk isoforms contain specific deletions, including several $trkB_{TK-}$ and $trkC_{TK-}$ receptors in which the entire kinase domain is deleted.[38] Both full-length and kinase-deleted or **truncated receptors** are widely expressed on neurons throughout the nervous system. Truncated receptors, which are also expressed on glial cells, can bind and internalize their cognate ligand, but they do not initiate the phosphorylation events required for signal transduction. As a result, the distribution and membrane concentration of truncated receptors could potentially modulate neurotrophin activity by restricting the availability of factors to full-length receptors.[39]

Although trk receptors account for most of the biological responses of neurons to neurotrophins, $p75^{LNTR}$ can facilitate trk ligand binding and neurotrophin responses, and it can initiate intracellular signaling independent of trks.[12,30] Antibodies that block NGF binding to $p75^{LTNR}$ but not to trkA reduce high-affinity NGF-binding sites.[33,40] $p75^{LNTR}$ enhances trkA receptor phosphorylation. Sensory neurons from transgenic mice that lack $p75^{LNTR}$ require higher NGF concentrations for survival than normal.[41] Several mechanisms have been proposed to account for the accessory role of p75. The fast-on and fast-off kinetics of $p75^{LNTR}$ could increase the local concentration of NGF available to trkA receptors. Alternatively $p75^{LNTR}$ could form a transient heterodimer with trkA and thereby "hand off" NGF.[42] In addition to enhancing NGF binding to and activation of trkA, $p75^{LNTR}$ initiates NGF responses in cells that lack trkA. NGF binding to $p75^{LNTR}$ increases sphingomyelinase activity, producing the lipid second-messenger molecule **ceramide,**[43] and causes activation and translocation of the transcription factor **nuclear factor** $\boldsymbol{\kappa\beta}$ (NF$\kappa\beta$). $p75^{LNTR}$ receptors are structurally related to members of the **tumor necrosis factor receptor family** (TNFR),[30] many of which regulate the onset of cell death programs in the immune system. Under certain conditions, $p75^{LNTR}$ seems to mimic the killer function of the TNFR in the immune system. In cells that express $p75^{LNTR}$ but not trkA, NGF can induce cell death via $p75^{LNTR}$.[44] Although $p75^{LNTR}$ binds all neurotrophins, effects have been observed after NGF binding.

Many neurons have both high- and low-affinity binding sites for neurotrophins. Biological responses are associated with high-affinity binding and rapid phosphorylation signaling events. All neurotrophins bind $p75^{LNTR}$ or the low-affinity neurotrophin receptor. $p75^{LNTR}$ lacks a cytoplasmic kinase domain but can facilitate ligand binding to and enhance signaling through trkA and independently initiate signaling. There are three tyrosine receptor kinase or trk family members, trkA, trkB, and trkC. Each binds one or more members of the neurotrophin factor family. Splice variants of trks result in isoforms that include truncated receptors lacking signaling capabilities. These truncated receptors may modulate neurotrophin activity by limiting access of full-length receptors to factors during development.

The trk Receptors Are Similar to Other Growth Factor Receptors

A cellular response to a neurotrophin requires expression of the appropriate member of the trk receptor family. Once activated, the receptor initiates a cascade of intracellular signals in the cytoplasm that continues into the nucleus.[45,46] Receptor signal transduction involves multiple signaling pathways. Some pathways show very rapid and transient changes, whereas others continue as a cascade of events that produce slower and longer lasting cellular responses.[47,48] The signaling machinery of the catalytic domain of the trk receptors is similar to that employed by most growth factor receptors.[10,49] The molecular components for these pathways are so well conserved that many of the signaling proteins are interchangeable among flies, worms, and various vertebrate species. An important downstream effector of trk signal transduction is the proto-oncogene p21ras. Because ras is activated not only by trks but also by virtually all other growth factor, it is surprising that neurotrophin receptors more frequently promote cell survival, differentiation, maturation, and functional maintenance than rapid cell division. The unique biological responses to trk signal transduction appear to be related to the restricted expression of these receptors and neuron-specific intracellular effectors.

Neurotrophin binding to trk receptors at the cell surface causes the formation of trk dimers and activation of their tyrosine kinase activity. The ligand-mediated aggregation of the receptors allows them to phosphorylate one another on intracellular domains. The generation of phosphotyrosine residues in turn catalyzes the formation of large signaling complexes through the recruitment of cytosolic and membrane-associated proteins[47] (Fig. 21.7). Two phosphotyrosine residues, required for the enzymatic activity of the kinase, are generated within the catalytic core of the trk receptor. Three additional tyrosine residues located outside the kinase domain are phosphorylated, and each associates with specific signaling proteins. Three of the proteins that bind to the phosphotyrosines have been identified as the launching sites of the primary pathways for trk signal transduction.[45] All three proteins contain a structural motif, the **src homology domain 2** (SH2), which specifically recognizes the phosphotyrosine residue and flanking sequences. They are:

1. Phospholipase C (PLC-γ). Upon phosphorylation, PLC-γ catalyzes the hydrolysis of membrane phosphatidylinositol to generate two second-messenger molecules, diacylglycerol (DAG) and inositol triphosphate (IP_3). DAG activates protein kinase C, whereas IP_3 is a potent mobilizer of intracellular calcium. PLC-γ activity causes changes in intracellular calcium, pH, cytoskeletal responses, and transcriptional changes following treatment with NGF.
2. Phosphatidylinositol-3 kinase (PI-3K). When activated, PI-3K catalyzes the production of phosphoinositides, which bind to and activate a protein kinase, akt, leading to the activation of pathways necessary for growth-factor-mediated survival.[50]
3. The adapter protein Shc (SH-2 containing protein). The adapter protein Shc binds to a trk phosphotyrosine residue near the membrane and is then itself tyrosine phosphorylated by trk. Shc acts as an intermediate linking trk to a protein complex that includes ras and proteins that regulate the activation state of ras. This complex contains a second adapter protein, Grb2, the nucleotide exchange factor mSOS1 (mammalian son of sevenless), and p120 GAP (GTPase-activating protein). Association of this complex with trk causes the conversion of ras to an active conformation,

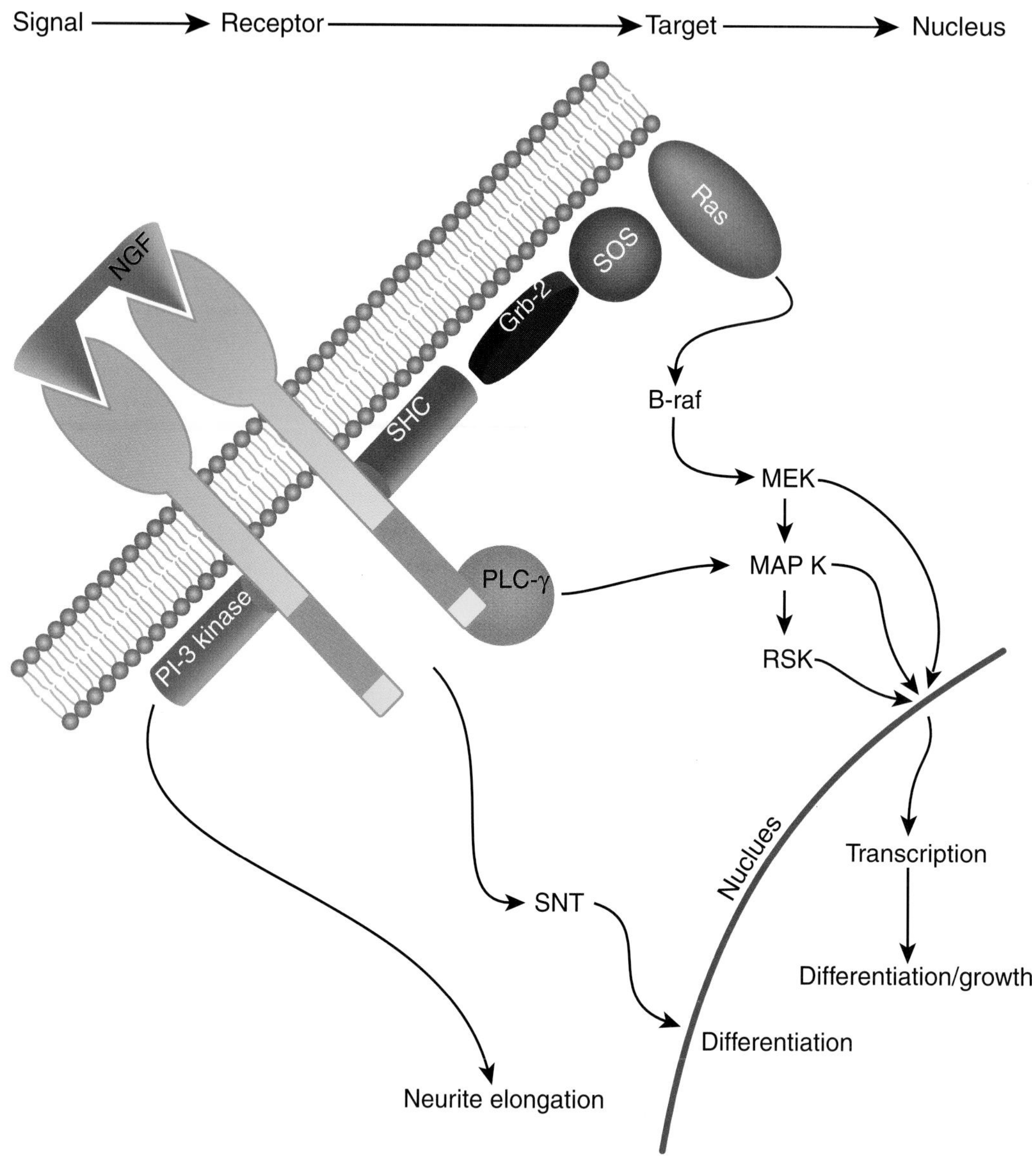

FIGURE 21.7 trk signaling pathways. NGF binds to two trk molecules, causing the formation of a homodimer, which in turn permits each trk molecule to phosphorylate tyrosine residues on its partner. Phosphorylation of specific tyrosine residues creates binding sites for PI-3, PLC-γ, and Shc, recruitment of these proteins into a complex, and initiation of a signaling cascade.

allowing transmission of signals to other downstream pathways.

The most prominent ras-dependent signaling pathway is the **MAP kinase cascade.** This pathway is composed of serine/threonine kinases that are serially phosphorylated and activated. The initial member of this cascade is raf, which directly binds to the active form of p21ras and becomes enzymatically activated. ras phosphorylates and activates MEK, which in turn phosphorylates the MAP kinases (ERK1 and ERK2), whose direct substrates include the protein kinase p90rsk. The MAP kinases phosphorylate a number of cytoplasmic and nuclear effectors. Importantly, activation of the MAP kinases and rsk causes their translocation to the nucleus. In the nucleus, they phosphorylate a number of transcription factors, including the immediate-early genes c-*fos* and c-*jun*, as well as delayed response genes like CREB (cAMP-response element-binding protein). These transcription factors cause rapid and long-lasting changes in gene expression.

The biological function of each of the three principal trk signal transduction pathways has been tested in

PC12-derived cell lines expressing targeted mutations of their individual tyrosine-binding sites.[46] Because point mutations of the tyrosine residues comprising the binding sites for Shc, PI-3K, or PLC-γ have only minor effects on trk signal transduction, redundancy must exist between the pathway and is probably mediated through overlapping cascades. One paradox in understanding neurotrophin and growth factor signaling is that although many growth factor receptors employ ras, the ultimate downstream effects of the different growth factors can be very different. For instance, the NGF-mediated trk activation of ras in PC12 cells stops cell division and induces neuronal differentiation and neurite outgrowth. Treatment with EGF activates the same ras pathway but causes a dramatic increase in cell proliferation. What distinguishes the actions of these two factors is that the duration of ras activity is different. NGF activation of ras continues much longer compared to its rapid and transient activity after EGF treatment. These results suggest that the duration of ras activation is a critical determinant of transcriptional activity and biological responses.[46–48] The requirement for ras-dependent pathways for biological responses varies among neuron types. DRG sensory neurons require ras activation for some neurotrophin responses but sympathetic neurons do not.

Trk signaling pathways also employ intracellular messengers that are expressed only in neurons. SNT (*suc*-associated neurotrophic factor-induced tyrosine-phosphorylated target) is phosphorylated and activated by a ras-independent pathway in PC12 cells and neurons where NGF induces neurite outgrowth, but not in nonneuronal cells where NGF stimulates proliferation.[47] SNT association with trk is dependent on binding to a 3-amino-acid motif (KFG) in the juxtamembrane region. This motif is highly conserved among full-length trk family members and is required for the NGF-induced differentiation of PC-12 cells but not for their survival.

Summary

Many neurons have both high- and low-affinity binding sites for neurotrophins. Biological responses are associated with high-affinity binding and rapid phosphorylation signaling events. All neurotrophins bind p75^{LNTR} or the low-affinity neurotrophin receptor. p75^{LNTR} lacks a cytoplasmic kinase domain but can facilitate ligand binding to and enhance signaling through trkA and independently initiate signaling. There are three tyrosine receptor kinase or trk family members, trkA, trkB, and trkC.

Signaling pathways used by trk family members are shared with those activated by most growth factors. Neurotrophin binding to trk causes receptor dimerization and phosphorylation of cytoplasmic tyrosine residues. The phosphotyrosines recruit cytosolic and include membrane-associated proteins PLC-γ, PI-3K, and the adapter protein, Shc, to the receptor.

THE DEVELOPMENTAL ROLES OF NEUROTROPHINS IN THE PERIPHERAL NERVOUS SYSTEM

Neurotrophins Can Regulate the Fate of Neuronal Precursors

Members of both the neurotrophin and trk receptor families are expressed in the developing nervous system long before the period of normal cell death. Expression of mRNA for trkB and trkC along with their preferred ligands, BDNF and NT-3, is generally earlier and more widespread than the expression of trkA and its preferred ligand, NGF. These factors may therefore be involved in the earliest stages of nervous system development. BDNF increases the commitment of neural crest cells to a sensory neuron lineage *in vitro*. Young sensory neurons not only express trkB and trkC receptors but also secrete BDNF before their axons approach synaptic targets. Migrating neural crest cells express trkC.[51] Treatment with NT-3 stimulates the proliferation of neural crest cells in culture. Experiments in which endogenous NT-3 is depleted in chick embryos treated with functional blocking antibodies or in mice with NT-3 null mutations suggest that NT-3 also plays an essential role in the differentiation and survival of neuronal precursors.[52–54] The number of sensory neurons appears to depend on NT-3 activity.[55–57] Treatment with antibodies that block NT-3 or trkC causes cell loss before the period of normal cell death.

The neurotrophins also influence neural precursors in the central nervous system. Combined treatment with NT-3 and PDGF induces the proliferation of cultured oligodendrocyte precursor cells, and injection of NT-3-specific antibodies into the developing optic nerve greatly reduces oligodendrocyte production, resulting in a smaller optic nerve. BDNF and NT-3 also appear to regulate the commitment of multipotential precursors to a neuronal fate in both the cortex and the hippocampus. The proliferation of multipotential stem cells in these tissues is stimulated by basic fibroblast growth F factor (bFGF), and bFGF and its receptor are found in the ventricular zone containing rapidly proliferating stem cells. Treatment of stem cells with NT-3 converts them into differentiated neurons by halting bFGF-stimulated mitosis and restricting the fate of the newly generated cells to a neuronal lineage.

Blocking the effects of endogenous NT-3 with specific antibodies interferes with neuronal differentiation but does not affect cell survival.

Neurotrophins Play a Role in Sensory Neuron Development

Remarkably detailed information is available on the effects of neurotrophins on subpopulations of neurons with different somatosensory functions in dorsal root ganglia (DRG). Neurons subserving different sensory modalities can be distinguished on the basis of cell body size, axon diameter, and myelination (and therefore signal conduction velocity) and the expression of specific cellular markers. Using these characteristics, researchers have matched sensory modalities with the expression of specific trk receptors.[58,59] For instance, small nociceptive cells that detect temperature and noxious stimuli or pain express the neuropeptides substance P and / or CGRP, have unmyelinated axons, are trkA positive. In contrast, slowly adapting mechanoreceptors with large myelinated axons are trkB or trkC positive. Large DRG neurons with large-diameter myelinated axons that innervate muscle spindles and Golgi tendon organs are trkC positive.[60] Transgenic mice carrying null mutations in a neurotrophin gene with the exception of NT-4, or a trk receptor will die at birth. Because sensory neurons develop early, it is possible to define anatomical and functional changes in specific sensory systems and correlate them with the null mutations.[7,18,61,62] DRG neuron number is significantly reduced in all trk receptor and neurotrophin-deficient mice (except NT-4). The properties of missing DRG neurons frequently match predictions based on the localization of trk receptor expression (Fig. 21.8). For instance, null mutations of either trkA or NGF

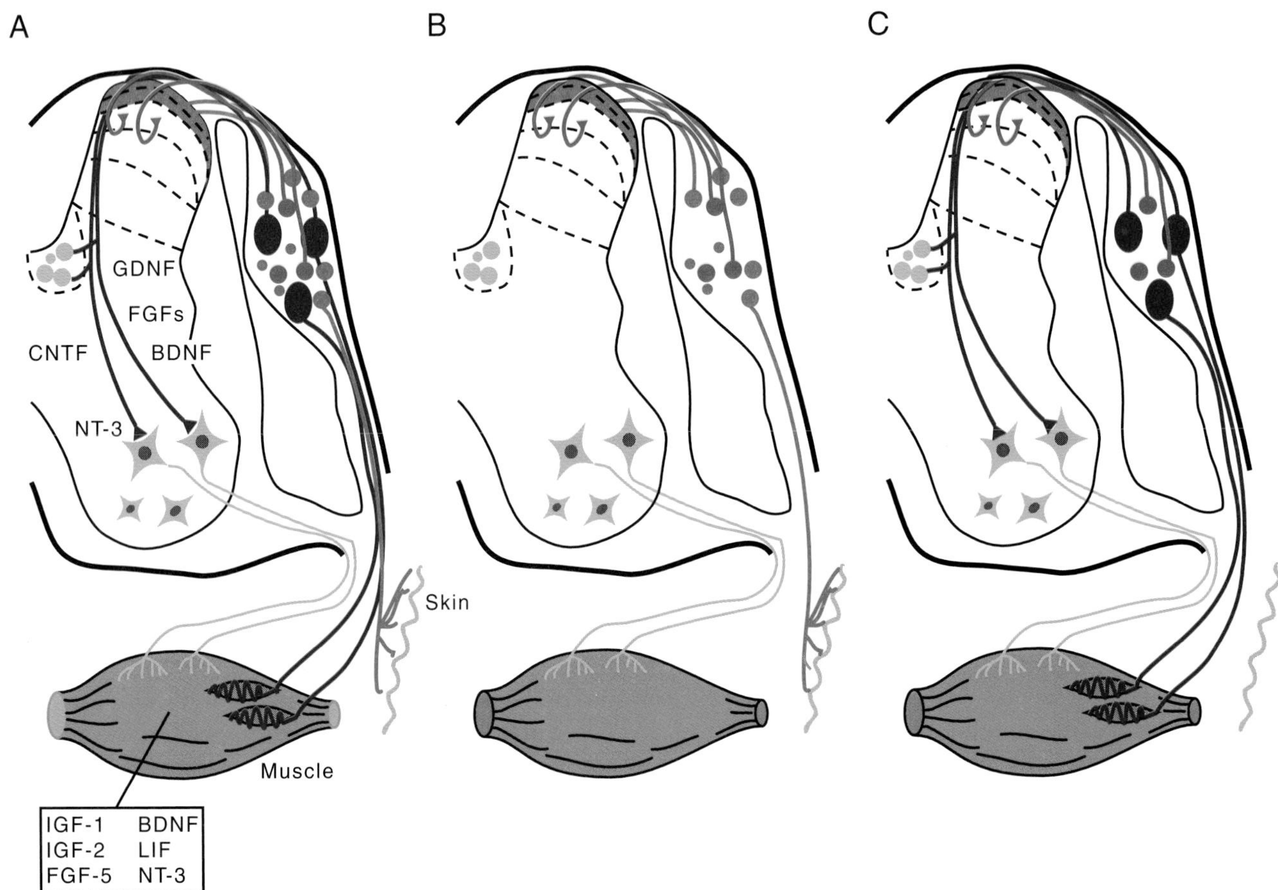

FIGURE 21.8 Phenotypic alterations in sensory motor pathways caused by null mutations in NGF / trkA and NT-3 / trkC. In the DRGs of normal mice, small-diameter (red), medium-diameter (green), and large-diameter (blue) neurons are present. Many of the small-diameter neurons innervate skin, respond to temperature and pain, and have terminations in the dorsal-most laminae of the spinal cord. These neurons are lost when NGF or trkA is absent (compare A and C). Large-diameter neurons innervate muscle spindles and other proprioceptive end organs and have axon terminations in the lowest laminae of the dorsal horn and in the ventral horn. These neurons are lost when NT-3 or trkC is absent (compare A and B).

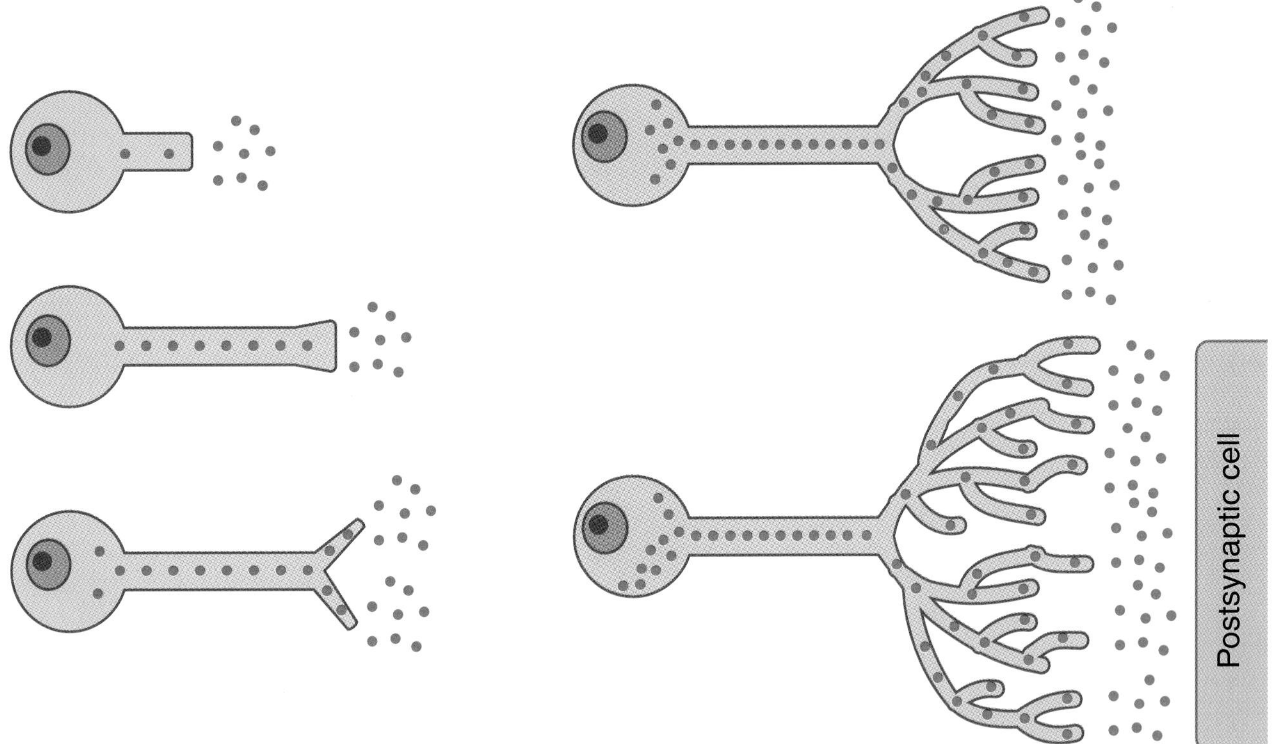

FIGURE 21.9 A model of trophic interactions during early to later stages of development when sensory neurons shift from "caretaker" neurotrophins supplied by tissues encountered on the journey to the appropriate target tissue. Once axons arrive at their final destination, neurons switch dependency to target-derived factors.

result in the loss of small SP- and/or CGRP-positive neurons that are associated with nociception, and trkC and NT-3 knockouts show a reduction in number of large neurons with myelinated axons that innervate muscle spindles.[63,64] Mice that are heterozygous for a neurotrophic deletion (+/−) have reduced levels of the trophic factor and have been used to determine whether the neurotrophic factor is present in limiting amounts as predicted by the neurotrophic hypothesis. For example, NT-$3^{+/-}$ animals have half the appropriate number of muscle spindle afferents, and $NGF^{+/-}$ mice have reduced sensitivity to pain.[61]

Sensory neurons—and presumably other neurons as well—differ in the onset and the duration of neurotrophin dependency. The life history of a typical sensory neuron is illustrated in Fig. 21.9. In sensory ganglia, autocrine or paracrine secretion of BDNF or NT-3 appears to be important for the initial differentiation of precursors into sensory neurons (see previous subsection).[3,6] Sensory neurons become dependent on target-derived neurotrophic factors for survival after their axons have grown to their peripheral and central targets. In the adult, neurotrophins are still supplied by target cells, but in addition, many sensory neurons receive BDNF through autocrine secretion in the ganglia.[65,66] When during development do sensory neurons become dependent on neurotrophins for survival and do they switch their dependency from one factor to another? Two different strategies by which sensory neurons can use neurotrophins to maintain survival have been described.

1. Neurons in some cranial ganglia derived from the placode (for example, vestibular, nodose, and petrosal neurons) do not become dependent on neurotrophins for survival until growing axons finally near their peripheral targets.[67] Each of these cranial ganglia differs in its proximity to the appropriate target tissue. The time that it can survive in culture in the absence of neurotrophin is directly correlated with the distance over which its axons must grow to reach its targets. Thus, neurons in these ganglia appear to have an intrinsic clock that allows their axons the appropriate amount of time to reach their targets; during this early time window, they do not require neurotrophins or target-derived factors for survival.
2. Sensory neurons in the DRG and trigeminal ganglia depend on neurotrophins to sustain them while

their axons grow to peripheral targets. These neurons initially utilize a "caretaker" neurotrophin supplied by tissues encountered by the growing axons. Trigeminal neurons that innervate facial skin undergo normal cell death when their axons reach the skin, where the neurons compete for target-derived NGF. When isolated very early in development, these neurons are initially neurotrophin- and target-independent, but subsequently die unless BDNF or NT-3 is provided. NGF does not support the survival of these early neurons. When trigeminal neurons are cultured later, during the period of final target innervation, they are no longer responsive to BDNF or NT-3 and instead require NGF. BDNF and NT-3 mRNA expression is present in the mesenchyme (through which axons must grow to reach skin) before the axons arrive and during their passage through the mesenchyme. In contrast, NGF expression is localized in the target epithelium and increases with the arrival of sensory axons. The existence and timing of this neurotrophin switch have been confirmed by studies examining when neurons die in mice with neurotrophin or trk null mutations. In $BDNF^{-/-}$, $trkB^{-/-}$, and $NT\text{-}3^{-/-}$ mice, trigeminal neurons die during the period of axonal growth and passage through mesenchyme. In $trkA^{-/-}$ mice, neuron death occurs later when the epithelium is being innervated.[68] Similar changes in neurotrophin dependency have been described for DRG neurons. trkC mRNA and receptor protein are expressed in almost all DRG neurons during very early periods of gangliogenesis. NT-3 mRNA is expressed near the early ganglion, and cells isolated during this early period require NT-3 or an autocrine supply of BDNF for neuronal differentiation. NT-3 is also made in tissues along the routes taken by sensory axons during their initial outgrowth. Analysis of $NT\text{-}3^{-/-}$ mice indicates that a proportion of DRG neurons require NT-3 during this early time while axons are en route to limb targets. As neurons mature, however, they restrict their trk expression and therefore their response to the appropriate target-derived neurotrophin required for cell survival.

Summary

NT-3 and BDNF are expressed in regions of neurogenesis and differentiation in both the CNS and the periphery. Early neuronal precursors respond by increasing cell proliferation, exiting mitosis, becoming restricted in a multipotential fate into a neuronal phenotype, and/or cell survival. Experiments that block neurotrophic activity (by ligand- or receptor-specific antibody treatment or in transgenic mice with null mutations) demonstrate that both NT-3 and BDNF are required for the early development of neurons. Evidence for an essential role is strongest in the PNS, where cell numbers are reduced. In the DRG, neurotrophin responsiveness can be correlated with somatosensory function. In general, small pain-sensitive neurons are dependent on NGF, some middle-size mechanoreceptors for touch are lost in BDNF knockouts, and large proprioceptive neurons are NT-3 dependent. Sensory neurons differ in when they become neurotrophin dependent and whether or not they alter their neurotrophin requirements during development.

NEUROTROPHINS IN THE CENTRAL NERVOUS SYSTEM

Neurotrophins Are Also Present in the Central Nervous System

The expression of neurotrophins and their receptors is carefully regulated in the central nervous system during development. In general, NT-3 mRNA reaches peak levels during embryonic development, while BDNF mRNA continues to increase to maximum levels in postnatal animals. No dramatic changes in the number of neurons, however, have been observed in the brains of any of the neurotrophin or trk receptor null mutant mice.[7,17,61] This observation was surprising, because significant cell death occurs in the central nervous system and neurotrophic factors and their receptors are widely expressed in the central nervous system during this period. The complexity and number of synaptic relationships established by CNS compared to those established by PNS neurons may partially explain why CNS neurons are not as sensitive to the loss of a single neurotrophin or neurotrophin receptor (Fig. 21.10). The trophic support to CNS neurons is likely to arise from multiple families of neurotrophic factors with possible synergistic and/or compensatory effects. It is also possible that losses do occur but have been difficult to detect in the null mutants because of the intermixture of subpopulations of neurons utilizing different neurotrophins. Consistent with this possibility, studies examining cell death rather than cell survival reveal significant increases in the number of dying cells in the cortex and hippocampus of trkB null mutant mice.[69] In addition, detailed morphological analyses of specific brain regions reveal abnormalities in patterning and neuronal maturation in the cerebellar cortex.[70]

The traditional view of the neurotrophic hypothesis has been that trophic support is derived from target tissues, but other sources of trophic support are now recognized. In many regions of the nervous system and during different stages of development, neurons

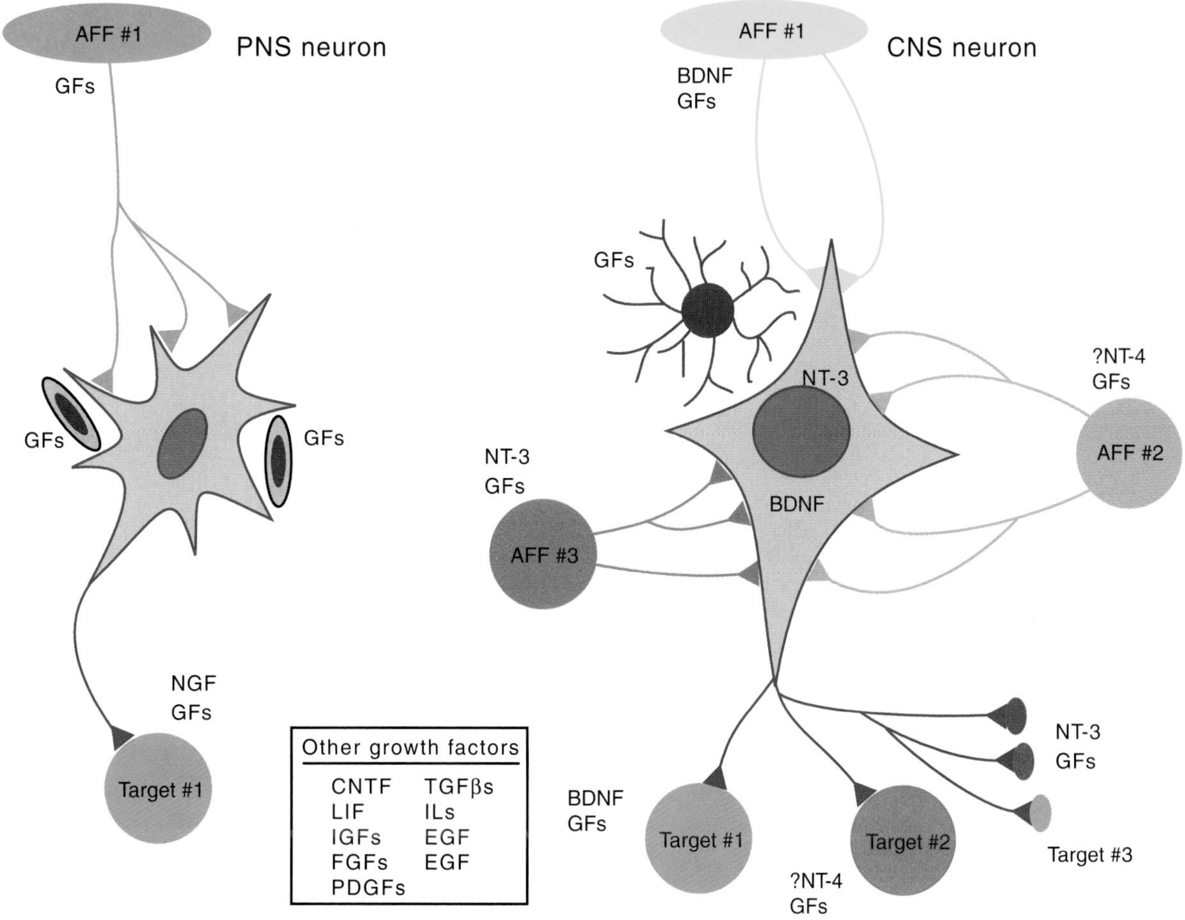

FIGURE 21.10 The possible sources of trophic support for peripheral (PNS) and central (CNS) neurons. Peripheral neurons like the DRG neuron in the diagram have only two targets that can provide support: one in the periphery (Target 1) and one in the spinal cord (Target 2). It is also possible that glial cells in the ganglion represented by the ovoid cells adjacent to the DRG neuron could secrete trophic factor(s). In contrast, central neurons like the one in the diagram receive synaptic input from many neurons (AFF 1 and 2), which could serve as a source of anterograde trophic support. The ability of neurons to synthesize and secrete neurotrophins is indicated by the presence of BDNF and NT-3 in the neuronal cell body. Central neurons may also project to several different targets (Targets 1–3) which could each provide retrograde trophic support. Candidate trophic factors are indicated adjacent to these hypothetical targets. Like glial cells in the periphery, astrocytes may also produce growth factors.

may coexpress mRNAs encoding both the neurotrophic factor and its receptor.[71–73] This coexpression is especially true for BDNF and NT-3. Such localization studies suggest that neurotrophic factors may also be derived by **autocrine** (self-secreting and stimulating) or **paracrine** mechanisms (factors provided by secretion from neighboring cells). Consistent with this notion, evidence from single neurons in cultures and antibody treatment of embryos or of transgenic null mutant mice supports the model of autocrine and paracrine routes of trophic support during normal development. Interpretation of the mRNA localization studies is complicated by the fact that neurotrophic factors may not simply be released locally in the region of the cell body but may also or instead be delivered to distant regions of the nervous system by anterograde axonal transport. This method of transport has been demonstrated with injections of radiolabeled factor.[74] Thus, although the original neurotrophic hypothesis that neurons depend on target-derived trophic factors still holds true for many neurons during critical periods of development (including sympathetic neuron dependence for target-derived NGF), other mechanisms of trophic support appear to play an important functional role in development.

Neurotrophins and their receptors are distributed throughout the mature brain[4,75,76] (see Fig. 21.11 for sampled brain sections). The localization of trk recep-

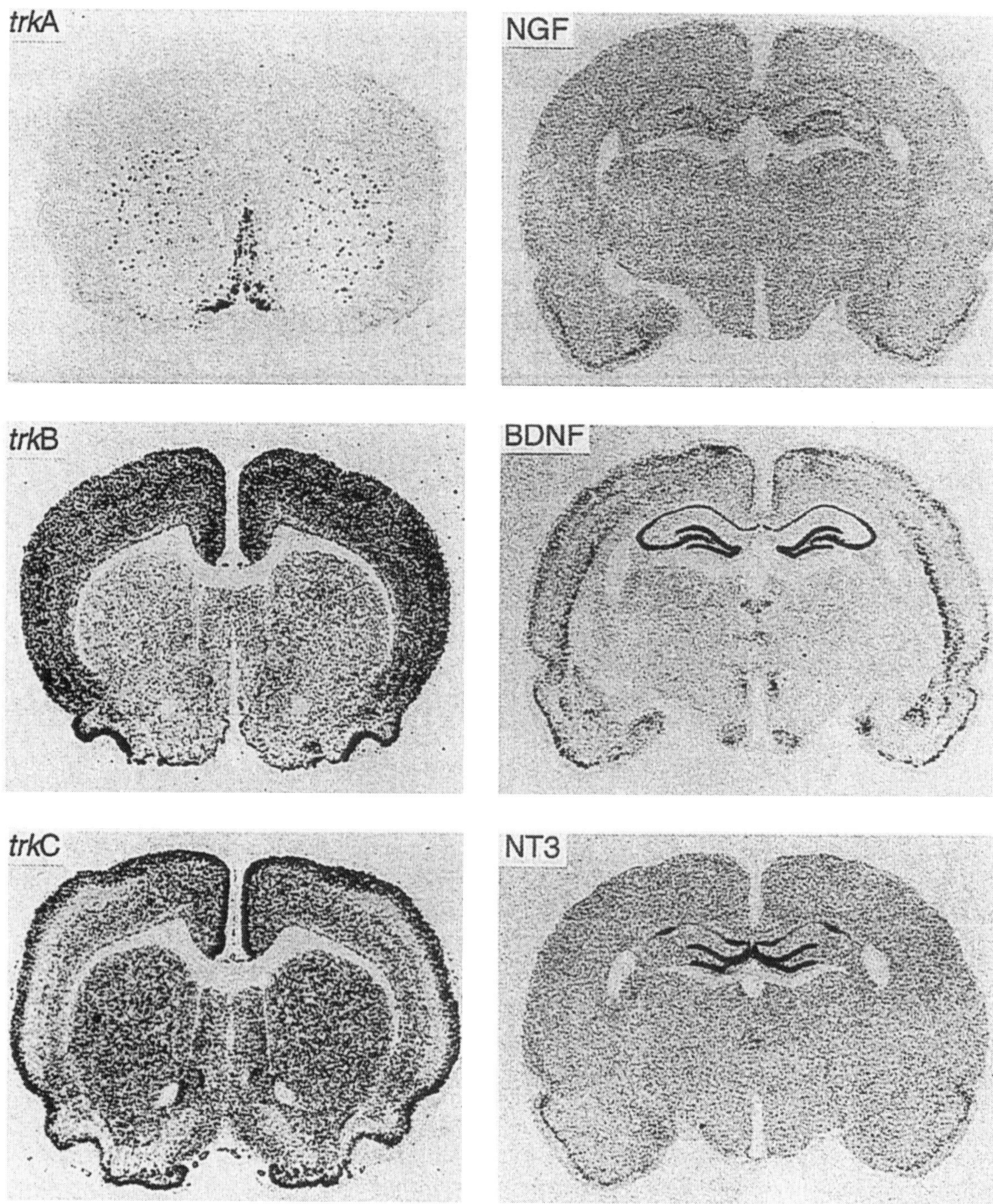

FIGURE 21.11 Distribution of neurotrophins and their receptors in the adult rat brain. *In situ* hybridization of neurotrophins and cognate trk receptors. Note that the expression of both the ligands and the receptors is specific to certain regions and that the amount and distribution of both BDNF and NT-3 mRNA (and their receptors) are more widespread than NGF. From Lindsay *et al.*[4]

tors corresponds to many neuronal cell types that are responsive to neurotrophins *in vitro.* NGF, BDNF, NT-3, and NT-4 are expressed in the cortex, and the richest source of all four factors is the hippocampus. In the adult, trophic interactions may play an especially vital role in these regions, because they are correlated with a high level of neural plasticity associated with learning and memory. Not surprisingly, neurons that project to these areas of the brain express the trk receptor appropriate for axonal binding and retrograde transport.[77] Cholinergic neurons expressing trkA mRNA in the medial septal nucleus, other basal forebrain areas, and the striatum appear to acquire NGF from their targets in the cortex and hippocampus. In general, both the quantity and the distribution of BDNF mRNA and NT-3 mRNA (and their receptors trkB mRNA and trkC mRNA) are greater and more widespread than those of NGF mRNA and trkA mRNA.

Physiological Activity Can Regulate Neurotrophin Synthesis

Neuronal activity can influence both neuron survival and morphology. In culture, in the absence of exogenous trophic factor, neuron death can be prevented by elevating the potassium ion concentration in the medium or by activating voltage-sensitive calcium ion channels. In many central neurons, depolarization with high potassium levels leads to an immediate opening of voltage-sensitive calcium channels, followed by a rapid increase in neurotrophin expression. For example, BDNF mRNA is rapidly and transiently induced in cerebellar, cortical, and hippocampal neurons within hours of a voltage-sensitive calcium ion influx.[78] Calcium channel blockade prevents the upregulation of BDNF. An increase in BDNF production and secretion appears to be required for the survival effects of high potassium levels on cortical neurons, because antibodies that block the biological activity of BDNF (but not NGF, NT-3, or NT-4) prevent this effect.[78]

Excitatory neurotransmission can also mediate changes in neurotrophin production. Activation of glutamate receptors upregulates BDNF expression in cultured cerebellar granule cells. Activation of kainate/glutamate receptors on hippocampal neurons rapidly increases NGF and BDNF mRNA expression 10-fold. Interestingly, activation of inhibitory GABAergic receptors reduces neurotrophin production in the same cells. *In vivo,* NGF and BDNF (but not NT-3) expression is dramatically increased within 30 min of seizure activity in the hippocampus. In addition, stimuli that produce long-term potentiation (LTP) in hippocampal neurons increase BDNF and NT-3 mRNA. BDNF production can also be regulated by normal physiological stimuli.[79] Rats maintained in the dark undergo a dramatic reduction in the expression of BDNF mRNA in the visual cortex (but not in other cortical areas). BDNF expression is rapidly restored when the animal is exposed to light. Taken together with evidence that neurotrophins alter synaptic function (see below), these data suggest that neurotrophic factors play an important positive feedback role. The transcriptional control of neurotrophin synthesis varies greatly with stimuli, brain region, and factor.[80] In the case of the BDNF gene alone, eight different mRNA isoforms are differentially regulated via different promoters in different tissues and through the actions of different stimuli.[80] This model of neuronal adaptation requires an extension of the original neurotrophic hypothesis to include target-mediated plasticity (as well as survival).

Neurotrophins Can Cause Short- and Long-Term Adaptive Changes in Synaptic and Neuronal Function

Expression of NGF, BDNF, and NT-4 increases during development. In many regions, including the cortex and hippocampus, levels of the factors and their receptors do not peak until adulthood. This temporal pattern suggests that these factors have important functional roles long after the period of normal cell death is completed. Trk receptor activation can lead to both short-term and long-term changes in synaptic activity. Short-term changes involve the transient modulation of synaptic transmission that lasts for only a few minutes to a few hours. These changes are likely to involve the immediate effects of Trk receptor signaling, including rapid protein phosphorylation by activated kinase enzymes and the activation of phosphoinositol pathways with the mobilization of intracellular calcium. Treatment of nerve muscle synapses developing in cultures from *Xenopus* embryos with BDNF or NT-3 causes a rapid increase in the frequency of spontaneous synaptic transmission[81] (Fig. 21.12). Although these factors have a potent, albeit transient, effect on the rate of firing, they do not influence the size of the postsynaptic currents. A similar phenomenon has also been observed at synapses in the central nervous system.[82] BDNF, NT-4/5, and NT-3 increase the synaptic efficacy of Schaffer collaterals on CA1 pyramidal cells in hippocampal slices and the synaptic transmission between hippocampal neurons in culture. Longer term changes in synaptic transmission include the maintenance of LTP for an extended period beyond the first few hours of induction and alterations in the morphology of pre- and postsynaptic elements that are likely to involve changes at the level of gene expression. Exogenous

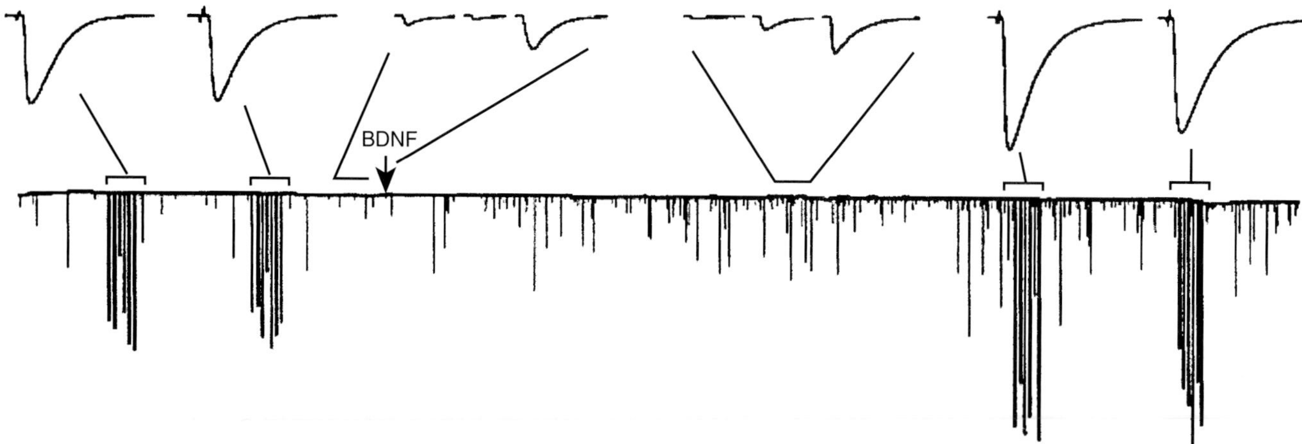

FIGURE 21.12 Changes in the spontaneous and evoked potentials observed in nerve-muscle cultures following administration of BDNF. When *Xenopus* spinal cord neurons and myocytes are grown in culture, the motor neurons form synapses on the myocytes. Typical recordings of end-plate potentials observed in a myocyte are shown at the left of the trace. The spikes present outside the bracketed area represent spontaneous events, and those within the bracketed area represent end-plate potentials resulting from stimulation of the neuron. The traces in the upper line are individual events shown at higher sweep speed. BDNF was added to the culture at the indicated time (arrow). Within a few minutes there is a significant increase in the incidence of spontaneous events and in the size of the end-plate potentials that follow nerve stimulation.

BDNF can increase the maintenance of LTP in some neurons,[83] and the capacity of hippocampal neurons to maintain LTP is impaired in neurons from transgenic mice that lack BDNF.

Neurotrophins influence aspects of neuronal physiology other than synaptic efficacy. Sympathetic neurons remain dependent on and responsive to NGF after the cell death period. Treatment with exogenous NGF increases the size of the cell body, the size and complexity of the dendritic arbor, the number of axon terminals in the target, and the production of neurotransmitter synthetic enzymes.[1,13] Depletion of endogenous NGF prevents the adaptive growth of responsive sympathetic and nociceptive sensory neurons. These target-mediated events are best characterized for NGF and sympathetic neurons, but similar adaptive changes have been observed in virtually all neuronal systems studied. For example, BDNF can modulate the complexity of dendritic arbors in specific cortical neurons in different layers of the cortex in an activity-dependent manner.[84]

Direct evidence for the regulation of synaptic connectivity by neurotrophins is available for neurons in both the visual system and the neuromuscular system. Retinal ganglion cell axon branching and remodeling can be altered by manipulating BDNF levels.[85] Physiological activity profoundly influences the formation of ocular dominance columns in the cat or ferret visual system (see Chapter 28 for details). Treatment with BDNF and NT-4/5 (but not NGF or NT-3) prevents the development of ocular dominance columns and maintains the broad overlapping terminal fields of lateral geniculate axons from the two eyes.[86] Visual activity also influences the size of lateral geniculate neurons during this critical period of development. As discussed above, physiological activity regulates the production of neurotrophins in the visual system.[79] Not surprisingly, light deprivation causes shrinkage of neurons in the lateral geniculate nucleus. Treatment with exogenous NT-4/5 (but not other neurotrophins) maintains the size of lateral geniculate in the absence of normal physiological activity. Similar interactions between activity of neurons and neurotrophins have been observed at the neuromuscular junction. The production of muscle-derived NT-4/5 is enhanced by the release of acetylcholine at the neuromuscular junction. NT-4/5 in turn stimulates the sprouting of presynaptic motor neuron terminals on muscle. Taken together, these observations suggest that specific neurotrophins regulate long-term changes in both the functional activity and the connectivity of neurons within different neural networks or systems.

Summary

Neural activity can regulate neurotrophin levels in the brain. Expression of the neurotrophins and their receptors is regionally regulated in the central nervous system during development. The NGF/trkA system is relatively restricted to cholinergic neurons in the basal forebrain and striatum that appear to utilize target-derived NGF. Regions expressing BDNF and NT-3 are more widespread, and these regions often coexpress the cognate receptors. Neurotrophins in the brain may be supplied by autocrine/paracrine secretion as well as being target derived. Despite the presence of neurotrophins and trk's in many regions of the CNS, dramatic changes in the neuron number have not been observed in the brains of null mutant mice. Neurotrophic factors can alter neural activity by rapid and long-term changes in synaptic transmission. Neurotrophins also play a role in modulating long-term changes in functional and anatomical plasticity by altering long-term potentiation and synaptic connectivity.

CYTOKINES IN THE NERVOUS SYSTEM

Cytokines Mediate Cell Interactions Both Outside and Within the Nervous System

Although some aspects of communication between neurons, including synaptic transmission and neurotrophin signaling, are highly specialized and restricted to the nervous system, others are not. All vertebrate organs and tissues regulate growth and maintenance through diffusible signaling molecules. In many tissues, the expression of these factors is increased in response to trauma, inflammation, infection, or tumor growth. In 1974 Stanley Cohen proposed that both lymphocyte-derived and non-lymphocyte-derived chemotactic and migration inhibitory factors be grouped into families of **cytokines** ("cell movement factors"). More recently, this term has been adopted as a general umbrella for many families of secreted proteins that mediate diverse biological responses including changes in the immune system (interleukins), tumor cytotoxicity (tumor necrosis factors), and inhibition of viral replication or cell growth (interferons) (see Table 21.2).

Many cytokines were named according to the particular biological activity that was the basis of their isolation, only to be later rediscovered or renamed as important mediators of other physiological processes. For example, some factors were isolated on the basis of their ability to enhance the survival of specific populations of neurons developing in culture. These include **ciliary neurotrophic factor** (CNTF) and **glial-derived neurotrophic factor** (GDNF). Other proteins that were originally identified as mitogens or chemotactic factors in nonneuronal tissues affect either the survival or the differentiation of neurons, including the **fibroblast growth factors** and **insulin-like growth factors.** The first neuronal function identified for **leukemia inhibitory factor** (LIF) was the induction of cholinergic properties in cultured sympathetic neurons, but it also supports the survival of several classes of neurons and induces neural precursors to become astrocytes.[87] Many cytokines that are important for the development or maintenance of other organs and tissues are also widely expressed within the nervous system. Their roles in the nervous system, however, remain to be defined. Likewise, factors first recognized as neuronal survival factors have mitogenic properties for either nonneuronal cells or neuronal precursors. As a result, these pleiotropic factors are grouped into families based on their protein sequences and receptor usage rather than on their biological properties. In this section, we focus on the CNTF-related family of neu-

TABLE 21.2 Cytokine and Growth Factor Families

Family	Representative members	Original biological activities
Neurotrophins	NGF, BDNF, NT-3, NT-4/5, NT-6	Neuronal survival and differentiation
Neuropoietic cytokines	CNTF, LIF, CT-1, ONCOM	Survival of ciliary neurons, leukemia inhibitory activity, increased cholinergic properties
Tissue growth factors	GDNF, TGF-α, TGF-β, FGFs, IGF-1α, IGF-1β, IGF-2, EGF, PDGF	Cell proliferation and differentiation in diverse tissues and organs, dopaminergic cell differentiation
Interleukins	IL-1α, IL-1β, IL-1ra, IL-2 through IL-15	Immunoregulation, diverse activities in the immune system
Tumor necrosis factors	TNF-α, TNF-β	Tumor cytotoxicity
Chemokines	MCAF, MGSA, RANTES, NAP-1, NAP-2, MIP-1	Leukocyte chemotaxis and cell activation
Colony-stimulating factors	G-CSF, M-CSF, GM-CSF	Hematopoietic cell proliferation and differentiation
Interferons	IFN-α, IFN-β, IFN-γ	Inhibition of viral replication, cell growth, or immunoregulation

rokines, the GDNF/TGF-related superfamily and the FGFs.

The Neuropoietic Cytokine Family Comprises CNTF, LIF, and Related Factors

CNTF was the third neurotrophic factor to be purified. Unlike the neurotrophin family members NGF and BDNF, which were isolated first, CNTF is a member of a broader family of **neuropoietic cytokines,** including LIF, oncostatin M, and cardiotrophin-1, that share a common three-dimensional structure and receptor subunits.[87,88] CNTF was originally isolated and named because it supports the survival of neurons cultured from parasympathetic ciliary ganglion. Surprisingly, CNTF is not widely expressed during early stages of development, but instead is highly expressed in myelinating Schwann cells in peripheral nerves. Many classes of neurons, however, express CNTF receptors during development and therefore respond to CNTF *in vitro* or when animals are treated with exogenous CNTF. CNTF promotes the survival of cultured parasympathetic ciliary ganglion neurons and sensory, hippocampal, and motor neurons and promotes cholinergic differentiation in sympathetic and motor neurons. LIF, which has a number of actions in the immune system and other nonneuronal tissues, shares receptor subunits with CNTF (as described later) and therefore can mimic both the survival and the cholinergic differentiation activities of CNTF observed in culture. In addition, developing motor neurons whose axons have been cut are protected from cell death *in vivo* by treatment with either CNTF or LIF. CNTF and LIF not only have effects on cultured neurons but also induce neural precursor cells to become astrocytes.

The LIF receptor is composed of two different transmembrane subunits, gp130 and LIFRβ. Neither of these receptor subunits contains a recognizable signaling domain; instead, they associate with cytosolic tyrosine kinases from the JAK/TYK family.[49] When LIF binds, the two subunits associate and initiate signal transduction by activating the associated JAK tyrosine kinases. Although the gp130 and LIFRβ subunits constitute the complete functional receptor for LIF, they are shared with the multicomponent receptors for other members of this cytokine family. CNTF, for example, uses the gp130 and LIFRβ subunits with a CNTF-binding protein or α subunit of the receptor (CNTFRα) that confers specificity for CNTF[89] (Fig. 21.13). CNTFRα conveys ligand specificity, but it is not capable of signal transduction alone. It lacks a cytoplasmic domain and is instead attached to the extracellular surface of the plasma membrane by a glycosylphosphatidylinositol (GPI) linkage. Once ligand is bound, the α subunit combines with the two components of the LIF receptor for signal transduction (gp130 and LIFR with their associated JAK tyrosine kinase). After assembly, the ligand-bound CNTFRα, gp130, and LIFRβ constitute a complete tripartite CNTF receptor capable of transduction (Fig. 21.13B). Treatment with LIF mimics CNTF activity in neurons because all CNTF-responsive neurons contain the LIF receptor as required subunits of the functional CNTF receptor complex that can be activated separately by LIF itself. Thus, even though the LIF receptor is found in tissues throughout the body, nature has devised an accessory binding protein, CNTFRα, to produce a tissue-specific LIF for the nervous system.

As described earlier, many neurons in culture respond to LIF and CNTF, but the physiological roles of these cytokines are not completely understood. Both LIF and CNTF null mutant mice survive into adulthood, suggesting that neither has a critical role during nervous system development. LIF is elevated in the nervous system after injury.[90,91] Antibody perturbation studies coupled with the analysis of LIF null mutant mice provide evidence that LIF is important for inducing changes in gene expression that occur in neurons after injury.[90,92] CNTF null mutant mice exhibit mild motor neuron loss in adulthood. This loss is greater in mice that lack both LIF and CNTF, suggesting that CNTF maintains motor neuron function in the adult and that LIF can, in part, compensate for the absence of CNTF.[93,94] Because CNTF does not contain signal peptide for secretion, the release of the factor may require reactive changes within Schwann cells associated with injury. In contrast to the relatively mild phenotypes observed in transgenic mice lacking the ligands, when the LIFRβ or CNTFRα receptor subunits are deleted, the mice die at birth and have significant loss of motor neurons.[95,96] The difference in phenotype between ligand-deficient mice and receptor-deficient mice suggests that additional, unidentified family members exist and that these ligands are required during development.

GDNF and Neurturin Are Members of the TGF Superfamily

Glial-derived neurotrophic factor and neurturin, its close relative, are among a small number of neurotrophic factors that were purified from a complex mixture of proteins secreted by nonneuronal cells growing in culture.[97] GDNF was isolated from conditioned medium produced by a glial cell line on the basis of its ability to increase dopamine uptake in cultured midbrain dopaminergic neurons, whereas neurturin was

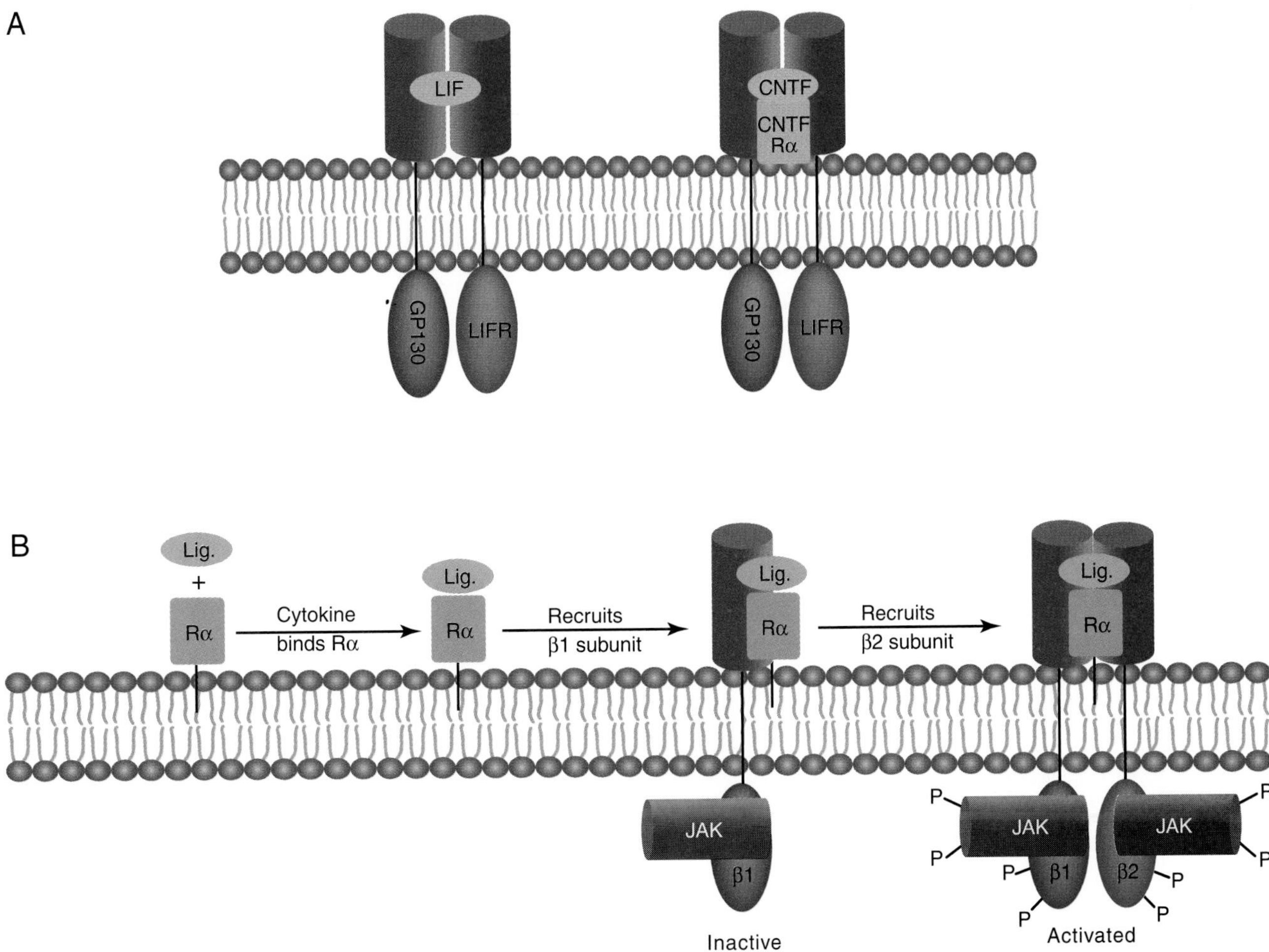

FIGURE 21.13 Binding and activation of the LIF/CNTF receptor complex. LIF receptor β and gp130 subunits form a functional LIF receptor, whereas the CNTF receptor requires an additional component, the CNTF receptor α subunit. The complex is formed by a stepwise assembly; once assembled, it associates with JAK kinases that can phosphorylate downstream targets in the signaling cascade.

purified on the basis of its ability to support sympathetic neuron survival in culture. The sequences of these isolated proteins reveal a distant structural relationship with members of the TGF-β family. Members of the β subclass of the TGF superfamily, especially TGF-β2 and TGF-β3, are expressed by developing neurons and reactive glial cells and enhance the survival of dopaminergic neurons *in vitro* and *in vivo*.[98] Striatal cells, a target region of dopaminergic neurons, make GDNF during development. Treatment *in vivo* with GDNF protects dopaminergic neurons in animal models for Parkinson disease.[99,100]

Whereas GDNF was originally identified by its activity on dopaminergic cells, many other neuronal populations are also GDNF responsive. It has potent effects on the survival, maturation, and maintenance of both developing and injured motor neurons both *in vitro* and *in vivo*.[101,102] Developing peripheral nerve and skeletal muscles contain GDNF mRNA, and expression is upregulated in both tissues by nerve section.[103] Subpopulations of other peripheral sensory and autonomic neurons are also GDNF responsive. In addition, nonneuronal tissues and organs express GDNF, suggesting that this growth factor may have functions outside the nervous system. In fact, the most dramatic consequence of null mutations of GDNF in mice is the absence of kidney tissue. Null mutant animals also have a significant reduction (35–40%) in neurons in some cranial sensory and sympathetic ganglia, as well as a marked loss of cells in the enteric nervous system. There are, however, no striking changes in the number of dopaminergic cells and only a minor loss of motor neurons.[104,105]

The identification and characterization of the GDNF

receptor subunits have shed further light on the biological activities of this factor. Investigators realized that the cellular protooncogene c-*ret*, which had been an orphan tyrosine kinase receptor (a receptor with an unidentified ligand), was one of the components of the GDNF receptor when null mutations of both c-*ret* and GDNF were serendipitously found to have similar kidney and nervous system deficits.[104–106] c-*ret* does not, however, bind GDNF. A GDNF-binding protein, or α subunit, was first identified using expression cloning[107] and GDNFRα and ret are coexpressed in many GDNF-responsive cells. Additional α subunits with different specificities for GDNF and neurturin have been identified. The GDNF- and neurturin-binding proteins lack a cytoplasmic domain and, like CNTFRα, are attached to the membrane by a GPI linkage. This protein associates with β components that are capable of cytoplasmic signaling. Once bound, the α subunit appears to assemble dimers of ret, which are then activated. The GDNF receptor complex resembles that of other cytokine receptors—in particular, the tripartite CNTF receptor complex[44]—more closely than the receptors of other members of the TGF superfamily, which are serine/threonine kinases.

The FGFs Are Present in the Developing and Mature Nervous System

Fibroblast growth factors are mitogenic for ectodermal and mesodermal cell types. Deletion of several of these factors or their receptors produces severe deficits in early embryonic development, consistent with the notion that these growth factors play important roles in the proliferation of many embryonic tissues. In addition to their broad expression in other tissues, several of these factors, including FGF-1 and 2 (acidic and basic FGF), are highly expressed in the brain. Another family member, FGF-3 (or Int-2), plays an early, significant but transient role in CNS development. Each of these factors has multiple tyrosine kinase receptors whose intracellular signaling cascades are similar to those described above for the trks and which are widespread in the brain. Early in development, both FGFs and their receptors are found in zones of stem cell proliferation. Extracellular FGFs are typically bound to heparin sulfate-binding sites in the extracellular matrix, which are thought to increase the local concentration of the factors and enhance their presentation to responsive cells. FGF expression remains high in the nervous system throughout life. FGFs promote the survival and differentiation of a broad spectrum of neurons *in vitro*. FGFs have been proposed as wound healing factors, but their physiological roles are not completely understood.[10]

Summary

CNTF and LIF belong to the neuropoietic cytokine family. The expression and biological properties of these cytokines distinguish them from neurotrophins. They possess widespread neurotrophic activity for many different neuronal populations *in vitro* and facilitate cholinergic differentiation in sympathetic and motor neurons. Their roles during normal development and in the mature nervous system remain to be defined. GDNF and neurturin are members of the TGF-B gene family and have effects on dopaminergic and motor neurons. FGFs may play important roles during development or after injury.

References

1. Purves, D. (1988). *Body and Brain. A Trophic Theory of Neural Connections.* Oxford University Press, Oxford.
2. Barde, Y. A. (1989). Trophic factors and neuronal survival. *Neuron* **2:** 1525–1534.
3. Davies, A. M. (1994). The role of neurotrophins in the developing nervous system. *J. Neurobiol.* **25:** 1334–1348.
4. Lindsay, R. M., Wiegand, S. J., Altar, C. A., and DiStefano, P.S. (1995). Neurotrophic factors: From molecule to man. *Trends Neurosci.* **17:** 182–190.
5. Lewin, G. R., and Barde, Y-A. (1996). Physiology of the neurotrophins. *Annu. Rev. Neurosci.* **19:** 289–317.
6. Davies, A. M. (1994). Switching neurotrophin dependence. *Curr. Biol.* **4:** 273–276.
7. Snider, W. D. (1994). Functions of the neurotrophins during nervous system development: What the knockouts are teaching us. *Cell (Cambridge, Mass.)* **77:** 627–638.
8. Klein, R. (1994). Role of neurotrophins in mouse neuronal development. *FASEB J.* **8:** 738–744.
9. Korsching, S. (1993). The neurotrophic factor concept: A reexamination. *J. Neurosci.* **13:** 2739–2748.
10. Eckenstein, F. (1994). Fibroblast growth factors in the nervous system. *J. Neurobiol.* **25:** 1467–1480.
11. Barbacid, M. (1994). The trk family of neurotrophin receptors. *J. Neurobiol.* **25:** 1386–1403.
12. Chao, M. V., and Hempstead, B. L. (1995). p75 and trk: A two-receptor system. *Trends Neurosci.* **18:** 321–326.
13. Levi-Montalcini, R. (1987). The nerve growth factor 35 years later. *Science* **237:** 1154–1162.
14. Levi-Montalcini, R. (1964). The nerve growth factor: Thirty-five years later. *Science* **143:** 105–110.
15. Hamburger, V., Brunso-Bechtold, J. K., and Yip, J. W. (1981). Neuronal death in the spinal ganglia of the chick embryo and its reduction by nerve growth factor. *J. Neurosci.* **1:** 60–72.
16. Levi-Montalcini, R., and Booker, B. (1960). Destruction of the sympathetic ganglia in mammals by an antiserum to a nerve-growth protein. *Proc. Natl. Acad. Sci. U.S.A.* **46:** 384–391.
17. Crowley, C., Spencer, S. D., Nishimura, M. C., Chen, K. S., Pitts-Meek, S., Armanini, M. P., Ling, L. H., McMahon, S. B., Shelton, D. L., Levinson, A. D., and Phillips, H. S. (1994). Mice lacking nerve growth factor display perinatal loss of sensory and sympathetic neurons yet develop basal forebrain cholinergic neurons. *Cell (Cambridge, Mass.)* **76:** 1–20.
18. Smeyne, R. J., Klein, R., Schnapp, A., Long, L. K., Bryant, S., Lewin, A., Lira, S., and Barbacid, M. (1994). Severe sensory and

sympathetic neuropathies in mice carrying a disrupted Trk/NGF receptor gene. *Nature (London)* **368:** 246–249.

19. Heumann, R., Korsching, S., Bandtlow, C., and Thoenen, H. (1987). Changes of nerve growth factor synthesis in non-neuronal cells in responses to sciatic nerve transection. *J. Cell Biol.* **104:** 1623–1631.
20. Lindholm, D., Castrén, E., Berzaghi, M., Blochl, A., and Thoenen, H. (1994). Activity-dependent and hormonal regulation of neurotrophin mRNA levels in the brain—implications for neuronal plasticity. *J. Neurobiol.* **25**(11): 1362–1372.
21. Blöchl, A., and Thoenen, H. (1995). Characterization of nerve growth factor (NGF) release from hippocampal neurons: Evidence for a constitutive and an unconventional sodium-dependent regulated pathway. *Eur. J. Neurosci.* **7:** 1220–1228.
22. Hendry, I. A., Stöckel, K., Thoenen, H., and Iversen, L. L. (1974). The retrograde axonal transport of nerve growth factor. *Brain Res.* **68:** 103–121.
23. Campenot, R. B. (1994). NGF and the local control of nerve terminal growth. *J. Neurobiol.* **25:** 599–611.
24. Barde, Y.-A., Edgar, D., and Thoenen, H. (1982). Purification of a new neurotrophic factor from mammalian brain. *EMBO J.* **1:** 549–553.
25. Leibrock, J., Lottspeich, F., Hohn, A., Hofer, M., Gengerer, B., Masiakowski, P., Thoenen, H., and Barde, Y. (1989). Molecular cloning and expression of brain-derived neurotrophic factor. *Nature (London)* **341:** 149–152.
26. McDonald, N. Q., and Rust, J. M. (1995). Insights into neurotrophin function from structural analysis. In *Life and Death in the Nervous System* (C. F. Ibañez, T. Hokfelt, L. Olsow, K. Fuxe, M. Jornvall, and L. Ottoson, eds.), pp. 3–18. Pergamon, Oxford.
27. Ibañez, C. F., Ryden, M., and Ilag, L. L. (1995). Functional analysis of receptor binding determinates in the neurotrophin family. In *Life and Death in the Nervous System* (C. F. Ibañez, T. Hokfelt, L. Olsow, K. Fuxe, M. Jornvall, and L. Ottoson, eds.), pp. 19–36. Pergamon, Oxford.
28. Sutter, A., Riopelle, R. J., Harris-Warrick, R. M., and Shooter, E. M. (1979). Nerve growth factor receptors. Characterization of two distinct classes of binding sites on chick embryo sensory ganglia cells. *J. Biol. Chem.* **254:** 5972–5982.
29. Meakin, S. O., and Shooter, E. M. (1992). The nerve growth factor family of receptors. *Trends Neurosci.* **15:** 323–331.
30. Chao, M. V. (1994). The p75 neurotrophin receptor. *J. Neurobiol.* **25:** 1373–1385.
31. Cordon-Cardo, C., Tapley, P., Jing, S. Q., Nanduri, V., O'Rourke, E., Lamballe, F., Kovary, K., Klein, R., Jones, K. R., Reichardt, L. F., and Barbacid, M. (1991). The Trk tyrosine protein kinase mediates the mitogenic properties of nerve growth factor and neurotrophin-3. *Cell (Cambridge, Mass.)* **66:** 173–183.
32. Kaplan, D. R., Hempstead, B. L., Martin-Zanca, D., Chao, M. V., and Parada, L. F. (1991). The trk protooncogene product: A signal transducing receptor for nerve growth factor. *Science* **252:** 554–558.
33. Weskamp, G., and Reichardt, L. F. (1991). Evidence that biological activity of NGF is mediated through a novel subclass of high affinity receptors. *Neuron* **6:** 649–663.
34. Barbacid, M. (1995). Life and death in mice without Trk neurotrophin receptors. In *Life and Death in the Nervous System* (C. F. Ibañez, T. Hokfelt, L. Olsow, K. Fuxe, M. Jornvall, and L. Ottoson, eds.), pp. 345–360. Pergamon, Oxford.
35. Lamballe, F., Tapley, P., and Barbacid, M. (1993). trkC encodes multiple neurotrophin-3 receptors with distinct biological properties and substrate specificities. *EMBO J.* **12:** 3083–3094.
36. Tsoulfas, P., Soppet, D., Escandon, E., Tessarollo, L., Mendoza-Ramirez, J. L., Rosenthal, A., Nikolics, K., and Parada, L. F. (1993). The rat trkC locus encodes multiple neurogenic receptors that exhibit differential response to neurotrophin-3 in PC12 cells. *Neuron* **10:** 975–990.
37. Garner, A. S., and Large, T. H. (1994). Isoforms of the avian trkC receptor: A novel kinase insertion dissociates transformation and process outgrowth from survival. *Neuron* **13:** 457–472.
38. Middlemas, D. S., Lindberg, R. A., and Hunter, T. (1991). TrkB, a neural receptor protein-tyrosine kinase: Evidence for a full-length and two truncated receptors. *Mol. Cell. Biol.* **11:** 143–153.
39. Biffo, S., Offenhäuser, N., Carter, B. D., and Barde, Y.-A. (1995). Selective binding and internalisation by truncated receptors restrict the availability of BDNF during development. *Development (Cambridge, UK)* **121:** 2461–2470.
40. Barker, P. A., and Shooter, E. M. (1994). Disruption of NGF binding to the low-affinity neurotrophin receptor $p75^{LNTR}$ reduces NGF binding to trkA on PC12 cells. *Neuron* **13:** 203–215.
41. Davies, A. M., Lee, K.-F., and Jaenisch, R. (1993). p75-deficient trigeminal sensory neurons have an altered response to NGF but not to other neurotrophins. *Neuron* **11:** 565–574.
42. Bothwell, M. (1995). Functional interactions of neurotrophins and neurotrophin receptors. *Annu. Rev. Neurosci.* **18:** 223–253.
43. Dobrowsky, R. T., Werner, M. H., Castellino, A. M., Chao, M. V., and Hannun, Y. A. (1994). Activation of the sphingomyelin cycle through the low-affinity neurotrophin receptor. *Science* **265:** 1596–1599.
44. Frade, J. M., Rodriguez-Tebar, A., and Barde, Y.-A. (1996). Induction of cell death by endogenous nerve growth factor through its p75 receptor. *Nature (London)* **383:** 166–168.
45. Segal, R., and Greenberg, M. (1996). Intracellular signaling pathways activated by neurotrophic factors. *Annu. Rev. Neurosci.* **19:** 463–489.
46. Greene, L. A., and Kaplan, D. R. (1995). Early events in neurotrophin signaling via Trk and p75 receptors. *Curr. Opin. Neurobiol.* **5:** 579–587.
47. Heumann, R. (1994). Neurotrophin signaling. *Curr. Opin. Neurobiol.* **4:** 668–679.
48. Kaplan, D. R. (1995). Signal transduction by Trk receptors. In *Life and Death in the Nervous System* (C. F. Ibañez, T. Hokfelt, L. Olsow, K. Fuxe, M. Jornvall, and L. Ottoson, eds.), pp. 37–54. Pergamon, Oxford.
49. Ip, N., and Yancopoulos, G. (1996). The neurotrophins and CNTF: Two families of collaborative neurotrophic factors. *Annu. Rev. Neurosci.* **19:** 491–515.
50. Dudek, H., Datta, S., Franke, T., Birnbaum, M., Yao, R., Cooper, G., Segal, R., Kaplan, D., and Greenberg, M. (1997). Regulation of neuronal survival by the serine-threonine protein kinase Akt. *Science* **275:** 661–665.
51. Pincot, O., Carmeli, C., Rosenthal, A., Kalcheim, C. (1993). Neurotrophin-3 affects proliferation and differentiation of distinct neural crest cells and is present in the early neural tube of avian embryos. *J. Neurobiol.* **24:** 1626–1641.
52. Kalcheim, C., Carmeli, D., and Rosenthal, A. (1992). NT3 is a mitogen for cultured neural crest cells. *Proc. Natl. Acad. Sci. U.S.A.* **89:** 1661–1665.
53. Gaese, F., Kolbeck, R., and Barde, Y.-A. (1994). Sensory ganglia require neurotrophin-3 early in development. *Development (Cambridge, UK)* **120:** 1613–1619.
54. Farinas, I., Yoshida, C. K., Backus, C., and Reichardt, L. F. (1996). Lack of neurotrophin-3 results in death of spinal sensory neurons and premature differentiation of their precursors. *Neuron* **17:** 1068–1078.
55. Farinas, I., Jones, K., Backus, C., Wang, X., and Reichardt, L. F. (1994). Severe sensory and sympathetic deficits in mice lacking NT3. *Nature (London)* **369:** 658–661.

56. Lefcort, F., Clary, D. O., Rusoff, A. C., and Reichardt, L. F. (1996). Inhibition of the NT3 receptor TrkC, early in chick embryogenesis, results in severe reductions in multiple neuronal subpopulations in the dorsal root ganglia. *J. Neurosci.* **16:** 3704–3713.
57. Ockel, M., Lewin, G. R., and Barde, Y.-A. (1996). *In vivo* effects of neurotrophin-3 during sensory neurogenesis. *Development (Cambridge, UK)* **122:** 301–307.
58. Mu, X., Silos-Santiago, I., Carroll, S. L., and Snider, W. D. (1993). Neurotrophin receptor genes are expressed in distinct patterns in developing dorsal root ganglia. *J. Neurosci.* **9:** 4029–4041.
59. Wright, D. E., and Snider, W. D. (1995). Neurotrophin receptor mRNA expression defines distinct populations of neurons in rat dorsal root ganglion. *J. Comp. Neurol.* **351:** 329–338.
60. Copray, J. C., and Brouwer, N. (1994). Selective expression of neurotrophin-3 messenger RNA in muscle spindles of the rat. *Neuroscience* **63:** 1125–1135.
61. Reichardt, L. F., Farinas, I., Backus, C., Yoshida, C. K., and Jones, K. R. (1995). Neurotrophins: Essential functions in vivo characterized by target gene mutations. In *Life and Death in the Nervous System* (C. F. Ibañez, T. Hokfelt, L. Olsow, K. Fuxe, M. Jornvall, and L. Ottoson, eds.), pp. 315–334. Pergamon, Oxford.
62. Liu, X., Ernfors, P., Wu, H., and Jaenisch, R. (1995). Sensory but not motor neuron deficits in mice lacking NT4 and BDNF. *Nature (London)* **375:** 238–241.
63. Klein, R., Silos-Santiago, I., Smeyne, R. J., Lira, S. A., Brambilla, R., Bryant, S., Zhang, L., Snider, W. D., and Barbacid, M. (1994). Disruption of the neurotrophin-3 receptor gene trkC eliminates Ia muscle afferents and results in abnormal movements. *Nature (London)* **368:** 249–251.
64. Ernfors, P., Lee, K.-F., Kucera, J., and Jaenisch, R. (1994). Lack of neurotrophin-3 leads to deficiencies in the peripheral nervous system and loss of limb proprioceptive afferents. *Cell (Cambridge, Mass.)* **77:** 503–512.
65. Lindsay, R. M. (1988). Nerve growth factors (NGF, BDNF) enhance axonal regeneration but are not required for survival of adult sensory neurons. *J. Neurosci.* **8:** 2394–2405.
66. Acheson, A., Conover, J. C., Fandl, J. P., DeChyiara, T. M., Russell, M., Thadani, A., Squinto, S. P., Yancopoulos, G. D., and Lindsay, R. M. (1995). A BDNF autocrine loop in adult sensory neurons prevents cell death. *Nature (London)* **374:** 450–453.
67. Vogel, K. S., and Davies, A. M. (1991). The duration of neurotrophic factor independence in early sensory neurons is matched to the time course of target field innervation. *Neuron* **7:** 819–830.
68. Pinon, L. G. P., Minichiello, L., Klein, R., and Davies, A. M. (1996). Timing of neuronal death in trkA, trkB and trkC mutant embryos reveals developmental changes in sensory neuron dependence on Trk signaling. *Development (Cambridge, UK)* **122:** 3255–3261.
69. Alcantara, S., Frisen, J., del Rio, J., Soriano, E., Barbacid, M., and Silos-Santiago, I. (1997). TrkB signaling is required for postnatal survival of CNS neurons and protects hippocampal and motor neurons from axotomy-induced cell death. *J. Neurosci.* **15:** 3623–3633.
70. Schwartz, P., Borghesani, P., Levy, R., Pomeroy, S., and Segal, R. (1997). Abnormal cerebellar development and foliation in BDNF−/− mice reveals a role for neurotrophins in CNS patterning. *Neuron* **19:** 269–281.
71. Kokaia, Z., Bengzon, J., Metsis, M., Kokaia, M., Persson, H., and Lindvall, O. (1993). Coexpression of neurotrophins and their receptors in neurons of the central nervous system. *Proc. Natl. Acad. Sci. U.S.A.* **90:** 6711–6715.
72. Kokaia, Z., Gido, G., Ringstedt, T., Bengzon, J., Kokaia, M., Sisjo, B. K., Persson, H., and Lindvall, O. (1993). Rapid increase of BDNF mRNA levels in cortical neurons following spreading depression: Regulation by glutamatergic mechanisms independent of seizure activity. *Mol. Brain Res.* **19:** 277–286.
73. Miranda, R. C., Sohrabji, F., and Toran-Allerand, C. D. (1993). Neuronal co-localization of mRNAs for neurotrophins and their receptors in the developing central nervous system suggest a potential for autocrine interactions. *Proc. Natl. Acad. Sci. U.S.A.* **90:** 6439–6443.
74. von Bartheld, C. S., Byers, M. R., Williams, R., and Bothwell, M. (1996). Anterograde transport and axodendritic transfer of neurotrophins in the developing visual system. *Nature (London)* **379:** 830–833.
75. Ernfors, P., Merlio, J. P., and Persson, H. (1992). Cells expressing mRNA for neurotrophins and their receptors during embryonic rat development. *Eur. J. Neurosci.* **4:** 1140–1158.
76. Maisonpierre, P. C., Belluscio, L., Friedman, B., Alderson, R. F. J. W. S., Furth, M. E., Lindsay, R. M., and Yancopoulos, G. D. (1990). NT-3, BDNF and NGF in the developing rat nervous system: Parallel as well as reciprocal patterns of expression. *Neuron* **5:** 501–509.
77. Seiler, M., and Schwab, M. E. (1984). Specific retrograde transport of nerve growth factor (NGF) from neocortex to nucleus basalis in the rat. *Brain Res.* **300:** 33–39.
78. Ghosh, A., Carnahan, J., and Greenberg, M. E. (1994). Requirement for BDNF in activity-dependent survival of cortical neurons. *Science* **263:** 1618–1623.
79. Castrén, E., Zafra, F., Thoenen, H., and Lindholm, D. (1992). Light regulates expression of brain-derived neurotrophic factor mRNA in rat visual cortex. *Proc. Natl. Acad. Sci. U.S.A.* **89:** 9444–9448.
80. Metsis, M. T., Timmusk, T., and Salin, T. (1995). Structure and regulation of BDNF and NT-4 genes. In *Life and Death in the Nervous System* (C. F. Ibañez, T. Hokfelt, L. Olsow, K. Fuxe, M. Jornvall, and L. Ottoson, eds.), pp. 235–260. Pergamon, Oxford.
81. Lohof, A. M., Ip, N. Y., and Poo, M.-M. (1993). Potentiation of developing neuromuscular synapses by the neurotrophins NT-3 and BDNF. *Nature (London)* **363:** 350–353.
82. Kim, H. G., Wang, T., Olafsson, P., and Lu, B. (1994). Neurotrophin 3 potentiates neuronal activity and inhibits gamma-aminobutyratergic synaptic transmission in cortical neurons. *Proc. Natl. Acad. Sci. U.S.A.* **91:** 12341–12345.
83. Kang, H., and Schuman, E. M. (1995). Long-lasting neurotrophin-induced enhancement of synaptic transmission in the adult hippocampus. *Science* **267:** 1658–1662.
84. McAllister, A. K., Katz, L. C., and Lo, D. C. (1996). Neurotrophin regulation of cortical dendritic growth requires activity. *Neuron* **17:** 1057–1064.
85. Cohen-Cory, S., and Fraser, S. E. (1995). Effects of brain-derived neurotrophic factor on optic axon branching and remodeling in vivo. *Nature (London)* **378:** 192–196.
86. Cabelli, R. J., Hohn, A., and Shatz, C. J. (1995). Inhibition of ocular dominance column formation by infusion of NT-4/5 or BDNF. *Science* **267:** 1662–1666.
87. Patterson, P. (1991). The emerging neuropoietic cytokine family: First CDF/LIF, CNF and IL-11; next ONC, MGF, GCSF? *Curr. Opin. Neurobiol.* **2:** 94–97.
88. Bazan, J. (1991). Neuropoietic cytokines in the hematopoietic fold. *Neuron* **7:** 197–208.
89. Stahl, N., and Yancopoulos, G. (1994). The tripartite CNTF receptor complex: Activation and signaling involves components shared with other cytokines. *J. Neurobiol.* **25:** 1454–1466.
90. Sun, Y., Zigmond, R., and Landis, S. (1994). Regulation of vaso-

active intestinal peptide expression in sympathetic neurons in culture and after axotomy: The role of cholinergic differentiation factor/leukemia inhibitory factor. *J. Neurobiol.* **25:** 415–430.

91. Banner, L., Moayeri, N., and Patterson, P., (1997). Leukemia inhibitory factor is expressed in astrocytes following cortical brain injury. *Exp. Neurol.* **147:** 1–9.
92. Rao, M., Sun, Y., Escary, J., Perreau, J., Tresser, S., Patterson, P., Zigmond, R., Brulet, P., and Landis, S. (1993). Leukemia inhibitory factor mediates an injury response but not a target-directed developmental transmitter switch in sympathetic neurons. *Neuron* **11:** 1175–1185.
93. Masu, Y., Wolf, E., Holtmann, B., Sendtner, M., Brem, G., and Thoenen, H. (1993). Disruption of the CNTF gene results in motor neuron degeneration. *Nature (London)* **365:** 27–32.
94. Sendtner, M., Gotz, R., Holtmann, B., Escary, J., Masu, Y., Wolf, E., Brem, G., Brulet, P., and Thoenen, H. (1996). Cryptic physiological trophic support of motorneurons by LIF revealed by double gene targeting of CNTF and LIF. *Curr. Biol.* **6:** 686–694.
95. DeChiara, T. M., Vejsada, R., Poueymirou, W. T., Acheson, A., Suri, C., Conover, J. C., Friedman, B., McClain, J., Pan, L., Stahl, N., and Yancopolous, G. (1995). Mice lacking the CNTF receptor, unlike mice lacking CNTF, exhibit profound motor neuron deficits at birth. *Cell (Cambridge, Mass.)* **83:** 313–322.
96. Li, M., Sendtner, M., and Smith, A. (1995). Essential function of LIF-receptor on motor neurons. *Nature (London)* **378:** 724–727.
97. Kotzbauer, P., Lampe, P., Heuckeroth, R., Golden, J., Creedon, D., Johnson, E., and Milbrandt, J. (1996). Neurturin, a relative of glial-cell-line derived neurotrophic factor. *Nature (London)* **384:** 467–470.
98. Poulsen, K. T., Armanini, M. P., Klein, R. D., Hynes, M. A., Phillips, H. S., and Rosenthal, A. (1994). TGFb2 and TGFb3 are potent survival factors of midbrain dopaminergic neurons. *Neuron* **13:** 1245–1252.
99. Gash, D., Zhang, Z., Ovadia, A., Cass, W., Yi, A., Simmerman, L., Russell, D., Martin, D., Lapchak, P., Colins, F., Hoffer, B., and Gerhardt, G. (1996). Functional recovery in Parkinsonian monkeys treated with GDNF. *Nature (London)* **380:** 252–255.
100. Olson, L. (1997). The coming of age of the GDNF family and its receptors: Gene delivery in a rat Parkinsonian model may have clinical implications. *Trends Neurosci.* **20:** 277–279.
101. Henderson, C. E., Camu, W., Mettling, C., Gouin, A., Poulsen, K., Karihaloo, M., Rullamas, J., Evans, T., McMahon, S. B., Armanini, M. P., Berkemeier, L., Phillips, H. S., and Rosenthal, A. (1993). Neurotrophins promote motor neuron survival and are present in embryonic limb bud. *Nature (London)* **363:** 266–270.
102. Oppenheim, R. W., Houenou, L. J., Johnson, J. E., Lin, L. F., Li, L., Lo, A. C., Newsome, A. L., Prevette, S. M., and Wang, S. (1995). Developing motor neurons rescued from programmed and axotomy-induced cell death by GDNF. *Nature (London)* **373:** 344–346.
103. Henderson, C. E., Phillips, H. S., Pollock, R. A., Davies, A. M., Lemeulle, C., Amanini, M. P., Simpson, L. C., Moffet, B., Vandlen, R. A., Koliatsos, V. E., and Rosenthal, A. (1994). GDNF: A potent survival factor for motoneurons present in peripheral nerve and muscle. *Science* **266:** 1062–1064.
104. Sanchez, M., Silos-Santiago, I., Frisen, J., He, B., Lira, S., and Barbacid, M. (1996). Renal agenesis and the absence of enteric neurons in mice lacking GDNF. *Nature (London)* **382:** 70–73.
105. Moore, M., Klein, K., Farinas, I., Sauer, H., Armanini, M., Phillips, H., Reichardt, L., Ryan, A., Carver-Moore, K., and Rosenthal, A. (1996). Renal and neuronal abnormalities in mice lacking GDNF. *Nature (London)* **382:** 76–79.
106. Schuchardt, A., D-Agati, V., Larsson-Blomberg, L., Costantini, F., and Pachnis, V. (1994). Defects in the kidney and enteric nervous system of mice lacking the tyrosine kinase receptor Ret. *Nature (London)* **367:** 380–383.
107. Lindsay, R., and Yancopoulos, G. (1996). GDNF in a bind with known orphan: Accessory implicated in new twist. *Neuron* **17:** 571–574.

CHAPTER

22

Early Experience and Critical Periods

Eric I. Knudsen

The nervous system has evolved to cope with an environment that is in many ways largely predictable. Therefore, much of the brain's structure and function can be specified by genetic determinants that reflect the common experience of previous generations. Not all aspects of an animal's world are certain, however: Details of an animal's physical characteristics vary, as do habitats and social conditions. The nervous system deals with such uncertainties, in part, by maintaining a degree of adaptive plasticity that allows experience to adjust and modify its innately determined patterns of neuronal connections. By the ingenious method of adaptive adjustment based on use or quality of performance, the developing nervous system customizes its connections to the individual animal with a precision that does not need to be, and sometimes cannot be, encoded in the genome.

Although the patterns and strengths of synaptic connections in the nervous system are capable of some degree of adaptive adjustment throughout the lifetime of an animal, many connections pass through a period during the later stages of their development when the capacity for adjustment is substantially greater than it is in the adult brain. This period is referred to as the pathway's sensitive or critical period. A **sensitive period** is a developmental stage during which neurons select their permanent repertoire of inputs from a wider array of possible inputs. Experimentally, it is a period during which the anatomical and functional properties of neurons are particularly sensitive to modification by experience.

An extreme form of a sensitive period is referred to as a **critical period,** a stage when appropriate experience is essential for the normal development of a pathway or a set of connections. During a critical period, the pathway awaits specific instructional information, encoded by impulse activity, to continue developing normally. This information causes the pathway to commit irreversibly to one of a number of possible patterns of connectivity. If appropriate experience is not gained during the critical period, the pathway never attains the ability to process information in a normal fashion and, as a result, perception or behavior is permanently impaired. For example, there are critical periods for the development of form vision and stereopsis in primates[1,2]; for the development of appropriate social and emotional responses to members of the same species, referred to as "imprinting," in birds and mammals[3–8]; and for the development of language skills in humans.[9–13]

Many experimental models are currently being explored in an attempt to understand how early experience transforms the nervous system's initially crude wiring plan into the exquisitely precise patterns of connectivity that are required to mediate adaptive behavior. In this chapter, we discuss four model systems that have been relatively well studied. None of these systems is understood in satisfying detail. Together, however, they illustrate a number of important principles, not the least of which is the profound influence that early experience can exert on the development of the brain and behavior.

SOUND LOCALIZATION: CALIBRATED BY EARLY EXPERIENCE IN THE OWL

A model system that is highly modifiable during development is the sound localization pathway that creates a map of auditory space in the midbrain of the barn owl (Fig. 22.1). This pathway transforms a representation of auditory spatial cues that exists in the central nucleus of the inferior colliculus (ICC; Chapter 27) into a topographic representation of space in the external nucleus of the inferior colliculus (ICX). The auditory map of space is then sent on to the optic tectum, the avian equivalent of the mammalian superior colliculus, where it aligns with and is integrated with a visual map of space. The function of this pathway is to extract spatial information that can be used to direct orienting movements of the eyes and head toward auditory stimuli[14] (Chapter 36).

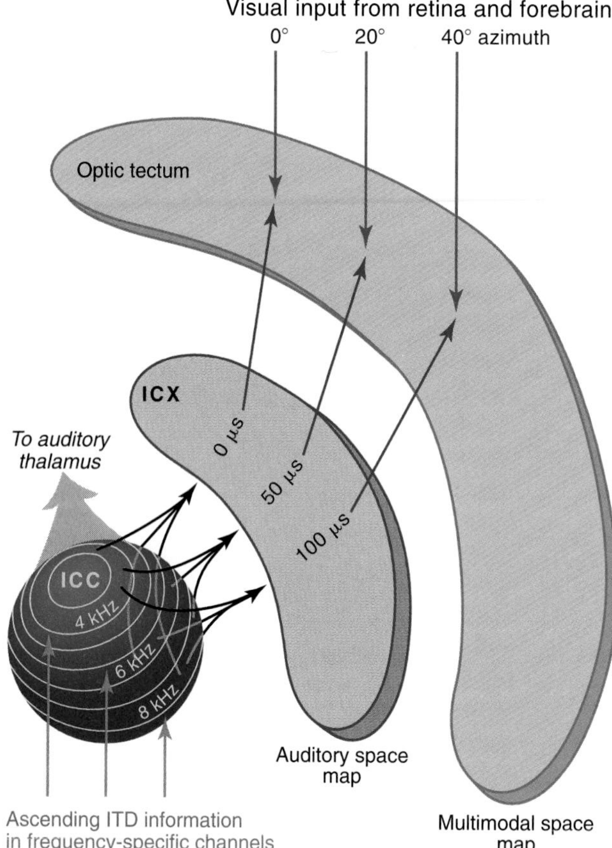

FIGURE 22.1 The ascending auditory pathway to the optic tectum in the barn owl. Auditory inputs enter the optic tectum from the brainstem (bottom arrows); these inputs already encode frequency-specific information about interaural time difference (ITD). These inputs project into the central nucleus of the inferior colliculus (ICC), where they are organized topographically by frequency. The bands in the ICC represent these frequencies (e.g., 4 kHz, 6 kHz, 8 kHz). Neurons in the ICC convey information both to the auditory thalamus (the primary pathway) and to the external nucleus of the inferior colliculus (ICX). In the ICX, ITD information is combined across frequency channels to synthesize a map of auditory space. For example, an ITD of 0 μs is generated by sound stimuli directly in front of the animal, such that auditory cues reach the two ears at exactly the same time. At the position marked 0 μs in the ICX are neurons that respond maximally to sounds with an ITD value of 0 μs and thus respond selectively to sounds originating in front of the animal. Sounds originating, for example, from positions that are further to the left-hand side will reach the ears with progressively greater delays and thus stimulate neurons with progressively larger best ITDs. From the ICX, the auditory map of space is conveyed via a topographic projection to the optic tectum. Here the auditory map is merged and aligned with a visual map of space (top arrows, representing inputs from the retina and the forebrain) to produce a multimodal space map.

The pathway derives the location of a sound source by evaluating spatial cues that are present in the auditory signals at the two ears. For owls, as for most animals, the most important cues for sound localization are interaural timing differences (ITDs) and interaural level differences (ILDs). ITD varies systematically with the horizontal (azimuthal) location of a sound source (Fig. 22.2A); ILD varies both with the azimuthal and with the elevational location of a sound source in spatial patterns that depend on sound frequency.[15]

In creating the **map of auditory space,** the nervous system can only roughly anticipate the relationship between encoded values of ITD and ILD and the locations of sound sources that produce them. The correspondence of ITDs and ILDs with locations in space changes with the size and shape of the head and ears, features that vary across individuals, as well as for a given individual during growth. Moreover, the encoded values of sound timing and level that are transmitted to the central nervous system depend on the relative sensitivity and transduction properties of each ear, and these can differ between the two ears. Therefore, to establish and maintain an accurate map of space in the optic tectum, the midbrain pathway must learn the exact relationship between the encoded cue values and the stimulus location in space.

The influence of early experience on the owl's auditory space map has been demonstrated using a variety of techniques that change the relationship between cue values and locations in space: For example, the external ears have been altered drastically or the auditory canal of one ear has been plugged chronically.[16,17] The midbrain pathway responds adaptively to such manipulations by adjusting the tuning of neurons in the ICX and optic tectum to ITDs and ILDs that restore an accurate map of space.[18] In young animals, this plasticity enables the recovery of a substantially normal auditory map even after severe disruptions in the spatial patterns of ITD and ILD. In adult animals, recovery is more limited in extent.[19]

The instructive signal that adjusts the tuning of ICX and tectal neurons is provided by the visual system. The instructive role of vision in guiding the tuning of ICX and tectal neurons has been demonstrated in experiments in which owls wear optical displacing prisms that chronically shift the visual field.[20] Owls cannot counterrotate their eyes (as humans do) to com-

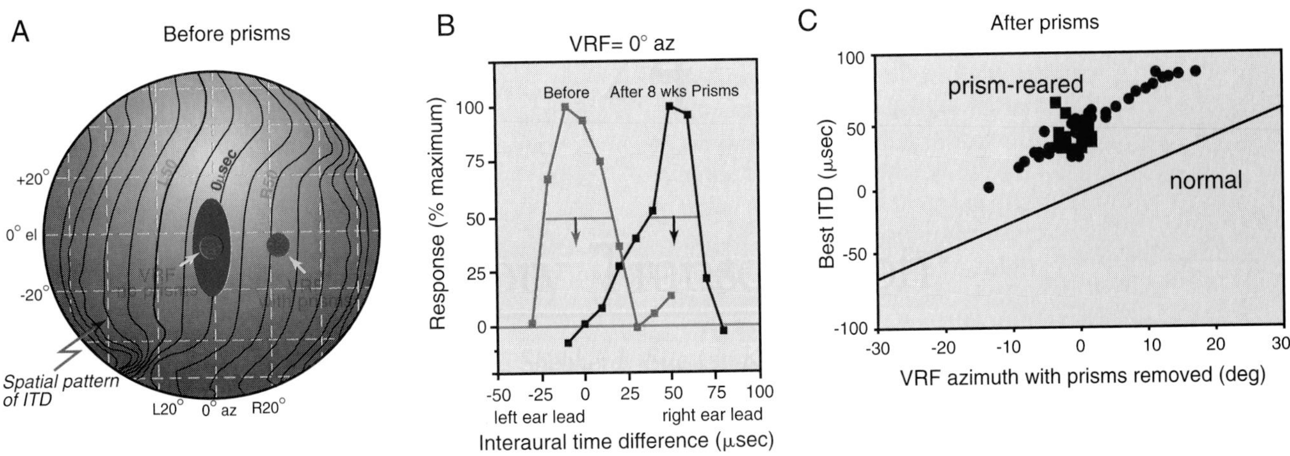

FIGURE 22.2 Rearing owls with laterally displacing, optical prisms causes an adaptive shift in the tuning of neurons in the optic tectum for ITD. (A) This map represents the space in front of the owl, showing both the elevation and the azimuth of a stimulus in space. The contour lines indicate the correspondence of ITD values (in microseconds) with particular locations in space. The point at which the 0 degree axes intersect represents the point in space directly in front of the owl's head. The auditory (A) and visual (V) receptive fields of one tectal neuron are shown in the center of the map. This neuron responds optimally when the stimulus is directly in front of the animal. Normally, the auditory and visual receptive fields are aligned. Optical prisms induce a horizontal displacement of the neuron's visual receptive field (VRF), resulting in a misalignment between A and V. (B) Tuning for ITD is shifted by prism experience. These ITD tuning curves were recorded from similar sites in the optic tectum before (blue) and after (purple) 8 weeks of prism experience. Both sites had a VRF at 0° azimuth. After 8 weeks of experience, the neuron is tuned for the ITD produced by an acoustic stimulus at the location of the optically displaced VRF, as shown in A. The arrows indicate the best ITD for each site; the best ITD is defined as the center of the range of ITDs to which the neuron responded with more than 50% of its maximum response. (C) The relationship between best ITD and VRF azimuth is shifted systematically from normal in prism-reared owls. The black line indicates the regression of best ITD on VRF azimuth that is observed in normal owls. The dots represent individual sites in a prism-reared owl. The map of ITD is shifted systematically relative to the visual map of space.

pensate for the prisms. Therefore, to maintain the alignment of the auditory and visual maps of space in the optic tectum, the midbrain pathway learns new associations between auditory cue values and locations in the visual field.

The effect of experience with displacing prisms on auditory spatial tuning is most apparent in the optic tectum, where the visual receptive field of each neuron indicates the location in auditory space to which that neuron should normally be tuned. When prisms are placed in front of the eyes that displace the visual field in azimuth, for example, the visual receptive field of a tectal neuron is shifted horizontally and out of alignment with the neuron's auditory receptive field (Fig. 22.2A). In juvenile birds, continuous experience with such prisms over a period of 6 to 8 weeks causes the auditory receptive fields of tectal neurons to realign with their visual receptive fields: The tectal neurons become tuned to the values of auditory cues that correspond with an auditory stimulus at the location of their optically displaced visual receptive fields (Figs. 22.2B and 22.2C). As a result, the auditory map of space is shifted across the optic tectum to match the optically shifted visual map.[21] This adjustment is adaptive because, by making this adjustment, the animal alters its orientation toward sounds so that it sees the source of the sound through the prisms.

The magnitude of the shift in neuronal ITD tuning that can be induced by a prismatic displacement of the visual field depends greatly on the developmental stage of the animal (Fig. 22.3). Large shifts in ITD tuning, of up to 70 μs, occur only in juvenile owls. In adult owls, experience with prisms rarely shifts the best ITDs (the ITDs that elicit a maximal neuronal response) by more than 10 μs, even after many months of prism experience. The stage during which prism experience induces large-scale changes in ITD tuning, the sensitive period, ends as the owls approach sexual maturity, at about 200–250 days old.

Although an experience-dependent shift in ITD tuning is most easily observed in the optic tectum (due to the physiological reference provided by each neuron's visual receptive field), the site in the pathway where the plasticity actually takes place is in the ICX: The maps of ITD in the ICX and in the optic tectum are shifted by equivalent amounts in prism-reared owls, whereas the representation of ITD in the ICC remains unaltered.[21]

The shift of the space map in the ICX is associated with an anatomical change in the pattern of axonal projections from the ICC to the ICX.[22] A topographic projection from the ICC to the ICX brings ITD information to the appropriate site in the ICX, where the information is integrated across frequency channels to create spatial receptive fields (Fig. 22.1). The normal topographic projection is established early in development, before prism experience exerts its effects (Fig. 22.4A). Prism experience causes neurons in the portion of the ICC that represents the shifted values of ITD to project strongly to novel regions of the ICX that then become tuned to those abnormal values of ITD. This novel projection coexists with the normal projection in owls with shifted space maps (Fig. 22.4B). These data suggest that experience induces the growth and elaboration of axons at sites where they support appropriate responses in the ICX.

The newly learned responses that result from prism experience are mediated differentially by a special class of glutamate receptor, the *N*-methyl-D-aspartate receptor (NMDA) receptor. Drugs that specifically block this receptor, such as AP5, eliminate or severely reduce the responses of ICX neurons to the newly learned value of ITD while having substantially less effect on their

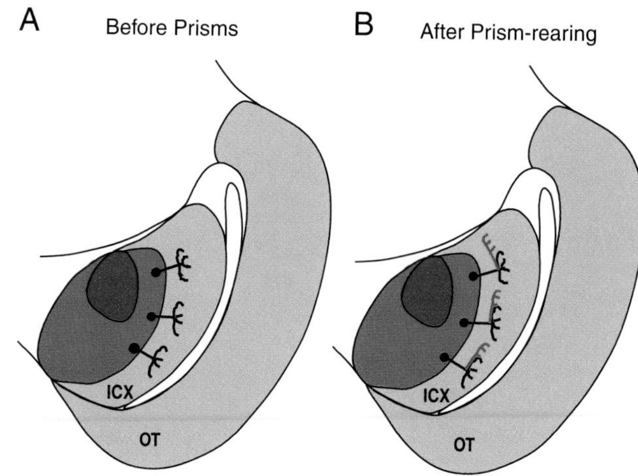

FIGURE 22.4 Schematic model of the change in the pattern of axonal projections from the ICC to the ICX that are thought to accompany the shift in the map of ITD in the ICX. Based on Feldman and Knudsen.[22] (A) The initial state of the projection before prism experience. (B) After prism experience, axonal projections from the ICC to the ICX are shifted systematically as indicated by the red arbors.

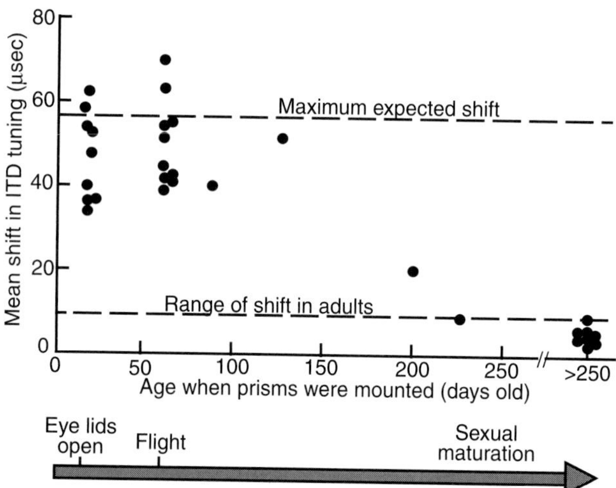

FIGURE 22.3 The sensitive period for visual calibration of neuronal ITD tuning in the optic tectum. Each dot represents data from a single owl. The large arrow below is a timeline, indicating important developmental stages in an owl's life. Each owl experienced a 23° displacement of the visual field for at least 60 days. ITD tuning was then measured at 15 to 23 sites in the optic tectum. The difference between the best ITD measured and the best ITD expected normally based on the location of the site's VRF (see Fig. 22.2C) was taken as the "shift in ITD tuning." The figure plots the mean shift in ITD tuning for the population of sampled sites as a function of the age of the owl when prisms were first mounted.

responses to the normal value.[23] Thus, the expression of newly learned responses in this pathway depends heavily on the activation of NMDA receptors. As we see later in this chapter, the NMDA receptor plays a critical role in many other examples of experience-dependent plasticity as well.

As mentioned earlier, large shifts in ITD tuning in response to visual field displacement occur only in juvenile owls during a sensitive period. In contrast, removal of prisms from adult owls that have been raised from the day of eye opening wearing prisms results in a shift of the map of ITD back to normal. Thus, the genetically programmed, normal pattern of connectivity persists into adulthood even without validation by experience. In owls that have been raised with prisms, the adult circuit is able to switch back, over a period of weeks, from the abnormal representation of ITD to the normal representation of ITD, depending on the visual world the animal experiences. In this case, patterns of connectivity learned during the sensitive period, together with the genetically programmed pattern of connectivity, establish the range of connectional states that the circuit can assume later in adult life.

Summary

The location of a sound source is derived by evaluating spatial cues that are present in the auditory signals at the two ears. Interaural timing differences and interaural level differences are used to calculate the azi-

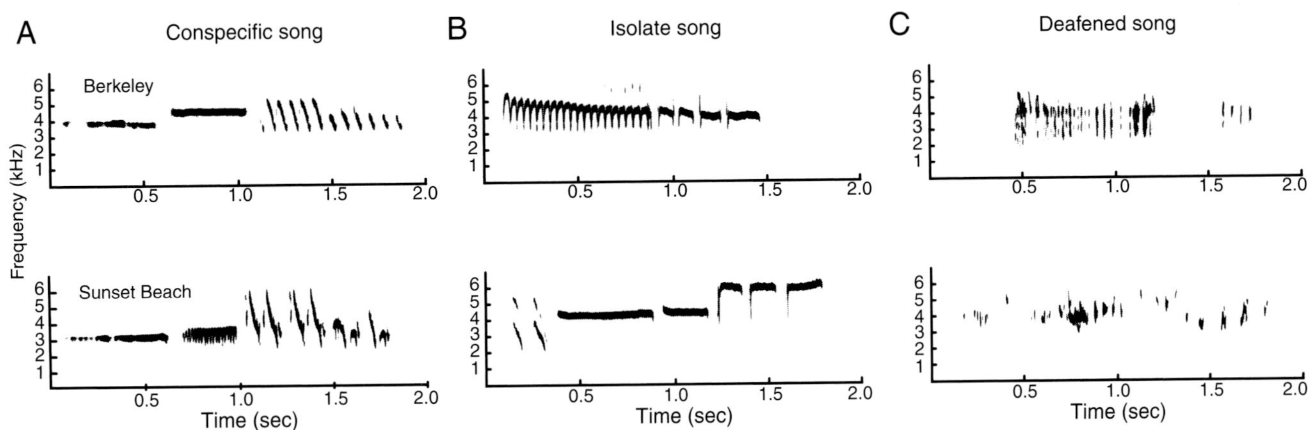

FIGURE 22.5 Songs of white-crowned sparrows. These are sonograms (time–frequency sound spectrograms) of songs from birds with different kinds of early experience. Sound energy in each frequency band is indicated by the darkness of the trace. (A) Song dialects. Birds raised in different areas sing slightly different songs. These dialects are stable for many years and are transmitted by learning. (B) Isolate songs. These simpler songs develop in birds raised in acoustic isolation or in birds that fail to copy a tutor song. (C) Songs of deafened birds. These kinds of songs develop in birds that are deafened after the critical period for song memorization but before the period of vocal learning. The birds need to hear their own voice to develop normal song. From Konishi.[24]

muth and elevation of a sound in space. In owls, this information is used to create a map of auditory space, which is aligned closely with a visual map of space in the optic tectum. The process by which these two maps are aligned relies on early experience during a sensitive period in development. The process can be altered by rearing owls with prisms, to shift the position of the visual field, or with ear plugs, which change the relationship between auditory cues and the locations of sound sources in space. The alignment of the visual and auditory maps requires the function of the NMDA subtype of glutamate receptor, a molecule that plays a critical role in other examples of experience-dependent plasticity.

BIRDSONG: LEARNED BY EXPERIENCE

Song is a special form of vocal communication used by certain species of birds to identify neighbors, defend territories, and attract mates.[24,25] Songs are distinguished from other communication sounds by their length, spectral complexity, and periodic structure—properties that give **bird song** its melodic quality. The songs sung by birds are characteristic of the species ("conspecific song"); dialects of the species' song often reflect the geographical area in which the bird was raised (Fig. 22.5A).

Songs are passed on from one generation to the next by a combination of genetic instruction and learning. In most species of song birds, the contribution of learning is great, and in some of these species, the learning takes place only during a critical period in development.[25,26]

White-crowned sparrows and zebra finches are model species that learn their songs during a critical period.[6,24] The extent of the critical period in each species has been determined by raising birds in acoustic isolation and then exposing them to conspecific song for brief periods in development. The effect of this experience on song learning is assessed by observing the song that the male eventually sings (in these species, only the male sings). Birds raised in acoustic isolation throughout the critical period sing an "isolate" song (Fig. 22.5B) that lacks the spectral and temporal complexity typical of normal song. When baby birds are allowed to hear conspecific song even for a few days during the critical period, however, they memorize that particular song and reproduce it accurately when they later learn to sing.

Song learning in these species illustrates an important principle that pertains to most critical period learning: The nervous system is genetically predisposed to accept only a limited range of potential stimuli as appropriate for learning.[27,28] For example, baby birds that are allowed to hear only alien songs that differ substantially from their conspecific song develop isolate song, indicating that they reject these distinctly alien songs as models for learning. Even within the range of songs that a bird will learn, it strongly prefers a conspecific song when given a choice of several similar song types. Moreover, babies learn a conspecific song rapidly, whereas they learn slightly different alien songs only after much longer periods of experience. Thus, the pathway responsible for song memorization contains genetically determined filters that require certain spectral and temporal features before the stimulus is accepted as appropriate, and within the range of stimuli that is deemed acceptable, some song patterns are preferred over others.

Song learning involves two components: **song memorization** and **vocal learning.** In white-crowned sparrows, these components are separated by many months, whereas in zebra finches, which develop much more rapidly, they overlap. During the critical period for song memorization, according to a current hypothesis, high-order sensory neurons become tuned to respond selectively to the acoustic patterns of the songs that the bird memorizes.[24] During the period of vocal learning, these high-order neurons act as templates for evaluating the bird's own song, guiding the development of song so that it matches the previously memorized song pattern.

There Is a Critical Period for Song Memorization

The critical period for song memorization begins at about 2 weeks of age and lasts for about 8 weeks in both zebra finches and white-crowned sparrows.[6,26] Baby birds that are exposed to a conspecific song before the critical period opens do not learn the song, even though they can hear at this early age. This suggests that the neuronal substrate for song memorization is not yet ready to be shaped by experience. Similarly, babies that do not hear a normal song until after 3–4 months of age do not learn to sing a normal song. Apparently, the neuronal substrate for song memorization has lost its ability to be shaped by experience.

The time at which the critical period for song memorization closes for a given individual is determined by the individual's own experience. Once the critical period has opened, exposure of a baby bird to normal song for 1 week is enough for the bird to learn the song; it is unaffected by songs heard subsequently. For this bird, the critical period closed after a week of experience. If, on the other hand, a baby bird is kept in acoustic isolation (or hears only songs that are suboptimal as models for learning) for many weeks past the opening of the critical period and then hears normal song, it learns the normal song. Thus, during the critical period the nervous system waits in a receptive state for appropriate experience-dependent instruction. Once this instruction is received, the nervous system presumably establishes a particular pattern of connectivity that is irreversible, thus closing the critical period.

When a baby bird is continuously deprived of appropriate auditory experience, its capacity to memorize song eventually diminishes with age. Under these conditions, the critical period closes gradually because of additional factors (discussed later) that reduce the plasticity of the relevant pathway. As a bird approaches this age, experience with appropriate stimuli must be richer in order to have an effect.[29] For example, white-crowned sparrows raised in acoustic isolation until 50 days of age no longer memorize songs presented from loudspeakers, but do memorize songs presented by live tutors.[30] Thus, the enrichment of the sensory experience provided by social interactions with the tutor overcomes the relative loss in the pathway's facility for song learning.

Evidence Favors a Critical Period for Vocal Learning

Learning to sing requires the interaction of vocal practice and auditory feedback and may also be limited to a critical period. A young bird that is deafened after song memorization but before the onset of vocal learning, and is thereby prevented from hearing its own voice, will not develop a normal song (Fig. 22.5C).[31] In contrast, a young bird that is deafened after it has already learned to sing a stable, "crystallized" song continues to sing a normal song. Clearly, auditory feedback is essential for shaping the patterns of connectivity in the song producton pathway while the bird is learning to sing.

In addition, exposure of a juvenile bird to high levels of testosterone causes its song to crystallize prematurely in an abnormal state.[32,33] Conversely, juvenile birds that are castrated before they learn to sing produce inconsistent song patterns throughout life. Thus, an abrupt increase in steroid hormone levels, such as accompanies sexual maturation, may close a critical period for song production, and without an increase in steroid hormone levels, the period of vocal learning remains open indefinitely.

These facts, although suggestive, do not conclusively demonstrate a critical period for song motor learning. If there is a critical period for vocal learning, then preventing a bird from singing (or hearing) during the normal period of song learning and then restoring the capacity to sing (or hear) later in life should leave the bird permanently incapable of developing normal song. Neither of these conclusive experiments has been done.

A Neural Pathway Exists for Song Learning

The neural mechanisms that underly song memorization are being explored in many laboratories but, as yet, we know little about this aspect of song learning. In contrast, a great deal is known about the neural mechanisms that underlie song production. The pathway for song production was identified by its sexual dimorphism in species in which only males sing.[34] In these species, there is a conspicuous network of hypertrophied nuclei, referred to as the **song system,** that is found only in males (Fig. 22.6). The song system consists of two distinct groups of nuclei: one group in the posterior forebrain that is responsible for song production and another in the anterior forebrain that is critical for vocal learning.

The posterior, vocal motor pathway consists of three serially connected nuclei: the higher vocal center (HVC) and the robust nucleus of the archistriatum (RA) in the forebrain and the hypoglossal nucleus in the brainstem (Fig. 22.6). As a bird prepares to sing, a wave of neural activity spreads from the HVC to the RA, and finally to the hypoglossal nucleus, which contains the motor neurons that control the vocal musculature.[35] Bilateral lesions of the HVC or the RA leave birds permanently incapable of producing song, although they still can make other kinds of unlearned vocalizations.[34]

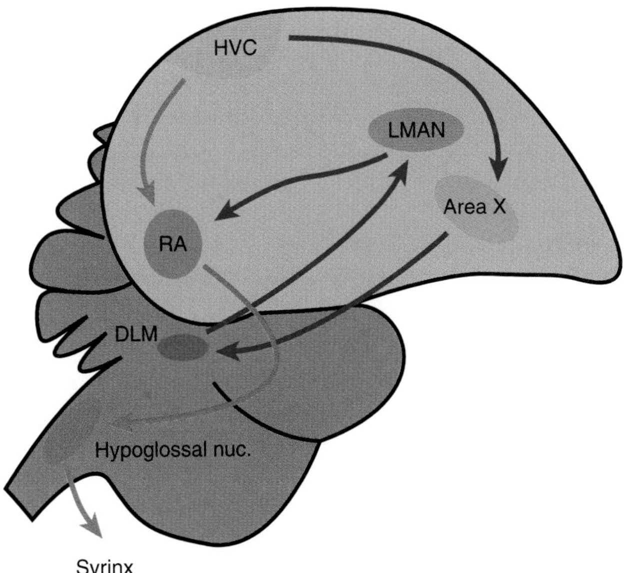

FIGURE 22.6 The song system in songbirds. This is a schematic diagram of a side view of a songbird's brain. The posterior, vocal motor pathway, shown in red, consists of the higher vocal center (HVC), the robust nucleus of the archistriatum (RA), and the hypoglossal nucleus. The anterior pathway, shown in blue, consists of area X, the medial portion of the dorsolateral nucleus of the thalamus (DLM), and the lateral portion of the magnocellular nucleus of the anterior neostriatum (LMAN).

The anterior pathway (Fig. 22.6), consisting of area X, a thalamic nucleus (DLM), and the lateral portion of the magnocellular nucleus of the anterior neostriatum (LMAN), is essential for normal song development.[36–38] Lesions made in the LMAN while a bird is learning to sing cause a dramatic cessation of song development, freezing the young bird's song in an immature state; this freezing process resembles song crystallization. In contrast, lesions in area X prevent the bird from ever achieving a stable, adult song. Lesions of these nuclei in adult birds have no apparent effect.[33] Thus, input from the anterior pathway is necessary to permit or to instruct the changes that take place in the song motor pathway during vocal learning.

There is some evidence that the anterior pathway plays an instructive role. The anterior pathway, which receives auditory input from the HVC, could compare the song that a bird produces with a template of the memorized song, and the result of this comparison could be used to instruct the development of connections in the song motor pathway. Consistent with this interpretation, area X and the LMAN contain neurons that, at least in adults, respond maximally to the sound of the bird's own song (Fig. 22.7).[39] In addition, the connections of the LMAN with the song production pathway are consistent with an instructive role. Axons from the LMAN are the first to innervate the RA during development.[40] Information transmitted by this pathway is mediated predominantly by NMDA receptors,[41] a class of glutamate receptors that, when activated, is known to induce synaptic plasticity in other systems. As zebra finches begin to sing, axons from the HVC enter the RA and begin making glutamergic synapses with RA neurons. These later connections may be guided by the activity of the preexisting, LMAN–RA synapses.

The period of vocal learning closes as birds reach sexual maturity and circulating levels of steroid hormones rise. Neurons in the LMAN, HVC, RA, and hypoglossal nuclei bind and accumulate androgens. As the period of vocal learning closes, the density of dendritic spines on LMAN neurons decreases sharply, suggesting that synaptic selection has occurred, the total volume of the LMAN regresses precipitously, and the influence of LMAN activity on the song motor nuclei declines.[42,43] Thus, the close of the period for vocal learning may be due to a loss of the instructive influence of LMAN activity on the song motor pathway, as triggered by a rise in steroid hormone levels.

Summary

Song is a learned vocal communication used by certain species of birds to attract mates, defend their terri-

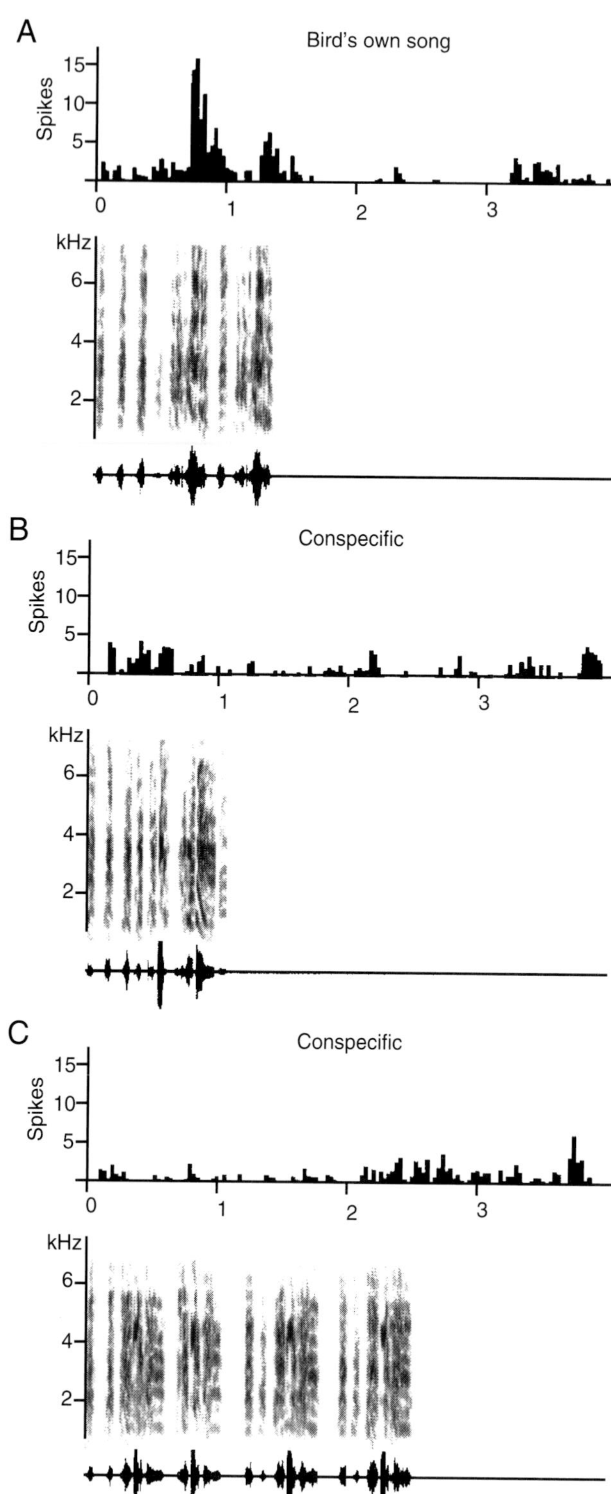

FIGURE 22.7. Selectivity of an LMAN neuron for the bird's own song. In each panel, the upper plot is a peristimulus histogram of the neuron's spike responses to the song stimulus; the middle plot is the sonogram (see Fig. 22.5) of the song; the lower plot is an oscillogram (amplitude waveform) of the song. (A) Strong responses to the bird's own song. (B) This conspecific song elicits a weak response. (C) This conspecific song suppresses the baseline activity of the neuron. From Doupe.[39]

tories, and identify their neighbors. Songs are learned in two phases: the first is song memorization, in which a song is heard and memorized during a critical period early in life; the second is vocal learning, in which vocal practice and auditory feedback shape the final form of the song during a later period. The neural pathway for song production is sexually dimorphic in many species in which only males sing. A set of nuclei in the anterior forebrain appears to play a special role in vocal learning. The period of vocal learning closes when birds reach sexual maturity and circulating levels of steroid hormones rise.

FILIAL IMPRINTING: BABIES LEARN TO RECOGNIZE THEIR PARENTS

For many species, particularly birds and mammals, parental care is essential for the survival of the young. The young of these species learn rapidly to distinguish their parents from all other individuals, and they form a unique and close relationship with their parents from that point on—a process referred to as **filial imprinting.**[3,5,44] Filial imprinting can involve the learning of visual, auditory, olfactory, and gustatory cues that identify a parent. The learning of these cues takes place during short, well-defined critical periods in early postnatal life.

The visual component of the learning process is usually preceded by the auditory, olfactory, and/or gustatory components. In many species, the babies learn to recognize the vocalizations of the mother based on experience that begins before or soon after the animal is born.[45–47] In addition, babies may learn the odor and/or taste of the mother from the odors and tastes experienced immediately after birth. The recognition of the parent based on acoustic and/or chemical cues helps the young select the correct individual for visual imprinting, once the eyes and nervous system are capable of adequate form vision.

The critical periods for filial imprinting are relatively discrete and can be as short as a few hours in some species (Fig. 22.8).[48] If a baby is deprived of a suitable object for imprinting throughout the critical period, it never learns to respond appropriately to the social signals offered later by a member of its species.[4,6,49] If a baby is in contact throughout the critical period only with an individual of another species, as often occurs when animals are raised by humans, the baby will imprint on that individual and may, from then on, ignore members of its own species. In the classic experiments by Konrad Lorenz, for example, baby geese that had been raised by

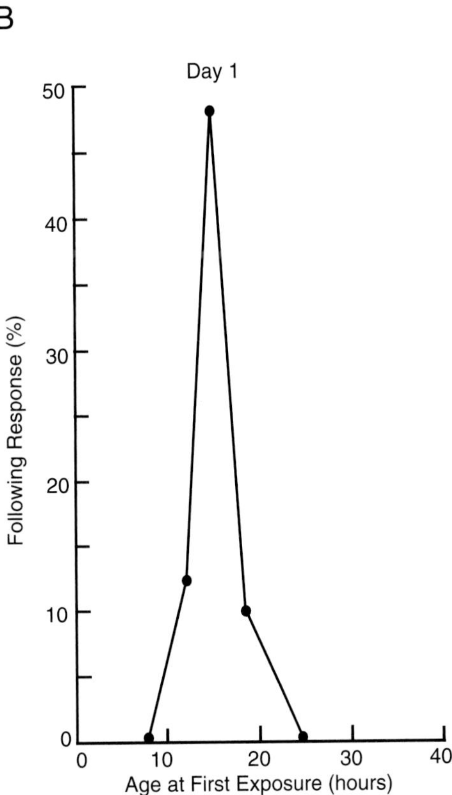

FIGURE 22.8 Filial imprinting. The critical period for parental imprinting in ducklings occurs during a few hours of the first day of life. Ducklings were exposed once, for 10 min, to one of several models of a male duck. Imprinting was assessed 5 to 70 h later by offering the ducklings a choice between the previously presented model and a model of a female duck and noting which of the models the ducklings followed. (A) This is one of the four different tests that were applied. In this test, the model of the male duck was located much further away than the model of the female duck. This test demonstrated that the duckling would respond to the imprinting object even though the female model was closer and louder. (B) The plot indicates the percentage of the ducklings that scored perfectly in the assessment of their following responses to the imprinting model. From Ramsay and Hess.[48]

Lorenz from the time of hatching followed him about as if he were their mother.

As in the previous examples of developmental learning, young animals exhibit an innate preference to imprint on normal stimuli. When given a choice, babies in the process of imprinting attend preferentially to images that more closely resemble members of their own species. Thus, when baby ducks are given the choice of imprinting on geese or on people, they imprint on the (ducklike) geese.[50] This predilection is based on genetically programmed preferences for simple, conspicuous features, referred to as **sign stimuli** by ethologists, that tend to distinguish the species from all others.[3] This implies that the neural circuitry involved in filial imprinting, like that involved in song learning, contains genetically determined neuronal filters that help to identify stimuli that are appropriate models for learning. As imprinting proceeds, learning causes these filters to become more selective until ultimately the young are capable of discriminating one individual from all others.

Filial Imprinting Has a Neural Correlate

In one model system, the guinea fowl, changes in neuronal morphology correlate with auditory imprinting. In this species, auditory imprinting causes neurons in a particular region of the anterior forebrain, the medial neo- and hyperstriatum (MNH), to be activated strongly and specifically by the imprinted acoustic stimulus.[44] In birds that are imprinted, the dendrites of large principal neurons in the MNH exhibit about half the density of spines as do the same class of neurons in animals that are not imprinted on an auditory stimulus. This effect, which is reminiscent of the effect of song learning on the dendrites of LMAN neurons, suggests that, in this pathway, experience during the critical period causes a selective elimination of inputs from a large initial repertoire of inputs. The inputs that are eliminated are presumably those that do not contribute to the representation of the imprinted auditory stimulus.

Summary

Young animals of many species learn rapidly to distinguish their parents from other individuals, a process known as filial imprinting. During a brief, early critical period, animals learn to identify a parent's vocalizations, odor, taste, and / or appearance. Young animals exhibit an innate preference to imprint on stimuli that are characteristic of their own species. This implies that the neural circuitry involved in filial imprinting contains genetically determined neuronal filters that help identify stimuli that are appropriate models for learning.

BINOCULAR VISION

Animals that have eyes oriented forward see a large portion of frontal space with both eyes. Normally, the views of frontal space that are provided by each eye are combined ("fused") into a single binocular percept. Binocular fusion improves the ability to detect weak signals under adverse conditions and enables the ability to see depth on the basis of small disparities in the images on the two retinas, referred to as "stereoscopic vision."

Binocular fusion and **stereoscopic vision** develop only in animals that experience normal binocular vision during early life.[51,52] Binocular fusion requires that the eyes be properly aligned and that signals from corresponding points on the two retinas (for example, the centers of the foveas) activate the same neurons in the visual cortex. The alignment of the eyes and the convergence of visual inputs onto neurons in the cortex are guided by early experience. For binocular fusion to develop, matched visual inputs from the two eyes must persist throughout a critical period. When this does not occur, as when the eyes are not properly aligned or when the visual input from one eye is substantially degraded relative to that from the other eye, the capacity for binocular fusion may be permanently lost.[53–55] Under these conditions, animals suppress information coming from one (the weaker) eye, a condition referred to as **amblyopia,** and they perceive the world in front of them based on inputs from only one eye.[51]

There Is a Critical Period for Binocular Fusion

The critical period for binocular fusion has been explored in monkeys and cats using a variety of manipulations that deprive baby animals of binocular vision. One manipulation, which mimics the effects of a monocular cataract, is suturing closed the lids of one eye (monocular deprivation). Based on the effects of this manipulation, the critical period for binocular fusion in kittens lasts approximately the first 3 months of postnatal life. If a kitten experiences monocular deprivation for just a few weeks during this period, visually guided behaviors mediated by the deprived eye are severely and permanently impaired.[51] In contrast, an equivalent visual impairment experienced after the end of the critical period has no apparent effect on

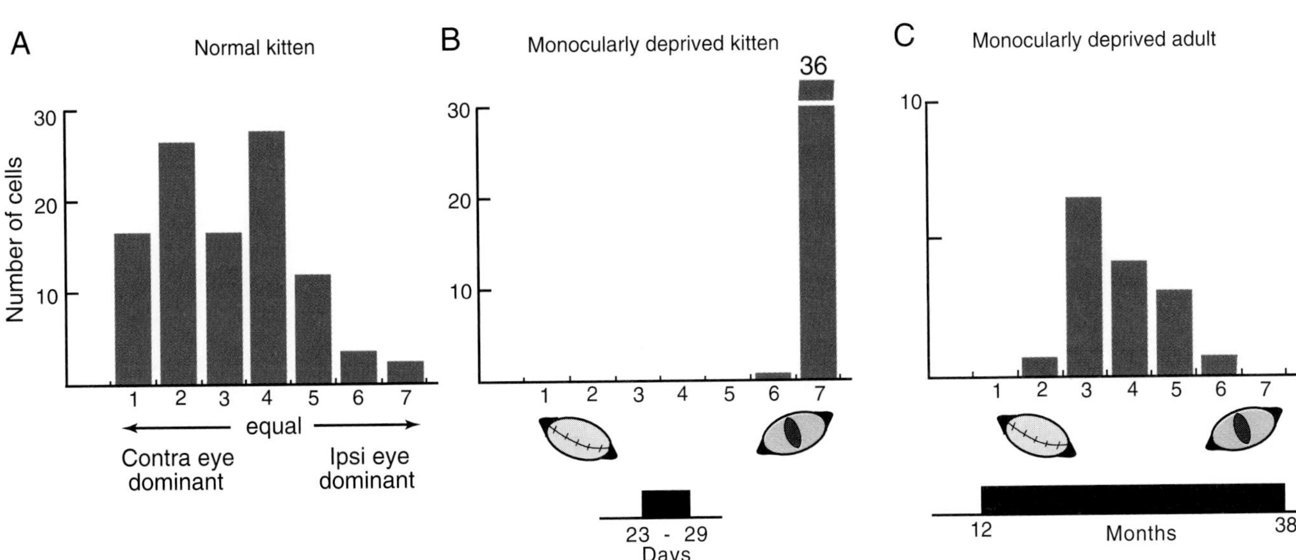

FIGURE 22.9 Effect of chronic closure of one eye on the responsiveness of visual cortical neurons to input from each eye. (A) The ocular dominance distribution in the primary visual cortex of two normal kittens, 3 to 4 weeks old. Cells in Group 1 were driven only by the contralateral eye; for Group 2, the contralateral eye was markedly dominant; for Group 3, the contralateral eye was slightly dominant; for Group 4, there was no apparent difference in the drive from the two eyes; for Group 5, the ipsilateral eye dominated slightly; for Group 6, it dominated markedly; and for Group 7, the cells were driven only by the ipsilateral eye. (B) The ocular dominance distribution was altered dramatically in a kitten exposed to contralateral eye closure for 1 week (from 23 to 29 days of age). (C) The ocular dominance distribution was essentially normal in an adult cat exposed to contralateral eye closure for 26 months. From Hubel and Wiesel.[56]

binocular fusion. Similar critical periods occur in monkeys and humans.

Experience Shapes Ocular Representation in the Visual Cortex

In the mammalian nervous system, visual information from the two eyes first comes together at the level of the primary visual cortex (Chapter 28). Visual experience during a critical period determines how much of the visual cortex is devoted to processing input from each eye and the degree to which binocular inputs are combined.

During ontogeny, genetic mechanisms establish overlapping left-eye and right-eye afferent projections from the lateral geniculate nucleus (LGN) to layer 4 in the visual cortex, as well as binocularly driven neurons throughout the cortical layers. As long as the eyes are coordinated and used equally, the afferents representing the left and right eyes compete for territory in layer 4 on an equal basis, and the normal final state, consisting of equally wide ocular dominance columns, is achieved (Fig. 22.9A and Fig. 22.10).[56] If, on the other hand, vision is impaired in one eye, due to monocular lid closure in an experimental animal or to a cataract in a human, for example, the balance between LGN afferents in their competition for layer 4 territory is disrupted: LGN afferents that convey input from the impaired eye lose the ability to drive layer 4 neurons in an abnormally large region of the cortex, while LGN afferents that convey input from the normal eye gain the ability to drive layer 4 neurons in an abnormally large portion of the cortex. As a consequence, activity throughout most of the visual cortex becomes driven by LGN afferents from the normal eye (Fig. 22.9B and Fig. 22.10).

The competition between LGN afferents for control of layer 4 neurons is in a state of dynamic equilibrium throughout the critical period.[57,58] Afferents from a previously deprived eye can regain territory in layer 4 if the lids of the deprived eye are opened and the lids of the previously open eye are sutured closed, a procedure referred to as "reverse suture."

Anatomical correlates of the functional takeover of layer 4 neurons by inputs from one eye are found in the patterns of LGN afferent terminations in layer 4.[59] In animals that experience monocular impairment during the critical period, the layer 4 termination zones for afferents from the deprived eye shrink while those from the nondeprived eye expand. At the cellular level, axons conveying input from the deprived eye decrease in total length and branch less in layer 4 compared to normal, whereas axons conveying input from the nondeprived eye branch even more profusely than normal (Fig. 22.10).[60]

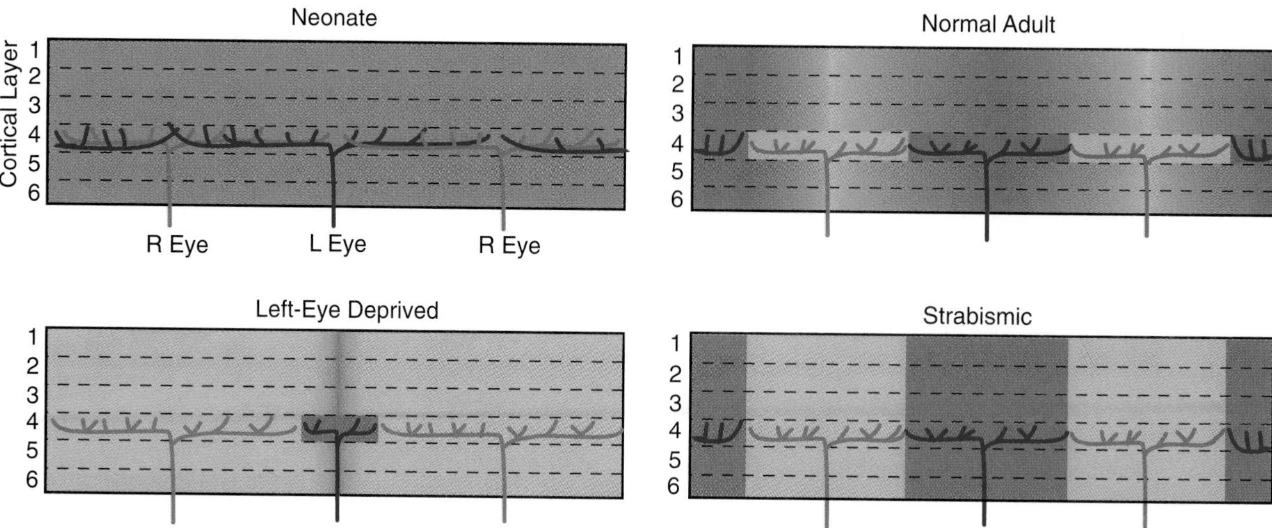

FIGURE 22.10 Schematic diagram of ocular representation in the primary visual cortex of monkeys. Right-eye input is represented as red; left-eye input is represented as dark purple. Neonate: LGN afferents representing the left and right eyes, respectively, terminate in layer 4, but their zones of termination overlap extensively. Neurons in all layers are driven by either eye. Normal adult: After development, the LGN afferent termination zones for the left and right eyes are segregate from each other, and the neurons in layer 4 are monocularly driven. Neurons in the upper and lower layers are driven by input from either eye, the relative strength of the left eye and right eye inputs varying systematically across the cortex. Left-eye deprived: After chronic closure of the left eye throughout development, the termination zones of LGN afferents from the left eye are decreased, while those of LGN afferents from the right eye have expanded. Most neurons in the upper and lower layers are driven by input from the right eye. Strabismic: After chronic misalignment of the eyes throughout development, the termination zones of LGN afferents from the left and right eyes are completely segregated from each other and equal in size. Neurons in all cortical layers are driven by input from only one eye or the other.

Most neurons in the layers above and below layer 4 are normally driven binocularly, with the relative dominance of left-eye versus right-eye inputs varying systematically across the cortex (Fig. 22.10). Ocular dominance in these upper and lower layers is determined not only by the relative amounts of activity originating from the left and right eyes but also by the temporal correlation of that activity. Misalignment of the eyes (strabismus), which can be induced experimentally by cutting the medial rectus muscles, leads to equal visual stimulation of the two eyes, but a loss of synchrony of activity from the two eyes that results from the animal viewing the same objects with both eyes. If the eyes are strabismic during the critical period, cortical ocular dominance columns develop and are of normal width, but binocular responses in the upper and lower layers are permanently lost (Fig. 22.10).[55] The crucial role of synchronous binocular activity in the development of cortical binocular responses has been demonstrated directly in kittens by blocking neural activity from both eyes, by injecting the eyes with tetrodotoxin, and by imposing various patterns of activity on the optic nerves by electrical stimulation.[61] When both optic nerves are stimulated synchronously, neurons in the cortex remain binocularly driven. In contrast, when the left and right optic nerves are stimulated equally but asynchronously, neurons in the cortex become monocularly driven with approximately equal numbers of neurons responding to each eye.

Cellular mechanisms by which the amount and synchrony of synaptic activity might shape the functional and anatomical architecture of the visual cortex are described in Chapter 19. In brief, they include the adjustment of synaptic strength, by both long-term potentiation and long-term depression, through a process that depends on the activation of NMDA receptors in the cortex.[62] In addition, the anatomical remodeling of LGN axons, which underlies ocular dominance column formation in layer 4, apparently depends on the availability of neurotrophins—BDNF and NT-4—as well as on the expression of their cognate receptor, TrkB.[63]

A Critical Period for Ocular Representation Exists in the Visual Cortex

The critical period for ocular representation in the visual cortex has been studied particularly carefully in cats by measuring the age dependence of the effects of monocular lid closure (Fig. 22.11).[56,64,65] The onset of the critical period is rapid, beginning at about 3 weeks in cats. By 4 to 6 weeks of age, the cortex is maximally sensitive to monocular deprivation: A few days of monocular deprivation causes a complete shift in the distribution of ocular dominance, leaving the cortex almost entirely driven by input from the nondeprived eye. Beyond 6 weeks of age, the critical period gradually closes: Over the next 10 months, the rate at which ocular dominance can be shifted by monocular deprivation and the degree to which it can be shifted both decrease. Once a cat is about 1 year old, monocular deprivation even for months no longer affects ocular dominance in the cortex.[66] Similar critical periods, but extending later in life, exist for the visual cortex in monkeys and humans.

The close of the critical period in cats can be delayed substantially by raising animals in complete darkness.[67,68] At birth, layer 4 neurons respond to inputs from both eyes, but the responses tend to be weak relative to those in the adult cortex (Fig. 22.10). In cats that are raised in the dark until well past the end of the critical period (as defined by monocular occlusion), layer 4 neurons continue to be driven binocularly and their responses remain weak. When these animals are finally allowed visual experience, cortical responses gradually increase in strength and the relative representation of left-eye and right-eye inputs in the cortex is shaped by the animal's experience. In monocularly deprived cats, nondeprived eye inputs become predominant in the cortex, and in cats that experience binocular vision, normal ocular dominance columns develop. This indicates that the critical period has remained open. Thus, without experience-driven input, the mechanisms that control ocular representation in the cortex remain in an uncommitted state, waiting for instruction for a prolonged, if not indefinite, period of time.

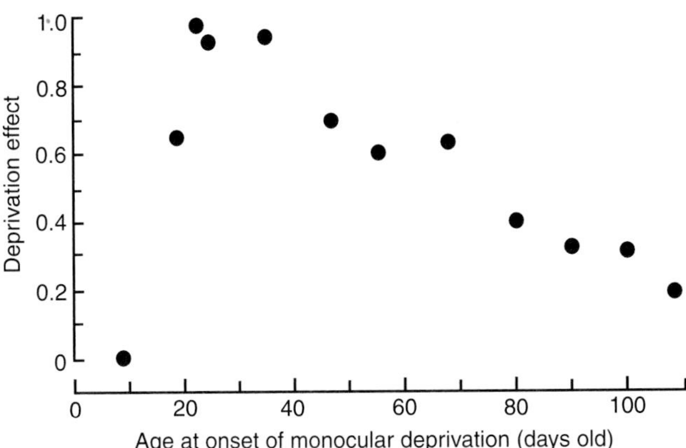

FIGURE 22.11 The critical period for ocular representation in the primary visual cortex of the cat. The degree of functional disconnection of cortical neurons from the deprived eye is quantified and plotted as a function of the kitten's age at the time of monocular closure. Chronic monocular closure lasted 10 to 12 days. Each point represents data from a single animal. Functional disconnection was based on the ocular dominance distribution (see Fig. 22.9) and indicated the degree to which the influence of the closed eye was weakened or lost. The index was defined such that the mean value for normal cats was 0, while total disconnection resulted in a value of 1. From Olson and Freeman.[65]

The critical period for ocular representation in the cortex is atypical in one respect: There is no predisposition to establish a normal pattern of connectivity based on normal experience. Even after baby cats or monkeys have experienced normal binocular vision for several weeks, monocular deprivation still causes the responses in the cortex to become dominated by the nondeprived eye. Moreover, once the responses in the cortex become dominated by one eye, reinstating normal visual input to the previously deprived eye does not restore normal binocular responses in the cortex (Fig. 22.9B). Instead, the nondeprived eye continues to dominate the responses of cortical neurons for as long as animals have been studied (up to 5 years after restoration of binocular input).[56] Thus, the pattern of neural connectivity that supports a normal binocular representation in the cortex is not stabilized immediately by exposure to normal binocular vision. Instead, normal binocular vision must persist throughout the entire critical period to prevent the cortex from becoming dominated by monocular responses. An adaptive advantage of this characteristic of the binocular pathway has yet to be recognized.

Summary

Binocular fusion occurs when signals from corresponding points on the two retinas activate the same neurons in visual cortex, a process that is guided by early experience. Early in development, thalamic axons representing inputs from the two eyes overlap extensively within layer 4 of the visual cortex. During normal development, the inputs from the left and right eyes segregate from each other to form ocular dominance columns of roughly equal width. If vision is impaired in one eye due to monocular occlusion during a critical period, the inputs carrying information from the deprived eye shrink and those from the normal eye expand. If synchronous visual stimulation of the two eyes is disrupted, as in strabismus, ocular dominance columns develop and are of normal width, but the neurons in the upper and lower layers fail to develop binocular responses. The end of the critical period can be delayed by rearing animals in complete darkness.

PRINCIPLES OF DEVELOPMENTAL LEARNING

During the later stages in the development of neural pathways, impulse activity shapes the strength and patterns of connections that are being formed between neurons. From a range of possible patterns of connectivity, the shaping process selects a pattern that is appropriate for the individual's experience.

For some pathways, the influence of experience-driven activity is not critical; it simply adjusts and fine-tunes connections that are largely genetically determined. This is the case with the owl's auditory space processing pathway, which can return to a genetically programmed, normal pattern of connectivity throughout the animal's life, once the animal experiences normal sensory input.

For other pathways, however, genetic programming is less specific or persistent, and experience is essential for the selection of one particular set of connections over all others. Such pathways, which include the song pathway in birds and the pathways that subserve filial imprinting and binocular vision, depend on specific instruction during a critical period to make a commitment to a pattern of connectivity that is appropriate for the individual.

Such **developmental learning** is distinguished from learning that can occur in adults by the magnitude and the permanence of the changes. Developmental learning can cause large-scale changes in the anatomy and/or functional response properties of neurons—well beyond the range of changes that occur in adults. Moreover, changes that result from early experience often persist throughout the lifetime of an animal.

Developmental learning is influenced heavily by genetic predisposition. Only a limited range of stimuli are allowed to operate as an instructive influence for a particular pathway; within this acceptable range, some stimuli are preferred over others. The predisposition of the nervous system to be instructed by "normal" experience probably originates in the selectivity of the response properties, genetically determined as well as shaped by experience, of the neurons that provide input to the sites in the pathway where the adjustments take place. As learning progresses, the selectivity of the pathway for acceptable input becomes progressively higher.

Whether or not a particular pathway passes through a critical period can vary across species. For example, some songbirds, such as canaries and mockingbirds, learn new songs seasonally throughout life, whereas others, such as white-crowned sparrows and zebra finches, learn their songs only during a critical period. Such species differences may provide a useful tool for uncovering the mechanisms that are responsible for critical periods.

The magnitude of changes that may result from experience-driven adjustments varies greatly across pathways and across species. The magnitude of changes depends on the degree of genetic specification of the inputs to the site of change. When the selection of appropriate inputs is from a large potential range of inputs, the effect of experience can have a profound influence on a pathway. Conversely, when the range of potential inputs is highly restricted by genetic specification, the effect of experience is correspondingly small.

The duration of different critical periods also varies greatly. At one end of the spectrum are the critical periods for imprinting, which may open and close within hours (Fig. 22.8).[3] At the other end are critical periods for acquiring complex cognitive capabilities (described in Chapter 51), such as language, which may involve several component critical periods. These are highly variable across individuals, and may last for many years.[25,69]

Deprivation Prolongs Critical Periods

Critical periods close once an animal receives adequate experience. When the animal is deprived of appropriate experience, the critical period is prolonged. For example, raising songbirds in acoustic isolation extends the critical period for song memorization, and raising cats in complete darkness extends the critical period for ocular representation in the visual cortex. This characteristic of critical periods indicates that the event that triggers critical period adjustments is the powerful and repeated activation of neurons at the site where changes take place. Without the vigorous activation of these neurons, the pathway remains in an uncommitted state. This characteristic suggests that young animals (including humans) suffering from a peripheral or central abnormality should be deprived of relevant sensory input, until the abnormality can be corrected. Otherwise, abnormal sensory experience may close the critical period, resulting in a commitment to an abnormal pattern of connectivity that cannot later be reversed.

Developmental Learning Has a Cellular Basis

Experience-driven changes in neural connectivity may involve the remodeling of axons and dendrites, the elaboration of new synapes, and/or the regulation of synaptic efficacy. Neuronal remodeling and the establishment of new synapses could be guided by the same mechanisms that control synaptogenesis during ontogeny (Chapter 19). Neurotrophins (described in Chapter 21), for example, could regulate axonal outgrowth based on experience-driven activity if they were secreted by highly active postsynaptic neurons and were taken up selectively by recently active, presynaptic axonal arbors. Uptake of neurotrophins by active arbors would induce them to grow and elaborate new synaptic connections, whereas inactive arbors would regress due to inadequate trophic support. Evidence for this hypothesis has been found in the visual cortex.[70]

Changes in connectivity patterns could also involve the regulation of synaptic efficacy within the preexisting synaptic repertoire of a neuron. The mechanisms that regulate synaptic strength include those that underlie synaptic plasticity in the adult nervous system (Chapter 55). Long-term potentiation (LTP) and long-term depression (LTD), for example, have been shown to operate in many models of developmental learning. Moreover, the ubiquitous presence of NMDA receptors, which are known to participate in LTP and LTD, at sites of change in the various models of developmental learning indicates that this class of glutamate receptor plays a key role in adjusting patterns of connectivity during sensitive periods.

Opening of Critical Periods Depends on Neuronal Maturation

Critical periods cannot open until the relevant neural pathways have developed to a point where they can support plasticity. An inability to support plasticity may be caused by the absence of adequate neuronal connectivity, neurotransmitters, receptors, or second-messenger systems. In addition, critical periods cannot open until the nervous system is capable of conveying the information that will be used to shape the patterns of connectivity. For example, critical periods that involve form vision cannot open until afferent activity encodes visual spatial information in adequate detail. This dependence implies that critical periods for regions of the brain that process high-level information cannot open until relevant information from lower level areas is sufficiently precise and reliable. The reliable encoding of low-level information may, in turn, depend on earlier critical period experience. Thus, the development of complex capabilities may involve cascades of critical periods affecting different levels of processing at different ages.[64,66]

The Closing of Critical Periods May Involve Several Mechanisms

Critical periods end once an individual has received adequate experience and the relevant pathway is irreversibly committed to a particular pattern of connectivity. The factors that render the commitment irreversible are not known. However, many factors may play a role and the factors that are most important may differ across different pathways.

One factor is that the molecular mechanisms that support changes in synaptic efficacy (described in Chapter 55), such as LTP and LTD, may be permanently altered as a consequence of adequate experience or age. Evidence supporting this possibility comes again from the visual cortex. As the critical period for ocular representation in layer 4 ends, the abundance of NMDA receptors decreases sharply in layer 4 and the kinetic properties of NMDA receptors change, making them less effective in modifying synaptic efficacy.[71,72] In addition, the effect of stimulating metabotropic glutamate receptors, which also play a role in regulating synaptic efficacy, changes markedly as the critical period closes.

A second factor is that the capacity for large-scale axonal growth may be lost. In those pathways in which axonal outgrowth is a necessary component of experience-based changes in connectivity, the loss of the mechanisms that support axonal growth would end the critical period. In the visual cortex of cats, for example, levels of the growth-associated protein GAP-43, which is thought to be necessary for axonal growth, decrease precipitously during the critical period.[73] A loss of responsiveness of presynaptic axonal arbors to neurotrophins secreted by postsynaptic neurons would also diminish the capacity for axonal elaboration. Indeed, in the visual cortex of ferrets, receptors for neurotrophins that mediate axonal remodeling are transformed from an active into an inactive form as the critical period ends.[70]

Each of the above mechanisms could be enabled by the repeated, vigorous activation of postsynaptic neurons. Hence, they could explain the resistance of a pathway to further change following exposure to adequate experience. In addition, these mechanisms could be enabled as a function of the animal's age.

A host of other factors impede anatomical and/or functional change that accompany the aging process and, therefore, could contribute to the irreversibility of critical period learning: the myelination of axons, preventing them from growing or retracting; the stabilization of synapses by the extracellular matrix or by proteoglycans; the appearance of molecules that prevent growth; and the disappearance of molecules that enable growth. Also, the action of inhibitory circuits, which become effective relatively late in development, can impede or prevent LTP.

Other factors that are of major importance are attention and arousal: Without adequate attention to the stimulus or arousal from the experience, experience-dependent changes do not take place. Conversely, after a critical period is essentially over, heightening an animal's attention or arousal can still trigger learning, as exemplified by song learning in birds. Therefore, an age-dependent decrease in the release of the neuromodulators norepinephrine (NE) and acetylcholine (ACh), which mediate the effects of attention and arousal, or in the responsiveness of neurons to these molecules could diminish the capacity of experience to induce changes. In the cat visual cortex, depletion of NE and ACh has been shown to decrease ocular dominance plasticity.[74] Conversely, administration of NE to the visual cortex of adult cats increases its modifiability.[75]

Finally, there is the possibility that a hormonally triggered switch may bring developmental learning to an end independent of experience. In many examples of developmental learning, the capacity for change declines abruptly when animals reach sexual maturity. This is the case for adjustments in the auditory space map in owls and for song learning in birds. Steroid hormones—in particular, estrogen—are known to regulate the density of synapses and various neurotransmitter receptors, the kinetics of NMDA receptors, and the responsiveness of neurons to sensory stimulation. Thus, an increase in steroid hormone levels or the expression of hormone receptors on neurons could trigger mechanisms in neurons that make them resistant to further large-scale changes.

Summary

Developmental learning occurs at all levels in the nervous system to shape the functional properties of pathways in response to the experience of the individual. In pathways that pass through a sensitive period, experience-driven activity has the opportunity to specify, from a range of possible patterns of connectivity, the pattern that is optimal for the individual's experience. For many pathways, the information gained from this experience is essential for guiding the normal development of the pathway. In such cases, this highly plastic period is referred to as a critical period.

Learning that occurs during a critical period is distinguishable from learning that occurs in adult animals in several respects. First, the changes occur readily only during a restricted period in the lifetime of the animal. Second, critical period learning involves the selection of a particular pattern of connectivity from a range of possible patterns. For example, a baby imprints on a particular individual as its parent, or a songbird selects particular songs to learn to sing. Third, the changes in the nervous system that occur during critical periods persist throughout life.

Critical periods vary in timing and duration across pathways and across species; some last only a few hours, whereas others last until the individual reaches sexual maturity. Critical periods open once the information conveyed to a pathway is sufficiently precise and the pathway is competent to support plastic change. The signal that induces change is probably the repeated, vigorous activation of postsynaptic neurons by presynaptic activity representing the occurrence of an appropriate stimulus. The range of stimuli that are effective in driving plastic change is specified by genetic preprogramming, with most pathways biased heavily to prefer normal patterns of stimulation. Critical periods close once an irreversible commitment to a pattern of connectivity has been made. This commitment can be triggered by the experience itself, or it can occur eventually as a consequence of age.

The mechanisms that close a critical period probably vary for different pathways. When the experience-induced changes require anatomical remodeling, the end of the critical period may be controlled by factors that regulate cell growth. Alternatively, when the induced changes require adjustments in synaptic efficacy, the critical period will be controlled by factors that influence the capacity of synapses to modify their efficacy. At this time, however, the specific mechanisms that are responsible for closing a particular critical period remain unknown.

References

1. Riesen, A. (1961). Stimulation as a requirement for growth and function in behavioral development. In *Functions of Varied Experience* (D. W. Fiske and S. R. Maddi, eds.), pp. 57–105. Dorsey Press, Homewood, IL.
2. von Senden, M. (1932). *Raum- und Gestaltauffassung bei Operierten Blindgeborenen vor und nach der Operation* (*translated as Space and Sight*). Free Press, Leipzig.
3. Gould, J. (1982). *Ethology: The Mechanisms and Evolution of Behavior.* Norton, New York.
4. Harlow, H., Dodsworth, R., and Harlow, M. (1965). Total social isolation in monkeys. *Proc. Natl. Acad. Sci. U.S.A.* **54:** 90–97.
5. Hess, E. H. (1973). *Imprinting: Early Experience and the Developmental Psychobiology of Attachment.* Van Nostrand-Reinhold, New York.
6. Immelmann, K. (1972). Sexual imprinting in birds. *Adv. Study Behav.* **4:** 147–174.
7. Leiderman, P. (1981). Human mother–infant social bonding: Is there a sensitive phase? In *Behavioral Development* (K. Immelmann, G. W. Barlow, L. Petrinovich, and M. Main, eds.), pp. 454–468. Cambridge University Press, Cambridge, UK.

8. Spitz, R. (1945). Hospitalism: An inquiry into the genesis of psychiatric conditions in early childhood. *Psychoanal. Study Child* **1:** 53–74.
9. Clarkson, R., Eimas, P., and Marean, G. (1989). Speech perception in children with histories of recurrent otitis media. *J. Acoust. Soc. Am.* **85**(2): 926–933.
10. Conrad, R. (1979). *The Deaf School Child.* Harper & Row, London.
11. Kuhl, P. (1991). Perception, cognition, and the ontogenetic and phylogenetic emergence of human speech. In *Plasticity of Development* (S. E. Brauth, W. S. Hall, and R. J. Dooling, eds.), pp. 73–106. MIT Press, Cambridge, MA.
12. Needleman, H. (1977). Effects of hearing loss from early recurrent otitis media on speech and language development. In *Hearing Loss in Children* (B. Jaffee, ed.), pp. 640–649. University Park Press, Baltimore, MD.
13. Ruben, R., and Rapin I. (1980). Plasticity of the developing auditory system. *Ann. Otol.* **89:** 303–311.
14. Stein, B. E., and Meredith, M. A. (1993). *The Merging of the Senses.* MIT Press, Cambridge, MA.
15. Brainard, M. D., Knudsen, E. I., and Esterly, S. D. (1992). Neural derivation of sound source location: Resolution of spatial ambiguity in binaural cues. *J. Acoust. Soc. Am.* **91:** 1015–1027.
16. Knudsen, E. I., Esterly, S. D., and Olsen, J. F. (1994). Adaptive plasticity of the auditory space map in the optic tectum of adult and baby barn owls in response to external ear modification. *J. Neurophysiol.* **71:** 79–94.
17. Knudsen, E. I. (1985). Experience alters spatial tuning of auditory units in the optic tectum during a sensitive period in the barn owl. *J. Neurosci.* **5:** 3094–3109.
18. Mogdans, J., and Knudsen, E. I. (1992). Adaptive adjustment of unit tuning to sound localization cues in response to monaural occlusion in developing owl optic tectum. *J. Neurosci.* **12:** 3473–3484.
19. Knudsen, E. I. (1988). Early blindness results in a degraded auditory map of space in the owl's optic tectum. *Proc. Natl. Acad. Sci. USA* **85:** 6211–6214.
20. Knudsen, E. I., and Brainard, M. S. (1991). Visual instruction of the neural map of auditory space in the developing optic tectum. *Science* **253:** 85–87.
21. Brainard, M. S., and Knudsen, E. I. (1993). Experience-dependent plasticity in the inferior colliculus: A site for visual calibration of the neural representation of auditory space in the barn owl. *J. Neurosci.* **13:** 4589–4608.
22. Feldman, D. E., and Knudsen, E. I. (1997). An anatomical basis for visual calibration of the auditory space map in the barn owl's midbrain. *J. Neurosci.* **17:** 6820–6837.
23. Feldman, D. E., Brainard, M. S., and Knudsen, E. I. (1996). Newly learned auditory responses mediated by NMDA receptors in the owl inferior colliculus. *Science* **271:** 525–528.
24. Konishi, M. (1985). Birdsong: From behavior to neuron. *Annu. Rev. Neurosci.* **8:** 125–170.
25. Marler, P. (1970). Birdsong and speech development: Could there be parallels? *Am. Sci.* **58:** 669–673.
26. Marler, P. (1970). A comparative approach to vocal learning: Song development in white-crowned sparrows. *J. Comp. Physiol. Psychol.* **71:** 1–25.
27. Hinde, R. A. (1982). *Acoustic Communication in Birds,* Vol. 2, D. E. Kroodsma, E. H. Miller (Eds.) *Song Learning.* Academic Press, New York.
28. Eales, L. A. (1987). Song learning in female-raised zebra finches: Another look at the sensitive phase. *Anim. Behav.* **35:** 1356–1365.
29. Eales, L. A. (1987). Do zebra finch males that have been raised by another species still tend to select a conspecific song tutor? *Anim. Behav.* **35:** 1347–1355.
30. Petrinovich, L., and Baptista, L. (1987). Song development in the white-crowned sparrow: Modification of learned song. *Anim. Behav.* **35:** 961–974.
31. Konishi, M. (1965). Effects of deafening on song development in American robins and black-headed grosbeaks. *Z. Tierpsychol.* **22:** 585–599.
32. Marler, P., Peters, S., Ball, G. F., Dufty, A. M., and Wingfield, J. C. (1988). The role of sex steroids in the acquisition and production of birdsong. *Nature* **336:** 770–772.
33. Bottjer, S. W., and Johnson, F. (1992). Matters of life and death in the songbird forebrain. *J. Neurobiol.* **23:** 1172–1191.
34. Nottebohm, F., Stokes, T. M., and Leonard, C. M. (1976). Central control of song in the canary, *Serinus canarius. J. Comp. Neurol.* 165, 457–486.
35. McCasland, J. S. (1987). Neuronal control of bird song production. *J. Neurosci.* **7:** 23–39.
36. Bottjer, S. W., Meisner, E. A., and Arnold, A. P. (1984). Forebrain lesions disrupt development but not maintenance of song in passerine birds. *Science* **224:** 901–903.
37. Sohrabji, S. W., Nordeen, E. J., and Nordeen, K. W. (1990). Selective impairment of song learning following lesions of a forebrain nucleus in the juvenile zebra finch. *Behav. Neural Biol.* **53:** 51–63.
38. Scharff, C., and Nottebohm, F. (1991). A comparative study of the behavioral deficits following lesions of various parts of the zebra finch song system: Implications for vocal learning. *J. Neurosci.* **11:** 2896–2913.
39. Doupe, A. J. (1997). Song- and order-selective neurons in the songbird anterior forebrain and their emergence during vocal development. *J. Neurosci.* **17:** 1147–1167.
40. Mooney, R., and Rao, M. (1994). Waiting periods versus early innervation: The development of axonal connections in the zebra finch song system. *J. Neurosci.* **14:** 6532–6543.
41. Mooney, R., and Konishi, M. (1991). Two distinct inputs to an avian song nucleus activate different glutamate receptor subtypes on individual neurons. *Proc. Natl. Acad. Sci. USA* **88:** 4075–4079.
42. Wallhausser-Franke, E., Nixdorf-Bergweiler, B. E., and DeVoogd, T. J. (1995). Song isolation is associated with maintaining high spine frequencies on zebra finch lMAN neurons. *Neurobiol. Learn. Mem.* **64:** 25–35.
43. Bottjer, S. W., Glaessner, S. L., and Arnold, A. P. (1985). Ontogeny of brain nuclei controlling song learning and behavior in zebra finches. *J. Neurosci.* **5:** 1556–1562.
44. Scheich, H. (1987). Neural correlates of auditory filial imprinting. *J. Comp. Physiol. A* **161:** 605–619.
45. Gottlieb, G. (1976). Early development of species-specific auditory perception in birds. In *Studies on the Development of Behavior and the Nervous System* (G. Gottlieb, ed.), Vol. 3, pp. 237–280. Academic Press, New York.
46. Grier, J., Counter, S., and Shearer, W. (1967). Prenatal auditory imprinting in chickens. *Science* **155:** 1692–1693.
47. Kuhl, P. (1976). Speech perception in early infancy: The acquisition of speech-sound categories. In *Hearing and Davis: Essays Honoring Hallowell Davis* (S. K. Hirsh, D. H. Eldredge, I. J. Hirsh, and S. R. Silverman, eds.), pp. 265–280. Washington University Press, St. Louis, MO.
48. Ramsay, A. O., and Hess, E. H. (1954). A laboratory approach to the study of imprinting. *Wilson Bull.* **66:** 196–206.
49. Vidal, J.-M. (1980). Relations between filial and sexual imprinting in domestic fowl. *Anim. Behav.* **28:** 880–891.
50. Miller, D., and Gottlieb, G. (1978). Maternal vocalizations of mallard ducks. *Anim. Behav.* **26:** 1178–1194.

51. Jampolsky, A. (1978). Unequal visual inputs and strabismus management: A comparison of human and animal strabismus. In *Symposium on Strabismus. Trans. New Orleans Acad. Ophthalmol.* **26:** 358–492.
52. Shatz, C. (1990). Impulse activity and the patterning of connections during CNS development. *Neuron* **5:** 745–756.
53. Blake, R., and Hirsch, H. (1975). Deficits in binocular depth perception in cats after alternating monocular deprivation. *Science* **190:** 1114–1116.
54. Hubel, D. (1979). The visual cortex of normal and deprived monkeys. *Am. Sci.* **67:** 532–543.
55. Wiesel, T. N., and Hubel, D. H. (1965). Extent of recovery from the effects of visual deprivation in kittens. *J. Neurophysiol.* **28:** 1060–1072.
56. Hubel, D. H., and Wiesel, T. N. (1970). The period of susceptibility to the physiological effects of unilateral eye closure in kittens. *J. Physiol.* (*London*) **206:** 419–436.
57. Blakemore, C., Vital-Durand, F., and Garey, L. (1981). Recovery from monocular deprivation in the monkey. I. Recovery of physiological effects in the visual cortex. *Proc. R. Soc. London [Biol.]* **213:** 399–423.
58. Movshon, J. (1976). Reversal of the physiological effects of monocular deprivation in the kitten's visual cortex. *J. Physiol. (London)* **261:** 125–175.
59. Hubel, D., Wiesel, T., and LeVay, S. (1977). Plasticity of ocular dominance columns in the monkey striate cortex. *Philos. Trans. R. Soc. London, Ser. B* **278:** 377–409.
60. Antonini, A., and Stryker, M. (1993). Rapid remodeling of axonal arbors in the visual cortex. *Science* **260:** 1819–1821.
61. Stryker, M. P., and Strickland, S. L. (1984). Physiological segregation of ocular dominance columns depends on the pattern of afferent electrical activity. *Vis. Sci. [Suppl.]* **25:** 278.
62. Kirkwood, A., and Bear, M. F. (1994). Hebbian synapses in visual cortex. *J. Neurosci.* **14:** 1634–1645.
63. Cabelli, R. J., Hohn, A., and Shatz, C. J. (1995). Inhibition of ocular dominance column formation by infusion of NT-4/5 or BDNF. *Science* **267:** 1662–1666.
64. LeVay, S., Wiesel, T. N., and Hubel, D. H. (1980). The development of ocular dominance columns in normal and visually deprived monkeys. *J. Comp. Neurol.* **191:** 1–51.
65. Olson, C. R., and Freeman, R. D. (1980). Profile of the sensitive period for monocular deprivation in kittens. *Exp. Brain Res.* **39:** 17–21.
66. Daw, N., Fox, K., Sato, H., and Czepita, D. (1992). Critical period for monocular deprivation in the cat visual cortex. *J. Neurophysiol.* **67**(1): 197–202.
67. Cynader, M., and Mitchell, D. E. (1980). Prolonged sensitivity to monocular deprivation in dark-reared cats. *J. Neurophysiol.* **4:** 1026–1040.
68. Mower, G., and Christen, W. (1985). Role of visual experience in activating critical period in cat visual cortex. *J. Neurophysiol.* **53**(2): 572–589.
69. Bates, E., Bretherton, L., and Snyder, L. (1988). *From First Words to Grammar.* Cambridge University Press, Cambridge, UK.
70. Katz, L. C., and Shatz, C. J. (1996). Synaptic activity and the construction of cortical circuits. *Science* **274:** 1133–1138.
71. Bode-Greuel, K. M., and Singer, W. (1989). The development of *N*-methyl-D-asparate receptors in cat visual cortex. *Dev. Brain. Res.* **46:** 197–204.
72. Daw, N. W. (1994). Mechanisms of plasticity in the visual cortex. *Invest. Ophthal. Vis. Sci.* **35:** 4168–4179.
73. McIntosh, J., Daw, N. W., and Parkinson, D. (1990). GAP-43 in the cat visual cortex during postnatal development. *Neuroscience* **4:** 585–594.
74. Bear, M. F., and Singer, W. (1986). Modulation of visual cortical plasticity by acetylcholine and noradrenaline. *Nature* **320:** 172–176.
75. Kasamatsu, T., Pettigrew, J., and Amy, M. (1979). Restoration of visual cortical plasticity by local microperfusion of norepinephrin. *J. Comp. Neurol.* **185:** 163–181.

S E C T I O N IV

SENSORY SYSTEMS

C H A P T E R

23

Fundamentals of Sensory Systems

Stewart H. C. Hendry, Steven S. Hsiao, and M. Christian Brown

In bringing information about the world to an individual, sensory systems perform a series of common functions. At its most basic, each system responds with some specificity to a stimulus and each employs specialized cells—the peripheral receptors—to translate the stimulus into a signal that all neurons can use. Because of their physical or chemical specialization, the many types of receptors transduce the energy in light, sound, mechanical, or thermal stimulation into a change in membrane potential. That initial electrical event begins the process by which the central nervous system (CNS) constructs an orderly representation of the body and of things visible or audible. To bridge the distance between peripheral transduction and central representation, messages are carried along lines dedicated to telling the CNS what has taken place in the external world and where it has happened. Such precision requires that labor be divided among neurons so that not only different stimulus energies (sound vs light vs mechanical deformation of skin or hair) but also different stimulus qualities (e.g., low-frequency flutter vs high-frequency vibration in the somatosensory system) are analyzed by separate groups of neurons.

In addition to their organization along parallel lines, sensory systems perform common types of operations. Foremost among these is the ability of each system to compare events that occur simultaneously at different receptors, a process that serves to bring out the greatest response where the difference in stimulus strength (contrast) is greatest. At late stages in sensory processing, systems make comparisons with past events and with sensations received by other sensory systems. These comparisons are the fundamental bases of perception, recognition, and comprehension.

In this chapter, we give an overview of the functional attributes and patterns of organization displayed by the auditory, somatosensory, and visual systems and outline the physiological and anatomical principles common to all sensory systems. When variations on a common theme exist, they are discussed with the goal of bringing the general pattern into sharper focus.

SENSATION AND PERCEPTION

The Function of Each Sensory System Is to Provide the CNS with a Representation of the External World

Because of the changes that occur around an individual, each sensory system has the task of providing a constantly updated representation of the external world. Accomplishing this task is no simple feat because it requires a close interaction between ascending or stimulus-driven mechanisms and descending or goal-directed mechanisms. Together these two mechanisms evoke sensations, give rise to perceptions, and activate stored memories to form the basis of conscious experience. Ascending mechanisms begin with the activity of peripheral receptors, which together form an initial neural representation of the external world. Descending mechanisms work to sort out from the large amount of sensory input those events that require immediate attention. In doing so, the descending mechanisms alter ascending inputs in ways that optimize perception.

Because of the interplay between ascending and descending mechanisms, perception differs from sensation. A classic example of the difference between the two is seen in the image of a vase that can also be

FIGURE 23.1 An example of a figure that can elicit different perceptions (faces or vase) even though stimulus and sensation remain constant. The mind can "see" purple figures against a blue background or a blue figure against a purple background.

perceived as two faces, pointed nose to nose (Fig. 23.1). In this case the image remains the same—the sensory input remains constant—but the perception of what is being viewed changes as the goal of the viewer changes or as his or her attention wanders. Using this example, we can see that detection of a stimulus and recognition that an event has occurred are what we usually call sensation; interpretation and appreciation of that event constitute perception.[1]

Neurons in Sensory Systems Signal Events by a Combination of Rate, Spatial, and Temporal Codes

Peripheral receptors and the central neurons with which they communicate signal the presence of a stimulus by their activity; they signal the intensity of a stimulus by the rate of that activity.[2] This signal is a rate code in which the number of action potentials generated by a neuron signals the strength of the sensory input it receives. The perceived intensity arises from an interaction between the number of neurons activated by a stimulus and the average rate of their response.

Sensation also depends on the location of active groups of neurons. For example, in reading Braille, the ability to identify letters is based on a refined spatial input of activity and comparison across adjacent regions, rather than on the total or average intensity within a large neuronal population. Comparison of this sort relies on the existence of a receptor density sufficiently large to capture the details of a stimulus. In this way peripheral innervation density is tightly correlated with spatial acuity.[3]

There is a temporal quality to sensation. Sounds that make up music or speech carry not only loudness (intensity) and tone (which for the auditory system is a matter of which place along the cochlea is active) but also rhythm—the precise interaction of sound and silence. In addition, all sensory systems must deal with the fact that stimuli can move, as with vibratory stimuli on the skin. This temporal information in a stimulus is carried by the time-varying pattern of activity in small groups of receptors and central neurons.

Psychophysics Is the Quantitative Study of Sensory Performance

A psychophysical experiment determines the quantitative relationship between a stimulus and a sensation in order to establish the limits of sensory performance.[4] Such an experiment relies on reports from a subject who is asked to judge quantitatively the presence or magnitude of a stimulus as careful adjustments in the physical attributes are made. One example of threshold detection is the **two-point limen,** in which two blunt probes, separated by a distance that is progressively enlarged or reduced over a series of trials, are applied to the skin surface. The minimum separation distance at which a subject reports two stimuli half the time and one stimulus the other half is taken as the detection threshold. That distance can be measured accurately and is found to vary markedly across the body surface; the two-point limen is smallest for the finger tips and largest for the skin of the back.[5] Other studies, such as those exploring the detection of relative magnitudes of stimuli, can include assessments of object heaviness, loudness of sound, or brightness of light. Studies of this sort have been combined with neurophysiological experiments to compare reports from subjects (sensory behavior) with the responses of single cells (neuronal physiology). Through this procedure the neural mechanisms underlying sensory perception can be examined.

RECEPTORS

Receptors Are Specific for a Narrow Range of Input

Neurons of the brain and spinal cord do not respond when they are touched, bombarded with sound, or exposed to light. Each of these forms of energy must be first transduced by specialized cells, thereby converting the stimulus into a signal that produces a neuronal response. In every sensory system cells that perform such a transduction are called **receptors**[6] (Fig. 23.2). For each of the fundamental types of stimuli (touch, chemicals, sound, or light) there is a separate population of receptors selective for the particular form of energy. Even within a single sensory system, classes of receptors that are particularly sensitive to one stimulus (e.g., heat or cold) and not another (muscle stretch) exist. This specificity in the receptor response is a direct function of differences in receptor structure and chemistry.

Receptor Types Vary across Sensory Systems

Systems differ in the number of distinct receptor types they incorporate. In the auditory system, two classes of receptor—the inner and outer hair cells of the cochlea—transduce mechanical energy of the basilar membrane, set in motion by sound.[7] Transduction in the visual system is performed by two broad classes of receptor in the retina—the rods and the cones.[8] The number of cone types varies from one type in some species to two types in many species to three types in a few species.[9] All photoreceptors transduce light energy, but the rods and the various types of cones are maximally sensitive to different wavelengths of light.[10] By comparison, the somatosensory system is unique in the large number of receptor types it contains. Separate types exist to transduce a variety of mechanical stimuli, including light touching of hairless skin, deformation of hair, vibration, increased or decreased skin temperature, tissue destruction, and stretch of muscles or tendons[11] (Fig. 23.2). A strong correlation exists, then, between the number of receptor types displayed by a system and the types of stimuli that system is able to detect.

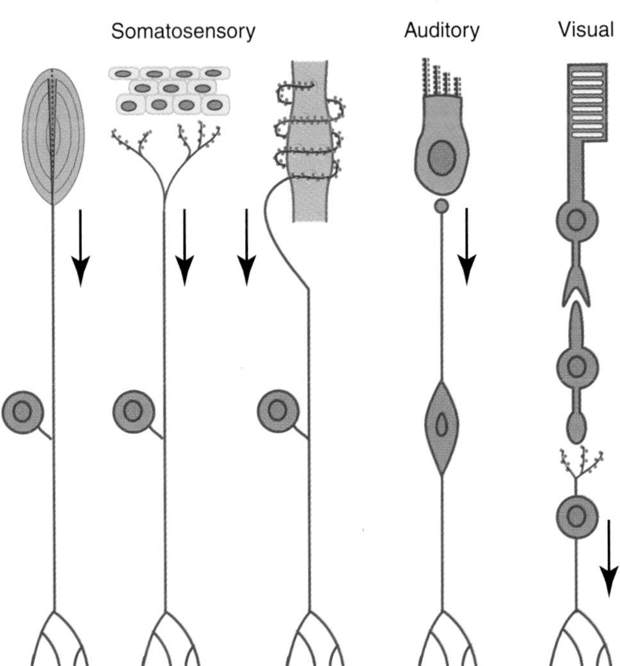

FIGURE 23.2 Receptor morphology and its relationship to ganglion cells in the somatosensory, auditory, and visual systems. Receptors are specialized structures that adopt different shapes depending on their function. The neural part of a receptor is the ganglion cell axon for each somatosensory receptor, but is a distinct type of cell in auditory and visual systems. In the auditory periphery, the receptor (hair cell) and ganglion cells communicate directly, whereas in the visual system an interneuron collects photoreceptor input and relays it to the retinal ganglion cell. Adapted from Bodian, D. (1967). Neurons, circuits, and neuroglia. In *The Neurosciences: A Study Program* (G. C. Quarton, T. Melnechuk, and F. O. Schmitt, eds.). New York: Rockefeller University Press, pp. 6–24.

Receptors Perform a Common Function in Unique Fashion

All receptors transduce the energy to which they are sensitive into a change in membrane voltage. The receptor's task is to transmit that voltage change by one route or another to a class of neurons—universally referred to as ganglion cells—that send their axons into the brain or spinal cord (Fig. 23.2). Systems vary in the mechanism whereby receptors and ganglion cells interact. Most receptors in the somatosensory system are part of multicellular organs, the neural components of which are the terminal specializations of ganglion cell axons.[11] An appropriate stimulus applied to a somatosensory receptor produces a generator potential—a graded change in membrane voltage[12]—that, when large enough, leads to action potentials that can be carried over a considerable distance into the central nervous system.

Receptors of the auditory and visual systems are separate specialized cells that transduce a stimulus and then transmit the resulting signal to the nearby process of a second-order neuron. Because the distances between receptor and target neuron are short, auditory hair cells and photoreceptors do not generate action potentials but signal their response by passive flow of current. Visual and auditory systems differ in the path between receptor and ganglion cell. In the cochlea, auditory receptors form chemical synapses directly with the processes of ganglion cells,[13] so that the response properties of inner hair cells are donated directly to the ganglion cells on which they synapse. That is not the case in the retina, where photoreceptors relay their response through populations of interneurons interposed between them and retinal ganglion cells[14] (Fig. 23.2). Because of this additional synapse and the opportunity it affords for summation and comparison of receptor signals, the retinal ganglion cell response differs appreciably from that of photoreceptors.

The mechanisms whereby receptors transduce and transmit signals are known in greater or lesser detail for each system. Visual transduction is a well-understood, rapid process in which a weak signal (a single photon)[15] can be greatly amplified through a biochemical cascade, leading to closure of thousands of Na^+ channels and a hyperpolarizing response.[16,17] For auditory hair cells and somatosensory mechanoreceptors, the mechanical deformation of a part of the cell is transduced into a change in membrane voltage.[18,19] The response of mechanoreceptors is similar to that of photoreceptors in being of one sign only, but it is a sign opposite that of photoreceptors, as an appropriate tactile stimulus leads to the opening of Na^+ channels and a depolarizing response. The requirement for depolarization may result from the demands placed on the somatosensory ganglion cell to generate action potentials and transmit information over long distances. Auditory receptors, in contrast, can generate a biphasic response. When protruding villi of the hair cell, called stereocilia, are deflected in one direction, transducer channels open and the cell is depolarized. Yet with deflection of stereocilia in the opposite direction, the same channels close and the cell is hyperpolarized.[19] Because sound usually produces a back-and-forth deflection of stereocilia, the result is a back-and-forth movement of the receptor potential—one that permits the receptor output to signal information about the waveform of an acoustic stimulus.

Receptors Are the Sites of Convergence and Divergence

The relationship between receptor and ganglion cell is seldom exclusive. Most commonly, a single ganglion cell receives input from several receptors and in many cases a single receptor sends information to two or more ganglion cells. **Convergence** and **divergence** go hand in hand for the somatosensory system as an individual receptor is often innervated by axons of several ganglion cells while at the same time the axon of a single ganglion cell can branch to end as part of several receptor organs.[20] Yet in the somatosensory system, the amount of divergence and convergence varies with the class of receptor involved (e.g., thermal receptor vs mechanoreceptor) and the location of the receptor on the body surface (e.g., shoulder vs finger tip). Similar features are seen in the visual system, as divergence and convergence dominate different parts of the retina populated by different receptor types. In the cone-rich central retina, each cone provides as many as four ganglion cells with their main visual drive,[21] whereas in the rod-rich periphery, a few dozen rods supply each ganglion cell with its visual input. In its precision and in its implications for sensory processing, nothing approaches the divergence seen in the cochlea, where a single inner hair cell can be the source of all input received by 20 ganglion cells.[13] Thus, what emerges from a comparison across systems is that convergence and divergence from receptor to ganglion cell vary directly with the demands placed on the system at the specific location. When spatial resolution is a requirement, convergence of receptor inputs onto individual ganglion cells is low. When detection of weak signals is necessary, convergence is high. And when receptor input is used for a complex function or for multiple functions, divergence of input from a single receptor onto many ganglion cells occurs.

Receptors Vary in Their Embryonic Origin

For auditory and somatosensory systems, the various classes of receptors and ganglion cells are part of the peripheral nervous system, generated as progeny of neuroblasts located in neural crests and sensory placodes.[22] That is not the case for photoreceptors and retinal ganglion cells. The retina is generated as a protrusion of the embryonic diencephalon and thus all its neurons and supporting cells are CNS derivatives of neural tube origin.[23] As a result of their origin, receptors and ganglion cells of the auditory and somatosensory system are supported by a class of nonneuronal cells (the Schwann cells), whereas photoreceptors and retinal ganglion cells are supported by CNS neuroglial cells. Most dramatic of all the consequences resulting from this difference in origin is the ability of axons in somatosensory peripheral nerves to regenerate and reinnervate targets after they are damaged, as opposed to the complete and permanent loss of visual function when optic nerves are cut or crushed.

Receptors Adopt Characteristic Patterns of Position and Density

Receptors are not scattered randomly across the sensory surface. An orderly arrangement of receptors exists along the skin, the basilar membrane, and the retina. In the retina, for example, photoreceptors adopt an hexagonal packing array,[24] and in the cochlea, a single row of inner hair cells lines up parallel to three rows of outer hair cells.[7] The arrangement of receptors in the skin is less orderly. Yet a nonrandom distribution is immediately evident in a comparison of the density of cutaneous receptors across the skin surface. By far the greatest density of receptor terminals is found at the finger tips and the mouth, whereas receptors along the surface of the back are at least an order of magnitude less frequent.[5]

PARALLEL PROCESSING

Sensory Information Is Transmitted along Labeled Lines

A long-appreciated principle that unites structure and function in a sensory system is the doctrine of specific energy, or the **labeled line principle.** This principle states that when a particular population of neurons is active, the conscious perception is of a specific stimulus at a defined location (Fig. 23.3). For example, in one particular population of somatosensory neurons, activity is always interpreted by the CNS as a painful stimulus occurring in the big toe, no matter whether the stimulus is natural (a sharp pin jabbed into the skin) or artificial (electrical stimulation of the appropriate axons). Different populations would signal vibration, heat, and light touch in the big toe, just as entirely different populations would signal pain in the second toe, the ball of the foot, or the heel. Why this is so can be seen from the fact that receptors are selective not only in what drives them but also in the postsynaptic targets with which they communicate. Each ganglion cell transmits its activity into a well-defined region of the CNS, after which a strictly organized series of synaptic connections relays information in a sequence that leads to the cerebral cortex.[25] It is this orderly relay from receptor to ganglion cell to central neurons at each of several stations that makes up a labeled line. All sensory information arising from a single class of receptors is referred to as a **modality.**

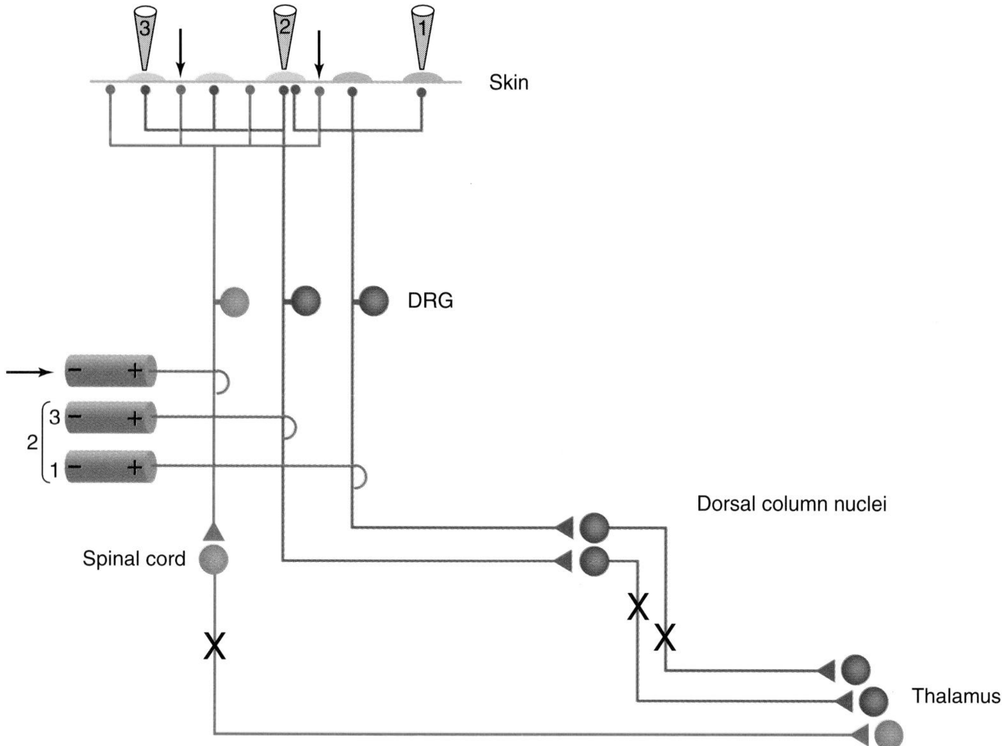

FIGURE 23.3 Example of labeled lines in the somatosensory system. Two dorsal root ganglion (DRG) cells (blue) send axons to be part of a touch receptor, whereas a third (red) gives off axons as pain receptors. Direct touching of the skin with a blunt probe (flat-bottom V) or electrical stimulation of an appropriate axon produces the sensation of light touch at a defined location. Note convergence of two DRG axons onto a single touch receptor on the skin. This convergence permits touch stimulus 2 to be localized precisely. Electrical stimulation of both axons produces the same sensation. A sharp stimulus (arrow) applied to nearby skin regions selectively activates the third ganglion cell, eliciting the sensation of pain. Electrical stimulation of that ganglion cell or of any cell along that pathway also produces a sensation of pain along that region of skin.

(For example, the sensations of heat and roughness involve distinct modalities.) Thus, the existence of labeled lines means that neurons in sensory systems are specific to both modality and location.

Topographic Projections Dominate the Anatomy and Physiology of Sensory Systems

Receptors in the retina and body surface are organized as two-dimensional sheets, whereas those of the cochlea form a one-dimensional line along the cochlear length. Receptors in these organs communicate with ganglion cells and those ganglion cells with central neurons in a strictly ordered fashion, such that relationships with neighbors are maintained throughout. This type of pattern, in which neurons positioned side by side in one region communicate with neurons so positioned in the next region, is called a **topographic pattern.** The end result is a map of the sensory surface (retina, cochlea, or skin) in each region. In addition to the labeled line principle, the topography of sensory systems shows that in any sensory region each neuron is specific for both the place at which a stimulus occurred and the modality of that stimulus.

Multiple Maps of the Sensory Surface Are Found in All Systems

To accommodate the many lines labeled for different modalities and the many maps organized to reflect the sensory surface, regions of the CNS often contain multiple maps. The division of labor seen earliest in sensory processing occurs in the auditory system, where axons of spiral ganglion cells divide into branches as they enter the CNS and terminate in three divisions of the cochlear nuclei.[26] Each division contains its own map of sound frequency (tonotopic map) that was originally established by the cochlea. The greatest number of maps generated from ganglion cell input is found in the visual system of primates, in which as many as six separate retinotopic maps are stacked on top of one another in the lateral geniculate nucleus (LGN) (in the thalamus), which receives direct input from the retina.[27] Such a large number of distinct maps in the LGN is indicative of inputs from ganglion cells that vary in location, structure, and function.[28]

Parallel Paths Maintain a Division of Labor from Periphery to Cortex

Where multiple maps of the sensory surface exist, the information entering and leaving the region of one map is kept separate from that entering and leaving the region of a second map. That is, parallel paths exist to handle separate modalities. For somatic sensation the most easily detected parallel paths handle discriminative touch and body position separately from pain and temperature.[29] For vision, surface features such as color and form are carried along a path separate from that which handles three-dimensional features of motion and stereopsis.[30] What is handled separately in multiple maps of the cochlea is not so clear. In each case, however, the need for multiple parallel paths exists because of the relatively slow speed and limited capacity of single neurons. So rather than have the same group of neurons perform different functions in serial order, each of several parallel groups performs a separate function. This leads eventually to the problem of binding together all features of a stimulus into a coherent precept, the neural basis for which may be the synchronized activity of neurons across several areas of cerebral cortex.[31]

CENTRAL PROCESSING

Receptive Fields Are Modified by Synapses in the CNS

Each sensory neuron possesses a receptive field, defined physiologically as the region of the periphery that when stimulated produces a change in the neuron's activity. This definition serves well for peripheral receptors and for central neurons. A second, more anatomically based definition states that the receptive field of a CNS neuron is composed of all peripheral receptors from which that neuron receives an input, directly or indirectly. Most neurons of the CNS are responsive to stimuli that occur along a very small part of the skin, retina, or basilar membrane. Thus, this majority population is innervated directly or indirectly by a relatively small proportion of peripheral receptors. For the most part, receptive fields in each sensory system tend to become larger and more complex at higher levels, as the contributions from a large number of receptors are added and compared with one another.

Neurons of the CNS Are Specialized and Form Distinct Classes

Groups of neurons at any level in a sensory system display unique characteristics. When these are significant enough to produce variations in physiology, separate classes are said to exist. An example of a cellular characteristic that produces a fundamental division in cell class is found in the retina, at the synapse between photoreceptors and neurons of the next stage of visual processing—the retinal bipolar cells. Even though all photoreceptors release the neurotransmitter glutamate, separate classes of bipolar cells express and insert into their dendrites different types of glutamate receptors.[32] One type produces a postsynaptic excitatory response; the other leads to a postsynaptic inhibitory response. This is the basis for the early division of the visual system into populations that respond when a light stimulus is turned off (OFF response) and those that respond when a light stimulus is turned on (ON response).

Lateral Mechanisms of Processing Are Found at All Levels of the CNS

A hallmark of all sensory systems is the ability of neurons at even the earliest stages of central processing to integrate the activity of more than one receptor (Fig. 23.4). The most common and easily understood of these mechanisms is **lateral** (or surround) **inhibition.** By this mechanism a sensory neuron in the CNS displays a receptive field with an excitatory center and an inhibitory surround.[33] Such a mechanism serves to turn sensory neurons of the CNS into contrast detectors; each responds optimally to a stimulus that occupies most of its center but little of its surround. In some cases the comparisons involve receptors of different types so that the center and surround differ not only in sign (excitation vs inhibition, ON vs OFF) but also in the stimulus quality to which they respond. One such example occurs in neurons of the visual system that possess centers and surrounds responsive to stimulation of different types of cones.[34] These cells display a combination of spatial contrast (the difference in the location of cones that produce center and surround) and chromatic contrast (the difference in the visible wavelengths to which these cones respond best). Similar types of responses are evident in the somatosensory system, where the difference between center and surround is the location on the skin from which each is activated.[29] In this case, skin mechanics[3] and neural mechanisms at each of several levels[6] produce receptive fields with a central hot spot of activity and a surrounding inactive zone. Mechanical mechanisms also generate the auditory system's lateral or two-tone suppressive areas, displayed by peripheral neurons, whereas larger lateral inhibitory areas generated by neural inhibition are evident in responses of some central neurons[35] (Fig. 23.4C). In each case, whether by CNS or peripheral mechanisms, center/surround organization serves to sharpen the selectivity of a neuron either for the position of the stimulus or for its exact quality by subtracting responses to stimuli of a general or diffuse nature.

Synaptic Mechanisms Exist for Coincidence Detection

Comparison of activity in a population of receptors of the same kind is sometimes necessary for a central neuron to respond at all. That is, input from two or more receptors (or the neurons to which they send inputs) is required to reach a neuron at about the same time so that the summation of their signals is strong enough to produce a response. The most compelling case for the detection of such a coincidence is seen in the medial superior olivary nucleus of the brainstem. Here neurons receive a bilateral input from the cochlear nuclei and are thus innervated by the pathways from both cochleas.[36] These neurons respond only when there is a coincident input from neurons on the two sides of the brain.[35] This circuit is involved in localization of sounds: A neural delay in input from one side serves to make up for the delay produced by the arrival of sound at one ear prior to the other, as occurs whenever the sound source is not directly in front of or behind the listener (see Chapter 27).

The Central Representations of Some Parts of the Periphery Are Magnified

The distribution of somatosensory and visual receptors is uneven. The site of central vision in primate retina—the fovea or macula—and the fingertips of the hand in primates are regions that possess a high density of receptors with small receptive fields (Fig. 23.5). Such an uneven distribution of neurons devoted to a structure is further amplified in the CNS so that a greater percentage of neural machinery subserves the representation of the retinal fovea or the fingertips than the representation of other regions of the retina or body surface.[37,38] This expansion of a representation in the CNS, referred to as a **magnification factor,** appears particularly impressive in humans, in whom a very large part of primary visual cortex is devoted to the couple of millimeters of retina in and around the fovea.[39]

Synthesis of Various Inputs Occurs to Produce a Coherent Precept

At very early stages in sensory processing, the CNS begins the task of reconstructing a complete representation of the world. This task involves comparisons of activity in groups of receptors large enough to construct a central representation of at least part of a stimu-

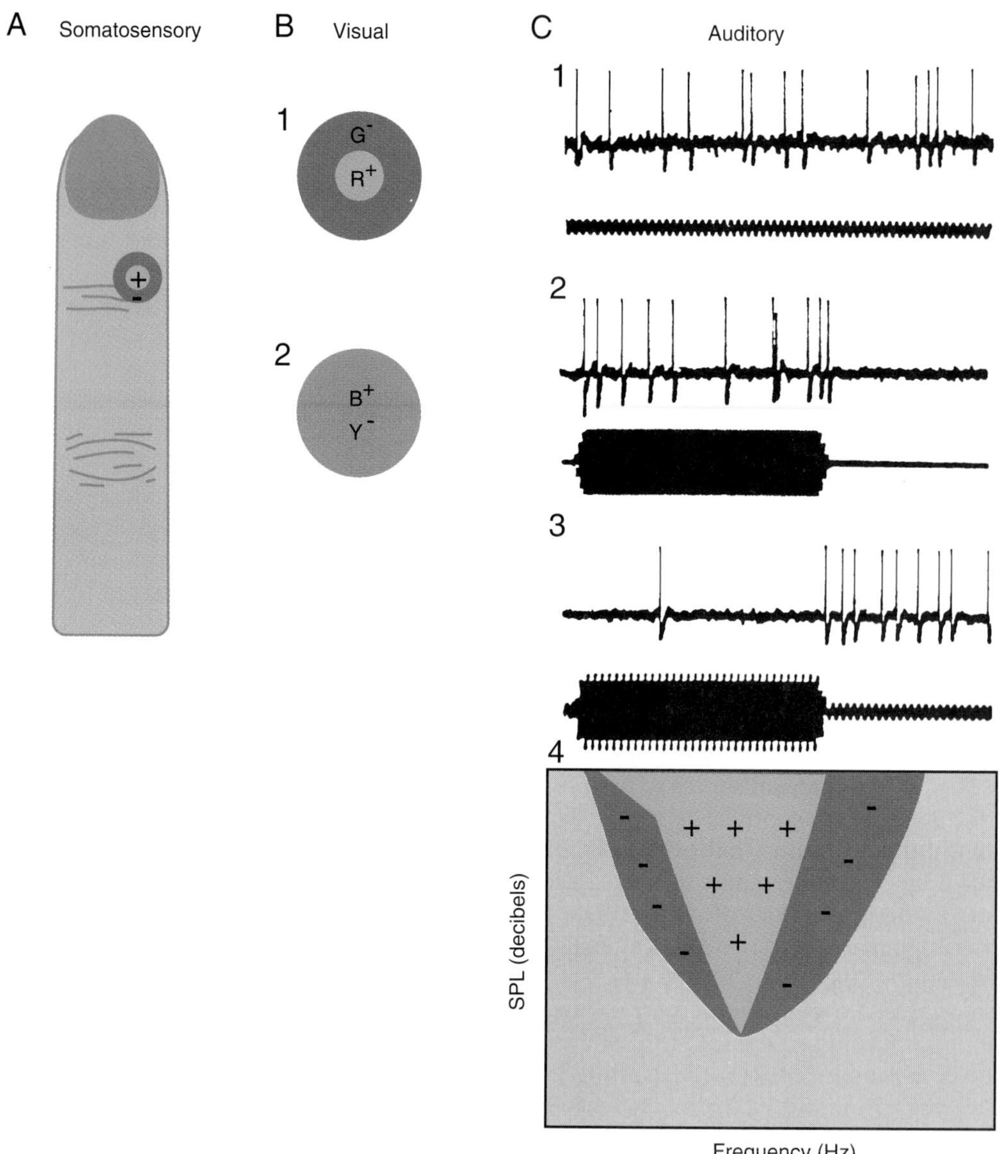

FIGURE 23.4 Center/surround organization of receptive fields. (A) Receptive fields of somatosensory neurons display antagonistic centers and surrounds because of skin mechanics. (B) A common type of receptive field in the retina and visual thalamus is antagonistic for location and for wavelength. Receptive field 1 is sensitive to turning on red light (R) at its center and turning off green light (G) in its surround. Receptive field 2 is less common and is antagonistic for wavelength (blue vs yellow) without being antagonistic for the location of the stimuli. Both are generated by neural processing in the retina. (C) Examples of peripheral (1–3) and central (4) mechanisms of surround suppression–inhibition in the auditory system. Records in 1–3 show the response recorded from the axon of an auditory ganglion cell (upper waveform) to two different tones (lower waveform), presented individually (1 and 2) or together (3). Either elicits a response from this auditory afferent but the two exert a suppressive effect when presented together. The graph in 4 shows the response of a central auditory neuron to changes in loudness or sound pressure level (SPL) and frequency of a tone. At a characteristic frequency the neuron responds well to a relatively quiet stimulus (low SPL); even slight changes from that frequency, however, produce inhibition (−) rather than excitation (+).

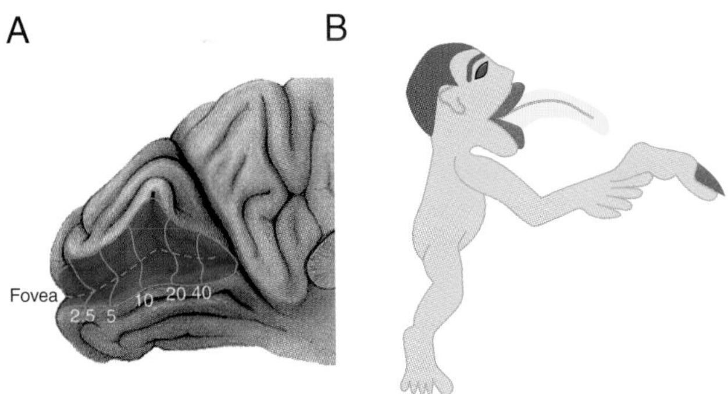

FIGURE 23.5 Examples of sensory magnification in the visual and somatosensory systems. (A) Recent determination of visual field map in human primary visual cortex shows that more than half this area is devoted to the central 10° of visual field. Very little is devoted to the visual periphery beyond 40°. From Horton and Hoyt (1991).[39] (B) Figurine of how the human body would appear if the body surface were a perfect reflection of the map in the first somatosensory cortex. The mouth and tongue and the tip of the index finger enjoy a greatly enlarged representation in the thalamus and cortex.

lus. One example is seen in the primary visual area of the cerebral cortex, where neurons are responsive to stimuli not as concentric circles (center and surround) but as elongated lines possessing a specific orientation.[40] Comparable synthesis of simpler inputs to reconstruct more complex features of stimulus is apparent at higher levels in the visual system[41,42] and in the somatosensory[43] and auditory areas of the cerebral cortex.[44]

COMMON ANATOMICAL PLAN

Axons in Each System Cross the Midline on Their Way to the Thalamus

Axons of ganglion cells enter the CNS and either directly, in the case of the visual system, or through at least one synaptic relay reach the dorsal thalamus (Fig. 23.6). Axons in all three systems cross the midline—they **decussate**—prior to reaching the thalamus. A single, incomplete decussation occurs in the visual system of primates, where slightly more than half the axons of the optic nerve cross the midline at the optic chiasm.[45] Decussation in the somatosensory system also occurs only once and is nearly total, as all but a small group of axons cross the midline in the spinal cord or brainstem.[46] These decussations serve the broad functions of bringing together all axons carrying visual information from half the visual world or of bringing somatosensory information into alignment with motor output, which is itself a largely crossed system. In contrast, multiple decussations occur in the auditory system prior to the thalamus,[47] as comparison of input from the two ears is the dominant requirement of sound source localization. Nevertheless, at high levels in the auditory system one side of the brain is concerned mainly with processing information about sound sources located toward the opposite side of the body. In all of these ascending systems a common final pattern exists in which a prominent, heavily myelinated tract carries rapidly transmitted messages into the thalamus.

Specific Thalamic Nuclei Exist for Each Sensory System

Information from each of the sensory systems must be relayed through the thalamus on its way to the cerebral cortex.[48] That relay involves either a single large nucleus or, in the case of the somatosensory systems, two nuclei—one for the body and one for the face. In each nucleus, synaptic circuits are said to be

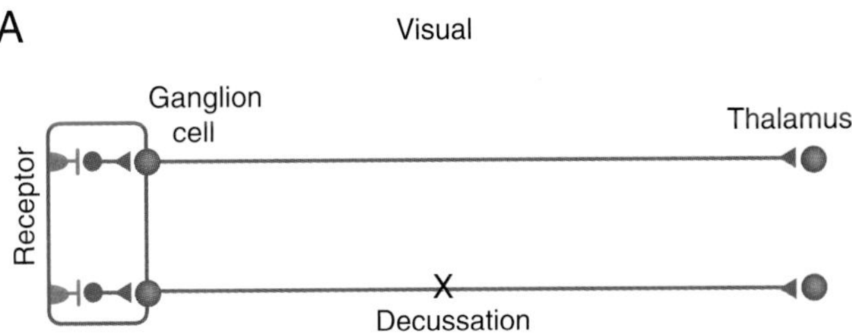

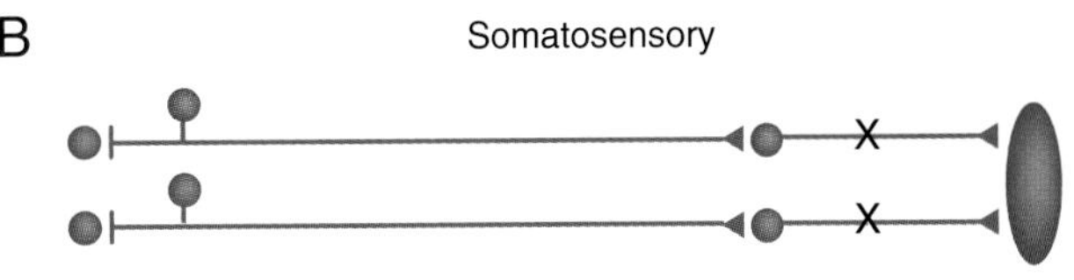

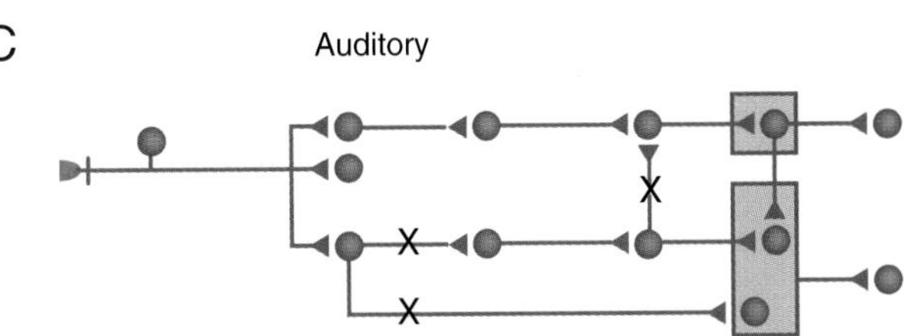

FIGURE 23.6 Comparison of central organization of sensory system pathways. In every case decussations are donated by A's in the pathway. Major relay paths include: (A) partial decussation of ganglion cell axons in the visual system and direct projection to the thalamus; (B) complete decussation of second-order axons in the somatosensory system and their termination in the thalamus; and (C) multiple decussations in the auditory brainstem with an obligatory synapse prior to termination in the thalamus.

"secure" because activity in presynaptic axons usually leads to a postsynaptic response. Each of the sensory relay nuclei is heterogeneous, with neurons performing one function (e.g., relay of discriminative touch) segregated from those performing another (e.g., relay of pain and temperature). For the most part, this segregation of function involves a population of large neurons and one or two populations of small neurons for each sensory thalamic nucleus.[49] In each case the larger neurons carry the most rapidly transmitted signals from the periphery to the cortex.

STRUCTURE, FUNCTION, AND CONNECTIONS OF SENSORY CORTEX

Sensory Areas Include Primary and Association Areas of the Cortex

Axons of sensory relay nuclei of the thalamus innervate a single area or a collection of neighboring areas of the cerebral cortex, thereby providing them with a precise topographic map of the sensory periphery.[48] These parts of cortex are frequently referred to as **primary sensory areas.** Most areas with which the primary areas communicate directly or by a single intervening relay area are sensory association areas.

A Common Structure Exists for Sensory Cortex

Neurons in areas of sensory cortex (and most other areas of the cerebral cortex) are organized into six layers. The small neurons of the middle layers (i.e., layers III and IV), which receive axons from thalamic relay nuclei, come to dominate areas of primary sensory cortex.[50] Because these cells resemble grains of sand in standard histological preparations, the sensory areas are themselves referred to as granular areas of cortex.[51]

Sensory Areas Are Organized into Columns and Other Compartments

Each area of sensory cortex shares with its subcortical components a map of at least part of the sensory periphery. Thus, retinotopic, somatotopic, and tonotopic maps are evident in the relevant areas of cortex. Yet because the retina and skin are two-dimensional sheets, the map of the sensory periphery on the surface of the cortex is a simple transformation of the peripheral representation onto the cortex. In auditory cortex, one dimension is reserved for tonotopic mapping as a faithful representation of the one dimension along the length of the basilar membrane.[52] The orthogonal direction is likely to encode for a second, as yet undiscovered, property.

Properties other than place in the periphery are mapped in primary sensory areas of cortex. The third spatial dimension of cortex, that of depth, arranges neurons in adjacent 0.5-mm-wide to 1-mm-wide regions, referred to as **columns.**[53] In these columns, neurons stacked above and below one another are fundamentally similar but differ significantly from neurons on either side of them. One example of columns with a clear anatomical correlate is the division of primary visual cortex of most primates and some carnivores into a series of alternating regions dominated by the right and left retinas. Each ocular dominance column contains cells driven exclusively or predominantly by one eye; adjacent columns are dominated by the other eye.[40] Other properties such as selectivity for the orientation of a visual stimulus and the contrast between it and the surround are also arranged in columns of primary visual cortex.[54] Similar types of columns are evident in the somatosensory system, as regions of modality and place specificity,[55] and in the auditory system, as regions of alternating summation and suppression of inputs from the two ears.[56] Moreover, in areas of nonprimary cortex the feature most commonly displayed by neurons of a particular area is one that often comes to occupy columns. A good example is found in the middle temporal area (MT) of association visual cortex, where neurons are tuned for the direction of a moving visual stimulus. Organized into columns through the depth of MT are neurons selective for one particular direction of visual stimulus movement; these are flanked by columns of neurons tuned for other directions of movement.[57] So consistent are these findings among sensory, motor, and association areas that columnar organization is viewed as a principal organizing feature for all of the cerebral cortex.[53]

Stereotype Connections Exist for Areas of Sensory Cortex

Areas of the cerebral cortex communicate most heavily with other areas of cortex and also send axons to subcortical regions throughout the neuraxis (Fig. 23.7). These include:

1. Areas in the same hemisphere. Well-organized connections among primary and association areas of sensory cortex serve to maintain parallel paths so that different aspects of vision, audition, and somatic sensation come to be handled by different areas of cortex. These connections also establish a hierarchy within a

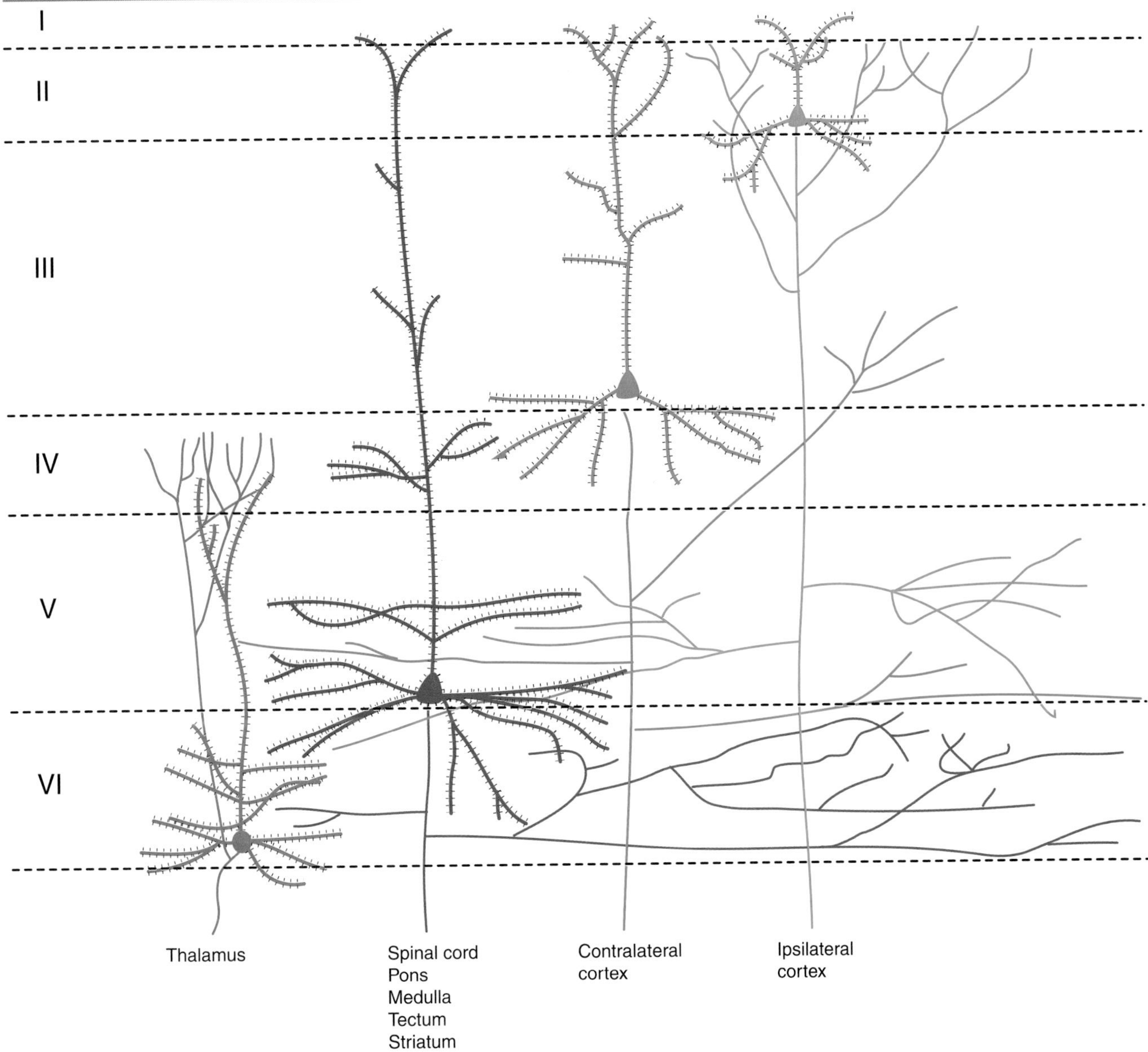

FIGURE 23.7 Organization of cortical outputs. Neurons sending their axons to different targets are distributed in different layers. Deep in layer IV arise subcortical projections back to thalamus (neurons in layer VI) or to the spinal cord, pons and medulla, tectum or striatum (neurons at various levels in layer V). Above layer IV are the neurons sending axons to other areas of cerebral cortex, either in the same (layer II) or the opposite (layer III) hemisphere. Adapted from Jones (1985).[50]

system, whereby selectivity for stimulus features becomes progressively greater from one area to the next.[58,59]

2. Areas in the contralateral hemisphere. Axons of each sensory area enter the corpus callosum (a large commissure or fiber tract connecting the two sides of the brain) and terminate in corresponding areas of the opposite hemisphere. In visual and somatosensory systems, these commissural connections are restricted in origin and termination; they exist to unite the representation of midline structures into a coherent precept.[54]

3. Subcortical regions. Areas of sensory cortex send axons to those nuclei in the thalamus and brainstem that provide ascending sensory information. By far the most prominent of these is the corticothalamic system of axons that arises in a primary area and terminates in the same thalamic nucleus that provides the area with its ascending input. This system of connections

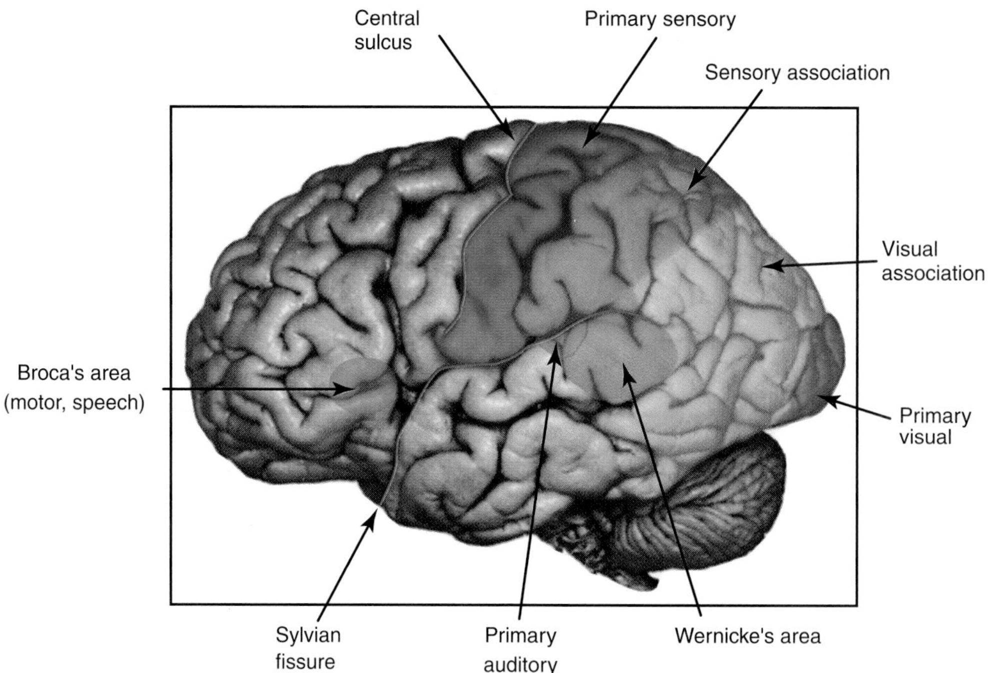

FIGURE 23.8 The location of primary sensory and association areas of human cerebral cortex. For each system separate higher order sensory areas integrate sensory inputs into a coherent precept or serve as an interface between sensory and motor functions. From Guyton, A. C. (1987). *Basic Neuroscience: Anatomy and Physiology*, W. B. Saunders, Philadelphia.

is truly impressive, as the number of corticothalamic axons innervating any nucleus of the thalamus greatly exceeds the number of ascending sensory axons.[50] Such a prominent set of connections permits a sensory area to control the activity of the very neurons that relay information to it. One role for descending control of thalamic and brainstem neurons is likely to be the focusing of activity, so that relay neurons most activated by a sensory stimulus are more strongly driven and those in surrounding less well activated regions are further suppressed.

Association Areas of Sensory Cortex Perform Broad Functions

All primary sensory areas parcel out ipsilateral corticocortical connections to areas that respond to sensory stimulation but do so either less robustly or with

CASE 4: SOUND PRACTICES

While attending a national conference, George O'Hara, a senior scientist, hears a presentation by Marie Shields, a graduate student, on the development of a new device for the high-fidelity amplification of sound. This is an area on which Dr. O'Hara has been focusing his recent efforts. Ms. Shields seems to have overcome one of the difficulties with which he has been struggling, although she is not yet ready to publish her work. After her presentation, Dr. O'Hara approaches Ms. Shields and invites her to join him for lunch and a discussion "of her outstanding seminar." Ms. Shields is elated by the attention from such a prominent neuroscientist and accepts his invitation with enthusiasm. During their meal together, Dr. O'Hara asks Ms. Shields about various aspects of her project, including the area that has been problematic for him. She answers all of his questions, volunteering a considerable amount of information not contained within her formal presentation. When Ms. Shields asks about his own research, Dr. O'Hara makes only a brief general comment and quickly turns the conversation back to her work. Has Dr. O'Hara acted responsibly? Has Ms. Shields acted sensibly?

See Appendix for discussion questions.

greater stimulus selectivity than the primary area. Invariably, several nonprimary areas are involved and arranged so that additional or novel parallel paths are generated (Fig. 23.8). In the visual system, separate "streams" involved in visuomotor and visuosensory functions have been described; one is responsible for using visual cues to drive appropriate eye movements and the other for dealing with the tasks of visual perception.[58] In the somatosensory system separate motor and limbic paths exist to perform much the same functions for the entire body, supplying sensory input to coordinate and adjust motor output and using complex input from many receptor types to match the shape of a tactual stimulus with one already stored in memory.[60,61] If a similar dichotomy exists in the auditory system, it is most easily found in specializations unique to humans—the speech areas of cortex. One of these exists at the interface of auditory input and motor commands to produce speech (Broca's area), the other at the matching of auditory signals with prior experience to interpret speech (Wernicke's area). Apparent from this pattern in association areas of cortex is the continued pressure for a division of labor within each sensory system, not one that produces separate paths for analyzing elemental features of a stimulus but one that combines those features either to elicit appropriate movements or to match a stimulus with an internal representation of the world.

Summary

A basic plan for the functional organization of sensory systems is not difficult to produce. Common themes of transduction, relay, parallel processing, and central modification are so numerous it is no surprise that a case has been made for a common phylogenetic origin of sensory systems.[62] Differences among the systems, on the other hand, betray the fact that each has existed and operated independently for as long as there have been vertebrates.[63] Thus, specializations are numerous both across and within sensory systems of vertebrates in general and mammals in particular, as each system has responded to pressures unique to it. What remains in overview, then, is a well-ordered basic plan from periphery to perception, one that has been modified in its details as variations in niche have lead to specializations in function.

References

1. Levine, M. W., and Shefner, J. M. (1991). *Fundamentals of Sensation and Perception.* Brooks/Cole, Pacific Grove, CA.
2. Somjen, G. (1972). *Sensory Coding in the Mammalian Nervous System.* Appleton-Century-Crofts, New York.
3. Phillips, J. R., and Johnson, K. O. (1981). Tactile spatial resolution: II. Neural representation of bars, edges, and gratings in monkey afferents. *J. Neurophysiol.* **46:** 1192–1203.
4. Stevens, S. S. (1957). On the psychophysical law. *Psychol. Rev.* **64:** 153–181.
5. Weinstein, S. (1968). Intensive and extensive aspects of tactile sensitivity as a function of body part, sex and laterality. In *The Skin Senses* (D. R. Kenshalo, ed.), pp. 195–220. Thomas, Springfield, IL.
6. Mountcastle, V. B. (1980). Sensory receptors and neural encoding: Introduction to sensory processes. In *Medical Physiology* (V. B. Mountcastle, ed.), 14th ed., Vol. 1, pp. 327–347. Mosby, St. Louis, MO.
7. Dallos, P. (1996). Overview: Cochlear neurobiology. In *The Cochlea* (P. Dallos, A. N. Popper, and R. R. Fay, eds.), pp. 1–43. Springer-Verlag, New York.
8. Schnapf, J. L., and Baylor, D. A. (1987). How photoreceptor cells respond to light. *Sci. Am.* **256:** 40–47.
9. Nathans, J. (1987). Molecular biology of visual pigments. *Annu. Rev. Neurosci.* **10:** 163–194.
10. Dartnall, H., Bowmaker, J. K., and Mollon, J. D. (1983). Microspectrophotometry of human photoreceptors. In *Colour Vision: Physiology and Psychophysics* (J. D. Mollon and L. T. Sharpe, eds.), pp. 69–80. Academic Press, New York.
11. Zelena, J. (1994). *Nerves and Mechanoreceptors.* Chapman & Hall, London.
12. Katz, B. (1950). Depolarization of sensory terminals and the initiation of impulses in the muscle spindle. *J. Physiol. (London)* **111:** 261–282.
13. Slepecky, N. B. (1996). Structure of the mammalian cochlea. In *The Cochlea* (P. Dallos, A. N. Popper, and R. R. Fay, eds.), pp. 44–129. Springer-Verlag, New York.
14. Dowling, J. E. (1987). *The Retina: An Approachable Part of the Brain.* Belknap Press, Cambridge, MA.
15. Baylor, D. A., Lamb, T. D., and Yau, K.-Y. (1979). Responses of retinal rods to single photons. *J. Physiol. (London)* **288:** 613–624.
16. Stryer, L. (1987). The molecules of visual excitation. *Sci. Am.* **257:** 42–50.
17. Yau, K.-W., and Baylor, D. A. (1989). Cyclic GMP-activated conductance of retinal photoreceptor cells. *Annu. Rev. Neurosci.* **12** pp. 289–328.
18. Burgess, P. R., and Perl, E. R. (1973). Cutaneous mechanoreceptors and nociceptors. In *Handbook of Sensory Physiology* (A. Iggo, ed.), Vol. 2, pp. 29–78. Springer, New York.
19. Hudspeth, A. J. (1985). The cellular basis of hearing: The biophysics of hair cells. *Science* **230:** 745–752.
20. Darian-Smith, I. (1984). The sense of touch: Performance and peripheral neural processes. In *Handbook of Physiology* (D. Smith, ed.), Sect. 1, Vol. III, Part 2, pp. 739–788. Am. Physiol. Soc., Bethesda, MD.
21. Wässle, H., Grünert, U., Röhrenbeck, J., and Boycott, B. B. (1990). Retinal ganglion cell density and cortical magnification factor in the primate. *Vision Res.* **30:** 1897–1911.
22. Hughes, A. F. W. (1969). *Aspects of Neural Ontogeny.* Academic Press, New York.
23. Jacobson, M. (1970). *Developmental Neurobiology.* Holt, Rinehart & Winston, New York.
24. Wässle, H., and Boycott, B. B. (1991). Functional architecture of the mammalian retina. *Physiol. Rev.* **71:** 447–480.
25. Darian-Smith, I., Galea, M. P., Darian-Smith, C., Sugitani, M., Tan, A., and Burman, K. (1996). The anatomy of manual dexterity: The new connectivity of the primate sensorimotor thalamus and cerebral cortex. *Adv. Anat. Cell Biol.* **133:** 1–142.
26. Ryugo, D. K. (1992). The auditory nerve: Peripheral innervation,

cell body morphology, and central projections. In *The Mammalian Auditory Pathway: Neuroanatomy* (D. B. Webster, A. N. Popper, and R. R. Fay, eds.), pp. 23–65. Springer-Verlag, New York.
27. Kaas, J. H. Guillery, R. W., and Allman, J. M. (1972). Some principles of organization in the dorsal lateral geniculate nucleus. *Brain, Behav. Evol.* **6:** 253–299.
28. Rodieck, R. W., and Watanabe, M. (1993). Survey of the morphology of macaque retinal ganglion cells that project to the pretectum, superior colliculus, and the parvicellular laminae of the lateral geniculate nucleus. *J. Comp. Neurol.* **338:** 289–303.
29. Darian-Smith, I. (1982). Touch in primates. *Annu. Rev. Psychol.* **33:** 155–194.
30. Merigan, W. H., and Maunsell, J. H. R. (1993). How parallel are the primate visual pathways. *Annu. Rev. Neurosci.* **16:** 369–402.
31. Singer, W. (1995). Time as coding space in neocortical processing: A hypothesis. In *The Cognitive Neurosciences* (M. S. Gazzaniga, ed.), pp. 91–104. MIT Press, Cambridge, MA.
32. Shiells, R. A., and Falk, G. (1995). Signal transduction in retinal bipolar cells. *Prog. Retinal Res.* **14:** 223–247.
33. Kuffler, S. W. (1953). Discharge patterns and functional organization of mammalian retina. *J. Neurophysiol.* **16:** 37–68.
34. Gouras, P. (1984). Color vision. *Prog. Retinal Res.* **3:** 227–261.
35. Irvine, D. R. F. (1992). Physiology of the auditory brainstem. In *The Mammalian Auditory Pathway: Physiology* (D. B. Webster, A. N. Popper, and R. R. Fay, eds.), pp. 153–231. Springer-Verlag, New York.
36. Stotler, W. A. (1953). An experimental study of the cells and connections of the superior olivary complex of the cat. *J. Comp. Neurol.* **98:** 401–432.
37. Azzopardi, P., and Cowey, A. (1993). Preferential representation of the fovea in the primary visual cortex. *Nature (London)* **361:** 719–721.
38. Silveira, L. C. L., Picano-Diniz, C. W., Sampaio, L. F. S., and Oswaldo-Cruz, E. (1989). Retinal ganglion cell distribution in the Cebus monkey: A comparison with the cortical magnification factors. *Vision Res.* **29:** 1471–1483.
39. Horton, J. C., and Hoyt, W. F. (1991). The representation of the visual field in human striate cortex. *Arch. Ophthalmol. (Chicago)* **109:** 816–824.
40. Hubel, D. H., and Wiesel, T. (1968). Receptive fields and functional architecture of monkey striate cortex. *J. Physiol. (London)* **193:** 215–243.
41. Mountcastle, V. B. (1995). The parietal system and some higher brain functions. *Cereb. Cortex* **5:** 377–390.
42. Logothetis, N. K., and Sheinberg, D. L. (1996). Visual object recognition. *Annu. Rev. Neurosci.* **19:** 577–621.
43. Costanzo, R. M., and Gardner, E. P. (1980). A quantitative analysis of responses of direction-selective neurons in somatosensory cortex of awake monkeys. *J. Neurophysiol.* **43:** 1319–1341.
44. Glass, I., and Wolberg, Z. (1983). Auditory cortex responses to sequences of normal and reversed squirrel monkey vocalizations. *Brain, Behav. Evol.* **22:** 13–21.
45. Hoyt, W. F., and Luis, O. (1963). The primate chiasm. *Arch. Ophthalmol. (Chicago)* **70:** 69–85.
46. Boivie, J. (1978). Anatomical observations on the dorsal column nuclei, their thalamic projection and the cytoarchitecture of some somatosensory thalamic nuclei in the monkey. *J. Comp. Neurol.* **178:** 17–47.
47. Aitkin, L. M., Irvine, D. R. F., and Webster, W. R. (1977). Central neural mechanisms of hearing. In *Handbook of Physiology* (J. M. Brookhart, V. B. Mountcastle, and I. Darian-Smith, eds.), Sect. 1, Vol. III, Part 2, pp. 675–737. Am. Physiol. Soc., Bethesda, MD.
48. Jones, E. G. (1977). Organization of the thalamocortical complex and its relation to sensory processes. In *Handbook of Physiology* (J. M. Brookhart, V. B. Mountcastle, and I. Darian-Smith, eds.), Sect. 1, Vol. III, Part 2, pp. 149–212. Am. Physiol. Soc., Bethesda, MD.
49. Jones, E. G. (1981). Functional subdivision and synaptic organization of the mammalian thalamus. *Int. Rev. Physiol.* **25:** 173–245.
50. Jones, E. G. (1985). *The Thalamus.* Plenum, New York.
51. Kemper, T. L. B., and Galaburda, A. M. (1984). Principles of cytoarchitectonics. *Cereb. Cortex* **1:** 35–57.
52. Brugge, J. F., and Merzenich, M. M. (1973). Response of neurons in auditory cortex of the macaque monkey to monaural and binaural stimulation. *J. Neurophysiol.* **36:** 1138–1158.
53. Mountcastle, V. B. (1997). The columnar organization of the neocortex. *Brain* **120:** 701–722.
54. Hubel, D. H. (1988). *Eye, Brain and Vision.* Freeman, New York.
55. Mountcastle, V. B. (1957). Modality and topographic properties of single neurons of cat's somatic sensory cortex. *J. Neurophysiol.* **20:** 408–434.
56. Brugge, J. F., and Reale, R. A. (1985). Auditory cortex. *Cereb. Cortex* **4:** 229–271.
57. Albright, T. D., Desimone, R., and Gross, C. G. (1984). Columnar organization of directionally selective cells in visual area MT of the macaque. *J. Neurophysiol.* **51:** 16–31.
58. Gallant, J. L., and Van Essen, D. C. (1994). Neural mechanisms of form and motion processing in the primate visual system. *Neuron* **13:** 1–10.
59. Pons, T. P., Garraghty, P. E., Friedmann, D. P., and Mishkin, M. (1987). Physiological evidence for serial processing in somatosensory cortex. *Science* **237:** 417–420.
60. Phillips, J. R., Johnson, K. O., and Hsiao, S. S. (1988). Spatial pattern representation and transformation in monkey somatosensory cortex. *Proc. Natl. Acad. Sci. U.S.A.* **85:** 1317–1321.
61. Johnson, K. O., and Hsiao, S. S. (1992). Tactual form and texture perception. *Annu. Rev. Neurosci.* **15:** 227–250.
62. Gregory, R. L. (1967). Origin of eyes and brains. *Nature (London)* **213:** 269–372.
63. Kruger, L., and Stein, B. E. (1973). Primordial sense organs and the evolution of sensory systems. In *Handbook of Perception* (E. C. Carterette, and M. P. Friedmann, eds.), Vol. 3, pp. 63–88. Academic Press, New York.

CHAPTER

24

Sensory Transduction

Peter R. Mac Leish, Gordon M. Shepherd, Sue C. Kinnamon, and Joseph Santos-Sacchi

From the early 19th century, the prevailing understanding of sensory perception has been based on the idea that each sensory modality has its own type of receptor. Modern research is replacing this idea with a new concept based on the molecular and cellular biology of sensory transduction. This work is showing that sensory transduction in each type of receptor represents adaptations of common molecular signaling mechanisms found in cells throughout the body.

A summary of some of these receptors and their signaling mechanisms is shown in Fig. 24.1. It can be seen that the diversity of sensory mechanisms is encompassed within an overall framework of membrane signaling mechanisms and second-messenger systems. Within this framework, each sensory modality has its unique series of molecular steps, from the initial interaction of the stimulus energy with its receptor to the final generation of the electrical response by the receptor cell membrane. Thus, a common language of signaling mechanisms unites the study of sensory transduction, which in turn is part of the much larger study of membrane signaling mechanisms in cells throughout the body. In addition, this framework of sensory signaling mechanisms applies across phyla, to both vertebrate and invertebrate species.

In this chapter, we focus on four of the main types of sensory receptors and show how these principles apply.

PHOTOTRANSDUCTION

Vision in Vertebrates Is Subserved by Two Types of Photoreceptors: Rods and Cones

Diurnal animals have a dual system of photoreceptors. Rod photoreceptor cells (rods) subserve vision in dim light, called scotopic conditions. Cone photoreceptor cells (cones) subserve vision in bright light, called photopic conditions. Rods and cones are thought to share essential features of phototransduction—even though more experimentation has been carried out on rods.

Rods are modified neuroepithelial cells that are highly polarized in structure and function. The conversion of light energy to an electrical signal (phototransduction) occurs at one end, and the electrical signal is transmitted to the other end, where it modifies the release of neurotransmitter onto second-order neurons. Rods consist of three principal compartments (Figs. 24.2 and 24.3): (1) The **outer segment** is composed of a stack of flattened discs, surrounded by the plasma membrane, that act to increase the sensory membrane area. The visual pigment rhodopsin is densely packed in the disc membrane but is also found to a lesser degree in the plasma membrane. Available evidence suggests no effective connection between the vast majority of the discs and the plasma membrane. At the base of the outer segment where the discs are formed, a small number of newly forming discs are continuous with the plasma membrane. (2) The ***inner segment*** is attached to the outer segment via a connecting cilium and contains a region of densely packed mitochondria called the myoid region (Fig. 24.4). (3) The cell body contains the nucleus and perinuclear assortment of organelles involved in macromolecular synthesis and metabolism. A fine axonlike process connects the cell body to the rod output terminal (spherule), which contains ribbons and associated vesicles involved in neurotransmitter storage and release.

The cone outer segment differs from that of the rod in that increased surface area is achieved by repeated infolding of the plasma membrane (Figs. 24.2 and 24.3). The cone outer segment is usually shorter than that of

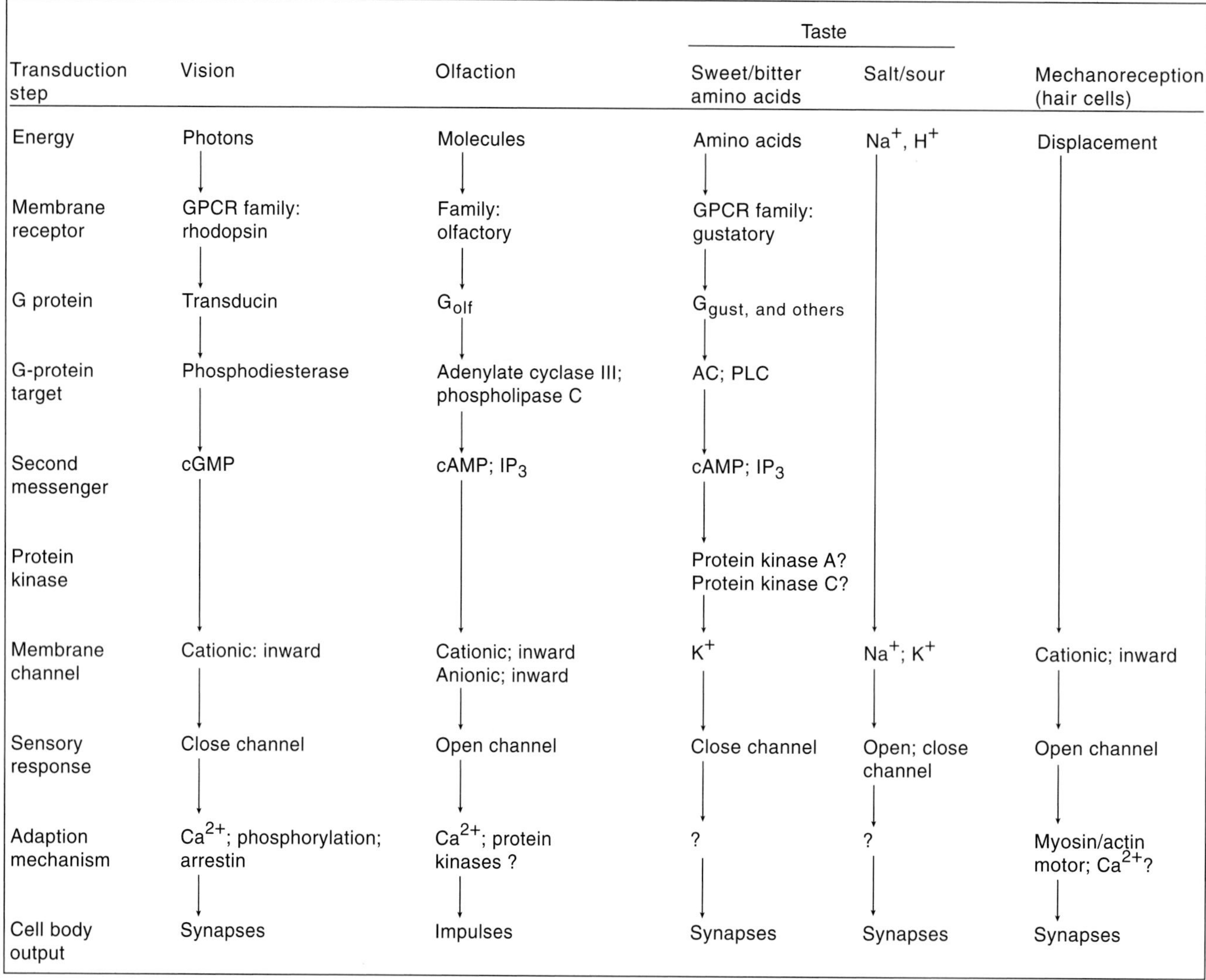

Transduction step	Vision	Olfaction	Taste: Sweet/bitter amino acids	Taste: Salt/sour	Mechanoreception (hair cells)
Energy	Photons	Molecules	Amino acids	Na^+, H^+	Displacement
Membrane receptor	GPCR family: rhodopsin	Family: olfactory	GPCR family: gustatory		
G protein	Transducin	G_{olf}	G_{gust}, and others		
G-protein target	Phosphodiesterase	Adenylate cyclase III; phospholipase C	AC; PLC		
Second messenger	cGMP	cAMP; IP_3	cAMP; IP_3		
Protein kinase			Protein kinase A? Protein kinase C?		
Membrane channel	Cationic: inward	Cationic; inward Anionic; inward	K^+	Na^+; K^+	Cationic; inward
Sensory response	Close channel	Open channel	Close channel	Open; close channel	Open channel
Adaption mechanism	Ca^{2+}; phosphorylation; arrestin	Ca^{2+}; protein kinases ?	?	?	Myosin/actin motor; Ca^{2+}?
Cell body output	Synapses	Impulses	Synapses	Synapses	Synapses

FIGURE 24.1 Summary of second-messenger pathways underlying sensory transduction in different sensory receptor cells GPCR, G-protein receptor family. Modified from Shepherd.[1]

the rod and tapers in the distal direction. As in the rod, the inner segment contains a dense array of mitochondria and connects to the cell body, which contains the nucleus and macromolecular synthesizing organelles. The axonlike process connecting the cell body to the cone pedicle differs considerably in length among species. In the human, the connecting fiber at the fovea is called the fiber of Henle and can measure up to several hundred micrometers in length because of the lateral displacement of the output terminals (pedicles) from the fovea. The cone pedicle contains ribbons and vesicles involved in neurotransmitter storage and release.

Light Hyperpolarizes the Photoreceptor Membrane

Intracellular recording from fish cones in the 1960s[2] first showed that light absorption leads to **hyperpolarization** of the membrane of vertebrate photoreceptors. The original observation came as a surprise because the adequate stimulus for known sense organs at that time such as stretch receptors led to a depolarization and excitation. Rods from many species have also been found to hyperpolarize in response to light. Rods and cones do not normally generate action potentials but rather respond to light with slow, graded hyperpolarizatons (Fig. 24.5). The ionic basis of the hyperpolarization was found to be suppression of an inward current carried mainly by sodium ions.[3]

In darkness, there is a steady-standing current that enters the outer segment and circulates in a loop that includes the inner segment (Fig. 24.6). The amplitude of the current is transiently decreased by dim flashes or steps of light and reduced to zero by bright light (Fig. 24.7). For dark-adapted rods, the absorption of approximately 30 photons is estimated to cause a 50% reduction in the amplitude of the light-regulated current, and 100 photons are sufficient for total suppression.[3] In dark-adapted humans, the behavioral perception of light is achieved when a small number (5–7) of photons generated by a brief flash arrive at a restricted area of retina.[4] Under these conditions the probability of two photons arriving at the same single cell is very low. Isolated rods from amphibians produce detectable responses to single photons.[5] The single-photon response has an amplitude of about 1 mV and 1 pA, corresponding to the suppression of 10^6 monovalent cations at the dark resting potential; lasts for several seconds; and has a peak approximately 1 s after light absorption.

The light-regulated current decreases in amplitude when external sodium ions are partially withdrawn and disappears altogether when sodium is completely replaced by an impermeant ion.[3,6] The simplest interpretation of these results is that the light-regulated current is carried mainly by sodium ions but more complex explanations involving other ions cannot be ruled out. Suppression of an inward sodium current by light explains the hyperpolarization of the membrane observed with intracellular voltage recording. The reversal potential of the light response is in the range of 0 to +10 mV, thereby suggesting the additional involvement of ions other than sodium[7] (Fig. 24.8) because the equilibrium potential for sodium ions is considered to occur at a more positive potential. Ion selectivity studies have shown that other monovalent (e.g., potassium) and divalent (e.g., calcium) ions can permeate the light-regulated conductance mechanism in the outer segment.[8,9] In fact, calcium is more permeant than sodium, but the large sodium current

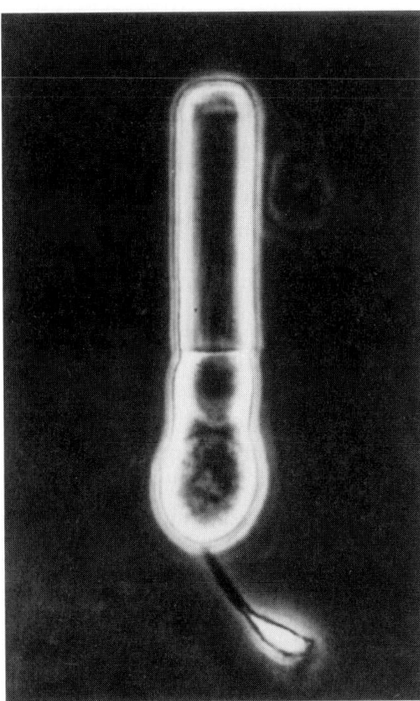

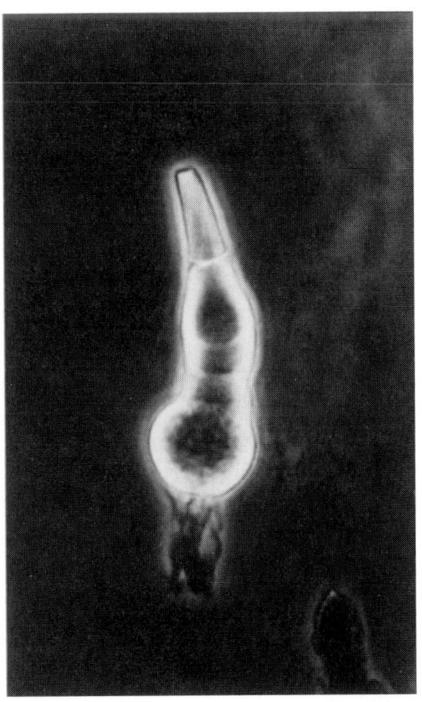

FIGURE 24.2 Phase-contrast micrographs of freshly dissociated rod (left) and cone (right) photoreceptor cells from the tiger salamander retina. Cells were obtained after papain treatment and mechanical disruption of tissue. From MacLeish *et al.*[10]

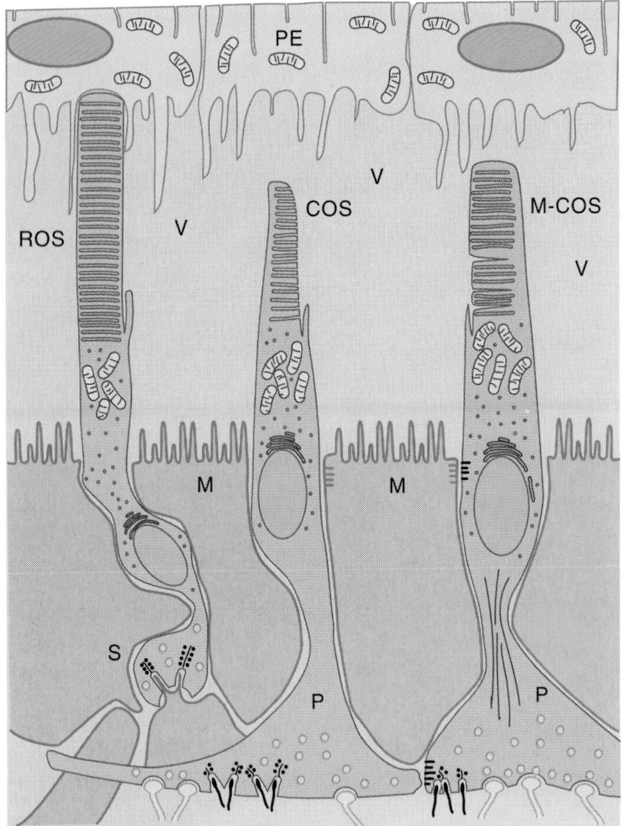

FIGURE 24.3 Schematic drawing of vertebrate rod and cone cells showing different outer segment arrangements. The rod outer segment consists of detached flattened discs that contain the visual pigment. The cone outer segment is thrown into folds that are continuous with the plasma membrane. PE, pigment epithelium; ROS, rod outer segment; COS, cone outer segment; M-COS, mammalian cone outer segment; V, ventricle; M, Müller cell; S, spherule; P, pedicle. Reprinted with permission from Cohen.[11]

arises from the higher concentration of sodium in the bathing medium. The total suppression of the light-regulated current by the removal of sodium has been explained by proposing that the conductance mechanism requires the presence of sodium for its activation.

Phototransduction Involves an Internal Messenger

Several lines of evidence support the claim for an internal messenger. In the case of rods, the bulk of rhodopsin is stored in the flattened discs in the outer segment, and the discs are isolated from the plasma membrane of the outer segment in which the light-regulated current is present. Also, the time course of the single-photon response is on the order of seconds, which is much longer than the open time of known membrane conductance mechanisms. It is easy to explain the time course by assuming that light activates a process with effective molecular intermediates that lasts seconds.

Ion substitution experiments indicate that reducing the concentration of external calcium dramatically increases the amplitude of light-regulated current.[3] Inhibition of the cGMP phosphodiesterase by IBMX also leads to an increase of the light-regulated current. Also, intracellular injection of cGMP increases the amplitude and latency of the photoresponse[12] and the amplitude of the light-regulated current[13] (Fig. 24.9). The findings on the effect of calcium led originally to the reasonable hypothesis that calcium is the internal messenger. In the calcium hypothesis, the activity of intracellular calcium is low in the dark and rises in response to light to block the light-regulated current from the cytoplasmic side. A counter view was forwarded when a light-activated cGMP phosphodiesterase was discovered[14,15] along with a fall in the amount of extractable cGMP in light. According to the cGMP hypothesis, the level of intracellular cGMP is high and sufficient to maintain a cGMP-dependent conductance. An effect of light is to decrease the level of cGMP, which in turn leads to suppression of the inward current.

Biochemical studies have indicated that the level of extractable cGMP increases as the activity of calcium ions decreases in the external solution.[16,17] This result pointed to an interrelationship between calcium and cGMP and highlighted the difficulty in establishing causality when changes in the level of one or the other of these two agents were seen to have an effect. The more likely site of action of calcium is on the guanylate cyclase, which shows increased activity in lowered calcium. The sensitivity of the cyclase to calcium ions will be considered in the context of the recovery of the light response and as a component of light adaptation.

Using the patch-clamp technique, Fesenko and colleagues[18] were the first to show that cGMP increases the conductance of inside-out patches of outer segment membrane when applied from the cytoplasmic side (Fig. 24.10). The action of cGMP is direct and does not require the presence of ATP; and therefore does not seem to involve cGMP-dependent protein kinases and protein phosphorylation. Activation of the cGMP-gated conductance by cGMP shows cooperativity (Fig. 24.11) suggesting that three to four cGMP molecules are required for channel activation.[18–21] In addition, the channel does not desensitize to cGMP, a property expected because the levels of cGMP are high in the dark. Calcium ions, in the presence of magnesium, were ineffective in controlling membrane conductance from the

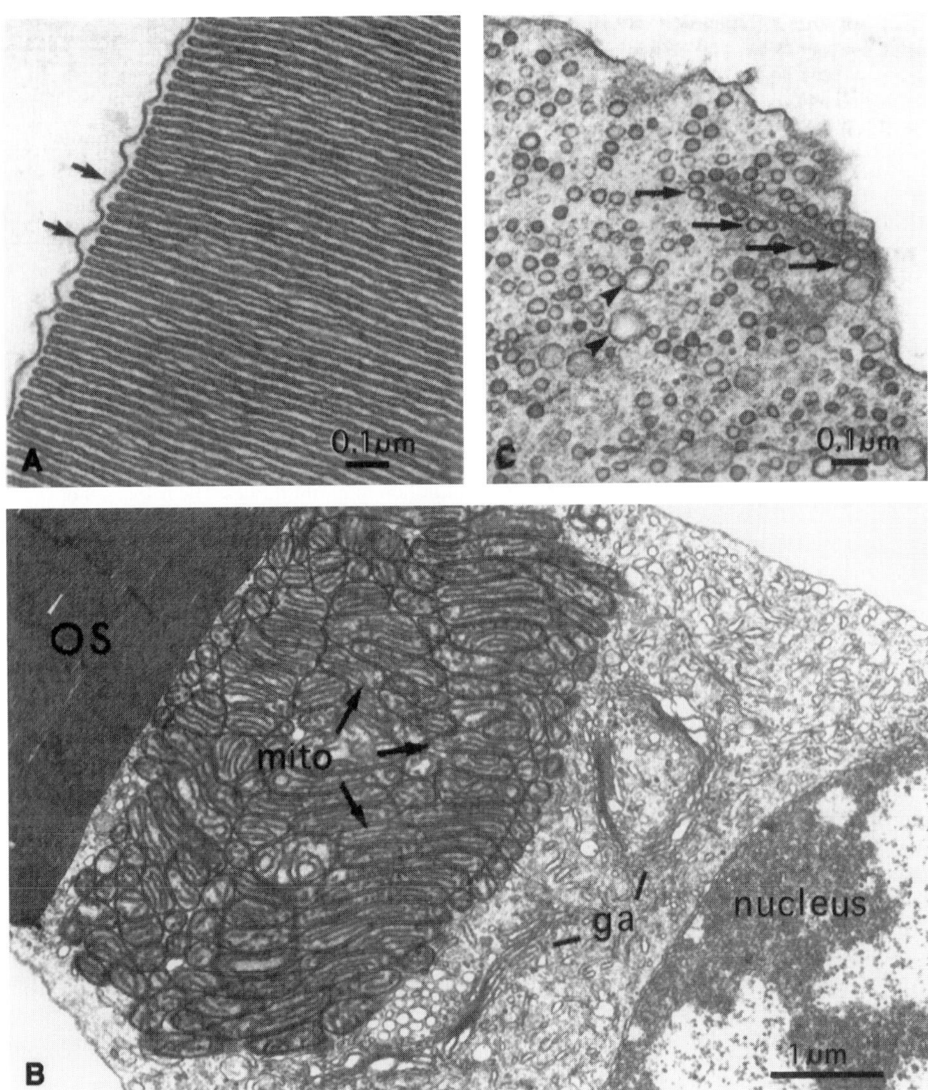

FIGURE 24.4 Electron microscopy of regions of the rod photoreceptor. Outer segment (upper left): Arrows point to plasma membrane that encloses detached flattened membranous discs. Spherule (upper right): Arrows point to synaptic ribbon with associated vesicles. Inner segment (bottom): Arrows point to large accumulation of mitochondria (mito). Also shown are a portion of the cell nucleus (lower right), Golgi apparatus (ga), smooth and rough endoplasmic reticulum, and portion of outer segment (OS). From MacLeish *et al.*[10]

cytoplasmic side. This finding led to the establishment of cGMP as the internal messenger and to the rejection of the calcium hypothesis.

Rhodopsin Is a Member of a Superfamily of Signaling Molecules

The rhodopsin molecule is composed of a protein component, opsin, and an organic molecule, 11-*cis*-retinal.[22] Opsin is a member of the seven-transmembrane domain family of molecules that modify their interaction with G proteins in response to the binding of effectors. Other members of this family include olfactory receptors and likely some taste receptors (see below). Opsin is a single polypeptide made up of 348 amino acids (Fig. 24.12). The transmembrane domains form α-helices that are connected by shorter linear sequences. 11-*cis*-Retinal sits in a pocket formed by the transmembrane α-helices and on absorption of a photon is converted to the all-*trans* isomer. A number of intermediates of rhodopsin have been

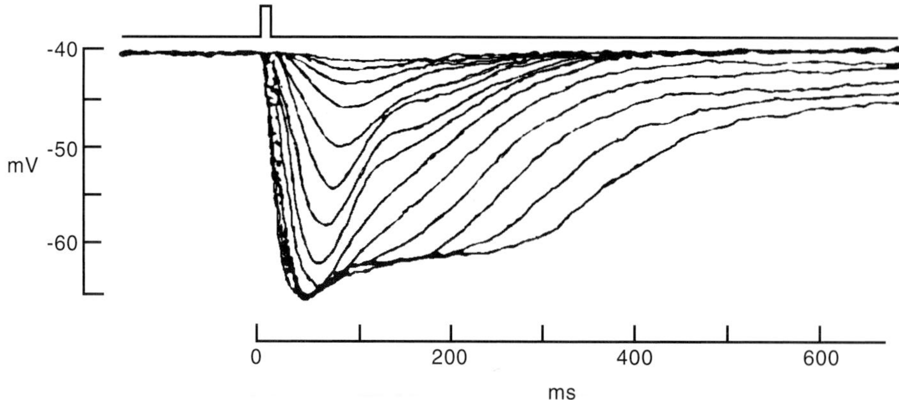

FIGURE 24.5 Photoresponse of cone. Intracellular recordings from cone in the intact turtle retina showing superimposed responses to brief flashes of light of increasing intensity. Responses are slow, graded hyperpolarizations that show amplitude saturation to bright flashes. The responses of rods share essential features but are slower and rods are more sensitive to light. From Baylor.[24]

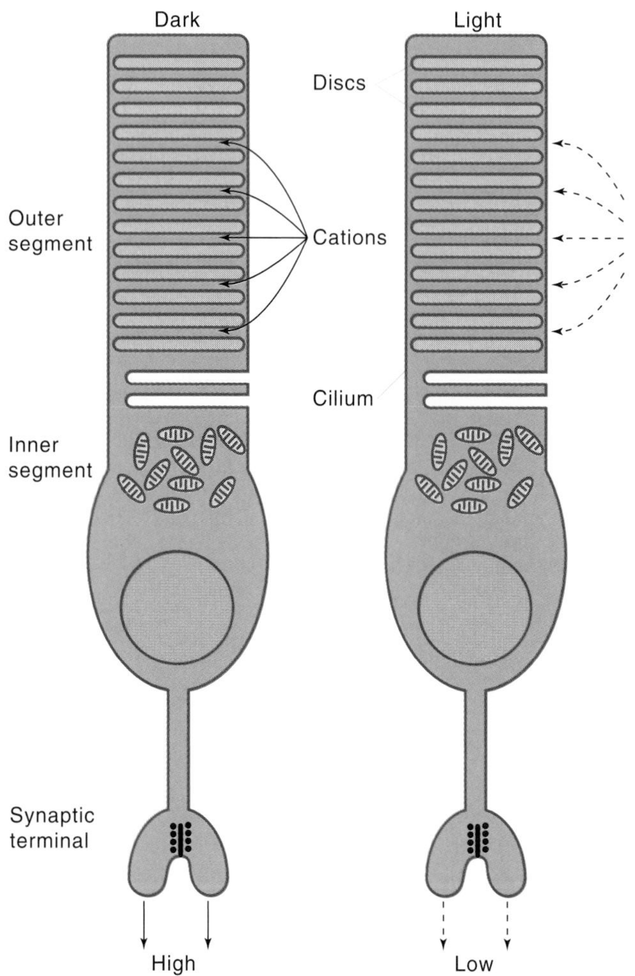

FIGURE 24.6 Schematic drawings of light suppression of current in outer segment. In darkness (left), there is a standing cationic current that enters the outer segment. In light (right), the current is reduced or eliminated altogether if the light is sufficiently bright. Because the current in the dark is carried mainly by sodium ions, the response to light is a hyperpolarization. From Yau.[25]

identified following light absorption. Based on its time of appearance, metarhodopsin II is thought to be the active intermediate in phototransduction. Following further conformational changes in the protein, the all-*trans*-retinal dissociates from opsin and is transported to the retinal pigment epithelium for reisomerization to 11-*cis*-retinal before retransport to the photoreceptor.[23]

The Biochemical Cascade Involves Transducin, a G Protein

Several biochemical studies contributed to the model described by Fung, Hurley, and Stryer[26] (Fig. 24.13). In that model, photoactivated opsin, R*, interacts with a photoreceptor-specific G protein called

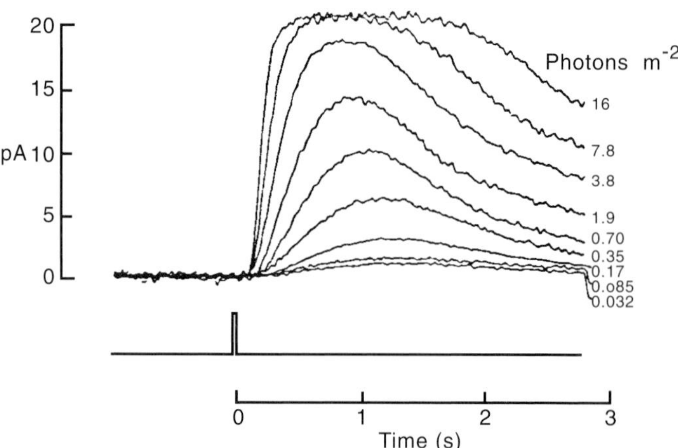

FIGURE 24.7 Light-suppressed rod currents vs light intensity. Traces are superimposed responses showing the transient suppression by light of the current entering the outer segment. From Baylor *et al.*[5]

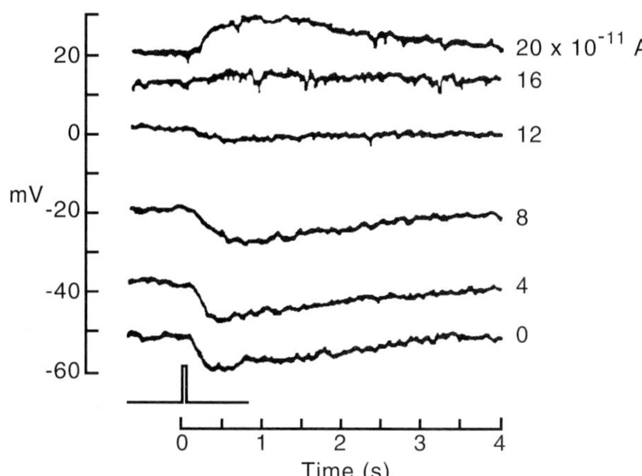

FIGURE 24.8 Reversal potential of the light response. Traces show the responses to the same intensity flash of light at different membrane potentials achieved by injecting currents as shown. At rest (0 injected current), the response was a hyperpolarization. As the membrane potential in darkness was shifted upward by injecting current of the magnitude shown on the right, the response eventually decreased in amplitude and reversed in polarity in the range of 0 to +10 mV. From Bader *et al.*[27]

transducin (T), which exists as the heterotrimeric complex T$\alpha\beta\gamma$, with GDP bound to the α subunit. Interaction with R* leads to an exchange of GDP for GTP and a dissociation of the T complex to form Tα–GTP and the T$\beta\gamma$ subunits. A single R* may generate several hundred Tα–GTP molecules, providing amplification or gain in the pathway. The Tα–GTP subunit binds to an inactive form of a cGMP phosphodiesterase which itself exists in the heterotrimeric complex $\alpha\beta\gamma$–phosphodiesterase (PDE). The activation of the PDE is achieved by removing an inhibitory action brought about by the binding of the γ subunit of PDE to Tα-GTP. The $\alpha\beta$–PDE complex contains the PDE activity; several hundred cGMP molecules are hydrolyzed per activated PDE, thereby providing a second amplification step in the transduction pathway.

Restoration of the System Involves Several Molecular Events

The presence of GTPase in the outer segment converts Tα–GTP to Tα–GDP, which leads to a dissociation of Tα–GDP from the PDE–$\alpha\beta$ subunit. The PDE–γ subunit then reassociates with the PDE-$\alpha\beta$ subunits and inhibits the PDE activity. In addition, R* undergoes phosphorylation by rhodopsin kinase,[28] which is thought to diminish the ability of R* to interact with transducin. Finally, arrestin, a 48-kDa protein of the outer segment, is proposed to interact with R* to prevent interaction with transducin.[29]

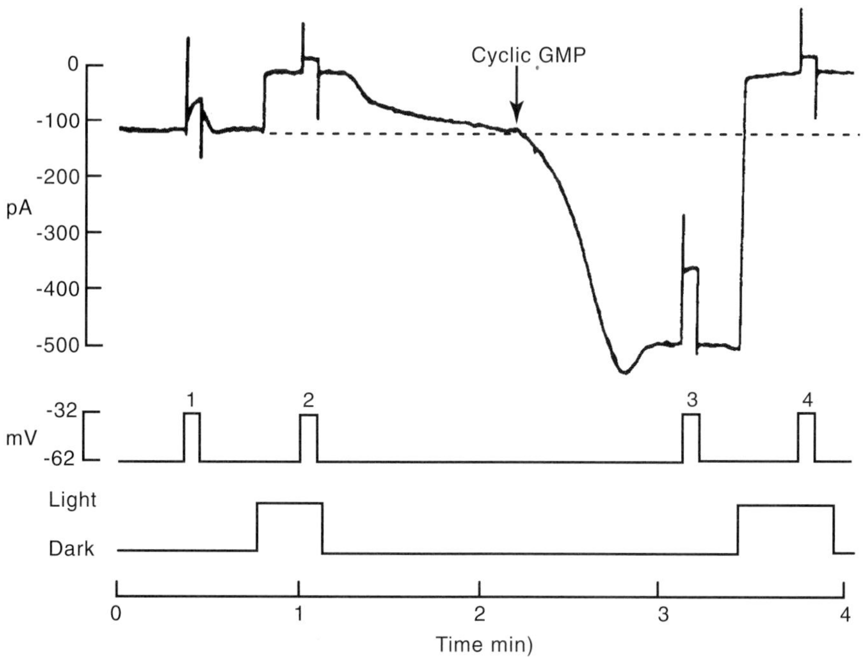

FIGURE 24.9 Response to cGMP injection in a rod. The top trace shows the magnitude of the current entering the outer segment in response to the iontophoretic injection of cGMP. The lower trace marks the presentation of a light bright enough to suppress the generator current. The current increased many fold from its value before injection. From MacLeish *et al.*[13]

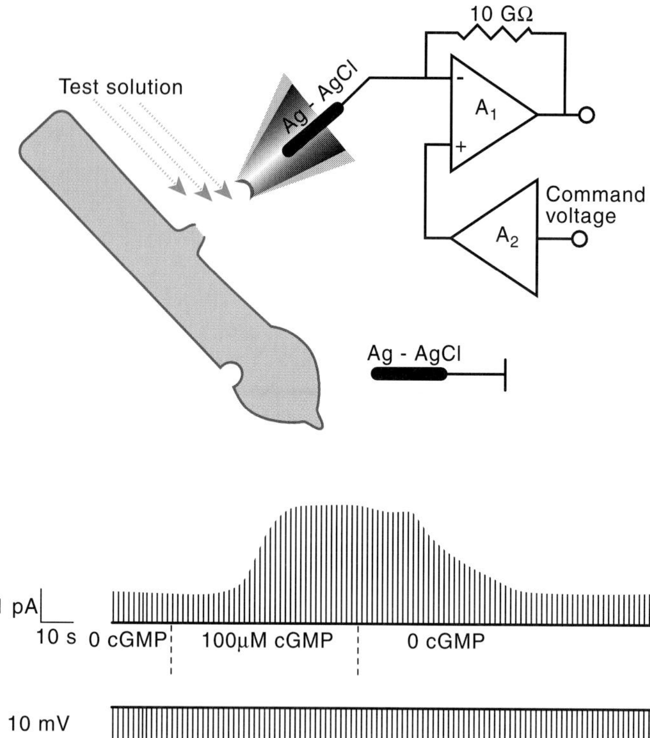

FIGURE 24.10 Sensitivity of rod outer segment excised patch to cGMP. The top electrical trace shows the current through an excised patch of outer segment membrane in response to 10-mV voltage pulses in the presence or absence of cGMP. The application of cGMP to the cytoplasmic side of the excised patch was accompanied by an increase in current indicating the activation of a conductance mechanism by cGMP. From Fesenko *et al.*[18]

The GMP-Gated Channel Is an Integral Membrane Protein

The functional cGMP-gated channel complex is thought to be composed of an as-yet-undetermined number of 63-kDa subunit polypeptides.[30] Hydropathicity plots suggest four or six putative transmembrane segments. The cGMP-binding region is situated near the carboxy terminus on the cytoplasmic surface of the membrane. In excised patches from rod outer segments, the application of 10 μM 1-*cis*-diltiazem reversibly and completely blocked the current induced by 90 μM cyclic GMP when both agents were applied from the cytoplasmic side.[31] Channels expressed in oocytes are blocked by higher concentrations of 1-*cis*-diltiazem,[21] and reconstituted channels are reported to show little or no 1-*cis*-diltiazem sensitivity. The composition of lipids in the bilayer is thought to influence the ability of 1-*cis*-diltiazem to block the action of cGMP.

A Small Fraction of Available cGMP Channels Are Open in the Dark

Under physiological conditions the maximal light response of amphibian rods is in the range 40–60 pA. Yet when high levels of cGMP are injected into the cell, light responses of >500 pA are observed.[13] This finding indicates that under normal conditions the vast majority, >90% and as high as 99%, of the cGMP-gated channels in the outer segment are already closed in the dark. The reason for the large reservoir of cGMP channels is not clear, but a consequence of working at the foot of the dose–response curve is relative linearity in the relationship between conductance induced by cGMP and the concentration of cGMP. Using the size of the cGMP current as a calibrator of the levels of cGMP, researchers have estimated that the free cGMP concentration in the dark is 1–5 μM. The extractable amounts of cGMP are considerably higher, indicating that a substantial fraction of the extractable cGMP is actually bound within the cells. A number of binding sites, including sites on the enzyme, PDE, and others on the cGMP-gated channels, have been suggested.

cGMP-Gated Channels Have Properties Critical for Phototransduction

In the presence of normal levels of external calcium, single-channel activity is not discernible; power spectrum analyses provide estimates of the single-channel conductance in the range of 100 fS and a mean open time of 1–2 ms.[18,32–34] Single-channel activity becomes discernible when the external calcium is reduced.[20,35,36] The absence of channel noise with normal levels of calcium provides a good background for detecting small photoresponses.

Under physiological conditions, the cGMP conductance mechanism shows outward rectification[7] (Fig. 24.14). In the normal operating range of −35 to −60 mV, the current–voltage curve is relatively flat, producing a constant current region. On approaching 0 mV, the *I–V* curve changes slope, crosses the voltage axis near 0 mV, and increases rapidly as the inside is made positive. The constant current region in the normal operating range ensures that changes in the light-regulated current arise from transduction events and not from changes in the voltage in response to light. That is, the current in open channels during a light response does not change due to the change in voltage.

The early sodium replacement experiments showed that the removal of sodium ions leads to the abolishment of the light response. Subsequent experiments

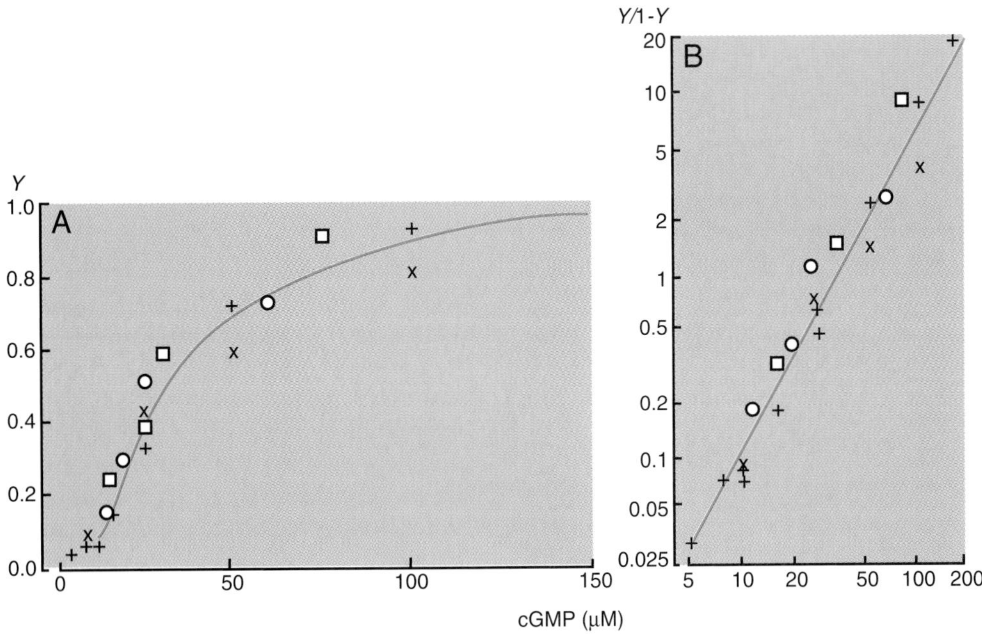

FIGURE 24.11 Dose response of the cGMP-induced current in an excised patch of ROS. (A) The normalized response as a function of the concentration of cGMP is shown on the left. (B) The slope of the curve on the right gives an estimate of the Hill coefficient for the activation reaction and suggests that two, or possibly three, molecules of cGMP are required to activate the conductance mechanism. From Fesenko *et al.*[18]

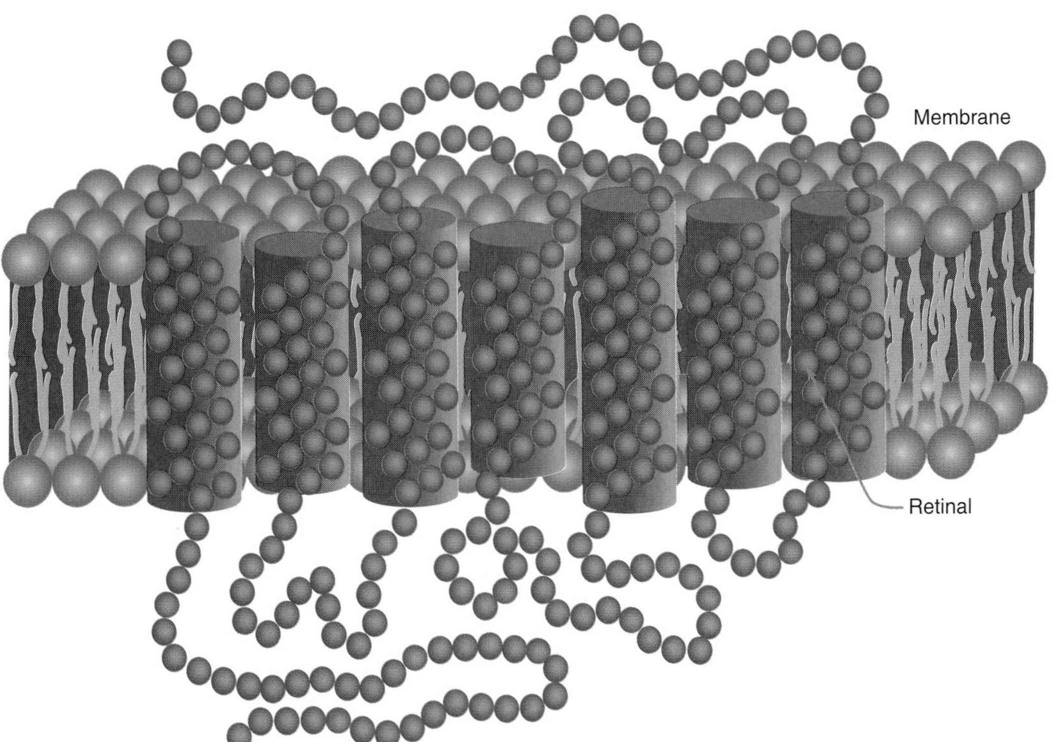

FIGURE 24.12 Proposed arrangement of a rhodopsin molecule within the plasma membrane of a rod. There are seven transmembrane domains and three cytoplasmic and three extracellular loops. The carboxy terminus faces the cytoplasm. From Hargrave and McDowell.[39]

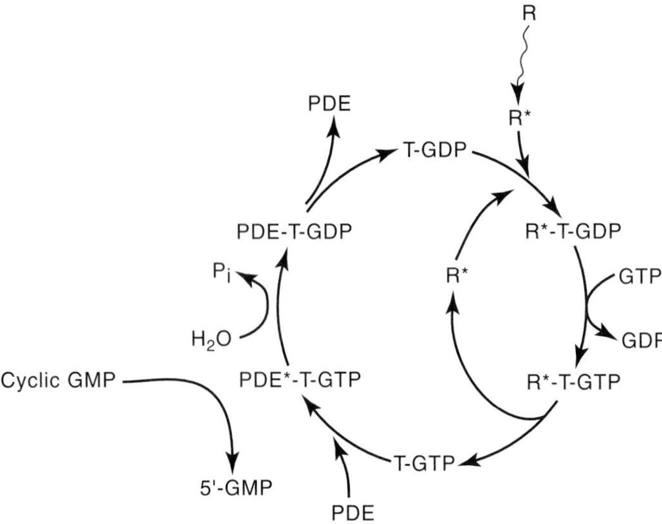

FIGURE 24.13 Proposed phototransduction biochemical scheme. Light causes the conversion of rhodopsin (R) to photolyzed rhodopsin (R*), which eventually leads to the hydrolysis of cGMP by the activation of phosphodiesterase. The proposed scheme contains two amplification steps whereby a single R* generates hundreds of T–GTP molecules and a single activated phosphodiesterase molecule hydrolyzes hundreds of cGMP molecules. From Fung *et al.*[26]

using excised plasma membrane patches from the outer segment revealed that a variety of cations are capable of permeating the conductance mechanism. The rank order is Ca : Na : K = 12 : 1 : 0.7.[8,19] At rest, the fraction of current carried by sodium is largest because sodium is the most abundant ion present.

Extrusion Mechanisms Restore Ionic Balance

Two mechanisms of ion extrusion are prominent in rods. The first is an energy-dependent Na,K-ATPase located in the inner segment. This mechanism pumps sodium ions out and potassium ions into the cell, particularly in the dark when the inward sodium current is highest. The second mechanism is a Na–K–Ca exchanger that is found in the outer segment[37,38] (Fig. 24.15). This mechanism seems to regulate internal calcium levels in the face of calcium entry through the cGMP-gated channels. During the light response, when the inward sodium current through the cGMP-gated channels is reduced, the activity of the exchanger is maintained, serving to lower intracellular free calcium. This lowering of intracellular free calcium has been proposed to increase the activity of the guanylate cyclase, which boosts the return of cGMP levels and returns the cell to the prelight condition.

Phototransduction Shows Adaptation to Light

Photoreceptors adapt to steady background light by decreasing their sensitivity to light.[40] The presence of adaptation improves the dynamic range of rods to cover roughly 3 orders of magnitude of light intensity. This means that flash intensities that give saturating responses in fully dark-adapted cells give submaximal responses in the presence of steady illumination. The adaptation is fairly rapid and is thought to involve a number of the steps in the phototransduction pathway. Research interest is centered on the role that lowered intracellular calcium might play in mediating light adaptation.

Intracellular activity of calcium falls in the presence of light because the influx of calcium is reduced by

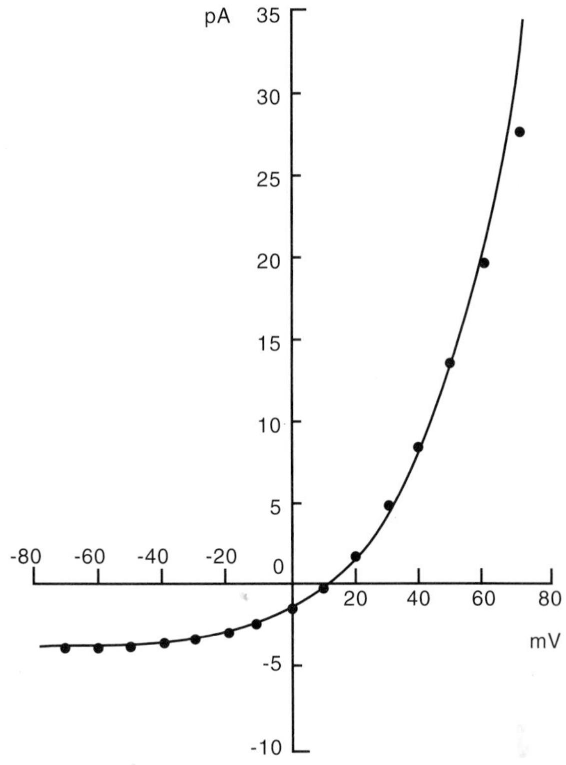

FIGURE 24.14 Current–voltage relationship of the light-suppressed rod current. The curve shows how the light-suppressed current varies with the membrane potential. In the assumed normal operating range (−35 to −60 mV), the size of the current is fairly constant. As the membrane potential approaches 0 to +10 mV, the current approaches zero. As the inside of the cell is made progressively more positive, the current rises rapidly as shown. From Yau.[25]

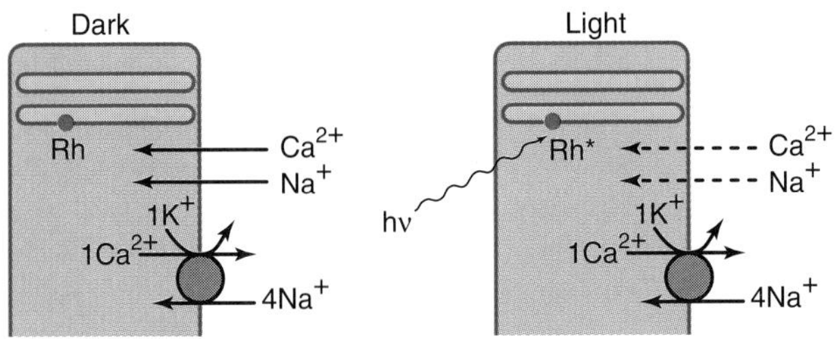

FIGURE 24.15 Calcium flux and the Na–K–Ca rod outer segment exchanger. In the dark (left), both sodium and calcium ions enter the interior of the rod outer segment (Ras) through the cGMP-gated conductance mechanism. To maintain a balance, calcium ions are extruded via an exchange mechanism, with the stoichiometry as shown, that utilizes the energy in the sodium and potassium gradients. In bright light (right), the calcium influx is eliminated but the calcium extrusion process continues, thereby reducing the concentration of free calcium in the ROS. From Yau.[25]

the suppression of the light-regulated current, but Ca efflux is maintained through the activity of the Na–K–Ca exchanger. A well-established effect of the fall in intracellular activity is an increase in the activity of guanylate cyclase, which acts to restore the level of cGMP that was reduced by light.

Invertebrate Phototransduction Takes Place in Microvillar Photoreceptor Cells

A variety of model systems have been used to study invertebrate phototransduction. These systems include cells from *Limulus,* barnacle, squid, and flies. Despite the great morphological variety in invertebrate photoreceptors, the following features appear common to most. The soma contains organelles specialized for phototransduction, as well as the nucleus and biosynthetic apparatus found in most cells. The visual pigment is stored in a microvillar-rich compartment called a rhabdomere. The microvilli are formed from plasma membrane extensions. In close association with the rhabdomere is an intracellular compartment called the submicrovillar cisternae, which is thought to function in phototransduction possibly as a source and sink of calcium ions.

Light Depolarizes the Photoreceptor Membrane in Invertebrates

Invertebrate photoreceptors respond to light with depolarization[41] (e.g., *Limulus*). Depolarization arises from a conductance increase and an increase in the current carried by sodium ions. Potassium ions also permeate the conductance mechanism, but the permeability change to potassium is estimated to be about half that to sodium, and at the resting potential of −50 mV the sodium current is considerably larger than the potassium current.

Intracellular recordings from invertebrate photoreceptors reveal small transient depolarizations, called bumps, that are observed in the dark or in response to dim light.[42] The amplitude, latency, and duration of the bumps vary from response to response. In *Limulus,* where bumps have been studied the most, the mean amplitude is 0.4 nA, the mean latency is 150 ms, and the mean duration is 80 ms. Background illumination (i.e., light adaptation) leads to a decrease in the amplitude of the bumps as well as a decrease in the mean latency and duration. Decreases in the concentration of bathing calcium lead to increases in the amplitude, latency, and duration of the bumps.

There is overwhelming evidence, arising mainly from statistical analyses of responses to dim lights, that bumps arise from the absorption of single photons of light. From the average size and duration of a bump, it has been estimated that 10^8 monovalent ions are translocated across the membrane. To account for the charge movement, thousands of channels are presumed to open more or less simultaneously, thereby evoking the production of a diffusible messenger(s) in the phototransduction process to account for the amplification step.

The responses to bright light are thought to arise from the summation of elementary bumps. The mean duration and latency of the response to bright light are shorter than those of a population of bumps. The shorter duration can be qualitatively accounted for by considering that the later occurring bumps in the response are in effect somewhat light adapted, and the decreased latency can be accounted for by considering that within the population of evoked bumps there will be a number with short latencies. A complete explanation of the differences observed in the responses of individual bumps and the macroscopic response is not currently available.

Phototransduction in Invertebrates Involves an Internal Messenger

On the basis of the amplification step in the generation of bumps and on evidence to be presented below, the existence of internal messenger(s) in the phototransduction pathway has been proposed. The following scheme is widely accepted. Light absorption by the visual pigment leads to the activation of the enzyme phospholipase C (PLC) through the involvement of a G protein.[43] The activated PLC causes the release of inositol trisphosphate (IP_3) from phosphoinositol 4,5-bisphosphate, which in turn stimulates the release of calcium from intracellular stores. The rise in free calcium is then proposed to lead to the activation of cation-selective channels in the plasma membrane through an unidentified intermediate.[44,45] The movements of calcium are complex and poorly understood. Measurements of extracellular calcium suggest that considerable amounts of calcium leave the cell in response to light. This calcium is probably derived from intracellular stores that must be replenished for proper continued transduction. A maintained rise in intracellular calcium in response to steady light is further proposed to be the signal for light adaptation under which the sensitivity to light and bump size decreases. cGMP has been proposed as an internal messenger based on reports that cGMP is able to activate a conductance in excised patches of *Limulus* photoreceptors,[46] but no biochemical evidence has been reported to substantiate this physiological finding.

Supportive evidence for the above scheme is provided by the following findings:

1. The *norpA* (*no receptor potential*) mutants of *Drosophila*, which are defective in PLC, are also defective in phototransduction.
2. Injection of IP_3 leads to a depolarization and bursting activity resembling bumps. The reversal potential of the IP_3-induced response is the same as that induced by light. Also, injection of IP_3 leads to a decrease in the light response and the response to repeated injection of IP_3.
3. In a number of species, illumination leads to an increase in labeled IP_3 following incubation with labeled inositol.
4. Illumination leads to the activity of a GTPase, which has been shown to be a termination step in the mobilization of the G protein.
5. Light-dependent and IP_3-dependent rises in intracellular free calcium have been reported.
6. Injection of the hydrolysis-resistant GTP analog GTPγS leads to persistent activation of the phototransduction pathway and thereby mimics light.

Rhodopsin and Metarhodopsin Are Interconvertible by Light

A striking difference between the molecular mechanisms in vertebrate and invertebrate transduction is the behavior of the chromophore in response to light. In vertebrates, the 11-*cis* isomer of vitamin A aldehyde is isomerized to the all-*trans* isomer, which then dissociates from the protein moiety, opsin, over a time course of seconds to minutes. The all-*trans* isomer diffuses out of the cell, whereupon it is transported to the retinal pigment epithelium for reisomerization to the 11-*cis* isomer and retransport to the photoreceptor. In invertebrates, the chromophore remains covalently linked to the protein moiety and the interconversion from rhodopsin to metarhodopsin is driven by light. Blue light ($<$490 nm) drives the reaction from rhodopsin to metarhodopsin, whereas longer wavelength light ($>$580 nm) drives the reaction from metarhodopsin back to rhodopsin. Slower mechanisms have been described whereby metarhodopsin is converted to rhodopsin in the dark.

Invertebrates Have a Prolonged Depolarizing Afterpotential

Many invertebrate photoreceptors demonstrate a prolonged depolarizing afterpotential (PDA) when a substantial amount of rhodopsin is converted to metarhodopsin by light. The duration of the PDA can be terminated by the application of long-wavelength light, which converts metarhodopsin to rhodopsin. A number of similarities have been reported between PDA and a prolongation of the light-suppressed current in vertebrates observed in response to bright flashes. A specific molecular explanation for the PDA involves the inability to phosphorylate metarhodopsin formed by light. The implication is that unphosphorylated metarhodopsin leads to persistent activation of the phototransduction cascade and upon phosphorylation or reconversion to rhodopsin the PDA is terminated. A number of mutants have been isolated on the basis of the effect on the PDA.

The Study of Mutants Can Provide Insight into Transduction Mechanisms

One of the advantages of working with insects, in particular *Drosophila,* is their short life span and the increased opportunities to generate and study specific mutations within the visual system.[47] A number of mutations involve degeneration of specific photoreceptor cells, whereas others affect aspects of the electrical signaling that can be used to shed light on the biochemical cascade of events in transduction.[48] Photoreceptor degeneration mutants include the following:

The mutant *ninaE* was selected on the basis of an electrical phenotype. The response to blue light showed neither inactivation nor an afterpotential, hence the name *nina*. Mutations in the *ninaE* locus show defects in the visual pigment rhodopsin, which is contained in the R1–R6 photoreceptors of *Drosophila*. The result of this mutation is degeneration of the R1–R6 photoreceptors.

The *rdgB* (*retinal degeneration B*) mutant of *Drosophila* is a conditional mutation that requires the presence of light for the degeneration of R1–R6 photoreceptors. In darkness, virtually no degeneration occurs. Treatment with hydrolysis-resistant analogs of GTP, GTPγS, or Gpp(NH)p as well as with fluoride ions causes degeneration in the dark presumably by activating the transduction pathway at an early stage. Interestingly, the double mutant *rdgB* and *norpA* does not show degeneration.

The phenotype of homozygotes ranges from unresponsive cells to cells with only modest response to light. The *norpA* gene (no receptor potential) is expressed in photoreceptors and codes for a phospholipase C enzyme. The existence of the *norpA* mutation strongly implicates PLC in the phototransduction cascade. Neither the rhodopsin content nor the conversion of rhodopsin to metarhodopsin measured spectrophotometrically seems defective in *norpA* mutants.

The phenotype of the *trp* (*transient receptor potential*) mutation in *Drosophila* is evident in the response to bright lights. The responses to dim light appear normal except for bright steps, the response relaxes to values close to baseline in the mutant, and there is a maintained or plateau value for wild-type cells. The electrical response is similar to that seen when the calcium blocker lanthanum is applied, suggesting that the *trp* mutation leads to a decrease in calcium entry. One suggestion is that the *trp* gene codes for a type of calcium channel expressed in the plasma membrane of invertebrate photoreceptors. The entry of calcium is thought to be essential in the maintenance of calcium stores inside the photoreceptors. The bump size is unaffected by the mutation, but the frequency of occurrence is severely reduced following the initial response to light. Also, the response latency in the presence of background light is reduced in the mutant. These results indicate that different mechanisms control bump size and the frequency of occurrence. The *trp* mutation in *Drosophila* is similar to the *nss* (*no steady state*) mutation in the blowfly, *Lucilia*.

Summary

Diurnal vertebrates have two classes of photoreceptors—rods and cones. Rods are very sensitive to light and subserve vision under scotopic conditions. Cones are less sensitive and subserve vision under photopic conditions. The conversion of light to an electrical signal depends on the presence of visual pigment molecules that are concentrated in the outer segment of rods and cones. These molecules are composed of a seven-transmembrane protein component and the 11-*cis*-retinal isomer of vitamin A. Light absorption by the visual pigment causes the isomerization of the 11-*cis*-retinal to all-*trans*-retinal. This is the only light-sensitive step in the light-response pathway.

The isomerization of vitamin A triggers a cascade of biochemical reactions and results in the activation of cyclic GMP phosphodiesterase. Activated cyclic GMP phosphodiesterase hydrolyzes cyclic GMP, which causes a decrease in a depolarizing cationic current. The result is a membrane hyperpolarization.

The cascade of biochemical reactions contains amplification steps. The electrical response to light is slow and graded. Invertebrate photoreceptors depolarize in response to light. Several mutants are available for possible deciphering of the biochemical steps in the light response of invertebrates.

OLFACTORY TRANSDUCTION

Odor detection and discrimination constitute a fundamental capacity of nearly all animals. In most species, odor signals play critical roles in feeding, mating, reproduction, and social organization.

The odor molecules are first encoded through the processes of olfactory transduction in olfactory sensory neurons. The first step involves absorption and transport of the odor molecules in the mucus. The odor molecules are then believed to interact with members of a large gene family of olfactory receptors belonging to the superfamily of seven-transmembrane, G-protein-coupled receptors. Functional groups on the odor molecules interact with specific subsites within the receptors to generate broad spectra of receptor responses.

The receptors activate G-protein-mediated second-messenger cascades, leading to the production of cAMP, which then directly activates a cyclic-nucleotide-gated, nonspecific cation channel, which generates a depolarizing sensory current response. Other second-messenger pathways that have been identified include an IP_3 pathway that activates Ca conductance in the ciliary plasma membrane; activation of Cl conductance, which contributes to the sensory response; and activation of K conductance, which hyperpolarizes the membrane and thereby generates inhibitory sensory responses in some species. Modulation of the sensory responses is mediated by many molecular pathways, including phosphorylation of second-messenger intermediates and gaseous messengers acting through Ca on the membrane channels. Different combinations of these second-messenger pathways are present in different species, making the olfactory sensory neuron a complex integrative unit finely tuned to the particular odor molecules relevant for that species.

These principles have emerged mainly from work on the main olfactory receptors of vertebrates, lobsters, and insects. Parallel studies are beginning to reveal equivalent molecular components of the signaling mechanisms in the receptor cells of the vomeronasal organ in vertebrates and in the chemosensory cells of nematodes. These studies should lead to an understanding of the cross-phyla principles uniting these different systems and of the specific adaptations of each species for its particular range of odor molecules.

Odor Molecules Are Transduced by Olfactory Sensory Neurons

Most vertebrate animals sense odor molecules by means of sensory neurons located in a pseudostratified epithelium within the nasal cavity. These are bipolar neurons; a thin dendrite arises from one pole, ending in a knob from which arise 6–12 cilia (see Fig. 24.16). These contain the 9 + 2 pairs of microtubules character-

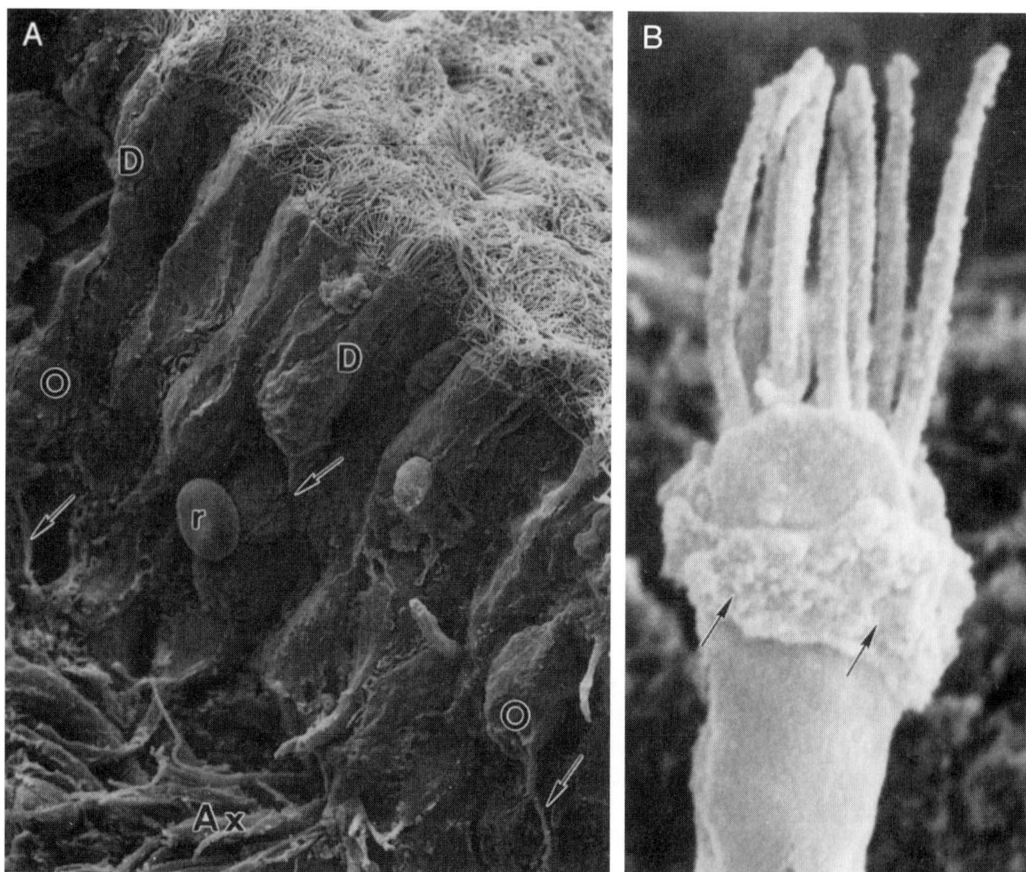

FIGURE 24.16 Olfactory receptor neurons are bipolar cells within the pseudostratified olfactory epithelium. (A): Scanning electron micrograph of the human olfactory epithelium, showing cell bodies of the olfactory receptor neurons (O) with their dendrites (D) ending in cilia that form a mat within the mucus layer overlying the epithelium. From the deeper aspect an axon (arrows) arises, forming bundles (Ax) in the submucosa. Red blood cell (r). (B) High-magnification view of the distal dendritic knob giving rise to olfactory cilia. The terminal web is visible encircling the knob (arrows). From Morrison and Costanzo.[49]

istic of true cilia in other cells of the body. The cilia are thin (0.2 mm in diameter near the knob, tapering to 0.1 μm near their tips), and they vary in length in different species, from 5–10 mm in humans[49] to 200 mm in frogs. The cilia contain no other organelles. The knobs and cilia are embedded in the mucus overlying the epithelium. The cilia greatly increase the surface area containing the olfactory receptors. The large number of cilia form a dense mat within the mucus layer that provides an effective device for capturing odor molecules that are absorbed from the air into the mucus. The mucus is viscous (secreted by the supporting cells) except for a watery surface layer (secreted by Bowman's glands). From the other pole of the neuron, a thin unmyelinated axon arises and joins other axons in the submucosa to form bundles that connect to the olfactory bulb.

Invertebrates such as crustacea (lobsters) and insects also have bipolar olfactory sensory neurons. These generally have longer and more numerous cilia surrounded by lymph and encased in antennal hairs.[50] The cilia may or may not contain microtubules. In insects, odor molecules access the cilia through pores in the hair, which empty into small spaces called "kettles," where the molecules are absorbed and diffuse to the ciliary membrane.[51]

Odor Stimuli Consist of a Wide Range of Small Signal Molecules

Odor molecules are given off by a variety of objects that play essential roles in such behaviors as feeding, mating, and social organization. They are low-molecular-weight molecules that fall into several broad classes. In aquatic animals, the molecules tend to be water soluble and include various amino acids that are important for food recognition. Bile salts are also effective stimuli for species such as fish and may function as alarm signals to warn of the presence of predators. In terrestrial animals, the molecules tend to be small (under 200 Da) and volatile, so that they can readily vaporize and be carried in the air; they also tend to be lipid soluble. Some of these are acids, alcohols, and esters found in various plant and animal foods. Some are essential oils. Others are aromatic compounds given off by flowering plants. They may function for long-distance signaling of the presence of food objects in the organism's environment, as well as for the palatability of those objects during eating. An important category consists of molecules used in reproductive activities, extending from signals used in attracting mates, identifying them, copulating, blocking pregnancy, facilitating nipple attachment by infants, and infant identification. Some of these activities are mediated by complex mixtures of acids, esters, and other types of common molecules; others are mediated by individual larger and more complex molecules like musks; still others are mediated by specific types of molecules for conspecific signaling known as **pheromones**. Many types of odor molecules have molecular weights and geometrical sizes and shapes that are in the same range as common neurotransmitters such as acetylcholine, glutamate, γ-aminobutyric acid, and glycine. It is not surprising that, as we shall see, their receptors may belong to the same superfamily.

Odor-Binding Proteins May Link Odor Molecules to Odor Receptors

The hydrophobic nature of most odor molecules important for terrestrial animals has implied that special mechanisms may be needed to transport the odor molecules through the lymph or mucus to receptive sites on the cilia. Vogt and Riddiford[52] first showed that the male silkworm antenna lymph contains a 15-kDa protein with high affinity for the female sex attractant pheromone; they called it **pheromone-binding protein** (PBP). They postulated that the PBP binds the pheromone molecules, thereby solubilizing them,[53] and transports them to the cilia receptors; these researchers also obtained evidence for an esterase in the lymph that could be involved in inactivating the pheromone molecules. Subsequent research has provided evidence as well for a family of **odor-binding proteins** (OBP) in various insect species. Several of the PBPs and OBPs have been cloned and sequenced[54] and expressed.[55] They are predominantly helical proteins with relatively high and narrow specificities for their ligands. By means of photoaffinity labeling of bacterially expressed recombinant PBP, specific amino acid residues that form the binding site for the pheromone ligand have been identified.[56] PBPs may present a combined binding protein–pheromone surface to the receptor, similar to the manner in which MHC molecules are involved in presenting antigens to antibodies.[57] It is also possible that PBPs may be involved in both presentation and inactivation of pheromone components.[58] These possibilities are under current investigation.

Proteins that bind odor molecules have also been found in the mucus of the vertebrate nasal cavity.[59–61] At first, these proteins were believed to be specific to the olfactory mucus, and homologous therefore to the OBPs in insects. It soon became apparent, however, that vertebrate OBPs are secreted by nasal glands and are found in the mucus covering respiratory as well as olfactory nasal epithelium. The vertebrate OBPs are small (ca. 20 kDa), soluble proteins. Interestingly, the cloned and sequenced vertebrate OBPs have an eight-stranded barrel structure[62–64] that is unrelated to the residue sequence and helical structure of the insect OBPs. In addition, vertebrate OBPs have broad odor–ligand affinities, in contrast to the narrower binding affinities of the insect OBPs.

To date, no direct physiological evidence has been reported for functions of vertebrate OBPs. Patch recordings from freshly isolated salamander olfactory neurons bathed in artificial medium show responses to odors, suggesting that the mucus, including OBPs, is not necessary for odor molecules to stimulate olfactory receptor cells (ORCs).[65] Nevertheless, vertebrate OBPs normally may enhance odor responses by concentrating odor molecules in the mucus, presenting them to the receptors, and facilitating their inactivation and removal.

G-Protein-Coupled Receptors Are Believed to Be the Initial Site of Odor Transduction in Mammals

Given the lipid solubility of many odor molecules, they could act at several receptor sites: on or within the membrane or within the cytoplasm. The best candidate at present is a family of G-protein-coupled membrane receptors. These were first anticipated in 1985 with the demonstration that odors stimulate the cAMP second-messenger system in isolated cilia preparations[66] and were finally demonstrated in 1991.[67] Beginning with oligonucleotide primers conserved in other G-protein-coupled neurotransmitter receptors, the polymerase chain reaction (PCR) was used to amplify homologous sequences of cDNA prepared from rat olfactory epithelium. The PCR bands on gels were subjected to restriction endonuclease digestion, yielding products whose total molecular weight was greater than that of the original band, suggesting the presence of multiple different genes. Since the original study, numerous members of this gene family have been isolated in a variety of species, from catfish (in which a few dozen to 100 are expressed) to mice, rats, and humans (up to 1000 members expressed).[68] Chromosome mapping shows that the olfactory receptor genes are commonly found in clusters and distributed broadly in different chromosomes.[69]

This extremely large gene family presents special problems for laboratories to coordinate their sequencing efforts and integrate the sequence information with other types of data. To support this effort, an Olfactory Receptor Database has been built and is accessible over the World Wide Web. It contains both unpublished and published sequences, as well as other types of data, such as molecular models and chromosome maps, to aid in analyzing the mechanisms of odor ligand–odor receptor interactions underlying odor detection and discrimination.

Determinants on Odor Molecules Interact with Residue Subsites in a Binding Pocket in Olfactory Receptors

It has been suggested[67] that a high degree of sequence diversity in transmembrane domains IV, V, and VI might be correlated with sites of binding for different odor ligands or classes of ligands. Computer models have indicated that odor ligands may bind in a pocket similar to that formed by the β-adrenergic receptor (another member of the G-protein-coupled receptor superfamily) to interact with its neurotransmitter ligand (epinephrine; see Fig. 24.17A). Specific residues within the pocket that appear to be characteristic of olfactory receptors have been identified. These residues appear to confer on a given receptor the ability to bind with relatively low and variable affinities to a broad range of different odor ligands. This binding is the basis for the ability of the animal to discriminate between many different odors (see Chapter 25). Two further methods of computational analysis have been applied to the receptors (see Box 24.1).

Experimental analysis of binding sites in these receptors has been slow to get under way. The model for this type of analysis in G-protein-coupled receptors is the β-adrenergic receptor, in which expression of the receptor in a heterologous cell type has enabled the residue sites involved in binding its preferred ligand, epinephrine, to be identified by the usual methods of point mutations (see Fig. 24.17B). The problem in olfactory receptors is much more difficult, however. First, expressing the receptors in heterologous systems has turned out to be very difficult. Second, although there is evidence that a single sensory neuron may express only one receptor type, this has not yet been established (see Chapter 26). Third, in contrast to most G-protein-coupled receptors, which have narrow affinities for known ligands, olfactory receptors are likely to interact with variable affinities with a range of ligands. Finally, because there may be thousands of odor ligands, defining the full range of preferred ligands for a given receptor may turn out to be impossible.

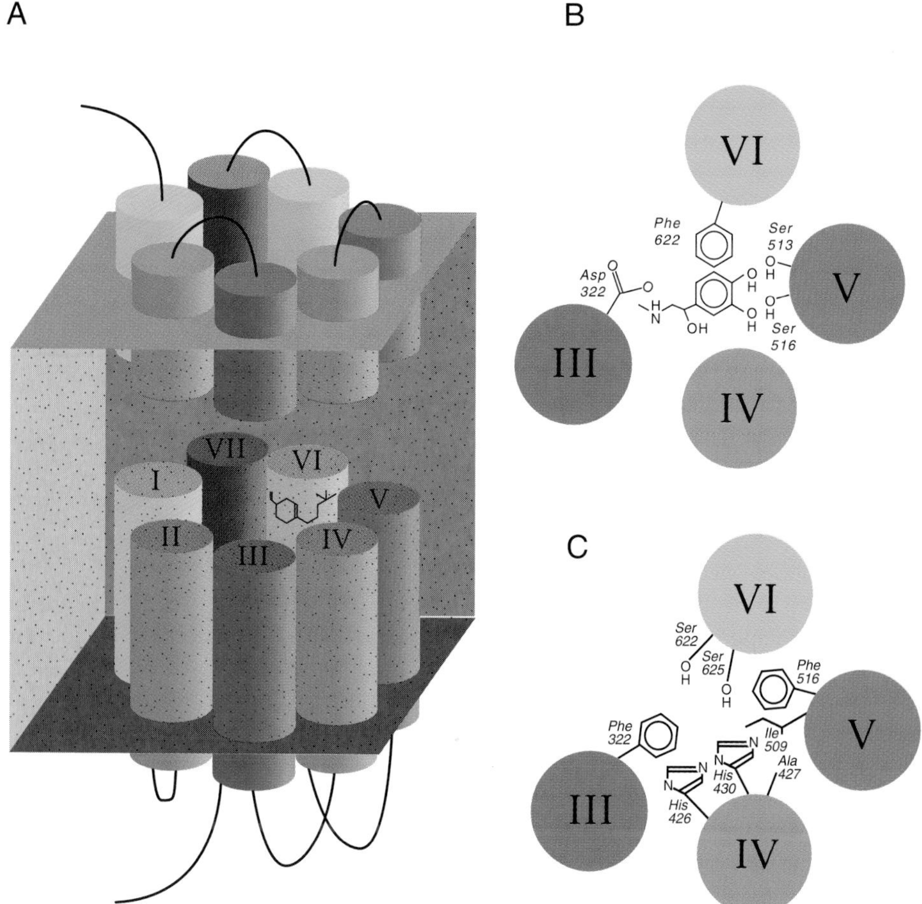

FIGURE 24.17 Molecular modeling and computational analysis have provided evidence that odor molecules may activate olfactory receptors within a binding pocket similar to that formed by the transmembrane domains (TMs) in β-adrenergic receptors. (A) Schematic model shows how an odor molecule, lyral, may interact with its receptor at a depth within the membrane similar to that at which epinephrine interacts with the β-adrenergic receptor. (B) Specific determinants on the epinephrine molecule are believed to interact with specific amino acid residues in the β-adrenergic receptor. These interactions include coulombic interactions between the cationic amine group of epinephrine and aspartate on TM III; aryl–aryl interactions between the phenyl group and phenylalanine on TM IV; and sterospecific hydrogen bonds between the catechol hydroxyl groups and dual serines on TM V. (C) Postulated residue sites in olfactory receptors that may be especially significant in interacting with odor molecules. The sites on TM IV bearing N-rich residues appear to be particularly characteristic of olfactory receptors. Other important sites are the dual serines on TM VI, the bulky phenyl group on TM III, and diverse sites on TM V. Based on Singer *et al.*[70] and Shepherd *et al.*[71]

To address these problems, researchers have used several approaches to provide evidence for the preferred ligands for several receptor types. The rat receptor OR5 was reported to show preference for binding the odor ligands lyral and lilial in a baculovirus expression vector.[74] In *Caenorhabditis elegans*, the seven-transmembrane domain receptor Odr-10 was shown to be associated with the odor ligand diacetyl in behavioral assays.[75] In mice, a major gene locus on chromosome 4 and additional loci on other chromosomes, including chromosome 6, have been found to produce hyposmia for isovaleric acid.[76] The clearest evidence to date appears to be provided by overexpression of a specific receptor gene in rat olfactory epithelium through transfection by an adenovirus vector;[77] tests of the responses of the transfected cells to a wide range of some 80 odors showed a peak preference for octyl aldehyde (see below). As these experimental approaches are developed to the stage at which point mutations can be made to test for residues involved in preferential binding, the computational methods described above will become essential tools in guiding

BOX 24.1

COMPUTATIONAL ANALYSIS OF PROTEIN SEQUENCES

Functionally significant residue sites in olfactory receptors have been identified by two methods for computational analysis of protein sequences. Correlated mutation analysis (CMA) is based on the hypothesis that during evolution single mutations are usually harmful—by disrupting the protein structure or degrading its function—unless followed by a later mutation that restores or enhances the structural effect or functional capacity. CMA involves a computer search of sequences of a protein family for evidence of correlated mutation changes between different pairs of amino acid residues. In the case of the olfactory receptors, this search has revealed correlated mutations involving several of the residues that were previously identified in the computer model, giving independent support to the possible functional importance of those residues in binding odor ligands.[72,73] Of particular interest are two histidine residues in transmembrane IV (see Fig. 24.17); histidine has the ability to form either positive or neutral charges on its nitrogen groups depending on the charge environment, and researchers speculate that this could contribute to broad affinities of olfactory receptors for different odor ligands.

Another method of identifying residues in receptors that may be functionally significant in binding ligands is to search for mutations in the nucleotide sequences that show positive selection. Mutations can result in either a codon that codes for the same amino acid (synonymous, or neutral selection) or a different amino acid (nonsynonymous, or positive selection). In a protein that binds its ligands in a highly selective manner, nonsynonymous mutations of codons for critical residues are usually harmful and are weeded out by selective pressures. In contrast, in a protein family like that of the olfactory receptors, where there is pressure to diversify in order to be able to respond to wider ranges of odor ligands, positive selection for nonsynonymous mutations is a potential advantage. Receptors in catfish have a number of residues showing positive selection. In mammals, transmembrane VI shows positive selection for a serine residue site[70] that was already identified by the models and by CMA as possibly playing a potential role in hydrogen bonding to odor ligands (cf. Fig. 24.17B).

which residue sites to target and in interpreting the results.

The initial computational studies provide evidence that odor transduction begins with the interactions of a limited number of determinants on odor molecules with a limited number of residue subsites in a binding pocket in olfactory receptor proteins. The set of determinants constitutes a kind of **epitope**.[78,79] Epitope is a term from the immune system, where it typically is a large structure formed by 6–10 amino acids, whereas many odor ligands are the size of amino acids, whose determinants are at the atomic level. **Odortype** or **odotope** may therefore be more appropriate and more specific for an odor epitope.[78,80,81] Alternatively, the similarity with the **pharmacophores** of molecules that bind other members of the G-protein-coupled receptor family suggests that the set of determinants on an odor ligand may be referred to as an **olfactophore**.[82] Theoretical studies suggest that odor ligands commonly comprise 3–4 determinants, which interact with 2–6 receptor subsites. Using these estimates, theoretical and computational models are being generated that account for the ability of up to 1000 receptors in the mammal to discriminate up to 10,000 or more different odors.[68,83,84]

cAMP and IP_3 Are Second Messengers in Mediating Odor Responses

The finding that olfactory cilia contain an adenylate cyclase that is sensitive to odor stimuli led quickly to the molecular cloning and sequencing of all of the components of this second-messenger system (Fig. 24.18). These include an olfactory-specific G_s protein (G_{olf}) and an adenylate cyclase Type III.[85] This pathway shows interesting adaptations for olfactory transduction. Cyclic AMP production is rapid; in rapid stop-flow experiments, exposure of an isolated cilia preparation to brief olfactory stimuli elicits an abrupt rise in cAMP within 50 ms, with a transient return to baseline[86,87] (Fig. 24.19A).

Evidence for the involvement of the phosphotidylinositol pathway in odor transduction in some species has also been adduced. In stop-flow experiments on preparations of cockroach antennae and rat cilia, odor stimulation elicits short-latency transient IP_3 produc-

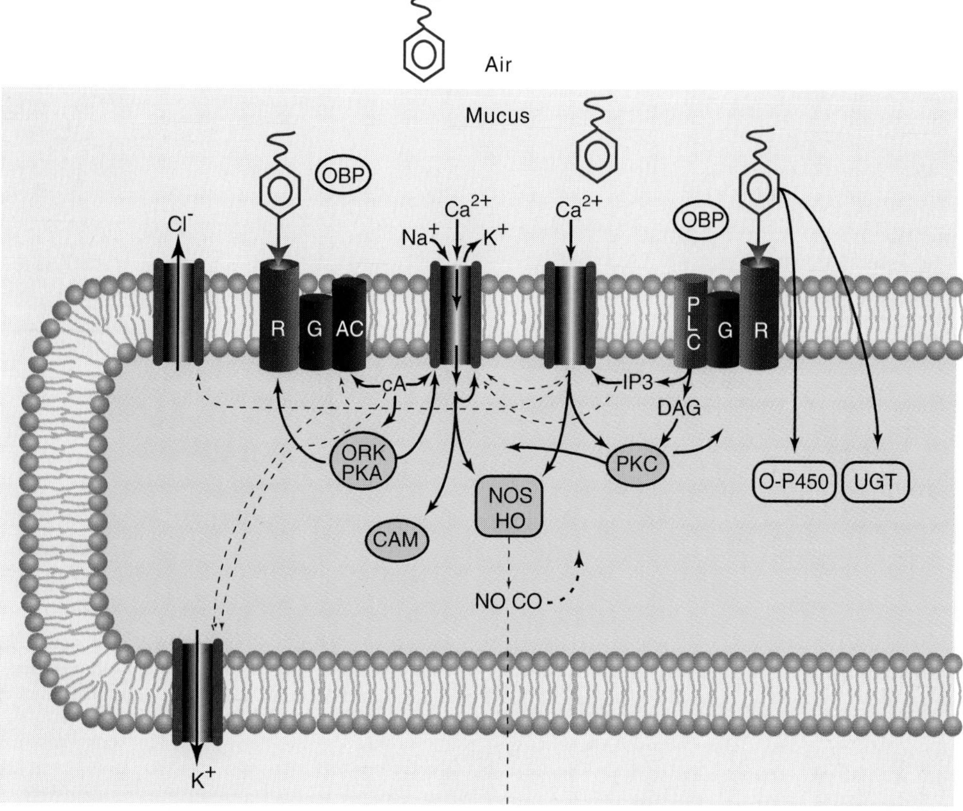

FIGURE 24.18 Sensory transduction of odor molecules involves complex second-messenger pathways. Odor molecules are initially absorbed into the olfactory mucus, where they may bind to olfactory-binding protein (OBP), which carries them to the olfactory cilia. The main transduction mechanism in many species is the cyclic AMP pathway, which involves the activation by odor molecules of a receptor (currently believed to be represented mainly by the large gene family of olfactory receptors), a GTP-binding protein (G); an adenylate cyclase (AC), which produces cyclic AMP (cA); and a nonspecific cationic cyclic-nucleotide-gated (CNG) channel. The CNG channel is also gated by cyclic GMP (not shown). In some species there is evidence for activation of a phospholipase (PLC)–inositol trisphosphate pathway that acts on a plasma membrane Ca channel. Ca also gates a Cl conductance that contributes substantially to the sensory current in many species. Ca^{2+} and cA also gate K currents in some species to produce suppressive responses, especially in invertebrates. Solid lines show pathways that have been demonstrated in the rat; dashed lines show pathways demonstrated in other species, including lobster, insect, catfish, mudpuppy, salamander, frog and toad. Second-messenger pathways through nitric oxide synthase (NOS) and heme oxygenase (HO) producing the gaseous messengers NO and CO, respectively, are also indicated by dashed lines. Pathways for desensitization and other types of modulation include olfactory receptor kinase (ORK), phosphokinase A (PKA), and C (PKC), diacyl glycerol (DAG), and Ca–calmodulin (CAM). Clearing of odors and other exogenous molecules may take place by olfactory cytochrome P-450 (O-P450) and uridyl glucuronic transferase (UGT). Based on many authors; adapted from Shepherd.[82]

tion similar to that shown by cAMP (Fig. 24.19B). An important question is whether different odors are associated with the different pathways. In the stop-flow experiments on isolated cilia, it has been reported that odors are associated with either the cAMP or the IP_3 pathway, but not both.[88] However, in cultured olfactory cells, coactivation of the pathways by several different types of odors has been reported.[89] In lobster olfactory neurons, both pathways are present; odor stimulation of a cell leads either to depolarization or to hyperpolarization through activation of several types of membrane conductances;[50] see Fig. 24.18 and later in this chapter).

A Cyclic-Nucleotide-Gated Channel Similar to That in Photoreceptors Is Involved in the Odor Response

Patch recordings from the cilia have shown that in inside-out configurations, cAMP directly activates a

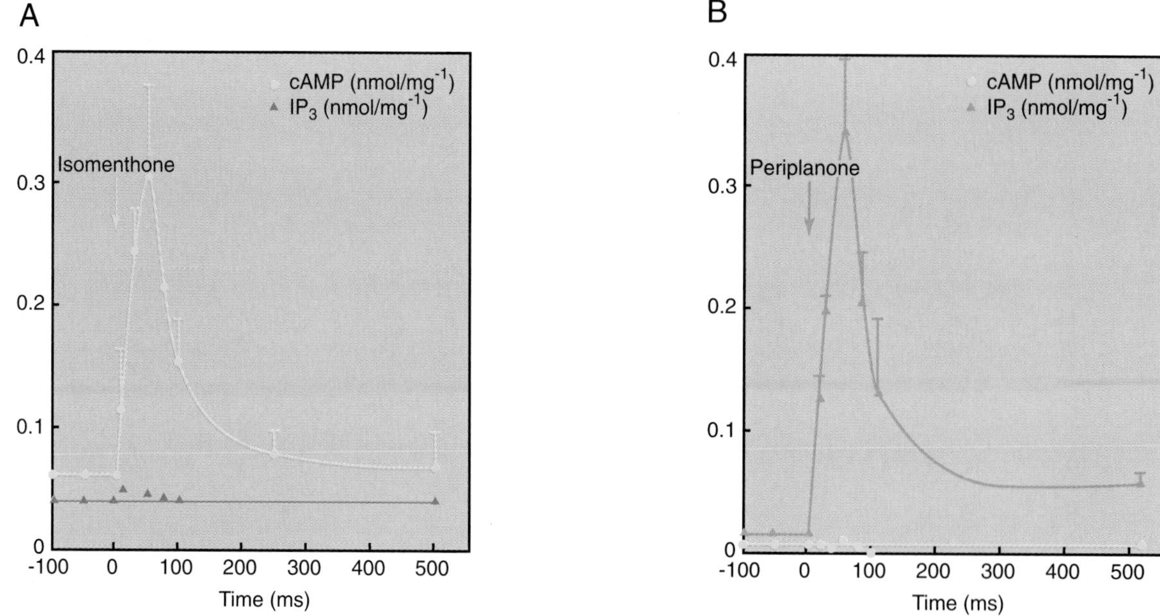

FIGURE 24.19 Rapid stop-flow experiments demonstrate that odor stimulation induces the rapid and transient generation of second messengers in olfactory sensory cells. (A) Time course of production of cyclic AMP, but not inositol trisphosphate (IP_3), in an isolated rat cilia preparation. (B) Time course of production of IP_3, but not cyclic AMP, in antennal homogenates from cockroaches, *Periplaneta americana*. From Breer *et al.*[98]

membrane conductance.[90] In single-channel recordings in the attached patch mode, the same channels are activated by both cAMP and odors, showing that this is indeed the sensory conductance[91–93] (Fig. 24.20). The channel has been cloned, sequenced, and shown to have high homology with the cyclic-nucleotide-gated (CNG) channel in photoreceptors.[94] Surprisingly, the native olfactory channel has a higher affinity ($K_D = 4$ μM) for cGMP (the natural ligand in the photoreceptor) than for cAMP ($K_D = 20$ μM). A similar difference has

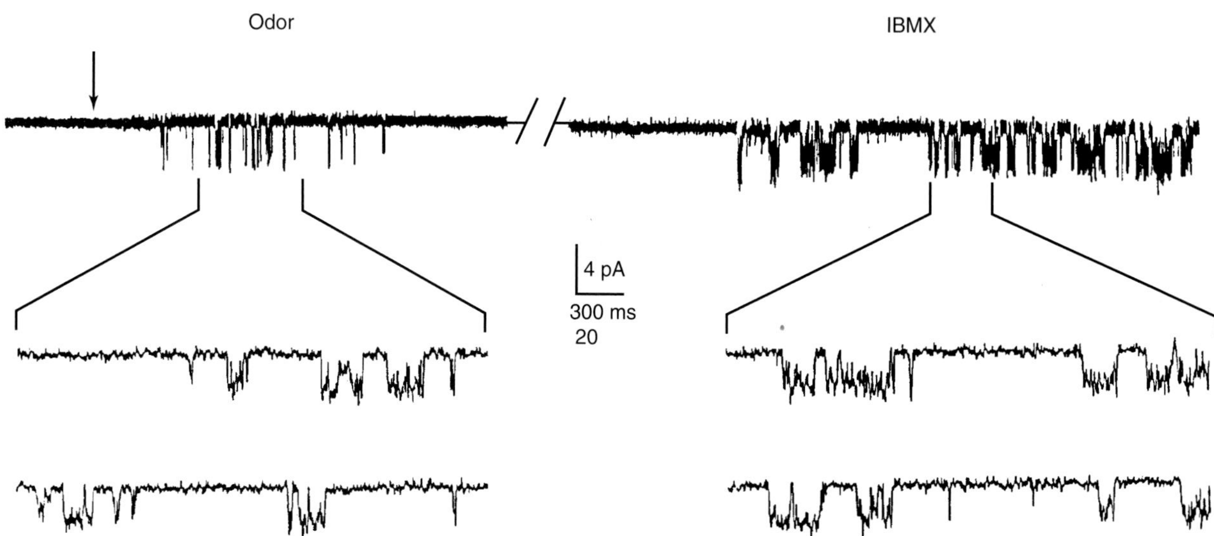

FIGURE 24.20 Patch-clamp recordings from olfactory sensory neurons show that the odors and cyclic nucleotides activate the same channel. IBMX suppresses phosphodiesterase, decreasing hydrolysis of cyclic AMP, causing an increase in its concentration and increased activation of the cyclic-nucleotide-gated channel. From Firestein *et al.*[92]

BOX 24.2

ONLY A SMALL FRACTION OF THE CHANNELS ARE ACTIVATED BY ODOR STIMULI

It is of interest to estimate the number of channels in the cilia and the fraction that generate a sensory response. The density of channels has been estimated at 500–2000 μm^{-2}, somewhat higher than the density of similar channels in rod outer segments (500–800 μm^{-2}). A single cilium in the salamander is 0.25 μm in diameter and 40 μm in length, giving a surface area of approximately 30 μm^2; a typical cell with 10 cilia therefore has a combined membrane surface area of 300 μm^2, giving a total of some 360,000 channels.

The maximum fraction of channels activated during an odor response may be estimated from the finding that in normal Ringer solution a cell at a resting potential of 60 mV can respond with a maximum whole cell sensory current in the range of 500–600 pA. At that resting potential the single-channel current (in the absence of divalent cations) is approximately 2–3 pA. If the single channel current in normal Ringer solution is 2 orders of magnitude smaller (i.e., 20–30 fA), it would imply the activation of some 20,000–30,000 channels, or approximately 6–8% of the total. If in addition up to half the current is due to a chloride conductance, it would imply that the proportion of open cAMP channels is only 3–4%. For comparison, some 1–2% of the available rod channels are open when the dark current is maximal.

been found in cloned channels. The role of cGMP may be related to gaseous second messengers in the odor response. A Hill coefficient of approximately 2, for both cAMP and cGMP, indicates that channel opening is cooperative, requiring the simultaneous binding of at least two ligand molecules. Selective mutation analysis has identified the nucleotide-binding sites that are specific for the rod photoreceptor channel and the olfactory receptor cell channel (Fig. 24.21).

Like the photoreceptor channel, the olfactory CNG channel is nonselective for cations. Unlike the photoreceptor, the olfactory channel is closed in the absence of sensory stimulation. When odor molecules bind to the receptor and lead to production of cAMP, the cAMP activates the channel, causing a net inflow of cations that depolarizes the membrane toward an equilibrium potential around zero. This depolarization spreads from the site of sensory transduction in the cilia and dendritic knob through the dendrite to the cell body and axon hillock, activating voltage-gated channels that generate action potentials. In this way, the amplitude and time course of the graded sensory potentials generated by odor stimuli are transduced into a frequency code of impulses that propagate through the axon to its terminals in the olfactory bulb.[95]

Olfactory Neurons Are Complex Integrative Units

In some species, such as the salamander, transduction involves mainly the depolarizing conductance gated by cAMP together with a depolarizing Ca^{2+}-gated Cl^- (see Fig. 24.18). In other species there has been evidence for an IP_3-gated Ca^{2+} conductance in the plasma membrane,[96,97] but this is controversial in the rat because G_{olf} knockout mice, presumably specific for the cAMP pathway, show no other responses as measured by the electro-olfactogram. In still other species, such as the lobster, K^+ conductances, modulated either by cAMP or by Ca^{2+}, are present.[50] These conductances tend to move the membrane potential toward the equilibrium potential for K^+, hyperpolarizing the membrane and opposing the generation of impulses. This series of events produces an interplay of depolarizing and hyperpolarizing sensory potentials that is similar to the interplay of excitatory and inhibitory synaptic potentials in central neurons. These olfactory sensory neurons thus function as complex integrative units in processing their odor stimuli.[50,99]

Olfactory neurons vary widely in their responsiveness to different odors, presumably reflecting different affinities of the odor ligands for the species of receptor molecule that they express. These differences mean that cells differ in both their threshold and their range of responsiveness to different odors. However, any given cell shows a limited concentration range to a given odor, usually only 1–2 orders of magnitude. This limited range has been found both in extracellular recordings of receptor neuron responses to square odor pulses and in patch recordings of responses of isolated receptor cells to rapid pulses delivered in a bath (see Fig. 24.22). Thus, the total concentration range to which the organism is sensitive is due to parallel

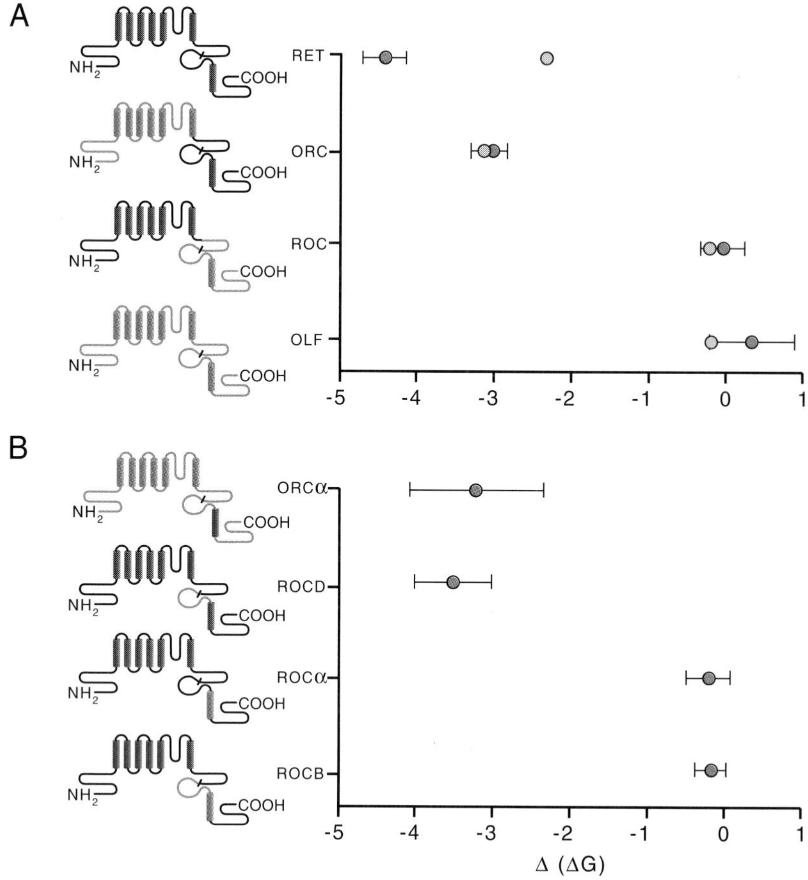

FIGURE 24.21 Chimeras of the retinal and olfactory cyclic-nucleotide-gated (CNG) channels show the segments responsible for differing cyclic nucleotide selectivity. (A) The differing affinities of the wild-type retinal (RET) and olfactory (OLF) channels are little affected by substitutions of the transmembrane domains. (B) Localization of the site of CNG selectivity to the C-terminal intracellular helix. ROCB, RET channel that contains the 132 amino acid residues of the putative OLF CNG-binding domain. ROCD, similar to ROCB, but retains the RET C helix. ORCα and ROCα, only the 24 amino acid residues of the C helices have been exchanged. Graphs show ratio of free energy change of cyclic AMP binding according to the del Castillo and Katz scheme (red circles and standard deviations) and the Monod-Wyman-Changeux model (gray circles). From Goulding *et al.*[104]

processing through different subsets of sensory neurons. Evidence indicates that the different concentration ranges of different olfactory receptor neurons (ORNs) for a given odor reflect the relative affinities of olfactory receptors in different ORN subsets for that odor ligand.

Calcium Ions Play a Central Role in Olfactory Adaptation

Ca^{2+} is an important factor in shaping the sensory response. During sustained odor stimulation, the sensory response declines from its initial, phasic peak to a lower tonic level. This decline is associated with the action of Ca^{2+}; in the absence of Ca^{2+}, there is no decline, and patch recordings show continued channel activity with no desensitization. The decline of a sensory response during sustained stimulation is referred to as **adaptation**, and these experiments suggest that adaptation in olfactory sensory neurons involves the action of internal Ca^{2+}. Single-channel analysis has shown that an increase in internal Ca^{2+} reduces the channel open probability. This effect appears to be mediated by an intermediate Ca^{2+}-binding protein, possibly calcium–calmodulin, which binds to the channel protein to reduce its affinity for cyclic nucleotides. Increases in intracellular Ca^{2+} following odor stimulation have also been documented using Ca^{2+}-sensitive dyes.[100] It is now possible to image the Ca^{2+} increase caused by

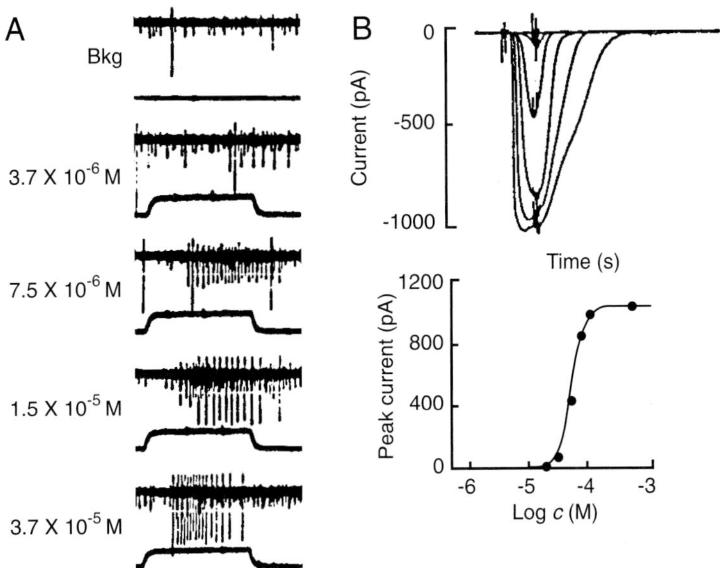

FIGURE 24.22 Olfactory receptor neurons show narrow response ranges to odor concentration. (A) A single salamander olfactory receptor cell responds with increasing impulse discharge to increasing concentrations of amyl acetate odor (the highest concentration of 3.7×10^{-5} was near maximal for the frequency of the impulse response before spike decrement was observed). From Getchell and Shepherd, 1978. (B) Patch recordings show membrane current responses to increasing odor concentration. Above: Membrane current responses to increasing concentrations of isoamyl acetate. Small spikes are artifacts showing the onset and offset of the odor pulse. Below: Graph of peak current versus odor concentration shows the narrow concentration range of this cell covering less than one log step from threshold to maximum response. From Firestein *et al.*, 1993.

odor stimuli in individual cilia (Fig. 24.23). Such analysis at the level of the individual cilium is comparable to the imaging of Ca^{2+} changes in individual cilia of hair cells.[101]

Calcium ions also act externally to reduce the conductance of the channel. In the absence of calcium, the channel has a unitary conductance of some 45 pS; in normal extracellular Ca^{2+}, Ca^{2+} entering the channel induces a "flicker block," reducing the conductance to less than 1 pS. This block is removed by depolarizing the membrane,[102,103] suggesting that in normal Ca^{2+} olfactory sensory neurons act as coincidence detectors for cyclic nucleotide production plus membrane depolarization. In normal Ca^{2+} and at normal resting potential, most of the channels appear to be in the blocked state. This mechanism may enhance the signal-to-noise ratio of the sensory response, as in photoreceptors.

Gaseous Messengers Appear to Modulate Odor Responses

The fact that the olfactory CNG channel is more sensitive to cGMP than to cAMP has suggested that the former may also play a role in olfactory transduction. At high odor concentrations, isolated cilia preparations generate slow accumulations of cGMP.[86] This accumulation was first shown to be blocked by blockers of nitric oxide synthase (NOS), which suggested that NO may be a gaseous second-messenger in the olfactory epithelium. There is controversy about whether the neuronal form of NOS is present in adults. NO may instead play a role as a second messenger between receptor neurons during development.[105]

More direct evidence of the role of a gaseous second messenger in sensory transduction has recently been obtained for carbon monoxide (CO). Heme oxygenase-2 (HO-2), the isoform of the enzyme that synthesizes CO in the brain, is present at high concentration in the olfactory epithelium. Odor stimulation of cultured receptor cells elicits production of cGMP that is blocked by hemoglobin, a blocker of HO-2. In the whole-cell recording mode, internal perfusion of a receptor cell with cGMP causes a slow inward current that is closely mimicked by superfusion of CO. During internal perfusion with cGMP, superfusion with CO has no effect, suggesting that CO acts through GC

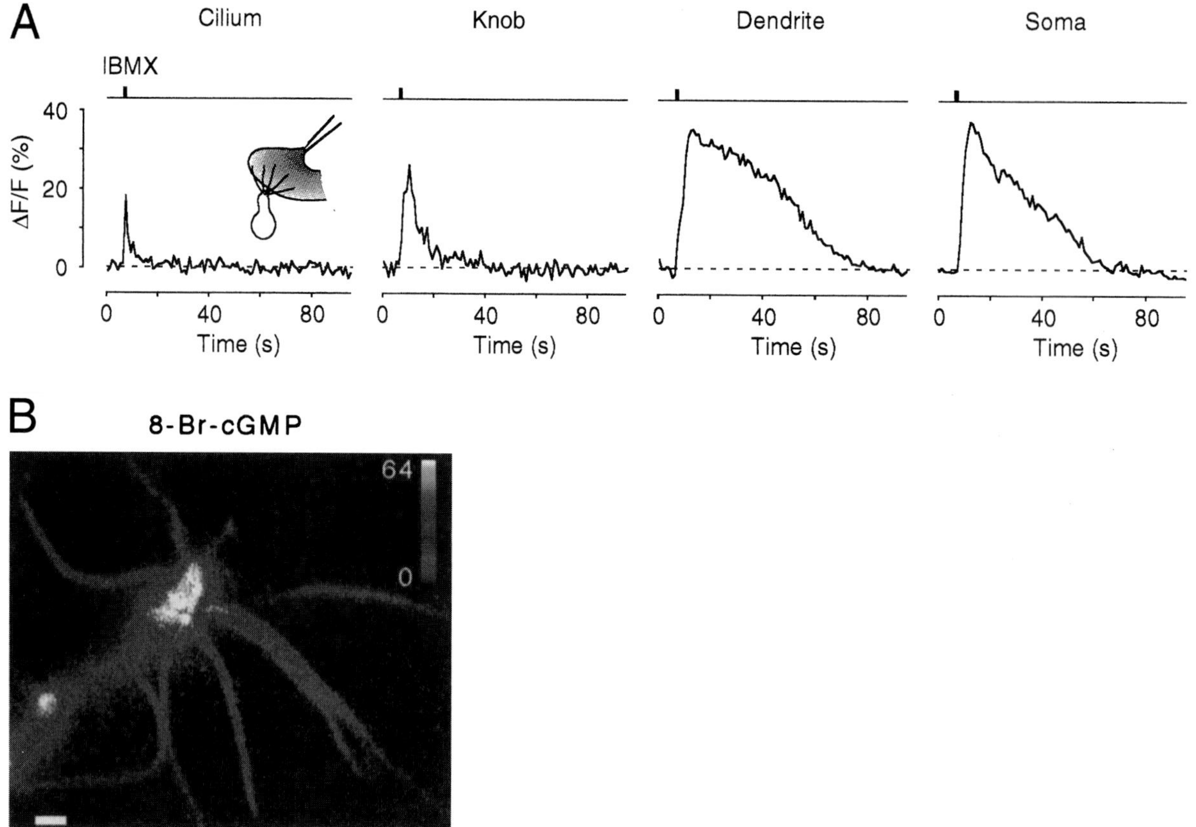

FIGURE 24.23 Calcium fluxes can be imaged in single olfactory cilia. (A) An isolated salamander olfactory receptor neuron was stimulated with a pulse of IBMX restricted to the cilia (inset). IBMX blocks phosphodiesterase, elevating cAMP concentration and activating the CNG channel, which increases the flow of Ca into the cilia. The measured changes in fluorescence of the Ca-sensitive dye fluo-3 are shown in the graphs for a cilium, knob, dendrite, and soma of the cell. Note that the earliest and most transient signal is seen in the cilium, indicating the site of sensory transduction. Similar changes in Ca fluorescence are seen with an odor pulse restricted to the cilia. (B) Ca changes are also elicited in the cilia by 8-bromo-cyclic GMP, a membrane-permeable analog of cyclic GMP, which activates the CNG channel in the cilia, increasing the flux of Ca into the cilia. The figure shows that Ca enters everywhere within the cilia; there is no compartmentation or localized sites of Ca flux. From Leinders-Zufall *et al.*[108]

and not directly on the CNG channel; this interpretation has been supported by experiments in which the inward current elicited by superfused CO is blocked by blockers of soluble GC. Evidence from olfactory cells in culture indicates that they produce CO. These combined results have supported the idea that CO may provide for modulation of receptor cells, contributing to their state of adaptation. It also points to a possible role for cGMP in mediating long-term adaptation of the ORNs through modulation of the cyclic-nucleotide-gated channel. Similar roles for cGMP in plasticity of central neurons have been postulated.

Odor Responses Encode Odor Molecules by Their Sensory Currents

The outcome of these transduction steps is the generation of a sensory current by the CNG channels. In response to stimulation with a particular odor, the amplitudes and time courses of this sensory current vary in different neurons, reflecting the differing affinities of the receptors and the properties of the second-messenger pathways. These differences across the whole population of sensory neurons provide the basis for encoding the information carried in particular odor molecules.

The extracellular field potentials recorded from the olfactory epithelium in response to odor stimulation provided the first evidence regarding the sensory currents generated by odor stimuli. These field potentials were called the electro-olfactogram (EOG),[105], analogous to the electroretinogram recorded from the retina and to field potentials recorded from the brain. The EOG represents the summed extracellular currents generated by many thousands of activated sensory neurons. Although giving limited insight into the actual mechanisms of generation of the sensory current, it has been a valuable tool for monitoring the population responses of sensory neurons to different stimuli and continues to be a valuable adjunct in contemporary studies of olfactory transduction.

The most direct evidence regarding odor-induced currents comes from patch recordings from isolated cells. The problem in these experiments is discovering the response spectrum (the "molecular receptive range" in the terminology of)[106] of the recorded cell. This information is in general not known; furthermore, this spectrum is likely to cover only a small part of the whole range of odors. One way of dealing with this problem is to use a cocktail of odors shown by tradition to be effective in eliciting responses, so that a reasonable proportion of recorded cells will show a response. A second way is to use a series of compounds with variable structures and smells and test them sequentially. A third is to use homologous chemical series, such as alcohols or aldehydes. This method, introduced by,[106] has turned out to be the most effective to date in activating receptor neurons in ways that give insight into the relations between odor structure and the strength of the current response.

An example of this approach is a study by [107] using the calcium-sensitive dye fura-2 to measure Ca^{2+} changes in ORNs during stimulation with different odors. The cells were isolated by tissue printing and exposed to several homologous series of straight-chain fatty acids and alcohols (containing from 3 to 9 carbon atoms). In a typical preparation of 5–10 cells, 1 or 2 responded to one of the series at the lowest concentration used; as the odor concentration was increased, activation spread to neighboring members of the chain. This experiment showed that the receptors in these cells can discriminate determinants down to a single carbon atom of chain length. In addition, some cells responded to compounds in only one series, whereas others responded to more than one. This result showed the ability to discriminate between functional groups, such as an OH or a COOH group. The authors concluded that individual ORNs are able to discriminate structural features of odor molecules such as hydrocarbon length, electrical charge, and relative electronegativities of functional groups. The results confirm the predictions made by many authors regarding the importance of stereochemical properties of odor molecules and by the molecular modeling of interactions between odor determinants and receptor residues discussed earlier.

To correlate specific odor determinants with specific residues in a known receptor, expression of the receptor in a heterologous cell system, such as an oocyte, is the preparation of choice. However, thus far such expression has proven to be difficult. Zhao and colleagues[77] used the alternative strategy of transfection with a recombinant adenovirus to overexpress a given receptor in the olfactory epithelium of the rat. They then tested the EOG responses of the epithelium to a battery of odors that included several homologous series as well as various other odorous compounds. Among some 80 compounds tested, only longer-chain aldehydes gave increased responses over controls, and of these octyl aldehyde gave the peak response (see Fig. 24.24A). By including a green fluorescent protein tag, the authors were able to dissociate the cells, make patch recordings from labeled cells overexpressing this receptor, and show the sensory currents elicited by octyl aldehyde (Figs. 24.24B–24.24E). These experiments provide the first direct evidence that a member of the large gene family of G-protein-coupled (GPC) receptors is specifically sensitive to odor stimuli. With the computational studies as a guide, the way is now open to analyzing, with point mutations and related methods, the binding sites and mechanisms by which detection and discrimination of this odor ligand by this odor receptor take place.

Transduction Mechanisms in the Vomeronasal Organ Are Similar and Different

In addition to the main olfactory epithelium, a second site of odor transduction exists in vertebrates. This site is Jacobson's organ, also known as the vomeronasal organ (VNO; see Chapter 25). It is present in a variety of vertebrate species and appears to be specialized for transmitting signals from less volatile or nonvolatile odorous compounds. Phylogenetically, it is first differentiated clearly in snakes, where it is involved in several functions, including mating behavior and responses to prey odors that are sampled from the tongue as it is drawn over the inlet to the organ. In rodents, the organ is well developed and is believed to be stimulated by sexually active substances that access the inlet

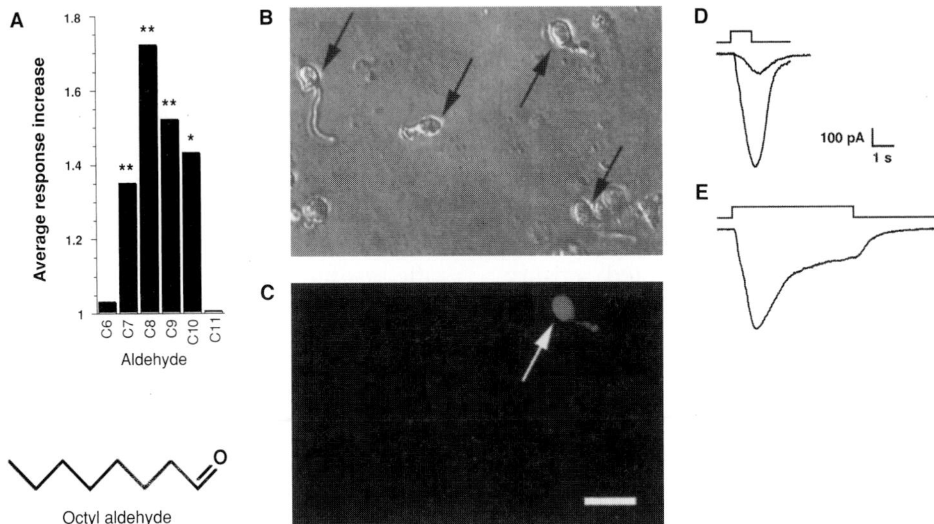

FIGURE 24.24 Overexpression of the I7 receptor in rat olfactory epithelium is associated with increased responsiveness to longer chain aliphatic aldehydes. (A) Average electro-olfactogram responses recorded from transfected rat olfactory epithelia to C6-C11 aliphatic aldehydes. The bars indicate the differences between responses in infected and uninfected animals. The responses to C6 and C11 are similar to control responses to other odors in the battery of 80 odors tested. The responses to C7–C10 show increased responsiveness in the infected animals, with a peak at C8, octyl aldehyde (chemical structure is shown below). The asterisks indicate statistical *P* values of less than 0.001 and 0.01. (B) Freshly dissociated olfactory cells from an infected epithelium (arrows) have characteristic single dendrites and multiple cilia. (C) The same field under fluorescence illumination shows a cell infected with the I7 receptor tagged with green fluorescent protein (GFP) (arrow). (D) A GFP-labeled cell shows, in a whole-cell patch recording, a typical inward current response to a brief pulse of octyl aldehyde at two concentrations. (E) The response of this same cell to a long-duration pulse of octyl aldehyde shows a typical dynamic overshoot and static plateau. From Zhao *et al.*[77]

to the organ as a male directly investigates the female's vaginal opening. In ungulates such as deer and horses, the inlet is exposed by a nasal movement called a flehmen reaction, in which the male investigates the urine of the female to determine her mating receptivity.

A family of genes encoding membrane proteins has been isolated from the vomeronasal organ in rats.[109] These proteins appear to be G-protein-coupled receptors specific to this tissue. Nevertheless, they exhibit little homology to the putative receptor proteins of the main olfactory epithelium or to other members of the GPC receptor superfamily. Although it is widely believed that they function as pheromone receptors, there is as yet no evidence that they have a receptor function. In addition, the only well-documented pheromone in mammals, androstenedione in pigs, mediates its effects through the main olfactory pathway rather than the VNO.[110] The receptor functions of these proteins thus await further study.

Summary

Olfactory transduction begins with the interaction of odor molecules with receptors in the cilia of olfactory receptor neurons. Increasing evidence indicates that these receptors belong to the superfamily of G-protein-coupled receptors. The receptor gene family is very large, with a sequence diversity that enables it to interact with a wide range of odor molecules. An individual cell may express only one or very few receptor types. Computational studies provide evidence that determinants on the odor molecules (carbon length, functional groups, stereochemical shapes) interact with amino acid residues in a receptor-binding pocket. Experimental studies are beginning to be carried out in expression systems so that the binding pockets and odor ligand specificities of specific receptors can be identified.

The activated receptors trigger a G-protein-mediated second-messenger cascade that results in production of cyclic AMP that modulates a cyclic-nucleotide-gated channel. The CNG channel is similar to the dark current channel in photoreceptors; this type of channel is also being found in neurons throughout the nervous system. In different species, the second messengers activated by odors include Ca^{2+}, IP_3, cyclic GMP, and CO, which can modulate not only the CNG channels but also Cl^-, K^+, and Ca^{2+} channels. These channels also add to the depolarizing CNG channel current or bring about hyperpolarizing responses in some cells. In addition, multiple mechanisms for desensitization and adaptation over both short (tens of milliseconds) and long (minutes) time scales act at all levels of the second-messenger pathways, from the receptors to the CNG channels.

The olfactory receptor cell thus appears to be a complex neuron, in which broad affinity receptors activate multiple second-messenger and desensitization tems to transduce the information carried in odor molecules into sensory currents and ultimately convert these currents into impulse discharges in the individual sensory cells. The information carried in the odor molecules is encoded by the ensemble of differentially responding cells with their overlapping response spectra and projected to higher centers for the neural processing that gives rise to the perception of smell.

TASTE

Taste Stimuli Are Transduced by Taste Receptor Cells

The sense of taste is mediated by taste receptor cells, which are organized into tiny onion-shaped end organs called taste buds. Taste buds are found primarily within papillae of the lingual epithelium, although in mammals some taste buds are found in other parts of the oral cavity and in fish they are also abundant on the barbels and over much of the body surface. A typical taste bud contains 50–150 spindle-shaped receptor cells (taste cells) that extend from the basal lamina to the mucosal surface of the tongue (Fig. 24.25). Taste cells, like olfactory neurons, continue to turn over throughout adult life. Basal stem cells in the basolateral margin of the taste bud give rise to taste receptor cells; a typical taste cell has a life span of approximately 10 days to 2 weeks in mammals. The apical tip of each receptor cell contains microvilli that project into the mucus of the oral environment. The basolateral membrane of each taste cell forms one or more chemical synapses with primary gustatory nerve fibers that enter the base of the taste bud. These sensory fibers travel in the facial, glossopharyngeal, or vagus nerves to gustatory nuclei in the brainstem.[111]

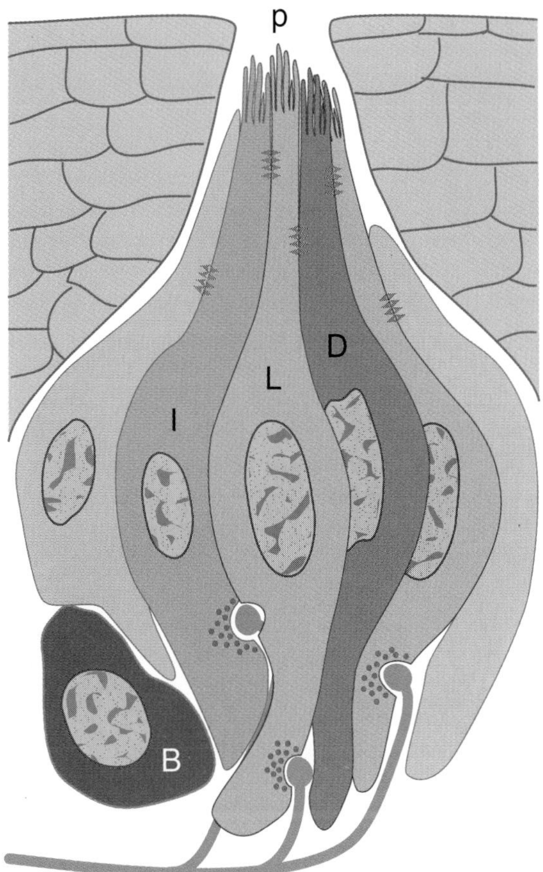

FIGURE 24.25 Diagram of a taste bud, showing basal stem cells (B) and taste receptor cells. Most taste buds contain dark (D), light (L), and intermediate (I) taste cells. The apical tips of the taste cells contain microvilli that protrude through the taste pore (p) into the oral environment, while the basolateral membrane forms chemical synapses with afferent nerve fibers. A typical taste bud contains 50–150 taste receptor cells.

In contrast to odorants, taste stimuli generally are water-soluble, nonvolatile compounds encountered at relatively high concentrations. Four primary taste qualities—salty, sweet, sour, and bitter—describe most gustatory sensations in humans. This classification scheme is based on electrophysiological and psychophysical studies showing that adaptation to any one of the primary taste qualities has no effect on the others. For example, when a bitter-tasting compound is placed on the tongue, the response to subsequent presentations of bitter stimuli will be reduced due to adaptation, but the taste of sweet compounds will be unaffected. Some compounds, however, do not fit into any of the primary tastes. An example is monosodium glutamate, which is referred to as "umami" or "delicious taste" in some Asian cultures. Most taste stimuli are hydrophilic molecules, including Na^+ salt (salty), divalent salts and KCl (bitter), acids (sour), sugars (sweet), amino acids (sweet, bitter, and umami), and proteins (sweet and bitter). Some taste stimuli are lipophilic, including the bitter-tasting alkaloids and many synthetic sweeteners. Since diffusion through the aqueous saliva is slow for lipophilic compounds, carrier proteins analogous to odorant-binding protein may transport such molecules to the apical microvilli.

Taste transduction is initiated when sapid molecules interact with sites on the apical microvilli of taste receptor cells. The interaction leads to a membrane conductance change, depolarization, and transmitter release from the taste cell onto gustatory fibers (Fig. 24.26). Although taste cells were once thought to be passive transducers, it is now clear that they possess voltage-gated Na^+, Ca^{2+}, and K^+ channels and regularly generate action potentials in response to most taste stimuli. The precise role of the action potential in the transduction process is not known, although it may be involved in activation of the Ca^{2+} channels underlying transmitter release and in the coding of stimulus intensity. Because the chemical structures of different taste stimuli differ greatly from one another, it is not surprising that taste cells use a diversity of mechanisms for signal transduction. Such mechanisms include direct interaction of taste stimuli with apically located ion channels, G-protein-coupled receptors, and ligand-gated ion channels. How these mechanisms are utilized by taste receptor cells to transduce the different taste qualities is considered below.

Sodium Ions Permeate Apically Located Na^+ Channels to Depolarize Taste Cells

Direct and indirect evidence suggests that Na^+ salt taste is transduced by passive, amiloride-sensitive Na^+ channels on the apical membrane of salt-sensitive taste cells. The mechanism is illustrated in Fig. 24.27. Sodium simply diffuses through the open channels to depolarize taste cells; presumably the Na^+ is pumped out by a Na^+, K^+-ATPase on the basolateral membrane. The first evidence for a role of amiloride-sensitive Na^+ channels in taste came from experiments showing that the gustatory nerve response to NaCl was inhibited by amiloride, a diuretic drug known to block a specific class of Na^+ channels (amiloride-sensitive Na^+ channels) in other transporting epithelial tissues. In addition, psychophysical studies on humans have shown that amiloride reduces the perceived intensity of NaCl stimulation. More recently, patch-clamp recordings have demonstrated directly the presence of amiloride-sensitive Na^+ channels in taste cell membranes of frogs and rodents. In rodents, this channel has properties that are similar to the well-studied amiloride-sensitive Na^+ channel of kidney and frog skin. These properties include a high selectivity for Na^+, a low single-channel conductance (5 pS), and regulation by hormones such as vasopressin and aldosterone.[112–119]

The importance of the amiloride-sensitive Na^+ channel to the detection of Na^+ has been shown by behavioral studies. In the presence of amiloride, most animals are unable to distinguish Na^+ salts from K^+ salts. Additional mechanisms for Na^+ salt detection are necessary, however, because approximately 30% of the afferent nerve response to NaCl remains after amiloride treatment and because amiloride does not affect the afferent nerve response to NaCl in some species. One of these mechanisms is paracellular, involving diffusion of NaCl through tight junctions at the apex of the taste bud, thereby increasing Na^+ concentrations in the extracellular space along the basolateral membranes of taste cells. Presumably, this Na^+ enters the taste cells to depolarize them, but the channels or transport proteins involved have not been identified.

Acids Depolarize Taste Cells by Modulating Ion Channels Sensitive to Changes in Proton Concentration

Another taste quality that does not require specific membrane receptors for transduction is sour taste. Sour taste is produced by acids, and the degree of sourness depends primarily on proton concentration. Recent patch-clamp studies suggest that several apically located ion channels may participate in sour transduction, which is not surprising, because protons are capable of modulating most ion channels. Some of these mechanisms are illustrated in Fig. 24.28. One channel that has been found to transduce H^+ in hamster taste cells is the amiloride-sensitive Na^+ channel, the same channel that transduces Na^+ salt. Both loose-patch recordings from taste buds *in situ* and whole-cell recordings from isolated taste cells showed that, in the absence of Na^+, proton influx through the amiloride-sensitive Na^+ channels depolarized taste cells and contributed to the detection of acids. Because Na^+ salt can be distinguished easily from the taste of acids, additional mechanisms must exist for the detection of H^+. In the mudpuppy, acid stimuli are detected by direct proton-block of K^+ channels that are restricted to the apical membrane of the taste cells. These voltage-dependent K^+ channels have a small but significant open probability at rest; accordingly, proton block of the resting outward K^+ current depolarizes the taste cells. Similar apically located K^+ channels may participate in H^+ transduction in mammals. Several additional mechanisms have been proposed for sour transduction, including a proton-gated Ca^{2+} conductance,

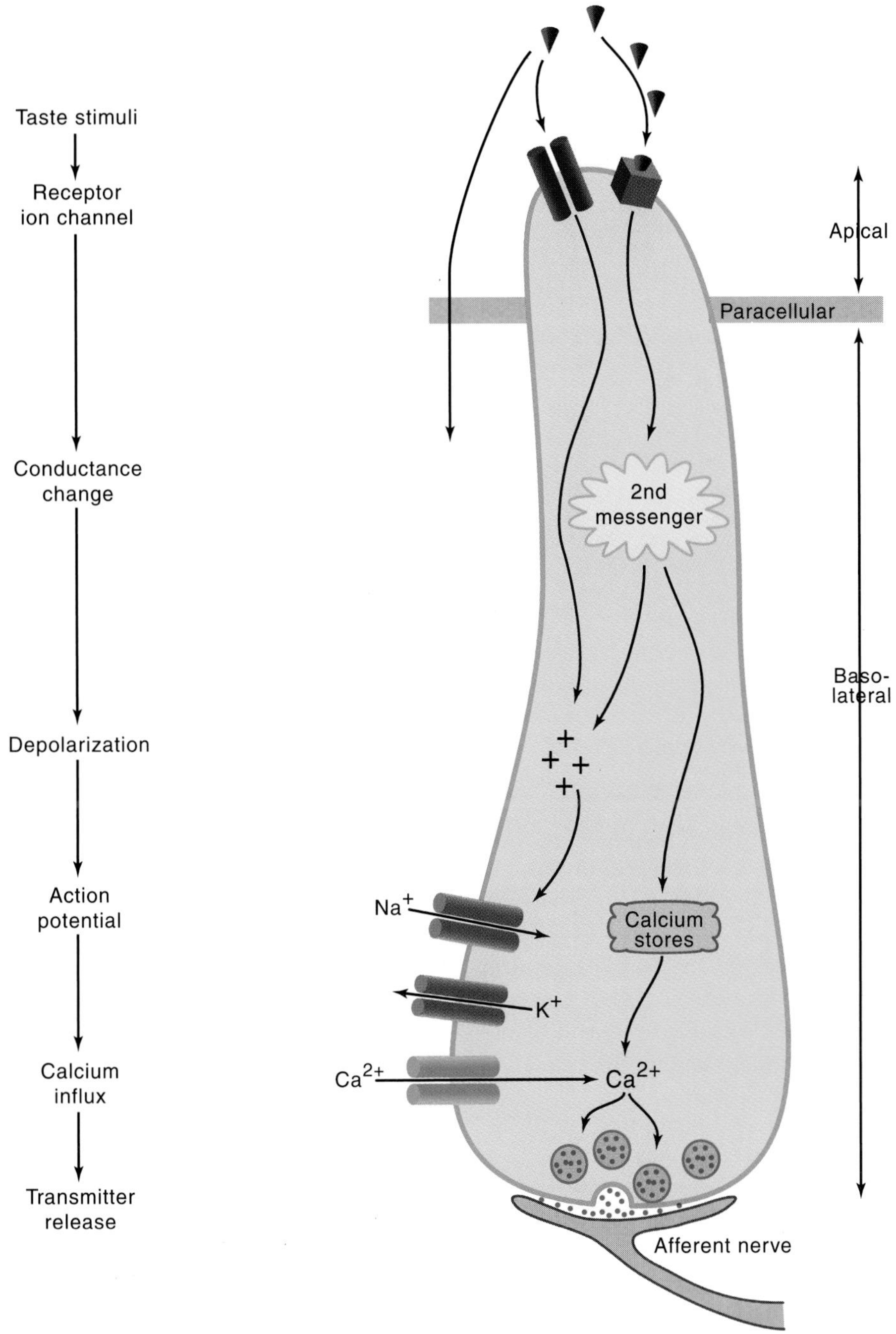

FIGURE 24.26 Generalized scheme of sensory transduction in a taste receptor cell. Taste stimuli interact with the apical membrane, either by binding to specific membrane receptors or by modulating apically located ion channels. The interaction usually leads to membrane conductance change, membrane depolarization, action potentials, Ca^{2+} influx, and transmitter release. Some taste stimuli activate second-messenger pathways that trigger release of Ca^{2+} from intracellular stores. Whether Ca^{2+} release is sufficient to cause release of neurotransmitter is not known.

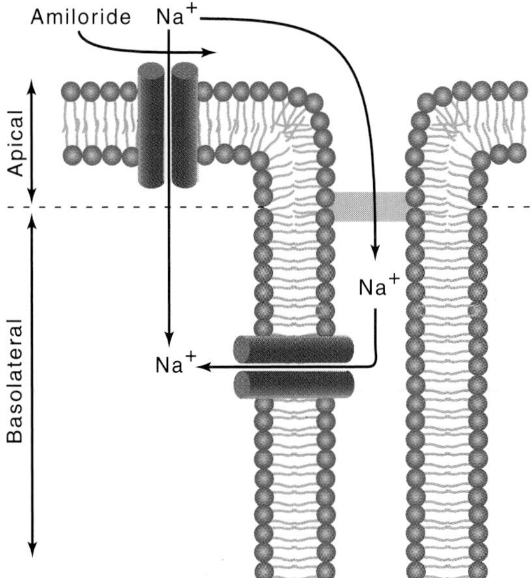

FIGURE 24.27 Sodium salt transduction. Sodium permeates apically located amiloride-sensitive Na^+ channels; the Na^+ simply flows down its electrochemical gradient to depolarize the taste cell. Some Na^+ also penetrates the tight junctions at the apex of the taste bud. This Na^+ likely enters the cell via Na^+-permeable channels on the basolateral membrane (the paracellular pathway). Whether these basolateral channels are the same amiloride-sensitive channels that are expressed on the apical membrane is not known. Sodium that enters the cell is pumped out by a Na^+, K^+-ATPase on the basolateral membrane (not shown).

a proton-gated anion conductance, and a proton transporter, all found in frog taste cells. Whether these additional mechanisms contribute to acid transduction in mammalian species remains to be determined.[120–126]

Sweet Taste Involves Receptors Linked to the cAMP and IP_3 Second-Messenger Pathways

In contrast to the ionic taste stimuli described above, specific membrane receptors appear to be required for the transduction of sugars, synthetic, sweetners, amino acids, and many bitter tasting compounds. Several different receptors are likely to be involved in sweet taste transduction; however, to date not a single sweet receptor has been purified biochemically or cloned. Receptors for sugars are thought to be coupled to G_S, the GTP-binding protein that stimulates adenylate cyclase. Taste cell depolarization is thought to involve a cyclic-nucleotide-dependent closure of K^+ channels (Fig. 24.29). The first evidence for a role of cyclic nucleotides in sweet transduction came from biochemical studies in which sucrose stimulated adenylate cyclase in a preparation of rat taste buds. The increase in cAMP required GTP, suggesting the involvement of G-protein-coupled receptors. The involvement of K^+ channels in the transduction cascade comes from electrophysiological studies showing that sweet stimuli depolarize taste cells by decreasing K^+ conductance. The effect is mimicked by membrane-permeant analogs of cAMP and cGMP. Whether the cAMP blocks the K^+ channels directly or whether activation of cAMP-dependent protein kinase is required has not been resolved.

Recently, biochemical and Ca^{2+} imaging studies have indicated that synthetic sweeteners may use a pathway for transduction different from that sugars use. The evidence comes from biochemical assays, showing that synthetic sweeteners stimulate IP_3 rather than cAMP in rat taste buds (Fig. 24.29). Calcium imaging studies using fura-2 are consistent with these findings; stimulation of taste cells with synthetic sweeteners causes release of Ca^{2+} from intracellular stores, whereas sucrose stimulation causes Ca^{2+} influx in the same taste cells. How release of IP_3 leads to transmitter release in taste cells is not known. If the Ca^{2+} released from intracellular stores is sufficient to

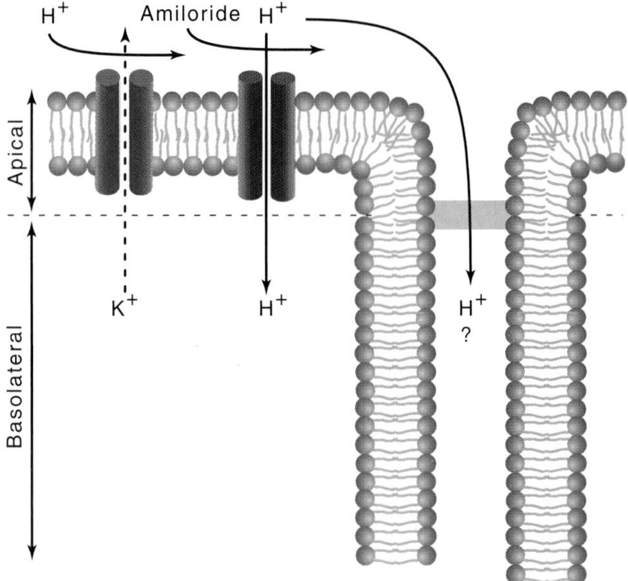

FIGURE 24.28 Acid (sour) transduction. Protons likely utilize several mechanisms for transduction. One mechanism involves proton permeation of the amiloride-sensitive Na^+ channel, and another mechanism involves proton block of apically located K^+ channels. Both mechanisms result in taste cell depolarization. Protons probably also permeate the paracellular pathway, but the effects of protons on basolateral channels have not been determined.

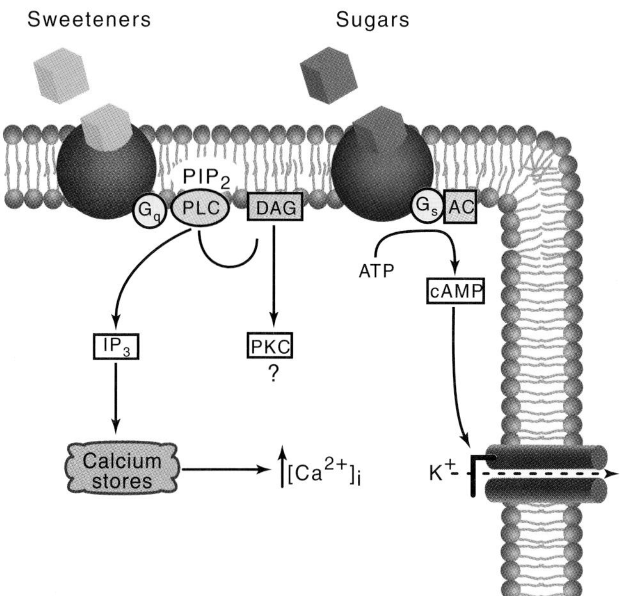

FIGURE 24.29 Sweet transduction. Sugars have been found to activate adenylate cyclase (AC), resulting in a cAMP-dependent closure of K^+ channels and membrane depolarization. Synthetic sweeteners activate phospholipase C (PLC), producing the second messengers IP_3 and diacylglycerol (DAG). IP_3 causes release of Ca^{2+} from intracellular stores, while DAG activates protein kinase C (PKC). Whether PKC is involved in the transduction of synthetic sweeteners is not known, but additional steps are likely, since sweeteners elicit trains of action potentials in taste cells.

cause transmitter release, taste cells should not be depolarized by synthetic sweeteners. Recent patch-clamp studies suggest that saccharin and other sweeteners elicit trains of action potentials in taste cells, however, and other mechanisms must contribute to transduction.[127–132]

Bitter Taste Involves Both G-Protein-Coupled Receptors and Apically Located Ion Channels

The large number of bitter tasting compounds and the diversity of their molecular structures suggest that bitter taste involves multiple mechanisms of transduction. Indeed, several mechanisms have been proposed, but the evidence for each is inconclusive at this writing. These mechanisms are summarized in Fig. 24.30. One mechanism that has received much attention involves activation of phosphodiesterase. This interest is based on the recent cloning of gustducin, a G protein that is specifically expressed in taste cells. Gustducin has considerable sequence homology to the transducins, G proteins that activate phosphodiesterase in the photoreceptor transduction cascade. Recently, transducin has been identified in taste cells as well. Evidence for the role of transducin in bitter taste comes from biochemical studies showing that denatonium, an intensely bitter tasting compound, stimulates transducin in taste cells, resulting in activation of phosphodiesterase and a decrease in cyclic nucleotide concentration. How the decrease in cyclic nucleotides results in release of transmitter is not known, although cyclic-nucleotide-suppressible conductance may play a role. More direct evidence for the role of phosphodiesterase in bitter taste has been obtained. Transgenic mice lacking the gustducin protein have been produced. These gustducin "knockout" mice are less sensitive than normal mice to bitter compounds, suggesting that gustducin (or transducin) likely plays an important role in bitter transduction. The gustducin knockout mice are also less sensitive to sweet stimuli. Thus, further experiments required to elucidate the role of gustducin in taste.

Other studies suggest that bitter stimuli activate phospholipase C in taste cells. Calcium imaging studies of isolated rat taste buds showed that denatonium increases intracellular Ca^{2+} in a subset of taste cells. The response is independent of extracellular Ca^{2+}, suggesting that Ca^{2+} is released from intracellular stores. More recently, biochemical studies have shown that IP_3-sensitive Ca^{2+} stores are located in rat taste buds and that denatonium stimulation increases IP_3 in taste cells. These data, taken together, suggest that denatonium activates phospholipase C, causing IP_3 production and subsequent release of Ca^{2+} from intracellular stores. Whether the Ca^{2+} released from intracellular stores is sufficient to trigger transmitter release is unknown. Also unclear is the identity of the G protein involved in the activation of phospholipase C. Although G_q-like G proteins are usually involved in the activation of phospholipase C, gustducin and/or transducin may activate phospholipase C as well as phosphodiesterase. Further studies are required to evaluate the respective roles of these G proteins in bitter transduction.

Finally, apically located K^+ channels mediate the transduction of several bitter compounds in mudpuppy taste cells, including quinine, K^+ salts, and divalent salts. Quinine and divalent salts, like H^+, directly block a resting efflux of K^+, causing depolarization of taste cells. Potassium salts depolarize cells by passive influx of K^+ through the channels. Whether apical K^+ channels contribute significantly to bitter transduction in mammals remains to be seen.[133–137]

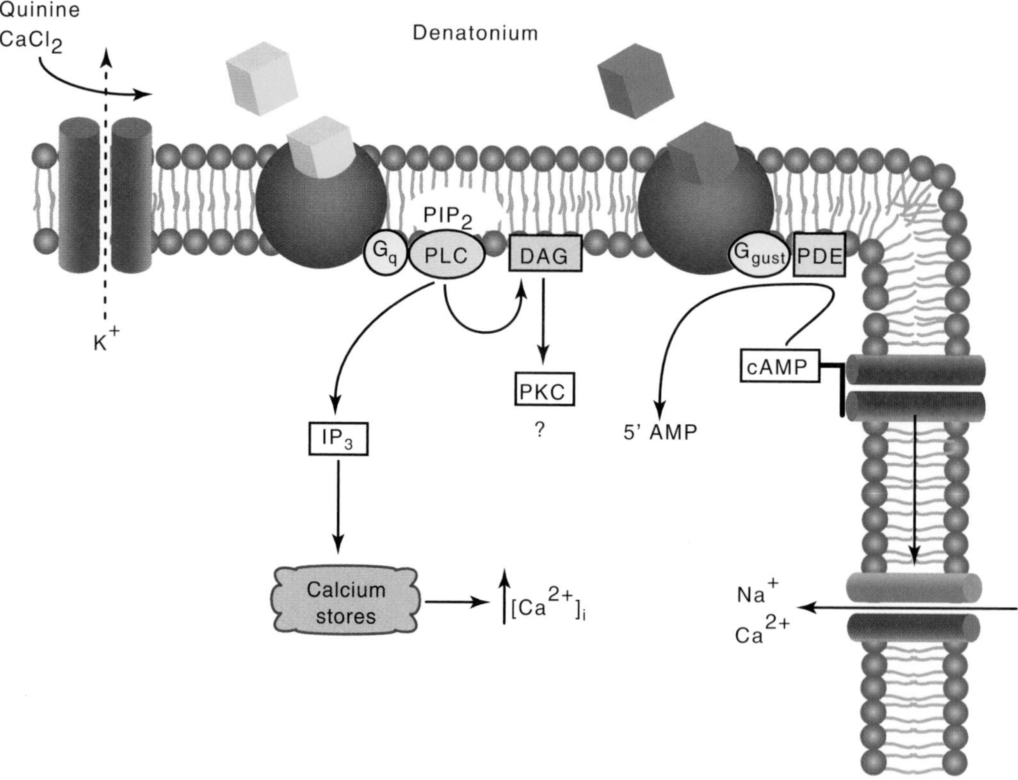

FIGURE 24.30 Bitter transduction. Several mechanisms likely contribute to bitter transduction. Denatonium has been shown to activate gustducin (Ggust) and transducin, causing a decrease in cAMP. The ion channels that mediate this denatonium response have not been identified, but direct cyclic-nucleotide-blocked cation channels may be involved. In this case, denatonium would depolarize taste cells by removing the cAMP block of the cation channels, allowing influx of cations. Denatonium has also been shown to activate PLC, presumably by activating a G_q-like G protein. Subsequent production of IP_3 causes release of Ca^{2+} from intracellular stores. It is not known whether this Ca^{2+} is sufficient to trigger transmitter release or whether additional steps in the transduction cascade are required. Another mechanism for bitter transduction involves direct block of apically located K^+ channels by quinine and divalent salts. Block of K^+ channels causes a reduced efflux of K^+, resulting in membrane depolarization.

Amino Acids Utilize Ligand-Gated Channels and G-Protein-Coupled Receptors for Transduction

The mechanisms involved in the transduction of amino acids are illustrated in Fig. 24.31. Amino acids have been studied extensively in catfish, where the barbels contain a high density of taste buds and the taste cells are extremely sensitive to amino acids. Biochemical and electrophysiological studies indicate that L-arginine and L-proline are transduced by ligand-gated cation channels on the apical membrane of taste cells. Membrane vesicles from catfish taste epithelia have been incorporated into bilayers on the tips of patch pipettes to study the properties of these channels. Both L-arginine and L-proline activate nonselective cation channels in these bilayers, suggesting that the channels are coupled directly to their receptors. The L-arginine-gated channel has a conductance of 45 pS and is activated maximally by 100–200 μM L-arginine. The L-proline-gated channel has a conductance of 49 pS and is activated maximally by 2–4 mM L-proline. These values are consistent with the binding affinities and electrophysiological responses to these amino acids.

The only amino acid that has been studied extensively as a taste stimulus in mammalian taste cells is L-glutamate, which is believed to elicit the "umami" sensation. A recent study utilizing PCR cloning strategies has isolated the metabotropic glutamate receptor mGluR4 from taste-derived mRNA. *In situ* hybridization has shown that mGluR4 is expressed in taste buds,

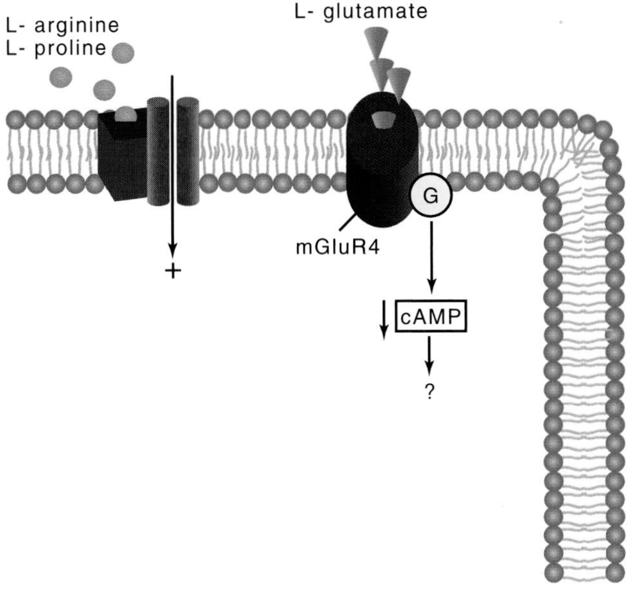

FIGURE 24.31 Amino acid transduction. Taste cells located in catfish barbels are extremely sensitive to particular amino acids. Both L-arginine and L-proline directly activate ligand-gated cation channels to depolarize taste cells. In contrast, in mammalian taste cells, L-glutamate likely activates the metabotropic glutamate receptor mGluR4, resulting in a decrease in cAMP. How the decrease in cAMP leads to membrane depolarization is not understood.

but not in the surrounding nongustatory epithelium. Evidence suggesting that this receptor has a role in glutamate taste comes from studies showing that L-AP4, the specific ligand for mGluR4, evokes behaviors in rats that are similar to those evoked by glutamate. Electrophysiological studies are required to confirm the role of mGluR4 in taste transduction. If the electrophysiological studies support the molecular and behavioral studies, mGluR4 will represent the first taste receptor to be cloned.[138–140]

Current research interests are focused on identifying the molecular components involved in the different transduction pathways, as well as how the different components are segregated into different cells.[6] For example, do cells that express the amiloride-sensitive Na^+ channel respond only to NaCl or do these cells also respond to other taste modalities? A considerable effort is focused on identifying the specific role of gustducin in taste transduction.[141–144]

Summary

Taste cells use a diversity of mechanisms for transduction. Ionic stimuli (e.g., salts and acids) interact directly with ion channels to depolarize taste cells, while more complex stimuli (e.g., sugars and amino acids) bind to receptor proteins that are coupled either to G proteins and second messengers or directly to ion channels. Transduction ultimately results in an increase in intracellular calcium and release of transmitter from the taste cell onto gustatory afferent fibers.

MECHANORECEPTION

Organisms are capable of detecting both remotely generated mechanical perturbations in the environment (sound and vibration) and self-generated mechanical perturbations induced by body movement. The organ system responsible for this capability is known as the acoustico (or octavo)-lateralis system, and it uses as its basic sensory unit a modified epithelial cell—the hair cell. Hair cells are located in a variety of specialized sensory organs. For example, in the mammal, the organ of Corti detects sound, and the vestibular sensory structures detect angular and linear acceleration through space. The lateral line system in fishes and amphibia detects waterborne vibrations.

Hair Cells Transduce Mechanical Energy Directly into Electrical Energy

Hair cells are polarized epithelial cells whose major functions are partitioned into apical and basal cellular compartments (Fig. 24.32). The apical end of the cell is specialized for the reception and translation of mechanical energy into receptor currents, whereas the basal end is specialized for the transmission of information to the central nervous system via synaptic contacts with the primary afferent neuron.

Stereocilia are modified microvilli, a fraction of a micrometer in width, that project from the cell apex and contain an abundant supply of tightly packed actin filaments, bound by fimbrin, coursing along their length. Depending on which specific organ the hair cells reside in, the number of these stiff, rodlike stereocilia ranges from about 10 to 300, and their lengths range from a fraction to tens of micrometers. The stereocilia, which are bundled together by extracellular filamentous linkages, rapidly taper as they insert into the cuticular plate, an actin-rich apical

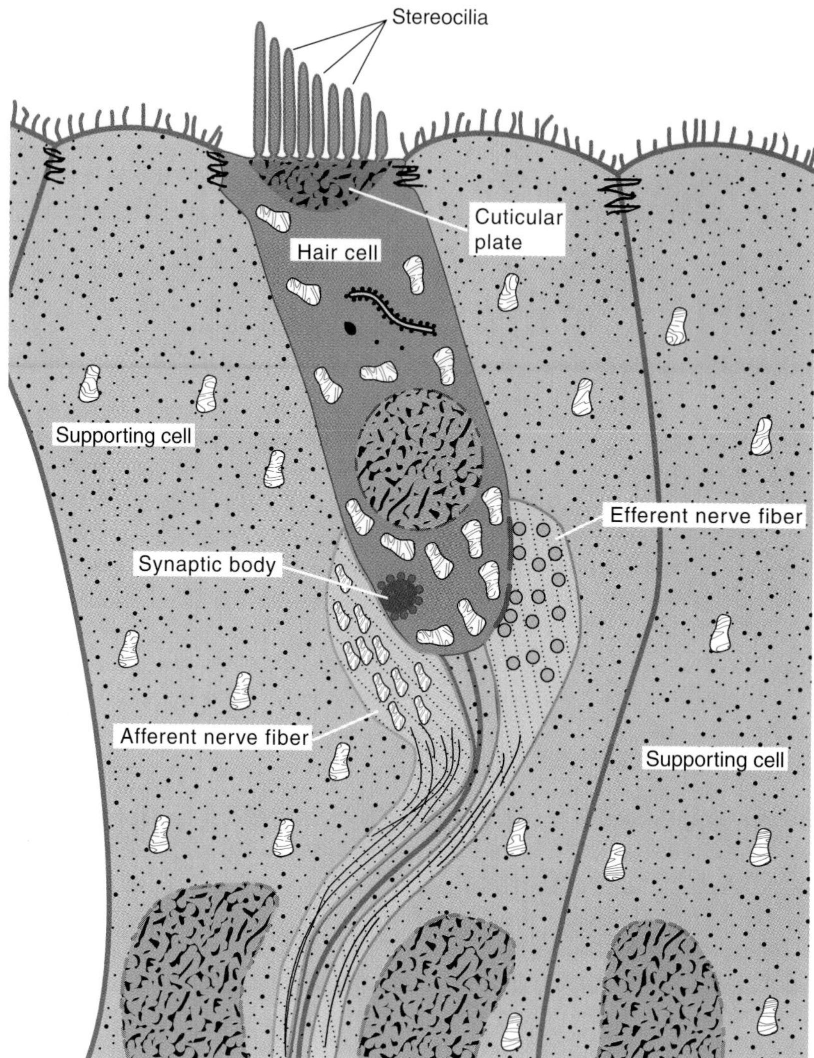

FIGURE 24.32 Schematic of a hair cell with supporting cells. Reprinted with permission from Hillman, D. E. *Frog Neurobiology*, Llinas, R., and Precht, W., Eds., Springer-Verlag, Berlin, 1976, p. 452.

cytoplasmic structure. Because the stereocilia are stiff, they pivot at their insertion when deflected. All hair cells, at one point in their differentiation, possess an additional apical protrusion, the kinocilium. This is a true cilium and contains the characteristic 9 + 2 microtubule doublets. In the organ of Corti, mature hair cells have lost this kinocilium and possess only stereocilia. The stereocilia of all hair cells are arranged hexagonally in rows and graded in height, with the tallest stereocilia row adjacent to the kinocilium or, in cells lacking the kinocilium, adjacent to its residual basal body. This characteristic morphologic polarization of the stereocilia bundle identifies the orientation of the bundle's responsiveness to mechanical deflection.

Through a variety of accessory mechanisms specific to each sensory organ, mechanical sensory stimuli ultimately cause a deflection of the hair bundle. When the bundle is deflected toward the tallest stereocilia row, a depolarization of the cell from its normal negative resting potential occurs, resulting in an increase in neurotransmitter release and excitation of the afferent nerve fiber (see Fig. 24.33). When the deflection is in the opposite direction, hyperpolarization occurs, resulting in a decrease in transmitter release and inhibition of fiber activity.[145–147]

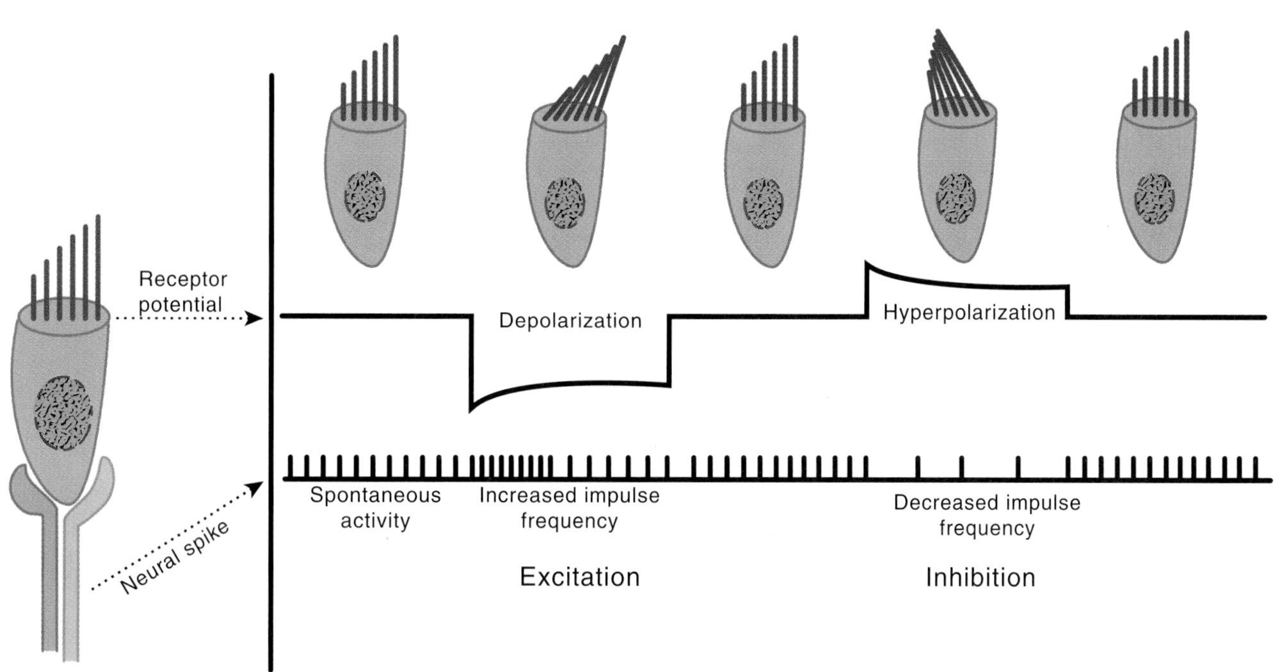

FIGURE 24.33 Illustration of hair cell stimulation, receptor potential response, and afferent fiber discharge. From Chapter 12, Flock, A. Ultrastructure and Function in the Lateral Line Organs. p. 182, In: Lateral Line Detectors. Chan, P. H. Ed. Indiana U. Press, Bloomington.

Receptor Potentials Are Evoked by Mechanically Gated Ion Channels within Stereocilia

With the stereocilia bundle in its resting, unperturbed position, a standing inward current exists through a small proportion (10–25%) of mechanically activated channels thought to be located within each stereocilium. Because these channels are nonselective for cations, this inward, positively charged flux tends to depolarize the hair cell somewhat. In many hair cell sensory systems, including the organ of Corti, the ionic milieu surrounding the hair bundle is richest in potassium; thus, the major charge carrier for the transduction current is K^+. However, small amounts of Ca^{2+} are also required to sustain stereociliar channel activity. Several lines of evidence indicate that the flow of transduction current into hair cells occurs near the top of the hair bundle; that is, the channels are located near the tips of the stereocilia. As implied above, displacement of the bundle toward the tallest stereocilium increases the proportion of open channels, thereby producing an increase above the inward resting current. The subsequent flow of current across the basolateral membrane produces a depolarizing voltage change, a receptor potential, capable of activating a variety of voltage-dependent conductances in that membrane. Conversely, closure of transduction channels during bundle movement away from the tallest stereociliar row reduces the inward current, effectively hyperpolarizing the basolateral membrane. Maximum sensitivity to deflection is achieved only along this axis; orthogonal deflection produces no response, whereas intermediate angles of deflection produce responses whose magnitude depends on the size of the vectoral component along the most sensitive axis (Fig. 24.34). The degree of

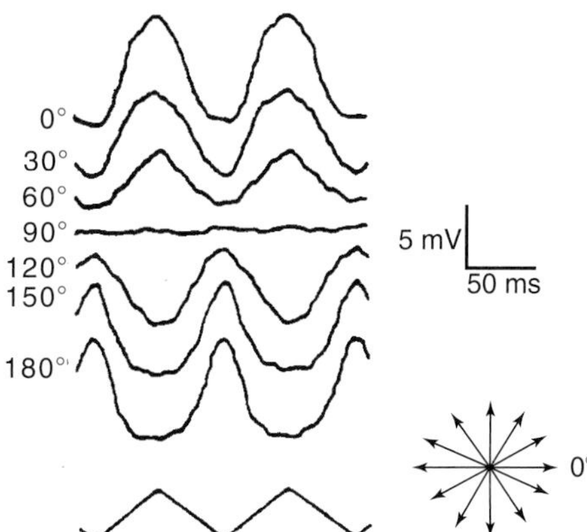

FIGURE 24.34 Evaluation of stereocilia directional sensitivity. Maximal sensitivity occurs when displacements are toward or away from the tallest stereociliar row. From Shotwell, S. L., Jacobs, R. and Hudspeth, A. J. (1981). Directional sensitivity of individual vertebrate hair cells to controlled deflection of their hair bundles. *Ann. N.Y. Acad. Sci.* **374:** 1–10.

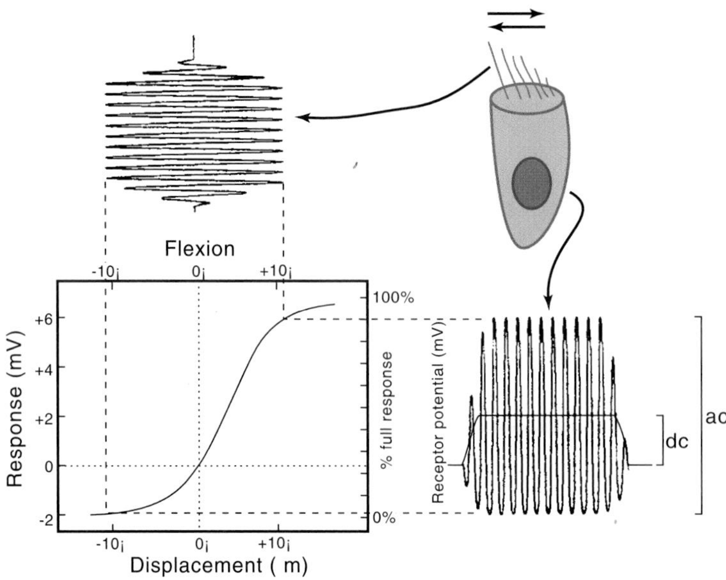

FIGURE 24.35 Sigmoidal input–output function of hair cell. Symmetrical sinusoidal displacement of stereocilia produces ac and dc receptor potential components. From: Hudspeth, A. J. and Corey, D. P. (1977). Sensitivity, polarity and conductance change in the response of vertebrate hair cells to controlled mechanical stimuli. *Proc. Natl. Acad. Sci. U.S.A.* **74:** 2047–2411.

bundle deflection, corresponding to the intensity of the mechanical stimulus, produces graded changes in the magnitude of the receptor potential. However, the relation between degree of bundle deflection and receptor potential magnitude is neither linear nor symmetric. Bundle displacements in the depolarizing direction are more effective than equal displacements in the opposite direction. The displacement–response function is sigmoidal and shifted from its midpoint (Fig. 24.35), with saturating electrical responses evoked by deflections as small as 300 nm. Thus, symmetrical sinusoidal deflections of the bundle (as might occur with acoustic stimuli) will produce both sinusoidal (ac) and superimposed depolarizing steady-state (dc) changes in membrane potential. Maximal transducer conductance changes up to about 10 nS have been observed, and single unit conductances on the order of 20–100 pS have been either measured or estimated. From such measures, the number of channels per stereocilium has been computed to be one to two.[148–151]

Extracellular Stereocilia Tip Links May Underlie Transducer Gating

The molecular basis of the hair bundle's response polarity appears to reside in specialized structural attachments at the tips of stereocilia (Fig. 24.36). These "tip links" are elastic filaments ("springs") that link the top of each stereocilium with a dense membranous plaque on the upper side of the adjacent taller stereocilium and occur in line with the axis of maximal bundle sensitivity. They are believed to provide the tension required to open transduction channels during bundle deflection, one end of the filament being anchored and the other pulling on the channel gate. As the hair bundle tilts during deflection in the excitatory direction, adjacent stereocilia shear against one another, stretching and increasing the tension of tip links, thereby increasing the probability that transducer channels will open. When the deflection is in the hyperpolarizing direction, the tip link tension slackens and the channels tend to close. In line with the tip link or gating spring hypothesis, destruction of the tip links by enzymatic (elastase) or chemical (Ca^{2+} chelators) treatments can abolish mechanical transduction. In addition, if tip link tension accounts for much of the bundle's stiffness, as expected, bundle compliance varies with the extent of deflection. The deflection versus bundle compliance function is bell shaped, with maximum compliance occurring when half the transduction channels are open. Furthermore, compliance changes are abolished by blocking stereociliar transduction channels with aminoglycoside antibiotics.[152–154]

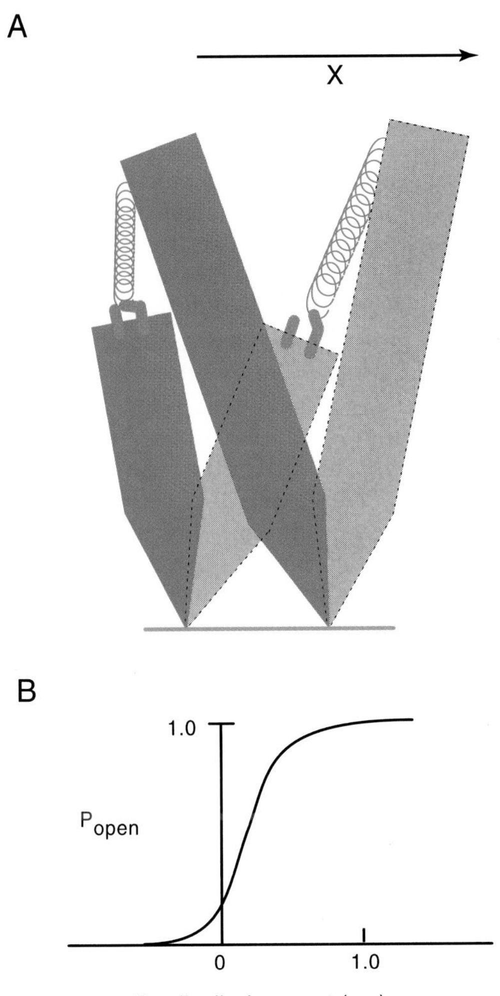

FIGURE 24.36 Gating spring model of hair cell transduction. (A) Tip links connecting channel gate to adjacent taller stereocilium tense during displacement toward the taller stereocilium, thus increasing the probability that the channel will open (B). From Pickles and Corey, *TINS* 15, p. 256, 1992.

Hair Bundle Sensitivity Resets during Static Deflection

In hair cells from a variety of organs, the induced receptor current does not remain constant when a hair bundle is statically deflected, but decays with a time constant of a few tens of milliseconds to about 20% of its initial value. This adaptation, which is Ca^{2+} dependent, results from a shift in the bundle's sigmoidal displacement-response function along the displacement axis in the direction of the deflection (Fig. 24.37). If adaptation did not occur, then during a static deflection superimposed deflections would produce little response. Essentially this adaptation shift may be viewed as a functional return of the bundle toward its resting position, where bundle deflections are most efficient in transducing mechanical stimuli. Necessarily, however, under constant bundle deflection, the reestablishment of high sensitivity must occur at the level of the channel-gating process itself.

Adaptation is lacking in the absence of extracellular Ca^{2+} and in the presence of intracellular Ca^{2+} chelators. As Ca^{2+} levels increase, adaptation occurs more rapidly and to a greater extent. The adaptation process may be related to direct actions of Ca^{2+} on the transduction channels themselves or on a mechanism responsible for tip link tension control. The latter hypothesis envisions a molecular motor (perhaps myosin I) that maintains a resting tension on the tip link by constantly attempting to move the tip link's upper insertional plaque up the length of the stereocilium. During bundle deflection in the excitatory direction, tip links are initially further tensed, thereby opening transduction channels that permit the influx of Ca^{2+} ions. The Ca^{2+} ions are believed to cause the molecular motor to slip during its climb up the stereocilium, thereby slackening the link's tension and allowing the channel's gate to close under constant bundle deflection. Reestablishment of resting tip link tension follows, because the motor renews its climb as Ca^{2+} influx is halted and the ion is buffered intracellularly. With this restablishment of resting tip link tension, the hair

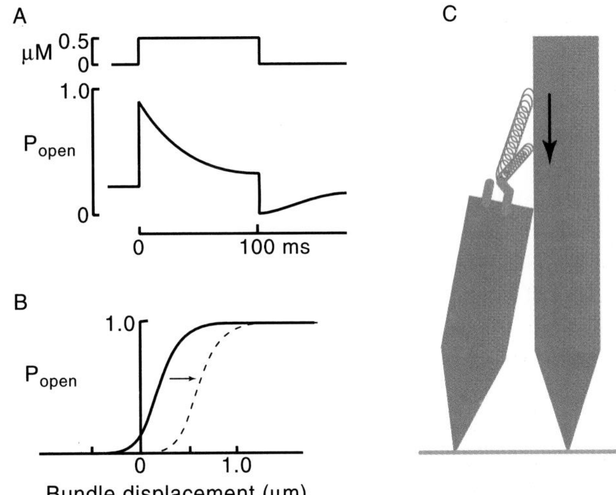

FIGURE 24.37 Hair cell response adaptation. (A) When a constant displacement stimulus is delivered to the bundle, the response (open probability) declines over time. (B) During this time the sigmoidal input–output function is shifted along the displacement axis in the direction of the stimulus. (C) The tip link attachment is believed to slip, causing a decrease in tip tension and channel closure during the constant displacement. From Pickles and Corey, *TINS* 15, p. 258, 1992.

cell is prepared to signal efficiently small mechanical perturbations superimposed on the initial static one. Static deflections in the inhibitory direction also evoke adaptation; as a consequence of reduced Ca^{2+} influx, the motor will attempt to reinstate resting tip link tension by climbing. However, adaptation occurs to a greater extent for deflections in the excitatory direction.

Adaptation is a relatively slow process and may be useful for maintaining high sensitivity in sensory organs responding to relatively slow or static deflections of stereocilia, such as the vestibular organs. In turtle auditory hair cells, however, adaptation time constants have been measured below 0.5 ms, a speed that may warrant reevaluation of the myosin adaptation hypothesis. Nevertheless, the usefulness of adaptation in auditory sensory organs is not obvious, because acoustic stimuli, being rapid and balanced about zero in nature, produce no static displacements. Thus, even though adaptation to static bundle deflection has been demonstrated in mammalian auditory hair cells, acoustically evoked receptor potentials (both ac and dc) of these hair cells do not normally decrease in magnitude over the time course of stimulation. However, other membrane characteristics, principally those of the basolateral membrane, can significantly affect the magnitude of receptor potentials during stimulation across the acoustic spectrum.[155–159]

Electrical Properties of the Basolateral Membrane Shape Receptor Potentials

The speed of the hair cell transduction process is incredibly fast compared to transduction in other sensory systems, such as vision, olfaction, and the taste modalities of sweet and bitter. The delay between a bundle deflection and the onset of receptor current is estimated to be about 10 μs at 37°C. This rapid response is a consequence of direct gating of transduction channels, and such speed is essential for auditory hair cells to detect acoustically evoked bundle deflections in the kilohertz (thousand per second) range. Humans can detect frequencies up to about 20–30 kHz, and some mammals, such as bats, can hear above 100 kHz. Although receptor currents may be generated without attenuation across frequency, receptor potentials, which ultimately are responsible for the release of neurotransmitter at the hair cell synapse, are susceptible to the *RC* filter characteristics of the basolateral membrane. The *RC* time constant of auditory hair cells ranges from a fraction of a millisecond to a few milliseconds, at the resting potential. This translates in the frequency domain to a low-pass filter whose cutoff frequency (f_c, the frequency at which the response energy is halved) ranges from tens of hertz to about 1 kHz. As detailed earlier, both ac and dc receptor potentials are generated by sinusoidal stimulation of the hair cell bundle. The ac potentials are susceptible to the membrane filter, such that as the frequency of constant amplitude stimulation increases above f_c, the receptor potential magnitude will halve for every octave increase (Fig. 24.38). Ultimately, at very high frequencies, ac responses will be negligible, but the dc component will remain unperturbed—a process termed rectification. It is this depolarizing dc component of the receptor potential, arising from the asymmetrical nature of the transduction process, that drives the release of neurotransmitter during high-frequency stimulation. The actual cutoff frequency may be considered dynamic, because receptor potentials themselves may activate voltage-dependent ionic conductances in the basolateral membrane that will modify the resistive component of the *RC* product. In outer hair cells from the organ of Corti, the capacitance of the basolateral membrane is also highly voltage dependent, and therefore in this cell type variations in both resistive and capacitive components may influence the membrane filter.[160–163]

Frequency Selective Sensitivity Is Achieved by Hair Cells through a Variety of Mechanisms

Hair cells in auditory organs typically respond best to a particular frequency of stimulation, a characteristic frequency. In the intact animal, hair cells are spatially arrayed along the length of the sensory epithelium according to increasing characteristic frequency; that is, they are **tonotopically** organized. The mechanism underlying such frequency selectivity may reside within the hair cell itself or arise from accessory structures that selectively enhance a particular stimulus frequency prior to detection by the hair cell.

In hair cells of some lower vertebrate auditory or vibration-sensing organs, when the bundles are sinusoidally deflected across a range of stimulus frequencies, the ac receptor potential may not be governed simply by the attenuation effects of a low-pass membrane filter. The activation and interaction of voltage-dependent ionic conductances in the basolateral membrane, namely, K(Ca) and Ca conductances, can under certain conditions promote the amplification of the re-

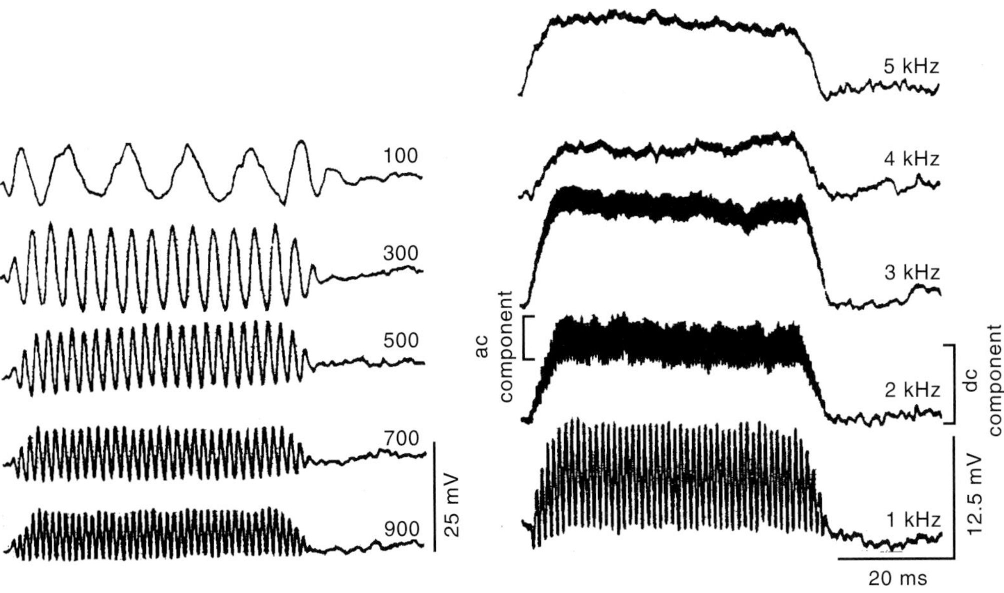

FIGURE 24.38 Receptor potentials from the mammalian inner hair cell in response to acoustic bursts of increasing frequency. Because of the cell's *RC* time constant, the ac component diminishes as frequency increases. However, the dc component remains intact. From Russell, I. J. and Sellick, P. M. (1983). Low frequency characteristics of intracellularly recorded receptor potentials in mammalian hair cells. *J. Physiol. (London)*, **338:** 179–206.

sponse to a particular stimulus frequency, the cell's **resonant frequency.** To illustrate, when a depolarizing current pulse, which is a wide band stimulus, is injected via an electrode into a hair cell from the turtle's basilar papilla, the membrane potential demonstrates a damped oscillation or ringing (Fig. 24.39). The frequency of the oscillation corresponds to the acoustically determined characteristic frequency that the hair cell would have had in the intact epithelium. Blocking the cell's basolateral ionic conductances abolishes the ringing phenomenon. The particular frequency that is enhanced in cells exhibiting ringing appears to be governed by the kinetics of the K channels residing in the basolateral membrane. Cells tuned to high frequencies have channels that gate at faster rates than those responsible for low-frequency tuning. Although the electrical resonant frequency observed in hair cells from a variety of acoustic and vibration sensitive organs corresponds roughly to the range of characteristic frequencies determined by natural stimuli in the intact animal, the occurrence of such electrical tuning does not necessarily compel the cell to utilize this process in the intact organ. Indeed, hair cells with *in vivo* characteristic frequencies in the kilohertz range may exhibit electrical resonances an order of magnitude lower. In any event, electrical tuning has not been measured and probably cannot be sustained at frequencies above 500 Hz due to the limitations of channel kinetics. Other mechanisms must be invoked to account for selectivity at high frequencies.

In most auditory organs, systematic variations in hair cell structure occur along the tonotopic axis of the epithelium. In particular, the height of stereocilia bundles increases toward the low-frequency region of the organ. This systematic change in bundle height underlies a systematic change in the mechanical resonance of the bundles, similar to the variation of pitch conferred by variation of string length in a harp. Cells with tall bundles have low characteristic frequencies because the bundles preferentially oscillate at low frequencies. Short-bundled cells have high characteristic frequencies. This pretransduction mechanism appears to account satisfactorily for frequency selectivity in some lower vertebrates; however, in higher vertebrates, especially mammals, more elaborate mechanical tuning mechanisms exist.

The mammalian organ of Corti rests upon an acellular basilar membrane (BM) that extends along the coiled cochlea. Two types of hair cells, the inner hair cells (IHC) and the outer hair cells (OHC), reside within the organ. Cells at the basal end of the coiled BM have high characteristic frequencies, and those at the apex have low ones. Von Bekesy, who won the Nobel prize

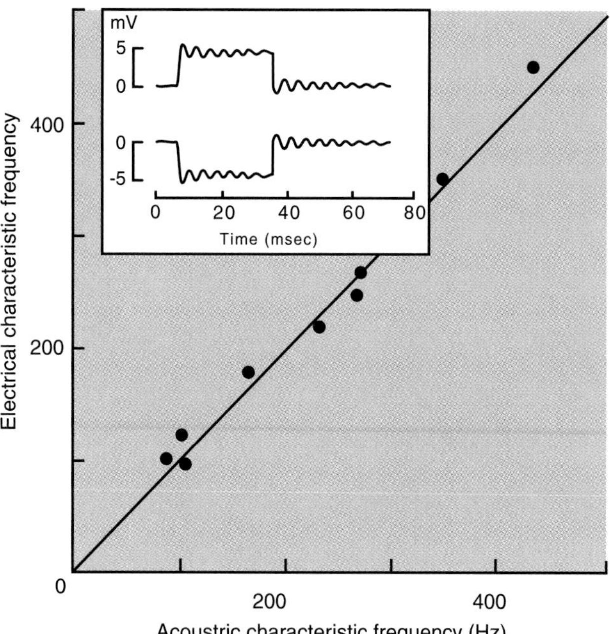

FIGURE 24.39 Electrical tuning in turtle hair cells. When a current pulse is injected into a hair cell, a damped oscillation is observed at stimulus onset and offset (inset). The frequency of the electrically induced oscillation corresponds to the acoustically determined best frequency of that cell. From Crawford, A. C. and Fettiplace, R. (1981). An electrical tuning mechanism in turtle cochlear hair cells. *J. Physiol. (London)*, **312:** Fig. 6, p. 389 and Fig. 4, p. 388.

in 1968, discovered that different regions of the BM are tuned to particular frequencies; low-frequency tones cause maximal vibrations of the BM near the apex, whereas high-frequency tones are most effective at the base. Characteristic frequencies are distributed tonotopically and are derived from the passive mechanical characteristics of the BM. The vibration of the BM induces bending of the stereocilia bundles, and consequently hair cells located at a particular location along the BM respond best to that frequency determined by BM tuning. However, the intrinsic frequency selectivity afforded by passive BM tuning is not great enough to account for the very selective responses observed in hair cells and eighth nerve fibers. OHCs, probably through a mechanical feedback scheme, are required to boost BM motion and enhance frequency selectively. In the absence of OHCs or under conditions in which OHCs are selectively impaired, frequency selectivity is likewise impaired. OHCs are unique because they function as both receptors and effectors, transducing mechanical stimuli via hair bundle displacement and changing length in response to the generated receptor potentials. These length changes presumably provide an energetic boost to BM motion, giving an enhanced stimulus to the IHCs, which are predominantly innervated by the eighth nerve fibers.[164–172]

The Outer Hair Cell Rapidly Alters Its Shape as a Function of Voltage

The guinea pig OHC is cylindrically shaped and varies in length from about 20 μm in the high-frequency region of the cochlea to about 80 μm in the low-frequency region. When an isolated OHC is electrically stimulated by an electrode *in vitro*, it responds by altering its length. No other cell type responds in this manner. The mechanical response is voltage dependent; depolarizing stimuli induce contractions and hyperpolarizing stimuli induce elongations. The length change versus voltage (ΔL vs ΔV) function (Fig. 24.40A) is sigmoidal, and like the stereocilia trans-

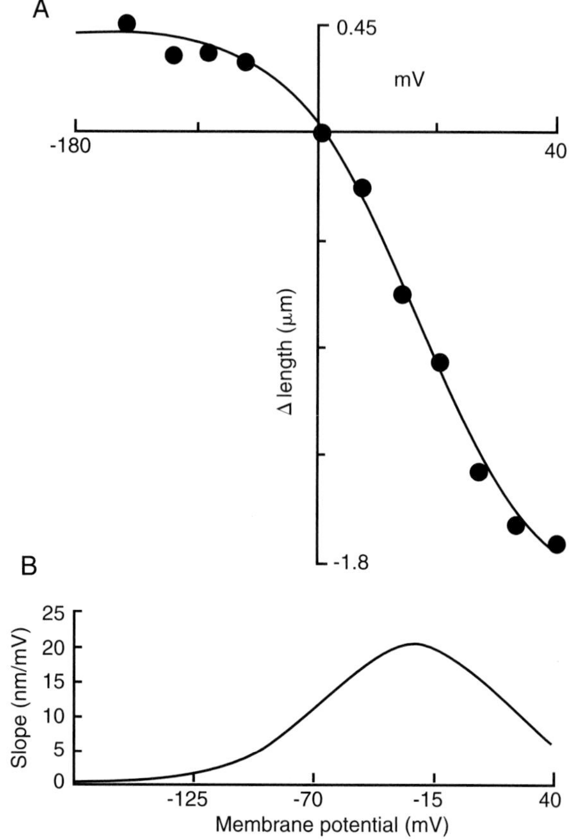

FIGURE 24.40 Mechanical response of mammalian outer hair cell (OMC) under voltage clamp. The OHC changes its length when the cell is held at different membrane potentials (A). The slope of the sigmoidal input–output function defines the cell's sensitivity to membrane potential change (B). From Santos-Sacchi, J. (1992). On the frequency limit and phase of outer hair cell motility: Effects of the membrane filter. *J. Neurosci.*, **12:** Fig. 2, 1909. Used with permission.

ducer function it is operatively offset from its midpoint; the midpoint voltage is near −30 mV and the OHC resting potential is near −70 mV. The slope of the function (dL/dV; Fig. 24.41B) indicates the sensitivity of the mechanical response to voltage change, and responses as large as 30 nm/mV have been found. *In vitro*, at least, this maximum sensitivity or gain resides at a voltage that is depolarized relative to the cell's resting potential. Thus, at the resting potential, although the gain is not maximal, sinusoidal voltage stimuli produce oscillatory (ac) as well as steady-state (dc) length changes. Although the response is voltage dependent, it is not evoked by activation of any particular voltage-dependent ionic conductance. In fact, it is independent of Ca^{2+} and ATP and not akin to any other known form of cellular motility. OHC motility appears to be directly governed by voltage-dependent membrane-bound proteinaceous motors within the basolateral plasma membrane. Freeze–fracture electron microscopy reveals a vast array of membrane-bound 10-nm particles within the lateral plasma membrane; their density approaches 6000 particles per square micrometer. These particles may underlie the mechanical activity of the cell.

As might be expected for a voltage-dependent process, a charged voltage sensor must be associated with the motor molecule, just as voltage-dependent ion channels have voltage sensors. The existence of an OHC motility voltage sensor is confirmed by measuring gating charge movements (capacitive-like currents) under voltage clamp while blocking ionic conductances. These gating currents represent the restricted movement of the charged voltage sensor within the plane of the membrane; increasing voltage will move more charge (thus activating more motors) according to Boltzmann statistics. Maximum charge moved is about 7000 e μm^{-2}. The plot of charge versus voltage (Q/V) is sigmoidal (Fig. 24.41A) and has the same shape and characteristics as the ΔL versus ΔV function. The slope of the Q/V function is defined as capacitance, and thus the OHC's capacitance is a bell-shaped function of voltage (Fig. 24.41B). This nonlinear capacitance rides atop the cell's intrinsic linear membrane capacitance of 1 $\mu F\ cm^{-2}$. Thus, in an OHC of about 70 μm in length, at the point where motile gain is maximum (i.e., where half the motors are activated) the capacitance peaks at about double the cell's linear capacitance. As mentioned above, such nonlinear capacitance may have significant effects on membrane-filtering characteristics.

The ΔL vs ΔV function (and correspondingly, the Q/V function) is not static. It can be shifted along the voltage axis. One of the more effective means of shift-

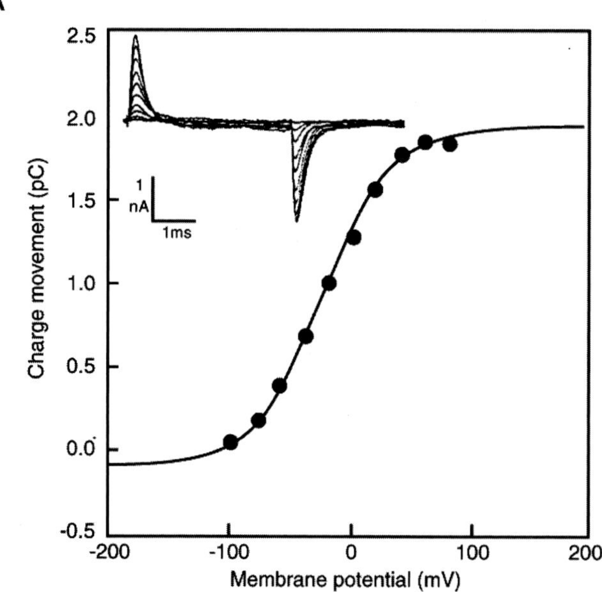

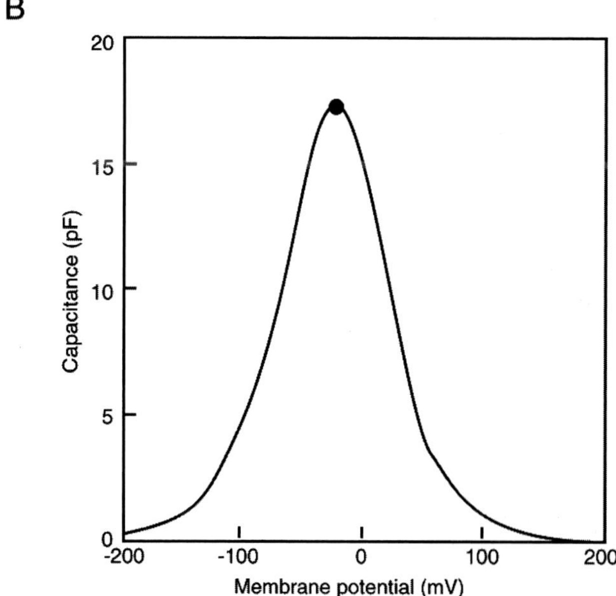

FIGURE 24.41 Gating charge associated with OHC motility voltage sensor. When the membrane potential is stepped with increasingly larger depolarizing voltages from a negative holding potential, nonlinear capacitive currents are generated and are obvious after linear capacitive currents are subtracted (inset). Integrating the onset currents, a measure of the amount of charge moved within the membrane can be obtained (A). The function is sigmoidal and has characteristics similar to the mechanical response. The first derivative of the charge with respect to membrane voltage defines the cell's nonlinear capacitance (B). From Santos-Sacchi, J. (1991). Reversible inhibition of voltage dependent outer hair cell motility and capacitance. *J. Neurosci.* **11:** Figs. 6 and 4.

ing the motility function is to exert tension on the plasma membrane. Reducing membrane tension shifts the function in the hyperpolarized direction, toward the cell's resting potential, whereas increasing tension shifts the function in the opposite direction. Intracellular turgor pressure effectively alters membrane tension; thus, the control of cell turgor may provide the cell with a means to control the gain of motility by shifting the function toward or away from the resting potential. Drugs are also capable of affecting motility. For example, salicylate (aspirin), which can cause hearing loss and ringing in the ears, can reduce the magnitude of motility and linearize and ΔL vs ΔV function.

Since hearing sensitivity and frequency selectivity in mammals span the kilohertz range, any mechanism designed to augment hearing must function at these rates. Indeed, OHC motility has been demonstrated, *in vitro*, to extend into the tens of kilohertz range. The cell can move as fast as a voltage can be placed across the lateral membrane. However, because the mechanical response is voltage dependent, it will be affected by the *RC* time constant of the OHC. Thus, at high frequencies ac receptor potentials, which presumably drive motility *in vivo*, will be greatly attenuated. It has been estimated that OHC motility will be smaller by an order of magnitude than basilar membrane motion near threshold at very high frequencies. Thus, how the cell could boost BM vibrations is difficult to imagine. Nevertheless, these calculations are based on motility characteristics obtained *in vitro*. The potential ability of the OHC to modify its mechanical gain through turgor control could overcome the membrane filter problem. In addition, recent evidence indicates that far-field extracellular components of the receptor potentials may provide an additional drive for the motile mechanism.[173–180]

Summary

Hair cells are modified epithelial cells that function to transduce mechanical energy from the environment into electrical energy. The gating of mechanically sensitive nonselective ionic channels within apical membrane specializations, termed stereocilia, induces modulation of a standing inward receptor current. In turn, this current evokes a change in membrane potential, a receptor potential, across the basolateral membrane. The receptor potential, which is shaped by basolateral membrane conductances, ultimately controls the release of hair cell neurotransmitter and afferent spike activity. Frequency specificity can arise from many mechanisms intrinsic and extrinsic to the hair cell. In the mammal, mechanical tuning of the sensory epithelium enhanced by active mechanical feedback from the outer hair cell provides for our exquisite ability to resolve frequency information.

References

General

Amoore, J. E., Johnston, J. W. J., and Rubin, M. (1965) The stereochemical theory of odor. *Sci. Am.* **210:** 42–49.

Bekesy, G. von, (1960). *Experiments in Hearing,* McGraw-Hill, New York.

Chadwick, D., Marsh, J., and Goode, J. (1993). *The Molecular Basis of Smell and Taste Transduction,* Ciba Foundation Symposium 179. Wiley, Chichester.

Finger, T. E., and Silver, W. L. (1987). *Neurobiology of Taste and Smell.* Wiley, New York.

Getchell, T. V., Doty, R. L., Bartoshuk, L. M., and Snow, J. B. (1991). *Smell and Taste in Health and Disease.* Raven Press, New York.

Kinnamon, S. C., and Margolskee, R. F. (1996). Mechanisms of taste transduction. *Curr. Opin. Neurobiol.* **6:** 506–513.

Lancet, D. (1986). Vertebrate olfactory reception. *Annu. Rev. Neurosci.* **9:** 329–355.

Lancet, D., Chen, Z., Ciobotariu, A., Eckstein, F., Khen, M., Heldman, J., Ophir, D., Shafir, I., and Pace, U. (1987). Toward a comprehensive molecular analysis of olfactory transduction. *Ann. N.Y. Acad. Sci.* **510:** 27–32.

McLaughlin, S., and Margolskee, R. (1994). The sense of taste. *American Scientist* **82:** 538.

Reed, R. R. (1994). The molecular basis of sensitivity and specificity in olfaction. *Sem. Cell. Biol.* **5:** 33–38.

Roper, S. D. (1989). The cell biology of vertebrate taste receptors. *Annu. Rev. Neurosci.* **12:** 329–353.

Roper, S. D. (1992). The microphysiology of peripheral taste organs. *J. Neurosci.* **12:** 1127–1134.

Shepherd, G. M. (1994). Discrimination of molecular signals by the olfactory receptor neuron. *Neuron.* **13:** 771–790.

Shepherd, G. M., and Firestein, S. (1991). Toward a pharmacology of odor receptors and the processing of odor images. *J. Ster. Biochem. Mol. Biol.* **39:** 583–592.

Simon, S. A., and Roper, S. D. (1993). *Mechanisms of Taste Transduction.* CRC Press, Boca Raton.

Spielman, A. I., Huque, T., Nagai, H., Whitney, G., and Brand, J. G. (1994). Generation of inositol phosphates in bitter taste transduction. *Physiol. Behav.* **56:** 1149–1155.

Cited

1. Shepherd, G. M. (1991). Sensory transduction: Entering the mainstream of membrane signaling. *Cell* **67:** 845–851.
2. Tomita, T. (1965). Electrophysiological study of the mechanisms subserving color coding in the fish retina. *Cold Spring Harbor Symposia on Quantitative Biology* **30:** 559–566.
3. Hagins, W. A., Penn, R. D., and Yoshikami, S. (1970). Dark current and photocurrent in retinal rods. *Biophys. J.* **10:** 380–412.
4. Hecht, S., Shlaer, S., and Pirenne, M. H. (1942). Energy, quanta, and vision. *J. Gen. Physiol.* **25:** 831–850.
5. Baylor, D. A., Lamb, T. D., and Yau, K.-W. (1979). Responses of retinal rods to single photons. *J. Physiol.* **288:** 613–634.

6. Brown, J. E., and Pinto, L. H. (1974). Ionic mechanisms for the photoreceptor potential of the retina of *Bufo Marinus*. *J. Physiol.* **236:** 575–591.
7. Bader, C. R., MacLeish, P. R., and Schwartz, E. A. (1979). A voltage-clamp study of the light response in solitary rods of the tiger salamander. *J. Physiol.* **296:** 1–26.
8. Hodgkin, A. L., McNaughton, P. A., and Nunn, B. J. (1985). The ionic selectivity and calcium dependence of the light-sensitive pathway in toad rods. *J. Physiol.* **358:** 447–468.
9. Yau, K.-W., and Nakatani, K. (1984). Cation selectivity of light-sensitive conductance in retinal rods. *Nature* **309:** 352–354.
10. MacLeish, P., Tachibana, M., and Townes-Anderson, E. (1982). Morphological and electrophysiological properties of dissociated retinal neurons. In *Advances in Pharmacology and Therapeutics II* (H. Yoshida, Y. Hagihara, and E. Ebashi, eds.), vol. 2, pp. 245–253, Pergamon Press, Oxford and New York.
11. Cohen, A. I. (1972). Rods and cones. In *Handbook of Sensory Physiology* (M. G. F. Fuortes, ed.), vol. VII/2, pp. 63–110, Springer-Verlag.
12. Nicol, G. D., and Miller, W. H. (1978). Cyclic GMP injected into retinal rod outer segments increases latency and amplitude of responses to illumination. *Proc. Natl. Acad. Sci. U.S.A.* **75:** 5217–5220.
13. MacLeish, P. R., Schwartz, E. A., and Tachibana, M. (1984). Control of the generator current in solitary rods of the *Ambystoma Tigrinum* retina. *J. Physiol.* **348:** 645–664.
14. Miki, N., Keirns, J. J., Marcus, F. R., Freeman, J., and Bitensky, M. W. (1973). Regulation of cyclic nucleotide concentration in photoreceptors: An ATP-dependent stimulation of cyclic nucleotide phosphodiesterase by light. *Proc. Natl. Acad. Sci. U.S.A.* **70:** 3820–3824.
15. Yee, R., and Liebman, P. A. (1978). Light-activated phosphodiesterase of the rod outer segment. *J. Biol. Chem.* **253:** 8902–8909.
16. Cohen, A. I., Hall, I. A., and Ferrendelli, J. A. (1978). Calcium and cyclic nucleotide regulation in incubated mouse retinas. *J. Gen. Physiol.* **71:** 595–612.
17. Polans, A. S., Kawamura, S. and Bownds, M. D. (1981). Influence of calcium on guanosine 3′,5′-cyclic monophosphate levels in frog rod outer segments. *J. Gen. Physiol.* **77:** 41–48.
18. Fesenko, E. E., Kolesnikov, S. S., and Lyubarsky, A. L. (1985). Induction by cyclic GMP of cationic conductance in plasma membrane of retinal rod outer segment. *Nature* **313:** 310–313.
19. Yau, K.-W., and Nakatani, K. (1985). Light-suppressible, cyclic GMP-sensitive conductance in the plasma membrane of a truncated rod outer segment. *Nature* **317:** 252–255.
20. Zimmerman, A. L., and Baylor, D. A. (1986). Cyclic GMP-sensitive conductance of retinal rods consists of aqueous pores. *Nature* **321:** 70–72.
21. Kaupp, U. B., Niidome, T., Tanabe, T., Terada, S., Bönigk, W., Stühmer, W., Cook, N. J., Kangawa, K., Matsuo, T., Miyata, T., and Numa, S. (1989). Primary structure and functional expression from complementary DNA of the rod photoreceptor cycle GMP-gated channel. *Nature* **342:** 762–766.
22. Wald, G. (1935). Carotenoids and the visual cycle. *J. Gen. Physiol.* **19:** 351–371.
23. Dowling, J. E. (1960). The chemistry of visual adaptation in the rat. *Nature* **188:** 114–118.
24. Baylor, D. A. (1987). Photoreceptor signals and vision. Proctor lecture. *Invest. Ophthal. Vis. Sci.* **28:** 34–49.
25. Yau, K.-W. (1994). Phototransduction mechanism in retinal rods and cones. The Friedenwald lecture. *Invest. Ophthal. Vis. Sci.* **35:** 9–32.
26. Fung, B. K.-K., Hurley, J. B., and Stryer, L. (1981). Flow of information in the light-triggered cyclic nucleotide cascade of vision. *Proc. Natl. Acad. Sci. U.S.A.* **78:** 152–156.
27. Bader, C. R., MacLeish, P. R., and Schwartz, E. A. (1978). Responses to light of solitary rod photoreceptors isolated from tiger salamander retina. *Proc. Natl. Acad. Sci. U.S.A.* **75:** 3507–3511.
28. Wilden, U., and Kühn, H. (1982). Light-dependent phosphorylation of rhodopsin: Number of phosphorylation sites. *Biochemistry* **21:** 3014–3022.
29. Kühn, H., Hall, S. W., and Wilden, U. (1984). Light-induced binding of 48-kDa protein to photoreceptor membranes is highly enhanced by phosphorylation of rhodopsin. *FEBS Lett.* **176:** 473–478.
30. Cook, N. J., Hanke, W., and Kaupp, U. B. (1987). Identification, purification and functional recognition of cyclic GMP-dependent channel from rod photoreceptors. *Proc. Natl. Acad. Sci. U.S.A* **84:** 585–589.
31. Stern, J. H., Kaupp, U. B., and MacLeish, P. R. (1986). Control of the light-regulated current in rod photoreceptors by cyclic GMP, calcium, and 1-*cis*-diltiazem. *Proc. Natl. Acad. Sci. U.S.A.* **83:** 1163–1167.
32. Bodia, R. D., and Detwiler, P. B. (1985). Patch-clamp recordings of the light-sensitive dark noise in retinal rods from the lizard and frog. *J. Physiol.* **367:** 183–216.
33. Detwiler, P. B., Conner, J. D., and Bodia, R. D. (1982). Gigaseal patch clamp recordings from the outer segments of intact retinal rods. *Nature* **300:** 59–61.
34. Gray, P., and Attwell, D. (1985). Kinetics of the light-sensitive channels in vertebrate photoreceptors. *Proc. Roy. Soc. B* **223:** 379–388.
35. Haynes, L. W., Kay, A. R., and Yau, K.-W. (1986). Single cyclic GMP-activated channel activity in excised patches of rod outer segment membrane. *Nature* **321:** 66–70.
36. Matthews, G., and Watanabe, S. I. (1997). Properties of ion channels closed by light and opened by guanosine 3′,5′-cyclic monophosphate in toad retinal rods. *J. Physiol.* **394:** 691–716.
37. Cervetto, L., Lagnado, L., Perry, R. J., Robinson, D. W., and McNaughton, P. A. (1989). Extrusion of calcium from rod outer segments is driven by sodium and potassium gradients. *Nature* **337:** 740–743.
38. Schnetkamp, P. P. M., Basu, D. K., and Szerencsei, R. T. (1989). Na^+-Ca^{2+} exchange in bovine rod outer segments requires and transports K^+. *Am. J. Physiol.* **257:** C153–157.
39. Hargrave, P. A., and McDowell, J. H. (1992). Rhodopsin and phototransduction: A model for G protein-linked receptors. *FASEB J.* **6:** 2323–2331.
40. Dowling, J. E. (1963). Neural and photochemical mechanisms of visual adaptation in the rat. *J. Gen. Physiol.* **46:** 459–474.
41. Millecchia, R., and Mauro, A. (1969). The ventral photoreceptor cells of limulus II. The basic photoresponse. *J. Gen. Physiol.* **54:** 310–330.
42. Dodge, F., Knight, B. W., and Toyoda, J.-I. (1968). Voltage noise in limulus visceral cells. *Science* **160:** 88–90.
43. Fein, A. (1986). Blockade of visual excitation and adaptation in *Limulus* photoreceptors by GDP-β-S. *Science* **232:** 1543–1545.
44. Peretz, A., Suss-Toby, E., Rom-Glas, A., Arnon, A., Payne, R., and Minke, B. (1994). The light response of drosophila photoreceptors is accompanied by an increase in cellular calcium: Effects of specific mutations. *Neuron* **12:** 1257–1267.
45. Ranganathan, R., Backsai, B. J., Tsien, R. Y., and Zucker, C. S. (1994). Cytosolic calcium transients: Spatial localization and role in drosophila photoreceptor cell function. *Neuron* **13:** 837–848.
46. Bacigalupo, J., Johnson, E. C., Vergara, C., and Lisman, J. E. (1991). Light-dependent channels from excised patches of *Limulus* ventral photoreceptors are opened by cyclic GMP. *Proc. Natl. Acad. Sci. U.S.A.* **88:** 7938–7942.

47. Pak, W. L. (1979). Study of photoreceptor function using Drosophila mutants. In *Neurogenetics: Genetic Approaches to the Nervous System* (X. Breakfield, ed.), pp. 67–99. Elsevier/North-Holland, New York.
48. Zucker, C. S. (1996). The biology of vision in Drosophila. *Proc. Natl. Acad. Sci. U.S.A.* **93:** 571–576.
49. Morrison, E. E., and Constanzo, R. M. (1990). Morphology of the human olfactory epithelium. *J. Comp. Neurol.* **297:** 1–13.
50. Ache, B. W. (1994). Towards a common strategy for transducing olfactory information. *Sem. Cell Biol.* **5:** 55–64.
51. Kaissling, K. E., Zack, S. C., and Rumbo, E. R. (1987). Adaptation processes in insect olfactory receptors: Mechanisms and behavioral significance. [Review]. *Ann. N.Y. Acad. Sci.* **510:** 104–112.
52. Vogt, R. G., and Riddiford, L. M. (1981). Pheromone binding and inactivation by moth antennae. *Nature* **293:** 161–163.
53. Vogt, R. G., and Riddiford, L. M. (1986). Pheromone reception: a kinetic equilibrium. In *Mechanisms in Insect Olfaction.* (T. L. Payne, M. C. Birch, and C. E. J. Kennedy, eds.), Oxford: Clarendon, pp. 201–208.
54. Raming, K., Krieger, J., and Breer, H. (1989). Molecular cloning of an insect pheromone-binding protein. *Febs Lett.* **256:** 215–218.
55. Krieger, J., Raming, K., Prestwich, G. D., Frith, D., Stabel, S., and Breer, H. (1992). Expression of a pheromone binding protein in insect cells using a baculovirus vector. *Eur. J. Biochem.* **203:** 161–166.
56. Du, G., Ng, C., and Prestwich, G. D. (1994). Odorant binding by a pheromone binding protein: Active site mapping by photoaffinity labeling. *Biochemistry* **33:** 4812–4819.
57. Prestwich, G. D., and Du, G. (1996). Pheromone binding proteins, phermone recognition, and signal transduction in moth olfaction. In *Pheromone Research: New Directions* (R. Cardé and A. K. Minks, eds.) Chapman & Hall, New York.
58. Ziegelberger, G., van den, Berg, M., Kaissling, K. E., Klumpp, S., and Schultz, J. E. (1990). Cyclic GMP levels and guanylate cyclase activity in pheromone-sensitive antennae of the silkmoths Antheraea polyphemus and Bombyx mori. *J. Neurosci.* **10:** 1217–1225.
59. Pelosi, P., Baldaccini, N. E., and Pisanelli, A. M. (1982). Identification of a specific olfactory receptor for 2-isobutyl-3-methoxypyrazine. *Biochem. J.* **201:** 245–248.
60. Pevsner, J., Trifiletti, R. R., Strittmatter, S. M., and Snyder, S. H. (1985). Isolation and characterization of an olfactory receptor protein for odorant pyrazines. *Proc. Natl. Acad. Sci. U.S.A.* **82:** 3050–3054.
61. Snyder, S. H., Sklar, P. B., Hwang, P. M., and Pevsner, J. (1989). Molecular mechanisms of olfaction. *Trends Neurosci.* **12:** 35–38.
62. Pelosi, P., and Maida, R. (1990). Odorant binding proteins in vertebrates and insects: Similarities and possible common function. *Chem. Senses* **15:** 205–215.
63. Pevsner, J., Hwang, P. M., Sklar, P. B., Venable, J. C., and Snyder, S. H. (1988). Odorant-binding protein and its mRNA are localized to lateral nasal gland implying a carrier function. *Proc. Natl. Acad. Sci. USA.* **85:** 2383–2387.
64. Pevsner, J., Reed, R. R., Feinstein, P. G., and Snyder, S. H. (1988). Molecular cloning of odorant-binding protein: Member of a ligand carrier family. *Science* **241:** 336–9.
65. Firestein, S., Shepherd, G. M., and Werblin, F. S. (1990). Time course of the membrane current underlying sensory transduction in salamander olfactory receptor neurones. *J. Physiol. (London)* **430:** 135–158.
66. Pace, U., Hansky, E., Salomon, Y., and Lancet, D. (1985). Odorant sensitive adenylate cyclase may mediate olfactory reception. *Nature* **316:** 255–258.
67. Buck, L. D., and Axel, R. (1991). A novel multigene family may encode odorant receptors: A molecular basis for odorant recognition. *Cell.* **65:** 175–187.
68. Lancet, D., and Ben-Arie, N. (1993). Olfactory receptors. *Current Biology.* **3:** 668–674.
69. Sullivan, S. L., Adamson, M. C., Ressler, K. J., Kozak, C. A., and Buck, L. B. (1996). The chromosomal distribution of mouse odorant receptor genes. *Proc. Natl. Acad. Sci. U.S.A.* **93:** 884–888.
70. Singer, M. S., Shepherd, G. M., Hughes, T. E., and Greer, C. A. (1996). Olfactory receptors: molecular basis for a functional map in the olfactory bulb. *AChemS Absts.* XVIII:
71. Shepherd, G. M., Singer, M. S., and Greer, C. A. (1996). Olfactory receptors: a large gene family with broad affinities and multiple functions. *The Neuroscientist* **2.**
72. Singer, M. S., Oliveira, L., Vriend, G., and Shepherd, G. M. (1995). Potential ligand-binding residues in rat olfactory receptors identified by correlated mutation analysis. *Receptors & Channels* **3:** 89–95.
73. Singer, M. S., Shepherd, G. M., and Greer, C. A. (1995). Olfactory receptors guide axons. *Nature.* **377:** 19–20.
74. Raming, K., Krieger, J., Strotmann, J., Boekhoff, I., Kubick, S., Baumstark, C., and Breer, H. (1993). Cloning and expression of odorant receptors. *Nature.* **361:** 353–356.
75. Sengupta, P., Chou, J. H., and Bargmann, C. I. (1996). Odr-10 encodes a seven transmembrane domain olfactory receptor required for responses to the odorant diacetyl. *Cell* **84:** 899–909.
76. Griff, I. C., and Reed, R. R. (1995). The genetic basis for specific anosmia to isovaleric acid in the mouse. *Cell* **83:** 407–414.
77. Zhao, H., Ivic, L., Otaki, J. M., Hashimoto, M., Mikoshiba, K., and Firestein, S. (1998). Functional expression of a mammalian odorant receptor. *Science* **279:** 237–242.
78. Shepherd, G. M. (1987). A molecular vocabulary for olfaction. *Ann. N.Y. Acad. Sci.* **510:** 98–103.
79. Ressler, K. J., Sullivan, S. L., and Buck, L. B. (1994). Information coding in the olfactory system: Evidence for a stereotyped and highly organized epitope map in the olfactory bulb. *Cell* **79:** 1245–1255.
80. Mori, K., and Yoshihara, Y. (1995). Molecular recognition and olfactory processing in the mammalian olfactory system. *Progr. Neurobiol.* **45:** 585–619.
81. Hildebrand, J. G. (1995). Analysis of chemical signals by nervous systems. *Proc. Natl. Acad. Sci. U.S.A.* **92:** 67–74.
82. Shepherd, G. M. (1994). Discrimination of molecular signals by the olfactory receptor neuron. *Neuron.* **13:** 771–790.
83. Lancet, D., Sadovsky, E., and Seidemann, E. (1993). Probability model for molecular recognition in biological receptor repertoires: Significance to the olfactory system. *Proc. Natl. Acad. Sci. U.S.A.* **90:** 3715–3719.
84. Shepherd, G. M., and Singer, M. S. (1995). Determinant based model for ligand-receptor interactions in olfactory receptors. *Assoc. Chemorecep. Sci. Absts.* **17:** 306.
85. Reed, R. (1992). Signaling pathways in odorant detection. *Neuron* **8:** 205–209.
86. Breer, H. (1991). Molecular reaction cascades in olfactory signal transduction. [Review]. *J Steroid Biochem. Mol. Biol.* **39:** 621–625.
87. Boekhoff, I., Tarelius, E., Strottmann, J., and Breer, H. (1990). Rapid activation of alternative second messenger pathways in olfactory cilia from rats by different odorants. *EMBO J.* **9:** 2453–2458.
88. Breer, H., Klemm, T., and Boekhoff, I. (1992). Nitric oxide mediated formation of cyclic GMP in the olfactory system. *NeuroReport* **3:** 1030–1032.
89. Ronnett, G. V., Cho, H., Hester, L. D., Wood, S. F., and Snyder, S. H. (1993). Odorants differentially enhance phosphoinositide turnover and adenylyl cyclase in olfactory receptor neuronal cultures. *J. Neurosci.* **13:** 1751–1758.

90. Nakamura, T., and Gold, G. H. (1987). A cyclic nucleotide-gated conductance in olfactory receptor cilia. *Nature* **325:** 442–444.

91. Firestein, S., Darrow, B., and Shepherd, G. M. (1991). Activation of the sensory current in salamander olfactory receptor neurons depends on a G protein-mediated cAMP second messenger system. *Neuron* **6:** 825–835.

92. Firestein, S., Zufall, F., and Shepherd, G. M. (1991). Single odor-sensitive channels in olfactory receptor neurons are also gated by cyclic nucleotides. *J. Neurosci.* **11:** 3565–3572.

93. Firestein, S., and Shepherd, G. M. (1991). A kinetic model of the odor response in single olfactory receptor neurons. *J. Steroid Biochem. Mol. Biol.* **39:** 615–620.

94. Ludwig, J., Margalit, T., Eismann, E., Lancet, D., and Kaupp, U. B. (1990). Primary structure of cAMP-gated channel from bovine olfactory epithelium. *Febs Lett.* **270:** 24–29.

95. Leinders-Zufall, T., Shepherd, G. M., and Zufall, F. (1995). Regulation of cyclic nucleotide-gated channels and membrane excitability in olfactory receptor cells by carbon monoxide. *J. Neurophysiol.* **74:** 1498–1508.

96. Restrepo, D., Teeter, J. H., Honda, E., Boyle, A. G., Marecek, J. F., Prestwich, G. D., and Kalinoski, D. L. (1992). Evidence for an InsP3-gated channel protein in isolated rat olfactory cilia. *Am. J. Physiol.*

97. Miyamoto, T., Restrepo, D., Cragoe, E. J., and Teeter, J. H. (1992). IP3- and cAMP-induced responses in isolated olfactory receptor neurons from the channel catfish. *J. Membr. Biol.* **127:** 173–183.

98. Breer, H., Boekhoff, I., and Tarelius, E. (1990). Rapid kinetics of second messenger formation in olfactory transduction. *Nature* **345:** 65–68.

99. Dionne, V. E. (1994). Emerging complexity of odor transduction. *Proc. Natl. Acad. Sci. U.S.A.* **91:** 6253–6254.

100. Schild, D., Lischka, F. W., and Restrepo, D. (1995). InsP3 causes an increase in apical $[Ca^{2+}]_i$ by activating two distinct current components in vertebrate olfactory receptor cells. *J Neurophysiol.* **73:** 862–866.

101. Denk, W., Holt, J. R., Shepherd, G. M. G., and Corey, D. P. (1995). Calcium imaging of single sterocilia in hair cells: Localization of transduction channels at both ends of tip links. *Neuron* **15:** 1311–1321.

102. Zufall, F., Firestein, S., and Shepherd, G. M. (1991). Analysis of single cyclic nucleotide-gated channels in olfactory receptor cells. *J. Neurosci.* **11:** 3573–3580.

103. Zufall, F., Shepherd, G. M., and Firestein, S. (1991). Inhibition of the olfactory cyclic nucleotide gated ion channel by intracellular calcium. *Proc. Royal Soc. London B: Biol. Sci.* **246:** 225–230.

104. Goulding, E. H., Tibbs, G. R., and Siegelbaum, S. A. (1994). Molecular mechanism of cyclic-nucleotide-gated channel activation. *Nature* **372:** 369–74.

105. Roskams, A. J., Bredt, D. S., Dawson, T. M., and Ronnett, G. V. (1994). Nitric oxide mediates the formation of synaptic connections in developing and regenerating olfactory receptor neurons. *Neuron* **13:** 289–299.

106. Firestein, S., Picco, C., and Menini, A. (1993). The relation between stimulus and response in olfactory receptor cells of the tiger salamander. *J. Physiol. (London).* **468:** 1–10.

107. Sato, T., Hirono, J., Tonoike, M., and Takebayashi, M. (1994). Tuning specificities to aliphatic odorants in mouse olfactory receptor neurons and their local distribution. *J. Neurophysiol.* **72:** 2980–2989.

108. Leinders-Zufall, T., Rand, M. N., Shepherd, G. M., and Greer, C. A. (1997). Calcium entry through cyclic nucleotide-gated channels in individual cilia of olfactory receptor cells: Spatiotemporal dynamics. *J. Neurosci.* **17:** 4136–4148.

109. Dulac, C., and Axel, R. (1995). A novel family of genes encoding putative pheromone receptors in mammals. *Cell* **83:** 195–206.

110. Dorries, K. M., Adkins-Regan, E., and Halpern, B. P. (1996). Sensitivity and behavioral responses to the pheromone androstenone are not mediated by the vomeronasal organ in domestic pigs. *Brain Behav. Evol.*

111. Deleted.

112. Avenet, P. (1992). Role of amiloride-sensitive Na^+ channels in taste. In *Sensory Transduction* (D. P. Corey, and S. D. Roper, eds.), New York: Rockefeller Univ., pp. 271–281.

113. Avenet, P., and Lindemann, B. (1988). Amiloride-blockable sodium currents in isolated taste receptor cells. *J. Membrane Biol.* **105:** 245–255.

114. Formaker, B. K., and Hill, D. L. (1988). An analysis of residual NaCl taste response after amiloride. *Am. J. Physiol.* **255:** R1002–R1007.

115. Heck, G. L., Mierson, S., and DeSimone, J. A. (1984). Salt taste transduction occurs through an amiloride-sensitive sodium transport pathway. *Science* **223:** 403–405.

116. Schiffman, S. S., Lockhead, E., and Maes, F. W. (1983). Amiloride reduces the taste intensity of Na and Li salts and sweeteners. *Proc. Natl. Acad. Sci. U.S.A.* **80:** 6136–6140.

117. Spector, A. C., and Grill, H. J. (1992). Salt taste discrimination after bilateral section of the chorda tympani or glossopharyngeal nerves. *Am. J. Physiol.* **263:** R169–R176.

118. Ye, Q., Heck, G. L., and DeSimone, J. A. (1991). The anion paradox in sodium taste reception: Resolution by voltage-clamp studies. *Science* **254:** 724–726.

119. Ye, Q., Heck, G. L., and DeSimone, J. A. (1993). Voltage-dependence of the rat chorda tympani responses to Na^+ salts: implications for the functional organization of taste receptor cells. *J. Neurophysiol.* **70:** 167–178.

120. Cummings, T. A., and Kinnamon, S. C. (1992). Apical K^+ channels in *Necturus* taste cells: Modulation by intracellular factors and taste stimuli. *J. Gen. Physiol.* **99:** 591–613.

121. Gilbertson, T. A., Avenet, P., Kinnamon, S. C., and Roper, S. D. (1992). Proton currents through amiloride-sensitive Na^+ channels in hamster taste cells: role in sour taste transduction. *J. Gen. Physiol.* **100:** 803–824.

122. Gilbertson, T. A., Roper, S. D., and Kinnamon, S. C. (1993). Proton current through amiloride-sensitive Na^+ channels in isolated hamster taste cells: enhancement by vasopressin and cAMP. *Neuron* **10:** 931–942.

123. Kinnamon, S. C. (1993). Role of apical ion channels in sour taste transduction. In: The Molecular Basis of Smell and Taste Transduction, Ciba Foundation Symposium 179 (D. J. Chadwick, Marsh, J. Goode, eds.), Chichester: John Wiley and Sons.

124. Kinnamon, S. C., Dionne, V. E., and Beam, K. G. (1988). Apical localization of K^+ channels in taste cells provides the basis for sour taste transduction. *Proc. Natl. Acad. Sci. U.S.A.* **85:** 7023–7027.

125. Okada, Y., Miyamoto, T., and Sato, T. (1993). Contribution of proton transporter to acid-induced receptor potential in frog taste cells. *Comp. Biochem. Physiol.* **105A:** 725–728.

126. Okada, Y., Miyamoto, T., and Sato, T. (1994). Activation of a cation conductance by acetic acid in taste cells isolated from the bullfrog. *J. Exp. Biol.* **187:** 19–32.

127. Avenet, P., Hofmann, F., and Lindemann, B. (1988). Transduction in taste receptor cells requires cAMP-dependent protein kinase. *Nature* **331:** 351–354.

128. Béhé, P., DeSimone, J. A., Avenet, P., and Lindemann, B. (1990). Membrane currents in taste cells of the rat fungiform papilla: Evidence for two types of Ca currents and inhibition of K currents by saccharin. *J. Gen. Physiol.* **96:** 1061–1084.

129. Cummings, T. A., Powell, J., and Kinnamon, S. C. (1993). Sweet taste transduction in hamster taste cells: evidence for the role of cyclic nucleotides. *J. Neurophysiol.* **70:** 2326–2336.
130. Striem, B. J., Pace, U., Zehavi, U., Naim, M., and Lancet, D. (1989). Sweet tastants stimulate adenylate cyclase coupled to GTP-binding protein in rat tongue membranes. *Biochem. J.* **260:** 121–126.
131. Striem, B. J., Yamamoto, T., Naim, M., Lancet, D., Jakinovich, W. Jr., and Zehavi, U. (1990). The sweet taste inhibitor methyl 4,6-dichloro-4,6-dideoxy-D-galactopyranoside inhibits sucrose stimulation of the chorda tympani nerve and of the adenylate cyclase in anterior lingual membranes of rats. *Chem. Senses* **15:** 529–536.
132. Striem, B. J., Naim, M., and Lindemann, B. (1991). Generation of cyclic AMP in taste buds of the rat circumvallate papilla in response to sucrose. *Cell Physiol. Biochem.* **1:** 46–54.
133. Akabas, M. H., Dodd, J., and Al-Awqati, Q. (1988). A bitter substance induces a rise in intracellular calcium in a subpopulation of rat taste cells. *Science* **242:** 1047–1050.
134. Bigiani, A. R., and Roper, S. D. (1991). Mediation of responses to calcium in taste cells by modulation of a potassium conductance. *Science* **252:** 126–128.
135. Hwang, P. M., Verma, A., Bredt, D. S., and Snyder, S. H. (1990). Localization of phosphatidylinositol signaling components in rat taste cells: Role in bitter taste transduction. *Proc. Natl. Acad. Sci. U.S.A.* **87:** 7395–7399.
136. Kinnamon, S. C. (1992). Role of K^+ channels in taste transduction. In *Sensory Transduction* (D. P. Corey and S. D. Roper, ed.), Rockefeller Univ. Press, New York, pp. 261–270.
137. McLaughlin, S. K., McKinnon, P. J., and Margolskee, R. F. (1992). Gustducin is a taste-cell specific G protein closely related to the transducins. *Nature* **357:** 563–569.
138. Caprio, J. (1975). High sensitivity of catfish taste receptors to amino acids. *Comp. Biochem. Physiol.* **52A:** 247–251.
139. Teeter, J. H., Brand, J. G., and Kumazawa, T. (1990). A stimulus-activated conductance in isolated taste epithelial membranes. *Biophys. J.* **58:** 253–259.
140. Brand, J. G., Teeter, J. H., Kumazawa, T., Huque, T., and Bayley, D. L. (1992). Transduction mechanisms for the taste of amino acids. *Physiol. Behav.* **49:** 899–904.
141. Gilbertson, T. (1993). The physiology of vertebrate taste reception. *Curr. Opin. Neurobiol.* **3:** 532–539.
142. Kinnamon, S. C. (1988). Taste transduction: A diversity of mechanisms. *Trends Neurosci.* **11:** 491–496.
143. Kinnamon, S. C., and Cummings, T. A. (1992). Chemosensory transduction mechanisms in taste. *Annu. Rev. Physiol.* **54:** 715–731.
144. Margolskee, R. R. (1993). The biochemistry and molecular biology of taste transduction. *Curr. Opin. Neurobiol.* **3:** 526–531.
145. Duvall, A. J., Flock, A., and Wersall, J. (1966). The ultrastructure of the sensory hairs and associated organelles of the cochlear inner hair cell, with reference to directional sensivity. *J. Cell Biol.* **29:** 497–505.
146. Harris, G. G., Frishkopf, L. S., and Flock, A. (1970). Receptor potentials from hair cells of the lateral line. *Science* **167:** 76–79.
147. Wersall, J., Flock, A., and Lundquist, P. G. (1965). Structural basis for directional sensitivity in cochlear and vestibular sensory receptors. *Cold Spring Harbor Symposia on Quantitative Biology* **30:** 115–132.
148. Corey, D. P., and Hudspeth, A. J. (1979). Ionic basis of the receptor potential in a vertebrate hair cell. *Nature* **281:** 675–677.
149. Hudspeth, A. J., and Corey, D. P. (1977). Sensitivity, polarity and conductance change in the response of vertebrate hair cells to controlled mechanical stimuli. *Proc. Natl. Acad. Sci. U.S.A.* **74:** 2047–2411.
150. Russell, I. J., Richardson, G. P., and Cody, A. R. (1986). Mechanosensitivity of mammalian auditory hair cells in vitro. *Nature* **321:** 517–519.
151. Shotwell, S. L., Jacobs, R., and Hudspeth, A. J. (1981). Directional sensitivity of individual vertebrate hair cells to controlled deflection of their hair bundles. *Ann. N.Y. Acad. Sci.* **374:** 1–10.
152. Assad, J. A., Shepherd, G. M., and Corey, D. P. (1991). Tip-link integrity and mechanical transduction in vertebrate hair cells. *Neuron* **7:** 985–994.
153. Pickles, J. O., Comis, S. D., and Osborne, M. P. (1984). Cross-links between stereocilia in the guinea pig organ of corti and their possible relation to sensory transduction. *Hear. Res.* **15:** 103–112.
154. Howard, J., and Hudspeth, A. J. (1988). Compliance of the hair bundle associated with gating of mechanoelectrical transduction channels in the bullfrog's saccular hair cell. *Neuron* **1:** 189–99.
155. Crawford, A. C., Evans, M. G., and Fettiplace, R. (1989). Activation and adaptation of transducer currents in turtle hair cells. *J. Physiol. (London)* **419:** 405–434.
156. Eatock, R. A., Corey, D. P., and Hudspeth, A. J. (1987). Adaptation of mechanoelectrical transduction in hair cells of the bullfrog's sacculus. *J. Neurosci.* **7:** 2821–2836.
157. Hacohen, N., Assad, J. A., Smith, W. J., and Corey, D. P. (1989). Regulation of tension on hair-cell transduction channels: Displacement and calcium dependence. *J. Neurosci.* **9:** 3988–3997.
158. Ricci, A. J., and Fettiplace, R. (1997). The effects of calcium buffering and cyclic AMP on mechano-electrical transduction in turtle auditory hair cells. *J. Physiol. (London)* **501:** 111–124.
159. Russell, I. J., Richardson, G. P., and Kossl, M. (1989). The responses of cochlear hair cells to tonic displacements of the sensory hair bundle. *Hear. Res.* **43:** 55–70.
160. Corey, D. P., and Hudspeth, A. J. (1983). Kinetics of the receptor current in bullfrog saccular hair cells. *J. Neurosci.* **3:** 962–976.
161. Dallos, P., Santos-Sacchi, J., and Flock C. (1982). Intracellular recordings from outer hair cells. *Science* **218:** 582–584.
162. Kros, C. J., and Crawford, A. C. (1990). Potassium currents in inner hair cells isolated from the guinea pig. *J. Physiol. (London)* **421:** 263–291.
163. Palmer, A. R., and Russell, I. J. (1986). Phase-locking in the cochlear nerve of the guinea-pig and its relation to the receptor potential of inner hair cells. *Hear. Res.* **24:** 1–16.
164. Art, J. J., Crawford, A. C., Fettiplace, R., and Fuchs, P. A. (1985). Efferent modulation of hair cell tuning in the cochlea of the turtle. *J. Physiol.* **360:** 397–421.
165. Dallos, P., and Harris, D. (1978). Properties of auditory nerve responses in absence of outer hair cells. *J. Neurophysiol.* **41:** 365–382.
166. Eatock, R. A., Saeki, M., and Hutzler, M. J. (1993). Electrical resonance of isolated hair cells does not account for acoustic tuning in the free-standing region of the alligator lizard's cochlea. *J. Neurosci.* **13:** 1767–1783.
167. Fettiplace, R., and Crawford, A. C. (1978). The coding of sound pressure and frequency in cochlear hair cells of the terrapin. *Proc. R. Soc. London-Ser. B.* **203:** 209–218.
168. Fettiplace, R., and Crawford, A. C. (1980). The origin of tuning in turtle cochlear hair cells. *Hear. Res.* **2(3–4):** 447–454.
169. Frishkopf, L. S., and DeRosier, D. J. (1983). Mechanical tuning of free-standing stereociliary bundles and frequency analysis in the alligator lizard cochlea. *Hear. Res.* **12:** 393–404.
170. Holton, T., and Hudspeth, A. J. (1983). A micromechanical contribution to cochlear tuning and tonotopic organization. *Science* **222:** 508–510.

171. Ruggero, M. A., and Rich, N. C. (1991). Furosemide alters organ of Corti mechanics: Evidence for feedback of outer hair cells upon the basilar membrane. *J. Neurosci.* **11:** 1057–1067.
172. Sellick, P. M., Patuzzi, R., and Johnstone, B. M. (1983). Comparison between the tuning properties of inner hair cells and basilar membrane motion. *Hear. Res.* **10:** 93–100.
173. Ashmore, J. F. (1987). A fast motile response in guinea-pig outer hair cells: The cellular basis of the cochlear amplifier. *J. Physiol. (London)* **388:** 323–347.
174. Brownell, W. E., Bader, C. R., Bertrand, D., and De Ribaupierre, Y. (1985). Evoked mechanical response of isolated cochlear outer hair cells. *Science* **227:** 194–196.
175. Dallos, P., Evans, B. N., and Hallworth, R. (1991). On the nature of the motor element in cochlear outer hair cells. *Nature* **350:** 155–157.
176. Dallos, P., and Evans, B. N. (1995). High-frequency motility of outer hair cells and the cochlear amplifier. *Science* **267:** 2006–2009.
177. Gulley, R. L., and Reese, T. S. (1977). Regional specialization of the hair cell plasmalemma in the organ of Corti. *Anat. Rec.* **189:** 109–124.
178. Iwasa, K. H. (1993). Effect of stress on the membrane capacitance of the auditory outer hair cell. *Biophys. J.* **65:** 492–498.
179. Kakehata, S., and Santos-Sacchi, J. (1995). Membrane tension directly shifts voltage dependence of outer hair cell motility and associated gating charge. *Biophys. J.* **68:** 2190–2197.
180. Santos-Sacchi, J. (1992). On the frequency limit and phase of outer hair cell motility: Effects of the membrane filter. *J. Neurosci.* **12:** 1906–1916.

CHAPTER

25

Chemical Senses: Taste and Olfaction

David V. Smith and Gordon M. Shepherd

The chemical senses of taste and olfaction have several elements in common, but differ in a number of significant ways. The taste and olfactory systems are both concerned with extracting information from chemical stimuli in the environment. Both respond to a wide array of chemicals and both use G-protein-coupled receptors, although their function in the taste system is limited to sweet- and bitter-tasting stimuli. Both taste and olfactory receptors undergo continual turnover and replacement throughout life. Taste receptors, however, are modified epithelial cells, whereas olfactory receptors are neurons. More is known about the coding of taste quality than of odor quality, partly due to the relative agreement concerning the existence of four elementary gustatory sensations; olfactory stimuli give rise to many sensations and there is less agreement on what constitutes basic odor qualities. Topographic arrangements are more important in the representation of odor information than in the coding of taste quality, where they have little influence. Both of these chemical sensory systems show strong adaptation in the face of continual stimulation, although the neural mechanisms for adaptation are not well understood in either system. Information provided by these two sensory systems is important for the survival of the organism and the species. Both taste and olfactory inputs play a major role in food selection and in avoiding the ingestion of toxins. Olfactory stimuli provide important social cues, especially those used in reproductive behavior and mother–infant relationships.

TASTE

The term "taste" often refers to the complex of sensations known as **flavor perception,** which includes sensory information from the olfactory, gustatory, and trigeminal systems. More strictly defined, **taste** refers to the sensations arising from stimulation of gustatory receptors. Throughout this chapter, the terms "taste" and "gustation" are used interchangeably to refer to the gustatory system.

The transduction of specific chemical stimuli (e.g., sodium ions, sugars, acids, or alkaloids) by taste receptor cells gives rise to activity in several types of gustatory nerve fibers. Understanding the neural coding of taste information must begin with knowledge about how chemical sensitivities, represented by specific receptor transduction mechanisms (see Chapter 24), are distributed and organized among peripheral and central gustatory neurons. The role of an individual taste fiber or central neuron in the coding of taste quality must be considered in the context of the multiple sensitivities of these cells. In addition to producing taste sensations (**salty, sweet, sour,** or **bitter**), chemical stimulation of gustatory receptors provides critical input for several somatic and visceral responses related to food ingestion and rejection. Viewing taste as an oral component of the visceral afferent system provides an important perspective on the involvement of gustatory information in the control of taste-mediated behaviors.

Taste Receptors Are Situated within Taste Buds Located in Several Distinct Subpopulations

The sense of taste provides a gateway for monitoring and controlling the ingestion of food. It responds to chemical substances in the oral cavity and helps to regulate the interaction between ingestive behavior and the internal milieu. Taste is mediated through chemical stimulation of gustatory receptor cells, which

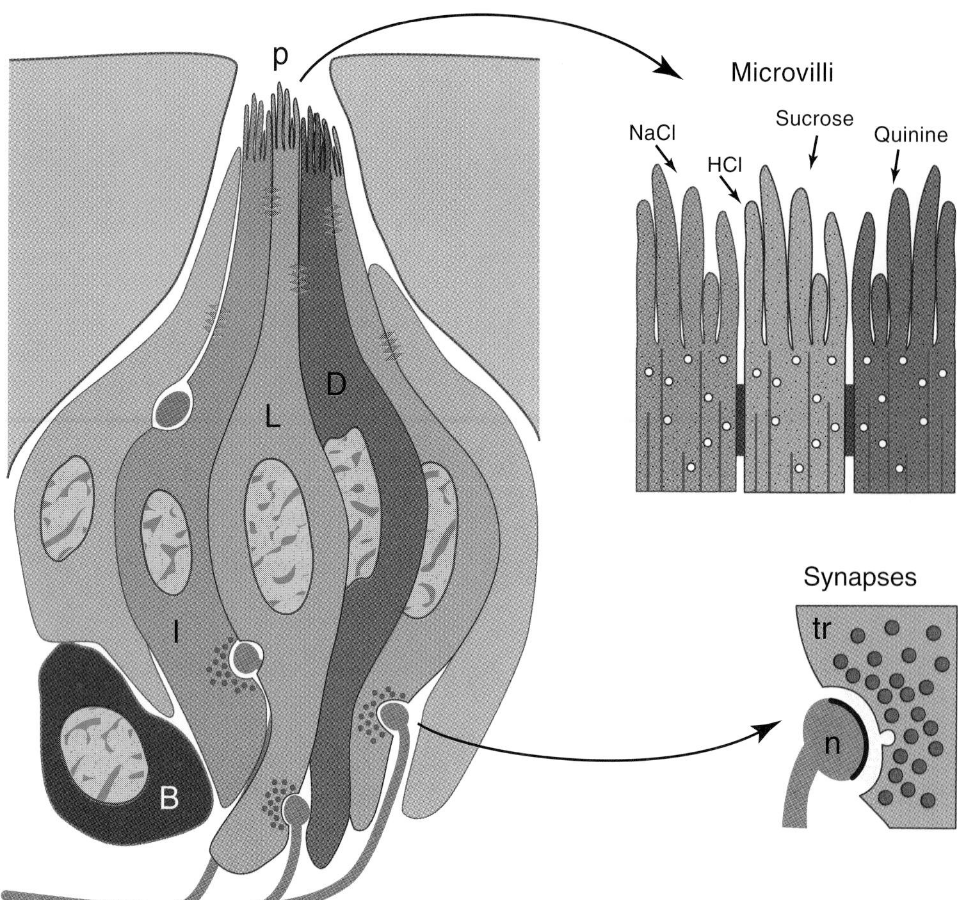

FIGURE 25.1 Schematic drawing of a mammalian taste bud. This barrel-shaped structure contains different cell types, including basal cells (B), dark cells (D), light cells (L), and intermediate cells (I). These epithelial receptor cells make synaptic contact with distal processes of cranial nerves (n) VII, IX, or X, whose cell bodies lie within the cranial nerve ganglia. The microvilli of the taste receptor cells (tr) project into an opening in the epithelium, the taste pore (p), where they make contact with gustatory stimuli. From Smith and Shipley,[1] with permission from Lippincott Williams & Wilkens.

are located within taste buds distributed within the oral, pharyngeal, and laryngeal mucosa. Taste buds on the tongue are contained within distinct papillae; those in other areas are distributed across the surface of the epithelium. At the ultrastructural level, at least two kinds of cells can be discerned within the taste bud, as indicated in Fig. 25.1.[1] They are termed **dark cells** and **light cells** on the basis of their ultrastructural appearance and the presence or lack of dense granules in their apical portion; **intermediate cells** with characteristics between these extremes are also present.[2] Cells within a taste bud are arranged in a concentric columnar fashion, with their apical microvilli projecting toward a pore that opens through the epithelium into the oral cavity (Fig. 25.1); gustatory stimuli interact with receptors and ion channels on these apical microvilli (see Chapter 24). The base of the taste bud is penetrated by terminal branches of the afferent nerve, which make synaptic contact with the receptor cells (Fig. 25.1). All three cell types have been shown to exhibit synaptic specializations, suggesting that they all may be receptor cells. A single nerve fiber may innervate cells in more than one taste bud, each of which is innervated by several different afferent fibers.

Taste receptors in mammals are distributed on the tongue and the oral, pharyngeal, and laryngeal epithelium within several subpopulations of taste buds; this distribution in the hamster is shown schematically in Fig. 25.2. About 18% of the hamster's taste buds are located in the fungiform papillae (F, Fig. 25.2) on the anterior portion of the tongue, 32% are within the foliate papillae (FO) on the posterior sides of the tongue, 23% are in the single midline vallate papilla (V) on the posterior tongue, about 14% are on the palate—distributed between the nasoincisive papillae (IP; 2%) and the soft palate (SP; 12%)—and about 10% are on

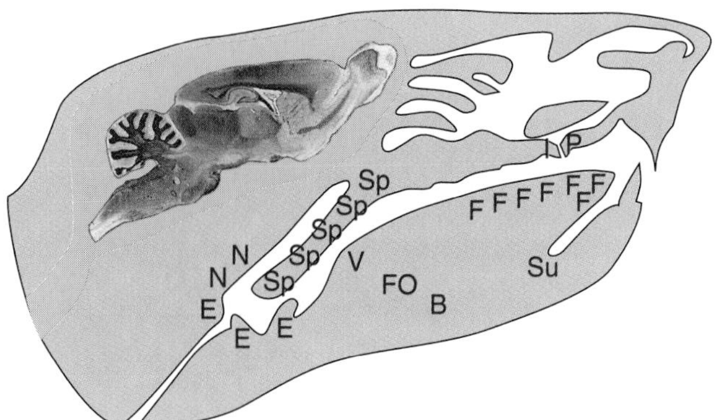

FIGURE 25.2 Diagram of a parasaggital section through the hamster oral cavity, showing the distribution of various taste bud populations, which are found in the fungiform (F) papillae on the anterior tongue, the vallate (V) and foliate (FO) papillae on the posterior tongue, the soft palate (SP), the incisive papillae (IP) on the hard palate, and the laryngeal surface of the epiglottis (E). Small numbers of taste buds are also found on the buccal wall (B), the sublingual organ (Su), and the nasopharynx (N). These taste buds are innervated by several different cranial nerves, which are branches of the VIIth, IXth, and Xth nerves (see text).

the laryngeal surface of the epiglottis (E) and the aryepiglottal folds.[3] A small number of taste buds are also within the sublingual organ (Su), the buccal walls (B), the nasopharynx (N), and the upper reaches of the esophagus. Similar distributions occur in the rat and other mammalian species that have been examined, including humans.

The Turnover and Replacement of Taste Bud Cells Are Continuous Processes

Taste receptor cells arise continually from an underlying population of basal epithelial cells. Whether the cell types identifiable on structural grounds are different cell types or a single type at different stages of maturation is not clear, primarily because the cells are in a constant state of turnover. In rats, the life span of a taste cell in a fungiform papilla is approximately 10 days.[4] The afferent nerve maintains a trophic influence over the taste buds, which degenerate when their nerve supply is removed. Although the innervation by gustatory nerve fibers is necessary to maintain the structural integrity of the taste bud, the gustatory sensitivities of the receptor cells appear to be determined by the epithelium itself (see Box 25.1).[5] Consistent with this observation, the several branches of a chorda tympani (CT) axon that innervate different fungiform papillae have similar profiles of sensitivity. Combined with the fact that the sensitivity of a given receptor field appears to be determined by the epithelium, this suggests that during cell turnover the nerve fibers are guided to make contact with particular types of receptor cells. Alternatively, the sensory code for taste could be maintained during taste cell turnover by reorganization of synaptic connections within the brainstem.

Although taste cells are modified epithelial cells, they possess many characteristics of neurons. Several recent investigations have demonstrated the presence of a variety of cell-surface molecules and other neural

BOX 25.1

TASTE RECEPTOR CELL SENSITIVITY IS DETERMINED BY THE EPITHELIUM

The formation and maintenance of taste buds are dependent on their innervation by gustatory nerve fibers, but the nerve itself does not dictate the sensory responsiveness of the taste buds. In a now classic experiment, Bruce Oakley[5] showed that altering the innervation of the taste buds had no influence on their response characteristics. In this experiment, Oakley transected the chorda tympani (CT) and glossopharyngeal (IXth) nerves of the rat and cross-anastomosed one to the other, resulting in either the fungiform taste buds being reinnervated by the IXth nerve or the vallate taste buds being reinnervated by the CT nerve following regeneration. Electrophysiological recording experiments then showed that when the IXth nerve had been rerouted to the anterior tongue, its fibers responded better to sodium chloride than to quinine, like those of the normal CT nerve. Similarly, when CT fibers had been routed to the posterior tongue, they responded more to quinine than to sodium chloride, like those of the normal IXth nerve. This experiment demonstrates that the receptor phenotype is a property of the target epithelium rather than the innervating nerve; thus, the trophic influence of the nerve over taste bud differentiation and maintenance does not extend to the receptor expression within the taste cells.

antigens on cells in mammalian taste buds. The neural cell adhesion molecule (NCAM) is expressed on a subset of vallate taste bud cells in the rat and mouse and also on the innervating fibers of the glossopharyngeal nerve. Transection of the nerve results in a loss of NCAM expression as the taste buds degenerate. Reinnervation of the vallate papilla following bilateral nerve crush is accompanied by NCAM expression in the nerve, followed by differentiation of the epithelium and the subsequent expression of NCAM in the differentiated taste cells.[6] A similar temporal sequence is seen during taste bud development in the mouse. These results are compatible with the idea that NCAM could play some role in triggering taste cell differentiation and/or in subsequent axon–taste cell recognition, which must occur during cell turnover. Any of a number of cell-surface molecules could play a role in either the structural integrity of the taste bud or mediation of axon–taste cell recognition.

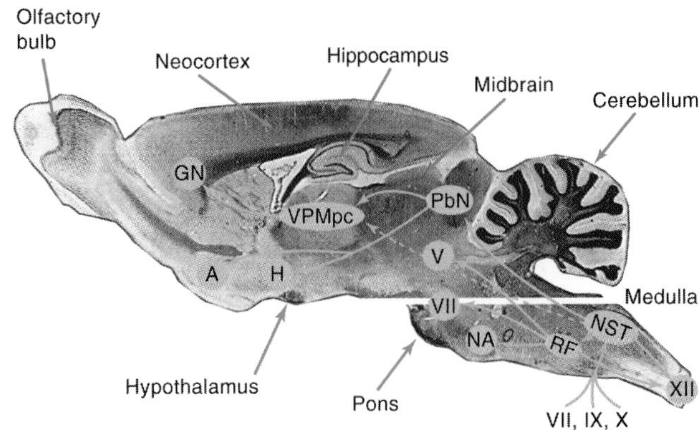

FIGURE 25.3 Schematic diagram of the ascending gustatory pathway; descending projections are not shown. Connections of the rodent gustatory system within the CNS are shown by solid lines; the projection from NST to VPMpc in primates is indicated by a dashed line. NST, nucleus of the solitary tract; PbN, parabrachial nuclei; VPMpc, venteroposteromedial nucleus (parvi cellularis) of the thalamus; GN, gustatory neocortex; A, amygdala; H, hypothalamus; NA, nucleus ambiguus; RF, reticular formation; V, VII, and XII, trigeminal, facial, and hypoglossal motor nuclei; VII, IX, and X, axons of peripheral gustatory fibers in the facial, glossopharyngeal, and vagal cranial nerves.

Taste Buds Are Innervated by One of Three Cranial Nerves

Taste buds in the fungiform papillae on the anterior portion of the tongue and in the more rostral of the foliate papillae on the sides of the tongue are innervated by the chorda tympani branch of the facial (VIIth) nerve. Axons of the CT travel to the anterior tongue along with the lingual nerve (a branch of the mandibular division of the Vth nerve), which carries somatosensory innervation from the same area. The greater superficial petrosal (GSP) branch of the VIIth cranial nerve innervates taste buds on the soft palate via the lesser palatine nerve and in the nasoincisor ducts via the nasopalatine nerve. The neurons giving rise to the gustatory fibers of the CT and GSP are located within the geniculate ganglion of the facial nerve. These two branches of the VIIth nerve carry gustatory information to the rostral pole of the nucleus of the solitary tract (NST), where their afferent terminations are largely coextensive.

The vallate and foliate papillae on the posterior tongue contain taste buds innervated by the lingual–tonsillar branch of the glossopharyngeal (IXth) nerve, which also supplies taste fibers to the nasopharynx and general somatosensory fibers to the posterior third of the tongue. In rodents, over half of all the taste buds are distributed within the vallate and foliate papillae. Afferent gustatory fibers of the IXth nerve, the cell bodies of which lie in the petrosal ganglion, project into the medulla and terminate within the NST somewhat caudal to, but overlapping with, the termination of the VIIth nerve.

Taste buds distributed on the laryngeal surface of the epiglottis, on the aryepiglottal folds, and in the upper reaches of the esophagus are innervated by the internal branch of the superior laryngeal nerve (SLN), which is a branch of the vagus (Xth) nerve. This nerve also carries somatosensory innervation from the supraglottic portion of the laryngeal mucosa. Chemosensitive fibers of the SLN, whose cell bodies lie within the nodose ganglion of the vagus nerve, project into the NST caudal to those of the VIIth and IXth cranial nerves. Epiglottal taste buds are found in all mammalian species that have been studied and in the hamster are as numerous as those on the soft palate and almost as abundant as those in the fungiform papillae on the anterior tongue.

Gustatory Afferent Information Flows into Two Major Ascending Pathways

Afferent fibers of the VIIth, IXth, and Xth cranial nerves carry gustatory information to the NST—the medullary relay for the gustatory and visceral afferent systems. These fibers terminate in the rostral pole of the NST (VIIth nerve) and at intermediate (IXth nerve) and more caudal (Xth nerve) levels. There is some overlap in their terminal fields within the NST, which lie predominantly rostral to the projection of general visceral afferent fibers of the vagus. A schematic diagram of the major ascending projections within the gustatory pathway is shown in Fig. 25.3. From the NST, ascending fibers project in most species to third-order cells within the parabrachial nuclei (PbN) of the pons, more or less parallel to the projection of general visceral sensation from the caudal NST. A thalamocortical projection arises from the PbN to carry taste information to the parvicellular portion of the ventroposteromedial nucleus of the thalamus (VPMpc) and on to gustatory neocortex (GN). In primates, taste fibers bypass the pontine relay and project directly to the VPMpc, as indicated by the dashed line in Fig. 25.3. From the thalamus, taste information passes to cells in the GN, located within the agranular insular cortex.

Arising in parallel with the thalamocortical projection is a second projection that carries gustatory afferent information into the limbic forebrain areas involved in feeding and autonomic regulation, including the lateral hypothalamus, the central nucleus of the amygdala, and the bed nucleus of the stria terminalis. Descending projections within the gustatory system (not shown in Fig. 25.3) occur between the insular cortex and ventral forebrain and the PbN and NST. There are also numerous local connections among neurons within the NST and with cells of the oral, facial, and pharyngeal motor nuclei (V, VII, ambiguus, and XII), either directly (as with XII) or via interneurons in the reticular formation. These hindbrain systems form the substrate for many taste-mediated somatic and visceral responses related to ingestion and rejection of tastants.

Gustatory Afferent Neurons Extract Several Types of Sensory Information

Most neurophysiological studies of the taste system have focused on the neural representation of the gustatory qualities of salty, sour, sweet, and bitter. Single peripheral gustatory fibers and central neurons are broadly tuned across the four taste qualities and often respond to tactile and thermal stimuli as well. Taste fibers in the facial, glossopharyngeal, and vagal nerves respond differentially to taste stimuli. These diverse sensitivities, which reflect both the quality and the hedonic value of the stimuli, provide input to neural systems related to ingestive and protective responses.

The gustatory system extracts three types of information from chemical stimuli: quality, intensity, and hedonic value. The unique perception of taste **quality** is the defining feature of this sense. Most researchers agree that in the absence of olfactory cues much of gustatory experience can be described by the sweet, salty, sour, and bitter qualities. However, considerable debate continues over whether some other qualities (e.g., umami) should be included or whether any qualities are unique categories of taste perception.[7,8] **Intensity** is a dimension common to all sensory systems, reflecting the magnitude of the evoked sensation. **Hedonic value,** the perceived pleasantness or unpleasantness of a taste sensation, is a response based on genetic, physiologic, and experiential factors as well as on the characteristics of the stimulus. Taste is an inherently hedonic sense, relating strongly to motivated behavior.[9] Although these dimensions can be assessed separately, they are not independent. For example, the perceived qualities of many taste stimuli change with stimulus concentration. Moreover, the hedonic value of a stimulus is largely determined by its quality and intensity. Many omnivorous mammals share concentration-dependent preferences for substances humans describe as tasting sweet or salty and aversions to substances humans term sour or bitter. Presumably, these predispositions reflect evolutionary pressures related to the ingestional consequences (i.e., nutritional or toxic) of potential foods.

The organization of the gustatory system is determined largely by genetic and developmental factors that configure the system and produce many "hardwired" functions. However, there are also mechanisms allowing experiential and physiologic factors to influence gustatory neural processing and perception. Species-specific predispositions toward the hedonic value of a stimulus can be overcome in acquired preferences or aversions or in response to metabolic or pharmacologic manipulations. Even the perception of intensity and quality can be influenced by experience, as demonstrated by the performance of "expert tasters" and by improvements in the capacity of naive subjects to discriminate small differences during psychophysical testing. Evidence also indicates that experiential factors and physiologic state can influence the neural processing of gustatory information. Thus, gustatory afferent input provides at least three types of information that are interrelated in complex ways. How taste intensity, quality, and hedonic value are represented in the nervous system is the problem of gustatory neural coding. Neurobiological research has approached the coding of these three dimensions as separate issues, with little attention to how they interrelate. In this section, we summarize current views of coding in the gustatory system.

At the outset, we note two features of this system that have important implications for gustatory coding. First, both peripheral and central gustatory neurons in a variety of mammalian species typically respond to more than one of the stimuli representing the salty, sweet, sour, or bitter taste qualities,[10–14] often to as many as three or four. The responses of a broadly tuned neuron in the rostral NST of the hamster are shown in Fig. 25.4.[15] This neuron was excited by sodium and nonsodium salts, by acids, and by the bitter stimulus

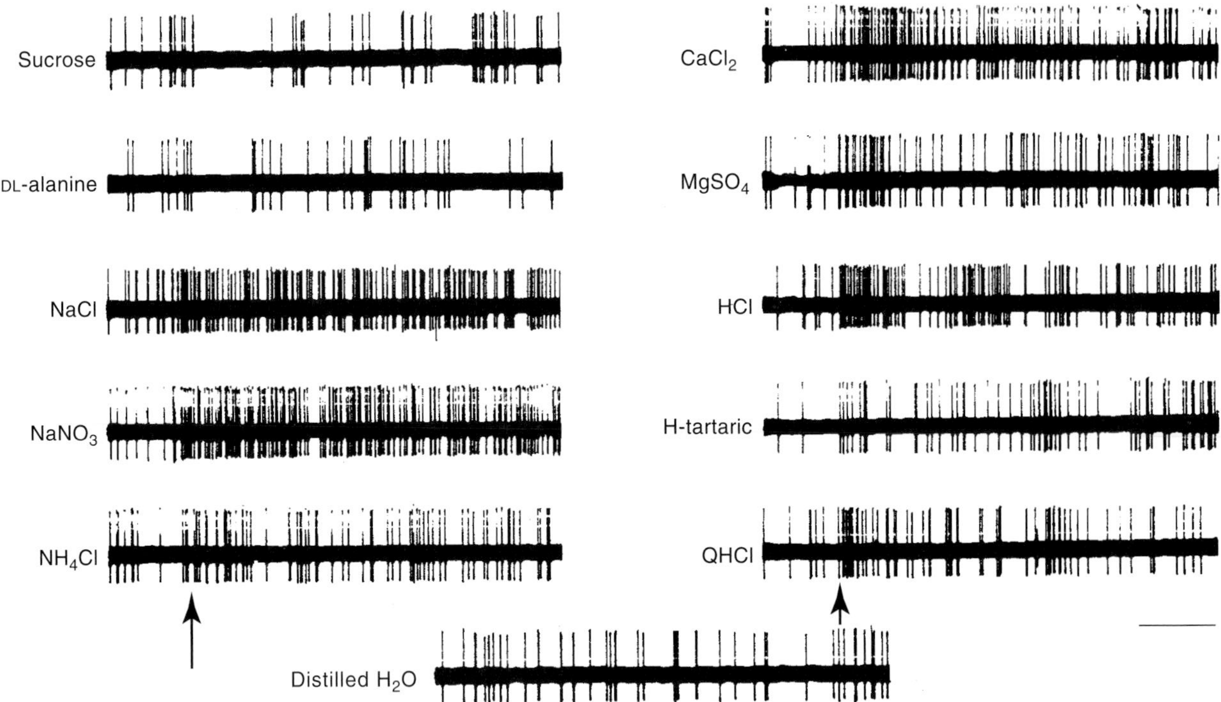

FIGURE 25.4 Responses of a neuron in the nucleus of the solitary tract of the hamster to several taste stimuli applied to the fungiform papillae. The arrows indicate the onset of the response, of which about five s are shown, preceded by about 1 s of response to distilled water. The concentrations of the stimuli are those that produce a half-maximal response to these chemicals in the hamster's chorda tympani nerve. This cell shows a positive excitatory response to all of these stimuli except sucrose and DL-alanine, which produce an inhibition of ongoing activity. From Smith *et al.*,[15] with permission from Elsevier Science Inc.

quinine hydrochloride (QHCl). It was inhibited by sucrose and DL-alanine, both of which taste sweet to humans. Because the responses of such taste neurons can be modulated by both quality and intensity, the response of any one neuron alone is entirely ambiguous with respect to either parameter. In addition, gustatory neurons are often responsive to thermal and tactile stimuli. Thus, impulse traffic in a single neuron may be related to several stimulus parameters, making the unambiguous interpretation of that signal impossible without comparing it to activity in other cells.[16,17] Therefore, in thinking about how sensory information is coded in the gustatory system, it is important to remember that cells at all levels of the pathway are broadly responsive to stimuli that vary in perceptual quality, are more broadly responsive at high than at low intensities, and are often sensitive to other modalities, such as touch and temperature.

Another important feature of the taste system is that, unlike most other sensory systems, it has no distinct topographic arrangement in its central neural organization. This lack of topography is not surprising because neither the molecules that constitute taste stimuli nor the perceptions of sweet, salty, sour, or bitter correspond to any continuous dimension of matter, space, or energy. There is some segregation of peripheral nerve terminations within the NST, and the taste bud subpopulations innervated by these nerves display somewhat different patterns of chemical sensitivity. This differential sensitivity results in some rough topographic differences in responsiveness within the NST. This segregation continues throughout the gustatory pathway to the cortex, where there are separate terminal fields for VIIth and IXth nerve inputs. This spatial separation has been proposed to be important in the neural coding of taste quality.[18] However, central taste neurons at all levels have broadly tuned response characteristics and many have receptive fields in two or more receptor populations. At present, there is little compelling evidence that taste quality is represented by a strict topographic code.

It is generally assumed, if not explicitly stated, that gustatory stimulus intensity is coded by neural impulse frequency. This assumption follows from observations that increases in stimulus concentration are associated with increases in perceived taste intensity and in neural response frequency. All neurons responsive to taste stimuli show some modulation by stimulus concentration; there is no evidence that only a specific subset of cells is responsible for coding stimulus intensity. Unlike gustatory intensity and quality, the issue of hedonic coding has not been systematically addressed in neurobiological studies of the taste system, probably because hedonic value is not independent of either quality or intensity and can be modified by both experience and physiologic state. Throughout this chapter, we relate the literature on gustatory physiology to the underlying hedonic dimension and to the appetitive and aversive responses that reflect hedonic value. This hedonic dimension is critically important in the control of many taste-mediated responses related to food ingestion and rejection.

Peripheral Taste Fibers Are Broadly Tuned across Qualities

The various subpopulations of taste buds are differentially sensitive to taste quality, resulting in differences among the gustatory nerves in the sensitivities of the afferent axons. Facial nerve fibers are relatively more responsive to preferred stimuli (sugars and salt), whereas taste axons of the glossopharyngeal nerve respond preferentially to aversive stimuli (acids and quinine). Vagal chemosensory fibers are responsive to stimuli that deviate from the normal pH and ionic milieu of the larynx, but they do not discriminate well among stimuli representing different taste qualities.

Facial Nerve Taste Fibers

Since the earliest electrophysiological studies of single taste fibers,[11,12] it has been recognized that individual fibers of the CT branch of the facial nerve are responsive to stimuli representing more than one of the four taste qualities. Nevertheless, fibers within the CT nerve can be grouped into classes based on their relative sensitivities. When the stimuli 0.1 *M* sucrose, 0.03 *M* NaCl, 3 m*M* HCl, and 1 m*M* quinine HCl are ordered hedonically from most to least preferred, the response profiles of hamster CT fibers show a single peak as sucrose-, NaCl-, or HCl-best fibers.[10] Few fibers ($<1\%$) most responsive to this concentration of QHCl are found in the CT nerve. Thus, taste fibers of the hamster CT nerve have an organization to their sensitivities; there are three neuron classes defined by their sensitivities to four basic stimuli applied to the anterior portion of the tongue: sucrose-, NaCl- and HCl-best fibers.

The appropriateness of this best-stimulus classification of CT fibers has been examined by analyzing the responses of 40 CT fibers to an array of 13 stimuli.[19] The response profiles of these 40 fibers are shown in Fig. 25.5, which allows a comparison among them. Within this figure, the fibers are arranged according to their best stimulus, with fibers 1–10 being sucrose-best, fibers 11–32 NaCl-best, and fibers 33–40 HCl-best. The green bars in Fig. 25.5 represent responses to four prototypical stimuli: sucrose (sweet), NaCl (salty), HCl (sour), and QHCl (bitter). The blue bars represent responses to other stimuli, shown along the abscissa. Although the response profiles within a best-stimulus group are not identical, inspection of Fig. 25.5 gives the impression that there are essential similarities among profiles of fibers within a group and striking differences between profiles in different groups.

The response profiles shown in Fig. 25.5 were subjected to a hierarchical cluster analysis, which addressed whether it is reasonable to assume that these profiles were sampled from distinct subpopulations rather than from a single population. In this analysis, the most similar pairs of profiles are clustered together first, followed by the clustering of pairs of profiles that are more dissimilar. The resulting dendrogram depicting the hierarchical arrangement of this clustering is shown in Fig. 25.6. At the right of the figure, the fiber numbers are indicated as they are specified in Fig. 25.5. The analysis segregated the CT fiber profiles into three major clusters, members of which are connected by solid lines in Fig. 25.6. This conclusion is based on a regular, stepwise increase in the intercluster distance as the linking proceeds, until, in moving from three clusters to two, a dramatic increase in the intercluster distance occurs. The fiber classes defined by the cluster analysis are labeled S, H, and N in Fig. 25.6, corresponding to the sucrose-, HCl-, and NaCl-best fibers, respectively. Thus, within the hamster CT nerve, classification of fibers using four prototypical stimuli produces the same classification as a hierarchical cluster analysis based on response profiles across 13 stimuli. Similar classes emerge from hierarchical clustering of second- and third-order brainstem neurons in the hamster when as few as 3 (McPheeters *et al.*[20]) or as many as 18 (Smith *et al.*[21]) stimuli are applied to the anterior portion of the tongue. The stimulus array must, however, include at least one example of three stimulus classes: (1) sweeteners, (2) sodium salts, and (3) nonsodium salts and acids.

When this array of 13 stimuli was applied to the hamster's fungiform papillae, the responses of the CT fibers reflected the perceptual similarities and differences among the stimuli, as determined by studies of behavioral generalization among taste stimuli by hamsters. Stimuli with similar taste quality produce patterns of activity across CT fibers that are highly correlated. The across-fiber patterns for 13 stimuli (data from Fig. 25.5) are depicted in Fig. 25.7, which shows that stimuli with similar tastes produce similar patterns of activity. For example, the correlation between

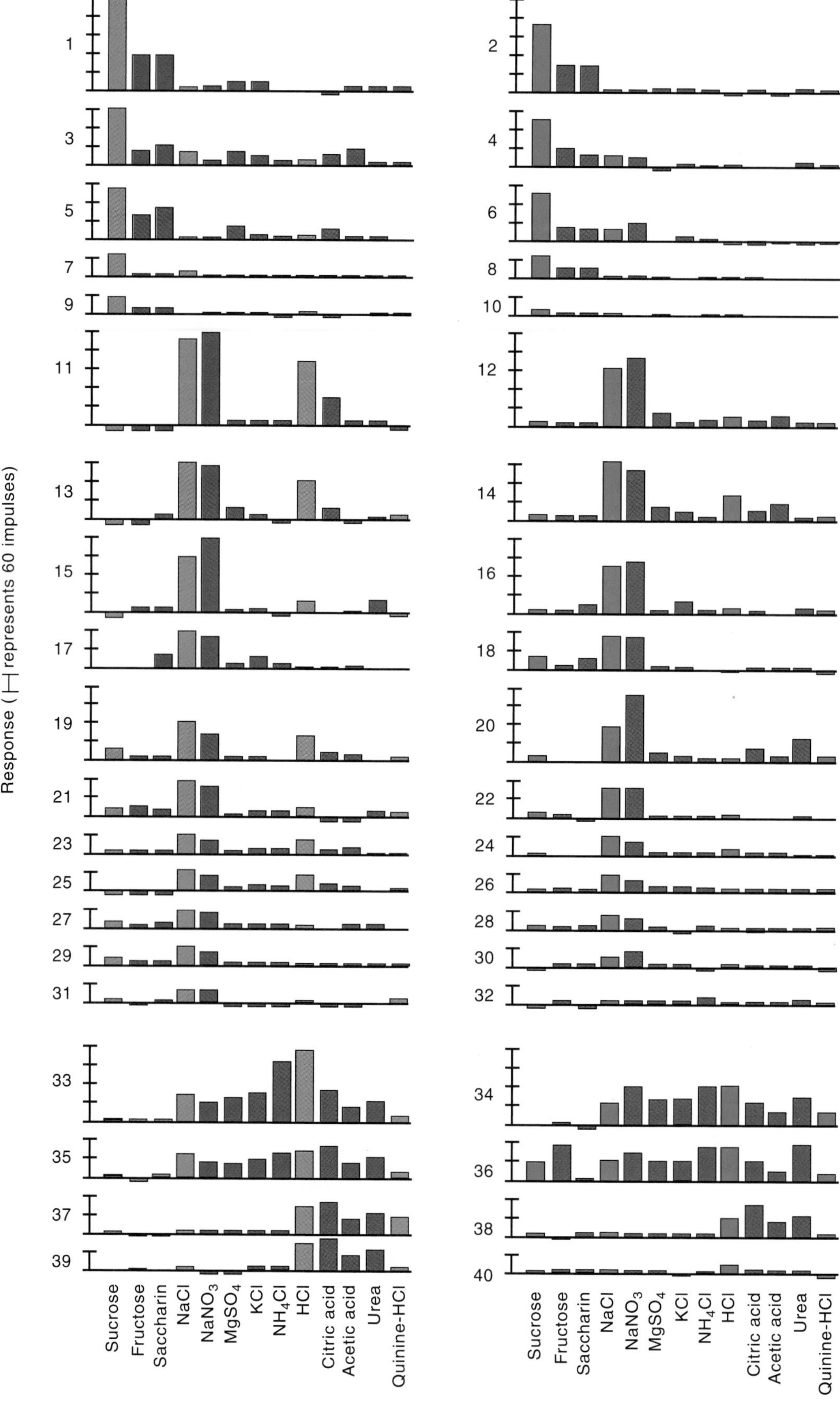
Response (⊢⊣ represents 60 impulses)
1
2
3
4
5
6
7
8
9
10
11
12
13
14
15
16
17
18
19
20
21
22
23
24
25
26
27
28
29
30
31
32
33
34
35
36
37
38
39
40
Sucrose
Fructose
Saccharin
NaCl
NaNO3
MgSO4
KCl
NH4Cl
HCl
Citric acid
Acetic acid
Urea
Quinine-HCl

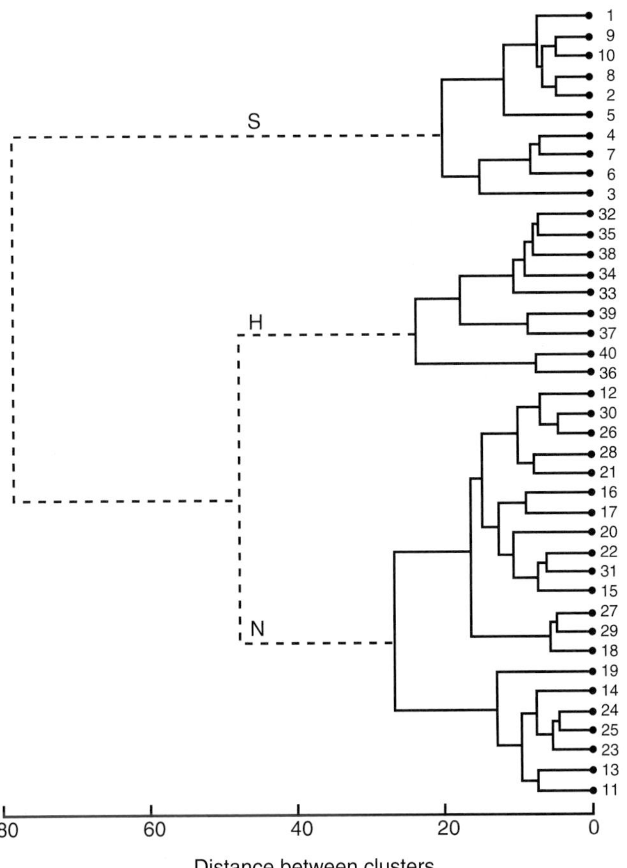

FIGURE 25.6 Cluster analysis of hamster (CT) fiber response profiles. The parallel horizontal lines of the dendrogram represent profiles, or groups of profiles, of fibers indicated at the right and numbered as in Fig. 25.5. The major profile clusters (S, H, N) are identified to the left of the defining vertical lines. The distances between profiles (or groups of profiles) are obtained by projecting the vertical lines to the distance scale along the abscissa. Modified from a figure in Frank *et al.*,[19] with permission of the Rockefeller University Press.

the patterns produced by sucrose and sodium saccharin is +0.89, between NaCl and $NaNO_3$ is +0.93, and between KCl and NH_4Cl is +0.91. Within this stimulus array, three distinctly different patterns are seen. One is elicited by sucrose, fructose, and sodium saccharin. A second pattern is elicited by NaCl and $NaNO_3$. A third, more variable pattern is evoked by the remaining stimuli, including the acids, nonsodium salts, urea, and QHCl. Within these patterns, the most responsive neurons for a particular group of stimuli tend to fall within one of the best-stimulus classes of fibers. For example, for the patterns evoked by sucrose, fructose, and sodium-saccharin, the sucrose-best fibers (fibers 1–10) are the most responsive. For the sodium salts, the NaCl-best fibers (fibers 11–32) are most responsive; however, the HCl-best fibers are often quite responsive as well. For the nonsodium salts and acids the HCl-best fibers (fibers 33–40) are most responsive, although HCl also activates NaCl-best fibers. Thus, within the activity elicited in the CT nerve, the responses of particular sets of fibers (S, N, or H fibers) typically dominate the patterns evoked by particular sets of stimuli (sweet-tasting, sodium salts, or nonsodium salts and acids).

FIGURE 25.5 Response profiles of hamster CT nerve fibers. The numbers to the left of each profile identify the fibers. The left-hand column shows profiles for odd-numbered fibers and the right-hand column shows profiles for even-numbered fibers. Fibers 1–10 are sucrose-best, fibers 11–32 are NaCl-best, and fibers 33–40 are HCl-best. Test stimuli are listed along the abscissa, beneath bars whose heights represent response rates for 5 s. Each tic mark represents 60 impulses per 5 s above the spontaneous rate. Response rates that are lower than the spontaneous rate are seen as bars extending below the horizontal zero line. The green bars represent responses to prototypical stimuli (sucrose, NaCl, HCl, and QHCl), and the blue bars represent responses to other stimuli. Reprinted from Frank *et al.*,[19] with permission of the Rockefeller University Press.

Taste buds in the nasoincisor ducts and on the soft palate are innervated by fibers of the GSP nerve. Although it has not yet been possible to analyze the responses of single gustatory fibers of the GSP, the responsiveness of the whole GSP nerve in both the rat and the hamster has been examined. In addition, responses from single neurons in the rat's NST to stimulation of the nasoincisor ducts and soft palate have been recorded. In general, the palate of both rats and hamsters is more responsive than the anterior tongue to sweet-tasting stimuli, although this difference is more striking in the rat.

Glossopharyngeal Taste Fibers

Studies of the responsiveness of the glossopharyngeal (IXth) nerve in several mammalian species show that its sensitivities to gustatory stimuli are different from those of the CT. For example, fibers of the hamster's IXth nerve are predominantly responsive to HCl and QHCl and show much less responsiveness to sucrose and NaCl over a wide range of concentrations.[22] Classification of hamster IXth nerve fibers using hierarchical cluster analysis resulted in 8 sucrose-, 4 NaCl-, 52 HCl-, and 19 QHCl-best fibers. A comparison of the mean response profiles of CT and IXth nerve fibers of the hamster is shown in Fig. 25.8, which demonstrates differences in both the numbers of fibers of different types and their relative responsiveness to the four stimuli. Fibers in the IXth nerve are mostly responsive to HCl or QHCl (Fig. 25.8A), whereas those in the CT nerve respond predominantly to sucrose or NaCl (Fig. 25.8B). In the rat, the IXth and CT nerves show a similar pattern of complementary responses to taste, with the IXth nerve containing many fibers responding best to QHC1 and sucrose, which are poor stimuli for the rat CT nerve.[23]

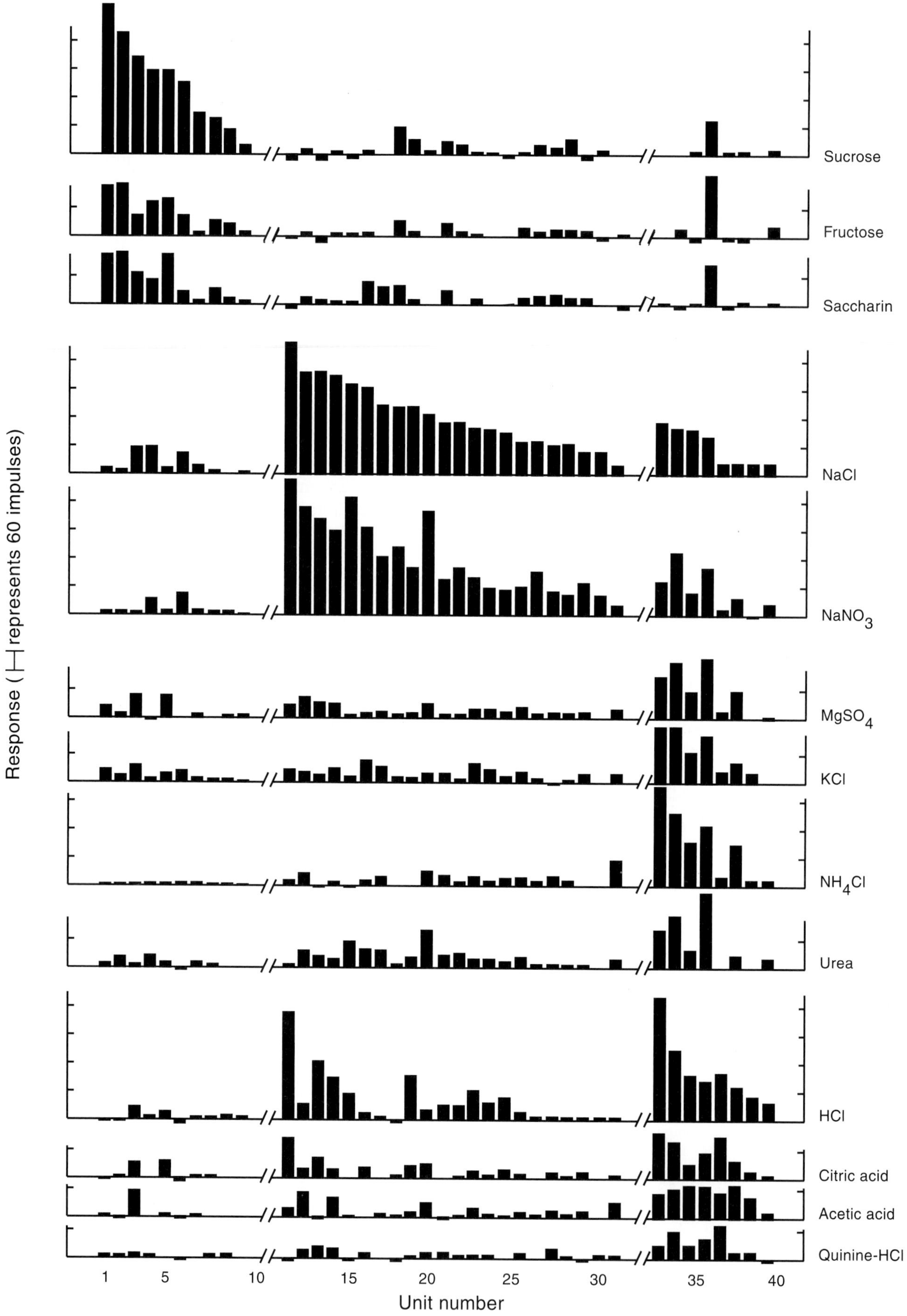

Response (├┤ represents 60 impulses)

Sucrose

Fructose

Saccharin

NaCl

$NaNO_3$

$MgSO_4$

KCl

NH_4Cl

Urea

HCl

Citric acid

Acetic acid

Quinine-HCl

1 5 10 15 20 25 30 35 40

Unit number

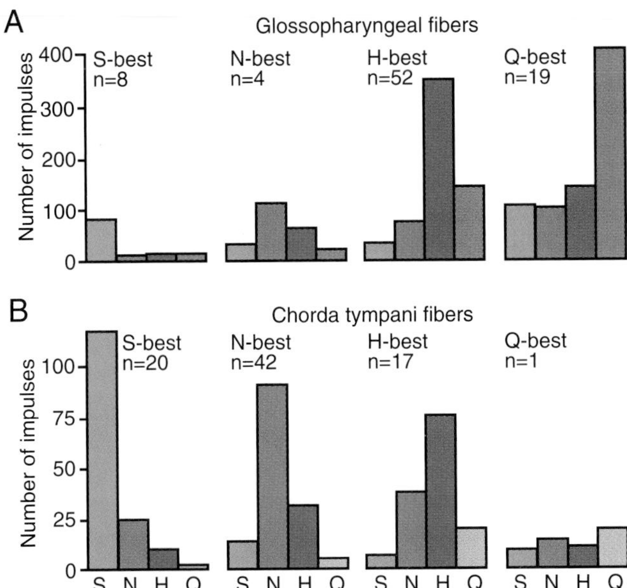

FIGURE 25.8 Mean response profiles for 83 fibers in the hamster IXth nerve (A) and 80 fibers in the hamster CT nerve (B). Number of impulses is the total number of impulses in 10 s across five concentrations in (A) and number of impulses in 5 s to a single midrange concentration in (B). S, N, H, and Q are as in Fig. 25.9. n = number of fibers. Reprinted from Hanamori *et al.*,[22] with permission.

Vagal Chemosensory Fibers

The responsiveness of afferent fibers in the SLN to chemical stimulation of the larynx has been studied in several species. Electrophysiological studies that directly compared the responsiveness of the SLN to that of other gustatory nerves have shown some striking differences in their sensitivities. In the hamster, distilled water, HCl, and high concentrations of NaCl are much more effective stimuli for SLN fibers than QHCl or sucrose.[24] These fibers respond most to distilled water and as the concentration of NaCl in water increases the response of SLN fibers decreases, reaching a minimum around the adapting concentration of 0.154 *M* NaCl. Further increases in NaCl concentration produce increasing levels of response in these fibers. Similar concentration-dependent relationships have been shown for SLN fibers in other species. Because increases in the concentration of NaCl but not of nonchloride sodium salts decrease the response to water, the response to water is thought to be mediated through the outward movement of Cl^- ions through the receptor membrane.[25] However, there are as yet no direct electrophysiological studies on transduction by laryngeal chemoreceptors to support this hypothesis.

Responses of fibers in the hamster's SLN primarily reflect the input from three receptor mechanisms: water, acid, and sodium. Classifying 65 SLN fibers according to which of five stimuli (distilled water, 1.0 *M* NaCl, 0.03 *M* HCl, 0.03 *M* QHCl, or 1.0 *M* sucrose) was the most effective stimulus resulted in 26 water-, 17 NaCl-, 20 HCl-, and 2 QHCl-best fibers.[24] Within these best-stimulus classes, fibers were not specifically tuned to their best stimulus. Water-best fibers (which also responded to hypotonic NaCl solutions) were also responsive to HCl and hypertonic NaCl. Similarly, NaCl-best fibers also responded moderately to water (and hypotonic NaCl) and to strong HCl. Fibers responding best to HCl also responded moderately to water and NaCl and somewhat to strong QHCl. These best-stimulus classes of cells were not as distinct from one another as those in the hamster CT or IXth nerve. The results of a hierarchical cluster analysis of the response profiles of these 65 SLN fibers indicated that there are not distinct clusters of chemosensitive fibers in the SLN. Rather, they appear to represent a continuum of response profiles, each somewhat different from the others.

FIGURE 25.7 Across-fiber patterns for hamster CT fibers (replot of data of Fig. 25.5). The response rates elicited for 5 s in CT fibers 1–40 are represented by consecutive filled bars from left to right. Each row depicts the pattern elicited by the stimuli listed at the right. The horizontal lines are broken twice with two short parallel diagonals at the transitions between sucrose-best and NaCl-best (between fibers 10 and 11) and NaCl-best and HCl-best (between fibers 32 and 33) fibers. Fiber numbers are indicated along the abscissa. Each tic mark represents 60 nerve impulses in a 5-s period. The bars extending below the zero line indicate response rates lower than the spontaneous rate. Reprinted from Frank *et al.*,[19] with permission of the Rockefeller University Press.

Gustatory Inputs to the Brainstem Are Differently Distributed across Several Afferent Nerves

The various populations of taste buds differ in their sensitivities and contribute different kinds of afferent information to the brainstem. Although there are species differences in the distributions of some of these sensitivities, the general conclusion is that the various taste bud populations provide different kinds and amounts of gustatory information. It is likely that these variable inputs are important for different kinds of taste-mediated behavior.

Receptors on the anterior tongue (CT) and palate (GSP) provide relatively more information about NaCl and sucrose than receptors on the posterior tongue (IXth) or in the larynx (SLN). Sensitivity to HCl is relatively similar in every gustatory nerve; QHCl clearly has its greatest relative effect in the IXth nerve. Only the SLN of the hamster responds to water. A summary of the responsiveness of hamster CT, IXth,

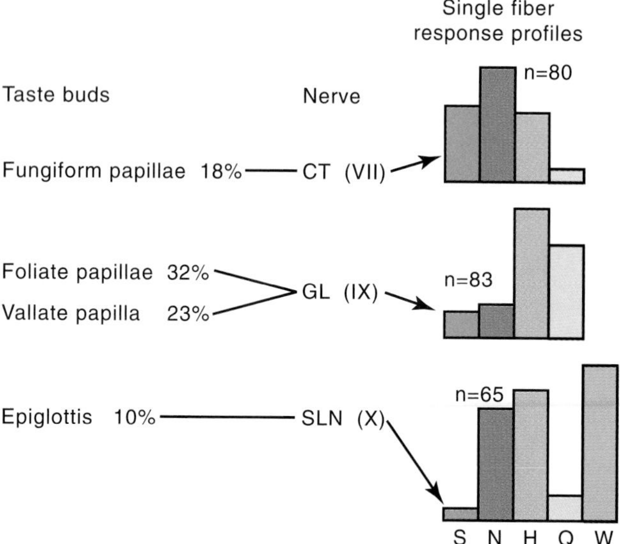

FIGURE 25.9 Profiles of mean response of single fibers in the hamster chorda tympani (CT), glossopharyngeal (GL), and superior laryngeal (SLN) nerves to four representative taste stimuli and distilled water applied to the fungiform, foliate, vallate, or epiglottal taste buds. Stimuli: S, sucrose; N, sodium chloride; H, hydrochloric acid; Q, quinine hydrochloride; W, distilled water. Data are from studies on the CT nerve,[19] the IXth nerve,[22] and the SLN.[24]

and SLN taste fibers is shown in Fig. 25.9, which depicts the mean response profiles of fibers in these nerves. The GSP nerve, which is not shown because no single-fiber data are available, is relatively more responsive to sucrose than the CT nerve. The differential information arising from these various gustatory nerves projects into the nucleus of the solitary tract of the medulla, where appropriate connections provide for the reflexive control of ingestive and protective responses that are triggered by taste stimulation.

Behavioral studies have begun to define taste quality for a number of mammalian species, including rats and hamsters.[15,26,27] These rodents easily discriminate among sucrose, NaCl, HCl, and QHCl. They group the tastes of other sugars and sodium saccharin with sucrose, other acids and some nonsodium salts like NH_4Cl with HCl, other sodium salts with NaCl, and some bitter-tasting salts like $MgSO_4$ with QHCl. Input from the fungiform papillae of the hamster is sufficient to allow neural and behavioral discrimination among sugars, sodium salts, and acids. In the rat, discrimination of sugars from other stimuli may depend primarily on input from the GSP nerve. However, neural activity in the CT nerve does not discriminate well between QHCl and the nonsodium salts and acids; this discrimination is much more dramatic in fibers of the IXth nerve. On the other hand, discrimination between NaCl and KCl appears to require the CT nerve; this discrimination is disrupted in rats by bilateral CT section.[28] Thus, the behavioral distinctions among stimuli with different taste qualities may rely somewhat on input from different cranial nerves. Fibers of the SLN innervating laryngeal chemoreceptors, however, do not appear to discriminate among stimuli with different taste qualities. Chemosensitive fibers of the SLN appear to be suited to a role in airway protection, by signaling deviations from the normal pH and ionic milieu of the larynx, rather than in the discrimination among gustatory qualities.

The Mechanisms of Taste Quality Coding Are Controversial

There has been considerable controversy over whether taste quality is represented in the nervous system by activity in specific neural channels (labeled lines) or by the relative activity across the population of responsive neurons (across-fiber patterns). The multiple sensitivity of taste-sensitive neurons makes a strict labeled-line hypothesis difficult to accept, although there is compelling evidence for taste neuron types based on similarities in their profiles of sensitivity. A consideration of the relationships between neuron types and across-fiber patterns suggests that taste quality coding can best be accounted for by the relative activity across neuron types.

The nature of the neural representation of taste quality has been vigorously debated for many years.[15,19,21,29–34] Even the existence of four basic taste qualities is not universally accepted, with some authors insisting on additional qualities and others arguing that taste experience is a continuum upon which the familiar qualities are merely arbitrary points.

Prior to the development of neurophysiological recording methods, a long tradition of human psychophysical research had provided considerable support for the notion that taste experience could be reduced to a few basic qualities, although not necessarily the traditional four. This idea, combined with Meuller's doctrine of specific nerve energies, led to the expectation that the perception of taste quality would arise from the activation of one of a few neuron types, each coding a single taste quality. This strict "labeled-line" theory was discounted by early neurophysiological recordings showing that peripheral taste fibers in several species are responsive to stimuli representing more than one taste quality.[11,12] As a result, an "across-fiber pattern" theory suggesting that taste quality is coded by the relative activity across a population of neurons was proposed.[30,35] This theory accommodates the multiple sensitivity of taste fibers and requires neither specific fiber types nor taste primaries. However, the per-

BOX 25.2

THE EARLIEST RECORDINGS OF SINGLE PERIPHERAL TASTE FIBERS REVEALED MULTIPLE SENSITIVITIES

The earliest electrophysiological recordings of afferent taste fiber activity were made by Carl Pfaffmann, who recorded the activity of single chorda tympani (CT) nerve fibers in the rat[11,12] and also in the cat and rabbit.[12] At that time, he was expecting to find individual nerve fibers that responded specifically to stimuli representing each of the basic human taste qualities of salty, sweet, sour, and bitter. To his surprise, most single fibers in the CT neve responded to stimuli representing more than one taste quality, often as many as three or four. This led Pfaffmann to propose that taste quality must be represented by the relative amounts of activity across a number of afferent fibers,[30] an idea that came to be known as the "across-fiber pattern theory" of taste quality coding. This notion accounted well for the multiple sensitivity of taste afferent neurons at all levels of the gustatory system. Although there has been considerable ensuing controversy over the nature of taste quality coding, the basic idea of a pattern code is still the most viable explanation for the neural representation of taste quality.

sisting view of the importance of taste primaries later led to a modification of the labeled-line theory proposing that taste quality is coded by the activity in a few "best-stimulus" channels—that is, by neurons that respond best, but not specifically, to one of the basic taste qualities.[31,32]

Although each coding theory has its strengths, both struggle to encompass the full range of data. For example, accumulating evidence suggests that there are functional classes of neurons that correspond in some way to primary taste qualities.[33] On the other hand, recent analyses show that no single class of neurons in isolation can discriminate well between different taste qualities.[33,34] The neural coding problem essentially rests on whether the activity in a given taste fiber is an unambiguous representation of the quality of the stimulus applied to its receptors or whether this activity is meaningful only in the context of activity in other afferent fibers. In this section we review the relevant neurophysiological data that bear on this issue and suggest that taste quality is coded in the relative rates of activity across several neuron types.

Across-Fiber Patterns and Taste Quality

Multiple sensitivity of fibers in the CT nerve (reviewed in Box 25.2) first led Pfaffmann[11,12,30] to propose that taste quality is coded by the pattern of activity across taste fibers. With this coding hypothesis, taste quality remains invariant with increased intensity even though any single neuron may increase its breadth of responsiveness. The pattern of activity generated across the entire array of taste neurons at a higher concentration is similar in shape, but varies in amplitude.[36] The across-fiber patterns to an array of 13 stimuli are shown in Fig. 25.7 for 40 hamster CT fibers. Stimuli with similar tastes, such as the three sweeteners or the two sodium salts, generate highly similar patterns of activity across these fibers. These similarities are typically measured by calculating the across-fiber correlation between pairs of stimuli,[35] although other indices have been proposed. Several behavioral investigations have shown that experimental animals judge stimuli that evoke highly correlated neural patterns to have similar tastes. This across-fiber pattern view of quality coding makes the multiple sensitivity of gustatory neurons an essential part of the neural code for taste quality; it stresses that the code for quality is given in the response of the entire population of cells, placing little or no emphasis on the role of an individual neuron. Erickson[17,29,37,38] has argued that such a coding mechanism could operate for many sensory systems, particularly for nontopographic modalities employing neurons that are broadly tuned across their stimulus array.

When the across-neuron correlations are calculated for an array of gustatory stimuli across either peripheral or central neurons, stimuli with similar tastes correlate highly and those with different tastes correlate less. Almost every neurophysiological study that has taken this approach to analyzing the responses of gustatory cells has shown that the across-neuron patterns reflect the qualitative similarities among taste stimuli. Often the across-neuron correlations serve as input to a multivariate statistical procedure to generate a "taste space" that represents the neural similarities and differences among the stimuli. A taste space for 18 stimuli is shown in Fig. 25.10; this three-dimensional space was derived from the responses of 31 neurons in the

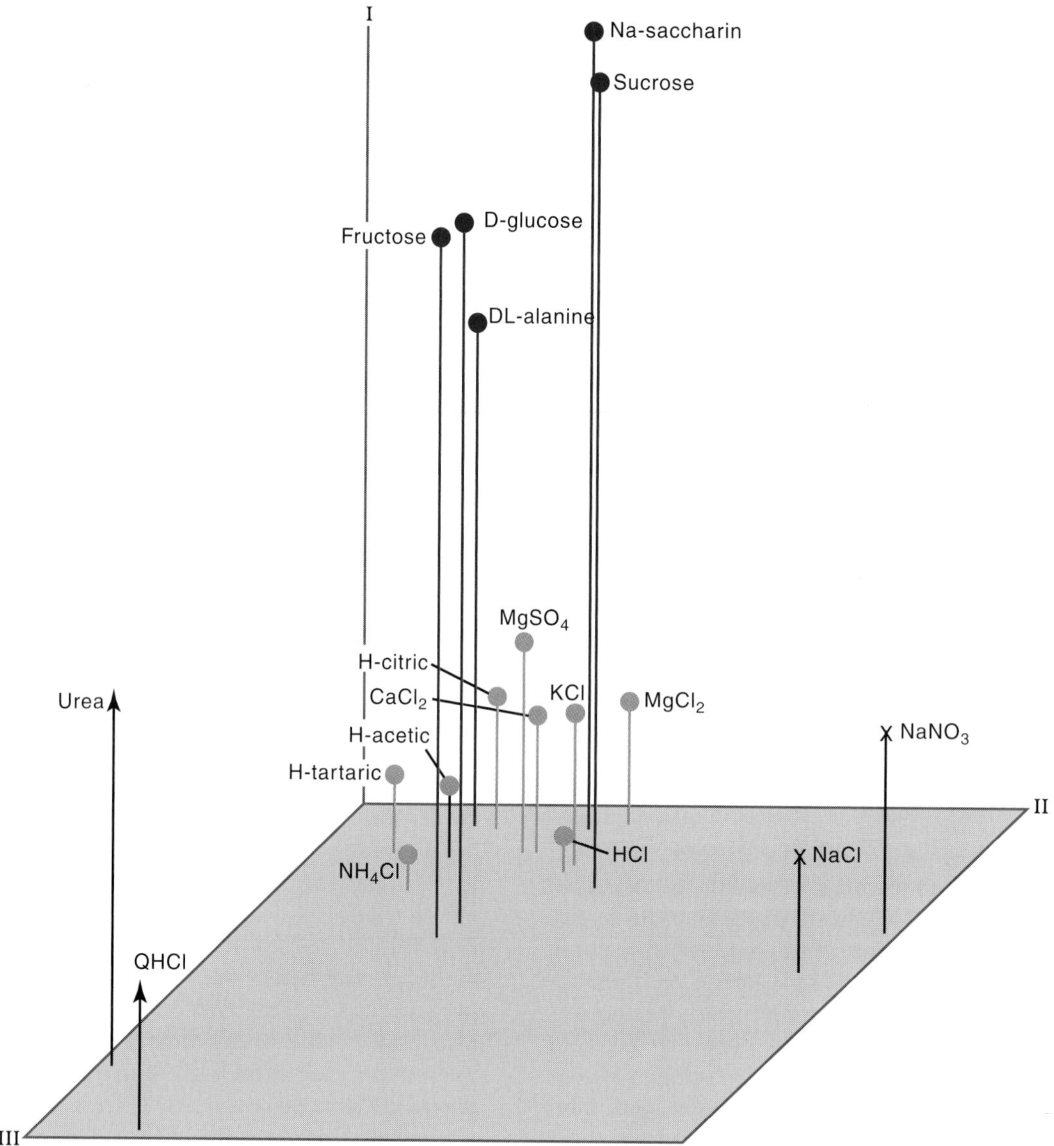

FIGURE 25.10 Three-dimensional "taste space" showing the similarities and differences among 18 stimuli delivered to the anterior tongue of the hamster. This space was derived from multidimensional scaling (KYST, Bell Laboratories) of the across-neuron correlations among these stimuli recorded from neurons in the parabrachial nuclei of the hamster. Four groups of stimuli are indicated by different symbols. Modified from Smith *et al.*,[34] with permission.

hamster PbN and was generated using multidimensional scaling (KYST). Within this space, the sweet-tasting stimuli (blue circles), the sodium salts (×s), the nonsodium salts and acids (red circles), and the two bitter-tasting stimuli (triangles) are clearly separated. This arrangement of stimuli based on similarities among their across-neuron patterns suggests that the information within these patterns is sufficient to discriminate among these four groups of stimuli, even though any one cell in the hamster PbN is very likely to respond to stimuli of more than one group.

Labeled Lines

Although mammalian taste neurons are broadly tuned, many investigators have attempted to group them into functionally meaningful categories. The discussion about the organization of sensitivities in the hamster's CT and IXth nerves shows that these taste fibers can be grouped into classes according to their best stimulus. Indeed, a hierarchical cluster analysis of the similarities and differences in the shapes of their response profiles across a broad array of stimuli results in distinct groups of CT fibers (Fig. 25.6) that correspond to these best-stimulus groups. The implication of distinct fiber types in the coding of taste quality began with Frank's[10] categorization of hamster CT fibers into best-stimulus groups. This categorization became the focus of an ensuing controversy over the neural representation of taste quality when Pfaffmann proposed that these fiber types code taste quality in a labeled-line fashion.[31,32] This hypothesis suggests that "sweetness" is coded by activity in sucrose-best neurons, "saltiness" by activity in NaCl-best neurons, etc. Thus, in contrast to a "population" approach to taste coding (across-neuron patterns), this labeled-line position advocates a "feature extraction" approach, in which particular neurons (or groups of neurons) play specific roles in the representation of taste quality.

Gustatory Neuron Types: Is Taste Quality Coded by Labeled Lines?

The labeled-line hypothesis requires the existence of neuron types for the coding of taste quality, whereas the across-neuron pattern theory does not. The number of labeled lines would equal the number of discrete taste qualities, which would each be signaled by activity in separate afferent channels. Consequently, the existence of gustatory neuron types has been sharply contested, on the assumption that their existence somehow implicates them as labeled lines. However, the mere existence of fiber types (defined by their best stimulus, similarities in their profiles, or other criteria) does not necessarily imply that these classes of cells comprise labeled lines. A classic example where receptor types are evident but where there is general agreement about the existence of a pattern code is in vertebrate color vision, as discussed later in this chapter.

The Controversy over the Existence of Gustatory Fiber Types

Following the introduction of the best-stimulus classification of CT fibers, Woolston and Erickson[39] correctly noted that the subdivision of neurons into groups based on their response to one or a few stimuli could be an arbitrary division of a continuous population of cells. Further, the experimenter's choice of stimuli and their concentrations could greatly influence the resulting classification. These considerations are particularly applicable to a sensory system such as taste, in which no stimulus continuum has been identified. Because of such considerations, these investigators argued for an approach to the classification of gustatory neurons based on traditional taxonomic procedures.[40,41] Using this approach, Erickson and his colleagues examined the classification of neurons in the rat CT nerve[42] and NST[39] using hierarchical cluster analysis. The solutions obtained in each case provided no support for distinct neuron types, suggesting that the subdivision of these cells into best-stimulus categories might be an arbitrary exercise. However, the anterior tongue of the rat primarily possesses only two sets of sensitivities: those to sodium salts and those to acids and other electrolytes, which overlap considerably in NaCl- and HCl-best fibers.[43]

As seen above, fiber types are readily distinguishable within the CT and IXth nerves of the hamster, based on the relative similarities and differences among their response profiles. Although the recognition of neuron types depends on the strictness of one's criteria when examining a cluster dendrogram, the dendrograms for the hamster CT (e.g., Fig. 25.6) and IXth nerves[22] strongly suggest fiber types. These hierarchical arrangements are strikingly different from those for SLN fibers,[24] which suggest a continuous distribution of fiber profiles. At all levels of the hamster gustatory system that have been examined, except in the SLN, there is strong evidence that taste sensitivities are organized into relatively distinct sets of fibers and neurons. Of course, the real issue with respect to sensory coding is what role these fiber types play in the neural code for taste quality.

Gustatory Neuron Types and Across-Neuron Patterns

Smith and colleagues examined the roles played by neuron types in the hamster brainstem in the definitions of the across-neuron patterns.[21,34,44] These investigators concluded that the discrimination among stimuli with different tastes (such as sodium and nonsodium salts) depends on comparisons of the activity in different neuron types (such as NaCl- and HCl-best cells) and that one neuron type alone was insufficient to discriminate between stimuli with different taste qualities. This coding mechanism is similar to the coding of stimulus wavelength by the vertebrate visual system, where three types of broadly sensitive photoreceptor pigments are involved.[45] The color of the wavelength of light falling on the retina can be accurately encoded by considering the relative activity in these three photoreceptors, that is, by a pattern.[37,46,47] Deficiencies in one or more of the photoreceptor pigments result in various forms of visual chromatic deficiency or "color blindness." Data on color-blind individuals show that the absence of any one of the three photoreceptor types results in the inability to discriminate among particular sets of wavelengths (see Smith[44] and Smith and Frank[33] for additional analysis and discussion of this point).

The experiments of Scott and colleagues[48] on the rat NST reveal a gustatory analog to visual color blindness. After blocking the "sodium receptor" (i.e., the NaCl-best neurons) with amiloride, these investigators demonstrated that cells in the NST could not discriminate between sodium and nonsodium salts; that is, the across-neuron patterns evoked by these stimuli were not distinct. However, as previously shown the across-neuron patterns for sodium salts can be distinguished from those for nonsodium salts and acids only if the activities of both NaCl-best and HCl-best cells are considered.[34,44] Without input from NaCl-best neurons (or the HCl-best neurons) there is a lack of separation within the multidimensional taste space between the sodium and the nonsodium salts and acids exactly like that reported after NaCl-best NST cells are blocked with amiloride. All three neuron types (S, N, H) are necessary for the gustatory system to sort out three groups of stimuli (sweeteners, sodium salts, and nonsodium salts and acids) based on their across-neuron patterns. These results imply that taste quality discrimination depends on a comparison of activity across broadly tuned neuron types, comparable to the coding of color vision by broadly tuned photoreceptors.

Taste Information Plays a Role in Ingestive Behavior

The relationship of taste quality to gustatory hedonics reflects the role of taste in the control of ingestive behavior. Sucrose and other sweet-tasting (hedonically positive) stimuli drive neurons that ultimately connect to cells controlling the ingestion of nutritive substances. Quinine and other aversive (hedonically negative) stimuli feed into neural systems controlling protective reflexes that prevent the ingestion of toxic substances. Both inhibitory modulation and excitatory modulation of the taste-responsive cells in the NST take place, providing mechanisms through which several parameters can influence taste sensitivity and taste-mediated behavior.

Taste physiologists have focused largely on the role of gustatory neurons in taste quality perception, but a number of taste-mediated somatic and visceral responses, ranging from tongue movements to salivation to preabsorptive insulin release, have their neuronal substrate within the brainstem. The differential sensitivities of the VIIth, IXth, and Xth nerves, the organization of their projections into the brainstem, the sensitivities of NST neurons, and the contribution of gustatory afferent input to taste-mediated behaviors are summarized in Fig. 25.11.

Taste may be considered the oral component of the visceral afferent system, which includes gustatory, respiratory, cardiovascular, and gastrointestinal functions. Taste buds innervated by the VIIth, IXth, and Xth nerves contribute differentially to this visceral continuum, with VIIth nerve fibers responsive primarily to hedonically positive stimuli such as sucrose and NaCl, IXth nerve fibers most sensitive to aversive stimuli such as HCl and QHCl, and Xth nerve fibers responsive to stimuli that deviate from the normal pH and ionic milieu of the larynx. For example, VIIth nerve fibers activated by sucrose project into the NST, where sucrose-best cells also respond to NaCl and to HCl, but are often inhibited by QHCl. Ultimately, the output of these second-order neurons ascends to the forebrain to give rise to the perception of sweetness (Fig. 25.11). Simultaneously, these cells provide input to somatic and visceral motor systems that drive the ingestive components of feeding behavior, including mouth and tongue movements, salivation, insulin release, and swallowing. Conversely, QHCl stimulates predominantly fibers of the IXth nerve. These fibers project into the NST, where they drive cells that are also responsive to HCl and NaCl but not to sucrose. Quinine-sensitive cells of the NST send ascending projections to the forebrain to give rise to sensations of bitterness (Fig. 25.11), but they also provide input to motor systems that drive behaviors associated with rejection. The superior laryngeal branch of the Xth nerve is involved in swallowing, airway protection, and a number of other visceral reflexes. Respiratory apnea is produced by laryngeal stimulation with water,[49] and chemosensory fibers of the rat SLN mediate diuresis in response to stimulation of the laryngeal mucosa with water.[50] In addition to its obvious role in regulating ingestive behavior, taste triggers a number of metabolic responses, including salivary, gastric, and pancreatic secretions, although the specific contributions of particular cranial nerves to these responses are not well understood. Thus, in addition to their mediation of gustatory sensation, taste buds may have a number of roles related to gustatory–visceral regulation, depending on their peripheral distribution and innervation.

Measures of Taste Reactivity Reflect the Hedonic Aspects of Taste

In addition to evoking the perception of taste quality, gustatory stimuli trigger several reflexive response sequences that are related to the ingestion and rejection of food substances. These behavioral sequences range from ingestive and protective somatic motor responses to visceral motor activity associted with gastrointesti-

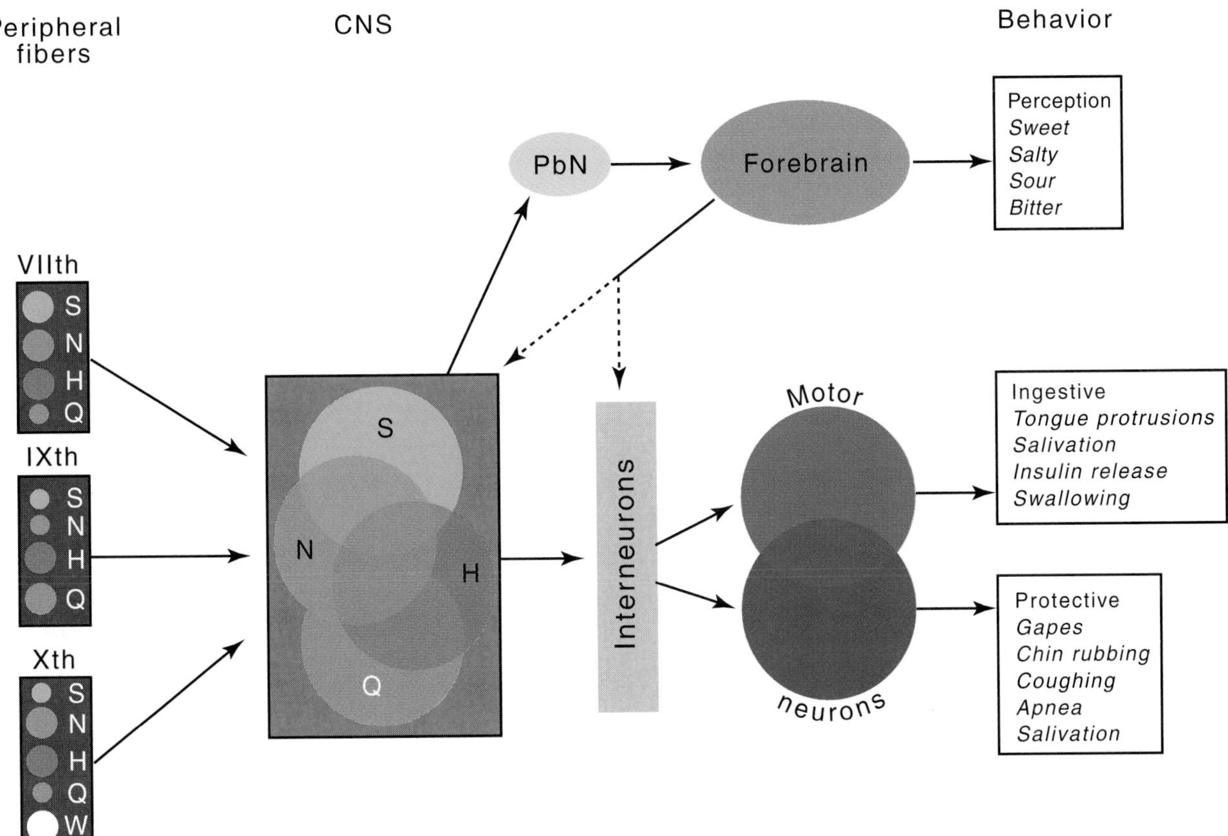

FIGURE 25.11 Schematic diagram of the chemosensory inputs of three cranial nerves to the taste-responsive portion of the nucleus of the solitary tract (NST) and their putative role in taste-mediated behaviors. The size of the filled circles for each of the peripheral nerves (VIIth, IXth, and Xth) depicts the relative responsiveness of these nerves to sucrose (S), NaCl (N), HCl (H), QHCl (Q), and water (W). Sensitivities of NST cells are largely overlapping, with each cell type somewhat responsive to two or three of the basic stimuli.[13] Sucrose and QHCl stimulate few of the same NST cells, however. Output from the NST ascends in the classic taste pathway to give rise to perceptions of sweetness, saltiness, sourness, and bitterness and to hedonic tone (not depicted). Local reflex circuits within the brainstem control ingestive and protective responses evoked by taste stimulation. Behavioral data suggest that both ingestive and protective responses can be triggered in parallel, depending on the quality of the stimulus.[52,53] Reprinted with permission from Smith and Frank.[33] Copyright CRC Press, Boca Raton, Florida.

nal function. A number of overt motor responses to taste stimulation can be quantified and measured; these responses have been termed "taste reactivity" and are useful indexes of the hedonic value of a gustatory stimulus.[51]

Taste reactivity in the rat consists of sequences of ingestive or protective behaviors that reflect the palatability (i.e., hedonic value) of a gustatory stimulus. Ingestive responses begin with rhythmic mouth movements, followed by midline tongue protrusions, lateral tongue protrusions, and swallowing; this sequence is triggered by sucrose and other hedonically positive (appetitive) stimuli. Protective responses include oral gapes and a number of somatic motor sequences such as head shaking, chin rubbing, forelimb flailing, paw pushing, face washing, and increased locomotion, all elicited by quinine and other hedonically negative (aversive) stimuli. Results from taste reactivity tests typically correspond with other short-term palatability measures such as lick-rate tests. In the rat, sucrose and quinine produce opposite patterns of ingestive and protective taste reactivity, and a combination of these behaviors can be triggered by mixtures of sucrose and quinine.[52] Similarly, in the hamster the patterns of taste reactivity to sucrose and quinine are quite different, whereas sodium salts and acids produce patterns consisting of combinations of both ingestive and protective behaviors.[53] The taste quality of the stimulus is directly related to the specific pattern of taste reactivity.

Decerebrate rats are able to exhibit normal patterns of taste reactivity to stimuli infused into their mouths.[54] Both ingestive and aversive oral and somatic motor responses are elicited by gustatory stimulation in these animals, suggesting that the neural substrate important for discriminating among taste stimuli is intact within the hindbrain. Similarly, anencephalic human neonates produce normal facial expressions in response to gustatory stimulation. Thus, information arising from the peripheral gustatory apparatus projects into the brainstem and makes connections at that level to produce the appropriate response sequences. Data presented above show that VIIth and IXth nerve fibers are differentially sensitive, particularly to sweet and bitter stimuli. This differential sensitivity is compatible with the idea that afferent input from the VIIth nerve is more important for ingestive behavior and that from the IXth nerve is more important for rejection.[55] However, transecting either the CT or the IXth nerve produces only partial effects on ingestive or aversive responses. Nevertheless, to produce ingestive responses, peripheral fibers carrying information about sweet stimuli, which are numerous in the CT and GSP nerves, must ultimately provide input to a specific set of motor neurons that control tongue protrusions, lateral tongue movements, and swallowing (see Fig. 25.11). Similarly, the oral and somatic motor outputs characteristic of the responses to quinine must arise from motor neurons that receive input arriving at the NST from peripheral taste fibers carrying information about bitter stimuli, which are most numerous in the IXth nerve (Fig. 25.11). Second-order gustatory cells in the NST project indirectly, through interneurons in the reticular formation, to brainstem motor nuclei that control oromotor responses.

One can view ingestive and protective motor sequences as parallel processes that can be driven one at a time, as by sucrose or quinine, or simultaneously, as by sucrose–quinine mixtures. Since most peripheral gustatory fibers and brainstem neurons have multiple sensitivities to different taste qualities, many of the cells contributing to each of these output systems may respond to several stimuli; thus, a stimulus like NaCl or HCl might evoke output in both systems. These multiple sensitivities, however, do not extend to sucrose and quinine, which do not stimulate the same cells and which are often mutually inhibitory in brainstem cells. Thus, sweet and bitter stimuli produce relatively specific afferent input and are characterized by specific and opposite patterns of motor output. These motor patterns can be generated by other stimuli to varying degrees and can be modified in the intact animal by conditioning, presumably via descending influences from the forebrain.

Taste Activity Is Modulated in the Medulla by Several Neurotransmitters

Both *in vitro*[56] and *in vivo*[57] experiments have provided good evidence that a major excitatory neurotransmitter between peripheral fibers and gustatory cells in the NST is glutamate, acting on both *N*-methyl-D-aspartate (NMDA) and non-NMDA receptors. In this respect, the gustatory NST is very similar to the visceral portion of the NST, which processes information from vagal afferent fibers. In addition, substance P exerts an excitatory influence on taste-responsive cells of the NST,[58,59] which are also tonically suppressed by the inhibitory neurotransmitter γ-aminobutyric acid (GABA).[59a,60] Several metabolic and environmental factors can modulate taste activity in the NST; these transmitter systems form part of a neural substrate for such modulation.

Responses of brainstem cells to gustatory stimulation are subject to several modulatory influences. For example, glucose, insulin, and pancreatic glucagon systemically administered alter the responses of cells in the rat NST to tongue stimulation with glucose.[61] The mechanisms underlying these inhibitory effects are unknown; they could involve a direct effect of the increased availability of glucose on the recorded cells or an inhibitory synaptic influence descending from the forebrain. That descending pathways can exert a modulatory influence over brainstem taste cells has been shown by electrophysiological studies on decerebrate rats. In addition, reversible blockade of the GN with procaine shows that PbN cells are both facilitated and inhibited by descending corticofugal inputs.[62] Electrical stimulation of GN produces both excitatory (via direct synaptic input) and inhibitory influences on PbN cells. There are direct descending projections from insular cortex to both parabrachial nuclei[63,64] and NST.[65] Ipsilateral GN stimulation both excites and inhibits the activity of cells of the rostral NST; these inhibitory responses can be blocked by the $GABA_A$ receptor antagonist bicuculline.[66]

Inhibitory Interactions in the Brainstem

Recent studies have begun to reveal mechanisms of inhibition within the gustatory region of the NST. The inhibitory neurotransmitter GABA has been shown to play a role in the processing of respiratory, cardiovascular, and other information in the visceral portion of the NST. Many small ovoid interneurons within the gustatory NST express GABA or its degradative enzymes. Similar GABAergic cells are also distributed within caudal regions of the NST. Electrophysiological recordings from cells in the rostral NST in *in vitro* slices from both rats[59a] and hamsters[60] have shown that GABA produces inhibition of activity in these cells, which is mediated predominantly by the $GABA_A$ receptor subtype. These studies suggest that the gustatory portion of the NST is under the influence of a tonic GABAergic inhibitory network. However, *in vitro* studies alone do not confirm the functional significance of such a system, or even that GABA influences taste (as opposed to somatosensory or visceral) responses. The inhibitory action of GABA on taste-elicited responses of cells in the NST (and its reversal by bicuculline) has been demonstrated by extracellular recording *in vivo* combined with local micropressure injection of these agents into the nucleus.[67] These latter data and those recorded *in vitro* strongly implicate GABAergic inhibitory mechanisms in the processing of gustatory information through the NST.

Glutamate—A Major Excitatory Neurotransmitter in the Nucleus of the Solitary Tract

The responses of cells in the gustatory zone of the NST can be blocked by glutamate antagonists. Excitatory postsynaptic potentials (EPSPs) recorded from rat NST cells *in vitro* in response to electrical stimulation of the solitary tract are reduced by both CNQX and APV, antagonists to the AMPA–kainate and NMDA glutamate receptors, respectively.[56] Although it is not possible to establish a cell recorded *in vitro* as definitively taste-responsive, because many cells within the NST are also responsive to touch and temperature, these data are supported by *in vivo* experiments. Both of these agents reversibly block or reduce the responses to chemical stimulation of the anterior tongue in hamster NST cells recorded *in vivo*.[57] All cells responsive to taste stimulation are blocked by CNQX, regardless of their profiles of sensitivity; there is no evidence that the neurotransmitter is different for cells of different types (i.e., sucrose- vs NaCl-best). Therefore, it is very likely that glutamate acts as a neurotransmitter between gustatory afferent fibers and taste-responsive cells in the NST.

Evidence also indicates that taste-responsive cells in the NST are excited by substance P (SP). Immunocytochemical studies have shown that SP-containing neurons are present within the gustatory zone of the NST and that SP-containing fibers enter this nucleus from a number of yet unknown sources. *In vitro* experiments on rat brainstem slices have shown that bath application of SP excites a number of cells in the gustatory zone of the NST.[59] The role of these SP-responsive NST cells in gustatory processing has been demonstrated in the hamster NST *in vivo*,[58] where responses to anterior tongue stimulation with NaCl or sucrose are enhanced by local microinjection of SP.

Summary

Taste receptors respond to a variety of chemical compounds to give rise to a limited number of sensations (saltiness, sweetness, sourness, and bitterness). The transduction mechanisms for taste stimuli are located on receptor cells within taste buds distributed in several subpopulations, innervated by one of four different peripheral nerves. These nerves project into the nucleus of the solitary tract in the medulla, and they contain different distributions of gustatory neuron types. From there, projections arise to the parabrachial nuclei in the pons and then to the thalamus and gustatory neocortex. A parallel pathway carries taste information into the ventral forebrain to areas involved in autonomic regulation. Facial nerve fibers respond predominantly to sweet-tasting stimuli and sodium salts, whereas those of the glossopharyngeal nerve are predominantly responsive to aversive stimuli such as bitter-tasting stimuli and acids. The gustatory system extracts information about taste intensity and quality and about the hedonic value of the stimuli. Gustatory neurons are broadly tuned to stimuli of different quality and often respond to tactile and temperature stimulation as well. Although researchers traditionally have disagreed about the nature of taste quality coding, there is good evidence that taste quality is represented by the relative activity across several well-defined neuron types in both the peripheral and central nervous systems. Taste information plays a key role in the control of ingestive behavior, and the consequences of ingestion and experience can feed back onto the gustatory system via both excitatory and inhibitory mechanisms to alter taste sensitivity.

OLFACTION

The olfactory system must satisfy several operational criteria that are essential for the survival of most animal species. First, it must be able to detect and discriminate the considerable range of signal molecules that mediate instinctive behaviors involved in prey–predator interactions, food selection, mating and reproduction, and social organization. Second, it must be able to detect and discriminate novel odors that may enter the environment unpredictably and be significant for one or more of these behaviors.

To meet these criteria, animals have evolved olfactory systems that share a number of features. Because the conservation of mechanisms across phyla is so fundamental[68] it will be useful to begin by summarizing the common features at the first two stages of the olfactory pathway, beginning with the receptor cells fol-

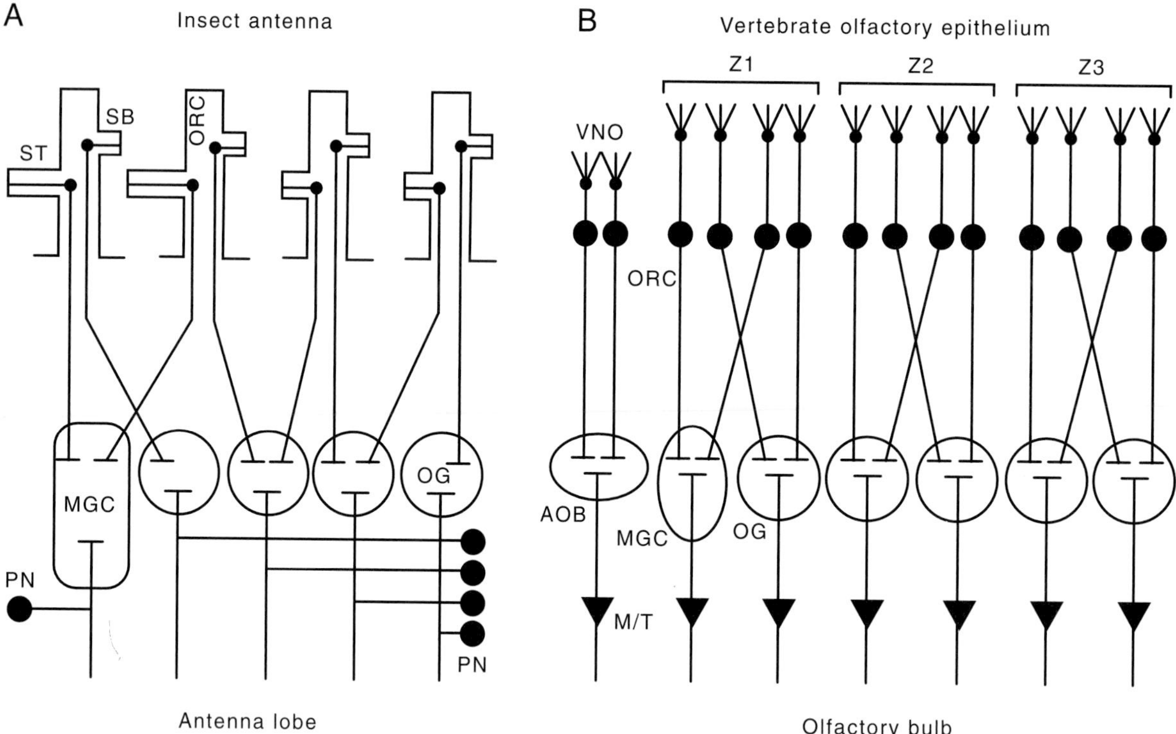

FIGURE 25.12 Comparison between the olfactory pathways of invertebrates and vertebrates. (A) Insect: SB, sensillum basiconica; ST, sensillum trichodea; ORC, olfactory receptor cells; MGC, macroglomerular complex; OG, ordinary glomeruli; PN, principal neuron. Not shown are local interneurons involved in intraglomerular processing between ORC terminals and PN dendrites. (B) Vertebrate: VNO, vomeronasal organ; Z1–Z3, expression zones for different olfactory receptor proteins; ORC, olfactory receptor cells; AOB, accessory olfactory bulb; MGC, modified glomerular complex; M/T, mitral/tufted cells. Not shown are local interneurons (periglomerular cells and granule cells) involved in intrabulbar processing at the glomerular and M/T cell body levels. From Hildebrand and Shepherd.[68]

lowed by the first relay station, the antennal lobe in insects and the olfactory bulb in mammals (Fig. 25.12). This will provide an integrated framework for subsequent discussions of specific mechanisms.

Olfactory responses begin with mechanisms for transduction and encoding of the information carried in odor-stimulating chemical agents (see Chapter 24). The encoded information is projected by subsets of olfactory receptor cells (ORCs) expressing different olfactory receptor genes onto corresponding convergence units called olfactory glomeruli. Glomeruli are the universal sites of the first synaptic relay in the olfactory bulbs of vertebrates and in the antennal lobes of many invertebrates (see Fig. 25.12). The differential patterns of activation of glomerular units constitute a neural "image" of the odor stimulus, which serves for the spatial and temporal encoding of the odor information within the glomerular sheet. The neural mechanisms underlying olfactory discrimination involve synaptic circuits that extract and compare the information carried in different glomeruli. This process begins in invertebrates at the glomerular level through interactions between the principal neurons and interneurons, and in vertebrates between mitral/tufted (M/T) cells and the periglomerular interneurons. The second level of synaptic processing occurs at the level of impulse output from the principal neurons through interactions with granule cells. In most vertebrates, a parallel pathway that mediates responses to less volatile odors runs from the vomeronasal organ to the accessory olfactory bulb. In mammals, synaptic mechanisms underlying olfactory memory have been identified in the accessory olfactory bulb at the granule cell level.

From the olfactory bulb, information in vertebrates is projected to the olfactory cortex, which consists of several subdivisions. In insects, the information is projected to higher brain centers called mushroom bodies. Different areas of olfactory cortex project to two types of targets. One target is the thalamus (mediodorsal nucleus), leading to the frontal cortex, where odor perception is believed to occur. The other target consists of regions (hypothalamus, entorhinal area) where limbic system responses to odors are mediated.

Odor Stimuli Consist of a Wide Range of Small Signal Molecules

Odor stimuli fall into several broad classes. As pointed out in Chapter 24, odor-generating compounds in aquatic species tend to be amino acids or bile salts. In terrestrial animals there is a great diversity of acids, alcohols, esters, and aromatic compounds, as well as longer chain fatty acids and more complex molecules such as musks and steroids, some of which act as components of pheromones.

Experimental and theoretical analyses of the mechanisms of odor stimulation and odor processing are usually carried out using single odor types, much as the analysis of visual processing rested initially on the use of simple spots and edges of light. However, in nature, behaviorally significant objects are more complex. In vision, we are very good at identifying complex patterns such as faces. Similarly, in olfaction, animals are very good at identifying the complex odors that identify individuals of a species. In most cases, such an **odor object** is signaled by a blend of two or more compounds; the task of the olfactory system is thus to identify not just a single odor molecule but a complex blend representing an odor object of behavioral significance to the organism. This is important to keep in mind when assessing the results of experimental analyses of the olfactory system using single odors.

Olfactory Receptor Cells Respond to Odors as Specialists or Generalists

The responses to different odors have traditionally been studied using extracellular unitary recordings from cells exposed to pulses of odor. The best stimulus control has been achieved in insects, where the recording electrode samples the activity of a receptor cell in an individual antennal hair while it is subjected to quantitatively controlled odor pulses.

The classical studies of Dietrich Schneider and his colleagues[69] in the silk moth showed that olfactory receptor neurons (ORNs) can be classified into two groups. In one group are cells that respond narrowly to only one type of molecule or at most a small number of closely related types. These types consist mainly of the sex-attractant pheromone molecules used by females to attract males during mating. The cells that respond to these molecules are called **specialists.** In contrast are cells that respond to a wide range of different types of molecules, such as the alcohols or esters, that are associated with different types of food objects in the environment. These cells are referred to as **generalists.** Some in-between categories of cells may respond somewhat more broadly to related types of molecules (broad specialists) or somewhat more narrowly to broad classes of odors (food specialists).

In the vertebrates, the classical studies of Robert Gesteland and his colleagues[70] revealed that ORNs in the frog tend to respond to a broad range of odor stimuli with a variety of patterns of impulse discharges. From that time, researchers have assumed that vertebrate ORNs are all generalists. When the odor stimuli are controlled as brief square-wave pulses and the stimulus headspace is actively cleared, ORN responses in extracellular single-unit recordings of spike discharges are reduced to mostly simple excitatory responses (Fig. 25.13A).[71] This reduction is also seen in responses to odors delivered in a bath using patch recordings from isolated cells,[72] giving assurance that the responses of the isolated cells are relatively physiological. A small proportion of salamander cells show more complex responses, both *in vivo* and *in vitro*. In other species, the responses tend to be more complex; for example, invertebrate receptor cells commonly show both excitation and suppression[69,73] (see Fig. 25.13B),[74] and significant degrees of suppression are also seen in some mammalian species.[75] The membrane basis for these differing properties is discussed in Chapter 24.

The classical studies have been extended by using the calcium-sensitive dye fura-2 to measure Ca^{2+} changes in ORNs during stimulation with odors.[76] As discussed in Chapter 24, these experiments showed that individual ORNs are able to discriminate structural features of odor molecules such as hydrocarbon length, electrical charge, and relative electronegativities of functional groups (see Fig. 25.13C). This evidence is the most direct support for the hypothesis that this information is transduced into the electrical response of the sensory neuron. The different overlapping response spectra constitute the basis for further processing by the circuits of the olfactory pathway.

All Known Vertebrate ORNs Are Generalists

All of the vertebrate receptor cells studied thus far tend to fall into the generalist class. The fact that no specialist cells have been found in vertebrates is somewhat puzzling, because increasing evidence indicates the importance of pheromones or pheromonelike substances in a range of vertebrate behaviors, such as mating preferences[77] and territorial marking. In many vertebrates the pheromones may be special blends of different types of molecules (e.g., acids and ketones), which implies that many cells may be able to respond to any one type, but only a few may respond maximally to the blend. A reasonable working hypothesis is that

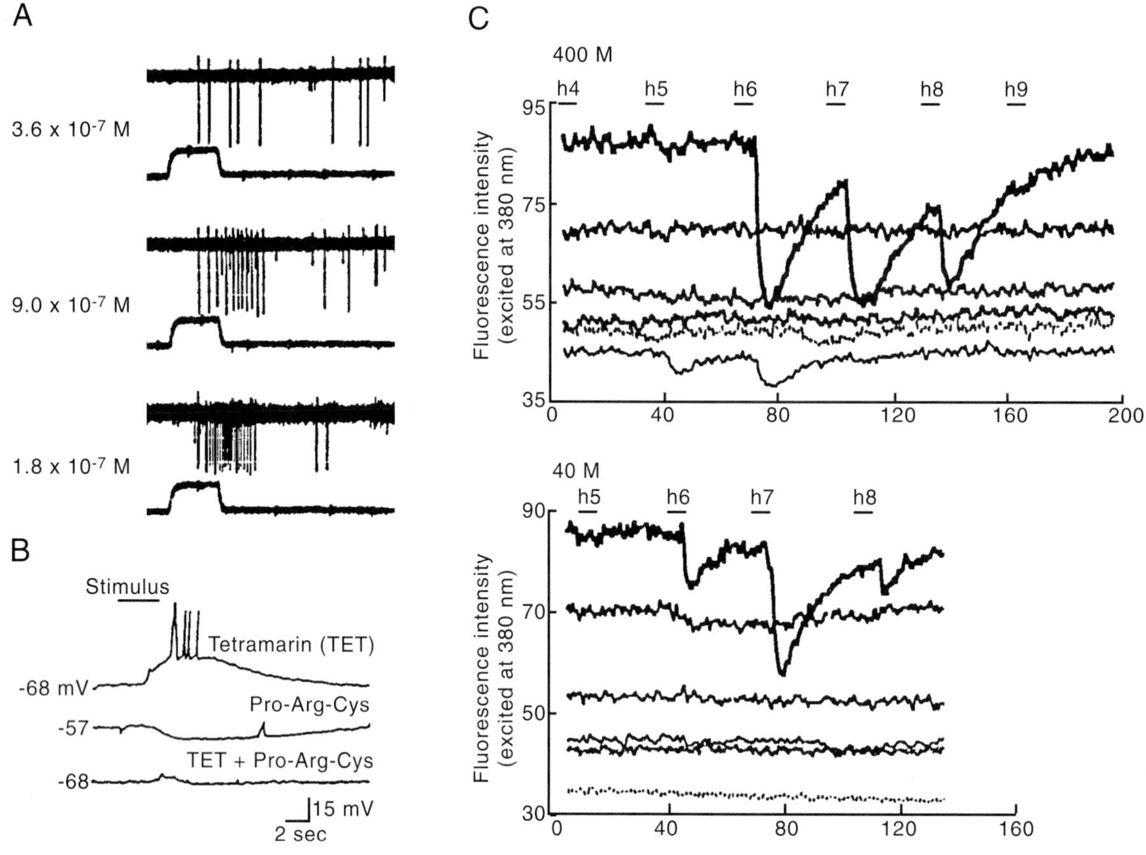

FIGURE 25.13 Examples of odor responses of different types of olfactory receptor neurons in different types of experimental preparations. (A) Extracellular unit recordings of excitatory single cell responses (upper traces) to increasing odor concentrations (lower traces) in the *in vivo* salamander olfactory epithelium. From Getchell and Shepherd.[71] (B) Lobster receptor neurons respond to different types of stimuli with either excitatory or inhibitory responses. From McClintock and Ache.[74] (C) Changes in fura-2 fluorescence with increasing concentrations (40 and 400 μM) of a homologous series of *n*-aliphatic alcohols (h4–h9) recorded in six isolated cells of the rat olfactory epithelium. From Sato *et al.*[76]

specialist ORNs tuned to vertebrate pheromones do exist.

Olfactory Cells Have Molecular Receptive Ranges

The spectrum of odors to which an individual ORN can respond has been termed its **molecular receptive range,** (MRR) in analogy with the spatial receptive field of a sensory cell in the visual or somatosensory systems.[78] A key question is whether the molecular receptive range depends on a single type of receptor molecule or whether a cell must express several receptor types to cover its range. For specialists, a single type of receptor is probably involved, in analogy with neurotransmitter receptors for their specific types of neurotransmitter molecules and the expression of a single type of opsin in cone photoreceptors. This question has not yet been answered, however, because candidate receptor molecules for pheromones in the invertebrates have not yet been identified. For generalists, the theoretical[79] and experimental[80] evidence thus far suggests the same rule—that a single ORN expresses mainly one type of receptor molecule. This rule means that to account for the broad responsivity of a cell a single receptor type must have affinities for a broad range of different types of molecules. Such differing affinities are consistent with studies of odor ligand–odor receptor interactions using molecular modeling techniques (see Chapter 24). The narrow responsiveness at threshold and the broadening responsiveness with higher odor concentrations seen in the experiments of Fig. 25.13 are consistent with the interpretation of a single receptor type having preferential affinities for a given set of determinants but broad affinities for related sets (see Box 25.3). Of course, they are also compatible with the presence of multiple types of receptors. Further experiments are required to test these hypotheses.

BOX 25.3

BROAD SPECTRA ARE THE BASIS FOR SPECIFIC ODOR DISCRIMINATION

The finding that many olfactory receptor cells display broad overlapping response spectra to different odors is often thought by students to be inconsistent with the ability of animals to make exquisite discriminations between similar odors. It seems more intuitive that responses should be narrowly tuned and distinctive for each odor rather than broadly tuned with a lot of overlap.

The corresponding question has been the subject of considerable controversy in the taste system; the current consensus is that taste cells tend to respond best to one of the submodalities but with lesser overlapping responses to the other submodalities.

Another instructive comparison is with the color system in vision, which is based on three subsets of cones, each expressing a receptor differentially tuned to wavelengths of light. Although these cones are called red, green, and blue, these names refer only to the wavelength of the cone's peak response; all have broad flanks of lesser responsiveness that cover most of the visible light spectrum. It is well recognized (see Chapter 24) that by itself a given type of cone gives no intrinsic information about wavelength; in fact, it is unable to distinguish between the wavelength and the intensity of a given light source. It is only through the differential overlapping responses of the cone types across the visible spectrum, and through downstream neural circuits that compare the responses, that wavelength is distinguished independently of intensity, and color perception is possible. This involves synaptic interactions among the pathways originating in the three cone subsets, interactions that heighten the contrast among the responses and are therefore called color opponent mechanisms.

To what extent can these principles apply to odor discrimination? The principles are particularly clearly understood in color vision because the stimulus varies only along one dimension, wavelength. In olfaction, a given series of chemical compounds can be arranged similarly in one dimension, such as in straight chains of two to ten or so carbon atoms (aliphatic compounds) ending in the same functional group (e.g., alcohols). However, intersecting with this series are a countless number of other series with different side groups (chains, rings, etc.) and functional groups. Typically, odors change systematically with increasing numbers of carbon atoms in a series up to a point, but then change dramatically, presumably reflecting the intersection with other series with different properties.

Because of the many different types of chemical compounds involved, odor space is termed multidimensional. It is therefore vastly larger and more complicated than color space. Nonetheless, it is a reasonable working hypothesis that some of the same principles should apply: the spectra of the receptor molecules and the receptor cells that contain them are likely to overlap considerably, and the microcircuits at the first stages of synaptic processing in the olfactory bulb are likely to be involved in the interactions necessary for distinguishing odor ligand properties from odor intensity. The experimental evidence for these principles is discussed in the text.

Further evidence in support of these principles is provided by recent work on artificial noses. In one prototype, polymer matrices with different physicochemical properties are dipped in a fluorescent indicator dye. The tips give different fluorescence to different vapor stimuli; the fiber optic responses are then read by an artificial neural network that compares and contrasts them. The device readily distinguishes the stimulus compounds on the basis of their overlapping responses to the different types of tips. The principles are thus similar to those explained above. The authors point out that the responses need not have any common or systematic molecular basis; all that is required is that the responses are different and that they overlap.

Is the Olfactory Projection Organized Topographically?

An old problem in olfactory studies is whether the projection from the olfactory epithelium to the olfactory bulb is organized in a diffuse or topographic manner. The visual and somatosensory systems process spatial information, and the pathways clearly reflect this in their topographic organization. In contrast, the common view has been that the olfactory system must be organized diffusely, because there is no apparent need for the kinds of topographic mapping of spatial stimuli that are present in the visual or somatosensory systems. However, the classical studies of Edgar Adrian[81] showed that different odor stimuli elicit different gradations of activity along the extent of the olfactory bulb, suggesting that at least a crude topographical organization of the olfactory receptor cells and their projections from the olfactory epithelium to the olfactory bulb may be present. Early evidence for this organization was obtained by Clark.[82] Modern studies, in fact, have provided increasing evidence for topographical organization of the olfactory system. We first review the studies using tract-tracing methods and then the studies using molecular biological probes to analyze this question.

Tract-tracing methods, including fiber degeneration stains,[83] radioactively labeled amino acid transport,[82] horseradish peroxidase (HRP) transport,[84,85] and monoclonal antibody staining,[86–88] have provided a wealth of evidence for the topographical organization of the olfactory epithelium and its projection to the bulb in the mammal.[89] The picture that has emerged is that a given glomerulus or group of neighboring glomeruli receives its input from sensory cells arranged within anterior–posterior strips of cells within the epithelium (see Fig. 25.14A). This pattern of projection has been observed directly by *in situ* hybridization for olfactory receptors (see Fig. 25.14B),[90] and its significance is discussed later in this chapter.

In contrast to the tract-tracing methods used with mammals, those used in fish and amphibians have provided little evidence of topographical organization between epithelium and bulb.[91,92] This seeming inconsistency appears to have been resolved by comparing the sizes of the systems: fish and amphibia have relatively small numbers of receptor cells (of the order of 10^6 on a side) contained in correspondingly small patches of olfactory epithelium, whereas most mammals have large numbers of receptor cells (e.g., 15 ×

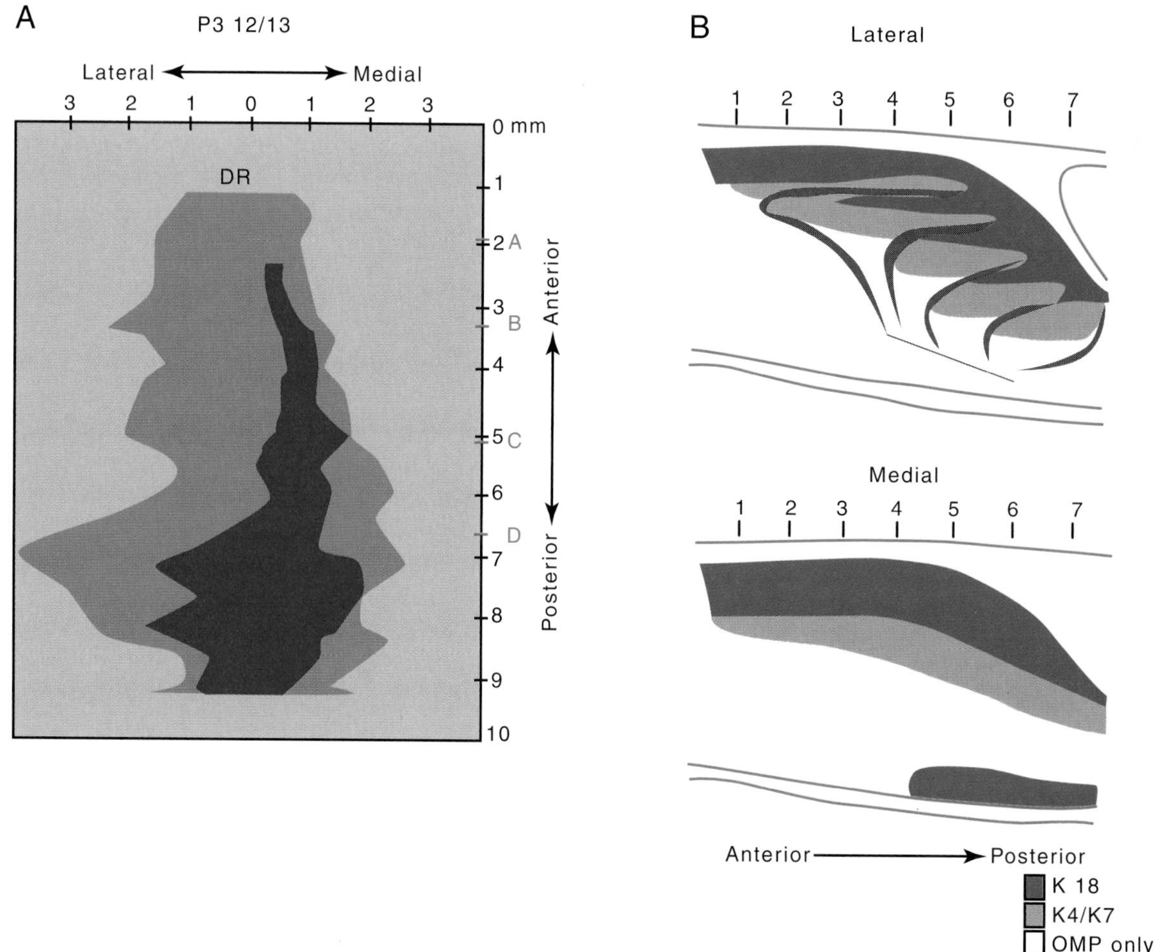

FIGURE 25.14 Both anatomical and molecular approaches show that the olfactory epithelium is organized into longitudinal strips of olfactory sensory cells. (A) Map of the main part of the olfactory epithelium showing the septal region containing cells retrogradely labeled by horseradish peroxidase injection into a small group of glomeruli in the caudal medial olfactory bulb of a 12-day-old rat pup. From Pedersen *et al.*[84] (B) Map of the expression zones of olfactory receptors as shown by *in situ* hybridization in the mouse, on the lateral turbinates (above) and the medial septal wall (below). From Ressler *et al.*[90]

10^6 in rat; 50×10^6 in rabbit) spread over large extents of epithelium. The scaling rule therefore seems to be that a small system, such as that of a fish or frog, is equivalent to a small part of a large system, such as that of a mammal. This interpretation is supported by the *in situ* hybridization studies of receptors (see below).

The Olfactory Projection Shows a High Degree of Convergence

Within the olfactory bulb the receptor cell axons terminate in rounded regions of neuropil termed glomeruli. Anatomical studies from the time of Ramón y Cajal to the present have shown that the glomerulus is an anatomical unit for convergence of axons from many ORNs (we will discuss the structure of the glomerulus further). This convergence is considerable; in the rabbit, for example, it has been estimated that 50×10^6 receptor cells project to 2000 glomeruli, making an overall average convergence of approximately 25,000:1.[93,94] Within the olfactory bulb, approximately 25 mitral cells and 50 tufted cells are connected through their primary dendrites to a given glomerulus, implying convergence ratios of 1000:1 and 500:1, respectively. These high convergence ratios imply that only a small proportion of the receptor cells projecting to a glomerulus need be activated to provide significant input to that glomerulus and the mitral/tufted cells connected to it.[95]

In invertebrates, the olfactory axons project to structures in the antennal lobe that resemble the glomeruli of vertebrates. The numbers of glomeruli in insects are modest, ranging from 9 to more than 1000, with many species in the range 50–300.[96] On the input side, insects have 200,000–350,000 ORNs.[97] Thus, the convergence ratio of ORCs to glomeruli in these insects is on the order of 1000:1 (about 1500–4500:1), up to an order of magnitude lower than the ratio for mammals. On the output side of a glomerulus, the numbers of uniglomerular projection (or principal) neurons are relatively small: 260 in the cockroach and about 300 in the tobacco worm, reflecting modest overall divergence from the glomeruli. In the tobacco worm, in addition to the uniglomerular output neurons associated with the ordinary glomeruli of the antennal lobe, 40 such neurons are also associated with the macroglomerular complex (MGC) and wide-field projection neurons that make connections with several or many glomeruli. There are also numerous wide-field local interneurons, with arborizations in many or all glomeruli.[98] Later we discuss the implications of these findings for more complex processing in insect glomeruli.

Olfactory Glomeruli Are Units for Processing Specific Odor Information

The **olfactory glomerulus** is the universal anatomical and functional unit for olfactory processing found across phyla. In mammals, the glomerulus is a spheroidal region of neuropil consisting of the preterminal axons and terminal boutons of ORC axons and the distal dendritic tufts of mitral (M), tufted (T), and periglomerular (PG) cells. The border of the glomerulus is demarcated by several layers of glial processes and by a ring of cell bodies of the PG cells. In mammals, a glomerulus ranges from 100–150 μm in diameter in rat to 150–200 μm in rabbit and is thus comparable in size to a barrel in rat somatosensory cortex or an orientation column in visual cortex. In amphibia and fish, the glomeruli are smaller, 20–50 μm in diameter, and much less distinct, partly owing to a paucity of surrounding PG cells.

In insects, the glomeruli are formed by the preterminal axons and terminals of the olfactory receptor neurons, which make synapses on the terminal neurites of the principal neurons and local interneurons of the antennal lobe.[97] The large size and reproducible positions of the glomeruli have made it possible to demonstrate unique identities and to provide detailed glomerular maps of several species of insects.[96]

Olfactory Glomeruli Are Also Functional Units for Processing Specific Odor Information

The functional significance of glomerular units in vertebrates was first shown by researchers using the 2-deoxyglucose (2DG) activity mapping technique.[99] In awake behaving rats exposed to a given odor (e.g., amyl acetate), the lowest concentrations elicit activity in only one or a few glomeruli (Fig. 25.15A). Stimulation with higher concentrations activates larger numbers of glomeruli (see Figs. 25.15B and 25.15C). These results led to an important insight: The few glomeruli activated at the lowest concentration represent input from the subset of ORNs whose receptors have the highest affinity for that particular odor. They further imply that higher concentrations activate other ORN subsets whose receptors have lower affinities for that odor. The basis for these properties of molecular encoding is hypothesized to be the affinities of the determinants of odor molecules for given residue sites in the binding pockets of the odor receptors (these postulated mechanisms are discussed in Chapter 24).

In some cases the elicited activity can be correlated with histologically defined glomeruli; one such example is the modified glomerular complex (MGC) that is

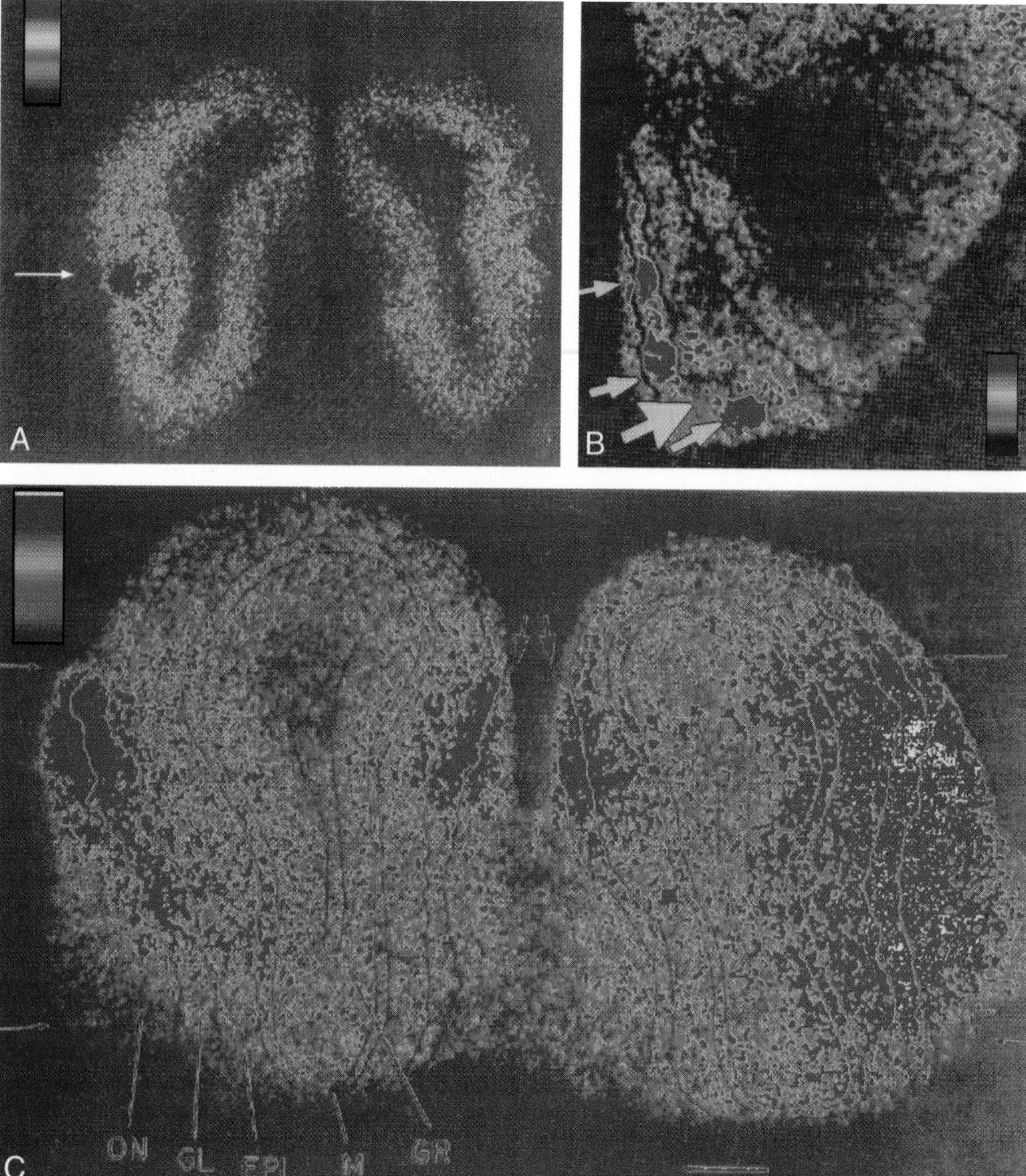

FIGURE 25.15 The 2-deoxyglucose (2DG) method reveals the functional organization of the olfactory glomerular sheet. (A) Patterns of 2-deoxyglucose utilization in an X-ray film autoradiograph of a frontal section through the olfactory bulb of a rat exposed to a low concentration of the odor of amyl acetate. A single focus associated with one glomerulus or a small group of neighboring glomeruli is seen in one of the olfactory bulbs. (B) With a moderate concentration of amyl acetate, the activity induced in the glomerular layer is characterized by activation of several glomeruli or groups of glomeruli (white lines outline the histological layers). (C) With a high concentration of odor of amyl acetate, the induced activity consists of broad regions of increased 2DG uptake, centered on the glomerular layer in medial and lateral regions of the olfactory bulb, that are roughly bilaterally symmetrical. From Stewart *et al.*,[99] reprocessed by Adobe Photoshop.

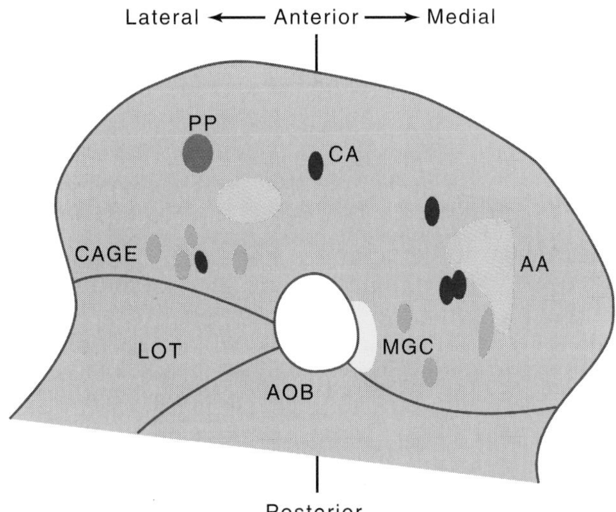

FIGURE 25.16 Consensus map of the glomerular layer of the rat olfactory bulb, showing the locations of foci of 2DG uptake in response to stimulation with different odors. AA, amyl acetate; CA, camphor; PP, peppermint; MGC, modified glomerular complex, activated by suckling; CAGE, exposure to air of home cage. Also: LOT, lateral olfactory tract; AOB, accessory olfactory bulb.

active in suckling rat pups (Figs. 25.12 and 25.16).[100] This set of glomeruli was the first to be characterized by both its anatomical identity and its functional specificity. Where are the olfactory receptor cells that project to this anatomically and functionally defined glomerular group? Injections of HRP into the MGC have shown labeling of cells primarily within a strip along the septal epithelium and in smaller strips over the turbinates[84,85] (see Fig. 25.15A). The combined 2DG functional studies and HRP anatomical studies thus suggested that a glomerulus is a **functional unit,** or **molecular module,** in the processing of specific odor information converging on it from receptor cells preferentially sensitive to a given odor or odors.

Olfactory Glomeruli Form Molecular Images of Odor Molecules

The patterns of 2DG activation in response to different odors give further insight into the mechanisms underlying odor discrimination. The key observation is that different odors evoke different patterns of active glomeruli located in distinct domains within the olfactory bulb. Thus, as shown in Fig. 25.17, the focal glomerular activity elicited by the odor of amyl acetate is localized in two broad zones, one medial and one lateral, within the olfactory bulb glomerular sheet.[99] In contrast, the activity elicited by camphor is distributed in a curving line of smaller glomerular patches. Although the two domains overlap, their overall patterns are distinct and different. Other domains associated with other types of odor stimuli are also shown in Fig. 25.16. These results suggest that each type of odor elicits a characteristic pattern of glomerular activation in the olfactory bulb. These patterns may be considered to constitute **odor images** in neural space.

Other methods have confirmed and extended the 2DG results. *In situ* hybridization for c-*fos* mRNA has shown expression in mitral, tufted, and PG cells in clusters within the olfactory bulb in response to different types of odors (see Fig. 25.17B).[102] The pattern for amyl acetate, for example, is similar to the zonal pattern of glomerular activation found with 2DG, although the clusters are more widely dispersed, perhaps reflecting the greater sensitivity of the method or the fact that the 2DG maps thus far have tended to emphasize the most intense foci.

Another approach is the use of voltage-sensitive dyes (VSD), which reveal patterns of odor-elicited activity during real time. The salamander is particularly attractive for this method because the different layers of the bulb are not concentric but abut the dorsal bulbar surface, and thus both sequences and extents of laminar activity can be registered. Odor-induced VSD patterns have been localized to compartments within a glomerulus, PG cells near that glomerulus, and mitral and granule cell layers deep to that focus, thus revealing a radial module.[103] This pattern is strikingly similar to that found in the 2DG and c-*fos* studies of mammals and is designated a radial translaminar module (see Fig. 25.17C). Odor responses involve activation of many modules in parallel, and the neural elements may be part of one module when responding to one odor but components of another module when responding to a different odor. Imaging of Ca^{2+} fluorescence in glomeruli of zebra fish[104] and honeybee[105] has revealed similar properties.

Olfactory Receptor Expression Is Correlated with Anatomical Projection Patterns

Anatomical studies of olfactory projections and functional studies of glomerular activation have provided a basic outline for the functional organization of the peripheral olfactory pathway. This outline has been confirmed and extended by localization of cells expressing olfactory receptors (cf. Chapter 24). *In situ* hybridization for receptor mRNA revealed that individual members of the olfactory G-protein-coupled receptor family are expressed within longitudinal zones along the septal and turbinate epithelium (see Fig. 25.14B).[90,106] These zones are similar in their orientations to the strips demonstrated in the anatomical studies. Three nonoverlapping zones have been identified; a

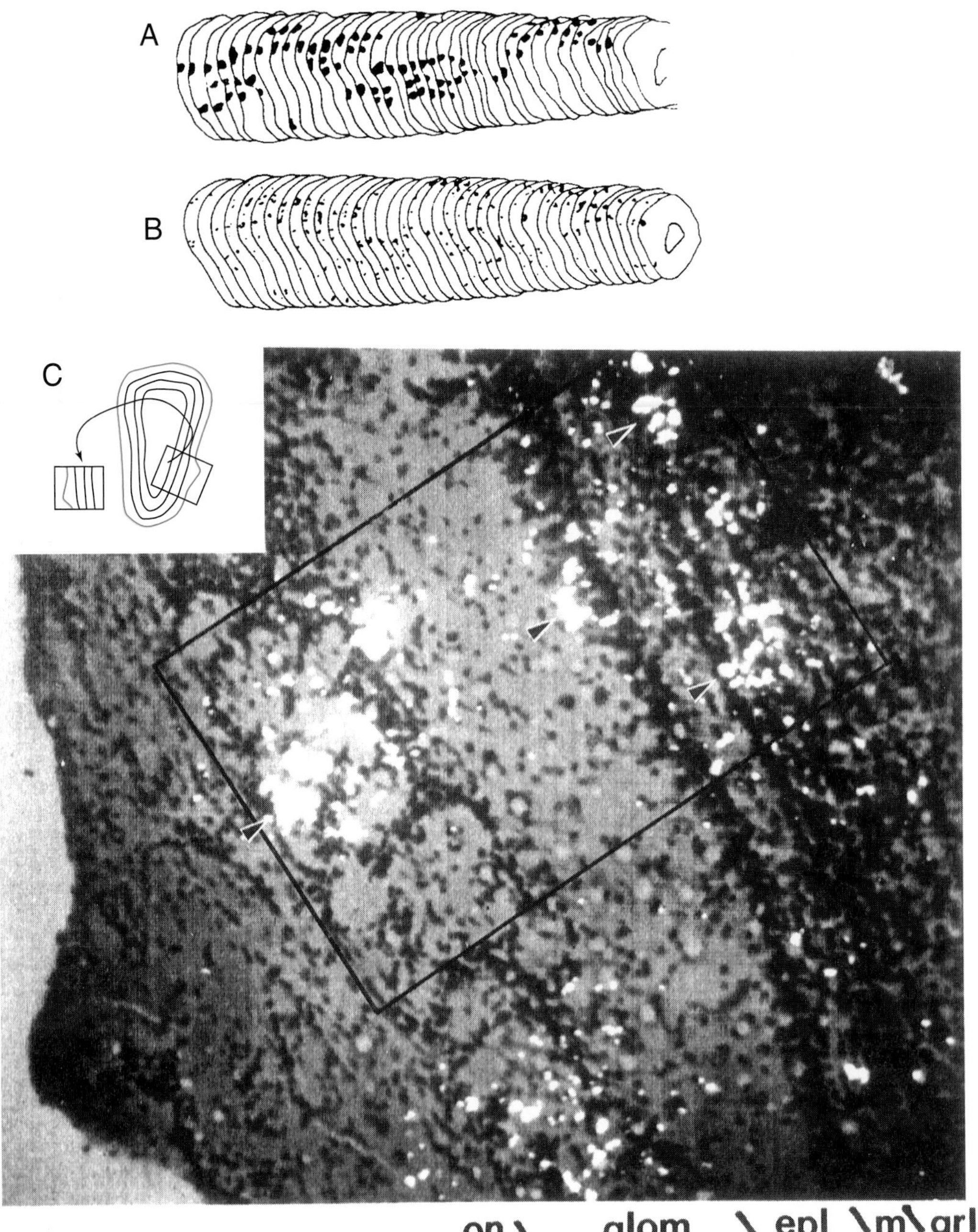

FIGURE 25.17 Different activity markers yield complementary results on the functional organization of the olfactory bulb. (A and B) Localization of mRNA for c-*fos* (A) in response to stimulation with amyl acetate in the rat reveals a spatial pattern of activation similar to that shown by 2DG (B). From Guthrie *et al.*[102] (C) Localization of voltage-sensitive dye fluorescence in the olfactory bulb of the salamander in response to odor stimulation shows activation of individual glomeruli or small groups of glomeruli and radial columns of activated cells. From Kauer and Cinelli.[103]

fourth smaller zone overlaps two of these. The significance of the overlapping and nonoverlapping zones is not yet understood. One possibility is that it is related to the developmental specificity of the olfactory projections (see below).

The anatomical relation between the epithelial expression zones and the olfactory bulb has been revealed in *in situ* hybridization experiments to test for expression of receptors in the olfactory bulb. These results have shown that receptor mRNA is indeed expressed, at low levels, in the olfactory bulb, and for a given receptor it is characteristically localized entirely

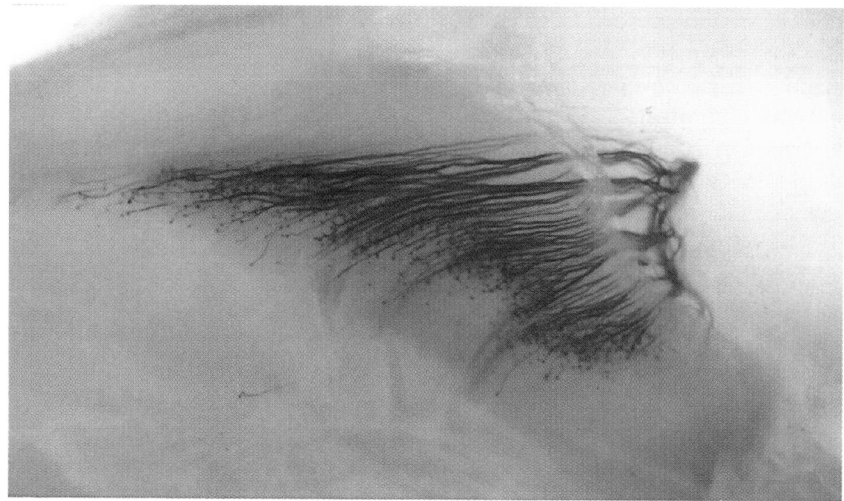

FIGURE 25.18 Whole mount of the nose of a rat shows olfactory receptor axons converging on a single glomerulus. This subset of cells is stained for a *lacZ* reporter linked to mRNA for one type of olfactory receptor and the microtubule-associated protein tau. From Mombaerts *et al.*[109]

to one or several glomeruli.[107,108] In further experiments, mRNA constructs were made to include coding regions for the microtubule-associated protein tau; when tau is linked to a reporter sequence (*lacZ*), the entire extent of the neuron can be seen in whole mounts of the nasal chamber and olfactory bulb (Fig. 25.18).[109] This procedure has provided clear visualization of subsets of ORNs expressing a given receptor and their axons gathering into bundles to converge onto a single glomerulus in the olfactory bulb. These experiments thus provide strong experimental evidence for the concept that subsets of ORNs expressing a single receptor gene project their axons as a labeled line onto one or a few target glomeruli. However, as the physiological and metabolic data suggest, this labeled line is complex and broadly tuned, overlapping in specificity with many others (see below).

In contrast with studies in the mammal, *in situ* hybridization studies of mRNA expression in the olfactory epithelium of fish have shown a random distribution of an ORN subset, with no evidence of anatomical localization or expression zones.[110] This lack of localization may be related to the fact that fish have a much smaller extent of olfactory epithelia (a frog olfactory epithelium is only a few percent of a rat, rabbit, or dog epithelium). As noted earlier, this result can be reconciled with the multiple expression zones in the mammal if the differences in epithelial sizes are taken into account; the extent of the fish epithelium is in fact much less than the extent of one mammalian expression zone. The entire fish olfactory epithelium appears to express only a limited number of different receptor types (perhaps a few dozen up to 100) compared with the large number (up to 1000) believed to be expressed by the entire rat olfactory epithelium. Thus, the rule for scaling between fish and mammals based on molecular biology appears to be the same as that inferred from the anatomy and behavior. Recent studies suggest that there may be more organization within the mammalian zones and within the small epithelia of submammalian species than was at first apparent.

Individual ORN Axons May Use Local Cues to Find Their Glomerular Targets

In considering the topographical organization of the olfactory projection, a critical question is: How does an ORN expressing a given olfactory receptor type make connection to the appropriate glomerulus in the olfactory bulb? Current experiments studying the patterns of expression of receptors and other molecular constituents of the ORNs during early development should help to answer that question. One factor is the degree of dispersion of the ORNs of a given subset within the olfactory epithelium; too great a dispersion could make the task of a particular axon finding its way to its appropriate glomerular target more difficult. The small epithelia of fish and amphibia and the zones of mammals seem to indicate the extent of epithelial regions within which random dispersion is still consistent with the abilities of individual axons to follow a succession of local cues in finding their way from the epithelium to their appropriate glomerular targets. Anatomical studies give evidence that axons and axon fascicles follow local cues in arriving at specific glomeruli and intraglomerular compartments.[111]

What is the mechanism for this local cue hypothesis? An intriguing possibility may be present in the receptors themselves. As described in Chapter 24, correlated mutation analysis has identified residues that appear to form a binding pocket that serves as the site for the initial transduction of odor signal molecules. In addition, this method has identified residues in the external loops of the receptors that are correlated with specific residues in the binding pocket. These external residues therefore serve as markers for the binding specificity of the pocket in enabling any receptors expressed in the axon and axon terminals to take part in cell–cell interactions mediating axonal guidance and target recognition for the establishment of appropriate synapses in the glomeruli.

Odor Processing by Olfactory Glomeruli Is Mediated by Excitatory and Inhibitory Microcircuits

The olfactory bulb provides the first stage of synaptic processing of the sensory information in the olfactory pathway. It is thus analogous in position to the retina in the initial processing of visual information (see Box 25.4).[112]

Within a glomerulus, the olfactory axons make excitatory synapses onto the dendrites of the principal neurons (M/T cells), as well as the dendrites of a type of short-axon cell, the PG cell, in most species (see Fig. 25.20).[113] In addition, there is a wealth of synapses between the M/T cell dendrites and the PG cell dendrites. These synapses are believed to provide for numerous types of interactions, including serial excitatory synapses (which spread excitation widely within a glomerulus), recurrent and lateral inhibitory synaptic circuits, and disinhibitory synaptic interactions. These interactions can be carried out within compartments within a given glomerulus; they may also allow activity to spread throughout a glomerulus. A glomerulus may therefore contain several levels of organization.[114,115]

In addition to this *intra*glomerular processing, there is *inter*glomerular processing through the axons of the PG cells, which make Type II synapses on PG cells related to neighboring glomeruli and on the dendritic shafts of M/T cells as they emerge from the glomeruli. One action of these synapses may be to inhibit PG cells and M/T dendrites, thus providing contrast enhancement between neighboring glomeruli. Another possibility is that the action could be excitatory, by means of a network of presynaptic PG cell inhibitory actions and by GABA-activated synapses acting through a reversed chloride gradient.

The Relative Activation of Different Glomeruli Is Crucial in Processing Odor Information

Indirect experimental and theoretical evidence indicates that intraglomerular processing may enhance the unitary operation of a glomerulus with regard to its specific input. Glomerular activation may even have an all-or-nothing property,[116] as seen in slow potentials recorded from the glomerular layer. This enhancement is also supported by the appearance of intense 2DG foci related to individual glomeruli even at very weak levels of odor stimulation.[99] This all-or-nothing property could arise from positive feedback types of mechanisms within a glomerulus, as noted earlier: disinhibitory synaptic sequences; excitatory synaptic interactions, enhanced by reverse chloride gradient responses; and active dendritic hot spots. Gaseous second messengers may also contribute to this unitary operation. The olfactory bulb stains for nitric oxide synthase (NOS), which is particularly localized in PG cell dendrites.[117] Nitric oxide synthesized in these dendrites could serve as a second messenger in activating guanylate cyclase in neighboring dendrites, thus adding to the dendrodendritic interactions taking place within the glomeruli. Because NO acts only briefly within a few micrometers before being inactivated, it is ideally suited to functioning within but not between glomeruli.

In contrast, interglomerular processing is believed to enhance the contrast between the specificities of neighboring glomeruli. A question arises whether this interglomerular mechanism acts throughout the range of odor concentrations. Both 2DG and VSD studies have shown that as odor concentration increases, activity is recruited in neighboring glomeruli, thus forming larger domains of activated glomeruli that are associated with the processing of that odor. One possibility is that this recruitment represents spread of excitatory interglomerular actions. However, it seems more likely at present that these recruited glomeruli represent inputs from other ORN subsets whose receptor proteins have lower affinities for that odor ligand. Further experiments are needed to test these specific hypotheses.

Insect Glomeruli Appear to Mediate More Complex Processing

As noted earlier, in the insect, olfactory axons commonly terminate on interneuronal neurites, so that there are complex sequences of synaptic connections between the olfactory input and the output of the principal neurons. The synaptic connections within the glomeruli of the insect antennal lobe thus may provide

BOX 25.4

THE OLFACTORY BULB AND RETINA HAVE SIMILAR BASIC PLANS

Although the olfactory bulb and the retina have distinctive types of cells and circuits, they are similar in their overall plan and in many aspects of their microcircuit organization. Each has straight-through pathways for direct transmission of the sensory information (see Fig. 25.19).[110] In addition, both regions provide for two levels of lateral processing, one at the level of sensory input and the other at the control of output. The significance of these two levels is best understood in the retina, where the lateral interactions can be clearly related to such obvious properties as enhancement of spatial contrast. Similar microcircuits for feedback and lateral inhibition exist at both levels in the olfactory bulb. These microcircuits may be involved in contrast enhancement between molecular stimuli. Research provides strong support for this function (see text).

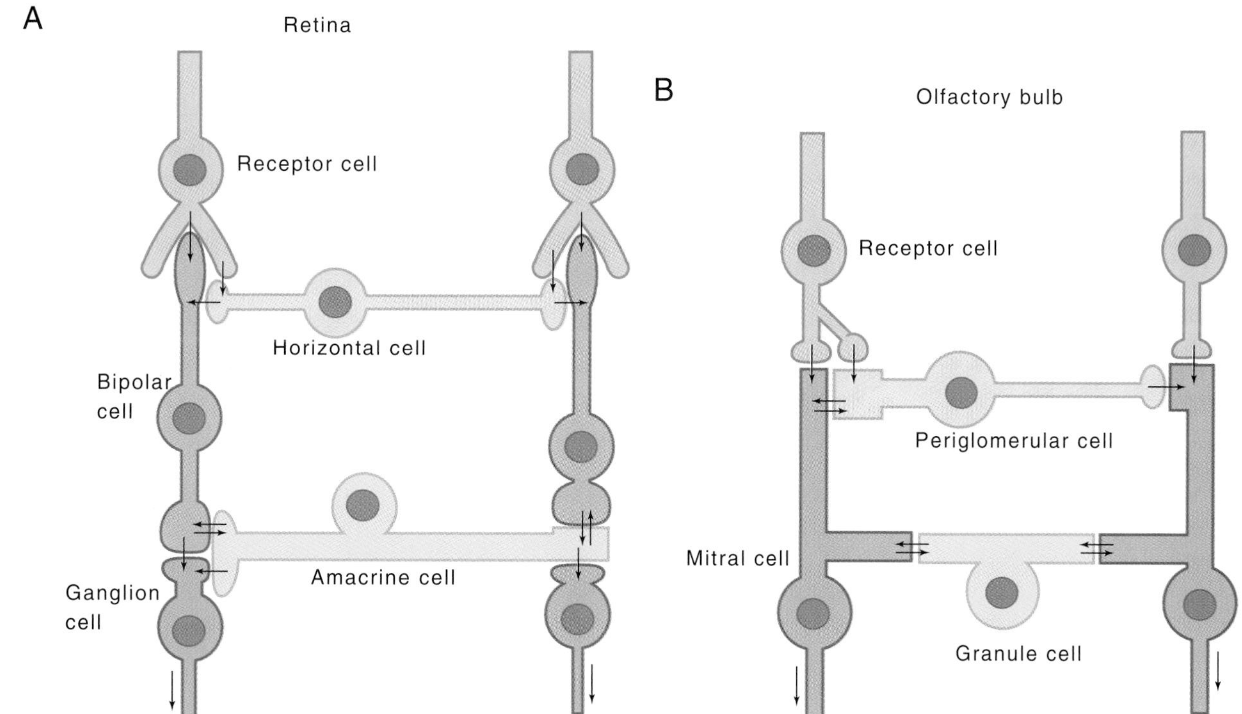

FIGURE 25.19 Comparison of the basic circuits of the olfactory bulb (B) and the retina (A). Although these regions process distinctly different types of sensory information, the overall similarity of their organization, and the detailed similarity of some of their local circuits, indicates conserved principles in the neural mechanisms for processing both types of information. Adapted from Shepherd.[112]

for more complex processing of afferent information than in the glomeruli of vertebrates.[68] This scheme would be in accord with the general principle in the invertebrate of delegating more processing to more peripheral structures. An analogy in this respect is the complex retina of submammalian species, characterized by multiple layers of synaptic processing through the neurites of amacrine cells. Similar multiple sequences of processing within the glomeruli of insects would account for the ability of those creatures to accomplish complex odor discrimination despite the relatively few glomeruli in their olfactory centers compared with those of mammals.

In addition to the ordinary glomeruli, the antennal lobes of males of certain species of insects contain an enlarged, sexually dimorphic glomerular structure. In

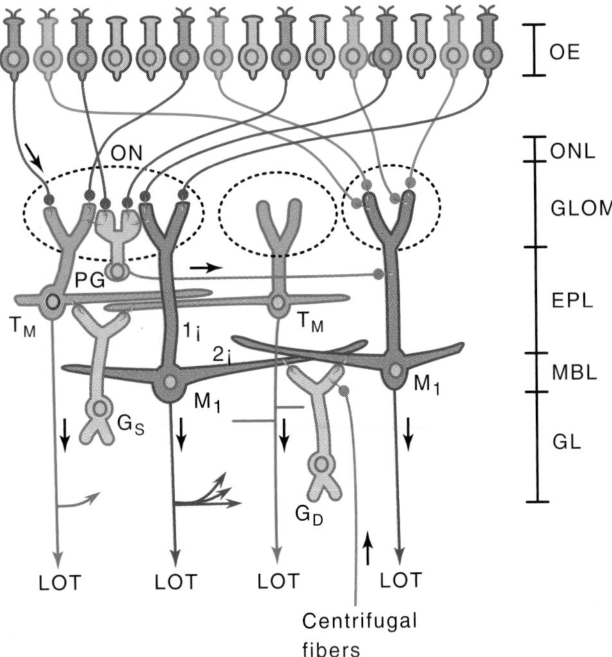

FIGURE 25.20 Summary diagram of the main types of synaptic connections within the mammalian olfactory bulb. Abbreviations: ON, olfactory nerves; PG, periglomerular cell; T_M, middle tufted cell; G_s, superficial granule cell; M_1, mitral cell, 1°, primary dendrite; 2°, secondary dendrite; G_D, deep granule cell; LOT, lateral olfactory tract. Layers: OE, olfactory epithelium; ONL, olfactory nerve layer; GLOM, glomerular layer; EPL, external plexiform layer; MBL, mitral cell body layer; GL, granule cell layer. After Mori and Shepherd.[113]

the cockroach this structure is called the macroglomerulus and in the tobacco worm the macroglomerular complex (reviewed in Hildebrand[68]). These structures constitute a male-specific olfactory labeled line dedicated to detection and sensory analysis of the female's species-specific sex pheromone. In tobacco worm, the MGC is the site of primary synaptic processing of afferent inputs of antennal ORNs narrowly tuned to respond to components A and B and at least one other component of the female's sex pheromone.

Dendrodendritic Synapses Mediate Contextual Molecular Contrast Enhancement

The second level of synaptic processing in the olfactory bulb depends mainly on one type of microcircuit, composed of reciprocal dendrodendritic synapses that mediate M/T-to-granule excitation and granule-to-M/T inhibition[118,119] (see Fig. 25.21). Through this means, activated M/T cells mediate feedback inhibition on themselves and lateral inhibition on their neighbors. These inhibitory interactions control the frequency of impulse output from the M/T cells and thus are the basis of the temporal encoding of odor information that is of increasing interest.[112,119,120] Lateral inhibition is activated by retrograde spread of the impulse into the secondary dendrites, so it directly reflects the output of the neuron. This was an early example of the type of impulse backpropagation that is of current interest in the functional organization of the neuron (see Chapter 15). The secondary dendrites are relatively long, thus providing for graded lateral inhibition onto a large population of neighboring cells receiving input from neighboring glomeruli. This inhibition thus may contribute a more complex, more contextual type of contrast enhancement between cells belonging to different glomerular modules. Formations of single and higher order odor opponent cells may be present at both levels, in analogy with color processing in the retina.

Odor Stimuli Give Rise to a Complex Array of Responses among Bulbar Cells

Responses of subsets of ORNs to odor stimulation vary in their specificity and intensity coding (cf. Fig. 25.13), which is the basis for processing by the olfactory bulb circuits. The responses in the olfactory bulb are also complex, but some patterns can be discerned. The simplest case is the salamander, in which carefully

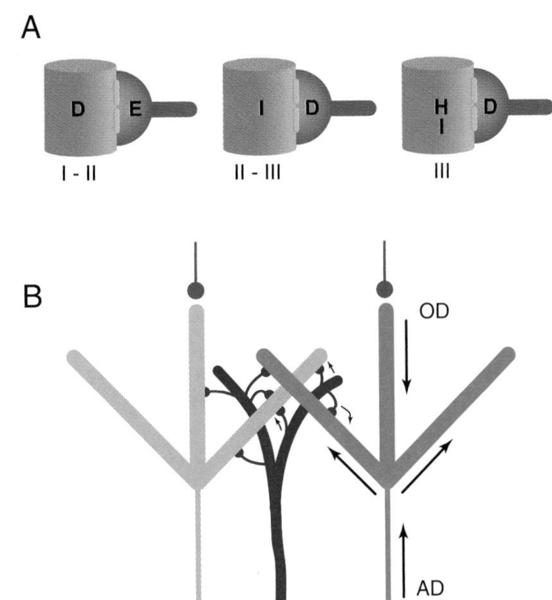

FIGURE 25.21 (A) Model for the action of the dendrodendritic synaptic pathway between mitral (pink profiles) and granule (blue profiles) cells, during successive time periods I, II, and III following generation of the impulse at the soma. D, depolarization; H, hyperpolarization; E, excitation; I, inhibition. (B) Diagram of the circuit connections between mitral and granule cell dendrites that mediate self- and lateral inhibition of the mitral cells. OD, orthodromic activation; AD, antidromic activation. Adapted from Rall and Shepherd.[119]

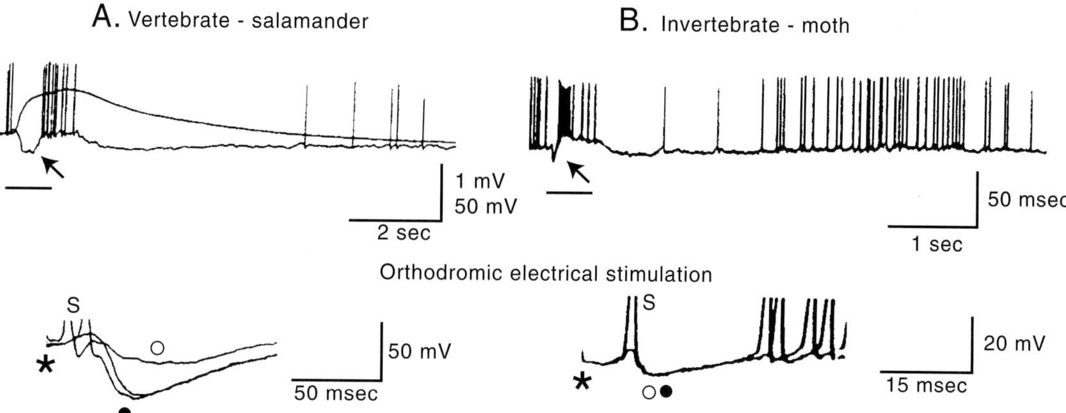

FIGURE 25.22 Electrophysiological recordings of odor responses of a vertebrate mitral cell (A) and an invertebrate principal neuron (B), showing similarities in their response properties. See text for full explanation. (A) From Hamilton and Kauer[121]; (B) from Christensen *et al.*[122]

controlled pulses of odor, combined with active clearing of the headspace, produce varying degrees of excitatory spike discharge in the ORNs.[71] When these methods are used to record from olfactory bulb cells, the responses of a given cell to a given odor may show one of several clearly defined types[121]: no response; excitation at threshold odor concentration, replaced by a brief excitatory burst followed by suppression at higher concentrations; only suppression at all levels of concentration. The excitatory responses are usually preceded by a brief period of suppression, caused by hyperpolarization of the membrane. Surprisingly, the corresponding cells in the antennal lobe of insects show a very similar initial hyperpolarization in response to odor stimuli (see Fig. 25.22).[121,122] The mammal shows similar categories of response, but with more variations on these simple patterns.[123]

The threshold excitatory responses are due primarily to excitatory synaptic drive from the subset of ORNs that projects to the glomerulus to which the M/T or PG cell is connected. At higher concentration, the initial excitatory burst is due mainly to the larger EPSP produced by the larger numbers of active ORN axons converging on this cell. However, feedback mechanisms may also be acting through recurrent synaptic excitation, synaptic disinhibition, or GABAergic inputs affecting reversed chloride gradients. The subsequent suppression could reflect synaptic inhibition at the glomerular level (either intra- or extraglomerular actions) or granule cell level. Responses that are inhibitory at all concentration levels might reflect the actions of interglomerular inputs from more active glomeruli, or granule cells. The initial brief hyperpolarization may be caused by an initial action of granule cells.

Our understanding of the neural basis of processing in the olfactory bulb thus requires much further experimental testing. However, we have some clues. Simultaneous recordings from pairs of mitral cells have shown that cells close together (within 40 μm), and therefore more likely to be connected to the same or a neighboring glomerulus, respond similarly to a given odor, whereas cells farther apart (more than 150 μm) tended to show opposite types of responses.[123] This result, together with a variety of other studies, has supported the idea that a main function of the dendrodendritic synapses present at both the glomerular and granule cell levels is to mediate lateral inhibition and that the role of this lateral inhibition is to enhance contrast between different odors.

Bulbar Circuits Underlie Odor Discrimination

The current model suggests that the excitatory circuits within a glomerulus help to amplify the specific input to it, whereas the inhibitory circuits between glomeruli and at the granule cell level contribute to contrast enhancement. One of the effects of these operations may be to narrow the molecular receptive range of the M/T cell output from a glomerular module compared to the range for the ORNs projecting to that module. This hypothesis has been tested in experiments in which multiple electrode penetrations have been made in the olfactory bulbs of rabbits stimulated with different types of odor molecules.[78,87] The recordings have shown that M/T cells preferentially responsive to specific classes of odor molecules (e.g., acids, alcohols, esters) are located in specific domains of the olfactory bulb, as suggested by the 2DG studies.

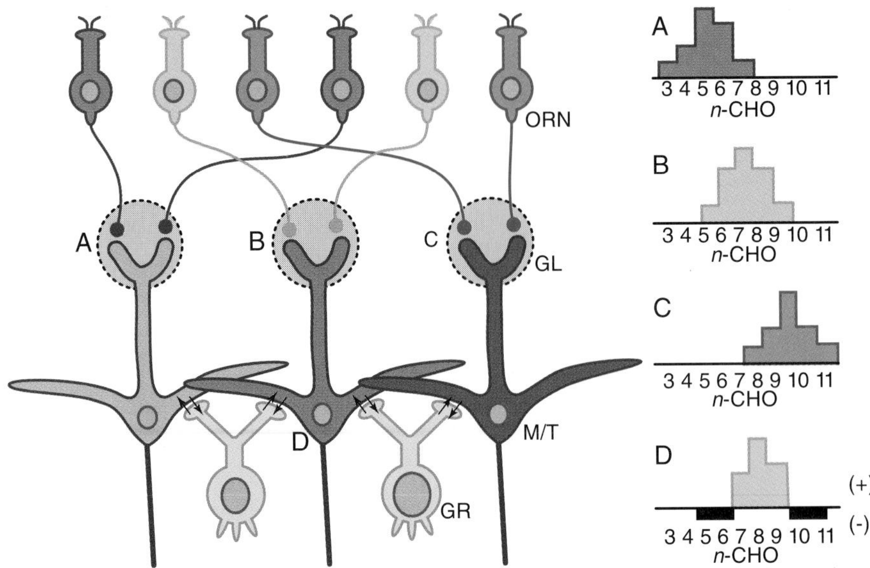

FIGURE 25.23 Summary of physiological evidence for molecular contrast enhancement through lateral inhibitory microcircuits in the olfactory bulb. Summary diagram of the functional organization underlying contrast enhancement between the responses of mitral cells to neighboring members of a homologous series (*n*-CHO) of odor molecules. The broad responses mediated from an ORN subset through glomerulus (GL) B are sharpened in the mitral/tufted (M/T) cell D by inhibitory interactions mediated by reciprocal dendrodendritic synaptic circuits through granules cells (GR). See text for details. From Yokoi *et al.*[124]

Within a region, M/T cells tend to show narrow specificities for two or three neighboring members of a particular carbon series (Fig. 25.23).[124] These narrow specificities are also seen for corresponding members of parallel carbon series (e.g., for corresponding acids, alcohols, or esters). Contributing to this narrow specificity is inhibition of responses to closely related molecules. This type of surround inhibition mediates contrast enhancement between odor ligands with closely related determinants as described earlier. Pharmacological analysis has provided evidence that this inhibition is mediated by the reciprocal dendrodendritic circuit between M/T and granule cells (see Fig. 25.23).

Many Systems Modulate the Behavioral State of the Olfactory Bulb

In discussing the organization of the olfactory system, we have focused on its most obvious function—processing odor information as a basis for the perception of odors. However, like most sensory pathways it is also under control by intrinsic peptidergic systems and by centrifugal fibers from centers in the brain, so that its sensory function is subject to modulation. In fact, the olfactory bulb contains a wealth of peptidergic and centrifugal inputs, which probably put it under more **modulatory control** by more different brain states than any other system. A moment's reflection gives a reason: The sense of smell is crucial to the two basic behaviors—feeding and mating—that are at the core of most animal life. In each case the significance of a given smell in eliciting a given behavior depends closely on the behavioral state of the animal. For example, the smell of food is attractive when we are hungry but not when we are full. The neural basis of this has been tested in rats; recordings from mitral cells in rats exposed to food odors showed strong responses when the rats were hungry but suppression when they were sated.[125]

Intrinsic Modulators

Dopamine D2 receptors have been localized to the glomerular and olfactory nerve layer and are possible sites of action by dopamine-containing PG cells. Although the role of dopamine (DA) remains unclear, several studies have indicated that DA has a role in olfactory processing. For example, the dopamine receptor agonist apomorphine blocks a 2DG pattern of glomerular activity induced by odor stimulation; this effect is prevented by pretreatment with the DA receptor antagonist haloperidol.[126] Odor learning increases dopamine levels in the olfactory bulb,[127] whereas odor deprivation increases D2 receptor density present on olfactory nerve terminals. These studies suggest that DA exerts a neuromodulatory action on sensory input.

Centrifugal Systems

Two centrifugal systems arise in the brainstem: the noradrenergic (NA) system, originating in the locus ceruleus; and the serotonergic system, arising in the dorsal raphe. NA is probably involved in modulating the olfactory system at both the bulbar and olfactory cortical levels, at different stages of development. NA reduces granule cell inhibition of mitral cells; experiments on cultured cells suggest that this is due to reduction of glutamate release from mitral cells through a presynaptic α-adrenergic inhibition of high threshold calcium currents, and possibly also a presynaptic reduction in GABA release from granule cells.[128] This NA mechanism could mediate some forms of olfactory learning. Another important centrifugal system consists of cholinergic fibers arising from the basal forebrain.

The Vomeronasal-Accessory Bulb System Mediates Specific Odor Information in Parallel

In addition to the main olfactory pathway, a parallel pathway exists for transmitting signals from less volatile or nonvolatile odorous compounds. This pathway originates in the **vomeronasal organ** (VNO), also referred to as Jacobson's organ (see Fig. 25.12). It is present in a variety of vertebrate species. Phylogenetically, it is first differentiated clearly in the snakes, where it is involved in several functions, including mating behavior and responses to prey odors that are sampled from the tongue as it is drawn over the inlet to the organ. In rodents, the organ is well developed and is believed to be stimulated by sexually active substances that access the inlet to the organ as a male directly investigates the female's vaginal opening. In ungulates such as deer and horses, the inlet is exposed by a nasal movement called a flehmen reaction in which the male investigates the urine of the female to determine her mating receptivity.

The VNO projects to a structure called the **accessory olfactory bulb** (AOB). In rodents, this bulb is located at the posterior dorsal surface of the main olfactory bulb (MOB). It contains the same types of cells and the same laminae as the main olfactory bulb, though they are less clearly differentiated. The AOB and MOB are anatomically distinct, and this separation continues also in their central pathways.

How are the various signals transduced in the VNO for eventual processing in the AOB? The first evidence came from a novel approach in which differential screening of cDNA libraries constructed from single VNO cells in the rat led to the identification of a family of presumed seven-transmembrane, G-coupled receptors that was distinct from the gene family of putative receptors in the main olfactory epithelium.[129] Further studies revealed a second family in the rat[130] and mouse[131] that has a very long N-terminal extracellular domain, and shares homology with Ca^{2+} sensory receptors and metabotropic glutamate receptors. These two classes of putative receptors are associated with G proteins, which themselves belong to two distinct classes that define separate anatomical subsystems. By *in situ* hybridization and immunocytochemical antibody staining, Giα2 was found to be present in receptor neurons whose cell bodies are located in the middle layer of the VNO[132] and that project to the anterior part of the AOB.[133] In contrast, Goα is expressed in receptor neurons whose cell bodies are located in the basal layer of the VNO and whose axons project to the posterior part of the AOB.

Although it is widely believed that these membrane proteins function as pheromone receptors, there is as yet no evidence that they have such a function. In addition, the only well-documented pheromone in mammals, androstenedione in pigs, mediates its effects through the main olfactory pathway rather than through the VNO.[77] The receptor functions of these proteins thus await further study.

Olfactory Memory Is Mediated by Dendrodendritic Synapses in the Accessory Olfactory Bulb

Changes in glomerular structure and function associated with learning of odors can be readily demonstrated in the main olfactory bulb in the postnatal period.[134] The accessory olfactory bulb provides evidence that olfactory learning can also take place in adults. A dramatic example is the so-called Bruce effect, in which a pregnant female mouse will abort its fetus if exposed within the first few days to the odor of a strange male but not a familiar male, implying that it has learned and remembered the familiar but not the strange odor.[135]

It was first shown that this effect is mediated through the VNO–AOB pathway. Interest then became focused on the dendrodendritic synapses between mitral/tufted and granule cells.[136] More recent studies indicate that changes in the efficacy of these synapses mediate the olfactory learning represented by the Bruce effect. The mGluR2 subtype of the metabotropic glutamate receptor family, found predominantly on granule cell dendrites, may play a critical role in this learning.[137,138] The mechanism may be summarized as follows (see Fig. 25.24, lower left). Release of glutamate from a mitral cell activates the mGluR2 receptor on the granule cells it contacts and reduces reciprocal inhibitory transmission from those granule cells, thereby

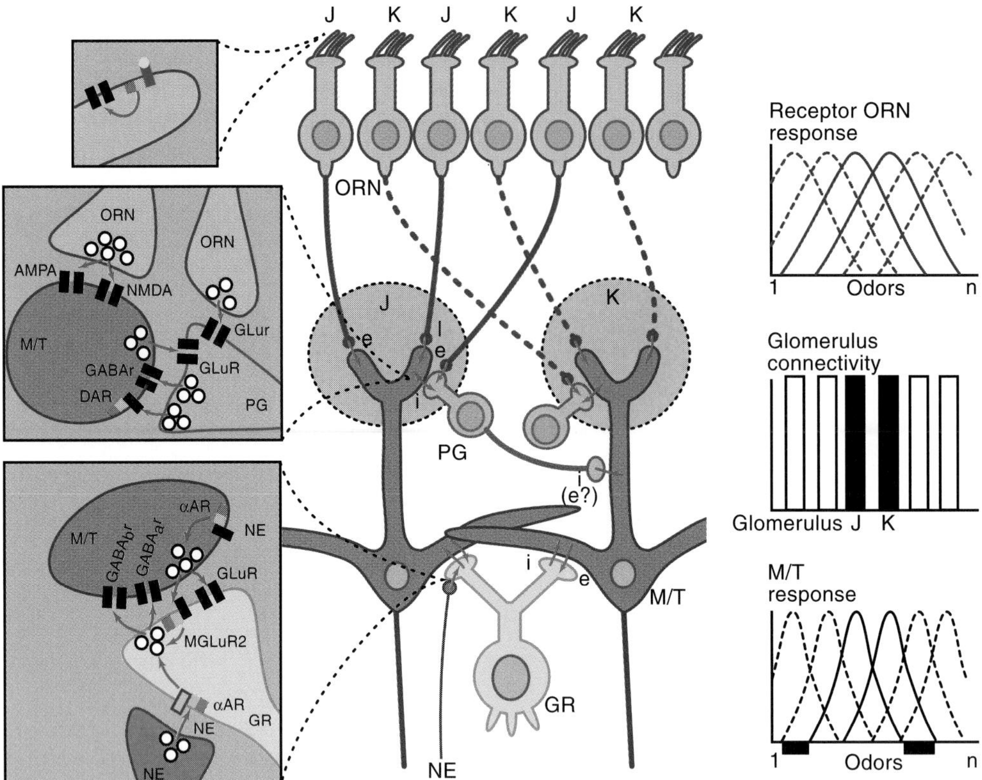

FIGURE 25.24 Summary of several of the key types of synaptic receptors and their involvement in olfactory bulb microcircuits underlying odor processing and odor memory. See text for full explanation. From Shepherd and Greer.[114]

enhancing the mitral cell's input to the cortex. Infusions of a specific mGluR2 agonist, DCG-IV, into the AOB of a female mouse, coupled with exposure to a pheromone of a male mouse, induces the formation of a memory of that pheromone that ordinarily would occur only during mating to this male. If the female now mates with a second male, she forms a memory for the second male's pheromone in the usual manner. However, the memory of the first pheromone, formed by mGluR2 activation but without mating, prevents the pregnancy block that ordinarily would occur on reexposure to the first male after the female has mated with the second male. Thus, a reduction of reciprocal inhibition from granule cells to mitral cells, through mGluR2 activation, mimicks the memory formation that occurs during mating. Noradrenergic modulation of the granule cell spines also contributes to the formation of the memory by presynaptically reducing the activation of the granule cell spines. Thus, these mechanisms of odor learning involve the same microcircuits as those involved in odor discrimination, as described earlier, but modulated by specific subsets of synaptic receptors.

Olfactory Bulb Output Goes Directly to Olfactory Cortex

The output of the olfactory bulb is carried by the axons of mitral cells and their smaller counterparts, the tufted cells (see Fig. 25.12). These axons project directly to olfactory cortex in the forebrain, the only sensory system to have this immediate access to the forebrain (all other sensory systems project first to the spinal cord, brainstem, or diencephalon, as noted in other chapters). Olfactory cortex has a three-layer structure that represents the primitive anlage of forebrain cortex found in fish, amphibia, and reptiles (see Fig. 25.25). The principal neuron is the pyramidal cell, with apical and basal dendrites bearing spines and recurrent collaterals connecting both to inhibitory interneurons and directly to other pyramidal cells. The M/T axons make excitatory connections to spines on the distal apical dendrites. Processing in the cortex takes place by means of the intrinsic excitatory and inhibitory synaptic circuits. Together these neural elements and their connections constitute a basic, or canonical, circuit. This circuit may be present in other

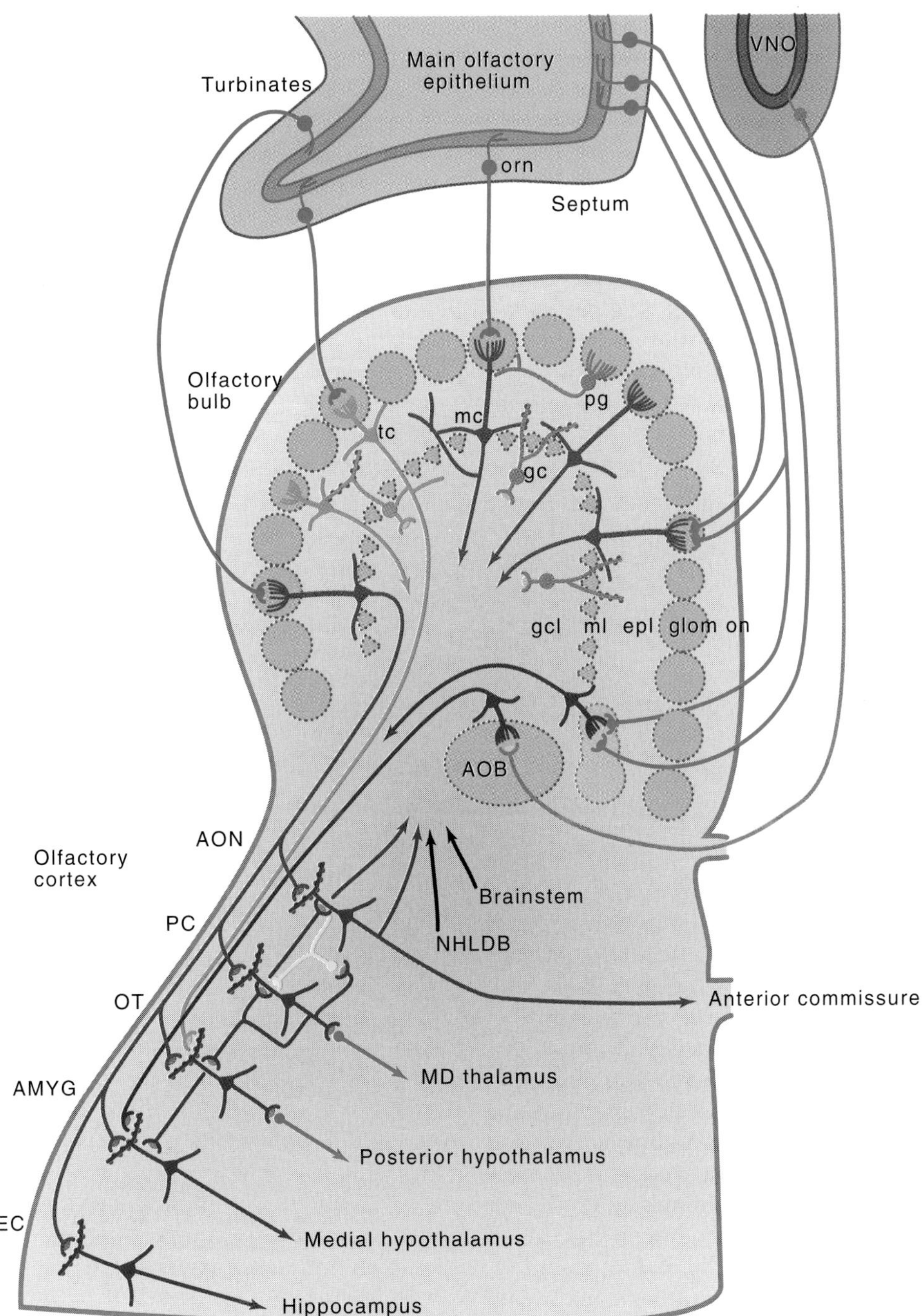

FIGURE 25.25 Summary of main projection pathways in the olfactory system. AON, anterior olfactory nucleus; PC, pyriform cortex; OT, olfactory tubercle; AMYG, amygdala; TEC, transitional entorhinal cortex; NHLDB, nucleus of horizontal limb of diagonal band; MD, mediodorsal; other abbreviations as before. From Shepherd.[89]

types of cortex, such hippocampus and neocortex, suggesting that it represents the simplest type of cortical circuit that is adapted and elaborated in the other types to carry out different or more complex types of functional operations.

Like cortical regions in other systems, the olfactory cortex is differentiated into several different areas. The main area is the **pyriform** (sometimes called the prepyriform) cortex. This area receives input from both M and T cells. It projects to mediodorsal thalamus, which in turn projects to medial and lateral orbitofrontal areas of the neocortex. It is at this level that conscious perception of odors presumably takes place. Second is the olfactory **tubercle,** which receives input mainly from T cells. In the primate this is called the anterior perforated substance because of the numerous blood vessels that penetrate its surface at the base of the brain. Its structure is modified by accumulations of small cells, called islets of Calleja, which contain high densities of dopaminergic nerve terminals. Third is the **cortico–medial** group of amygdalar nuclei, which receive specific input from the accessory olfactory bulb. Fourth is the lateral **entorhinal** area, which projects to the hippocampus. Finally is the **anterior olfactory** nucleus, a sheet of cells just posterior to the olfactory bulb in subprimates.

Summary

Taste receptors give rise to a limited number of sensations. The gustatory system processes these signals and extracts information about taste intensity and quality. The olfactory system must detect and discriminate between expected and unpredictable odors. The neural mechanisms underlying olfactory discrimination involve synaptic circuits that extract and compare the signals processed in glomeruli. Information within the glomeruli is processed through a series of excitatory and inhibitory signals mediated by various neurotransmitters and second messengers. The excitatory circuits amplify the signal; the inhibitory circuits serve to discriminate between the stimuli. Animals are very good at recognizing the complex odors that identify individuals of the species. This is usually signaled by a blend of two or more compounds representing an odor object of behavioral significance to the organism. Many cells may be able to respond to one molecular type but only a few may respond maximally to the blend. Anatomically, the olfactory system is organized topographically. Actual perception of odors is believed to occur in the frontal cortex of mammals and in higher brain centers called mushroom bodies in insects. In addition to the main olfactory pathway in vertebrates, a parallel pathway exists for transmitting signals from less volatile odorous compounds. This is important in reptiles and mammals for detecting odors that stimulate sexual responses.

References

Cited

1. Smith, D. V., and Shipley, M. T. (1995). The gustatory system. In *Neuroscience in Medicine* (P. M. Conn, ed.), pp. 511–519. Lippincott, Philadelphia.
2. Delay, R. J., Kinnamon, J. C., and Roper, S. D. (1986). Ultrastructure of mouse vallate taste buds: II. Cell types and cell lineage. *J. Comp. Neurol.* **253:** 242–252.
3. Miller, I. J., Jr., and Smith, D. V. (1984). Quantitative taste bud distribution in the hamster. *Physiol. Behav.* **32:** 275–285.
4. Beidler, L. M., and Smallman, R. (1965). Renewal of cells within taste buds. *J. Cell Biol.* **27:** 263–272.
5. Oakley, B. (1967). Altered taste responses from cross-regenerated taste nerves in the rat. In *Olfaction and Taste II* (T. Hayashi, ed.), pp. 535–547. Pergamon, London.
6. Smith, D. V., Klevitsky, R., Akeson, R. A., and Shipley, M. T. (1994). Expression of the neural cell adhesion molecule (NCAM) and polysialic acid during taste bud degeneration and regeneration. *J. Comp. Neurol.* **347:** 187–196.
7. Erickson, R. P. (1977). The role of "primaries" in taste research. In *Olfaction and Taste VI* (J. LeMagnen and P. MacLeod, eds.), pp. 369–376. Information Retrieval, London.
8. McBurney, D. H. (1974). Are there primary tastes for man? *Chem. Senses Flavour* **1:** 17–28.
9. Pfaffmann, C. (1964). Taste, its sensory and motivating properties. *Am. Sci.* **52:** 187–206.
10. Frank, M. (1973). An analysis of hamster afferent taste nerve response functions. *J. Gen. Physiol.* **61:** 588–618.
11. Pfaffman, C. (1941). Gustatory afferent impulses. *J. Cell. Comp. Physiol.* **17:** 243–258.
12. Pfaffmann, C. (1955). Gustatory nerve impulses in rat, cat and rabbit. *J. Neurophysiol.* **18:** 429–440.
13. Travers, J. B., and Smith, D. V. (1979). Gustatory sensitivities in neurons of the hamster nucleus tractus solitarius. *Sens. Processes* **3:** 1–26.
14. Van Buskirk, R. L., and Smith, D. V. (1981). Taste sensitivity of hamster parabrachial pontine neurons. *J. Neurophysiol.* **45:** 144–171.
15. Smith, D. V., Travers, J. B., and Van Buskirk, R. L. (1979). Brainstem correlates of gustatory similarity in the hamster. *Brain Res. Bull.* **4:** 359–372.
16. Crick, F. H. C. (1979). Thinking about the brain. *Sci. Am.* **241:** 219–232.
17. Erickson, R. P. (1970). Parallel "population" neural coding in feature extraction. In *The Neurosciences: Third Study Program* (F. O. Schmitt and F. G. Worden, eds.), pp. 155–170. MIT Press, Cambridge, MA.
18. Yamamoto, T., and Yuyama, N. (1987). On a neural mechanism for cortical processing of taste quality in the rat. *Brain Res.* **400:** 312–320.
19. Frank, M. E., Bieber, S. L., and Smith, D. V. (1988). The organization of taste sensibilities in hamster chorda tympani nerve fibers. *J. Gen. Physiol.* **91:** 861–896.
20. McPheeters, M., Hettinger, T. P., Nuding, S. C., Savoy, L. D., Whitehead, M. C., and Frank, M. E. (1990). Taste-responsiveness neurons and their locations in the solitary nucleus of the hamster. *Neuroscience* **34:** 745–758.
21. Smith, D. V., Van Buskirk, R. L., Travers, J. B., and Bieber, S. L. (1983). Gustatory neuron types in hamster brain stem. *J. Neurophysiol.* **50:** 522–540.
22. Hanamori, T., Miller, I. J., Jr., and Smith, D. V. (1988). Gustatory responsiveness of fibers in the hamster glossopharyngeal nerve. *J. Neurophysiol.* **60:** 478–498.
23. Frank, M. E. (1991). Taste-responsive neurons of the glossopharyngeal nerve of the rat. *J. Neurophysiol.* **65:** 1452–1463.
24. Smith, D. V., and Hanamori, T. (1991). Organization of gustatory sensitivities in hamster superior laryngeal nerve fibers. *J. Neurophysiol.* **65:** 1098–1114.
25. Shingai, T. (1977). Ionic mechanisms of water receptors in the laryngeal mucosa of the rabbit. *Jpn. J. Physiol.* **27:** 27–42.
26. Frank, M. E., and Nowlis, G. H. (1989). Learned aversions and taste qualities in hamsters. *Chem. Senses* **14:** 379–394.
27. Spector, A. C., and Grill, H. J. (1988). Differences in the taste

quality of maltose and sucrose in rats: Issues involving the generalizations of conditioned taste aversions. *Chem. Senses* **13:** 95–113.
28. Spector, A. C., and Grill, H. J. (1992). Salt taste discrimination after bilateral section of the chorda tympani or glossopharyngeal nerves. *Am. J. Physiol.* **263:** R169–R176.
29. Erickson, R. P. (1982). The "across-fiber pattern" theory: An organizing principle for molar neural function. *Contrib. Sens. Physiol.* **6:** 79–110.
30. Pfaffmann, C. (1959). The afferent code for sensory quality. *Am. Psychol.* **14:** 226–232.
31. Pfaffmann, C. (1974). Specificity of the sweet receptors of the squirrel monkey. *Chem. Senses Flavour* **1:** 61–67.
32. Pfaffmann, C., Frank, M., Bartoshuk, L. M., and Snell, T. C. (1976). Coding gustatory information in the squirrel monkey chorda tympani. *Prog. Psychobiol. Physiolog. Psychol.* **6:** 1–27.
33. Smith, D. V., and Frank, M. E. (1993). Sensory coding by peripheral taste fibers. In *Mechanisms of Taste Transduction* (S. A. Simon and S. D. Roper, eds.), pp. 295–338. CRC Press, Boca Raton, FL.
34. Smith, D. V., Van Buskirk, R. L., Travers, J. B., and Bieber, S. L. (1983). Coding of taste stimuli by hamster brain stem neurons. *J. Neurophysiol.* **50:** 541–558.
35. Erickson, R. P., Doetsch, G. S., and Marshall, D. A. (1965). The gustatory neural response function. *J. Gen. Physiol.* **49:** 247–263.
36. Ganchrow, J. R., and Erickson, R. P. (1970). Neural correlates of gustatory intensity and quality. *J. Neurophysiol.* **33:** 768–783.
37. Erickson, R. P. (1968). Stimulus coding in topographic and nontopographic afferent modalities: On the significance of the activity of individual sensory neurons. *Psychol. Rev.* **75:** 447–465.
38. Erickson, R. P. (1984). On the neural basis of behavior. *Am. Sci.* **72:** 233–241.
39. Woolston, D. C., and Erickson, R. P. (1979). Concept of neuron types in gustation in the rat. *J. Neurophysiol.* **42:** 1390–1409.
40. Rowe, M. H., and Stone, J. (1977). Naming of neurones: Classification and naming of cat retinal ganglion cells. *Brain, Behav. Evol.* **14:** 185–216.
41. Tyner, C. F. (1975). The naming of neurons: Applications of taxonomic theory to the study of cellular populations. *Brain, Behav. Evol.* **12:** 75–96.
42. Erickson, R. P., Covey, E., and Doetsch, G. S. (1980). Neuron and stimulus typologies in the rat gustatory system. *Brain Res.* **196:** 513–519.
43. Frank, M. E., Contreras, R. J., and Hettinger, T. P. (1983). Nerve fibers sensitive to ionic taste stimuli in chorda tympani of the rat. *J. Neurophysiol.* **50:** 941–960.
44. Smith, D. V. (1985). The neural representation of gustatory quality. *Prog. Clin. Biol. Res.* **176:** 75–97.
45. Marks, W. B., Dobelle, W. H., and MacNichol, E. F., Jr. (1964). Visual pigments of single primate cones. *Science* **143:** 1181–1183.
46. Boynton, R. M. (1966). Vision. In *Experimental Methods and Instrumentation in Psychology* (J. Sidowski, ed.), pp. 273–330. McGraw Hill, New York.
47. Boynton, R. M. (1971). Color vision. In *Woodworth and Schlosberg's Experimental Psychology* (J. W. Kling and L. A. Riggs, eds.), pp. 315–368. Holt, Rinehart & Winston, New York.
48. Scott, T. R., and Giza, B. K. (1990). Coding channels in the taste system of the rat. *Science* **249:** 1585–1587.
49. Boggs, D. F., and Bartlett, D., Jr. (1982). Chemical specificity of a laryngeal apneic reflex in puppies. *J. Appl. Physiol.* **53:** 455–462.
50. Shingai, T., Miyaoka, Y., and Shimada, K. (1988). Diuresis mediated by the superior laryngeal nerve in rats. *Physiol. Behav.* **44:** 431–433.
51. Grill, H. J., and Norgren, R. (1978). The taste reactivity test. I. Mimetic responses to gustatory stimuli in neurologically normal rats. *Brain Res.* **143:** 263–280.
52. Berridge, K. C., and Grill, H. J. (1984). Isohedonic tastes support a two-dimensional hypothesis of palatability. *Appetite* **4:** 221–231.
53. Brining, S. K., Belecky, T. L., and Smith, D. V. (1991). Taste reactivity in the hamster. *Physiol. Behav.* **49:** 1265–1272.
54. Grill, H. J., and Norgren, R. (1978). The taste reactivity test. II. Mimetic responses to gustatory stimuli in chronic thalamic and decerebrate rats. *Brain Res.* **143:** 281–297.
55. Nowlis, G. H. (1977). From reflex to representation: Taste-elicited tongue movements in the human newborn. In *Taste and Development: The Genesis of Sweet Preference* (J. M. Weiffenbach, ed.), DHEW Publ. No. (NIH) 77-1068, pp. 190–203. USDHEW, Bethesda, MD.
56. Wang, L., and Bradley, R. M. (1995). In vito study of different synaptic transmission in the rostral gustatory zone of the rat nucleus of the solitary tract. *Brain Res.* **702:** 188–198.
57. Li, C.-S., and Smith, D. V. (1997). Glutamate receptor antagonists block gustatory afferent input to the nucleus of the solitary tract. *J. Neurophysiol.* **77:** 1514–1525.
58. Davis, B. J., and Smith, D. V. (1997). Substance P modulates taste responses in the nucleus of the solitary tract of the hamster. *Neuroreport* **8:** 1723–1727.
59. King, M. S., Wang, L., and Bradley, R. M. (1993). Substance P excites neurons in the gustatory zone of the rat nucleus tractus solitarius. *Brain Res.* **619:** 120–130.
59a. Wang, L., and Bradley, R. M. (1993). Influence of GABA on neurons of the gustatory zone of the rat nucleus of the solitary tract. *Brain Res.* **616:** 144–153.
60. Liu, H., Behbehani, M., and Smith, D. V. (1993). The influence of GABA on cells in the gustatory region of the hamster solitary nucleus. *Chem. Senses* **18:** 285–305.
61. Giza, B. K., and Scott, T. R. (1991). The effect of amiloride on taste-evoked activity in the nucleus tractus solitarius of the rat. *Brain Res.* **550:** 247–256.
62. DiLorenzo, P. M. (1990). Corticofugal influence on taste responses in the parabrachial pons of the rat. *Brain Res.* **530:** 73–84.
63. Saper, C. B. (1982). Reciprocal parabrachial-cortical connections in the rat. *Brain Res.* **242:** 33–40.
64. Shipley, M. T., and Sanders, M. S. (1982). Special senses are really special: Evidence for a reciprocal, bilateral pathway between insular cortex and nucleus parabrachialis. *Brain Res. Bull.* **8:** 493–501.
65. Shipley, M. T. (1982). Insular cortex projections to the nucleus of the solitary tract and brainstem visceromotor nuclei in the mouse. *Brain Res. Bull.* **8:** 139–148.
66. Liu, H., Behbehani, M., and Smith, D. V. (1993). The influence of gustatory cortex on taste cells of the solitary nucleus of the hamster. *Neurosci. Abstr.* **19:** 1430.
67. Smith, D. V., Liu, H., and Vogt, M. B. (1994). Neural coding of aversive and appetitive gustatory stimuli: Interactions in the hamster brainstem. *Physiol. Behav.* **56:** 1189–1196.
68. Hildebrand, J. G., and Shepherd, G. M. (1997). Molecular mechanisms of olfactory discrimination: Converging evidence for common principles across phyla. *Annu. Rev. Neurosci.*
69. Boeckh, J., Kaissling, K. E., and Schneider, D. (1966). Insect olfactory receptors. *Cold Spring Harbor Symp. Quant. Biol.*
70. Gesteland, R. C., Lettvin, J. Y., and Pitts, W. H. (1965). Chemical transmission in the nose of the frog. *J. Physiol. (London)* **181:** 525–559.
71. Getchell, T. V., and Shepherd, G. M. (1978). Responses of olfactory receptor cells to step pulses of odour at different concentrations in the salamander. *J. Physiol. (London)* **282:** 521–540.

72. Firestein, S., Shepherd, G. M., and Werblin, F. S. (1990). Time course of the membrane current underlying sensory transduction in salamander olfactory receptor neurones. *J. Physiol. (London)* **430:** 135–158.

73. Ache, B. W. (1994). Towards a common strategy for transducing olfactory information. *Semin. Cell Biol.* **5:** 55–64.

74. McClintock, T. S., and Ache, B. W. (1989). Hyperpolarizing receptor potentials in lobster olfactory receptor cells: Implications for transduction and mixture suppression. *Chem. Senses* **14:** 637–647.

75. Dionne, V. E. (1994). Emerging complexity of odor transduction. *Proc. Natl. Acad. Sci. U.S.A.* **91:** 6253–6254.

76. Sato, T., Hirono, J., Tonoike, M., and Takebayashi, M. (1994). Tuning specificities to aliphatic odorants in mouse olfactory receptor neurons and their local distribution. *J. Neurophysiol.* **72:** 2980–2989.

77. Dorries, K. M., Adkins-Regan, E., and Halpern, B. P. (1995). Olfactory sensitivity to the pheromone, androstenone, is sexually dimorphic in the pig. *Physiol. Behav.* **57:** 255–259.

78. Mori, K. (1992). Differential specificities of single mitral cells in rabbit olfactory bulb for a homologous series of fatty acid odor molecules. *J. Neurophysiol.* **67:** 786–789.

79. Lancet, D. (1986). Vertebrate olfactory reception. *Annu. Rev. Neurosci.* **9:** 329–355.

80. Chess, A., Simon, I., Cedar, H., and Axel, R. (1994). Allelic inactivation regulates olfactory receptor gene expression. *Cell (Cambridge, Mass.)* **78:** 823–834.

81. Adrian, E. D. (1950). The electrical activity of the mammalian olfactory bulb. *Electroencephalogr. Clin. Neurophysiol.* **2:** 377–388.

82. Clark, W. E. le Gros (1957). Inquiries into the anatomical basis of olfactory discrimination. *Proc. R. Soc. London, Ser. B* **146:** 299–319.

83. Land, L. J. (1973), Localized projection of olfactory nerves to rabbit olfactory bulb. *Brain Res.* **63:** 153–166.

84. Pedersen, P. E., Jastreboff, P. J., Stewart, W. B., and Shepherd, G. M. (1986). Mapping of an olfactory receptor population that projects to a specific region in the rat olfactory bulb. *J. Comp. Neurol.* **250:** 93–108.

85. Astic, L., and Saucier, D. (1986). Anatomical mapping of the neuroepithelial projection to the olfactory bulb in the rat. *Brain Res. Bull.* **16:** 445–454.

86. Mori, K., Fujita, S. C., Imamura, K., and Obata, K. (1985). *J. Comp. Neurol.* **242:** 214–229.

87. Mori, K., and Yoshihara, Y. (1995). Molecular recognition and olfactory processing in the mammalian olfactory system. *Prog. Neurobiol.* **45:** 585–619.

88. Schwob, J. E. (1992). The biochemistry of olfactory neurons: Stages of differentiation and neuronal subsets. In *Science of Olfaction* (M. J. Serby and K. L. Chobor, eds.), pp. 80–125. Springer-Verlag, New York.

89. Shepherd, G. M. (1994). *Neurobiology* 4th ed. Oxford University Press, New York.

90. Ressler, K. J., Sullivan, S. L., and Buck, L. B. (1993). A zonal organization of odorant receptor gene expression in the olfactory epithelium. *Cell (Cambridge, Mass.)* **73:** 597–609.

91. Kauer, J. S. (1981). Olfactory receptor cell staining using horseradish peroxidase. *Anat. Rec.* **200:** 331–336.

92. Riddle, D. R., and Oakley, B. (1991). Evaluation of projection patterns in the primary olfactory system of rainbow trout. *J. Neurosci.* **11:** 3752–3762.

93. Allison, A. C. (1952). The morphology of the olfactory system in the vertebrates. *Biol. Rev. Cambridge Philos. Soc.* **28:** 195–244.

94. Meisami, E., and Sendera, T. J. (1993). Morphometry of rat olfactory bulbs stained for cytochrome oxidase reveals that the entire population of glomeruli forms early in the neonatal period. *Brain Res. Dev. Brain Res.* **71:** 253–257.

95. van Drongelen, W., Holley, A., and Doving, K. B. (1978). Convergence in the olfactory system: Quantitative aspects of odour sensitivity. *J. Theor. Biol.* **71:** 39–48.

96. Rospars, J. P., and Hildebrand, J. G. (1992). Anatomical identification of glomeruli in the antennal lobes of the male sphinx moth. *Manduca sexta. Cell Tissue Res.* **270:** 205–227.

97. Boeckh, J., and Tolbert, L. P. (1993). Synaptic organization and development of the antennal lobe in insects. *Microsc. Res. Tech.* **24:** 260–280.

98. Matsumoto, S. G., and Hildebrand, J. G. (1981). Olfactory mechanisms in the moth *Manduca sexta*: Response characteristics and morphology of central neurons in the antennal lobes. *Proc. R. Soc. London, Ser. B* **213:** 249–277.

99. Stewart, W. B., Kauer, J. S., and Shepherd, G. M. (1979). Functional organization of rat olfactory bulb analyzed by the 2-deoxyglucose method. *J. Comp. Neurol.* **185:** 715–734.

100. Teicher, M. H., Stewart, W. B., Kauer, J. S., and Shepherd, G. M. (1980). Suckling pheromone stimulation of a modified glomerular region in the developing rat olfactory bulb revealed by the 2-deoxyglucose method. *Brain Res.* **194:** 530–535.

101. Deleted at proof.

102. Guthrie, K. M., Anderson, A. J., Leon, M., and Gall, C. (1993). Odor-induced increases in *c-fos* mRNA expression reveal an anatomical 'unit' for odor processing in olfactory bulb. *Proc. Natl. Acad. Sci. U.S.A.* **90:** 3329–3333.

103. Kauer, J. S., and Cinelli, A. R. (1993). Are there structural and functional modules in the vertebrate olfactory bulb? *Microsc. Res. Tech.* **24:** 157–167.

104. Friedrich, R., and Korshing, S. I. (1996). Combinatorial and chemotopic odorant coding in the zebra fish olfactory bulb visualized by optical imaging. *Neuron* **18:** 737–752.

105. Joerges, J., Küttner, A., Galizia, C. G., and Menzel, R. (1997). Representations of odours and odour mixtures visualized in the honeybee brain. *Nature* **387:** 285–288.

106. Vassar, R., Ngai, J., and Axel, R. (1993). Spatial segregation of odorant receptor expression in the mammalian olfactory epithelium. *Cell (Cambridge, Mass.)* **74:** 309–318.

107. Vassar, R., Chou, S. K., Sitcheran, R., Nuñez, J. M., Vosshall, L. B., and Axel, R. (1994). Topographic organization of sensory projections to the olfactory bulb. *Cell (Cambridge, Mass.)* **79:** 981–991.

108. Ressler, K. J., Sullivan, S. L., and Buck, L. B. (1994). Information coding in the olfactory system: Evidence for a stereotyped and highly organized epitope map in the olfactory bulb. *Cell (Cambridge, Mass.)* **79:** 1245–1255.

109. Mombaerts, P., Wang, F., Dulac, C., Chao, S. K., Nemes, A., Mendelsohn, M., Edmondson, J., and Axel, R. (1996). Visualizing an olfactory sensory map. *Cell (Cambridge, Mass.)* **87:** 675–686.

110. Goulding, E. H., Ngai, J., Kramer, R. H., Colicos, S., Axel, R., Siegelbaum, S. A., and Chess, A. (1992). Molecular cloning and single-channel properties of the cyclic nucleotide-gated channel from catfish olfactory neurons. *Neuron* **8:** 45–48.

111. Halasz, N., and Greer, C. A. (1993). Terminal arborizations of olfactory nerve fibers in the glomeruli of the olfactory bulb. *J. Comp. Neurobiol.* **337:** 307–316.

112. Shepherd, G. M., ed. (1990). *The Synaptic Organization of the Brain.* Oxford University Press, New York.

113. Mori, K., and Shepherd, G. M. (1994). Emerging principles of molecular signal processing by mitral/tufted cells in the olfactory bulb. *Semin. Cell Biol.* **5:** 65–74.

114. Shepherd, G. M., and Greer, C. A. (1998). Olfactory bulb. In

The Synaptic Organization of the Brain (G. M. Shepherd, ed.), 4th ed., pp. 159–203. Oxford University Press, New York.

115. Treloar, H., Walters, E., Margolis, F., and Key, B. (1996). Olfactory glomeruli are innervated by more than one distinct subset of primary sensory olfactory neurons in mice. *J. Comp. Neurol.* **367:** 550–567.
116. Leveteau, J., and MacLeod, P. (1965). Olfactory discrimination in the rabbit olfactory glomerulus. *Science* **175:** 170–178.
117. Breer, H., and Shepherd, G. M. (1993). Implications of the NO/cGMP system for olfaction. *Trends Neurosci.* **16:** 5–9.
118. Rall, W., Shepherd, G. M., Reese, T. S., and Brightman, M. W. (1966). Dendrodendritic synaptic pathway for inhibition in the olfactory bulb. *Exp. Neurol.* **14:** 44–56.
119. Rall, W., and Shepherd, G. M. (1968). Theoretical reconstruction of field potentials and dendrodendritic synaptic interactions in olfactory bulb. *J. Neurophysiol.* **31:** 884–915.
120. Laurent, G., Wehr, M., and Davidowitz, H. 1996. Temporal representations of odors in an olfactory network. *J. Neurosci.* **16:** 3837–3847.
121. Hamilton, K., and Kauer, J. S. (1989). Patterns of intracellular potentials in salamander mitral/tufted cells in response to odor stimulation. *J. Neurophysiol.* **62:** 609–625.
122. Christensen, T. A., Waldrop, B. R., Harrow, I. D., and Hildebrand, J. G. (1993). Local interneurons and information processing in the olfactory glomeruli of the moth *Manduca sexta*. *J. Comp. Physiol. A* **173:** 385–399.
123. Wellis, D. P., and Scott, J. W. (1991). Localized denervation demonstrates the innervation pattern of olfactory bulb glomeruli and second order cells. *J. Comp. Neurol.* **304:** 544–554.
124. Yokoi, M., Mori, K., and Nakanishi, S. (1995). Refinement of odor molecule tuning by dendrodendritic synaptic inhibition in the olfactory bulb. *Proc. Natl. Acad. Sci. U.S.A.* **92:** 3371–3375.
125. Pager, J. (1978). Ascending olfactory information and centrifugal influxes contributing to a nutritional modulation of the rat mitral cell responses. *Brain Res.* **140:** 251–269.
126. Sallaz, M., and Jourdan, F. (1992). Apomorphine disrupts odour-induced patterns of glomerular activation in the olfactory bulb. *NeuroReport* **3:** 833–836.
127. Coopersmith, R., Weihmuller, F. B., Kirstein, C. L., Marshall, J. F., and Leon, M. (1991). Extracellular dopamine increases in the neonatal olfactory bulb during odor preference training. *Brain Res.* **564:** 149–153.
128. Trombley, P. Q., and Shepherd, G. M. (1994). Glycine exerts potent inhibitory actions on mammalian olfactory bulb neurons. *J. Neurophysiol.* **71:** 761–767.
129. Dulac, C., and Axel, R. (1995). A novel family of genes encoding putative pheromone receptors in mammals. *Cell (Cambridge, Mass.)* **83:** 195–206.
130. Herrada, G., and Dulac, C. (1997). A novel family of putative pheromone receptors in mammals with a topographically organized and sexually dimorphic distribution. *Cell (Cambridge, Mass.)* **90:** 763–773.
131. Matsunami, H., and Buck, L. B. (1997). A multigene family encoding a diverse array of putative pheromone receptors in mammals. *Cell (Cambridge, Mass.)* **90:** 775–784.
132. Halpern, M., Shapiro, L. S., and Jia, C. (1995). Differential localization of G proteins in the opposum vomeronasal system. *Brain Res.* **677:** 157–161.
133. Jia, C., and Halpern, M. (1996). Subclasses of vomeronasal receptor neurons: differential expression of G proteins (G and G) and segregated projections to the accessory olfactory bulb. *Brain Res.* **719:** 117–128.
134. Woo, C. C., Coopersmith, R., and Leon, M. (1987). Localized changes in olfactory bulb morphology associated with early olfactory learning. *J. Comp. Neurol.* **263:** 113–125.
135. Bruce, H. M. (1959). An exteroceptive block to pregnancy in the mouse. *Nature (London)* **184:** 105.
136. Brennan, P., Kaba, H., and Keverne, E. B. (1990). Olfactory recognition: A simple memory system. *Science* **250:** 1223–1226.
137. Hayashi, Y., Momiyama, A., Takahashi, T., Ohishi, H., Ogawa-Meguro, R., Shigemoto, R., Mizuno, N., and Nakanishi, S. (1993). Role of a metabotropic glutamate receptor in synaptic modulation in the accessory olfactory bulb.. *Nature (London)* **336:** 687–690.
138. Kaba, H., Hayashi, Y., Higuchi, T., and Nakanishi, S. (1994). Induction of an olfactory memory by the activation of a metabotropic glutamate receptor. *Science* **265:** 262–264.

General

Axel, R. (1995). The molecular logic of smell. *Sci. Am.* 154–159.

Berkowicz, D. A., Trombley, P. Q., and Shepherd, G. M. (1994). Evidence for glutamate as the olfactory receptor cell neurotransmitter. *J. Neurophysiol.* **71:** 2557–2561.

Chen, W. R., Midtgaard, J., and Shepherd, G. M. (1997). Forward and backward propagation of dendritic impulses and their synaptic control in mitral cells. *Science* **278:** 463–467.

Ennis, M., Zimmer, L. A., and Shipley, M. T. (1996). Olfactory nerve stimulation activates rat mitral cells via NMDA and non-NMDA receptors in vitro. *NeuroReport* **7:** 989–992.

Firestein, S., and Shepherd, G. M. (1991). A kinetic model of the odor response in single olfactory receptor neurons. *J. Steroid Biochem. Mole. Biol.* **39:** 615–620.

Firestein, S., Darrow, B., and Shepherd, G. M. (1991). Activation of the sensory current in salamander olfactory receptor neurons depends on a G protein-mediated cAMP second messenger system. *Neuron* **6:** 825–835.

Firestein, S., Zufall, F., and Shepherd, G. M. (1991). Single odor-sensitive channels in olfactory receptor neurons are also gated by cyclic nucleotides. *J. Neurosci.* **11:** 3565–3572.

Hildebrand, J. G. (1995). Analysis of chemical signals by nervous systems. *Proc. Natl. Acad. Sci. U.S.A.* **92:** 67–74.

Hildebrand, J. G. (1995). Olfactory control of behavior in moths: Central processing of odor information and the functional significance of olfactory glomeruli. *J. Comp. Physiol.*

Shepherd, G. M. (1992). Modules for molecules. *Nature (London)* **358:** 457–458.

Shepherd, G. M. (1994). Discrimination of molecular signals by the olfactory receptor neuron. *Neuron* **13:** 771–790.

Siklos, L., Rickmann, M., Joo, F., Freeman, W. J., and Wolff, J. R. (1995). Chloride is preferentially accumulated in a subpopulation of dendrites and periglomerular cells of the main olfactory bulb in adult rats. *Neuroscience* **64:** 165–172.

C H A P T E R

26

Somatic Sensation

Stewart H. C. Hendry, Steven S. Hsiao, and Mary C. Bushnell

Sensory systems provide a continuous representation of the external world in a way that makes sense for the organism—a difficult task because the capacity of an individual neuron to carry information is small, whereas the amount of information that needs to be carried is huge. As with other sensory systems, the somatosensory system solves this problem by breaking down each sensory event into well-defined modalities that are carried forward along paths reserved for each modality. The somatosensory system differs qualitatively from other sensory systems in its multiple roles: it provides the central nervous system (CNS) with a continuous representation of the external and the internal state of the body and serves both sensory and motor functions. The many roles played by the somatosensory system can be divided into three essential functions:

A. **Exteroceptive functions** include the sensations of touch, temperature, and pain. These tell an animal about environmental stimuli and are further divided into three modalities:

1. **mechanoreception,** the sensation of all nonpainful mechanical stimuli;
2. **thermoreception,** the sensation of heat and cold;
3. **nociception**, the sensation of pain, both burning pain and sharp pain.

B. **Proprioceptive functions** include the kinesthetic senses of position and movement.[1] They rely on input from muscles, tendons, and joints to provide information about relative location of the body and limbs and the direction, force, and speed of their movement.

C. **Interoceptive functions** arise from sensory receptors in the internal organs and provide information about the health and well-being of the viscera. Included in these functions is some information that reaches consciousness and some that does not.

Each of the broad somatosensory modalities (e.g., mechanoreception) is further divided into submodalities (e.g., flutter vs vibration). At its most fundamental, a sensory submodality is the sensation produced when a single type of primary sensory axon is active. This definition makes plain the principles of receptor specificity and modality segregation. Together, they form the basis for the widely accepted view that stimulation of a single receptor produces activity along a select path of neurons in the CNS. It is this information that permits the organism to accurately determine both the particular kind of stimulus that has occurred and its location on the body.

In this chapter we review how each of the somatosensory modalities is sensed by the peripheral nervous system, carried into the CNS, and processed to produce a conscious perception. Beginning with a discussion of peripheral mechanisms of somesthesis and moving progressively through the CNS toward a merger of sensory systems with the motor system, we make the point that the function of the somatosensory system can be appreciated from the physiology of individual neurons and their anatomical relationships with one another. In this discussion, three themes will be repeated:

1. **modality segregation,** meaning the grouping together of neurons and axons that carry one type of information and their separation from neurons and axons that carry other types of information;
2. **somatotopy,** the orderly mapping of the body surface throughout the CNS;
3. **neural coding,** the means by which neurons communicate their information to one another and ulti-

mately to consciousness. Neural coding can be studied in the relationship between the behavior of the animal and the activity of the neuron. Studies of neural coding compare quantitative measures of behavior (psychophysics) with neuronal response (neurophysiology) to determine which groups of cells might be responsible for an observed behavior and how their activity mediates that behavior. Because they are complex and involve large numbers of neurons, the codes underlying only some aspects of tactile perception have been discovered. These will be discussed at greatest length.

PERIPHERAL MECHANISMS OF SOMATIC SENSATION

Mechanoreception Includes Perceptions of Form, Texture, and Vibration

Form Perception

The classical example of tactile form discrimination is the ability of a subject to detect when two points along the skin are stimulated. This test involves the application of two blunt points to the skin at a known separation, during which a subject is asked whether the sensation is that of a single point or two. When the separation between the two points is small, one point is perceived, but as the separation increases the sensation changes to that of two points. The minimal separation between two points that permits each to be perceived separately, referred to as the **two-point limen,** is a simple measure of **spatial acuity.** This acuity varies markedly across the skin surface (Fig. 26.1), with locations of highest acuity such as at the fingertips and around the mouth (two-point limens of 0.9 and 0.5 mm) being at least 2 orders of magnitude more sensitive than the region of lowest acuity—the back (60–70 mm).[2] Other means of measuring spatial acuity, such as detection of embossed letters that vary in height or bars that vary in spacing and orientation, demonstrate that the limits of tactile spatial acuity approach those imposed by the innervation density of the skin (Fig. 26.2).[3] Further, human subjects can read embossed dots that form Braille characters at rates of 100 characters per minute, thereby demonstrating that the somatosensory system is capable of not only high spatial resolution but also high temporal resolution.[4]

Texture Perception

Whereas form is easy to describe and to define in quantitative terms, the second feature associated with all surfaces—texture—is neither easily definable nor quantitatively accessible. Surfaces of different texture can be subjectively divided into groups that include slippery, rough, leathery, and wet, but relatively little is known of the number and character of elemental features in texture perception.

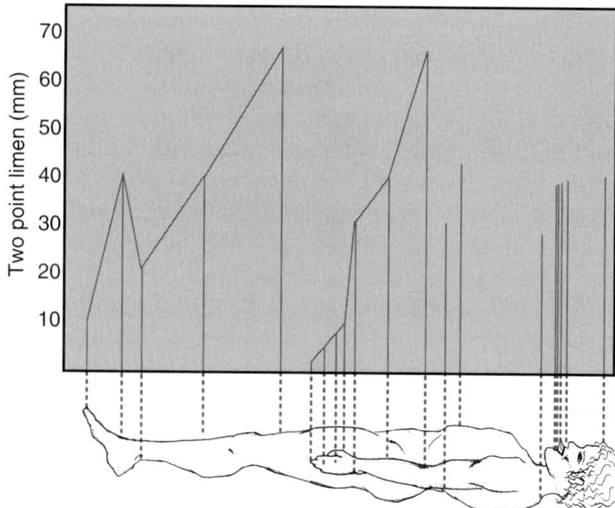

FIGURE 26.1 Variation in two-point limen (threshold) across the body surface. The graph plots the distance necessary for a human subject to detect two blunt probes as separate stimuli. That distance is lowest for the fingertips and mouth (approximately 10 mm) and highest for the legs, shoulders, and back (as much as 70 mm). From Patton, H. D., Sundsten, J. W., Crill, W. E., and Swanson, P.D ., eds. (1976). *Introduction to Basic Neurology,* p. 160. W. B. Saunders, Philadelphia.

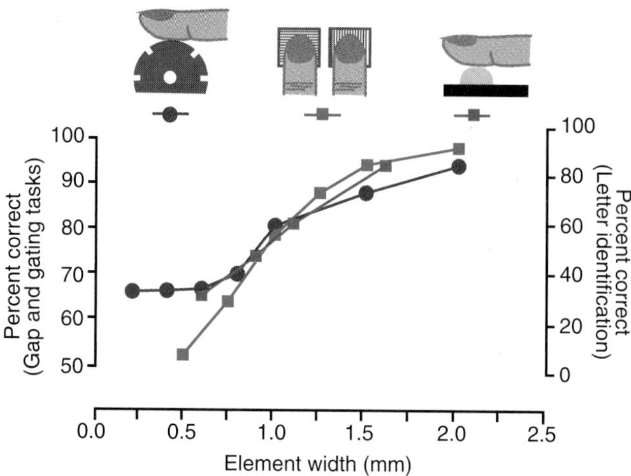

FIGURE 26.2 Results of psychophysical experiment illustrating that the threshold for tactile acuity on the finger pad is about 1 mm. In the experiments, subjects were required to correctly identify the presence of gaps that varied in width, the orientation of gratings that varied in spacing, or the letter embossed onto an otherwise smooth surface. An increase in stimulus dimension (width of the gap, spacing between gratings, or height of the letter) produced an increase in psychophysical performance in all three tasks.

The aspect of texture that has been studied most extensively is the perception of roughness. This perception is greatly affected by the density and height of the individual surface elements[5] but is less affected by changes in the force applied to a surface or the velocity in which it is scanned.

Vibration Perception

The tactile system easily discriminates mechanical vibrations transmitted through objects that are grasped by a human hand. From these vibrations arise the human ability to use and manipulate objects and to make sense of what is occurring at the working ends of tools. As an example, one can easily tell how smooth a road surface is by the vibrations transmitted through the steering wheel to the hands. Perceptually divided into two separate sensations—flutter, at frequencies of less than 40 Hz, and vibration at higher frequencies—the dual sense of flutter/vibration spans the range of frequencies from 5 to 400 Hz, with a definite maximal sensitivity around 200 Hz. Detection threshold, or the amount of skin indentation that produces a detectable stimulus, is a U-shaped curve with 50-μm indentations required at 10 Hz, less than 1 μm at 200 Hz, and more than 65 μm at 400 Hz. Once the detection threshold is exceeded, any further increase in stimulus amplitude produces a perception that the strength of the stimulus has increased.[6]

Peripheral Receptors Include Mechanoreceptors, Nociceptors, and Thermoreceptors

Mechanoreceptors

The body surface is covered by hairy skin and hairless or **glabrous skin,** embedded in which are four types of mechanoreceptors responsible for the detection of light mechanical stimuli.[7,8] Each mechanoreceptor can transduce a particular mechanical stimulus into a change in membrane potential. What differs among the various receptor types and what makes them uniquely sensitive to particular stimuli is where they are located in the skin and what surrounds their terminals (see Table 26.1).

Transduction of mechanical stimuli into neuronal activity begins with four well-characterized peripheral receptors in glabrous skin, two of which occupy superficial regions of the skin and two others deeper tissue. In each position, one type of receptor fires only briefly with the beginning and end of the stimulus and is therefore referred to as rapidly adapting (RA). In contrast, two other types of receptors (one deep and one superficial) maintain their activity so long as a stimulus is in place and are therefore referred to as slowly adapting (SA) (Fig. 26.3). As outlined below, these two subdivisions—deep versus cutaneous and rapidly adapting versus slowly adapting—are fundamental to the roles these receptors play in the discrimination and localization of mechanical stimuli.

Cutaneous receptors Superficial or cutaneous receptors respond to low-energy mechanical stimuli (light touch) delivered to the skin. They include Meissner corpuscles having rapidly adapting responses and Merkel disks having slowly adapting Type I (SAI) responses (Fig. 26.4).[8] The RA axons ending in Meissner corpuscles are responsible for the perception of localized movement along the skin, most noticeably as somatosensory feedback when objects are grasped. Comparisons of human psychophysics and physiology of RA afferents show that these receptors are responsible for the ability of humans to detect

TABLE 26.1 Summary of Primary Afferent Fibers and Their Roles

Modality	Submodality	Receptor	Fiber type	Conduction velocity (m s^{-1})	Role in perception
Mechanoreception	SAI	Merkel cell	Aβ	42–72	Pressure, form, texture
	RA	Meissner corpuscle	Aβ	42–72	Flutter, motion
	SAII	Ruffini corpuscle	Aβ	42–72	Unknown, possibly skin stretch
	PC	Pacinian corpuscle	Aβ	42–72	Vibration
Thermoreception	Warm	Bare nerve endings	C	0.5–1.2	Warmth
	Cold	Bare nerve endings	Aδ	12–36	Cold
Nociception	Small, myelinated	Bare nerve endings	Aδ	12–36	Sharp pain
	Unmyelinated	Bare nerve endings	C	0.5–1.2	Burning pain
Propioception	Joint afferents	Ruffini-like and paciniform-like endings, bare nerve endings	Aβ	42–72	Protective function against hyperextention
	Golgi tendon organs	Golgi endings	Aα	72–120	Muscle tension
	Muscle spindles	Type I	Aα	72–120	Muscle length and velocity
		Type II	Aβ	42–72	Muscle length
	SAII	Ruffini endings	Aβ	42–72	Joint angle?

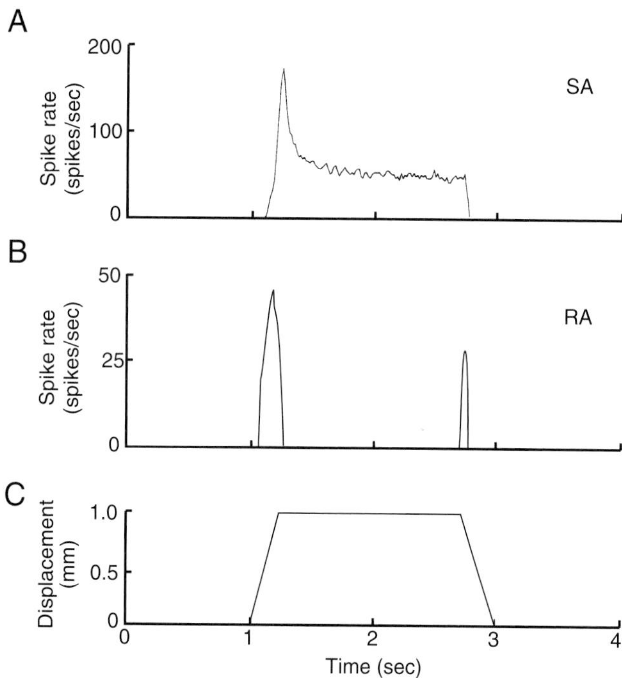

FIGURE 26.3 Response of slowly adapting (SA) and rapidly adapting (RA) peripheral afferents to as sustained indentation of the skin surface. SA afferents (A) respond with an early peak in activity and a lowered but sustained discharge that persists so long as the identation continues (C). In contrast, RA afferents (B) respond to the onset and termination of the stimulus and not to the continued indentation.

low-frequency vibration, a sensation referred to as flutter.[6]

A major function of Meissner corpuscles/RA afferents is the adjustment of grip force during the time that the object is lifted. These afferents respond with a brief burst of action potentials when objects move a small distance within the hand during the early stages of lifting.[9] In response to RA afferent activity, the motor system is able to adjust force levels through spinal reflex until the gripped object no longer moves.

The second type of cutaneous receptor, Merkel disks, and the slowly adapting type I axons they innervate are responsible for form and texture perception.[10] As would be expected for receptors mediating form perception, Merkel disks are present at high density in the digits and around the mouth (50 mm^{-2} of skin surface), are at lower density in other glabrous surfaces, and are at very low density in hairy skin. This innervation density shrinks progressively with the passage of time so that by the age of 50, the density in human digits is reduced to 10 mm^{-2}.[11]

The SAI axons contacted by Merkel cells display slowly adapting, low-threshold responses to cutaneous stimuli. Unlike the RA axons, the SAI fibers respond not only to the initial indentation of skin but also to a sustained indentation, up to several seconds in duration. Receptive fields of single SAI axons include multiple points of maximal sensitivity ("hot spots"). Because SAI afferents are particularly sensitive to local skin curvature, they respond best to the edges of objects pressed into the skin.[12]

Deep mechanoreceptors Two separate classes of peripheral receptors in deep tissue produce rapidly and slowly adapting responses to somatosensory stimuli. Pacinian corpuscles are rapidly adapting receptors and Ruffini endings are slowly adapting (Fig. 26.4). Pacinian afferents operate at the extremes of sensory function, by being exquisitely sensitive to minute vibrations on the skin, with a threshold of 10 nm at 200 Hz, but at the same time having very large receptive fields that usually cover several digits and in some cases an entire hand. They are the receptors responsible for the sensation of high-frequency vibration.

Sensory axons at the core of Ruffini corpuscles (referred to as SAII axons) display slowly adapting responses to the lateral movement or stretching of skin, usually in one direction only. Their receptive fields are large and diffuse, producing responses to movements of limbs and digits. Yet because direct stimulation of SAII axons produces no conscious sensations in humans, their role in somatosensory perception is unknown.[13]

Correlation of function and structure Much of the selectivity of each cutaneous receptor to a particular submodality is a product of its structure (Figs. 26.4 and 26.5). Meissner corpuscles are encapsulated nerve endings tethered to specialized skin cells by collagen fibers, thereby making RA axons very sensitive to rapid skin movement. Moreover, the ability to localize small movements over large areas of skin surface results from the innervation of many, widely displaced (3–4 mm) Meissner corpuscles by a single RA axon. Merkel disks, on the other hand, have a much simpler structure, as each of two to five terminals given off by a single SAI axon ends in close apposition to a Merkel cell. Such a one-to-one correspondence between terminal and Merkel cell allows for maximum spatial resolution (see Box 26.1).[14–16]

So far as deep receptors are concerned, Pacinian afferents derive their rapidly adapting properties from the structure of the corpuscle that envelops the axon terminal. Surrounded by capsules of supporting cells and fluid-filled spaces that filter out the contribution of sustained stresses, the central Pacinian axon terminal is left to respond only to high-frequency indentation of the skin surface. In contrast, each Ruffini corpuscle is innervated by a core axon that breaks up into thin

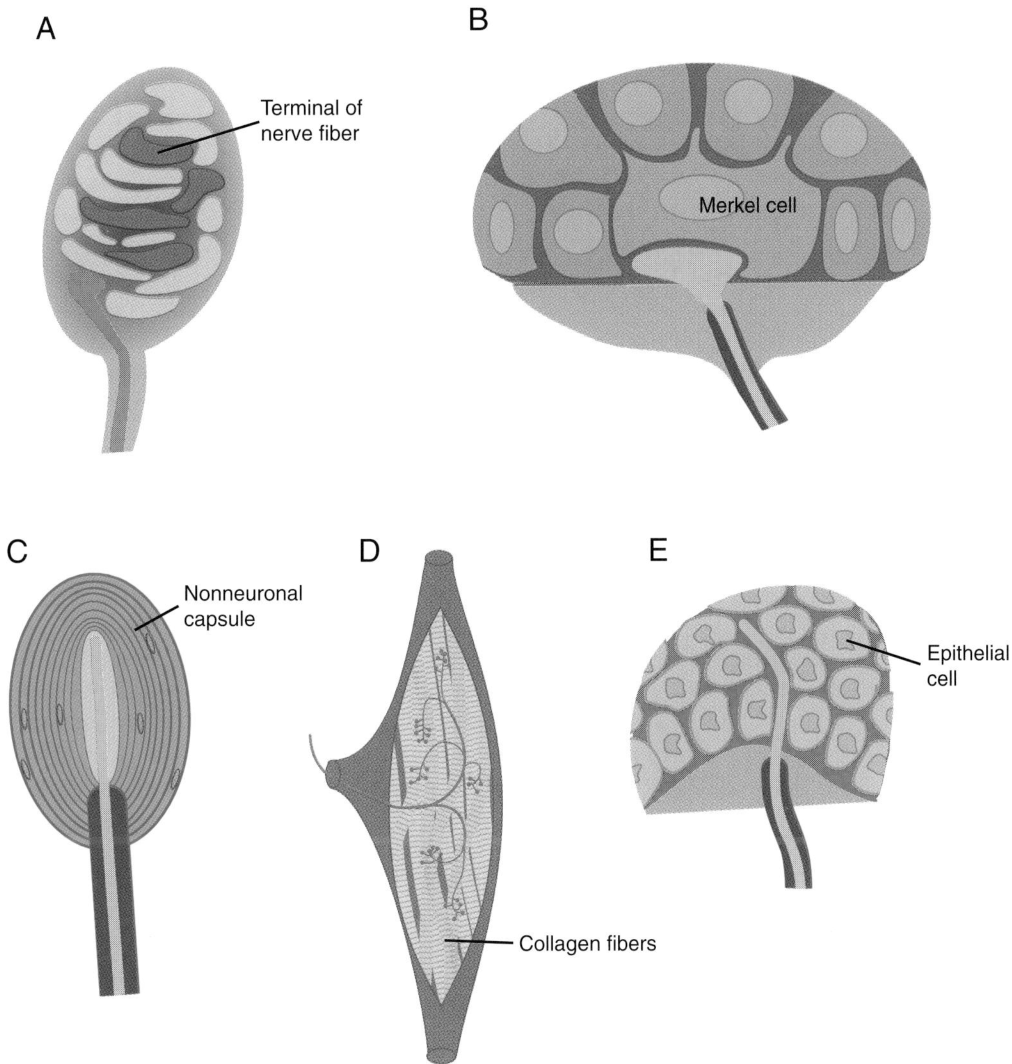

FIGURE 26.4 Morphological features of somatosensory receptors, including the variation in nonneural components. (A) Meissner corpuscles are composed of axonal loops, separated by nonneuronal, supporting cells; (B) Merkel disks are characterized by the close association between afferent axons and Merkel cells. Because of their shape and rolein fine cutaneous discrimination, they are often referred to as "touch domes"; (C) Pacinian corpuscles include a central sensory axon, surrounded by a fluid-filled capsule that filters out all sustained stimuli; (D) Ruffini endings are driven by skin stretch because of the termination of primary afferents among collagen fibrils of the skin; (E) free nerve endings, characteristic of nociceptors, are left unprotected from chemicals that are secreted or applied to the skin.

fibers, arranged so that physical stretching of the corpuscle leads to deformation of the axon itself.[17]

Innervation of hairs Each of several types of hairs is innervated by mechanoreceptors that also occur in dermis and epidermis, such as Merkel disks and Meissner corpuscles. Two additional types of mechanoreceptors, Lanceolate endings and pilo-Ruffini receptors, innervate only hairs. Lanceolate endings are made up of long axon terminals running parallel to the hair shaft and surrounded by a thin layer of supporting cells. These rapidly adapting receptors are exquisitely sensitive to minute movements of hairs and encode the velocity of a stimulus by increasing action potential frequency as stimulus velocity increases. Pilo-Ruffini receptors closely resemble Ruffini corpuscles but possess no capsule. As seen for Ruffini corpuscles, pilo-Ruffini receptors depolarize when they are deformed.

Nociceptors

As is the case for other somatosensory modalities, the perception of pain is mediated by specialized recep-

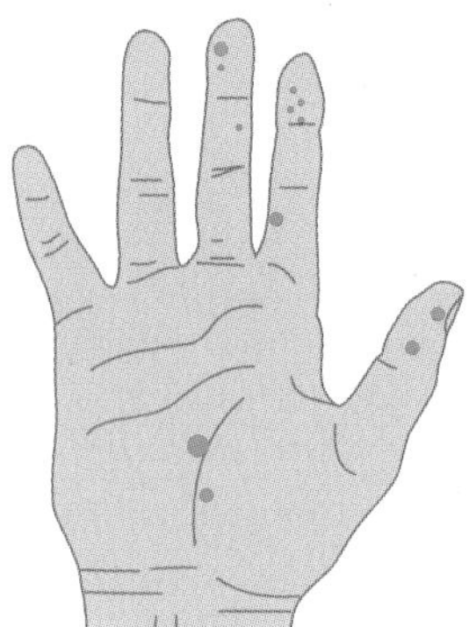

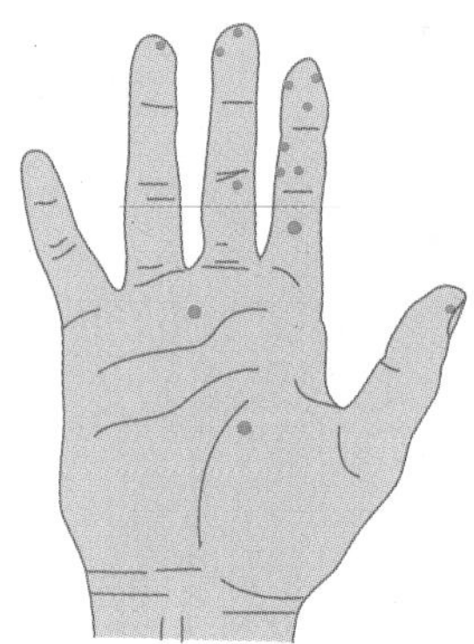

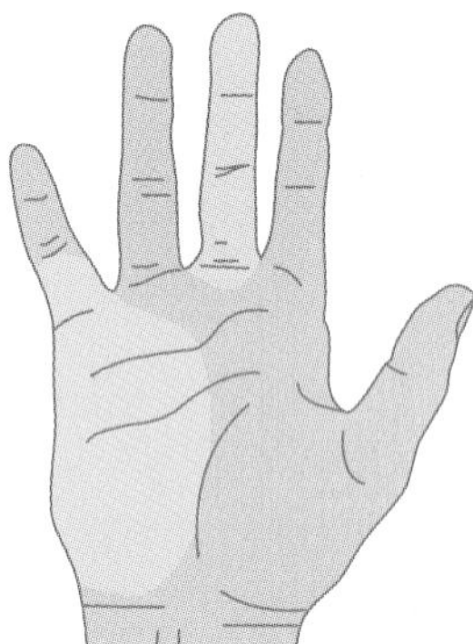

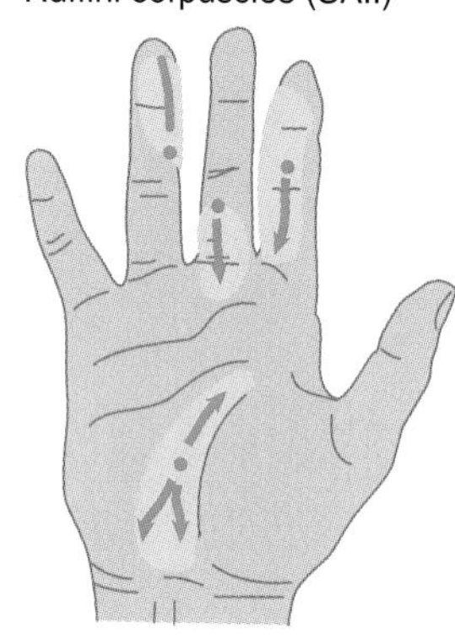

FIGURE 26.5 Map of receptive fields on the human hand displayed by the various receptor types. Receptive fields vary in overall size from punctate zones displayed by RA and SAI afferents, to broad regions of the palm or entire fingers with Pacinians. SAII afferents respond to stimuli that produce skin stretch and are often selective for the direction of stretch.

tors that activate neurons in specific regions of the CNS devoted to processing pain. Yet there is an affective component to pain that leads to different perceptions and interpretations, depending on the subject's mood, attentiveness, personality, and past experience. The role played by pain's affective component is clear in the observation that pain during childbirth is objectively more intense than that associated with solid malignant tumors but is subjectively far less unpleasant. Furthermore, the unpleasantness of pain can be reduced with training even though the intensity remains at an undiminished level.[18]

Many psychophysical studies of pain have shown thresholds to vary among individuals and among body sites on an individual. So whereas a single grain of sand under the eyelid is very painful, many grains of sand under the feet evoke no pain sensations. For this reason the use of mechanical stimuli is avoided in psychophysical studies and thermal stimuli, which are much less variable, are commonly used. These studies have found that the normal threshold for thermal pain is 45°C (113°F), the temperature at which heat produces tissue damage.[19]

With regard to the peripheral components of nociception, it is necessary to point out that specific nociceptors exist in cutaneous and deep tissues and in the viscera and that mechanoreceptors do not signal pain by a change in their own firing rate.

Nociceptors can be divided into two functionally distinct groups—one responsive to intense mechanical stimuli only, the other to a variety of noxious stimuli. These differ little between glaborous and hairy skin and are essentially similar across mammalian species.

Mechanical nociceptors Careful study of peripheral nerves has shown that axons responding to mechanical stimuli only if it is very intense (i.e., high-threshold mechanoreceptors) have a broad range of conduction velocities, from less than 10 to more than 50 m s^{-1}. Most are in Aδ range (15–30 m s^{-1}). (See Box 26.2 for notation.) Each possesses a receptive field distributed as 5–20 small spots over an area approximately 2–3 mm in diameter. These spots are widely distributed as islands within a sea of tissue that is otherwise unresponsive to noxious stimuli. In many cases, only those stimuli sufficient to produce tissue damage lead to well-defined responses.[20]

Axon terminals of nociceptive axons possess no connective tissue sheaths and, for that reason, are often referred to as bare nerve endings. Because they are not protected by physical barriers, nociceptor terminals are sensitive to chemical agents produced and released at the site of injury. These agents diffuse over distances of several millimeters and can initiate or modulate activity in the surrounding nociceptors.

Mechanical nociceptors are notable for their very high threshold to thermal stimulation when it is initially applied. When heat is applied repeatedly, however, the threshold to this stimulus is greatly reduced and the response to suprathreshold stimuli is increased. This phenomenon, referred to as **sensitization,** does not extend to mechanical stimulation. That is, repeated application of heat does not increase the nociceptor's sensitivity or response to a mechanical stimulus.

Polymodal nociceptors Almost half of the unmyelinated axons of a peripheral nerve respond well not only to intense mechanical stimuli but also to heat and noxious chemicals.[21] Axons of these polymodal nociceptors make up the majority of very slowly conducting (<1 m s^{-1}) C fibers in a peripheral nerve. Their receptors respond to minute punctures of the epithelium, with a response magnitude that depends on the

BOX 26.1

NEURAL CODING

The contribution of each receptor type to perception of spatial form and texture can be compared in an experiment in which Braille characters are used as a stimulus (Fig. 26.6).[14] Spatial details of the characters are well preserved in the response of Merkel cell/SAI afferents, are less well preserved for the Meissner corpuscle/RA afferents, and are absent entirely in the response of Pacinian afferents or Ruffini/SAII afferents. These findings indicate that SAI afferents are the source of the information by which Braille characters are perceived; Pacinian and SAII afferents are useless for this task, not only because they fail to resolve the details of a tactile stimulus but also because their innervation density is far too low to support the representation of a detailed image. Responses such as those shown in Fig. 26.6 are typical for each member of the four receptor classes, indicating that SAI afferents provide information about the fine spatial structure of a stimulus pressed into the skin. Moreover, SAI afferents appear to convey information about texture, specifically about the roughness and possibly the hardness of an object. The code for roughness exists in the difference in firing rates between adjacent SAI afferents: similar firing rates in neighboring afferents would signal a smooth stimulus (e.g., glass), whereas marked spatial variation in firing would be interpreted as a rough stimulus (e.g., sandpaper). The coarser the grain of the sandpaper, the greater the difference in firing rates among adjacent SAI receptors.[15,16]

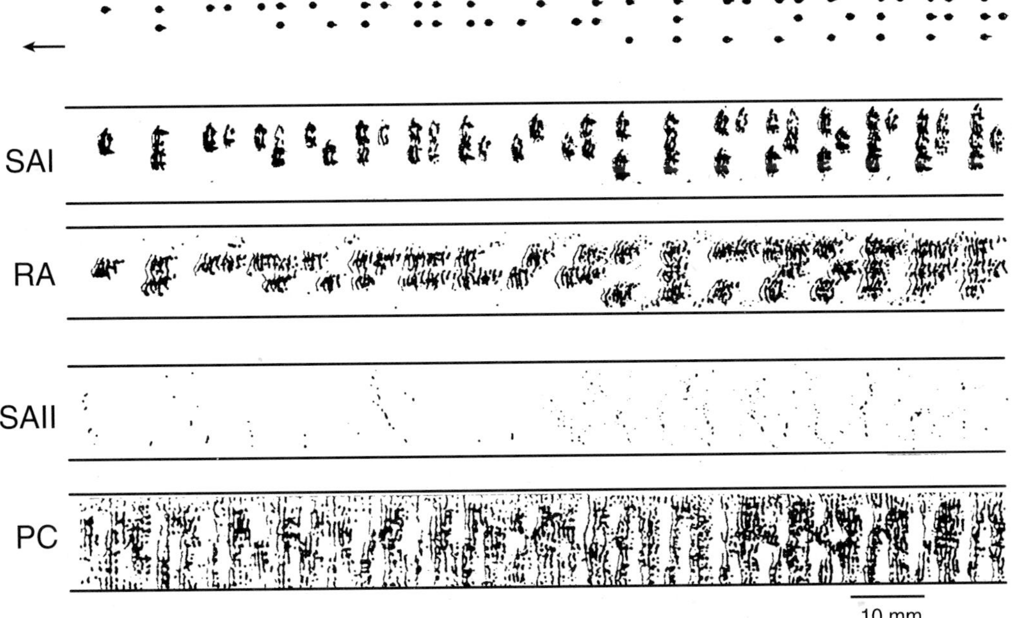

FIGURE 26.6 Response of peripheral axons to a Braille pattern of dots scanned over the surface of a human fingertip at a rate of 60 mm/s, with 200-μm shifts in position after each pass. Dots represent individual action potentials. Only the response of the SAI afferents (Merkel disk receptors) follows the Braille pattern faithfully, whereas RA afferents and Pacinians (PC) produce a response that distorts the input. SAIIs display little response to this stimulus. Adapted from Phillips *et al.* (1990).[14]

degree of tissue deformation. They also respond to temperatures in the range 40–60°C and change their response rates as a linear function of warming when temperatures exceed 46°C (in contrast with the saturating responses displayed by nonnoxious thermoreceptors at these high temperatures). Mechanical and thermal receptive fields of the polymodal receptors overlap extensively, and both enlarge predictably with increased stimulus intensity. Much like mechanical nociceptors, the polymodal class possesses no cellular capsule that would serve as a barrier to chemical mediators of pain.

BOX 26.2

PERIPHERAL NERVE

The peripheral processes of the dorsal root ganglion cells run in peripheral nerves as they extend to the skin surface or other peripheral targets. These axons vary in diameter in a manner that is consistent with the morphology and function of their terminal receptors. By a commonly used letter code:

$A\alpha$ fibers are the largest (15–20 μm) and most heavily myelinated ones that conduct action potentials most rapidly (approximately 100 m s^{-1}).

$A\beta$ fibers are medium-size (5–15 μm) and well-myelinated axons of Pacinian and Meissner corpuscles and of Merkel disks, with conduction velocities near 50 m s^{-1}.

$A\delta$ fibers are thin (1–5 μm), poorly myelinated axons of mechanical nociceptors, thermal receptors, and mechanoreceptors with large receptive fields; axon potential conduction velocities range from less than 10 to slightly more than 30 m s^{-1}.

C fibers are very thin (less than 1 μm in diameter), poorly conducting axons (as slow as 0.4 m s^{-1}) that terminate without capsules or other types of end organs in skin. See also Table 26.1.

Pain qualities carried by the two fiber types The relatively rapidly conducting $A\delta$ and the slowly conducting C fiber nociceptors are responsible for two very different qualities to pain. The rapidly transmitted signal, often with high spatial resolution, is called first pain or cutaneous pricking pain. It is well localized and easily tolerated, although it is frequently accompanied by a reflexive withdrawal response. The much slower, highly affective component with poor localization is called second pain or burning pain. Because second pain is carried by slowly conducting C fibers, it follows pricking pain by a significant delay (e.g., 1 s for pain at the fingertips). This pain is poorly localized and very poorly tolerated.

Some sources describe the presence of a third pain arising from viscera, musculature, and other deep tissues. Deep pain is poorly localized and is often associated with referred pain, in which tissue damage at one site is interpreted as occurring at a second site (e.g., heart attacks are often accompanied by reports of pain along the ulnar surface of the left arm). The existence of referred pain is explained by the convergence of visceral and peripheral nociceptive afferents onto a common population of spinal neurons. Because of the extreme affective component to deep pain, it is poorly tolerated and thus infrequently studied and poorly understood.

Thermoreceptors

By definition, specific thermoreceptors respond with a sustained response over a select range of skin temperatures but do not respond to skin indentation. As a group, thermoreceptors can be divided into warm receptors and cold receptors, both of which end as unencapsulated terminals. Axons of **warm receptors** are unmyelinated, slowly conducting fibers (C fibers) that make up a significant fraction of axons in a typical peripheral nerve, whereas axons of **cold receptors** are lightly myelinated, more quickly conducting fibers ($A\delta$ fibers) and constitute at least a quarter of the axons in a peripheral nerve.[22]

Receptive fields of thermoreceptors are very small spots, 1 mm in diameter in glabrous skin and 3–5 mm in hairy skin, three or four of which are innervated by a single primary axon. At a temperature of 30–35°C, both warm spots and cold spots discharge, but as temperatures increase, cold spots reduce their firing frequency whereas warm spots increase firing. Reductions in temperature produce the opposite result (Fig. 26.7).

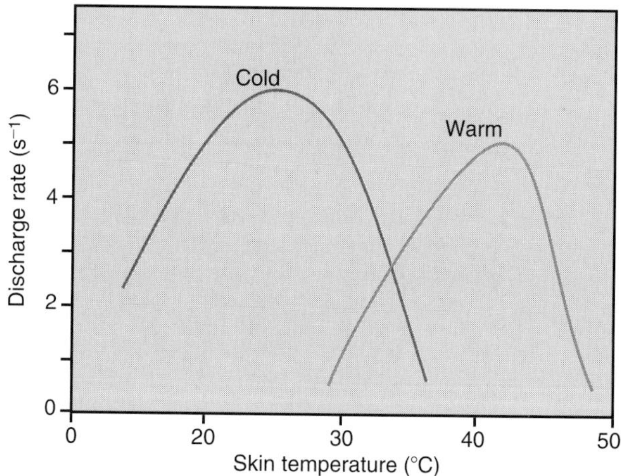

FIGURE 26.7 Rate of firing of thermoreceptors in monkey hand with variation in skin temperature. Cold receptors are most responsive to temperatures at or slightly above 20°C, whereas warm receptors show a peak response at or above 40°C. Fluctuations near body temperature produce modulations in the response of both receptors.

BOX 26.3

HYPERALGESIA AND ALLODYNIA

Unlike other somatosensory modalities, which show adaptation to the continuous presentation of a stimulus, the sensation of pain becomes greater, not less, when a painful stimulus is repeatedly presented. That is, thresholds for both mechanical and thermal nociceptors can be greatly lowered by a prior, painful stimulus. This process, called **hyperalgesia,** includes a primary effect at the site of injury and a secondary hyperalgesia in undamaged tissue surrounding the wound.[25] **Primary hyperalgesia** includes a lowered threshold for both mechanical and thermal stimuli and probably occurs through the local release of one or more chemical agents. A particularly strong case can be made for the neuropeptide bradykinin as a chemical mediator of primary hyperalgesia, with direct effects either on C fiber polymodal nociceptors or on mechanical nociceptors. Other chemical agents, including prostaglandin E_2, do not directly drive nociceptors to respond but lead to a greatly heightened response to subsequent nonnoxious mechanical stimuli. Inhibition of these chemical agents is the route whereby aspirin and ibuprofen work as analgesics.

In contrast to the primary hyperalgesia, **secondary hyperalgesia** exists with a lowered threshold only for subsequent mechanical stimuli. This secondary effect is associated with an area of erythemia or flare that is smaller than the more diffuse region of primary hyperalgesia. Studies using local stimulation and local anesthetics have shown secondary hyperalgesia to be of neural origin. A CNS component to secondary hyperalgesia is inferred from the observation that the lower threshold to nociceptive stimuli extends over too great a distance to be accounted for by strictly peripheral mechanisms.

A phenomenon that resembles secondary hyperalgesia is **allodynia,** a condition in which a painful response is produced by an innocuous mechanical stimulus. As with secondary hyperalgesia, allodynia is the result of a sensitization of spinothalamic neurons in the dorsal horn and the failure of descending systems to control the activity of these neurons.[26]

A simple experiment illustrates the fact that cold and warm spots respond in opposite directions to a change in temperature and signal that change to the CNS. If one hand is submerged in frigid water and the other in very warm water and then both are plunged into tepid water (30–35°C), the previously chilled hand will feel warm and the previously heated hand will feel cold. This result shows that thermoreceptors are very poor indicators of absolute temperature but are very sensitive to changes in skin temperature.

Thermoreceptors are extremely sensitive to localized changes in temperature and can signal very small changes if they are applied rapidly (5°C per minute). In contrast, slow changes of 0.5°C per minute produce no change in receptor activity and no report by human subjects of a change in perceived temperature.[23,24] When the thermal stimulus is applied by touching a hot or cold object to the skin, localization is extremely precise because of the tactile component of the stimulus. Yet when temperature changes are imposed by a radiant heat source, localization is extremely imprecise with very gross misplacement (e.g., front versus back) on the trunk (Box 26.3).[25,26]

Proprioception Is the Kinesthetic Sense

One part of somatic sensation deals with the state of the body itself, rather than its relationship with the external environment. This proprioceptive, or **kinesthetic** sense, is related to the capacity to sense position of joints, to sense their direction and velocity of movement, and to determine the effort needed to grasp and lift objects. Because proprioception is involved with movements of the joints and limbs, it is generally considered to be closely associated with the motor system. Because signals for voluntary movements are generated by commands originating in regions of the forebrain, the CNS is able to sense the position of limbs by keeping track of these commands. This process is usually referred to as efferent copy or corollary discharge.[27] This process is clearly seen in the fact that objects appear heavier when muscles fatigue, even though sensory input does not change.[1]

Despite the existence of CNS-generated signals of position, sensory input from the periphery is required for movements imposed on a limb and to ensure that visually or even auditory guided movements are effected as limbs come in contact with the external world. Yet humans have a high capacity to discriminate both position and movement of limbs without visual or auditory feedback and can do so for changes in proximal joint angles as little as 0.2°.

The sense of limb position at rest and the sense of limb movement or kinesthesia are the products of inputs from cutaneous mechanoreceptors, joint recep-

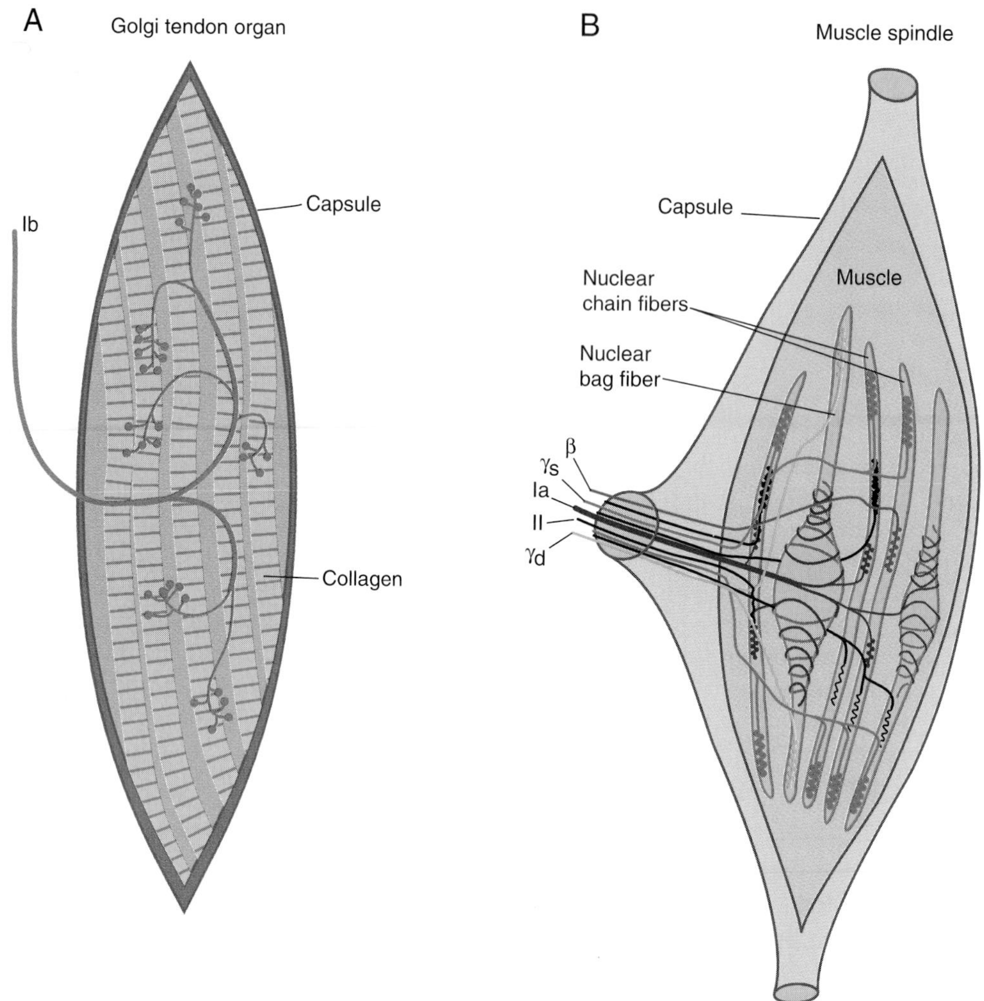

FIGURE 26.8 Proprioceptive afferents. (A) Golgi tendon organs and their termination along the collagen fibers of the tendon capsule. These afferents respond when the entire capsule is stretched, usually by overvigorous contraction of the muscle. (B) Muscle spindle afferents (Ia and II) terminate on the noncontractile portions of intrafusal muscle fibers. They are arranged in parallel with the work muscle fibers and respond to stretch of the entire muscle. Specialized motoneurons (γ) provide the motor innervation of the intrafusal muscle fibers and control the overall sensitivity of the muscle spindle.

tors, and two specialized proprioceptors—muscle spindles and Golgi tendon organs[28] (Fig. 26.8).

Role of Mechanoreceptors

Of the cutaneous mechanoreceptors described above, only the Ruffini/SAII afferents could encode joint position by responding to skin stretch in a directionally selective manner. Yet because stimulation of SAII afferents produces no conscious sensation, either these afferents play no role in encoding limb position or they do so as a population rather than as individual axons.

Experiments in which SAIIs are blocked by local anesthesia indicate that their role varies with location. When skin around the knee is anesthetized, subjects experience no change in the capacity to determine joint position, yet when skin around the mouth, hands, or feet is anesthetized, the ability to use these structures or to detect their passive movement is severely reduced. For some body parts, then, SAII afferents may play an active part in proprioception.

Role of Joint Receptors

Several types of receptors are located in the joint capsule and respond to the bending of joints. These include slowly adapting responses in the joint capsule, arising from Ruffini-type endings and from paciniform corpuscles (small, elongated Pacinian corpuscles). Yet because joint afferents respond primarily at the extremes of flexion or extension and because humans who have had their joint capsules anesthetized or surgically removed experience no loss of limb position sense, joint capsule receptors are not involved in coding joint position. Instead, they are thought to play a protective role by signaling and thereby preventing hyperextension or hyperflexion of the joint.[1,29]

Role of Muscle Spindles

These most complex peripheral receptors are a type of encapsulated ending, as much as 10 mm in length, each of which includes a single, large-diameter (group Ia) primary sensory axon and a single thinner (group II) secondary sensory axon[30] (Fig. 26.8). The sensory axons terminate as tightly wound coils around the central, noncontractile regions of muscle fibers, called **intrafusal fibers,** that vary in structure and have the common trait of being too small to exert significant force (i.e., they are not work muscle fibers). Intrafusal fibers and their sensory axons are sensitive to elongation of the muscle and to the subsequent recovery from stretch.

Diversity in the structure of intrafusal muscle fibers and of sensory axons permits muscle spindles to sense both dynamic and static components of muscle stretch. Primary axons and the intrafusal fibers they innervate are particularly sensitive to the earliest, most rapid change in muscle length and fire at a rate that varies with the velocity of change and length of the muscle. In contrast, secondary axons and their intrafusal fibers are more sensitive to new static positions of the muscle produced by sustained stretching or contraction.

One function of muscle spindles can be seen in the patellar tendon or **knee jerk reflex.** To elicit this reflex, intrafusal muscle fibers of leg flexors are tonically stretched by crossing the leg and then quickly lengthened by a sharp tap on the patellar tendon. This process of making the spindle afferents respond to lengthening of the muscle is referred to as "loading" the muscle spindle. A very rapid contraction of the flexor muscles follows. Because muscle contraction occurs through physical shortening of extrafusal fibers, the intrafusal fibers are also shortened and the spindles are said to be "unloaded." Thus, one major function of the spindles is to provide the sensory component of a spinal reflex. Muscle spindle afferents also convey nonreflexive sensory information to higher stations in the somatosensory system, which permits an animal to sense the location of its limbs in space.

Role of Golgi Tendon Organs

These receptor organs are located in the fibrous tendons of muscles, where 10–20 individual muscle fibers join the ends of collagen fibers. Axons of Group Ib afferents terminate in and among the collagen fibers, so that when the tendon is stretched the axons and terminals are compressed, causing them to discharge. By this arrangement, contraction of the muscle and the consequent pull on the organ's collagen fibers cause the sensory axon to respond (Fig. 26.8).

The most easily demonstrated effect of Ib afferent activity is to halt contraction of the muscle of which its Golgi tendon organ is a part. This effect, known as **autogenic inhibition,** is produced by a simple spinal cord circuit, through which contractions that threaten to pull the muscle away from its tendon are inhibited. So far as their proprioceptive functions are concerned, Golgi tendon organs do not respond to passively maintained limb position or to imposed changes in that position.

Dorsal Root Ganglion Cells Carry Information from the Somatosensory Periphery to the Central Nervous System

Each of the receptor types described above is a primary sensory axon arising from **dorsal root ganglion** (DRG) **cells** or **trigeminal ganglion cells** (in the case of the neck and head). These cells are organized as collections of neurons in the peripheral nervous system, referred to as **ganglia,** and form two parallel chains along either side of the spinal cord.

Morphology

DRG neurons give rise to no dendrites and receive no synapses. The one process each cell does give off is an axon, which bifurcates close to the soma, sending one process out to the periphery and a second into the CNS. These peripheral and central processes serve as parts of a continuous cable carrying action potentials from their peripheral terminal sites to their central terminal sites.

Dorsal root ganglion cells can be grouped into different classes by variations in the common morphological plan, specifically by variations in the size of somata, the diameter of axons, the morphology of peripheral terminals, and the site of central terminations.[31] A division into two size classes has a clear functional correlate, because large DRG cells relay low-threshold mechanical and proprioceptive stimuli, whereas small DRG cells are responsible for nociception and thermoreception.

Dermatomes

The peripheral axons of any individual dorsal root innervate a region of skin that is common across subjects. As examples, the dorsal root ganglion at the 4th

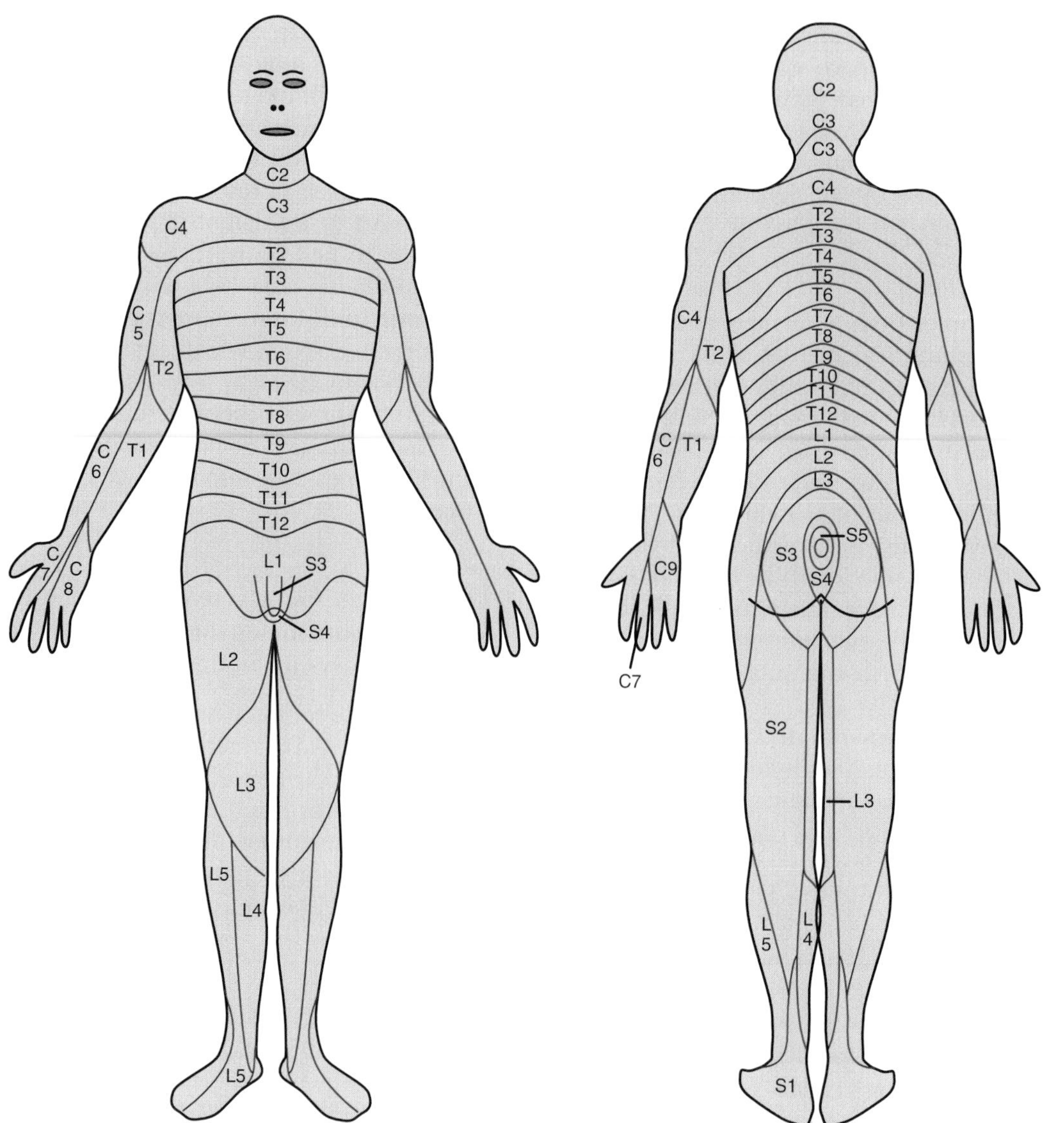

FIGURE 26.9 Classic dermatomal map, showing the distribution of spinal nerves and the segments from which they arise. Despite extensive overlap between nerves arising from adjacent segements, this map permits localization of injuries and other conditions that give rise to restricted sensory deficits.

thoracic level innervates the region around the nipples, whereas the ganglion at the 10th thoracic level innervates the region around the umbilicus. Each of these regions is called a **dermatome** and because of the stereotyped pattern of their organization, a **dermatomal map** can be generated (Fig. 26.9). Missing from most maps is the fact that the boundaries between dermatomes are not rigid, because somata in adjacent dorsal roots send axons to partially overlapping regions of skin. Nevertheless, dermatomal maps are valuable in evaluating injuries or infections restricted to a small number of dorsal root ganglia, because careful testing with a fine probe applied to the skin can reveal the extent of damage or inflammation.

Summary

Peripheral receptors begin the division of labor that characterizes the somatosensory system. Because they are the peripheral terminals of different classes of dorsal root ganglion cells, each of which has its own sites of termination in the CNS, the receptors are the basis for parallel processing at the earliest stages in somatic sensation. Experimental studies that compared the physiology of receptors with the behavior of humans and other primates established the role that certain types of receptors play in the perception of specific stimuli. It remains for the rest of the somatosensory system to select which peripheral information is relevant, to make it useful for motor behavior, and to bring it to consciousness.

SPINAL AND BRAINSTEM COMPONENTS OF THE SOMATOSENSORY SYSTEM

Large- and Small-Diameter Fibers Have Separate Paths

A basic principle of somatosensory functional organization correlates the physiological properties of a DRG's peripheral axon with the site at which its central axon terminates. Information from each class of mechanoreceptor, proprioceptor, nociceptor, and thermoreceptor reaches a unique group of neurons in the CNS. This principle of organization, referred to as **modality segregation,** is the mechanism whereby neurons responsible for different sensations make up separate pathways into and through the CNS. Such a division begins in the peripheral nerves and continues as dorsal root axons enter the spinal cord (Fig. 26.10; Box 26.4).[32] There the central processes of DRGs take two different routes (Fig. 26.11).[33]

Most small-diameter, lightly myelinated and unmyelinated axons that carry information about pain and temperature enter the dorsal horn in a lateral division of fibers and terminate in layers I and IIa of the dorsal horn and in layers V, VI, and X of the intermediate horn (Fig. 26.11B).

Medium- and large-diameter axons that carry discriminative touch and proprioception enter in the medial division of the dorsal root and either terminate in layers IIb and III or turn to ascend in the gracile and cuneate fasciculi (the dorsal columns). Axons in the dorsal columns include not only the primary dorsal root axons but also the axons of cells in layer III, referred to as postsynaptic dorsal column axons. These axons relay information from the layer III neurons similar to that carried by medial-division fibers of the dorsal root (Fig. 26.11A).

Although identical in the sizes of axons they contain and the sensory modalities they carry, the gracile and cuneate fasciculi differ fundamentally in the parts of the body from which they convey somatosensory information. The **gracile fasciculus** exists through the full length of the cord. Its axons include the central processes of dorsal root ganglion and axons of spinal neurons from the lower half of the spinal cord, including thoracic segments 7 through 12 (T7–T12), all six lumbar segments (L1–L6), and the single coccygeal segment. As a result, this fasciculus carries somatosensory input from the feet, legs, and lower trunk (approximately the level of the last rib).

The cuneate fasciculus is found only from the middle of the thoracic cord to the junction of the spinal cord with the medulla because it is made up of ganglion cell central processes and spinal axons from only the upper thoracic segments (T1–T6) and all eight cervical segments (C1–C8). These axons carry information from the hands, arms, and upper body.

A Basic Outline of Central Somatosensory Pathways Includes Two Parallel Groups of Neurons and Axons

By way of the dorsal columns, discriminative somatosensory inputs are carried to the gracile and cuneate nuclei (dorsal column nuclei) of the lower medulla.

BOX 26.4

ANATOMY OF THE SPINAL CORD

As in any region of the CNS, groups of cell bodies and bundles of axons occupy different regions in the spinal cord.[32] In a reversal from what is seen in other prominent regions of the CNS such as the cerebellar cortex and cerebral cortex, axonal bundles (referred to as tracts or fasciculi) occupy the perimeter of the spinal cord whereas cell bodies occupy its central core.

Fiber tracts directly relevant to somatic sensation are ones that carry sensory information to the brain (ascending tracts) and those that carry regulatory influences from brain to spinal neurons (descending tracts). Ascending tracts include axons that are the central processes of dorsal root ganglion cells as well as axons of spinal neurons. Descending axons originate in the cerebral cortex and in subcortical regions and terminate on neurons of the cord. These include many axons that control voluntary movements and others that regulate the tonic sensitivity of motoneurons (Fig. 26.10).

Neurons of the cord occupy three large regions, in which they are arranged in groups that resemble layers (Fig. 26.10):

1. Dorsal horn (layers I–V). The dorsal horn contains

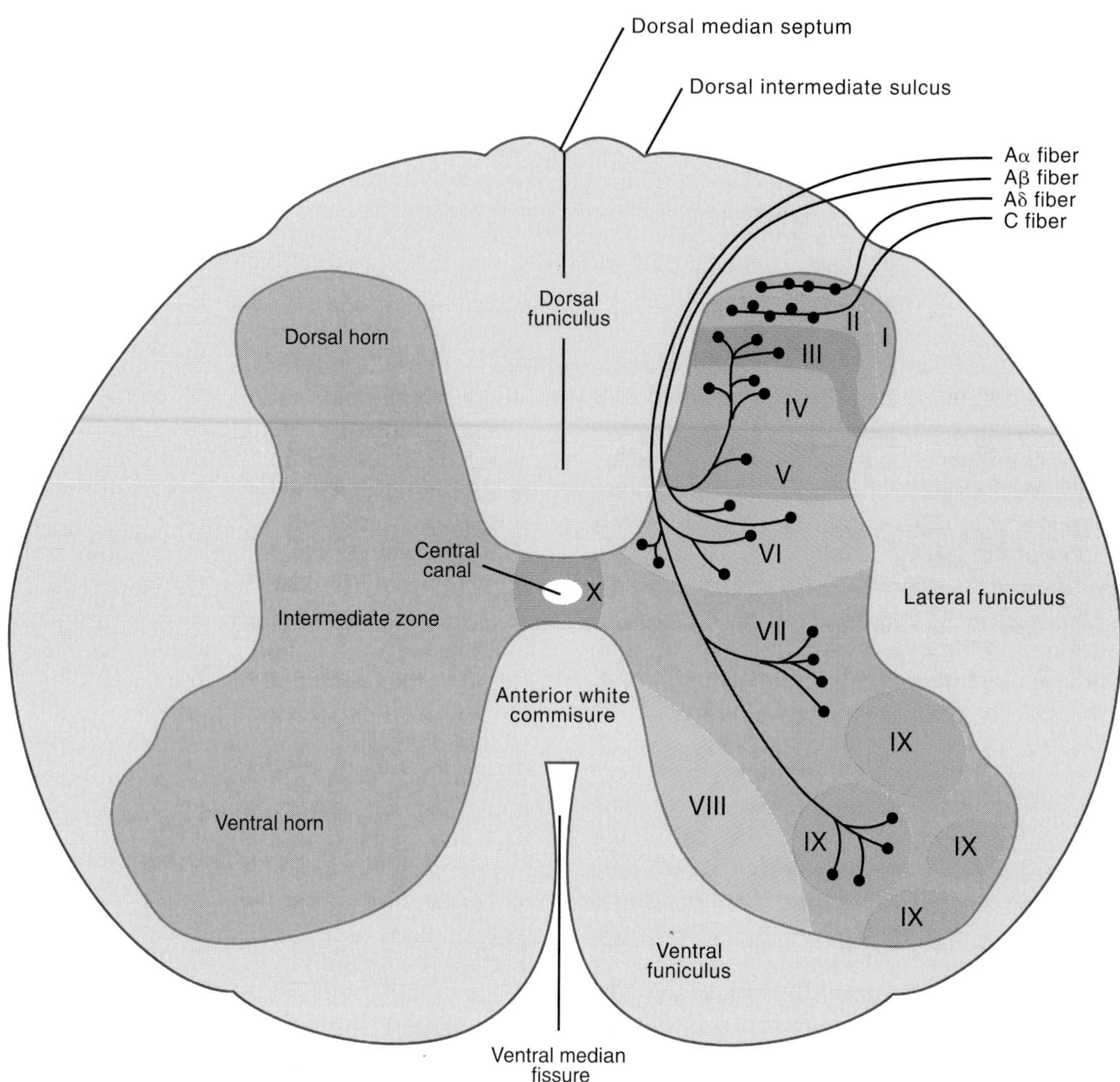

FIGURE 26.10 Anatomy of the spinal cord at a cervical level. Gray matter can be divided into groups of neurons that form layers in both dorsal (sensory) and ventral (motor) horns. Termination of large (Aα and Aβ) and small (Aδ and C) afferent axons in the cord vary by depth. The two groups enter the cord separately and terminate in regions that overlap very little.

neurons that receive input from the dorsal root ganglia and process and relay somatosensory information to other neurons of the CNS. The dorsal horn contains three broad groups of neurons, arranged as layers. These are lamina I, lamina II (substantia gelatinosa), and laminae III–V (nucleus proprius).

2. Intermediate cord (layers VI–VIII). The intermediate horn consists of many propriospinal neurons (those whose axons do not leave the spinal cord but that terminate in segments above or below their parent somata), and others that relay somatosensory information to higher levels of the CNS both for conscious appreciation of sensory inputs and for coordination of movements.

3. Ventral horn (layers IX and X). The ventral horn contains motor neurons that provide the direct innervation of muscles and interneurons that modulate motor neuron activity.

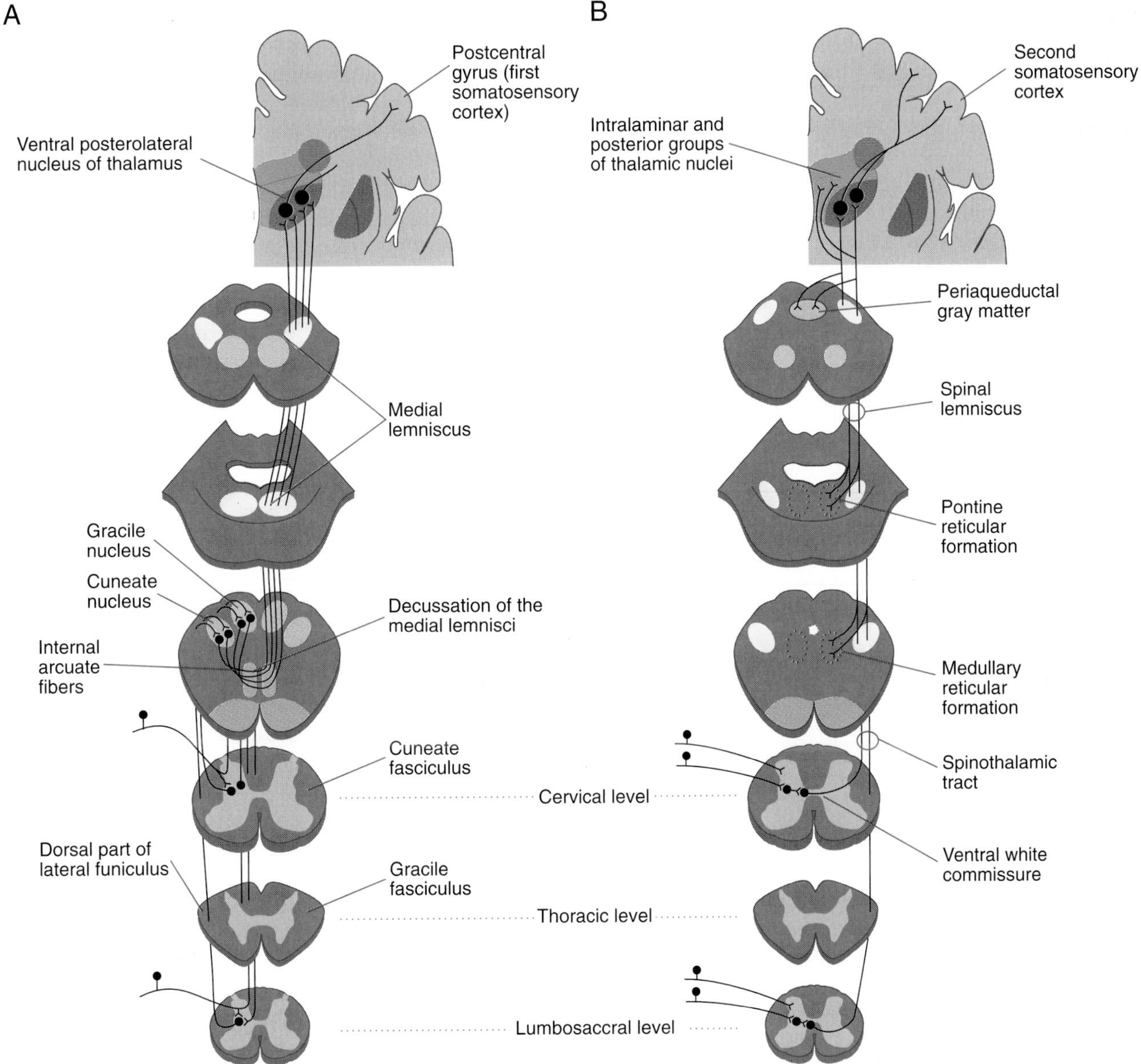

FIGURE 26.11 Anatomy of ascending somatosensory paths. (A) Organization of the dorsal column–medial lemniscal system from entry of large-diameter afferents into the spinal cord to the termination of thalamocortical axons in the first somatosensory area of the cerebral cortex. An obligatory synapse occurs in the gracile and cuneate nuclei, from which second-order axons cross the midline and ascend to the ventral posterolateral nucleus of thalamus (VPL) by way of the medial lemniscus. (B) Organization of the spinothalamic tract and the remainder of the anterolateral system. Primary axons terminate the spinal cord itself. Second-order axons cross the midline and ascend through the spinal cord and brainstem to terminate in VPL and other nuclei of the thalamus. Collaterals of these axons terminate in the reticular formation of the pons and medulla.

In turn, neurons in the dorsal column nuclei give rise to axons that cross the midline of the medulla and ascend in a fiber bundle called the medial lemniscus. These terminate in the lateral division of the ventroposterior nucleus (VPL) in the dorsal thalamus (Fig. 26.11A). A secondary pathway relays medial division inputs through neurons of nucleus proprius to the lateral cervical nucleus of the spinal cord, the axons of which cross the midline and merge with the medial lemniscus to terminate in VPL. In contrast, axons of nociceptors and thermoreceptors terminate in the spinal cord itself (i.e., in layer I, layers IV and V of nucleus proprius, and layers VI–VIII of the intermediate cord). These spinal neurons then send their axons across the midline of the spinal cord and ascend as the anterolateral system to terminate either in the brainstem or in several nuclei of the dorsal thalamus (Fig. 26.11B).

The Dorsal Column–Medial Lemniscal System Is Organized to Relay Fine Touch

Synaptic inputs reaching the dorsal column nuclei and those carried away from it are notable for the strength of the connections they form, for the modality specificity imposed upon the neurons in the system, and for the precise body map observed across the entire population of neurons. These are the cardinal properties of the dorsal column–medial lemniscal system that recur in the ventrobasal complex of the thalamus and in the first somatosensory area of the cerebral cortex.[33]

During their ascent to the gracile and cuneate nuclei, axons of the dorsal columns are sorted by place and modality. Somatotopic sorting takes place as those axons entering each of the dorsal columns earliest are displaced medially while later entering axons form sheets or lamellae more laterally. Modality sorting also takes place, at least for the gracile fasciculus, as only RA inputs remain in that tract prior to its termination in the gracile nucleus. SA inputs reach the gracile nucleus but do so through other spinal pathways, such as those of the spinocervicothalamic system.

A second level of functional organization is seen in the body map contained within the two dorsal column nuclei, with the representation of the feet, legs, and lower trunk in the gracile nucleus, and the hands, arms, and upper trunk in the cuneate nucleus. Thus, in the human somatosensory brainstem is the body map of a "small man," or homunculus. Similar body maps are present in the subsequent stages of somatosensory processing, but at each level they are distorted largely because of the greater number of receptors on some parts of the skin surface (the fingertips) than on others (the back and shoulders) and partly because the amount of neural machinery devoted to the representation of certain body parts is greater than that devoted to others.

The Anterolateral System Is a Complex Group of Neurons

Neurons in layer I and in layers V–VIII of the intermediate cord give rise to axons that terminate in the dorsal thalamus, the midbrain, and the reticular formation of the pons and medulla.[19] Because each group of axons crosses the midline and ascends in the anterolateral quadrant of the spinal cord, they are referred to collectively as the **anterolateral system.** Spinal neurons of the anterolateral system are innervated by axons of the lateral division of the dorsal roots and thus respond to mechanical nociceptive stimuli, thermal stimuli (whether nociceptive or innocuous), and innocuous mechanical stimuli carried by mechanoreceptors with large receptive fields (i.e., crude touch).

Fibers of the anterolateral system terminate at three levels in the CNS (Fig. 26.11B). A sizable fraction of axons terminate in the medulla and pons upon loosely organized groups of neurons interspersed among thin bundles of axons, in a region referred to as the **reticular formation.** This ascending system is the **spinoreticular pathway,** which provides pain inputs for producing forebrain arousal and affective response rather than for discriminating the location of the stimulus. Spinoreticular axons arise predominantly from the cervical cord, where approximately the same number of cells contribute to it as provide axons for the spinothalamic tract.

A smaller group of anterolateral axons, the spinomesencephalic axons, terminates in the superior colliculus of the midbrain and in the region surrounding the cerebral aqueduct (periaqueductal gray region or PAG). These spinomesencephalic axons carry purely nociceptive information and include, in part, collaterals of anterolateral axons innervating the dorsal thalamus. Axons terminating in the PAG are implicated in descending mechanisms for controlling pain[34] (Fig. 26.12). The bulk of the anterolateral system is composed of spinothalamic axons, which terminate in the dorsal thalamus. These axons are present in all mammals and are particularly robust in primates.[19,35] They terminate in three thalamic nuclei: the ventroposterolateral nucleus, the medial nucleus of the posterior complex, and the central lateral nucleus.

The **ventroposterolateral nucleus** (VPL) is the principal relay nucleus for discriminative somatosensory information. It receives both spinothalamic and medial lemniscal inputs. The two systems of input axons do not converge onto the same VPL neurons but innervate different collections of cells in this nucleus. Spinothalamic neurons innervating VPL are found in layer I and layer V of the monkey spinal cord and include separate groups of cells with nociceptive, thermoreceptive, and mechanoreceptive properties.

Terminations in the **medial nucleus of the posterior complex** (POm) carry a nondiscriminative, affective component of a painful stimulus. Receptive fields of POm cells are usually large and include separate, noncontiguous regions on both sides of the body. In most cases, only nociceptive inputs succeed in driving POm neurons, although responses of individual neurons are insecure and change markedly with variations in skin temperature or anesthetic state.

The **central lateral nucleus** (CL) is part of a general

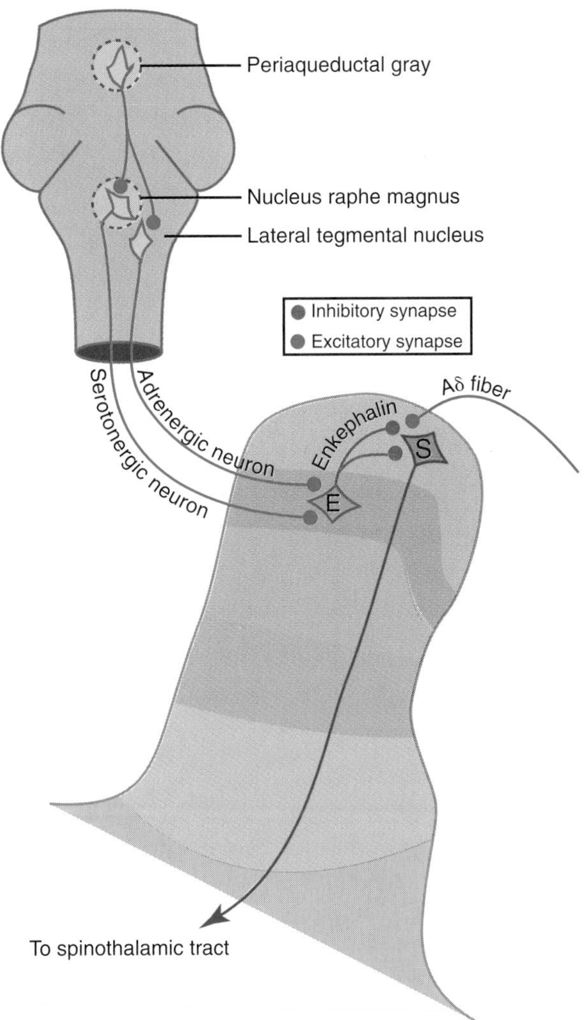

FIGURE 26.12 Descending control of pain. Serotoninergic axons arise from neurons in the nucleus raphe magnus and adrenergic axons from neurons in the lateral tegmental nucleus. Neurons in each nucleus are innervated by neurons of the periaqueductal gray area and both form excitatory synapses onto spinal interneurons (E). Those interneurons use opiatelike peptides (enkephalins) as neurotransmitters; release of the enkephalins inhibits both the incoming nociceptive axons and the spinothalamic neurons (S) on which they synapse.

system for cortical activation, neurons of which innervate many areas of cerebral cortex. That spinothalamic innervation of CL is not part of a discriminative pathway can be seen from studies of humans, in which stimulation of intralaminar nuclei produces reports of burning sensations over most of the body.

The Trigeminal System Has Parallels with the Spinal Somatosensory System

Much as sensory axons for the trunk and limbs are processes of DRG cells, so the axons conveying somatosensory inputs from the face are processes of the **trigeminal** or **semilunar ganglion** and make up the afferent component of the trigeminal or fifth (V) cranial nerve. The trigeminal nerve divides into three large branches—the ophthalmic, maxillary, and mandibular nerves—which innervate the skin in nonoverlapping regions of the face. In doing so the axons of the trigeminal ganglion end as mechanoreceptors, thermoreceptors, and nociceptors in a manner precisely analogous to that of a dorsal root ganglion.

Central processes of trigeminal ganglion cells enter the CNS at the middle of the pons and adopt a path for discriminative touch that is distinct from the path for pain and temperature. Most large-diameter axons carrying fine tactile inputs terminate near the level of the trigeminal nerve's entry, in the principal or main sensory nucleus, whereas others descend in the spinal tract of V to terminate in the pars oralis of the spinal trigeminal nucleus (Fig. 26.13A). The majority of axons given off by these nuclei cross the midline, ascend as trigeminothalamic axons, join with the medial lemniscus caudal to the thalamus, and terminate in the ventroposteromedial nucleus (VPM). In most regards, then, this is the trigeminal equivalent of the dorsal column–medial lemniscal system.

Small, lightly myelinated and unmyelinated axons entering in the trigeminal nerve descend in the spinal trigeminal tract to terminate in the **pars caudalis** of the spinal trigeminal nucleus (Fig. 26.13B). The pars caudalis is that part of the spinal trigeminal nucleus found in the caudal medulla and the first two segments of the cervical cord. It most closely resembles the anterolateral system in its structure and function and is the site of termination for nociceptors and thermoreceptors.[36] Neurons of this nucleus give off crossed and uncrossed axons, some of which terminate in VPM and others in POm and CL.

Most aspects of trigeminal structure and function, however, are unlike those of the spinal somatosensory system. The most obvious of these is the displacement of trigeminal ganglion cells that innervate spindles of the muscles of mastication. Although of an origin (neural crests) similar to that of the neurons of the semilunar ganglion and of the DRGs, these cells do not occupy a position in the ganglion itself or in any part of the peripheral nervous system. Instead the neurons make up a distinct nucleus in the midbrain called the trigeminal mesencephalic nucleus and, as such, are the only documented example of CNS neurons derived from neural crest rather than from neural tube.

A second feature unique to the trigeminal system is the innervation of specialized structures. Most prominent among these is the tooth pulp, which is thought to be innervated solely by C and Aδ nociceptors. The

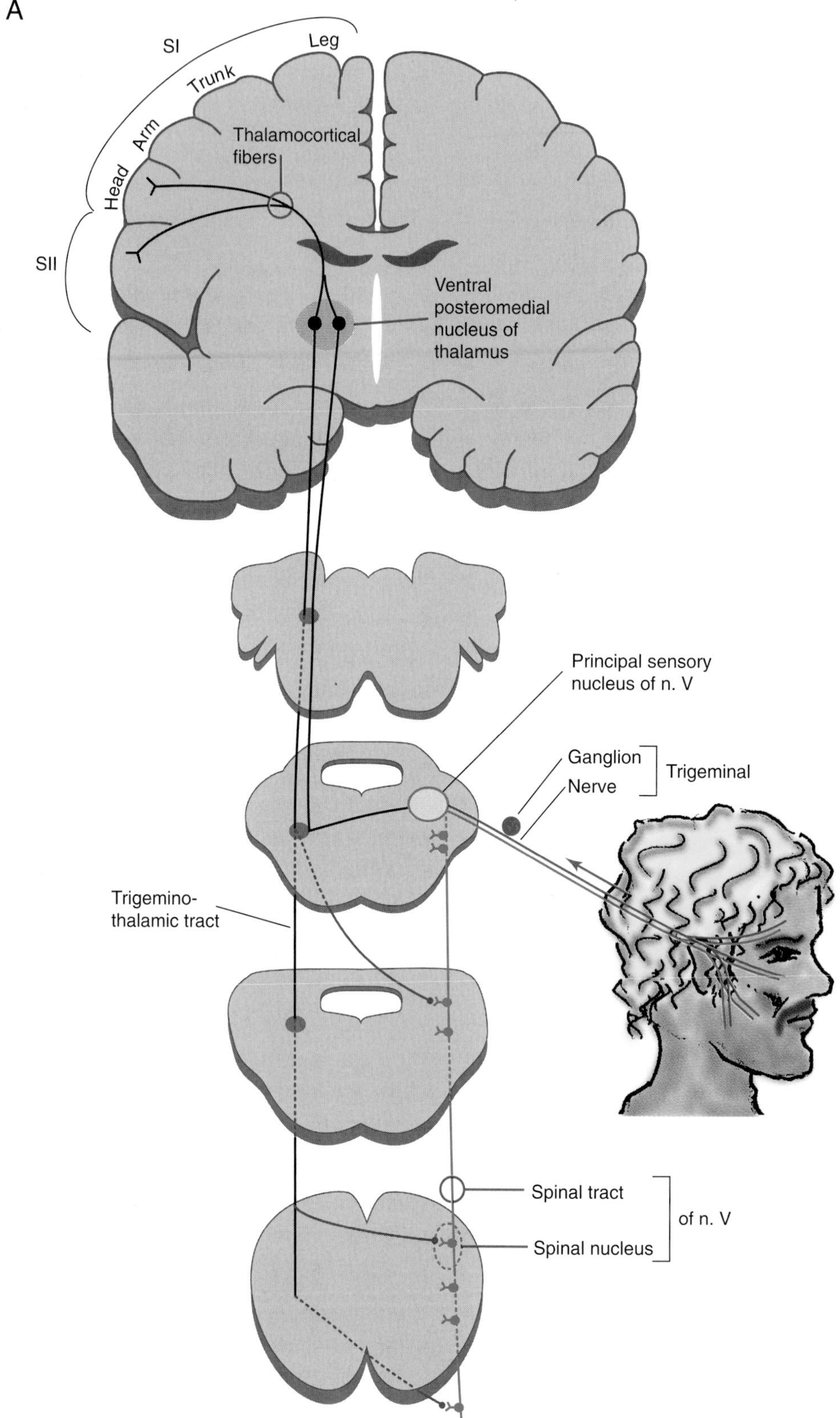

FIGURE 26.13 Sensory components of the trigeminal system. (A) Path for discriminative touch. Large-diameter afferents from the face innervate second-order neurons in the spinal trigeminal nucleus (pars oralis) and the principal sensory nucleus. Neurons in these nuclei give rise to axons that cross the midline, ascend in the trigeminothalamic tract, and terminate in the ventral posteromedial (VPM) nucleus of the thalamus.

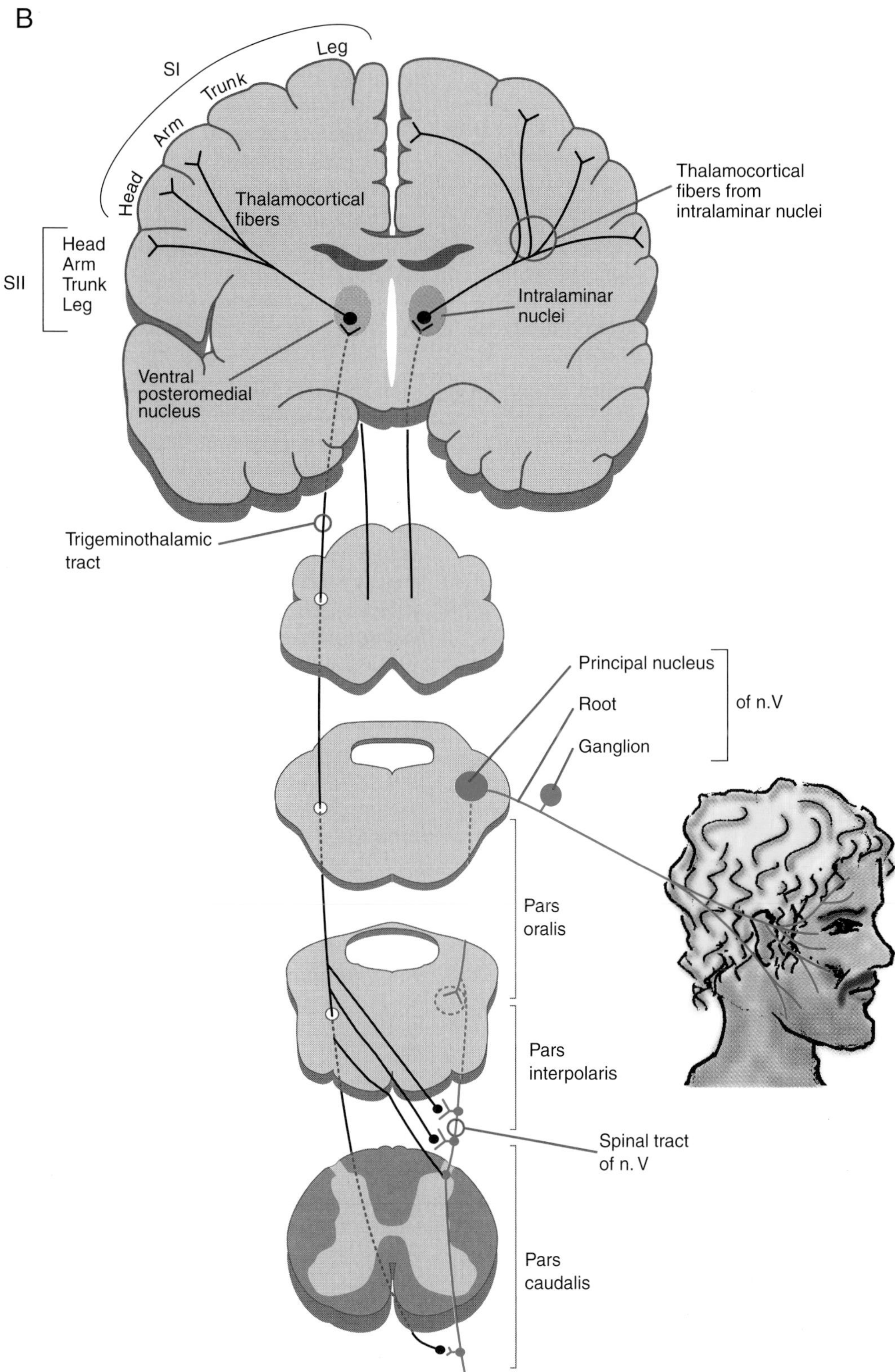

FIGURE 26.13 (B) Path for pain and temperature the trigeminal system. Small-diameter afferent axons descend in the spinal trigeminal tract and terminate in the pars caudalis of the spinal nucleus. The second-order axons cross the midline and ascend to the thalamus.

majority of these axons terminate in the pars interpolaris of the spinal nucleus.

Summary

Parallel paths exist in both the spinal somatosensory and the trigeminal systems. Separate paths exist to process and relay discriminative sensations, such as fine touch, and the more poorly localized sensations of pain and temperature. These different modalities are carried by different groups of neurons, whose axons occupy separate parts of the spinal cord and brainstem until they converge in the ventrobasal complex.

THE THALAMIC VENTROBASAL COMPLEX

The **ventrobasal complex** (VB) includes the two divisions of the ventroposterior nucleus that receive somatosensory input from the body and face. Axons of both the medial lemniscus and the spinothalamic tract terminate in the VPL; trigeminothalamic fibers from the principal sensory nucleus and from the spinal trigeminal nucleus innervate the VPM. A third nucleus can be included in VB of primates. This, the ventroposterior inferior nucleus (VPI), has a unique cell architecture, with neurons smaller than those in the rest of VB. Yet it is the cortical projection of the VPI that serves to best distinguish it from VPL and VPM, for neurons in VPI innervate exclusively the second somatosensory cortex (SII).[37]

VPL and VPM Are Somatotopically Organized

Neurons responding to stimulation of one region of the contralateral body surface are segregated from those responding to other regions.[38] In the body map for the ventrobasal complex, the representation of the mouth is most medial and the neck most lateral in VPM, and the hand is most medial and the feet most lateral in VPL. Each part of the body is represented in a sheet of cells, called **lamellae,** that take a curved path from dorsal to ventral in VB.[39] All neurons in a particular lamella respond to stimulation of the same region on the surface of the body or face. As the stimulus is moved along the body surface, then, activity in VB moves from one lamella to its immediate neighbor.

The VB Is Divided into Functional Subdivisions

The termination of medial lemniscal axons in VPL divides it into functional subdivisions. At a coarse level, the nucleus is divided into a core region that receives predominantly cutaneous inputs and a shell region that receives predominantly deep tissue inputs. At a finer level, the lemniscal axons terminate in narrow (200–300 μm in diameter) elongated rods that provide a group of thalamocortical neurons with their somatosensory input. These neurons, in turn, project to a zone in the cerebral cortex less than 1 mm in diameter.[40]

Neurons in VB Have Receptive Field Properties

A property characteristic of VB neurons innervated by the medial lemniscus is extreme synaptic security, with the ability to follow activity in presynaptic axons up to rates of more than 100 Hz.[39,41] Separate populations of VB neurons display rapidly and slowly adapting responses to cutaneous simulation and rapidly adapting responses to pressure, all of which suggest they are driven indirectly by SAI, RA, and Pacinian afferents. These findings accent the relay properties of VB and suggest that much of the circuitry in this nucleus is devoted to transferring a faithful replica of medial lemniscal and trigeminothalamic inputs to the cortex.

Neurons in VB driven by inputs from the anterolateral system include both nociceptive and thermoreceptive cells.[42] The anterolateral fibers terminate most densely in a small-celled peripheral part of VPL, displaced from the leminiscal terminations in the core.[43] Nevertheless, nociceptive and thermoreceptive neurons in VPL receive convergent input from mechanoreceptors, which may be the basis for localization of painful stimuli.

Summary

Variations in function and structure divide the ventrobasal complex into several parts. Separate nuclei, VPL and VPM, receive and process inputs from the body and head, respectively. Each nucleus is, itself, subdivided into regions, the physiology of which is dominated either by discriminative sensations or by pain and temperature.

SOMATOSENSORY AREAS OF THE CEREBRAL CORTEX

Areas of cerebral cortex are defined by three properties: function, structure, and connectivity. Connectivity and function are a matter of cause and effect because the physiology of somatosensory areas of cortex arises principally from their connections, particularly inputs from VB and from other areas of cerebral cortex.[44–46]

In the somatosensory system, two areas of cerebral cortex receive direct synaptic inputs from VB: The first somatosensory area (SI) in monkeys and humans is in the posterior bank of the central sulcus and on the crown of the postcentral gyrus; the second somatosensory area (SII) is on the lip and upper bank of the lateral fissure. These two are innervated not only by axons from VB but also from one another, as a dense reciprocal projection exists between the two.[47] Together, SI and SII then send axons to areas adjacent to them in the parietal lobe and insula, all of which can be considered part of the somatosensory system, and to areas of motor cortex.

The First Somatic Sensory Area Has Four Distinct Areas

Modern studies have identified four physiologically and anatomically distinct areas in SI, analagous to the areas of human cortex originally designated 3a, 3b, 1, and 2.[48,49] Each area contains neurons responsive to somatic stimuli and each receives direct axonal terminations from VB (Fig. 26.14). The precise source of those inputs varies, however, since few VB neurons send collaterals to two areas in SI.[50] As a result the physiological properties of neurons in one area differ appreciably from those of other areas.

At their most basic, cortical areas in SI perform different functions. Neurons in areas 3b and 1 are respon-

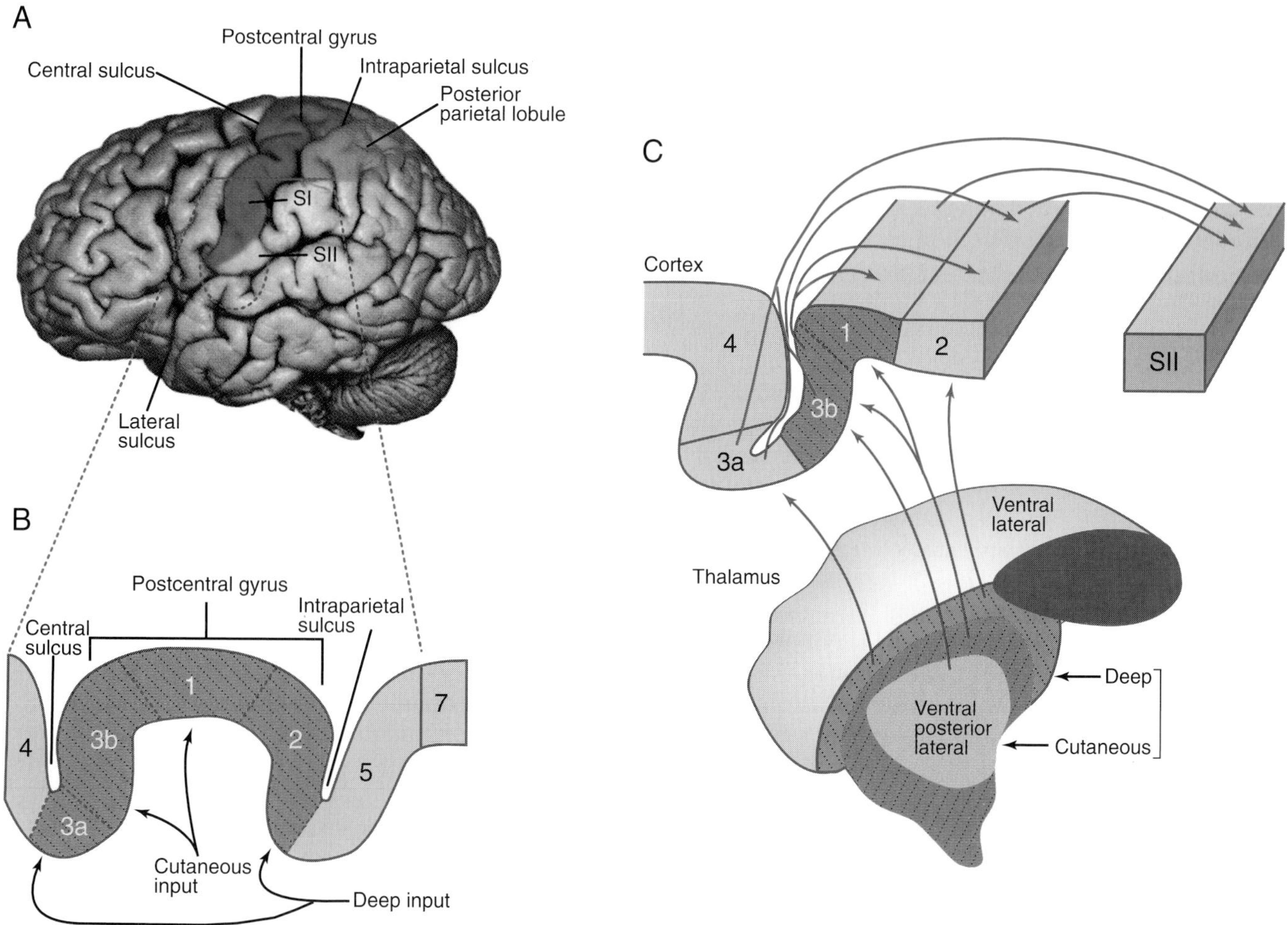

FIGURE 26.14 Functional organization of the ventrobasal complex and first somatosensory cortex (SI). (A) Location of SI in the postcentral gyrus and its relationship to SII and somatosensory association cortex in the posterior parietal lobe. (B) Cross section through the postcentral gyrus, cut orthogonal to the central sulcus. SI is divided into four anatomically and functionally distinct areas. They are bordered by area 4 of the precentral motor cortex and by area 5 of the parietal association cortex. (C) Relationship between regions of cutaneous and deep input to VPL and the termination of thalamocortical axons in SI. The serial processing of somatosensory inputs is also indicated by the projections from one area of SI to others and from all areas in SI to the second somatosensory area (SII). Adapted from Jones and Friedman (1982).[40]

sive to cutaneous inputs, both rapidly adapting and slowly adapting. In contrast, areas 3a and 2 respond to deep stimuli, with area 3a being particularly responsive to muscle afferents and area 2 to both cutaneous inputs and muscle afferents. In each area, receptive fields are larger than those displayed by primary sensory axons but are nevertheless specifically RA-like, SA-like, or Pacinian-like. Thus, SI clearly shows the division of labor that began at the periphery with the elaboration of different receptor types and the preservation of their selectivity for stimulus quality.

Lesion studies indicate that area 3b is critical for the performance of tactile discrimination based on the shape or texture of a stimulus.[51,52] Removal or inactivation of this area leads to a severe deficit in all aspects of tactile sensibility that translates to a lack of appreciation in the quality or even the existence of tactile stimuli. Lesions of area 1 disrupt performance based on texture but leave intact performance based on the size of objects, whereas lesions in area 2 produce the opposite result. These findings indicate that area 3b is a conduit for all cutaneous sensibility, that area 1 is specialized for analysis of SAI and RA inputs related to texture perception, and that area 2 integrates positional information with edge detection to form an accurate impression of an object's three-dimensional shape (also termed stereognosis).

A complete map of the body surface exists in each of the four areas of SI in Old World monkeys and thus it is assumed that four homunculi exist in human SI. Although complete, the body maps contain many distortions, the most dramatic of which is the greatly enlarged representations of the hand, particularly the digits, and of the face. Representation of the digits occupies more than 100 times the cortical surface area devoted to the trunk (Fig. 26.15). By this relative enlargement in cortical representation, the digits and lips are said to be magnified and the degree of overrepresentation is called the magnification factor.[53]

Area 3b is most densely innervated by axons of the core region in VB and displays the typical structure of primary sensory areas (Fig. 26.14). In fact, a compelling argument has been made that area 3b in Old World monkeys is equivalent to the entire SI of other mammals.[48] The adjacent area 3a varies in structure along the length of the central sulcus but can be seen as a region of hybrid structure, with many small cells, typical of area 3b, but also groups of larger cells, typical of the bordering precentral motor cortex.[54] Areas 1 and 2 display a structural pattern characteristic of most areas of cerebral cortex. So similar is their structure that determining where area 1 ends and area 2 begins can be extremely difficult when only anatomical criteria are used.[55]

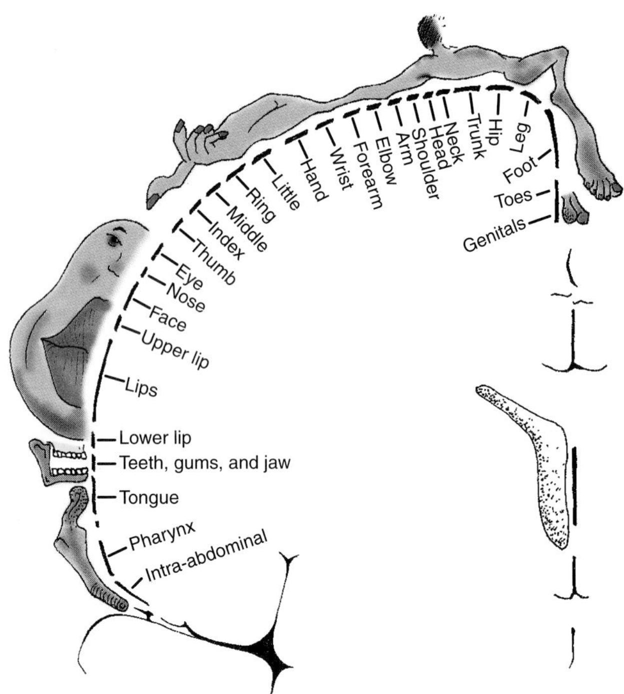

FIGURE 26.15 Somatotopic organization of human SI. The body map produces a homunculus with foot representation most medial and face representation most lateral. Note the expanded representation of some structures such as the mouth and hand. Modified from Penfield and Rasmussen, *The Cerebral Cortex of Man: A Clinical Study of Localization of Function, 1950,* courtesy of MacMillan.

In each area of SI, responses to stimuli are recorded for neurons from just below the pial surface of the cortex, in layer II, to just above the white matter, in layer VI. A consistent feature of cortex is the basic similarity in physiological properties displayed by neurons in a radial traverse through the cortex, so that cells in layers II–VI along a true radial path in SI respond to the same stimulus applied to the same part of the body surface. That is, neurons exhibiting place- and modality-specific responses are organized as radial arrays or columns.[56] These columns originate from the patchy termination of thalamocortical, intracortical, and callosal axons in areas of SI and are carried to all neurons in a column by radially organized axons that arise from neurons in one layer and terminate upon neurons in another layer.

Seven of 10 neurons in monkey VB send their axons to area 3b, where they terminate in the middle layers (layers III and IV). Neurons in layers II and III of area 3b then relay inputs to layer IV of the other areas in SI. This pattern in which layer III neurons in one area send axons to layer IV of another is typical of a pattern referred to as "feedforward" because the connections occur for a primary sensory area communicating with a higher order area. In this sense, area 3b is a first step

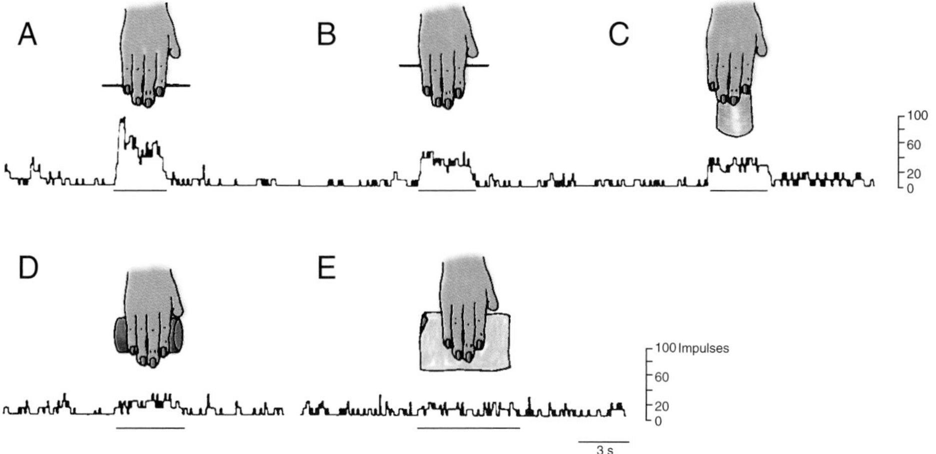

FIGURE 26.16 Response of neurons in monkey SI to the active grasping of objects. Variations in the position and shape of complex objects elicit responses of different strengths from neurons in this region of cortex. Most effective for this particular neuron is an edge applied to the tips of the fingers (A). Least effective is a flat sheet of paper (E).

and areas 1 and 2 a second cortical step in the analysis of somatosensory inputs. These patterns of thalamocortical and corticocortical connections suggest, then, that overlaid on the parallel processing of cutaneous versus deep inputs in SI is the serial processing of information. As an example, the function of area 3b inputs to area 2 is to contribute information from cutaneous receptors to an area dominated by deep inputs, providing for a unified representation of a stimulating object.

Differences in the receptive field properties of neurons in the areas of SI subscribe to a certain logic, given the varying sources of somatosensory inputs.[57] In the VB-dominated area 3b, neurons display very small, simple receptive fields, with neurons in layer IV of area 3b possessing receptive fields most similar to those of peripheral afferents. Neurons in overlying layers (II and III) display more complex responses (e.g., the presence of distinct excitatory and inhibitory subregions) over larger areas of the body surface. Those receptive fields are then donated by layer II–III neurons to area 2, where convergence and processing of inputs produce receptive fields with complex properties such as selectivity for the three-dimensional shape of an object (Fig. 26.16).

Because area 3a is located between the precentral motor area (area 4) and area 3b of SI, it could be seen as a sensory area with a motor function. Its connectivity suggests that is the case because thalamocortical inputs arise from neurons in VB responsive to proprioceptive stimuli, whereas densest intracortical inputs arise from cortical areas that also innervate the precentral motor area. Yet the path of information out of area 3a is not to motor cortex but to area 2 and to an area of parietal association cortex.[47] Only from those areas does sensory information reach the precentral motor and premotor areas. Area 3a, then, is not a direct conduit for proprioceptive input to motor cortex but is an intermediate stage of somatosensory processing, one whose output is combined with those from other somatosensory areas before that information is sent to the motor cortex.

From their innervation of motor and association areas, areas of SI can be seen to integrate somatosensory information and to relay such information to areas that control and coordinate body and limb movements. Other regions receiving information from SI include SII and the cortical areas around it and a series of subcortical nuclei. Most of the latter are, themselves, part of the somatosensory system, including VB, the dorsal column nuclei, and the dorsal and intermediate horns of the spinal cord. Such descending output from cortex serves to selectively activate neurons that are processing information from a specific body location and modality. Much of it can be seen as the anatomical substrate for the influence of attention on somatosensory processing. Attentional mechanisms help to limit the amount of information that the CNS needs to process simultaneously and ensures that irrelevant stimuli, such as the constant sensation of clothes in contact with the skin, do not unduly occupy the limited resources available for cortical processing. Thus, the responses of neurons in SI and particularly in SII are greatly affected by the attentional state of an animal.[58]

Fundamental changes take place in the somatosensory cortex when peripheral receptors or their axons are damaged. Because there is a limit to the time in development during which manipulations produce the most robust changes in cortical anatomy and physiology (a time referred to as the critical period), the general impression had grown that SI is largely immutable in adult life. Research over the past decade has shown repeatedly that such an impression was mistaken. Manipulations such as digit amputation or nerve section that eliminate input from a part of the body surface lead to a rearrangement of the body map in SI. Through this process, a part of SI normally responsive to one body region, such as the first digit, comes to respond to adjacent regions (neighboring digits). This type of somatosensory rearrangement can be extremely rapid, occurring within minutes of a manipulation, and thus depends on the ability of preexisting but ineffectual synaptic contacts in the cortex to now drive cortical neurons. Moreover, body map rearrangements can occur without the production of trauma anywhere in the somatosensory system but with only subtle manipulations such as coordinated stimulation of body regions and classical conditioning of cortical responses. A search for the mechanism of plasticity indicates that for SI itself, enhancement of connections formed by thalamocortical and intracortical axons permits a limited rearrangement in the body map, one that spans a distance of 2–3 mm.[59] Thus, the ability of inputs from one finger to capture cortical territory previously driven by another finger can be seen as a strictly intracortical event, driven by changes in intracortical excitation and inhibition. For much larger expansions that occur over 10–12 mm of SI, such as those that occur after limb amputation or the sectioning of several dorsal roots, the rearrangement in body map includes expansion in body maps not only in SI and SII but also in the dorsal column nuclei and VB. So extensive is this rearrangement that parts of SI previously responsive to the hand and arm come to respond to stimulation of the face and head.[60]

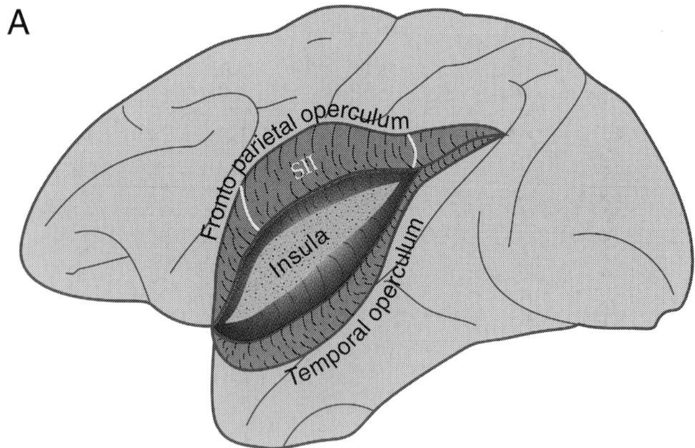

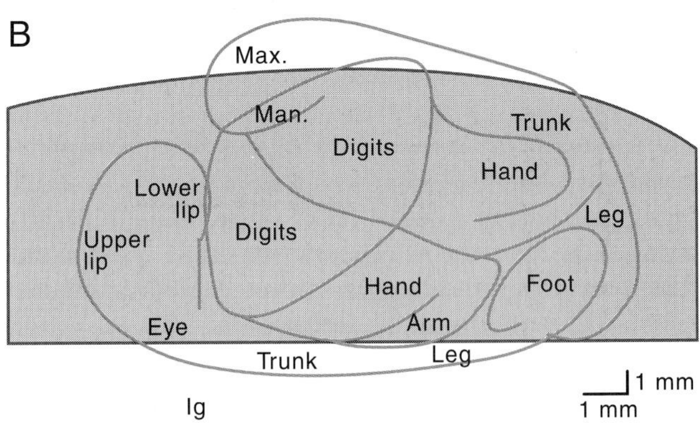

FIGURE 26.17 Location and somatotopic organization of the second somatosensory area in rhesus monkeys. (A) Partially unfolded view of cortex in the lateral sulcus. SII is located in the upper bank of that sulcus; its borders are indicated by the yellow lines. (B) Map of the body surface in SII, indicating the presence of two separate maps in this area and the relative expansion of the hand and digit representation.

The Second Somatic Sensory Area Receives Direct Input from VB

SII is the area of cerebral cortex in the upper bank of the lateral fissure (Fig. 26.17) that receives direct inputs from VB and whose neurons respond robustly to cutaneous stimulation of low intensity. By this definition, SII is approximately one-fourth the size of SI in surface area and contains at least one and probably two complete representations of the body (Fig. 26.17).[61,62] Complete destruction of SII leaves a monkey permanently incapable of discriminating objects on the basis of their texture and permanently impaired in discriminating among objects of different sizes.[63]

SII is the first stage of cortical somatosensory processing in which both sides of the body surface are represented in a sizable proportion of neurons. Inputs from the ipsilateral body surface reach SII predominantly from the contralateral hemisphere by way of axons in the corpus callosum. The transcallosal input to SII serves the obvious function of midline fusion. By this process, receptive fields along the body midline are generated in SII and extend for some distance into each half of the body, thus forming a coherent percept of a single body map. A less obvious function of the callosal input to SII is seen in studies of humans and nonhuman primates. To learn a tactile discrimination task with one hand and to perform it with the other is an ability easily and quickly accomplished by an intact human or monkey. Yet it is a task that is lost when the corpus callosum is cut or SII is surgically removed, thereby demonstrating a major role for SII in the interhemispheric transfer of tactile discrimination.

Many neurons in SII (more than 80%) are directly

affected by attentional state, with approximately half the responsive population showing enhanced responses when a stimulating object is attended to and half showing suppressed responses to the same condition.[58] These responses, being more complex than the ones sampled in any area of SI, have raised the strong possibility that SII is a higher order stage in a hierarchy of somatosensory areas. Evidence for such a hierarchy has come from studies of rhesus monkeys in which the somatosensory receptive fields of SII neurons were eliminated after surgical removal of SI.[64]

In primates, SII is the recipient of inputs from all four areas of SI, and in each case the intracortical axons terminate densely in layer IV of SII. Neurons of SII, in turn, give rise to axons that innervate two neighboring areas of insular cortex and from there somatosensory information reaches the amygdala and hippocampus (Fig. 26.18). Thus, SII in rhesus monkeys and presumably in other primates can be seen as a funnel for the relay of somatosensory information into the limbic system.[65] By this scheme SII is vital as the obligatory route taken by sensory inputs mediating tactual learning and memory.

A second major role for SII apparent from its intracortical connectivity is that of sensory–motor integration. One of the central components of coordinated movements is a continuous somatosensory feedback that permits changes in a motor program to occur. As an example, the act of precisely grasping an object requires strict coordination between somatosensory feedback and motor program. As indicated from studies in which lesions are placed within the CNS, that feedback makes its way to the brainstem through the dorsal columns. Finding that neurons in areas of motor cortex display relatively low-threshold somatosensory responses is not surprising in this context, and the conclusion had been that such responses are a function of the input to motor areas from SI. Such responses survive complete removal of SI, however, showing that the connections from this area to motor cortex are neither necessary nor sufficient. Cutaneous and deep responses in motor areas cannot arise from thalamocortical inputs because these inputs originate in thalamic nuclei other than VB, whose somatosensory responses are weak and require very strong stimuli. The remaining and obvious sources of somatosensory inputs to motor cortex are SII and the posterior parietal areas, 5 and 7.

Posterior Parietal Areas Perform Complex Somatosensory Functions

Various descriptors and definitions are used for the areas of parietal cortex posterior to area 2. If corticocortical inputs are combined with a traditional scheme for numbering areas of cortex, then two cortical areas (areas 5 and 7) with two subdivisions each (a and b) may be considered part of the somatosensory system.

The rostral half of the posterior parietal cortex is made up of areas 5a and 7b. These are the areas directly innervated by area 2 in monkeys and in which somatosensory responses to low-threshold stimuli can be easily mapped. Their output to the precentral motor area indicates that they play a role in integrating somatosensory information with motor behavior. Specifically, they are implicated in attentional and motivational control of movements that are related to tactile stimuli.[66]

The caudal half of the posterior parietal cortex, especially area 7a, is a site for convergence of somatosensory and visual inputs. It is a region very strongly implicated in visual functions of localizing a stimulus and of directing attention to that stimulus. These caudal parietal regions, in the bank of the intraparietal sulcus of Old World monkeys, are clearly involved in directing eye movements and are thus at a pivot point in somatosensory, visual, and motor systems. Although neurons are responsive to both somatosensory and visual stimuli in this area, it cannot be said that neurons display receptive fields in the same sense as neurons in SI. Instead, responses can be elicited from any place in the sensory periphery but in a manner that depends on the context of the stimulus.[67]

Both halves of the posterior parietal cortex appear to function, then, as stations for the higher order analysis and relay of somatosensory inputs to areas of motor and possibly attentional control.[68] Yet it should be appreciated that unilateral removal of the posterior parietal areas in monkeys leads to few somatosensory deficits, amounting to only a partial neglect of tactile stimuli delivered to the contralateral body surface. Most importantly, no region of cortex undergoes the dramatic increase in size and shift in function that the posterior parietal cortex does in going from nonprimates to primates and especially from nonhuman primates to humans.

Summary

Over the past few decades, the early concepts of somatosensory system function and organization have been challenged, only to be reaffirmed and refined by further work. Thus, the concept of labeled lines beginning in the periphery and continuing centrally has been firmly established. Similarly, the broad division of the somatosensory system into lemniscal and

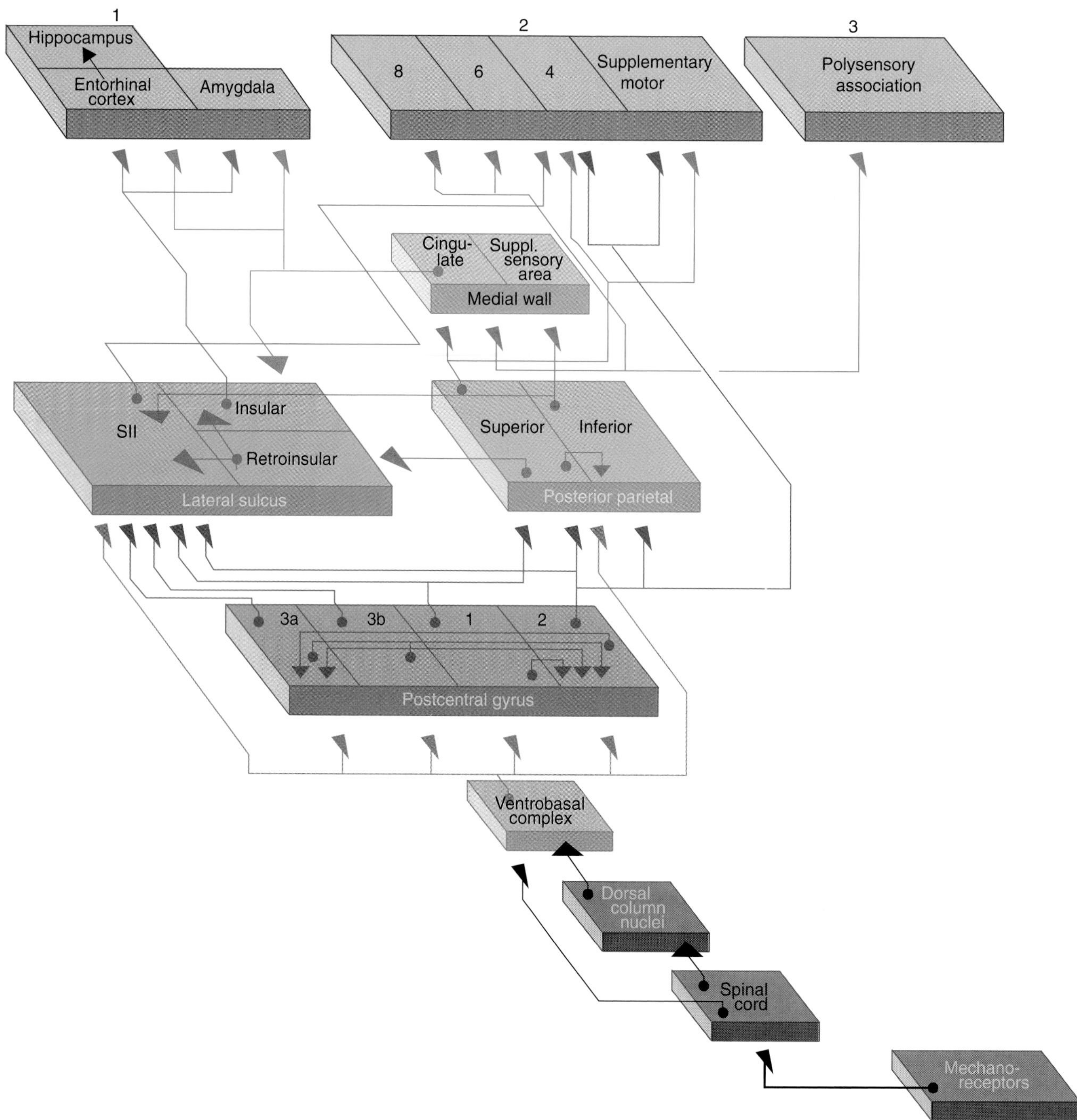

FIGURE 26.18 Schematic representation of the path taken by mechanoreceptor input to eventually reach three cortical targets. All relevant information reaches the ventrobasal complex and most is relayed to the areas of SI. From there, by steps through SII and the posterior parietal areas, somatosensory information reaches: (1) the limbic system (entorhinal cortex and hippocampus), as a means for becoming part of or gaining access to stored memories; (2) the motor system (primary and supplementary motor cortex), where the continuous sensory feedback onto motor system occurs; and (3) the polysensory cortex in the superior temporal gyrus, in which creation of a complete and abstract sensory map of the external world is thought to occur. Adapted from Wall, J. T. (1988). Trends in Neurosci. **11:** 549–557, with permission.

BOX 26.5

CORRELATION OF PSYCHOPHYSICS AND NEUROPHYSIOLOGY

Most understanding of the neural basis for perception comes from experiments that combine psychophysics with neurophysiology. First introduced into studies of somatic sensation by Vernon Mountcastle in the early 1960s, this approach assumes that perception is directly related to the neural activity in populations of sensory neurons. Mountcastle and his colleagues performed psychophysical experiments in which humans were tested with vibratory stimuli that varied in frequency and intensity. They showed that the detection threshold for vibration was a U-shaped curve, where the minimum intensity for detecting a vibration was at a frequency of 200 Hz. In companion neurophysiological experiments on monkeys, these same investigators systematically tested the thresholds for eliciting action potentials from hundreds of peripheral afferents, using the same stimulus as that employed in the human psychophysical studies. Their results showed that the U-shaped curve could be accounted for only by the presence of two separate populations of sensory afferents: the RA afferents at low frequency and the Pacinian afferents at high frequency.

One problem well recognized by Mountcastle and his group was the use of different species for psychophysical and neurophysiological experiments, a design based on the assumption that monkeys and people are essentially identical in sensory processes. To directly test this assumption, Mountcastle began studies in which monkeys were trained to detect and to signal the presence of a vibration. These studies showed that thresholds in humans and monkeys are practically identical, thus confirming the similarity of the two species in the initial processing of tactile stimuli. This pioneering study provided both the technological and philosophical means for solving what was once thought to be an intractable problem. An entire field of investigation has followed, providing vital insights into not only the processing of tactile stimuli but also the steps involved in the perception of auditory and visual stimuli.

anterolateral groups remains one of the earlier appreciated and more clearly documented functional divisions of a sensory system into parallel paths. The greatest single advance has come from the simultaneous application of psychophysical and neurophysiological approaches of studying somatic sensation in alert, trained monkeys (see Box 26.5). With this approach the contribution of single neurons to the perception of form and texture has been demonstrated and the dynamic processing of tactile information has been accented. It is the latter, the dynamic aspects of somatosensory function, where the future of somatosensory research lies. From studies of rearrangements in somatotopy following peripheral manipulations and from those documenting the role of attention on the response properties of neurons, the static image of the somatosensory system is being replaced by one in which the context of a stimulus is a key component of a neuron's response.

References

1. Clark, F. J., and Horch, K. W. (1986). Kinesthesia. In *Handbook of Perception and Human Performance: Sensory Processes and Perception* (K. R. Boff, L. Kaufman, and J. P. Thomas, eds.), pp. 1–62. Wiley, New York.
2. Weinstein, S. (1968). Intensive and extensive aspects of tactile sensitivity as a function of body part, sex and laterality. In *The Skin Senses* (D. R. Kenshalo, ed.), pp. 195–222. Thomas, Springfield, IL.
3. Johnson, K. O., Hsiao, S. S., and Twombly, I. A. (1995). Neural mechanisms of tactile form recognition. In *The Cognitive Sciences* (M. Gazzaniga, ed.), pp. 253–268. MIT Press, Cambridge, MA.
4. Foulke, E. (1991). Braille. In *The Psychology of Touch* (M. A. Heller and W. Schiff, eds.), pp. 219–234. Erlbaum, Hillsdale, NJ.
5. Connor, C. E., Hsiao, S. S., Phillips, J. R., and Johnson, K. O. (1990). Tactile roughness: Neural codes that account for psychophysical magnitude estimates. *J. Neurosci.* **10:** 3823–3836.
6. Talbot, W. H., Darian-Smith, I., Kornhuber, H. H., and Mountcastle, V. B. (1968). The sense of flutter-vibration: Comparison of the human capacity with response patterns of mechanoreceptive afferents from the monkey hand. *J. Neurophysiol.* **31:** 301–334.
7. Iggo, A., and Andres, K. H. (1982). Morphology of cutaneous receptors. *Annu. Rev. Neurosci.* **5:** 1–32.
8. Zelena, J. (1994). Nerves and Mechanoreceptors. Chapman & Hall, London.
9. Westling, G., and Johansson, R. S. (1987). Responses in glabrous skin mechanoreceptors during precision grip in humans. *Exp. Brain Res.* **66:** 128–140.
10. Johnson, K. O., and Hsiao, S. S. (1992). Tactual form and texture perception. *Ann. Rev. Neurosci.* **15:** 227–250.
11. Stevens, J. C., Cruz, L. A., and Pierce, J. B. (1996). Spatial acuity of touch: Ubiquitous decline with aging revealed by repeated threshold testing. *Somatosensory Motor Res.* **13**(1): 1–10.
12. Phillips, J. R., and Johnson, K. O. (1981). Tactile spatial resolution: II. Neural representation of bars, edges, and gratings in monkey afferents. *J. Neurophysiol.* **46:** 1192–1203.

13. Torebjork, H. E., Vallbo, A. B., and Ochoa, J. L. (1987). Intraneural microstimulation in man: Its relation to specificity of tactile sensations. *Brain* **110:** 1509–1529.
14. Phillips, J. R., Johansson, R. S., and Johnson, K. O. (1990). Representation of braille characters in human nerve fibers. *Exp. Brain Res.* **81:** 589–592.
15. Johnson, K. O., and Hsiao, S. S. (1994). Evaluation of the relative roles of slowly and rapidly adapting afferent fibers in roughness perception. *Can. J. Physiol. Pharmacol.* **72:** 488–497.
16. Hsiao, S. S., Johnson, K. O., and Twombly, I. A. (1993). Roughness coding in the somatosensory system. *Acta Psychol.* **84:** 53–67.
17. Bell, J., Bolanowski, S. J., and Holmes, M. H. (1994). The structure and function of Pacinian corpuscles: A review. *Prog. Neurobiol.* **42:** 79–128.
18. Willis, W. D. (1985). *The Pain System: The Neural Basis of Nociceptive Transmission in the Mammalian Nervous System.* Karger, New York.
19. Willis, W. D. (1989). Peripheral neural mechanisms of nociception. In *Textbook of Pain* (P. D. Wall and R. Melzack, eds.), pp. 112–127. Churchill-Livingstone, New York.
20. Burgess, P. R., and Perl, E. R. (1973). Cutaneous mechanoreceptors and nociceptors. In *Handbook of Sensory Physiology* (A. Iggo, ed.), Vol. 2, pp. 30–78. Springer-Verlag, New York.
21. Perl, E. R. (1984). Pain and nociception. In *Handbook of Physiology* (I. Darian-Smith, J. M. Brookhart, and V. B. Mountcastle, eds.), Sect. 1, Vol. III, Part 2, pp. 915–975. Am. Physiol. Soc., Bethesda, MD.
22. Darian-Smith, I. (1984). Thermal sensibility. In *Handbook of Physiology* (I. Darian-Smith, J. M. Brookhart, and V. B. Mountcastle, eds.), Sect. 1, Vol. III, Part 2, pp. 879–914. Am. Physiol. Soc., Bethesda, MD.
23. Darian-Smith, I., Johnson, K. O., and Dykes, R. W. (1973). "Cold" fiber population innervating palmar and digital skin of the monkey: Responses to cooling pulses. *J. Neurophysiol.* **36:** 325–346.
24. Johnson, K. O., Darian-Smith, I., and LaMotte, C. (1973). Peripheral neural determinants of temperature discrimination in man: A correlative study of responses to cooling skin. *J. Neurophysiol.* **36:** 347–370.
25. Campbell, J. N., and Meyer, R. A. (1986). Primary afferents and hyperalgesia, In *Spinal Afferent Processing* (T. L. Yaksh, ed.), pp. 59–81. Plenum, New York.
26. Lin, Q., Peng, Y. B., and Willis, W. D. (1996). Possible role of protein kinase C in the sensitization of primate spinothalamic tract neurons. *J. Neurosci.* **16:** 3026–3034.
27. Matthews, P. B. C. (1982). Where does Sherrington's "muscle sense" originate? Muscles, joints, or corollary discharge? *Annu. Rev. Neurosci.* **5:** 189–218.
28. Burgess, P. R., Wei, J. Y., Clark, F. J., and Simon, J. (1982). Signaling of kinesthetic information by peripheral sensory receptors. *Annu. Rev. Neurosci.* **5:** 171–187.
29. McCloskey, D. I. (1978). Kinesthetic sensibility. *Physiol. Rev.* **58: 763–820.**
30. Hasan, Z., and Stuart, D. G. (1984). Mammalian muscle spindle receptors. In *Handbook of the Spinal Cord* (R. A. Davidoff, ed.), pp. 559–607. Dekker, New York.
31. Lawson, S. N. (1992). Morphological and biochemical cell types of sensory neurons. In *Sensory Neurons: Diversity, Development and Plasticity* (S. A. Scott, ed.), pp. 27–59. Oxford University Press, Oxford.
32. Brown, A. G. (1981). *Organization in the Spinal Cord.* Springer-Verlag, New York.
33. Mountcastle, V. B. (1984). Central nervous mechanisms in mechanoreceptive sensibility. In *Handbook of Physiology* (I. Darian-Smith, J. M. Brookhart, and V. B. Mountcastle, eds.), Sect. 1, Vol. III, Part 2, pp. 789–878. Am. Physiol. Soc., Bethesda, MD.
34. Basbaum, A. I., and Fields, H. L. (1984). Endogenous pain control systems: Brainstem spinal pathways and endorphin circuitry. *Annu. Rev. Neurosci.* **7:** 223–255.
35. Trevino, D. L. (1976). The origin and projections of a spinal nociceptive and thermoreceptive pathway. In *Sensory Functions of the Skin in Primates, with Special Reference to Man* (Y. Zotterman, ed.), pp. 367–376. Pergamon, New York.
36. Dubner, R., and Bennett, G. J. (1983). Spinal and trigeminal mechanisms of nociception. *Annu. Rev. Neurosci.* **6:** 381–418.
37. Friedman, D. P., and Murray, E. A. (1986). Thalamic connectivity of the second somatosensory area and neighboring somatosensory fields of the lateral sulcus of the macaque. *J. Comp. Neurol.* **252:** 348–373.
38. Mountcastle, V. B., and Henneman, E. (1952). The representation of tactile sensibility in the thalamus of the monkey. *J. Comp. Neurol.* **97:** 409–440.
39. Poggio, G. F., and Mountcastle, V. B. (1963). The functional properties of ventrobasal thalamic neurons studied in unanesthetized monkeys. *J. Neurophysiol.* **26:** 775–806.
40. Jones, E. G., and Friedman, D. P. (1982). Projection pattern of functional components of thalamic ventrobasal complex on monkey somatosensory cortex. *J. Neurophysiol.* **48:** 521–544.
41. Poggio, G. F., and Mountcastle, V. B. (1960). A study of the functional contributions of the lemniscal and spinothalamic systems to somatic sensibility. *Bull. Johns Hopkins Hosp.* **108:** 266–316.
42. Kenshalo, D. R., Giesler, G. J., Leonard, R. B., and Willis, W. D. (1980). Responses of neurons in primate ventral posterior lateral nucleus to noxious stimuli. *J. Neurophysiol.* **43:** 1594–1614.
43. Rausell, E., Bae, C. S., Viñuela, A., Huntley, G. W., and Jones, E. G. (1992). Calbindin and parvalbumin cells in monkey VPL thalamic nucleus: Distribution, laminar cortical projections, and relations to spinothalamic terminations. *J. Neurosci.* **12:** 4088–4111.
44. Jones, E. G., and Powell, T. P. (1969). Connexions of the somatic sensory cortex of the rhesus monkey. I. Ipsilateral cortical connexions. *Brain* **92:** 477–502.
45. Jones, E. G., and Powell, T. P. (1969). Connexions of the somatic sensory cortex of the rhesus monkey. II. Contralateral cortical connexions. *Brain* **92:** 717–730.
46. Jones, E. G., and Powell, T. P. (1970). Connexions of the somatic sensory cortex of the rhesus monkey. III. Thalamic connexions. *Brain* **93:** 37–56.
47. Jones, E. G., Coulter, J. D., and Hendry, S. H. C. (1978). Intracortical connectivity of architectonic fields in the somatic sensory, motor and parietal cortex of the monkey. *J. Comp. Neurol.* **181:** 291–348.
48. Kaas, J. H. (1996). The somatosensory cortex. In *Somesthesis and the Neurobiology of the Somatosensory Cortex* (O. Franzen, R. S. Johansson, and L. Terenius, eds.), pp. 163–172. Birkhäuser, Basel.
49. Kaas, J. H., Nelson, R. J., Sur, M., Lin, C. S., and Merzenich, M. M. (1979). Multiple representations of the body within the primary somatosensory cortex of primates. *Science* **204:** 521–523.
50. Jones, E. G. (1983). Lack of collateral thalamocortical projections to fields of the first somatic sensory cortex in monkeys. *Exp. Brain Res.* **52:** 375–384.
51. Carlson, M. (1980). Characteristics of sensory deficits following lesions of Brodmann's areas 1 and 2 in the postcentral gyrus of Macaca mulatta. *Brain Res.* **204:** 424–430.
52. Randolph, M., and Semmes, G. (1974). Behavioral consequences of selective subtotal ablations in the postcentral gyrus of *macaca mulatta. Brain Res.* **70:** 55–70.
53. Sur, M., Merzenich, M. M., and Kaas, J. H. (1980). Magnification, receptive-field area, and hypercolumn size in areas 3b and 1 of somatosensory cortex in owl monkeys. *J. Neurophysiol.* **44:** 295–311.

54. Jones, E. G., and Porter, R. (1980). What is area 3a? *Brain Res. Rev.* **2:** 1–43.
55. Powell, T. P. S., and Mountcastle, V. B. (1959). The cytoarchitecture of the post-central gyrus of the monkey, *Macaca mulatta. Bull. Johns Hopkins Hosp.* **105:** 108–131.
56. Mountcastle, V. B. (1957). Modality and topographic properties of single neurons of cat's somatic sensory cortex. *J. Neurophysiol.* **20:** 408–434.
57. Iwamura, Y., and Tanaka, M. (1978). Postcentral neurons in hand region of area 2: Their possible role in the form discrimination of tactile objects. *Brain Res.* **150:** 662–666.
58. Hsiao, S. S., O'Shaughnessy, D. M., and Johnson, K. O. (1993). Effects of selective attention on spatial form processing in monkey primary and secondary somatosensory cortex. *J. Neurophysiol.* **70:** 444–447.
59. Merzenich, M. M., Kaas, J. H., Wall, J. T., Sur, M., Nelson, R. J., and Felleman, D. J. (1983). Progression of change following nerve section in the cortical representation of the hand in areas 3b and 1 in adult owl and squirrel monkeys. *Neuroscience* **10:** 639–665.
60. Pons, T. P., Garraghty, P. E., Ommaya, A. K., Kaas, J. H., Taub, E., and Mishkin, M. (1991). Massive cortical reorganization after sensory deafferentation in adult macaques. *Science* **252:** 1857–1860.
61. Burton, H., Fabri, M., and Alloway, K. D. (1995). Cortical areas within the lateral sulcus connected to cutaneous representations in areas 3b and 1: A revised interpretation of the second somatosensory area in macaque monkeys. *J. Comp. Neurol.* **355:** 539–562.
62. Krubitzer, L. A. (1996). The organization of lateral somatosensory cortex in primates and other mammals. In *Somesthesis and the Neurobiology of the Somatosensory Cortex* (O. Franzen, R. S. Johansson, and L. Terenius, eds.), pp. 173–186. Birkhäuser, Basel.
63. Murray, E. A., and Mishkin, M. (1984). Relative contributions of SII and area 5 to tactile discrimination in monkeys. *Behav. Brain Res.* **11:** 67–83.
64. Pons, T. P., Garraghty, P. E., and Mishkin, M. (1992). Serial and parallel processing of tactual information in somatosensory cortex of rhesus monkey. *J. Neurophysiol.* **68:** 518–527.
65. Friedman, D. P., Murray, E. A., O'Neill, J. B., and Mishkin, M. (1986). Cortical connections of the somatosensory fields of the lateral sulcus of macaques: Evidence for a corticolimbic pathway for touch. *J. Comp. Neurol.* **252:** 323–347.
66. LaMotte, R. H., and Mountcastle, V. B. (1979). Disorders in somesthesis following lesions of parietal lobe. *J. Neurophysiol.* **42:** 400–419.
67. Mountcastle, V. B. (1995). The parietal system and some higher brain. *Cereb. Cortex* **5:** 377–390.
68. Steinmetz, M. A., Connor, C. E., Constantinidis, C., and McLaughlin, J. R. (1994). Covert attention suppresses neuronal responses in area 7a of the posterior parietal cortex. *J. Neurophysiol.* **72:** 1020–1023.

C H A P T E R

27

Audition

M. Christian Brown

The auditory system detects sound and uses acoustic cues to identify and locate sounds in the environment. The auditory system shares functional and evolutionary similarities with other mechanoreceptive systems, such as the vestibular system and the lateral-line system of lower vertebrates. All of these systems use the same type of receptor cell—the hair cell—and all are specialized to detect some external stimulus that eventually causes the stereocilia of the hair cells to be displaced. Unlike other mechanoreceptive systems, the auditory system is sensitive to sound. In this chapter, we explore the characteristics of the auditory system that make it sensitive to sound and that make it sensitive to the location of a sound source. We emphasize the generalized mammalian auditory system but also take examples from studies of animals with specialized auditory systems such as bats and owls, which have greatly advanced our knowledge of audition.

A major difference between the auditory system and other sensory systems is the fast time scale on which the auditory system works. Sounds are oscillations of air pressure that vary rapidly with time, often thousands of oscillations per second (Fig. 27.1). These oscillations are mimicked by the receptor potentials of the hair cells and then transformed into a spike code by the auditory nerve and transmitted to the brain. Within the brain, specialized auditory neurons extract information from the spike code. Such information can, for example, determine that a sound source is located to one side of the head, using interaural time differences as small as 10 μs. This impressive time sensitivity mentioned often in this chapter and is a unique characteristic of the auditory system.

AMPLITUDE AND FREQUENCY RANGES OF HEARING

Sound is quantified by specifying its amplitude and frequency content (Fig. 27.1). **Amplitude** of sound pressure is usually specified by a scale of sound pressure level (SPL, in decibels or dB), which logarithmically compresses the huge differences between the pressures that are just audible and those that are very loud. The range of levels over which hearing is possible begins at about 0 dB, the threshold of human hearing in the most sensitive frequency range. As an example of the exquisite sensitivity of hearing, at 0 dB, the amplitude of air particle movements is about 0.01 nm in extent! The upper limit of hearing is about 120–140 dB, at which sounds cause damage to the ear and at which a sensation called auditory feeling or pain begins.

Sound frequency is the number of oscillations of air pressure per second, measured in hertz (Hz) (Fig. 27.1). Humans are sensitive to frequencies from about 20 to 20,000 Hz, with the most sensitive range being 1000 to 4000 Hz (1 to 4 kHz). Most energy in human speech is between about 0.25 and 3 kHz. Smaller animals have frequency ranges that are higher than that of humans. For instance, mice and bats are able to hear sound frequencies higher than 50 kHz, at the expense of relatively poor hearing at low frequencies. Although auditory experiments often use pure tone stimuli that contain a single frequency (Fig. 27.1), most naturally occurring stimuli are complex and contain a multitude of frequencies, each having a different amplitude and time course. Complicated stimuli can be broken down

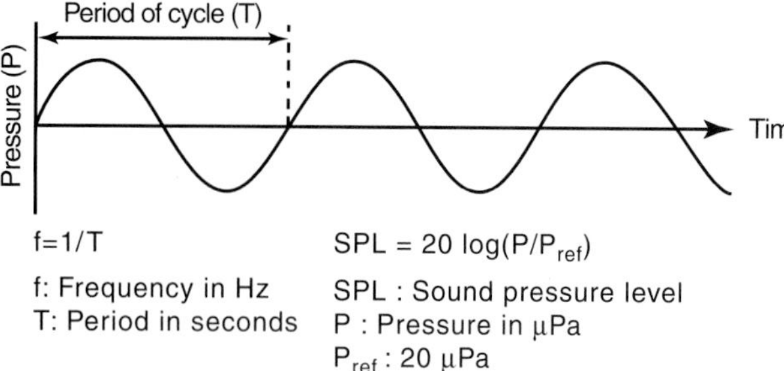

FIGURE 27.1 Sound pressure as a function of time for the sinusoidal pressure of a pure tone. The two important characteristics of this sound are its frequency (*f*, in Hz) and its sound pressure level (SPL, in dB). As shown, frequency is the reciprocal of the period of the cycle. Periods of sound waves in the audible range are very fast: the period of a 1000-Hz tone is 1 ms. SPL is a logarithmic function of acoustic pressure and is related to sound pressure by the equation shown.

into simple components by Fourier analysis. Because of the **nonlinear** behavior of the auditory system, however, its responses to a complex stimulus are not always predictable from the sum of the responses to its individual components.

EXTERNAL AND MIDDLE EAR

The peripheral auditory system is divided into the external, the middle, and the inner ear (Fig. 27.2). The **external ear** is composed of the pinna and external auditory canal. These structures convey sound to the middle ear, but not without influencing it. This influence emphasizes and deemphasizes certain sound frequencies, resulting in peaks and notches in the sound spectrum.[1] The positions of the peaks and notches depend on the location of the sound source, so they provide information about location, even when only one ear is being used (**monaural sound localization**). Such information may be especially important for determining the elevation of a sound source, because spectral peaks and notches are among the few cues that depend strongly on a sound source's elevation.

Mechanosensitive organs in lower vertebrates, such as the lateral line of fish, are sensitive to vibrations in aquatic environments. When vertebrates evolved onto land, they faced the problem of converting sound in air to sound in body fluids because the inner ear of vertebrates remains filled with body fluids. Because of the different physical characteristics of air and body fluids, sound at the air–fluid interface is almost completely reflected back into the air, rather than being transmitted into the fluid. The function of the **middle ear** is to ensure efficient transmission of sound from air into the fluid of the inner ear. The middle ear begins at the **tympanic membrane** (eardrum), continues with the three middle ear **ossicles** (malleus, incus, and stapes), and ends at the footplate of the **stapes**, which contacts the inner-ear fluids at the oval window of the cochlea (Fig. 27.2). In addition to the ossicles, the middle ear has large air spaces and two middle-ear muscles. The middle ear can increase the transmission of sound into the inner ear in several ways. Most importantly, the area of the eardrum is larger (by about 35 times) than the area of the stapes footplate, so there is a corresponding increase in pressure from the eardrum to the stapes footplate. Additionally, there may be small contributions from a lever action of the ossicles and a buckling motion of the tympanic membrane, both increasing the force applied to the footplate. Together, these mechanisms provide a pressure gain of about 25 to 30 dB in the middle frequencies over what would be achieved by sound striking the oval window directly.[2] This amount of gain means that for middle frequencies, most of the acoustic energy that strikes the eardum is transmitted by the middle ear into the inner ear. For lower and higher frequencies, however, energy is lost. When sound conduction through the middle ear is compromised, a patient has a conductive hearing loss. One disease that causes a conductive hearing loss is **otosclerosis**, in which bony growths around the stapes cause it to adhere to surrounding bone and lessen its transmission of vibration. A surgical procedure called a stapedectomy usually restores hearing by replacing the stapes with an artificial stapes.

THE COCHLEA

The inner ear is located deep within the head (Fig. 27.2). The inner ear contains the **cochlea**, which is the sensory endorgan for the auditory system. It also contains the utricle, saccule, and cristae of the three semicircular canals, which are the sensory endorgans for the vestibular system (see Chapter 36). The word cochlea comes from the Greek word *kokhlias*, meaning "snail," since the cochlea is coiled like a snail's shell. The long spiraled tube of the cochlea in most species has two to four turns, which are visible in cross section (Fig. 27.3A). The sensory organ, the **organ of Corti**, contains the receptor cells (hair cells) and supporting cells. The organ of Corti rests on the basilar membrane and is covered by the tectorial membrane (Fig. 27.3B). Hair cells are of two types: **inner hair cells** and **outer hair cells.** Their names are derived from the position of the hair cells along the cochlear spiral: inner hair cells are located innermost along the spiral and outer hair cells

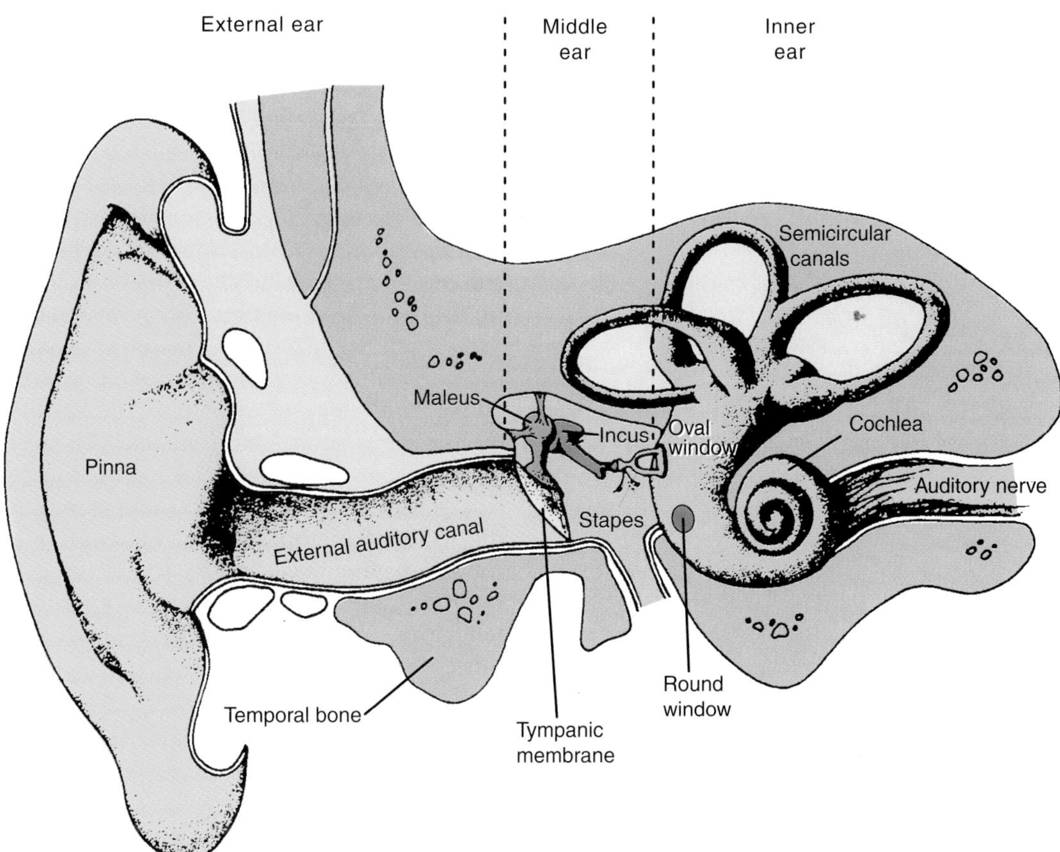

FIGURE 27.2 Drawing of the auditory periphery within the human head. Shown are the external ear (pinna and external auditory canal) and the middle ear (tympanic membrane or eardrum, and the three middle ear ossicles: malleus, incus, stapes). Also shown is the inner ear, which includes the cochlea of the auditory system and the semicircular canals of the vestibular system. There are two cochlear windows, the oval and round windows. The oval window is the window through which the stapes conveys sound vibrations to the inner-ear fluids. From Lindsey and Norman (1972) *Human Information Processing* Academic Press, New York.

are located outermost. There is one row of inner hair cells and usually three rows of outer hair cells. In the human cochlea, there are about 3500 inner hair cells and about 14,000 outer hair cells.[3]

Outer Hair Cells Contribute to Auditory Sensitivity

Sound-induced vibrations of the middle ear are transmitted into the cochlear fluids and then to the **basilar membrane** and organ of Corti. Early experiments by von Bekesy[4] determined that the pattern of basilar membrane motion was a **traveling wave** that begins at the base of the cochlea and proceeds apically. Furthermore, the pattern was different for different sound frequencies, with high frequencies causing maximal motion at the base of the cochlea and lower frequencies causing motion more apically. This difference is likely caused by the fact that the basilar membrane is narrower and stiffer at the base of the cochlea and becomes wider and less stiff at the apex. Modern methods have determined that the motion of the basilar membrane is extremely sensitive in that it responds at very low sound pressures and it is very sharply tuned to sound frequency.[5,6] This sensitivity and tuning are dependent on the health of the cochlea and are especially susceptible to injury of the outer hair cells. For instance, in experimental animals in which outer hair cells have been selectively lesioned with aminoglycoside antibiotics, the high sensitivity and sharp tuning disappear.[7] Outer hair cells may contribute to basilar membrane motion because they themselves can be motile.[8,9] The outer hair cells change their length when depolarized and hyperpolarized *in vitro* (reviewed in Chapter 24). *In vivo*, these cells are depolarized and hyperpolarized by the receptor potentials that they produce in response to sound. Their contribution to boosting the response of the basilar membrane has

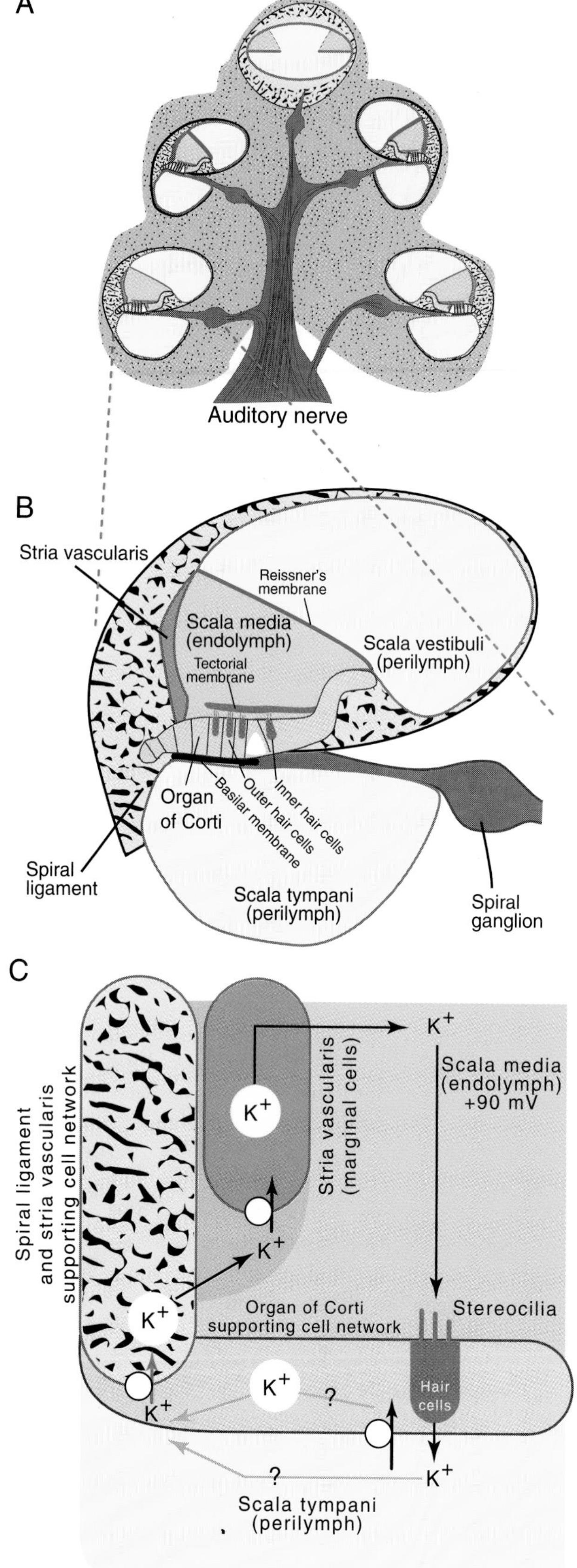

led investigators to designate the outer hair cells as a **cochlear amplifier** of basilar membrane motion. This amplification is a key functional role for outer hair cells. The motility and amplification of outer hair cells are the likely causes of sounds that are emitted by the ear, "otoacoustic emissions" (Box 27.1).

Hair cells transduce the mechanical energy of sound into electrical receptor potentials when the hair-cell **stereocilia** are displaced[14,15] (reviewed in Chapter 24). In the sound-stimulated cochlea, stereocilia are deflected when the tectorial membrane, which overlies the stereocilia, moves differently than the bodies of the hair cells in the organ of Coti on top of the basilar membrane. The tips of outer hair cell stereocilia may directly contact the tectorial membrane, whereas the tips of inner hair cell stereocilia may end just beneath the tectorial membrane and be displaced by nearby fluid movements caused by the tectorial membrane's motion. When stereocilia are displaced toward the taller rows of stereocilia, the cell is depolarized, and this causes the hair cell to release an excitatory neurotransmitter. When stereocilia are displaced in the other direction, the cell is hyperpolarized and release of transmitter is decreased. Although the identity of the transmitter is not known with certainty, it interacts with a receptor, likely one of the glutamate receptors, on the auditory nerve terminals. The terminals are then depolarized and generate impulses that are conveyed to the brain.

Endolymph Increases Auditory Sensitivity

An increase in sensitivity of hair cells is made possible by the unique composition of the inner-ear fluids.

FIGURE 27.3 (A) Cross section through the cochlea. The cross section of this human cochlea shows the approximately three turns that spiral around a central core (modiolus) containing the auditory nerve. (B) Cross section through one cochlear turn to illustrate important cell groups (organ of Corti, spiral ligament, and stria vascularis) and the main fluid compartments (scala vestibuli, scala media, and scala tympani). Within the organ of Corti, sensory or hair cells are colored dark blue, whereas supporting cells are colored light blue. These supporting cells are coupled by gap junctions. (C) A schematic of one turn of the cochlea showing the cycle for potassium ion (K^+) flow in the cochlea. Marginal cells (red) in the stria vascularis accumulate K^+ via active transport (circle with adjacent arrow) and generate the endolymph's high K^+ concentration and high electrical potential. When sound causes the stereocilia to move, K^+ flows down its electrochemical gradient into the hair cells, and eventually out their basal–lateral surfaces. Hypothetical return pathways back to the stria are via perilymph or possibly through gap junctions in supporting cell networks. Part B modified from T. Kikuchi, R. S. Kimura, D. L. Paul, and J. C. Adams (1995). Gap junctions in the rat cochlea: immunohistochemical and ultrastructural analysis. *Anat. Embryol.* **191:** 101–118, copyright Springer-Verlag. Part C courtesy of Drs. E.A. Mroz and J. C. Adams.

BOX 27.1

OTOACOUSTIC EMISSIONS

In 1978, David Kemp made a surprising discovery: the ear can sometimes *emit* sounds.[10–12] These otoacoustic emissions are now the focus of much interest because basic researchers can use them to study the function of the ear and because clinicians can use them as tests of hearing. Emissions are almost always so low in level that they are inaudible unless the individual is in an exceptionally quiet environment. Thus, for measurement of emissions, a sensitive microphone is placed in the external ear canal. Many studies indicate that the cochlea (inner ear) is the source of emissions. Within the cochlea, the outer hair cells are likely to be the generators of emissions; these cells are motile and probably generate movements of the basilar membrane and cochlear fluids via this motility. After these movements are generated, they travel in reverse of the normal pathway for sound into the inner ear: the emissions propagate from their point of generation along the basilar membrane to the oval window, then through the middle ear via the ossicles, and finally move the tympanic membrane to result in airborne sound.

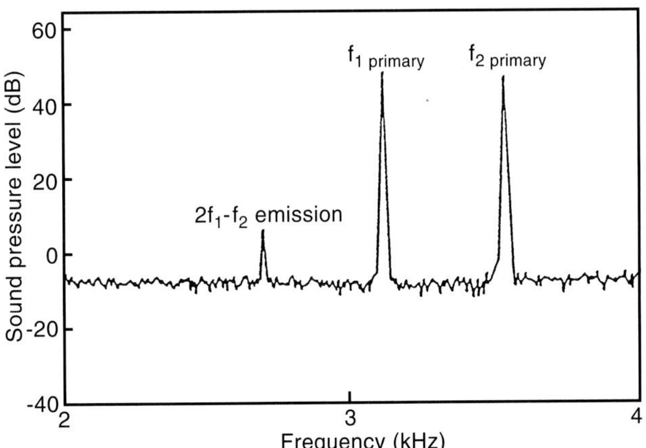

FIGURE 27.4 Distortion-product otoacoustic emission from a human subject. On the figure is plotted the amplitude of the two primary tones (frequencies f_1 = 3.164 kHz and f_2 = 3.828 kHz, each 50 dB SPL) that were used to evoke the emission at $2f_1 - f_2$ (2.5 kHz at 12 dB SPL). From B. L. Lonsbury-Martin and G. K. Martin (1990). Distortion-product emissions. *Ear and Hear.* **11:** 144–154, copyright Williams & Wilkins.

There are two main types of emissions—spontaneous emissions and evoked emissions. The latter are evoked in response to an externally presented sound. Spontaneous emissions are detected from the ears of about one-third of normal hearing humans, but these emissions are rare in laboratory animals. They are almost always pure tones. Transient evoked emissions are evoked by a short sound such as a click and appear several to tens of milliseconds later. These emissions were first called the "cochlear echo," but they are not a real echo because more energy appears in the emission than was present in the evoking sound. Distortion-product evoked emissions (Fig. 27.4) are evoked by two tones ("primaries" of frequencies f_1 and f_2) and occur at combinations of the primary frequencies (such as at frequency $2f_1 - f_2$).[25] The two primary tones each produce traveling waves along the basilar membrane, and a likely point of generation of the emission is where these waves overlap maximally.

Otoacoustic emissions can be used clinically as a screening tool in hearing tests, because subjects with sensory hearing losses greater than 30 dB typically lack emissions. Transient evoked or distortion-product-evoked emissions are used in such tests. Emission-based tests are especially valuable for infants, who are difficult to test by conventional audiometry. Otoacoustic emissions only rarely are the cause of **tinnitus,** the sensation of ringing in one's ears. Most individuals who have tinnitus do not have emissions corresponding to the tinnitus. Thus, tinnitus arises by some other mechanism, almost certainly within the peripheral or central nervous system.

Within the inner ear, fluids are contained in three compartments known as scalae: scala tympani, scala media, and scala vestibuli (Fig. 27.3B). These scalae extend in parallel along the length of the cochlea from the base to the apex. Scala tympani and scala vestibuli contain perilymph, which is high in Na^+ and low in K^+, similar to other extracellular fluids. Scala media contains **endolymph**, a specialized fluid with a low concentration of Na^+ and a high concentration of K^+ (about 160 m*M*). The endolymph is also unusual because it has a positive electrical potential (about 90 mV), observable even in the absence of sound. The endolymph's high K^+ concentration and positive electrical potential are not found elsewhere in the body. The organ of Corti, which contains the hair cells, is located at the junction between endolymph and perilymph (Figs. 27.3A and 27.3B). The stereocilia are surrounded by endolymph, whereas the remainder of the hair cell is surrounded by perilymph. The endolymph increases the sensitivity of the hair cells because it increases the transduction current,[16] a K^+ current that flows from the endolymph into the hair cells (Fig. 27.3 C). The endolymph increases this current because the high concentration of K^+ in endolymph forms a concentration gradient that favors K^+ flow into the cells, and because the positive potential of the endolymph forms a large electrical gradient that also favors K^+ flow into the hair cells. Without the endolymph, these driving forces would decrease, the transduction current would decrease, and the sensitivity of hearing would decrease.

Once the endolymph's chemical and electrical properties are established and sound stimulates the cochlea, K^+ flows into the hair cells with little energy expenditure by the hair cells, since K^+ is flowing down its electrochemical gradient. The K^+ leaves the hair cells through channels in their basal–lateral surfaces, again without energy expenditure by the hair cells, because of the low K^+ concentration in the perilymph surrounding the basal–lateral surfaces. In this cycle for K^+ flow, hair cells can be considered simply as "gates," turning on and off the flow of the transduction current when sound deflects the stereocilia. The cycle depends on the electrochemical characteristics of the endolymph, which are generated by a tissue in the lateral edge of the cochlea, the stria vascularis (Figs. 27.3B and 27.3C).[17,18] The stria's marginal cells have a high concentration of Na^+,K^+-ATPase,[19] an enzyme that probably helps in the accumulation of K^+ in the scala media and in the generation of the endolymphatic potential. The energy demands required to generate the endolymph are placed on the stria vascularis, which is highly metabolically active and richly endowed with blood vessels and which is remote from the organ of Corti in the lateral part of the cochlea. This placement results in fewer energy demands being made on the hair cells so that they do not require a high blood flow. Blood flow might bring noise to the organ of Corti, interfering with sound reception. In fact, there are only a few blood vessels near the organ of Corti.

Sensorineural Hearing Loss Often Results from Damage to Hair Cells

Sensorineural **hearing loss** results from damage to hair cells or, less commonly, from damage to afferent nerve fibers. Hair cells can be destroyed or have their stereocilia damaged by intense sounds.[20,21] Damaging sounds are generated by guns, jet engines, or music amplified to high sound levels. Hair-cell loss is permanent in the mammalian cochlea, but in the bird cochlea, hair cells are regenerated from nearby supporting cells.[22] Damage from intense sounds can be minimized by decreasing the duration of the sound exposure and by decreasing the level of the sound at the tympanic membrane (wearing protectors like ear muffs or ear plugs). Hair cells can also be destroyed by chemical agents such as aminoglycoside antibiotics (e.g., streptomycin, kanamycin).[23] These agents block the transduction channels, but their mechanism of hair-cell destruction is unknown. In individuals with sensorineural hearing loss, some hearing can be restored with a cochlear implant (Box 27.2).[24,25]

BOX 27.2

COCHLEAR IMPLANTS

The cochlear implant is one of the more successful prostheses designed to stimulate the nervous system. The cochlear implant can provide partial restoration of hearing for individuals with sensorineural hearing loss. In sensorineural hearing loss, there is usually a partial or complete loss of the sensory cells (hair cells) in the inner ear (cochlea). Hair cells normally transduce the mechanical energy of sound into the electrical energy of receptor potentials. They synapse on primary auditory nerve fibers, which send information to the brain. Hair cells can be irreversibly damaged by intense sound, ototoxic drugs, or the aging process. Once lost, hair cells are not regenerated in mammals. Often, however, individuals with hair-cell loss retain a portion of their auditory nerve fibers. It is these fibers that are stimulated by the cochlear implant.

The cochlear implant consists of a microphone to record sound, an electronic "processor" that transforms the sound waveform into a code of electrical stimuli, and an array of stimulating electrodes in the cochlea.[13,24] The electrode array (Fig. 27.5) is inserted through the round window into scala tympani, where it lies close to the peripheral axons of primary auditory neurons. Usually, the implant consists of about a dozen electrodes that begin in the base and are spaced apically along the cochlear spiral. Those electrodes in the most basal regions are positioned to stimulate nerve fibers that originally responded

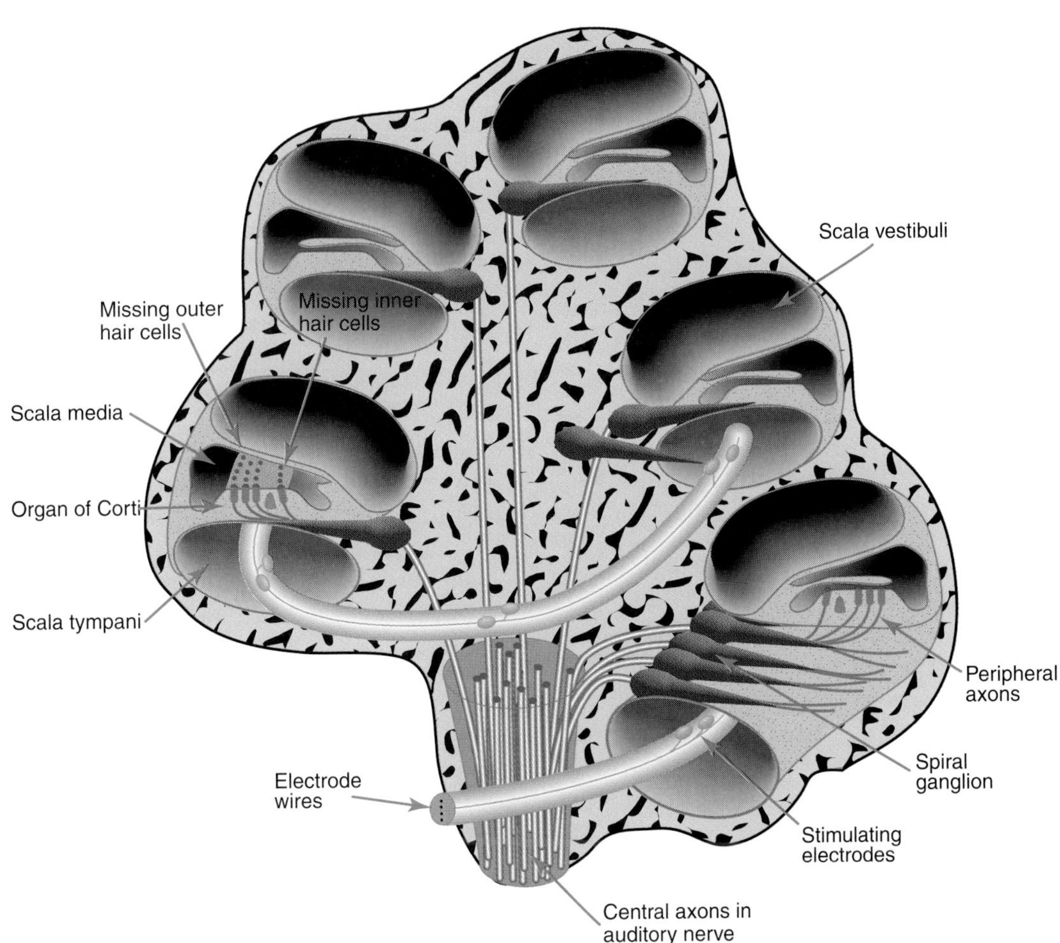

FIGURE 27.5 Drawing of the human cochlea showing the cochlear implant electrodes. The electrode array is inserted through the round window of the cochlea into the fluid-filled space called scala tympani. It likely stimulates the peripheral axons of the primary auditory neurons, which carry messages via the auditory nerve into the brain. In the normal cochlea, frequency is mapped along the cochlear spiral, with the lowest frequencies at the apex of the cochlea (at the top). The electrodes of the cochlear implant are spaced along the cochlear spiral and are designed to stimulate groups of nerve fibers that originally responded to different frequencies. From G. E. Loeb. (1985). The functional replacement of the ear. *Scientific Am.* **252:** 104–111.

to high frequencies, and those in more apical regions are positioned to stimulate fibers that originally responded to lower frequencies.

In some individuals who have received implants, comprehension of speech is possible, even when there are no other cues such as lip reading. These individuals can carry on a normal conversation, even via telephone. In other individuals, however, full speech comprehension is not restored, but the implant, together with lip reading ability, enables conversation in quiet, one-on-one situations. It also provides for the detection of important sounds such as a telephone's ring and the approach of a vehicle. The success of the implant may vary from patient to patient, depending on the number of surviving primary auditory neurons, the exact orientation of the electrodes with respect to the neurons, and the type of processor that is used. The individual's motivation and the assistance received from clinicians are also likely to be important factors. Finally, individuals who have become deaf after the acquisition of spoken language reacquire language ability more easily than prelingually deafened individuals, probably because of differences in the central nervous system. Cochlear implant research is focused on making improved designs for the processor and electrodes, so future implant recipients may be able to more fully comprehend speech.

Summary

Current research on the cochlea is centered on the mechanisms of outer hair cell motility and how this motility contributes to basilar membrane motion. The identity of the hair cell neurotransmitter is also an open question. Much interest is focused on the processes and factors involved in hair-cell regeneration, with the eventual hope that regeneration can be encouraged to take place in mammalian cochleas. The improvement of cochlear implants is also a very active area of clinical research.

THE AUDITORY NERVE

Hair cells receive their afferent innervation from neurons of the spiral ganglion, located in the central core, or modiolus, of the cochlea (see Fig. 27.3). These primary auditory neurons send peripheral axons to the hair cells and central axons into the brain by way of the auditory subdivision of the eighth cranial nerve (Fig. 27.6).[26] Two types of afferent neurons separately innervate the inner and outer hair cells.[27,28] The first type of afferent neuron (the **type I neuron**) sends processes to contact inner hair cells, almost always contacting a single hair cell, whereas the second type of afferent neuron (the **type II neuron**) sends processes to contact from 5 to 100 outer hair cells.[29,30] Fibers from type I neurons are relatively large in diameter and myelinated; thus, their information reaches the brain quickly, within a few tenths of a millisecond. Fibers from type II neurons are thin and unmyelinated and transmit information much more slowly. Both types of afferent fibers project centrally into the cochlear nucleus in the brainstem, with overlapping terminations

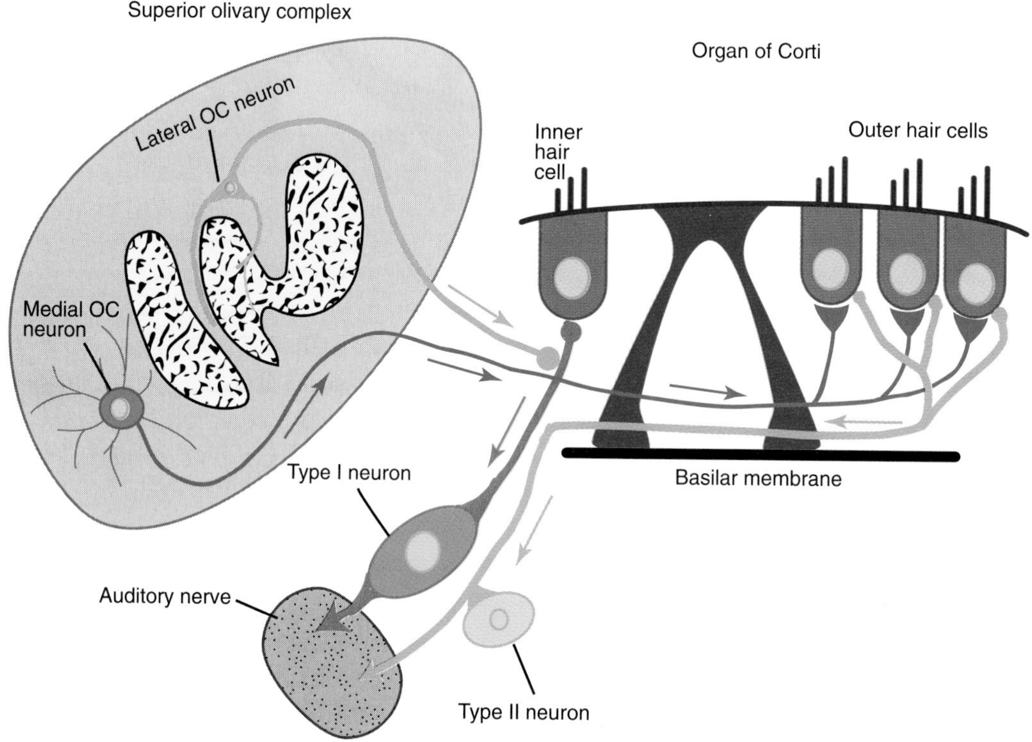

FIGURE 27.6 Innervation patterns of afferent and efferent neurons in the organ of Corti. The afferent innervation is provided by neurons of the spiral ganglion in the cochlea. There are two types: (1) type I neurons, which receive synapses from inner hair cells; and (2) type II neurons, which receive synapses from outer hair cells. The central axons of these neurons form the auditory nerve. The efferent innervation is provided by superior olivary complex neurons that send axons to the cochlea and are hence called olivocochlear (OC) neurons. There are two types of OC neurons: (1) lateral OC neurons, which innervate type I dendrites near inner hair cells; and (2) medial OC neurons, which innervate outer hair cells. Lateral OC neurons are distributed mainly ipsilateral to the innervated cochlea, whereas medial OC neurons are distributed bilaterally to the innervated cochlea, with approximately two-thirds on the contralateral side (not illustrated) and one-third on the ipsilateral side of the brain. From W. B. Warr, J. J. Guinan Jr., and J. S. White (1986). Organization of the efferent fibers: The lateral and medial olivocochlear systems. In *Neurobiology of Hearing*. R. A. Altschuler, D. W. Hoffman, and R. P. Bobbin, eds. pp. 333–348. Raven Press, New York.

in the main body of the nucleus, and additional type II projections into granule-cell regions.[26,31] Interestingly, type I neurons total about 95% of the afferent population (about 30,000 in humans[32]), whereas the type II neurons total only about 5%. Thus, outer hair cells, which number over three-quarters of the receptor cell population, are innervated by only a small minority of the afferent neurons. This innervation plan strongly suggests that the functional role for inner hair cells and type I neurons is to serve as the main channel for sound-evoked information flow into the brain. The functional role for outer hair cells was mentioned earlier: to serve as the cochlear amplifier and enhance basilar membrane vibration and tuning, thus increasing the responses of inner hair cell and type I neurons (see above and Chapter 24). Thus, outer hair cells do make a large contribution to information sent to the brain, and this contribution is via the inner hair cells and type I neurons. Outer hair cells may also transmit information via their type II afferent neurons. What type of information these type II neurons transmit is unknown; their responses have not been determined because of the difficulty recording from their thin, uncommon fibers.

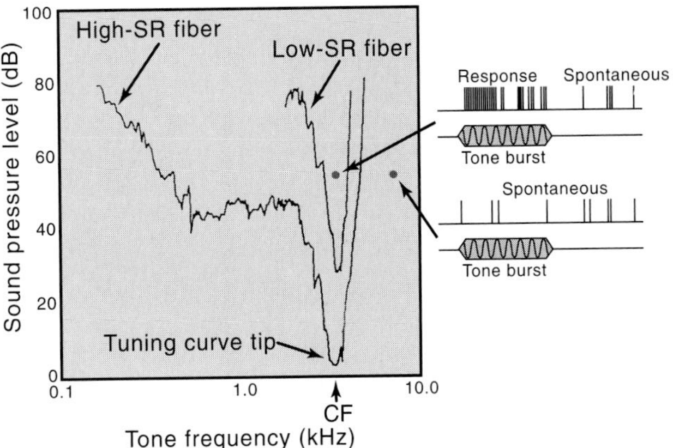

FIGURE 27.7 Tuning curves of two type I auditory nerve fibers. These curves plot the sound pressure level necessary to cause a response as a function of sound frequency. Above the tuning curve, the fiber responds to sound, whereas below the tuning curve, there is only spontaneous firing (insets at right). The lowest point on the tuning curve is at the characteristic frequency (CF); it is the point of maximal sensitivity. The sharply tuned region near the CF is called the tuning curve tip. The sharp tuning and high sensitivity of this region are generated by the mechanical properties of the outer hair cells. Tuning curves from two fibers—a high-SR (spontaneous rate) fiber and a low-SR fiber—are shown. As is typical, the high-SR fiber has the highest sensitivity. From N. Y. S. Kiang (1984). Peripheral neural processing of auditory information. In *Handbook of Physiology* (J. M. Brookhart and V. B. Mountcastle, eds), Vol. 3, pp. 639–674. American Physiological Society, Bethesda, MD.

Responses Are Sharply Tuned

Auditory nerve fibers respond to sound and then transmit these responses to the brain via discrete action potentials. The brain must extract information from these spikes and process this information to eventually form a percept of the sound that we hear. The information available to the brain via the auditory nerve includes which nerve fibers are responding and the rate and time pattern of the spikes in each fiber. The information sent to the brain via the auditory nerve has been extensively studied by recording the sound-evoked responses of single type I auditory nerve fibers.[33,34] When the responses of a fiber are studied as a function of sound frequency, they show sharp tuning. Graphs of minimum sound pressure level for neural response versus frequency are known as **tuning curves** (Fig. 27.7). The lowest point on the tuning curve is the **characteristic frequency (CF).** This is the frequency that evokes a response at the lowest sound pressure level; at CF, auditory nerve fibers can respond to sound levels as low as 0 dB in the most sensitive range of hearing. At low sound levels, the tuning curve is impressively narrow, indicating that the fiber responds only to a narrow band of frequencies near CF. This sharply tuned "tip" region (Fig. 27.7) is likely generated by contributions to basilar membrane motion provided by outer hair cells. At high sound levels, the tuning curve becomes much wider, especially for frequencies below CF. This response to a broad range of frequencies likely reflects the mechanical characteristics of basilar membrane motion without contributions from outer hair cells.

The relationship between a type I fiber's CF and its point of innervation has been studied by single-unit labeling.[35] The distance to the point of innervation along the length of the cochlea is logarithmically related to fiber CF. Fibers with the lowest CFs innervate the apex of the cochlea, and fibers with progressively higher CFs innervate progressively more basal positions, as expected from the pattern of basilar membrane vibration. This precise mapping of frequency to position is known as a **tonotopic mapping**. It is preserved as the auditory nerve projects centrally into the cochlear nucleus and for much of the central pathway. This observation strongly suggests that frequency is coded in the auditory pathway via a **place code**, with neurons at different places coding for different frequencies.

Phase Locking of Responses Is a Property of Auditory Nerve Fibers

Responses of auditory nerve fibers can show time-locked discharges at particular phases within the cycle

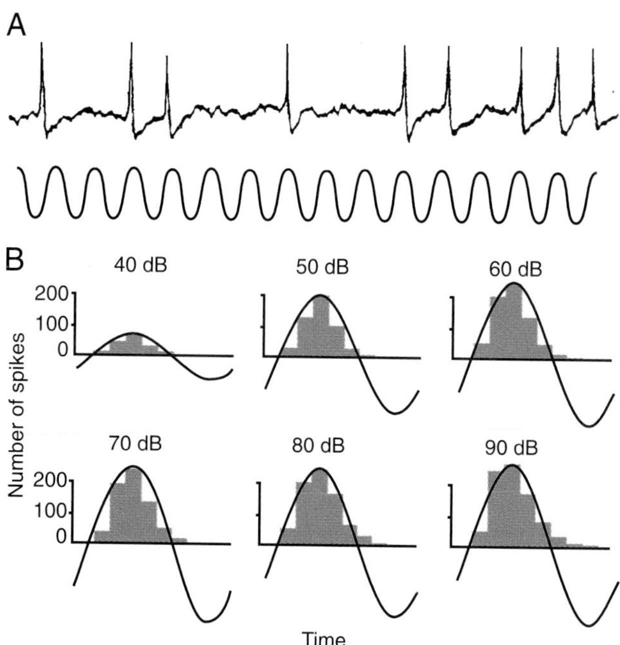

FIGURE 27.8 (A) Preferential firing of an auditory nerve fiber at a certain phase of the sound waveform. Although the pattern is "phase-locked," there is not firing for every cycle of the waveform. Stimulus frequency was 0.3 kHz. (B) Histograms that quantify the time of firing plotted within one cycle of the sound waveform. Response of the fiber is phase-locked at the moderate and high SPLs shown. Stimulus frequency was 1.1 kHz. From E. F. Evans (1975). Cochlear nerve and cochlear nucleus. In *Handbook of Sensory Physiology.* (W. D. Keidel and W. D. Neff, eds), Vol. 5, part 2, pp. 1–108. Springer Verlag, Berlin by permission; and from Rose, J. E., J. Hind, and D. J. Anderson (1971). Some effects of stimulus intensity on response of auditory nerve fibers in the squirrel monkey. *J. Neurophysiol.* **34:** 685–699.

of the sound waveform, a property known as **phase locking** (Fig. 27.8).[34] Although responses are locked to a particular phase, there is generally not a spike for every waveform peak. Phase locking in nerve fibers results from the fact that in inner hair cells, the receptor potential's ac component mimics the sound waveform (see Chapter 24). Presumably, during each depolarization of the waveform, there is an increased probability of transmitter release to the auditory nerve, resulting in an increased probability of neural discharge during this phase. Phase locking decreases for frequencies above 1 to 3 kHz, mainly because of the decline in ac receptor potential at high frequencies. For low frequencies, phase-locked information is carried by auditory nerve fibers to the brainstem. There, information may be extracted from these phase-locked patterns about the frequency of a sound. Such a **temporal code** for sound frequency may be important for low sound frequencies where phase locking is robust. It is less important for the high frequencies where phase locking is diminished, where coding for sound frequency is almost certainly via a place code.

Response Is a Function of Sound Level and Spontaneous Activity

The response of a single auditory nerve fiber increases with sound level until a point at which the fiber's rate no longer increases (Fig. 27.9A, solid line). At this point, the response is said to be saturated. The **dynamic range** over which the rate of most fibers increases is generally 20 or 30 dB, with some fibers showing somewhat greater dynamic ranges.[36] How then can the auditory nerve signal the large range in level of audible sound, from 0 to 100 dB? First, it is likely that as the level of a tone increases, more and more fibers that are tuned to other CFs begin to respond, because tuning curves become broader at higher sound levels (Fig. 27.7). Second, auditory nerve fibers vary in their sensitivity to sound, and as sound level is increased, the less sensitive fibers begin to respond. Sensitivity of fibers at a given CF varies by as much as 70 dB.[37] The sensitivity of response has been correlated with the rate of spontaneous firing, which is the rate of firing when there is no stimulus or when the stimulus is outside the tuning curve (Fig. 27.7). These spontaneous rates (SRs) vary from one fiber to another over the range of 0 to 100 spikes per second.[33] Although there may be a continuum of SR, three main groups of fibers have been defined (low SR: $<$0.5 spike per second; medium SR: 0.5 to 17.5 spikes per second; high SR: $>$17.5 spikes per second), and these groups predict many physiological and anatomical characteristics of auditory nerve fibers. The high-SR fibers have higher sensitivities than medium- and low-SR fibers (Fig. 27.7). Low- and medium-SR fibers give off the largest number of terminals in the cochlear nucleus of the brainstem and preferentially innervate certain regions such as the peripheral cap of small cells, suggesting that the information carried by the different SR groups may be kept somewhat separate in the brainstem.[38] The low-SR fibers may be less sensitive, but they likely play important roles in detecting changes in sounds at high sound levels. Low-SR fibers can signal changes at high sound levels because their low sensitivity causes them to respond mostly at higher sound levels, and they have less tendency to saturate because their response often grows more slowly with sound level.

Masking Involves Adaptation and Suppression

Auditory nerve response to one stimulus may be masked, or hidden, by the presence of other stimuli. **Masking** involves two properties of auditory nerve response: adaptation and two-tone suppression, as well as "line-busy" or refractory properties. In **adaptation**, firing to a tone burst is high initially and then lessens, or adapts, to a steady state over time (Fig.

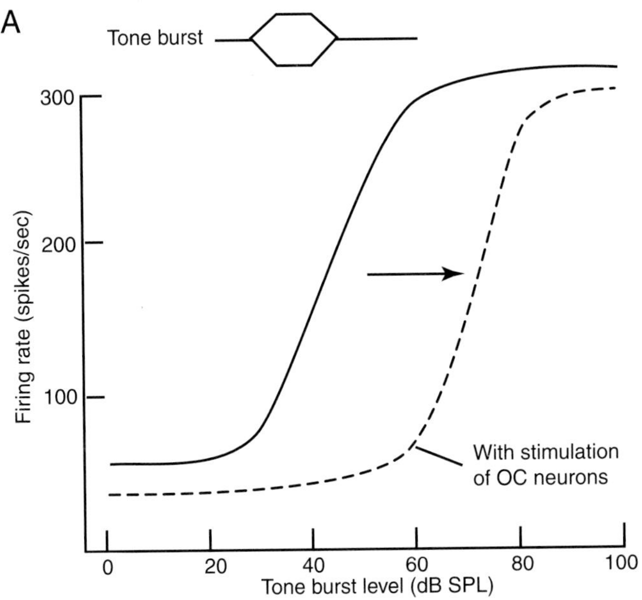

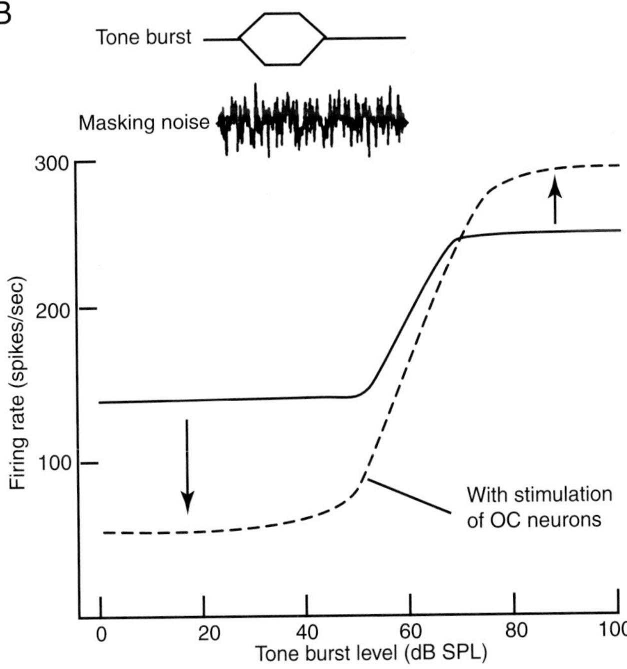

FIGURE 27.9 Rate-level function for an auditory nerve fiber in response to tone bursts, without (solid lines) and with (dashed lines) electrical stimulation of olivocochlear (OC) neurons. (A) With tone bursts alone, the discharge rate rises with sound level until it reaches a maximum and no longer increases (saturation). Stimulation of the OC neurons shifts the function to the right, toward higher tone-burst levels (arrow). This shift adjusts the dynamic range of the fiber so that it can signal changes in tone-burst level even for high sound levels; this is a likely function of the OC neurons. (B) When the tone bursts are accompanied by continuous masking noise (insets at top), the function in response to tone bursts is changed (solid curve). At low tone burst levels, the fiber has a significant firing rate because it is responding to the noise. At high tone burst levels, it is still responding to the noise and is adapted (see Fig. 27.10), so its response is lower than the function with tone bursts alone (A). In this case, stimulation of OC neurons (dashed line) decreases the response to the noise, thus decreasing the fiber's rate at low levels of tone bursts (left arrow). Because the fiber is responding less to the noise, it is less adapted and has a greater response at high levels of tone bursts (right arrow). The fiber now has a greater ability to signal changes in level of the tone burst; this effect has been called antimasking and may be another important function of the OC system. Adapted from R. Winslow and M. B. Sachs, (1987). Effect of electrical stimulation of the crossed olivocochlear bundle on auditory nerve response to tones in noise. *J Neurophysiol.* **57**:1002–1021.

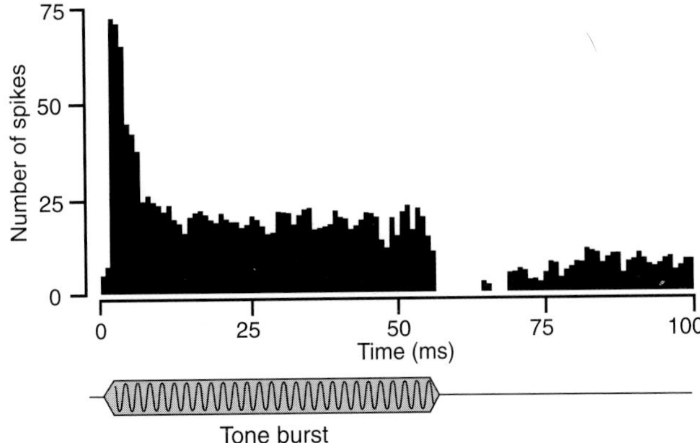

FIGURE 27.10 Poststimulus time (PST) histogram from an auditory nerve fiber in response to a tone burst (outline indicated below). A PST histogram is constructed by repeatedly presenting a stimulus while counting the number of action potentials that fall into bins of time during and after the stimulus. The PST can be thought of as the probability of firing as a function of time. This function has an initial peak and then a decrease in firing (adaptation) during the burst. After the burst ends, spontaneous firing is lessened but then returns gradually.

27.10).[39] Adaptation probably takes place at the hair-cell / nerve fiber synapse, since there is little adaptation in receptor potentials of hair cells for these short times (see Chapter 24). Because of adaptation to one stimulus, the fiber is less likely to respond to a second stimulus: that is, the first stimulus masks the second stimulus. Masking by continuous noise greatly changes the dynamic range and the firing rates of responses to tone bursts. With tone bursts alone (Fig. 27.9A, solid line), there is a moderate dynamic range and a large difference in firing rate from low to high tone-burst levels. With tone bursts in masking noise (Fig. 27.9B, solid line), there is a substantial rate at low tone-burst levels because the fiber is now responding to the masking noise. At high tone-burst levels, the rate is decreased because the fiber is adapted by the noise and is less likely to respond to the tone burst. Thus, with masking noise, there is much less difference in the fiber's rate as a function of tone-burst level as well as a lower dynamic range: these effects decrease the ability of the fiber to signal changes in tone-burst level.

An additional type of masking, referred to as suppressive masking, involves a phenomenon called **two-tone suppression.**[40] In two-tone suppression, one tone lowers the response to a second tone, even though the first tone does not excite the auditory nerve fiber. Two-tone suppression is present in the motion of the basilar membrane. It may help to control the amount of gain provided by the cochlear amplifier, because as stimuli composed of several frequencies increase in sound level, two-tone suppression decreases the nerve fiber's response so that it does not saturate. Whether there is adaptive masking or suppressive masking depends on the frequencies and levels of signals relative to the fiber's response area. Masking is important in the auditory system because many auditory processes, such as speech comprehension, are greatly affected by maskers and because background or masking signals are common in many everyday situations.

Summary

A gap in current knowledge is how the afferent fibers of the outer hair cells, the type II auditory nerve fibers, function in the hearing process. Similarly, future experiments will provide insight into the roles played by the different spontaneous-rate groups of type I auditory nerve fibers. Insight is needed into the mechanisms used to prevent degradation of signals by masking noise; potentially these mechanisms could be applied clinically in the design of hearing aids and cochlear implants.

DESCENDING SYSTEMS TO THE PERIPHERY

Efferent neurons send information from the brain to the periphery. Three systems of efferent neurons send information to the auditory periphery: (1) olivocochlear efferents, which send fibers to the organ of Corti; (2) middle-ear muscle motor neurons, which send fibers to the middle-ear muscles; and (3) inner-ear sympathetics, which send fibers to cochlear blood vessels and possibly other targets.[41] Because little is known about the function of the sympathetics, they will not be discussed. The other two systems are composed of neurons that originate in the brainstem and project to the periphery in order to control incoming information.

Olivocochlear Efferents Alter the Responses of Hair Cells and Nerve Fibers

Almost all hair-cell systems have abundant efferent innervations of the sensory endorgans. The cochlear efferent neurons have cell bodies in the brainstem's superior olivary complex and project to the cochlea and hence are called **olivocochlear (OC) neurons**. There are two groups of OC neurons—medial OC and lateral OC neurons (Fig. 27.6)[42]—named according to the positions of their cell bodies in the superior olive. As for the afferent fibers, the olivocochlear fibers separately innervate the two types of hair cells in the base of the cochlea[43] although probably not in the apex. Medial OC neurons innervate outer hair cells,[44] whereas lateral OC neurons innervate the inner hair cell region by synapsing on dendrites of type I auditory nerve fibers.[45] Little is known about the lateral OC neurons, because their very thin axons are difficult to study. We will mainly describe the medial OC neurons.

Activation of the medial OC neurons by electrical stimulation causes them to release the neurotransmitter acetylcholine. At the outer hair cell, acetylcholine acts on a nicotinic receptor that allows Ca^{2+} influx, which then opens Ca^{2+}-activated K^+ channels, allowing K^+ efflux that hyperpolarizes the cell.[46,47] A hyperpolarization would be expected to reduce the electromotility of the outer hair cell, decrease basilar membrane motion, and reduce the responses of inner hair cells[48] and auditory nerve fibers (Fig. 27.9A, dashed line). These decreases shift responses of auditory nerve fibers to higher sound levels (Fig. 27.9A, arrow).[49] This shift means that sound levels that previously saturated the discharge rates are now within the increasing portion of the fiber's rate-level curve, so the fiber can now signal changes in sound level even at higher sound levels. Thus, one function of medial OC neurons may be to provide control of the gain of the auditory system to prevent saturation of responses. This function is accomplished via synapses on outer hair cells to control the gain of the cochlear amplifier.

Medial OC neurons may also reduce the effects of masking noise on the responses of auditory nerve fibers.[50] We have discussed how maskers can decrease responses by adaptation and suppression. OC stimulation on masked responses to tone bursts can *enhance* the response (Fig. 27.9B, dashed line). Responses at low tone-burst levels are decreased because the fiber's response to the noise is decreased (left arrow on Fig. 27.9B); responses at high tone-burst levels are increased because there is less noise-induced adaptation and a greater response to the tone bursts (right arrow on Fig. 27.9B). The fiber now has a greater ability to signal changes in level of the tone burst; this effect has been called antimasking and may be an important function of the OC system. An additional function of medial OC neurons may be to protect the cochlea from damage due to intense sounds.[51,52] Medial OC neurons may protect via their large synaptic endings on outer hair cells, the cells that are often damaged by intense sound.

The above-mentioned functions for the medial OC neurons (shifting the gain of the cochlear amplifier, antimasking, and protecting the cochlea from damage) would require that the OC system have its most important effects at high levels of sound. Studies of the OC neurons have shown that they do respond to sound, and in fact their responses are highest at high sound levels.[53,54] Indeed, some OC neurons have rate-level functions that show little tendency to saturate over large ranges of sound level. About two-thirds of OC neurons are best activated by sounds presented to the innervated ear, whereas the other third are best activated by sounds presented to the opposite ear. The OC reflex could thus be described as consensual because a stimulus applied to only one ear will evoke the reflex going to the contralateral as well as the ipsilateral side. An individual OC neuron has the opportunity to control information in a relatively restricted frequency band because a single neuron projects to a restricted band of outer hair cells not more than an octave distance along the cochlea.[44] The OC innervation of the outer hair cells is mainly to the base and middle of the cochlea, where high and middle frequencies are represented.

Middle-Ear Muscles Decrease Transmission through the Middle Ear

Two muscles are attached via tendons to the middle ear ossicles: the **tensor tympani** to the malleus and the **stapedius** to the stapes. The tensor tympani is innervated by motor neurons from the trigeminal or fifth cranial nerve, whereas the stapedius is innervated by motor neurons from the facial or seventh cranial nerve. These muscles are abundantly innervated by motor neurons, receiving almost one motor neuron per muscle fiber.[55] High ratios such as this are found in other muscles only where a high degree of control is necessary, such as the muscles that control the position of the eye. Like the OC reflex, the **middle-ear muscle reflex** is consensual, with contractions of the muscles on one side in response to high-level sound in either ear and the largest contractions for binaural sound. Contractions of the muscles decrease transmission of sound through the middle ear. The effect is to decrease transmission broadly over all low frequencies (<1 kHz), where decreases are as much as 25 dB.[56] This broad, low-frequency pattern is different from the effects of the OC system, which may be narrow and are mainly at high and middle frequencies. Functions of the middle-ear muscles have been postulated mostly for the stapedius muscle. Like the OC system, the stapedius may prevent damage due to intense sounds[57] and, by attenuating low frequencies, may prevent these frequencies from masking responses of high frequencies, thus improving speech discrimination in noise.[58] The middle-ear muscles may also decrease responses to self-generated stimuli such as speech, because they contract during vocalization.

Summary

Auditory information from the ear is affected by efferent signals from the brain to the periphery. Most is known about the medial olivocochlear (OC) neurons innervating the outer hair cells. Activation of these neurons shifts the response of the hair cells so that they operate over a higher volume range. Another function may be to allow discrimination of sounds within a volume range ("antimasking") and protect the cochlea from damage from intense sounds. Of course, the signal from the OC neurons feeding back on the auditory system is generated by sound incident upon the ipsilateral or contralateral ear. The auditory system also enjoys the benefit of protection through the control of muscles attached to the middle ear ossicles. These muscles offer protection, as well as enhanced discrimination of vocal sounds through suppression of the subject's own vocalizations.

CENTRAL NERVOUS SYSTEM

Auditory Pathways Are Tonotopically Organized

The auditory nerve terminates centrally in the cochlear nucleus, which in turn projects to the other auditory nuclei of the brainstem: the superior olivary complex and inferior colliculus (Fig. 27.11). These multiple brainstem nuclei are important for the auditory system's determination of the sound location (see Auditory Brainstem discussion below). The external location of a sound source is not represented directly along the auditory system's receptor organ, in contrast to other systems such as the somatosensory system, where position of a stimulus is mapped by sensory endings along the body surface. Instead, the cochlea maps frequency. Thus, locational information must then be determined by neural processing that compares interaural differences in responses; this processing is accomplished mainly in the brainstem centers. Above the brainstem, auditory information proceeds to the thalamus and cortex, analogous to other sensory systems. At these highest stages of the auditory pathway are the medial geniculate body of the thalamus and the auditory fields of cerebral cortex (Fig. 27.11). In addition to the ascending pathways shown in Fig. 27.11, descending systems link "higher" to "lower" centers in the auditory pathway.[59] The func-

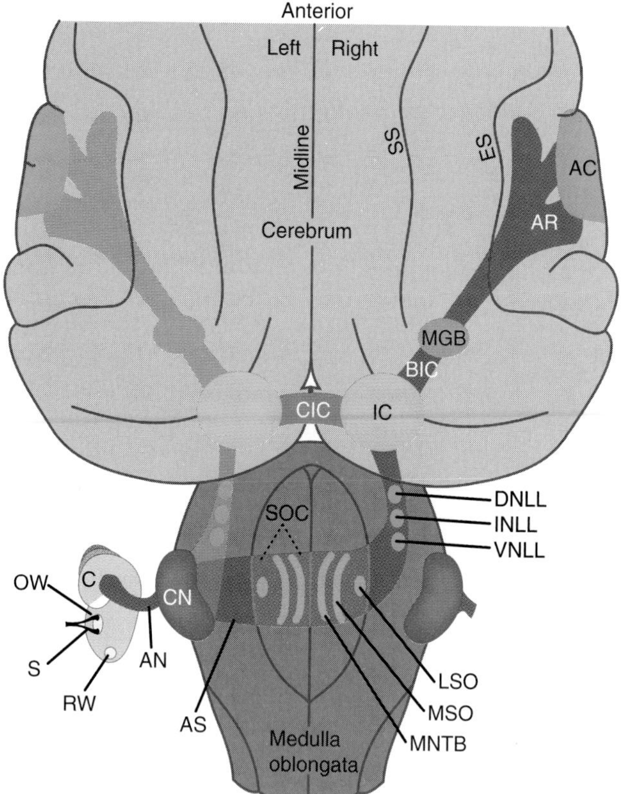

FIGURE 27.11 Simplified schematic of the pathways of the ascending auditory system of a generalized mammal. The pathway begins at lower left with the spiral ganglion and ends at top with the auditory cortex in frontal section plane. The schematic is drawn as if the viewer were looking down on the brain from a dorsal position. AC, auditory cortex; AN, auditory nerve; AR, auditory radiations; BIC, brachium of the inferior colliculus; C, cochlea; CIC, commissure of the inferior colliculus; CN, cochlear nucleus; DNLL, dorsal nucleus of the lateral lemniscus; ES, ectosylvian sulcus; IC, inferior colliculus; INLL, intermediate nucleus of the lateral lemniscus; LSO, lateral superior olive; MGB, medial geniculate body; MNTB, medial nucleus of the trapezoid body; MSO, medial superior olive; OW, oval window; RW, round window; S, stapes; SOC, superior olivary complex; SS, suprasylvian sulcus; VNLL, ventral nucleus of the lateral lemniscus. From N. Y. S. Kiang and W. T. Peake (1988). Physics and physiology of hearing. In (R. C. Atkinson *et al.*, eds.), *Handbook of Experimental Psychology*, pp. 277–326. Wiley, New York.

tions of these descending systems have not been well explored, except for the olivocochlear and middle-ear muscle systems (see above).

An important characteristic of most central auditory nuclei is **tonotopic organization**, the mapping of neural CF onto position.[60] This tonotopy is established by the basilar membrane and relayed into the central nervous system by the auditory nerve. Such inputs result in isofrequency laminae, sheets of tissue in which neurons have the same CF. These observations support a place code for sound frequency in much of the auditory central nervous system. This is especially true at higher nuclei because these neurons have a decreased ability to phase lock to the sound waveform, making a temporal code less plausible. In most auditory nuclei, there are not large overrepresentations of certain frequencies, although, as we will see below, a given nucleus may be more devoted to low frequencies (e.g., medial superior olive) or to high frequencies (e.g., lateral superior olive). An important exception is the case of echolocating bats that use a constant frequency in their echolocating pulse; in these species there is an overrepresentation of the constant frequency that begins in the cochlea and is preserved in central nuclei.[61] In these bats, much cortical area is devoted to the constant frequency, analogous to the large somatosensory cortical areas devoted to important areas such as the hands and face.

Under certain conditions, tonotopic mappings have been shown to be capable of **plastic changes.** After peripheral hearing loss, tonotopic mapping of the auditory cortex is altered such that a region that originally processed frequencies within the hearing loss begins to respond to adjacent frequencies.[62] For instance, when the cochlea is damaged so that it no longer responds to high frequencies, the high-frequency portion of the cortex does not stay unresponsive, but over time becomes responsive to middle frequencies where hearing is still normal. Plasticity is of interest to humans because of a common condition called **presbycusis,** which is hearing loss with advanced age. Presbycusis generally begins with a loss at high frequencies and spreads to lower frequencies with advancing age. Although presbycusis is likely caused by peripheral changes, it may result in plastic changes in the central pathways that change the way sound is processed in the brain.

Units Are Classified by Their Responses to Sound

Classification by PST Histograms

The cochlear nucleus is the auditory center that is understood best at the cellular level. Cochlear nucleus neurons have been well classified both anatomically and physiologically, and structure–function correlations can be made between these classifications. Physiologically, excitation of cochlear nucleus neurons arises from their auditory nerve inputs.[26] Single-unit recordings from cochlear nucleus neurons reveal that the auditory nerve spike pattern is changed to many new patterns; these patterns may be used to classify units into different unit types. The patterns are distinguished by the shape of the unit's **poststimulus time (PST) histogram**, which plots the unit's spike pattern as a function of time for short-duration tone bursts. Unit types are called pauser, onset, primarylike with notch,

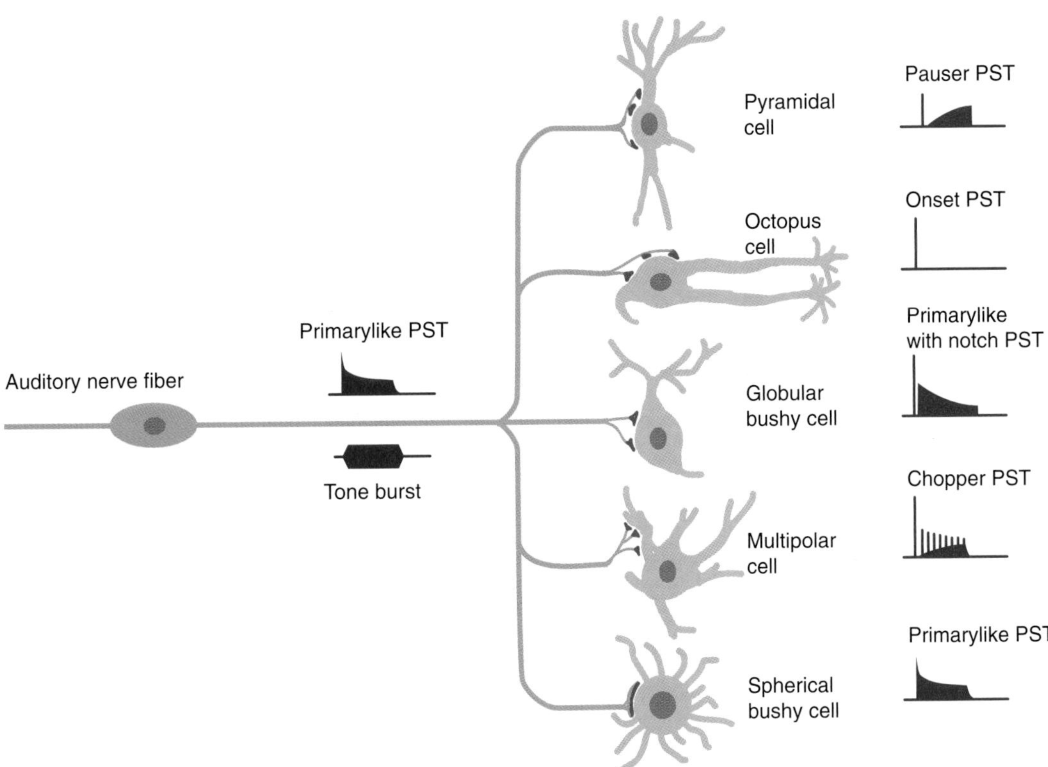

FIGURE 27.12 Schematic of the main anatomical cell types of the cochlear nucleus and their corresponding poststimulus time (PST) histograms. At left, an auditory nerve fiber is shown with its typical response, a primarylike PST histogram (shown in Fig. 27.10). At center, the auditory nerve fiber divides to innervate the main cochlear nucleus cell types. At right, the PST histograms corresponding to these cell types are shown. For the histograms, the sound stimulus is typically a 25-ms tone burst with frequency at the neuron's CF and sound level at 30 dB above threshold. From Kiang, N.Y.S. (1975). Stimulus representation in the discharge pattern of auditory neurons. In *The Nervous System* (D. B. Tower, ed.), Vol. 3, Human Communication and Its Disorders, pp. 81–96. Raven Press, New York.

chopper, and primarylike (Fig. 27.12).[63,64] A correspondence between these unit types and anatomical cell types of the cochlear nucleus has been established. The correspondence was first suggested by the regional distributions of unit and cell types; for instance, there is a region of the cochlear nucleus in which mostly "octopus" cells are found and from which mostly onset units are recorded.[65] Direct correspondence has been made by single-unit labeling, in which a single unit is first classified physiologically according to PST type and subsequently injected with a neural tracer (e.g., horseradish peroxidase) that fills the neuron and its processes.[66,67] The anatomical cell type can then be determined from postexperiment histology. These types of experiments are difficult and low-yielding, but they firmly establish the structure–function correspondences, at least for neurons large enough to record and label *in vivo*. For instance, a major cell type in the ventral subdivision of the cochlear nucleus, spherical **bushy cells**, corresponds to a major unit type, the primarylike units (Fig. 27.12).

Use of PST histograms not only is helpful in classifying units, but also reveals functional properties about the neurons. Let us consider the example of primarylike units, which get their name from the similarity of their PSTs to those of primary auditory nerve fibers. In recordings with metal electrodes near primarylike units, an early response called a prepotential is observed at a specific time (about 0.5 ms) before the unit discharges[68] (see Box 27.3).[69–71] The prepotential is produced by a very large auditory nerve terminal called an **endbulb of Held**, which is one of the largest terminals in the brain. The endbulb completely envelops the large postsynaptic bushy cell and probably forms hundreds of synapses on the cell body.[72,73] The overwhelming influence of the endbulb ensures that a spike in the auditory nerve fiber is always followed by a spike in the bushy cell, and ensures that there is low jitter in the synaptic delay so that the postsynaptic spike occurs regularly at a specific time after the auditory nerve spike. This means that there will be a close correspondence between the auditory nerve fiber's spike pattern and the bushy cell's spike pattern. The large influence of the endbulb would, for most neurons, last many milliseconds, so that two closely spaced presynaptic spikes would produce only one postsyn-

BOX 27.3

GIANT SYNAPTIC TERMINALS: ENDBULBS AND CALYCES

The largest synaptic terminals in the brain are contained in the central auditory pathway. There are two types of giant synaptic terminals in the auditory pathway: (1) endbulbs of Held (see A), which are found in the ventral cochlear nucleus; and (2) calyceal endings, which are found in the medial nucleus of the trapezoid body. These endings enable secure transmission of information to their postsynaptic neurons.

Endbulbs of Held are formed by primary auditory nerve fibers; each nerve fiber forms one or sometimes two endbulbs. The endbulbs contact and completely encircle their postsynaptic target, the spherical bushy cells of the cochlear nucleus (see A). The endbulb probably forms hundreds of synapses directly onto the soma of the spherical bushy cell. In single-unit recordings near bushy cells, a metal microelectrode records a complex waveform that differs from recordings in other regions of the brain (see B). The waveform consists of a prepotential followed about 0.5 ms later by a spike. The prepotential is likely from the presynaptic endbulb, and the spike is from the postsynaptic bushy cell. The delay between the two events is the synaptic delay. This unusual synapse has several important properties. First, the prepotential is almost always followed by a spike, indicating that the discharge in the endbulb is securely followed by a discharge in the bushy cell. Second, the delay between the prepotential and the spike is almost always the same, indicating that the synapse has low jitter, or variability in time (see C). This low jitter is important because the endbulb is the only central synapse in the pathway to the medial superior olivary nucleus, a nucleus where timing information from the two ears is compared to localize sound sources.

Calyceal endings are formed in the medial nucleus of the trapezoid body, a nucleus in the superior olivary complex. They originate from axons of globular bushy cells of the cochlear nucleus. Each axon probably forms a single calyx. The calyces encircle and synapse on principal neurons in the medial nucleus of the trapezoid body. As with endbulbs, recordings from this synapse show prepotentials, and the synapse is secure and has low jitter. This synapse conveys input to the lateral superior olive, where level information from the two ears is compared in order to localize sound sources. Calyces are so large that it is possible to use patch electrodes to record and clamp the presynaptic terminal while simultaneously doing the same with their postsynaptic target, in *in vitro* preparations.[69] These methods have given insight into presynaptic and postsynaptic regulation of transmitter release at this glutamatergic synapse.

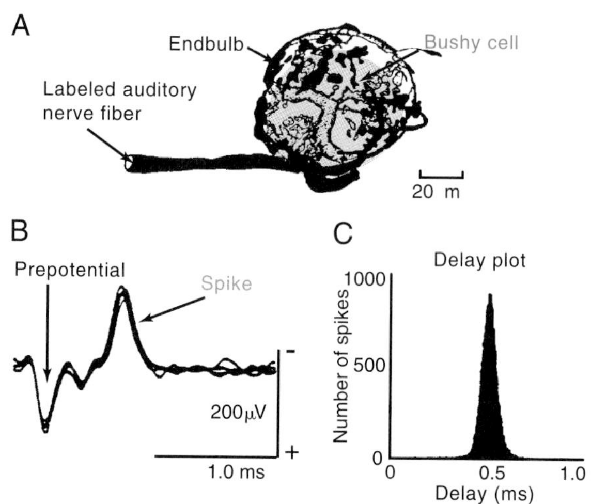

FIGURE 27.13 (A) Drawing of a labeled auditory nerve fiber forming an endbulb of Held on a spherical bushy cell in the anteroventral cochlear nucleus.[70] (B) Waveforms recorded by an extracellular metal electrode in the anteroventral cochlear nucleus. The prepotential is likely recorded from the endbulb, whereas the spike is likely recorded from the bushy cell.[68] (C) Histogram of the delay time between prepotential and spike. This represents the synaptic delay between endbulb and bushy cell. The delay of this synapse has exceptionally low jitter in time.[71] (A) From E. M. Rouiller, R. Cronin-Schreiber, D. M. Fekete, and D. K. Ryugo (1986). The central projections of intracellularly labeled auditory nerve fibers in cats: An analysis of terminal morphology. *J. Comp. Neurol.* **249:** 261–278. Copyright © Wiley-Liss, Inc. (B) From R. R. Pfeiffer (1966). Anteroventral cochlear nucleus: Wave forms of extracellularly recorded spike potentials. *Science* **154:** 667–668. (C) From C. E. Molnar and R. R. Pfeiffer (1968). Interpretation of spontaneous spike discharge patterns of neurons in the cochlear nucleus. *Proc. IEEE* **56:** 993–1004. Copyright © 1968 IEEE.

aptic spike or a second spike that was delayed, thus smearing in time the pattern of input spikes. However, the bushy cell membrane recovers quickly,[74] because it contains specialized membrane channels that allow the cell to repolarize after firing an impulse so it is reset and ready to fire again.[75] These channels are K^+ channels that have a very quick time course; they are blocked by 4-aminopyridine but are only somewhat affected by tetraethylammonium. The overall effect of the endbulb–bushy cell specializations is to replicate the auditory nerve fiber's spike pattern, producing a primarylike PST histogram and phase-locking pattern like that of a primary auditory nerve fiber. These patterns are conveyed to the targets of the spherical bushy cell in a nucleus called the medial superior olive (see Fig. 27.16). Here, the bushy cell timing information from one side is compared to that from the opposite side of the brain, an important comparison that helps to establish the location of a sound source.

In contrast, other types of cochlear nucleus neurons have PST histograms that look very different in shape from those of auditory nerve fibers. These neurons do not preserve the timing of the auditory nerve discharge and presumably have other functions. For instance, onset units respond mainly at the onset of a short tone burst (Fig. 27.12). One subclass of onset units can increase its response over a large range of SPL and might be involved in signaling sound level.[64] Tests of such hypotheses are easier in birds than in mammals. Birds have a much more regional segregation of neurons by anatomical and physiological type in the cochlear nucleus.[76] In birds, bushy cells are segregated in one region (nucleus magnocellularis), whereas other cell types such as multipolar cells are confined to a second region (nucleus angularis). The bushy cells in nucleus magnocellularis have excellent phase locking but poor dynamic range of response when sound level is increased. Multipolar neurons in nucleus angularis have complementary properties: poor phase locking but excellent dynamic ranges. This regional segregation has been used to separately manipulate neurons coding for these two properties.[77] Overall, these results suggest that in the auditory system of diverse animal species, separate neural pathways exist for sound level coding and for time coding.

Classification by Response Map

Another important way to classify neurons in the cochlear nucleus, as well as throughout the auditory nervous system, is by a neuron's **response map** (Fig. 27.14).[78] Response maps are plotted on graphs of sound level versus frequency; like tuning curves, these maps show areas of excitation but they additionally show areas of inhibition. They are especially valuable for centers where inhibitory influences play a role in shaping responses, such as in the dorsal subdivision of the cochlear nucleus, the inferior colliculus, and at higher stages of the auditory system. In the **dorsal cochlear nucleus**, five response types have been defined (Fig. 27.14). Type I neurons have excitatory tuning curves similar to those of the auditory nerve (Fig. 27.7) and have no inhibitory areas. Other response types have progressively larger inhibitory areas; for instance, type IV neurons have only a small excitatory area near CF and a narrow, knife-sharp excitatory area above CF, with the rest of their area dominated by inhibition. This

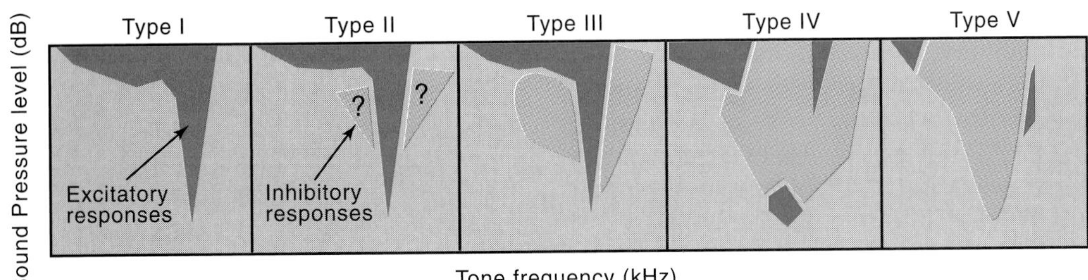

FIGURE 27.14 Unit classification by "response area." Shown are response areas for the five response types (types I–V) typically found in the cochlear nucleus. The response types are distinguished by the positions of their excitatory (green) and inhibitory (pink) areas. Question marks show variable or uncertain areas. Type I neurons have excitatory response areas similar to the tuning curves of auditory nerve fibers. Type II neurons have similar excitatory areas and are inferred to have inhibitory flanking areas because they have almost no response to broadband signals like white noise. Type III neurons have similar excitatory areas and definite inhibitory areas on either side. Type IV neurons have a small excitatory area at low levels (near the characteristic frequency), as well as a knife-sharp excitatory area at higher frequencies. Inhibition dominates much of the remainder of their response area. Type V neurons are similar to type IV neurons but lack a low-level excitatory area. From Young, E. D. (1984). Response characteristics of neurons of the cochlear nuclei. In *Hearing Science: Recent Advances*. (C. I. Berlin, ed.), pp. 423–460. College-Hill Press, San Diego.

inhibition is generated by inhibitory circuits within the dorsal cochlear nucleus, most likely from type II neurons.[79] Type IV neurons correspond to the main projection neurons of the dorsal cochlear nucleus, the pyramidal neurons, whereas type II neurons are likely to be inhibitory interneurons. One hypothesis for the functional role of type IV neurons is that their sharp borders between excitatory and inhibitory areas serve to detect the spectral notches that result from the acoustic characteristics of the external ear, especially the pinna. These notches could be used for sound localization, since their frequencies depend on sound source location.[1] The notches also depend on position of the pinna, and in fact, type IV neurons receive input from brainstem somatosensory nuclei that may inform the type IV neurons about the position of the animal's moveable pinna.[80] Animals that lack a movable pinna, such as humans and cetaceans (whales and porpoises), have a dorsal cochlear nucleus that differs greatly from that of other mammals, by being unlayered and possibly lacking in several cell types (granule and cartwheel cells).[81]

Classification by Laterality of Response: The Response to the Contralateral versus the Ipsilateral Ear

A final important way to classify neurons is by their **laterality of response**, which is defined as whether the neuron responds to the contralateral or ipsilateral ear and whether the response is excitatory or inhibitory. Many neurons in central auditory nuclei above the cochlear nucleus are binaural; that is, they can be influenced by sound presented to either ear. A predominant pattern, however, is for the neuron to be excited by sound in the contralateral ear (the side opposite to where the neuron is located). The ipsilateral ear can be excitatory, inhibitory, or mixed in its influence. The contralateral response results from the fact that many central auditory pathways cross to the opposite side of the brain (Fig. 27.11). There are also uncrossed pathways; these pathways generate the response to the ipsilateral ear. Despite an influence of the ipsilateral ear, lesion studies indicate the functional importance of excitation from the contralateral ear. For instance, damage to the inferior colliculus or auditory cortex on one side decreases the ability to localize sounds on the opposite side.[82] Thus, as in other sensory and in motor sytems, one side of the brain is primarily concerned with function on the opposite side of the body.

The Auditory Brainstem Uses Binaural Cues to Determine Sound Location

An important function of the auditory system is to determine the location of sound sources in space. When we use cues from both ears to locate sounds, we are performing **binaural sound localization**. This is the predominant type of localization for determining the azimuthal position of a sound source. Binaural localization uses two cues: **interaural time differences** (ITDs) and **interaural level differences** (ILDs). ITDs (Fig. 27.15A) result because sound reaches the ear closest to the source sooner than the ear farther from the source. ITDs are a good cue for localization because they depend greatly on the source's azimuth.[83] For ongoing sounds such as pure tones, they can be translated into phase differences in the sound waveforms at the two ears. These phase differences are useful at low frequencies but become ambiguous at frequencies above about 1.5 kHz because by the time sound reaches the ear away from the source, the waveform has repeated by a cycle or more. We have discussed how auditory neurons can phase-lock to the sound waveform. The decline in phase locking for frequencies above 1 to 3 kHz is a second reason that phase differences are less important for localizing sounds at high frequencies.

Interaural level differences (ILDs) result when the head forms a "sound shadow," reducing the level of sound at the ear away from the source (Fig. 27.15B). ILDs vary greatly with sound-source azimuth, but due to the directional characteristics of sound, ILDs are significantly large only at high frequencies and are much smaller at low frequencies.[84] Thus, for sound localization at low frequencies (<1 kHz), ITDs are the major cues, but for localization at high frequencies (>3 kHz), ILDs are the major cues. For human performance using pure tones, accuracy of azimuthal localization is good at low frequencies and at high frequencies, but somewhat less accurate at middle frequencies,[85] perhaps because the cues are somewhat more ambiguous at these middle frequencies. In psychophysical experiments in humans under optimal conditions, the minimum discriminable angle for localization of a sound source approaches one degree of azimuth. The physical cues corresponding to this angle are about 10 μs in ITD or 1 dB in ILD. When experiments are conducted with headphones to manipulate the ITDs and ILDs, such interaural differences are indeed discriminable in human subjects.[85]

Mechanisms of Interaural Time Sensitivity

Two neural circuits that provide sensitivity to ITD or ILD are within the superior olivary complex (Fig. 27.16).[86] The neural mechanisms that generate sensitivity to ITDs are impressive, given the small sizes of the differences. For instance, the central nervous system must be able to detect ITDs of 10 μs by comparing spikes coming in from the neural channels of the two sides that differ in time by 10 μs. Yet, 10 μs is less than

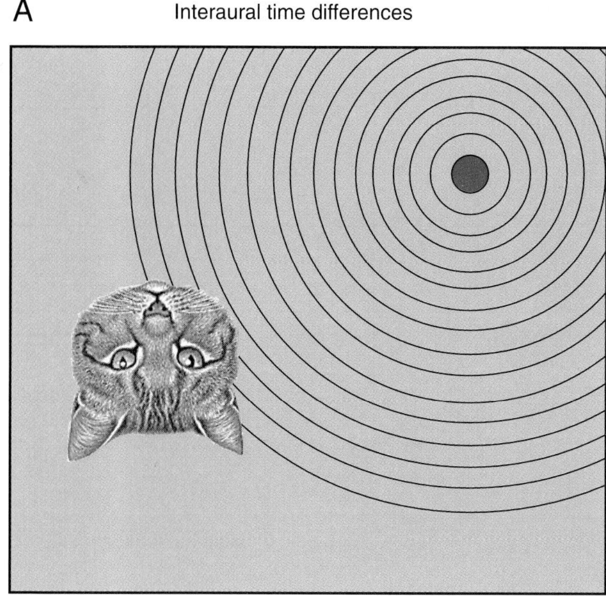

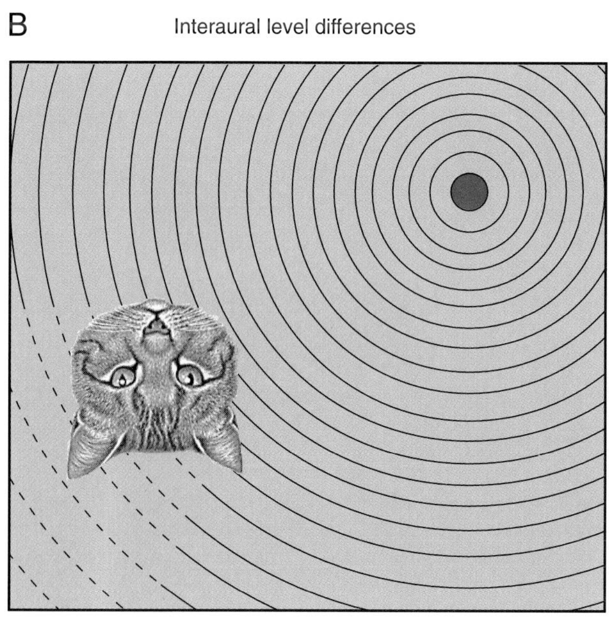

FIGURE 27.15 The two cues for binaural localization of sound. A sound source is shown as a solid dot to the right of the animal's head, and sound waves are shown as concentric lines. Interaural time differences (A) result from the longer time it takes sound to travel from the source to the ear away from the source. Interaural level differences (B) result from the head forming a "sound shadow," reducing the level of sound at the ear away from the source.

the rise time of neural spikes, making the incoming spikes almost identical. The neural circuit that is sensitive to ITDs in the mammal is the **medial superior olive** (MSO) and its inputs (Fig. 27.16A); a similar circuit is present in birds in nucleus laminaris.[89] The MSO inputs are from primarylike units (spherical bushy cells) of the left and right cochlear nuclei. These inputs preserve the phase-locking and timing characteristics of the auditory nerve because of the low jitter in the endbulb–bushy cell synapse (see Box 27.3). For a low-frequency sound with an ITD, phase-locked spikes from one side will have a time difference relative to the other side. The phase-locked spikes will repeat this time difference many times during the many waveforms of a continuous sound. **Neural delay lines** that "make up" for this time difference are formed by axons for both contralateral and ipsilateral inputs, in the model originally proposed by Jeffress[90] (Fig. 27.16A). However, recent observations indicate that only contralateral inputs are delayed.[88] An axon forms a delay line simply because it takes time for an impulse to travel along the axon. Within the medial superior olive, a neuron responds best when it receives coincident input from the two sides. Thus, a neuron in the middle of the drawing of the medial superior olive in Fig. 27.16A responds best when the signal reaches the ears at the same time and the delays are about equal. A neuron at the bottom of the drawing has a long contralateral axonal delay that makes up for spikes coming in later from the ipsilateral side. Thus, this neuron responds best when the sound to the contralateral ear is leading, which occurs for a sound source located on the contralateral side (Fig. 27.16B). Medial superior olive neurons are thus tuned to a particular ITD and respond less to other ITDs. There appears to be a mapping of best ITD along the anterior–posterior dimension, with neurons sensitive to zero ITD located anteriorly and those sensitive to greater lead of the contralateral stimulus located more posteriorly.[87] Thus, medial superior olive neurons on one side respond mainly to sound sources located on the contralateral side of the head. As mentioned earlier, ITDs are most important for sound localization at low frequencies, and the medial superior olive has a tonotopic organization that is predominantly composed of neurons with low characteristic frequencies. In fact, the medial superior olive is small or nonexistent in animals that hear poorly at low frequencies, and these animals are usually unable to localize low-frequency sounds.[91]

Mechanisms of Interaural Level Sensitivity

A second neural circuit in the brainstem, within the **lateral superior olive,** generates responses that are sensitive to ILDs (Fig. 27.16C).[92] Input to the lateral superior olive from the ipsilateral side is excitatory, by

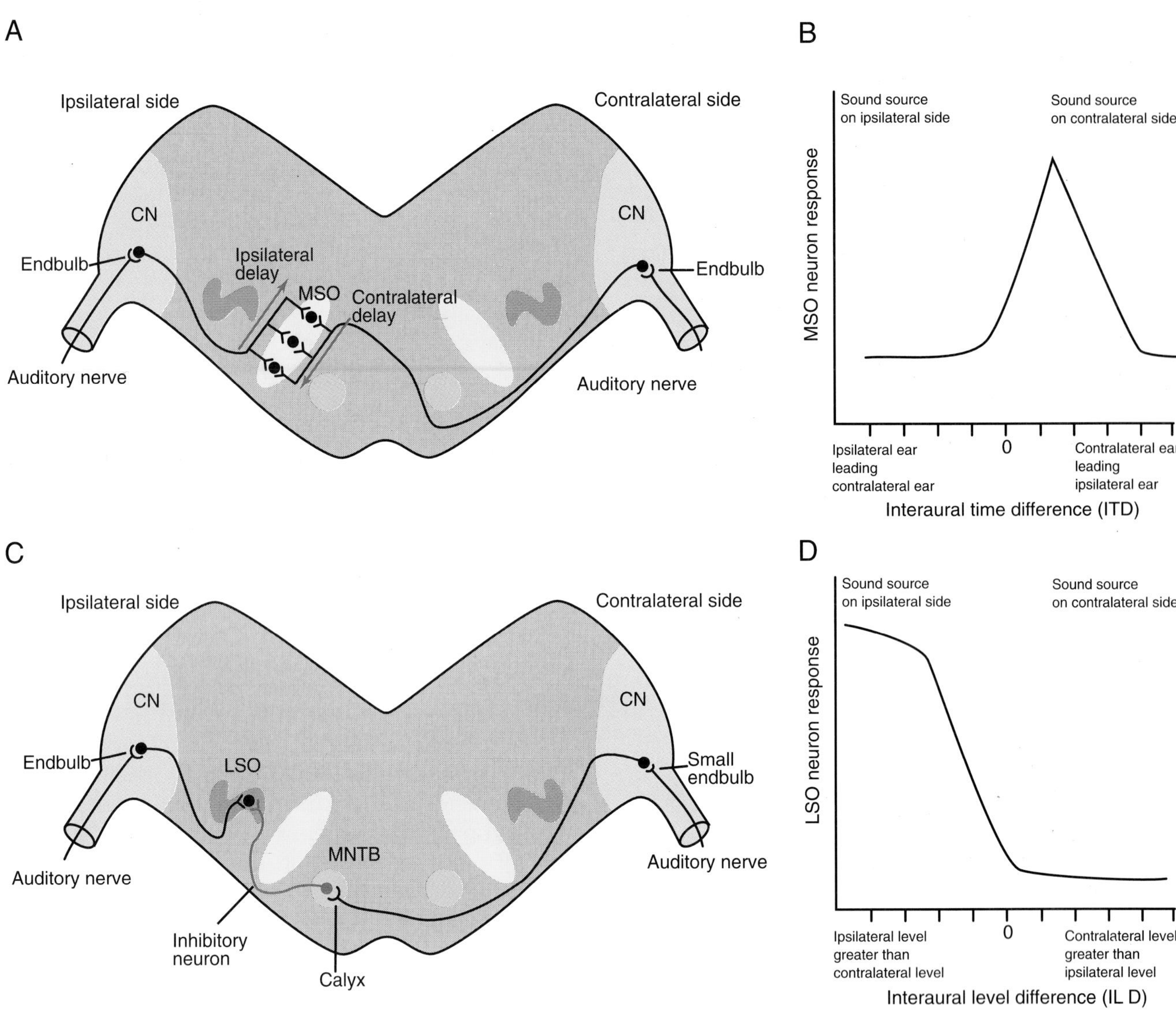

FIGURE 27.16 Innervation schematics and responses of two circuits in the lower brainstem that are important in binaural sound localization. Neuronal cell bodies are shown as dots, and fiber pathways are shown as lines; also indicated are positions of large synaptic terminals (endbulbs and calyces, see Box 27.3). (A) Circuit of the medial superior olive (MSO), which is sensitive to interaural time difference (ITD). Input to the cochlear nucleus (CN) from the auditory nerve terminates at the large endbulbs of Held that synapse onto spherical bushy cells. Bushy cells project bilaterally such that a single MSO receives input from both sides. The bushy cell inputs form delay lines such that ITD is mapped along the MSO. Recent data indicate that the delay line is oriented rostrocaudally and that only contralateral inputs are delayed.[87,88] (B) Response of an MSO neuron as a function of ITD. Neurons within the MSO respond when spikes from their two inputs arrive at the same time. The response plotted is that of a neuron in the lower part of the MSO drawn in A; there is a large response when the ipsilateral input lags, so that the early contralateral input has time to proceed down the axonal delay line to reach the neuron at the same time as the lagging ipsilateral input. This type of lagging ipsilateral input would be produced by a sound source located on the contralateral side, as would be the case for an MSO on the left side of the animal shown in Fig. 27.15. (C) Circuit of the lateral superior olive (LSO), which is sensitive to interaural level differences. Excitatory input arises from the ipsilateral CN. Inhibitory input (red line) from the contralateral side is through the medial nucleus of the trapezoid body (MNTB), a nucleus of inhibitory neurons. The large synaptic ending in the MNTB is called a **calyx**. (D) Response of an LSO neuron as a function of interaural level difference (ILD). There is a large response when sound is of higher level on the ipsilateral side and no response when sound is of higher level on the contralateral side. Thus, a response is produced by a sound source located on the ipsilateral side.

way of spherical bushy cells from the cochlear nucleus. Input from the contralateral side is inhibitory. This input originates from excitatory globular bushy cells of the cochlear nucleus and synapses by way of giant calyceal endings on neurons in the medial nucleus of the trapezoid body (Fig. 27.16C). Many of the neurons in the medial nucleus of the trapezoid body are inhibitory and use the neurotransmitter glycine,[93] which is a common inhibitory transmitter throughout the auditory brainstem. These inhibitory neurons then project to the lateral superior olive. Because of these inputs, lateral superior olivary neurons compare the difference in levels of the sound at the two ears: they are excited when sound in the ipsilateral ear is of higher level but are inhibited when sound in the contralateral ear is of higher level (Fig. 27.16D). When the sound is of equal level in the two ears, the strong contralateral inhibition usually dominates and there is little response. These neurons are thus excited by sound sources located on the ipsilateral side of the head. As the lateral superior olive projects centrally, this ipsilateral-side response is transformed to a contralateral-side response by crossing to the inferior colliculus on the opposite side.[94] (There is also an uncrossed projection, but it is inhibitory.) As mentioned above, ILDs are most important for sound localization at high frequencies, and the lateral superior olive has a tonotopic organization that is predominantly composed of neurons with high characteristic frequencies.

Inferior Colliculus

Ascending input from lower brainstem centers converges at the **inferior colliculus** (Fig. 27.11), which is an obligatory synaptic station for almost all ascending neurons. The inferior colliculus consists of several subdivisions, the best studied of which is the large, laminated, central nucleus. In the central nucleus, direct input from the cochlear nucleus interacts with binaurally responsive input from the medial and lateral superior olives. Terminals from the medial and lateral superior olives may have limited spatial overlap, however, because the central nucleus is tonotopically organized. Low-CF input (including that from the medial superior olive) projects to the dorsolateral part of the colliculus, and high-CF input (including that from the lateral superior olive) projects to the ventromedial part. Many low-CF collicular neurons are sensitive to ITDs, like their medial superior olive inputs, whereas many high-CF collicular neurons are sensitive to ILDs, like their lateral superior olive inputs.[95,96] Interestingly, large lesions of the superior olivary complex do not completely disrupt ILD sensitivity in the colliculus[97]; this is evidence that ILD sensitivity is created anew at levels above the lateral superior olive. ILD sensitivity may be created in part by the dorsal nucleus of the lateral lemniscus,[98] a nucleus within the lateral lemniscus that sends a large inhibitory projection to the colliculus. ILD sensitivity may also be created anew by inhibitory mechanisms within the colliculus. Additional circuits for generation of ITD sensitivity have not been identified; thus, the colliculus appears to be sensitive to ITD because of its inputs from the medial superior olive.

An important question is whether the colliculus uses its inputs to form a **space map**—a mapping of sound source location to position within the brain. Such a mapping has not been reported in the mammalian inferior colliculus, but it has been observed in the deep layers of the superior colliculus, where it is in register with a mapping of the visual field.[99] These deep layers of the superior colliculus have sensorimotor functions in orientation movements of the head, eyes, and pinnae. Another auditory space map has been observed in the barn owl, which hunts for prey in darkness using acoustic cues. In the owl, the mapping has been observed within a nucleus homologous to the external nucleus of the inferior colliculus (nucleus mesencephalicus lateralis dorsalis).[100] Here, spatial receptive fields of neurons are narrow in both azimuth and elevation. These receptive fields are arranged so that there is a mapping of sound source location within the brain. This mapping demonstrates that space maps do exist, but they do not appear to be a common feature of the auditory system of nonspecialized mammals.

The Medial Geniculate and Auditory Cortex Are the Highest Stages of the Auditory Pathway

The medial geniculate and auditory cortex contain subdivisions that have clear tonotopic organization as well as subdivisions with less obvious tonotopy.[101,102] For instance, in the cortex of the cat, four fields have clear tonotopic mappings (fields AI, A, P, VP), but other fields do not (Fig. 27.17). The tonotopic axis of field AI runs from high frequencies rostrally to low frequencies caudally; other adjacent fields (such as A) have mirror-image tonotopy (Fig. 27.17B). The major ascending pathway connecting tonotopic areas at the highest levels of the pathway begins in the laminated central nucleus of the inferior colliculus, forms synapses in the laminated ventral division of the geniculate, and continues to most of the tonotopic cortical fields. A **parallel pathway** connecting less tonotopic areas begins in the dorsal cortex of the colliculus, forms synapses in the dorsal division of the medial geniculate, and projects mainly to cortical field AII; this pathway has been termed diffuse.[103] Finally, a polysensory

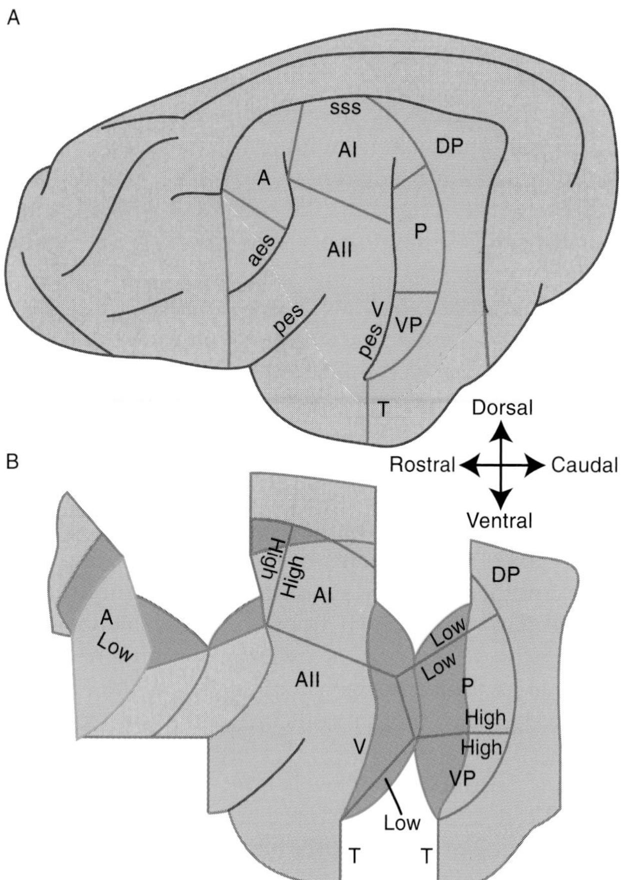

FIGURE 27.17 Auditory cortical fields in temporal cortex of the cat. (A) Lateral view, and (B) lateral view that is "unfolded" to show the parts of the fields that are normally hidden within the sulci (dark red). The four tonotopic fields are the anterior (A), primary (AI), posterior (P), and ventroposterior (VP) fields. The positions of the lowest and highest CFs in these fields are indicated in (B). Note that at the boundaries of the tonotopic fields, the direction of tonotopy is reversed so that adjacent fields have "mirror-image" tonotopy. Other cortical fields are secondary (AII), ventral (V), temporal (T), and dorsoposterior (DP) fields. Also indicated are suprasylvian sulcus (sss) and anterior and posterior ectosylvian sulci (aes, pes). From T. J. Imig and R. A. Reale (1980). Patterns of cortico-cortical connections related to tonotopic maps in cat auditory cortex. *J. Comp. Neurol.* **192:** 293–332, Copyright 1980 by Wiley, New York.

pathway begins in the external and dorsal nuclei of the colliculus and projects via the medial division of the geniculate to almost all the auditory cortical fields.

In general, the physiology of the tonotopic areas has been explored better than that of other areas. Units from the tonotopic areas, such as the geniculate's ventral division and cortical field AI, tend to have short latencies and sharply tuned tuning curves. Neurons in areas with less obvious tonotopy tend to have longer latencies, broader tuning curves, and responses that can habituate or stop responding after multiple presentations of the stimulus.[104] In humans, the **primary auditory cortex** is located on Heschl's gyrus, which is on the superior surface of the temporal lobe (Fig. 27.11). Electrophysiological data have been obtained from this region in human patients undergoing surgery for epilepsy. In these regions, there are large evoked potentials in response to sound,[105] and auditory sensations are reported after electrical stimulation.[106] In normal subjects, sound-evoked activation is seen in this region of temporal cortex, with imaging techniques such as positron emission tomography (PET) and functional magnetic resonance imaging (fMRI).[107]

The medial geniculate exerts its influence on ascending information, but it does so with extensive influence from the cortex. The medial geniculate receives extensive projections from auditory cortex: it probably receives more input from auditory cortex than from lower centers. One large projection is from the tonotopic cortical fields AI and A to the tonotopic ventral division of the medial geniculate. Apparently, however, the geniculate mediates some functions that do not require the cortex. For example, fear conditioning is a behavior that can be established by pairing a sound with a painful electric shock in rats. After conditioning is established, conditioned responses such as an increase in blood pressure can be elicited by sound alone. Lesions of the auditory pathway up to and including the geniculate have a large effect on such conditioning; however, lesions of the auditory cortex do not produce large alterations.[108] Apparently, pathways directly from the geniculate to the amygdala mediate such conditioned responses. Cortical neuron responses are also changed by conditioning; for example, the pairing of an acoustic stimulus with a noxious stimulus greatly alters the cortical neuron's response.[109] Such observations indicate the context-dependent nature of responses at these high levels of the pathway.

Cortical Columns

A fundamental feature of cortical organization is the **cortical column**, which is oriented normal to the cortical surface and runs across all six of the cortical layers. In cortex, neurons within a column tend to have similar response characteristics. For instance, in auditory cortex, neurons within a given column generally have similar CFs.[110] Neurons also tend to have similar types of responses to binaural sounds; these binaural interaction characteristics are tested in preparations in which each ear is stimulated with a separate sound source. Usually one ear, the main ear, excites a cortical neuron; most often this ear is the contralateral ear. The response of the opposite ear can be either to excite by itself or facilitate the neuron's main ear response (**summation interaction**) or to inhibit by itself or to suppress the main ear response (**suppression interac-**

tion). Typically, either summation interactions or suppression interactions are found for neurons within a column.[111] For the high-CF part of AI, summation and suppression columns show some organization, although not nearly as rigid as a checkerboard pattern with CF on one axis and alternating summation or suppression columns on the perpendicular axis. The binaural interaction classification described above is useful but oversimplified, because some neurons can show both summation and suppression, depending on factors such as sound level. However, one finding that supports summation/suppression columns as an organizational plan is the pattern of projections from a column in one hemisphere to the opposite cortical hemisphere. Neurons within a summation column tend to have large projections to the opposite hemisphere.[112] Suppression columns tend to have few projections (with the exception of less common columns in which the contralateral ear is inhibitory and the ipsilateral is excitatory). These findings support binaural interaction characteristics as being an important property of cortical columns.

Cortical Field AI and Sound Localization

Physiological studies suggest a role for cortical field AI in sound localization. In AI, many neurons are sensitive to interaural time and level differences, much as we have seen for neurons at lower stages of the pathway. When tested with a sound source in space, the response of many neurons depends on the azimuth of the source (Fig. 27.18). Of course, when a sound source in space is used, the receptive fields of cortical neurons will depend on the directional characteristics of the external ear[1] as well as neural mechanisms at all stages of the auditory pathway. As expected from the fact that the auditory pathways are predominantly crossed, a large number of cortical neurons respond to sound sources centered on the contralateral side, although some are centered on the ipsilateral side.[113] The receptive fields for many neurons occupy much of the azimuth on the contralateral side (Fig. 27.18A), and some have even wider fields that encompass both sides (omnidirectional fields). Other neurons, however, have receptive fields that are very narrow (Fig. 27.18B). Units within a given column tend to have receptive fields that are similar, probably because of the similar binaural interaction characteristics within a column. It is easy to imagine that neurons with summation characteristics would tend to have receptive fields that would be large and encompass both contralateral and ipsilateral sides, because of their excitatory input from both sides. Units with suppression characteristics, however, would tend to have narrower fields located mainly on one side, because they receive inhibitory

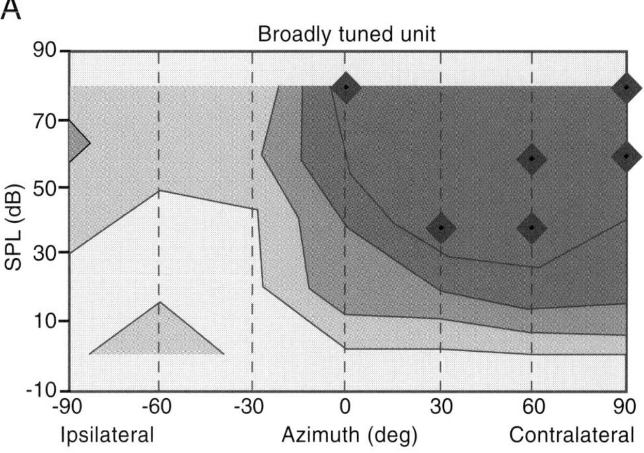

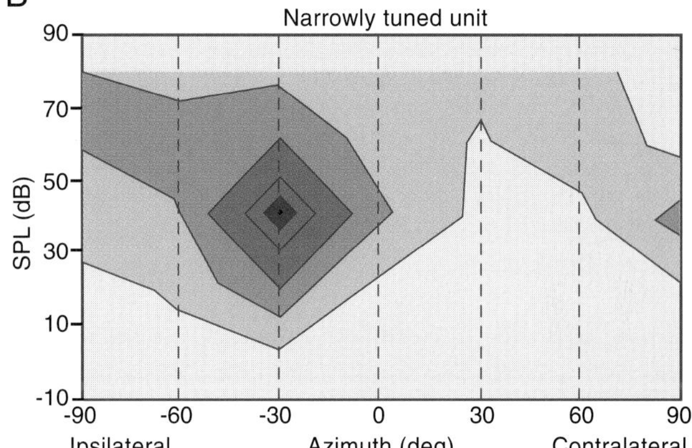

FIGURE 27.18 Receptive fields of two auditory cortex neurons (A, B) plotted as a function of sound pressure level (SPL) and azimuth in the frontal hemifield. Noise bursts were used as stimuli. Small diamonds show points of maximal response, and progressively lighter shading shows regions of progressively smaller response. Zero degrees azimuth refers to directly ahead, and positive azimuths refer to points in the contralateral hemifield. From J. C. Clarey, P. Barone, and T. J. Imig (1994). Functional organization of sound direction and sound pressure level in primary auditory cortex of the cat. *J. Neurophysiol.* **72:** 2383–2405.

input from the other side. Finally, auditory cortex has not yet been shown to have an organized space map of a sound's position in external space onto a dimension within the cortex.

Behavioral studies also indicate that AI plays a role in sound localization. Cats with lesions of AI on one side have a deficit for localizing sounds on the contralateral side.[114] Lesions of other fields that spare AI do not produce deficits. Furthermore, the deficit is frequency specific: when the lesion is in areas of AI tuned to certain frequencies, the deficit is observed only for those frequencies.[114] The deficit is most pronounced when the task is for a subject to move toward the sound source and is not seen when the task is simply to lateralize the sound—that is, to press a bar on the right

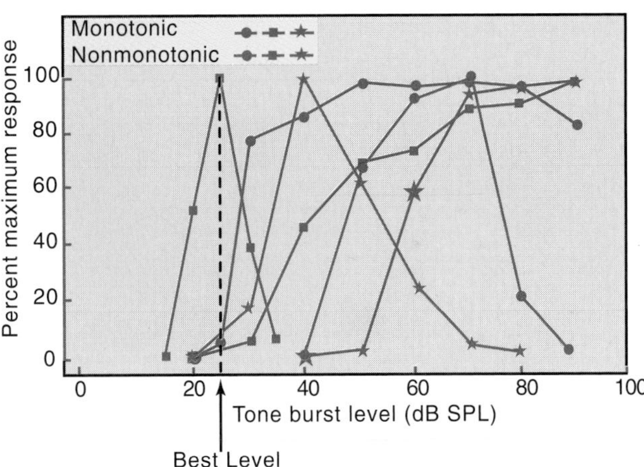

FIGURE 27.19 Response-level functions for neurons from the auditory cortex. Functions from three "monotonic" neurons have an increasing response until saturation; functions from three "nonmonotonic" neurons have an increasing response until a certain level ("best level"), after which the response falls. From D. P. Phillips, S. S. Orman, A. D. Musicant, and G. F. Wilson (1985) Neurons in the cat's primary auditory cortex distinguished by their responses to tones and wide-spectrum noise. *Hearing Res.* **18:** 73–86, with permission from Elsevier Science, Amsterdam, The Netherlands.

or left side corresponding to the side of the sound source.[115] This finding suggests that the simpler lateralization task is processed at a subcortical location, but the more difficult task of forming an image of a sound source's position in space and moving toward that position is processed in the cortex.

Coding of Sound Level

For auditory nerve fibers, and for many other neurons in the auditory system, the neuron's firing rate increases monotonically with sound level until saturation (Fig. 27.19, monotonic units). At high stages of the auditory pathway, however, more neurons are encountered with rate-level functions that are nonmonotonic and have prominent peaks with a well-defined "best level" (Fig. 27.19, nonmonotonic units).[116] For some neurons, the rate at high sound levels returns to zero, and tuning curves can be "closed" at high sound levels rather than being open like auditory nerve fibers (Fig. 27.7). Nonmonotonic neurons can be seen in the dorsal subdivision of the cochlear nucleus and the inferior colliculus[117] and are especially common in cortical field P. Such nonmonotonicities likely result from inhibitory influences, which, at higher stages of the auditory pathway, are often mediated by the inhibitory transmitter γ-aminobutyric acid (GABA).[118,119] Possibly because of these inhibitory influences, nonmonotonic units tend to have narrower response areas for sounds in space. For instance, the y axis of Fig. 27.18 plots the neuron's response as a function of sound level. The broadly tuned unit (Fig. 27.18A) has a monotonic level function, whereas the narrowly tuned unit (Fig. 27.18B) has a nonmonotonic level function. Hypothetically, the best level could be an organizing principle for central auditory nuclei, but so far, organized mappings of best level have not been reported in most species, with the exception of echolocating bats.[120]

Processing of Complex Signals in Cortex

Animals and humans emit a variety of vocal signals. These signals make possible a wide range of behaviors, including communication and even echolocation in bats (Box 27.4). Are there specific "call detectors" in the auditory cortex? This area is relatively unexplored; however, available evidence suggests that this type of detector may exist only rarely and that the response to vocalizations is probably represented by spatially dispersed, synchronized assemblies of cortical neurons, rather than by individual neurons.[125] However, cortical neurons do show selectivity to complex sounds like noise bands and especially species-specific calls over what would be predicted from their pure-tone frequency selectivity.[126,127] For instance, a neuron that responds well to a particular type of call does not usually respond as well to the call played backward in time, even though it has an identical frequency content. Similar results in response to speech stimuli have been found in recordings of units from auditory areas in the superior temporal gyrus of human patients undergoing surgery for epilepsy.[128]

A number of studies using lesions of the auditory cortex indicate a strong role of the cortex in processing complex acoustic signals. After bilateral lesions of the auditory cortex, experimental animals cannot discriminate between different temporal patterns of sounds, such as a sequence in which the sound frequency pattern is low–high–low and a sequence in which the pattern is high–low–high.[129] In primates, lesions of the cortex impair discrimination of species-specific vocalizations.[130] This impairment is more pronounced after lesion of the left cortex, indicating lateralization of processing of these vocalizations at the cortical level. Human speech is an especially complex acoustical signal; its intelligibility and production can be greatly decreased by a stroke that creates a lesion of the cortex in humans. Although the extent and effect of such lesions vary greatly, language processing is most interrupted by lesions of perisylvian cortex regions, especially in Wernicke's area and Broca's area (see Chapter 57). Wernicke's area is especially close to auditory cortex and can be considered an auditory association area. Lesions lateralized in the left hemisphere in right-handed individuals are most disruptive of speech comprehension and production. The lateralization of lan-

BOX 27.4

BAT ECHOLOCATION

Bats offer unique opportunities for researchers studying the auditory system. Echolocating bats emit high-frequency pulses of sound and use the return echoes to locate and capture their flying insect prey. These pulses are above the upper frequency limit of human hearing. They were discovered in the 1940s by Donald Griffin,[123] who was then an undergraduate student at Harvard University. The bat's echolocation performance is impressive: bats are adept enough to find a mosquito above a golf course at night. Indeed, Griffin demonstrated that bats can avoid wires as thin as 0.3 mm in diameter while flying in a darkened room.

There are more than 800 species of echolocating bats, all within the suborder Microchiroptera. One of the best-studied bats is the mustached bat, *Pteronotus parnellii.* It emits echolocating pulses that have an initial part of constant frequency, followed by a part of decreasing frequency (frequency-modulated). This bat is thus called a CF-FM bat (see B). Some other species of bats emit only the FM portion and are called FM bats. Bats use differences between the emitted pulse and the returned echo to locate targets. Relative to the pulse, the returned echo is delayed because of the sound's round-trip travel time between the bat and the target. The delay between the pulse and echo can thus be used as a measure of target range. The echo can also be changed in frequency, or Doppler-shifted, because the bat is moving relative to the reflecting surface. Bats that are moving toward a reflecting surface will have an echo that is Doppler-shifted toward higher frequency. Most background surfaces at a given direction will be

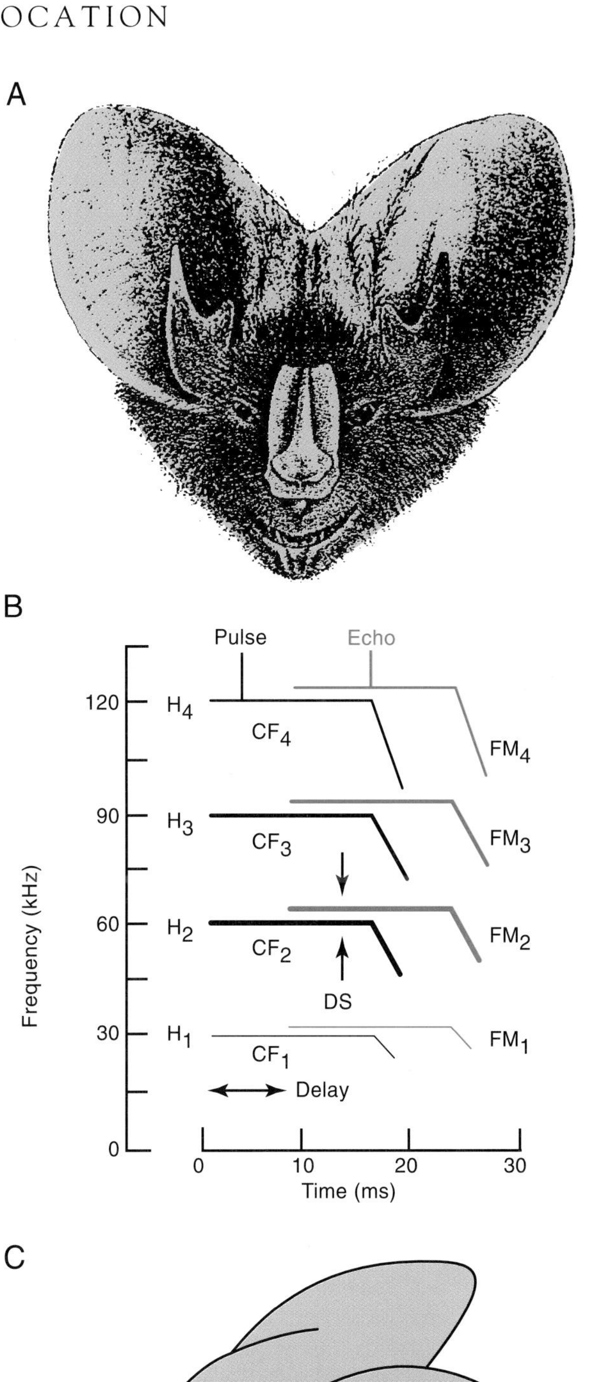

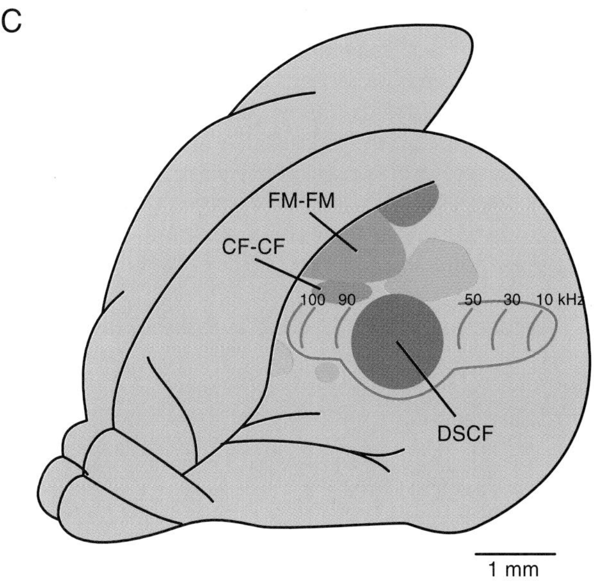

FIGURE 27.20 (A) Close-up view of an echolocating bat, *Megaderma lyra.* Like many echolocating bats, this bat has an enlarged nose leaf that probably focuses the echolocating pulse ahead. Also, like many echolocating bats, this bat has enlarged external ears that make the bat more sensitive to echoes coming from ahead (from Griffin,[123] originally from Dobson[124]). (B) Emitted pulse and returned echo of the mustached bat, *Pteronotus parnellii.* The emitted pulse consists of four harmonics (H_1–H_4), the strongest of which is H_2 at about 60 kHz. Each harmonic has an initial part of constant frequency (CF) and a later part of changing frequency (frequency modulation, FM). Echo delays and Doppler shift (DS) are indicated on the figure. (C) Dorsolateral view of the auditory cortex of the mustached bat, showing several of the areas specialized for processing the echolocation signals. The primary auditory cortex, AI, is exceptionally large (isofrequency contours are indicated in kHz). AI contains a greatly expanded region devoted to the most prominent component of the Doppler-shifted echo (60 to 63 kHz); this region is called the Doppler-shifted CF region (DSCF). Other regions contain neurons that respond to specific combinations of the pulse and echo, often at certain delays. Neurons that respond to pulse/echo CF combinations are in the CF–CF region. Those that respond to pulse/echo FM combinations are in the FM-FM region. (B and C) From D. C. Fitzpatrick, J. S. Kanwai, J. A. Butman, and N. Suga (1993). Combination-sensitive neurons in the primary auditory cortex of the mustached bat. *J. Neurosci.* **13:** 931–940.

Doppler-shifted about the same. However, targets that are moving differently from the background will generate different Doppler shifts. For instance, a moth with moving wings will reflect an echo with a moving Doppler shift that is quite different from the stationary background. Such differences are presumably used by the CF-FM bat to locate moving targets. Insects are not always passive in the face of such predatory behavior. For instance, some moths have good ultrasonic hearing and take evasive flight maneuvers when exposed to a bat's pulse.

Work on the auditory system of bats has been greatly aided by knowledge of the "relevant" stimulus; much of the time the bat hears an emitted pulse followed a short time later by an echo. Work by Suga and his colleagues[121,122] has demonstrated that the auditory cortex of the mustached bat contains many specialized areas (see C). One large area (DSCF area) is devoted to processing the Doppler-shifted echo for the strongest harmonic of the pulse, near 60 kHz. These frequencies also have large representations throughout the bat's auditory system beginning at the cochlea. Within the DSCF area, there is a mapping of neuronal best level as well as characteristic frequency. In other cortical regions, some neurons have response properties that allow them to detect various features of the pulse and echo. For instance, neurons in the FM-FM region respond preferentially to two FM pulses separated by a specific delay. The fact that these neurons respond to certain features of the pulse, echo, and delay suggests that they could be called feature detectors. The best delays for these neurons range from 0.4 to 18 ms, which would correspond to target ranges of 7 to 310 cm. Furthermore, these best delays are mapped along cortical distance. Work on the bat cortex has resulted in specific hypotheses about the function of most of the auditory cortical fields. Our state of knowledge of the cortical fields in other animals is by contrast much more primitive.

BOX 27.5

INTRAOPERATIVE NEUROPHYSIOLOGIC MONITORING

Intraoperative recordings of evoked potentials can provide early warning about surgically induced injuries to specific parts of the nervous system. Evoked potentials reflect function, and changes in function often occur before an injury becomes so severe that it results in permanent neurologic deficits. Such early warning can therefore make it possible for the surgeon to intervene and reverse an injury in time to avoid permanent neurologic deficits. The use of intraoperative monitoring can also often give surgeons an increased feeling of security because they know that the function of the parts of the nervous system that may be subject to surgical injuries are being continuously monitored. Sometimes intraoperative monitoring makes it possible to perform an operation in a shorter time. Intraoperative neurophysiologic recordings make it possible to monitor the function of specific neural systems continuously during an operation, which no other method offers. Imaging techniques, widely used for diagnostics, only provide information about structure, and present imaging techniques are not suitable for continuous monitoring in the operating room.

Brainstem auditory evoked potentials (BAEP) and evoked potentials recorded directly from exposed structures of the auditory nervous system are now used routinely to monitor the auditory system in operations where the auditory nerve or other parts of the auditory system are at risk. Monitoring of auditory evoked potentials can also make it possible to detect injuries to the brainstem from surgical manipulations before any other signs become manifest. Intraoperative neurophysiologic monitoring has helped to decrease surgical-induced hearing deficits from injuries to the auditory nerve, and it has been an effective early warning for brainstem injuries.

The introduction of neurophysiologic methods in the neurosurgical operating room has opened the possibility for studies not previously possible. Thus, the ability to place recording electrodes directly on specific parts of the ascending auditory pathway during neurosurgical operations has provided a wealth of information about the auditory nervous system. It has specifically contributed to understanding how far-field auditory evoked potentials such as the BAEP are generated. Recordings of evoked potentials directly from exposed structures of the auditory nervous system have identified important differences between the human auditory system and that of animals commonly used in studies of the physiology of the auditory system. Intraoperative studies have also provided information about pathologies such as tinnitus and certain cochlear injuries that could not have been obtained in conventional studies in human or animals.

Aage R. Møller, Ph.D.

From Møller, A. R. (1995). *Intraoperative Neurophysiologic Monitoring.* Harwood Academic Publishers, Luxembourg.

guage processing in one hemisphere is a unique finding of asymmetry in brain function, very different from the symmetry of the subcortical nuclei and primary auditory cortical fields.

Imaging studies (PET, fMRI) in normal subjects suggest that acoustic stimuli such as noise and modulated tones activate primary auditory cortical fields but do not activate surrounding areas. These surrounding areas, including Wernicke's and Broca's areas, can be activated by speech stimuli.[107,131,132] Furthermore, the activation by speech stimuli is usually lateralized to the left hemisphere of right-handed individuals. Taken together, the lesion and imaging studies suggest a hierarchical pattern of cortical activation with simple stimuli being processed in the primary cortical fields and more complex stimuli such as speech processed in association areas that are lateralized in one hemisphere. Further imaging studies will be very useful in showing more specifically the functions of the auditory areas in cortex.

Summary

Much about the central auditory pathways remains to be explored. Although these pathways are tonotopically mapped, whether there are other mappings in orthogonal dimensions is generally unknown. Much current research is focused on plasticity of central auditory responses with auditory experience and after hearing loss and whether this plasticity is generally present at the many subcortical auditory centers. The fact that there are descending systems at many levels of the pathways is known, but future research is necessary to show how these systems alter processing of auditory information. Finally, the medial geniculate and auditory cortex likely play a role in sound localization, but the specifics of this role and their functions in many of the other hearing processes remain to be discovered.

References

General

Dallos, P., Popper, A. N., and Fay, R. R., eds. (1996). *The Cochlea.* Springer-Verlag, New York.

Guinan, J. J., Jr. (1996). The physiology of olivocochlear efferents. In *The Cochlea* (P. Dallos, A. N. Popper, and R. R. Fay, eds.), pp. 435–502. Springer-Verlag, New York.

Irvine, D. R. F. (1992). Physiology of the auditory brainstem. In *The Mammalian Auditory Pathway: Neurophysiology* (A. N. Popper and R. R. Fay, eds.), pp. 153–231. Springer-Verlag, New York.

Pickles, J. O. (1988). *An Introduction to the Physiology of Hearing, 2nd ed.* Academic Press, London.

Popper, A. N., and Fay, R. R., eds. (1992). *The Mammalian Auditory Pathway: Neurophysiology.* Springer-Verlag, New York.

Popper, A. N., and Fay, R. R., eds. (1995). *Hearing by Bats.* Springer-Verlag, New York.

Ruggero, M. A. (1992). Physiology and coding of sound in the auditory nerve. In *The Mammalian Auditory Pathway: Neurophysiology* (A. N. Popper and R. R. Fay, eds.), pp. 34–93. Springer-Verlag, New York.

Schuknecht, H. F. (1993). *Pathology of the Ear, 2nd ed.* Lea & Febiger, Philadelphia.

Webster, D. B., Popper, A. N., and Fay, R. R., eds. (1992). *The Mammalian Auditory Pathway: Neuroanatomy.* Springer-Verlag, New York.

Wightman, F. L., and Kistler, D. J. (1993). Sound localization. In *Human Psychophysics* (W. A. Yost, A. N. Popper, and R. R. Fay, eds.), pp. 155–192. Springer-Verlag, New York.

Cited

1. Rice, J. J., May, B. J., Spirou, G. A., and Young, E. D. (1992). Pinna-based spectral cues for sound localization in cat. *Hear. Res.* **58:** 132–152.
2. Nedzelnitsky, V. (1980). Sound pressures in the basal turn of the cat cochlea. *J. Acoust. Soc. Am.* **68:** 1676–1689.
3. Bredberg, G. (1968). Cellular pattern and nerve supply of the human organ of Corti. *Acta Oto-Laryngol., Suppl. 236:* 1–135.
4. von Bekesy, G. (1960). *Experiments in Hearing.* McGraw Hill, New York.
5. Rhode, W. S. (1971). Observations of the vibration of the basilar membrane in squirrel monkeys using the Mössbauer technique. *J. Acoust. Soc. Am.* **49:** 1218–1231.
6. Ruggero, M. A., Rich, N. C., Recico, A., Narayan, S. S., and Robles, L. (1997). Basilar-membrane responses to tones at the base of the chinchilla cochlea. *J. Acoust. Soc. Am.* **101:** 2151–2163.
7. Dallos, P., and Harris, D. (1978). Properties of auditory nerve responses in absence of outer hair cells. *J. Neurophysiol.* **41:** 365–383.
8. Ashmore, J. F. (1987). A fast motile response in guinea-pig outer hair cells: The cellular basis of the cochlear amplifier. *J. Physiol. (London)* **388:** 323–347.
9. Santos-Sacchi, J. (1992). On the frequency limit and phase of outer hair cell motility: Effects of the membrane filter. *J. Neurosci.* **12:** 1906–1916.
10. Kemp, D. T. (1978). Stimulated acoustic emissions from within the human auditory system. *J. Acoust. Soc. Am.* **64:** 1386–1391.
11. Zurek, P. M. (1981). Spontaneous narrowband signals emitted by human ears. *J. Acoust. Soc. Am.* **69:** 514–523.
12. Probst, R., Lonsbury-Martin, B. L., and Martin, G. K. (1991). A review of otoacoustic emissions. *J. Acoust. Soc. Am* **89:** 2027–2067.
13. Loeb, G. E. (1985). The functional replacement of the ear. *Sci. Am.* **252:** 104–111.
14. Russell, I. J., and Sellick, P. M. (1978). Intracellular studies of hair cells in the mammalian cochlea. *J. Physiol. (London)* **284:** 261–290.
15. Dallos, P. (1996). Overview: Cochlear neurobiology. In *The Cochlea* (P. Dallos, A. N. Popper, and R. R. Fay, eds.), pp. 1–43. Springer-Verlag, New York.
16. Davis, H. (1953). Energy into nerve impulses: The inner ear. *Adv. Sci.* **9:** 420–424.
17. Tasaki, I., and Spyropoulos, C. S. (1959). Stria vascularis as source of endocochlear potential. *J. Neurophysiol.* **22:** 149–155.
18. Salt, A. N., Melichar, I., and Thalmann, R. (1987). Mechanisms of endocochlear potential generation by stria vascularis. *Laryngoscope* **97:** 984–991.
19. Schulte, B. A., and Adams, J. C. (1989). Distribution of immunoreactive Na^+, K^+-ATPase in gerbil cochlea. *J. Histochem. Cytochem.* **37:** 127–134.
20. Johnsson, L.-G., and Hawkins, J. E., Jr. (1976). Degeneration patterns in human ears exposed to noise. *Ann. Otol., Rhinol., Laryngol.* **85:** 1–15.
21. Liberman, M. C. (1987). Chronic ultrastructural changes in

acoustic trauma: Serial-section reconstruction of stereocilia and cuticular plates. *Hear. Res.* **26:** 65–88.

22. Corwin, J. T., and Cotanche, D. A. (1988). Regeneration of sensory hair cells after acoustic trauma. *Science* **240:** 1772–1774.
23. Garetz, S. L., and Schacht, J. (1996). Ototoxicity: Of mice and men. In *Clinical Aspects of Hearing* (T. Van De Water, A. N. Popper, and R. R. Fay, eds.), pp. 116–154. Springer-Verlag, New York.
24. Tyler, R. S., ed. (1993). *Cochlear Implants. Audiological Foundations.* Singular Publishing Group, San Diego, CA.
25. Lonsbury-Martin, B. L., and Martin, G. K. (1990). Distortion-product emissions. *Ear and Hear.* **11:** 144–154.
26. Ryugo, D. K. (1992). The auditory nerve: Peripheral innervation, cell body morphology, and central projections. In *The Mammalian Auditory Pathway: Neuroanatomy* (D. B. Webster, A. N. Popper, and R. R. Fay, eds.), pp. 23–65. Springer-Verlag, New York.
27. Spoendlin, H. (1971). Degeneration behaviour of the cochlear nerve. *Arch. Klin. Exp. Ohren-, Nasen-Kehlkopfheilk.* **200:** 275–291.
28. Kiang, N. Y. S., Rho, J. M., Northrop, C. C., Liberman, M. C., and Ryugo, D. K. (1982). Hair-cell innervation by spiral ganglion cells in adult cats. *Science* **217:** 175–177.
29. Brown, M. C. (1987). Morphology of labeled afferent fibers in the guinea pig cochlea. *J. Comp. Neurol.* **260:** 591–604.
30. Simmons, D. D., and Liberman, M. C. (1988). Afferent innervation of outer hair cells in adult cats. I: Light microscopic analysis of fibers labeled with horseradish peroxidase. *J. Comp. Neurol.* **270:** 132–144.
31. Brown, M. C., Berglund, A. M., Kiang, N. Y. S., and Ryugo, D. K. (1988). Central trajectories of type II spiral ganglion neurons. *J. Comp. Neurol.* **278:** 581–590.
32. Nadol, J. B., Jr. (1988). Comparative anatomy of the cochlea and auditory nerve in mammals. *Hear. Res.* **34:** 253–266.
33. Kiang, N. Y. S., Watanabe, T., Thomas, E. C., and Clark, L. F. (1965). *Discharge Patterns of Single Fibers in the Cat's Auditory Nerve.* MIT Press, Cambridge, MA.
34. Rose, J. E., Hind, J., and Anderson, D. J. (1971). Some effects of stimulus intensity on response of auditory nerve fibers in the squirrel monkey. *J. Neurophysiol.* **34:** 685–699.
35. Liberman, M. C. (1982). The cochlear frequency map for the cat: Labeling auditory-nerve fibers of known characteristic frequency. *J. Acoust. Soc. Am.* **72:** 1441–1449.
36. Sachs, M. B., and Abbas, P. J. (1975). Rate versus level functions for auditory-nerve fibers in cats: tone-burst stimuli. *J. Acoust. Soc. Am.* **56:** 1835–1847.
37. Liberman, M. C. (1978). Auditory-nerve responses from cats raised in a low-noise chamber. *J. Acoust. Soc. Am* **63:** 442–455.
38. Liberman, M. C. (1991). Central projections of auditory-nerve fibers of differing spontaneous rates. I. Anteroventral cochlear nucleus. *J. Comp. Neurol.* **313:** 240–258.
39. Smith, R. L. (1979). Adaptation, saturation, and physiological masking in single auditory-nerve fibers. *J. Acoust. Soc. Am.* **65:** 166–178.
40. Sachs, M. B., and Kiang, N. Y. S. (1968). Two-tone inhibition in auditory-nerve fibers. *J. Acoust. Soc. Am.* **43:** 1120–1128.
41. Spoendlin, H. (1981). Autonomic innervation of the inner ear. *Adv. Oto-Rhino-Laryngol.* **27:** 1–13.
42. Warr, W. B. (1992). Organization of olivocochlear efferent systems in mammals. In *The Mammalian Auditory Pathway: Neuroanatomy* (D. B. Webster, A. N. Popper, and R. R. Fay, eds.), pp. 410–448. Springer-Verlag, New York.
43. Brown, M. C. (1987). Morphology of labeled efferent fibers in the guinea pig cochlea. *J. Comp. Neurol.* **260:** 605–618.
44. Liberman, M. C., and Brown, M. C. (1986). Physiology and anatomy of single olivocochlear neurons in the cat. *Hear. Res.* **24:** 17–36.
45. Liberman, M. C. (1980). Efferent synapses in the inner hair cell area of the cat cochlea: An electron microscopic study of serial sections. *Hear. Res.* **3:** 189–204.
46. Fuchs, P. A., and Murrow, B. W. (1992). Cholinergic inhibition of short (outer) hair cells of the chick's cochlea. *J. Neurosci.* **12:** 800–809.
47. Elgoyhen, A. B., Johnson, D. S., Boulter, J., Vetter, D. E., and Heinemann, S. (1994). Alpha 9: An acetylcholine receptor with novel pharmacological properties expressed in rat cochlear hair cells. *Cell (Cambridge, Mass.)* **79:** 705–715.
48. Brown, M. C., and Nuttall, A. L. (1984). Efferent control of cochlear inner hair cell responses in the guinea-pig. *J. Physiol. (London)* **354:** 625–646.
49. Wiederhold, M. L., and Kiang, N. Y. S. (1970). Effects of electric stimulation of the crossed olivocochlear bundle on single auditory-nerve fibers in the cat. *J. Acoust. Soc. Am.* **48:** 950–965.
50. Kawase, T., Delgutte, B., and Liberman, M. C. (1993). Antimasking effects of the olivocochlear reflex. II. Enhancement of auditory-nerve response to masked tones. *J. Neurophysiol.* **70:** 2533–2549.
51. Rajan, R., and Johnstone, B. M. (1988). Electrical stimulation of cochlear efferents at the round window reduces auditory desensitization in guinea pigs. I. Dependence on electrical stimulation parameters. *Hear. Res.* **36:** 53–74.
52. Reiter, E. R., and Liberman, M. C. (1995). Efferent mediated protection from acoustic overexposure: Relation to "slow" effects of olivocochlear stimulation. *J. Neurophysiol.* **73:** 506–514.
53. Liberman, M. C. (1988). Response properties of cochlear efferent neurons: Monaural vs. binaural stimulation and the effects of noise. *J. Neurophysiol.* **60:** 1779–1798.
54. Brown, M. C., Kujawa, S. G., and Duca, M. L. (1998). Single olivocochlear neurons in the guinea pig. I. Binaural facilitation of responses to high-level noise. *J. Neurophysiol.* **79:** 3077–3087.
55. Joseph, M. P., Guinan, J. J., Jr., Fullerton, B. C., Norris, B. E., and Kiang, N. Y. S. (1985). Number and distribution of stapedius motoneurons in cats. *J. Comp. Neurol.* **232:** 43–54.
56. Nuttall, A. L. (1974). Measurements of the guinea-pig middle-ear transfer characteristic. *J. Acoust. Soc. Am.* **56:** 1231–1238.
57. Zakrisson, J.-E., Borg, E., Liden, G., and Nilsson, R. (1980). Stapedius reflex in industrial impact noise: Fatigability and role for temporary threshold shift (TTS). *Scand. Audiol., Suppl.* **12:** 326–334.
58. Borg, E., and Zakrisson, J.-E. (1973). Stapedius reflex and speech features. *J. Acoust. Soc. Am.* **54:** 525–527.
59. Spangler, K. M., and Warr, W. B. (1991). The descending auditory system. In *Neurobiology of Hearing: The Central Auditory System,* (R. A. Altschuler, R. P. Bobbin, B. M. Clopton, and D. W. Hoffman, eds.), pp. 27–45. Raven Press, New York.
60. Clopton, B. M., Winfield, J. A., and Flammino, F. J. (1974). Tonotopic organization: Review and analysis. *Brain Res.* **76:** 1–20.
61. Suga, N., and Jen, P.H.-S. (1976). Disproportionate tonotopic representation for processing CF-FM sonar signals in the mustache bat auditory cortex. *Science* **94:** 542–544.
62. Robertson, D., and Irvine, D. R. F. (1989). Plasticity of frequency organization in auditory cortex of guinea pigs with partial unilateral deafness. *J. Comp. Neurol.* **282:** 456–471.
63. Pfeiffer, R. R. (1966). Classification of response patterns of spike discharges for units in the cochlear nucleus: tone-burst stimulation. *Exp. Brain Res.* **1:** 220–235.
64. Rhode, W. S., and Greenberg, S. (1992). Physiology of the cochlear nuclei. In *The Mammalian Auditory Pathway: Neurophysiology* (A. N. Popper and R. R. Fay, eds.), pp. 94–152. Springer-Verlag, New York.
65. Godfrey, D. A., Kiang, N. Y. S., and Norris, B. E. (1975). Single

unit activity in the posteroventral cochlear nucleus of the cat. *J. Comp. Neurol.* **162:** 247–268.

66. Rhode, W. S., Oertel, D., and Smith, P. H. (1983). Physiological response properties of cells labeled intracellularly with horseradish peroxidase in cat ventral cochlear nucleus. *J. Comp. Neurol.* **213:** 448–463.
67. Rouiller, E. M., and Ryugo, D. K. (1984). Intracellular marking of physiologically characterized cells in the ventral cochlear nucleus of the cat. *J. Comp. Neurol.* **225:** 167–186.
68. Pfeiffer, R. R. (1966). Anteroventral cochlear nucleus: Wave forms of extracellularly recorded spike potentials. *Science* **154:** 667–668.
69. Forsythe, I. D. (1994). Direct patch recording from identified presynaptic terminals mediating glutamatergic EPSCs in the rat CNS, *in vitro*. *J. Physiol. (London)* **479:** 381–387.
70. Rouiller, E. M., Cronin-Schreiber, R., Fekete, D. M., and Ryugo, D. K. (1986). The central projections of intracellularly labeled auditory nerve fibers in cats: An analysis of terminal morphology. *J. Comp. Neurol.* **249:** 261–278.
71. Molnar, C. E., and Pfeiffer, R. R. (1968). Interpretation of spontaneous spike discharge patterns of neurons in the cochlear nucleus. *Proc. IEEE* **56:** 993–1004.
72. Lenn, N. J., and Reese, T. S. (1966). The fine structure of nerve endings in the nucleus of the trapezoid body and the ventral cochlear nucleus. *Am. J. Anat.* **118:** 375–390.
73. Sento, S., and Ryugo, D. K. (1989). Endbulbs of Held and spherical bushy cells in cats: Morphological correlates with physiological properties. *J. Comp. Neurol.* **280:** 553–562.
74. Oertel, D. (1985). Use of brain slices in the study of the auditory system: Spatial and temporal summation of synaptic inputs in cells in the anteroventral cochlear nucleus of the mouse. *J. Acoust. Soc. Am.* **78:** 328–333.
75. Manis, P. B., and Marx, S. O. (1991). Outward currents in isolated ventral cochlear nucleus neurons. *J. Neurosci.* **11:** 2865–2880.
76. Sullivan, W. E., and Konishi, M. (1984). Segregation of stimulus phase and intensity coding in the cochlear nucleus of the barn owl. *J. Neurosci.* **4:** 1787–1799.
77. Takahashi, T., Moiseff, A., and Konishi, M. (1984). Time and intensity cues are processed independently in the auditory system of the owl. *J. Neurosci.* **7:** 1781–1786.
78. Young, E. D. (1984). Response characteristics of neurons of the cochlear nuclei. In *Hearing Science: Recent Advances* (C. I. Berlin, ed.), pp. 423–460. College-Hill Press, San Diego, CA.
79. Voigt, H. F., and Young, E. D. (1980). Evidence of inhibitory interactions between neurons in dorsal cochlear nucleus. *J. Neurophysiol.* **44:** 76–96.
80. Young, E. D., Nelken, I., and Conley, R. A. (1995). Somatosensory effects on neurons in dorsal cochlear nucleus. *J. Neurophysiol.* **73:** 743–765.
81. Moore, J. K., and Osen, K. K. (1979). The cochlear nuclei in man. *Am. J. Anat.* **154:** 393–418.
82. Jenkins, W. M., and Masterton, R. B. (1982). Sound localization: Effects of unilateral lesions in central auditory system. *J. Neurophysiol.* **47:** 987–1016.
83. Roth, G. L., Kochhar, R. K., and Hind, J. E. (1980). Interaural time differences: Implications regarding the neurophysiology of sound localization. *J. Acoust. Soc. Am.* **68:** 1643–1651.
84. Shaw, E. A. G. (1974). Transformation of sound pressure level from the free field to the eardrum in the horizontal plane. *J. Acoust. Soc. Am.* **56:** 1848–1861.
85. Mills, A. W. (1960). Lateralization of high-frequency tones. *J. Acoust. Soc. Am.* **32:** 132–134.
86. Irvine, D. R. F. (1986). *The Auditory Brainstem: Progress in Sensory Physiology*, Vol. 7. Springer-Verlag, Berlin.
87. Yin, T. C. T., and Chan, J. C. K. (1990). Interaural time sensitivity in medial superior olive of cat. *J. Neurophysiol.* **64:** 465–488.
88. Smith, P. H., Joris, P. X., and Yin, T. C. T. (1993). Projections of physiologically characterized spherical bushy cell axons from the cochlear nucleus of the cat: Evidence for delay lines to the medial superior olive. *J. Comp. Neurol.* **331:** 245–260.
89. Carr, C. E., and Konishi, M. (1990). A circuit for detection of interaural time differences in the brain stem of the barn owl. *J. Neurosci.* **10:** 3227–3246.
90. Jeffress, L. A. (1948). A place theory of sound localization. *J. Comp. Psychol.* **41:** 35–39.
91. Masterton, B., Thompson, G. C., Bechtold, J. K., and RoBards, M. J. (1975). Neuroanatomical basis of binaural phase-difference analysis for sound localization: A comparative study. *J. Comp. Physiol. Psychol.* **89:** 379–386.
92. Boudreau, J. C., and Tsuchitani, C. (1968). Binaural interaction in the cat superior olive S segment. *J. Neurophysiol.* **31:** 442–454.
93. Moore, M. J., and Caspary, D. M. (1983). Strychnine blocks binaural inhibition in lateral superior olivary neurons. *J. Neurosci.* **3:** 237–242.
94. Glendenning, K. K., Baker, B. N., Hutson, K. A., and Masterton, R. B. (1992). Acoustic chiasm V: Inhibition and excitation in the ipsilateral and contralateral projections of LSO. *J. Comp. Neurol.* **319:** 100–122.
95. Kuwada, S., and Yin, C. T. (1983). Binaural interaction in low-frequency neurons in inferior colliculus of the cat. I. Effects of long interaural delays, intensity, and repetition rate on interaural delay function. *J. Neurophysiol.* **50:** 981–999.
96. Irvine, D. R. F., and Gago, G. (1990). Binaural interaction in high-frequency neurons in inferior colliculus of the cat: Effects of variations in sound pressure level on sensitivity to interaural differences. *J. Neurophysiol.* **63:** 570–591.
97. Li, L., and Kelly, J. B. (1992a). Binaural responses in the rat inferior colliculus following kainic acid lesions of the superior olive: Interaural intensity difference functions. *Hear. Res.* **61:** 73–85.
98. Li, L., and Kelly, J. B. (1992b). Inhibitory influence of the dorsal nucleus of the lateral lemniscus on binaural responses in the rat's inferior colliculus. *J. Neurosci.* **12:** 4530–4539.
99. Middlebrooks, J. C., and Knudsen, E. I. (1984). A neural code for auditory space in the cat's superior colliculus. *J. Neurosci.* **4:** 2621–2634.
100. Knudsen, E. I., and Konishi, M. (1978). A neural map for auditory space in the owl. *Science* **200:** 795–797.
101. Clarey, J. C., Barone, P., and Imig, T. J. (1992). Physiology of thalamus and cortex. In *The Mammalian Auditory Pathway: Neurophysiology* (A. N. Popper and R. R. Fay, eds.), pp. 232–334. Springer-Verlag, New York.
102. de Ribaupierre, F. (1997). Acoustical information processing in the auditory thalamus and cerebral cortex. In *The Central Auditory System* (G. Ehret and R. Romand, eds.), pp. 317–397. Oxford University Press, New York.
103. Rouiller, E. M., Simm, G. M., Villa, A. E. P., de Ribaupierre, Y., and de Ribaupierre, F. (1991). Auditory corticocortical interconnections in the cat: Evidence for parallel and hierarchical arrangement of the auditory cortical areas. *Exp. Brain Res.* **86:** 483–505.
104. Schreiner, C. E., and Cynader, M. S. (1984). Basic functional organization of second auditory cortical field (AII) of the cat. *J. Neurophysiol.* **51:** 1284–1305.
105. Celesia, G. G., and Puletti, F. (1969). Auditory cortical areas of man. *Neurology* **19:** 211–220.
106. Penfield, W., and Perot, P. (1963). The brain's record of auditory and visual experience. *Brain* **86:** 595–696.

107. Binder, J. R., Rao, S. M., Hammeke, T. A., Yetkin, F. Z., Jesmanowicz, A., Bandettini, P. A., Wong, E. C., Estowski, L. D., Goldstein, M. C., Haughton, V. M., and Hyde, J. S. (1994). Functional magnetic resonance imaging of the human auditory cortex. *Ann. Neurol.* **35:** 662–672.
108. Romanski, L. M., and LeDoux, J. E. (1992). Bilateral destruction of neocortical and perirhinal projection targets of the acoustic thalamus does not disrupt auditory fear conditioning. *Neurosci. Lett.* **142:** 228–232.
109. Weinberger, N. M. (1993). Learning-induced changes of auditory receptive fields. *Curr. Opin. Neurobiol.* **3:** 570–577.
110. Merzenich, M. M., Knight, P. L., and Roth, G. L. (1975). Representation of cochlea within primary auditory cortex in the cat. *J. Neurophysiol.* **38:** 231–249.
111. Imig, T. J., and Adrian, H. O. (1977). Binaural columns in the primary field (AI) of cat auditory cortex. *Brain Res.* **138:** 241–257.
112. Imig, T. J., and Brugge, J. F. (1978). Sources and terminations of callosal axons related to binaural and frequency maps in primary auditory cortex of the cat. *J. Comp. Neurol.* **182:** 637–660.
113. Clarey, J. C., Barone, P., and Imig, T. J. (1994). Functional organization of sound direction and sound pressure level in primary auditory cortex of the cat. *J. Neurophysiol.* **72:** 2383–2405.
114. Jenkins, W. M., and Merzenich, R. B. (1984). Role of cat primary auditory cortex for sound localization behavior. *J. Neurophysiol.* **52:** 819–847.
115. Heffner, H. E., and Heffner, R. S. (1990). Effect of bilateral auditory cortex lesions on sound localization in Japanese macaques. *J. Neurophysiol.* **64:** 915–931.
116. Phillips, D. P., Orman, S. S., Musicant, A. D., and Wilson, G. F. (1985). Neurons in the cat's primary auditory cortex distinguished by their responses to tones and wide-spectrum noise. *Hear. Res.* **18:** 73–86.
117. Wang, J., Salvi, R., and Powers, N. (1996). Plasticity of response properties of inferior colliculus neurons following acute cochlear damage. *J. Neurophysiol.* **75:** 171–183.
118. Faingold, C. L., Boersma Anderson, C. A., and Caspary, D. M. (1991). Involvement of GABA in acoustically-evoked inhibition in inferior colliculus neurons. *Hear. Res.* **52:** 201–216.
119. Winer, J. A., Wenstrup, J. J., and Larue, D. T. (1992). Patterns of GABAergic immunoreactivity define subdivisions of the mustached bat's medial geniculate body. *J. Comp. Neurol.* **319:** 172–190.
120. Suga, N. (1977). Amplitude-spectrum representation in the Doppler-shifted-CF processing area of the auditory cortex of the mustache bat. *Science* **196:** 64–67.
121. Suga, N. (1990). Biosonar and neural computation in bats. *Sci. Am.* **262**(6): 60–68.
122. Fitzpatrick, D. C., Kanwai, J. S., Butman, J. A., and Suga, N. (1993). Combination-sensitive neurons in the primary auditory cortex of the mustached bat. *J. Neurosci.* **13:** 931–940.
123. Griffin, D. R. (1958). *Listening in the Dark.* Yale University Press, New Haven, CT (originally from Dobson[124]).
124. Dobson, G. E. (1876). *Monograph of the Asiatic Chiropteran and Catalogue of the Species of Bats in the Collection of the Indian Museum.* Indian Museum, Calcutta and London.
125. Wang, X., Merzenich, M. M., Beitel, R., and Schreiner, C. E. (1995). Representation of a species-specific vocalization in the primary auditory cortex of the common marmoset: Temporal and spectral characteristics. *J. Neurophysiol.* **74:** 2685–2706.
126. Winter, P., and Funkenstein, H. H. (1973). The effect of species-specific vocalization on the discharge of auditory cortical cells in the awake squirrel monkey (*Saimiri sciureus*). *Exp. Brain Res.* **18:** 489–504.
127. Rauschecker, J. P., Tian, B., and Hauser, M. (1995). Processing of complex sounds in the macaque nonprimary auditory cortex. *Science* **268:** 111–114.
128. Creutzfeldt, O., Ojemann, G., and Lettich, E. (1989). Neuronal activity in the human lateral temporal lobe. I. Responses to speech. *Exp. Brain Res.* **77:** 451–475.
129. Diamond, I. T., and Neff, W. D. (1957). Ablation of temporal cortex and discrimination of auditory patterns. *J. Neurophysiol.* **20:** 300–315.
130. Heffner, H. E., and Heffner, R. S. (1986). Effect of unilateral and bilateral auditory cortex lesions on the discrimination of vocalizations by Japanese macaques. *J. Neurophysiol.* **56:** 683–701.
131. Petersen, S. E., Fox, P. T., Posner, M. I., Mintum, M., and Raichle, M. E. (1988). Positron emission tomographic studies of the cortical anatomy of single-word processing. *Nature (London)* **331:** 585–589.
132. Zatorre, R. J., Evans, A. C., Meyer, E., and Gjedde, A. (1992). Lateralization of phonetic and pitch discrimination in speech processing. *Science* **256:** 846–849.

C H A P T E R

28

Vision

R. Clay Reid

Vision is the most studied and perhaps the best understood topic in sensory neuroscience. For this reason, a single chapter can cover only a portion of the subject. This chapter is concerned primarily with vision in mammals. In particular, we focus on the pathway in the visual system that has to do with perception: from the retina, to the lateral geniculate nucleus of the thalamus (LGN), and on to the multiple areas of visual cortex. Other regions of the brain (such as the superior colliculus) that receive visual input are dealt with briefly in this chapter and more extensively in the chapter on eye movements (Chapter 36).

In studying vision, we have the opportunity to explore the brain at many different levels, from the physical and biochemical mechanisms of phototransduction (Chapter 24) to the boundary between psychology and physiology (Chapters 52 and 53). At each of these levels, the visual system has evolved to solve a number of difficult problems. In terms of the physical stimulus, vision operates over extremely wide ranges of illumination. We can detect single photons in the dark[1–3] but can also see clearly in bright sunlight, when the retina is bombarded with over 10^{14} photons per second. At a much higher level of complexity, ensembles of neurons in the cerebral cortex are able to solve extremely difficult problems, such as extracting the three-dimensional motion of an object from two-dimensional retinal images.

At every moment, the visual system is confronted with the vast amount of information present in visual scenes, estimated to contain typically millions of bits per second. The complex circuitry of the retina has evolved so that much of this information is extensively processed and relayed to the rest of the central nervous system both efficiently and with great fidelity. But vision has not evolved to treat all of this information equally; instead, it appears to be best suited to extract the sort of information that may be useful to animals—including humans—in a natural environment. It is vision that helps us to navigate in the world; to judge the speed and distance of objects; to identify food, members of other species, and familiar or unfamiliar members of our own species.

In many animals, primates in particular, more of the brain is devoted to vision than to any other sensory function. This is perhaps because of the extreme complexity of the task required of vision: to classify and to interpret the wide range of visual stimuli that we confront in the physical world. At the highest levels of processing (discussed at the end of this chapter), the cerebral cortex extracts from the world the diverse qualities that we experience as visual perception: from motion, color, texture, and depth to the grouping of objects, defined by the combination of simple features.

THE RECEPTIVE FIELD: THE FUNDAMENTAL CONCEPT IN VISUAL PHYSIOLOGY

Perhaps because we are such visual animals, the strategies that the brain uses to solve the problems of vision can be understood at a very intuitive level. The most useful concept to aid this intuition is that of the **receptive field,** which is the cornerstone of visual physiology. As defined by H. K. Hartline,[4] the receptive field is the "region of the retina that must be illuminated in order to obtain a response in any given fiber." In this case, "fiber" refers to the axon of a retinal neuron, but any visual neuron, from a photoreceptor to a visual cortical neuron, has a receptive field. The definition was later extended to include not only the region of the retina that excited a neuron but also the specific properties of the stimulus that evoked the strongest response. Visual neurons can respond preferentially to the turning on or turning off of a light stimulus—termed **on** and **off** responses—or to more complex features such as color or the direction of motion. Any of these preferences can be expressed as attributes of the receptive field.

Sensory Systems Detect Contrast or Change

In the 1930s and 1940s, Hartline firmly developed the concept of the receptive field with studies of the axons of individual neurons that project from the lateral eye of the horseshoe crab (*Limulus*) and from the frog's eye. The lateral eye of the *Limulus* is a compound eye made up of about 300 large **ommatidia** arranged in a roughly hexagonal array. Each ommatidium contains optical elements, photoreceptors, and a single neuron whose axon joins the optic nerve. In his earliest work,[5] Hartline found that when an isolated ommatidium was illuminated, the firing rate of its axon increased. More surprisingly, it was later found that the firing of the same axon would be decreased by a light stimulus in any adjacent ommatidium.[6] This form of antagonistic behavior, known as **lateral inhibition,** serves to enhance responses to edges while reducing responses to constant surfaces. Without it, visual neurons would be just as sensitive to a featureless stimulus, such as a clean white wall, as to stimuli defined by edges, such as a white square on a black wall. In the following years, similar spatially antagonistic visual responses were found in mammals, as was first demonstrated by Kuffler in the retina of the cat.[7,8] Kuffler's study of retinal ganglion cells is discussed in Box 28.1.

Lateral inhibition represents the classic example of a general principle: most neurons in sensory systems are best adapted for detecting changes in the external environment. This principle can be explained in behavioral terms. As a rule, it is change that has the greatest *significance* for an animal: for example, the edge of an extended object, or a static object beginning to move. This principle can also be explained in terms of information processing. Given a world that is filled with constants—with uniform objects, with objects that move only rarely—it is most *efficient* to respond especially to changes.

In this chapter, we discuss several types of responses in the visual system in terms of detection of change. First, there is spatial contrast, the detection of which is enhanced by neurons in the retina that have lateral inhibition (center–surround organization; see Box 28.1). Next, there is temporal contrast, or change over time. Starting in the retina, visual neurons are affected very little by slow changes in illumination, but are extremely sensitive to more rapid changes. Finally, there is motion, which is distinguished by characteristic changes in a stimulus over both space and time. Many neurons in the visual system are selectively excited by objects that have a certain rate or direction of motion. In summary, contrast sensitivity can take on at least three forms: (1) sensitivity to spatial variations in a stimulus (spatial contrast), (2) sensitivity to changes over time (temporal contrast), and (3) sensitivity to changes in both space and time (motion; see Box 28.5).

Receptive Fields Encode Increasingly High-Order Features of the Visual World

From the photoreceptors to the multiple visual cortical areas, vision is a hierarchical system. One level provides input to the next in a feedforward progression, although lateral interactions and feedback are almost always present as well. As a general rule, receptive fields at successive stages of processing (from photoreceptors, bipolar cells, ganglion cells, and geniculate neurons, through neurons in multiple visual cortical areas) encode increasingly high-level features of the visual stimulus. The outer segment of a photoreceptor, which contains the visual pigment, is influenced only by a small point in visual space. It is therefore almost entirely insensitive to the spatial structure of a stimulus. At the opposite extreme, some neurons in the inferior-temporal region of visual cortex seem to respond best when the animal is viewing a specific face (see Chapter 52).

These two extremes of visual responses illustrate the visual system's dual task: to maintain generality—the ability to respond to any stimulus—while also being able to represent specific, environmentally "important" classes of stimuli. High-level neurons classify visual stimuli by integrating information that is present in the earlier stages of processing, but also by ignoring information that is independent of that classification. For instance, motion-sensitive neurons in area MT of cerebral cortex (see below) are exquisitely sensitive to the direction and rate of motion of an object, but very poor at distinguishing the object's color or its position. This lack of localization is quite common in high-level neurons: receptive fields become larger as the features they represent become increasingly complex. Thus, for instance, neurons that respond to faces typically have receptive fields that cover most of visual space. For these cells, large receptive fields have a distinct advantage: the preferred stimulus can be identified no matter where it is located on the retina.

Summary

The mammalian visual system is a complex, hierarchical system that can be studied from a number of different viewpoints. In this chapter, we concentrate on the physiology of visual neurons, which is based on the study of receptive fields. Originally, receptive fields were defined as the area of the retina that could evoke a responses in a visual neuron. The concept has evolved to include the stimulus attributes that lead to a neural response, such as color, motion, or even the complex features of a specific physical object. Within the hierarchy of the visual system—from retina to the multiple areas of visual cortex—neurons are selective for increasingly complex or high-order features.

THE EYE AND THE RETINA

The Optics of the Eye Project an Inverted Visual Image on the Retina

The study of vision begins with the eye (Fig. 28.1), whose refractive properties are determined by the curvature of the **cornea** and, behind it, the **lens.** These optical elements act to focus an inverted image on the retina, where the first stages of neural visual processing take place. The curvature of the cornea is fixed, but the curvature of the lens is adjusted by smooth muscles that flatten the lens when they contract, thus bringing more distant objects into focus. The amount of light that reaches the retina is controlled by the iris, whose aperture is the pupil. The **iris,** which is situated between the cornea and the lens in the **anterior chamber** of the eye, contracts at high light levels and expands in the dark. It is thus partially responsible for the ability to see over a broad range of light levels, but this ability is primarily due to light and dark adaptation, two complex processes that take place in the retina.[9]

Both the focusing of the eye, **accommodation,** and the control of the pupil size, the **pupillary light reflex,** are controlled by nuclei of the midbrain. The reflex pathway for both processes begins with branches of axons from the retina that are routed to the pretectum, just ventral to the superior colliculus. The pretectum provides input to the accessory oculomotor nucleus, also known as the Edinger–Westphal nucleus, which controls the muscles responsible for accommodation and pupillary constriction. Accommodation requires input from the visual cortex, while the pupillary light reflex relies purely on retinal input to the midbrain.

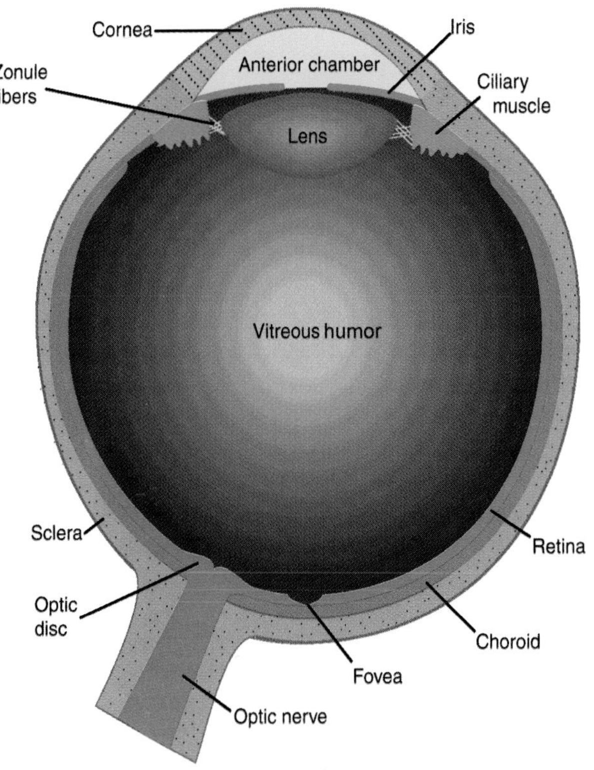

FIGURE 28.1 Schematic diagram of the human eye.

The Retina Is a Three-Layer Structure with Five Types of Neurons

For a number of reasons, the retina is an "approachable part of the brain"[10] whose circuitry is particularly amenable to study. Unlike the other sensory organs found in the periphery, the retina itself is part of the central nervous system; embryologically, it is formed from the optic cup, an outpouching of the neural tube (Chapter 15). The retina thus has much in common with the rest of the central nervous system (such as neurotransmitter and receptor families), but is far easier to study *in vitro.* Although other regions of the central nervous system can be studied in isolation, the retina is unique in that an isolated preparation preserves virtually all of the functions that are present *in vivo.* It thus presents the best of two worlds: the completeness of an intact sensory system and the accessibility of an isolated preparation. The retina serves as a model system for the study of visual physiology; it can be used to illustrate many of the principles of sensory processing relevant to higher stages. But even more so than with higher visual areas (for instance, the LGN, superior colliculus, and visual cortex), our understanding of the retina has been greatly enhanced by the powerful physiological and pharmacological tools that can be used *in vitro*.

The anatomy of the retina has an almost crystalline beauty, a beauty that is enhanced by the clear relationships between form and function.[11] It is composed of five principal layers: three layers of cell bodies separated by two layers of neural processes, dendrites and axons, as in Fig. 28.2.[12] The retina is oriented within

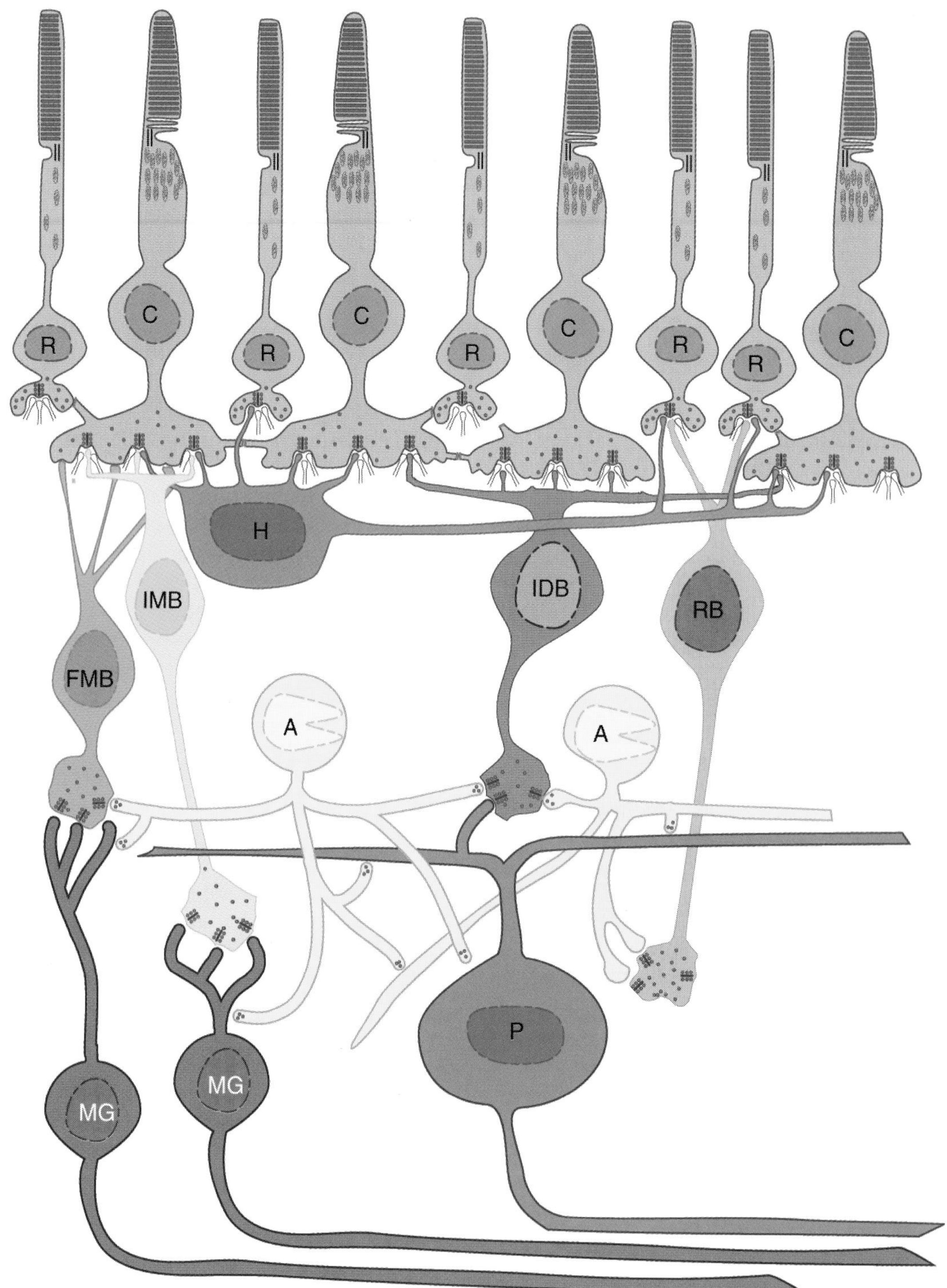

FIGURE 28.2 Summary diagram of the cell types and connections in the primate retina. R, rod; C, cone; H, horizontal cell; FMB, flat midget bipolar; IMB, invaginating midget bipolar; IDB, invaginating diffuse bipolar; RB, rod bipolar; A, amacrine cell; MG, midget ganglion cell; P, parasol cell. Adapted from Dowling.[12]

the eye so that light must travel through the entire thickness of the neuropil to reach the photoreceptors. Of the three cell layers, the first is farthest from the center of the eye and is thus called the **outer nuclear layer.** It contains the cell bodies of the photoreceptors, the rods and cones (Chapter 24). The next cell layer is the **inner nuclear layer,** which contains the cell bodies of the retina's interneurons, both excitatory and inhibitory. These include horizontal cells, bipolar cells, and amacrine cells. Finally, the **ganglion cell layer** is home to the retinal neurons whose axons form the optic nerve, the sole pathway from the retina to the rest of the central nervous system. Interposed between the cell-body layers are two layers of cell processes, the **inner** and **outer plexiform layers.** The two plexiform layers are the sites of all interactions between the retina's neurons.

The retina is one of the few circuits in the nervous system simple enough that cell types and connections can be learned without great effort. This is made even easier because the role of each of the five cell types can be placed within a simple functional scheme. The two main attributes of the retina's output—(1) a point-to-point representation of the world and (2) center–surround interactions in the receptive field (see Box 28.1)—can be understood in terms of the anatomy. The direct pathway photoreceptor → bipolar cell → ganglion cell is the substrate for the center of the ganglion cell's receptive field and thus for its spatial resolution. The lateral interactions in the retina, most notably the center–surround antagonism, or lateral inhibition, are mediated by the horizontal cells and amacrine cells.

Photoreceptor Are Hyperpolarized by Light

The photoreceptors have been discussed at length in the chapter on sensory transduction (Chapter 24). Here it is important to note that unlike most cells in the nervous system, the majority of cells in the retina—photoreceptors, bipolar cells, horizontal cells, and, arguably, most amacrine cells—do not normally fire action potentials. Instead, they have continuously graded membrane potentials that are modulated around a mean level. The photoreceptor cells have a tonic level of depolarization and of neurotransmitter release. They are hyperpolarized by an increment in light, via a cGMP-gated process that closes sodium channels. Thus, light acts to decrease the amount of neurotransmitter they release.

Bipolar Cells Can Be Hyperpolarized or Depolarized by Light

Bipolar cells are divided into two broad classes, termed **on** and **off** bipolars, that respond to light stimuli with depolarization and hyperpolarization, respectively. On bipolars are also known as **invaginating bipolars,** and off bipolars are known as **flat bipolars,** because of the shape of the synaptic contacts they receive from photoreceptors (Fig. 28.2). Because all photoreceptors use glutamate as their neurotransmitter, these opposite responses require that on and off bipolar cells respond to the same neurotransmitter in opposite ways.[13,14] Glutamate, typically an excitatory transmitter, is inhibitory for on bipolars. It acts by closing a cGMP-gated sodium channel, similar to that seen in the photoreceptors. Excitation in on bipolars is the result of the removal of a tonic blockade of these sodium channels by glutamate; this removal of inhibition occurs when photoreceptors are hyperpolarized by light. Off bipolars are excited by glutamate via more typical AMPA/kainate receptors (so named because of the pharmacological agents that activate them; see Chapter 10). When these cells are inhibited by light, the inhibition is in fact due to the removal of tonic excitation, which again occurs when the photoreceptors are hyperpolarized.

The functional importance of the on and the off pathways can best be understood in terms of contrast. From the bipolar cells onward—that is, once on and off pathways have been established—visual neurons respond better to spatial and temporal contrast than to absolute light levels.[15] Objects in the world are visible by the light they reflect; their borders are discerned usually because of different degrees of reflectance, which leads to contrast (while changes in illumination, except for shadows, tend to be much more gradual). Because the visual system is clearly adapted for seeing objects that can be either brighter or darker than their backgrounds, it is not too surprising that it is equally sensitive to positive and negative contrast steps.

Most ganglion cells—the output cells of the retina—receive their main excitatory input from one class of bipolar cells. Thus, these ganglion cells also have either on or off responses in the center of their receptive fields, according to which class of bipolar cells provides their excitatory input (see Box 28.1). In most species, there are additional ganglion cells, known as on–off cells, that respond to any transition, that is, to both light-on and light-off. These latter cells receive input from both classes of bipolar cells. Many of these cells respond preferentially to stimuli moving in a particular direction of motion (see Box 28.5).

Horizontal and Amacrine Cells Mediate Lateral Interactions in the Retina

There is a complex three-way synaptic relationship among the terminals of the photoreceptors, the

BOX 28.1

KUFFLER'S STUDY OF CENTER–SURROUND RETINAL GANGLION CELLS

The classic experiments that Kuffler[7,8] performed on retinal ganglion cells have formed the foundations for much of the subsequent physiological analysis of the mammalian visual system. Even beyond the study of vision, they represent a model for our understanding of the neurobiology of sensory systems. These experiments were performed *in vivo,* in anesthetized cats. The first step in this sort of experiment is the careful placement of a fine microelectrode close to a single neuron, so that action potentials can be recorded extracellularly. An oscilloscope trace of this neuron's firing pattern is important, but the sound of the action potentials on an audio monitor is even more critical. This immediate feedback allows the researcher to search for visual stimuli that excite or inhibit the neuron. Kuffler's first finding was that there were two categories of ganglion cells, as Hartline[4,16] had seen in the retina of the frog. The cells were either on—that is, excited by light increment—or off—excited by light decrement.

One of Kuffler's more important contributions was the careful mapping of lateral interactions in the retina, or what he termed the **center–surround** structure of the receptive field. When an on ganglion cell was being studied, a small light spot placed in the center of its receptive field would cause an immediate increase in the cell's firing rate (Fig. 28.3B, top). The **center** of the receptive field of an on ganglion cell was defined as all positions where the small spot evoked an on-excitatory response. When the same spot was placed just beyond the center, in the region termed the **surround,** the neuron decreased its firing rate (Fig. 28.3B, bottom). Kuffler mapped the spatial extent of the regions that evoked excitation or inhibition simply by listening to the responses to spots flashed at many different locations. To represent these maps, on regions were marked with crosses and off regions with triangles (Figs. 28.3A and 28.3F). Alternatively, Kuffler studied receptive fields by searching for an "optimal stimulus," one that most effectively increased the firing of a ganglion cell. The strongest stimulus for an on-center cell was a spot of light that entirely filled the receptive field center (Fig. 28.3C). Similarly, the most effective *inhibitory* stimulus was a bright annulus shown to the surround alone. Following such strong inhibition, the cell had an excitatory response when the stimulus was turned off (Fig. 28.3D). Finally, Kuffler studied interactions between receptive field subregions. A large, bright stimulus that covered both center and surround was found to evoke a much weaker response than a smaller spot confined to the center; the surround inhibition weakened or altogether eliminated the central excitation (Fig. 28.3E).

Kuffler's early experiments, along with those of Hartline, thus established the technical and conceptual foundations for the field of visual physiology. Almost all subsequent work in this field can be seen as falling into the three broad categories of experiments, exemplified by Kuffler's 1952[7] study: (1) the mapping of responses with isolated, suboptimal stimuli, (2) the search for an optimal stimulus, and (3) the study of interactions between responses evoked by two or more stimuli.

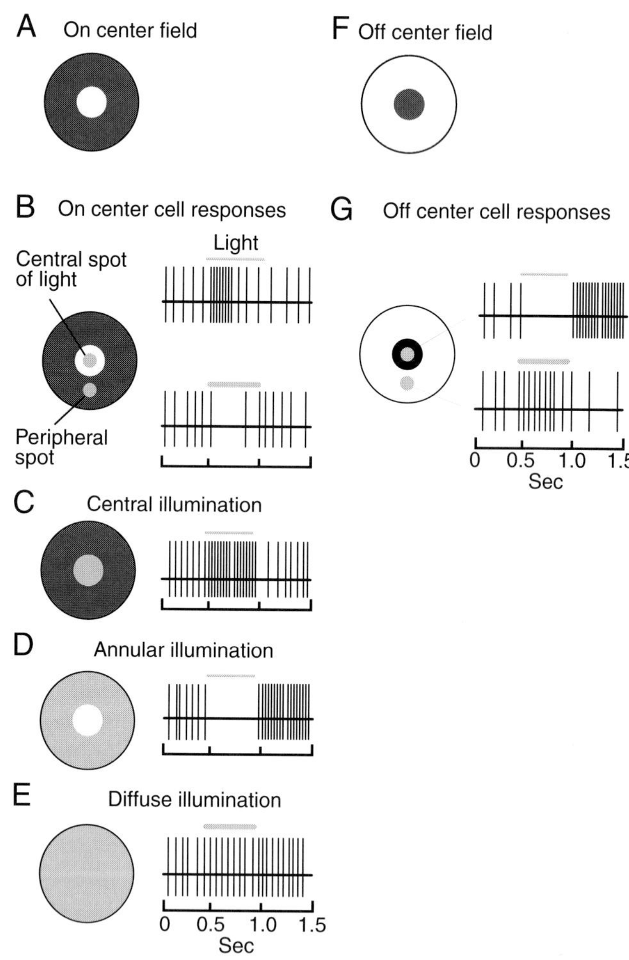

FIGURE 28.3 Visual responses of on-center (white) and off-center (dark gray) retinal ganglion cells. Visual stimuli are indicated in yellow and the responses to these stimuli are shown to the right. See text for details. Adapted from Kuffler *et al.*[17]

processes of horizontal cells, and the dendrites of bipolar cells (Fig. 28.2).[12] Horizontal cells are inhibitory (GABAergic) and, as the name implies, they contact photoreceptors over a much larger area of retina than do the bipolar cells. Thus, because they are the only neurons that sample over a sufficiently large area in the **outer plexiform layer,** horizontal cells are thought to be responsible for the antagonistic surround seen in the receptive fields of bipolar cells.

The second family of lateral interneurons in the retina, the amacrine cells (literally, cells with no axons), is a diverse class of cells that exhibit a wide range of morphologies. As is true of the horizontal cells, all processing takes place on the dendrites of amacrine cells (in the inner plexiform layer), which contain both pre- and postsynaptic elements (Fig. 28.2). Most amacrine cells use GABA, glycine, or both acetylcholine and GABA as neurotransmitters, but it is thought that virtually every transmitter found in the brain is used by some amacrine cell.[11] The functions of most of these diverse subclasses remain poorly understood. In addition to a possible influence on the antagonistic surround, it has been proposed that some amacrine cells are responsible for the nonlinear responses in Y cells of the cat (see Box 28.2) or for the direction selectivity seen in the rabbit retina (see Box 28.5).

Retinal Ganglion Cells Provide the Output of the Retina

Visual information leaves the eye via the optic nerve, which is composed of the axons of all of the different classes of ganglion cells. The optic nerve begins at the **optic disc** (see Fig. 28.1). Because there are no photoreceptors at the optic disc, this circular region constitutes a blind spot in the retina. The precise routing of ganglion cell axons to different parts of the brain provides a number of interesting problems for developmental neurobiology[11a] (see Chapters 19 and 22). This routing of axons is both macroscopic—different types of ganglion cells project to different regions of the brain—and microscopic—within any given target region, axons are sorted out in a precise manner. In each of two principal targets of retinal axons, the superior colliculus and LGN, a topographical map of visual space is created in which the precise visual–spatial relations are maintained between neighboring neurons.

In this chapter, we are concerned primarily with the classes of retinal ganglion cells that project to LGN neurons, which in turn project to the visual (striate) cortex. Although the cells in the LGN are more than mere relays of information from the retina, their receptive fields are quite similar to those of their ganglion cell inputs. The following discussion of retinal receptive fields, therefore, can serve equally well to describe receptive fields in the LGN.

Parallel Pathways Are Composed of Distinct Classes of Retinal Ganglion Cells in the Cat

Kuffler found that retinal ganglion cells in the cat have a stereotyped center–surround organization. Similar cells (both on and off) were found at every position across the entire retina. Researchers later discovered, however, that there are in fact several different functional classes of ganglion cells, each with distinct response properties. Although different cell classes have been found in different species, in none is the retina composed of a single mosaic of identical cells. The fact that there are multiple distinct types of output from the retina has had a profound effect on the study of visual processing in the brain. The degree to which these **parallel pathways** are combined or kept separate has been a major theme in the study of central visual pathways, particularly the visual cortex.

The idea that there are parallel sensory pathways into the brain is not new. At the beginning of the 19th century, both Bell and Müller argued for what Müller termed the "specific energy of nerves." This term is a precursor of the idea that sensory neurons are "labeled lines,"[18] each of which conveys distinct signals to the brain. Helmholtz gave a surprisingly modern version of this idea in the *Handbook of Physiological Optics* (1860)[18a] in which he expressed Thomas Young's theory of color vision (1801) in the following manner: "The eye is provided with three distinct sets of nervous fibers. Stimulation of the first excites the sensation of red, stimulation of the second the sensation of green, and stimulation of the third the sensation of violet" (quoted in Boring[19]; as explained below, however, this view of color vision is not quite accurate).

In one of the first studies using a quantitative approach to receptive field mapping (see Box 28.2), Enroth-Cugell and Robson[20] found that cat retinal ganglion cells could be classified into two categories: X and Y (more categories have been found subsequently). This classification was based on a simple criterion: did ganglion cells simply sum all of their excitatory and inhibitory inputs in a linear fashion, or was the integration of inputs more complicated and nonlinear? The linear / nonlinear distinction between X and Y cells[20,23,24] (see Box 28.2) may seem fairly abstract, but these cells turned out to be different in a number of other ways. Most notably, Y-cell receptive fields are, on average, three times larger than those of their neighboring X cells. X cells are therefore far more numerous, because many more X-cell receptive fields are needed to effectively "tile," or cover, the entire visual world. One

BOX 28.2

QUANTITATIVE METHODS IN THE STUDY OF VISUAL NEURONS: ENROTH-CUGELL AND ROBSON'S CLASSIFICATION OF RETINAL GANGLION CELLS

Although neuroscientists have learned a tremendous amount about the visual system using the tools developed by Kuffler, researchers have been following a parallel line of work on the visual system by asking different sorts of questions with the aid of more quantitative methods. In Kuffler's experiments and, most notably, many of Hubel and Wiesel's (Box 28.4), easily produced stimuli (such as spots, edges, and bars) were used to stimulate visual neurons. Action potentials were detected primarily with an oscilloscope and audio monitor. In the more quantitative studies of visual physiology, stimuli are shown primarily on cathode ray tubes (or video monitors) and data are recorded with computers. These differences are trivial in themselves, but the use of electronics has allowed a broad range of stimuli to be produced with great precision and reproducibility; the use of computers for data acquisition has simplified the detailed analysis of visual responses. The quantitative study of visual physiology constitutes a large field, which stems from the work of Hartline, Ratliff, Campbell, Barlow, and others.[21,22] The analysis of the receptive fields of retinal ganglion cells in the cat performed by Enroth-Cugell and Robson[20] represents an early and influential example of this line of research.

The stimuli used by Enroth-Cugell and Robson, and in many studies that followed theirs, were of **gratings**—light and dark bands whose luminance varied in a sinusoidal fashion across a screen. Gratings were not designed to be the "best" stimuli for visual neurons or to maximally excite them. The broad goal of this sort of experiment is to study not only what makes neurons respond best but also how they would respond to *any* stimulus and to probe what mechanisms they use to produce these responses.[23] The analytical framework that goes along with these experiments is called **systems theory,** the study of input–output (or stimulus–response) systems.

Linear systems, those that simply add up all of their inputs to produce a response, constitute an important part of this theory. Within this formalism, sine-wave gratings are in fact the simplest possible stimulus. If the input to a linear system—in particular, the optics of the eye—is a sine wave, then the output is also a sine wave. Unlike with stimuli such as spots and edges, if a sine wave is presented to the eye, the image on the retina will also be a sine wave.

Enroth-Cugell and Robson used a simple test of linearity in their study of retinal ganglion cells in the cat. They presented a grating at different positions (called *phases*) and recorded the responses to its introduction and removal. For each cell studied, they asked two questions. (1) If a certain position (whose bars were arranged white, black, white, . . .) excited the cell, did the "opposite" grating (black, white, black, . . .) inhibit it? More importantly, (2) was there was a *null* position for the grating that evoked no response, since excitation and inhibition were perfectly balanced?

One class of ganglion cells, which they called X cells, passed these tests for linear spatial summation (Fig. 28.4, left). A second class of cells, Y cells, behaved differently. Like X cells, these cells also had a center–surround receptive field when mapped with spots and annuli. When studied with two "opposite" gratings, however, the responses evoked were not equal and opposite. Instead, the introduction and removal of the gratings at all positions were excitatory and no null position could be found (Fig. 28.4, right).

The use of systems theory in the study of the visual system has had a number of notable successes. It has helped in the classification of different families of visual neurons, such as X and Y cells. Further, it has been used to elucidate some of the mechanisms responsible for the response characteristics of these different classes of cells.[24] Perhaps most importantly, it has helped create a framework in which the response properties of neurons can be exhaustively characterized and related to perception.

It is particularly easy to study a linear system with a well-chosen, "complete," set of stimuli, such as sine-wave gratings of different sizes and positions (phases). Once the responses to these inputs have been determined, the responses to any stimulus can be predicted (by using Fourier analysis, for instance, if the original stimuli were gratings). Conversely, if the responses of an array of linear detectors are known, then the stimulus that evoked these responses can be reconstructed in straightforward manner. If a system is grossly nonlinear—such as an on–off cell in the retina, which responds equally well to a light stimulus and its opposite, a dark stimulus—then reconstruction is more difficult, if not impossible. The visual system might have used several strategies to reconstruct the stimulus—or, more accurately, to have a complete representation of the pattern of light that made up a physical stimulus—given the activity of a group of neurons. It is therefore an important empirical finding that many visual neurons in the retina, LGN, and the first stages of visual cortex behave linearly; that is, the "early" visual system uses a particularly simple solution to the problem of image representation.

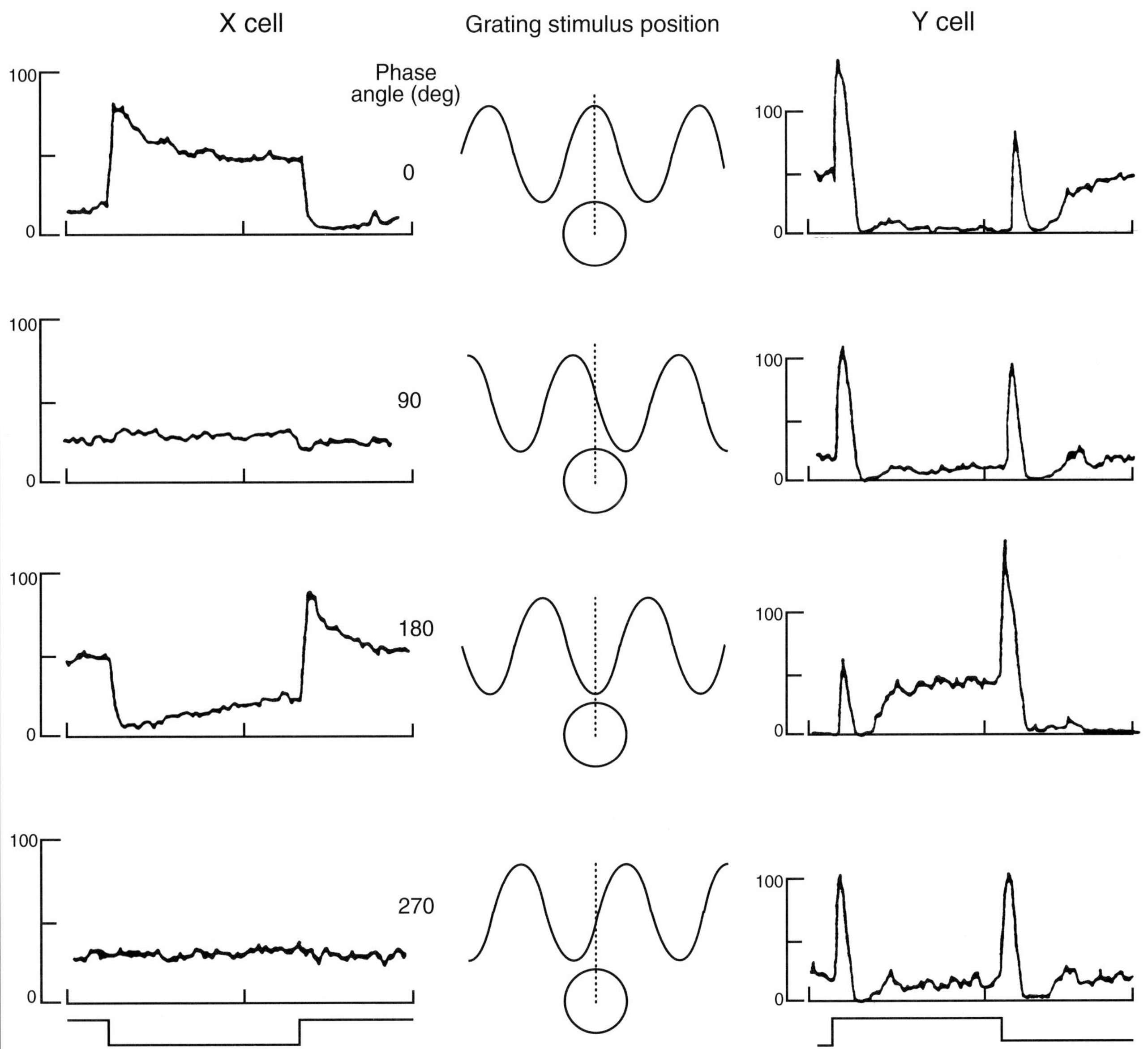

FIGURE 28.4 Visual responses of X and Y cells to contrast-reversing sine-wave gratings at different spatial phases (different positions, indicating schematically in the middle column). The visual responses, in spikes per second, are shown as poststimulus time histograms synchronized to the repetitive stimulus; the length of the abscissa is 2 s. Upward deflection of the lowest trace indicates introduction of the grating pattern (contrast on), and downward deflection indicates removal of the pattern (contrast off, but no change in mean luminance). Adapted from Enroth-Cugell and Robson.[20]

view is that the large, nonlinear receptive fields of Y cells make them well suited to detect change, while at the same time limiting their ability to signal the exact location or nature of the stimulus. According to this view, X cells are better at localizing more specific stimulus features.

Primate Ganglion Cells Project to Three Subdivisions of the LGN: Parvocellular, Magnocellular, and Koniocellular

Primates also have a number of different classes of retinal ganglion cells, each with distinct cellular morphology, projection patterns, and visual response properties. Here, we will concentrate only on ganglion cells that project to the LGN. There are many differences between primate species (nocturnal versus diurnal, Old World versus New World); for this discussion, we will concentrate on the macaque, a diurnal, Old World primate. The macaque visual system has been extensively studied with anatomical, physiological, and behavioral methods. Most importantly, macaque vision is very similar to human vision.[25]

The most numerous class of ganglion cells in the macaque retina is sometimes referred to as P cells, so-called because they project to the dorsal-most layers of the LGN, the **parvocellular layers** (small cells). The M cells, which project to the two ventral layers of the LGN, the **magnocellular layers** (large cells), constitute a second class of retinal neurons. P and M cells have distinct morphologies (Fig. 28.2). P cells (also known as, confusingly, midget ganglion cells) have very small dendritic fields. M cells (also known as parasol cells) have much larger dendritic fields. Finally, members of a third class of retinal cells project to the **intercalated layers** between the principal parvocellular and magnocellular layers. These intercalated layers are also termed **koniocellular** (dustlike, or tiny cells). There are roughly 1,000,000 P cells in the retina and parvocellular neurons in the LGN; there are 100,000 M and magnocellular neurons. Although the intercalated layers appear quite sparse and thin in standard histological sections, there are as many intercalated cells as there are magnocellular cells.[26] Because of their size and location, the intercalated cells have been difficult to study and little is known about them in the macaque. In the following section, we will discuss the distinct functional properties of the P and M pathways.

The P and M Pathways Have Different Response Properties

As noted above, the receptive field properties of the LGN relay cells match closely those of their retinal afferents. But the two parallel pathways, P → parvocellular and M → magnocellular, are quite different. Five main characteristics distinguish the responses of P cells and M cells[27–32] (see Figs. 28.5 and 28.6). (1) P-cell receptive fields are smaller than M-cell receptive fields at the same retinal position. (2) M-cell axons conduct impulses faster than P-cell axons. (3) The responses of P cells to a prolonged visual stimulus, particularly a color stimulus, can be very sustained, whereas M cells tend to respond more transiently. (4) Most P cells are sensitive to the color of a stimulus; M cells are not (Figs. 28.5A–28.5C). (5) M cells are much more sensitive than P cells to low-contrast stimuli (Fig. 28.5D). These last two differences, which have strong implications for the functional role of these pathways, are discussed below.

Color-Selective Responses in the P Pathway Are Derived from Antagonistic Inputs from L and M Cones

Color vision (see Box 28.3) depends on the distinct sensitivities of the three classes of cone photoreceptors to different wavelengths of light (the rods are active only under low light levels and are not involved in color vision). Although we are able to make very fine distinctions between different wavelengths, it is important to emphasize that each of the light-sensitive pigments in the three cone classes is sensitive to a broad range of wavelengths. The spectral sensitivities of these pigments overlap considerably (Fig. 28.6A). Consequently, the names sometimes used for these pigments—red-, green-, and blue-sensitive—are inaccurate. For instance, the "red" pigment is most sensitive to light whose wavelength is 564 nm, or yellow, but

FIGURE 28.5 Visual responses of magnocellular and parvocellular neurons in the macaque. (A) Responses of a color-opponent (red-on/green-off) parvocellular neuron to small and large stimuli. For small spots, roughly the size of the receptive-field center, the neuron was excited by both red and white and was weakly inhibited by blue. The responses to large spots were more selective. Red was excitory, blue was strongly inhibitory, and white stimuli were ineffective. (B) Responses of the same red-on/green-off parvocellular neuron to different wavelengths of light. For small spots, the neuron was excited (X) for a broad range of wavelengths. For large spots, it was excited above 550 nm, from yellow to red, and inhibited (△) below 550 nm, from blue to green. (C) Responses of a magnocellular neuron to different wavelengths of light presented in the receptive-field center. The neuron had off (△) responses at all wavelengths; i.e., no wavelength specificity was found. (D) Average contrast response functions of P (●) and M (○) cells, measured in spikes per second. P cells respond poorly to low contrasts and do not saturate at high contrasts. M cells respond better to low contrasts and saturate by 20–30%. (A–C) From Wiesel and Hubel.[28] (D) From Kaplan and Shapley.[32]

A

Light

Parvocellular red on

Red
640 nm

Red

Blue
480 nm

Blue

White

White

B

Parvocellular red on

Small spot

Big spot

Log sensitivity

3
2
1
0

400
500
600
700 nm

Wavelength

C

Magnocellular broad band

Log sensitivity

3
2
1
0

400
500
600
700 nm

Wavelength

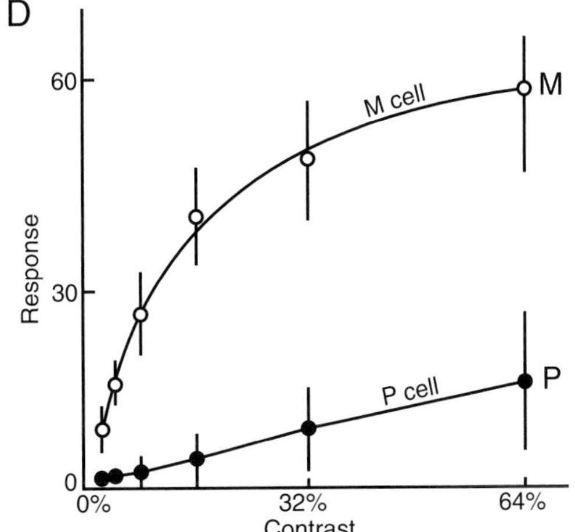

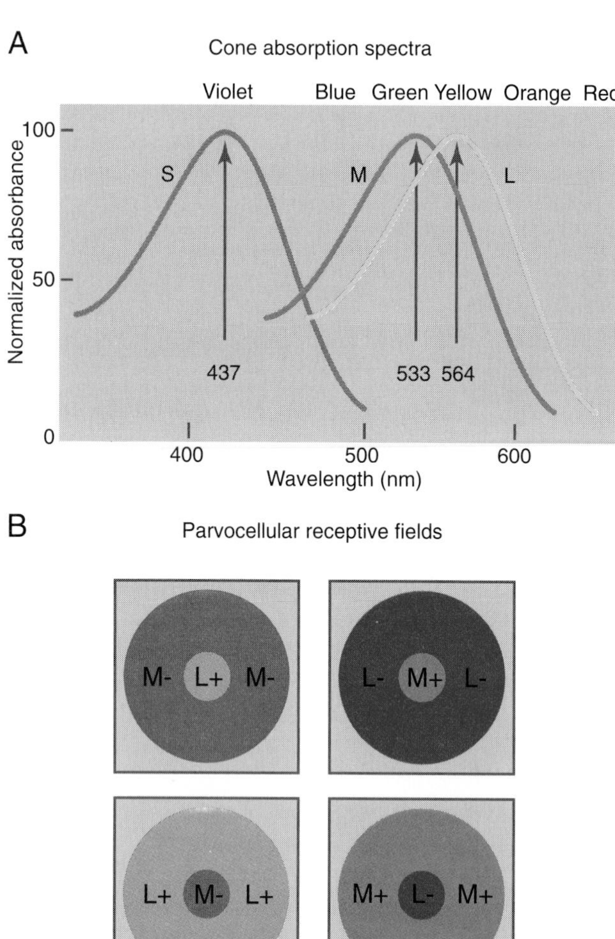

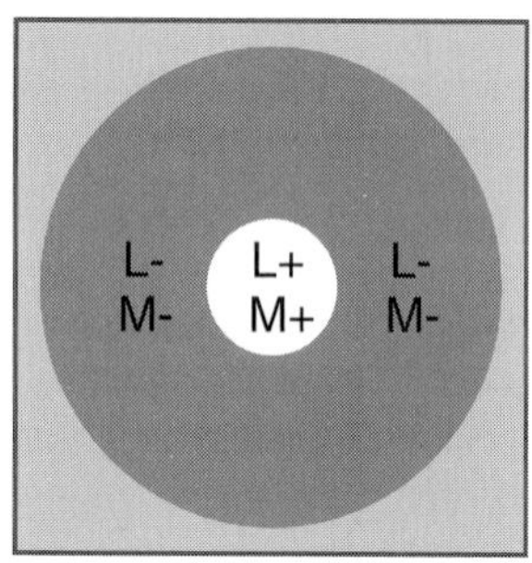

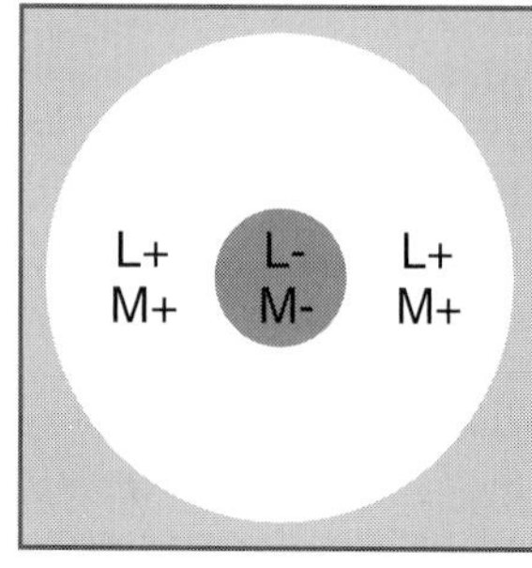

FIGURE 28.6 Aspects of color vision. (A) Absorption spectra of the three cone photoreceptors in humans: long-, middle-, and short-wavelength sensitive (L, M, and S). The L and the M cones in particular are sensitive to overlapping ranges of wavelengths. (B) Receptive field of the four types of red-green parvocellular cells in the macaque (labeled L+ and M+ or L− and M−, according to their on or off centers, respectively). Classically, these small receptive fields have been described as receiving antagonistic input from L cones in the centers and M cones in their surrounds, or vice versa. When probed with color stimuli, L-on center and the M-off center cells are excited by red and inhibited by green (and some blues: see Fig. 28.5A). M-on and L-off cells are excited by green and inhibited by red. When probed with small white spots, L-on and M-on cells are excited when the stimulus is turned off. (C) Receptive fields of the two main types of magnocellular cells. These larger receptive fields receive mixed L and M input to both center and surround. There are two types: on-center (M+L+) and off-center (L−M−).

is also quite sensitive at the 533-nm peak of the "green" pigment. A much more accurate terminology, one that identifies the relative sensitivities of the three pigment absorption spectra, is now usually employed: long-, middle-, and short-wavelength sensitive (or L, M, and S cones).

Because green light will excite both long- and middle-wavelength cones, the color green can be distinguished only by the fact that it excites middle-wavelength more strongly than it excites long-wavelength cones. This distinction can be made by neurons that are sensitive to the difference between the signals from two cone classes, or neurons that are **color-opponent.** In the retina and LGN, there are two categories of color-opponent ganglion cells: red-green and blue-yellow (yellow is made of the sum of long- and middle-wavelength cone signals). These are sometimes also termed red-minus-green cells and blue-minus-yellow cells. The most numerous color-opponent neurons in the primate retina are the red-green opponent P cells. These cells receive antagonistic input from the long- and middle-wavelength-sensitive (L and M) cones.

Near the fovea, the center of the retina, a P cell (also known as a midget ganglion cell) receives input from a single midget bipolar. The midget bipolar in turn receives input from a single cone (Fig. 28.2). This arrangement ensures not only that the center of the ganglion cell's receptive field is as small as possible but also that the center receives input from only one cone type, L or M. Classically,[27-29] the antagonistic surround of these P cells (or their counterparts in the LGN) has been thought to be dominated by the other main cone class, M or L, respectively. Although the exact nature of the surround in red-green P cells has been somewhat controversial,[33,34] this classical view is shown in Fig. 28.6B.

There are four different types of red-green opponent P cells in the retina (Fig. 28.6B), and hence parvocellular neurons in the LGN. L-on center and M-off center cells are excited by red and inhibited by green (and some blues; see Fig. 28.5A). M-on and L-off cells are excited by green and inhibited by red. As Wiesel and Hubel showed,[28] parvocellular neurons in the LGN are sensitive to small bright spots presented in their receptive field centers, but they are most *color-selective* when larger stimuli are used (see Figs. 28.5A and 28.5B). This is because only larger stimuli are effective in stimulat-

BOX 28.3

INHERITED AND ACQUIRED DEFECTS OF COLOR VISION: RETINAL AND CORTICAL MECHANISMS

Inherited defects of color vision have been studied for over 200 years, originally with psychophysical methods but more recently with the tools of molecular genetics. Normal color vision is **trichromatic** (literally, three-colored), because there are three different classes of cone photoreceptors. The most common form of color vision defect is found in trichromats with one or more abnormal, or anomalous, cone pigments. More severe defects are found in **dichromats,** who lack a single cone type entirely. The current terminology for the three types of dichromacy was proposed by von Kries in 1897: **protanopia** (literally, the first type of blindness, or "red-blindness"), **deuteranopia** (second type, or "green-blindness"), and **tritanopia** (third type, or "blue-blindness"). Dichromats are unable to make certain color distinctions, but only the very rare **monochromats**—people with one cone type or only rods—are truly color blind.

The genetics of red-green defects have long been known to be X-linked: they are inherited from the mother and are fairly common in men, but they are uncommon in women. Roughly 2% of European males are protanopes or deuteranopes and, depending on the population, between 2 and 6% are either protanomalous or, more commonly, deuteranomalous. By contrast, only 0.4% of women in similar populations have red-green defects. Tritanopia, found equally in men and women, is significantly rarer. It is inherited as an autosomal dominant trait thought to occur at low frequencies, estimated variously between 1 in 500 and 1 in over 10,000.

Because of the overlap in cone pigments, inherited color vision defects are not as simple as terms such as "red blindness" might suggest. In broad terms, protanopes and deuteranopes are unable to make specific discriminations along the red-green axis. Depending on the defect, they are unable to distinguish certain reds and greens from gray or from each other. Tritanopes are unable to discrimi-

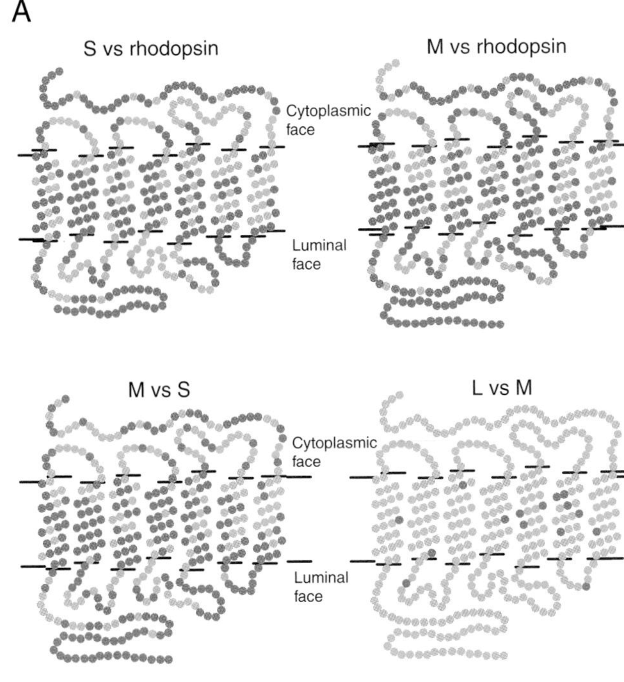

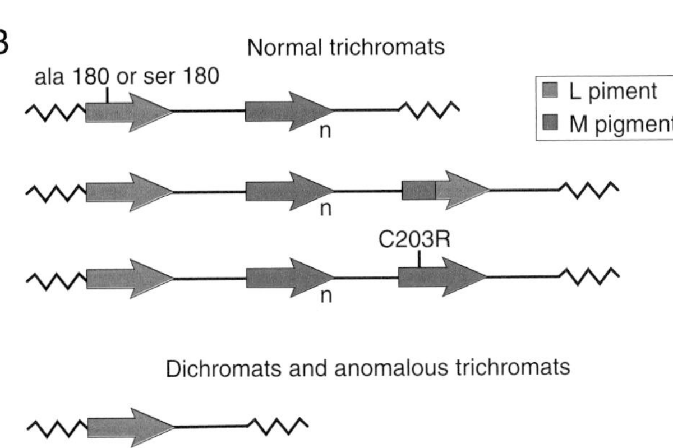

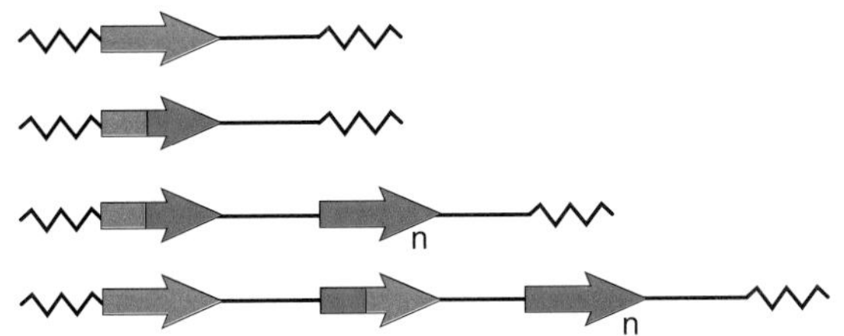

FIGURE 28.7 Molecular biology of the photopigment genes. (A) Transmembrane model of the cone photopigments. The homologies between the different photopigments are shown, with differences between proteins in gray. The amino acid sequences of the M and S cone pigments and rhodopsin are all approximately 40% identical (and 75% homologous), whereas the L and M pigments are 96% identical (99% homologous). (B) Structure of the portion of the X chromosome coding for the L and the M pigments. Normally, there is one L-pigment gene and several M-pigment genes. Because not all of these genes are expressed, a number of variants result in normal color vision (top). Many different patterns of recombination and deletion can be associated with a defect in red-green vision: either dichromacy or anomalous trichromacy (bottom). (A) From Nathans *et al.*[35] (B) From Nathans.[36]

nate between colors with and without a short-wavelength component, such as between gray and certain shades of violet or yellow.

In 1986, Nathans, Hogness, and colleagues[35] cloned and sequenced the three cone pigment genes and related them to color defects in humans. The cloning strategy was based on the predicted close homology between the pigments and rhodopsin (Fig. 28.7B).[36] As expected from the genetics of protanopia and deuteranopia, two very similar genes for the L and the M pigments were found on the X chromosome (see Fig. 28.7B). The third gene, which codes for the S pigment, was found on chromosome 7. In subsequent work by this group and others, the molecular genetics of the inherited color defects, including anomalous trichromacy, have been studied in great detail.

Although the inherited color deficiencies are fairly simple and well understood, acquired defects in color vision—found in a number of ocular, neurological, and systemic diseases—are far more varied. One such syndrome, cerebral achromatopsia, was described in the neurological literature in the 1880s. In rare patients with certain cortical lesions, color discrimination and color naming were severely impaired. In the majority of cases, there were other associated deficits—either an area of complete blindness (a **scotoma**) or an inability to recognize faces (**prosopagnosia;** see Chapter 52)—but in some cases vision was otherwise quite normal. From the location of the lesions, some neurologists early on inferred the existence of a color vision "center" near the inferior border of the primary visual cortex (V1).

The literature of cerebral achromatopsia, quite developed in the late 19th century, fell into eclipse for the first half of the 20th century when highly specific functional divisions of the cortex were questioned.[37] With the discovery in the 1970s of multiple visual areas in primate cerebral cortex, however, the existence of a cortical region devoted to color in humans seemed less farfetched. Thus, the same neurological findings that were once greeted with skepticism are now widely accepted, although some controversy remains over the identity of the color region in humans and its homology to regions in the brains of nonhuman primates.

ing simultaneously the color-opponent center and surround. As noted above, single cones are not very color-selective. Parvocellular neurons are most color-selective when the stimulus evokes antagonistic influences from two cone classes, one found in the center and the other found only in the surround (Fig. 28.6).

M Cells Are Highly Sensitive to Contrast

Because of their marked color sensitivity and small receptive fields, P cells have long been thought to be involved with our ability to make color discriminations and to see the finest details. When tested with black-and-white stimuli, however, P cells respond to low contrast very poorly compared to M cells. In a study that used quantitative methodology similar to Enroth-Cugell and Robson's (see Box 28.2), Kaplan and Shapley[32] measured the responses of P cells and M cells to sine-wave gratings of various contrasts (Fig. 28.5D). **Contrast** is defined as the fractional change in luminance, divided by the mean. Perceptually, we are able to see stimuli that have less than 1% contrast. Kaplan and Shapley found that M cells often responded well to contrasts of under 5% and that they gave their strongest responses at contrasts as low as 20%. P cells tended to respond poorly to contrasts below 10%, a stimulus that is easily visible, and rarely reached their strongest responses below 64%. Kaplan and Shapley concluded that our ability to see low contrasts is due primarily to the M-cell system.

The relatively poor sensitivity of P cells to low-contrast stimuli is not well understood,[38] but it may be partially the result of two factors: receptive-field centers receive input from a very small region of the retina, and the inputs from different cone classes are subtracted from each other, rather than added together. Whatever the reason, the poor performance of the P pathway in detecting low contrast implies an important role for M cells in the detection of the form of objects (which is robust at low contrasts), in addition to their well-known role in the motion pathway (discussed later).

Summary

The retina, part of the central nervous system, is a self-contained neuronal circuit whose anatomy and physiology have been studied in great detail. There are five types of cells in the retina. Photoreceptors, bipolar cells, and ganglion cells constitute the direct, feedforward pathway. Horizontal cells and amacrine cells subserve lateral interactions in the retina. Photoreceptors are all hyperpolarized by light, but bipolar cells can be either hyperpolarized (off cells) or depolarized by light (on cells). Bipolar cells provide the main excitatory input to retinal ganglion cells and thereby determine their on or off responses. There is a great variety of retinal ganglion cells, but most have an antagonistic center–surround organization. In the primate, the two best-studied classes of ganglion cells are P cells and M cells, which project to the parvocellular and magnocellular layers of the LGN, respectively. P cells have small receptive fields, are sensitive to the color of a stimulus, and are relatively insensitive to low-contrast black-and-white stimuli. M cells have larger receptive fields, are insensitive to color, and are very sensitive to low contrasts.

THE RETINOGENICULOCORTICAL PATHWAYS

Visual Information Is Relayed to Cortex via the Lateral Geniculate Nucleus

In mammals with forward-facing eyes, such as most carnivores and the primates, the retinal axons are routed so that visual information from the same points in space coming from the two eyes can be combined. From both eyes, ganglion cells whose receptive fields are in one half of the visual world project to the opposite cerebral hemisphere (Fig. 28.8).[39] This cross-routing occurs at the optic chiasm (from the Greek letter chi, χ). Here, axons from the medial (nasal, or nearer the nose) half of one retina crossover to join the axons from the lateral (temporal, or nearer the temples) half of the other retina. In other words, the temporal retina projects to the ipsilateral (same-side) hemipshere and the nasal retina projects to the contralateral (opposite-side) hemisphere. Unlike somatic sensation, which is entirely crossed (see Chapter 26), only half of the retinal axons cross. Like somatic sensation, however, the crossing of retinal axons results in each half of the external visual world being represented in the opposite cerebral hemisphere. In mammals whose eyes face laterally, such as rodents, most axons from each eye project to the contralateral hemipshere, although some fibers from a sliver of temporal retina project ipsilaterally.

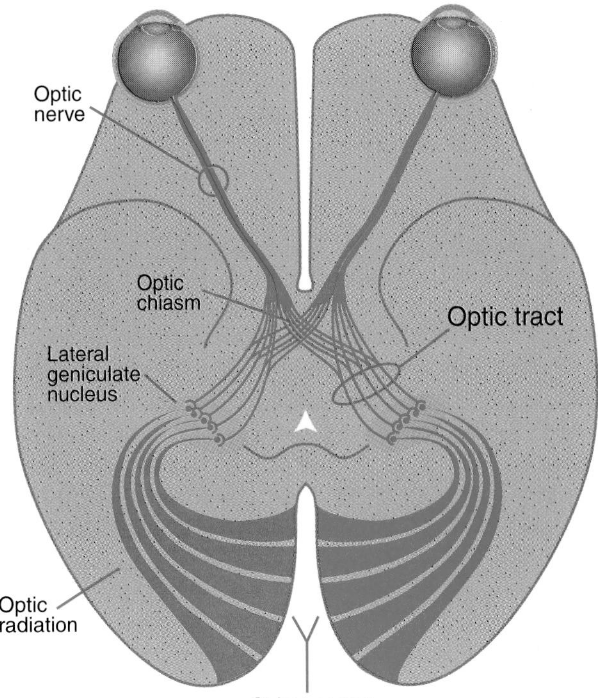

FIGURE 28.8 The retinogeniculocortical pathway in the human. Optic nerve axons from the nasal retina cross at the optic chiasm and join axons from the temporal retina of the other eye. Together, these contralateral and ipsilateral axons make up the optic tract, which projects to the LGN. Each of the six layers of the LGN receives input from only one eye. Axons from the LGN make up the optic radiations, which project to the striate cortex. Adapted from Polyak.[39]

The LGN Is a Layered Structure That Receives Segregated Input from the Two Eyes

As they leave the optic chiasm, retinal axons from the two eyes travel together in the optic tract, which terminates in the LGN of the thalamus (Fig. 28.8). The LGN is composed of layers—the number varies between species—each of which receives input from only one eye. In the macaque, the six principal layers contain most of the relay cells to primary visual cortex (Fig. 28.9).[40] The four parvocellular layers are found dorsally. They receive P-cell input from the two eyes in the order contra, ipsi, contra, ipsi. The magnocellular layers are found more ventrally. They receive M-cell input in the order ipsi, contra. Interposed between these principal layers are the intercalated layers, populated by koniocellular neurons. The retinal inputs to the koniocellular neurons are not well studied.

In the cat, the LGN has only two principal layers, called A and A1, which receive input from the contralateral and ipsilateral retinas, respectively. The neurons are again quite similar to either the retinal X cells or Y cells that innervate them. Cells that correspond to the koniocellular pathway (known as W cells) in the cat are found in the C laminae, which are ventral to layers A and A1.

The Primary Visual Cortex in the Cat Is an Example of a Functional Hierarchy

Cat primary visual cortex (Brodmann's area 17) is perhaps the best understood neocrotical area in any

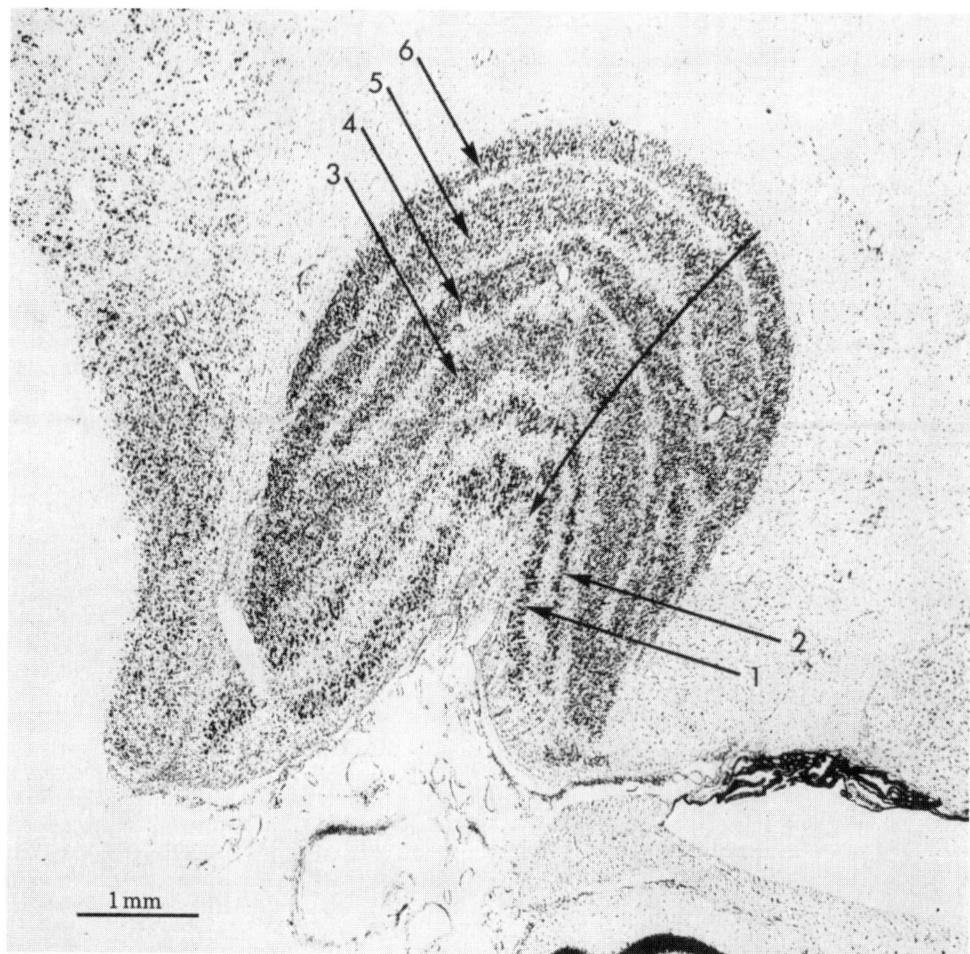

FIGURE 28.9 The six-layered LGN of the macaque monkey. The top four parvocellular layers (6, 5, 4, and 3) received input from the two eyes in the order contra, ipsi, contra, ipsi. The bottom two magnocellular layers (2 and 1) receive ipsi and contra input, respectively. In between these principal layers are the intercalated or koniocellular layers. The arrow from layer 6 to 1 indicates the organization of the precisely aligned retinotopic maps of the six layers. The receptive fields of neurons found along this line are located at the same position in visual space. From Hubel and Wiesel.[40]

species. The first studies of Hubel and Wiesel[41,42] form the foundation of this understanding. Hubel and Wiesel found cells whose responses differed dramatically from those in the retina and thalamus. Many of these cells could be excited by stimuli presented to either eye. Primary visual cortex thus represents the first level of the visual system at which binocular interactions could form a substrate for depth perception. Most strikingly, Hubel and Wiesel found that the vast majority of cortical cells responded best to linear contours of a specific orientation and gave no response at the orthogonal orientation. This was in sharp contrast to cells in the retina and LGN, which were not selective for orientation.

Hubel and Wiesel described two broad classes of neurons in area 17, simple cells and complex cells (see Box 28.4).[43–48] Both classes were orientation-selective; simple cells achieved this selectivity by having elongated on and off subregions, but the mechanism used by complex cells was less readily apparent. In their model of visual cortical organization, Hubel and Wiesel proposed that simple cells receive direct input from relay cells in the lateral geniculate nucleus (Fig. 28.10E). These simple cells would then project to complex cells to form a higher-order representation of the stimulus (Fig. 28.10F).

This original model is hierarchical or serial; information flows from one level to the next in a well-defined series. In contrast to this serial model of cortical processing, it has also been proposed that each region of the cerebral cortex is made up of several different streams of information that are all processed in paral-

BOX 28.4

HUBEL AND WIESEL'S STUDIES OF SIMPLE AND COMPLEX CELLS IN CAT VISUAL CORTEX

In experiments inspired by Kuffler's successful analysis of ganglion cell receptive fields, Hubel and Wiesel began the first of their many studies of visual cortex in the late 1950s. In their earliest experiments they used visual stimuli created by making spots on glass slides and projecting them onto a screen. Although such stimuli had worked well in the retina, cortical neurons were rarely responsive to them. When all else had failed, they noted that one cell responded best when a slide was being removed from their projection system. The edge of the glass slide projected a thin black line onto the screen and this turned out to excite the cell.[43]

Beginning with this serendipitous observation, Hubel and Wiesel went on to find that in fact most cells in visual cortex responded to elongated bars or edges. Moreover, the responses of each of these neurons depended strongly on the orientation of the stimulus. Each neuron had an orientation that evoked strong responses, but it responded poorly or not at all to stimuli at other orientations or to unoriented stimuli, such as round spots. These orientation-selective neurons came in two varieties, termed simple and complex cells[41,42] (see Movshon *et al.*[44,45] for an analysis of these categories within the quantitative framework outlined in Box 28.2). The receptive fields of simple cells were well segmented into on and off subregions (Figs. 28.10C and 28.10D). In these receptive-field subregions, responses were evoked by turning a light stimulus on or off, but not by both.

Given these well-defined on and off subregions in simple cells, Hubel and Wiesel suggested a straightforward hierarchical model to explain orientation selectivity. On-center neurons in the lateral geniculate nucleus whose receptive fields fall in a row could all converge to excite a specific simple cell (Fig. 28.10E). This simple cell would thus have an elongated on subregion with a pronounced orientation bias. Although this model has generated much controversy over the ensuing years, many of its elements have been demonstrated directly.[46–48]

The second class of cortical neurons, complex cells, also responded best to oriented stimuli, but their receptive fields were not elongated along a preferred orientation, nor were they found to be divided into distinct on and off subregions. It would therefore be difficult to imagine how the responses of these neurons could be constructed directly from the unoriented (or weakly oriented) input from the thalamus. Given the properties of simple cells, Hubel and Wiesel proposed a hierarchical scheme. Complex cells receive their orientation selectivity from convergent input from simple cells whose receptive fields have the same orientation preference, but have different spatial locations (Fig. 28.10F). The extent to which this model explains the behavior of complex cells remains an open question.

---

lel. As with most dichotomies, elements of both hierarchical and parallel processing have been found in the visual cortex of all mammals studied. For simplicity, an outline of the organization of visual cortex in the cat is here discussed in terms of a hierarchical model. Parallel processing will be illustrated with the example of primate visual cortex.

In terms of their probable function in perception, the receptive fields of complex cells furnish an early example of what was meant in the introduction by a higher-order representation. Complex cells convey information about orientation to later stages of processing, but that information has been combined and generalized. A simple cell responds to an oriented stimulus of a specific configuration and a specific location; in partiuclar, it has separate on and off subregions. A complex cell also responds to stimuli at one orientation, but the receptive field is not segregated into on and off subregions. Instead, it can respond to a light or dark stimulus of the correct orientation, independent of the exact location of the stimulus within the receptive field. This sort of generalization is a recurrent theme in the cortical processing of visual information (discussed later).

The hierarchical (serial) scheme has received support from several correlations between anatomy and physiology of area 17. In broad terms, simple cells are more common in the layers of cortex that receive direct input from the thalamus (layer 4 and to a lesser extent layer 6). Complex cells are found more frequently in layers that are more distant from the thalamic input[49]: in layers 2 + 3, which receive input primarily from layer 4, and in layer 5, which receives most of its input from layers 2 + 3 (Fig. 28.11).[52a]

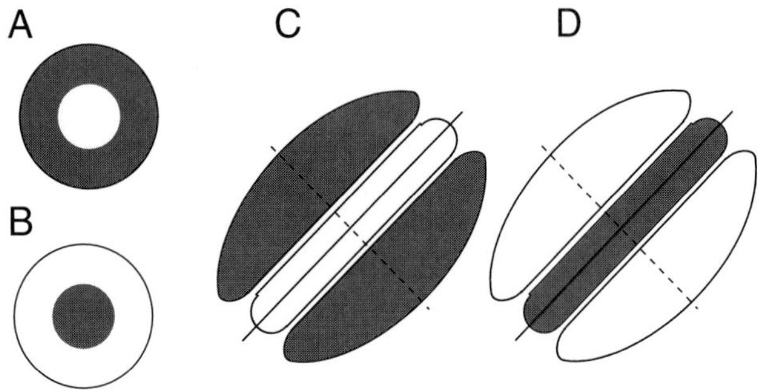

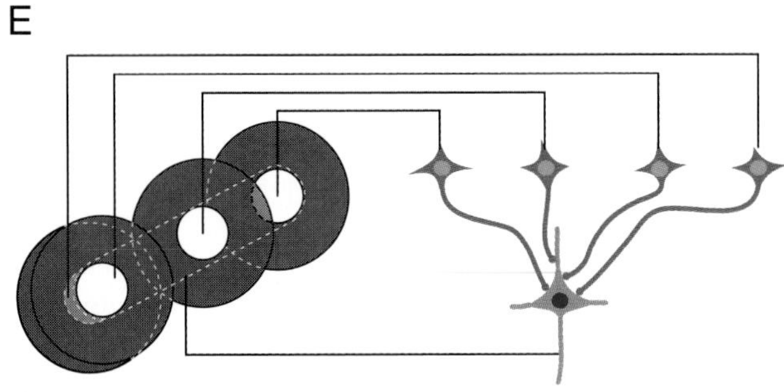

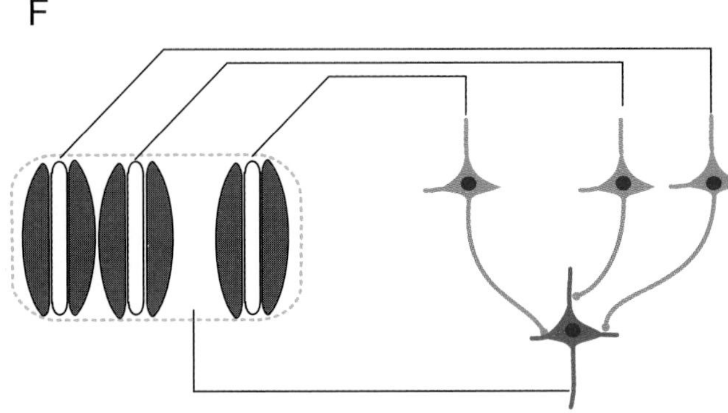

FIGURE 28.10 Hubel and Wiesel's original models of visual cortical hierarchy. (A,B) Receptive field maps of center–surround receptive fields in LGN. White, on responses; dark gray, off responses. (C,D) Receptive field maps of simple cells. (E) Model of convergent input from LGN neurons onto cortical simple cell. (F) Model of convergent input from simple cells onto complex cells. Adapted from Hubel and Wiesel.[42]

Several Parallel Streams Are Found in Macaque Primary Visual Cortex

In the macaque primary visual cortex (V1, or striate cortex), a hierarchical organization is certainly present, but there are also clearly several parallel streams. As we discussed above, at least three types of inputs to visual cortex (parvocellular, magnocellular, and koniocellular) are first segregated within the lateral geniculate nucleus. Each class of neurons projects to a specific subdivision of primary visual cortex. Most thalamic afferents terminate in layer 4C, which is split into two divisions. 4Cα receives its input from magnocellular neurons and 4Cβ from parvocellular neurons. Intercalated, or koniocellular, geniculate neurons project to layers 2 + 3, specifically to "blob" regions, discussed later, that stain densely for the enzyme cytochrome oxidase.[50–52,62a]

Thus, visual information from functionally and anatomically distinct M and P retinal neurons is kept separate through the LGN and at least up to the cortical neurons that receive direct thalamic input. The degree to which these pathways are kept separate within visual cortex remains an area of active research.

Functional Architecture Can Be Seen in the Columnar Structure of Visual Cortex

So far, the physiology of the visual cortex has been considered in terms of individual neurons and their response properties. Another major contribution of Hubel and Wiesel was their demonstration that cells with similar receptive field properties tended to be found near each other in the cortex. Further, they found that physiological response properties, such as orientation selectivity, were organized in an orderly fashion across the cortical surface. They termed the relationship between the anatomy and physiology the *functional architecture* of visual cortex.

Hubel and Wiesel's key observation in this arena was that as an electrode is advanced through the depth of the cortex, all neurons encountered have similar response properties. If a cell near the surface has a specific orientation and is dominated by input from one eye, then cells below it share these preferences. This finding is consistent with the idea, proposed by Lorente de Nó,[53] that the fundamental unit in cortical architecture is a vertically oriented column of neurons. Hubel and Wiesel proposed that a cortical column is both a physiological and an anatomical unit, as had Mountcastle[54] in his study of somatosensory cortex (see Chapter 26). A second observation was that the property of orientation preference varies smoothly over the cortical surface. If an electrode takes a tangential path through the cortex through many different columns, the orientation preference generally changes in a steady clockwise or counterclockwise progression, although occasionally there are discontinuous jumps (Fig. 28.12A).

In addition to orientation, at least two other parameters are mapped smoothly across the cortical surface. Cells in the visual cortex receive inputs from the two eyes in varying proportion, a property that Hubel and Wiesel termed **ocular dominance.** In tangential micro-

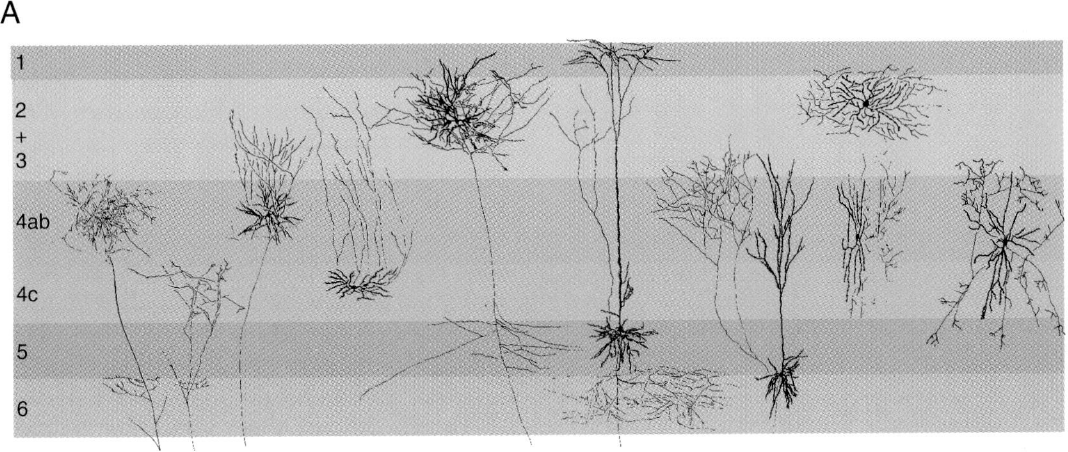

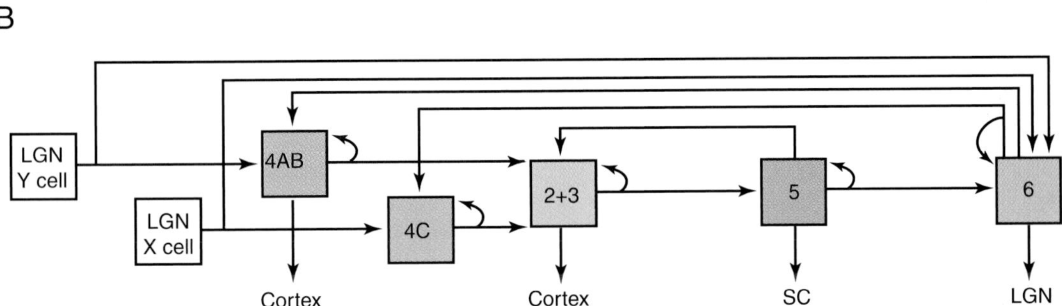

FIGURE 28.11 Circuitry of cat cortical area 17. (A) Morphology of individual cells stained with horseradish peroxidase. Thick lines, dendrites; thin lines, axons. (B) Schematic diagram of connections. Most thalamic (LGN) input is concentrated in layer 4 and to a lesser degree in layer 6. Y cells tend to project more superficially in layer 4 than do X cells (note that the sublayers 4AB and 4C are not strictly analogous to 4A, 4B, and 4C in the macaque). There is a fairly strict hierarchical pathway from layers 4 → 2 + 3 → 5 → 6 with feedback connections from 5 → 2 + 3 and 6 → 4. There are also many lateral connections between neurons within the same layer. Adapted from Gilbert and Wiesel.[52a]

electrode penetrations, cells are found that are successively dominated first by input from one eye and then the other are found. This provides evidence for **ocular dominant columns,** which have subsequently been demonstrated anatomically[55] as well as physiologically. Second, prior to Hubel and Wiesel's work, a precise map of visual space across the surface of the cortex had been demonstrated.[56,57] For any cortical column, receptive fields are all located at roughly the same position on the retina. Nearby columns represent nearby points in visual space in a precise and orderly arrangement. The position of a stimulus on the retina is termed its **retinotopy;** thus, a region of the brain (such as the superior colliculus, LGN, or the visual cortex) that maintains the relations between adjacent retinal regions is said to have a **retinotopic map.**

Given the existence of multiple functional maps, the obvious question is: How do these maps relate to each other? This question has been answered most definitely for the relationship between retinotopy and ocular dominance. Layer 4 in the primate is ideal for studying this question, because the receptive fields are quite small and the borders between ocular dominance columns are well defined. By making long, tangential penetrations through layer 4 of striate cortex, Hubel and Wiesel[40] found a precise interdigitating map from each eye. When eye dominance shifts, the receptive field location shifts to a point corresponding to the middle of the previous ocular dominance column (Fig. 28.12B). Thus, there is a 50% overlap in the spatial locations represented by adjacent ocular dominance columns. In this manner, a complete representation of space is attained for both eyes while ensuring that cells that respond to overlapping points in visual space are always nearby within the cortex.

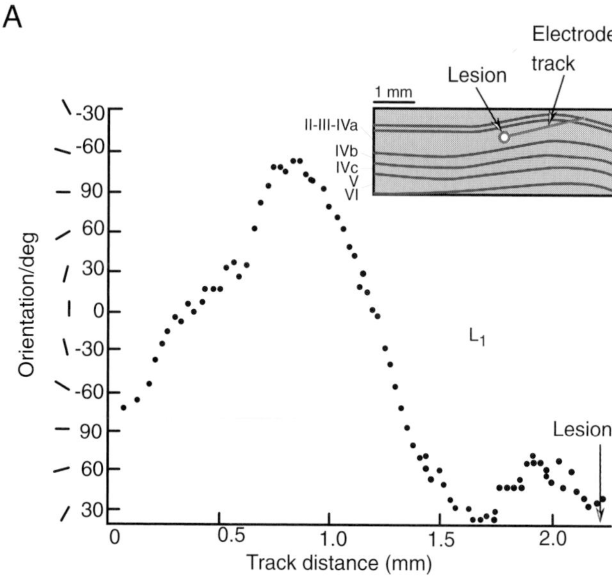

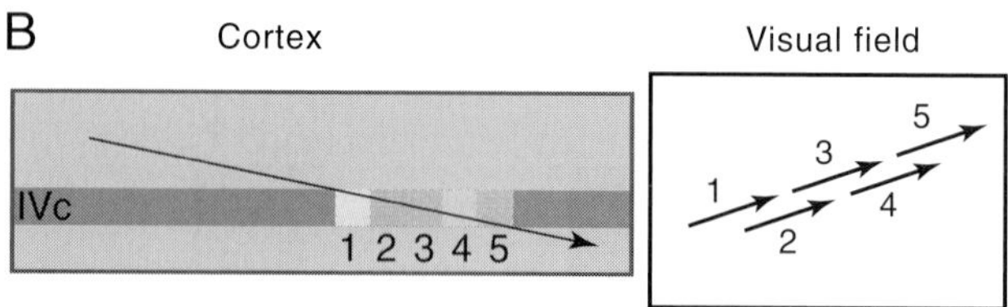

FIGURE 28.12 Two aspects of the functional architecture of macaque primary visual cortex. (A) Graph of the preferred orientation of neurons encountered in a long microelectrode penetration through layers 2 + 3 (inset). There was a steady, slow progression of preferred orientations, although there were a few positions where the orientations changed more rapidly. (B) Schematic diagram of the retinotopic positions of receptive fields encountered in layer 4C. At the border between ocular dominance columns (for instance between 1 and 2), the receptive location jumps back to a point represented near the middle of the previous ocular dominance column. There is a complete representation of visual space in columns dominated by each eye (1,3,5 or 2,4) and these representations are interleaved between the two sets of columns. Adapted from Hubel and Wiesel.[40]

Ocular Dominance and Orientation Columns Can Be Revealed with Optical Imaging

The technique of optical imaging has proven extremely useful in the study of the functional architecture of visual cortex. Optical imaging allows the direct visualization of the relative activity of small cortical ensembles, rather than relying on inferences made from single-unit studies. The technique produces pictures of regions where there is increased neural activity, with dyes that change color with neural activity or even in the absence of dyes.[58–62] When no dyes are used, brain activity is mapped with an intrinsic signal, caused primarily by changes in blood flow and blood oxygenation.

A typical optical imaging experiment works as follows (see Fig. 28.13).[58–61] First, a series of digitized images is taken of a region of visual cortex (~1 cm^2) while the animal is presented with visual stimuli through the left eye. Next, a similar series is captured during right-eye stimulation. When the right-eye images are digitally subtracted from the left-eye images, a striking picture that reveals the functional architecture of ocular dominance is created.

An important feature of optical imaging is that multiple images can be obtained from the same region of cortex. For instance, in addition to ocular dominance, maps of the preferred orientation can be made. Anatomical methods had been used to produce maps of ocular dominance prior to the advent of optical imaging,[55] and these maps appear similar to those found with optical imaging. Likewise, the orientation columns revealed by optical imaging were consistent with earlier microelectrode studies (compare Fig. 28.13e with Fig. 28.12A), but the images for the first time gave a detailed picture of the layout of orientation across the cortical surface. A useful way to present these data is in terms of a color code, in which each color represents a different preferred orientation (Fig. 28.13d). The details of these orientation maps were entirely new and could not have been predicted from previous techniques. In particular, orientation varied smoothly and continuously over some regions of cortex, but these regions were interrupted by linear fractures in the orientation map,[58] or by single points around which all orientations were seen ("pinwheels"[62]).

Cytochrome Oxidase Staining Reveals Blobs and Stripes in Cortical Areas V1 and V2

In the primate, there is a fourth feature of the functional architecture in addition to the retinotopy, orientation, and ocular dominance columns. When stained for the enzyme cytochrome oxidase, histological sections of V1 display striking patterns of high and low enzyme activity.[50,51] In superficial layers of V1 (layers 2 + 3), staining for cytochrome oxidase reveals a pattern of patches, or blobs, arranged in a gridlike fashion (Fig. 28.14). These blobs, which are the sites of termination of the koniocellular thalamic afferents,[62a] were reported to contain neurons whose receptive fields are color-selective, poorly oriented, and monocular,[52] although some later reports have challenged this view.

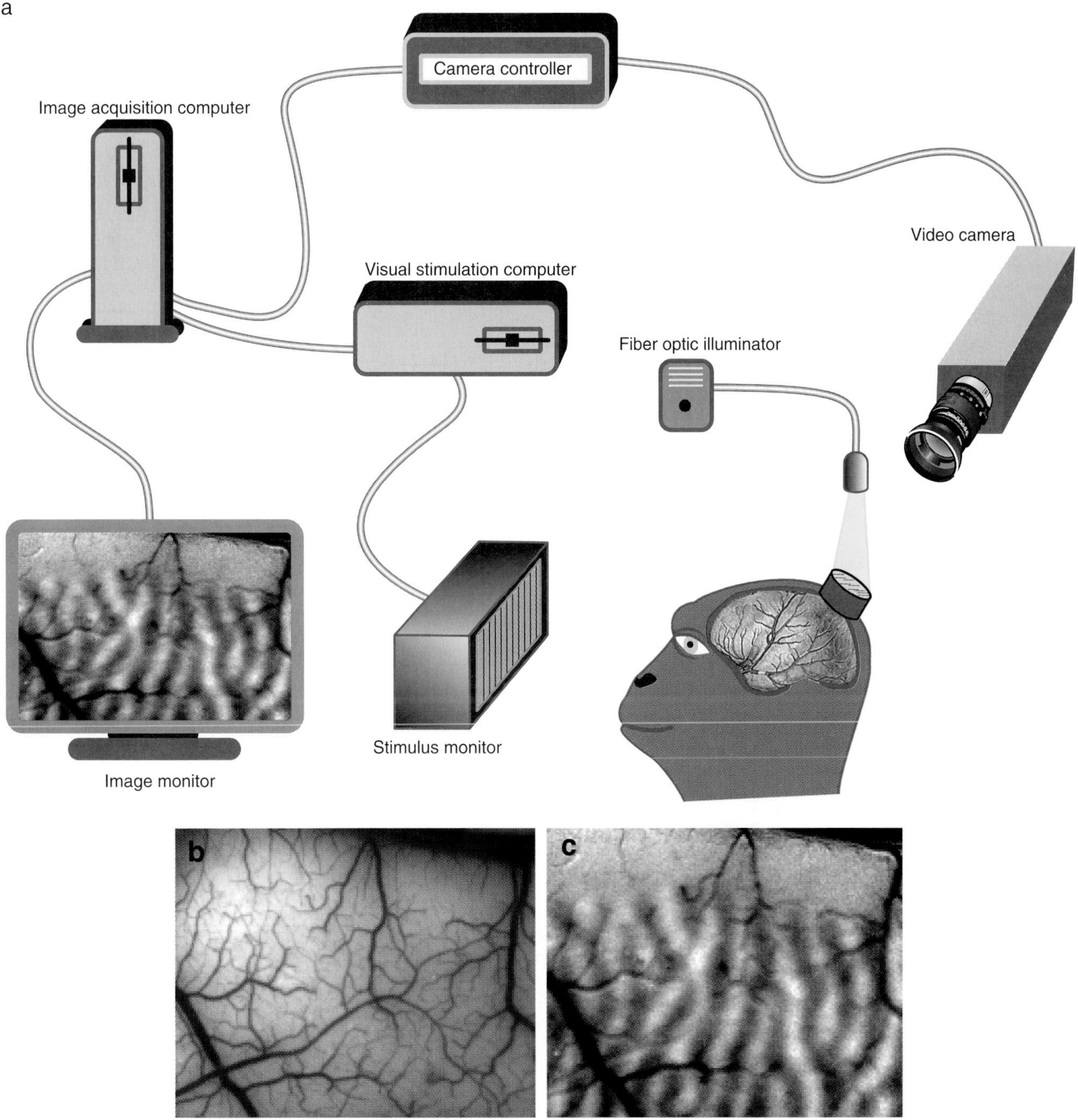

FIGURE 28.13 Optical imaging of functional architecture in primate visual cortex. (a) Schematic diagram of the experimental setup for optical imaging. Digitized images of a region of visual cortex (as in b) are taken with a CCD camera while the anesthetized, paralyzed animal is viewing a visual stimulus. These images are stored on a second computer for further analysis. (b) Individual image (9 × 6 mm) of a region of V1 and a portion of V2, taken with a special filter so that blood vessels stand out. (c) Ocular dominance map. Images of the brain during right-eye stimulation were digitally subtracted from images taken during left-eye stimulation. (*continued*)

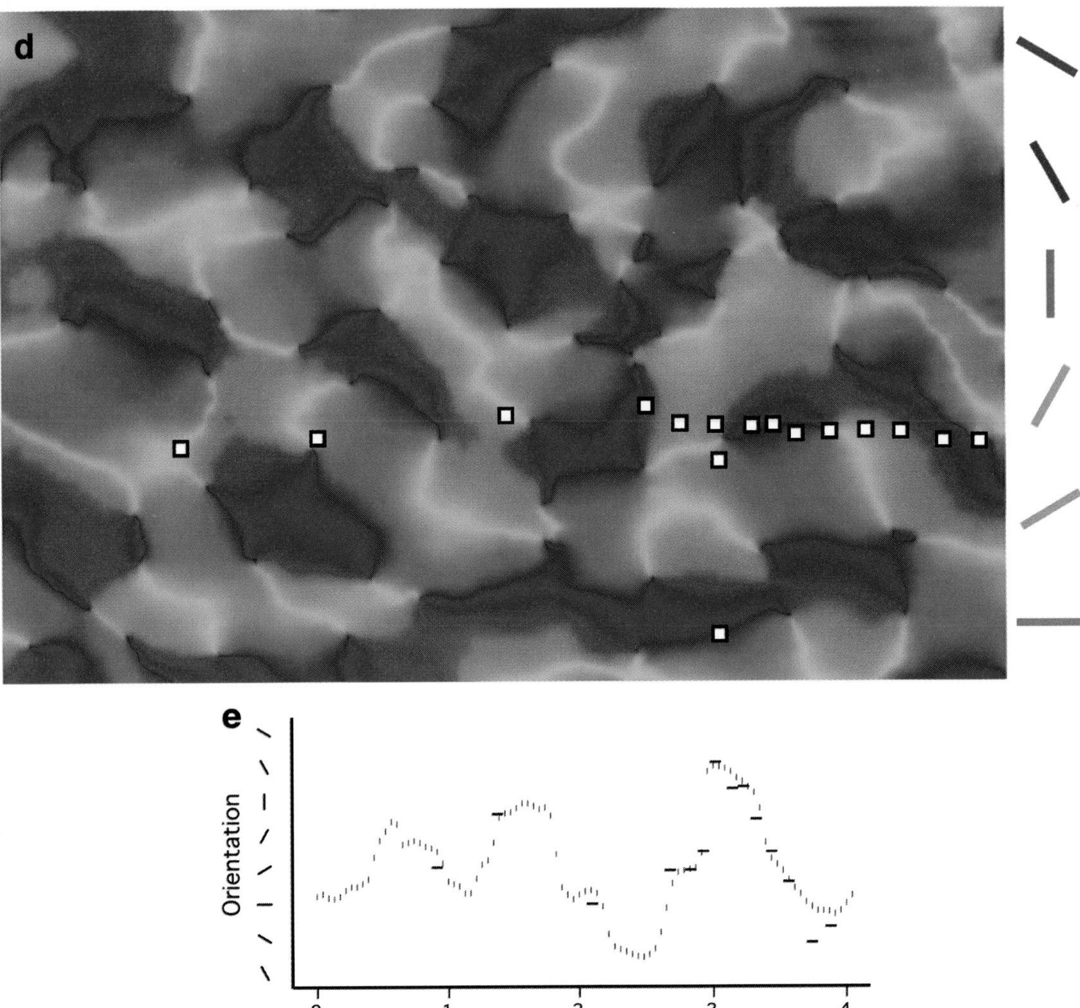

FIGURE 28.13 (*continued*) (d) Orientation map. Images of the brain were taken during stimulation at 12 different angles. The orientation of the stimuli that produced the strongest signal at each pixel are color coded. The key at right gives the correspondence between color and the optimal orientation. (e) Comparison of the preferred orientation of single neurons with the optical image. At each of the locations indicated by squares in (d), single neurons were recorded from with microelectrodes. The preferred orientations of the neurons (dashes) were compared with the preferred orientations measured in the optical image, sampled along the line connecting the recording sites (dots). (a) Adapted from Grinvald *et al.*[61] (b, c) Adapted from Ts'o *et al.*[60] (d,e) Adapted from Blasdel and Salama.[58]

In V2, the second visual area in the cerebral cortex (see below), cytochrome oxidase staining reveals regions of high and low activity arranged in parallel thin and thick stripes that are interrupted by unstained, inter-stripe regions (Fig. 28.14, along top). The anatomical connections between V1 and V2 are strongly constrained by the subdivisions revealed by cytochrome oxidase staining. Interblobs project to unstained stripes, blobs project to "thin" stained stripes, and neurons in layer 4B of V1 project to "thick" stained stripes.

The anatomy and physiology of the regions defined by cytochrome oxidase staining in V1 and V2 have since the early 1980s been the objects of much research, and of much controversy. Most importantly, the relationship between cytochrome oxidase staining and the magnocellular and parvocellular pathways is still an open question.[63–64] Consensus has been reached on one point, however: the magnocellular stream dominates the pathway from 4Cα to 4B in V1 and from there projects both directly and indirectly, via the thick stripes in V2, to regions of the brain that process visual

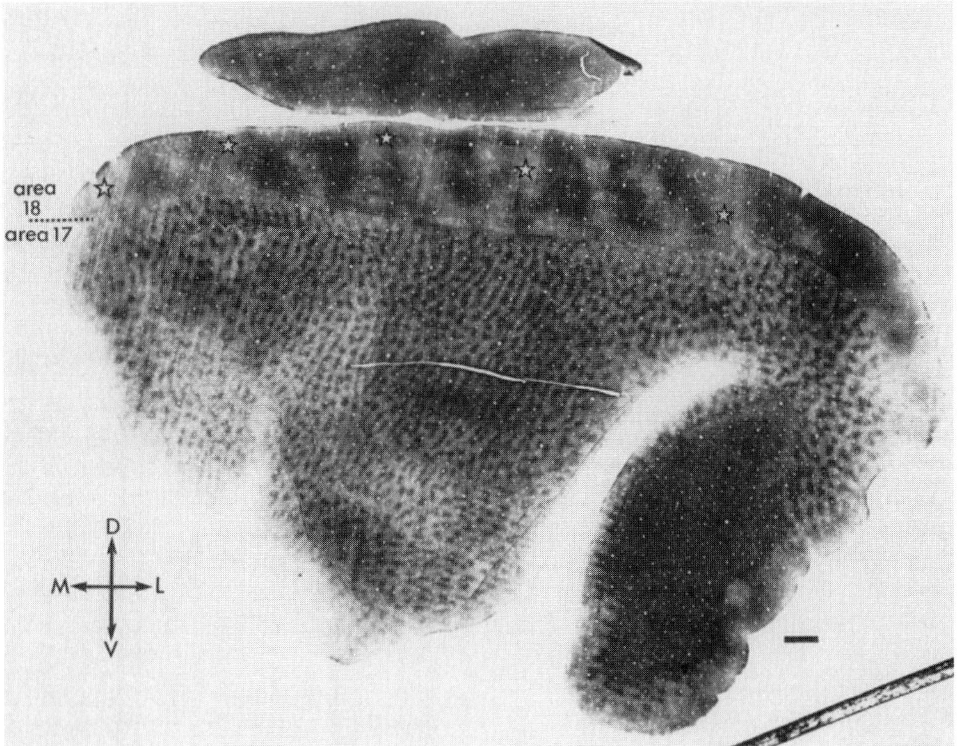

FIGURE 28.14 Macaque visual cortex stained for the metabolic enzyme cytochrome oxidase. Shown is a tangential section through layers of V1 or area 17 (below) and V2 or area 18 (above). In V1, "blobs" are seen in a roughly rectangular grid with a spacing of 400 nm. In V2, there are cytochrome oxidase-rich stripes with a much coarser spacing. The distinction between thick and thin stripes (see text) is less readily seen in the macaque than in the owl monkey. Scale bar: 1 mm. M, medial; L, lateral; D, dorsal; V, ventral. From Livingstone and Hubel.[52]

motion signals. Magnocellular neurons, with their rapidly conducting axons and high sensitivity to luminance contrast, are well suited to providing input to the motion-sensitive neurons in cortical areas MT and MST.

There Are Many Extrastriate Visual Areas That Perform Different Functions

In early studies of the cytoarchitecture of cerebral cortex, the visual cortex was divided into three areas according to Brodmann's classification: areas 17, 18, and 19. These divisions were based on differences in cell cytoarchitecture, or differences in the size, morphology, and distributions of cells within the six cortical laminae. Area 17 is primary visual cortex, or **striate cortex,** so named because of a heavily myelinated sublamina within layer 4, prominently visible as a stripe in transverse section. Areas 18 and 19 were known simply as visual association cortex. An assumption behind these designations was that areas defined by anatomical criteria would ultimately prove to be functionally specialized.

The existence of multiple visual cortical areas has been a significant discovery of the past quarter century in the field of sensory biology. A vast expanse of cerebral cortex—greater than 50% of the total in many primate species—is primarily or exclusively involved in the processing of visual information. The boundaries of striate cortex, or V1, have remained unchanged. **Extrastriate** cortex, however, now includes areas 18 and 19 as well as large regions of the temporal and parietal lobes (see Fig. 28.15 for a diagram of the four main regions of cerebral cortex: **occipital, parietal, temporal,** and **frontal**). Extrastriate cortex is composed of some 30 subdivisions that can be distinguished by their physiology, cytoarchitecture, histochemistry, and/or connections with other areas.[66,67] Each of these extrastriate visual areas is thought to make unique functional contributions to visual perception and visually guided behavior.

As a testament to the increasing complexity of the field, the naming of visual areas (see Fig. 28.15) has

A

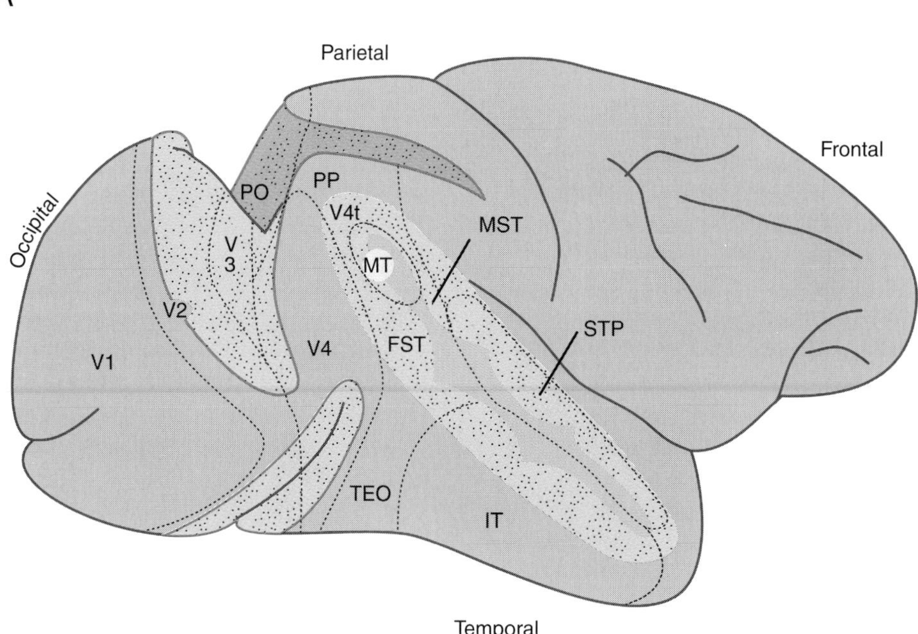

B

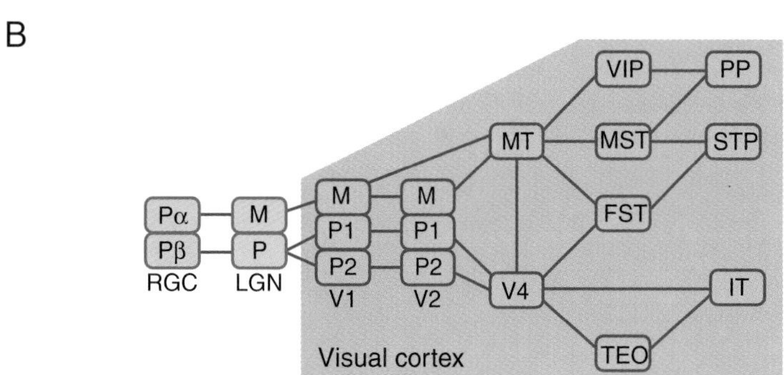

FIGURE 28.15 Extrastriate cortical regions. (A) Lateral view of the macaque brain, with the sulci partially opened to expose the areas within them. Shown are the rough outlines of the main visual areas, which take up all of occipital cortex and much of parietal and temporal cortex. (B) Partial diagram of the connections between visual area. Emphasis is placed on the hierarchical organization of the connections and on the partially segregated P (parvocellular) and M (magnocellular) pathways. Adapted from Albright.[65]

progressed from the use of simple labels—V1 through V4—to the use of more complex terms specifying anatomical location of each new area, such as MT (medial temporal, or V5), MST (medial superior temporal), or IT (inferotemporal, itself made up of several distinct areas).

The dual themes of parallel and hierarchical processing are central to the understanding of extrastriate cortex. Figure 28.15B is a vastly simplified version of a "wiring diagram" between visual areas.[67] Several criteria have been used to define new visual cortical areas. First, extrastriate regions have retinotopic maps of the visual world that can be demonstrated by physiological recordings. Second, a clear hierarchy between many cortical areas can be demonstrated anatomically. There is a stereotyped pattern of projections from one visual area to the next. Where strong connections between two areas exist, these connections tend to be bidirectional. The feedforward and feedback connections are distinguished by the layers that send and receive the connections. In such a manner, a clear hierarchy can be traced, for instance, along the pathway V1 → V2 → V3 → MT → MST (with several shortcuts, such as V1 → MT).[68]

While physiological studies of cortical areas revealed profound differences between two types of processing in extrastriate cortex, a series of studies by Ungerleider and Mishkin[69] uncovered a higher-order dichotomy. Using behavioral analyses of animals with anatomically defined cortical lesions, Ungerleider and Mishkin found a strong dissociation between the types of deficits exhibited by animals with lesions in their parietal cortex and those exhibited by animals with lesions in their temporal cortex (see Fig. 28.14). Animals with temporal lesions were often much worse at recognizing objects visually, although lower level visual function, such as acuity, was not appreciably lessened. Parietal lesions led to little or no deficit in object recognition, but visuospatial tasks, such as visually guided behavior, were profoundly impaired. From these studies and the growing body of physiological evidence, two distinct streams were postulated: a temporal or ventral stream devoted to object recognition and a parietal or dorsal stream devoted to action or spatial tasks. Put simply, the "what" and "where" functions in extrastriate cortex are divided into two distinct streams.

The temporal stream, V1 → V2 → V3 → V4 → IT . . . , is discussed in the chapter on object recognition (Chapter 52). In the present chapter, only the parietal stream, V1 → V2 → MT → MST (with several shortcuts; see Fig. 28.15) is considered. The parietal stream is dominated by the magnocellular cells and the temporal stream by parvocellular inputs, although the segregation is far from strict, particularly in the temporal stream.[63] One of the original themes in the study of extrastriate cortex was that each visual area was specialized for the study of a particular set of visual properties. Again, this strict segregation of functional properties has not held up to scrutiny in many cases. Nevertheless, the areas toward the end of the parietal stream, MT and MST, are highly specialized for the processing of visual motion.

In Parietal Cortex, Neurons Are Selective for Higher-Order Motion Cues

MT, or V5, is perhaps the best understood of the extrastriate visual areas. It has held particular interest ever since it was discovered in 1971,[70,71] primarily because it was the first area found that was strongly dominated by one visual function. Fully 95% of the neurons in MT are highly selective for the direction of motion of a stimulus.[70] In V1, a significant fraction of neurons are selective for the direction of motion, but the optimal speed may vary depending on the spatial structure of the object that is moving. In MT, speed tuning is less dependent on other stimulus attributes. Receptive fields of individual neurons in MT integrate motion information over large regions of visual space and are qualitatively less "picky" than neurons in primary visual cortex.[72] This generalization of motion signals can be achieved in a simple manner, such as by adding together inputs over space, or in a complex manner, such as by combining two component motions, in different directions, into a single coherent motion (see Box 28.5).[73–80] Of even greater interest, neurons in MT (and to a greater extent, those in MST) appear to be sensitive to more complex aspects of visual motion, such as the motion of extended objects, rather than to isolated features.[65]

The range of stimuli that a given MT neuron can respond to is impressively broad—the attributes, or form cues, that define a figure can be luminance, texture, or relative motion—but the preferred direction and speed are always the same for that neuron.[72] This is the extreme of what was termed *high-order responses* in the introduction to this chapter. Neurons at lower levels in the visual system are sensitive to isolated and specific features in visual scenes. Higher visual areas respond to very specific attributes, but these attributes are increasingly remote from the physical stimulus. Instead, they represent what we would think of as increasingly complex concepts, such as the motion of an extended object or the identity of a face.

A fundamental concept in the psychology of vision is that of **perceptual constancy.** Much of visual perception is invariant over vast differences in retinal image properties, provided that the elements of the visual scene that gave rise to the retinal image (the object) are constant. The higher-order representation found in areas such as MT provides a possible neural substrate for this important perceptual phenomenon.

Summary

The lateral geniculate nucleus of the thalamus (LGN) is a layered structure that receives segregated input from the two eyes, and it projects to primary visual cortex (striate cortex). Geniculate neurons have center–surround receptive fields that are similar to those of their retinal inputs. By contrast, most neurons in primary visual cortex are sensitive to the orientation of a stimulus. In all species, there are elements of both hierarchical and parallel processing in primary visual cortex. In this section, we have emphasized that the

BOX 28.5

THREE TYPES OF SELECTIVITY FOR MOTION

Motion is one of the more important aspects of the visual world. It is a powerful cue for navigating in the world, for segregating figures from their background, and for predicting the trajectory of objects. It is not surprising, therefore, that sensitivity to motion is a highly developed feature of the visual system. At the lowest level, neurons in the retina respond best to stimuli moving in a specific direction. These **directionally selective** neurons have been studied most intensively in the rabbit retina (first by Barlow and Levick[73,74]), but they have been observed in other species, including the cat. These neurons give on–off (±) responses to flashed lights, but are best excited by the motion of an object anywhere in their receptive fields (Fig. 28.16A). They can signal that motion in a particular range of directions is present, but because their receptive fields are relatively large and have both on and off responses, their responses cannot be used to identify the details of an object. Directionally selective retinal neurons do not project to the LGN, so the directional neurons found in the visual cortex[41,42] must create their selectivity anew.

Directionally selective simple cells in the cat visual cortex rely on an interesting mechanism that constitutes a second type of selectivity for motion. Unlike directionally selective ganglion cells, which signal that motion is present somewhere within a large region, directionally selective simple cells maintain detailed spatial information as well. These cells combine two characteristics of visual responses, described above: sensitivity to spatial and sensitivity to temporal contrast (here temporal refers to time). Neurons in the cat retina and LGN are very sensitive to spatial contrast, due to their center–surround receptive field (Fig. 28.3), and also temporal contrast, as seen in their rapid responses to changes in luminance. Directionally selective simple cells combine these attributes in a specific manner.[75–77]

A moving stimulus, such as a light bar moving to the left (Fig. 28.16B, left), is described by its trajectory in space over time. This trajectory can be plotted in an x, t (space–time) plot whose slope represents the object's direction and velocity. For instance, a bar moving to the right traces an oblique trajectory (up and to the left) in such a space–time plot (Fig. 28.16B, middle). When represented in a similar plot, the receptive fields of directionally selective simple cells can show a similar orientation (Fig. 28.16B, right).[78] This plot is exactly analogous to Kuffler's maps of ganglion cell receptive fields. It represents the responses of the cell to small stimuli at different positions, but it includes the time course of the responses as well. The on region of this receptive field is indicated with solid contour lines (and shown in white for added emphasis); the off flanks of the receptive field are indicated with dotted contour lines.

For directionally selective simple cells, the timing of the response is directly related to the position of the stimulus. In the illustration, the cell is sensitive to a bright bar at a range of positions, but the timing of the peak response changes with position. These responses to flashed bars explain the responses to moving stimuli. Just as on-center/off-surround ganglion cells respond best to a bright spot on a dark background (Fig. 28.6C), a directionally selective simple cell responds best to a bar moving in a specific direction. A moving bar is the stimulus that best matches the "template" formed by their receptive field. In this manner, simple-cell receptive fields can be strongly direction selective, but their responses preserve precise information about the position and structure of the stimulus (they are "linear," in the terminology of Enroth-Cugell and Robson; see Box 28.2).

A third kind of directionally selective cell is found in cortical area MT of the macaque. Receptive fields of individual neurons in MT integrate motion information over large regions of visual space. By comparison, receptive fields in the retina, LGN, and V1 can be thought of as viewing the world through much smaller apertures. If the goal of vision is to extract the properties of objects, rather than isolate features, then the existence of small receptive fields can lead to what is known as the aperture problem. As illustrated in Fig. 28.16C, two objects moving in different directions can appear to have the same direction of motion when viewed through an aperture. Given that direction-selective neurons in V1 in fact can be fooled in this manner, how is it possible that the visual system can discern the true direction of motion of extended objects?

In a dual study of perception in humans and of MT neurons in macaques, Movshon and colleagues[79] analyzed the responses to complex stimuli whose components moved in different directions (such as the edges of the square in the bottom half of Fig. 28.16C), but which were perceived as coherent patterns moving in an intermediate "pattern" direction. Unlike neurons in V1, a significant fraction of neurons in MT responded to the pattern direction rather than to the components. This would imply that some MT neurons combine their inputs in a complex

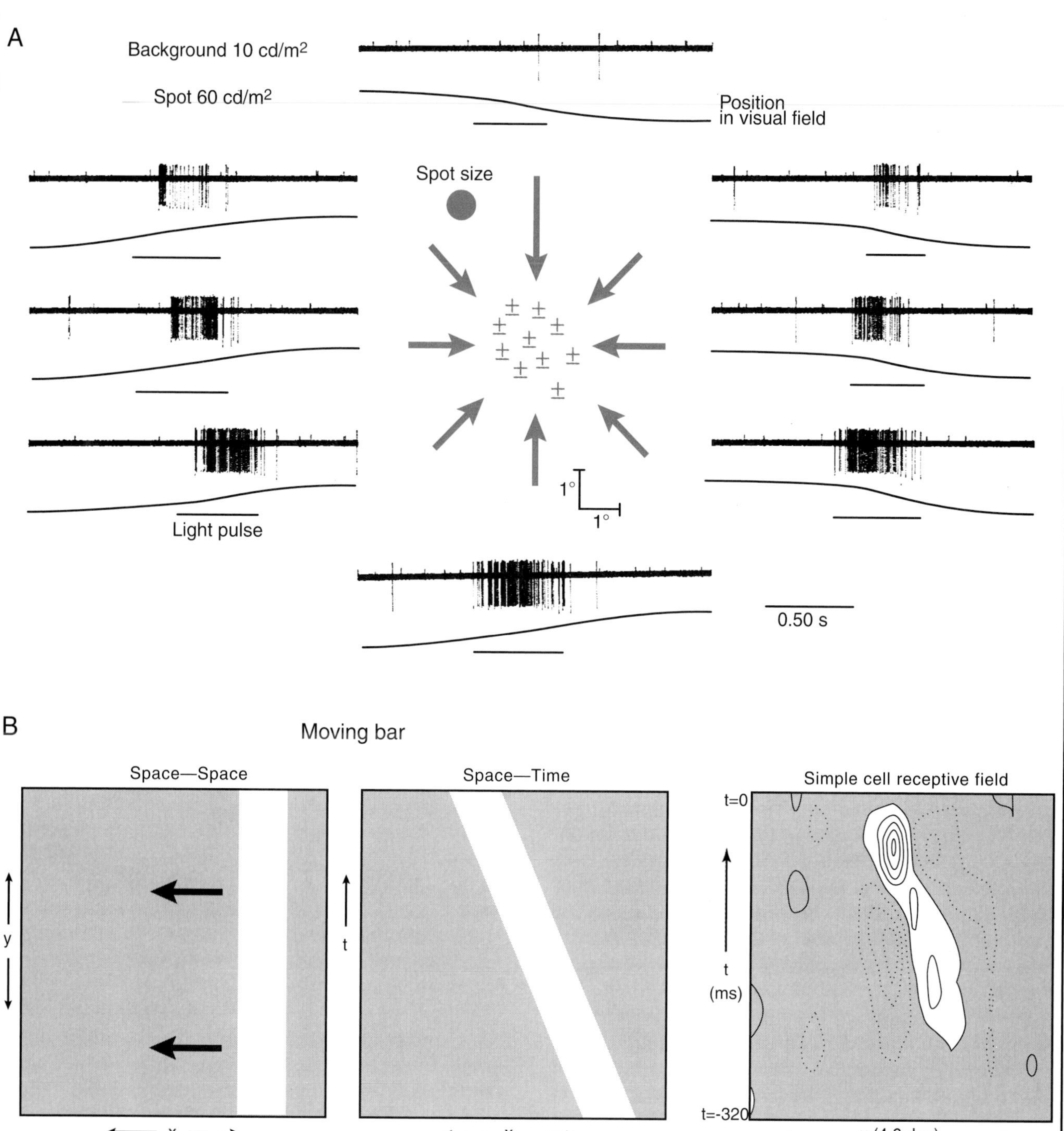

FIGURE 28.16 Three types of direction selectivity. (A) Receptive field map of a directionally selective ganglion cell in the rabbit (± indicates where neuron responded in an on-off manner). Surrounding it are individual responses to stimuli moving in eight different directions. The smooth traces below each train of action potentials correspond to the position of the stimulus as it moves in the indicated direction. The horizontal bars indicate when the spot was in the receptive field. (B) Direction selectivity in cortical simple cells of the cat. A bar moving to the left (shown in a space–time plot in the middle) matches the "template" formed by a directionally selective simple receptive field (shown at right). The vertical time axis in the right-hand panel corresponds to where the stimulus was *before* the neuron fired, from $t = -320$ to $t = 0$ ms. The bright regions in the receptive field correspond to the best location for a bright stimulus at each delay between stimulus and response.

(*Continued*)

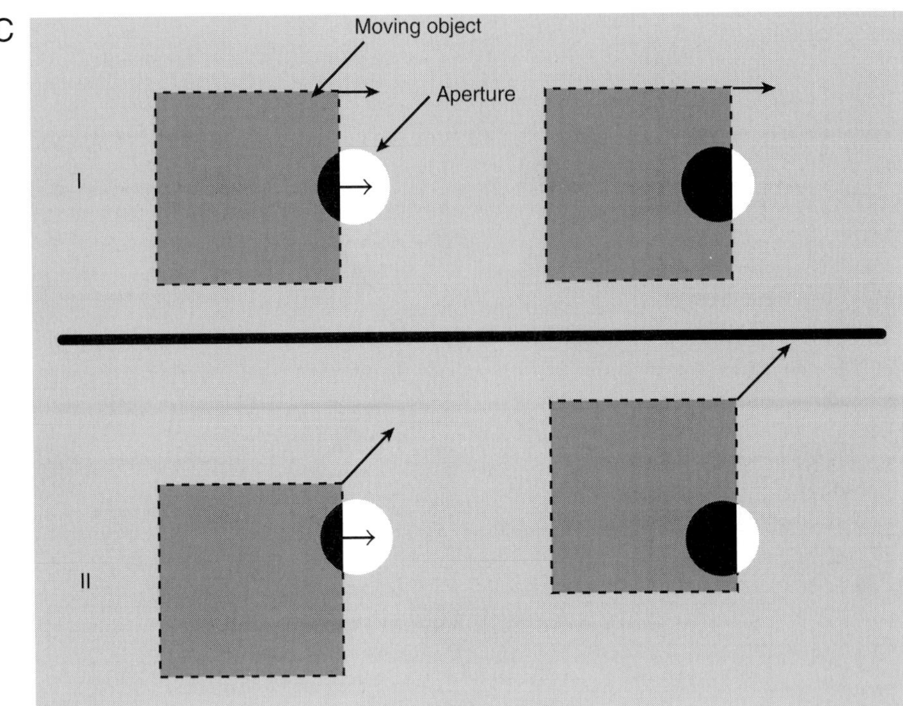

FIGURE 28.16 (*continued*) (C) The ambiguous motion of an extended object when viewed through a small aperture—known as the aperture problem—is partially resolved by some neurons in macaque cortical area MT. The squares in I and II (shown at times T1 and T2) are moving in different directions, but they appear identical when viewed through a small aperture. (A) Adapted from Barlow *et al.*[73] (B) Far right from McLean *et al.*[78]

manner to achieve a selectivity for the motion of extended objects rather than primitive features.

In a subsequent study, Stoner and Albright[80] found that the combination of motion signals by MT neurons was dependent on cues for image segmentation. If moving features (such as the edges in Fig. 28.16C) were interpreted as part of the same moving object, MT neurons would combine motion signals accordingly. If the same features were seen to arise from different moving objects, the signals would not be combined. These results emphasize the important role of a surface segmentation in high-level motion processing and indicate a critical contribution from cortical areas involved in form processing.

visual cortical circuit in the cat can be seen as a functional hierarchy that transforms the geniculate input into simple then complex receptive fields. For the macaque monkey, we have emphasized the parallel pathways that are kept relatively separate in striate and extrastriate cortex.

Visual cortex has an orderly functional architecture. Neurons within a cortical column have similar receptive field attributes, such as orientation selectivity, ocular dominance, and receptive field location. Each of these receptive field attributes varies smoothly over the cortical surface. The organization of ocular dominance columns and orientation columns across the cortical surface can be visualized with optical imaging.

Finally, in the macaque monkey, there are more than 30 extrastriate visual cortical regions, each of which performs different functions. These extrastriate regions can be divided into two pathways: the temporal stream—devoted to form recognition—and the parietal stream—devoted to action or to spatial tasks. The areas in each stream form a functional and anatomical hierarchy. Neurons in successive visual areas respond to increasingly high-order or abstract features of the visual world.

References

General

Boynton, R. M., and Kaiser, P. K. (1996). *Human Color Vision,* 2nd ed. Optical Society of America, Washington, DC.

Hubel, D. H. (1988). *Eye, Brain, and Vision.* Scientific American Library, Freeman, New York.

Marr, D. (1982). *Vision: A Computational Investigation into the Human Representation and Processing of Visual Information.* Freeman, New York.

McIlwain, T. T. (1996). *An Introduction to the Biology of Vision.* Cambridge University Press, Cambridge, UK.

Shatz, C., and Lam, D. M.-K. (1991). *Development of the Visual System.* MIT Press, Cambridge, MA.

Cited

1. Hecht, S., Schlaer, S., and Pirenne, M. H. (1942). Energy, quanta, and vision. *J. Gen. Physiol.* **47:** 443–463.
2. Baylor, D. A., Lamb, T. D., and Yau, K.-W. (1979). Responses of retinal rods to single photons. *J. Physiol.* (*London*) **288:** 613–634.
3. Baylor, D. A., Nunn, B. J., and Schnapf, J. L. (1984). The photocurrent, noise and spectral sensitivity of rods of the monkey *Macaca fascicularis. J. Physiol.* (*London*) **357:** 575–607.
4. Hartline, H. K. (1938). Response of single optic nerve fibers of the vertebrate eye to illumination of the retina. *Am. J. Physiol.* **121:** 400–415.
5. Hartline, H. K., and Graham, C. H. (1932). Nerve impulses from single receptors in the eye. *J. Cell. Comp. Physiol.* **1:** 277–295.
6. Hartline, H. K., Wagner, H. G., and MacNichol, E. F., Jr. (1952). The peripheral origin of nervous activity in the visual system. *Cold Spring Harbor Sym. Quant. Biol.* **17:** 125–141.
7. Kuffler, S. W. (1952). Neurons in the retina: Organization, inhibition and excitation problems. *Cold Spring Harbor Symp. Quant. Biol.* **17:** 281–292.
8. Kuffler, S. W. (1953). Discharge patterns and functional organization of the mammalian retina. *J. Neurophysiol.* **16:** 37–68.
9. Shapley, R., and Enroth-Cugell, C. (1985). Visual adaptation and retinal gain controls. *Prog. Retinal Res.* **3:** 263–343.
10. Dowling, J. E. (1987). *The Retina: An Approachable Part of the Brain.* Harvard University Press, Cambridge, MA.
11. Wässle, H., and Boycott, B. B. (1991). Functional architecture of the mammalian retina. *Physiol. Rev.* **71:** 447–480.

11a. Shatz, C., and Lam, D. M.-K. (1991). *Development of the Visual Systems.* MIT Press, Cambridge, MA.

12. Dowling, J. E. (1997). Retina. In *Encyclopedia of Human Biology* (Renato Dulbecco, ed.), 2nd ed, Vol. 7, pp. 571–587. Academic Press, San Diego, CA.
13. Wu, S. M. (1994). Synaptic transmission in the outer retina. *Annu. Rev. Physiol.* **56:** 141–168.
14. Schiller, P. H. (1992). The ON and OFF channels of the visual system. *Trends Neurosci.* **15:** 86–92.
15. Shapley, R. (1986). The importance of contrast for the activity of single neurons, the VEP and perception. *Vision Res.* **26:** 45–61.
16. Hartline, H. K. (1940). The receptive fields of optic nerve fibers. *Am. J. Physiol.* **130:** 690–699.
17. Kuffler, S. W., Nichols, J. G., and Martin, A. R. (1984). *From Neuron to Brain: A Cellular Approach to the Function of the Nervous System,* 2nd ed. Sinauer Assoc., Sunderland, MA.
18. Bullock, T. H., and Horridge, G. A. (1965). *Structure and Function in the Nervous Systems of Invertebrates.* Freeman, San Francisco.

18a. Helmholtz, H. von (1924). *Handbook of Physiological Optics,* 3rd ed. (J.P.C. Southall, trans.). Optical Society of America, Rochester, NY (originally published 1909).

19. Boring, E. G. (1950). *A History of Experimental Psychology,* 2nd ed. Prentice-Hall, Englewood Cliffs, NJ.
20. Enroth-Cugell, C., and Robson, J. G. (1966). The contrast sensitivity of retinal ganglion cells of the cat. *J. Physiol.* (*London*) **187:** 517–552.
21. Ratliff, F., ed (1974). *Studies on Excitation and Inhibition in the Retina. A Collection of Papers from the Laboratories of H. Heffer Hartline.* Rockefeller University Press, New York.
22. Wandell, B. A. (1993). *Foundations of Vision.* Sinauer Assoc., Sunderland, MA.
23. Enroth-Cugell, C., and Robson, J. G. (1984). Functional characteristics and diversity of cat retinal ganglion cells. Basic characteristics and quantitative description. *Invest. Ophthalmol. Visual Sci.* **25:** 250–267.
24. Hochstein, S., and Shapley, R. M. (1976). Quantitative analysis of retinal ganglion cell classifications. *J. Physiol.* (*London*) **262:** 237–264.
25. De Valois, R. L., Morgan, H. C., Polson, M. C., Mead, W. R., and Hull, E. M. (1974). Psychophysical studies of monkey vision: I. Macaque luminosity and color vision tests. *Vision Res.* **14:** 53–67.
26. Hendry, S. H., and Yoshioka, T. (1994). A neurochemically distinct third channel in the macaque dorsal lateral geniculate nucleus. *Science* **26:** 575–577.
27. De Valois, R. L. (1960). Color vision mechanisms in the monkey. *J. Gen. Physiol.* **43:** 115–128.
28. Wiesel, T. N., and Hubel, D. H. (1966). Spatial and chromatic interactions in the lateral geniculate body of the rhesus monkey. *J. Neurophysiol.* **29:** 1115–1156.
29. Gouras, P. (1968). Identification of cone mechanisms in monkey ganglion cells. *J. Physiol.* (*London*) **199:** 533–547.
30. De Monasterio, F. M., and Gouras, P. (1975). Functional properties of ganglion cells of the rhesus monkey retina. *J. Physiol.* (*London*) **251:** 167–195.
31. Schiller, P. H., and Malpeli, J. (1978). Functional specificity of lateral geniculate nucleus laminae of the rhesus monkey. *J. Neurophysiol.* **41:** 788–797.
32. Kaplan, E., and Shapley, R. M. (1986). The primate retina contains two types of ganglion cells, with high and low contrast sensitivity. *Proc. Natl. Acad. Sci. U.S.A.* **83:** 2755–2757.
33. Lennie, P., Haake, P. W., and Williams, D. R. (1991). The design of chromatically opponent receptive fields. In *Computational Models of Visual Processing* (M. S. Landy and J. A. Movshon, eds.), pp. 71–82. MIT Press, Cambridge, MA.
34. Reid, R. C., and Shapley, R. M. (1992). The spatial structure of L, M, and S cone inputs to receptive fields in primate lateral geniculate nucleus. *Nature* (*London*) **356:** 716–718.
35. Nathans, J., Thomas, D., and Hogness, D. S. (1986). Molecular genetics of human color vision: The genes encoding blue, green, and red pigments. *Science* **232:** 193–202.
36. Nathans, J. (1994). In the eye of the beholder: Visual pigments and inherited variations in human vision. *Cell* (*Cambridge, Mass.*) **78:** 357–360.

37. Zeki, S. (1990). A century of cerebral achromatopsia. *Brain* **113:** 1721–1777.
38. Shapley, R., and Perry, V. H. (1986). Cat and monkey retinal ganglion cells and their visual functional roles. *Trends Neurosci.* **9:** 229–235.
39. Polyak, S. L. (1941). *The Retina.* University of Chicago Press, Chicago.
40. Hubel, D. H., and Wiesel, T. N. (1977). Ferrier Lecture: Functional architecture of macaque monkey visual cortex. *Proc. R. Soc. Lond. B* **198:** 1–59.
41. Hubel, D. H., and Wiesel, T. N. (1959). Receptive fields of single neurones in the cat's visual cortex. *J. Physiol. (London)* **148:** 574–591.
42. Hubel, D. H., and Wiesel, T. N. (1962). Receptive fields, binocular interaction and functional architecture in the cat's visual cortex. *J. Physiol. (London)* **160:** 106–154.
43. Hubel, D. H. (1982). Exploration of the primary visual cortex, 1955–78. *Nature (London)* **299:** 515–524.
44. Movshon, J. A., Thompson, I. D., and Tolhurst, D. J. (1978). Spatial summation in the receptive field of simple cells in the cat's striate cortex. *J. Physiol. (London)* **283:** 53–77.
45. Movshon, J. A., Thompson, I. D., and Tolhurst, D. J. (1978). Receptive field organization of complex cells in the cat's striate cortex. *J. Physiol. (London)* **283:** 79–99.
46. Chapman, B., Zahs, K. R., and Stryker, M. P. (1991). Relation of cortical cell orientation selectivity to alignment of receptive fields of the geniculocortical afferents that arborize within a single orientation column in ferret visual cortex. *J. Neurosci.* **11:** 1347–1358.
47. Reid, R. C., and Alonso, J. M. (1995). Specificity of monosynaptic connections from thalamus to visual cortex. *Nature (London)* **378:** 281–284.
48. Ferster, D., Chung, S., and Wheat, H. (1996). Orientation selectivity of thalamic input to simple cells of cat visual cortex. *Nature (London)* **380:** 249–252.
49. Gilbert, C. (1978). Laminar differences in receptive field properties of cells in cat primary visual cortex. *J. Physiol. (London)* **268:** 391–421.
50. Hendrickson, A. E., Hunt, S. P., and Wu, J.-Y. (1981). Immunocytochemical localization of glutamic acid decarboxylase in monkey striate cortex. *Nature (London)* **292:** 605–607.
51. Horton, J. C., and Hubel, D. H. (1981). A regular patchy distribution of cytochrome-oxidase staining in primary visual cortex of the macaque monkey. *Nature (London)* **292:** 762–764.
52. Livingstone, M. S., and Hubel, D. H. (1984). Anatomy and physiology of a color system in the primate visual cortex. *J. Neurosci.* **4:** 309–356.
52a. Gilbert, C. D., and Wiesel, T. N. (1985). Intrinsic connectivity and receptive field properties in visual cortex. *Vision Res.* **25:** 365–374.
53. Lorente de Nó, R. (1938). The physiology of the nervous system. In *The Physiology of the Nervous System* (J. F. Fulton, ed.), pp. 291–329. Oxford University Press, New York.
54. Mountcastle, V. B. (1957). Modality and topographic properties of single neurons of cat's somatic sensory cortex. *J. Neurophysiol.* **20:** 408–434.
55. LeVay, S., Hubel, D. H., and Wiesel, T. N. (1975). The pattern of ocular dominance columns in macaque visual cortex revealed by a reduced silver stain. *J. Comp. Neurol.* **159:** 559–576.
56. Talbot, S. A., and Marshall, W. H. (1941). Physiological studies on neural mechanisms of visual localization and discrimination. *Am. J. Ophthalmol.* **24:** 1255–1263.
57. Daniel, P. M., and Whitteridge, D. (1959). The representation of the visual field on the cerebral cortex in monkeys. *J. Physiol. (London)* **159:** 203–231.
58. Blasdel, G. G., and Salama, G. (1986). Voltage-sensitive dyes reveal a modular organization in monkey striate cortex. *Nature (London)* **321:** 579–585.
59. Grinvald, A., Lieke, E., Frostig, R. D., Gilbert, C. D., and Wiesel, T. N. (1986). Functional architecture of cortex revealed by optical imaging of intrinsic signals. *Nature (London)* **324:** 361–364.
60. Ts'o, D. Y., Frostig, R. D., Lieke, E. E., and Grinvald, A. (1990). Functional organization of primate visual cortex revealed by high resolution optical imaging. *Science* **24:** 417–420.
61. Grinvald, A., Ts'o, D. Y., Frostig, R. D., Lieke, E., Arieli, A. and Hildesheim, R. (1988). Optical imaging of neuronal activity in the visual cortex. In *Neural Mechanisms of Visual Perception: Proceedings of the Second Retina Research Foundation Symposium* (D. M.-K. Lam and C. D. Gilbert, eds.). Gulf Publishing Co., Houston, TX.
62. Bonhoeffer, T., and Grinvald, A. (1991). Iso-orientation domains in visual cortex are arranged in pinwheel-like patterns. *Nature (London)* **353:** 429–431.
62a. Fitzpatrick, D., Itoh, K., and Diamond, I. T. (1983) The laminar organization of the lateral geniculate nucleus and the striate cortex in the squirrel monkey (*Saimiri sciureus*). *J. Neurosci.* **3:** 673–702.
63. Merigan, W. H., and Maunsell, J. H. R. (1994). How parallel are the primate visual pathways? *Annu. Rev. Neurosci.* **16:** 369–402.
64. Shipp, S., and Zeki, S. (1995). Segregation and convergence of specialised pathways in macaque monkey visual cortex. *J. Anat.* **187:** 547–562.
65. Albright, T. D. (1993). Cortical processing of visual motion. In *Visual Motion and Its Role in the Stabilization of Gaze* (F. A. Miles and J. Wallman, eds.), pp. 177–201. Elsevier Science Publishers, Amsterdam.
66. Zeki, S. M. (1978). Functional specialisation in the visual cortex of the rhesus monkey. *Nature (London)* **274:** 423–428.
67. Felleman, D. J., and van Essen, D. C. (1991). Distributed hierarchical processing in the primate cerebral cortex. *Cereb. Cortex* **1:** 1–47.
68. Maunsell, J. H., and van Essen, D. C. (1983). The connections of the middle temporal visual area (MT) and their relationship to a cortical hierarchy in the macaque monkey. *J. Neurosci.* **3:** 2563–2586.
69. Ungerleider, L. G., and Mishkin, M. (1982). Two cortical visual systems. In *Analysis of Visual Behavior* (D. J. Ingle, M. A. Goodale, and R. J. W. Mansfield, eds.), pp. 549–586. MIT Press, Cambridge, MA.
70. Allman, J. M., and Kaas, J. H. (1971). A representation of the visual field in the caudal third of the middle temporal gyrus of the owl monkey (*Aotus trivirgatus*). *Brain Res.* **31:** 85–105.
71. Dubner, R., and Zeki, S. M. (1971). Response properties and receptive fields of cells in an anatomically defined region of the superior temporal sulcus in the ronkey. *Brain Res.* **35:** 528–532.
72. Albright, T. D. (1992). Form-cue invariant processing in primate visual cortex. *Science* **225:** 1141–1143.
73. Barlow, H. B., Hill, R. M., and Levick, W. R. (1964). Retinal ganglion cells responding selectively to direction and speed of image motion in the rabbit. *J. Physiol. (London)* **173:** 377–407.
74. Barlow, H. B., and Levick, W. R. (1965). The mechanism of directionally selective units in rabbit's retina. *J. Physiol. (London)* **178:** 477–504.
75. Reid, R. C., Soodak, R. E., and Shapley, R. M. (1987). Linear mechanisms of directional selectivity in simple cells of cat striate cortex. *Proc. Natl. Acad. Sci. U.S.A.* **84:** 8740–8744.

76. McLean, J., and Palmer, L. A. (1989). Contribution of linear spatiotemporal receptive field structure to velocity selectivity of simple cells in area 17 of cat. *Vision Res.* **29:** 675–679.
77. Jagadeesh, B., Wheat, H. S., and Ferster, D. (1993). Linearity of summation of synaptic potentials underlying direction selectivity in simple cells of the cat visual cortex. *Science* **262:** 1901–1904.
78. McLean, J., Raab, S., and Palmer, L. A. (1994). Contribution of linear mechanisms to the specification of local motion by simple cells in areas 17 and 18 of the cat. *Visual Neurosci.* **11:** 271–294.
79. Movshon, J. A., Adelson, E. H., Gizzi, M., and Newsome, W. T. (1985). The analysis of moving visual patterns. In *Pattern Recognition Mechanisms* (C. Chagas, R. Gattass, and C. G. Gross, eds.), pp. 117–151. Vatican Press, Rome.
80. Stoner, G. R., and Albright, T. D. (1992). Neural correlates of perceptual motion coherence. *Nature (London)* **358:** 412–414.

S E C T I O N V

MOTOR SYSTEMS

C H A P T E R

29

Fundamentals of Motor Systems

W. Thomas Thach

In one way, the motor system is like the sensory system turned backward. Information enters the sensory system through receptors and branches at different stages to control lower processes or move to the top of the system. In the motor system (Fig. 29.1), programming begins partly at the top and partly at lower levels as motor information moves down through stages to the effectors, the muscles. A motor neuron and the individual muscle fibers it innervates constitute a **motor unit** (Fig. 29.2). Many motor neurons supply each muscle; the motor neurons for any one muscle are arranged in a cigar-shaped **motor neuron pool** that lies within the ventral horn of the gray matter of the spinal cord. The motor neurons are contacted by the axons of sensory neurons innervating the **muscle spindles,** by command axons descending from the brainstem and cerebral cortex, and by interneurons within the gray matter of the spinal cord. The interneurons are themselves activated by muscle spindle and Golgi tendon organ afferents, by brainstem and cortical command axons, and by still other interneurons within the gray matter. The interneurons constitute an "extra layer" between these inputs and the motor neurons, allowing a greater degree of complexity in movement control.

Posture—the ability to stand upright automatically against gravity—is controlled in part by the vestibulospinal, reticulospinal, and tectospinal pathways, which descend to the spinal cord from the vestibular nucleus, reticular nucleus, and superior colliculus in the brainstem, respectively. These pathways descend bilaterally within the ventromedial part of the spinal cord, in proximity to the motor neurons that control proximal body muscles, which lie in the medial part of the ventral horn.

Voluntary movement—movements that we think about and consciously plan—are controlled chiefly by pathways descending from the cerebral motor cortex and adjacent cortical areas. These pathways form the **corticospinal tract,** which descends via the corona radiata, the cerebral peduncle, and the base of the pons to the medullary pyramids. At the pyramids, a portion of the corticospinal tract fibers cross the neuraxis to enter the lateral column of the white matter of the spinal cord, where they contact some of the motor neurons that control the distal muscles in the arms and legs on the opposite side of the body. The remainder of the corticospinal tract fibers remain on the same side and descend in the most ventromedial part of the spinal cord, where they, like the axons in the postural control pathways, contact motor neurons projecting to trunk and other proximal muscles on the same side of the body.

Two additional parts of the motor system are the **basal ganglia,** which appear to permit chosen and inhibit unwanted movements, and the **cerebellum,** which coordinates the many muscles active in any given movement. Both structures receive input from almost all of the cerebral cortex. The cerebellum also receives input from the spinal cord (via the dorsal spinocerebellar and ventral spinocerebellar tracts), the vestibular and reticular nuclei, the superior colliculus, and the **inferior olive.** The cerebellum projects to all components of the postural and voluntary control systems as well as to the **red nucleus.**

THE SPINAL CORD AS A CENTRAL PATTERN GENERATOR: REFLEXES AND LOCOMOTION

In another way, the motor system is quite different from the sensory system. Whereas interruption of a sensory pathway generally results only in a loss of

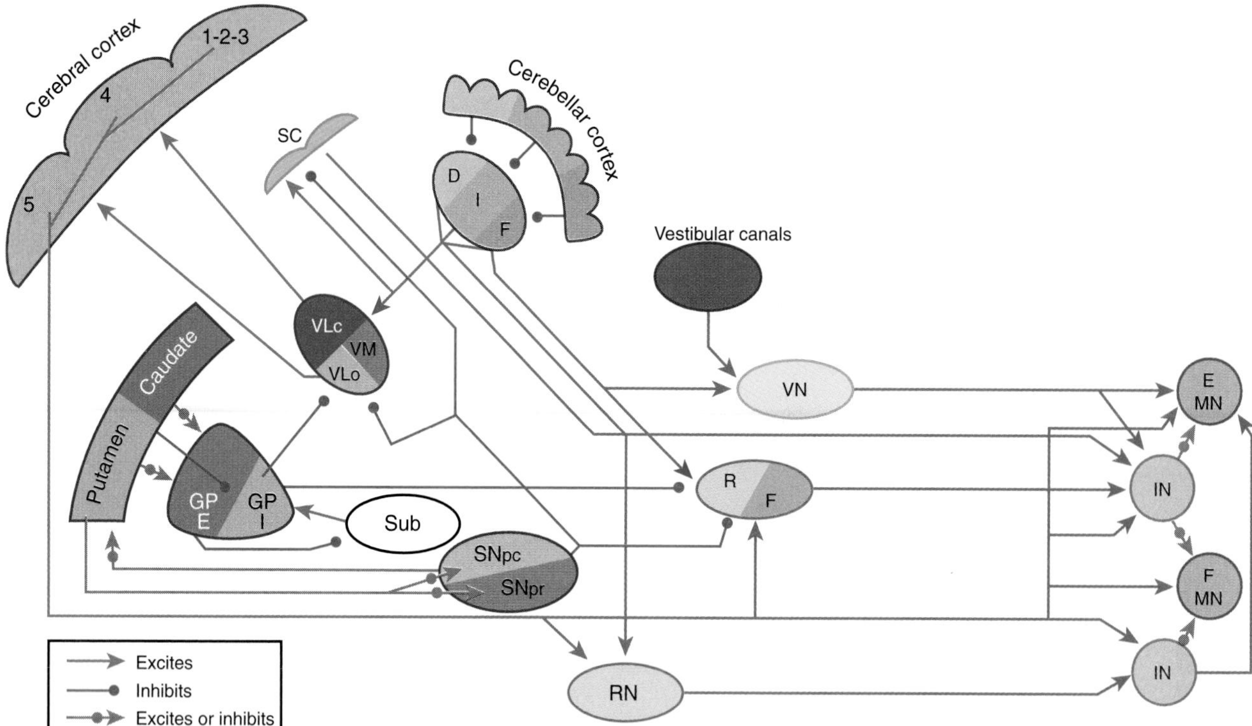

FIGURE 29.1 Descending pathways to the spinal cord and their origins in brainstem, cerebellum, and cerebrum. GP E, globus pallidus, external segment; GP I, globus pallidus, internal segment; VLc, caudal ventrolateral nucleus; VLo, oral ventrolateral nucleus; VM, ventromedial nucleus; Sub, subthalamic nucleus; D, dentate nucleus; I, interposed nucleus; F, fastigial nucleus; SNpc, substantia nigra pars compacta; SNpr, substantia nigra pars reticulata; SC, superior colliculus; RN, red nucleus; RF, reticular formation (e.g., reticular nucleus of the pontine tegmentum); VN, vestibular nuclei; IN, interneuron; E MN, extensor motor neuron; F MN, flexor motor neuron. Adapted from Thach and Montgomery, *Neurobiology of Disease*, Oxford University Press, New York, 1990.

sensation, interruption of a motor pathway usually gives two kinds of abnormal function: the inability to make an intended movement (negative deficit) and the spontaneous production of an unintended posture or movement (positive deficit). The characteristics of deficit can help the physician to locate the level of injury within the motor pathway. Many parts of the motor system can independently generate movement when cut off from other parts, as long as they are connected to the periphery. Each part then shows itself to be a **central pattern generator** (CPG) of movement.

A single impulse in a motor neuron causes all muscle fibers in the motor unit to contract simultaneously, producing a **twitch.** Stronger contractions result from the maintained firing of single motor units—rate coding—and the activation of additional motor units—recruitment. Contractile force is normally maintained by **temporal summation (fusion)** of the twitches of all active motor units. The motor neuron is the final common pathway for all motor programs, although interneurons appear to be the major summing point for descending control.

Damaging a muscle produces the same negative deficits—weakness and paralysis—as damaging the motor nerve that innervates the muscle. The positive deficits caused by these injuries are different, however. Whereas muscle damage produces **fibrillation** (spontaneous twitching of single muscle fibers), nerve damage causes **fasciculation** (spontaneous firing of motor axons and twitching of all of the muscle fibers they contact).

Spinal segmental reflexes further control motor unit properties. **Renshaw cells** (Fig. 29.3) are excited by alpha motor neurons and feed back to inhibit them; the inhibition limits the maximal rate of motor neuronal firing and coordinates the firing patterns of neighboring motor neurons. **Golgi tendon organs** (GTOs) sense active muscle stretch and inhibit motor neurons via inhibitory interneurons. This may help to protect against hurtful contractile forces. Muscle spindles supply excitation to motor neurons that is proportional to the length or velocity of muscle stretch. The segmental stretch reflexes provide a compliant interface with the environment. Firing at the same time as

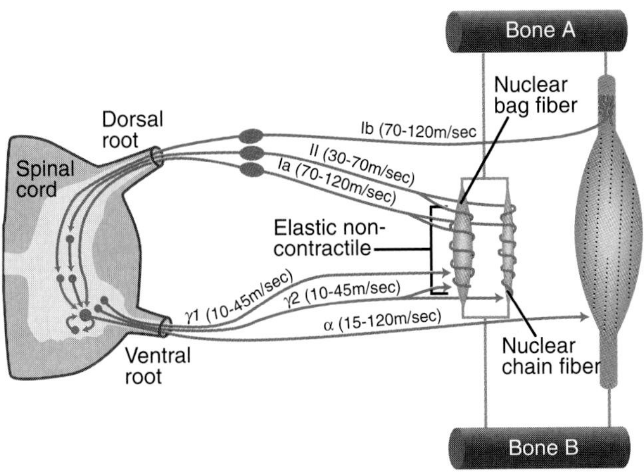

FIGURE 29.2 Diagram of muscles and muscle spindles and their motor and sensory innervation. The Ib endings (Golgi tendon organs) sense force that is actively generated by the muscle contraction and fire proportionately, returning to the spinal cord to inhibit the alpha motor neuron via inhibitory interneurons. By contrast, the Ia (primary annulospiral receptors) and II (secondary flower spray receptors) endings of the muscle spindles sense the length of the muscle and fire proportionately when it is stretched or shortened, returning to the spinal cord to excite the alpha motor neuron. In most kinds of movement, alpha and gamma motor neurons fire together (coactivation). The gamma motor neurons excite the spindle fibers and thereby the Ia and II endings to maintain spindle sensitivity to length despite muscle shortening. The tendon and spindle reflexes act as servomechanisms for force and length, respectively, of muscle contraction. Thus, if the muscle fatigues and produces less force, the Ib ending will be activated less, causing less inhibitory drive (via the interneuron) to the alpha motor neuron, which will allow it to increase its firing to drive the fatigued muscle to greater contraction. If the fatigued muscle fails to shorten as much as it otherwise would, that extra amount of length will add to the gamma motor neuronal drive of the Ia and II endings, which will then excite the alpha motor neuron more to make up the deficit in length. Adapted from Thach and Montgomery, *Neurobiology of Disease*, Oxford University Press, New York, 1990.

alpha motor neurons, **gamma motor neurons** contract the ends of the muscle spindles, keeping spindle sensitivity to passive stretch constant as a muscle shortens.

When descending pathways are damaged, as with cerebral or spinal cord lesions, stretch reflexes become autonomous and overactive (positive deficits). Tapping a tendon with a reflex hammer in such patients elicits exaggerated stretch reflexes. Passively extending the elbow or flexing the knee reveals spring-viscous resistance, the result of increasing muscle contraction due to stretching of the spindles. Resistance may increase up to a certain length and force of stretch and then suddenly relax as GTOs (and group II spindle afferents) are activated by the rising tension; this phenomenon is called the **claspknife reaction.** When one suddenly stretches a muscle in such a patient and attempts to hold the muscle at the longer length, the muscle undergoes an oscillating pattern of rhythmic contractions and relaxations called **clonus.** Clonus is caused by cyclic alternation of the stretch reflex, the GTO reflex, and Renshaw inhibition, all of which are positive deficits reflecting excessive activity of the stretch reflex arc. The movements reveal damage to the descending pathways that normally control the stretch reflex.

A painful stimulus to the skin or deep tissues causes withdrawal of the stimulated limb and extension of the opposite limb (Fig. 29.3). These reflexes protect a limb from injury due to an external threat and support the body as the hurt limb withdraws (another positive deficit). They also contribute to the essential spinal mechanism for producing locomotion. When set to oscillate, these spinal reflexes are sufficient to generate the rudiments of walking in nonprimate vertebrates. After injury of descending motor pathways, pain-sensing reflexes become hyperactive and may cause extreme maintained flexion of the leg at the foot, knee, and hip. The **Babinski response**—dorsiflexion of the hallux upon sharp stimulation of the lateral sole—is the first sign of this hyperactivity.

BRAIN PROJECTIONS TO THE SPINAL CORD: POSTURE AND VOLUNTARY MOVEMENT

Nuclei in the brainstem and cerebral cortex send axons down to excite interneurons and motor neurons (Fig. 29.1). These descending paths constitute the **postural** and **voluntary** motor control systems.

The Postural System Is Automatic

Vestibulospinal pathways project bilaterally to large numbers of spinal interneurons and motor neurons, causing many muscles to contract as the head moves in space. These mechanisms provide the automatic antigravity control of the trunk and limbs needed to maintain an upright stance. **Reticulospinal** and **tectospinal pathways** add somatosensory and visual control of posture. **Tonic neck reflexes** work with and against vestibulospinal reflexes. Otherwise, voluntary movements of the head would act upon the vestibulospinal reflexes and adversely change posture every time one turned or tilted one's head. Receptors in the neck detect movement of the head with respect to the body and subtract from or add to the effect of vestibulospinal reflexes. Tonic neck reflexes thus compensate for the fact that the gravity and body motion sensors of the vestibulospinal reflex are mounted in the head.

Direct damage to these brainstem components destroys these various functions, causing patients to fall (a negative deficit). When these brainstem components

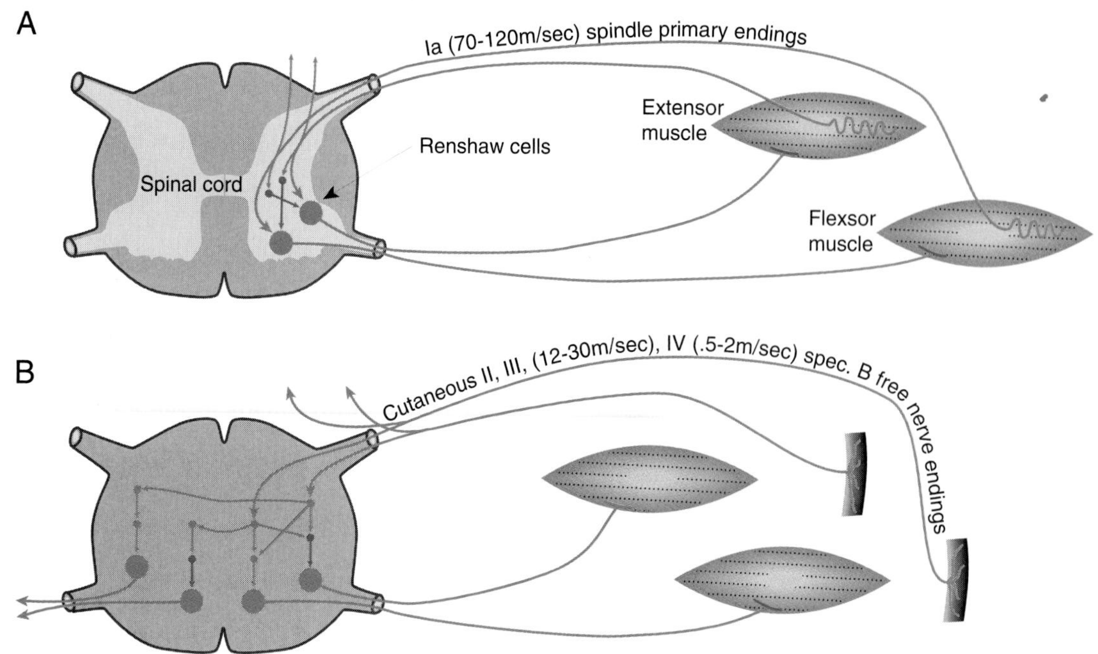

FIGURE 29.3 Circuitry for segmental spinal reflexes. Ia spindle reflexes are activated by stretch of the muscle and cause excitation of that muscle and its synergists and reciprocal inhibition of its antagonists. Skin reflexes (activated by a noxious stimulus) may cause withdrawal of the limb away from the stimulus with a supporting reaction in the opposite limb. Adapted from Thach and Montgomery, *Neurobiology of Disease,* Oxford University Press, New York, 1990.

are deprived of higher control, as in a stroke involving the upper brainstem or internal capsule, they become overactive and autonomous (a positive deficit). Lesions of the upper pons or midbrain result in overactive vestibulospinal reflexes, which cause the **decerebrate response**—extension of all four limbs and the neck (Fig. 29.4). Lesions of the internal capsule release both vestibulospinal and tonic neck reflexes from cortical control, producing the **decorticate posture**—flexed upper and extended lower extremities, reversing on inversion of the body—and the **obligatory tonic neck reflexes**—head turned toward the extended limbs and away from the flexed limbs (Figs. 29.4 and 29.5).

Decerebrate Decorticate Tonic neck reflex

FIGURE 29.4 Attitudes in patients with damage of upper brainstem (decerebrate) as motor cortex as internal capsule (decorticate and tonic neck reflex) which result from the continued activity of neural centers below the level of the lesion. Adapted from Thach and Montgomery, *Neurobiology of Disease,* Oxford University Press, New York, 1990.

FIGURE 29.5 Attitudes in normal humans during sports activities in which the tonic neck reflex is likely to play a role. Adapted from Fukuda, T. (1961). Studies on human dynamic postures from the viewpoint of postural reflexes. Acta Oto Laryngol. Suppl. **161:** 1–52.

The Voluntary Motor System Produces Consciously "Willed" Movements

The corticospinal tract arises from primary motor cortex (area 4, 30%; area 6, 30%) and the somatosensory cortex (40%). The **primary motor cortex** contains the large Betz cells in layer 5, and it produces movements in response to weak electrical stimulation. Like other portions of the neocortex, the motor cortex is basically columnar in structure. Each column appears to govern movements at or around one or a few joints in a certain direction. The primary motor cortex is somatotopically organized, with more area devoted to the control of distal parts of the body. It is accessed by conscious thought via pathways from the frontal and parietal lobes. Axons of neurons chiefly in layer 5 form the corticospinal and corticobulbar tracts, which project via the cerebral peduncle to the medullary pyramids. At the pyramids, about 90 percent of the axons cross to the lateral of the contralateral spinal cord, while about 10 percent remain ipsilateral in the ventral column of the cord. The voluntary system contacts fewer interneurons and motor neurons than the postural control system. The voluntary system thus provides for discrete movements involving a few muscles and joints.

Output from the motor cortex can also be gated by conscious intent from the **supplementary motor area** (SMA) in the **transcortical reflex** (Fig. 29.6). Once set by maintained discharge in the SMA, transcortical reflexes can be triggered by muscle stretch, causing contraction of the muscle that opposes the stretch and restoring the original intended length and joint position. Transcortical reflexes can also be triggered by skin contact, providing palpatory and grasping digit movements to and around a contacted object.

Slight damage to the lateral corticospinal tract impairs voluntary movements at one or few distal joints, whereas more extensive damage involves the face, arms, legs, and trunk of the opposite side of the body, producing **hemiparesis**—partial paralysis—or **hemiplegia**—complete paralysis—both negative deficits. Irritation of the motor cortex through electrical stimulation, tumor, stroke, trauma, or other means can cause seizures (a positive deficit). Because seizures continue after the stimulus, they are thought to depend on positive feedback combined with the loss of normal inhibition. Seizures may be focal (involving the face or an arm or leg), or they may "march" (e.g., from the face to an arm, and then to a leg).

When the lateral system is deprived of higher control, as in lesions of more anterior parts of the frontal lobe, the palpatory reflex may become automatic and hyperactive—the **involuntary grasp reflex.** The long loop stretch reflex after frontal lobe damage may become automatic and hyperactive as an unwitting resistance to limb displacement (**gegenhalten** = holding against) (Fig. 29.6).

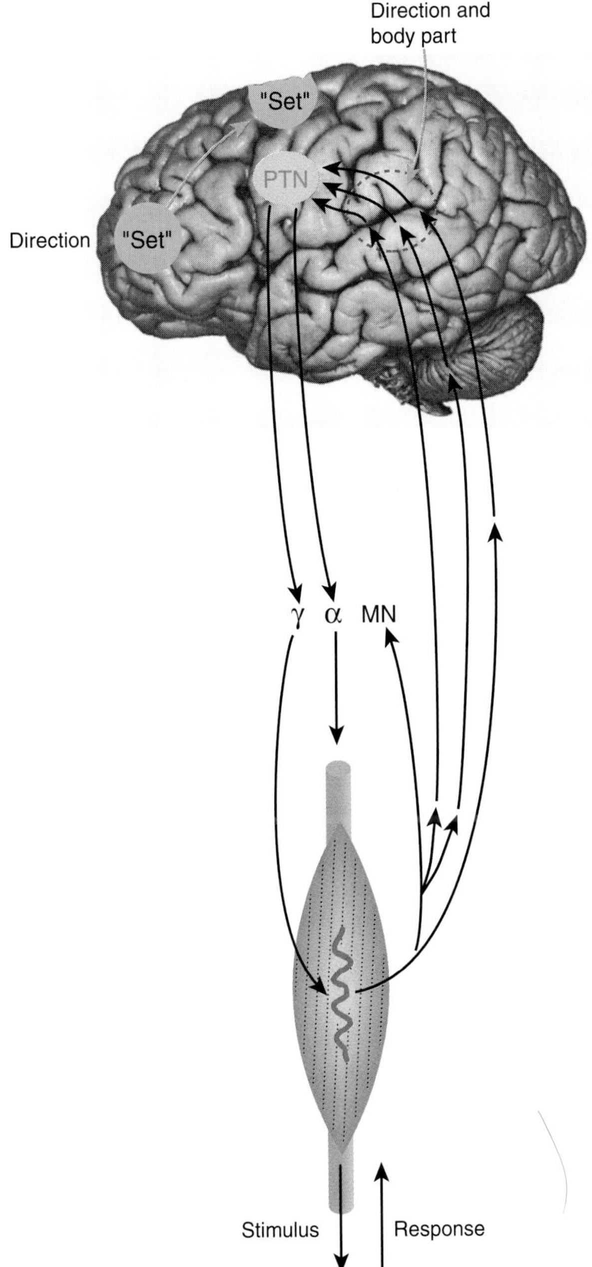

FIGURE 29.6 Diagram of the monosynaptic spinal and the transcortical ("long loop") reflex. α, alpha motor neuron; γ, gamma motor neuron; PTN, pyramidal tract neuron in motor cortex; "Set" shows areas in the supplementary motor area and the anterior frontal lobes that influence the transcortical reflex. The adequate stimulus is a stretch of the muscle; the response is a contraction of that muscle. The monosynaptic spinal reflex is automatic and obligatory; the transcortical reflex is voluntary and conditional—it can be gated "on" or "off."

The red nucleus receives input from the motor

CASE 5: CONCERNING CONFIDENTIALITY

Veronica Hernandez serves on the scientific advisory board for Bioprosthetics Corporation, a start-up company established by Mark Robbins, who is a professor of surgery at Waterford College of Medicine. Dr. Hernandez receives a yearly $2,000 honorarium in exchange for her advice. At their recent advisory board meeting, Dr. Robbins presented his 5-year plan for the company. Upon hearing his plan, Dr. Hernandez was immediately reminded of a manuscript on the central control of motor function that she recently reviewed and recommended for publication. That manuscript strongly suggests that the line of inquiry being proposed will be fruitless. Should Dr. Hernandez provide this information to Dr. Robbins?

See Appendix for discussion questions.

and especially premotor regions of the cerebral cortex. In humans, the relatively few rubrospinal axons cross and descend with axons of the motor cortex in the contralateral lateral column of the spinal cord, where they terminate on the same targets as the lateral corticospinal tract. Most of the output of the red nucleus projects to the principal portion of the inferior olive, which in turn projects exclusively to the cerebellum as climbing fibers. The red nucleus is thought by many to be concerned with the cerebellar role in motor learning.

THE BASAL NUCLEI AND CEREBELLUM: FOCUSING AND COORDINATING MOVEMENT

The basal ganglia inhibit the part of the thalamus that projects back to the cerebral cortex (for voluntary movement). The basal ganglia also inhibit brainstem cells called the "peripedunculopontine nuclei" (for posture). Input to the basal ganglia comes from the cerebral cortex and thalamus. The **basal nuclei** include the **globus pallidus** (internal and external segments), **putamen, subthalamic** and **caudate nuclei,** and **substantia nigra, pars compacta,** and **pars reticulata.**

According to the "brake hypothesis," the normal function of the basal nuclei is to disinhibit the **motor pattern generator** (MPG) involved in a particular movement and to inhibit all competing MPGs. MPGs include all of the components of the postural and the voluntary control systems. For example, when one reaches out to push an elevator button, that movement is commanded by the prefrontal, premotor, motor, and parietal cortices as well as the cerebellum. The premotor and motor cortices send a message to the arm area of the basal nuclei, which release their inhibitory "brake" on the voluntary system MPGs and apply the brake to the postural system MPGs. This mechanism focuses the movement and eliminates competition between MPGs.

Damage to the globus pallidus (usually as a result of stroke) or substantia nigra (in Parkinson disease) causes a sustained contraction in all muscles, agonist and antagonist, resulting in resting plastic rigidity, a positive deficit. Attempted voluntary movements are slow—**bradykinesia**—or absent—**akinesia;** both conditions represent negative deficits. Parkinson disease also features a "pill-rolling tremor." Damage to the caudate nucleus and putamen (Huntington disease) causes **chorea** ("dancing") and **athetosis** (changing posture), whereas damage to the subthalamic nucleus (in stroke) causes **hemiballismus** (throwing an object). Chorea, athetosis, and hemiballismus—all positive deficits—are sinuous, writhing, well-coordinated movements that often seem natural. They may resemble a normal facial grimace, a gesture of the hand in speech, or a change in the position of a crossed leg. Therefore, the names of these deficits are those for natural acts. For the same reason, it was long thought that the basal nuclei might be CPG for normal voluntary movements and postures. According to this view, cerebral cortical inputs to the basal nuclei triggered patterned motor outputs. When the basal nuclei were freed from cortical control by damage to the cerebral cortex, patterned involuntary movements were thought to be released. However, the evidence now suggests that the basal nuclei are inhibitory and control MPGs for movement downstream from them.

The output of the cerebellum projects to all components of the voluntary and postural motor systems. In contrast to the basal nuclei, however, the cerebellum produces excitatory rather than inhibitory output. To return to the example we used earlier, when one reaches out to push an elevator button, many of the more than 600 muscles in the body are involved. The cerebellum controls the muscle activities that one rarely thinks about, like contracting the anterior tibial muscle to keep one from falling over backward. The cerebellum selects and coordinates the timing, duration, and amplitude of activity in the many muscles that are used in even the simplest acts. It helps an individual learn new motor skills and modify old ones so that they may be performed unconsciously yet with perfect coordination.

The cerebellar circuit has two types of input. One pathway, terminating as mossy fibers, carries many kinds of interoceptive and exteroceptive information. This pathway ends on and excites granule cells, the proposed memory cells of the cerebellum. There are more granule cells in the cerebellum than there are neurons in all of the rest of the nervous system. Granule cell axons form parallel fibers that weakly excite Purkinje cells. The other input to the cerebellum comes from a single source, the inferior olive, which has relatively few cells. Inferior olivary axons, called climbing fibers, powerfully excite Purkinje cells. Climbing fiber input causes a Purkinje cell to change its responses to all of the inputs it receives and is thought to create new patterns of movement in response to those inputs. Motor learning in the cerebellum proceeds gradually by trial and error, but once a skilled movement is learned, it remains coded for a long time.

Damage to the lateral cerebellar cortex and dentate nucleus results in movements with curved trajectories, overshoot of endpoint, terminal tremor on the finger–nose–finger and heel–knee–shin tests, and irregularities of rapid alternating pronation–supination of the wrist and the finger–to–thumbcrease tests. Damage to the midline cerebellar cortex and fastigial nuclei causes patients to fall to the side of the lesion, especially on heel-to-toe gait. The cerebellar cortex and nuclei are somatotopically mapped: damage to anterior regions affects the legs; damage to the middle affects the arms; and damage to posterior regions affects the head, neck, and eyes.

Summary

In sum, like the sensory systems, the motor system has a number of discrete components. These are linked together in a network that is in general hierarchical, but there are many cross-connections and feedback loops. No one component functions in isolation without the cooperative activity of many other components.

References

General

Brookhart, J. M., Mountcastle, V. B., Brooks, V. B., and Geiger, S. R., eds. (1981). *Handbook of Physiology*, Sect. 1, Vol. 2, Parts 1 and 2. American Physiological Society, Bethesda, MD.

Creed, R. S., Denney-Brown, D. E., Eccles, J. C., Liddell, E. G. T., and Sherrington, C. S. (1932). *Reflex Activity of the Spinal Cord.* Clarendon Press, Oxford.

Denny-Brown, D. E. (1962). *The Basal Ganglia and Their Relation to Disorders of Movement.* Oxford University Press, London.

Dow, R. S., and Moruzzi, G. (1958). *The Physiology and Pathology of the Cerebellum.* University of Minnesota Press, Minneapolis.

Holmes, G. (1939). The cerebellum of man (The Hughlings Jackson Lecture). *Brain* **62:** 1–30.

Landau, W. M. (1969). Spasticity and rigidity. In *Recent Advances in Neurology* (F. Plum, ed.), pp. 1–32. Davis, Philadelphia.

Lawrence, D. G., and Kuypers, H. G. J. M. (1968). The functional organization of the motor system in the monkey. I. The effects of bilateral pyramidal lesions. *Brain* **91:** 1–14.

Lawrence, D. G., and Kuypers, H. G. J. M. (1968). The functional organization of the motor system in the monkey. II. The effects of lesions of the descending brainstem pathways. *Brain* **91:** 15–36.

Mink, J. W., and Thach, W. T. (1991). Basal ganglia motor control. III. Pallidal ablation: Normal reaction time, muscle cocontraction, and slow movement. *J. Neurophysiol.* **65:** 330–351.

Schieber, M. H. (1991). Individuated finger movements of Rhesus monkeys: A means of quantifying the independence of the digits. *J. Neurophysiol.* **65:** 1381–1391.

Thach, W. T., Goodkin, H. G., and Keating, J. G. (1992). Cerebellum and the adaptive coordination of movement. *Annu. Rev. Neurosci.* **15:** 403–442.

CHAPTER

30

Muscle, Motor Neurons, and Motor Neuron Pools

M. K. Floeter

Movement results from the action of muscles and external forces, such as gravity, on the skeleton or soft tissues. Skeletal muscles are often diagrammed for simplicity as springs and ratchets connected in series across a jointed arm. Such mechanical analogies are helpful in analyzing movements, but to appreciate how the nervous system controls movements we must understand the biological components of movement. In the past few decades, tremendous progress has been made in elucidating the cellular and biochemical makeup of muscle, the physiology and organization of motor neurons that drive muscles, and the specialized sensory receptors of muscle. In this chapter we investigate the organization of these most distal components of the motor system and the constraints they place on the central nervous system's coordination of movement.

SKELETAL MUSCLE

A skeletal muscle is made up of many individual cells, called **muscle fibers,** each only a few centimeters long. Fascicles, or bundles of muscle fibers, are encased in connective tissue. Fascicles end on tendons that attach to bones; to soft tissue, as in the muscles for facial expression; or to other muscles, such as the tongue muscle.

In general, muscles under voluntary control have a striped or striated appearance that results from the orderly arrangement of their contractile machinery. Many of the basic features of striated muscle are quite similar in vertebrates and invertebrates. Here we describe mammalian skeletal muscle; a few variations on the standard mammalian pattern are highlighted in Box 30.1.[1]

Muscle Proteins Are Spatially Organized within the Muscle Fiber

Mammalian skeletal muscle is composed of cylindrical, multinucleated fibers formed from the fusion of myoblast cells during development. The nuclei are positioned along the periphery of the muscle fiber, while the contractile apparatus, consisting of longitudinally oriented **myofibrils** about 1 μm in diameter, fills the interior (Fig. 30.1). Each myofibril consists of repeated units a few micrometers long, known as **sarcomeres.**

Sarcomeres contain longitudinal arrays of thick and thin filaments separated by perpendicular bands called **Z lines.**[2] Thin filaments are composed of actin filaments that are entwined by the protein tropomyosin. Binding to tropomyosin is another protein, troponin, which is a member of a family of calcium-binding proteins (Fig. 30.2). The thin filaments are anchored to the Z lines, which contain α-actinin.[3] Thick filaments primarily contain **myosin,** a large protein composed of two heavy chains and four light chains. Myosin heavy chains consist of a linear tail and a globular head to which the light chains attach. Myosin monomers assemble into thick filaments, with the tails aligned in the center and the heads protruding outward on either end of the sarcomere (Fig. 30.2). The myosin head functions as a weak ATPase whose activity increases enormously when myosin binds to actin. When the muscle fiber is at rest, the binding sites on actin are concealed from myosin by troponin and tropomyosin. A flexible

BOX 30.1

VARIATIONS IN MUSCLE DESIGN AND CONTROL

Many animals have evolved muscle adaptations that meet special requirements of their movements and that differ from the adaptation described for mammals.[1] These differences may involve the structure, biochemistry, or neural control of the muscle.

Some animals require muscles that generate great force or provide extreme resistance to stretch, and they meet this requirement in a variety of ways. The mussel, for example, uses the protein paramyosin instead of myosin in its retractor muscle. Paramyosin forms thicker filaments that contain additional sites for cross bridge formation. As discussed in the text, the amount of force a muscle can generate is related to the number of cross bridges it forms. Some mollusks and clams, in contrast, close their shells using a muscle in which the cross bridges remain tightly bound until they are actively released. This arrangement allows the clam to keep its shell closed while expending little energy.

Many marine animals move slowly and thus require muscles that can produce twitches much slower than those produced by most mammalian muscles. Slowness can be achieved by having longer sarcomeres, in part because Ca^{2+} diffusion throughout the sarcomere takes longer. Crustacean muscles have sarcomeres that range from 2 to 25 μm in length. In mammals, longer sarcomeres are occasionally found in muscles that stiffen but do not twitch, such as the tensor tympani muscle of the cat eardrum.

Although muscles composed of a single fiber type are unusual in mammals, they are common in fish. Salmon and tuna, for example, have distinct red muscles that they use for sustained swimming; these muscles consist entirely of slow fibers. For occasional leaping and rapid bursts of speed, they use another set of muscles consisting entirely of fast white fibers.

The structural arrangement of the components of a muscle fiber may differ from the standard arrangement of mammalian muscle fibers. In some insect flight muscles, for example, the contractile apparatus contains a spokelike array of myofibrils that radiate from a central cluster of nuclei. Differences in the arrangement of intracellular components are also found in the specialized intrafusal fibers of mammals, the nuclear bag and chain fibers.

The greatest variability in muscle organization occurs in how the nervous system controls muscles. Muscles in many nonmammalian animals are polyneuronally innervated; that is, more than one neuron innervates each muscle fiber. In some polyneuronally innervated muscles, the motor neurons have a similar or additive function. For example, in the fruit fly *Drosophila*, additional motor neurons can be recruited to produce graded contractions of a muscle fiber. In other animals, multiple motor neurons innervating a single muscle fiber may play distinct roles. The locust jumping muscle has a dual arrangement, with one motor neuron that produces a rapid and powerful excitation and one that produces a graded excitation and contraction. In most arthropod muscles, each muscle fiber receives input from excitatory and inhibitory motor neurons, and integration of postsynaptic potentials occurs in the muscle fiber. Presynaptic inhibition of the motor terminal has been described for the crustacean neuromuscular junction. Different excitatory neurotransmitters may be released at the neuromuscular junction. Some animals, such as the nematode *Caenorhabditis elegans*, use acetylcholine, the neurotransmitter of the mammalian neuromuscular junction; others, such as *Drosophila* and crustaceans, use glutamate.

Finally, there are differences in how the nervous system controls the activity of motor neurons. Mammals generally produce rhythmic muscle contractions through repetitive bursts of motor neuron firing. The frequency of repetition is limited by both the motor neuron's refractory period and the muscle fiber's speed of shortening and relaxation, and few mammalian limb movements are faster than 10 Hz. Some insects, however, can beat their wings at frequencies of 100–1000 Hz. Their muscle fibers produce such rapid movements by having very short contraction and relaxation times. In addition, some insects bypass the constraints of using neural mechanisms to maintain the wing beat. In these insects, muscle fibers are specialized to be activated by mechanical stretch, and sets of muscle fibers are arranged such that contraction of one set stretches another set, causing it to contract. The result is an oscillatory contraction of both sets of muscle fibers. Neural drive is used primarily to initiate the oscillation.

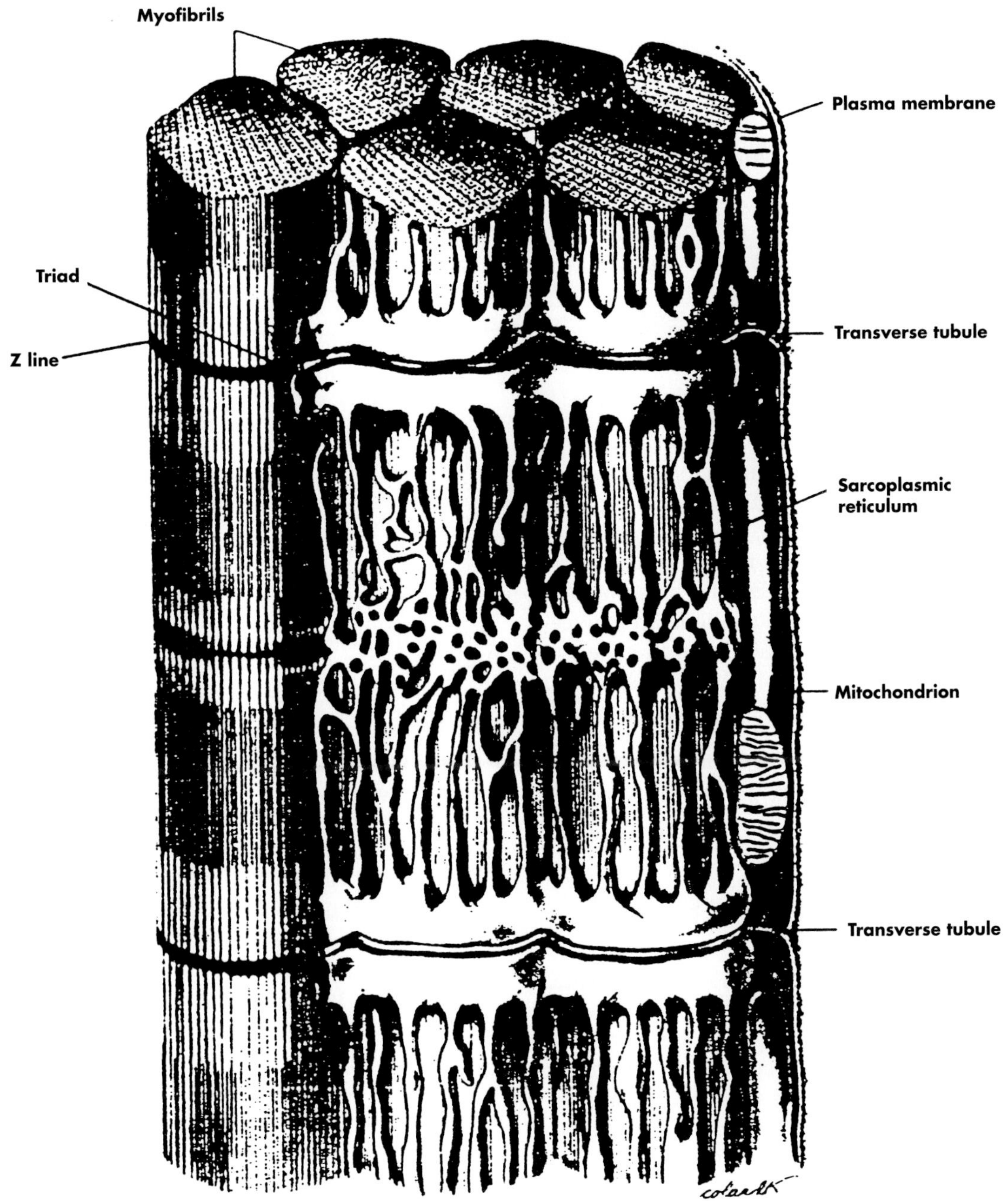

FIGURE 30.1 Structure of a vertebrate skeletal muscle fiber. Redrawn from Fawcett.[66]

hinge region of the myosin molecule allows the head to pivot as it undergoes conformational changes associated with actin binding and ATP hydrolysis.[4,5]

Cellular Structures Are Spatially Organized around the Contractile Proteins

The skeletal muscle fiber has a number of cellular specializations that function in controlling the myofibrils. The muscle fiber's plasma membrane has numerous infoldings, known as **transverse tubules** (T tubules), that penetrate deep into the interior of the muscle fiber. The T-tubule membrane is continuous with the plasma membrane but contains a higher concentration of several specific proteins, including channels for calcium and chloride ions. The "interior" of each T tubule is continuous with the extracellular space, but diffusion of substances into and out of the

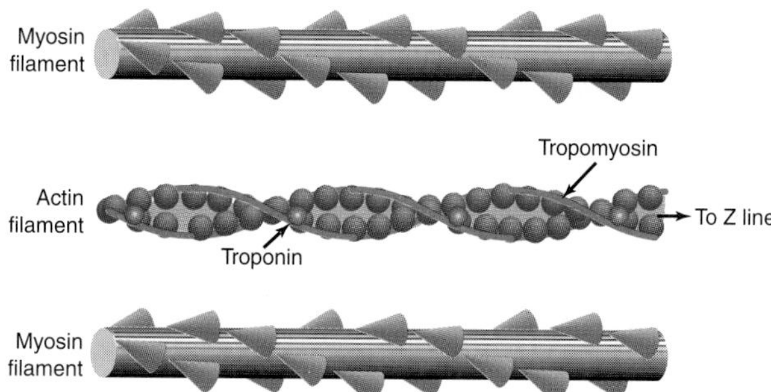

FIGURE 30.2 Thick and thin filaments. Intertwined arrays of actin, troponin, and tropomyosin make up thin filaments. Multiple myosin monomers assemble into thick filaments. Reproduced from Squire,[2] with permission from Elsevier.

T tubules occurs more slowly than at the cell surface. The ends of the T tubules come into close contact with the **sarcoplasmic reticulum** (SR), a form of endoplasmic reticulum specialized for the release and reuptake of calcium in muscle fibers. The SR encircles the myofibrils, creating a close physical relationship between this calcium-storage organelle and the contractile proteins. Mitochondria, the sites of aerobic respiration, and glycogen, the main energy source in the muscle fiber, are packed between the bundles of myofibrils. The junctions between the T tubules and the SR, called **triads,** play a key role in the coupling between muscle excitation and contraction (Fig. 30.3).

Sequence of Electrical and Chemical Events Leads to Muscle Contraction

Mammalian skeletal muscle fibers are innervated by the axon of a single alpha motor neuron at their **end plate,** a discrete region near the midpoint of the muscle fiber. The synapse between the motor neuron and the muscle fiber is called the **neuromuscular junction.** Acetylcholine released by the motor neuron binds to receptors in the muscle fiber membrane that allow cations to enter the muscle fiber. The entry of cations produces a local depolarization, known as the **end-plate potential,** that initiates a series of events culminating in the contraction of the muscle fiber.

1. *Membrane excitation.* The muscle fiber membrane contains voltage-activated sodium and potassium channels that can generate an action potential, as described for neurons in Chapter 6. When the end-plate potential reaches the threshold for activating the sodium channel, an action potential occurs. The action potential travels along the muscle fiber membrane and the continuous membrane of the T tubules.

2. *Calcium channel activation.* The T-tubule membrane contains voltage-activated Ca^{2+} channels that are sensitive to dihydropyridine (L channels, see Chapter 6). The action potential depolarization causes a conformational change in the Ca^{2+} channel proteins, opening the channels and allowing Ca^{2+} to enter the muscle fiber in the vicinity of the T tubules. However, Ca^{2+} flux through these channels does not seem to be necessary for coupling membrane excitation to contraction in skeletal muscle. Instead, the conformational change of the Ca^{2+} channel protein is of primary importance.

3. *Channel interactions.* The Ca^{2+} channels in the T-tubule membrane lie in close apposition to a second type of Ca^{2+} channel, known as the ryanodine receptor, which is anchored in the SR (Fig. 30.4)[6]. The conformational change in the T-tubule Ca^{2+} channel that occurs during depolarization opens the ryanodine receptor channel. Opening of the latter appears to be triggered by a direct interaction between the ryanodine receptor's large foot region and the T-tubule Ca^{2+} channel. This interaction rapidly couples membrane excitation and Ca^{2+} release.[7,8] (The role of voltage-activated ion channels in some muscle diseases is considered in Box 30.2.[9–11])

4. *Calcium release.* Opening of the ryanodine receptor channel releases Ca^{2+} from the SR into the muscle fiber's cytosol. The concentration of Ca^{2+} in the cytosol rises by an order of magnitude.

5. *Calcium binding.* Ca^{2+} binds to troponin, leading to the displacement of tropomyosin from actin. It has been hypothesized that this displacement exposes the myosin-binding sites on actin allowing **cross bridges** to form between actin and myosin.

6. *Cross-bridge attachment and detachment.* When a cross bridge forms, the ATPase activity of the myosin

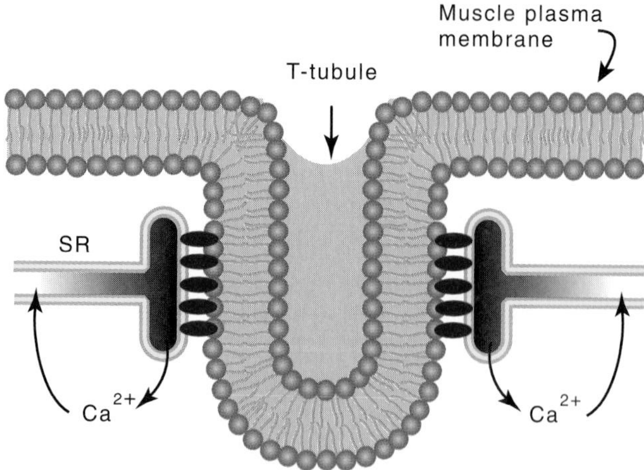

FIGURE 30.3 The triad, formed at the junction of a T tubule and the sarcoplasmic reticulum (SR), is the site where excitation–contraction coupling occurs. Reproduced from Catterall.[7] Copyright © 1991 Cell Press.

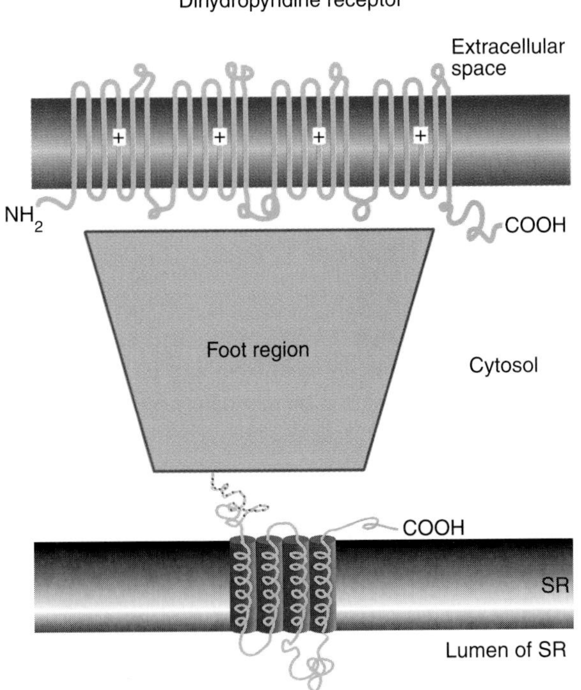

FIGURE 30.4 Diagram of the interaction between the dihydropyridine receptor (in the T tubule) and the large foot region of the ryanodine receptor (in the SR). A direct interaction between the two proteins is a key element in excitation–contraction coupling. Reproduced from Takeshima *et al.*[6] Copyright © 1989 Macmillan Magazines Limited.

head increases. The myosin head hydrolyzes ATP, causing detachment of the cross bridge. If Ca^{2+} levels in the cytosol remain high, binding sites for myosin remain exposed, and the formation and detachment of cross bridges continue. The repeated forming and breaking of cross bridges produce swiveling of the myosin heads[12] and cause the thin filaments to slide along the thick filaments. Since the thin filaments are anchored at the Z lines that delimit each sarcomere, tension is exerted on the Z lines and the sarcomere shortens.

7. *Relaxation.* Repolarization of the muscle fiber membrane initiates the process of relaxation. The voltage-activated channels return to their inactivated conformation, which leads to closing of the ryanodine receptor Ca^{2+} channels. Ca^{2+} ATPases in the SR pump Ca^{2+} from the muscle fiber's cytosol back into the SR. The Ca^{2+} concentration in the cytosol returns to its resting value relatively slowly compared to the quick rise that occurred during contraction. As Ca^{2+} levels fall, troponin and tropomyosin bind to actin, concealing binding sites for the myosin heads. The formation of cross bridges is blocked, and the muscle relaxes.

The Number of Cross-Bridges Determines the Force Produced by a Muscle Fiber

Cross bridges, the mechanical links between thick and thin filaments, contribute to muscle stiffness, or resistance to stretch. When a muscle is at rest, there are no cross bridges and the filaments slide easily past each other when the muscle is passively stretched. When a muscle is contracting, however, its resistance to stretch depends on the length of overlap between thick and thin filaments, which determines the number of cross bridges that can form. In Fig. 30.6A, the length of overlap between thick and thin filaments is diagrammed for a muscle sarcomere that can be stretched between 1 and 4 μm. Note that when the sarcomere is very short, as in the bottom diagram, or very long, as in the top diagram, few cross bridges form because there is little overlap between thick and thin filaments. An optimal range of overlap occurs with sarcomere lengths around 2.2–2.6 μm, as in the middle diagram. The relationship between sarcomere length and the force that is generated (Fig. 30.6B) shows that the force is maximal at those lengths where the overlap is greatest.[13] This relationship means that, when activated, a sarcomere may produce a variable amount of force that is determined by the length to which it is stretched. The optimal working lengths of individual sarcomeres underlie differences in the force generated by whole muscles that may undergo stretch during movements.

The Strength of Cross Bridges Varies throughout the Cycle

Another factor affecting muscle stiffness is the strength of cross bridges. At the beginning of the cross bridge cycle, myosin heads are loosely bound to actin, and the muscle can still be easily stretched. As the cycle proceeds, stronger cross bridges are formed, leading to a several hundred-fold increase in stiffness.[12] Muscles cannot be easily stretched during the late stages of the cross bridge cycle; strong stretches that would forcibly lengthen the muscle may lead to injury. However, weaker stretches that pull against strong cross bridges without breaking them can be used to generate springlike forces. Certain movements do appear to use the compliance of cross bridges in this way.[14]

Internal Connective Tissue Contributes to the Stiffness of Muscle

A third factor that affects muscle stiffness is the connective tissue in muscle. At muscle lengths longer than the optimal length, the tendons and connective tissue in a muscle will resist further stretch. Because

BOX 30.2

MUSCLE DISEASES RESULTING FROM ABNORMALITIES IN VOLTAGE-ACTIVATED CHANNELS

Several inherited skeletal muscle diseases result from mutations affecting the ion channels of the muscle fiber membrane. Different mutations lead to distinctive clinical syndromes.[9] Sodium channel abnormalities include the human and equine disorder hyperkalemic periodic paralysis. This disorder is characterized by attacks of paralysis, during which the muscle fiber membrane is electrically inexcitable. Attacks often follow a period of rest after strenuous exercise. In another sodium channel disorder, paramyotonia congenita, low temperatures cause myotonia, an excessive excitation of the muscle and transient weakness. Precisely how the mutations alter sodium channels and produce the functional changes in these two disorders is an area of active investigation.

Characteristic electrical discharges occur in myotonia. The discharges resemble individual muscle fiber action potentials repeating with high frequency upon an oscillating baseline as shown in Fig. 30.5. Since the amplitude and frequency of the discharges wax and wane, the discharges have a characteristic sound when amplified on an audio speaker, often compared to the sound of a dive-bombing airplane. Myotonic discharges are also seen in Thomsen myotonia, a hereditary disorder of voltage-activated chloride channels in muscle. Chloride channels play a role in maintaining a stable membrane potential. Muscle hypertrophy is another symptom of this disorder, and it has been speculated that the muscles are effectively experiencing a kind of continuous exercise.

Abnormalities in voltage-activated calcium channels may play a role in hypokalemic periodic paralysis, a disorder characterized by attacks of weakness without myotonia.[10] Mutations in the ryanodine receptor channel have been associated with malignant hyperthermia, a disease in which excessive muscle contraction and fever occur in humans when certain anesthetic agents are given and in swine under stress. Elevated calcium release from the sarcoplasmic reticulum is thought to underlie the excessive muscle contraction.[11]

FIGURE 30.5 Myotonic discharge in the muscle of a patient with myotonia congenita.

these components are less elastic than muscle fibers, tension rises quickly. Thus, the length–tension curves of whole muscles are affected by internal connective tissue arrangements, which vary for each muscle. The contribution to total tension from connective tissue is often referred to as passive, and the contribution from myofibrils is referred to as active. Passive contributions are different for healthy and diseased muscles. Degenerative muscle diseases or even the prolonged disuse of muscles, such as may occur after a stroke, can markedly increase the amount of connective tissue in a muscle, thereby increasing the muscle's resistance to stretch.

Muscles Have Several Energy Sources

The process of cross bridge cycling requires energy. In particular, the detachment of cross bridges from the strongly bound state requires the hydrolysis of ATP. During a maintained contraction, 50–80% of the ATP consumed by a muscle fiber fuels the cross bridge cycle, and another 20–30% powers the pumping of Ca^{2+} back

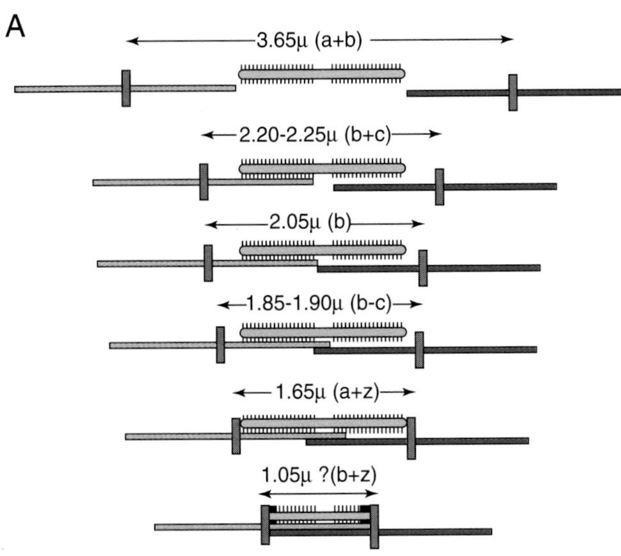

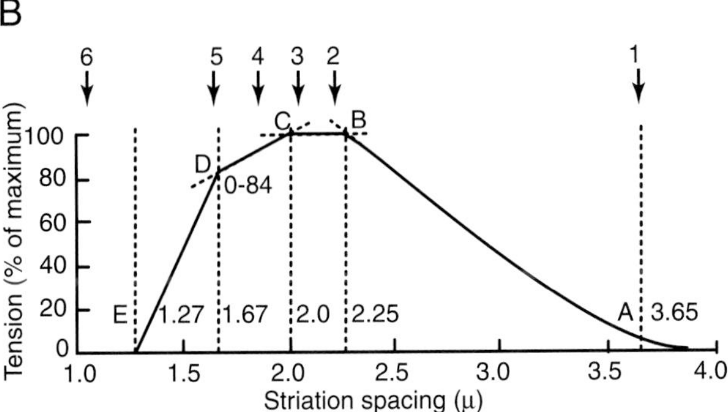

FIGURE 30.6 Sarcomere length–tension curves. (A) Diagram of thick and thin filaments at six sarcomere lengths. These lengths are indicated on a graph of tension versus sarcomere length (B). Note that optimal tension (points 2 and 3) is produced when there is maximal overlap between the thick and thin filaments. No tension is produced when the filaments do not overlap at all (point 1) and when the ends of the thin filaments collide with the Z lines (point 6). Reproduced from Gordon *et al.*[67]

into the SR. A smaller amount of ATP is used by the Na,K-ATPase that maintains the transmembrane Na^+ and K^+ gradients. In the absence of ATP, cross bridges remain in the strongly attached state and muscles cannot easily be stretched without injury, a condition known as **rigor.**

The muscle fiber has several different pathways for making ATP. When oxygen is available, ATP is generated most efficiently by oxidative phosphorylation in mitochondria, using fatty acids and carbohydrates for substrates. When the oxygen supply to a muscle is limited, as may occur during intense exercise, anaerobic pathways such as glycolysis and the breakdown of phosphocreatine become important for synthesizing ATP. The substrates used by a muscle to make ATP are also influenced by the muscle's physiological state. During fasting, for example, muscles make ATP from amino acids.

There Are Three Basic Types of Mammalian Skeletal Muscle Fibers

Even on gross examination, most muscles appear heterogeneous, containing different proportions of dark or red muscle fibers and pale or white fibers. With more refined techniques, we can distinguish at least three fiber types—designated Type 1, Type 2a, and Type 2b—in mammalian skeletal muscles. The differences between the three fiber types can be loosely divided into those that affect muscle metabolism and those that affect the characteristics of contraction.[15] The metabolic differences can be demonstrated histochemically, as shown in Fig. 30.7. Type 1 fibers tend to be thinner than Type 2a and Type 2b fibers (Fig. 30.7; see also Fig. 30.17). Differences in the cross-sectional area of the myofibrils, which are more loosely packed in Type 1 fibers, may contribute to differences in the amount of force the various fiber types can generate.

Type 1 Fibers Are Specialized for Slow, Sustained, Aerobic Exercise

Type 1, or slow red muscle, fibers have a rich capillary blood supply, many mitochondria, and high levels of myoglobin, a protein that binds oxygen and provides the fiber's red color. These features correspond to the Type 1 fiber's dependence on aerobic metabolism for generating ATP. At rest, Type 1 fibers have a higher resting blood flow than other fiber types.[16] The contractile characteristics of Type 1 fibers are determined by both the density of cellular specializations for contraction and the kinetics of the contractile proteins. Type 1 fibers have less abundant SR than other fiber types and a lower density of SR Ca^{2+}-ATPases, resulting in slower Ca^{2+} fluxes into the muscle fiber cytosol. The type of myosin expressed by Type 1 fibers has a relatively low rate of ATP hydrolysis, which limits the rate of detachment of cross bridges and thus the speed of contraction and relaxation. These cellular and molecular features cause Type 1 muscle fibers to produce a slow twitch when activated and give the fibers a metabolism optimal for aerobic conditions.

Type 2 Fibers Are Specialized for Rapid Contractions

Mammalian limb muscles contain at least two subtypes of fast-twitch fibers, designated Type 2a and

FIGURE 30.7 Adjacent sections from the medial gastrocnemius muscle of the cat, histochemically stained for ATPase activity at neutral (A) and acidic (B) pH and for the mitochondrial enzyme NADH dehydrogenase (C) allow identification of muscle fiber types. Type 1 fibers, for example, are darkly stained in (A) and (C). Courtesy of R. E. Burke.

Type 2b. The metabolic properties of Type 2b, or white, fibers lie at the opposite extreme from those of Type 1 fibers. Type 2b fibers are supplied by fewer capillaries and have sparse mitochondria, but they contain relatively large stores of glycogen. Glycogen is an energy store that can be broken down anaerobically through glycolysis, a relatively inefficient process for generating ATP that is accompanied by the buildup of lactic acid. However, Type 2b fibers contain abundant SR with a relatively high density of a "fast-twitch" isoform of Ca^{2+}-ATPase, permitting rapid Ca^{2+} fluxes between the cytosol and the SR. The form of myosin expressed by Type 2b fibers has a fast ATPase activity, resulting in more rapid cross bridge cycling. Thus, Type 2b fibers shorten rapidly and produce fast twitches, but they are limited by their metabolic machinery to brief bursts of exercise.

Type 2a fibers combine some of the features of Type 1 and Type 2b fibers. These pale red fibers are well vascularized and contain the metabolic machinery for both oxidative phosphorylation and glycolysis. Their contractile proteins, on the other hand, resemble those of Type 2b fibers: the myosin has a high rate of ATP hydrolysis, the SR is relatively abundant, and the SR Ca^{2+}-ATPase is similar to that of Type 2b fibers. Both Type 2 fibers produce fast twitches. Type 2a fibers can be thought of as switch-hitters, capable of rapid contractions that can be sustained for relatively long periods without fatigue.

Most Muscles Contain Both Fiber Types

A few mammalian muscles consist of a single fiber type, but most have a mixture of slow- and fast-twitch fibers, in proportions that vary with the typical usage of the muscle. For example, the soleus muscle, an ankle extensor that is usually active during standing, has a high proportion of slow fibers in both humans and cats. Another ankle extensor, the medial gastrocnemius, has a higher proportion of fast-twitch fibers and is generally relaxed during standing but active during running and jumping. The composition of the medial gastrocnemius varies considerably in different mammals: The proportion of fast Type 2 fibers is relatively high in predators such as lions and cats and relatively low in foragers such as skunks and sloths.

Muscle Fibers Contain Multiple Isoforms of Proteins

The preceding discussion highlights the point that many of the metabolic and mechanical differences between muscle fiber types result from the complement of proteins expressed in each fiber. Interestingly, the diversity of contractile proteins exceeds what would be needed to generate a simple dichotomy of slow- and fast-twitch fibers. A family of genes coding for different forms of myosin heavy chains has been cloned. At least seven isoforms are found in adult skeletal muscle, and additional isoforms are expressed during development. Distinct myosins are found in limb muscles, extraocular muscles, and muscles derived from the branchial arch. In limb muscles, the myosins made by Type 2a and Type 2b fibers are encoded by different genes. The diversity of myosins ensures a range of contractile speeds, providing a foundation for muscles that can be used for tasks with very different temporal demands. For example, extraocular muscles contain one set of fibers that are used for rapid saccades and another set that are activated during smooth pursuit.

In each muscle fiber, specific myosin isoforms are usually coexpressed with particular isoforms of a number of other muscle proteins, including the SR Ca^{2+}-ATPase and troponin. The diversity of these other proteins, which are expressed in varying amounts in different myofibers, also contributes to producing the range of muscle fiber contractile speeds. Although the regulation of muscle genes and their transcripts is beyond the scope of this chapter, it is important to note that motor neurons are primarily responsible for determining muscle fiber type. Motor neuron activity and trophic interactions between the motor neuron and muscle fiber play a role in the expression of muscle proteins during development and probably throughout adulthood.[17]

Muscle Fascicles Are Arranged in Pinnate or Parallel Architectures

The conduction velocity of a muscle fiber action potential is only a few meters per second. Since the sarcomeres along the fiber must be activated relatively synchronously to provide a useful mechanical action, muscle fiber conduction velocity limits the length of most muscle fibers to a few centimeters. Relatively few muscles, however, are so short that a single fiber can extend the entire length. Instead, most muscles are made of fascicles that may be arranged in a variety of ways.[18] The most common arrangements are described as pinnate and parallel (Fig. 30.8).

In muscles with a pinnate architecture, the fascicles are oriented at an angle to the primary direction of force produced by the muscle. The angle of pinnation affects the amount of leverage that can be achieved. Individual muscle fibers often attach to aponeuroses or tendinous sheaths running within the muscle, as shown in the unipinnate muscle in Fig. 30.8A, in which the fibers pull on two parallel tendons as they shorten. In a multipinnate muscle, multiple tendons may divide the muscle into parallel adjacent compartments that exert common force, as diagrammed in Fig. 30.8B. The claw-closing muscles of lobsters and crabs illustrate the tremendous force that can be generated in a very small space by a pinnate muscle. Although pinnation increases force, it limits the extensibility of a muscle. Therefore, it is most suitable for muscles with relatively short lever arms that operate over a limited range of lengths, such as the lateral gastrocnemius muscle of the leg.

Muscles that span multiple joints or have long lever arms, such as the knee flexor muscles, often undergo large changes in length during various movements. These muscles tend to have a parallel architecture, in which the fascicles are oriented in the same direction as the force produced by the muscle. Some parallel muscles, such as the sartorius, consist of staggered, interdigitated fascicles that allow a small amount of slippage past each other (Fig. 30.8D). Other parallel muscles such as the rectus abdominus, have serial compartments separated by tendinous partitions (Fig. 30.8C). Still others, such as the semitendinosis muscle of the leg, contain both staggered fascicles and serial compartments.[19] Parallel arrangements may require that the neural machinery synchronously activate all of the fibers along the length of the muscle. The occasional failure to activate fibers in different compartments of the hamstring muscle synchronously, for example, results in a "pulled" hamstring.

Muscles May Be Divided into Compartments

The muscle fibers of mammalian skeletal muscles are often partitioned into anatomical or functional compartments. In some muscles, such as the lateral gastrocnemius, all compartments act on a common tendon to exert a similar force. In other muscles, such as the biceps brachii, tendons from different compartments have separate insertions and produce slightly different mechanical actions. Functional compartments may also occur without gross anatomic demarcations. The deltoid muscle of the shoulder, for example, has broad tendinous attachments that allow different portions of the muscle to exert different force vectors. The masseter muscle, which closes the jaw, contains different regions that can be selectively activated to produce different types of bites. To use muscles for precise movements, therefore, the nervous system must exert control not only over muscles but also over the compartments within muscles.

A Variety of Terms Are Used to Describe Muscle Actions

When a muscle actively shortens, it undergoes what is called an **isotonic contraction.** Not all muscle activations produce muscle shortening, however. In an **isometric activation,** a muscle is activated against a resis-

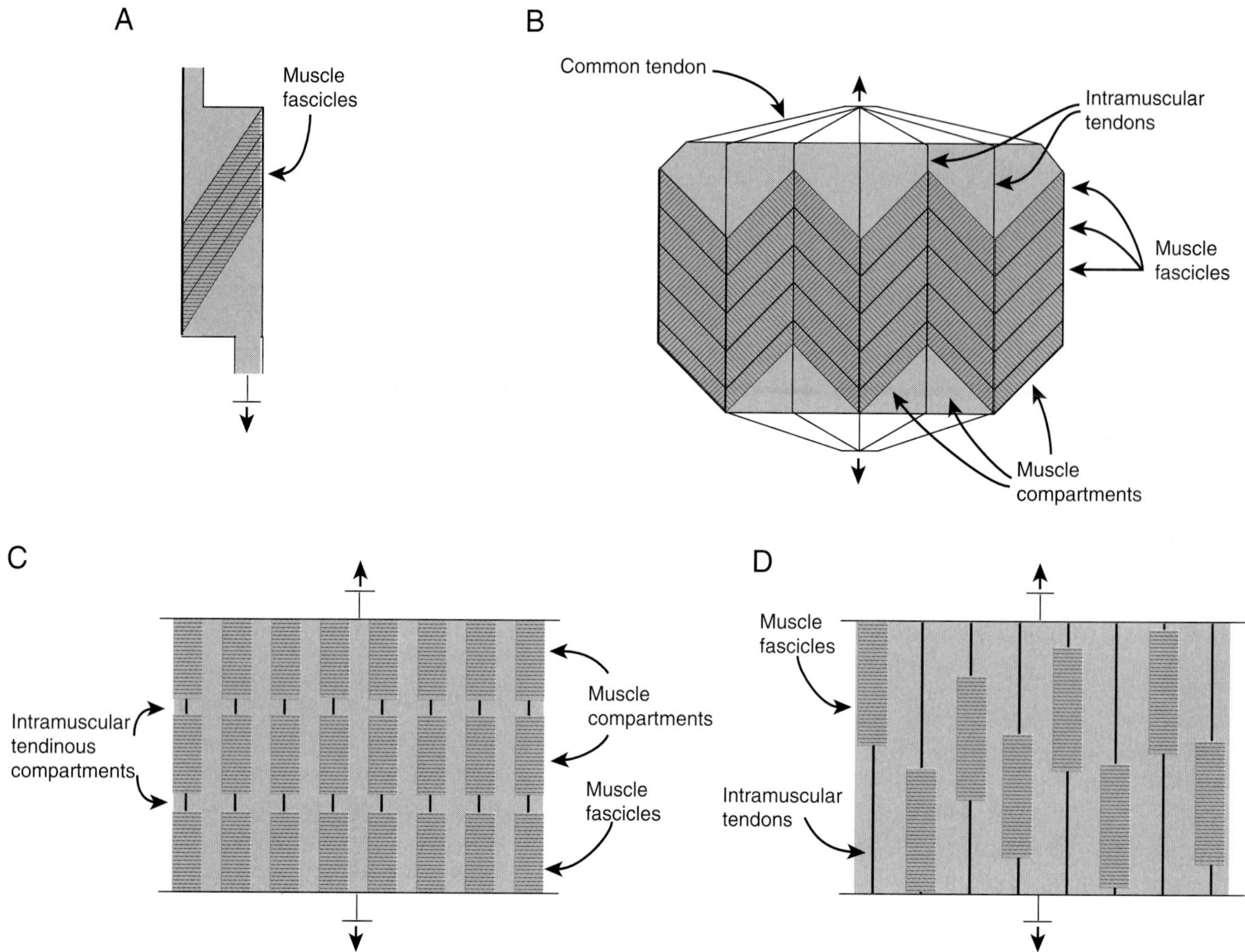

FIGURE 30.8 Architecture of muscles. (A) Unipinnate muscles: Fascicles are oriented at an angle to the direction of force. (B) Multipinnate muscles: Intramuscular tendons create parallel compartments within the muscle; force is exerted on a common tendon. (C) Parallel architecture in series: Intramuscular tendons separate compartments containing fascicles. (D) Parallel architecture: Interdigitated fascicles.

tance without shortening. Activation that occurs as a muscle is lengthened, as occurs in the ankle dorsiflexor muscles when a person walks downhill, is sometimes called an **eccentric contraction.**

Muscles that have similar actions across the same joint are referred to as **synergists,** while muscles that have opposite actions across a joint are called **antagonists.** However, minor differences in the location of tendinous insertions may cause synergists to produce slightly different mechanical actions, and muscles with complex insertions may exert different actions when contracting in combination with other muscles. Moreover, antagonists are often coactivated for movements that require reinforcing or stiffening a limb across a joint. Many muscles also span more than one joint and may have complex patterns of activation during movements. For this reason, studies of movements may need to begin with an analysis of the patterns of contraction and the detailed anatomy of the muscles that are involved.

Summary

Muscle contraction is produced by an orderly sequence of electrical and chemical events, beginning with an action potential originating at the neuromuscular junction. Skeletal muscle fibers translate the electrical signal into a mechanical movement as a result of the spatial organization of intramuscular contractile proteins and excitable membrane channels both on the plasma membrane and on the sarcoplasmic reticulum. Differences in the isozymes or the concentration of these proteins can produce a spectrum of contractile speeds in different muscle fibers. The profile of metabolic enzymes and mitochondrial content also produces a spectrum of fatigability and oxygen requirements among muscle fibers. Individual muscle fibers are classified into two types, with several subtypes, according to their contractile and metabolic properties. The properties of a whole muscle depend on the proportion of muscle fiber types it contains and on the architectural arrangement of muscle fascicles with respect to connective tissues, bones, and joints.

MOTOR UNITS

A Motor Unit Consists of One Motor Neuron and the Muscle Fibers It Innervates

In mammals, each skeletal muscle fiber is normally innervated by a single motor neuron, but that motor neuron may branch to innervate many muscle fibers. The combination of one motor neuron and all of the muscle fibers it innervates is called a **motor unit.** A motor unit is the smallest element of a muscle under neural control. All of the muscle fibers in a given motor unit are of the same type: 1, 2a, or 2b. The fibers belonging to a single motor unit, sometimes referred to as a **muscle unit,** are typically scattered in the muscle among fibers belonging to other motor units, as can be seen in Fig. 30.7 (see also Fig. 30.17). When a muscle is divided into multiple compartments as described above, however, the fibers of a given motor unit are usually confined to a single compartment.[20]

Twitch Properties Can Be Used to Characterize Motor Units

When a motor neuron fires slowly, the muscle fibers it innervates respond to each spike with a twitch. The time from the initial activation of the muscle fibers to the development of peak force is called the **twitch contraction time** (Fig. 30.9A). Muscle relaxation is often measured by the "half-relaxation time," the time required for the force to return to half the peak force. Although brief, the force resulting from a single twitch outlasts the action potential propagated along the muscle fiber membrane. In the human biceps muscle, for example, twitch contraction times range from 30 to 75 ms, and half-relaxation times are two to three times longer than that. In contrast, the average motor unit action potential lasts only about 7–13 ms.[21]

Motor neurons usually fire a series of spikes during natural movements. When the interval between spikes is shorter than the relaxation time, the tension generated by successive twitches can summate (Fig. 30.9B). At high motor neuron firing rates, twitches fuse to

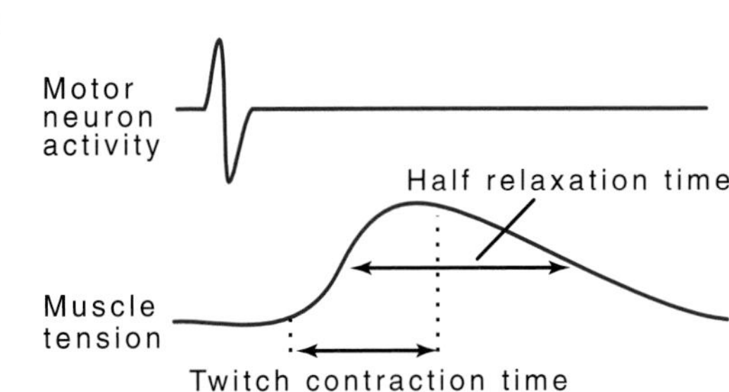

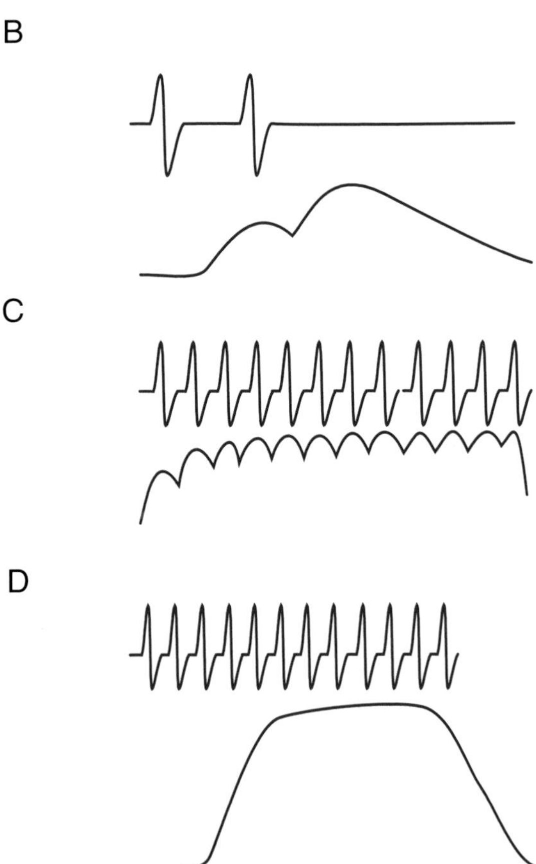

FIGURE 30.9 Muscle tension increases with motor neuron firing rate. (A) Single twitch. (B) Summation of two twitches. (C) Summation of multiple twitches. (D) Tetanus.

generate a steady level of force, or **tetanus** (Fig. 30.9C and 30.9D). Individual motor units can be characterized by their tetanic tension, which ranges from 0.5 mg to 120 g for motor units of the medial gastrocnemius of the cat.[22] The rate of firing needed to develop tetanus depends on relaxation time, which differs for Type 1 and Type 2 fibers. Motor units composed of Type 1 fibers develop peak tension most slowly and relax slowly; their twitches may fuse with firing rates as low as 15–20 Hz (Fig. 30.10). Motor units composed of Type 2 fibers may have twitch fusion frequencies of 40–60 Hz.

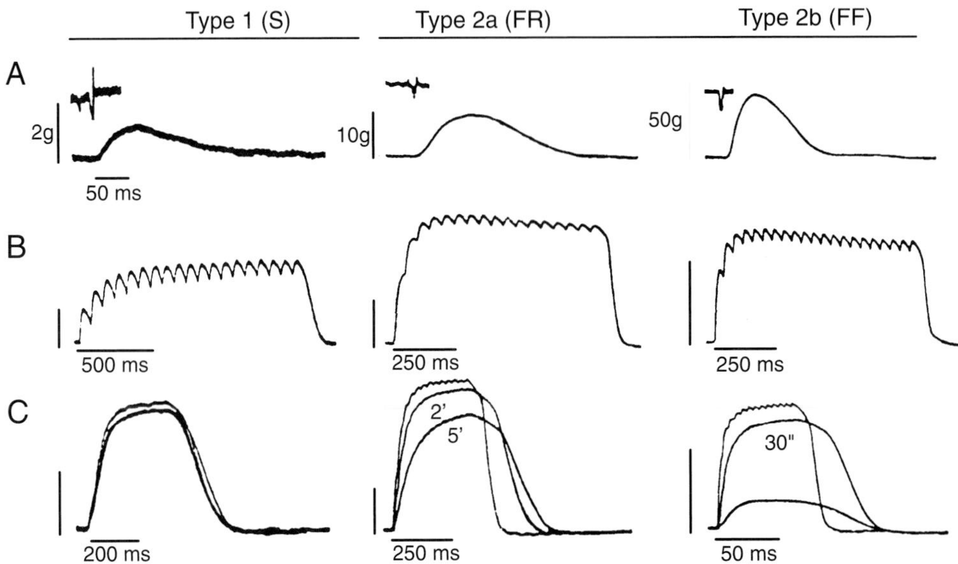

FIGURE 30.10 Contractile properties of different motor unit types (S, FR, and FF). (A) Single twitch. Note the different time scales and tension calibrations. (B) Summation of twitches. The "sag" property, a dropping off of tension during maintained stimulation, is seen in FR and FF units. (C) The tension produced by a single twitch is reduced after short periods of activation, indicating fatigue. Note that S units show little fatigue, whereas FF units fatigue within 30 s. Reproduced from Burke *et al.*[22]

The force produced by a motor unit is influenced by the pattern of motor neuron firing as well as its frequency. If a motor neuron fires an extra spike during a steady train of spikes (Fig. 30.11), the force produced increases abruptly. This phenomenon, termed the "catch" property, has been observed in all of the motor unit types described in the next section.[23] The sustained jump in force is thought to result from a change within the muscle, presumably involving the coupling between excitation and contraction. A similar phenomenon in barnacle muscles has been investigated with the Ca^{2+} indicator aequorin.[1] In this species, the extra spike elicits an abrupt rise in the cytosolic Ca^{2+} concentration of the muscle fiber, but this rise is short-lived compared to the increase in tension (Fig. 30.12).

There Are Three Basic Motor Unit Types

Although the anatomical and physiological properties of motor neurons vary, the properties of a given motor neuron generally match those of the muscle fiber type it innervates. Detailed studies of motor units in the cat triceps surae muscle have revealed that most motor units can be divided into three groups: S (slow), FR (fast fatigue-resistant), and FF (fast fatigable). The methods for distinguishing among these groups are described in Box 30.3.

Motor neurons of S motor units tend to have the smallest somas and dendritic trees, as well as relatively small-diameter axons and low conduction velocities. Their compact anatomy correlates with a high passive membrane resistance and a low rheobase (the amount

FIGURE 30.11 Catch property in cat motor unit. An extra spike occurring at the arrow triggers an abrupt increase in the tension produced by the motor unit. Reproduced from Burke *et al.*[23]

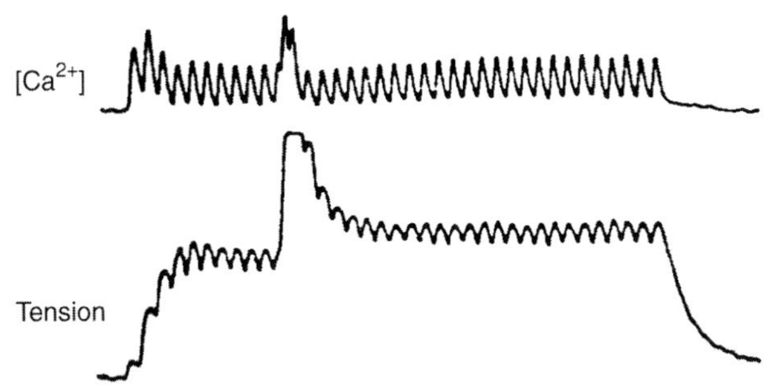

FIGURE 30.12 Catch property and Ca^{2+} flux in a barnacle muscle fiber. An extra muscle spike occurring at the arrow produces a sudden increase in Ca^{2+} concentration in the muscle fiber, accompanied by a sharp rise in tension. Reproduced with permission from Hoyle.[68] Copyright © 1983 Wiley & Sons, Inc.

of current required to fire an action potential). S motor neurons also have relatively long afterhyperpolarizations (AHPs) following each spike,[24] due to a relatively high density of Ca^{2+}-activated potassium channels. Long AHPs produce long refractory periods and limit the rate of repetitive firing. In aggregate, these physiological properties optimize S motor neurons for low rates of steady firing. Not surprisingly, S motor neurons innervate Type 1 muscle fibers. S motor units have a relatively long twitch contraction time and a small peak force (Fig. 30.10), but with prolonged activation the twitch tension remains high. Therefore, S motor units are suited to movements that require low levels of sustained or repetitive force.

FF motor units lie at the other end of the spectrum of motor unit types. They can rapidly develop large twitch forces but fatigue fairly quickly (Fig. 30.10). FF motor neurons have large somas and dendritic trees, low membrane resistance, high rheobase, large axons, and high conduction velocities. Their action potentials are followed by relatively short AHPs, allowing these neurons to attain high firing rates. FF motor neurons innervate Type 2b muscle fibers.

BOX 30.3

IDENTIFICATION OF MOTOR UNIT TYPES IN THE LABORATORY

Motor units can be characterized by a number of properties, many of which are related and vary along the same axis on a three-dimensional plot, as illustrated in Fig. 30.13. In practice, only a few of these properties are usually measured during an experiment. Burke and colleagues[22] have been able to place most motor units into three categories (S, FR, and FF) by examining two properties: fatigue sensitivity and the presence or absence of "sag" in an unfused tetanus. Their method has become a standard for physiological classification of motor units.

The fatigue test stimulation paradigm was chosen to minimize the contribution of fatigue at the neuromuscular junction. Mechanical and electrical responses of muscle units are recorded during a train of 13 motor neuron spikes at 40 Hz, repeated every second for several minutes. The responses are used to calculate the fatigue index (FI), defined as the maximum tension produced during the 120th train divided by that produced during the first. FI values below 0.25 are characteristic of FF units, whereas FI values above 0.75 correspond to FR and S units.

Sag is the slight decline in twitch tension that occurs after the maximal tension is reached with the first 6–7 stimulation pulses. It is measured by stimulating with 30 pulses, where the interpulse interval is 1.25 times the twitch contraction time. FR and FF motor units show sag but S motor units do not.

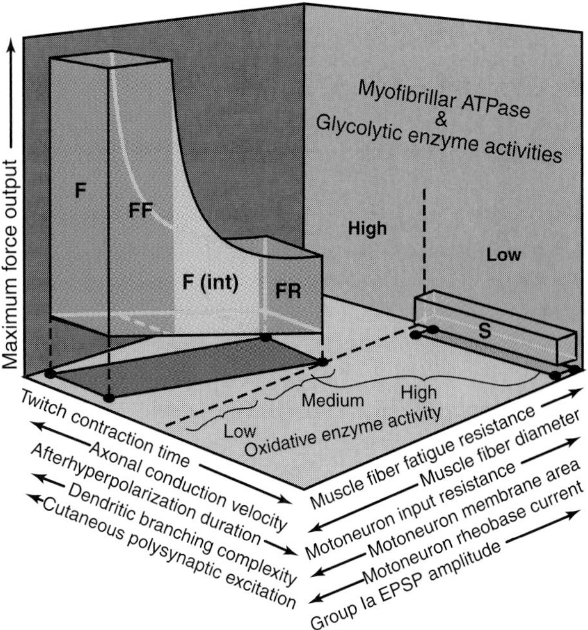

FIGURE 30.13 Three-dimensional plot of motor unit properties used to divide motor units into types S, FR, and FF. Reprinted from R. E. Burke. In *Muscle Afferents and Spinal Control of Movement* (L. Jami, E. Pierrot-Deseilligny, and D. Zytnicki, eds.), p. 271. Copyright 1992, with kind permission from Elsevier Science Ltd.

FR motor units are similar to FF motor units both anatomically and in their speed of contraction, but they produce smaller peak forces and are much more resistant to fatigue during repetitive activation. FR motor neurons innervate Type 2a muscle fibers.

Summary

The motor unit is defined as a single motor neuron and the group of muscle fibers it innervates. All muscle fibers in a single motor unit consist of the same muscle fiber type. The amount of force produced by the muscle fibers of a motor unit is governed by the pattern and frequency of action potentials produced by the motor neuron. The firing patterns of motor neurons are in turn determined by passive electrical properties and the types and density of ion channels contained in their membranes. Three types of motor units—S, FR, and FF—can be categorized on the basis of their twitch speed and fatigability. The properties of motor neurons are well matched to the contractile and metabolic properties of the muscle fibers they innervate.

MOTOR NEURON POOLS

A Muscle Is Innervated by a Pool of Motor Neurons

Motor neurons are located in the brainstem and in the ventral horn of the gray matter of the spinal cord (Fig. 30.14). Motor neurons that innervate the same muscle are grouped in clusters known as motor nuclei or motor columns. In the spinal cord, motor nuclei generally extend over several segments and have a cigar-shaped contour in longitudinal sections of the cord. The number of motor neurons innervating different muscles varies considerably, with estimates ranging from 30–40 for the cat tenuissimus muscle[25] to 300 for the human thumb muscles.[26]

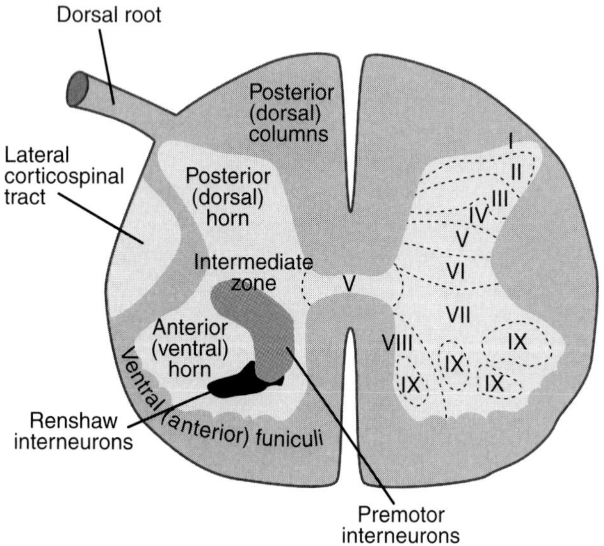

FIGURE 30.14 Cross section of spinal cord.

Axons of spinal motor neurons leave the ventral gray matter and enter the ventral root at the same segmental level. Before exiting the spinal cord, many motor axons send recurrent collateral branches into the ventrolateral white matter; these branches may travel one or two segments before they reenter the ventral gray. Outside the vertebral column, axons in the ventral and dorsal roots from the same segment join to form a spinal nerve. Motor axons innervating one muscle may be contained in multiple spinal nerves, corresponding to the segments of the spinal cord that contain the motor nucleus for that muscle. All of the motor axons that innervate a given muscle, as well as the sensory axons that innervate the specialized sensory receptors in that muscle, become sorted out to form a common muscle nerve. In limbed vertebrates, this sorting typically occurs in a nerve plexus formed from the spinal nerves. Because the innervation of most limb muscles comes from several roots, injuries involving single nerve roots generally lead to weakness, whereas injuries affecting a muscle nerve cause complete paralysis of a muscle. However, for some muscles, such as the intercostal muscles that lie between the ribs, innervation arises from a single spinal segment, an advantageous arrangement for neurologists seeking to localize spinal injuries and for developmental neurobiologists studying the specificity of segmental innervation.

Motor Neurons Are Usually Activated in a Characteristic Sequence

Motor neurons that innervate the same muscle belong to a common motor neuron "pool." Defining a motor neuron pool is not always a straightforward proposition, however, as the earlier discussion of the internal architecture of muscles and muscle compartments illustrates. A single "muscle" may contain several functional motor neuron pools.

During most movements, muscles are not maximally activated, and only a fraction of the motor units of a particular pool will be activated. How does the nervous system choose which motor units to activate? An early idea suggested by Sherrington[27] was that activity was simply rotated among all motor neurons in the pool. Later Denny-Brown and Pennybacker[28] recorded graded contractions in human muscles by inserting needles into the muscles; they found that the same motor units were activated in a characteristic sequence as the strength of contraction increased. Henneman[29] recorded from motor axons during reflex contractions in animals and showed that motor neurons with small extracellular spikes were activated first, followed by progressively larger motor neurons. This ordering of motor neuron activation is known as the **size principle.**

The Size Principle Results from Intrinsic Properties of Motor Neurons and Synaptic Inputs

The size principle generally holds true when motor neuron size is expressed by a number of measures, including axon diameter, conduction velocity, membrane resistance, rheobase, and motor unit force. Most of these properties can be considered intrinsic to the motor neuron, because they result from the anatomy or ion channels of the motor neuron. Many of the intrinsic properties associated with size also affect the ease with which a motor neuron can be activated by injected or synaptic current.

Intrinsic properties of motor neurons are not the sole determinant of recruitment order, however. The distribution of synaptic inputs is also important. Synaptic input from many, but not all, descending and sensory reflex pathways is distributed to the members of a motor neuron pool in a way that also activates them according to their size. Muscle spindle afferents from a particular muscle, for example, appear to synapse equally on every motor neuron in that muscle's motor neuron pool,[30] but excitatory postsynaptic potentials (EPSPs) from each afferent tend to be larger on small motor neurons than on large motor neurons. If each bouton releases the same amount of transmitter, generating the same synaptic current, differences in the membrane resistance of motor neurons of different sizes would be sufficient to cause a gradient of EPSP size.[31] Alternatively, differences in EPSP size could be produced from differences in the probability of transmitter release from boutons onto small motor neurons.[32]

It is the mixture of intrinsic cell properties and the action of synaptic inputs that produces the typical recruitment order of S → FR → FF for many pathways that activate motor neurons. Studies of motor neuron recruitment that have produced these principles have usually examined muscles undergoing isometric or isotonic activation as the prime mover. For technical reasons, these studies have generally focused on early-recruited motor units.

Some Synaptic Inputs May Produce Alternative Recruitment Sequences

Some inputs to motor neurons can produce recruitment sequences that disagree with the size principle. Cutaneous nerve stimulation, for example, differentially inhibits small motor neurons and excites high-threshold motor neurons in both humans and cats.[33,34] Because the intrinsic properties of motor neurons are relatively stable, this alternative sequence must be determined by the distribution of synaptic inputs. Cutaneous afferents activate excitatory and inhibitory neurons and their inputs to the motor neuron pool must be distributed or weighted differently. Another example of the selective recruitment of large motor units occurs during eccentric contraction of ankle extensor and elbow flexor muscles in humans when they are used to exert a braking action.[35,36] In this situation, this alternative recruitment sequence may be necessary to counteract the relatively long relaxation times of S motor units. Many natural movements do incorporate eccentric contractions, and the role of alternative recruitment sequences in controlling these movements deserves further research.

Motor Neuron Recruitment and Increased Firing Rates Increase Muscle Force

Higher levels of muscle force can be generated in two ways: Motor neurons can fire more rapidly, and additional motor units can be recruited. As Fig. 30.15

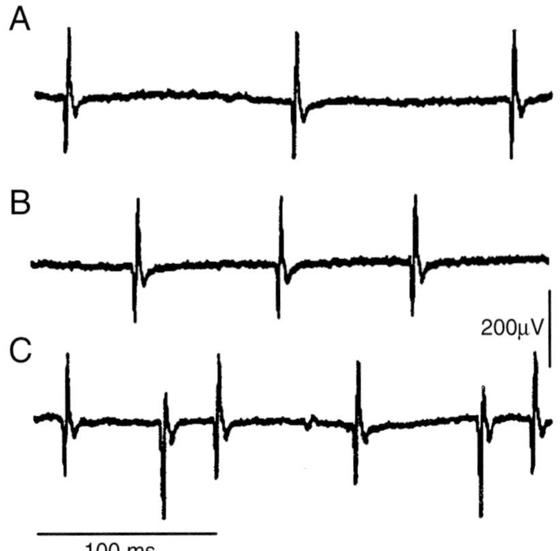

FIGURE 30.15 Increase in motor neuron firing rate and recruitment of additional motor units during voluntary contraction of a human finger extensor muscle. (A) Low force. (B) Increased firing rate, corresponding to greater force. (C) Recruitment of second motor unit, with still greater force.

illustrates, both mechanisms occur as a muscle is more strongly activated. In the neurological literature, increases in firing rate and recruitment of additional motor units are sometimes referred to as temporal and spatial recruitment, respectively. Evaluation of these processes can be helpful in the diagnosis of diseases and of injury to motor axons or motor neurons, as described later in this chapter.

The relative importance of recruitment of additional motor neurons and changes in firing frequency in a given muscle may vary with level of force. In the intrinsic hand muscles,[37] for example, many early-recruited motor units have a similar threshold for activation, and low-level force gradations rely primarily on faster firing by motor neurons that are already activated. For strong forces, the addition of more motor units may be necessary, particularly when active motor neurons are firing at a frequency that is producing near-tetanic levels of force. The spacing of thresholds among the motor neurons within a pool influences which mechanism is more likely at a particular level of force. However, motor neuron thresholds are not necessarily fixed; they can be modulated by synaptic inputs to the motor neuron pool,[38] for example. One can demonstrate this modulation by applying a short-acting anesthetic to a muscle nerve. The anesthetic blocks muscle contraction and eliminates sensory input from muscle spindle afferents. Without this input, the range over which motor neurons can be smoothly activated narrows, and it becomes difficult to activate the small numbers of motor neurons that would normally produce the lowest levels of force.[39]

The Gain of a Motor Neuron Pool Is Not Fixed

The relationship between the output of a motor neuron pool and the synaptic input to the pool can be termed the "gain" of the pool[40] (Fig. 30.16). The gain is affected by the range and spacing of motor neuron thresholds. Many inputs to motor neurons change the excitability of the entire motor neuron pool in a fairly uniform manner, and they essentially shift the threshold of the entire pool (Fig. 30.16, line B). Other synaptic inputs affect motor neurons within the pool in a nonuniform way, altering the slope of the input–output function (Fig. 30.16, line C). Changes in the characteristics of presynaptic terminals can appear to affect the gain of a motor neuron pool. For example, activation of cat muscle spindle afferents at high frequencies depresses transmission from presynaptic terminals onto low-threshold motor neurons, but it facilitates transmission from terminals onto high-threshold motor neurons.[41,42] As a result, the gain of the motor neuron pool changes in a nonlinear way during prolonged muscle spindle activation. Voltage-dependent membrane properties and channels activated by neuromodulators may also contribute to complicated, nonlinear input–output relationships for motor neuron pools (Fig. 30.16, line D).

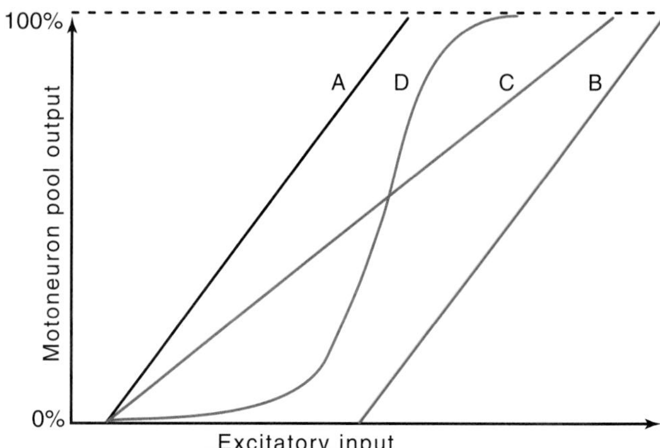

FIGURE 30.16 Gain of a motor neuron pool. (A) Standard gain. (B) Change in threshold. (C) Change in gain. (D) Nonlinear gain.

Motor Neuron Plateau Potentials Produce Sustained Firing

One example of a nonlinear input–output relationship is provided by motor neuron **plateau potentials,** sustained membrane depolarizations that do not depend on sustained synaptic input. In vertebrate motor neurons, a plateau potential may develop when a motor neuron receives excitatory inputs at the same time that membrane repolarization is suppressed by monoamines.[43] Thus, appearance of plateau potentials depends on the activation of the descending brainstem pathways that are the major source of monoamines in the spinal cord. The ionic mechanisms underlying motor neuron plateau potentials have been studied most carefully in turtle motor neurons.[44] In turtles, the monoamine serotonin reduces the AHP of the motor neuron, allowing activation of a voltage-gated Ca^{2+} channel that produces the depolarizing plateau. The motor neuron maintains a firing rate proportional to the level of depolarization as long as the plateau persists. Plateau potentials in cat motor neurons are inactivated by inhibitory or mixed synaptic inputs, such as those that occur during cutaneous stimulation.[45] Although plateau potentials would seem ideal for sustained postural contractions,[46] their role in motor control has not been elucidated.

Motor Neuron Firing Rates Accommodate during Sustained Activation

During a steady, voluntary contraction that produces a low level of force, the firing rate of motor neurons declines. This phenomenon is known as **late accommodation** or, more whimsically, muscular wisdom. The "wisdom" of such a decline stems from the observation that with sustained activation, the relaxation time of a muscle fiber increases, effectively decreasing the firing frequency needed to maintain a tetanus. During voluntary contractions, this decline may be largely due to changing input to motor neurons from muscle afferents.[47,48] Some late accommodation can also be intrinsic to motor neurons, as shown by prolonged current injection in motor neurons with severed axons: An initial decline in firing frequency, thought to reflect the effects of summed AHPs, is followed 30 s to minutes later by a further decline.[49] The second fall in firing rate, which is more prominent in motor neurons innervating fast twitch fibers, appears to represent the cumulative effects of many consecutive spikes, but its ionic mechanisms are not fully understood.

The pattern of motor neuron firing affects not only the production of force by a muscle,[50] as discussed above in relation to catch properties, but also the development of fatigue. When fast-twitch motor neurons were stimulated to fire in either a regular pattern or an "optimized" pattern, which consisted of a short burst of spikes followed by spikes at longer intervals, muscle force declined quickly with the regular pattern but remained high with the optimized pattern.[51] The nervous system may utilize such "optimized" patterns of firing to reduce fatigue in natural movements.

Motor Neurons Influence Muscle Fiber Type

The fiber type composition of a muscle depends to a large extent on the motor neurons that innervate it and their activity patterns. When a muscle nerve is partially injured, some motor axons degenerate and the remaining axons sprout new collaterals that innervate nearby denervated muscle fibers. The plasticity of muscle fibers—their ability to change their biochemical and physiological properties—can be demonstrated most clearly when denervation is followed by reinnervation by a different type of motor neuron. The reinnervated muscle fibers change many of their metabolic and contractile characteristics to conform to the new motor unit type, a process that may involve trophic interactions as well as new motor neuron firing patterns. Similar findings are seen after recovery from poliomyelitis, a disease that destroys some motor neurons and allows reinnervation by surviving motor neurons. Histochemical staining of muscle biopsies after partial nerve injury or poliomyelitis frequently shows that fibers of the same type are grouped (Fig. 30.17B) rather than scattered as in normal muscle (Fig. 30.17A). Grouping of muscle fibers reflects the expanded territories of the surviving motor units. Box 30.4 describes electrophysiological signs of motor unit changes that occur in muscle disease.

Muscles of trained athletes often show a fiber type composition appropriate for their sport. For example, marathon runners have a high proportion of fatigue-resistant muscle fibers, a finding that could result from athletic training or represent an underlying genetic difference in muscle composition that predisposes certain individuals to become marathon runners. Can muscle fiber types be modified by changing the activity of intact motor units through exercise? Nonathletes placed on an exercise training program showed changes in the metabolic characteristics of their muscle fibers; endurance exercise in particular resulted in elevated levels of oxidative enzymes in both Type 1 and Type 2 fibers.[52,53] Whether myosin isoforms and structural proteins also change with exercise training is unclear. Strength training can alter the relative areas of Type 1 and Type 2 fibers within muscles, but this alteration may reflect muscle fiber hypertrophy.[54]

A more extreme modification of muscle activity patterns can be examined by using chronic electrical stimulation of muscle nerves. With continuous low-frequency (2.5–10 Hz) stimulation, muscle fibers undergo an orderly sequence of transformation to predominantly Type 1 fibers. The initial change occurs in metabolism, with an increase in the concentration of oxidative enzymes. Later changes involve twitch properties, Ca^{2+} sequestration, and eventually myosin isoforms.[55] The metabolic changes in muscle seen after exercise training may thus represent an incomplete progression through this sequence.[56]

Summary

Each muscle is innervated by a pool of motor neurons, which typically contains a mixture of motor unit types, although in different proportions depending on the typical use of that muscle. An orderly sequence of motor neuron activation within a pool leads to activation of units producing the smallest amount of force before those producing larger amounts of force. This sequence, known as the size principle, results from passive electrical properties of motor neurons and their synaptic inputs. Alternative recruitment sequences

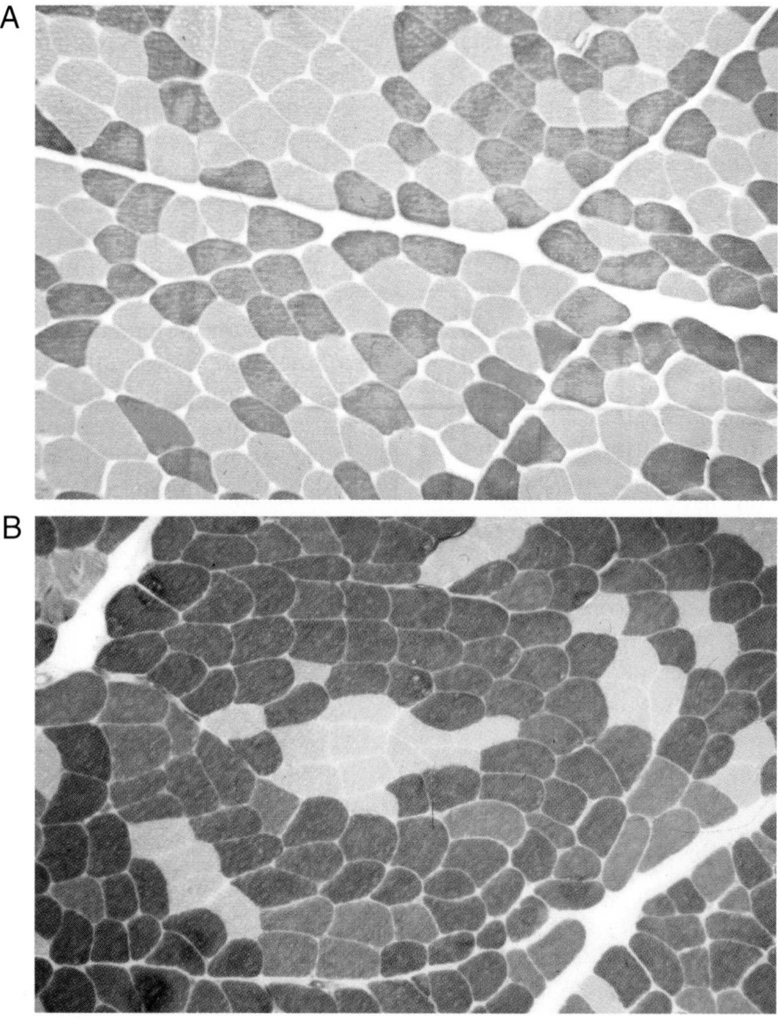

FIGURE 30.17 Histochemical staining for ATPase activity in human muscle biopsy specimens. (A) Normal muscle; note scattering of fiber types. (B) Postpolio muscle, showing grouping of fiber types caused by the expanded territories of surviving motor neurons. Courtesy of M. Dalakas.

can occur when synaptic inputs have a specialized distribution among motor neurons that overrides the contribution of the passive electrical properties of motor neurons.

MUSCLE AFFERENTS

Muscle Spindles Convey Information about Muscle Stretch

Muscle spindles are sensory organs that lie in parallel with skeletal muscle fibers and function primarily in sensing muscle stretch. A muscle spindle consists of a fusiform bundle of 5–10 specialized muscle fibers buried within the muscle (Fig. 30.19). The muscle fibers within the spindle are called intrafusal fibers to distinguish them from the extrafusal fibers that make up the bulk of the muscle and produce the vast majority of the muscle's contractile force. A typical muscle spindle contains two basic types of intrafusal fibers: nuclear bag fibers, which have a bulging center containing clusters of cell nuclei and sparse central myofibrils; and nuclear chain fibers, which have an elongated arrangement of nuclei and continuous myofibrils.[57,58] The nuclear bag fibers are subdivided into bag 1 and bag 2 fibers, each with a different composition of contractile proteins. All three types of intrafusal fibers detect muscle length, but bag 1 fibers also respond to sudden changes in muscle length.

Muscle Spindles Are Innervated by Primary and Secondary Sensory Axons

One large-diameter sensory axon, called the **Ia fiber**, or **primary afferent**, enters each spindle and branches to innervate each intrafusal fiber. The largest branch spirals around the central bulge of the bag 1 fiber, while smaller branches end on bag 2 and chain fibers. In mammals but not amphibians, smaller diameter sensory fibers known as Group II (or secondary) endings also enter the spindle and terminate on bag 2 and chain fibers.

Because the various intrafusal fibers respond differently to stretch, the sensory fibers that terminate on them provide different information about the stretch.[59,60] The primary afferents fire a burst of spikes at the onset of stretch (Fig. 30.20A), signaling a change in muscle length as detected by bag 1 fibers. The peak firing rate during the burst is proportional to the velocity of stretch.[61] Similar primary afferent bursts occur

BOX 30.4

DISEASES OF MUSCLE AND MOTOR NEURONS LEAD TO CHANGES IN MOTOR UNITS

A number of diseases can affect muscles, peripheral nerves, or motor neurons. Usually, such diseases cause weakness, a symptom that may result from a problem at any point in the motor system: the muscle, the neuromuscular junction, the peripheral nerve, the motor neuron, or neurons presynaptic to the motor neuron. Clues to the anatomical localization of the problem can be obtained by examining the pattern of weakness, which differs according to the particular structure involved, and by clinically assessing stretch reflexes, which are usually diminished in diseases involving the peripheral nerve, and signs of muscle atrophy. Fasciculations, the visible twitching of small portions of the muscle due to the involuntary firing of individual motor units, are a clinical sign of potential injury or disease to the motor neuron or its axon.

Electromyography, the recording of muscle electrical activity with needle electrodes, can be a useful adjunct to clinical examination in humans. When motor neurons are lost, as in polio, the remaining motor axons sprout, enlarging their peripheral territory to include the denervated muscle fibers, as Fig. 30.17B shows. Enlarged motor units may produce visible twitches within the muscle as they contract; such twitches are known as contraction fasciculations. Enlarged motor units also generate action potentials that are larger than normal when recorded with extracellular needle electrodes, as shown in the top recording in Fig. 30.18. This recording is an electromyogram from a man who had polio 40 years earlier but recovered much of his strength. He relied on high firing rates of his few remaining motor units to generate higher forces, since he was unable to recruit additional motor units.

In contrast, muscle fibers degenerate and the remaining muscle is smaller in diseases such as the muscular dystrophies. Furthermore, action potentials may not propagate the full length of the surviving muscle fibers. However, the number of motor neurons is generally normal. As a consequence, motor unit action potentials appear smaller than normal when measured with extracellular needle electrodes, as shown in the bottom recording in the Fig. 30.18. The ability to recruit additional motor units to generate higher levels of force remains intact.

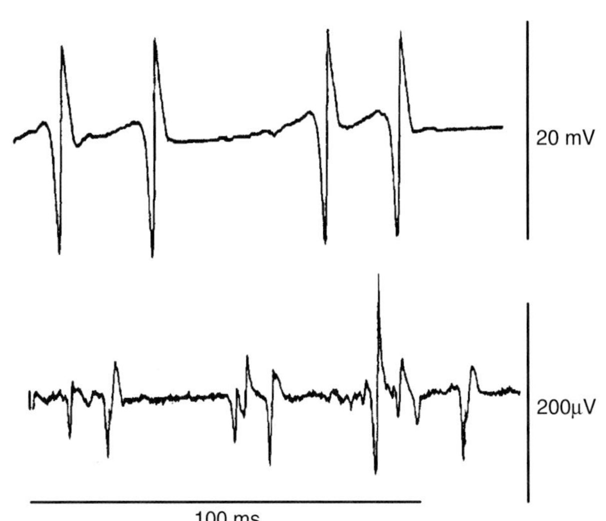

FIGURE 30.18 Electromyographic recordings from patients with motor neuron muscle diseases. (Top) Postpolio. While trying to produce steady force, the sole surviving motor unit is firing at near maximal rates of 40/s. (Bottom) Myopathy. Many motor units have been recruited but have small amplitudes compared to normal, as in Fig. 30.15.

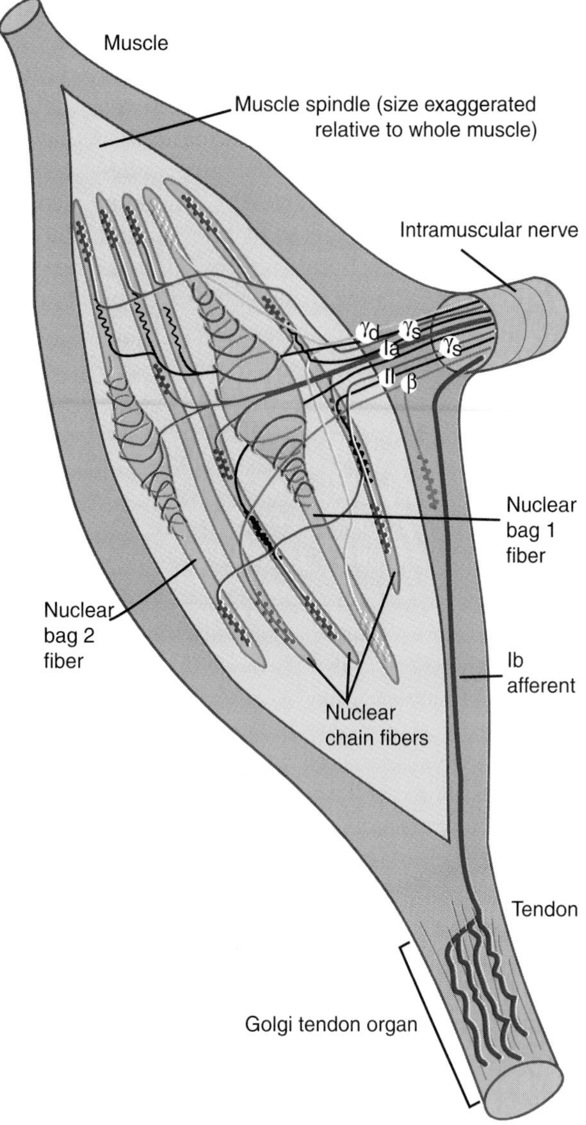

FIGURE 30.19 Structure and innervation of muscle spindles and Golgi tendon organs.

when a muscle is stretched with a brief tap (Fig. 30.20B). The primary afferents are exquisitely sensitive to very small stretches, such as those that occur when vibration is applied to the muscle (Fig. 30.20C). With sustained stretches, the primary afferents exhibit a slow decrease in firing rate, and when the stretch is released, they are momentarily silenced (Fig. 30.20D). Both primary and secondary afferents fire more rapidly at longer muscle lengths, because both innervate bag 2 and chain fibers. However, the secondary afferents do not respond to brief taps or vibrations, and they are not silenced by the release of stretch.

Specialized Motor Neurons Innervate Muscle Spindles

The ends of intrafusal fibers are innervated by two classes of motor neurons: gamma motor neurons (or fusimotor neurons), which innervate intrafusal fibers exclusively; and beta motor neurons (or skeletofusimotor neurons), which have branches that innervate both intra- and extrafusal fibers. Beta motor neurons are the only motor neuron type in amphibians, and they were once thought to be uncommon in mammals. However, it is now thought that a third or more of mammalian intrafusal fibers may be innervated by beta motor neurons,[62] although the specific role of these motor neurons has not been determined. Gamma and beta motor neurons can be classified as either dynamic, innervating bag 1 fibers or static, innervating bag 2 or chain fibers.

One function of the motor innervation of intrafusal fibers may be to maintain the sensitivity of the muscle spindle as the muscle contracts. When the gamma and beta motor neurons fire, the ends of the intrafusal fibers contract, elongating or stiffening the central portion of the fibers, where the afferents terminate. Without motor innervation, the spindles would slacken and the afferents would become silent when the muscle shortened during movements. During voluntary movements, however, the motor neurons innervating intra- and extrafusal fibers are generally coactivated. Therefore, when the muscle contracts, the spindles also stiffen or contract, allowing primary afferents to continue firing despite muscle shortening. Fusimotor fir-

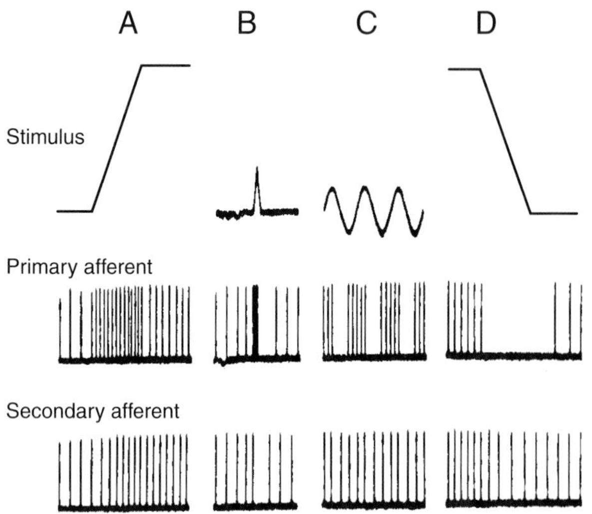

FIGURE 30.20 Responses of cat primary and secondary afferents to linear stretch (A), tap (B), vibration (C), and release from stretch (D). Reproduced from Matthews.[59]

ing alone may lead to contraction or stiffening of the spindle that could change the sensitivity of spindle afferents without muscle stretch. Independent function of the fusimotor system has been demonstrated in several species but has not been shown in awake, behaving humans.

Golgi Tendon Organs Convey Information about Muscle Tension

Another sensory structure, the **Golgi tendon organ** (GTO), lies in series between the muscle and the tendon.[63] The GTO consists of free nerve endings between collagen bundles aligned with muscle fascicles. The afferent fibers of the GTOs, known as Ib afferents, have large diameters and a range of conduction velocities that largely overlap those of the Ia spindle afferents. GTOs are sensitive to muscle force, particularly that generated by active contraction of extrafusal fibers. In early studies where muscles were passively stretched, the notion arose that GTOs only sense dangerously high tension levels. That idea has now been discarded.

However, the relationship between muscle force and the firing of individual GTOs is complicated. Each GTO may sense the force generated by only a small number of motor units that insert onto its local region of the tendon. Individual GTOs have been found to fire in a one-to-one fashion upon activation of a single motor unit.[64] Recruitment of additional motor units can decrease the firing rate of a GTO, perhaps because the parallel arrangement of different fascicles results in unloading of some GTOs when units in adjacent fascicles are activated. Unlike muscle spindles, GTOs do not have a motor innervation that allows their sensitivity to be adjusted during muscle contraction.

Muscle Afferents Send Central Branches to Spinal Segments and Higher Levels of the Central Nervous System

Primary, secondary, and GTO afferent fibers enter the spinal cord through the dorsal roots and distribute branches widely, often over several segments. Within the intermediate and ventral gray matter of the spinal cord, they synapse on many interneurons that play a role in local circuits and segmental reflexes, as discussed in Chapter 31. Muscle afferents also encode information concerning the actions of the muscles and positions of the limbs, and they transmit this information to higher levels of the central nervous system. Combined with information from joint and cutaneous receptors, signals from muscle afferents contribute to proprioception and kinesthesia, the sense of active movement.[65] Muscle afferents provide input to cells of Clarke's nucleus that give rise to the dorsal spinocerebellar tract, which is discussed in Chapter 35. Muscle afferent information is also relayed to the cerebral cortex via the dorsal column–lemniscal pathway and is represented in a subregion (3b) of the primary somatosensory cortex, as explained in Chapter 26.

Summary

Specialized sensory receptors in the muscle provide feedback to the central nervous system regarding the amount of muscle stretch and tension. Spindles are specialized muscle fibers embedded within the muscle and provide signals on the muscle length. The length of the muscle and changes in length are encoded by the pattern and frequency of action potentials in the primary or Ia afferents and secondary or Group II afferents. Gamma motor neurons innervate the spindle fibers and can adjust the sensitivity of the spindle. Golgi tendon organs lie within the musculotendinous junctions and are activated when tension is produced by nearby active motor units. Sensory information from muscle receptors is transmitted to higher levels of the central nervous system as well as to the spinal cord.

Muscles are responsible for executing the movements formulated by the central nervous system. Therefore, the biological properties of muscle place important constraints on how the nervous system operates. Muscles are made up of smaller fascicles of muscle fibers, surrounded by connective tissue. The arrangement of fascicles and connective tissue limits the power and distensibility of a muscle. Each muscle contains a mixture of different muscle fiber types in varying proportions. Muscle fiber types are classified according to properties determined by the intracellular specializations and the composition of the contractile proteins, ion channels, and metabolic enzymes in individual muscle fibers. These properties are strongly influenced by the motor neuron that innervates the muscle fiber and can undergo plastic changes after sustained activity or motor neuron injury.

The motor unit, consisting of one motor neuron and all the muscle fibers it innervates, is the smallest element that the nervous system controls. All muscle fibers of a motor unit are of the same type. Within a fascicle, however, muscle fibers from different motor units are intermixed in a mosaic pattern. The properties of motor neurons and muscle fibers are matched to produce motor units that can be categorized as slow twitch or fast twitch and as fatigable or fatigue-resistant. Motor neurons fire repetitively at a rate that

BOX 30.5

MYASTHENIC DISORDERS

The neuromuscular junction (NMJ) transmits signals from somatic motor nerves to skeletal muscle. Synaptic vesicles store quantal packets (5–10,000 molecules) of the neurotransmitter acetylcholine (ACh). The ACh receptor (AChR) is strategically deployed on the crests of the junctional folds at a density of about 10,000 molecules/μm^2 (Fig. 30.21). The AChR is composed of four homologous subunits with a stoichiometry of $\alpha 2\beta\delta\varepsilon$ at the adult, and $\alpha 2\beta\delta\gamma$ at the fetal, NMJ. Different genes encode each subunit.

Exocytotic release of single quanta occurs spontaneously in the resting state. Depolarization of the nerve terminal by nerve impulse opens presynaptic voltage-gated Ca^{2+} channels and the entry of Ca^{2+} ions triggers the release of multiple quanta. The number of released quanta (m) is a function of the probability of release (p), which depends mostly on the prevailing Ca^{2+} concentration near the intraterminal release sites, and the number of readily releasable quanta (n), so that $m = np$. ACh released into the synaptic space diffuses to the postsynaptic region where it binds to AChR, causing its cation-selective channel to open for a period distributed exponentially from a fraction of a millisecond to several milliseconds, allowing Na^+ and to a lesser extent Ca^{2+} to enter the muscle fiber. After ACh dissociates from AChR, it is rapidly hydrolyzed to choline and acetate by acetylcholinesterase (AChE), an enzyme embedded in the synaptic basal lamina. Choline is taken up by the nerve terminal by Na^+-dependent active transport. ACh is resynthesized in the terminal by choline acetyltransferase and is concentrated in synaptic vesicles by a proton-pump-dependent ACh transporter.

The ion flux into muscle generated by a single quantum gives rise to a miniature end-plate potential (MEPP); multiquantal release by nerve impulse generates an end-plate potential (EPP). When the EPP exceeds the threshold for activating perijunctional voltage-gated Na^+ channels, it triggers a muscle fiber action potential. The amplitude of the MEPP depends on the number of ACh molecules per quantum, the density of postsynaptic AChRs, and the end-plate geometry. The EPP amplitude is a function of m and the MEPP amplitude. *The safety margin of neuromuscular transmission is the difference between the actual EPP amplitude and the EPP amplitude required to trigger a muscle fiber action potential.*

Myasthenic disorders arise when the safety margin of transmission is compromised. This can be caused by derangements in (1) quantal release mechanisms, (2) the number of ACh molecules per quantum, and (3) the postsynaptic effect of the quantum, which is a function of (i) the end-plate geometry, (ii) the density and functional state of AChE, and (iii) the density, functional state, and

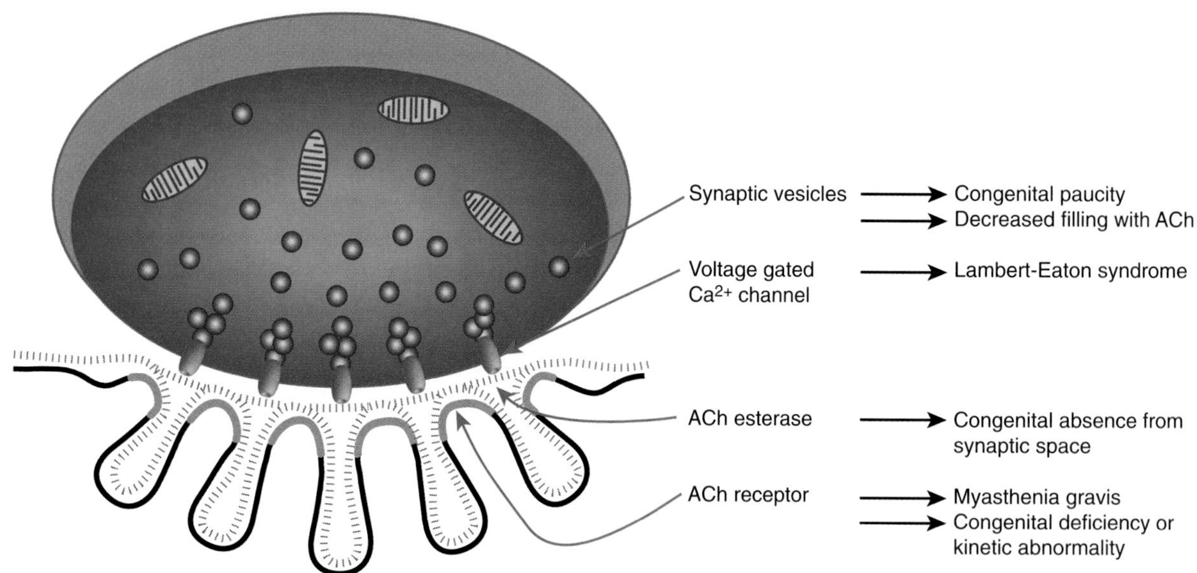

FIGURE 30.21 Schematic diagram of a neuromuscular junction showing key components subserving neuromuscular transmission and the myasthenic disorders associated with these components.

ion channel properties of AChRs. Figure 30.21 indicates categories of myasthenic disorders and the structures implicated in their pathogenesis.

The **presynaptic disorders** include the Lambert–Eaton myasthenic syndrome (LEMS) and congenital myasthenic syndromes (CMSs). In LEMS, pathogenic autoantibodies reduce the number of voltage-gated presynaptic Ca^{2+} channels. This curtails Ca^{2+} ingress into the nerve terminal and reduces p, and hence the EPP. LEMS is often associated with small-cell carcinoma of the lung because autoantibodies against Ca^{2+} channels expressed by cancer cells cross-react with Ca^{2+} channels on the presynaptic membrane. In the CMS due to a paucity of synaptic vesicles, quantal release, and hence the EPP, is reduced by a decrease in n. In the CMS caused by a defect in ACh resynthesis or vesicular packaging, sustained activity results in a progressive decrease in the number of ACH molecules per quantum, and hence in a progressive decrease of the MEPP and EPP.

In the CMS due to end-plate AChE deficiency, the absence of AChE from the synaptic basal lamina allows each ACh molecule to bind repeatedly to AChRs. This prolongs the synaptic current and overloads the postsynaptic region with cations, which injures the junctional folds. The postsynaptic effect is partially offset by the smallness of the nerve terminals, which reduces quantal release. The safety margin of transmission is compromised by loss of AChR from the injured junctional folds, a decrease in n and m stemming from the smallness of the nerve terminals, and a depolarization block due to temporal summation of the prolonged EPPs during physiological activity.

The **postsynaptic disorders** include autoimmune myasthenia gravis (MG) and congenital myasthenic syndromes. In autoimmune MG, pathogenic autoantibodies directed against epitopes on AChR cause AChR deficiency by complement-mediated lysis of the junctional folds, accelerated internalization of AChR, interference with ACH binding, or a combination of these mechanisms.

The postsynaptic CMSs stem from a deficiency and/or altered kinetic properties of AChR. AChR deficiency results from recessive, loss-of-function mutations in AChR subunit genes that either decrease subunit expression or prevent subunit assembly or glycosylation. Most of these mutations reside in the ε subunit, perhaps because deficiency of this subunit can be partially offset by compensatory expression of the fetal γ subunit. In the low-affinity fast-channel CMS, a loss-of-function mutation in the ε subunit of AChR (εP121L) decreases binding affinity for ACh. This reduces the quantal response and the MEPP amplitude and shortens the channel opening episodes, but there is no AChR deficiency. The mutation manifests clinically only when combined with a null mutation in the other ε allele. The slow-channel CMSs stem from dominant, gain-of-function mutations in different subunits and in different functional domains of the subunits. Each mutation prolongs the channel opening episodes, causing (1) cationic overloading of the postsynaptic region, destruction of the junctional folds, and loss of AChR, and (2) a depolarization block due to temporal summation of the prolonged EPPs during physiological activity. Some mutations act mainly by slowing the channel closing rate (for example, εP264P, a mutation in a transmembrane domain that lines the ion channel); others act mainly by enhancing the affinity for ACh (for example, αG153S in the extracellular domain of AChRs), so that the channel is forced to reopen repeatedly during its prolonged occupancy by ACh. Most slow-channel mutations also render the channel leaky so that it opens even in the absence of ACh and increases the extent of desensitization in the presence of ACh.

The CMSs caused by mutations in AChR subunit genes are experiments of nature that highlight functionally significant domains of the AChR. Identification of different CMSs is important in medicine, for it paves the way toward rational therapy.

Andrew G. Engel

allows the tension in individual units to summate. Slow-twitch units produce smaller amounts of force than fast-twitch units and are the easiest to activate. Increasing amounts of tension are produced by increasing the rate of motor neuron firing and by recruitment of additional motor units that produce greater force. Most movements utilize an orderly pattern of recruitment, in which motor units are activated in order of increasing force, allowing a smooth force profile and movement.

References

1. Hoyle, G. (1983). *Muscles and Their Neural Control.* Wiley, New York.
2. Squire, J. M. (1983). Molecular mechanisms in muscular contraction. *Trends Neurosci.* **10:** 409–413.
3. Vigoreaux, J. O. (1994). The muscle Z band: Lessons in stress management. *J. Muscle Res. Cell Motil.* **15:** 237–255.
4. Elliot, G. F., and Worthington, C. R. (1994). How muscle may contract. *Biochim. Biophys. Acta* **1200:** 109–116.
5. Vale, R. D. (1994). Getting a grip on myosin. *Cell (Cambridge, Mass.)* **78:** 733–737.

6. Takeshima, H., Nishimura, S., Matsumoto, T., Ishida, H., Kangawa, K., Minamino, N., Matsuo, H., Ueda, M., and Hanaoka, M. (1989). Primary structure and expression from complementary DNA of skeletal muscle ryanodine receptor. *Nature (London)* **339:** 439–445.
7. Catterall, W. A. (1991). Excitation-contraction coupling in vertebrate skeletal muscle: A tale of two calcium channels. *Cell (Cambridge, Mass.)* **64:** 871–874.
8. Rios, E., Pizarro, G., and Stefani, E. (1991). Charge movement and the nature of signal transduction in skeletal muscle excitation-contraction coupling. *Annu. Rev. Physiol.* **54:** 109–133.
9. Hoffman, E. P. (1995). Voltage-gated ion channelopathies: Inherited disorders caused by abnormal sodium, chloride and calcium regulation in skeletal muscle. *Annu. Rev. Med.* **46:** 431–441.
10. Ptacek, L. J., Tawil, R., Griggs, R. C. *et al.* (1994). Dihydropyridine receptor mutations cause hypokalemic periodic paralysis. *Cell (Cambridge, Mass.)* **77:** 863–868.
11. MacLennan, D. H., and Phillips, M. S. (1992). Malignant hyperthermia. *Science* **256:** 789–793.
12. Metzger, J. M., and Moss, R. L. (1990). Calcium-sensitive cross-bridge transitions in mammalian fast and slow skeletal muscle fibers. *Science* **247:** 1088–1090.
13. Gordon, A. M., Huxley, A. F., and Julian, F. J. (1966). The variation in isometric tension with sarcomere length in vertebrate muscle fibers. *J. Physiol. (London)* **184:** 170–192.
14. Goldspink, G. (1981). The use of muscles during flying, swimming, and running from the point of view of energy saving. In *Vertebrate Locomotion* (M. H. Day, ed.), pp. 219–238. Academic Press, London.
15. Pette, D., and Staron, R. S. (1990). Cellular and molecular diversities of mammalian skeletal muscle fibers. *Rev. Physiol. Biochem. Pharmacol.* **116:** 1–76.
16. Ong, T. C., Hayes, D. A., and Armstrong, R. B. (1988). Distribution of microspheres in plantaris muscles of resting and exercising rats as a function of fiber type. *Am. J. Anat.* **182:** 318–324.
17. Funakoshi, H., Belluardo, N., Arenas, E., Yamamoto, Y., Casabona, A., Persson, H., and Ibanez, C. F. (1995). Muscle-derived neurotrophin-4 as an activity dependent trophic signal for adult motor neurons. *Science* **268:** 1495–1499.
18. Gans, C., and Gant, A. S. (1992). Muscle architecture and control demands. *Brain, Behav., Evol.* **40:** 70–81.
19. Gans, C., Loeb, G. E., and deVree, F. (1989). Architecture and consequent physiological properties of the semitendinosus muscle in domestic goats. *J. Morphol.* **199:** 287–297.
20. Weijs, W. A., Juch, P. J. W., Kwa, S. H. S., and Korfage, J. A. M. (1993). Motor unit territories and fiber types in rabbit masseter muscle. *J. Dent. Res.* **72:** 1491–1498.
21. Buchthal, F., and Schalmbruch, H. (1970). Contraction times and fibre types in intact human muscles. *Acta Physiol. Scand.* **79:** 435–452.
22. Burke, R. E., Levine, D. N., Tsairis, P., and Zajac, F. E. (1973). Physiological types and histochemical profiles in motor units of the cat gastrocnemius. *J. Physiol. (London)* **234:** 723–748.
23. Burke, R. E., Rudomin, P., and Zajac, F. E. (1970). Catch property in single mammalian motor units. *Science* **168:** 122–124.
24. Zwaagstra, B., and Kernell, D. (1980). The duration of after-hyperpolarization in hindlimb alpha motoneurones of different sizes in the cat. *Neurosci. Lett.* **19:** 303–307.
25. Lev-Tov, A., Pratt, C. A., and Burke, R. E. (1988). The motor unit population of the cat tenuissimus muscle. *J. Neurophysiol.* **59:** 1128–1142.
26. McComas, A. J. (1991). Motor unit estimation: methods, results, and present status. *Muscle Nerve* **14:** 585–597.
27. Sherrington, C. S. (1906). *Integrative Action of the Nervous System.* Scribner's, New York.
28. Denny-Brown, D., and Pennybacker, J. B. (1938). Fibrillation and fasciculation in voluntary muscle. *Brain* **61:** 311–334.
29. Henneman, E. (1957). Relation between size of neurons and their susceptibility to discharge. *Science* **126:** 1345–1347.
30. Mendell, L. M., and Henneman, E. (1968). Terminals of single Ia fibers: Distribution within a pool of 300 homonymous motor neurons. *Science* **160:** 96–98.
31. Segev, I., Fleshman, J. W., and Burke, R. E. (1990). Computer simulation of group Ia EPSPs using morphologically realistic models of cat α-motor neurons. *J. Neurophysiol.* **64:** 648–660.
32. Heckman, C. J., and Binder, M. (1988). Analysis of effective synaptic currents generated by homonymous Ia afferent fibers in motor neurons of the cat. *J. Neurophysiol.* **60:** 1946–1966.
33. Nielsen, J., and Kagamihara, Y. (1993). Differential projection of the sural nerve to early and late recruited human tibialis anterior motor units: Change of recruitment gain. *Acta Physiol. Scand.* **147:** 385–401.
34. Kanda, K., Burke, R. E., and Walmsley, B. (1977). Differential control of fast and slow twitch units in the decerebrate cat. *Exp. Brain Res.* **29:** 57–74.
35. Nardone, A., Romano, C., and Schieppati, M. (1989). Selective recruitment of high threshold human motor units during voluntary isotonic lengthening of active muscles. *J. Physiol. (London)* **409:** 451–471.
36. Abbruzzese, G., Morena, M., Spadavecchia, L., and Schieppatti, M. (1994). Response of arm flexor muscles to magnetic and electrical brain stimulation during shortening and lengthening tasks in man. *J. Physiol. (London)* **481:** 499–507.
37. Milner-Brown, H. S., Stein, R. B., and Yemm, R. (1972). Mechanisms for increased force during voluntary contractions. *Proc. Physiol. Soc.* pp. 18P–19P.
38. Bakels, R., and Kernell, D. (1994). Threshold spacing in motoneurone pools of rat and cat: Possible relevance for manner of force gradation. *Exp. Brain Res.* **102:** 69–74.
39. Gandevia, S. C., Macefield, V. G., Bigland-Ritchie, B., Gorman, R. B., and Burke, D. (1993). Motor neuronal output and gradation of effort in attempts to contract acutely paralysed leg muscles in man. *J. Physiol.* **471:** 411–427.
40. Kernell, D., and Hultborn, H. (1990). Synaptic effects on recruitment gain: A mechanism of importance for the input output relations of motoneurone pools. *Brain Res.* **507:** 176–179.
41. Collins, W. F., Honig, M. G., and Mendell, L. M. (1984). Heterogeneity of group Ia synapses on homonymous α motor neurons as revealed by high frequency stimulation of Ia afferent fibers. *J. Neurophysiol.* **52:** 980–993.
42. Collins, W. F., Davis, B. M., and Mendell, L. M. (1988). Amplitude modulation of EPSPs in motor neurons in response to frequency modulated trains in single Ia afferent fibers. *J. Neurosci.* **6:** 1463–1468.
43. Kiehn, O. (1991). Plateau potentials and active integration in the final common pathways for motor behavior. *Trends Neurosci.* **14:** 68–73.
44. Hounsgaard, J., and Kiehn, O. (1989). Serotonin-induced bistability of turtle motoneurones caused by a nifedipine-sensitive calcium plateau potential. *J. Physiol. (London)* **414:** 265–282.
45. Crone, C., Hultborn, H., Kiehn, O., Mazieres, L., and Wigstrom, H. (1988). Maintained changes in motoneuronal excitability by short lasting synaptic inputs in the decerebrate cat. *J. Physiol. (London)* **405:** 321–343.
46. Eken, T., and Kiehn, O. (1989). Bistable firing properties of soleus motor units in unrestrained rats. *Acta Physiol. Scand.* **136:** 383–394.

47. Gandevia, S. G., Macefield, V. G., Burke, D., and McKenzie, D. K. (1990). Voluntary activation of human motor axons in the absence of muscle afferent feedback. *Brain* **113:** 1563–1581.
48. Macefield, V. G., Gandevia, S. C., Bigland-Ritchie, B., Gorman, R. B., and Burke, D. (1993). The firing rates of human motoneurones voluntarily activated in absence of muscle afferent feedback. *J. Physiol. (London)* **471:** 429–443.
49. Kernell, D., and Monster, A. W. (1982). Motoneurone properties and motor fatigue. *Exp. Brain Res.* **46:** 197–204.
50. Burke, R. E., Rudomin, P., and Zajac, F. E. (1976). The effect of activation history on tension production by individual motor units. *Brain Res.* **109:** 515–529.
51. Bevan, L., Laouris, Y., Reinking, R. M., and Stuart, D. G. (1992). The effect of the stimulation pattern on the fatigue of single motor units in adult cats. *J. Physiol. (London)* **449:** 85–108.
52. Holloszy, J. O., and Booth, F. W. (1976). Biochemical adaptations to endurance exercise in muscle. *Annu. Rev. Physiol.* **38:** 273–291.
53. Nemeth, P. M. (1990). Metabolic fiber types and influences on their transformation. In *The Segmental Motor System* (M. D. Binder and L. M. Mendell, eds.), pp. 258–277. Oxford University Press, New York.
54. Costill, D. L., Coyle, E. F., Fink, W. F., Lesmes, G. R., and Witzman, F. A. (1979). Adaptations in skeletal muscle following strength training. *J. Appl. Physiol.* **46:** 96–99.
55. Pette, D. (1992). Fiber transformation and fiber replacement in chronically stimulated muscle. *J. Heart Lung Transplant.* **11:** S299–S305.
56. Salmons, S. (1994). Exercise stimulation and type transformation of skeletal muscle. *Int. J. Sports Med.* **15:** 136–141.
57. Hunt, C. C. (1990). Mammalian muscle spindle: Peripheral mechanisms. *Physiol. Rev.* **70:** 643–663.
58. Barker, D., and Banks, R. W. (1994). The muscle spindle. In *Myology* (A. G. Engel and C. Franzini-Armstrong, eds.), pp. 333–360. McGraw-Hill, New York.
59. Matthews, P. B. C. (1964). Muscle spindles and their motor control. *Physiol. Rev.* **44:** 219–288.
60. Grill, S. E., Hallett, M., Marcus, C., and McShane, L. (1994). Disturbances of kinaesthesia in patients with cerebellar disorders. *Brain* **117:** 1433–1447.
61. Houk, J. C., Rymer, W. Z., and Crago, P. E. (1992). Responses of muscle spindle receptors to transitions in stretch velocity. In *Muscle Afferents and Spinal Control of Movement* (L. Jami, E. Pierrot-Deseilligny, and D. Zytnicki, eds.), pp. 53–61. Pergamon, Oxford.
62. Emonet-Denand, F., Petit, J., and Laporte, Y. (1992). Comparison of skeletofusimotor innervation in cat peroneus brevis and peroneus tertius muscles. *J. Physiol. (London)* **458:** 519–525.
63. Jami, L. (1992). Golgi tendon organs in mammalian skeletal muscle: Functional properties and central actions. *Physiol. Rev.* **72:** 623–710.
64. Houk, J., and Henneman, E. (1967). Responses of Golgi tendon organs to active contractions of the soleus muscle of the cat. *J. Neurophysiol.* **30:** 466–481.
65. Gandevia, S., McCloskey, D. I., and Burke, D. (1992). Kinaesthetic signals and muscle contraction. *Trends Neurosci.* **15:** 62–65.
66. Fawcett, D. W. (1986). *A Textbook of Histology.* Saunders, Philadelphia.
67. Gordon, A. M., Huxley, A. F., and Julian, J. F. (1966). The variation in isometric tension with sarcomere length in vertebrate muscle fibers. *J. Physiol.* **184:** 170–192.
68. Hoyle, G. (1983). *Muscles and Their Neural Control.* Wiley, New York.

CHAPTER

31

Spinal Motor Control, Reflexes, and Locomotion

M. K. Floeter

In the last chapter, we introduced the concept of the motor unit, the smallest element of movement controlled by the vertebrate nervous system. There is a fairly large gap, however, between our understanding of how motor units and motor neuron pools are organized and how motor behaviors are produced. Most behaviors involve activation of many muscles, demanding the coordinated control of motor units in different motor neuron pools. Each muscle must produce a quite specific amount of force with precisely the right timing in relation to the activation and relaxation of other muscles. The force and timing are regulated within each motor neuron pool, while activity patterns are coordinated between motor neuron pools. Imagine, for example, an act as simple as hammering a nail: while the hand firmly grasps the hammer, muscles acting across the shoulder, elbow, and wrist work together in an overlapping sequence to propel the hammer and land it precisely on the head of the nail. The coordination of several muscles that are used in this simple behavior seems to occur rather automatically. In fact, it reflects a complex integration of descending inputs from cortical and brainstem areas, activation of spinal circuits, and sensory feedback.

PRINCIPLES OF SPINAL MOTOR CONTROL

The Spinal Cord Participates in Coordinating Movement

In certain circumstances, the spinal cord itself can produce simple movements. Experiments conducted around the turn of the century demonstrated that animals with a spinal cord transection maintained the ability to scratch a spot of skin or walk on a treadmill as long as their weight was supported. These movements occurred even though the spinal cord was disconnected from input from the brain. Two contrasting viewpoints emerged to explain how the spinal cord generated such behaviors.

One school held that these behaviors were built from combinations of smaller, simple reflexes. Reflexes are stereotyped motor behaviors that are evoked by specific sensory stimuli. The stimuli may need to have a particular intensity or be restricted to certain regions of the body. A pinch of the foot but not the tail, for instance, will evoke a withdrawal reflex of the leg. The motor response is stereotyped, though not invariant, and may involve multiple muscles. Reflexes often habituate with repeated stimuli. In the early 1900s, Sir Charles Sherrington described many spinal reflexes in animals,[1] along with the anatomy of the nerves and muscles underlying each reflex. He was particularly interested in the consequences of eliciting reflexes in combinations and is often identified with the idea of reflex chains. A chain of reflexes would be one way to generate complex movements: the first sensory stimulus would evoke a reflex movement, which would lead to a changed sensory input and second reflex movement, and so on.

An alternative explanation was proposed around the same time by Graham Brown, who found that animals with spinal cord transection could walk on a treadmill even after the dorsal roots were severed.[2] Since no sensory feedback could reach the spinal cord to evoke a reflex in these animals, he suggested that a motor program within the spinal cord itself encoded the movement. Brown proposed that the spinal machinery for this central program consisted of two mutually inhibitory "half-centers," both under tonic excitation: one half-center drove muscles that flexed the legs, and the other drove muscles that extended the legs. We'll return to Brown's half-center proposal and other conceptions of central motor programs later in this chapter.

Models Are Often Used to Explain Motor Behaviors

Sherrington's rigorous approach of combining functional observations with analysis of anatomical circuits has had a tremendous influence on other scientists' attempts to understand the coordination of movement. For some simple movements, such as those involved in gill withdrawal and escape responses of invertebrates, it may be possible to examine the circuitry that produces the behavior directly. For many behaviors, however, the complexity of the underlying circuitry makes it too difficult to study the circuitry completely. This is generally true for behaviors coordinated in the vertebrate spinal cord. For this reason, models that simplify the spinal circuits are constructed to better understand how the circuitry produces the behavior. A model of a spinal motor circuit typically receives "inputs"—signals originating outside the spinal circuit, such as sensory information or descending commands—and generates an "output," which is generally some measure of a movement.

Most neuroscientists use models to guide experimental hypotheses and modify these models as they discover unpredicted facets of the circuitry. They usually start by identifying a simple, essential feature of the motor behavior: that movements alternate on opposite sides of the body, for example, or that the position of a moving limb at any instant represents a balance between the activity in two sets of muscles, as another example. The model is a proposal to explain as simply as possible how the nervous system produces this feature. Brown's proposal that locomotion on a treadmill resulted from two mutually inhibitory half-centers in the spinal cord is an example of such a proposal. A model formalizes the relationship between inputs and outputs but simplifies the intervening steps. The goal of a model is not only to simulate the motor output normally observed but also to predict the consequences of disturbances or novel inputs and to suggest testable hypotheses that will help us elucidate the intervening steps. As anatomical and physiological experiments refine the model, details of the underlying networks can be introduced.

Interneurons Are Integrative Elements in Spinal Network Models

The intervening steps in spinal network models usually involve spinal interneurons. An **interneuron** is a nerve cell whose cell body and axon reside entirely within the central nervous system. A key feature of interneurons in the mammalian spinal cord is that they generally receive inputs from multiple sources, allowing them to serve as a point of convergence and integration. Most interneurons have axons that branch to connect with many motor neurons and other interneurons. Consequently, there are very few interneurons that act as a private relay between a single stream of information and particular motor neurons.

Interneurons introduce an additional level of complexity to spinal circuits, but at the same time they provide flexibility. In one sense, interneurons assume the role of the logical elements in equations, performing "and" and "or" operations between different sets of inputs. When two input pathways share a common interneuron link, the information passing along these pathways is summed before it reaches the motor neurons. The timing of the two inputs must be very close for summation to occur. If both inputs are excitatory but weak, their summation may activate an interneuron that neither input could activate independently; this phenomenon is termed **spatial facilitation**. Conversely, if an inhibitory input shares an interneuron with a strong excitatory input, the two may sum to prevent activation of the interneuron, a phenomenon called **gating**. Repetitive firing of a single, relatively weak excitatory input may lead to a marked amplification of signal strength called **temporal facilitation**. Temporal facilitation results from the summation of EPSPs in individual interneurons as well as the progressive activation of a pool of interneurons. These combinatorial operations in interneurons can amplify, modulate, and reverse the signs of inputs to motor neurons and introduce delays during different phases of a movement.

A Network of Neurons Can Produce Different Motor Behaviors

Because behavior changes from moment to moment while anatomy is stable over the same time frame, it is reasonable to ask whether one network of neurons can produce more than one motor behavior. In the past, it was assumed that the anatomical connections of an ensemble of neurons would determine their actions, and most efforts were directed toward mapping neuronal connections. Certain patterns of connectivity do contribute to distinct firing patterns; for example, mutually excitatory connections between cells promote synchronous firing, whereas mutually inhibitory connections tend to produce oscillation. However, we now know that cellular and synaptic properties arising from receptors and ion channels expressed by individual neurons influence the strength of synaptic connections from moment to moment.[3] As we saw in earlier chapters, the behavior of many receptors and channels will vary depending on the membrane potential action of other neurotransmitters and whether they have been recently activated. A small change in the state of these "intrinsic" properties of individual neurons can lead to marked alterations of their firing and, consequently, different outputs from a network, as explained in Box 31.1[4–10] for the "simple" nervous system of the lobster.

Summary

A useful approach to understanding the spinal control of motor behavior is to construct a model of how spinal circuitry produces the behavior. The goal of such a model is to simulate the normal motor output and predict the effects of disturbances on the output. Most spinal network models involve spinal interneurons, which introduce complexity and flexibility to spinal circuits. Changes in the intrinsic membrane properties of neurons in these circuits can also influence the output from a network.

REFLEXES

In the preceding section, we discussed how neuronal networks can be built from simple circuits. But do such circuits exist in the spinal cord, and are they used by higher centers to elicit voluntary movements? It is difficult to answer that question directly, but it appears that spinal reflexes and descending motor pathways do share common spinal interneurons. Spinal reflexes produce fairly stereotyped movements, but the repertoire of possible voluntary movements is immense. If both movements are produced by the same neuronal networks, they must activate interneurons in a distinctly different manner. Although it is unlikely that descending commands produce voluntary movements simply by selecting a set of reflexes, spinal reflexes can be used to identify the common spinal circuitry. They are also useful for clinical evaluation of the nervous system in humans. In this section, we describe some of the more commonly observed mammalian spinal reflexes and their underlying circuitry, highlighting interneurons that also receive input from descending pathways.

Muscles Contract in Response to Stretch

The stretch reflex, or myotactic reflex, is the simplest spinal reflex, consisting of the contraction of a skeletal muscle when it is stretched. The contraction has a brief (phasic) component and a sustained (tonic) component, although the latter is difficult to elicit in most normal humans. The knee jerk is an example of the phasic stretch reflex: a sharp tap on the patellar tendon stretches the quadriceps muscle. Stretch activates muscle spindles in the quadriceps, leading to a burst of action potentials in spindle afferents, as described in Chapter 30. Ia afferents, as well as a few group II afferents, make monosynaptic excitatory synapses onto quadriceps alpha motor neurons. Some of the motor neurons reach threshold for firing an action potential, and the relatively synchronized activation of a portion of that motor neuron pool results in a brief muscle contraction.

The circuitry underlying the phasic stretch reflex is conceptually simple (Fig. 31.3). The synapse between Ia spindle afferents and motor neurons has been extensively studied as a source of information on central synapses and the role of muscle afferents during movement (see Box 31.2).[11–19] Ia afferents most potently excite motor neurons of the same muscle (**homonymous motor neurons**), but they also excite motor neurons that innervate other muscles, typically synergists (**heteronymous motor neurons**). The patterns and strength of heteronymous Ia connections vary considerably among different muscles and in different species. These variations may be important for the motor control needs of each species: quadrupedal versus bipedal gait, toe-walking versus walking on the sole of the foot, for example. In cats, Ia synapses are made primarily onto the dendrites of motor neurons.[20] The transmitter at this synapse is most likely glutamate, because transmission is blocked by glutamate antagonists; separate components of the Ia EPSP are sensitive to NMDA and non-NMDA antagonists.[21,22]

When a muscle is stretched and held at a new length, rather than briefly tapped, the phasic stretch reflex is sometimes followed by the tonic stretch reflex, a maintained contraction whose strength is proportional to the amount of stretch. This more variable component of the stretch reflex can be demonstrated most easily after brainstem transection in cats (Fig. 31.4).[23] The circuitry generating the tonic stretch reflex is still not entirely known, but the secondary spindles described in Chapter 30, which signal information regarding static muscle length, are likely to be involved.[24] These group II afferents provide a strong excitatory input to gamma motor neurons as well as to a variety of spinal interneurons. The tonic stretch reflex is thought to play a role in some disorders of excessive muscle tone in humans (see Box 31.3).[25–27]

Muscle Stretch Triggers Reciprocal Inhibition

Muscle spindle afferents also initiate a reflex relaxation of antagonist muscles known as **reciprocal inhibition**. Several different spinal circuits produce recip-

BOX 31.1

COMPLEXITIES OF A "SIMPLE" NERVOUS SYSTEM

Scientists once hoped that the study of invertebrate nervous systems would lead to the discovery of a few basic circuits that would be conserved in networks controlling movement in different organisms. Instead, invertebrates seem to have evolved a multiplicity of solutions for generating patterned or rhythmic movements. A few common principles have emerged:

- At least some neurons in the network will have the capacity to generate bursts of spikes, prolonged depolarizations, or endogenous oscillations.
- The expression of such active properties usually requires modulatory input from central or peripheral sources.
- Circuits tend to be more complex than minimally necessary: several redundant mechanisms reinforce particular network activity patterns.
- Pattern generation emerges from the activity of many components of the network: the same network may produce different rhythms through combinations or functional "reconfiguration" of the components.

The crustacean stomatogastric nervous system (STNS) is a particularly instructive example of these principles. The STNS consists of four ganglia that control the movement of the gut, including an organ called the gastric mill. The STNS produces at least four different rhythms, named for the four regions of the foregut. Separate sets of neurons generate these rhythms, although there is some overlap, and the neurons are distributed in more than one ganglion. The neurons controlling two rhythms—the slow gastric mill rhythm and the faster pyloric rhythm—reside mainly within stomatogastric ganglion (STG). Only a small number of neurons make up the networks for these two rhythms.

In the lobster, the gastric mill rhythm is generated by about 10 identified motor neurons and one interneuron.[4] The chemical and electrical synaptic connections between these neurons are shown in Fig. 31.1A. The core of the network is a motor neuron, DG, whose membrane potential undergoes an endogenous oscillation. This oscillation is reinforced by inputs from a half-center oscillator that is formed by inhibitory connections between two synergist motor neurons, LG and MG, and an interneuron. LG and MG have intrinsic properties that result in postinhibitory rebound, which promotes bursting. The intrinsic properties of the interneuron allow it to generate voltage plateaus; it also excites DG. This network is quiescent until activated by neurons in other ganglia or peripheral sensory neurons, which release a variety of neurotransmitters, including acetylcholine, peptides, and monoamines. The neurotransmitters modulate the conductances underlying the postsynaptic neurons' active membrane properties. Acetylcholine, for example, turns on the endogenous oscillation of DG.[4] Figure 31.1B[5] illustrates the slow rhythmic firing of neurons in the gastric mill network.

The network that generates the pyloric rhythm contains three electrically coupled endogenous oscillator neurons, one AB and two PDs, that inhibit all of the other pyloric neurons (Fig. 31.1C). Nearly all of the cells exhibit active membrane properties, including plateau potentials and postinhibitory rebound, that are reinforced by synaptic and electrical interconnections. These properties allow a variety of rhythmic outputs, one of which is shown in Fig. 31.1D.[6] As is true for the gastric mill rhythm, the pyloric rhythm can be modulated by synaptic inputs. The frequency of the rhythm, for instance, is increased by the activation of stretch receptors, which release serotonin on pyloric neurons.[7] Serotonin modifies the conductances that contribute to oscillation.[8]

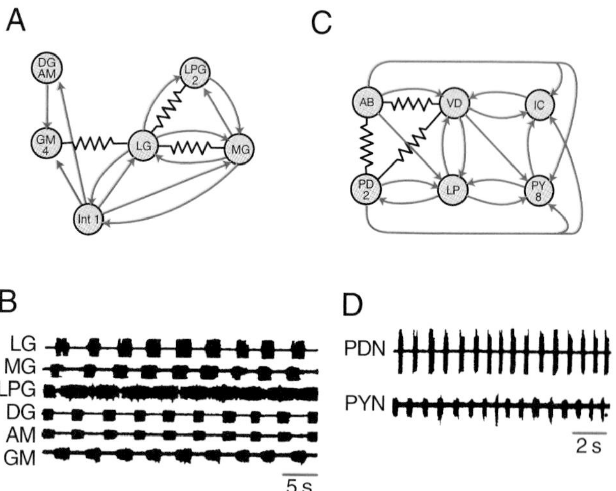

FIGURE 31.1 Diagram of excitatory (open triangles), inhibitory (filled circles), and electrical (zigzag lines) connections between neurons making up the gastric mill network (A) and pyloric network (C) in the lobster. The outputs of these networks are the gastric mill rhythm (B) and pyloric rhythm (D). Reproduced from Harris-Warwick[5] and Johnson.[6]

Although the rhythm-generating activities of the gastric mill and pyloric networks are fully independent, some of the neurons in these two networks are synaptically interconnected. For example, the PD neuron in the pyloric network inhibits the interneuron in the gastric mill network, and the gastric mill LPG neurons inhibit the pyloric PD neuron. In addition, neurons of both networks receive input from several common sources. A striking example of a common input is that from PS neurons, which are not part of either network. Activation of PS neurons triggers swallowing by "reconfiguring" selected cells in the pyloric, gastric mill, and esophageal networks (Fig. 31.2).[9,10] Of course, the PS neurons do not reconfigure the anatomy of these cells. Rather, they alter the functional interactions between neurons, resulting in the dramatic and unpredicted emergence of a new rhythm.

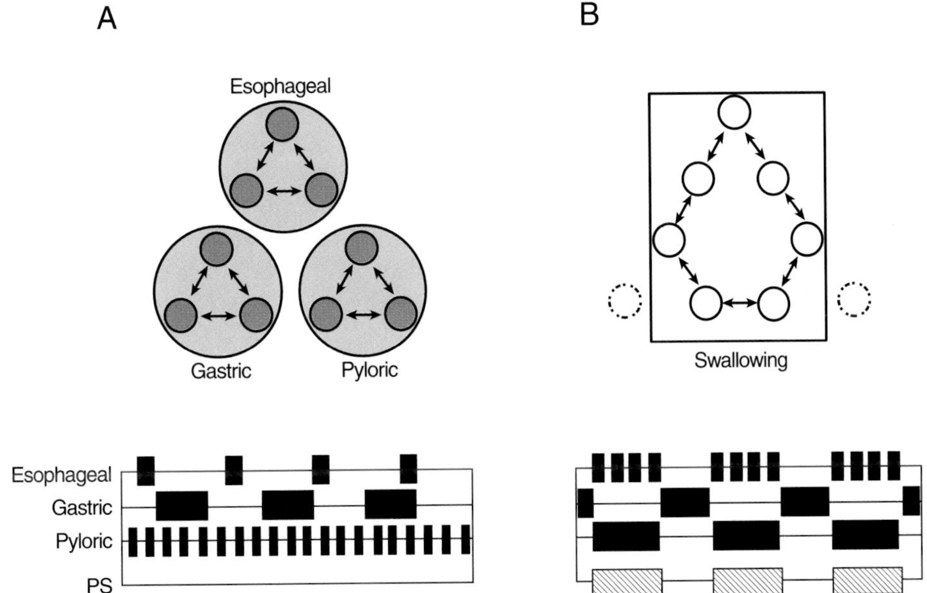

FIGURE 31.2 Dynamic configuration of networks. (A) When the PS neurons are silent, three neural networks of the STNS (gastric, pyloric, and esophageal) generate independent rhythms. (B) When the PS neurons are active, some of the neurons in these three networks are reorganized into a new network, creating a rhythm that produces swallowing. Reproduced from Meyrana.[10]

rocal inhibition. The shortest circuit is disynaptic, mediated through a single, glycinergic interneuron. This interneuron is called the Ia inhibitory interneuron (IaIN), because it is excited by Ia afferents and inhibits motor neurons. However, the IaIN is also excited by descending commands and by spinal networks that coordinate locomotion (Table 31.1). In humans, the IaIN can be activated through voluntary effort alone, after movement and feedback from stretch receptors have been eliminated by a local anesthetic nerve block.[28,29] The ability of the IaIN to serve as a multipurpose inhibitory relay results from its several sources of input.[30–32]

In general, any input that activates a motor neuron also activates its corresponding pool of IaINs. If this circuitry were completely hardwired, it could be difficult to perform motor acts, such as precision grips, that involve the simultaneous contraction of antagonist muscles. In reality, though, the strength of IaIN inhibition is continually subject to modification throughout movement, due to the many convergent inputs to the IaINs. Furthermore, the strength of reciprocal inhibition at rest differs for muscle pairs acting across different joints. For example, in humans the inhibition is relatively strong between wrist flexor and extensor muscles but relatively weak between ankle flexor and extensor muscles. During ankle dorsiflexion movements, however, reciprocal inhibition of ankle extensor motor neurons is enhanced, reflecting spatial facilitation of descending and peripheral inputs to the IaINs.[33] Within a motor neuron pool, the size of the IPSP, like the size of the Ia EPSP, is inversely related to a motor

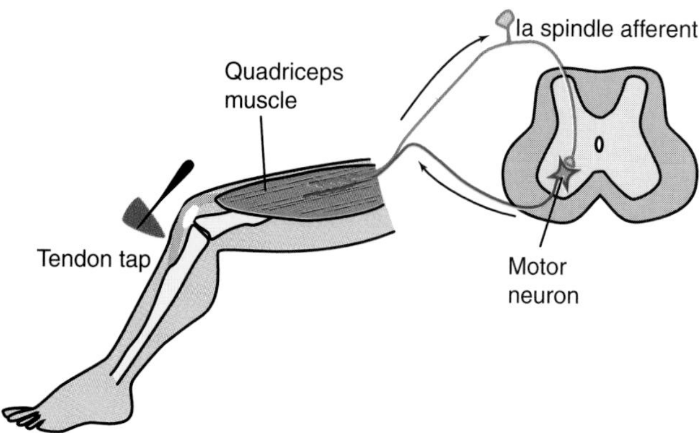

FIGURE 31.3 The basic circuitry underlying the knee-jerk stretch reflex. Ia spindle afferents from the quadriceps muscle make monosynaptic, excitatory connections on alpha motor neurons that innervate the quadriceps.

neuron's rheobase, suggesting that input from IaINs obeys the size principle.

The Stretch Reflex Is Modified by Presynaptic Inhibition

The presynaptic terminals of muscle afferents receive axoaxonic synapses from inhibitory interneurons in the spinal cord. Inhibition of the presynaptic terminals prevents transmission of muscle afferent input to motor neurons, gating the sensory signal. Different classes of interneurons mediate presynaptic inhibition of Ia, Ib, and group II muscle afferents, and each class has a characteristic pattern of descending and peripheral inputs.[34] Presynaptic inhibition has been characterized best in Ia afferents that are inhibited by stretching antagonist muscles. In the cat's hindlimb, Ia afferents from extensor muscles are presynaptically inhibited by interneurons that are activated by Ia afferents from flexor muscles. At least two interneurons are interposed in the circuit between the flexor and extensor

BOX 31.2

STRETCH REFLEXES AND MOVEMENT

Does the nervous system use stretch reflexes for normal movement? In 1953, Merton hypothesized that movements begin with the firing of gamma motor neurons, which causes a small contraction of intrafusal fibers and activates the alpha motor neuron pool through a stretch reflex.[11] This "follow-up servo-control" mechanism was a plausible idea, supported by the known anatomy, since gamma motor neurons receive descending inputs but not Ia afferent inputs. A key prediction of Merton's hypothesis was that the firing of gamma motor neurons should always precede that of alpha motor neurons. However, alpha and gamma motor neurons are now known to be coactivated in most natural movements, and the hypothesis in its original form has been rejected.

Nevertheless, a variation of Merton's original idea appears valid: gamma motor neuron firing allows spindles to remain sensitive during a contraction, thereby maintaining excitatory input to motor neurons from spindle afferents. When a muscle contracts, the intrafusal fibers momentarily slacken, leading to a pause of spindle afferent firing. Gamma motor neurons then fire, tightening the spindle and allowing it to maintain a fairly linear response to muscle stretch.[12] This "servo-assist" action ensures that sensory feedback is available to the CNS throughout a movement.

Although alpha and gamma motor neurons are generally coactivated, the coupling between them is not fixed, and the level of gamma motor neuron activity can be adjusted. The strength of gamma activation may depend on the task. For some slow movements, in which feedback can be used to alter the ongoing movement or counteract fatigue, a strong gamma activation may be useful.[13–15] For other situations, such as walking on a balance beam, it appears advantageous to suppress stretch reflexes,[16] possibly through a weak gamma activation.

Evidence is also accumulating that use can modify the stretch reflex. Monkeys have been trained to suppress or enhance phasic stretch reflexes through operant conditioning over a period of weeks.[17] These changes persist after spinal cord transection, indicating that the site of plasticity lies within the spinal cord. The changes appear to involve alpha rather than gamma motor neurons.[18] In humans, stretch reflexes may undergo long-lasting modifications that reflect the habitual use of certain muscles. In Royal Danish ballerinas, for example, the stretch reflexes of calf muscles have been found to be weaker than those of other trained athletes, presumably as a result of training that emphasizes the priority of descending motor commands over peripheral feedback.[19]

BOX 31.3

DISORDERS AFFECTING MUSCLE TONE

Muscle tone refers to the stiffness of a muscle, and it is usually assessed clinically by passively stretching the relaxed muscle and judging its resistance to stretch. Relaxed muscles normally offer little resistance to slow stretches, because slow stretching does not activate primary afferents very strongly and there is little, if any, background firing of spindle afferents or motor neurons at rest.

Excessive muscle tone is a hallmark of many neurological conditions. Lesions of the corticospinal tract, which may result from stroke, degenerative diseases, or injury, typically lead to an increase in tone called **spasticity.** Both tonic and phasic stretch reflexes are hyperexcitable in spasticity. Tendon taps elicit especially brisk reflex contractions, often setting up repetitive oscillations known as clonus. Muscles resist passive stretching, and their resistance increases with the velocity of the stretch. Thus, attempting to straighten a spastic limb rapidly will produce a reflex contraction, the "spastic catch," but slower stretches will not. The hyperactive stretch reflexes in people with stroke or spinal injury appear to result from changes in both monosynaptic and polysynaptic circuits activated by spindle afferents.[25] An earlier hypothesis, that spasticity results from an increase in the activity of gamma motor neurons, has not been supported by recordings of spindle activity in people with spasticity.[26]

Rigidity is a form of excessive muscle tone that frequently accompanies neurological diseases involving the basal ganglia, such as Parkinson disease. Phasic stretch reflexes are often normal in diseases with rigidity, but tonic stretch reflexes are increased and may even be present at rest. Muscles resist passive stretching at all speeds. These changes in tone may be characterized as "lead pipe" rigidity or, if there is superimposed tremor, as "cogwheeling." The loss of descending activation of inhibitory polysynaptic circuits may contribute to such rigidity.[27]

afferents. The inputs to the first- and last-order interneurons differ, as outlined in Table 31.1. By preventing the stretch reflex of antagonist muscles, presynaptic inhibition tends to reinforce reciprocal inhibition produced by IaINs. In humans, this mechanism is thought to produce a second period of reflex reciprocal inhibition.

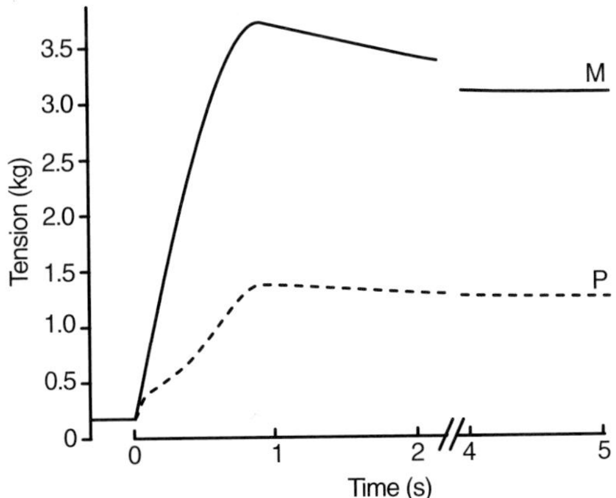

FIGURE 31.4 Phasic and tonic components of the stretch reflex in a decerebrate cat. The total tension of the quadriceps muscle (curve M) remains high for several seconds after the muscle is stretched and held at a new length; a portion of this maintained tension is due to the tonic stretch reflex. Denervation of the muscle eliminates the stretch reflex, revealing the contribution from passive tension (curve P). Reproduced from Liddell.[23]

GABA, the transmitter released by the last-order interneuron, activates at least two types of receptors on the presynaptic terminals of Ia afferents. Activation of $GABA_A$ receptors increases Cl^- conductance and depolarizes the afferent terminals. Since primary afferent depolarization (PAD) coincides with the timing of inhibition, PAD is used experimentally as an indication of presynaptic inhibition. However, activation of $GABA_B$ receptors on the primary afferents also contributes to presynaptic inhibition but not PAD; the effect of GABA binding to these receptors is mediated through second-messenger pathways involving G proteins.

Animal studies reveal that supraspinal descending inputs can activate presynaptic inhibitory interneurons. In humans, only some of these interneurons are activated during simple voluntary movements, allowing presynaptic inhibition to be selectively directed against afferents terminating on specific motor neuron pools. At the onset of movement, presynaptic inhibition is decreased on afferents synapsing on motor neurons of activated muscles, but it is increased on afferents synapsing on motor neurons of nonactivated muscles.[35] With sustained contractions, presynaptic inhibition returns to baseline levels.[36] These observations suggest that descending motor commands fractionate

TABLE 31.1 Characteristics of Selected Spinal Interneurons

Interneuron	Transmitter	Anatomy/physiology	Inputs	Outputs
IaIN	Glycine	Lamina VII; synapses on motor neuron soma; fires single spike to input volley	Corticospinal, vestibulospinal, rubrospinal, antagonist IaINs, Renshaw cells, locomotor networks	Antagonist motor neurons, antagonist IaINs
Ia presynaptic inhibitory (first-order)	Unknown	Intermediate zone?	Corticospinal, vestibulospinal, rubrospinal, cutaneous afferents	Last-order Ia presynaptic inhibitory interneurons
Ia presynaptic inhibitory (last-order)	GABA	Intermediate nucleus	Reticulospinal, locomotor networks?	Antagonist Ia afferents
Group II (excitatory)	Unknown	Intermediate zone?	Ia and/or Ib, propriospinal, descending?	Flexor motor neurons (excitatory)
Group II (inhibitory)	Unknown	Intermediate zone?	Ia and/or Ib, propriospinal, descending?	Extensor motor neurons (inhibitory)
Renshaw cell	Glycine (GABA subpopulation?)	Ventral horn, medial to motor neuron pools; synapses on motor neuron dendrites; fires in high-frequency bursts	Motor neurons, Renshaw cells, corticospinal, rubrospinal, descending monoaminergic, locomotor networks, cutaneous?	Alpha motor neurons (esp. synergists), gamma motor neurons, Renshaw cells, IaINs
IbIN	Glycine?	Intermediate zone; no tonic firing; single spikes when activated	Ib (extensor $\gg$ flexor), Ia, and cutaneous afferents (all excitatory); corticospinal, rubrospinal, reticulospinal (all inhibitory)	Motor neurons (esp. extensor), IbINs, neurons of Clarke's column (subgroup)

interneuron action to achieve a focused inhibition whose strength changes throughout a movement, quite different from peripheral reflex activation of the same interneurons. Presynaptic inhibition is also modulated during locomotion in cats,[37] gating the peripheral feedback that motor neurons receive at different phases of the step cycle. Box 31.4[38–40] describes how descending control of spinal inhibition is altered in some movement disorders.

Different Interneurons Cause Presynaptic Inhibition of Ib and Group II Muscle Afferents

Ib afferents are also subject to presynaptic inhibition and PAD, both of which are most effectively activated by Ib afferents. As is true for Ia afferents, presynaptic inhibition of Ib afferents involves at least two interneurons with a characteristic combination of descending and peripheral inputs.[41] Most descending inputs converge on the first-order interneurons. Cutaneous inputs excite or inhibit different subgroups of these interneurons. The existence of separate circuitry for presynaptic inhibition of Ia and Ib afferents suggests that the CNS can independently control the effectiveness of feedback from muscle spindles and GTOs. This flexibility may allow the CNS to switch between operating modes that respond to length (Ia) feedback and those that respond to tension (Ib) feedback.[42]

Other interneurons mediate presynaptic inhibition of secondary spindle afferents, which is most effectively produced by group II and cutaneous pathways from the same segmental level.[43] Most interneurons mediating presynaptic inhibition of muscle afferents are thought to be located in the intermediate zone of the spinal cord, whereas most interneurons that mediate presynaptic inhibition of cutaneous afferents have been localized to the dorsal horn.

Secondary Spindle Afferents Have Complex Effects on Motor Neurons

Group II spindle afferents project to motor neurons through monosynaptic and potent interneuronal connections. In general, reflex activation of these afferents tends to excite flexor motor neurons and inhibit extensor motor neurons. In recent years, however, a class of last-order interneurons that receive group II input with little input from the other flexor reflex afferents has been identified in animal experiments (Table 31.1). These interneurons, which include excitatory and inhibitory subpopulations, form a disynaptic circuit from secondary spindle afferents to motor neurons. They may play a role in postural adjustments and in coordinating the transition between the different phases of stepping. Whether descending commands can selectively activate these interneurons is not known.[44]

Motor Neurons Activate Inhibitory Interneurons

Collaterals of motor neuron axons excite inhibitory interneurons known as Renshaw cells, which project back onto motor neurons (Table 31.1).[45] Renshaw cells inhibit both extensor and flexor motor neurons, with stronger inhibition of motor neurons that are nearby and that innervate functional synergists.[46] Renshaw cell inhibition, or "recurrent inhibition," limits the firing frequency of motor neurons, but the role this limitation plays during movement is not clear.[47,48] A popular suggestion is that Renshaw cells produce a type of "lateral inhibition" among motor neurons innervating synergists, leading to enhanced contrast between activated and quiescent motor neurons. Still another suggestion is that stronger recurrent inhibition of early-recruited units within a motor neuron pool could shift activation to larger motor neurons during a sustained contraction. Renshaw cells receive inputs from several sources in addition to motor neurons. Supraspinal inputs could preset Renshaw cell excitability during voluntary movement, but the magnitude of recurrent inhibition may be too small to play a major role in shaping motor neuron output.[49]

When Renshaw cells are activated, they fire a characteristic high-frequency burst of action potentials, which permits temporal summation of their IPSPs on the motor neuron.[50] The blockage of these IPSPs by strychnine indicates that Renshaw cells use glycine as a neurotransmitter, although there is evidence for an additional GABAergic component that may be slower and more prolonged.[51,52] The strength of recurrent inhibition is quite variable among different motor neuron pools. This variability results partly from differences in the number of recurrent collaterals. Motor neurons innervating distal foot muscles, for example, have few if any recurrent collaterals,[53] which prevents these motor neurons from effectively activating Renshaw cells. The density of the Renshaw projection onto different motor neuron pools may also vary.

Renshaw cells, like IaINs, are rhythmically activated during locomotion in the cat. This rhythmicity occurs in part because motor neurons fire rhythmically during locomotion, providing Renshaw cells with rhythmic synaptic input. Renshaw cells also receive inputs from segmental interneurons active in locomotion.[32,54]

Golgi Tendon Organs Activate Nonreciprocal Inhibition

Activation of Ib or GTO afferents in cats inhibits homonymous and synergist motor neurons, a phenomenon known as autogenic or nonreciprocal inhibition. Nonreciprocal inhibition has been called the "inverse myotatic reflex," because its effect—a decreased agonist muscle tension—is the opposite of that produced by the activation of Ia afferents. Ib inhibitory circuits may be useful for regulating the ongoing force during movement, as would be needed in grasping a delicate object, for example. The interneurons that mediate this disynaptic effect have been termed Ib inhibitory interneurons (IbINs), because they receive a significant

BOX 31.4

MOVEMENT DISORDERS AND SPINAL INHIBITION

Some human movement disorders that involve excessive coactivation of muscles, such as writer's cramp and generalized dystonia, are characterized by defective activation of reciprocal inhibition, among other abnormalities.[38,39] These disorders are thought to originate from functional changes in the basal ganglia or the cerebral cortex rather than the spinal cord. The abnormalities of reciprocal inhibition involve short-latency polysynaptic circuits. These abnormalities reflect the loss of functional descending inputs onto many classes of spinal interneurons. Presynaptic inhibition of Ia afferents is also diminished in persons with spasticity following spinal injury, reflecting the loss of convergent descending input onto presynaptic inhibitory interneurons.[40]

input from Ib afferents (Table 31.1).[55] IbINs also receive convergent excitatory input from Ia afferents.[56] Unlike muscle spindles, the GTOs do not have a mechanism for altering their sensitivity during a contraction, and the Ia input may confer such sensitivity to the Ib pathway.[57] The relative strength of Ia and Ib afferent input to IbINs might be controlled through presynaptic inhibition by way of selective interneuron pathways.

Nonreciprocal inhibition was once thought to be responsible for a sign of spasticity called the "clasp-knife" phenomenon, in which resistance to muscle stretch disappears suddenly once a certain degree of stretch is achieved. The clasp-knife phenomenon is thought to be mediated through high-threshold muscle afferents, and interneurons in this pathway have been described.[58] The early attribution of the clasp-knife phenomenon to Ib afferents was based partly on the now-discarded belief that GTOs respond only to injuriously high levels of muscle tension.

Flexor Reflexes Result from the Mass Activation of Many Afferent Classes

A number of spinal reflexes are characterized by limb flexion or a flexion–extension movement. In 1910, Sherrington reported that flexor reflexes, consisting of hip, knee, and ankle flexion combined with extensor muscle relaxation, could be elicited by stimulating skin, mixed nerves, or entire dorsal roots in animals with spinal or brainstem transections.[59] Variations of the flexor reflex included extension of the contralateral limb, bilateral flexion, and "rebound" extension following flexion. These variations were influenced by the level of transection. Flexor reflexes were also recognized by neurologists of that time as a sign of impairment of the corticospinal tract. Testing for a Babinski sign, a dorsiflexion of the great toe when the sole of the foot is firmly stroked, is an example of a flexor reflex that remains part of standard neurological examinations to this day.

A variety of peripheral afferents elicit flexor reflexes: group II and III muscle afferents, joint afferents, and high- and low-threshold cutaneous afferents. Because they can elicit a common action, these afferents are sometimes grouped together under the label "flexor reflex afferents," or FRAs.[60] It is important to realize, however, that the normal function of FRAs is not just to elicit flexor reflexes, but to provide proprioceptive and cutaneous information to the spinal cord and ascending pathways. FRAs are likely to be activated quite differently during normal movements, each in a quite distinct way, signaling the movement of particular joints, pressure on particular regions of the skin, or stretch of particular muscles. It has been suggested that such "multisensory" signals might be used to reinforce selected movements.[61]

FRA effects on motor neurons are mediated through circuits involving several interneurons, both excitatory and inhibitory. We know little about the details of these circuits, such as which afferents terminate on first- and last-order interneurons and which interneurons serve as convergence points for cortico-, rubro-, vestibulo-, and propriospinal inputs. However, two major ideas concerning the organization of FRA interneurons have been highly influential. The first idea, championed by Lundberg,[44,61] is that different subsets of FRA interneurons can elicit either flexion or "alternative reflex pathways," such as those responsible for variations of the flexor reflex that were described by Sherrington. According to this idea, subsets of interneurons mediating alternative reflex pathways have inhibitory interconnections, meaning that descending motor commands can select subsets of interneurons whose action produces the desired movement and inhibits alternative subsets. As the movement occurred, it would activate afferents, particularly secondary afferents, that reinforce the activation of the selected subset.

A corollary idea is that subgroups of FRA interneurons with inhibitory interconnections could have a half-center organization that functions as a pattern generator for stepping. The basic circuit would consist of reciprocal inhibition between two sets of interneurons: one set would be activated by ipsilateral FRAs and excite flexor motor neurons, whereas the other set would be activated by contralateral FRAs and excite extensor motor neurons. Peripheral feedback would sculpt these crude alternating movements into a more refined locomotor pattern. Circuits that fit this description were first revealed in cord-transected animals that were treated with L-dopa. Under these conditions, the usual short-latency flexor reflexes are suppressed, but longer latency flexor reflexes that could form the crude half-center are enhanced.[62] Similar long-latency flexor reflexes have been discovered in persons with spinal injuries,[63] and an active area of research in clinical rehabilitation is directed at enhancing these reflexes through pharmacological and physical treatments to regain locomotor function after spinal injury.[64,65]

The short- and long-latency flexor reflexes are both distinct from the nociceptive flexion reflex, which produces a flexion of prolonged duration in response to painful stimuli. In contrast, the stimuli that evoke flexor reflexes are not necessarily painful or noxious. The nociceptive flexion reflex appears to serve a primarily protective function, withdrawing the stimulated limb from harm. This reflex takes priority when it is elicited during ongoing stepping: the stimulated limb assumes a flexed posture, no longer participating in stepping or alternative reflex pathways, while the nonstimulated limbs may continue the locomotor cycle. There is abundant evidence for descending and segmental modulation of interneurons in nociceptive reflex circuits, a topic covered in other chapters.

Exteroceptive Reflexes Activate a Limited Subset of Motor Neurons

Although cutaneous afferents participate in generalized flexor reflexes, local cutaneous stimulation can result in more specific reflex actions. These reflexes, sometimes referred to as exteroceptive reflexes, typically occur only in response to stimulation of a topographically limited area of skin (Fig. 31.5).[66] The motor neurons that participate in an exteroceptive reflex are also fairly limited. In men, for example, stroking the skin of the inner thigh reflexively activates the cremasteric muscle of the scrotum but not leg or abdominal muscles. Because the sensory and motor circuits of these reflexes are limited to a few spinal segments, exteroceptive reflexes are exceedingly useful for clinical evaluation of spinal cord function at distinct anatomical levels.

Another example of a specific cutaneous reflex is the stumbling corrective reaction.[67] This reflex consists of lifting the foot when the skin on the dorsum of the foot is stimulated during walking. The stumbling corrective reaction is phase dependent, meaning that it occurs only when the limb is in the flexion phase of the step cycle, when the limb is not bearing weight. This reflex seems most useful for stepping over obstacles the foot may contact as it swings forward. At least one interneuron that may participate in this reflex has been described; it receives input from the skin of the foot and projects to a subset of foot muscle motor neurons. Transmission through this disynaptic pathway is modulated during locomotion.[68]

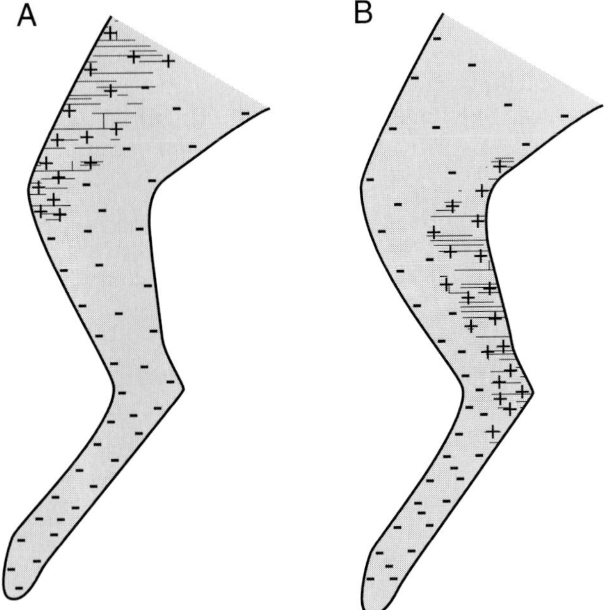

FIGURE 31.5 Regions on the skin of the cat hindlimb that excite (+) or inhibit (−) motor neurons that cause knee extension (A) and ankle extension (B). The density of the + and − signs is proportional to the strength of the response. Reproduced from Hagbarth.[66]

Summary

A variety of excitatory and inhibitory spinal reflexes are elicited by the activation of different classes of afferents. With the exception of the monosynaptic components of the stretch reflex, these reflexes are relayed through spinal interneurons. The interneurons typically receive convergent inputs from several sources, with distinct patterns of inputs for different classes of interneurons. Convergent inputs allow flexibility in the reflex movements. At least some interneuron classes can be activated independently by descending inputs. One proposal under active study is that descending commands selectively activate motor neurons through the same interneurons that are used in reflex circuits.

INTERNEURONS ASSOCIATED WITH MOVEMENTS

In the last section, we discussed a few of the spinal interneurons that have been identified through reflexes, that is, by peripheral activation. Such interneurons make up a small fraction of the interneurons in the spinal cord. Their existence and actions are known because they are relatively easy to identify and study, a feature that does not necessarily correlate with their importance for motor control. Our knowledge of other classes of spinal interneurons is still rudimentary. Even so, many more spinal interneurons are known than we can describe in the space allotted for this chapter. In this section we briefly describe some of the more recently discovered interneurons and the approaches that were used to investigate them. Most of these interneurons have been identified by their functional relationships to particular movements.

The Actions of Group I Excitatory Interneurons Are Revealed during Movement

Many reflex circuits were first studied in anesthetized, motionless animals, using electrical nerve stimulation to activate different classes of sensory fibers.

Under these conditions, spinal circuits that generate active movement may be quiescent, contributing little input to interneurons that participate in reflex circuits. Yet many of the sensory receptors, such as the GTOs, are best activated by changes that occur during active movement. Experiments on decerebrate cats suggest that some reflex pathways are "gated" open during movement.[69,70] In these experiments, Ib afferents were activated during different phases of stepping; this manipulation simulated the addition of a sudden load onto a contracting muscle, thereby increasing the tension on active motor units. Loading ankle extensor muscles during extension enhanced the extension and prevented the transition to flexion (Fig. 31.6). Unloading the limb at the very end of extension promoted a more vigorous flexion. These findings indicate that Ib inputs can reset the rhythm of stepping and excite extensor-related neurons. Excitation of motor neurons by Ib inputs is in contrast to the inhibition from Ib inputs that is normally observed at rest. Thus, these experiments revealed a previously unknown excitatory pathway from Ib afferents to motor neurons, a pathway that involves a novel population of interneurons. It was later shown that Ia afferents also activate this pathway, now known as the group I excitatory pathway. This pathway appears to function only during active movements, such as locomotion, when it reverses the usual inhibitory action of Ib afferents.

At least two factors appear to contribute to the activation of the group I excitatory pathway during locomotion. First, inputs from locomotor interneurons or other sources most likely undergo spatial facilitation on group I excitatory interneurons. Second, the EPSPs produced in motor neurons by group I excitatory interneurons are larger when the motor neurons are depolarized. This effect is similar to that produced by the activation of NMDA-receptor channels, whose nonlinear current–voltage relationship was described in an earlier chapter. Because of this voltage-dependent amplification of EPSPs, the group I excitatory pathway is gated open only in those motor neurons that receive coincident excitatory inputs.[71]

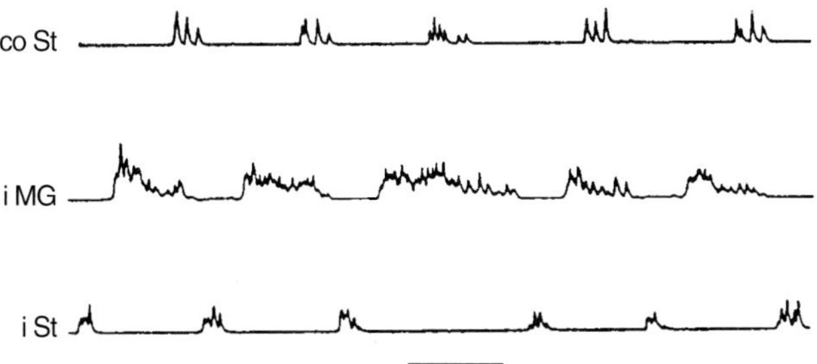

FIGURE 31.6 EMG records from three muscles in a decerebrate cat exhibiting spontaneous fictive locomotion. Stimulation of group I afferents (dark bar) prolongs the extensor phase of locomotion, as seen in the ankle extensor muscle (i MG). Activity in the ipsilateral knee flexor muscle (i St) is delayed until the stimulation ends. The EMG of the contralateral knee flexor muscle (co St) shows only a modest change. Reproduced from Whelan.[70]

Populations of Interneurons Can Be Identified by Their Activity Patterns

Some spinal interneurons that coordinate movement are not easily activated by peripheral inputs and can be identified only by their specific firing patterns during movement. One method for finding such cells has been to search with multiple microelectrode penetrations for units with particular activation patterns. More recently, a number of activity-dependent markers, such as fluorescent calcium- and voltage-sensitive dyes, have been used to reveal populations of active cells in slices or *in vitro* preparations of the spinal cord. This approach has shown that spontaneous, cyclic limb movements in embryonic chicks are associated with waves of neuronal activity that begin with interneurons and motor neurons in the ventrolateral spinal cord and spread dorsally (Fig. 31.7).[72]

In other experiments, populations of neurons that are active during prolonged movements have been labeled with markers that are taken up and retained by active cells. These populations can be viewed later in fixed tissue sections. This technique was used in the neonatal rat spinal cord to locate a cluster of interneurons near the central canal that are involved in pharmacologically induced locomotor activity.[73] Intracellular recordings have shown that interneurons in this area have oscillatory membrane potentials when exposed to NMDA.[74] Such neurons are candidates for the rhythm generator neurons of locomotor networks, which will be discussed later in this chapter.

The Fish Escape Circuit Uses Monosynaptic and Interneuronal Relays

The escape response of fish is a frequently cited example of how descending axons activate motor neurons to cause a simple movement. When attacked by predators, many fish quickly bend their body and tail away from the attacker, forming the shape of the letter "C" before swimming away. This escape behavior is triggered by the firing of a pair of brainstem reticulospinal neurons, the Mauthner cells, whose axons make monosynaptic excitatory connections with spinal motor neurons. The initial bending is not invariant during each escape, as might be predicted from a simple monosynaptic connection. When a Mauthner cell fires, the EPSP it produces in a motor neuron includes sev-

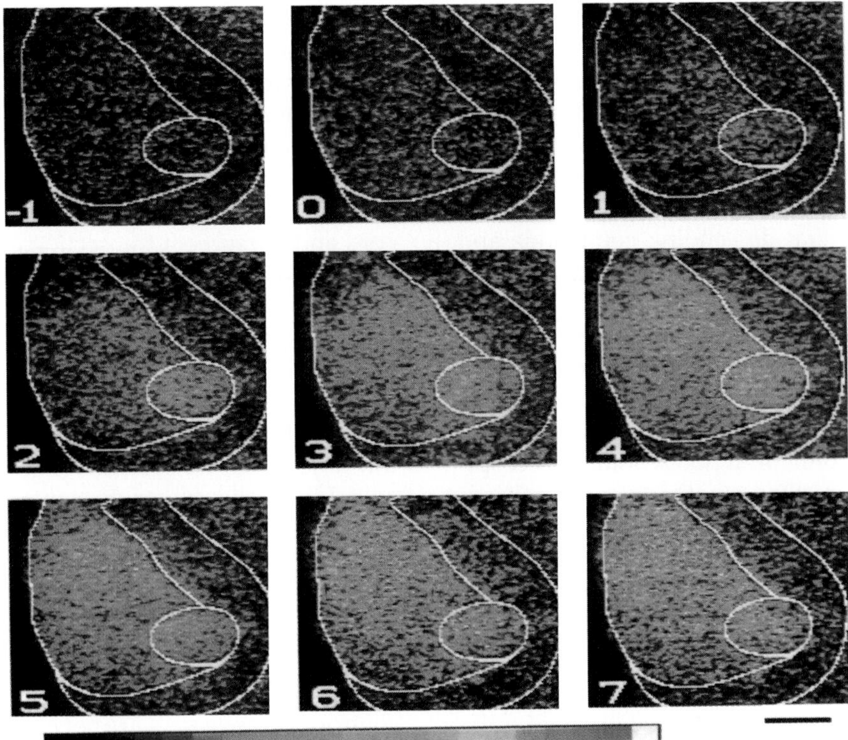

FIGURE 31.7 Optical recording of the sequence of neuronal activity in the embryonic chick spinal cord during spontaneous movement. Neuronal activity, indicated by a calcium-sensitive vital dye, began in the ventral gray matter (panels 1 and 2) and then spread to more dorsal areas of the cord (panels 3–6). Calcium concentrations are indicated by changes in color. Reproduced from O'Donovan.[72]

eral components in addition to the monosynaptic component. One of the other components results from a parallel excitatory relay through additional descending interneurons that are excited by the Mauthner cell and project to many motor neurons. These descending interneurons and their target motor neurons are electrically coupled, with the result that the depolarization of many interneurons is directly transmitted to each motor neuron. This component of the Mauthner-cell-evoked EPSP is generally larger than the monosynaptic component and depolarizes the motor neuron to its firing threshold.[75]

The C3-C4 Interneurons Relay Voluntary Commands to Forelimb Muscles

How does the spinal cord translate descending motor commands into targeted arm movements? This question has been addressed through behavioral, anatomical, and electrophysiological studies in cats. These studies indicate that motor neurons innervating the forelimb muscles used in such movements are activated by interneurons in the third and fourth cervical segments (C3 and C4) of the spinal cord. These C3-C4 interneurons, as they are called, receive potent direct inputs from the cortex, as well as inputs from many brainstem pathways, forelimb muscle afferents, and low-threshold cutaneous afferents. Thus, the C3-C4 interneurons are ideally situated to integrate descending motor commands with sensory feedback from the moving forelimbs. The C3-C4 interneurons are propriospinal neurons, that is, neurons whose axons project to other spinal segments. The axons of the C3-C4 interneurons travel in the ventral white matter to the sixth cervical and first thoracic segments, projecting to motor neuron pools for several forelimb muscles. Spinal lesions that sever the C3-C4 interneuron axons without interrupting corticospinal fibers eliminate a cat's ability to aim its forelimbs with accuracy.[76] However, cats with such lesions are not paralyzed and are still able to make limb movements. These experiments suggest that the command for wrist movements in cats is mediated by cortical and rubrospinal systems acting in parallel with the C3-C4 interneuron link.[77]

A similar propriospinal interneuron arrangement is thought to control wrist movements in humans.[78] Cutaneous stimulation depresses wrist extensors during low levels of voluntary activation and during acti-

A similar propriospinal interneuron arrangement is thought to control wrist movements in humans.[78] Cutaneous stimulation depresses wrist extensors during low levels of voluntary activation and during activation by transcranial magnetic stimulation of the motor cortex. This effect occurs without any change in the excitability of the stretch reflex involving these muscles, suggesting that descending commands and cutaneous input converge at a level presynaptic to the motor neuron.[79]

An interneuronal linkage is only one of several ways that descending commands activate motor neurons. In primates, corticospinal axons make a dense projection to the ventral gray matter of the spinal cord, including the region of the motor neuron pools. Some corticospinal axons synapse directly on motor neurons, particularly those innervating distal hand muscles. However, each corticospinal axon may innervate motor neurons in several different pools, and a single motor neuron may receive synapses from multiple corticospinal neurons. This divergence means that there is no simple relationship between the firing of an individual corticospinal neuron and the contraction of a particular muscle. Experiments on primate intrinsic hand muscles suggest that, with repetitive activation and temporal summation, monosynaptic connections from corticospinal axons may be strong enough to fire motor neurons.[80] Of course, this finding does not exclude the possibility of contributions from interneurons, which are probably activated by corticospinal axons. Monosynaptic connections between corticospinal neurons and motor neurons are likely to play an important role in directing independent control of digits in primates.

The Equilibrium Point Hypothesis Relates Movement Control to Limb Mechanics

A different approach to understanding the spinal control of movement is offered by the **equilibrium point hypothesis**, an idea with origins in biomechanics rather than neural circuitry. The hypothesis begins with the proposal that the posture of a limb results from interactions between the springlike properties of opposing muscles. The nervous system can regulate the stiffness and tone of opposing muscles, so that the limb will be in a stable balance at discrete equilibrium points. Movements of the limb occur when the equilibrium point is shifted. According to this hypothesis, the nervous system moves the limb by generating a motor program consisting of a sequence of equilibrium points. The trajectory of the limb represents its movement between equilibrium points.

The equilibrium point hypothesis is supported by experiments on the frog spinal cord.[81] In these experiments, microstimulation at a site in the intermediate gray always resulted in an arm movement to the same position, regardless of the initial starting point, and the limb trajectory was consistent with a series of calculated equilibrium points. Stimulation in different regions of the intermediate gray revealed a relatively small number of stable end positions. Frogs with spinal cord and dorsal root transections had similar limb trajectories, suggesting that a mechanism intrinsic to the spinal gray generated these trajectories. Neither microstimulation in the ventral horn nor computer simulations of random or topographic motor neuron recruitment could reproduce such trajectories, indicating that spinal interneurons were responsible for generating the trajectories. A second conclusion was that these spinal interneurons, or their inputs, must be spatially organized in the cord.

Summary

Many of the spinal circuits that are important for controlling movement are not organized as reflex pathways. Because these circuits may not be activated by stimulating sensory afferents, the challenge for the modern scientist is to find ways to identify such circuits and explain how they work. It is generally fruitful to study a circuit—often with combined anatomical, physiological, and mathematical approaches—while it is generating a motor behavior. The development of new techniques and reagents to visualize active neuronal populations offers another promising route of investigation.

LOCOMOTION

Locomotion is the action of moving from place to place. Depending on the organism, it may be accomplished by swimming, walking, slithering, or flying. In vertebrates, all modes of locomotion use the rhythmic repetition of a sequence of muscle activity, and the spinal cord plays a key role in coordinating this sequence. Different modes of locomotion can be characterized by the relationship between patterns of muscle activation on opposite sides of the body. When fish swim, they generate a propulsive wave by alternately contracting and relaxing trunk muscles on opposite sides. Birds, on the other hand, activate wings synchronously in flight. In stepping, homologous limbs are activated with alternate timings that may vary for different gaits used by bipedal and quadrupedal animals.

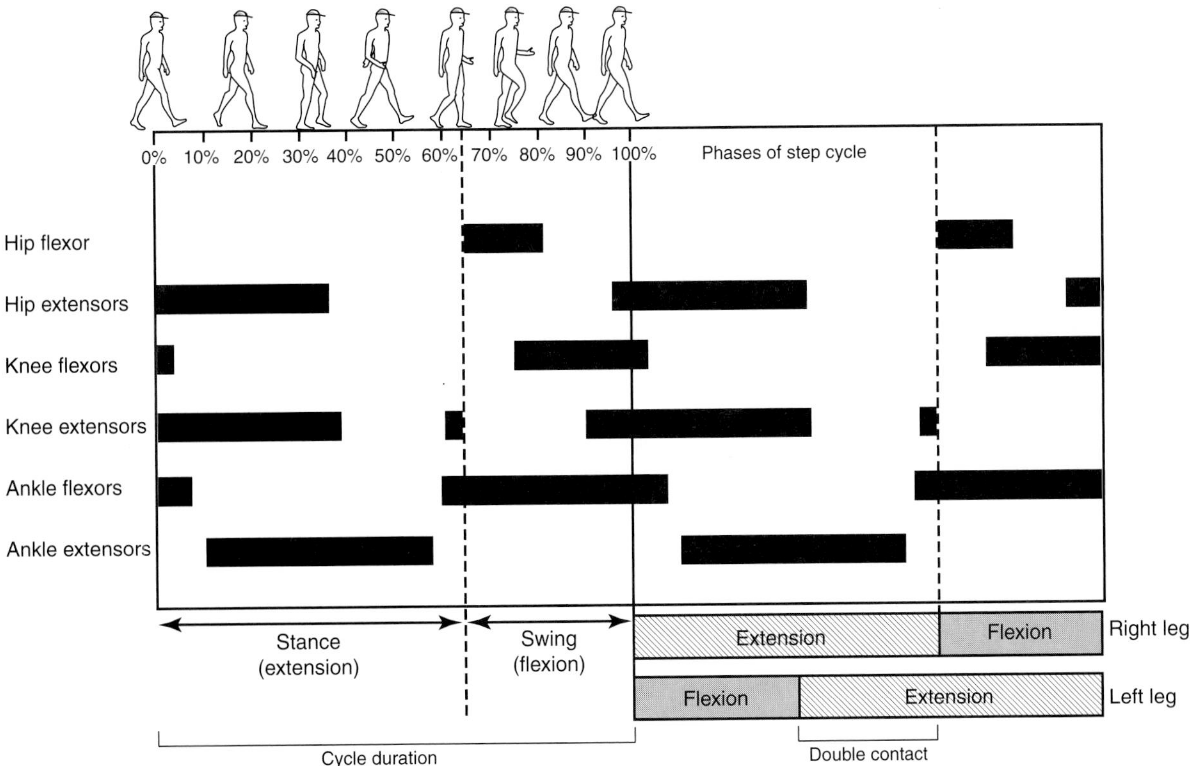

FIGURE 31.8 Schematic diagram of two step cycles in human locomotion. The drawings at the top illustrate the position of the limbs during one cycle. Dark horizontal bars below the drawings show the timing of activity in flexor and extensor muscles of the right leg. The division of each step cycle into stance (extension) and swing (flexion) phases is indicated at the bottom of the figure. Note that the stance phases of the two legs overlap during the time when both feet contact the ground.

human locomotion, the stance phase begins when the heel strikes the ground and begins to bear weight. Throughout stance, the weight is gradually shifted forward, rolling from the heel to the ball of the foot. The swing phase begins when the toe leaves the ground and the limb moves forward. To accomplish this sequence of movements, muscles moving the hip, knee, and ankle joints are activated in characteristic patterns, as diagrammed in the middle portion of Fig. 31.8. Although flexor muscles are generally more active in swing and extensors in stance, the activation patterns of individual muscles can be more elaborate and finely graded. Some muscles are activated twice per cycle, whereas others are activated during only a portion of one phase (Fig. 31.9).

Gaits can be described by several features: the duration of each cycle, the relative proportion of the cycle spent in swing and stance phases, and the phase relationships between limbs. At slow or moderate walking speeds (i.e., long cycle durations), extension is prolonged, and the extension phases of opposite legs overlap. At these speeds, both feet are in simultaneous contact with the ground for some period of time during each cycle (Fig. 31.8, lower right). As the rate of walking increases, the step cycle shortens largely because the extension phase becomes shorter, leading to a briefer period with simultaneous contact. At high speeds, there is no simultaneous contact at all, and the human gait switches recognizably from walking to running. Quadrupedal animals have a greater variety of gaits—including trot, canter, and gallop—each with characteristic phase relationships between front and hind limbs and between left and right sides.

The Energetic Costs of Locomotion Vary

During locomotion, muscles are used in a way that appears to minimize energy consumption.[82] Switching from one gait to another occurs naturally as an animal changes speed, and the rate of oxygen consumption increases linearly with speed. But if a gait is performed at speeds artificially lower or higher than the usual range of speeds, energy consumption rises dramatically.[83] This suggests that animals naturally assume the most efficient locomotor patterns for the desired speed. If the principle of minimizing energy consumption is

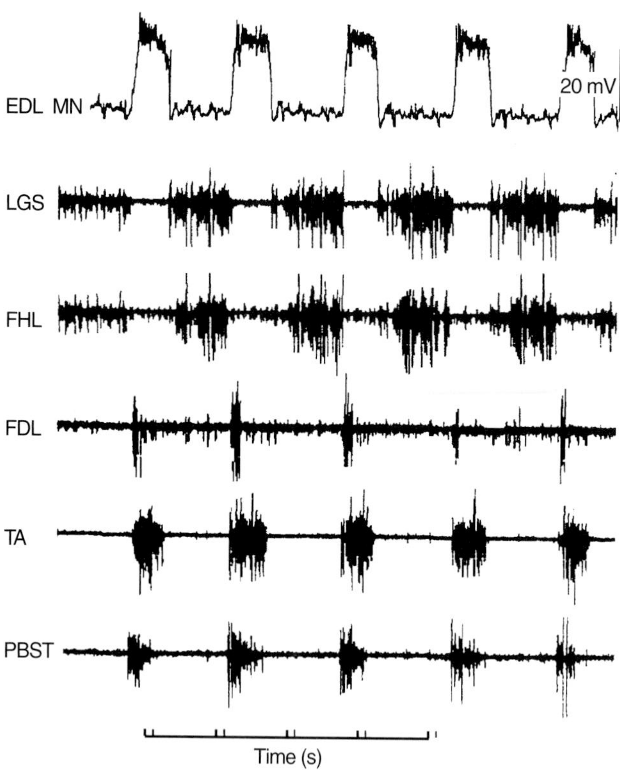

FIGURE 31.9 Motor neuron activity during five step cycles in the cat. The upper trace (EDL MN) is an intracellular recording from a motor neuron that innervates the extensor digitorum longus muscle, a toe and ankle dorsi flexor. Lower traces are muscle nerve recordings from two ankle and foot extensors (LGS and FHL), one toe extensor (FDL), one ankle flexor (TA), and the hamstring (PBST). The activation patterns differ for each muscle. During the flexion phase, the EDL motor neuron is depolarized by approximately 20 mV and there is activity in the recording TA nerve. Briefer bursts of activity are seen at the onset of the flexion phase in FDL and PBST. LGS and FHL are active throughout most of the extension phase. (Courtesy of R. E. Burke.)

changes speed, and the rate of oxygen consumption increases linearly with speed. But if a gait is performed at speeds artificially lower or higher than the usual range of speeds, energy consumption rises dramatically.[83] This suggests that animals naturally assume the most efficient locomotor patterns for the desired speed. If the principle of minimizing energy consumption is extended to individuals, gaits should also reflect aspects of an individual's own limb musculature, with preferred cadences and stride lengths.

Most of the work of terrestrial locomotion consists of shifting the center of gravity to allow the body to fall forward over the foot in stance. Some extensor muscles undergo a mostly isometric activation at the end of the swing phase (see Fig. 31.8), stiffening the limb to provide resistance for a controlled fall and a small bounce. These isometric activations minimize the metabolic cost associated with the formation and breaking of cross-bridges. Energy use is further minimized if the momentum of the fall is stored in the elasticity of muscles and tendons and used to power the following step. The contribution of elastic recoil is considerable and is obvious to anyone who has walked on a loose, sandy beach or other surface that absorbs and damps the energy of recoil. In some African tribes, women who carry loads on their heads use a pendular gait that exploits the transfer of kinetic energy of the load, allowing them to carry up to 20% of their body mass without additional energy consumption.[84] Interestingly, the kangaroo converts the energy of elastic recoil so well that, at faster speeds of hopping achieved by longer jumps, energy consumption actually decreases slightly.[85]

Several Levels of the Nervous System Participate in the Control of Locomotion

In normal individuals, coordinated locomotion is associated with activity in the spinal cord, brainstem, cerebellum, and cerebral cortex, each of which makes distinct contributions to the control of movement. These contributions include initiating locomotion, coordinating muscle activation patterns, responding to perturbations, making postural compensations, and implementing goal-directed changes in gait. Observations of the effects of lesions in different brain regions provide one source of information about a particular region's role in locomotion. However, species differences are important to keep in mind. In some nonmammalian vertebrates, supraspinal lesions disrupt the timing or phase relationships of muscle activity but often preserve a recognizable locomotor pattern. In cats, locomotion may appear fairly normal following removal of the cerebral cortex. In humans, however, even small cortical lesions can have markedly disruptive effects on locomotion (see Box 31.5).

Basic Patterns of Muscle Activation Are Coordinated in the Spinal Cord

Evidence for the existence of spinal circuitry controlling muscle activation patterns during locomotion has been found for many vertebrates, including lampreys, tadpoles, rats, cats, and marmosets. In some vertebrates with legs, a rhythmic motor output that resembles stepping can be elicited with various pharmacological manipulations after complete spinal transection. The rhythmic output persists without sensory feedback, demonstrating its spinal origin. Primitive stepping generators have also been inferred in ma-

BOX 31.5

ALTERED GAIT PATTERNS OCCUR IN NEUROLOGICAL DISEASES

Many neurologic conditions affect gait. Injuries or disease of peripheral nerves, muscles, or motor neurons can cause weakness of the muscles used in locomotion. Injury to motor areas of the cerebral cortex in humans leads to varied degrees of unilateral weakness as well as to stereotyped changes in gait. Many of these changes reflect weakness of leg flexor muscles. The stride length of the affected leg is shorter, because the swing is decreased and the foot fails to dorsiflex properly at the onset of the swing phase. Such changes may cause the foot to scuff the floor, or they may be compensated for by lifting and circumduction of the hip, resulting in a greater side-to-side movement.

Injuries to other supraspinal areas cause abnormalities of gait that are difficult to explain on the basis of weakness. Frontal lobe lesions lead to an apraxic gait, which is characterized by tiny, hesitant steps, as if the feet were stuck to the floor. Patients with such lesions have no clear sensory or motor deficit but seem to have difficulty organizing and producing the locomotor movement. In contrast, cerebellar lesions lead to an ataxic gait, in which stepping is unsteady and irregular. Patients with cerebellar lesions typically stand with their feet widely separated, and each step varies in length, timing, and force. In Parkinson disease, a disorder of the basal ganglia, patients have particular difficulty initiating locomotion. Once they begin to walk, they make small, shuffling steps that may accelerate as stepping proceeds, a characteristic called "festination." These clinical observations highlight the importance of supraspinal structures in the control of human locomotion.

caque monkeys and humans with partial but not complete spinal transections.[63,86–88]

Although the neurons that form central pattern generator (CPG) networks have not been identified, a number of models have been formulated to explain the organization of CPGs. We have already mentioned one of these models, Brown's half-center proposal, which maintains that the CPG is an oscillator composed of two half-centers, one driving flexors and another driving extensors. A variation on the half-center model proposes that limb movements are controlled by a mosaic of such oscillators, one for each muscle pair that produces opposite actions across a joint (Fig. 31.10).[89] Coupling between oscillators allows the multijoint coordination of flexor and extensor muscles during the step cycle, whereas looser coupling of oscillators in different limbs permits different gaits. A similar oscillator model has been used to explain the generation of the swimming rhythm in lampreys (see Box 31.6).[90–93] The validity of a CPG model is based on how well the model predicts the output—a change in locomotor rhythm—that results from a specific experimental perturbation.

Perturbations during locomotion can differentially affect either the timing or the strength of muscular contractions during the locomotor cycle. For example, activation of the group I excitatory pathway described earlier alters the timing of the step cycle. In contrast, some interneurons that provide inputs to motor neu-

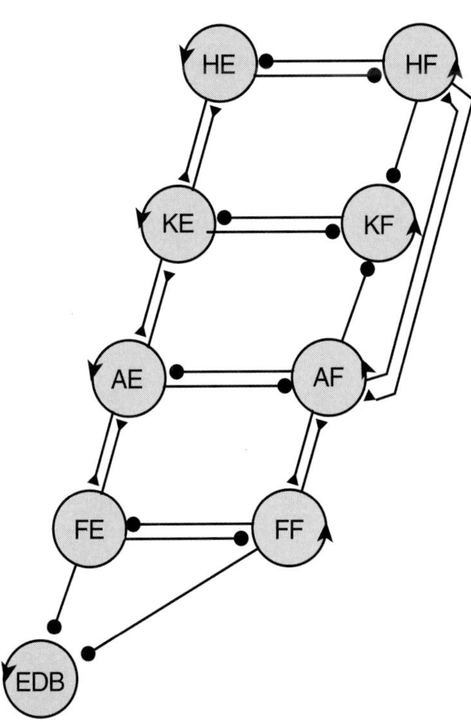

FIGURE 31.10 Scheme for multijoint coordination within a single limb using a mosaic of oscillators. Individual oscillators control extension and flexion at the hip (HE, HF), knee (KE, KF), ankle (AE, AF), and foot (FE, FF), as well as dorsiflexion of the toe by an intrinsic foot muscle (EDB). Changes in the strength of the interconnections between oscillators allow a variety of gaits. Excitatory connections are represented by triangles and inhibitory connections by filled circles. Reproduced from Grillner.[89]

BOX 31.6

SWIMMING IN LAMPREYS

The lamprey is a jawless fish that swims by propagating a wave of muscular contraction along its length. The contraction of muscles on one side of this primitive vertebrate is coupled with the relaxation of muscles of the opposite side. As the wave spreads from head to tail, there is a slight delay in muscle activation from segment to segment. The delay decreases with swimming speed, producing a constant phase lag of about 1% over a wide range of speeds. Pieces of spinal cord containing only a few spinal segments can sustain a basic swimming rhythm, which suggests that the pattern-generating circuitry underlying swimming is contained in those pieces. Since pieces from all levels of the spinal cord are capable of sustaining swimming, the underlying circuitry must be repeated in each spinal segment.

Several models have been proposed to explain the generation of the swimming rhythm in the lamprey, all of which involve a chain of oscillators. In some models, a network of neural interconnections creates the basic oscillator unit.[90] In others, the oscillator is represented mathematically by phase equations, which avoids specific assumptions about unknown circuitry.[91] According to a popular connectionist network model (Fig. 31.11), each segment of the cord contains a half-center circuit. This model is based on synaptic interconnections that have been observed among three sets of interneurons on each side of the spinal cord: excitatory, lateral, and contralaterally projecting interneurons. The excitatory interneurons drive ipsilateral motor neurons as well as the other two sets of interneurons. The contralaterally projecting interneurons inhibit all three classes of interneurons on the contralateral side of the cord, causing activity to alternate from side to side. All of the excitatory connections of this circuit, including the inputs from descending reticulospinal axons that initiate swimming, are glutamatergic, whereas the inhibitory connections are glycinergic. In this network model, the rhythm can be modulated by sensory or other inputs.

Grillner and colleagues expanded on the connectionist network model by incorporating known physiological properties of the three types of interneurons, including voltage- and neurotransmitter-modulated conductances.[92] The output generated by their expanded model resembled the normal swim pattern in many ways. In addition, their

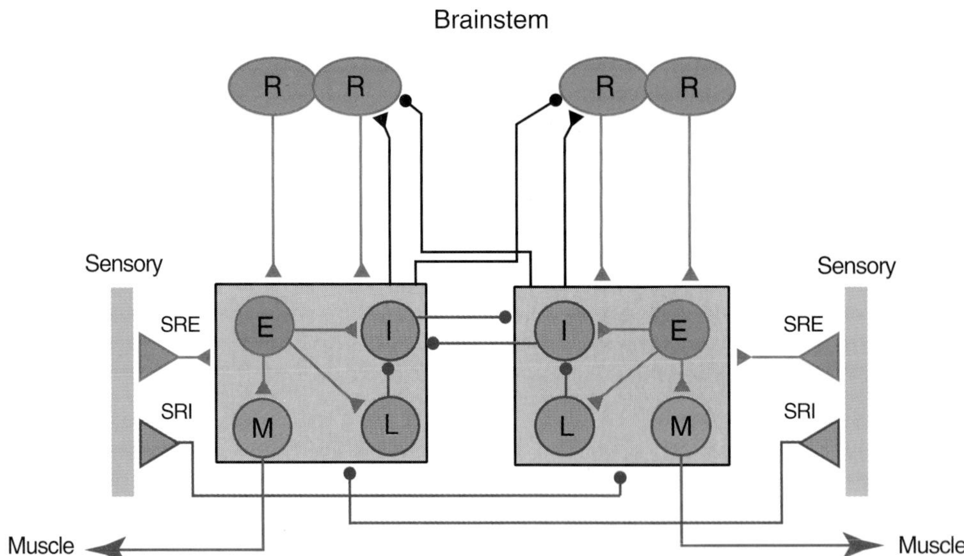

FIGURE 31.11 Model of the oscillator for swimming within each segment of the lamprey spinal cord. Abbreviations: E, excitatory interneuron; I, contralaterally projecting interneuron; L, lateral interneuron; M, motor neuron; R, reticulospinal neuron; SRE, excitatory sensory input; SRI, inhibitory sensory input. Excitatory connections are represented by triangles and inhibitory connections by circles. Reproduced from Grillner.[90]

model correctly predicted the changes expected from modulators such as serotonin (Fig. 31.12).

Although the connectionist network model does an admirable job of producing the basic swimming rhythm and certain variations for individual segments, it is somewhat less satisfactory for explaining intersegmental coordination or how the lamprey can swim backward as well as forward. Intersegmental coordination requires connections between oscillators. One proposal is that such coordination is mediated partly by collaterals of excitatory interneurons that may extend a few segments rostrally and caudally. Increased excitability of an individual segment could then be transmitted to adjacent segments.[93] Although this proposal provides a fairly reasonable approximation of real swimming, there are arguments in favor of longer-range interactions between segments. Clearly, this and other models will be refined as more is learned about the anatomy and physiology of lamprey spinal circuits.

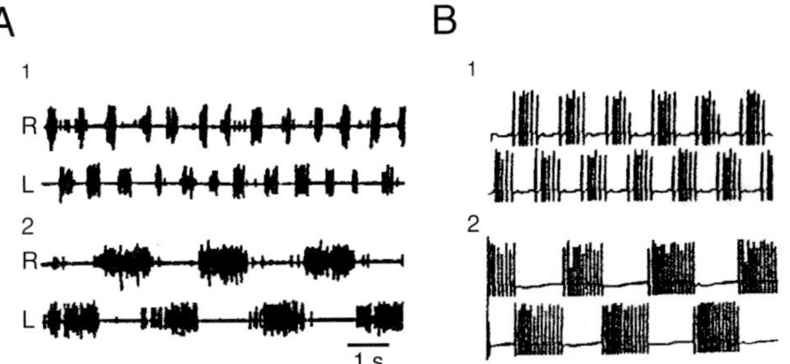

FIGURE 31.12 Real and simulated swimming motor patterns in the lamprey spinal cord. (A) Alternating motor output on the right (R) and left (L) sides of the cord produces the characteristic swimming rhythm in normal saline (1) and in the presence of 1 μM citalopram, a drug that increases the activation of serotonergic action. Note that the rhythm is slowed and bursts are prolonged by citalopram. (B) An expanded connectionist network model simulates the real rhythm in normal saline (1). When the effect of serotonin is incorporated into the model (2), the output of the model resembles the real swimming rhythm in citalopram. Reproduced from Grillner.[92]

rons, such as Renshaw cells or IaINs, may be driven by the CPG, affecting the amplitude of the motor output without influencing its timing or rhythm. These observations suggest that locomotor CPGs have separate portions for generating rhythms and for setting the amplitude of the motor output.[94]

Sensory Inputs Shape Details of the Locomotor Pattern

Although spinal networks may encode a basic sequence of muscle activity for locomotion, the final gait reflects a degree of fine-tuning by descending and peripheral inputs. This fact was recognized by Brown in his earliest description of spinal pattern generators[2]:

> A purely central mechanism of progression ungraded by proprioceptive stimuli would clearly be inefficient in determining the passage of an animal through an uneven environment. Across a plane of perfect evenness the central mechanism itself might drive an animal with precision. Or it might be efficient, for instance, in the case of an elephant charging over ground of moderate unevenness. But it alone would make impossible the fine stalking of a cat over rough ground. In such a case each step may be somewhat different to all others, and each must be graded to its condition if the whole progression of the animal is to be efficient.... This grading can only be brought about by peripheral stimuli.

Afferent inputs reinforce and refine the basic patterns of motor neuron activation. The rhythmic movements of the limbs produce rhythmic activity in cutaneous, joint, and muscle afferents. Spindle afferents fire in complicated patterns, both when muscles are passively stretched and during active contraction, when fusimotor drive enhances the afferents' sensitivity.[95] Deafferentation of a limb in cats disrupts the balance between flexion and extension movements at different joints, resulting in a disorganized but recognizable locomotor pattern with inaccurate placements of the limb.[96]

Another function of afferent input is to initiate compensatory changes when stepping is perturbed, as discussed earlier for the stumbling corrective reaction. Transmission of some sensory information is gated during the step cycle, suggesting that the interneurons relaying this information also receive inputs from CPG neurons.[97] The vestibular system and proprioceptors in neck muscles provide postural information to the CPG, affecting the rhythm and amplitude of extensor bursts.[98]

The Brainstem Is the Primary Center for Locomotor Control

In intact animals, brainstem structures play a key role in initiating and maintaining locomotion.[99] In decerebrate animals, electrical stimulation of the rostral mesencephalon causes a slow, tonic contraction of limb muscles followed by stepping. This functionally defined brainstem area, called the mesencephalic locomotor region (MLR), lies near the cuneiform nucleus. The stepping elicited by MLR stimulation persists for a short time after the stimulation ends, and the timing of the step cycle is not yoked to the frequency of stimulation. However, higher intensity stimulation produces faster stepping that may change into a trot or gallop.

How does the MLR transmit excitatory drive to the spinal cord? The MLR itself has few or no direct spinal projections, but it does project heavily to neurons in the reticular formation of the medial medulla. The axons of those neurons travel in the ventral spinal cord and are thought to project to the interneurons that form the spinal CPGs.[100] Reticulospinal neurons relay descending locomotor signals from the MLR, as well as signals originating outside the MLR in sensory areas of the pons.[101] Some reticulospinal neurons exhibit rhythmic firing patterns that can be correlated with the swing and stance phases of the locomotor cycle or with activity in individual motor neuron pools, which is often more finely graded. Most of the rhythmic firing patterns persist even when sensory feedback is removed, suggesting that these patterns are of central origin.[102,103] Whether the rhythmic activity of reticulospinal neurons is endogenously generated or results from rhythmic inputs from the MLR or feedback from spinal CPGs is not entirely clear. Brainstem rhythmicity could serve to reinforce or entrain spinal rhythm generators, but such interactions need further investigation.

Higher Levels of the CNS Also Influence Locomotor Patterns

In addition to formulating conscious decisions about initiating and maintaining walking, the cerebral cortex plays a role in producing adaptations of gait. During voluntary modifications of gait by cats trained to step over obstacles, many corticospinal neurons change their firing rates, often with a timing appropriate for the altered contraction of particular muscles.[104] The motor cortex can intervene, either directly or through spinal CPGs, to alter a limb's trajectory with a high degree of precision, in a manner similar to that used for generating a goal-directed reaching movement.[105] In humans, a greater influence of supraspinal regions in locomotor control can be inferred from the effects of clinical lesions (see Box 31.5).

Locomotor Rhythms May Arise from the Intrinsic Rhythmicity of CPG Neurons or Rhythmic Inputs

Many models of spinal locomotor CPGs rely on network connections rather than intrinsic membrane properties to simulate the rhythmicity of the locomotor cycle. This bias is partly the result of our rather limited knowledge of the membrane properties of vertebrate neurons. However, there are intriguing hints that such properties may contribute to the rhythmicity of spinal networks. One of the more consistent activators of rhythmic activity in many vertebrates is the direct application of excitatory amino acids, particularly NMDA, to the isolated spinal cord.[92,106,107] Moreover, antagonists of excitatory amino acids block locomotion resulting from brainstem stimulation.[108] In many neurons, NMDA alters voltage-dependent conductances, producing rhythmic membrane potential oscillations that could potentially support a locomotor rhythm.[90,109] On the other hand, NMDA may simply raise the overall excitability of a circuit, allowing rhythmic synaptic inputs to have a greater effect.[107]

A number of other drugs can induce or modulate rhythmic activity in spinal cord preparations in the laboratory, including serotonin, acetylcholine, dopamine, and opiate antagonists. Serotonin, for example, interacts with NMDA-induced rhythms in lampreys[92] and neonatal rats,[110] prolonging cycle durations and motor neuron bursts, most likely by modulating Ca^{2+}-activated K^+ channels. Not all of these drug-induced rhythms correspond to locomotion or even interpretable patterns of muscular activation.[111] Most animals have a varied behavioral repertoire, and these rhythms may represent fragments of other behaviors or other network configurations.

Synaptic connections, especially reciprocal inhibitory synapses, form an essential element in half-center models of locomotor CPGs. Glycine is the neurotransmitter used by neurons essential for coordination between opposite sides of the lamprey during swimming, as discussed in Box 31.6. A modulatory role for the inhibitory neurotransmitter GABA has also been suggested in lampreys; in tadpoles, GABA plays a key role in stopping locomotion in response to pressure on the head.[112] Since the pharmacology of locomotor networks is a relatively new area of investigation, we have much to learn about whether the use of particular neurotransmitters is conserved between species.

Summary

The circuitry of the spinal cord plays an important role in controlling the activation of motor neuron pools to produce coordinated movement. Sensory afferents and supraspinal inputs activate interneurons in the spinal cord, sometimes in parallel with direct connections to motor neurons. Different classes of spinal interneurons have characteristic patterns of inputs, outputs, and interconnections with other interneuron classes. Networks of spinal interneurons can integrate inputs from many sources to produce a complex motor command. Models of simple networks in vertebrates and invertebrates provide examples of how such networks could operate.

Sensory afferents and descending inputs share common spinal interneurons, but are capable of activating them in distinctive ways. Reflexes occur when sensory afferents are used to activate spinal circuitry. Specific reflexes that are activated by muscle stretch, muscle tension, and skin stimulation and the interneuronal circuits known to participate in these reflexes are described in this chapter. Although reflexes could play a role in generating or modifying normal movements, there is growing evidence that voluntary movements activate interneurons in a more selective manner. The study of reflexes provides information on the basic organization of spinal circuitry that is shared with descending pathways.

Not all spinal interneurons receive direct input from sensory afferents. The organization of intrinsic spinal circuits and how they participate in controlling movement must be studied during a movement itself, because these interneurons may be quiescent at other times. Studies of spinal circuits during simple movements using physiological recording or markers that permit imaging of neuronal activity offer the prospect of viewing the operations of such networks.

Spinal circuitry plays an important role in coordinating locomotion. The basic sequence of alternating muscle contraction is encoded by pattern-generating circuitry in the spinal cord, but is further refined by sensory feedback and inputs from a number of supraspinal centers. The brainstem plays a pivotal role in activating the spinal circuitry for locomotion.

References

1. Sherrington, C. S. (1906). *Integrative Action of the Nervous System.* Scribner's, New York.
2. Brown, T. G. (1911). The intrinsic factors in the act of progression in the mammal. *Proc. R. Soc. London* **84:** 308–319.
3. Getting, P. A. (1989). Emerging principles governing the operation of neural networks. *Annu. Rev. Neurosci.* **12:** 185–204.
4. Elson, R. C., and Selverston, A. I. (1992). Mechanisms of gastric rhythm generation in the isolated stomatogastric ganglion of spiny lobsters: Bursting pacemaker potentials, synaptic interactions, and muscarinic modulation. *J. Neurophysiol.* **68:** 890–907.
5. Harris-Warwick, R. M., Nagy, F., and Nusbaum, M. P. (1992). Neuromodulation of stomatogastric networks by identified neurons and transmitters. In *Dynamic Biological Networks* (R. M. Harris-Warwick, E. Marder, A. I. Selverston, and M. Moulins, eds.), pp. 87–137. MIT Press, Cambridge, MA.
6. Johnson, B. R., and Hooper, S. L. (1992). Overview of the stomatogastric nervous system. In *Dynamic Biological Networks* (R. M. Harris-Warwick, E. Marder, A. I. Selverston, and M. Moulins, eds.), pp. 1–30. MIT Press, Cambridge, MA.
7. Katz, P. S., and Harris-Warwick, R. M. (1990). Neuromodulation of the crab pyloric central pattern generator by serotonergic/cholinergic proprioceptive afferents. *J. Neurosci.* **10:** 1495–1512.
8. Kiehn, O., and Harris-Warwick, R. M. (1992). Serotonergic stretch receptors induce plateau properties in a crustacean motor neuron by a dual conductance mechanism. *J. Neurophysiol.* **68:** 485–495.
9. Meyrand, P., Simmers, J., and Moulins, M. (1991). Construction of a pattern generating circuit with neurons of different networks. *Nature (London)* **351:** 60–63.
10. Meyrand, P., Simmers, J., and Moulins, M. (1994). Dynamic construction of a neural network from multiple pattern generators in the lobster stomatogastric nervous system. *J. Neurosci.* **14:** 630–644.
11. Merton, P. A. (1953). Speculations on the servo-control of movement. In *The Spinal Cord* (J. L. Malcolm, J. A. B. Gray, and G. E. W. Wolstenholme, eds.), pp. 183–198. Little Brown, Boston.
12. Houk, J. C., and Rymer, W. Z. (1981). Neural control of muscle length and tension. In *Handbook of Physiology* (V. B. Brooks, ed.), Sect. 1. Vol. II, Part I, pp. 257–323. Am. Physiol. Soc., Washington, DC.
13. Hulliger, M., Durmuller, N., Prochazka, A., and Trend, P. (1989). Flexible fusimotor control of muscle spindle feedback during a variety of natural movements. *Prog. Brain Res.* **80:** 87–101.
14. Schieber, M. H., and Thach, W. T. (1985). Trained slow tracking. II. Bidirectional discharge patterns of cerebellar nuclear, motor cortex, and spindle afferent neurons. *J. Neurophysiol.* **54:** 1228–1270.
15. Hagbarth, K.-E. (1993). Microneurography and applications to issues of motor control: Fifth annual Stuart Reiner memorial lecture. *Muscle Nerve* **16:** 693–705.
16. Llewellyn, M., Yang, J. F., and Prochazka, A. (1990). Human H-reflexes are smaller in difficult beam walking than in normal treadmill walking. *Exp. Brain Res.* **83:** 22–28.
17. Wolpaw, J. R., and Carp, J. S. (1990). Memory traces in the spinal cord. *Trends Neurosci.* **31:** 145–152.
18. Carp, J. S., and Wolpaw, J. R. (1994). Motor neuron plasticity underlying operantly conditioned decrease in primate H-reflex. *J. Neurophysiol.* **72:** 431–442.
19. Nielsen, J., Crone, C., and Hultborn, H. (1993). H-reflexes are smaller in dancers from The Royal Danish Ballet than in well trained athletes. *Eur. J. Appl. Physiol.* **66:** 116–121.
20. Brown, A. G., and Fyffe, R. E. W. (1978). The morphology of group Ia afferent fibre collaterals in the spinal cord of the cat. *J. Physiol. (London)* **274:** 111–127.
21. Ziskind-Conhaim, L. (1990). NMDA receptors mediate poly- and monosynaptic potentials in motor neurons of rat embryos. *J. Neurosci.* **10:** 125–135.
22. Pinco, M., and Lev-Tov, A. (1993). Modulation of monosynaptic excitation in the neonatal rat spinal cord. *J. Neurophysiol.* **70:** 1151–1158.
23. Liddell, E. G. T., and Sherrington, C. S. (1924). Reflexes in response to stretch (myotatic reflexes). *Proc. R. Soc. London, Ser. B* **96:** 212–242.
24. McGrath, G. J., and Matthews, P. B. C. (1973). Evidence from the use of procaine nerve block that the spindle group II fibres contribute to the excitation in the tonic stretch reflex of the decerebrate cat. *J. Physiol. (London)* **235:** 371–408.
25. Pierrot-Deseilligny, E. (1990). Electrophysiological assessment of the spinal mechanisms underlying spasticity. In *New Trends and Advanced Techniques in Clinical Neurophysiology* (P. M. Rossini and F. Mauguieres, eds.), pp. 364–373. Elsevier, Amsterdam.
26. Hagbarth, K. E., Wallin, G., and Lofsted, L. (1973). Muscle spindle responses to stretch in normal and spastic subjects. *Scand. J. Rehabil. Med.* **5:** 156–159.
27. Delwaide, P. J., Pepin, J. L., and Maertens de Noordhoot, A. (1991). Short latency autogenetic inhibition in patients with Parkinsonian rigidity. *Ann. Neurol.* **30:** 83–89.

28. Nielsen, J., Crone, C., Sinkjaer, T., Toft, E., and Hultborn, H. (1995). Central control of reciprocal inhibition during fictive dorsiflexion in man. *Exp. Brain Res.* **104:** 99–106.
29. Nielsen, J., Kagamihara, Y., Crone, C., and Hultborn, H. (1992). Central facilitation of Ia inhibition during tonic ankle dorsiflexion revealed after blockade of peripheral feedback. *Exp. Brain Res.* **88:** 651–656.
30. Hultborn, H., Illert, M., and Santini, M. (1976a). Convergence on interneurones mediating the reciprocal Ia inhibition of motoneurones. I. Disynaptic Ia inhibition of Ia inhibitory interneurones. *Acta Physiol. Scand.* **96:** 193–201.
31. Hultborn, H., Illert, M., and Santini, M. (1976b). Convergence on interneurones mediating the reciprocal Ia inhibition of motoneurones. III. Effects from supraspinal pathways. *Acta Physiol. Scand.* **96:** 368–391.
32. Pratt, C. A., and Jordan, L. M. (1987). Ia inhibitory interneurons and Renshaw cells as contributors to the spinal mechanisms of fictive locomotion. *J. Neurophysiol.* **57:** 56–71.
33. Crone, C., and Nielsen, J. (1989). Spinal mechanisms in man contributing to reciprocal inhibition during voluntary dorsiflexion of the foot. *J. Physiol. (London)* **416:** 255–272.
34. Rudomin, P. (1990b). Presynaptic inhibition of muscle and tendon organ afferents in the mammalian spinal cord. *Trends Neurosci.* **13:** 499–505.
35. Hultborn, H., Meunier, S., Pierrot-Deseilligny, E., and Shindo, M. (1987). Changes in presynaptic inhibition of Ia fibers at the onset of voluntary contraction in man. *J. Physiol. (London)* **389:** 757–772.
36. Meunier, S., and Pierrot-Deseilligny, E. (1989). Gating of the afferent volley of the monosynaptic stretch reflex during movement in man. *J. Physiol. (London)* **419:** 753–763.
37. Gossard, J. P., Cabelguen, J. M., and Rossignol, S. (1991). An intracellular study of muscle primary afferents during fictive locomotion in the cat. *J. Neurophysiol.* **65:** 914–916.
38. Nakashima, K., Rothwell, J. C., and Day, B. L. D. (1989). Reciprocal inhibition between forearm muscles in patients with writer's cramp and other occupational cramps, symptomatic hemidystonia and hemiparesis due to stroke. *Brain* **112:** 681–697.
39. Panizza, M. E., Hallett, M., and Nilsson, J. (1989). Reciprocal inhibition in patients with hand cramps. *Neurology* **39:** 85–89.
40. Faist, M., Mazavet, D., Dietz, V., and Pierrot-Deseilligny, E. (1994). A quantitative assessment of presynaptic inhibition of Ia afferents in spastics. Differences in hemiplegics and paraplegics. *Brain* **117:** 1449–1455.
41. Rudomin, P., Solodkin, M., and Jimenez, I. (1986). PAD and PAH response patterns of group Ia- and Ib fibers to cutaneous and descending inputs in the cat spinal cord. *J. Neurophysiol.* **56:** 987–1006.
42. Rudomin, P. (1990). Presynaptic control of synaptic effectiveness of muscle spindle and tendon organ afferents in the mammalian spinal cord. In *The Segmental Motor System* (M. D. Binder and L. M. Mendell, eds.), pp. 349–380. Oxford University Press, Oxford.
43. Riddell, J. S., Jankowska, E., and Huber, J. (1995). Organization of neuronal systems mediating presynaptic inhibition of group II muscle afferents in the cat. *J. Physiol. (London)* **483:** 443–460.
44. Lundberg, A., Malmgren, K., and Schomburg, E. D. (1987). Reflex pathways from group II muscle afferents. 3. Secondary spindle afferents and the FRA: A new hypothesis. *Exp. Brain Res.* **65:** 294–306.
45. Eccles, J. C., Fatt, P., and Koketsu, K. (1954). Cholinergic and inhibitory synapses in a pathway from motor-axon collaterals to motoneurones. *J. Physiol. (London)* **126:** 524–562.
46. McCurdy, M. L., and Hamm, T. M. (1994). Topography of recurrent inhibitory postsynaptic potentials between individual motor neurons in the cat. *J. Neurophysiol.* **72:** 214–226.
47. Friedman, W. A., Sypert, G. W., Munson, J. B., and Fleshman, J. W. (1981). Recurrent inhibition in type identified motor neurons. *J. Neurophysiol.* **46:** 1349–1359.
48. Hultborn, H., Lipski, J., Mackel, R., and Wigstrom, H. (1988). Distribution of recurrent inhibition within a motor nucleus. I. Contribution from slow and fast units to the excitation of Renshaw cells. *Acta Physiol. Scand.* **134:** 347–361.
49. Lindsay, A., and Binder, M. D. (1991). Distribution of effective synaptic currents underlying recurrent inhibition in cat triceps surae motoneurons. *J. Neurophysiol.* **65:** 168–177.
50. Eccles, J. C., Eccles, R. M. Iggo, A., and Ito, M. (1961). Distribution of recurrent inhibition among motoneurones. *J. Physiol. (London)* **159:** 479–499.
51. Cullheim, S., and Kellerth, J.-O. (1981). Two kinds of recurrent inhibition of cat spinal alpha-motor neurones as differentiated pharmacologically. *J. Physiol. (London)* **312:** 209–224.
52. Schneider, S. P., and Fyffe, R. E. W. (1992). Involvement of GABA and glycine in recurrent inhibition of spinal motor neurons. *J. Neurophysiol.* **68:** 397–406.
53. Cullheim, S., and Kellerth, J.-O. (1978). A morphological study of the axons and recurrent axon collaterals of cat alpha-motoneurones supplying different hind-limb muscles. *J. Physiol. (London)* **281:** 285–299.
54. McCrea, D., Pratt, C. A., and Jordon, L. M. (1980). Renshaw cell activity and recurrent effects on motor neurons during fictive locomotion. *J. Neurophysiol.* **44:** 475–488.
55. Jankowska, E. (1992). Interneuronal relay in spinal pathways from proprioceptors. *Prog. Neurobiol.* **38:** 335–378.
56. Jankowska, E., Johannisson, T., and Lipski, J. (1981). Common interneurones in reflex pathways from group Ia and Ib afferents of ankle extensor muscles in the cat. *J. Physiol. (London)* **310:** 381–402.
57. Malmgren, K. (1988). On premotoneuronal integration in cat and man. *Acta Physiol. Scand., Suppl.* **576:** 1–53.
58. Cleland, C. L., and Rymer, W. Z. (1993). Functional properties of spinal interneurons activated by muscular free nerve endings and their potential contributions to the clasp knife reflex. *J. Neurophysiol.* **69:** 1181–1191.
59. Sherrington, C. S. (1910). Flexion-reflex of the limb, crossed extension-reflex, and reflex stepping and standing. *J. Physiol. (London)* **40:** 28–121.
60. Eccles, R. M., and Lundberg, A. (1959). Synaptic actions in motor neurons by afferents which may evoke the flexion reflex. *Arch. Ital. Biol.* **97:** 199–221.
61. Lundberg, A. (1979). Multisensory control of spinal reflex pathways. *Prog. Brain Res.* **50:** 11–28.
62. Jankowska, E., Jukes, M. G. M., Lund, S., and Lundberg, A. (1967). The effect of DOPA on the spinal cord. 6. Half-centre organization of interneurons transmitting effects from the flexor reflex afferents. *Acta Physiol. Scand.* **70:** 389–402.
63. Bussel, B., Roby-Brami, A., Yakovleff, A., and Bennis, N. (1989). Late flexion reflex in paraplegic patients: Evidence for a spinal stepping generator. *Brain Res. Bull.* **22:** 53–56.
64. Stewart, J. E., Barbeau, H., and Gauthier, S. (1991). Modulation of locomotor patterns and spasticity with clonidine in spinal cord injured patients. *Can. J. Neurol. Sci.* **18:** 321–332.
65. Dietz, V., Colombo, G., and Jensen, L. (1994). Locomotor activity in spinal man. *Lancet* **344:** 1260–1263.
66. Hagbarth, K. E. (1952). Excitatory and inhibitory skin areas for flexor and extensor motoneurones. *Acta Physiol. Scand.* **26** (Suppl. 94): 1–58.
67. Forssberg, H. (1979). Stumbling corrective reaction: A phase

dependent compensatory reaction during locomotion. *J. Neurophysiol.* **42:** 936–953.
68. Fleshman, J. W., Lev-Tov, A., and Burke, R. E. (1984). Peripheral and central control of flexor digitorum longus and flexor hallucis longus motor neurons: The synaptic basis of functional diversity. *Exp. Brain Res.* **54:** 133–149.
69. Conway, B. A., Hultborn, H., and Kiehn, O. (1987). Proprioceptive input resets central locomotor rhythm in the spinal cat. *Exp. Brain Res.* **68:** 643–656.
70. Whelan, P. J., Hiebert, G. W., and Pearson, K. G. (1995). Stimulation of the group I extensor afferents prolongs the stance phase in walking cats. *Exp. Brain Res.* **103:** 20–30.
71. Brownstone, R. M., Gossard, J.-P., and Hultborn, H. (1994). Voltage-dependent excitation of motoneurones from spinal locomotor centres in the cat. *Exp. Brain Res.* **102:** 34–44.
72. O'Donovan, M., Ho, S., and Yee, W. (1994). Calcium imaging of rhythmic network activity in the developing spinal cord of the chick embryo. *J. Neurosci.* **14:** 6354–6369.
73. Kjaerulff, O., Barajon, I., and Kiehn, O. (1994). Sulphorhodamine-labelled cells in the neonatal rat spinal cord following chemically induced locomotor activity in vitro. *J. Physiol. (London)* **478:** 265–273.
74. Hochman, S., Jordan, L. M., and MacDonald, J. F. (1994). N-methyl-D-aspartate receptor mediated voltage-oscillations in neurons surrounding the central canal in slices of rat spinal cord. *J. Neurophysiol.* **72:** 565–577.
75. Fetcho, J. R. (1992). Excitation of motor neurons by the Mauthner axon in goldfish: Complexities in a "simple" reticulospinal pathway. *J. Neurophysiol.* **67:** 1574–1586.
76. Alstermark, B., Lundberg, A., Norsell, U., and Sybirska, E. (1981). Integration in descending motor pathways controlling the forelimb in the cat. 9. Differential behavioral defects after spinal cord lesions interrupting defined pathways from higher centres to motor neurones. *Exp. Brain Res.* **42:** 299–318.
77. Alstermark, B., Lundberg, A., and Pettersson, L. G. (1991). The pathway from Ia forelimb afferents to the motor cortex: A new hypothesis. *Neurosci. Res.* **11:** 221–225.
78. Malmgren, K., and Pierrot-Deseilligny, E. (1988). Evidence for non-monosynaptic Ia excitation of human flexor motoneurones, possibly via propriospinal neurones. *J. Physiol. (London)* **405:** 747–764.
79. Burke, D., Gracies, J. M., Mazavet, D., Meunier, S., and Pierrot-Deseilligny, E. (1994). Non-monosynaptic transmission of the cortical command for voluntary movement in man. *J. Physiol. (London)* **480:** 191–202.
80. Porter, R., and Lemon, R. (1993). *Corticospinal Function and Voluntary Movement,* Monogr. Physiol. Soc., Vol. 45. Clarendon Press, Oxford.
81. Gizster, S. F., Mussa-Ivaldi, F. A., and Bizzi, E. (1993). Convergent force fields organized in the frog's spinal cord. *J. Neurosci.* **13:** 467–491.
82. Goldspink, G. (1981). The use of muscles during flying, swimming, and running from the point of view of energy saving. In *Vertebrate Locomotion* (M. H. Day, ed.), pp. 219–238. Academic Press, London.
83. Hoyt, D. F., and Taylor, C. R. (1981). Gait and the energetics of locomotion in horses. *Nature (London)* **292:** 239–240.
84. Heglund, N. C., Willems, P. A., Penta, M., and Cavagna, G. A. (1995). Energy-saving gait mechanics with head-supported loads. *Nature (London)* **375:** 52–54.
85. Dawson, T. J., and Taylor, C. R. (1973). Energetic cost of locomotion in kangaroos. *Nature (London)* **246:** 313–314.
86. Holmes, G. (1915). Spinal injuries of warfare. *Br. Med. J.* Dec. 4, Vol. 2, pp. 815–821.
87. Calancie, B., Needham-Shropshire, B., Jacobs, P., Willer, K., Zych, G., and Green, B. A. (1994). Involuntary stepping after chronic spinal cord injury. Evidence for a central rhythm generator for locomotion in man. *Brain* **117:** 1143–1159.
88. Eidelberg, E. (1981). Locomotor control in macaque monkeys. *Brain* **104:** 647–663.
89. Grillner, S. (1985). Neurobiological bases of rhythmic motor acts in vertebrates. *Science* **228:** 143–149.
90. Grillner, S., Deliagina, T., Eckberg, O., Manira, A. E., Hill, R. H., Lansner, A., Orlovsky, G. N., and Wallen, P. (1995). Neural networks that coordinate locomotion and body orientation in lamprey. *Trends Neurosci.* **18:** 270–279.
91. Cohen, A., Ementrout, B., Kiemel, T., Kopell, N., Sigvardt, K. A., and Williams, T. (1992). Modeling of intersegmental coordination in the lamprey central pattern generator for locomotion. *Trends Neurosci.* **15:** 434–438.
92. Grillner, S., and Matsushima, T. (1991). The neural network underlying locomotion in lamprey: Synaptic and cellular mechanisms. *Neuron* **7:** 1–15.
93. Matsushima, T., and Grillner, S. (1992). Neural mechanisms of intersegmental coordination in lamprey: Local excitability changes modify the phase coupling along the spinal cord. *J. Neurophysiol.* **67:** 373–388.
94. Gelfand, I. M., Orlovsky, G. N., and Shik, M. L. (1988). Locomotion and scratching in tetrapods. In *Neural Control of Rhythmic Movements in Vertebrates* (A. H. Cohen, S. Rossignol, and S. Grillner, eds.), pp. 167–199. Wiley, New York.
95. Loeb, G. E., Hoffer, A., and Pratt, C. A. (1985). Activity of spindle afferents from cat anterior thigh muscles. I. Identification and patterns during normal locomotion. *J. Neurophysiol.* **54:** 549–564.
96. Goldberger, M. E. (1988). Partial and complete deafferentation of cat hindlimb: The contribution of behavioral substitution to recovery of motor function. *Exp. Brain Res.* **73:** 343–353.
97. Moschavakis, A. K., Sholomenko, G. N., and Burke, R. E. (1991). Differential control of short latency cutaneous excitation in cat FDL motor neurons during fictive locomotion. *Exp. Brain Res.* **83:** 489–501.
98. Orlovsky, G. N. (1972). The effect of different descending systems on flexor and extensor activity during locomotion. *Brain Res.* **40:** 359–371.
99. Jordan, L. M. (1991). Brainstem and spinal cord mechanisms for the initiation of locomotion. In *Neurobiological Basis of Human Locomotion* (M. Shimamura, S. Grillner, and V. R. Edgerton, eds.), pp. 3–20. Japan Scientific Societies, Toyko.
100. Steeves, J. D., and Jordan, L. M. (1980). Localization of a descending pathway in the spinal cord which is necessary for controlled treadmill locomotion. *Neurosci. Lett.* **20:** 283–288.
101. Noga, B. R., Kriellaars, D. J., and Jordan, L. M. (1991). The effect of selective brainstem or spinal cord lesions on treadmill locomotion evoked by stimulation of the mesencephalic or pontomedullary locomotor regions. *J. Neurosci.* **11:** 1691–1700.
102. Drew, T., Dubuc, R., and Rossignol, S. (1986). Discharge pattern of reticulospinal and other reticular neurons in chronic, unrestrained cats walking on a treadmill. *J. Neurophysiol.* **55:** 375–401.
103. Perreault, M. C., Drew, T., and Rossignol, S. (1993). Activity of Medullary reticulospinal neurons during fictive locomotion. *J. Neurophysiol.* **69:** 2232–2247.
104. Drew, T. (1993). Motor cortical activity during voluntary gait modifications in the cat. 1. Cells related to the forelimbs. *J. Neurophysiol.* **70:** 179–199.
105. Georgopoulos, A. P., and Grillner, S. (1989). Visuomotor coordination in reaching and locomotion. *Science* **245:** 1209–1210.
106. Greer, J. J., Smith, J. C., and Feldman, J. L. (1992). Respiratory

and locomotor patterns generated in the fetal rat brain stem-spinal cord in vitro. *J. Neurophysiol.* **67:** 996–999.

107. Arshavsky, Y. I., Orlovsky, G. N., Panchin, Y. V., Roberts, A., and Soffe, S. R. (1993). Neuronal control of swimming locomotion: Analysis of the pteropod mollusc *Clione* and embryos of the amphibian *Xenopus. Trends Neurosci.* **16:** 227–233.
108. Douglas, J. R., Noga, B. R., Dai, X., and Jordan, L. M. (1993). The effects of intrathecal administration of excitatory amino acid agonists and antagonists on the initiation of locomotion in the adult cat. *J. Neurosci.* **13:** 990–1000.
109. Hochman, Jordan, and Schmidt (1994). TTX-resistant NMDA receptor mediated voltage oscillations in mammalian lumbar motor neurons. *J. Neurophysiol.* **72:** 2559–2562.
110. Cazalets, J. R., Squali-Houssaini, Y., and Clarac, F. (1992). Activation of central pattern generators for locomotion by serotonin and excitatory amino acids in neonatal rat. *J. Physiol. (London)* **455:** 187–204.
111. Cowley, K. C., and Schmidt, B. J. (1994). A comparison of motor patterns induced by N-methyl-D-aspartate, acetylcholine and serotonin in the in vitro neonatal rat spinal cord. *Neurosci. Lett.* **171:** 147–150.
112. Boothby, K. M., and Roberts, A. (1992). The stopping response of *Xenopus laevis* embryos: Pharmacology and intracellular physiology of rhythmic spinal neurones and hindbrain neurones. *J. Exp. Biol.* **169:** 65–86.

C H A P T E R

32

Supraspinal Descending Control: The Medial "Postural" System

J. Baker

Upright stance against gravity is an active process. Posture requires holding certain positions over time and making many corrective movements to maintain those positions. Many bones, joints, and muscles are active simultaneously.[1] Maintaining posture is largely automatic: we do not have to think about it. Indeed, the most remarkable and characteristic feature of posture is its automaticity. Vestibular, somatosensory, and visual information triggers rapid accurate responses using relatively simple neural circuits. As you sit or recline reading this text, you are almost surely maintaining your balance and posture. Only during sleep do we consistently assume stable body positions that require no postural control.[2] Among normal individuals, the span of skill levels in posture and balance is extraordinary, ranging from Olympic gymnasts and Tai Chi masters to those of us who have difficulty standing on one leg to put on pants. Surely the gymnast depends on more than simple reflexes, and we often refer to postural reactions, postural control, or postural strategies.

The presence of reflex responses as an underlying part of postural behaviors has been recognized for centuries. René Descartes referred to the natural reaction of thrusting out the hands during a fall; he believed that the sensations of falling produced some change in the brain that caused it to send "animal spirit" to the nerves to initiate the protective reflex without the influence of the mind.[3]

ABLATION AND TRANSECTION STUDIES

Ablation and transection of brain tissues have shown us the importance of brainstem and higher structures to posture.[4] We know that vision, proprioception, and vestibular sense all contribute to posture,[5] and a great deal is known especially about the vestibular signals carried to the spinal cord for postural responses.[6] Neurotransmitter systems and neuromodulators have specific effects on posture, providing further clues to the central structures involved.[7,7a] The responses of humans and experimental animals to the displacement of platforms have begun to reveal the strategies used to maintain balance and their alteration in patients with balance disorders (see Box 32.1).[8,8a]

Postural Control Elements Were Localized by Transection and Ablation Experiments

Some of the oldest and still most useful tools for understanding functions of neural circuits are ablation and pathway tracing. **Ablation** removes a component of an input, or an upper level of control from the circuit, and we see what the system can and cannot do in its absence. We use the same methods in troubleshooting electronic and computer circuits. Pathway tracing helps outline the circuits.

One of the important advances in neuroscience in the 19th century was the use of ablation and transection of brain structures to study the localization of CNS function, and one of the earliest applications was to localize the level of postural control along the neuraxis.[9] While the debate over the extent of cerebral localization was not fully resolved at that time, it became clear by the beginning of the 20th century that lower portions of the mammalian brain were capable of autonomously performing simple behaviors. Sir Charles Sherrington extensively studied spinal reflexes and the phenomenon of **decerebrate rigidity** produced by brain transection.[9] He found that complete separa-

BOX 32.1

GRAVITY SENSOR

Although most of the work on postural reflexes has concerned mammalian responses and neurophysiological mechanisms, invertebrate studies offer simpler systems that may be more directly manipulated, especially by neuropharmacological agents. The work of Kravitz and colleagues exemplifies this approach.[7] They found that systemic administration of the aminergic neurotransmitter serotonin (see Chapter 8) causes a lobster to assume a flexed posture characteristic of defensive responses. Octopamine, in contrast, causes the animal to lie flat with its legs extended. These responses are not due to the direct action of serotonin and octopamine on muscles; both agents stimulate muscular contraction. However, serotonin and octopamine have opposite effects on extensor and flexor motor neurons: serotonin excites flexor motor neurons and is selectively localized in a subset of interneurons. The overall conclusion is that serotonin acts on the lobster central nervous system to trigger the flexion posture, while octopamine triggers extension.

tion of the neuraxis near the level of the pons resulted in tonic contraction of the limb antigravity extensors in quadrupeds (Fig. 32.1). The result was an exaggerated standing posture, although the animal was not much more stable than one that had been stuffed by a taxidermist.

While a decerebrate animal does not exhibit effective stabilizing postural responses to perturbations, it does respond in a more organized fashion than a spinalized animal.[10] Depending on the level of transection and the time since it was performed, varying degrees of evidence of a "righting reaction" can be observed. Chronic bulbospinal cats, those with a transection above the medulla, show evidence of a righting reaction when placed on one side. The upper forelimb is flexed with gripping claws while the lower forelimb

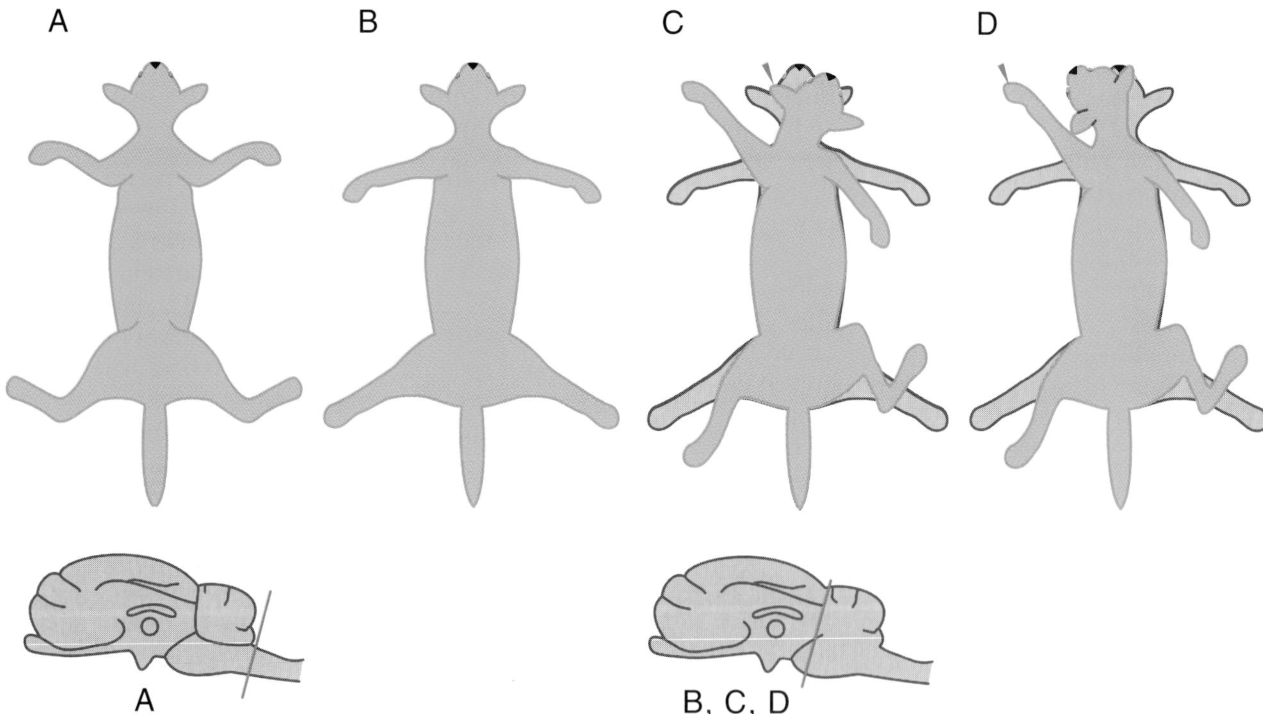

FIGURE 32.1 Posture in cats following transection of the neuraxis. (A) Immediately after separation of the spinal cord from the brain, the cat assumes a limp posture, with limbs neither flexed nor extended. The level of transection is shown below in a sagittal view. (B) When the transection is made through the pons, the cat assumes a rigid posture, with all four limbs extended. Stimulation of the pinna (C) or forepaw (D) causes the animal shown in (B) to adjust the position of its head and limbs. Based on reports by Sherrington.[9]

is extended under the body as if to push the body up off its side. When the transection is made above the mesencephalon, effective righting may be observed in chronically surviving animals. As the level of transection is raised, posture and balance become progressively closer to normal. The decorticate animal, produced by ablation of cerebral cortical tissue, has many apparently normal postural reactions, lacking only certain placing and stepping reactions, as we will describe later in this chapter.

Henricus Kuypers and colleagues used silver degeneration staining techniques to trace descending pathways from brainstem motor centers that lay below the transections in decerebrate animals.[11] They grouped the subcorticospinal pathways into ventromedial and lateral systems based on the placement of descending fibers in the spinal white matter. The lateral system arose from the magnocellular red nucleus and was thought to be allied with corticospinal control of the limbs (see Chapter 33). The ventromedial system arose from the vestibular nuclei, reticular formation, and other brainstem nuclei, including the interstitial nucleus of Cajal and superior colliculus. Ventromedial fibers terminated preferentially in the ventral and medial parts of the interneuronal zones of the spinal gray matter.[11]

Lawrence and Kuypers transected the ventromedial descending pathways of monkeys in the medulla.[12] The animals had great difficulty maintaining a normal posture, balancing, walking, and climbing. When reaching for an object, they appeared to have very poor control of the limb at the outset of the movement. When they were successful at approaching an intended target, they often displayed very good dexterity in making the fine movements required to grasp an object, presumably due to lateral descending pathways, which remained intact. While there was some improvement over a period of weeks following the operation, unsteadiness and a flexor bias of the trunk and limbs persisted, and the animals were unable to right themselves 40 days after the lesion. These observations led Lawrence and Kuypers to conclude that the ventromedial descending system is concerned with maintaining posture and integrating movements of the trunk and extremities. They proposed that the ventromedial system accomplished this via its projections predominantly to motor neurons that innervate the axial and proximal musculature.

Summary

The maintenance of a stable upright body position against the force of gravity during moving, standing, or reaching requires an integrated postural control motor system. Neurons of this system operate at all levels of the control nervous system, requiring visual, proprioceptive, and vestibular sensory information to be integrated tightly with spinal cord muscular adaptations. Transection of the pons produces a decerebrate animal with a rigid standing posture and an inability to adapt to positional perturbations. Transections at more rostral mesencephalic levels contributes to improved posture and balance. The brainstem postural control pathways, the subcorticospinal fibers, arise from the vestibular nuclei, as well as other brainstem nuclei, and course ventromedially to the ventral and medial spinal gray matter to control motor neurons innervating the axial and proximal limb muscles.

SENSORY INFORMATION ABOUT HEAD POSTURE

Other sensory inputs for postural responses are vision and proprioception, but vestibular sense is cardinal and has been the most extensively studied. Vestibular sensory signals provide direct information about rotation of the head and the head's orientation with respect to gravity.[13] To understand the neck and limb reflexes elicited by vestibular stimulation—the vestibulocollic and vestibulospinal reflexes—we must first consider the vestibular receptor organs of the inner ear.

The Vestibular Apparatus Senses Head Motion and Rotation

Two types of vestibular transducer organs, the **semicircular canals** and the **otolithic maculae,** are located within the **labyrinth** of the ear and respond to accelerations of the head in space.[14] The three semicircular canals and the two otolithic maculae are stimulated by rotational and linear acceleration, respectively. In both cases, it is the mechanical structure of the sense organ that determines the nature of the effective stimulus.

The labyrinth (Fig. 32.2) consists of the bony labyrinth, a set of passages in the skull. The bony labyrinth is lined with membranes that contain endolymph and which make up the membranous labyrinth. The membranous labyrinth has a large central vessel called the utricle, a swelling called the saccule, and three narrow passages that emerge from the utricle and loop around to rejoin it. These three loops form circular passages for endolymph and are known as the semicircular canals. The canals are oriented orthogonal to one another: there is a lateral or horizontal canal, an anterior or superior canal, and a posterior canal. The membranous passages of the vestibular labyrinth are joined with those of the auditory labyrinth by a thin tube (the ductus reuniens).

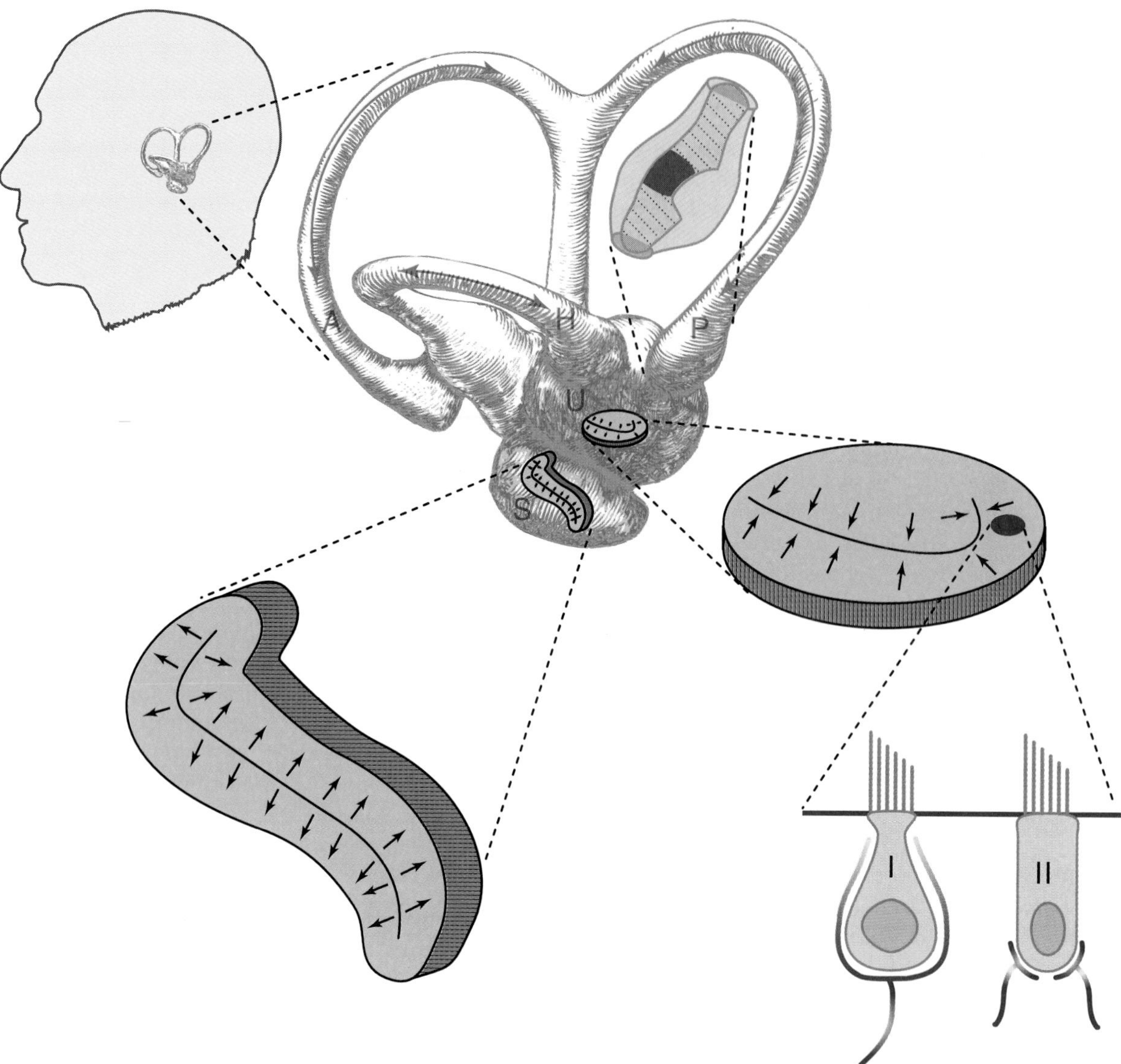

FIGURE 32.2 The vestibular canals and otoliths. The position and orientation of the labyrinth (not to scale) in the head are shown at the upper left of the figure. An enlarged view of the labyrinth at upper right shows the directions of head rotation and endolymph flow (red arrows) that excite each of the three semicircular canals. The horizontal orientation of the utricular macula and vertical orientation of the saccular macula are shown schematically. More highly magnified views of the receptor regions of a canal and of the otolith organs are shown with the best directions for excitation of otolith hair cells marked by black arrows. At the lower right are two anatomical types of hair cell, the calyx or type I and bouton-ending or type II receptor. The tallest cilial extension on each cell is the kinocilium. A, anterior semicircular canal; H, horizontal semicircular canal; P, posterior semicircular canal; S, saccule containing saccular macula; U, utricule containing utricular macula; I, type I receptor; II, type II receptor. Based on studies reviewed by Wilson and Melvill-Jones.[13]

The Semicircular Canals Are Stimulated by Rotational Head Acceleration

A great deal of research has helped specify just what aspects of motion the different parts of the membraneous labyrinth actually detect. In the semicircular canals, the inertial flow of a fluid is used to deflect a small vane upon head movement. Each semicircular canal contains a sensory end-organ ridge or crest (the crista) that rests in a swelling near one end of the canal, the ampulla. Hair cells extend cilia from the ampullary crest into a gelatinous mass, the cupula, that occludes the canal passage. These hair cells are like other hair cell receptors, such as those in the auditory system

(Chapter 27). They have many stereocilia and one kinocilium. Pressure of the endolymph on the cupula acts to deflect the stereocilia; deflection of the stereocilia toward the kinocilium depolarizes the hair cells, which make synaptic contact with vestibular afferents in cranial nerve VIII.

Pressure of the endolymph on the cupula results from any relative motion of the skull and endolymph. When the head accelerates, the inertia of the endolymph causes the endolymph to lag behind the head until the endolymph is accelerated by the pressure between it and the cupula. Because the canals form a complete fluid loop, there is no pressure difference across the cupula during linear head acceleration. In contrast, rotational acceleration of the head can build pressure on one side of the cupula, resulting in vestibular transduction. The hair cell receptors in a given canal will be stimulated when the rotational acceleration is in a direction that builds pressure on one side of the cupula in that canal, but they will not be stimulated if the rotational acceleration pushes the fluid to the sides of the canal walls instead of along their length. Thus, the three canals have different effective directions for stimulation. In general, left canals are excited by leftward rotation and right side canals by rightward rotation.

Mechanical factors complicate transduction in the semicircular canals. The canal passages are narrow, and the endolymph has a certain viscosity. In addition, the cupula is not a perfectly rigid pressure transducer, because it bends in response to pressure. (Of course, it must bend to allow hair cell depolarization.) These factors combine to convert the external acceleration stimulus into a hair cell stimulus that is largely a rotational velocity signal and only partly an acceleration signal. While it is very difficult to examine the actual mechanical stimulus to the hair cells, we do know, for example, that the cupula bends but does not move enough to allow endolymph to flow past it. A mechanical analysis of the semicircular canals has led to the "second-order linear system torsion pendulum" model of hair cell excitation, which assumes that endolymph mass, viscous forces, and cupula elasticity contribute to determining the stimulus at the hair cells (for a mathematical discussion, see Ref. 13).

Semicircular Canal Afferents Encode Rotational Velocity of the Head

Research has also shown that there are changes in the nature of the motion sensing information as if different stages in the circuit were performing mathematical integrations on the data stream. The signals in the vestibular portion of the VIIIth cranial nerve are much easier to monitor than those in hair cells, and we have a very good idea of their properties, thanks especially to the work of Cesar Fernandez and Jay Goldberg, who have studied both canal[15,15a] and otolith[16,16a] afferents. Earlier work in rays and other nonmammalian vertebrates had generally supported the torsion pendulum model of the vestibular transducer. Fernandez and Goldberg extended those findings by recording from semicircular canal primary afferents in anesthetized squirrel monkeys while subjecting the animals to periods of either constant angular acceleration or sinusoidal oscillation. They found that primary afferents had a spontaneous firing rate of about 75 spikes s^{-1} in the absence of any rotational acceleration stimulus, and that this spontaneous activity could either increase or decrease, depending on the direction of acceleration. Acceleration about the same axis as that of the canal innervated by the afferent was always the most effective stimulus for exciting an afferent. Excitation gave slightly larger responses than inhibition, and overall the afferent response was approximately linearly related to stimulus strength. The most telling result for understanding vestibular signals in the brain was that at intermediate frequencies of sinusoidal oscillation, roughly around 0.25 Hz, the afferent responses were approximately in phase with the velocity of the angular rotation. It is common now to refer to the vestibular primary afferent response as a velocity signal, generated by the mechanical integration of the transducer apparatus.

Fernandez and Goldberg showed that the velocity signals carried by semicircular canal afferents were gradually replaced by acceleration signals when the rotation frequency approached either a very low (0.01 Hz) or a very high (10 Hz) value. When they expressed canal afferent responses in the form of a Bode plot (Fig. 32.3), they found that the phase lead at low and high frequencies and the gain of the responses did not agree with the torsion-pendulum model. Therefore, Fernandez and Goldberg introduced a more complete model of afferent responses that included adaptation to prolonged acceleration and a phase lead effect at high frequencies (see Refs. 15 and 15a for mathematical details).

The final important finding from the work of Fernandez and Goldberg was that primary afferents could be divided into two groups based on a single parameter, the regularity of their resting discharge in the absence of stimulation. This regularity can be simply expressed by the coefficient of variation, the ratio of the standard deviation of interspike intervals to their mean. Units with low coefficients of variation, often as low as 0.05, were called regular afferents, and units

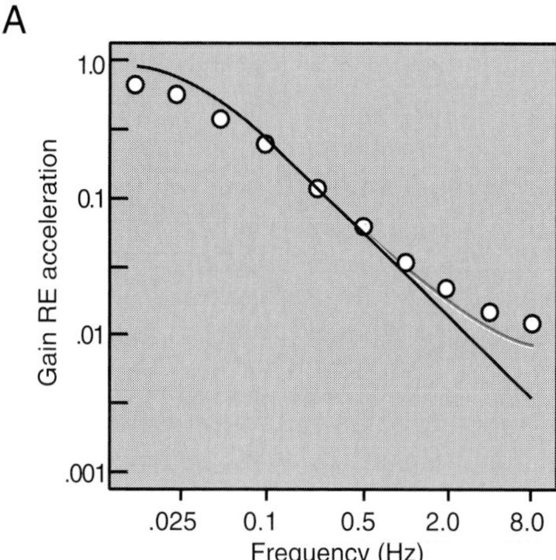

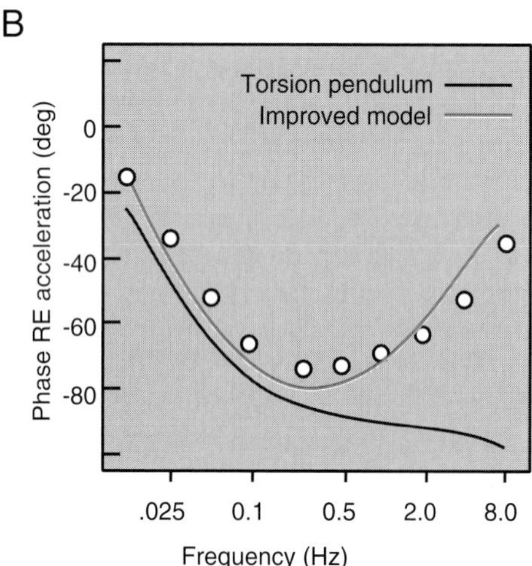

FIGURE 32.3 A Bode plot of the average gain and phase of responses of squirrel monkey semicircular canal primary afferents to various frequencies of sinusoidal oscillation. Responses are plotted as a function of the frequency of a rotational acceleration stimulus. (A) A response gain RE acceleration with a slope of −1 represents a "velocity" response and approximates the data in the middle range of frequencies. The term "gain" is used in a loose sense here as the ratio of neural activity modulation to the amplitude of the acceleration stimulus. In the strict sense, gain is a ratio of two quantities in the same units and therefore dimensionless. (B) A phase of −90° also corresponds to a "velocity" response, and data approach this value in the middle frequencies. At frequency extremes, data are closer to the 0° phase that characterizes an "acceleration" response. The approach toward an acceleration response at high frequencies was unexpected. Solid curves, representing the prediction of the traditional torsion pendulum model of the canal transducer mechanism, fit the data poorly, especially at high frequencies of rotation. The improved model of Fernandez and Goldberg (red curves) more accurately predicts the observed responses. Data and curves redrawn from Fernandez and Goldberg.[15,15a]

with high coefficients of variation, often over 0.4, were called irregular afferents. We now believe that regular and irregular afferents contribute selectively to different reflex responses.

The Otolith Organs Respond to Linear and Gravitational Acceleration

There are two otolith organs in mammals, the **utricle** (utriculus) and **saccule** (sacculus). In the utricle and saccule, forces of gravity and linear acceleration of the head act on small stones, which then bend hair cells proportionately. The names apply to the fluid chambers in which they lie, and the specific locations of the receptors are called the maculae. The two maculae are small regions that contain hair cells innervated by vestibular afferents. Like canal hair cells, macular hair cells have cilia embedded in a gelatinous mass above the cell bodies and are depolarized when the stereocilia are bent toward the kinocilium. The macular hair cells rest in large chambers, in which fluid motion is thought to exert little or no dynamic force on the cilia. Instead, the gelatinous mass holding the cilia contains otoconia or statoconia, dense crystals of a calcium compound. The entire mass above the hair cells is acted on by gravity or linear acceleration because of its higher density than the endolymph. For example, when the head tilts, the otoconial mass sags in the direction of the tilt. This sagging, or the equivalent lagging of the mass behind a linear acceleration, provides the natural stimulus for the hair cells.

The utricular macula lies on the floor of the utricle, the largest cavity of the vestibular labyrinth. When the body is not accelerated and the head is held approximately erect with respect to gravity, there is no stimulus to this organ. The same is approximately true when the head is upside down. However, the hair cells in the utricular macula are stimulated when the head is held at any other orientation with respect to gravity. Microscopic examination of the utricular macula shows that the hair cells have their kinocilia oriented in different directions, suggesting that different directions of tilt will excite different populations of utricular afferents. The direction of a hair cell indicated by its kinocilium is called its morphological polarization vector.

The saccular macula is located on the side of the saccule and is oriented in an approximately parasagittal plane. Thus, there is a strong acceleration stimulus to the saccular macula when the head is erect and little or no stimulus when the head is lying on either side. Saccular hair cells also have a variety of morphological polarization vectors.

Early studies of otolithic afferent responses in nonmammalian vertebrates have been extended to mammals, including squirrel monkeys[16] and cats.[17] As is true for canal afferents, otolithic afferents can be divided into regular and irregular afferents, both of which exhibit approximately linear response curves.

The responses of otolith afferents across frequencies are generally fairly closely related to the amplitude of a sinusoidal tilt or acceleration stimulus; response phases approximate the tilt angle amplitude, and response strength remains roughly constant with respect to stimulus amplitude across all frequencies. However, there is some evidence for velocity sensitivity and for adaptation to prolonged stimulation, and these effects result in deviations from pure tilt position signals in otolith afferents. The most pronounced deviation is a tendency for some afferents, typically irregular afferents, to give larger responses to constant-amplitude sinusoidal tilts as tilt frequency increases. Utricular afferents have a range of best (i.e., most excitatory) directions of tilt for excitation, including front-to-back pitch, side-to-side roll, and all tilts between and around these directions.

These studies of primary vestibular afferents indicate that two types of vestibular signals are available to assist balance: signals from the semicircular canals relating to rotational head velocity, and signals from the otoliths conveying information about head tilt or linear acceleration.

Summary

Sensory signals from the vestibular system define the position of the head with respect to gravity and its relative rate of rotation in any plane. The semicircular canal afferents provide information on rotational head velocity as their hair cells are activated in each of their three planes by the inertial flow of endolymph. Similarly, the hair cells of the two otolith organs are deformed and activated by head tilt and by linear acceleration of the head.

POSTURAL REFLEXES OF THE HEAD AND BODY: RELIANCE ON A NEGATIVE FEEDBACK SYSTEM

In engineering terminology, "negative feedback" is a signal that measures a performance error. The signal is used to "subtract" from the command signal to reduce the performance error. The same principle is widespread in biology. Both vestibular and proprioceptive sensory signals are used to generate negative feedback reflexes. Negative feedback reflexes serve to reduce the external stimulus that drives them, thereby stabilizing the body.[18] In the case of vestibular reflexes, this means that a head motion in some particular direction in space will excite vestibular afferents that send signals to central neurons; those neurons, in turn, excite motor neurons innervating muscles that move the head or whole body in the direction opposite to the original stimulus, thereby reducing further head motion. This reflex opposition occurs with a delay limited primarily by the speed of muscle contraction. In the case of proprioceptive reflexes, motions that stretch neck and other postural muscles are opposed by the reflex (see Chapter 31).

Vestibulocollic and Vestibulospinal Reflexes Stabilize the Head in Space

Vestibular signals act on neck, trunk, and limb muscles, as well as those moving the eyes. Vestibulocollic and vestibulospinal reflexes make use of canal and otolith signals to stabilize the posture of the head and body. These reflexes are thought to serve two functions, both involving negative feedback. The first function was mentioned in the preceding section: when the head and body rotate or tilt in any direction, the vestibular stimulus excites pathways that oppose the motion, reducing or correcting the undesired movement.[19,19a] Second, the biomechanical components of the head have a characteristic resonant frequency of around 2–3 Hz at which oscillation is especially likely to occur, and the vestibulocollic reflex effectively dampens this tendency for oscillatory motion. Figure 32.4 shows a block diagram of the vestibulocollic reflex, illustrating the closed-loop nature of the negative feedback circuit. The importance of the vestibulocollic and vestibulospinal reflexes is demonstrated by damage to the labyrinth or the VIIIth nerve, or mechanical blockage of the semicircular canals. Unilateral labyrinthectomy causes an initial postural disability in which subjects lean or fall toward the side of the lesion.[20] Bilaterally symmetrical plugging of the semicircular canals, which removes head velocity signals with little loss of or imbalance in tonic vestibular nerve activity, produces a severe head instability with oscillations that may persist for several days.[21,21a]

The neuroanatomical pathways that contribute to the vestibulocollic and vestibulospinal reflex responses (Fig. 32.5) have been elucidated primarily through electrical stimulation and other physiological methods.[22] The medial, lateral (Deiters'), and descending (inferior) vestibular nuclei of the brainstem contribute axons to the medial and lateral vestibulospinal tracts, which provide direct vestibular input to the spinal cord. Antidromic activation of vestibular nucleus neurons by spinal cord stimulation and orthodromic activation of spinal neurons by stimulation of vestibular structures show that vestibulocollic reflexes are mediated primarily by the bilaterally projecting medial vestibulospinal tract, but that ipsilateral excitation is carried via the lateral vestibulospinal tract. The bulk of the lateral

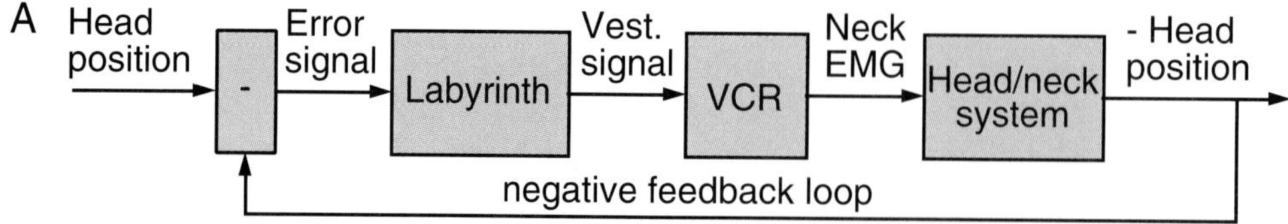

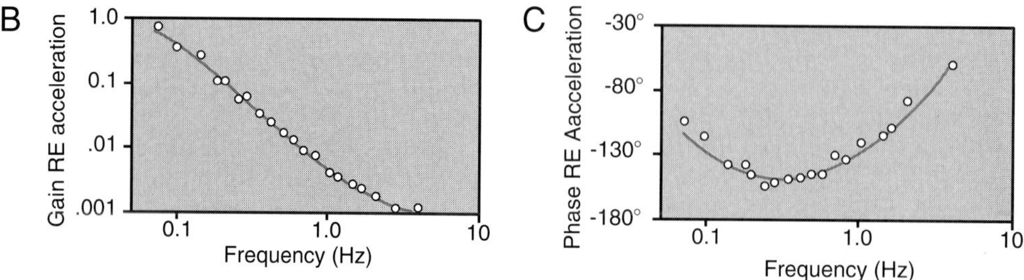

FIGURE 32.4 A block diagram of the vestibulocollic reflex (VCR, A) and Bode plots of vestibulocollic reflex excitation of the complexus neck muscle in a decerebrate cat (B, C). The block diagram illustrates the negative feedback loop nature of the vestibulocollic reflex: head rotation in one direction excites neck muscles that rotate the head in the opposite direction, reducing the motion. The curves in B and C are based on a two-pole, two-zero model of the reflex discussed in the text.[19a,23]

vestibulospinal tract projects from the lateral vestibular nucleus as far as the lumbar spinal cord. Note that the vestibulocollic reflex, although discussed separately, is as much a vestibulospinal reflex as are the vestibular limb reflexes. The only difference is that the vestibulocollic reflex exerts its primary action at the cervical rather than the lumbar spinal levels.

The Reticulospinal Pathway May Contribute Information on Head Pitch

Two lines of evidence demonstrate that anatomical projections responsible for vestibulocollic and vestibulospinal reflexes include more than the medial and lateral vestibulospinal tracts. First, interruption of the medial longitudinal fasciculus, which carries the medial vestibulospinal tract to the cervical spinal cord, has essentially no effect on vestibulocollic reflexes.[22,22a,23] Only lesions that also interrupt reticulospinal pathways substantially reduce the strength of vestibulocollic responses. Second, extensive analysis of the information carried by vestibular axons indicates that these axons do not transmit signals related to pitching motion (nose-up and nose-down head rotation, as in an affirmative nod). Such signals are needed by certain muscles for reflex muscle contraction to correct for head and body pitch.[24,24a] Unless pitch signals for vestibular reflexes are generated within the spinal cord, it is reasonable to infer that they must be carried by reticulospinal projections. However, reticulospinal contributions to vestibular reflexes have not been thoroughly studied.

The Vestibulocollic Reflexes Adapt Head Position Dynamically by Control of Neck Muscles

The vestibulocollic reflex circuitry includes a phase-lagging element that operates at low frequencies.[23] This element converts the velocity signal from the semicircular canals into a head position signal that is appropriate for repositioning the head in response to a slow change in head angle. At high frequencies, the circuitry appears to introduce a phase lead that works in conjunction with the high-frequency phase lead of primary canal afferents (see Fig. 32.3) to make two 90° phase leads. The result is that the reflex opposes head angular acceleration, as would be appropriate if the inertia of the head were an important factor to be compensated for during rapid head motion. In engineering terms, the phase-lagging elements residing in the brainstem and the mechanics of the semicircular canals are "poles," and the two phase lead elements are "zeroes." Therefore, the complete description of the vestibulocollic reflex is referred to as a two-pole, two-zero model. One pole and one zero are located in the periphery, while the other pole and zero are generated by the central neural circuitry of the vestibulocollic reflex. The mechanisms by which neurons in the brainstem accomplish these functions are unknown.

The timing of vestibulocollic responses is appropriate, given the function of the reflex and the mechanical properties of the load presented by the head. However, the mechanical properties of the multijointed limbs and trunk are far more complex,[25] and it is corre-

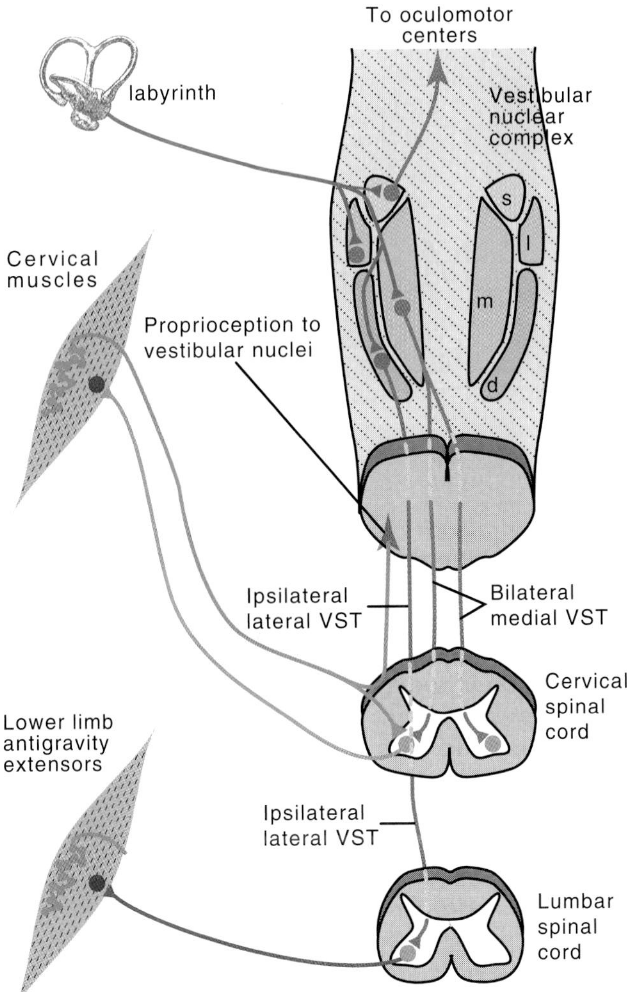

FIGURE 32.5 Vestibular and proprioceptive reflex pathways. The medial vestibulospinal tract (VST) projects bilaterally to the cervical spinal cord and mediates the vestibulocollic reflex. The lateral vestibulospinal tract projects to the lumbar spinal cord and influences limb extensors involved in balance. Neck muscle proprioceptors send signals to the vestibular nuclei that are involved in cervicocollic reflexes and interactions among reflexes. The medial and lateral VSTs arise from the medial (m), lateral (l), and descending (d) vestibular nuclei. The superior vestibular nucleus (s) is primarily concerned with the vestibuloocular reflex.

spondingly more difficult to predict what the dynamics of the controlling neural signals should be. Electromyographic recordings during vestibulospinal reflexes in decerebrate animals have shown that limb extensors are excited in phase with the position of the head at low frequencies of oscillation. Thus, when the head rolls to the left, the left forelimb extends as if to brace against further displacement.[24a] The likely source of the signals that elicit these responses is the otolith organs. As the frequency of head oscillation approaches 1 Hz, the phase of vestibulospinal responses advances toward a peak in phase with head velocity. The value of this timing is unclear,[24a] but the implication is that semicircular canal signals begin to predominate over otolith signals in vestibulospinal responses at higher frequencies.

A major focus of recent work on both vestibulocollic and vestibulospinal reflexes is the spatial organization of the responses and the possible interaction of spatial properties and dynamics. Early studies concentrated on left-to-right yaw motion (as in shaking the head to indicate "no") for vestibulocollic reflexes, and on left-to-right rolling motion (produced by tilting the top of the head to the left and then to the right while looking straight ahead) for vestibulospinal limb reflexes. Of course, the vestibular reflexes work to compensate for motion in any direction. The problem of producing the correct direction of reflex response to any direction of disturbance has been considered thoroughly for the vestibuloocular reflex that stabilizes the eyes (see Chapter 36), but the vestibulospinal reflexes present a more difficult situation.

What synergies or coordinations of muscle groups are used by the brain to generate compensatory vestibulocollic responses? There are any number of ways that the more than 30 muscles of the neck could be used to compensate for a particular direction of head rotation, and the mechanisms by which the brain organizes the activation of these muscles are unknown. However, some features of spatial organization have been elucidated. Each of the major neck muscles exhibits a characteristic directionality of excitation in response to vestibular stimulation by rotation in many different directions, but a muscle's excitation direction does not match the directional sensitivity of any single semicircular canal.[26] Instead, the responses to rapid motions reflect a weighted sum of canal inputs (Fig. 32.6), and various explanations have been proposed to account for the particular weightings observed. A complicating feature of vestibulocollic spatial organization is that the phase of vestibulocollic neuron or neck muscle activation often depends on the direction of the vestibular stimulus. This dependence, which has been termed spatial–temporal convergence, may reflect canal and otolith signal convergence to match a varying mechanical load presented by the head with different directions of rotation.

Another factor complicating the analysis of vestibulocollic responses is the presence of signals related to the velocity or direction of eye movements.[27] Adding the visual and proprioceptive signals that are present in vestibulospinal neural circuitry (discussed in the following sections) makes a rich and complex control system that we are only beginning to understand. Comparable information on the spatial organization

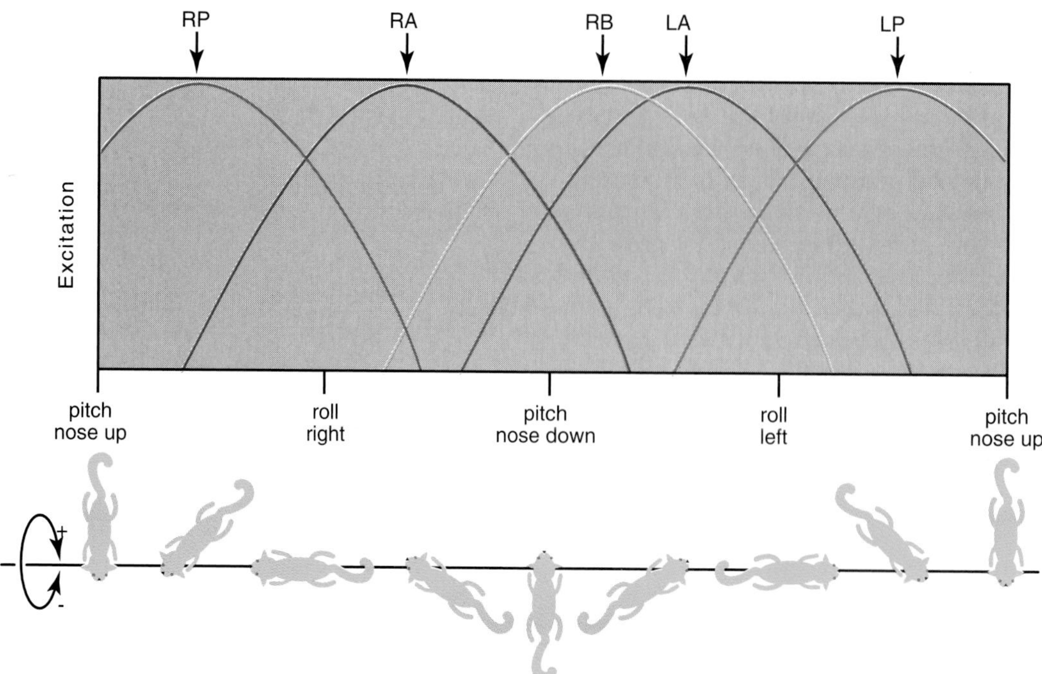

FIGURE 32.6 Directionality of responses of the four vertical semicircular canals (hypothetical data) and of a neck muscle, the right biventer cervicis (RB), activated via the vestibulocollic reflex neural circuitry. The abscissa represents the direction of vertical vestibular rotation, from pitch to roll and beyond, and the ordinate represents the strength of the neural or electromyographic responses to sinusoidal oscillation in each of the orientations. The peak of each curve represents the direction that produces the best excitation of the corresponding canal. For example, the right posterior (RP) canal is most excited when the head is rotated so that the nose tips up and the right ear tips down. This rotation is a combination of upward (also called backward) pitch and rightward roll of the head. Inhibitory responses have been omitted for clarity, and the curves are truncated at the ends of the graph. The electromyographic activity in neck muscles during the vestibulocollic reflex is best explained as the weighted sum of canal inputs. For example, the biventer cervicis could receive a strong input from the left anterior (LA) canal and a weaker input from the right anterior (RA) canal. The appropriately weighted sum of these signals could produce the shaded curve. The biventer cervicis also responds weakly to vestibular rotation in the yaw horizontal direction, which is not shown here. Also not shown are response phases, which would be important for determining the spatial–temporal convergence of vestibular signals.[28]

of vestibulospinal control of the limbs reveals a similar complexity and an unexpected paucity of responses to pitch motion, underscoring the incompleteness of our knowledge of these reflex mechanisms. The physiological responses of the vestibulospinal reflexes are paralleled in complexity by the reflexes' neuroanatomical interconnections, which include ascending as well as descending axon collaterals.[28,29]

The Cervicocollic Reflex Stabilizes the Head by Opposing Neck Muscle Stretch

Another sensory input that controls head position is from muscle spindles, which participate in neck muscle "stretch reflexes" as they do for most other skeletal muscles in the body.

The proprioceptive contribution to reflex stabilization of the head and body has been examined with many of the same methods used to examine vestibular contributions. The sensory situation for proprioceptive signals is more complicated than that for vestibular signals, since any of the muscles of the neck, trunk, or limbs could be the source of sensory signals that influence any other muscle or synergistic group of muscles. We will consider only the signals from neck proprioceptors that are involved in the neck stretch reflex or cervicocollic reflex. Like the stretch reflex for limb extensors, the cervicocollic reflex opposes muscle stretch and so is a negative feedback compensatory system. Other proprioceptive systems are often considered postural reactions rather than simple reflexes, and we will describe them later in this chapter.

The frequency domain of the cervicocollic reflex has been analyzed in decerebrate cats in which the trunk is rotated while the head is fixed in space.[30] This procedure stimulates neck proprioceptors without any vestibular input. For trunk rotation frequencies below about 1 Hz, neck muscle electromyographic activity is in phase with the extent of neck stretch, which is termed a position response. At higher frequencies, responses increase rapidly in gain and advance in phase toward an acceleration response. Therefore, the cervicocollic reflex has been described as having two phase lead terms or zeros. It has been argued that this type of responsiveness directly reflects the properties of the muscle spindle afferents that provide the input, meaning that the brainstem does little processing of inputs from neck muscle proprioceptors.

The cervicocollic and vestibulocollic reflexes resemble each other more in their spatial organization than in their dynamics. Although attempts to elicit the cervicocollic reflex in alert animals have not been entirely successful, in decerebrate preparations the directionality of neck muscle responses to stretch matches that of vestibulocollic responses fairly well. This observation indicates that vestibular and stretch reflexes involving neck muscles share some central circuitry. Not only is the directionality of neck muscle responses different from that of any single semicircular canal, it also does not appear to match the direction of pulling actions of the neck muscles under study. We are left to speculate on the principles of central organization of these reflexes.

The central pathways mediating the cervicocollic reflex are more varied and less well mapped than those that underlie the vestibulocollic reflex. There are homonymous monosynaptic stretch reflex connections, connections to a muscle from other muscles, and longer pathways that may involve connections through the medial, lateral, and descending vestibular nuclei (see Fig. 32.5) as well as reticulospinal neurons.[30]

Summary

Postural reflexes of the head and body allow for smooth attainment of stability despite unplanned movements or unexpected loss of balance. Vestibular signals and proprioceptive information from neck and limbs provides error detection information, which drives opposing muscles toward stabilized positions in the neck but coordinates balance through axial movements on the same side. The medial and lateral vestibular nuclei and their vestibulospinal projections, as well as the reticulospinal pathway, are required for this control. Neck muscle proprioceptors stabilize the head by opposing further movement of the head.

THE ROLE OF THE BRAINSTEM IN CONTROLLING COORDINATED POSTURAL REACTIONS

A variety of reflexes contribute to the maintenance of posture. All benefit from the integrity of connections with the brainstem[1] and in some cases with higher centers, but not all are as readily characterized by objective measures as the vestibulocollic, vestibulospinal, and cervicocollic reflexes we have already discussed. The tonic neck or cervicospinal reflexes are the best known of these, but the supporting, placing, righting, hopping or stepping, and other reactions are useful parts of the neural control of posture.

Tonic Neck Reflex Adjusts Limb Extension When Head Angle Shifts

The pattern of responses of this reflex (Fig. 32.7) was originally described by Magnus and later refined by Roberts. Newborns, humans with cerebral or vestibular damage, and decerebrate experimental animals most clearly display the tonic neck reflex, which interacts with vestibulospinal reflex. When the neck is flexed, pitching the head forward or down, both fore-

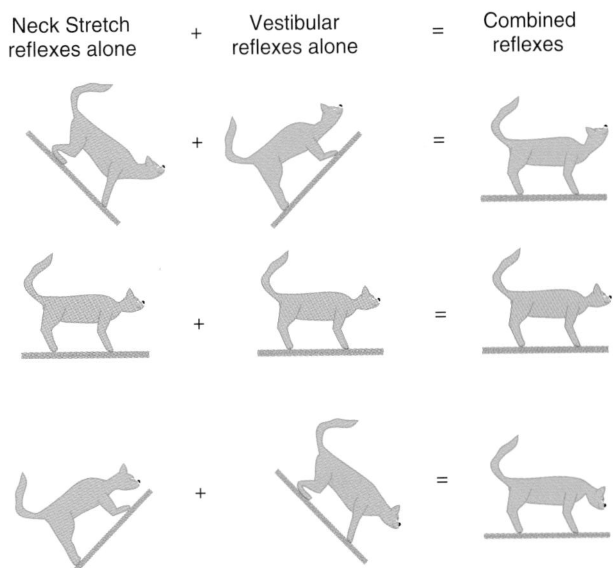

FIGURE 32.7 Operation of neck-to-limb proprioceptive reflexes (left), static vestibulospinal reflexes (middle), and the summed responses of these reflexes (right) in quadrupeds. A straight limb orthogonal to the trunk indicates a neutral posture, as in the middle row and right column. A limb extended away from the center of the trunk represents reflex extension (e.g., the forelimb in the upper left diagram), and a bent limb represents reflex flexion (e.g., the hindlimb in the upper left diagram).

limbs are flexed. Normally, the tonic neck reflex is opposed by the vestibulospinally mediated extension of the forelimbs (bottom row of Fig. 32.7), but if the spine is rotated without moving the head, the tonic neck reflex can be evoked alone. Roberts accomplished this by producing roll rotations in decerebrate cats and showed that stretching the neck with roll to one side elicited flexion of the ipsilateral forelimb.

The action of the tonic neck reflex on forelimb muscles has been studied with the directional testing techniques that have been used on vestibulocollic and cervicocollic reflexes.[24a] The tonic neck reflex is more sensitive to roll motion than to pitch rotation, although the difference in sensitivity is not as great as it is in the vestibulospinal reflex. The direction of neck stretch that excites a forelimb extensor muscle most effectively via the tonic neck reflex is typically opposite the best direction via the vestibulospinal reflex but the small component of pitch motion is larger in stretch-evoked than in vestibular-evoked responses.

Limb-Placing Reactions Rely on Brainstem Coordination

Placing a limb on the ground initiates a set of reflex reactions that stiffen the limb into a supporting pillar.[31] This response, called the positive supporting reaction, depends on the integrity of the brainstem. As discussed earlier in the chapter, righting reactions also depend on the brainstem, and the optical righting reflexes mediated by vision require an intact cerebral cortex. Stable posture requires not only that the legs be rigid but also that the feet be correctly placed on a supporting surface. The placing reactions of quadrupeds contribute to correct foot placement by moving the feet toward a visible surface (visual placing reaction) or onto a surface that has tactile contract with the chin, whiskers, or top of the foot (tactile placing reactions). Although a tactile placing reaction may be evoked in primitive form in a spinalized animal, it is generally held that at least the lower brainstem must be intact for effective tactile placing to occur. If balance reactions are insufficient to maintain a stable posture, as when the supporting surface is moved beneath the foot, the limb may hop to a new position where stable posture is possible (hopping reaction).[4] The action of the righting reflex of cats during falling is familiar to all. Humans show a similar reaction to an unexpected drop, measurable as a short latency electromyographic response in the gastrocnemius muscle. In cats, the righting reflex survives blockage of the semicircular canals but not total labyrinthectomy, so it appears to be otolith-mediated.[32] The role of these many postural reactions in the maintenance of posture and balance in intact humans has been the focus of several studies utilizing movable posture platforms, which we will discuss in the next section.

Experimental Approaches Have Further Revealed Brainstem Postural Response Elements

It is clear by now that transection and lesion experiments have been important in determining the level of the brainstem necessary for the execution of postural responses. Electrical stimulation of the brainstem has also been used to reveal the generally excitatory or inhibitory nature of brainstem centers for postural control. Rhines and Magoun[33] found that stimulation anywhere in a large region of the dorsal mesencephalon and pons markedly facilitated stretch reflexes and responses to cortical stimulation. When the pontine reticular formation was lesioned, stimulation in more rostral regions lost its facilitatory effect. Stimulation in the ventromedial medullary reticular formation had an inhibitory effect on all spinal reflexes and on cortically induced movement. The effect included a loss of muscle tone, and although strongest ipsilaterally, it extended to both sides of the body. Since this discovery, there have been many studies on the inhibitory potentials generated in spinal motor neurons and interneurons by stimulation of the medullary reticular formation. This inhibition is widespread and operative at many levels of signal processing between sensory inputs and motor outputs.

Axons from the pontine reticular formation descend in the medial reticulospinal tract, while axons from the medullary reticular formation descend in the lateral reticulospinal tracts. The actions of these reticulospinal pathways and the previously discussed medial and lateral vestibulospinal pathways are thought to be the main influences on basic postural mechanisms and the source of the residual capabilities of brain-transected animals.

Summary

During early development or following clinical or experimental damage to higher motor control responses, important postural control reflexes arising in the brainstem can be observed. These include the tonic neck reflex, which activates forelimbs to flex or extend in response to head movement, as well as limb-placing and trunk-righting reactions. Experimental stimulation of decerebrate brainstems reveals both facilitatory and inhibitory controls over spinal reflexes, arising in the medial and lateral reticulospinal tracts.

BALANCE AND CONTEXT-DEPENDENT POSTURAL STRATEGIES

How are the descending pathways from the brainstem coordinated to produce the postural behaviors of intact animals? An important tool for addressing this question has been the posture platform, a base that can be displaced as subjects stand on it.[34–36] Even on a perfectly stable supporting surface with vision, somesthesis, and vestibular sense all active, a standing person will sway slightly. This sway will increase as sensory input is distorted or removed, showing the importance of the multiple avenues of balance information as well as the adequacy of limited sensory input in maintaining upright posture.

The basic objective of standing posture is to keep the body's center of mass positioned over the base of support provided by the feet, so that the body does not topple.[37] The range of body positions that lie over the base of support defines the limits of stability. When the extremes of body sway extend beyond those limits, the body must reduce them, take a step, or fall.

The ability to maintain an upright posture is tested by exposing subjects to a variety of contexts or sensory environments and by displacing the support surface (Fig. 32.8).[41] We can draw several conclusions from such experiments. (1) Neurologically intact subjects sway little in normal visual surroundings on a stable surface. (2) When the eyes are closed, sway is slightly greater. This is the Romberg test used in clinical evaluation. (3) When the support surface is compliant, proprioceptive feedback is much less useful, and sway increases slightly. (4) When the visual surround is linked to the subject's head position in the condition called "sway referencing of vision," visual information is misleading and sway is increased. (5) When the tilt angle of the support surface is linked to the body tilt angle in the condition called "sway referencing of the support surface," proprioceptive information is misleading and sway is increased. (6) When both visual and proprioceptive information is misleading, sway is even greater, but normal subjects can still maintain an upright posture through the use of vestibular information.

Sudden displacement of the platform on which a subject stands allows measurement of the latencies and patterns of electromyographic activity in the postural muscles of the legs. If the platform is displaced forward or backward, the leg muscles contract in sequence from ankle to thigh to hip, and motion occurs primarily about the ankle joint. When the platform is displaced forward, the ankle flexor tibialis anterior on the front of the calf is the first to be excited, about 80–100 ms after the displacement. It causes toe elevation. This is followed about 20 ms later by contraction of the quadriceps thigh muscles, then later still by contraction of the trunk musculature. Backward displacement first elicits excitation of the gastrocnemius muscle at the back of the calf, extending the ankle, followed by excitation of thigh and trunk muscles antagonistic to those excited by forward displacement (Fig. 32.9). The overall postural sequence of distal to proximal excitation has been termed an **ankle strategy** for maintaining balance.[34]

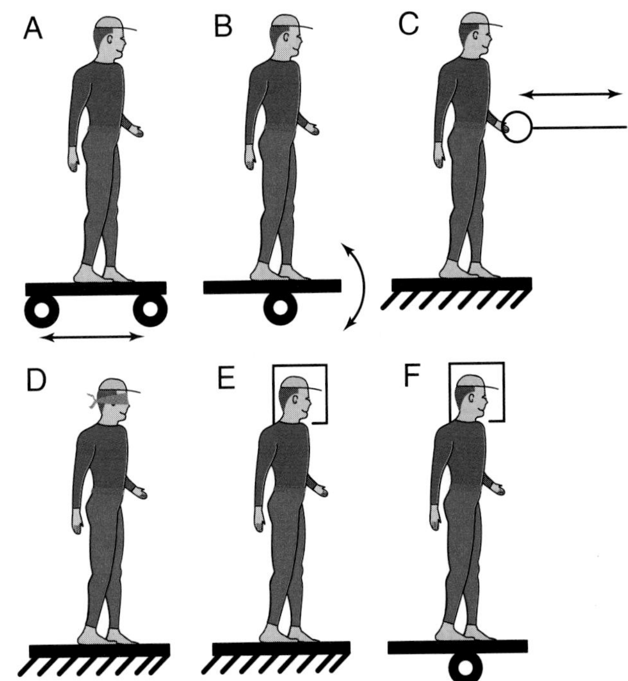

FIGURE 32.8 Tests of upright posture. (A) Sway can be measured during quiet upright stance, and reflex responses elicited by linear displacement of the supporting surface. (B) Rotation of the supporting surface may elicit a different postural response pattern, or the platform may be configured to rotate with ankle rotations for sway referencing of the support surface. (C) Displacement of a handle gripped by the subject produces postural adjustments that precede any arm muscle contraction. (D) Removal of visual input, as done in the Romberg test of vestibular function, increases sway. Normal subjects maintain balance without vision, whereas patients with vestibular deficits may not. (E) The visual surround can be sway referenced. (F) Both vision and ankle proprioception can be sway referenced, which substantially increases sway in normal subjects, who must then rely only on vestibular input.

Although the ankle strategy has been confirmed in all subjects tested with simple forward–backward displacements, it is not the only strategy available; postural reactions have been shown to adapt to alterations in the support surface or sensory inputs. Displacement of a support surface that is short compared to the foot demands a different postural response, because the torques produced by the ankle strategy are ineffective

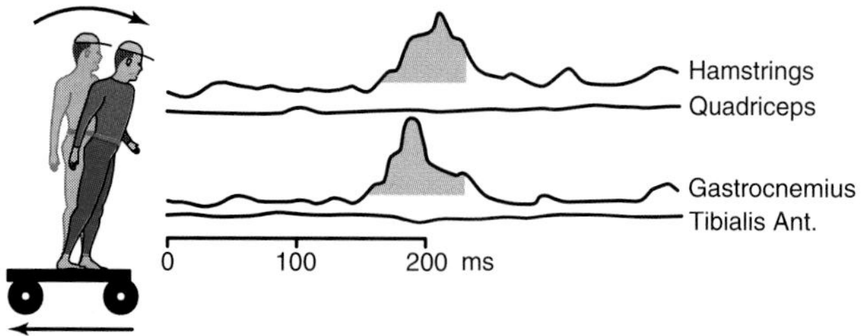

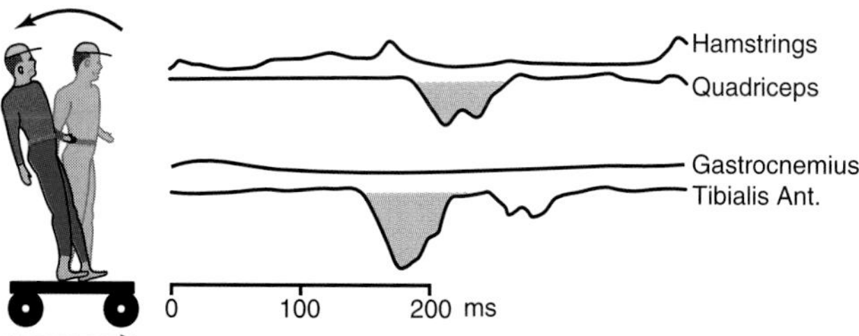

FIGURE 32.9 Sequencing of muscle activation in response to displacement of a supporting platform. (top) When the platform is displaced backward (at 0 ms), distal leg flexor muscles contract first (gastrocnemius, about 80 ms latency), followed by proximal leg flexors (hamstrings, about 100 ms latency). (bottom) Forward displacement of the platform activates distal leg extensors (tibialis anterior) followed by proximal leg extensors (quadriceps). The shaded areas mark the initial electromyographic responses to displacement.[39]

when there is no support to push against. Similarly, the ankle strategy is counterproductive when the base is rotated instead of displaced. Situations such as these require the use of the **hip strategy,** in which the body is bent at the hips and the lower half moves in the same direction as it does during the ankle strategy, while the upper half moves in the opposite direction. Thus, during a forward, front-downward tilt of a supporting platform, the hips move backward and the head forward. As a result, the center of mass, which had moved forward due to the displacement, is shifted backward so that it is again centered over the feet. Other work has questioned the prevalence of the ankle strategy and documented a stiffening strategy of muscle cocontraction in response to base rotation and a multilink strategy that includes ankle, hip, and neck joint motions in response to translation.[38] Stiffening, ankle, hip, and multilink strategies are applicable to the sway that occurs during normal standing on commonly encountered kinds of surfaces and may represent basic units of postural reaction.

Like simple reflexes, these postural reactions represent neuronally mediated negative feedback responses. However, postural reactions differ from ordinary reflex responses in the degree of their dependence on context and recent experience. It also appears that the various postural strategies are not mutually exclusive, but are more like additive units or building blocks. When subjects are placed on support surfaces intermediate in length between those associated with the ankle strategy and the hip strategy, they adopt complex strategies that may represent combinations of ankle and hip strategies with different magnitudes and temporal relations. In addition, during the first few trials after switching from one length of support surface to another, the subjects' responses partly reflect the previous surface, only gradually shifting from one strategy to another over several trials.

Postural responses are also elicited under feedforward control in anticipation of upcoming disturbances and in coordination with the overall motor program to be executed. For example, when subjects standing on a platform are cued by a tone to pull a rigid handle with their hands, the first electromyographic activity occurs in the postural muscles of the legs, not in the muscles of the arm used to pull the handle.[39] The same order of muscle activation accompanies self-initiated handle pulls, making it unlikely that the tone somehow triggered a postural response. Rather, the postural adjustment is in anticipation of the loss of balance that would occur if the pull were unopposed by a shift in stance. Even when the handle is pulled away from the subject while in the subject's grasp, the earliest strong response is not a biceps stretch reflex but a postural response of the gastrocnemius muscle. These findings suggest that postural responses are one component of coordinated movement, often the initial component since a stable platform is needed as a base for voluntary movements.

The range of postural reactions recorded from standing human subjects argues for a complexity beyond that observed in the vestibulocollic or vestibulospinal reflexes during rotation or tilting of animal subjects. However, it is not yet clear whether this complexity reflects the rich variety of strategies that can achieve the single goal of balance, or whether there are strong constraints on postural responses that arise from the complicated biomechanics of the multijoint system of the body. Balance is subject not only to the static requirement that the center of mass be located over the feet, but also to dynamic factors that accompany rapid movement of massive body parts. Inertia, viscosity, and elasticity act at each of the major joints, and the task of measuring or modeling these factors and their interactions has barely begun.

Experimental animals also can be placed on posture platforms, which in the case of quadrupeds can consist of four small pads for the limbs. These experiments

> **BOX 32.2**
>
> **VESTIBULAR PLASTICITY**
>
> The experience of sailors getting their "sea-legs" suggests that, in addition to the role of context and choice of strategies we have discussed, postural reflexes and balance are adapted gradually over time for better performance in new circumstances. Clear evidence for this general phenomenon comes from the study of postural control in astronauts. After a space flight, astronauts initially rely more heavily than before on visual cues for postural orientation, and they show degraded performance in their responses to disturbances generated by a posture platform. Sway during standing is dramatically increased when visual cues are removed, and the body segments move in a less coordinated manner than before space flight.[41,42] Still, the performance of astronauts after the experience of space flight is quite remarkable; they are able to balance adequately within hours of landing and regain their preflight postural performance within a few days.

demonstrate that animals with a spinal transection are incapable of maintaining an erect posture. They also indicate that even though vestibular information from head motion accompanying body displacement is vigorous and early enough to guide reflex responses, cats are able to maintain apparently good quadrupedal standing posture and responses to unexpected motion after total labyrinthectomy.[40] Clearly, we have a great deal to learn about how the brain manages the many systems that contribute to posture and balance (see Box 32.2).

Summary

The interplay between sensory systems coordinated by the brainstem to control postural behavior has been documented with an experimental posture platform that detects swaying movements of the body. Such studies document the importance of visual and proprioceptive cues and the degree to which misleading signals can initiate distal-to-proximal limb muscles to maintain the body's center of gravity over the feet. Similar strategies of postural adjustment can be triggered by anticipation of voluntary movements that preset the body base to avoid the loss of balance that would be caused by the unopposed voluntary movement.

VESTIBULAR DAMAGE AND DISORDERS OF POSTURAL CONTROL

Control of posture involves many levels within the nervous system, and it is not surprising that disorders of posture can result from damage to the sensory periphery or to telencephalic, cerebellar, brainstem, or spinal centers. The striking motor consequences of lesions of the basal ganglia may include profound effects on posture,[43] such as the rigidity and general poverty of movement associated with Parkinson disease (Chapter 35). Damage to the anterior vermis of the cerebellum can exaggerate decerebrate rigidity, and cerebellar patients show poorer performance in posture platform situations,[44] with less adaptive modification of responses as might be expected from our knowledge of cerebellar function (Chapter 35).

Many of the more plainly visible postural disorders stem from damage or diseases of the vestibular system, such as vestibular neuritis, peripheral or central tumors or infarction, and Meniere syndrome (see Box 32.3). Bilateral involvment and acute, episodic, or chronic time courses can occur in many vestibular disorders. The most obvious form of vestibular system damage is unilateral labyrinthectomy, either performed experimentally in animals or caused by disease or surgical intervention against disease in humans.[20] The postural symptoms that appear immediately after the loss of vestibular input to one side of the brain vary across species, with carnivores (cats) typically showing a more prominent tilting of the head and body toward the side of damage. Tilting results because the resting activity of the remaining vestibular apparatus is not balanced by equal resting activity on the lesioned side. This difference in activity is interpreted as motion toward the intact side. The brain responds by tilting the body away from the direction of apparent motion. The static postural effect of unilateral labyrinthectomy is accompanied by dynamic postural deficits, seen in experimental animals as weakened ipsilateral limb extensor responses and delayed responses to sudden drops. Compensation for unilateral labyrinthectomy occurs over a period of a few weeks, during which time responses may return to normal. Interestingly, vestibulo-ocular reflexes (Chapter 36) often take longer to recover

BOX 32.3

MENIERE SYNDROME

The typical patient with Meniere syndrome develops a sensation of fullness and pressure along with decreased hearing and tinnitus in one ear. Vertigo rapidly follows, reaching a maximum intensity within minutes and then slowly subsiding over several hours. Often the patient is left with a sense of unsteadiness and nonspecific dizziness that can go on for days after the acute vertiginous spell. In the early stages, the hearing loss is completely reversible, but as the disease progresses, residual hearing loss becomes a prominent feature. The tinnitus is typically described as a roaring sound similar to the sound of the ocean. These episodes occur at irregular intervals over years, with periods of remission unpredictably intermixed. Eventually most patients reach the so-called "burnt out phase," where the episodic vertigo disappears and severe permanent hearing loss remains.

The clinical syndrome was first described by Prosper Meniere in 1861, but Hallpike and Cairns made the initial clinical–pathological correlation with hydrops of the labyrinth in 1938. Patients with Meniere syndrome invariably show an increase in volume of endolymph associated with distention of the entire endolymphatic system. Herniations and ruptures in the membranous labyrinth commonly occur, which may explain the episodes of hearing loss and vertigo.

Delayed endolymphatic hydrops occurs in an ear that has been damaged years before, usually by infection. With this disorder, the patient reports a long history of hearing loss, typically since childhood, followed many years later by episodic vertigo but without the typical auditory symptoms. The pathologic findings are remarkably similar to idiopathic Meniere syndrome, suggesting a common etiology. A subclinical viral infection could damage the resorptive mechanism of the inner ear, leading to an eventual decompensation in the balance between secretion and resorption of endolymph.

The key to the diagnosis of Meniere syndrome is to document fluctuating hearing levels in a patient with the characteristic clinical history. In the early stages, the sensorineural hearing loss is usually greater in the low frequencies. Some patients with Meniere syndrome develop abrupt episodes of falling to the ground without loss of consciousness or associated neurologic symptoms. These episodes have been called "otolithic catastrophes" because they are thought to result from a sudden mechanical deformation of the otolith receptor organ. Patients often report feeling as though they were pushed to the ground by some external force.

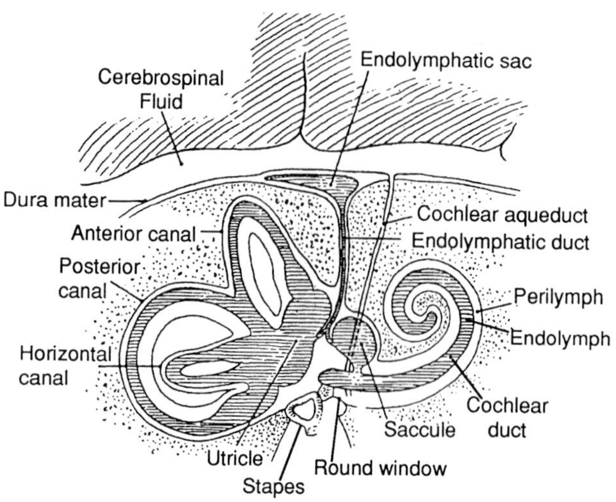

Cross section of the inner ear. Endolymph is produced by secretory cells in the membranous labyrinth and circulates through the endolymphatic duct to the endolymphatic sac where it is resorbed. Blockage of the endolymphatic duct in animals leads to endolymphatic hydrops.

Since the cause of Meniere syndrome is usually unknown, treatment is empiric. Medical management consists of symptomatic treatment with antivertiginous drugs and long-term prophylaxis with salt restriction and diuretics. Many different surgical procedures have been tried but none has been consistently effective. Shunt operations to decrease the endolymph pressure have not been successful because the implanted drain devices are rapidly encapsulated by fibrous tissue. Destructive surgeries (removing the labyrinth or cutting the vestibular nerve) can stop the episodes of vertigo but do not change the tinnitus and progressive hearing loss.

Robert W. Baloh

after unilateral labyrinthectomy and may fail to achieve prelesion performance.

Translating or tilting platforms provide a means for quantitatively assessing vestibular damage from unilateral labyrinthectomy or other sources, including those that result in total vestibular loss.[45,46] Patients with chronic bilateral loss may perform well on posture platforms when visual and somatosensory cues are present, but they fail completely to maintain an upright stance when the support surface and visual surround are *both* sway-referenced, so that only vestibular information is accurate. In contrast, patients with acute bilateral vestibular loss or patients who have not yet compensated for vestibular loss perform poorly on a posture platform if *either* vision or somatic sense is sway-referenced.

Summary

Many clinical disorders share postural control dysfunctions. Many arise from damage to other motor control regions such as basal ganglia or cerebellum in which motor output deteriorates. Direct damage to the vestibular organs will result in immediate and long-lasting abnormalities in posture, but these can usually be compensated through visual and proprioceptive feedback.

The control of "posture"—antigravity stance—is of enormous importance in biology and medicine. It has long been of interest to scientists and engineers because of its similarity to man-made systems that use rapid feedback from the performance itself to correct and improve the performance. Much of the theory about how such systems work, the methods by which they are studied, and the mathematical vigor with which they may be described is applicable to posture. As our human population ages, the postural control system becomes increasing vulnerable, and its damage is increasingly a cause of disability or death. Awareness of this area of science and engineering is therefore increasingly important in medicine.

References

General

Baloh, R., and Honrubia, V. (1990). *Clinical Neurophysiology of the Vestibular System.* 2nd ed. F. A. Davis, Philadelphia.

Horak, F., and Shupert, C. (1994). Role of the vestibular system in postural control. In *Vestibular Rehabilitation* (S. Herdman, ed.), F. A. Davis Co., Philadelphia.

Peterson, B., and Richmond, F. (1988). *Control of Head Movement.* Oxford University Press, New York.

Cited

1. Roberts, T. (1967). *Neurophysiology of Postural Mechanisms.* Plenum Press, New York.
2. Johansson, R., and Magnusson, M. (1991). Human postural dynamics. *Crit. Rev. Biomed. Engineer.* **18:** 413–437.
3. Clarke, E., and O'Malley, C. (1968). *The Human Brain and Spinal Cord.* Univ. Calif. Press, Berkeley.
4. Henneman, E. (1980). Motor functions of the brain stem and basal ganglia. In *Medical Physiology,* 14th ed., (V. C. V. Mountcastle, ed.), Mosby, St. Louis.
5. Paulus, W., Straube, A., and Brandt, T. (1984). Visual stabilization of posture: Physiological stimulus characteristics and clinical aspects. *Brain* **107:** 1143–1163.
6. Pompeiano, O., and Allum, J. (1988). *Vestibulospinal Control of Posture and Locomotion.* Elsevier, Amsterdam.
7. Kravitz, E., Beltz, B., Glusman, S., Goy, M., Harris-Warwick, R., Johnston, M., Livingstone, M., Schwarz, T., and Siwicki, K. (1985). The well modulated lobster: The roles of serotonin, octopamine, and proctolin in the lobster nervous system. In *Model Neural Networks and Behavior* (A. Selverston, ed.). Plenum, New York.

7a. Pompeiano, O. (1992). The role of noradrenergic locus coeruleus neurons in the dynamic control of posture during the vestibulospinal reflexes. In *Vestibular and Brain Stem Control of Eye, Head and Body Movements* (H. Shimazu and Y. Shinoda, eds.). Karger, Basel.

8. Keshner, E., and Allum, J. (1990). Muscle activation patterns coordinating postural stability from head to foot. In *Multiple Muscle Systems: Biomechanics and Movement Organization* (J. Winters and S. Woo, eds.). Springer-Verlag, New York.

8a. Nashner, L. (1990). Sensory, neuromuscular, and biomechanical contributions to human balance. In *Balance: Proceedings of the American Physical Therapy Association Forum* (P. Duncan, ed.), American Physical Therapy Association, Alexandria, VA.

9. Sherrington, C. (1898). Decerebrate rigidity and reflex coordination of movements. *J. Physiol.* **22:** 319–332.
10. Bazett, H., and Penfield W. (1922). A study of the Sherrington decerebrate animal in the chronic as well as the acute condition. *Brain* **45:** 185–265.
11. Kuypers, H., Fleming, W., and Farinholt, J. (1962). Subcorticospinal projections in the rhesus monkey. *J. Comp. Neurol.* **118:** 107–137.
12. Lawrence, D. G., and Kuypers, H. G. J. M. (1968). The functional organization of the motor system in the monkey. II. The effects of lesions of the descending brain-stem pathways. *Brain* **91:** 15–36.
13. Wilson, V., and Melvill-Jones, G. (1979). *Mammalian Vestibular Physiology.* Plenum Press, New York.
14. Netter, F. (1983). *The CIBA Collection of Medical Illustrations.* Vol. 1, *Nervous System.* CIBA Pharmaceutical Company, West Caldwell, NJ.
15. Fernandez, C., and Goldberg, J. (1971). Physiology of peripheral neurons innervating semicircular canals of the squirrel monkey. II. Response to sinusoidal stimulation and dynamics of peripheral vestibular system. *J. Neurophysiol.* **34:** 661–675.

15a. Goldberg, J., and Fernandez, C. (1971). Physiology of peripheral neurons innervating semicircular canals of the squirrel monkey. I. Resting discharge and response to constant angular accelerations. *J. Neurophysiol.* **34:** 635–660.

16. Fernandez, C., and Goldberg, J. (1976). Physiology of peripheral neurons innervating otolith organs of the squirrel monkey. I. Response to static tilts and to long duration centrifugal force. *J. Neurophysiol.* **39:** 970–984.

16a. Fernandez, C., Goldberg, J., and Abend, W. (1972). Response to static tilts of peripheral neurons innervating otolith organs of the squirrel monkey. *J. Neurophysiol.* **35:** 978–997.

17. Loe, P., Tomko, D., and Werner, G. (1973). The neural signal of angular head position in primary afferent vestibular nerve axons. *J. Physiol.* **230:** 29–50.

18. Shimazu, H., and Shinoda, Y. (1992). *Vestibular and Brain Stem Control of Eye, Head and Body Movements.* Karger, Basel.
19. Suzuki, J.-I., and Cohen, B. (1964). Head, eye, body and limb movements from semicircular canal nerves. *Exp. Neurol.* **10:** 393–405.
19a. Schor, R., Kearney, R., and Dieringer, N. (1988). Reflex stabilization of the head. In *Control of Head Movement* (B. Peterson and F. Richmond, eds.). Oxford University Press, New York.
20. Smith, P., and Curthoys, I. (1989). Mechanisms of recovery following unilateral labyrinthectomy: A review. *Brain Res. Rev.* **14:** 155–180.
21. Schor, R. (1974). Responses of cat vestibular neurons to sinusoidal roll tilt. *Exp. Brain Res.* **20:** 347–362.
21a. Baker, J., Goldberg, J., Peterson, B., and Schor, R. (1982). Oculomotor reflexes after semicircular canal plugging in cats. *Brain Res.* **252:** 151–155.
22. Wilson, V., and Maeda, M. (1974). Connections between semicircular canals and neck motoneurons in the cat. *J. Neurophysiol.* **37:** 346–357.
22a. Wilson, V., and Peterson, B. (1988). Vestibular and reticular projections to the neck. In *Control of Head Movement* (B. Peterson and F. Richmond, eds.). Oxford University Press, New York.
23. Bilotto, G., Goldberg, J., Peterson, B., and Wilson, V. (1982). Dynamic properties of vestibular reflexes in the decerebrate cat. *Exp. Brain Res.* **47:** 343–352.
24. Baker, J., Goldberg, J., and Peterson, B. (1985). Spatial and temporal response properties of the vestibulocollic reflex in decerebrate cats. *J. Neurophysiol.* **54:** 735–756.
24a. Wilson, V., Schor, R., Suzuki, I., and Park, B. (1986). Spatial organization of neck and vestibular reflexes acting on the forelimbs of the decerebrate cat. *J. Neurophysiol.* **55:** 514–526.
25. Kuo, A., and Zajac, F. (1993). Human standing posture: Multijoint movement strategies based on biomechanical constraints. *Prog. Brain Res.* **97:** 349–358.
26. Banovetz, J., Peterson, B., and Baker, J. (1995). Spatial coordination by descending vestibular signals. 1. Reflex excitation of neck muscles in alert and decerebrate cats. *Exp. Brain Res.* [In press]
27. Boyle, R. (1993). Activity of medial vestibulospinal tract cells during rotation and ocular movement in the alert squirrel monkey. *J. Neurophysiol.* **70:** 2176–2180.
28. Uchino, Y., Isu, N., Ichikawa, T., Satoh, S., and Watanabe, S. (1988). Properties and localization of the anterior semicircular canal-activated vestibulocollic neurons in the cat. *Exp. Brain Res.* **71:** 345–352.
29. Isu, N., Sakuma, A., Hiranuma, K., Uchino, H., Sasaki, S., Imagawa, M., and Uchino, Y. (1991). The neuronal organization of horizontal semicircular canal-activated inhibitory vestibulocollic neurons in the cat. *Exp. Brain Res.* **86:** 9–17.
30. Peterson, B., Goldberg, J., Bilotto, G., and Fuller, J. (1985). Cervicocollic reflex: Its dynamic properties and interaction with vestibular reflexes. *J. Neurophysiol.* **54:** 90–109.
31. Magnus, R. (1926). Some results of studies in the physiology of posture. *Lancet* **211:** 531–536.
32. Watt, D. (1976). Responses of cats to sudden falls: An otolith-originating reflex assisting landing. *J. Neurophysiol.* **39:** 257–265.
33. Rhines, R., and Magoun, H. (1946). Brain stem facilitation of cortical motor response. *J. Neurophysiol.* **9:** 219–229.
34. Horak, F., and Nashner, L. (1986). Central programming of postural movements: Adaptation to altered support-surface configurations. *J. Neurophysiol.* **55:** 1369–1381.
35. Nashner, L., Woollacott, M., and Tuma, G. (1979). Organization of rapid responses to postural and locomotor-like perturbations of standing man. *Exp. Brain Res.* **36:** 463–476.
36. Nashner, L. (1982). Adaptation of human movement to altered environments. *Trends Neurosci.* **5:** 358–361.
37. Lacquaniti, F. (1992). Automatic control of limb movement and posture. *Curr. Opin. Neurobiol.* **2:** 807–814.
38. Allum, J., Honegger, F., and Pfaltz, C. (1989). The role of stretch and vestibulospinal reflexes in the generation of human equilibrating reactions. *Prog. Brain Res.* **80:** 399–409.
39. Cordo, P., and Nashner, L. (1982). Properties of postural adjustments associated with rapid arm movements. *J. Neurophysiol.* **47:** 287–302.
40. Macpherson, J., and Inglis, J. (1993). Stance and balance following bilateral labyrinthectomy. *Prog. Brain Res.* **97:** 219–228.
41. Anderson, D., Reschke, M., Homick, J., and Werness, S. (1986). Dynamic posture analysis of Spacelab-1 crew members. *Exp. Brain Res.* **64:** 380–391.
42. Paloski, W., Black, F., Reschke, M., Calkins, D., and Shupert, C. (1993). Vestibular ataxia following shuttle flights: Effects of microgravity on otolith-mediated sensorimotor control of posture. *Am. J. Otol.* **14:** 9–17.
43. Martin, J. (1967). *The Basal Ganglia and Posture.* Pitman Medical, London.
44. Nashner, L. (1976). Adapting reflexes controlling the human posture. *Exp. Brain Res.* **26:** 59–72.
45. Keshner, E., Allum, J., and Pfaltz, C. (1987). Postural coactivation and adaptation in the sway stabilizing responses of normals and patients with bilateral vestibular deficit. *Exp. Brain Res.* **69:** 77–92.
46. Allum, J., Honegger, F., and Schicks, H. (1994). The influence of a bilateral vestibular deficit on postural synergies. *J. Vestibular Res.* **4:** 49–70.

CHAPTER

33

Voluntary Descending Control

Marc H. Schieber

In the early 19th century, phrenologists claimed that intellectual abilities correlated with variations in skull shape, while neurologists and neuroscientists generally believed that different brain functions were distributed throughout the cerebral hemispheres.[1] Things began to change in 1861, when Paul Broca asserted that the posterior portion of the inferior frontal gyrus in the left hemisphere was a unique area in humans, specialized for language production. In 1870, Hughlings Jackson hypothesized that the brain contained another specialized area where motor output was represented somatotopically, that is, according to an organized map of the body. Jackson based his hypothesis on observations of epileptic patients whose motor convulsions spread systematically from one part of their body to adjacent parts. In the same year, Fritsch and Hitzig reported that electrical stimulation of a restricted portion of the frontal cortex in anesthetized dogs could evoke movements of the contralateral face, forelimb, and hindlimb, with movements of different body parts evoked from different locations in the cortex. These observations localized motor function to somatotopically organized, electrically excitable regions of the cerebral cortex.

The cortical control of movement has been confirmed in numerous species of mammals, including humans. The "excitable cortex," where electrical stimulation can evoke contralateral movement, has been parsed into an increasing number of motor areas. With progressively more sophisticated techniques, neuroscientists have explored the interconnections between these areas and other parts of the cortex, subcortical centers, and the spinal cord and have studied the physiology of cortical neuronal activity during a variety of voluntary movements. In this chapter, we will examine how these areas of the cerebral cortex contribute to the production of voluntary movement.

CORTICAL PATHWAYS TO MOTOR NEURONS

Both old work and new work demonstrate that a number of different sites in the cerebral cortex project to the brainstem and spinal cord. Nevertheless, the dramatic deficits produced by damaging primary motor cortex and the lack of knowledge of deficits produced by damage of other cortical motor areas have focused attention on motor cortex. While motor cortex is not "the whole story," it is clearly the place to begin.

The Corticospinal Projection Is the Most Direct Pathway from the Cerebral Cortex to Spinal Motor Neurons

In monkeys, apes, and humans, cortical neurons with axons projecting to the spinal cord are found most densely in the anterior bank of the central sulcus (Rolandic fissure). The density of such neurons decreases from there rostrally to the posterior bank of the arcuate sulcus and medially to the cingulate sulcus (Fig. 33.1). This territory corresponds to cytoarchitectonic areas 4 and 6 of Brodmann. Although additional corticospinal neurons are present in areas 1, 2, 3, 5, and 7 of the parietal lobe, those neurons probably project to the dorsal horn of the spinal cord to regulate sensory inflow, rather than having a motor function.

The axons of neurons that project from the cerebral

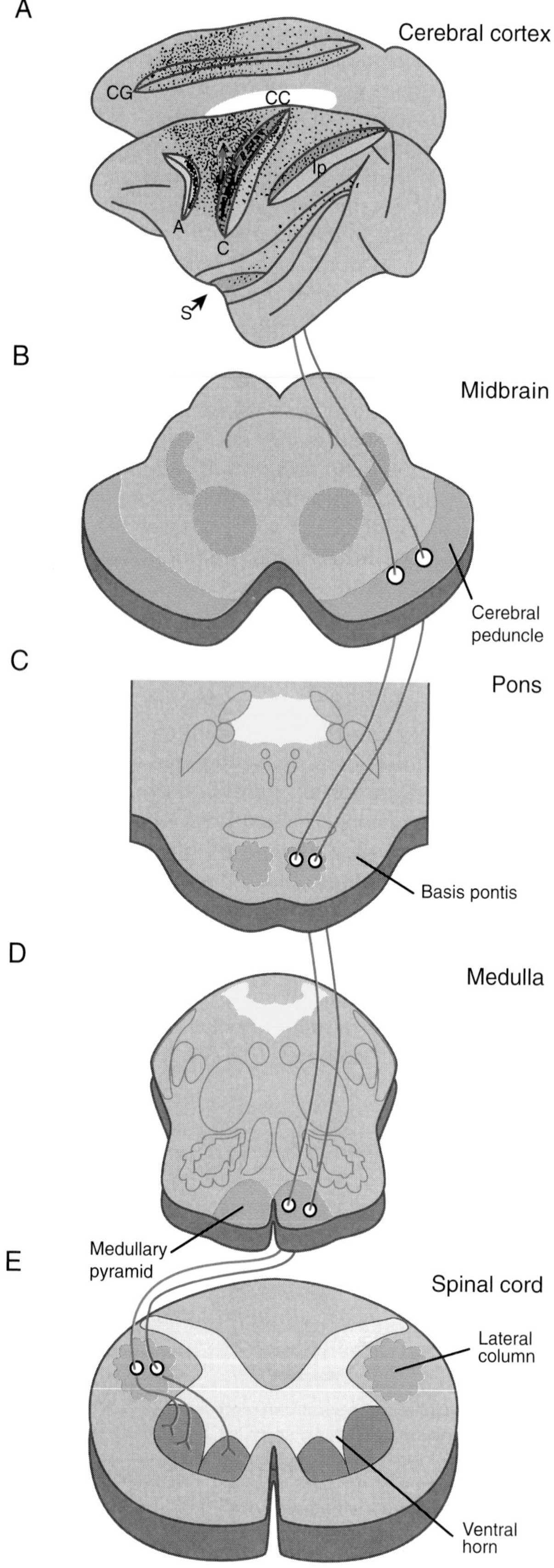

cortex to the spinal cord constitute the corticospinal tract. Corticospinal neurons have large pyramid-shaped somata in cortical layer Vb. Their axons leave the cortex, pass through the centrum semiovale, and enter the internal capsule, along with many other axons from other cortical areas. The corticospinal axons are most heavily concentrated in the middle third of the internal capsule's posterior limb. As axons descend from the internal capsule below the thalamus, they come to lie on the ventral surface of the brainstem. Here, they form the cerebral peduncle of the midbrain, where they are again concentrated in the middle third (Fig. 33.1). The axons of the peduncle become intermixed with nuclear neurons at the base of the pons (**basis pontis**). Most of these axons synapse on pontine neurons and end here, providing input from the cerebral cortex to the cerebellum. The continuing corticospinal axons collect to form the **medullary pyramid** (Box 33.1). As the medulla blends into the spinal cord, the vast majority of corticospinal axons cross the midline and enter the lateral column of white matter on the opposite side of the spinal cord. Because of this decussation of the pyramidal tract, the left motor cortex controls movements on the right side of the body and vice versa. A small minority of corticospinal axons remain uncrossed and continue caudally as the ventral (or anterior) corticospinal tract near the ventral midline of the spinal cord.

As descending corticospinal axons reach their target levels in the spinal cord, they enter the spinal gray matter, where they ramify and synapse. A small fraction of these axons synapse directly on motor neurons in Rexed's lamina IX. Most of the corticospinal neurons that make such monosynaptic connections to motor neurons have their somata in the anterior bank of the central sulcus, in the portions of the somatotopic map that correspond to the hands and feet. These monosynaptic connections are generally made on the motor neurons of distal limb muscles, whose somata are clus-

FIGURE 33.1 The corticospinal projection in the macaque monkey. (A) The density of corticospinal neuronal somata is shown by stippling in this lateral view of the left cerebral hemisphere; the superior medial surface of the hemisphere is also shown (above) as if reflected in a mirror. The central sulcus (C), arcuate sulcus (A), cingulate sulcus (Cg), and Sylvian fissure (S) are drawn as if pulled open to reveal the neurons in their banks. Two schematic corticospinal neurons, one in the anterior bank of the central sulcus and the other on the convexity anterior to the central sulcus, send their axons down through the midbrain (B), pons (C), medulla (D), and spinal cord (E), which are drawn in cross section. In the spinal cord, one corticospinal axon leaves the lateral column to terminate in the dorsolateral ventral horn, while the other axon terminates in the ventromedial ventral horn. After Toyoshima and Sakai.[2]

BOX 33.1

PYRAMIDS IN THE BRAIN

Gross anatomic inspection of cross sections through the medulla's ventral surface reveals a structure that looks like a small pyramid. This medullary pyramid turns out to be the collected bundle of corticospinal axons. The corticospinal tract therefore is often referred to as the pyramidal tract, which has nothing to do with the fact that the somata of corticospinal neurons are also pyramidal in shape.

tered in the dorsolateral ventral horn. Such connections are found most often in primates, especially humans. Corticospinal axons from neurons located farther anterior to the central sulcus typically synapse on premotor interneurons in the intermediate zone and ventromedial portion of the ventral horn (Rexed's laminae VII and VIII), where the motor neurons of proximal limb muscles and axial muscles are located. These axons constitute the vast majority of corticospinal axons. Some of them cross the midline spinal gray matter to reach the ventromedial ventral horn ipsilateral to their origin; such doubly decussating corticospinal axons, along with the uncrossed ventral corticospinal tract, may be partly responsible for the relative preservation of trunk and proximal limb movements after unilateral damage to the cortex.

Indirect Pathways to the Spinal Cord Involve Centers in the Brainstem

The corticospinal tract is not the only output pathway through which the cerebral cortex contributes to motor control[3] (Box 33.2). Woolsey and his co-workers demonstrated the presence of other, indirect pathways in the macaque by cutting the medullary pyramid on one side; they found that stimulation of the cortex on that side still evoked contralateral movements.[4] The somatotopic organization of the cortex in the operated animals was similar to that in normal macaques although the thresholds for stimulation were raised and small, distal movements were evoked less often.

Intermixed with corticospinal neurons in layer V of areas 4 and 6 are corticorubral neurons, whose axons project to the red nucleus (RN). Some corticospinal axons also send collaterals to the RN. Many RN neurons, particularly those in the caudal, magnocellular portion of the RN, in turn send their axons across the midline and into the lateral column of the spinal cord, terminating most heavily in the dorsolateral region of the ventral horn. These descending axons from the RN are called the rubrospinal tract. A noncorticospinal pathway thus exists from the cortex to the RN to the spinal cord. Although the rubrospinal tract is less prominent in humans than in nonhuman primates and carnivores, the activity of rubrospinal neurons indicates that they also play a significant role during voluntary movements of the arm, hand, and fingers.[5,6]

A second noncorticospinal pathway involves neurons scattered in the medial reticular formation of the pons and medulla. The medial reticular formation re-

BOX 33.2

OUTSIDE THE PYRAMIDS

Axons of noncorticospinal descending pathways do not pass through the medullary pyramid and therefore can be described collectively as **extrapyramidal pathways**. At one time these pathways were thought to receive their major controlling inputs from the basal ganglia. Human neurologic disorders that result from dysfunction of the basal ganglia thus came to be known as "extrapyramidal syndromes." This term is misleading, however. More recent work has shown that many of the brainstem nuclei giving rise to extrapyramidal pathways receive cortical input, and that much of the output of the basal ganglia is directed via the thalamus back to cortical motor areas. Many manifestations of extrapyramidal syndromes may therefore be played out through cortical motor areas, even via the pyramidal tract. Indeed, surgical lesions of the pyramidal tract were once used to treat some extrapyramidal syndromes.

ceives input from cortical motor areas and projects via the ventral column of the spinal cord to the ventral horn, chiefly its ventromedial portion. The axons that make this projection constitute the reticulospinal tract. Additional noncorticospinal motor pathways to the spinal cord arise from neurons in the midbrain tectum, interstitial nucleus of Cajal, and vestibular nuclei. The axons of these neurons descend as the tectospinal, interstitiospinal, and vestibulospinal tracts, respectively. Direct projections from cortical motor areas to these brainstem centers have not been described.

There are functional differences between the laterally located corticospinal and rubrospinal tracts and the medially located reticulospinal and vestibulospinal tracts. Monkeys with transected corticospinal and rubrospinal tracts rapidly recover the use of all four extremities in activities such as ambulation and climbing, but they remain permanently unable to make the relatively independent finger movements needed to extract small pieces of food from narrow holes.[7] In contrast, monkeys with transected reticulospinal and vestibulospinal tracts remain permanently unable to ambulate and climb, but when supported, they can use their hands and fingers adeptly in retrieving food pieces from narrow holes.[8] These differences in the functional deficits produced by experimental lesions correlate with the heavier projection of the lateral descending pathways to the dorsolateral ventral horn, where the motor neurons for distal muscles are located, and with the heavier projection of the medial descending pathways to the ventromedial ventral horn, where the motor neurons for proximal limb and axial muscles are located.

Some Cortical Motor Output Projects to and Is Processed by the Basal Ganglia and Cerebellum and Then Returns to the Cortex

In man-made movement control systems, commands for movement are constantly monitored and compared to performance errors so that they may be corrected and improved. In biological motor control, the commands are many and are often potentially in conflict. They must be coordinated at higher levels to optimize performance and prevent conflicts. The basal ganglia and the cerebellum are important for these operations.

Not all of the output of cortical motor areas is directed at the spinal cord. Many axons from layer V neurons of the motor cortex project to two major subcortical centers, the basal ganglia (corpus striatum and globus pallidus; Chapter 34) and the cerebellum (Chapter 35). Almost all regions of cerebral cortex project diffusely to the corpus striatum, which in turn projects to the globus pallidus. Most of the output of the globus pallidus is sent via the thalamus back to the cortex, particularly to motor areas. Almost all regions of the cerebral cortex also project to the cerebellum via the nuclei of the basis pontis. Cortical motor areas send a second projection to the cerebellum via the parvocellular portion of the red nucleus and then the inferior olive. Much of the cerebellar output, especially that from the dentate and interposed nuclei, in turn projects via the thalamus back to cortical motor areas. Thus, the basal ganglia and cerebellum can be viewed as funnels that process information gathered from all of the cerebral cortex and send this processed information back to cortical motor areas.

Summary

The voluntary motor control system contains corticospinal projections arising from neurons just rostral to the central sulcus in Brodmann areas 4 and 6, as well as in areas 1, 2, 3, 5, and 7. Their axons constitute the corticospinal tracts whose axons descend through the internal capsule, eventually converging at the base of the medulla into the pyramidal tracts, which mainly cross over (decussate) as they extend to their spinal targets. In addition, neurons of cortical areas 4 and 6 can influence spinal motor responses indirectly through synaptic relays in the red nucleus or in the medial reticular formation of the pons and medulla. The corticorubrospinal projections, together with the direct corticospinal system, control fine movements of the distal extremities, while the more medial corticoreticulospinal system controls waking and postural movements.

ORGANIZATION OF THE MOTOR CORTEX

The original "primary motor cortex" is now appreciated to be only one of the several cortical areas projecting to brainstem and spinal cord. These areas are defined as "motor" if (1) they project to other motor structures, (2) their ablation causes deficits in movement, and (3) their stimulation causes movements.

The Motor Cortex Is Subdivided into Multiple Cortical Motor Areas

The use of electrical stimulation perhaps more so than anatomy and ablation information has been of importance in defining the "motor" areas of cerebral cortex. Early in the 20th century, neuroanatomists recognized that the motor cortex could be distinguished from the rest of the cerebral cortex on the basis of two major features of its cell arrangement (cytoarchitectonics). First, the somata of many pyramidal neurons in layer V, the output layer, are exceptionally large. Second, the neurons of layer IV, the granular layer that receives thalamic input, are very sparse compared to layer IV neurons in other areas of the neocortex. The motor cortex is not a uniform field, however. For example, Brodmann divided it into two areas, designated 4 and 6. Area 4 has extremely large layer V neurons (Betz cells) and almost no layer IV neurons (agranular cortex). Area 6, in contrast, has somewhat smaller layer V neurons and a few layer IV neurons (dysgranular cortex).

Subsequent investigators have further subdivided these areas on the basis of cytoarchitectonics, the patterns of myelinated fibers (myeloarchitectonics), and more recently neurotransmitter receptor distribution (Fig. 33.2). Although the nomenclature and boundaries of cortical subdivisions differ, the various parcellation schemes show two general features. First, there is a sequence of mediolaterally oriented strips of cortex, beginning in area 4 and passing from the caudal to the rostral portion of area 6. Second, each strip of area 6 is subdivided; one subdivision is on the medial wall of the hemisphere, a second is on the dorsal convexity, and a third is on the ventral convexity. In addition to subdivisions of areas 4 and 6, Brodmann's areas 23 and 24 in the banks of the cingulate sulcus and on the medial surface of the hemisphere in the cingulate gyrus are now thought to contain at least two additional cortical motor areas. Table 33.1 summarizes how parcellation of the cortical motor areas has progressed over the past century and provides a rough correlation between the various schemes.

Cortical motor areas differ in their connections with the thalamus. For example, cortical motor areas M1 (the primary motor cortex), PMv, and SMA connect primarily with VPLo/VLc, area X, and VLo in the thalamus, respectively. These differences are significant because thalamic nuclei VPLo/VLc and area X receive major inputs from the cerebellum, while VLo receives major input from the basal ganglia. Thus, information processed by the cerebellum is directed largely to M1 and PMv, while information from the basal ganglia is sent largely to SMA.

Cortical motor areas also differ in their connections with one another and with nonmotor regions of the cortex (Fig. 33.3). For example, when horseradish peroxidase (HRP) is injected into the hand area of M1,

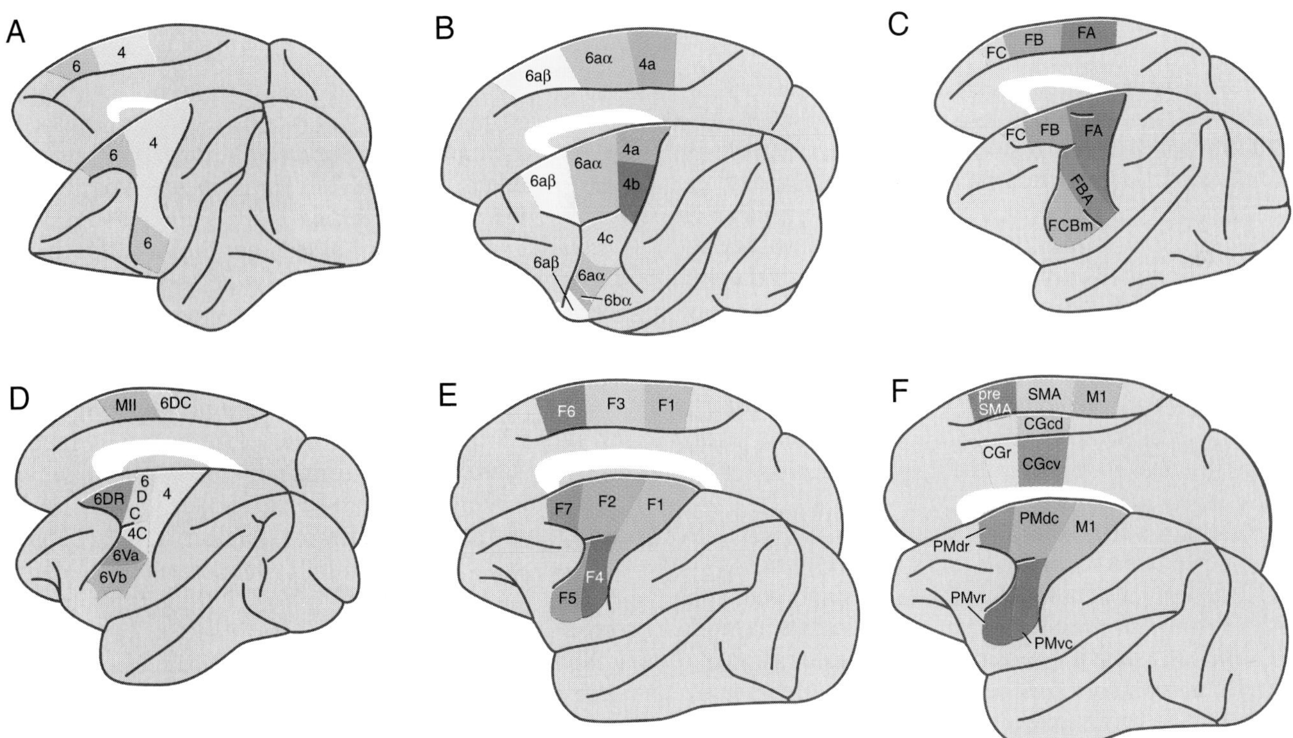

FIGURE 33.2 Cortical motor areas. Diagrams of a macaque brain show how the motor cortex of the frontal lobe has been parceled in various cytoarchitectonic studies over the past century. Modified from Matelli *et al.*[9] (A) Brodmann, 1903; (B) Vogt and Vogt, 1919; (C) Von Bonin and Bailey, 1947; (D) Barbas and Pandya, 1987; (E) Matteli *et al.*, 1991; (F) general abbreviations.

TABLE 33.1 Cortical Motor Areas and Cytoarchitectonics

<table>
<tr><th>Generic description</th><th>Generic abbreviation</th><th>Matelli et al.[9]</th><th>Barbas and Pandya</th><th>von Bonin and Bailey</th><th>Vogt and Vogt</th><th>Brodmann</th></tr>
<tr><td>Primary motor cortex</td><td>M1</td><td>F1</td><td>4</td><td>FA</td><td>4a, 4b, 4c</td><td>4</td></tr>
<tr><td>Premotor cortex, dorsal caudal</td><td>PMdc</td><td>F2</td><td rowspan="2">6DC</td><td rowspan="2">FB</td><td rowspan="3">6aα</td><td rowspan="7">6</td></tr>
<tr><td>Supplementary motor area-proper</td><td>SMA</td><td>F3</td></tr>
<tr><td>Premotor cortex, ventral, caudal</td><td>PMvc</td><td>F4</td><td>6Va</td><td>FBA</td></tr>
<tr><td>Premotor cortex, ventral, rostral</td><td>PMvr</td><td>F5</td><td>6Vb</td><td>FCBm</td><td>6bα,β</td></tr>
<tr><td>Pre-SMA</td><td>Pre-SMA</td><td>F6</td><td>MII</td><td rowspan="2">FC</td><td rowspan="2">6aβ</td></tr>
<tr><td>Premotor cortex, dorsal, rostral</td><td>PMdr</td><td>F7</td><td>6DR</td></tr>
<tr><td>Cingulate motor area, caudal</td><td>CGc</td><td>24d</td><td colspan="3"></td><td>23</td></tr>
<tr><td>Cingulate motor area, rostral</td><td>CGr</td><td>24c</td><td colspan="3"></td><td>24</td></tr>
</table>

separate pockets of retrogradely labeled neuronal somata are found in PMv, PMd, SMA, CGc, and CGr, indicating that each of these areas sends a separate projection to the hand area of M1.[10,11] In contrast, PMvr, PMdr, and pre-SMA do not project directly to M1. Instead, PMvr projects to PMvc, PMdr projects to PMdc, and pre-SMA projects to PMvr. Different cortical motor areas also receive input from different cortical sensory and association areas: M1 receives input from the primary somatosensory area (S1), PMv receives input from visual association area 7b, and PMd receives input from somatosensory association area 5.

Because of their sensory inputs, many M1 neurons have somatosensory receptive fields. Neurons located caudally in M1 tend to respond to cutaneous modalities, while neurons located rostrally in M1 tend to respond to deep modalities. An M1 neuron's somatosensory input is generally related to that neuron's output function. For example, caudally located M1 neurons that control the muscles that move the fingers may have cutaneous receptive fields on the fingers (Fig. 33.4A), while rostrally located M1 neurons that control the biceps or triceps may have deep receptive fields in those muscles. Somatosensory inputs to M1 neurons may be involved in some muscle responses to sudden muscle stretch (Box 33.3).

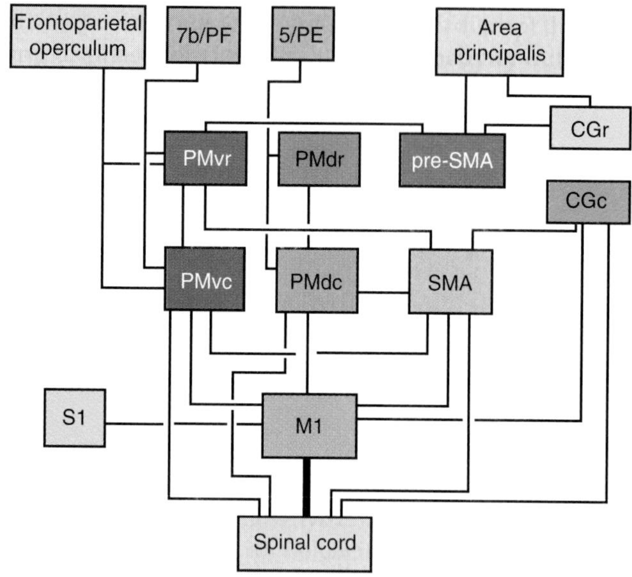

FIGURE 33.3 Connections of the cortical motor areas. Most corticocortical connections are reciprocal. Thin lines to the spinal cord from PMvc, PMdc, SMA, and CGc indicate that corticospinal projections from these areas are not as strong as that from M1.

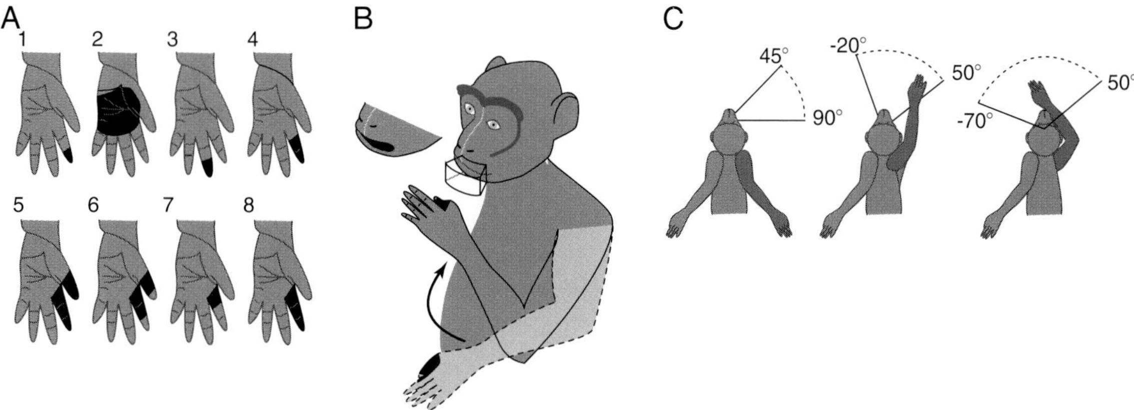

FIGURE 33.4 Sensory receptive fields in M1 and PMv. (A) Black regions show the tactile receptive fields of eight M1 neurons recorded at loci where intracortical microstimulation evoked flexion of the monkey's index and ring fingers. Other neurons at the same loci responded to passive extension of those fingers. From Rosen and Asanuma.[12] (B) A single PMv neuron responded to visual stimuli moving near the mouth, to tactile stimulation of the lips and of the skin between the thumb and index finger, and to flexion of the elbow. From Rizzolatti *et al.*[13] (C) Another PMv neuron with a tactile receptive field covering the entire right arm had a visual receptive field for objects moving near the face. The visual receptive field shifted from right to left as the right arm was moved from right to left. Reprinted with permission from Graziano *et al.*[14] Copyright 1994 American Association for the Advancement of Science.

PMv receives both somatosensory and visual input via area 7b. Both the somatosensory and the visual receptive fields of PMv neurons tend to be large, and when single PMv neurons receive both types of sensory information, the fields tend to be related (Fig. 33.4B). A neuron with a somatosensory receptive field covering the forearm, for instance, may respond to visual stimuli moving near the forearm. Interestingly, if the

BOX 33.3

LONG-LOOP RESPONSES

Somatosensory inputs to M1 help mediate long-loop responses, i.e., muscular responses that occur too slowly to be mediated by the monosynaptic stretch reflex but too quickly to be considered voluntary reactions. For example, when the handle a subject is holding is suddenly jerked away from the subject, extending the elbow and stretching the biceps, three distinguishable waves of contraction may be recorded in the biceps (Fig. 33.5). Timing considerations indicate that the first wave is the monosynaptic reflex produced by stretching the muscle (MR), and that the third wave is the subject voluntarily pulling back on the handle (V). The middle wave (LL) occurs at a latency consistent with conduction of impulses from muscle afferents to the cortex and then almost directly from M1 to spinal motor neurons. Many biceps-related M1 neurons may discharge a burst of impulses at a time appropriate to contribute to this long-loop response. Interestingly, the strength of the long-loop response may be increased if the subject plans to pull on the handle by contracting the biceps, and decreased if the subject plans to push on the handle by relaxing the biceps; parallel changes may occur in the bursts of the M1 neurons. Thus, long-loop responses are affected by the subject's motor plans.[18]

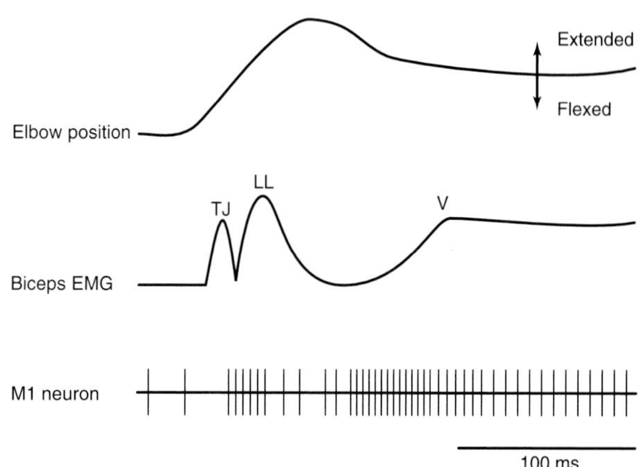

FIGURE 33.5 The long-loop response.

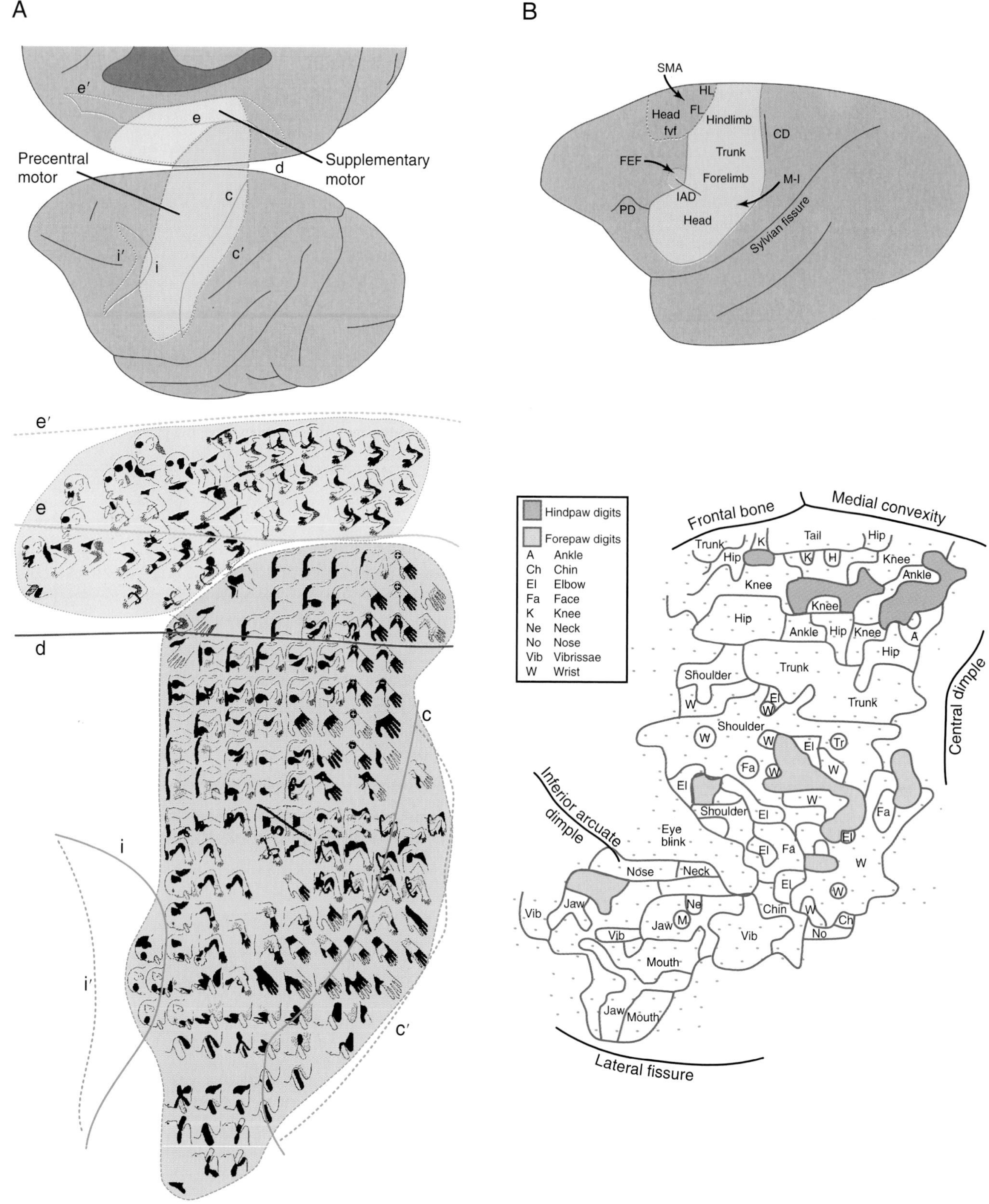

A
B
e′
e
Precentral motor
Supplementary motor
d
c
c′
i′
i
SMA
HL
FL
Head fvf
Hindlimb
CD
Trunk
FEF
Forelimb
M-I
IAD
PD
Head
Sylvian fissure
Hindpaw digits
Forepaw digits
A Ankle
Ch Chin
El Elbow
Fa Face
K Knee
Ne Neck
No Nose
Vib Vibrissae
W Wrist
Frontal bone
Medial convexity
Central dimple
Inferior arcuate dimple
Lateral fissure
Trunk
Tail
Hip
Knee
Ankle
Shoulder
Eye blink
Nose
Neck
Jaw
Vib
Mouth
Chin

BOX 33.4

CLINICAL ASPECTS OF M1 SOMATOTOPY

The overall somatotopic organization of M1 becomes evident in the clinical practice of neurology. Lesions on the lateral convexity of M1 cause weakness or paralysis of the contralateral face, more medial lesions on the convexity affect the contralateral hand and arm, and lesions on the medial wall of the hemisphere affect the leg and foot.

forearm is moved to a different position, the visual receptive field of the PMv neuron moves with the forearm (Fig. 33.4C).

Somatotopic Organization in the Motor Cortex Is Not a One-to-One Map of Body Parts, Muscles, or Movements

Somatotopic organization is the hallmark of the motor cortex.[15,16] Within the primary motor cortex, the face is represented laterally, the lower extremity (or hindlimb and tail) medially, and the upper extremity (or forelimb) in between (Fig. 33.6). Distal parts of the extremities and acral parts of the face (lips and tongue) are most heavily represented caudally, often in the anterior bank of the central sulcus, close to the primary somatosensory cortex; proximal parts of the extremities and axial movements are most heavily represented rostrally (Box 33.4). This overall organization of M1 according to major body parts is termed **somatotopic**. Those parts of the body that are used for fine manipulative movements (such as lips, tongue, and fingers in primates) are generally represented over a wider cortical territory than body parts used in larger movements such as ambulation. Penfield, in his cartoon of the motor **homunculus** (little man), and Woolsey, in his cartoon of the motor **simiusculus** (little monkey), conveyed this apparent magnification of certain body parts with respect to cortical territory by distorting the size of body parts relative to their normal proportions.

The cortical motor areas contain multiple somatotopic maps of the body. In the early 1950s, Penfield and Welch and Woolsey and his collaborators found that a second, somatotopically organized body map lies anterior to the M1 foot representation on the medial aspect of the cerebral hemisphere.[19,19a] Although the leg representation in the second map blended with that of M1 on the hemisphere's medial wall, the secondary arm and face representations on the medial wall were spatially separate from those of M1 on the hemisphere's convexity (Fig. 33.6). These investigators therefore described this region as a "supplementary" motor area (SMA). More recent studies using intracortical microstimulation have confirmed the second somatotopic map of the body in the SMA and have shown additional maps in areas pre-SMA, CGc, CGr, and PMv.

Recent advances have shown that M1's somatotopic organization is not, however, a one-to-one mapping of body parts, muscles, or movements. Within the arm representation, for example, the cortical territory representing any particular part of the arm overlaps considerably with the territory representing nearby parts. This overlap results partly from the convergence of outputs from a wide M1 territory to the motor neuron pools that control muscles moving a given body part. Convergence of M1 outputs has been confirmed by intracortical microstimulation coupled with electromyography (EMG). Maps of which body parts move or which muscles contract on threshold stimulation at different cortical sites look like a complex mosaic (Fig. 33.6). As the stimulation current is increased, the mosaic pieces representing a given muscle coalesce into

FIGURE 33.6 Somatotopic maps in M1. (A) Map by Woolsey and co-workers[19a] in which each figurine represents in black and gray the body parts that moved a lot or a little, respectively, when the cortical surface at that site was stimulated. In addition to the primary representation on the convexity, their map shows a secondary representation on the medial surface of the hemisphere, called the supplementary motor area (SMA). As defined in this study, M1 and SMA each included several of the currently defined cortical motor areas. (B) Intracortical microstimulation of M1 in an owl monkey produced this map, consisting of a complex mosaic of different body parts. In this species, the central sulcus is only a shallow dimple, and M1 is entirely on the hemisphere's surface. Each dot represents a stimulated locus, and lines surround adjacent loci from which movement of the same body part was evoked. Note that the forepaw digits (purple) and the hindpaw digits (green) are represented in multiple areas separated by areas representing nearby body parts. From Gould *et al.*[17] In both (A) and (B), the inset at the top indicates the region of the frontal lobe enlarged below.

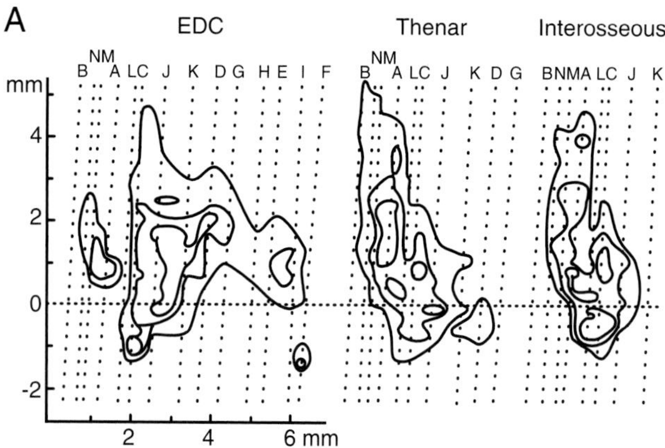

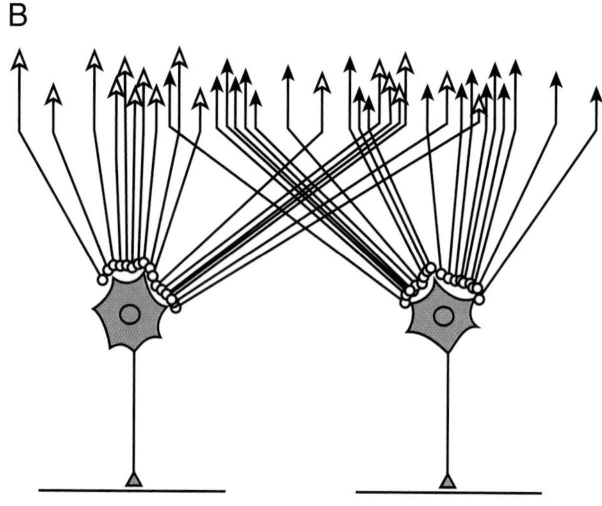

FIGURE 33.7 Convergence of M1 outputs to single muscles. (A) Isothreshold contours show the points at which EMG responses were evoked in three different muscles—extensor digitorum communis (EDC), thenar, and first dorsal interosseus (1DI)—by intracortical microstimulation in the anterior bank of the central sulcus. Modified from Andersen *et al.*[20] (B) The data shown in (A) indicate that the cortical input to any muscle's motor neurons originates from a wide territory in M1 and that the cortical territory providing input to a given muscle overlaps extensively with the cortical territory providing input to other muscles in the same part of the body. Modified from Andersen *et al.*[20]

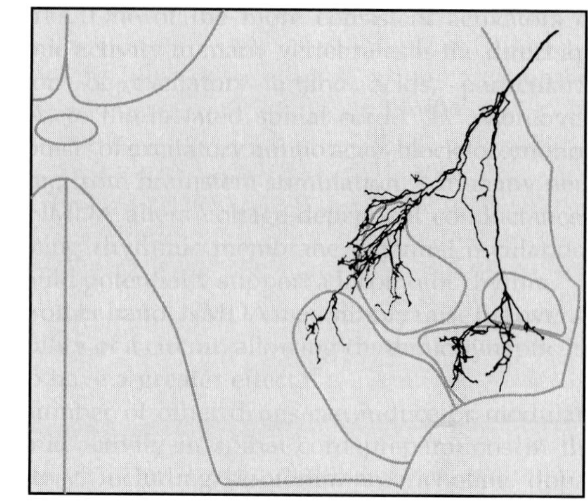

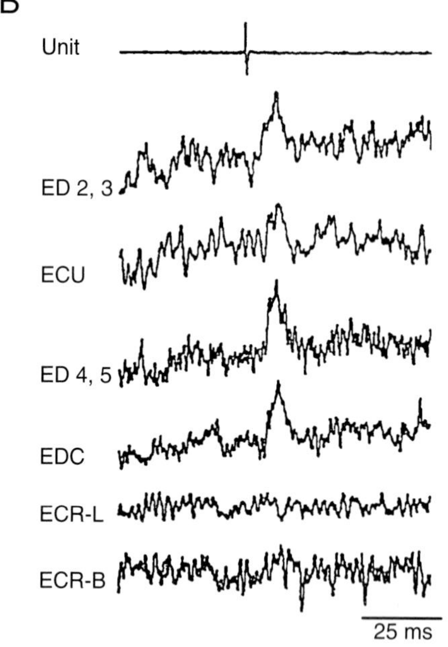

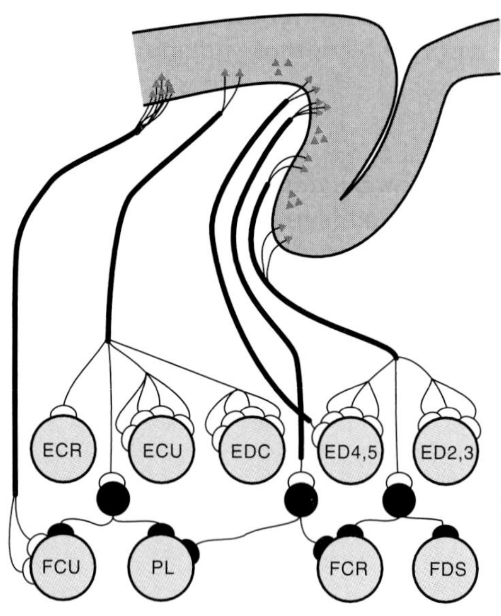

FIGURE 33.8 Divergence of M1 outputs to multiple muscles. (A) Tracing of a single corticospinal axon ramifying in the ventral horn of the spinal cord shows terminal fields in the motor neuron pools of four forearm muscles. From Shinoda *et al.*[22] (B) Action potentials in a cortical neuron (top trace) are followed at a fixed latency by peaks of post-spike facilitation in EMGs recorded from four forearm muscles (lower traces), consistent with monosynaptic excitation of all four motor neuron pools by that cortical neuron. The EMGs are rectified and averaged responses to 7051 action potentials in the cortical neuron. From Fetz and Cheney.[23] (C) These anatomic and physiologic findings indicate that the output of single corticospinal neurons often diverges to influence multiple muscles. Taken from Cheney *et al.*[24] (Fig. 11).

a larger and larger territory that overlaps more and more with the territories of other muscles (Fig. 33.7A). These findings indicate that a given muscle is controlled by a large territory in M1 and that the territories for different muscles overlap[21] (Fig. 33.7B).

Another factor contributing to the overlap of territories in M1 is the divergence of output from single cortical neurons to multiple motor neuron pools. Intracellular staining has shown that a single corticospinal axon may have terminal ramifications within the motor neuron pools of multiple muscles over several segmental levels of the spinal cord[22] (Fig. 33.8A). Moreover, spike-triggered averaging of EMG activity has demonstrated that single M1 neurons can have relatively direct effects on multiple muscles[24–29] (Fig. 33.8B).

During natural movements of discrete body parts, activity is distributed across a wide territory in M1. In monkeys trained to perform individuated movements of each finger, single M1 neurons are active during movements of multiple fingers, and neurons throughout the M1 hand area are active during movements of any given finger.[30] Likewise, in humans performing movements of different fingers, activity is distributed over the primary sensorimotor hand area whether the subject is moving a single finger or the whole hand.[31,32] Although the entire hand area may be activated for movement of any given finger, monkey and human studies have shown a tendency for the center of activation during movements of the thumb to be located laterally to that for movements of other fingers,[30,33] consistent with the somatotopic orientation of the hand in the classic simiusculus and homunculus. Horizontal intracortical interconnections within the M1 hand area may be partly responsible for the distributed activation of the entire hand area during movement of any given finger.

The somatotopic representation in M1, like that in the primary somatosensory cortex, has a certain degree of plasticity. The cortical territory representing a given muscle can enlarge when that muscle is stretched or when nearby body parts are experimentally denervated.[33,34] Threshold stimulation in the cortical territory that had represented a denervated body part comes to evoke movements in nearby body parts. Furthermore, in normal humans who are actively practicing a complex sequence of finger movements, the cortical territory representing a given finger muscle enlarges as the subjects become skilled at performing the sequence.[35] Because such changes can occur within several minutes, they probably are mediated by long-term potentiation and/or depression at existing synapses. This ability of M1 cortex to reorganize may in part underlie motor recovery seen in humans after damage to M1 or the corticospinal tract.[36]

Summary

The motor cortex is subdivided into multiple cortical areas. The principal motor areas 4 and 6 are typified by large layer V efferent pyramid neurons (Betz cells) from which the corticospinal projections originate and by few neurons in layer IV, generally the primary recipients of extracortical input. In addition, areas 23 and 24 of the cingulate gyrus and sulcus also contain cortical motor neurons. These regions differ in their internal organization with respect to their interconnections with thalamic relays and in their interconnections with other cortical motor areas. Finally, each cortical motor area receives distinctive afferents from selected cortical sensory and cortical association areas. These differences result in multiple somatotopic maps of motor output functions, with each region capable of controlling those motor units with specific forms of voluntary movement. A given corticospinal neuron may control multiple muscles over several spinal segments. Furthermore, the cortical area representing a given muscle can vary with the workload of the muscles involved.

CONTROL OF VOLUNTARY MOVEMENTS BY THE MOTOR CORTEX

A new criterion for classifying cortical areas as "motor" come with techniques for recording signals of neural discharge that correlate with movement. These have included electroencephalographic measurement of currents generated by many cells, microelectrode recording of the action potentials of a single cell, and radiologic imaging methods that measure changes in blood flow or oxygenation of hemoglobin that are proportionate to neural activity.

Multiple Cortical Areas Are Active When the Brain Generates a Voluntary Movement

The different methodologies now make it clear that many cortical areas in addition to the primary motor cortex are active in correlation with movement. The generation of a voluntary movement may involve many parts of the motor cortex. During performance of either a simple keypress or a complex finger-movement sequence with one hand, for example, functional imaging studies in humans have shown bilateral activation of the primary sensorimotor hand area, the supplementary motor area, and the ventrolateral premotor cortex, plus contralateral activation of the dorsolateral premotor cortex and the medial cortex rostral to the SMA.[37–40] Whereas such techniques provide information on the parts of the cortex that are active in a given situation, studies of electrical potentials provide information on the time course of activation. For simple self-paced movements, cortical electrical potentials over the SMA and M1 begin to change as early as 1 s prior to the movement. As the time of movement onset approaches, the amplitude of these bilateral electrical potential shifts increases (the Bereischaft potential). At the time of the movement, a further increase in amplitude occurs over the somatotopically appropriate region of M1 contralateral to the moving body part.[41–43] Measurements of cortical activation made by functional imaging or by recording surface potentials represent the net activity of thousands of cortical neurons and millions of synapses.

M1 Neurons Control Movement Kinematics and Dynamics

Given that cortical areas are active in controlling movement, the question remains: What does each area contribute to control? Primary motor cortex appears to control the number of muscles and movement forces and trajectories.

Recording the activity of single neurons during movements performed by awake animals has provided further insight into the manner in which cortical motor areas generate voluntary movements. In one of the earlier of such studies, Evarts recorded the activity of M1 pyramidal tract neurons in monkeys trained to raise and lower weights using flexion and extension wrist movements[44] (Fig. 33.9). The discharge frequency of many M1 neurons changed systematically in temporal relation to either flexion or extension. A typical flexion-related neuron, for example, began to discharge several hundred milliseconds before flexion began. As the beginning of flexion approached, the neuron's discharge frequency increased, accelerating still more when flexion began. The neuron was silent during extension. The time course of these movement-related changes in single-neuron activity parallels the time course of cortical electrical potential shifts.

Evarts went on to demonstrate that the discharge frequency of M1 pyramidal tract neurons (PTNs) varied in relation to a number of mechanical parameters of the movement the monkey was making. By changing the weights the monkeys had to lift, Evarts showed that PTN discharge frequency varied with the *force* the monkey exerted. Comparison of PTN discharge with simultaneous force recordings revealed that bursts of PTN firing were often coupled to sudden increases in the exerted force, indicating a relationship between firing frequency and the *rate of change of force*. Subsequent studies have confirmed these findings and also

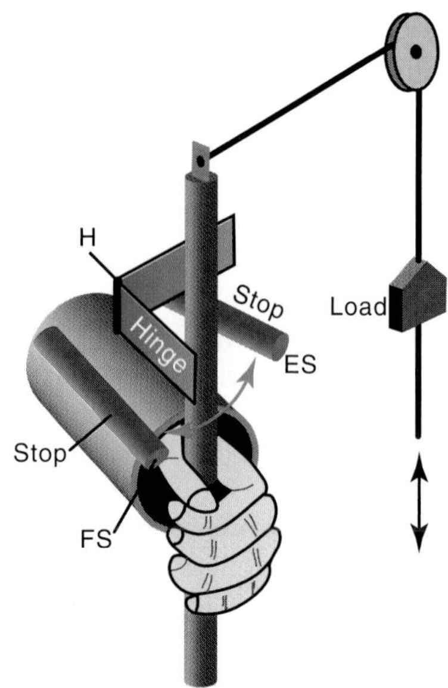

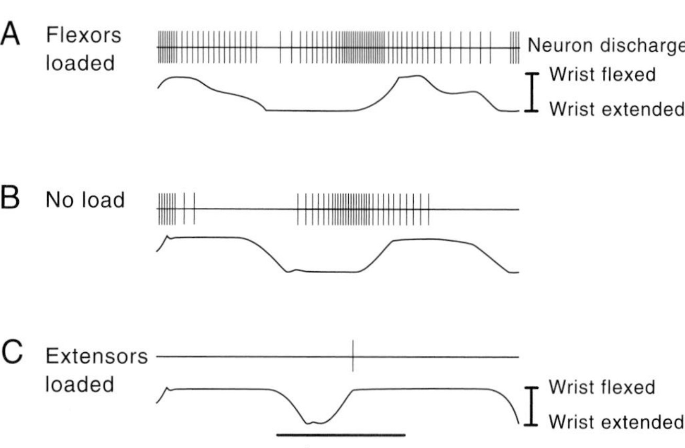

FIGURE 33.9 Discharge of a single M1 neuron in a monkey making flexion and extension wrist movements with the wrist flexors loaded (A) and unloaded (B), and with the wrist extensors loaded (C). The discharge rate of this neuron was greatest when the monkey used its wrist flexor muscles against a load. From Evarts.[44]

have shown that the discharge of M1 neurons can be related to the *direction* of movement, the *position* of a particular joint, or the *velocity* of movement.[45–47] Cortical neurons whose firing is related to kinematic and dynamic parameters of movement are not found only in M1. Many neurons in the SMA, PMd, and parietal area 5 (which projects to SMA and PMd) fire in relation to movement direction,[48,49] and some PMv neurons fire in relation to movement force.[50] Therefore, neurons in several nonprimary cortical motor areas may participate with those in M1 to control movement parameters such as direction, force, position, and velocity.

Although very strong correlations can be found between a given neuron's discharge frequency and a particular movement parameter, every M1 neuron's discharge does not simply encode a single parameter. For example, examination of the encoding of muscular force, joint position, and direction of impending wrist movements revealed that the discharge of single M1 neurons is often related to two or even all three of those parameters.[47] In monkeys making reaching movements, single M1 neurons show a variety of correlations to the direction of movement and the direction of load.[51] Similarly, the discharge of most task-related M1 neurons can be correlated with the direction, position, velocity, and acceleration of reaching movements.[45] In the premotor cortex, most PMd and PMv neurons appear to fire in relation to the direction and amplitude of wrist movements.[52] Thus, the discharge of a single neuron in the motor cortex may affect several movement parameters.

Conversely, any given parameter or other feature of a movement is probably represented not by the discharge of a single M1 neuron, but by the ensemble activity of a distributed population of cortical neurons. Researchers have correlated the force, rate of change of force, position, and velocity of flexion and extension wrist movements more accurately with the summed, weighted activity of a number of simultaneously recorded M1 neurons than with the discharge of any single neuron.[53] Although single M1 neurons are broadly tuned for movement direction, when the activity of many M1 neurons is summed, the resultant population vector may represent movement direction with considerable precision (Fig. 33.10). The neurons that contribute their activity to the ensemble control of any given movement parameter appear to be distributed throughout the region of M1 that controls the relevant body part, without an obvious mapping of direction, force, position, velocity, or acceleration. Even the body part that is moved—the feature most often mapped in M1—seems to be controlled by the ensemble activity of a widely distributed population of M1 neurons.[30]

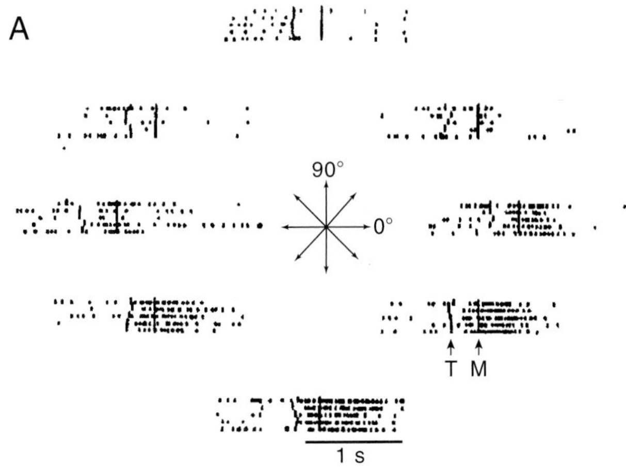

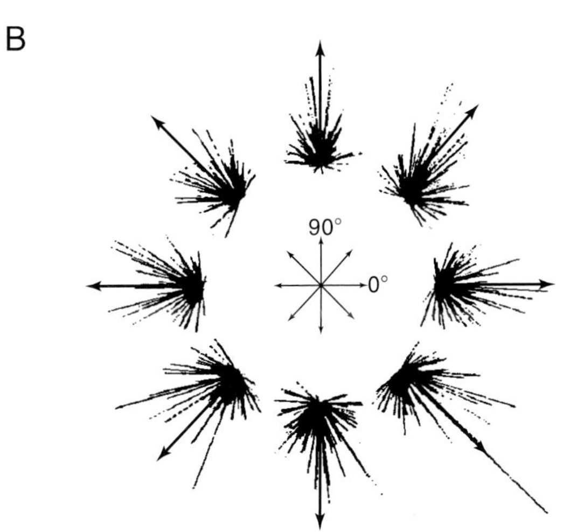

FIGURE 33.10 (A) Discharge of a single M1 neuron before and during arm movements in a monkey. Movements (represented by arrows) started from the same central point and ended at eight different points on a circle. The eight rasters show that this neuron's activity was related to movements in four of the eight directions. The neuron discharged most intensely for movements down and to the right and was inhibited during movements up and to the left. From Georgopoulos.[54] (B) For each of the eight movements, the discharge of each M1 neuron is shown as a line pointing in the neuron's preferred direction. Each line starts at the movement endpoint, and its length is proportional to the intensity of the discharge of that neuron during movement in that direction. Although the discharge of single neurons rarely identified any single movement direction with accuracy, the population vectors (arrows) summing the discharge of an ensemble of M1 neurons adequately specify each of the eight movement directions. From Georgopoulos.[54]

Cortical Motor Areas Prepare Voluntary Movements Based on a Variety of Cues

Cortical areas outside primary motor cortex seem to be especially concerned with using a wide variety of sensory and other information as "cues" to trigger and guide movements.

Further insight into the cortical processes controlling movement has been obtained by separating in time the *instruction* to move from the *trigger* to execute the instruction. Neuronal discharge during such an **instructed delay period** is often referred to as **set-related activity**. The feature most clearly represented in set-related activity is direction. During an instructed delay period, many neurons in M1, SMA, and PMd discharge at the highest rate while the subject waits to

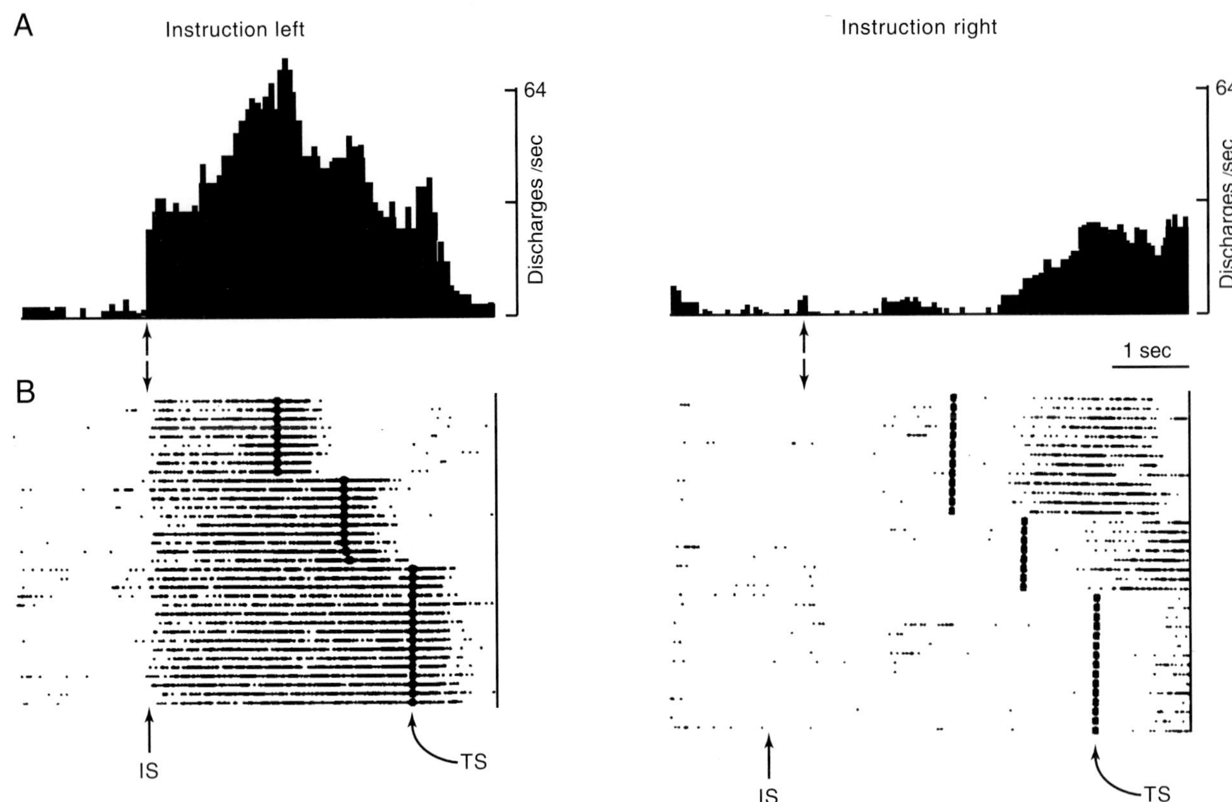

FIGURE 33.11 Directional set in a PM neuron. (A) As a monkey performed a delayed-reaction paradigm, this neuron began to discharge shortly after receiving instructions (IS) to perform a leftward movement. Discharge continued until after the monkey had subsequently received a separate triggering signal (TS, which occurred at three different time intervals after the IS) and performed the movement. During the delay between IS and TS, while the monkey did not move, the neuron's discharge encoded the direction of the instruction, the direction of the impending movement, or both. (B) When the instruction was for rightward movement, this neuron did not discharge until after the movement had been made, presumably as the monkey was then preparing to move back to its original position. From Wise and Strick.[55]

move in a particular direction (Fig. 33.11). Such directional set is more common in PMd and SMA than in M1, where activity during movement execution predominates.[49,56–58] During the delay between instruction and trigger, PMd, SMA, and other areas appear to store information on the direction of the impending movement. Indeed, neurons sometimes discharge in error during the delay, as if the monkey has seen a cue other than the one actually given and is preparing to move in the wrong direction. When such error discharges occur, the monkey often does make the wrong movement. The delay-period discharge of such neurons thus represents stored information, not about which cue the monkey has seen, but rather about what movement the monkey will make.

In most instructed delay tasks, the direction of the cue is the same as the direction of the movement. To pick up a pencil, for example, you may glance at the pencil and then move your hand to the same place. Insight into how cue direction is transformed into movement direction has come from tasks in which these two features were experimentally dissociated, similar to glancing at your pencil in a mirror and then reaching to pick up the real pencil instead of the mirror image. To dissociate cue direction and movement direction experimentally, researchers train monkeys to perform mental rotation tasks (Fig. 33.12). For example, a monkey may be presented with an array of four buttons located up, down, left, and right. In one condition, a brief lighting of the button instructs the monkey to touch the same button when triggered after a delay; here cue direction and movement direction are the same. In another condition, the same monkey learns that when either the up button or the down button is lit, it should touch the button located 90° clockwise. Lighting the upper button thus instructs the monkey

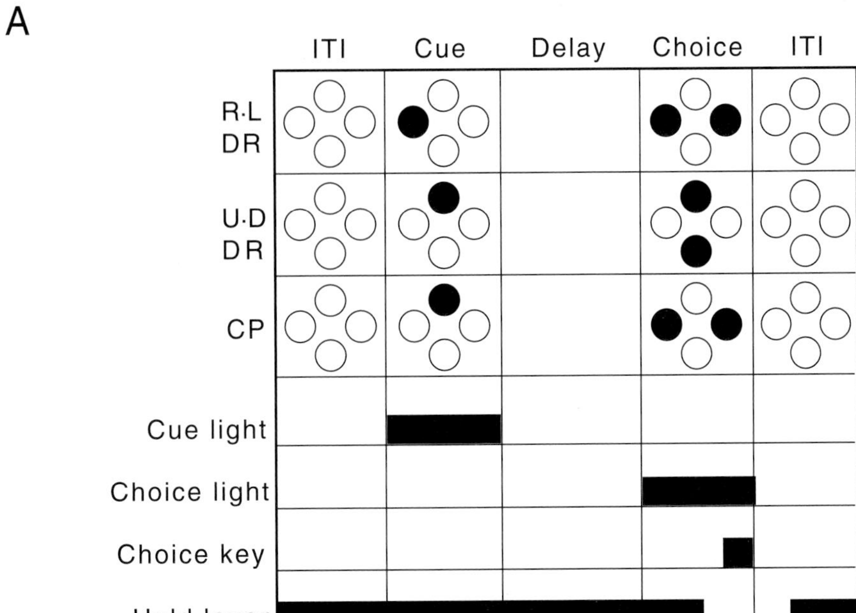

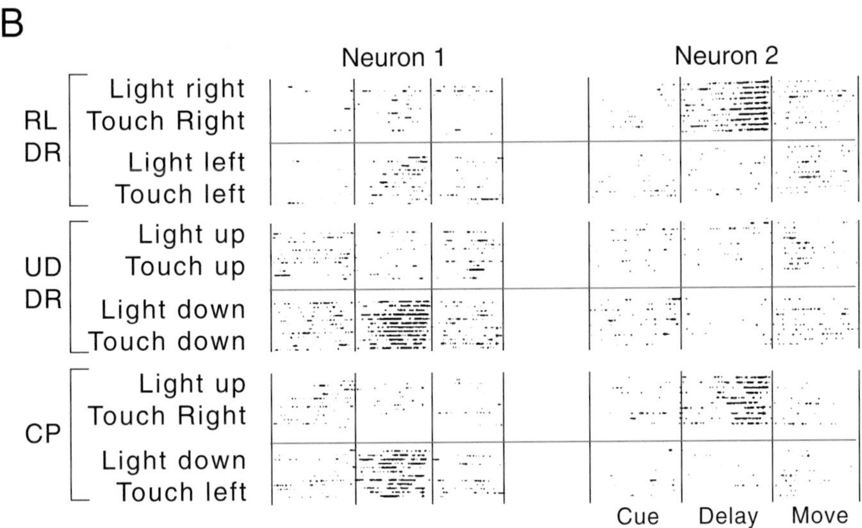

FIGURE 33.12 Dissociation of instruction direction and movement direction in area principalis neurons. (A) In this experiment, monkeys were trained to press one of four illuminated buttons in three different task paradigms: right/left delayed response (RL-DR), up/down delayed respone (UD-DR), and a conditional position (CP) task. In RL-DR, either the left or the right button was briefly illuminated. The light was turned off for 3 s, and then both the left and right buttons were lit simultaneously as a trigger. To receive a reward, the monkey had to respond by pressing the button that previously had been lit. UD-DR was performed similarly, except that the up and down buttons were used. In both RL-DR and UD-DR, instruction direction and movement direction were the same. In the CP paradigm, however, the instruction was delivered with the up and down buttons, but the trigger was delivered with the right and left buttons. In this situation, the monkey learned to press the right button if the up button was lit and the left button if the down button was lit. Here the instruction direction differed from the movement direction. (B) Responses of two neurons in the area principalis. Neuron 1 did not discharge during the delay period of RL-DR but discharged during the delay of downward trials during UD-DR. In the CP paradigm, it discharged during the delay period of trials in which the instruction was delivered with the down light and the monkey touched the right button. Neuron 1 thus discharged during the delay whenever an instruction had been delivered via the down light, whether the monkey subsequently touched the down button or the right button. The discharge of neuron 1 was therefore coupled to the instruction direction. Neuron 2 discharged during the delay period of RL-DR trials in which the instruction had been on the right and the monkey touched the right button. It did not discharge during UD-DR. During the delay period of the CP paradigm, Neuron 2 discharged during trials in which the instruction had been delivered with the up light and the monkey touched the right button. Neuron 2 thus discharged whenever the monkey was going to press the right button, whether the instruction had been delivered via the right light or the up light. Its discharge was coupled to the impending movement direction.

to touch the right button; lighting the down button instructs it to touch the left button. Here cue direction and movement direction are dissociated.

Investigators have used such a task to study neurons in the **area principalis** of the dorsolateral frontal lobe, another cortical area known from lesion studies to be critical for performance of such spatial delay tasks.[59] Each area principalis neuron showed delay-period activity that was coupled either to a particular cue direction or to a particular movement direction. This finding was interpreted initially to mean that cue direction is transformed into movement direction in the area principalis during the delay period, and that information about the appropriate movement direction is sent back to M1 at the time of execution.

Additional experiments, however, have shown that the transformation process is not quite so discretely localized. In the SMA and even in M1, many neurons discharge in relation to cue direction independent of movement direction, during the instructed delay period and during movement execution.[46,60] Representations of both cue direction and movement direction thus are present in SMA and M1 during movement preparation and execution. Within each area, the representations of cue and movement direction do not necessarily involve two different neuronal populations. In a task that dissociated cue direction and movement direction, single PMd neuron activity during the instructed delay period encoded cue direction initially and actual movement direction later.[61] In a similar study of M1, the vector representing the summed activity of a large M1 neuronal population was shown to point initially in the direction of the cue and then to rotate progressively toward the movement direction prior to actual movement onset.[62] Transformation of information on cue direction into information on movement direction therefore appears to be distributed over at least the area principalis, SMA, and M1.

Some Cortical Motor Areas Are Involved in Movements in Response to either Internal or External Cues

Another aspect of movement preparation that differentially involves certain cortical motor areas has to do with whether the instructions about what to do come from internally remembered or externally delivered cues. In one experiment, for example, monkeys were trained to touch three of four pads in randomly selected sequences that were cued when the pads were lit in sequence.[63] Once a monkey was accustomed to a given sequence, the lights were gradually dimmed until the monkey was performing the correct sequence based only on internally remembered cues. After several of these remembered trials, the pads were lit in a different sequence for several trials. Whereas neurons in M1 showed similar discharge rates during the internally remembered and externally cued trials for a given sequence, SMA neurons were generally more active during the internally remembered trials, and PMv neurons were generally more active during the externally cued trials (Fig. 33.13).

These differences in SMA and PMv neuronal activities during internally remembered and externally cued movements are consistent with earlier studies of the effects of experimental lesions of the SMA or premotor cortex (PMv and PMd together). Experimental lesions of the SMA impaired monkeys' ability to open latchboxes, a task that required undoing three different latches in a sequence the monkeys had learned by trial and error.[64] The same monkeys had little trouble operating a handle in different ways when the color of the handle (an external cue) told them which way to move the handle. Conversely, monkeys with bilateral premotor cortex lesions had great difficulty operating the handles properly based on the external color cue, but had little trouble with the internally remembered sequences needed to open the latchboxes. Thus, both lesion studies and neuronal recordings indicate that the SMA is particularly involved when a movement is based on internally stored information, whereas the PMv is particularly involved when a movement is based on available visual cues.

Context May Affect Activity in the Motor Cortex

Given the focus of motor cortex on muscles, of SMA on "internal" inputs, and of premotor cortex on "external" (especially visual) inputs, how does each coordinate with the other?

Some studies have suggested that neuronal activity in cortical motor areas is dependent on certain behavioral contexts. Even in M1, for example, the discharge of many neurons may depend on whether the subject is trying to hold still in the face of perturbing forces or trying to execute an overt movement.[65] The discharge of other M1 neurons depends on whether the subject is executing a small precise movement or a large, gross movement.[66] Certain cortical motor areas may play even more specialized roles in particular behavioral contexts. For example, in bimanual tasks, when cooperation between the two hands is essential, the SMA is critically involved.[67] Studies have suggested that area F5 has an important function when the hands are used in particular configurations.[68,69] Some F5 neurons discharge vigorously during a power grasp with

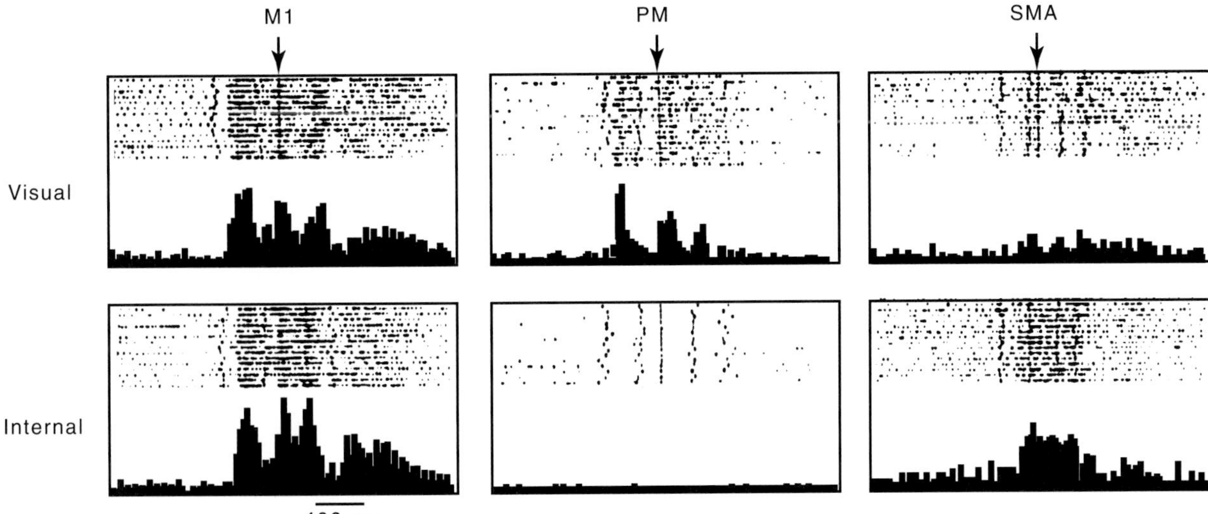

FIGURE 33.13 Activity of three neurons—one in M1, one in PM, and one in SMA—recorded as a monkey pressed three buttons in sequence. The sequence was first visually cued by lighting the buttons and then internally cued. The M1 neuron showed similar activity whether the monkey performed from visual or internal cues. The PM neuron, however, was much more active in response to visual than internal cues, while the opposite was true for the SMA neuron. Modified from Mushiake et al., 1991.

the whole hand but not during a delicate pinch, while other F5 neurons exhibit the opposite discharge pattern. Especially intriguing is the observation that F5 neurons that discharge during a particular type of hand movement may also discharge as the monkey watches a human perform a similar hand movement. Further investigations are needed to reveal how the various cortical motor areas contribute to movements performed in different behavioral contexts.

Summary

Control of voluntary movement involves much of the cerebral cortex anterior to the central sulcus. In addition to the classically described primary motor cortex (M1) and supplementary motor area (SMA), a number of separately identifiable motor areas are found in the premotor cortex anterior to M1 and the SMA and in the cingulate sulcus inferior to the SMA. These cortical motor areas are connected with one another and receive input from prefrontal and parietal cortical areas as well as from the basal ganglia and cerebellum via the thalamus.

Cortical motor areas mediate control of voluntary movement via their descending projections, which arise most heavily from M1. The corticospinal tract provides a descending pathway directly from the cortex to spinal premotor interneurons and some motor neurons. Less direct descending pathways from the cortex involve the rubrospinal, reticulospinal, and vestibulospinal tracts. The corticospinal and rubrospinal pathways project most heavily to spinal motor neurons that control distal limb muscles in behaviors such as manipulation of small items. The reticulospinal and vestibulospinal pathways project most heavily to motor neurons that control axial and proximal limb muscles during behaviors such as ambulation.

Generation of a voluntary movement involves neuronal activity in somatotopically organized regions of the cortical motor areas. Although M1 has distinguishable regions for control of the face, arms, and legs, within these regions the neurons controlling different body parts, muscles, or movements are intermingled. The discharge of M1 neurons transmits information on features of movement including direction, force, rate of change of force, joint position, and velocity. The discharge of any single M1 neuron may contain only broadly tuned information on one or more kinematic and dynamic parameters, but the ensemble discharge of a large population of M1 neurons provides an accurate representation of movement parameters. Nonprimary cortical motor areas also participate in the control of some kinematic and dynamic movement parameters. The nonprimary areas appear more specialized, however, for selecting and controlling movements made in particular behavioral contexts, such as when the direction of a movement to be made must be remembered or when a movement must be selected on the basis of an available visual cue.

References

1. Walshe, F. M. R. (1948). *Critical Studies in Neurology.* Livingstone, London.
2. Toyoshima, K., and Sakai, H. (1982). Exact cortical extent of the origin of the corticospinal tract (CST) and the quantitative contribution to the CST in different cytoarchitectonic areas. A study with horseradish peroxidase in the monkey. *J. Hirnforschung* **23:** 257–269.
3. Kuypers, H. G. J. M. (1987). Some aspects of the organization of the output of the motor cortex. In *Motor Areas of the Cerebral Cortex* (G. Bock, M. O'Connor, and J. Marsh, eds.), pp. 63–82. Wiley, New York.
4. Woolsey, C. N., Gorska, T., Wetzel, A., Erickson, T. C., Earls, F. J., and Allman, J. M. (1972). Complete unilateral section of the pyramidal tract at the medullary level in *macaca mulatta. Brain Res* **40:** 119–123.
5. Mewes, K., and Cheney, P. D. (1991). Facilitation and suppression of wrist and digit muscles from single rubromotoneuronal cells in the awake monkey. *J. Neurophysiol.* **66:** 1965–1977.
6. Sinkjaer, T., Miller, L., Andersen, T., and Houk, J. C. (1995). Synaptic linkages between red nucleus cells and limb muscles during a multi-joint motor task. *Exp. Brain Res.* **102:** 546–550.
7. Lawrence, D. G., and Kuypers, H. G. J. M. (1968). The functional organization of the motor system of the monkey. I. The effects of bilateral pyramidal lesions. *Brain* **91:** 1–14.
8. Lawrence, D. G., and Kuypers, H. G. J. M. (1968). The functional organization of the motor system in the monkey. II. The effects of lesions of the descending brain-stem pathways. *Brain* **91:** 15–41.
9. Matelli, M., Luppino, G., and Rizzolatti, G. (1991). Architecture of superior and mesial area 6 and the adjacent cingulate cortex in the macaque monkey. *J. Comp. Neurol.* **311:** 445–462.
10. Muakkassa, K. F., and Strick, P. L. (1979). Frontal lobe inputs to primate motor cortex: evidence for four somatotopically organized "premotor" areas. *Brain Res.* **177:** 176–182.
11. Shima, K., Aya, K., Mushiake, H., Inase, M., Aizawa, H., and Tanji, J. (1991). Two movement-related foci in the primate cingulate cortex observed in signal-triggered and self-paced forelimb movements. *J. Neurophysiol.* **65:** 188–202.
12. Rosen, I., and Asanuma, H. (1972). Peripheral afferent inputs to the forelimb area of the monkey motor cortex: Input-output relations. *Exp. Brain Res.* **14:** 257–273.
13. Rizzolatti, G., Scandolara, C., Matelli, M., and Gentilucci, M. (1981). Afferent properties of periarcuate neurons in macaque monkeys. II. Visual responses. *Behav. Brain Res.* **2:** 147–163.
14. Graziano, M. S., Yap, G. S., and Gross, C. G. (1994). Coding of visual space by premotor neurons. *Science* **266:** 1054–1057.
15. Leyton, A. S. F., and Sherrington, C. S. (1917). Observations on the excitable cortex of the chimpanzee, orangutan, and gorilla. *Quart. J. Exp. Physiol.* **11:** 137–222.
16. Penfield, W., and Boldrey, E. (1937). Somatic motor and sensory representation in the cerebral cortex of man as studied by electrical stimulation. *Brain* **37:** 389–443.
17. Gould, H. J., 3d, Cusick, C. G., Pons, T. P., and Kaas, J. H. (1986). The relationship of corpus callosum connections to electrical stimulation maps of motor, supplementary motor, and the frontal eye fields in owl monkeys. *J. Comp. Neurol.* **247:** 297–325.
18. Cheney, P. D., and Fetz, E. E. (1984). Corticomotoneuronal cells contribute to long-latency stretch reflexes in the rhesus monkey. *J. Physiol.* **349:** 249–272.
19. Penfield, W., and Welch, K. (1951). The supplementary motor area of the cerebral cortex. *Arch. Neurol. Psychiatry* **66:** 289–316.

19a. Woolsey, C. N., Settlage, P. H., Meyer, D. R., Sencer, W., Hamuy, T. P., and Travis, A. M. (1951). Patterns of localization in precentral and "supplementary" motor areas and their relation to the concept of a premotor area. *Res. Pub. Assoc. Res. Nerv. Ment. Dis.* **30:** 238–264.

20. Andersen, P., Hagan, P. J., Phillips, C. G., and Powell, T. P. (1975). Mapping by microstimulation of overlapping projections from area 4 to motor units of the baboon's hand. *Proc. R. Soc. London–Series B: Biol. Sci.* **188:** 31–36.
21. Humphrey, D. R. (1986). Representation of movements and muscles within the primate precentral motor cortex: historical and current perspectives. *Fed. Proc.* **45:** 2687–2699.
22. Shinoda, Y., Yokota, J., Futami, T., (1981). Divergent projection of individual corticospinal axons to motoneurons of multiple muscles in the monkey. *Neurosci. Lett.* **23:** 7–12.
23. Fetz, E. E., and Cheney, P. D. (1980). Postspike facilitation of forelimb muscle activity by primate corticomotoneuronal cells. *J. Neurophysiol.* **44:** 751–772.
24. Cheney, P. D., Fetz, E. E., and Palmer, S. S. (1985) Patterns of facilitation and suppression of antagonist forelimb muscles from motor cortex sites in the awake monkey. *J. Neurophysiol.* **53:** 805–820.
25. Buys, E. J., Lemon, R. N., Mantel, G. W. H., and Muir, R. B. (1986). Selective facilitation of different hand muscles by single corticospinal neurones in the concious monkey. *J. Physiol.* **381:** 529–549.
26. Cheney, P. D., and Fetz, E. E. (1985). Comparable patterns of muscle facilitation evoked by individual corticomotoneuronal (CM) cells and by single intracortical microstimuli in primates: Evidence for functional groups of CM cells. *J. Neurophysiol.* **53:** 786–804.
27. Cheney, P. D., Fetz, E. E., and Mewes, K. (1991). Neural mechanisms underlying corticospinal and rubrospinal control of limb movements. In Progress in Brain Research (G. Holstege, ed.), pp. 213–252. Elsevier Science, Amsterdam.
28. Fetz, E. E., Cheney, P. D., Mewes, K., and Palmer, S. (1989). Control of forelimb muscle activity by populations of corticomotoneuronal and rubromotoneuronal cells. *Prog. Brain Res.* **80:** 437–449.
29. Lemon, R. N., Mantel, G. W. H., and Muir, R. B. (1986). Corticospinal facilitation of hand muscles during voluntary movement in the conscious monkey. *J. Physiol.* **381:** 497–527.
30. Schieber, M. H., and Hibbard, L. S. (1993). How somatotopic is the motor cortex hand area? *Science* **261:** 489–492.
31. Colebatch, J. G., Deiber, M. P., Passingham, R. E., Friston, K. J., and Frackowiak, R. S. J. (1991). Regional cerebral blood flow during voluntary arm and hand movements in human subjects. *J. Neurophysiol.* **65:** 1392–1401.
32. Sanes, J. N., Donoghue, J. P., Thangaraj, V., Edelman, R. R., Warach, S. (1995). Shared neural substrates controlling hand movements in human motor cortex. *Science* **268:** 1775–1777.
33. Grafton, S. T., Woods, R. P., and Mazziotta, J. C. (1993). Within-arm somatotopy in human motor areas determined by positron emission tomography imaging of cerebral blood flow. *Exp. Brain Res.* **95:** 172–176.
34. Sanes, J. N., Wang, J., and Donoghue, J. P. (1992). Immediate and delayed changes of rat motor cortical output representation with new forelimb configurations. *Cereb. Cortex* **2:** 141–152.
35. Pascual-Leone, A., Grafman, J., and Hallett, M. (1994). Modulation of cortical motor output maps during development of implicit and explicit knowledge. *Science* **263:** 1287–1289.
36. Weiller, C., Ramsay, S. C., Wise, R. J. S., Friston, K. J., and Frackowiak, R. S. J. (1993). Individual patterns of functional reorganization in the human cerebral cortex after capsular infarction. *Ann. Neurol.* **33:** 181–189.

37. Kawashima, R., Roland, P. E., and O'Sullivan, B. T. (1994). Fields in human motor areas involved in preparation for reaching, actual reaching, and visuomotor learning: A positron emission tomography study. *J. Neurosci.* **14:** 3462–3474.
38. Kawashima, R., Yamada, K., Kinomura, S., Yamaguchi, T., Matsui, H., Yoshioka, S., and Fukuda, H. (1993). Regional cerebral blood flow changes of cortical motor areas and prefrontal areas in humans related to ipsilateral and contralateral hand movement. *Brain Res* **623:** 33–40.
39. Roland, P. E., Larsen, B., Lassen, N. A., and Skinhoj, E. (1980). Supplementary motor area and other cortical areas in organization of voluntary movements in man. *J. Neurophysiol.* **43:** 118–136.
40. Roland, P. E., Skinhoj, E., Lassen, N. A., and Larsen, B. (1980). Different cortical areas in man in organization of voluntary movements in extrapersonal space. *J. Neurophysiol* **43:** 137–150.
41. Ikeda, A., and Shibasaki, H. (1992). Invasive recording of movement-related cortical potentials in humans. *J. Clin. Neurophysiol.* **9:** 509–520.
42. Tarkka, I. M., and Hallett, M. (1991). Topography of scalp-recorded motor potentials in human finger movements. *J. Clin. Neurophysiol.* **8:** 331–341.
43. Tarkka, I. M., and Hallett, M. (1990). Cortical topography of premotor and motor potentials preceding self-paced, voluntary movement of dominant and non-dominant hands. *Electroencephalogr. & Clin. Neurophysiol.* **75:** 36–43.
44. Evarts, E. V. (1968). Relation of pyramidal tract activity to force exerted during voluntary movement. *J. Neurophysiol.* **31:** 14–27.
45. Ashe, J., and Georgopoulos, A. P. (1994). Movement parameters and neural activity in motor cortex and area 5. *Cereb. Cortex* **4:** 590–600.
46. Crutcher, M. D., and Alexander, G. E. (1990). Movement-related neuronal activity selectively coding either direction or muscle pattern in three motor areas of the monkey. *J. Neurophysiol.* **64:** 151–163.
47. Thach, W. T. (1978). Correlation of neural discharge with pattern and force of muscular activity, joint position, and direction of intended next movement in motor cortex and cerebellum. *J. Neurophysiol.* **41:** 654–676.
48. Kalaska, J. F., Cohen, D. A., Prud'homme, M., and Hyde, M. L. (1990). Parietal area 5 neuronal activity encodes movement kinematics, not movement dynamics. *Exp. Brain Res.* **80:** 351–364.
49. Weinrich, M., Wise, S. P., Mauritz, K. H. (1984). A neurophysiological study of the premotor cortex in the rhesus monkey. *Brain* **107:** 385–414.
50. Hepp-Reymond, M. C., Husler, E. J., Maier, M. A., and Qi, H. X. (1995). Force-related neuronal activity in two regions of primate ventral premotor cortex. *Canadian J. Physiol. & Pharmacology* **72:** 571–579.
51. Kalaska, J. F., Cohen, D. A., Hyde, M. L., and Prud'homme, M. (1989). A comparison of movement direction-related versus load direction-related activity in primate motor cortex, using a two-dimensional reaching task. *J. Neurosci.* **9:** 2080–2102.
52. Kurata, K. (1993). Premotor cortex of monkeys: Set- and movement-related activity reflecting amplitude and direction of wrist movements. *J. Neurophysiol.* **69:** 187–200.
53. Humphrey, D. R., Schmidt, E. M., and Thompson, W. D. (1970). Predicting measures of motor performance from multiple cortical spike trains. *Science* **170:** 758–762.
54. Georgopoulos, A. P. (1988). Neural integration of movement: role of motor cortex in reaching. *FASEB J.* **2:** 2849–2857.
55. Wise, S. P., and Strick, P. L. (1996). Anatomical and physiological organization of the nonprimary motor cortex. *Trends Neurol. Sci.* **7:** 442–446.
56. Kurata, K. (1989). Distribution of neurons with set- and movement-related activity before hand and foot movements in the premotor cortex of rhesus monkeys. *Exp. Brain Res.* **77:** 245–256.
57. Tanji, J., and Kurata, K. (1982). Comparison of movement-related activity in two cortical motor areas of primates. *J. Neurophysiol.* **48:** 633–653.
58. Wise, S. P., Weinrich, M., and Mauritz, K. H. (1986). Movement-related activity in the premotor cortex of rhesus macaques. *Prog. Brain Res.* **64:** 117–131.
59. Niki, H., and Watanabe, M. (1976). Prefrontal unit activity and delayed response: relation to cue location versus direction of response. *Brain Res.* **105:** 79–88.
60. Alexander, G. E., and Crutcher, M. D. (1990). Neural representations of the target (goal) of visually guided arm movements in three motor areas of the monkey. *J. Neurophysiol.* **64:** 164–178.
61. Crammond, D. J., and Kalaska, J. F. (1994). Modulation of preparatory neuronal activity in dorsal premotor cortex due to stimulus-response compatibility. *J. Neurophysiol.* **71:** 1281–1284.
62. Georgopoulos, A. P., Lurito, J. T., Petrides, M., Schwartz, A. B., and Massey, J. T. (1989). Mental rotation of the neuronal population vector. *Science* **243:** 234–236.
63. Mushiake, H., Inase, M., and Tanji, J. (1991). Neuronal activity in the primate premotor, supplementary, and precentral motor cortex during visually guided and internally determined sequential movements. *J. Neurophysiol.* **66:** 705–718.
64. Passingham, R. E. (1987). Two cortical systems for directing movement. Ciba Foundation Symposium **132:** 151–164. [Review]
65. Humphrey, D. R., and Reed, D. J. (1983). Separate cortical systems for control of joint movement and joint stiffness: Reciprocal activation and coactivation of antagonist muscles. *Adv. Neurol.* **39:** 347–372.
66. Evarts, E. V., Fromm, C., Kroller, J., and Jennings, V. A. (1983). Motor cortex control of finely graded forces. *J. Neurophysiol.* **49:** 1199–1215.
67. Brinkman, C. (1981). Lesions in supplementary motor area interfere with a monkey's performance of a bimanual coordination task. *Neurosci. Lett.* **27:** 267–270.
68. di Pellegrino, G., Fadiga, L., Fogassi, L., Gallese, V., and Rizzolatti, G. (1992). Understanding motor events: A neurophysiological study. *Exp Brain Res* **91:** 176–180.
69. Rizzolatti, G., Camarda, R., Fogassi, L., Gentilucci, M., Luppino, G., and Matelli, M. (1988). Functional organization of inferior area 6 in the macaque monkey. II. Area F5 and the control of distal movements. *Exp. Brain Res.* **71:** 491–507.

C H A P T E R

34

Basal Ganglia

Jonathan W. Mink

Two large subcortical motor systems send output via the thalamus to the cerebral cortex. These systems are the basal ganglia and the cerebellum. Although they appear to influence the same cortical areas, they project to the cortex via separate areas of the thalamus. Furthermore, the output of basal ganglia is inhibitory and that of the cerebellum is excitatory. We consider the basal ganglia in this chapter and the cerebellum in Chapter 35.

The basal ganglia are large subcortical structures comprising several interconnected nuclei in the forebrain, midbrain, and diencephalon (Fig. 34.1). It is generally agreed (see Box 34.1)[1–3] that the basal ganglia participate in the control of movement, for three reasons. First, most basal ganglia inputs and outputs are connected with motor areas. Second, the discharge of many basal ganglia neurons correlates with movement. Third, basal ganglia lesions can cause severe movement abnormalities. The connections and lesion effects of the basal ganglia suggest that these brain nuclei may also participate in some cognitive and emotional aspects of behavior. In this chapter, we concentrate on the motor functions of the basal ganglia (see Box 34.2). We begin with anatomy (structure) because it is anatomy that provides the infrastructure for physiology (function). Next we consider the activity of individual components of the basal ganglia during movement, and we describe the effect of placing a selective lesion in one component. Finally, we discuss some of the current hypotheses of basal ganglia motor function.

ANATOMY OF THE BASAL GANGLIA

The basal ganglia receive a broad spectrum of cortical inputs. The information conveyed to the basal ganglia is processed to produce a focused output to areas of the frontal lobes and brainstem that are involved in the planning and production of movement. As stated in the introduction, the basal ganglia output is inhibitory, which means that an increase in the basal ganglia output leads to a reduction in the activity of its targets. The fact that the basal ganglia output is inhibitory to other motor mechanisms is important to understanding its normal function.

The basal ganglia include the **striatum** (**caudate** and **putamen**), the **subthalamic nucleus,** the **globus pallidus** (internal and external segments) and the **substantia nigra** (**pars compacta** and **pars reticulata,** Fig. 34.2). At first glance, this anatomy may seem confusing. There are several component nuclei at different levels in the brain, and two of the nuclei (the substantia nigra and globus pallidus) are divided into functionally different components. Furthermore, the names of some structures are not the same in all mammals, and the names have changed over the years, so that an individual structure may have more than one name. However, with consistent use of modern terminology and a functional context in which to place the anatomy, it is easy to understand the organization of the basal ganglia.

Most inputs to the basal ganglia originate in the cerebral cortex and terminate in the striatum and subthalamic nucleus. There are no direct inputs from peripheral sensory or motor systems. The bulk of the output from the basal ganglia arises from the internal segment of the globus pallidus and the substantia nigra pars reticulata and projects to the thalamus and to an area in the brainstem. There are no direct outputs from the basal ganglia to spinal motor circuits.

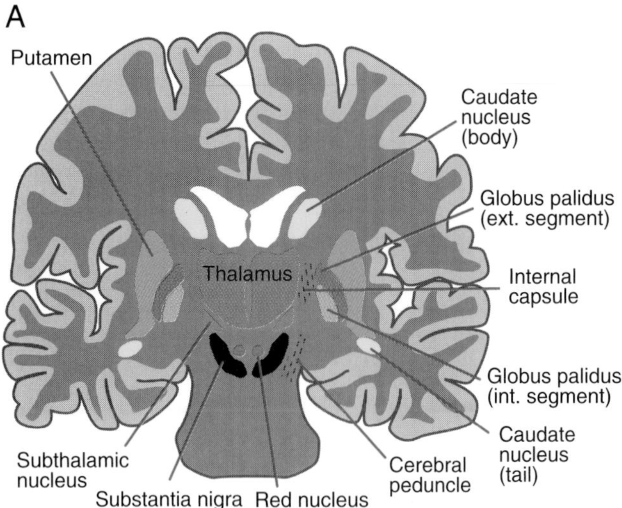

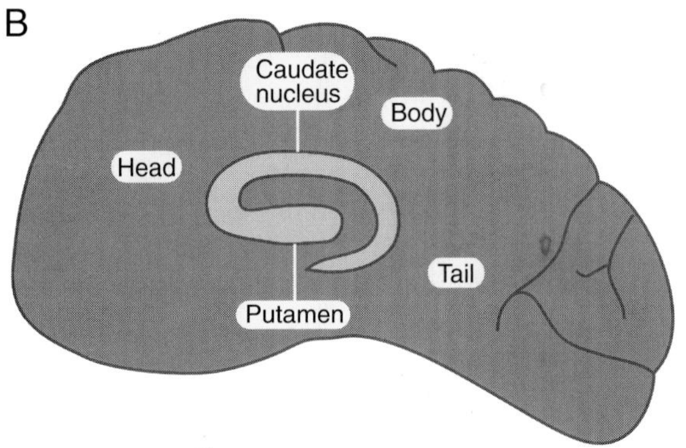

FIGURE 34.1 The location of the basal ganglia in the human brain. (A) Coronal section. (B) Sagittal section.

The Striatum Receives Most of the Inputs to the Basal Ganglia

The striatum is located in the forebrain and is composed of the caudate nucleus and putamen (the dorsal striatum or neostriatum).[4] Embryologically, the striatum develops from a basal region of the lateral telencephalic vesicle (see Chapter 2).[5] Its name is based on its striped appearance (Latin *stria*, furrow), which is due to the myelinated axons that pass through it. In rodents, the caudate and putamen are a single structure through which axons of the internal capsule course, but in carnivores and primates the caudate and putamen are separated by the internal capsule. The caudate and putamen receive input from the neocortex, and the size of these nuclei parallels the size of the neocortex throughout phylogeny.

Golgi staining and horseradish peroxidase labeling have revealed three major morphological types of neurons in the striatum,[6] which differ in the size of their somata and in the presence or absence of dendritic spines. By far the most numerous type is the medium spiny neuron[7] (Fig. 34.3).[8] These constitute 95% of striatal neurons and carry the output of the striatum to the globus pallidus (GP) and substantia nigra (SN). Medium spiny neurons have large dendritic trees that span 200–500 μm, and their extensive local axon collaterals may inhibit neighboring striatal neurons.[8] Although medium spiny neurons are morphologically homogeneous and use γ-aminobutyric acid (GABA) as one of their transmitters, they show considerable heterogeneity, as we shall see. The second type of striatal neuron, the large aspiny neuron, makes up 1–2% of the striatal population. These striatal interneurons are thought to use acetylcholine (ACh) as a neurotransmitter[9] and have extensive axon collaterals in the striatum that terminate on medium spiny neurons. The third type of neuron is the medium aspiny cell, which is thought to use somatostatin as a neurotransmitter.[10] (Neurotransmitters are discussed in detail in Chapter 8.)

The striatum receives excitatory input from all of the cerebral cortex with the exception of the primary auditory and visual cortex.[11] Cortical inputs use glutamate as a neurotransmitter and terminate largely on the heads of the dendritic spines of medium spiny neurons[12,13] (Fig. 34.4). The projection from the cerebral cortex to the striatum has a roughly topographical organization.[4] For example, the somatosensory and motor cortices project to the putamen, and the prefrontal cortex projects to the caudate.[14,15] Somatotopy is preserved within the somatosensory and motor projections,[16] which may provide a basis for the segregation of functionally different circuits in the basal ganglia[17] (Fig. 34.5).

Although somatotopy implies a certain degree of parallel organization in the corticostriatal projection, convergence and divergence also take place in this projection. The large dendritic fields of medium spiny neurons allow them to receive input from adjacent projections arising from different areas of the cortex.[18] Within the somatosensory and motor projections, inputs from more than one cortical area overlap,[19] and a single cortical area diverges to several striatal zones (Fig. 34.6).[18,19] Convergence and divergence provide an anatomical framework for the integration and transformation of information from several areas of the cerebral cortex.[20]

In addition to cortical inputs, medium spiny striatal neurons receive a number of other inputs, including excitatory and presumed glutamatergic inputs from the centromedian and parafascicular nuclei of the thalamus[21,22]; cholinergic inputs from large aspiny neurons[23]; inputs from adjacent medium spiny striatal neurons using GABA, substance P, and enkephalin[24]; and

BOX 34.1

THE CONCEPT OF THE EXTRAPYRAMIDAL MOTOR SYSTEM

Participation of the basal ganglia in normal motor control is an idea that dates back to the early part of the century. The British neurologist S. A. Kinnier Wilson described a disease whose symptoms included muscular rigidity, tremor, and weakness and was associated with pathological changes in the liver and the putamen (hepatolenticular degeneration).[1] Wilson noted that several symptoms of damage to the corticospinal tracts were not present in this disease, which led him to postulate that the motor abnormalities were due to disease of another motor system that functions independently of the pyramidal (corticospinal) motor system. He further postulated that the basal ganglia (striatum and globus pallidus) were the major constituents of this other motor system. In later writing, Wilson developed a view of the two motor systems, the phylogenetically old "extrapyramidal" system and the phylogenetically new pyramidal system.[2] He thought that the extrapyramidal system has an automatic, postural, and static function that is minimally modifiable, while the pyramidal system has a voluntary, phasic function that can be modified.

Wilson and others thought that the output of the basal ganglia went directly to the spinal cord. In the 1960s, however, more modern anatomical techniques showed that the bulk of the basal ganglia output projects via the thalamus to motor cortical areas.[3] In this sense, the basal ganglia output is prepyramidal, not extrapyramidal. With the developing model of initiation of movement by the basal ganglia, the prepyramidal function was emphasized as the most important aspect of basal ganglia output. More recently, the injection of fluorescent dyes has shown that the vast majority of neurons in the GPi branch and project to both the thalamus and the brainstem.[43] Hence, the basal ganglia can be considered both prepyramidal and extrapyramidal. Although we now know that the basal ganglia can act through the pyramidal system and that there are many extrapyramidal motor systems that project to the spinal cord independently of the pyramidal tract, the phase "extrapyramidal motor system" is still used to refer to the basal ganglia and to disorders that result from basal ganglia damage.

BOX 34.2

THE VENTRAL SYSTEM OF THE BASAL GANGLIA

Some nuclei in the brain historically have not been included in the basal ganglia but are analogous to the traditional components. These nuclei lie ventral to the neostriatum and globus pallidus and are called the ventral striatum (nucleus accumbens and olfactory tubercle) and the ventral pallidum. The ventral striatum receives input from the limbic and olfactory areas of the cortex, including the amygdala and hippocampus. Like the neostriatum, the ventral striatum receives a dopaminergic input, but it is from the ventral tegmental area (VTA), which lies medial to the substantia nigra. The ventral striatum sends a projection back to the VTA and to the adjacent SNpr. The ventral pallidum is analogous to both the GPe and GPi. It receives input from the ventral striatum and possibly from the STN, but unlike the globus pallidus, it also receives direct input from the amygdala. The output of the ventral pallidum projects to the dorsomedial nucleus of the thalamus (DM), and from there to the limbic area of the cortex. By virtue of its inputs and outputs, the ventral system is closely linked to the limbic system. This linkage suggests that the ventral system may be involved to some degree in motivation and emotion. The exact nature of this role is unclear, but it may be analogous to the motor role of the basal ganglia, with the inhibitory output of the ventral pallidum acting to suppress or select potentially competing limbic mechanisms.

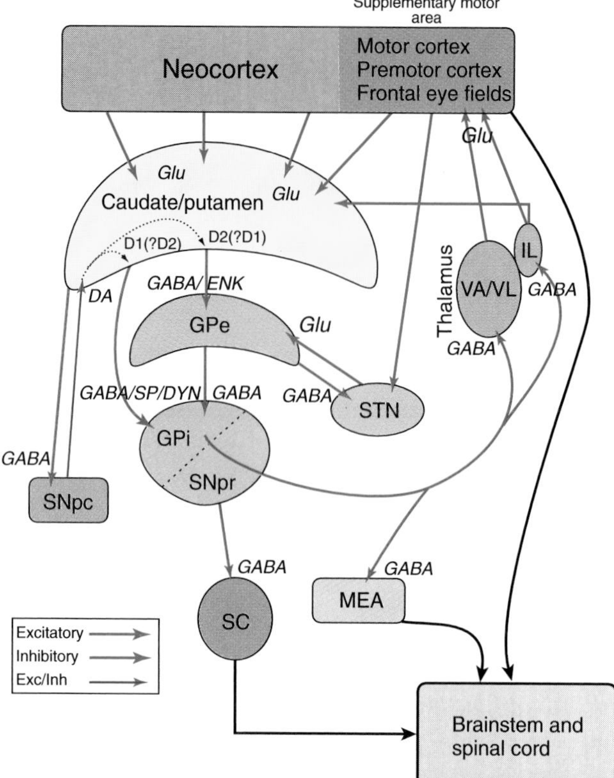

FIGURE 34.2 Schematic drawing of the basal ganglia circuitry. Excitatory connections are indicated with red arrows and inhibitory connections with green arrows. The dopamine-containing connection from the substantia nigra pars compacta (SNpc) is both excitatory and inhibitory, depending on the postsynaptic receptor. Structural abbreviations: GPe, globus pallidus pars externa; GPi, globus pallidus pars interna; IL, intralaminar thalamic nuclei; MEA, midbrain extrapyramidal area; SC, superior colliculus; SNpc, substantia nigra pars compacta; SNpr, substantia nigra pars reticulata; STN, subthalamic nucleus. Neurotransmitter abbreviations: DA, dopamine; D1 and D2, dopamine receptor types 1 and 2; DYN, dynorphin; ENK, enkephalin; GABA, γ-aminobutyric acid; Glu, glutamate; SP, substance P; VA/VL, ventral anterior and ventral lateral nuclei of the thalamus.

dopaminergic inputs from the substantia nigra pars compacta (SNpc).[4]

The dopaminergic input to medium spiny neurons is of particular interest because of its role in Parkinson disease, which we discuss later in the chapter. These inputs terminate largely on the shafts of dendritic spines (see Fig. 34.4),[13] putting them in a position to modulate transmission from the cerebral cortex to the striatum. The action of dopamine on striatal neurons depends on which of the five types of G-protein-coupled dopamine receptors are involved. D1 and D5 receptors stimulate adenylate cyclase activity and may potentiate the effect of cortical input to striatal neurons. D2, D3, and D4 receptors inhibit adenylate cyclase activity and may have the opposite effect on cortical input.[25]

Medium spiny neurons contain the inhibitory neurotransmitter GABA as well as various peptide neurotransmitters.[24,26] On the basis of the particular peptide neurotransmitters they contain and the type of dopamine receptor they express, medium spiny neurons can be divided into two populations. One population contains dynorphin and substance P and primarily expresses D1 receptors. These neurons send axons directly to the internal segment of the globus pallidus (GPi) and to the substantia nigra pars reticulata

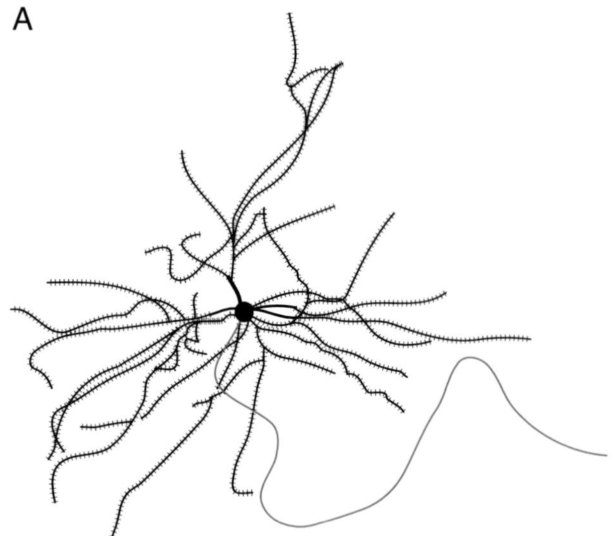

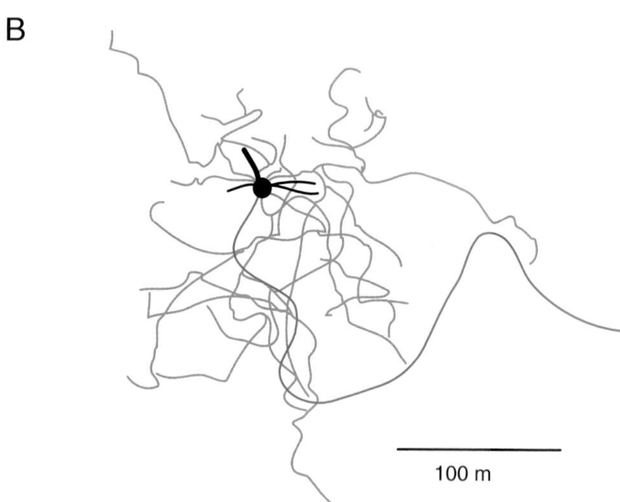

FIGURE 34.3 Two representations of a striatal medium spiny neuron that has been filled with HRP. (A) The soma and dendritic tree, with numerous dendritic spines. The thin process is the axon, which has been drawn without its collaterals. (B) The same neuron drawn to show the axonal collaterals, which branch extensively within the same field as the dendritic tree. From Wilson and Groves.[8]

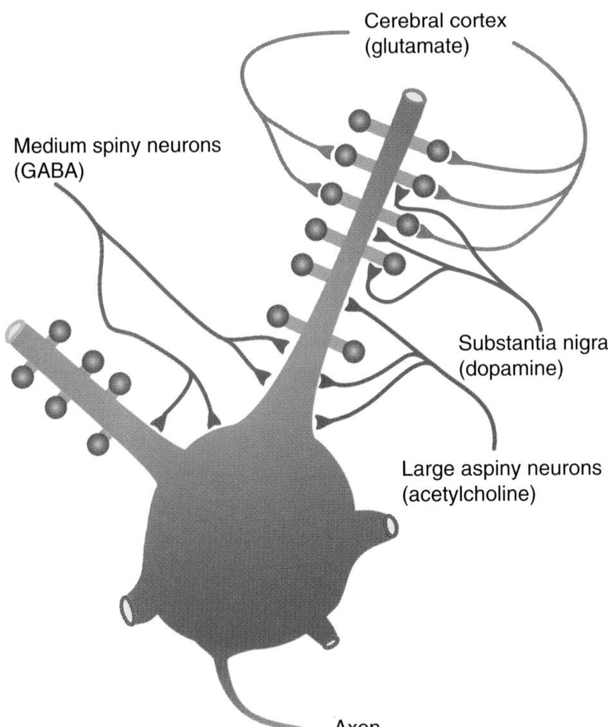

FIGURE 34.4 Pattern of termination of afferents on a medium spiny neuron. Shown here are the soma and the proximal section of two dendrites with their spines. Modified from Smith and Bolam, 1990.

(SNpr).[27-29] Although substance P is generally thought to be an excitatory neurotransmitter, the predominant effect of these neurons is inhibition of their targets. The second population contains enkephalin and primarily expresses D2 receptors. These neurons project to the external segment of the globus pallidus (GPe) and are inhibitory,[27-29] and thus their influence on GPi and SNpr is only expressed *indirectly*. The two populations of medium spiny neurons are morphologically indistinguishable and are not topographically segregated within the striatum[28] (Fig. 34.7). This commingling of neurons suggests that they receive similar inputs and thus may convey similar information to their respective targets. However, the different targets and transmitter types of the two populations may represent one level of functional segregation within the striatum.

Although no regional differences in the striatum are apparent from cell morphology, staining for calbindin or for acetylcholinesterase (AChE) activity reveals a patchy distribution of lightly stained regions, called **striosomes,** surrounded by more heavily stained regions, termed the **extrastriosomal matrix.**[30] The matrix forms the bulk of the striatal volume and receives input from most areas of the cerebral cortex. Within the matrix are clusters of neurons with similar inputs; these clusters are called **matrisomes.**[20] The bulk of the output from cells in the matrix is to both segments of the GP and to the SNpr. The striosomes receive input from the prefrontal cortex and send their output to the SNpc.[31] Immunohistochemical techniques have demonstrated that substance P, dynorphin, enkephalin, and other substances have a patchy distribution that may be partly or wholly in register with the striosomes.[32] The striosome matrix organization suggests another level of functional segregation within the striatum.

The Subthalamic Nucleus Receives Inputs from Motor Areas of Cerebral Cortex

The subthalamic nucleus (STN) is located at the junction of the diencephalon and midbrain, ventral to the thalamus and rostral and lateral to the red nucleus. Embryologically, it develops from the lateral hypothalamic cell column.[4,5] Phylogenetically, it increases in size in proportion to the neocortex. The STN receives an excitatory, glutamatergic input from motor areas of the cortex, including the primary motor cortex (area 4), premotor and supplementary motor cortices (area 6), and frontal eye fields (area 8).[33-35] The STN also receives an inhibitory GABAergic input from the GPe.[36] The output from the STN is excitatory and glutamatergic[37,38] and projects to the GPi, SNpr, and GPe.[39]

Although the STN is similar to the striatum in terms of its inputs and projection patterns, it differs from the striatum in that its cortical input is exclusively from motor areas and its output is excitatory. Of the two routes from the cortex to the GPi, GPe, and SNpr, the excitatory route through the STN is the faster.[40]

Globus Pallidus Internal Segment Is the Basal Ganglia Output for Limb Movements

The globus pallidus lies medial to the putamen and rostral to the hypothalamus. Embryologically, it arises from the lateral hypothalamic cell column.[4,5] In primates, the globus pallidus is separated into a medial or internal segment and a lateral or external segment by a fiber tract called the **internal medullary lamina.** In rodents and carnivores, the GPi lies within the internal capsule and is called the entopeduncular nucleus. The GPe is not a principal source of output from the basal ganglia, and we consider it in a later section.

The GPi is composed primarily of large neurons that project outside the basal ganglia.[41,42] The dendritic tree of a GPi neuron radiates from the soma in a disk-like distribution and is oriented so that the face of the disk is perpendicular to incoming striatal axons. The disk of an individual GPi neuron can be up to 1 mm

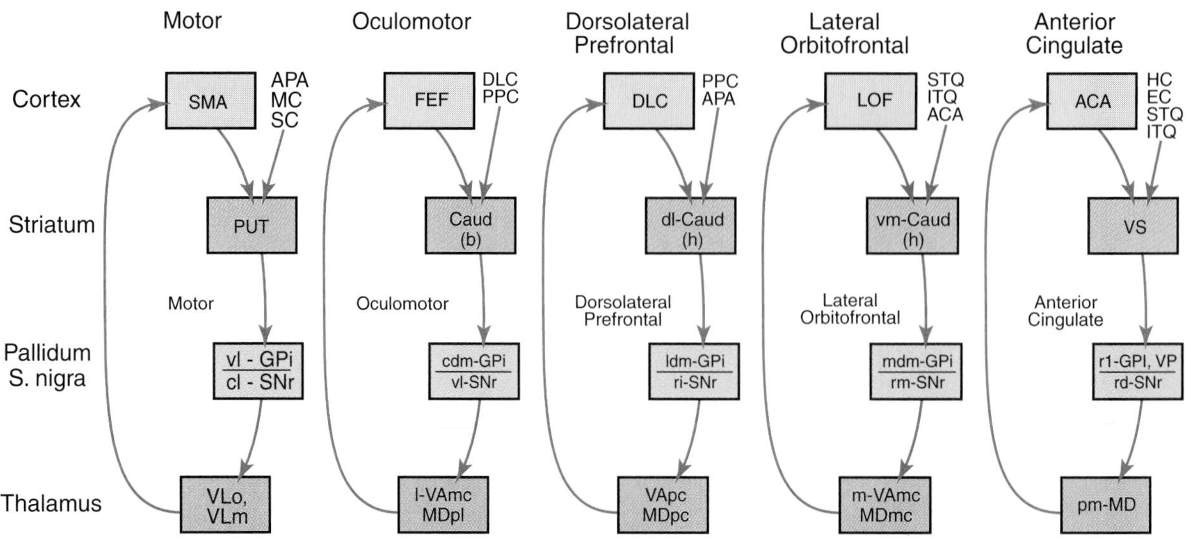

FIGURE 34.5 Hypothetical parallel segregated circuits connecting the basal ganglia, thalamus, and cerebral cortex. The five circuits are named according to the primary cortical target of the output from the basal ganglia: motor, oculomotor, dorsolateral prefrontal, lateral orbitofrontal, and anterior cingulate.[17] Abbreviations: ACA, anterior cingulate area; APA, arcuate premotor area; CAUD, caudate; (b) body; (h) head; DLC, dorsolateral prefrontal cortex; EC, entorhinal cortex; FEF, frontal eye fields; GPi, internal segment of globus pallidus; HC, hippocampal cortex; ITG, inferior temporal gyrus; LOF, lateral orbitofrontal cortex; MC, motor cortex; MDpl, mediulis dorsalis pars paralamellaris; MDme, medialis dorsalis pars magnocellularis; MDpc, medialis dorsalis pars parvocellularis; PPC, posterior parietal cortex; PUT, putamen; SC, somatosensory cortex; SMA, supplementary motor area; SNr, substantia nigra pars reticulata; STG, superior temporal gyrus; VAmc, ventralis anterior pars magnocellularis; Vapc, ventralis anterior pars parvocellularis; VLm, ventralis lateralis pars medialis; VLo, ventralis lateralis pars oralis; VP, ventral pallidum; VS, ventral striatum; cl, caudolateral; cdm, caudal dorsomedial; dl, dorsolateral; l, lateral; ldm, lateral dorsomedial; m, medial; mdm, medial dorsomedial; pm, posteromedial; rd, rostrodorsal; rl, rostrolateral; rm, rostromedial; vm, ventromedial; vl, ventrolateral.

in diameter, giving these neurons the potential to receive a large number of converging inputs.[43]

The principal inputs to the GPi are from the striatum and the STN.[39] As we noted above, the striatal inputs contain GABA, substance P, and dynorphin and are inhibitory. Each striatal axon enters the GPi and sparsely contacts several neurons in passing before surrounding a single neuron with a dense termination.[44] The excitatory, glutamatergic projection from the STN to the GPi is highly divergent: each STN axon synapses on many GPi neurons[44] (Fig. 34.8). Recall that the striatal projection to the GPi is relatively slower than the STN projection. Thus, the GPi receives fast, widespread, divergent excitation from the STN and slower, focused, convergent inhibition from the striatum.

The output from the GPi is inhibitory and involves GABA as a neurotransmitter.[45] The majority of the output is sent via collaterals to both the thalamus and the brainstem.[46] In the thalamus, axons from the GPi terminate in the oral part of the ventrolateral nucleus (VLo) and in the principal part of the ventral anterior nucleus (VApc).[47] In turn, these thalamic nuclei project to the motor, premotor, supplementary motor, and possibly the prefrontal cortices.[48,49] Evidence indicates that an individual GPi neuron sends output via the thalamus to only one area of the cortex.[48] This means that GPi neurons that project to the motor cortex, for example, are adjacent to those that project to the premotor cortex. Thus, just as there appear to be parallel inputs from the cortex to the striatum, there also may be functionally parallel outputs from the GPi.

Collaterals of the axons that project from the GPi to the thalamus terminate in the midbrain extrapyramidal area, a region at the junction of the midbrain and pons near the pedunculopontine area.[50] The midbrain extrapyramidal area projects in turn to the reticulospinal motor system. Other GPi neurons (20%) project to the centromedian–parafascicular complex of the thalamus or to the lateral habenula.[46] The role of these projections is unknown.

Substantia Nigra Pars Reticulata Is the Basal Ganglia Output for Eye Movements

Like the globus pallidus, the substantia nigra is divided into two segments: the densely cellular

SNpc and the more sparsely cellular SNpr.[4] The SNpc contains dopamine cells and is not a principal output nucleus of the basal ganglia. We consider it later.

The SNpr is similar to the GPi in many ways, including the size of its neurons, their histochemistry, and their connectional anatomy. The SNpr contains large neurons that project outside the basal ganglia. The dendritic trees of these neurons are less discoidal than those of GPi neurons, but like those of GPi neurons they extend up to 1 mm and thus receive a wide field of inputs.[81] Like the GPi, the SNpr receives inhibitory inputs from the striatum, mediated by GABA, SP, and dynorphin, and excitatory glutamatergic inputs from the STN. The output of the SNpr is GABAergic and inhibitory to the medial part of ventrolateral thalamus

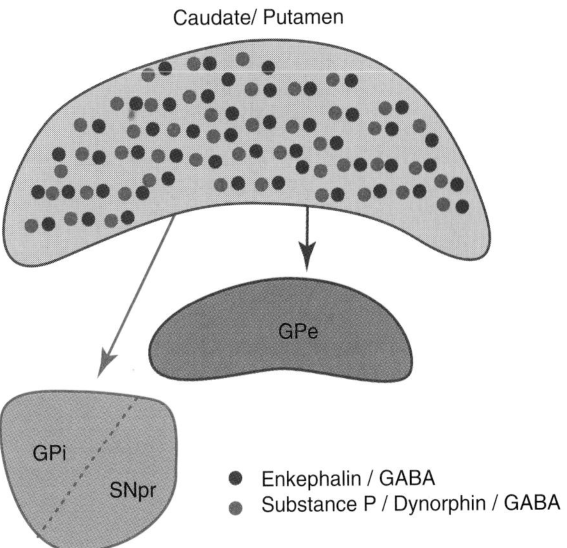

FIGURE 34.7 The two chemically defined populations of medium spiny neurons are intermixed in the striatum. One population (blue) projects to the globus pallidus pars externa (GPe) and contains GABA and enkephalin. The other population (red) projects to the globus pallidus pars interna (GPi) and substantia nigra pars reticulata (SNpr) and contains GABA, dynorphin, and substance P.

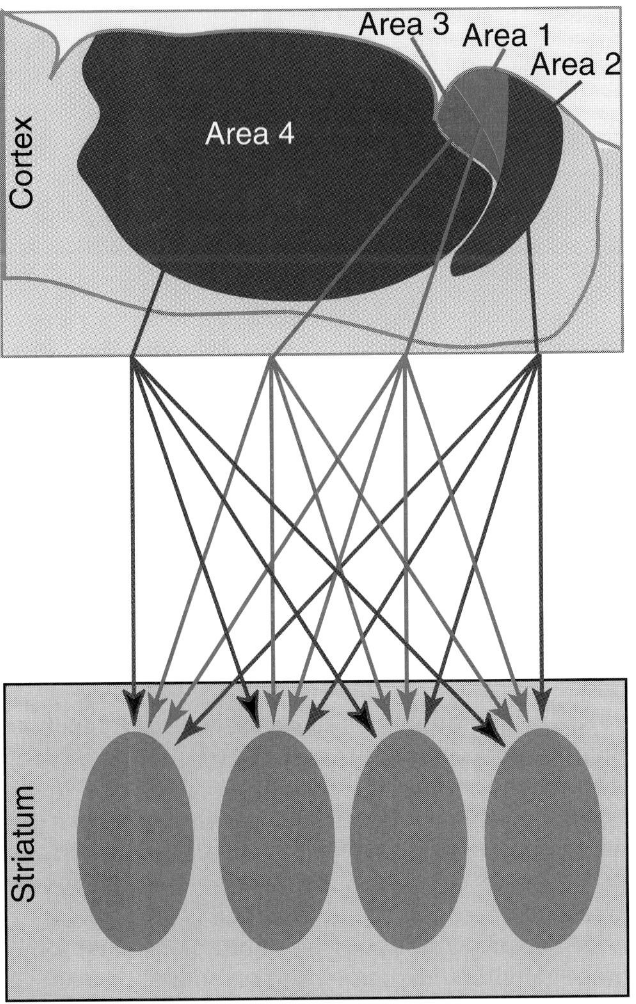

FIGURE 34.6 Schematic representation of projections to the striatum from arm areas in the somatosensory cortex (areas 1, 2, and 3) and motor cortex (area 4). Notice that each cortical area projects to several striatal zones and that several functionally related cortical areas project to a single striatal zone. After Flaherty and Graybiel.[19]

(VLm) and to the magnocellular part of ventral anterior thalamus (VAmc).[52–54] These thalamic areas in turn project to the premotor and prefrontal cortices.[55] Like the GPi, the SNpr sends collaterals to the midbrain extrapyramidal area and the centromedian–parafascicular complex of the thalamus.[56,57] The primary difference in the connectivity patterns of the GPi and SNpr is that the lateral portion of the SNpr sends an inhibitory projection to the superior colliculus and to the paralaminar part of the dorsal medial thalamus (DMpl).[52,58,59] The DMpl projects in turn to the frontal eye fields. Thus, the lateral portion of the SNpr is connected with cortical and brainstem areas that control eye movements.

Globus Pallidus External Segment Projects Primarily to the Subthalamic Nucleus

The GPe is one of two nuclei that may be viewed as intrinsic nuclei of the basal ganglia. The other is the SNpc, which we consider in the next section. Both the GPe and the SNpc receive the bulk of their input from and send the bulk of their output to other basal ganglia nuclei. The GPe is similar in some ways to the GPi. Its inputs are an inhibitory projection from the striatum and an excitatory projection from the STN. The patterns of termination of the striatal and STN afferents are similar, in that the striatal input is focused and convergent and the STN input is diver-

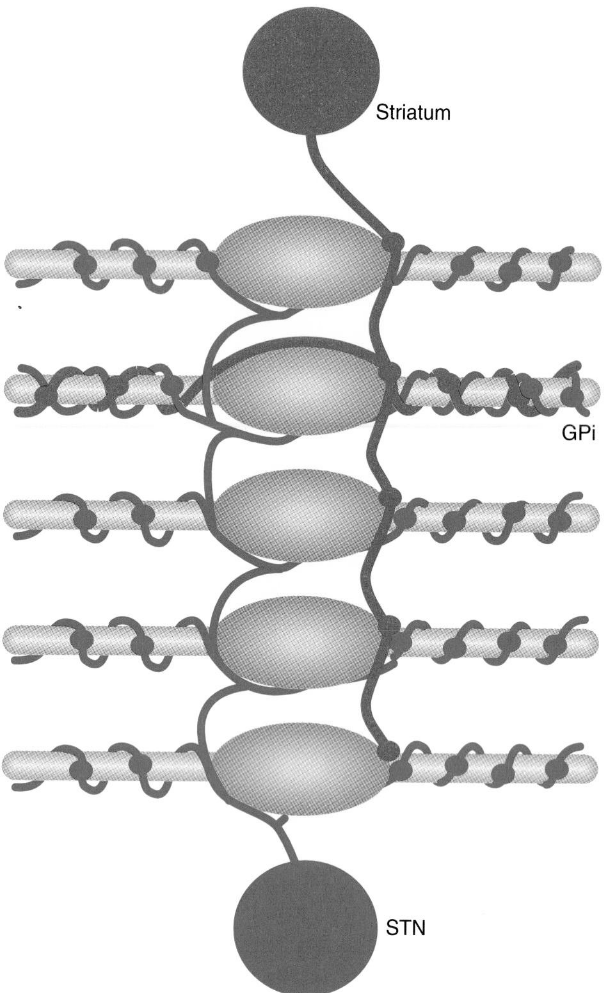

FIGURE 34.8 The two primary inputs to the globus pallidus pars interna (GPi) have different patterns of termination. Axons from the subthalamic nucleus (green) are excitatory and terminate extensively on multiple GPi neurons. Axons from the striatum (red) contact several GPi neurons weakly in passing and terminate densely on single neuron. Modified from Parent and Hazrati.[44]

gent.[44] Unlike the GPi, however, the GPe receives input from the striatum mediated by GABA and enkephalin but not substance P.[28,29] Furthermore, the output of the GPe is GABAergic and inhibitory and projects primarily back to the STN.[60] There is also a GABAergic inhibitory output from the GPe directly to the GPi and the SNpr.[61] As we noted above, the GPe and GPi receive input from neighboring striatal neurons and therefore are likely to receive similar information. The fact that the GPe inhibits the GPi directly or via the STN (the GPe inhibits the STN, and the STN inhibits the GPi, so the net effect is inhibition) suggests that the GPe may act to oppose, limit, or focus the effect of the striatal projection to the GPi.

Substantia Nigra Pars Compacta Provides Dopamine Input to Striatum

The SNpc is perhaps the most thoroughly studied structure in the basal ganglia. Its large dopamine-containing cells are the neurons that degenerate in Parkinson disease, which is characterized by abnormal movement. These neurons also contain neuromelanin, a dark pigment that makes the SNpc appear black and is the basis for the name substantia nigra (Latin, black substance). The SNpc receives GABAergic inhibitory input from the striatum, specifically from the striosomes.[62] Other inputs to the SNpc have been difficult to assess, because the dendrites of SNpc and SNpr neurons overlap. Thus, whether axons ending in the substantia nigra terminate on SNpc neurons, SNpr neurons, or both is not always clear. SNpc neurons project to all of the caudate and putamen in a topographic manner.[63] The action of the dopamine released by these neurons appears to be primarily a modulation of the excitatory corticostriatal input, with the nature of that modulation depending on the receptors expressed by the postsynaptic neurons, as we discusssed earlier.

Summary

Now that we have described the anatomy of the individual components of the basal ganglia, let us step back and summarize their connections with each other and with the rest of the brain.

1. The striatum receives input from nearly all of the cerebral cortex. Several functionally related cortical areas project to overlapping striatal zones, and an individual cortical area projects to several striatal zones. Cortical areas that are not functionally related project to separate zones of the striatum, although there may be some common projections to adjacent zones.
2. The striatum sends a focused and convergent inhibitory projection to the basal ganglia output nuclei, the GPi and SNpr.
3. The subthalamic nucleus receives input from the motor, premotor, and supplementary motor cortices and from the frontal eye fields. It sends a fast, divergent, excitatory projection to the GPi and SNpr.
4. Reciprocal and looplike connections among the basal ganglia nuclei may play a negative or positive feedback role or may result in focusing of signals.
5. The output from the GPi and SNpr is inhibitory and projects to motor areas in the brainstem and thalamus.

6. There are no direct connections between the basal ganglia and spinal sensory or motor circuits.

Researchers disagree whether the overall anatomic organization of the basal ganglia should be viewed as a convergence (or funneling) of information that produces a focused output or as a system of multiple, parallel, segregated loops, each with a separate output. Several observations support the convergence view: (1) there is a very marked reduction in the number of neurons at each level from the cortex to the striatum to the GPi and SNpr; (2) a large number of synapses are made on each striatal neuron; and (3) striatal, GPi, and SNpr neurons have large dendritic trees. Other observations support the idea of parallel segregated loops: (1) somatopy is preserved in the cortex, striatum, and GPi/SNpr, with separate representations of the face, arm, and leg; (2) topography is relatively well preserved through the basal ganglia, for example, from the prefrontal cortex to the caudate to the SNpr to the VA thalamus and back to the prefrontal cortex; and (3) separate groups of GPi neurons project via the thalamus to separate motor areas of the cortex. Clearly, there is convergence on a local scale and parallelism on a global scale, but what we still do not know is whether the parallel pathways are completely functionally segregated or interact with each other at their interfaces.

SIGNALING IN THE BASAL GANGLIA

Although the anatomic organization of the basal ganglia may provide some clues about their function, inference of function from anatomy is highly speculative. A direct way to study the function of an area of the central nervous system is to record the electrical activity of individual neurons with an extracellular electrode in awake, behaving animals. By sampling the activity of a part of the brain during behavior, we can gain some insight into what role that part might play in behavior. If an animal is trained to perform a task consistently, the activity of single neurons can be correlated with individual aspects of the task performance. Furthermore, the timing of neural activity in one part can be compared with the timing of activity in other parts and with the timing of the movement. This approach has shown that neurons within the different basal ganglia nuclei have characteristic baseline discharge patterns that change with movement. In this section, we describe some of the signals in the basal ganglia that are correlated with movement or the preparation for movement.

The Striatum Has Low Spontaneous Activity That Increases during Movement

Most striatal neurons have low baseline discharge rates of 0.1–1 s^{-1} (Fig. 34.9).[64] These neurons project outside the striatum and therefore are probably medium spiny neurons.[65] In general, the activity of these neurons reflects the activity of the areas of cerebral cortex from which they receive inputs, with less modality specificity.[17,66] For example, neurons in areas of the putamen that receive input from the somatosensory and motor cortices have activity correlated with active and passive movement, but not with specific tactile modalities such as light touch, vibration, or joint position.

Neurons related to movement are somatotopically distributed in the striatum: neurons whose activity correlates with facial movements or leg movements are located in ventromedial or dorsolateral areas of the striatum, respectively[64]; neurons whose activity correlates with arm movements are located between the "face" and "leg" regions. Neurons with similar discharge characteristics tend to occur in clusters that may correspond to the matrisomes mentioned earlier. Movement is associated with an increase in the firing rate of these neurons above their very low baseline rates.[67] Movement-related striatal neurons fire an average of 20 ms prior to movement (Fig. 34.10), and half fire in relation to the direction of movement. Firing is correlated with the start of movement in some neurons and with the cessation of movement in others.[68] Neurons in the putamen may fire in relation to self-initiated movements, stimulus-triggered movements, or both.[69] Some neurons in the anterior part of the putamen and

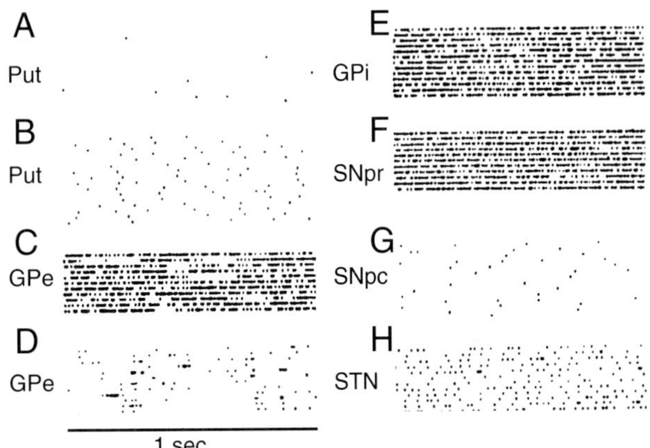

FIGURE 34.9 Representative neural discharge patterns from the various basal ganglia nuclei. In these raster displays, each dot indicates the occurrence of an action potential. Each horizontal raster line represents a one-second period of discharge. Several such periods are arranged vertically for each nucleus. From Crutcher and DeLong.[112]

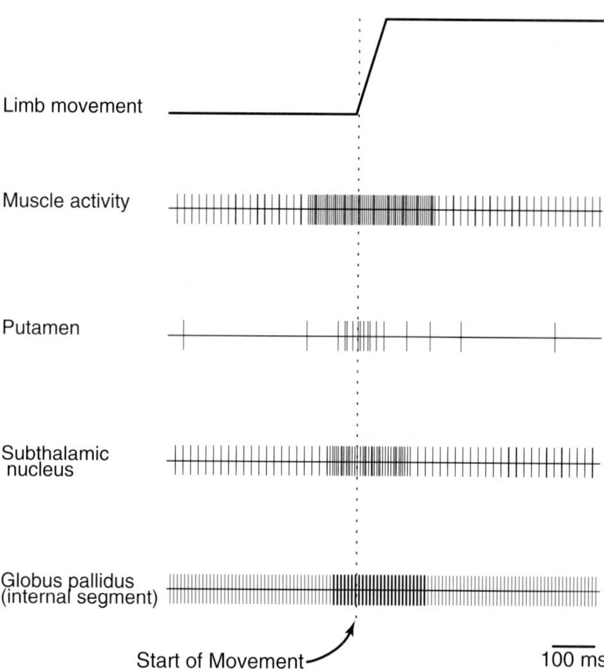

FIGURE 34.10 Schematic representation of the timing of neuronal activity in three nuclei of the basal ganglia in relation to limb movement and the muscle activity used to make the movement.

in the caudate nucleus that receive input from the premotor or prefrontal cortex are active during the preparation for movement.[70,71] Their activity is time-locked to instructional cues but not to the movement itself. In some neurons, firing is correlated with the instruction of whether or not to move ("set"); in others, it is correlated with the signal to move ("go"). Although particular neurons may have activity patterns that differently relate to specific tasks or task parameters, as a whole the striatum is not exclusively active in relation to any of these tasks or parameters.[69,70]

Some striatal neurons fire tonically at rates of 2–10 s^{-1}.[65] These neurons are distributed throughout the striatum. Although their discharge bears no specific relation to movement, it is related to certain sensory stimuli that are associated with reward. For example, a tonically active neuron may fire if a clicking sound precedes a fruit juice reward but not if the click or reward occurs alone.[72] For this reason, it has been suggested that these neurons signal aspects of tasks that are related to learning and reinforcement. The tonically active neurons are not activated by electrical stimulation of the globus pallidus; they may correspond to the cholinergic large aspiny neurons.[65] If so, that would place them in a position to modify the sensitivity of the medium spiny neurons to cortical input in relation to specific behavioral contexts.

Subthalamic Nucleus Has Moderate Spontaneous Activity That Increases during Movement

Neurons in the subthalamic nucleus are tonically active, with average baseline discharge rates of about 20 s^{-1} (Fig. 34.9).[73] They are organized somatotopically and change their activity in relation to eye or limb movement.[73–75] For 90% of the neurons, the change is an increase in firing rate that occurs an average of 50 ms prior to the movement (Fig. 34.10).[76] The activity of approximately half of all movement-related STN neurons is correlated with movement direction.

Globus Pallidus Internal Segment and Substantia Nigra Pars Reticulata Have High Spontaneous Activity That Increases or Decreases after Movement Initiation

As described above, the GPi and SNpr generate the output of the basal ganglia. Just as they are anatomically similar, they are physiologically similar. Neurons in these nuclei are tonically active, with average firing rates of 60–80 s^{-1} (Fig. 34.9).[77] They are organized somatotopically, with the leg and arm represented in the GPi and the face and eyes in the SNpr.[75,76,78,79] Because of this somatotopy, studies of limb movements have focused on the GPi, and studies of eye movements have focused on the SNpr. Because limb and eye movements are controlled differently, we discuss these studies separately.

Seventy percent of arm movement-related GPi neurons increase their activity during movement.[80] During wrist movement, GPi neurons change their firing rate after the wrist muscles become active (Fig. 34.10),[80] suggesting that the output of the basal ganglia does not initiate movement. The activity of GPi neurons does not consistently correlate with the amplitude or velocity of movement or with muscle activity or length.[80] In some tasks, GPi activity correlates with the direction of movement, but the correlation is not consistent across different tasks. The weak and inconsistent parameter coding suggests that the GPi is involved in some aspect of movement other than parameter control.

Like limb-movement neurons in the GPi, SNpr neurons that are related to saccadic eye movements are tonically active.[78] During saccades, SNpr activity begins after activity in the superior colliculus, a structure that initiates saccades.[56] Thus, for eye movements as well as limb movements, the basal ganglia are unlikely to initiate movement. Unlike GPi limb-movement neurons, however, all SNpr neurons related to saccades decrease their activity during the saccade. Whether this difference between GPi neurons and SNpr neurons indicates a fundamental distinction between eye and limb movement control or whether it reflects task differences is not known. Other differences between GPi limb-movement neurons and SNpr saccade neurons have been noted. While the former have weak sensory responses, some of the latter respond strongly to visual stimuli.[81] For the visually responsive SNpr neurons, the spatial location of the stimulus seems to be the most salient feature. The activity of some SNpr neurons is related most strongly to saccades that are made to remembered targets.[82] For example, when a visual target is presented and then removed and a monkey is trained to look to where the target had been, some SNpr cells will decrease their firing rate more than when a saccade is made to a visible target. Whether a similar phenomenon exists for GPi neurons is not known. However, few GPi neurons change their activity in a task where monkeys must remember the direction, velocity, and amplitude of a self-initiated wrist movement.[83]

Globus Pallidus External Segment Has Irregular Activity That Increases or Decreases after Movement Initiation

Two types of neurons in the GPe have been described on the basis of their baseline activity patterns.[77] Most neurons fire in high-frequency (70 s^{-1}) bursts interrupted by long pauses. A smaller number of neurons fire in lower frequency (10 s^{-1}) bursts that occur more often. Both types of neurons change their activities in relation to limb movement, and in most cases these changes are increases in activity.[77,80] As has been described for the GPi, the coding of movement amplitude and velocity and the coding of muscle length and force are weak in the GPe.[80] Like the other nuclei of the basal ganglia, the GPe is unlikely to initiate movement.[76,80]

Substantia Nigra Pars Compacta Has Low Spontaneous Activity That Does Not Change with Movement

The activity of single neurons in the SNpc of trained animals is different from that of neurons in the other basal ganglia nuclei. SNpc neurons fire at a baseline rate of about 2 s^{-1}, and their firing is not related to movement itself. There is no apparent somatotopy in the SNpc,[79] and the neurons in this nucleus carry little specific information regarding sensory modality or spatial properties. The activity of SNpc neurons does change in relation to behaviorally significant events such as reward or the presentation of instructional cues.[84] The only responses to stimuli are those that occur when a stimulus is presented in the context of a movement task.[85] Furthermore, SNpc neuronal activity changes with conditioning. For example, if a reward is preceded by a tone, an SNpc neuron that had fired in relation to the reward will, after several trials, begin to fire in relation to the tone that predicts the reward.

Thus, SNpc dopamine neurons apparently can predictively signal the occurrence of a behavioral event. In this way, SNpc neurons are similar to tonically active striatal neurons. Remember that SNpc neurons also synapse extensively on the shafts of the dendritic spines of medium spiny striatal neurons. It has been suggested that the dopamine input from the SNpc changes the sensitivity of striatal neurons to cortical inputs that terminate on the heads of the dendritic spines. The activity of SNpc neurons could modify the response of striatal neurons to cortical input that occurs in a specific behavioral context.

Summary

We can make several general statements about the discharge of movement-related neurons in the basal ganglia:

1. Movement-related neurons in the striatum, subthalamic nucleus, globus pallidus, and substantia nigra pars reticulata are arranged somatotopically.
2. Neurons in the striatum are quiet at rest and increase their firing rate during movement. Neurons in STN are tonically active and also increase their firing rate during movement. Thus, GPi neurons receive a widespread, tonically active excitatory input and a focused, intermittent inhibitory input.
3. Neurons in the GPe and GPi are tonically active. Most increase their activity during limb movement, but up to one-third decrease their activity.
4. Neurons in the SNpr are tonically active. Those that are related to saccadic eye movements decrease their activity during the movement.
5. Neurons in the SNpc discharge in relation to rewards and behaviorally relevant stimuli but not to movement.
6. Activity changes in the basal ganglia begin at the onset of movement but after the muscles are already active. Thus, the basal ganglia are unlikely to initiate movement.

THE EFFECT OF BASAL GANGLIA DAMAGE ON BEHAVIOR

Valuable clues to the function of the basal ganglia have come from recording the activity of single neurons in the basal ganglia during behavior. However, correlation of neural activity with an aspect of behavior does not necessarily mean that neural activity causes that aspect of behavior. Studying behavior after a specific component had been selectively removed from an otherwise intact system would aid in determining the role of the basal ganglia in behavior. Selective removal occurs in certain human neurological diseases that cause degeneration of neurons in the basal ganglia. Historically, these diseases have fueled great interest and have provided some insight into basal ganglia function. The movement disorders that result from basal ganglia damage are often dramatic. Depending on the site of the pathology, they range from extreme slowness of movement and rigidity to uncontrollable involuntary movements.

Although human diseases are of great interest, they often affect more than one structure. This necessarily limits the power of functional models derived from the study of human basal ganglia diseases. More selective lesions can be made in experimental animals, but until recently, reproducing the movement disorders associated with human basal ganglia disease was difficult. Experimental lesions can be made in a number of ways. Electric current can be passed through an electrode to permanently destroy both neuronal somata and axons in the area surrounding the electrode. This method has the disadvantage of destroying axons that pass through the area but which are not necessarily part of the structure of interest. Alternatively, a small amount of a toxic chemical (e.g., the potent excitotoxic amino acids kainic acid and ibotenic acid) can be injected into a restricted area of the brain and can be used to kill neurons whose somata are in the area of the injection, sparing axons that pass through the area. 6-Hydroxydopamine or MPTP (see Box 34.3) can be used to destroy dopamine neurons selectively. Agonists and antagonists of GABA can also be injected into the brain to cause temporary focal inactivation or disinhibition of neurons; the effects of these chemicals last for several hours and are followed by a complete return to the normal state. In this section, we review the results of selective basal ganglia lesions produced by these techniques in animals, and we discuss human basal ganglia diseases in the context of these experiments.

Damage to the Striatum Causes Slow Voluntary Movements or Involuntary Postures and Movements

Lesions in the striatum produce varying results that depend on the location of the lesion, the lesion method, and the parameter that is measured. Many studies of unilateral striatal lesions have described only minimal

BOX 34.3

THE MPTP STORY

Until the early 1980s, the quest for an complete animal model of Parkinson disease was largely unsuccessful. Although some of the abnormalities of Parkinson disease could be caused by electrolytic lesion of the SNpc or by injecting the neurotoxin 6-hydroxydopamine into SNpc, neither of these methods produced the full syndrome of Parkinson disease. In 1982, an unfortunate but fortuitous accident happened. Four young drug users in northern California developed the symptoms of Parkinson disease. Because the disease is highly unusual in young adults, the neurologists caring for these patients began a search for the cause.[98] They discovered that each of the patients had recently used a new synthetic heroin that contained an analog of the narcotic meperidine, 1-methyl-4-phenylproprionoxypiperidine (MPPP), as well as a contaminant, 1-methyl-4-phenyl-1,2,5,6-tetrahydropyridine (MPTP). It turned out that MPTP was the agent responsible for the parkinsonian symptoms. MPTP is oxidized in the brain to MPP^+ by monoamine oxidase. When MPP^+ is taken up by dopamine neurons, it kills them by inhibiting oxidative metabolism in the mitochondria.[99]

MPTP also produces a syndrome that resembles Parkinson disease in several species of monkeys.[100] Monkeys given MPTP develop tremors as well as slowness of movement, paucity of movement, and rigidity. In these monkeys, there is a nearly complete degeneration of dopamine neurons in the SNpc and the ventral tegmental area and a variable degeneration in the locus coeruleus. Like humans with Parkinson disease, MPTP monkeys improve when given the dopamine precursor L-dopa, and they have side effects of chorea when they are given too much L-dopa. Thus, by behavioral, pharmacological, and pathological measures, the MPTP monkey is an excellent model of human Parkinson disease. It is currently used to study the pathophysiology and pharmacology of Parkinson disease and has led to new ideas about possible causes of the disease.

BOX 34.4

OBSESSIVE–COMPULSIVE DISORDER

Obsessive–compulsive disorder (OCD) is a chronic disorder characterized by recurrent intrusive thoughts and ritualistic behaviors that consume much or most of the afflicted individual's attentional and goal-directed processes.[1] Among the more agonizing illnesses in clinical medicine, OCD is classified as an anxiety disorder because of the marked tension and distress produced by resisting the obsessions and compulsions. The most common obsessions involve thoughts about harming oneself or others (e.g., a mother who repeatedly thinks about taking her infant's life, despite her complete lack of desire or intent to do so and her horror over having such thoughts) or of contamination. Compulsions may be a response to obsessive thoughts (e.g., repetitive hand-washing following skin contact with any object due to obsessive worries of having contacted germs) or may instead reflect cognitive–behavioral rituals performed according to stereotyped rules (e.g., counting one's footsteps to avoid ending on certain numbers). Even though individuals with OCD often recognize that such thoughts and behaviors are irrational, they describe feeling irresistibly compelled to engage in them.

The onset of OCD usually occurs between late childhood and early adulthood. Without treatment, OCD is frequently disabling. However, the amount of time engaged in obsessions and compulsions and the magnitude of the associated anxiety can often be reduced by chronic treatment with drugs that potently inhibit serotonin reuptake.[2] Behavioral therapy involving repeated *in vivo* exposure and response prevention (e.g., having patients touch a toilet seat and subsequently preventing them from hand-washing) may also facilitate extinction of the anxiety responses generated by resisting the obsessive thoughts and compulsive behaviors.[1]

Although the etiology and pathophysiology of OCD are unknown, the anatomical circuits involved in the production of obsessions and compulsions have been elucidated by converging evidence from functional neuroimaging studies of OCD, analysis of the lesions that result in obsessive–compulsive symptoms, and observations regarding the neurosurgical interventions that can ameliorate OCD.[1–7] Positron emission tomographic (PET) imaging studies of primary OCD have shown that "resting" cerebral blood flow and glucose metabolism are abnormally increased in the orbital cortex and the caudate nucleus bilaterally in primary OCD.[3] With further symptom provocation during exposure to relevant phobic stimuli (e.g., skin contact with "contaminated" objects for OCD subjects with germ phobias), blood flow increases further in the orbital cortex, the caudate, the putamen, the thalamus, and the anterior cingulate cortex.[4] During effective pharmacotherapy, orbital metabolism decreases toward normal, and both drug treatment and behavioral therapy are associated with a reduction of caudate metabolism.[3] The baseline areas of hypermetabolism in the orbital cortex and the caudate may thus reflect physiological concomitants of obsessive thoughts and/or chronic anxiety, and conversely, the reduction in caudate metabolism associated with effective (but not ineffective) treatment may reflect a physiological correlate of symptom resolution rather than a primary mechanism of treatment. Moreover, given the evidence from electrophysiological and lesion analysis studies indicating that the orbital cortex participates in the correction of behavioral responses that have become inappropriate as reinforcement contingencies change, some orbital areas may be specifically activated as an endogenous attempt to interrupt the reverberating patterns of nonreinforced thought and behavior in OCD.[8] Compatible with this hypothesis, the posterior orbital cortex BF increases during symptom provocation in OCD, but the magnitude of this BF increase correlates *inversely* with the corresponding rise in obsession ratings ($r = -0.83$).[4]

Evidence that dysfunction within these basal ganglia and ventral prefrontal cortical structures or the circuits they form with other structures may be related to the etiopathology of OCD is provided by analysis of the neurological conditions that are associated with the development of secondary obsessions and compulsions. Such conditions include lesions of the lentiform nuclei that include involvement of the globus pallidus, Sydenham chorea (a poststreptococcal autoimmune disorder associated with neuronal atrophy in the caudate and putamen), Tourette disorder (an idiopathic syndrome characterized by motoric and phonic tics that may have a genetic relationship with OCD), chronic motor tic disorder, and lesions of the ventromedial prefrontal cortex.[1,5–7] Several of these conditions are associated with complex motor tics (repetitive, coordinated, involuntary movements occurring in patterned sequences in a spontaneous, unpredictable, and transient manner). Complex tics and obsessive thoughts may reflect homologous, aberrant neural processes that are manifested within the motor and cognitive–behavioral domains, respectively, because of their origination in distinct portions of the cortical–striatal–pallidal–thalamic circuitry.[9] Nevertheless, it is noteworthy that imaging studies of obsessive–compulsive syndromes arising in the setting of Tourette syndrome or basal ganglia lesions have not found elevated BF and metabolism in the caudate and, in some cases, have found reduced metabolism in the orbital cortex in such subjects relative to controls.[5]

The differences in the functional anatomical correlates of primary versus secondary OCD suggest a neural model in which dysfunction arising at various points within the ventral prefrontal cortical–striatal–pallidal–thalamic circuitry may result in pathological obsessions and compulsions. This circuitry in general appears to be involved in the organization of internally guided behavior toward a reward, switching of response strategies, habit formation, and stereotypic behavior.[9] These circuits have also been implicated in the pathophysiology of major depressive disorder (MDD), another illness in which intrusive, distressing thoughts recur to the extent that the ability to switch to goal-oriented, rewarding cognitive–behavioral sets appears impaired. Although MDD and OCD appear distinct in their course, prognosis, genetics, and neurochemical concomitants, substantial comorbidity exists across these syndromes. For example, major depressive episodes occur in about one-half of patients with OCD, pathological obsessions commonly arise in MDD, and the pharmacological interventions that ameliorate OCD can also effectively treat MDD.[1]

The clinical comorbidity across these two disorders may conceivably reflect involvement of an overlapping neural circuitry by otherwise distinct pathophysiological processes. Consistent with this hypothesis, neurosurgical procedures that are effective at reducing both obsessive–compulsive and depressive symptoms in intractable cases of OCD and MDD all interrupt the white matter tracts that carry neural projections between the frontal lobe, the basal ganglia, and the thalamus.[1] Although the therapeutic mechanisms of these treatments are unknown, the locations of the surgical lesions placed in such procedures provide further support for the hypothesis that dysfunction involving the connections between the ventral PFC and the basal ganglia may be involved in the pathophysiology of obsessive thoughts and compulsive behaviors.

Wayne C. Drevets

References

1. Jenike, M. A., Baer, L., and Minichiello, W. E. *Obsessive Compulsive Disorders: Theory and Management.* Year Book Medical Publishers, Inc., Chicago.
2. Zohar, J., Murphy, D. L., Zohar-Kadouch, R. C., Pato, M. A. T., Wozniak, K. M., and Insel, T. R. (1990). Serotonin in obsessive compulsive disorder. In: *Serotonin in Major Psychiatric Disorders* (E. F. Coccaro and D. L. Murphy, eds.), pp. 99–126. American Psychiatric Press, Washington DC.
3. Baxter, L. R. (1995). Neuroimaging studies of human anxiety disorders. In *Psychopharmacology: The Fourth Generation of Progress* (F. E. Bloom and D. J. Kupfer, eds.), pp. 921–932. Raven Press, New York.
4. Rauch, S. L., Jenike, M. A., Alpert, N. M., *et al.* (1994). Regional cerebral blood flow measured during symptom provocation in obsessive-compulsive disorder using oxygen 15-labeled carbon dioxide and positron emission tomography. *Arch. Gen. Psychiat.* **51:** 62–70.
5. LaPlane, D., *et al.* (1989). Obsessive-compulsive and other behavioural changes with bilateral basal ganglia lesions. *Brain* **112:** 699–725.
6. Swedo, S. E., Rapoport, J. L., Cheslow, D. L., *et al.* (1989). High prevalence of obsessive-compulsive symptoms in patients with Sydenham's chorea. *Am. J. Psychiat.* **146:** 246–249.
7. Eslinger, P. J., and Damasio, A. R. (1985). Severe disturbance of higher cognition after bilateral frontal lobe ablation: patient EVR. *Neurology* **35:** 1731–1741.
8. Rolls, E. T. (1995). A theory of emotion and consciousness, and its application to understanding the neural basis of emotion. In *The Cognitive Neurosciences* (M. Gazzaniga, ed.), pp. 1091–1106. MIT Press, Cambridge, MA.
9. Nauta, W. J. H. (1989). Reciprocal links of the corpus striatum with the cerebral cortex and limbic system: a common substrate for movement and thought? In *Neurology and Psychiatry: A Meeting of Minds* (J. Mueller, ed.). Karger, New York.

deficits.[86] If the putamen is unilaterally inactivated with the GABA agonist muscimol, the result is slightly slowed movement of the contralateral limb associated with increased activity of antagonist muscles.[87] Reaction time is generally normal, however, indicating that movement initiation is intact. Bilateral electrolytic lesions have had little effect in some studies. In other studies, they have resulted in paucity of movement, severe slowness of movement bilaterally, and postural abnormalities.[86] The reason for this discrepancy is not clear, but it may be due to differences in lesion size.

Huntington disease (or Huntington chorea) is a genetically based, degenerative disease in humans that results in disabling involuntary movements. These movements are called **chorea** (Greek, dance). They are frequent, brief, sudden, random, twitchlike movements that involve all parts of the body and resemble fragments of normal voluntary movement. In contrast to these excessive involuntary movements, the voluntary movements of patients with Huntington disease are slower than normal.[88] As the disease progresses, muscular rigidity appears. The pathologic hallmark of Huntington disease is a marked loss of neurons in the striatum. Surprisingly, however, experimental destruction of striatal neurons in monkeys does not result in chorea,[86] perhaps because the destruction involves neurons that project to the GPe as well as those that project to the GPi. Blocking the striatal–GPe pathway with a GABA antagonist does produce chorea.[89] A possible mechanism for this effect is that disinhibition of the GPe causes inhibition of the STN and ultimately decreased activity in the GPi. This results in abnormal overactivity of motor cortical and brainstem circuits, producing chorea.[29]

Damage to Subthalamic Nucleus Causes Large-Scale Involuntary Movements

In monkeys and humans, electrolytic or pharmacological lesions in the subthalamic nucleus cause dramatic involuntary flinging movements of the contralateral arm and leg.[86,90] These movements resemble chorea in their brief, random, and sudden nature, but they tend to be much larger in amplitude. Because of the flinging quality of these movements, they are referred to as **hemiballismus.** After a lesion in the STN, hemiballismus lasts for days to weeks before gradually resolving. Humans and experimental animals with hemiballismus can still make quite normal voluntary movements.[90] It has been suggested that the mechanism underlying hemiballismus is a loss of excitatory input to GPi, resulting in decreased GPi activity and ultimately in disinhibition of cortical and brainstem motor mechanisms.[29] In fact, blocking excitatory transmission from the STN to the GPi with the glutamate antagonist kynurenate also causes involuntary movements.[91] However, when hemiballismus is produced by an STN lesion in monkeys, it is abolished by a second lesion placed in the GPi.[92] Furthermore, in monkeys with STN lesions, the level of GPi activity is reduced even after hemiballismus resolves.[93] This reduction in activity suggests that hemiballismus is not caused simply by a tonic reduction of GPi activity. It seems more likely that hemiballismus reflects a fluctuating or bursting output from the basal ganglia, but the validity of this idea remains to be demonstrated.

Damage to Globus Pallidus Causes Slow Voluntary Movements and Involuntary Postures and Does Not Delay Movement Initiation

Because of the close proximity of the GPi and the GPe, it is difficult to lesion one without including part of the other. Therefore, one must use caution when interpreting the results of GP lesions. In most cases, however, combined GPe and GPi lesions have an effect similar to the effects of lesions of the GPi alone.[94] Unilateral lesions of the GPe and GPi cause slowness of movement and abnormal cocontraction of agonist and antagonist muscles, but they do not affect the initiation of movement. Bilateral lesions of the GPe and GPi result in even more severely abnormal flexed postures, which affected individuals are apparently unable to move out of.[95] Electrolytic lesions that have produced this severe abnormality have been large, involving both the GPe and the GPi as well as part of the internal capsule. Similar abnormalities are seen with carbon monoxide or carbon disulfide poisoning, which causes neuronal death in the GPi and SNpr.[86]

Lesions restricted to the GPi result in slowness of movement of the contralateral limbs. Reaction time is normal, however, indicating that the mechanisms involved in the initiation of movement are intact. In some studies, the slowness of movement was accompanied by cocontraction of agonist and antagonist muscles, producing rigidity.[91] In most cases, there is relatively more activity in flexor muscles, which is reflected in a tendency for the limbs to assume an abnormally flexed posture. If particular muscles are already contracting, GPi lesions cause movements to be more impaired when these muscles are relaxed than when they are more fully contracted (Fig. 34.11). Thus, lesions that remove the inhibitory output of the basal ganglia appear to interfere with the ability to turn off unwanted muscle activity.[94]

Lesions of Substantia Nigra Pars Reticulata Cause Involuntary Eye Movements

It is difficult to produce electrolytic lesions exclusively in the SNpr because of its proximity to the SNpc. However, it is possible to inactivate neurons focally in the SNpr by using the GABA agonist muscimol.[96] Injection of muscimol into the lateral SNpr inactivates neurons that are normally involved in saccadic eye movements, abolishing the ability to maintain visual fixation because involuntary saccades cannot be suppressed (Fig. 34.12). This defect appears to result from disinhibition of the superior colliculus, because injection of the GABA antagonist bicuculline into the superior colliculus mimics the effects of muscimol injection into the SNpr.[97] Thus, just as GPi inactivation results in abnormal excess limb and trunk muscle activity, SNpr inactivation results in abnormal excess eye movements.

Lesions of Substantia Nigra Pars Compacta Cause Symptoms of Parkinson Disease

Lesions of the SNpc are of particular interest because the dopamine neurons in this nucleus die in **Parkinson**

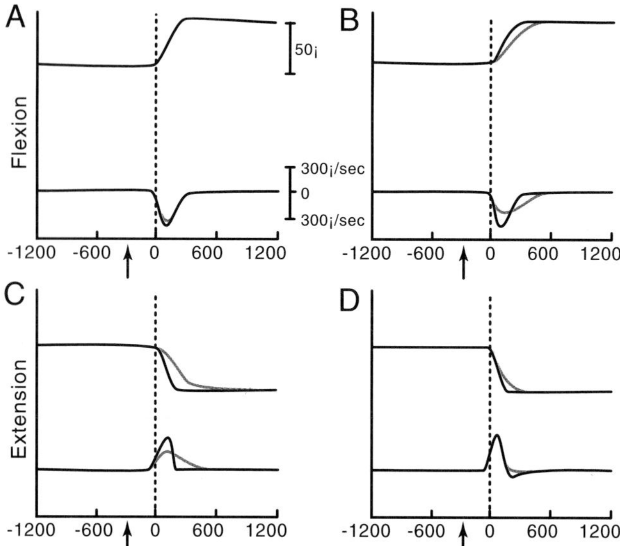

FIGURE 34.11 Wrist position and velocity in visually guided wrist movements before (black traces) and after (blue traces) a lesion of the globus pallidus pars interna. In each graph, the top traces represent wrist position and the lower traces represent wrist velocity. (A) Flexion with the flexor muscles loaded (movement made by further activating the loaded muscles). (B) Flexion with the extensor muscles loaded (movement made by turning off the loaded muscles). (C) Extension with the flexor muscles loaded (movement made by turning off the loaded muscles). (D) Extension with the extensor muscles loaded (movement made by further activating the loaded muscles). After the lesion, the peak velocity was lower for movements made by decreasing the activity of the loaded muscle than for those made by increasing the activity of the loaded muscle. From Mink and Thach.[94]

disease, a neurological disorder that affects older adults. The main symptoms of Parkinson disease are resting tremor that decreases during movement, slowness of movement (**bradykinesia**), paucity of movement (**akinesia**), muscular rigidity, and unstable posture. The primary pathology of the disease is a progressive degeneration of neurons in the SNpc. There is also some loss of dopamine neurons in the ventral tegmental area and of norepinephrine neurons in the locus coeruleus. Although Parkinson disease has been recognized since it was first described by James Parkinson in 1817, a reasonable animal model of the disease was not available until fairly recently. As we noted above, the interdigitation of the SNpc and SNpr has made selective electrolytic lesions of each area difficult to produce. In the 1970s, however, researchers discovered that injection of 6-hydroxydopamine (6-OHDA) bilaterally along the nigrastriatal projection causes selective degeneration of SNpc dopamine neurons. Lesions made in this way result in some of the abnormalities of Parkinson disease, namely, the slowness of movement and rigidity, but they do not produce tremor.[86] In the 1980s, a street drug contaminant called MPTP (see Box 34.3)[98–100] was found to produce all of the symptoms of Parkinson disease in humans and in certain species of monkeys.

Despite extensive investigation, the fundamental mechanism underlying the tremor in Parkinson disease is not known. Some evidence suggests that it results from abnormal bursting of neurons in the thalamus.[101] The slowness of movement in Parkinson disease has been associated with reduced magnitude and duration of muscle activity during movement.[86] In monkeys that have been given 6-OHDA or MPTP, the activity of motor cortex neurons during arm movements is also reduced compared with that in normal monkeys.[102] Some MPTP monkeys have abnormally increased neuronal activity in the STN and GPi and decreased activity in the GPe.[103] GPi neurons in the MPTP monkey have abnormal bursting activity and abnormally increased responses to somatosensory stimuli. It has been suggested that the increased activity of GPi neurons causes excessive inhibition of motor

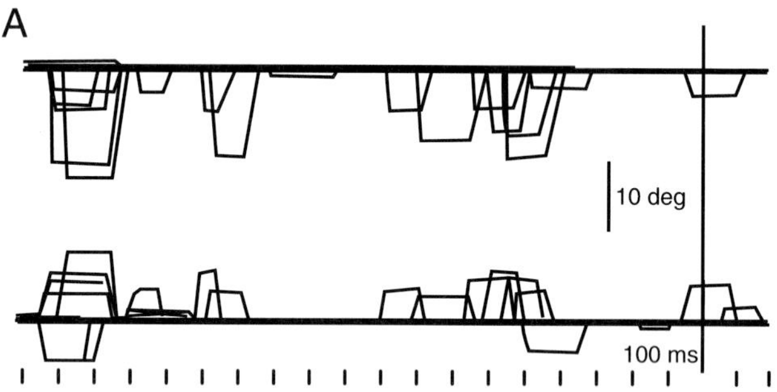

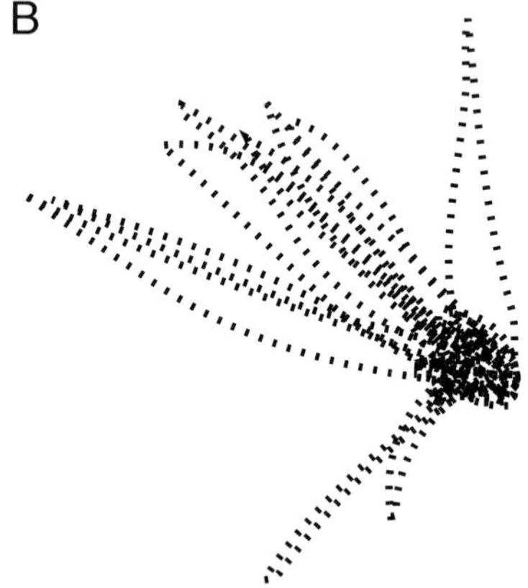

FIGURE 34.12 After inactivation of the substantia nigra pars reticulata, monkeys are unable to maintain fixation of gaze because of involuntary contraction of the eye muscles. (A) Vertical (top traces) and horizontal (bottom traces) eye position during attempted visual fixation. (B) The trajectory of involuntary eye movements in a monkey after injection of muscimol into the lateral SNpr. The monkey was instructed to maintain its gaze at the center dot. From Hikosaka and Wurtz.[96]

mechanisms in the cortex and brainstem, resulting in slower movements.[29,104]

The rigidity of Parkinson disease has been attributed in part to hyperactivity of the transcortical stretch reflex. Normally, this reflex acts to resist displacement from an actively held posture, but it is inhibited when subjects are instructed not to resist the displacement. People with Parkinson disease have abnormally active transcortical stretch reflexes and are unable to suppress them in response to instruction.[105] The inability to inhibit long-loop reflexes may also account for the postural instability of Parkinson disease. Parkinson patients have an inappropriate cocontraction of leg and back muscles in response to perturbation from an upright stance. When the same subjects are perturbed from a sitting position, they are unable to inhibit the postural reflexes that were active during stance.[106] This observation suggests that both rigidity and postural instability may involve an inability to suppress unwanted reflex activity.

Summary

1. Damage to any basal ganglia structures may cause slowness of voluntary movements, involuntary movements, involuntary postures, or a combination of these.
2. Damage to the striatum causes voluntary movements to be slow and may produce involuntary movements or postures depending on the mechanism of damage.
3. Damage to the subthalamic nucleus causes large-amplitude involuntary limb movements.
4. Damage to the globus pallidus causes slowness of movement, abnormal postures, and difficulty relaxing muscles, but does not delay movement initiation.
5. Damage to substantia nigra pars reticulata causes abnormal eye movements, but does not delay the initiation of eye movements.
6. Damage to substantia nigra pars compacta causes tremor at rest, slowness of movement, rigidity, and postural instability, which are the main features of Parkinson disease.

FUNDAMENTAL PRINCIPLES OF BASAL GANGLIA OPERATION

An old model of basal ganglia function proposed that the basal ganglia initiate movement. This model was based in large part on the manifestation of basal ganglia diseases. The paucity and slowness of movement in Parkinson disease were attributed to an inability to initiate movements, and the involuntary movements of chorea and hemiballismus were attributed to the release of normal motor systems from basal ganglia control. This model gained support from the fact that much of the output from the basal ganglia goes to parts of thalamus that project to the premotor and motor cortices. According to the model, motor programs are stored in the basal ganglia and are called up and sent to the motor cortex for execution. This model is no longer widely accepted, because it is now apparent that the basal ganglia are active relatively late in relation to movement and brain mechanisms that are known to be involved in the initiation of movement. Furthermore, lesions of the basal ganglia output nuclei do not delay the initiation of movement.

If the basal ganglia do not initiate movement, what do they do? We consider three current hypotheses. The first states that the basal ganglia contribute to the automatic execution of movement sequences. This hypothesis suggests that other mechanisms initiate the first component in a sequence, but the basal ganglia contain the programs for completing the sequence. The second hypothesis states that the basal ganglia circuitry is made up of opposing parallel pathways that adjust the magnitude of the inhibitory GPi output to increase or decrease movement. According to this hypothesis, increased GPi output slows movement and decreased GPi output increases movement. The third hypothesis states that the basal ganglia output is analogous to a brake. It proposes that a small part of the output decreases during voluntary movement to remove inhibition from the desired motor mechanism, while the majority of the output increases to prevent other motor mechanisms from competing with the desired mechanism.

Do the Basal Ganglia Automatically Generate Learned Movement Sequences?

The sequencing hypothesis states that the basal ganglia are responsible for the automatic execution of learned movement sequences.[107,108] Patients with Parkinson disease have difficulty moving several body parts simultaneously or sequentially, and this difficulty is more than one would expect from a simple addition of the deficits of each component of the movement. An example of difficulty with sequential movements in Parkinson disease is the phenomenon of **micrographia** (small writing). A patient begins to write a sentence with nearly normal-sized writing, but after several letters are written, the writing becomes progressively smaller so that by the end of the sentence, it may be illegible. In micrographia, the early components of the sequence are larger and faster than the subsequent components. One experiment compared the performance of elbow flexion and hand grip individually and in sequence.[109] Patients with Parkinson disease performed each movement more slowly than did normal subjects. However, when each movement was part of a sequence, it was slowed to an even greater degree than when it was performed separately. In monkeys trained to perform two prompt wrist movements in sequence, some GPi neurons fired after the first component of the movement but before the second component.[108] Proponents of the sequencing hypothesis speculate that the loss of the GPi output signal in Parkinson disease is responsible for the relatively greater difficulty in producing sequential movements than in producing individual movements.

Do the Basal Ganglia Produce or Prevent Movement by Using Opposing Direct and Indirect Pathways?

The opponent parallel pathway hypothesis emphasizes two major paths of information flow from the striatum to the GPi and SNpr (Fig. 34.13).[29,104,110] One is an inhibitory "direct" pathway from the striatum to the GPi/SNpr. The other is a net excitatory "indirect" pathway from the striatum to the GPe (inhibitory), from the GPe to the STN (inhibitory), and from the STN to the GPi/SNpr (excitatory). This hypothesis maintains that the two pathways are in balance such that increased activity in the "direct" pathway causes decreased GPi/SNpr output, and increased activity in the "indirect" pathway causes increased GPi/SNpr output. By adjusting the balance, the cortical targets of the basal ganglia can be facilitated or inhibited. The hypothesis predicts that abnormally decreased output results in excessive movement (chorea) and abnormally increased output results in decreased movement (Parkinson disease). The primary evidence for this hypothesis is the finding that activity in the STN and GPi is increased in MPTP monkeys but decreased in monkeys with chorea.[93,103] How the physiology in these pathological states relates to the normal physiology of the basal ganglia output remains unclear.

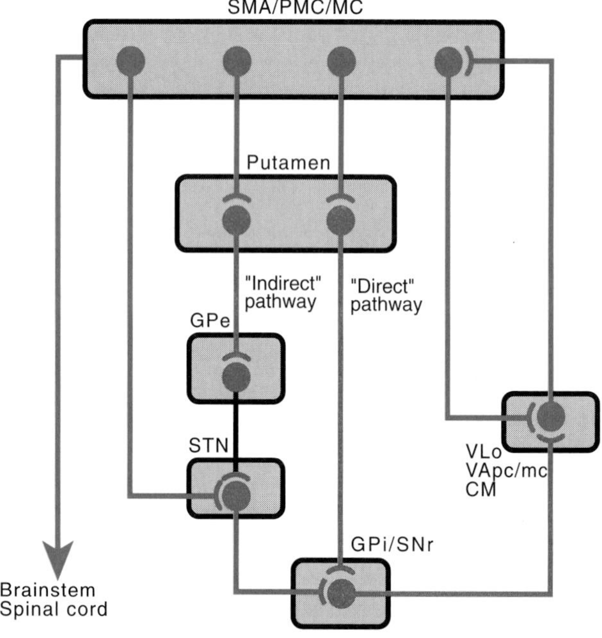

FIGURE 34.13 Schematic diagram of proposed "direct" and "indirect" pathways from the putamen to the GPi. See the text for a description. Red symbols represent inhibitory pathways, and green symbols represent excitatory pathways. From Alexander and Crutcher.[110]

Do the Basal Ganglia Act as a "Brake" to Prevent Unwanted Movement?

The output of the basal ganglia is inhibitory to posture and movement pattern generators in the cerebral cortex (via the thalamus) and in the brainstem. The inhibitory output neurons of the basal ganglia fire tonically at high frequencies. The brake hypothesis states that when a movement is initiated by a particular motor pattern generator, GPi neurons projecting to that generator decrease their firing frequency, thereby removing tonic inhibition and "releasing the brake" on that generator. GPi neurons projecting to other movement pattern generators increase their firing frequency, thereby increasing inhibition and "applying the brake" on those generators.[94,111] Thus, other postures and movements are prevented from interfering with the one selected.

Figure 34.14 illustrates how this mechanism might work. When one makes a voluntary movement, that movement is initiated by the prefrontal, premotor, and motor cortices and the cerebellum. The premotor and motor cortices send a corollary signal to the STN, exciting it. The STN projects to the GPi in a widespread pattern and excites it. In parallel, signals are sent from the cortex to the striatum, which inhibits the GPi focally via a direct pathway. The striatum can also disinhibit the GPi via two indirect pathways (striatum to GPe to GPi, and striatum to GPe to STN to SPi). The indirect pathways further focus the effects of the fast, excitatory, cortico-STN pathway and the slower, inhibitory, corticostriatal pathway to the GPi. The net result is to release the brake from the selected voluntary movement pattern generator and to apply the brake on potentially competing posture-holding pattern generators (transcortical, vestibular, tonic neck, and other postural reflexes).

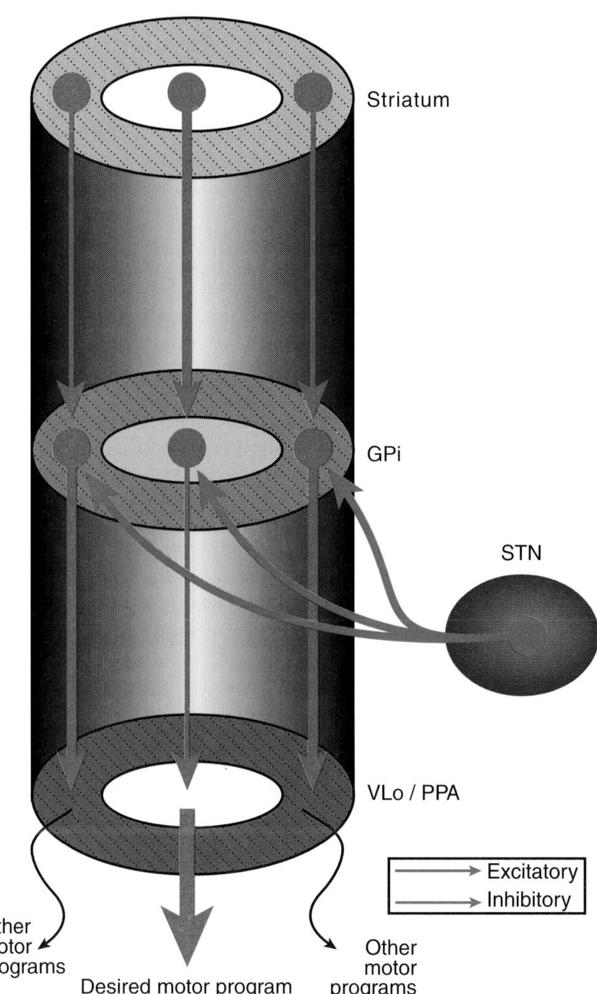

FIGURE 34.14 Relationship of proposed center-surround organization of the GPi to inputs from the striatum and subthalamic nucleus. During voluntary movement, excitatory STN neurons increase the activity of GPi neurons in the surround territory. At the same time, striatal neurons inhibit the functional center of the GPi in a focused manner. The GPi activity changes are conveyed to targets in the thalamus (VLo) and midbrain pedunculopontine area (PPA), causing disinhibition of neurons involved in the desired motor program and inhibition of surrounding neurons involved in competing motor programs. Excitatory projections are indicated by green arrows, and inhibitory projections are indicated by red arrows. The relative magnitude of activity is represented by line thickness.

Summary

The basal ganglia continue to be a target of active investigation. Their circuitry and chemistry are complicated and are still being defined. Diseases of the basal ganglia are relatively common, yet their causes are poorly understood at both a molecular and a systemic level. Although the prevailing hypotheses of basal ganglia differ substantially, they are not necessarily mutually exclusive. With further investigation, these hypotheses may be reconciled, consolidated, or superseded.

References

General

Adams, R. D., and Victor, M. (1993). *Principles of Neurology*, 5th ed. McGraw-Hill, New York.

Houk, J. C., Davis, J. L., and Beiser, D. G., eds. (1995). Models of information processing in the basal ganglia. In *Computational Neuroscience* (T. J. Sejnowski and T. A. Poggio, eds.). MIT Press, Cambridge, MA.

Mano, N., Hamada, I., and DeLong, M. R., eds. (1993). *Role of the Cerebellum and Basal Ganglia in Voluntary Movement.* Int. Congr. Ser. Elsevier, Amsterdam.

Parent, A. (1986). *Comparative Neurobiology of the Basal Ganglia.* Wiley, New York.

Penney, J. B., and Young, A. B. (1983). Speculations on the functional anatomy of basal ganglia disorders. *Annu. Rev. Neurosci.* **6:** 73–94.

Cited

1. Wilson, S. A. K. (1912). Progressive lenticular degeneration: A familial nervous system disease associated with cirrhosis of the liver. *Brain* **34:** 295–207.
2. Wilson, S. A. K. (1928). *Modern Problems in Neurology.* Arnold, London.
3. Nauta, W. J. H., and Mehler, W. H. (1966). Projections of the lentiform nucleus in the monkey. *Brain Res.* **1:** 3–42.
4. Carpenter, M. B. (1981). Anatomy of the corpus striatum and brain stem integrating systems. In *Handbook of Physiology* (V. B. Brooks, ed.), pp. 947–995, Sect. 1, Vol. II, Part 1. Am. Physiol. Soc. Bethesda, MD.
5. O'Rahilly, R., and Muller, F. (1994). *The Embryonic Human Brain.* Wiley-Liss, New York.
6. Gerfen, C. R. (1988). Synaptic organization of the striatum. *J. Electron. Microsc. Tech.* **10:** 265–281.
7. Kemp, J. M., and Powell, P. S. (1971). The structure of the caudate nucleus of the cat: Light and electron microscopy. *Philos. Trans. R. Soc. London, Ser. B* **262:** 383–401.
8. Wilson, C. J., and Groves, P. M. (1980). Fine structure and synaptic connections of the common spiny neuron of the rat neostriatum: A study employing intracellular injection of horseradish peroxidase. *J. Comp. Neurol.* **194:** 599–614.
9. Phelps, P. E., Houser, C. R., and Vaughn, J. E. (1985). Immunocytochemical localization of choline acetyltransferase within the rat neostriatum: A correlated light and electron microscopic study of cholinergic neurons and synapses. *J. Comp. Neurol.* **238:** 286–307.
10. DiFiglia, M., and Aronin, N. (1982). Ultrastructural features of immunoreactive somatostatin neurons in the rat caudate nucleus. *J. Neurosci.* **2:** 1267–1274.
11. Kemp, J. M., and Powell, T. P. S. (1970). The corticostriate projection in the monkey. *Brain* **93:** 525–546.
12. Cherubini, E., Herrling, P. L., Lanfumey, L., and Stanzione, P. (1988). Excitatory amino acids in synaptic excitation of rat striatal neurones in vitro. *J. Physiol. (London)* **400:** 677–690.
13. Bouyer, J. J., Park, D. H., Joh, T. H., and Pickel, V. M. (1984). Chemical and structural analysis of the relation between cortical inputs and tyrosine hydroxylase-containing terminals in rat neostriatum. *Brain Res.* **302:** 267–275.
14. Jones, E. G., Coulter, J. D., Burton, H., and Porter, R. (1977). Cells of origin and terminal distribution of corticostriatal fibers

arising in the sensory-motor cortex of monkeys. *J. Comp. Neurol.* **173:** 53–80.

15. Goldman, P. S., and Nauta, W. J. H. (1977). An intricately patterned prefronto-caudate projection in the rhesus monkey. *J. Comp. Neurol.* **171:** 369–386.
16. Kunzle, H. (1975). Bilateral projections from precentral motor cortex to putamen and other parts of the basal ganglia. An autoradiographic study in *Macaca fascicularis. Brain Res.* **88:** 195–209.
17. Alexander, G. E., DeLong, M. R., and Strick, P. L. (1986). Parallel organization of functionally segregated circuits linking basal ganglia and cortex. *Annu. Rev. Neurosci.* **9:** 357–381.
18. Selemon, L. D., and Goldman-Rakic, P. S. (1985). Longitudinal topography and interdigitation of corticostriatal projections in the rhesus monkey. *J. Neurosci.* **5:** 776–794.
19. Flaherty, A. W., and Graybiel, A. M. (1991). Corticostriatal transformations in the primate somatosensory system. Projections from physiologically mapped body-part representations. *J. Neurophysiol.* **66:** 1249–1263.
20. Graybiel, A. M., Aosaki, T., Flaherty, A. W., and Kimura, M. (1994). The basal ganglia and adaptive motor control. *Science* **265:** 1826–1831.
21. Lapper, S. R., and Bolam, J. P. (1992). Input from the frontal cortex and the parafascicular nucleus to cholinergic interneurons in the dorsal striatum of the rat. *Neuroscience* **51:** 533–545.
22. Sadikot, A. F., Parent, A., and Francois, C. (1992). Efferent connections of the centromedian and parafascicular thalamic nuclei in the squirrel monkey: A PHA-L study of subcortical projections. *J. Comp. Neurol.* **315:** 137–159.
23. Izzo, P. N., and Bolam, J. P. (1988). Cholinergic synaptic input to different parts of spiny striatonigral neurons in the rat. *J. Comp. Neurol.* **269:** 219–234.
24. Penny, G. R., Afsharpour, S., and Kitai, S. T. (1986). The glutamate decarboxylase-, leucine enkephalin-, methionine enkephalin- and substance P-immunoreactive neurons in the neostriatum of the rat and cat: Evidence for partial population overlap. *Neuroscience* **17:** 1011–1045.
25. Surmeier, D. J., Reiner, A., Levine, M. S., and Ariano, M. A. (1993). Are neostriatal dopamine receptors co-localized? *Trends Neurosci.* **16:** 299–305.
26. Ribak, C. E., Vaughn, J. E., and Roberts, E. (1979). The GABA neurons and their axon terminals in rat corpus striatum as demonstrated by GAD immunocytochemistry. *J. Comp. Neurol.* **187:** 261–283.
27. Gerfen, C. R., Engber, T. M., Mahan, L. C., Susel, Z., Chase, T. N., Monsma, F. J., and Sibley, D. R. (1990). D_1 and D_2 dopamine receptor-regulated gene expression of striatonigral and striatopallidal neurons. *Science* **250:** 1429–1432.
28. Gerfen, C. R., and Young, W. S., III (1988). Distribution of striatonigral and striatopallidal peptidergic neurons in both patch and matrix compartments: An in situ hybridization histochemistry and fluorescent retrograde tracing study. *Brain Res.* **460:** 161–167.
29. Albin, R. L., Young, A. B., and Penney, J. B. (1989). The functional anatomy of basal ganglia disorders. *Trends Neurosci.* **12:** 366–375.
30. Graybiel, A. M., and Ragsdale, C. W. (1978). Histochemically distinct compartments in the striatum of human, monkey and cat demonstrated by acetylcholinesterase staining. *Proc. Natl. Acad. Sci. U.S.A.* **75:** 5723–5726.
31. Gerfen, C. R. (1992). The neostriatal mosaic: Multiple levels of compartmental organization in the basal ganglia. *Annu. Rev. Neurosci.* **15:** 285–320.
32. Graybiel, A. M., Ragsdale, C. W., Yoneika, E. S., and Elde, R. P. (1981). An immunohistochemical study of enkephalins and other neuropeptides in the striatum of the cat with evidence that the opiate peptides are arranged to form mosaic patterns in register with striosomal compartments visible with acetylcholinesterase staining. *Neuroscience* **6:** 377–397.
33. Rouzaire-Dubois, B., and Scarnati, E. (1987). Pharmacological study of the cortical-induced excitation of subthalamic nucleus neurons in the rat: Evidence for amino acids as putative neurotransmitters. *Neuroscience* **21:** 429–440.
34. Fujimoto, K., and Kita, H. (1993). Response characteristics of subthalamic neurons to the stimulation of the sensimotor cortex in the rat. *Brain Res.* **609:** 185–192.
35. Hartmann-von Monakow, K., Akert, K., and Kunzle, H. (1978). Projections of the precentral motor cortex and other cortical areas of the frontal lobe to the subthalamic nucleus in the monkey. *Exp. Brain Res.* **33:** 395–403.
36. Kita, H., Chang, H. T., and Kitai, S. T. (1983). Pallidal inputs to subthalamus: Intracellular analysis. *Brain Res.* **264:** 255–265.
37. Rinvik, E., and Ottersen, O. P. (1993). Terminals of subthalamonigral fibres are enriched with glutamate-like immunoreactivity: An electron microscopic, immunogold analysis in the cat. *J. Chem. Neuroanat.* **6:** 19–30.
38. Brotchie, J. M., and Crossman, A. R. (1991). D-[^{3}H]Aspartate and [^{14}C]GABA uptake in the basal ganglia of rats following lesions in the subthalamic region suggest a role for excitatory amino acid but not GABA-mediated transmission in subthalamic nucleus efferents. *Exp. Neurol.* **113:** 171–181.
39. Parent, A., Smith, Y., Filion, M., and Dumas, J. (1989). Distinct afferents to internal and external pallidal segments in the squirrel monkey. *Neurosci. Lett.* **96:** 140–144.
40. Kita, H. (1992). Responses of globus pallidus neurons to cortical stimulation: Intracellular study in the rat. *Brain Res.* **589:** 84–90.
41. DiFiglia, M., and Rafols, J. A. (1988). Synaptic organization of the globus pallidus. *J. Electron. Microsc. Tech.* **10:** 247–263.
42. Francois, C., Percheron, G., Yelnik, J., and Heyner, S. (1984). Golgi analysis of the primate globus pallidus. I. Inconstant processes of large neurons, other neuronal types, and afferent axons. *J. Comp. Neurol.* **227:** 182–199.
43. Percheron, G., Yelnik, J., and Francois, C. (1984). A Golgi analysis of the primate globus pallidus. III. Spatial organization of the striato-pallidal complex. *J. Comp. Neurol.* **227:** 214–227.
44. Parent, A., and Hazrati, L.-N. (1993). Anatomical aspects of information processing in primate basal ganglia. *Trends Neurosci.* **16:** 111–116.
45. Penney, J. B., and Young, A. B. (1981). GABA as the pallidothalamic neurotransmitter: Implications for basal ganglia function. *Brain Res.* **207:** 195–199.
46. Parent, A., and De Bellefeuille, L. (1982). Organization of efferent projections from the internal segment of globus pallidus in primate as revealed by fluorescence retrograde labelling method. *Brain Res.* **245:** 201–213.
47. DeVito, J. L., and Anderson, M. E. (1982). An autoradiographic study of efferent connections of the globus pallidus in *Macaca mulatta. Exp. Brain Res.* **46:** 107–117.
48. Middleton, F. A., and Strick, P. L. (1994). Anatomical evidence for cerebellar and basal ganglia involvement in higher cognitive function. *Science* **266:** 458–461.
49. Hoover, J. E., and Strick, P. L. (1993). Multiple output channels in the basal ganglia. *Science* **259:** 819–821.
50. Rye, D. B., Lee, H. J., Saper, C. B., and Wainer, B. H. (1988). Medullary and spinal efferents of the pedunculopontine tegmental nucleus and adjacent mesopontine tegmentum in the rat. *J. Comp. Neurol.* **269:** 315–341.
51. Francois, C., Yelnik, J., and Percheron, G. (1987). Golgi study of the primate substantia nigra. II. Spatial organization of dendritic arborizations in relation to the cytoarchitectonic bound-

aries and to the striatonigral bundle. *J. Comp. Neurol.* **265:** 473–493.

52. Carpenter, M. B., Nakano, K., and Kim, R. (1976). Nigrothalamic projections in the monkey demonstrated by autoradiographic techniques. *J. Comp. Neurol.* **165:** 401–416.
53. Ueki, A. (1983). The mode of nigro-thalamic transmission investigated with intracellular recording in the cat. *Exp. Brain Res.* **49:** 116–124.
54. Oertel, W. H., and Mugnaini, E. (1984). Immunocytochemical studies of GABAergic neurons in rat basal ganglia and their relations to other neuronal systems. *Neurosci. Lett.* **47:** 233–238.
55. Kievit, J., and Kuypers, H. G. J. M. (1977). Organization of the thalamo-cortical connexions to the frontal lobe in the rhesus monkey. *Exp. Brain Res.* **29:** 299–322.
56. von Krosigk, M., Smith, Y., Bolam, J. P., and Smith, A. D. (1992). Synaptic organization of GABAergic inputs from the striatum and the globus pallidus onto neurons in the substantia nigra and retrorubral field which project to the medullary reticular formation. *Neuroscience* **50:** 531–549.
57. Francois, C., Percheron, G., Yelnik, J., and Tande, D. (1988). A topographic study of the course of nigral axons and of the distribution of pallidal axonal endings in the centre median-parafascicular complex of macaques. *Brain Res.* **473:** 181–186.
58. Rinvik, E., Grofova, I., and Ottersen, O. P. (1976). Demonstration of nigrotectal and nigroreticular projections in the cat by axonal transport of proteins. *Brain Res.* **112:** 388–394.
59. Hikosaka, O., and Wurtz, R. H. (1983). Visual and oculomotor functions of monkey substantia nigra pars reticulata. IV. Relation of substantia nigra to superior colliculus. *J. Neurophysiol.* **49:** 1285–1301.
60. Rouzaire-Dubois, B., Hammond, C., Hamon, B., and Feger, J. (1980). Pharmacological blockade of the globus pallidus-induced inhibitory response of subthalamic cells in the rat. *Brain Res.* **200:** 321–329.
61. Bolam, J. P., and Smith, Y. (1992). The striatum and the globus pallidus send convergent synaptic inputs onto single cells in the entopeduncular nucleus of the rat: A double anterograde labelling study combined with postembedding immunocytochemistry for GABA. *J. Comp. Neurol.* **321:** 456–476.
62. Graybiel, A. M. (1990). Neurotransmitters and neuromodulators in the basal ganglia. *Trends Neurosci.* **13:** 244–254.
63. Hedreen, J. C., and DeLong, M. R. (1991). Organization of striatopallidal, striatonigral, and nigrostriatal projections in the macaque. *J. Comp. Neurol.* **304:** 569–595.
64. Crutcher, M. D., and DeLong, M. R. (1984). Single cell studies of the primate putamen. I. Functional organization. *Exp. Brain Res.* **53:** 233–243.
65. Kimura, M., Kato, M., and Shimazaki, H. (1990). Physiological properties of projection neurons in the monkey striatum to the globus pallidus. *Exp. Brain Res.* **82:** 672–676.
66. Alexander, G. E., and DeLong, M. R. (1985). Microstimulation of the primate striatum. II. Somatopic organization of striatal microexcitable zones and their relation to neuronal response properties. *J. Neurophysiol.* **53:** 1417–1430.
67. Crutcher, M. D., and DeLong, M. R. (1984). Single cell studies of the primate putamen. II. Relations to direction of movements and patterns of muscular activity. *Exp. Brain Res.* **53:** 244–258.
68. Montgomery, E. B., and Buchholz, S. R. (1991). The striatum and motor cortex in motor initiation and execution. *Brain Res.* **549:** 222–229.
69. Romo, R., Scarnati, E., and Schultz, W. (1992). Role of primate basal ganglia and frontal cortex in the internal generation of movements. II. Movement-related activity in the anterior striatum. *Exp. Brain Res.* **91:** 385–395.
70. Schultz, W., and Romo, R. (1992). Role of primate basal ganglia and frontal cortex in the internal generation of movements. I. Preparatory activity in the anterior striatum. *Exp. Brain Res.* **91:** 363–384.
71. Alexander, G. E. (1987). Selective neuronal discharge in monkey putamen reflects intended direction of planned limb movements. *Exp. Brain Res.* **67:** 623–634.
72. Aosaki, T., Tsubokawa, H., Ishida, A., Watanabe, K., Graybiel, A. M., and Kimura, M. (1994). Responses of tonically active neurons in the primate's striatum undergo systematic changes during behavioral sensorimotor conditioning. *J. Neurosci.* **14:** 3969–3984.
73. Wichmann, T., Bergman, H., and DeLong, M. R. (1994). The primate subthalamic nucleus. I. Functional properties in intact animals. *J. Neurophysiol.* **72:** 494–506.
74. Hikosaka, O., Matsumura, M., Kojima, J., and Gardiner, T. W. (1993). Role of the basal ganglia in initiation and suppression of saccadic eye movements. In *Role of the Cerebellum and Basal Ganglia in Voluntary Movement*, (N. Mano, I. Hamada, and M. R. DeLong, eds.). Elsevier, Amsterdam.
75. DeLong, M. R., Crutcher, M. D., and Georgopoulos, A. P. (1985). Primate globus pallidus and subthalamic nucleus: functional organization. *J. Neurophysiol.* **53:** 530–543.
76. Georgopoulos, A. P., DeLong, M. R., and Crutcher, M. D. (1983). Relation between parameters of step-tracking movements and single cell discharge in the globus pallidus and subthalamic nucleus of the behaving monkey. *J. Neurosci.* **3:** 1586–1598.
77. DeLong, M. R. (1971). Activity of pallidal neurons during movement. *J. Neurophysiol.* **34:** 414–427.
78. Hikosaka, O., and Wurtz, R. H. (1983). Visual and oculomotor functions of monkey substantia nigra pars reticulata. I. Relation of visual and auditory responses to saccades. *J. Neurophysiol.* **49:** 1230–1253.
79. DeLong, M. R., Crutcher, M. D., and Georgopoulos, A. P. (1983). Relations between movement and single cell discharge in the substantia nigra of the behaving monkey. *J. Neurosci.* **3:** 1599–1606.
80. Mink, J. W., and Thach, W. T. (1991). Basal ganglia motor control. II. Late pallidal timing relative to movement onset and inconsistent pallidal coding of movement parameters. *J. Neurophysiol.* **65:** 301–329.
81. Hikosaka, O., and Wurtz, R. H. (1983). Visual and oculomotor functions of monkey substantia nigra pars reticulata. II. Visual responses related to fixation of gaze. *J. Neurophysiol.* **49:** 1254–1267.
82. Hikosaka, O., and Wurtz, R. H. (1983). Visual and oculomotor functions of monkey substantia nigra pars reticulata. III. Memory-contingent visual and saccade responses. *J. Neurophysiol.* **49:** 1268–1284.
83. Mink, J. W., and Thach, W. T. (1991). Basal ganglia motor control. I. Nonexclusive relation of pallidal discharge to five movement modes. *J. Neurophysiol.* **65:** 273–300.
84. Schultz, W., Apicella, P., and Ljungberg, T. (1993). Responses of monkey dopamine neurons to reward and conditioned stimuli during successive steps of learning a delayed response task. *J. Neurosci.* **13:** 900–913.
85. Schultz, W., and Romo, R. (1990). Dopamine neurons of the monkey midbrain: Contingencies of responses to stimuli eliciting immediate behavioral reactions. *J. Neurophysiol.* **63:** 607–624.
86. DeLong, M. R., and Georgopoulos, A. P. (1981). Motor functions of the basal ganglia. In *Handbook of Physiology* (V. B. Brooks, ed.), pp. 1017–1062, Sect. 1, Vol. II, Part 1. Am. Physiol. Soc., Bethesda, MD.

87. Kato, M., and Kimura, M. (1992). Effects of reversible blockade of basal ganglia on a voluntary arm movement. *J. Neurophysiol.* **68:** 1516–1534.

88. Thompson, P. D., Berardelli, A., Rothwell, J. C., Day, B. L., Dick, J. P. R., Benecke, R., and Marsden, C. D. (1988). The coexistence of bradykinesia and chorea in Huntington's disease and its implications for theories of basal ganglia control of movement. *Brain* **111:** 223–244.

89. Crossman, A. R. (1987). Primate models of dyskinesia: The experimental approach to the study of basal ganglia-related involuntary movement disorders. *Neuroscience* **21:** 1–40.

90. Hamada, I., and DeLong, M. R. (1992). Excitotoxic acid lesions of the primate subthalamic nucleus result in transient dyskinesias of the contralateral limbs. *J. Neurophysiol.* **68:** 1850–1858.

91. Robertson, R. G. Farmery, S. M., Sambrook, M. A., and Crossman, A. R. (1989). Dyskinesia in the primate following injection of an excitatory amino acid antagonist into the medial segment of the globus pallidus. *Brain Res.* **476:** 317–322.

92. Carpenter, M. B., Whittier, J. R., and Mettle, F. A. (1950). Analysis of choreoid hyperkinesia in the rhesus monkey. Surgical and pharmacological analysis of hyperkinesia resulting from lesions in the subthalamic nucleus of Luys. *J. Comp. Neurol.* **92:** 293–331.

93. Hamada, I., and DeLong, M. R. (1992). Excitotoxic acid lesions of the primate subthalamic nucleus result in reduced pallidal neuronal activity during active holding. *J. Neurophysiol.* **68:** 1859–1866.

94. Mink, J. W., and Thach, W. T. (1991). Basal ganglia motor control. III. Pallidal ablation: Normal reaction time, muscle cocontraction, and slow movement. *J. Neurophysiol.* **63:** 330–351.

95. Denny-Brown, D. (1962). *The Basal Ganglia.* Oxford University Press, London.

96. Hikosaka, O., and Wurtz, R. H. (1985). Modification of saccadic eye movements by GABA-related substances. II. Effects of muscimol in monkey substantia nigra pars reticulata. *J. Neurophysiol.* **53:** 292–308.

97. Hikosaka, O., and Wurtz, R. H. (1985). Modification of saccadic eye movements by GABA-related substances. I. Effect of muscimol and bicuculline in monkey superior colliculus. *J. Neurophysiol.* **53:** 266–291.

98. Langston, J. W., Ballard, P., Tetrud, J., and Irwin, I. (1983). Chronic Parkinsonism in humans due to a product of meperidine-analog synthesis. *Science* **219:** 979–980.

99. Tipton, K. F., and Singer, T. P. (1993). Advances in our understanding of the mechanisms of the neurotoxicity of MPTP and related compounds. *J. Neurochem.* **61:** 1191–1206.

100. Crossman, A. R., Clarke, C. E., Boyce, S., Robertson, R. G., and Sambrook, M. A. (1987). MPTP-induced Parkinsonism in the monkey: Neurochemical pathology, complications of treatment and pathophysiological mechanisms. *Can. J. Neurol. Sci.* **14:** 428–435.

101. Pare, D., Curro'Dossi, R., and Steriade, M. (1990). Neuronal basis of the parkinsonian resting tremor: A hypothesis and its implications for treatment. *Neuroscience* **35:** 217–226.

102. Watts, R. L., and Mandir, A. S. (1992). The role of motor cortex in the pathophysiology of voluntary movement deficits associated with Parkinsonism. *Neurol. Clin.* **10:** 451–469.

103. Wichmann, T., Bergman, H., and DeLong, M. R. (1994). The primate subthalamic nucleus. III. Changes in motor behavior and neuronal activity in the internal pallidum induced by subthalamic inactivation in the MPTP model of Parkinsonism. *J. Neurophysiol.* **72:** 521–530.

104. DeLong, M. R. (1990). Primate models of movement disorders of basal ganglia origin. *Trends Neurosci.* **13:** 281–285.

105. Tatton, W. G., and Lee, R. G. (1975). Evidence for abnormal long-loop reflexes in rigid Parkinsonian patients. *Brain Res.* **100:** 671–676.

106. Horak, F. B., Nutt, J. G., and Nashner, L. M. (1992). Postural inflexibility in Parkinsonian subjects. *J. Neurol. Sci.* **111:** 46–58.

107. Marsden, C. D. (1987). What do the basal ganglia tell premotor cortical areas? *Ciba Found. Symp.* **132:** 282–300.

108. Brotchie, P., Iansek, R., and Horne, M. K. (1991). Motor function of the monkey globus pallidus. 2. Cognitive aspects of movement and phasic neuronal activity. *Brain* **114:** 1685–1702.

109. Benecke, R., Rothwell, J. C., Dick, J. P. R., Day, B. L., and Marsden, C. D. (1986). Performance of simultaneous movements in patients with Parkinson's disease. *Brain* **109:** 739–757.

110. Alexander, G. E., and Crutcher, M. D. (1990). Functional architecture of basal ganglia circuits: Neural substrates of parallel processing. *Trends Neurosci.* **13:** 266–271.

111. Mink, J. W., and Thach, W. T. (1993). Basal ganglia intrinsic circuits and their role in behavior. *Curr. Opin. Neurobiol.* **3:** 950–957.

112. DeLong, M. R., Georgopoulos, A. P., Crutcher, M. D., Mitchell, S. J., Richardson, R. T., and Alexander, G. E. (1984). Functions of the basal ganglia. *Ciba Found. Symp.* **107:** 64–82.

CHAPTER

35

Cerebellum

Amy J. Bastian, Enrico Mugnaini, and W. Thomas Thach

The cerebellum is a major part of the brain, occupying between a third and a quarter of the cranial capacity in humans. It receives sensory, motor, perceptual, and cognitive information from all parts of the nervous system, and its output is sent to all parts of the motor system, except the basal ganglia (see Chapter 34). The cerebellum also projects to areas of the frontal lobe in the cerebral cortex that may be involved in generating movement and planning future behavior. The recognized role of the cerebellum is to provide for coordination and fine control of movement. It is thought to accomplish this by building up through trial and error complex motor responses that may be triggered automatically.

ANATOMY AND PHYLOGENETIC DEVELOPMENT OF THE CEREBELLUM

The cerebellum is present in all vertebrates and in the most primitive prevertebrates (myxinoids) up through the most advanced vertebrates (primates).[1–4] In agnathans (lampreys and hagfish), it is a rudimentary structure that assists the functions of the well-developed vestibuloocular, vestibulospinal, and reticulospinal systems. The cerebellum is somewhat larger in fishes, where, on the input side, it processes sensory information from the vestibular, lateral line, and, to a lesser extent, proprioceptive and somatosensory systems; on the output side, it is connected to the vestibular and reticular nuclei (see Box 35.1). In amphibians, the region of the cerebellum that receives proprioceptive and other sensory information is expanded. This region, called the corpus cerebella, increases further in reptiles, birds, and mammals. In these vertebrate classes, it constitutes the largest portion of the cerebellum, receiving proprioceptive, somatosensory, visual, and auditory information and projecting to the tectum, the red nucleus, and the cerebral cortex via the thalamus. In primates, the hugely expanded lateral hemispheres of the corpus cerebella are connected with the enlarged cerebral cortex (Fig. 35.1). The hemispheres receive information from the frontal, parietal, and visual cortices by way of pontine nuclei and project to the motor and premotor cortices as well as to more anterior portions of the frontal lobe (Fig. 35.2).[5–12]

The Cerebellum Can Be Subdivided on the Basis of Phylogeny, Anatomy, and the Effect of Lesions

Superficially, the cerebellum consists of a three-layered cortex folded in thin, parallel strips called **folia** (leaves), which in most species run roughly transverse to the long axis of the body (Fig. 35.2). The cerebellar cortex surrounds three pairs of deep cerebellar nuclei. From medial to lateral, the deep cerebellar nuclei are the **fastigius,** the **interpositus** (which is further divided into the globose and emboliform nuclei in humans), and the **dentate.** The deep cerebellar nuclei and the **vestibular nuclei** constitute the output structures of the cerebellum. An inner mass of white matter contains axons that run between the cerebellar cortex and the deep cerebellar nuclei.

The cerebellum is divided into three lobes.[1] The **flocculonodular lobe** (vestibulocerebellum) is located on the inferior surface and is separated from the **posterior lobe** via the posterolateral fissure. Superior to the posterior lobe is the **anterior lobe:** these two lobes are separated by the primary fissure. The lobes are further divided into **lobules**[2–4] (Fig. 35.2), which are numbered I–X beginning at the dorsal anterior vermis and ending

BOX 35.1

THE GIGANTOCEREBELLUM

The weakly electric fish (family Mormyridae) have an enormous cerebellar structure called the gigantocerebellum. On a per body-weight basis, the gigantocerebellum is comparable in weight to the human cerebellum.[124] The largest portion of the gigantocerebellum, called the valvula, has a Purkinje cell layer that would stretch to approximately 1 m if unfolded. That length is similar to the length of the Purkinje cell layer in the entire human cerebellum.[124] The valvula receives inputs from the electrosensory organs, the lateral line, and possibly the visual system. The functional significance of this massive expansion of the cerebellum is a mystery.[125]

at the inferior posterior vermis. Each lobule contains a number of folia. Lobulation is fairly consistent across individuals of the same species and extends with few exceptions across species, despite great variation in hemispheric development.

The corpus cerebella can be divided into three longitudinal zones (medial, intermediate, and lateral) based on the projection of the cortex onto the three deep nuclei.[1] These zones differ in the type of information that comes into them over mossy fibers. The medial zone is dominated by information from vestibular, somatosensory, visual, and auditory regions. The intermediate zone receives proprioceptive and somatosensory information from the spinal cord, as well as information from the motor cortex via the pontocerebellar nuclei.[13] The lateral zone receives information via the pontine nuclei from the motor cortex, the premotor cortex (area 6), and perhaps all of the rest of the cerebral cortex, with the possible exception of portions of the temporal lobes.[14] It was once thought that the outputs of the zones (and nuclei) were also segregated—flocculonodular lobe to vestibular nuclei, fastigius to vestibular and reticulospinal systems, interpositus to red nucleus, and dentate (via thalamus) to motor cortex—but we now know that this picture is greatly oversimplified. Although there may be a predominance to projection along these lines, there is also a great deal of overlap. Thus, vestibular, fastigial, interposed, and dentate nuclei all project via the thalamus to the motor cortex, and vestibular, fastigial, and interposed nuclei all project directly to the spinal cord.[5–8]

Staining for acetylcholinesterase and many other markers reveals strips running sagittally within the longitudinal zones.[15–18] This dimension seems equally important in embryogenesis and in function as the mediolateral development of the parallel fiber system. The strips, which have been given names (c1, c2, etc.), are constant in their presence and location within a species and to some extent across species. They have been used chiefly as anatomical markers for physiolog-

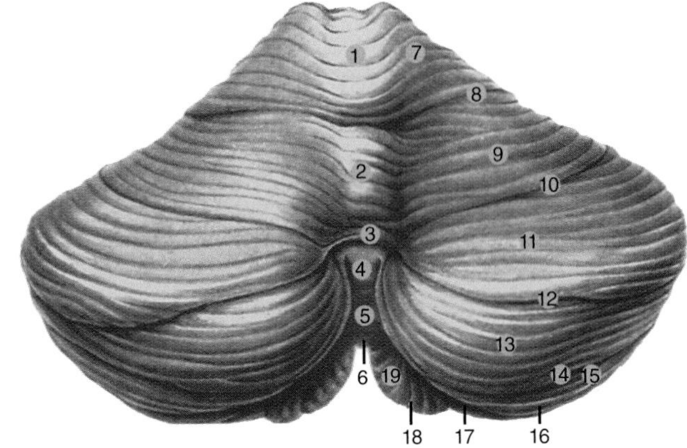

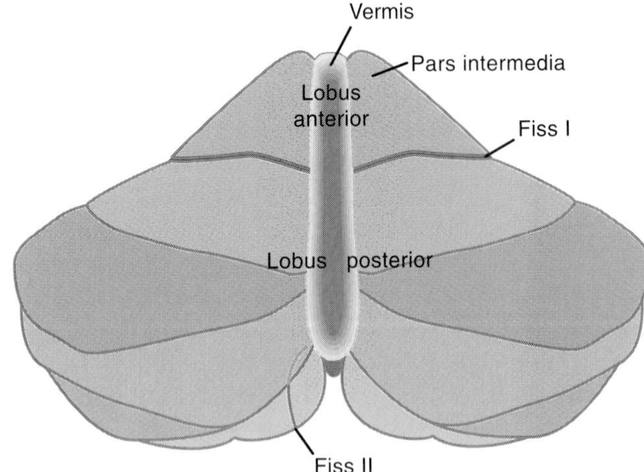

FIGURE 35.1 Cerebellar structure and functional subdivisions. (A) Dorsal view of the human cerebellum. (B) Functional subdivisions. Adapted from Nieuwenhuys, Voogd, and van Huijzen (1979).

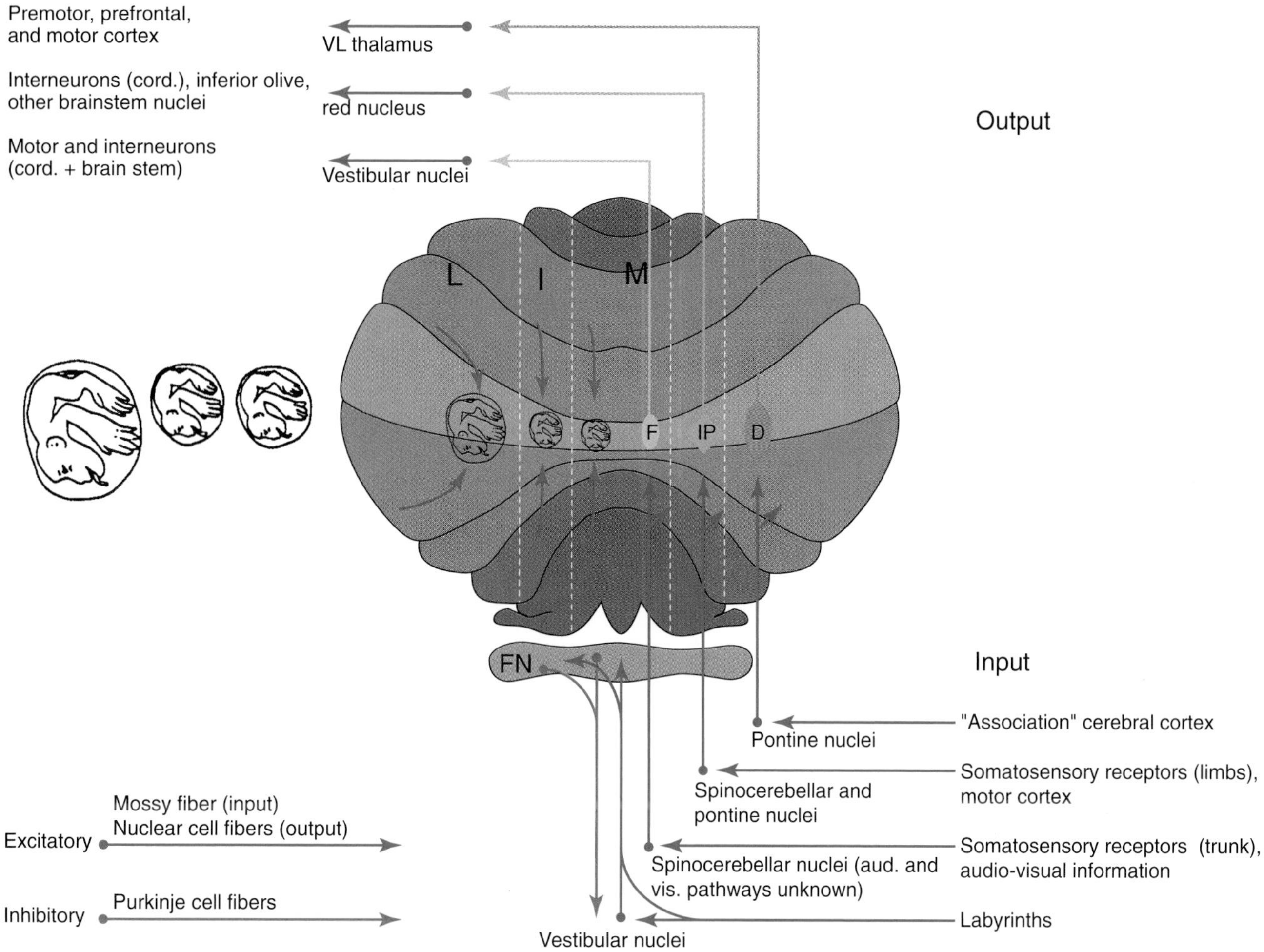

FIGURE 35.2 Cerebellar inputs and outputs. The cerebellum is shown schematically with the flocculonodular (FN) lobe unfolded and represented at the inferior surface. Green arrows indicate excitatory projections into and out of the cerebellum; red arrows indicate the inhibitory projections from cerebellar cortex to the deep cerebellar nuclei and the vestibular nuclei. Adapted from Thach, Fig. 31-3. In: Mountcastle, J. B. (1980). *Medical Physiology,* Volume I. 14 Ed. C. V. Mosby Co., St. Louis.

ical experiments, although whether they represent afferent mossy and climbing fibers, efferent Purkinje fibers, or boundaries between them is not clear.

Various attempts have been made to divide the cerebellum according to its functional organization. Fulton and Dow[19–21] described three divisions in the monkey based on different behavioral abnormalities that resulted when each was damaged. Lesion of the **vestibulocerebellum** (flocculonodular lobe) caused ipsilateral jerk nystagmus, head tilt (occiput to the side of the lesion), and circling gait.[21] These deficits were interpreted as consistent with disturbed vestibular function. Lesion of the **spinocerebellum** (anterior lobe and lobulus simplex) impaired gait without impairing reaching, deficits interpreted as consistent with abnormal spinal control of walking.[19] Lesion of the **cerebrocerebellum** (**pontocerebellum**) caused inaccuracy in reaching and clumsiness of hand movements, suggesting impaired voluntary control of body parts.[20] These results were confirmed and extended with lesions of the deep nuclei in the cat.[22–24]

Another scheme based on functional organization arose from cerebellar input mapping studies that revealed a somatotopic map in the anterior lobe of the cerebellum, with trunk in the midline, limbs lateral, tail anterior, and head posterior.[25–27] Each paramedian lobule also has a small ipsilateral map whose head region is contiguous with that of the anterior lobe map. It has been argued from these maps that the midline cerebellum controls the trunk, the lateral cerebellum controls distal limb parts, and the intermediate zone controls proximal limb parts. This scheme differs from that of Fulton and Dow, which holds that each major subdivision controls all parts of the body for a specific range of behaviors (e.g., behaviors under vestibular control, reflex control, and voluntary control).

Most Cerebellar Input Arrives over Mossy Fibers and Climbing Fibers

The **mossy fiber** is the main operational input to the cerebellum, carrying afferent information from both the periphery and other brain centers[28–30] (Table 35.1). Because mossy fibers originate from second-order sensory neurons, some processing of even the most direct afferent information occurs before that information is sent to the cerebellum. All mossy fiber input into the cerebellum is excitatory (glutamate),[31,32] and many mossy fibers send a branch to excite the nuclear cells before the main trunk ascends to the cortex. In the cortex, mossy fibers make complex synapses with granule cells and Golgi cells in the **granule cell layer**; these synapses cause granule cell axons (also called parallel fibers) to excite Purkinje cells to generate "simple spikes" and other cerebellar cortical neurons (Figs. 35.3 and 35.4).

Mossy fibers that project to the vestibulocerebellum come from neurons in the vestibular nuclei, while those that project to vermal cerebellar cortical regions and the fastigius nucleus come from the spinocerebellar pathway, the vestibular nuclei, and the reticular nuclei. The intermediate zone of the cerebellar cortex and the interpositus nuclei receive mossy fibers from the periphery via the spinocerebellar tracts and from the motor cortex via the pons.[29,30] Finally, mossy fibers that project to the lateral zone of the cerebellar cortex and

TABLE 35.1 Afferent Systems to Cerebellum

Tract	Origin	Via	Distribution	Impulses transmitted
Dorsal spino-cerebellar	Clarke's column (T_1-L_2)	ICP	Chiefly uncrossed to vermis and intermediate part of anterior lobe and pyramis; some fibers to tuber, uvula, and medial part of paramedian lobule	Proprioceptive (muscles and joints) and exteroceptive (skin), from trunk, hind limb, and tail
Ventral spino-cerebellar	"Border" cells of ventral horn	SCP	Crossed and uncrossed to vermis of anterior lobe	Proprioceptive (muscles and joints) and exteroceptive (skin), from all parts of body
Cuneocere-bellar	External arcuate nucleus	ICP	Uncrossed to vermis and intermediate part of anterior lobe and pyramis; some fibers to uvula and tuber	Proprioceptive, from upper limb and neck
Olivocere-bellar	All parts of inferior olive	ICP	Chiefly crossed to all parts of cortex and all intracerebellar nuclei; partly uncrossed to nucleus fastigii	From all levels of spinal cord; from higher nuclei and from cerebral cortex
Pontocere-bellar	All parts of pontine gray	MCP	Chiefly crossed to all cortex except nodulofloccular lobe; partly uncrossed to vermis	From all four lobes of cerebrum, spinal cord, and other centers
Reticulo-cerebellar	Lateral reticular nucleus	ICP	Uncrossed to entire cerebellar cortex	From all levels of spinal cord and from higher levels
	Paramedian reticular nucleus	ICP	More than half uncrossed to anterior lobe; some to pyramis, uvula, and nucleus fastigii	From higher levels, including cerebral cortex
Vestibulo-cerebellar	Vestibular nuclei, chiefly medial and descending	ICP	Secondary fibers (crossed and uncrossed) to nodulofloccular lobe, some to uvula and nucleus fastigii	Vestibular
Perihypo-glosso-cerebellar	Nucleus of roller Nuclear praepositus Nucleus intercalatus	ICP	More than half uncrossed to anterior lobe; some to pyramis, uvula, and nucleus fastigii	
Tectocere-bellar	Quadrigeminal bodies	SCP	Chiefly crossed, probably to declive, folium, and tuber	Auditory and visual
Trigemino-cerebellar	Secondary fibers from all parts of trigeminal nucleus	ICP	Forming part of commissura cerebelli	Tactile and proprioceptive, from face and jaw

Note. ICP, inferior cerebellar peduncle; MCP, middle cerebellar peduncle; SCP, superior cerebellar peduncle.

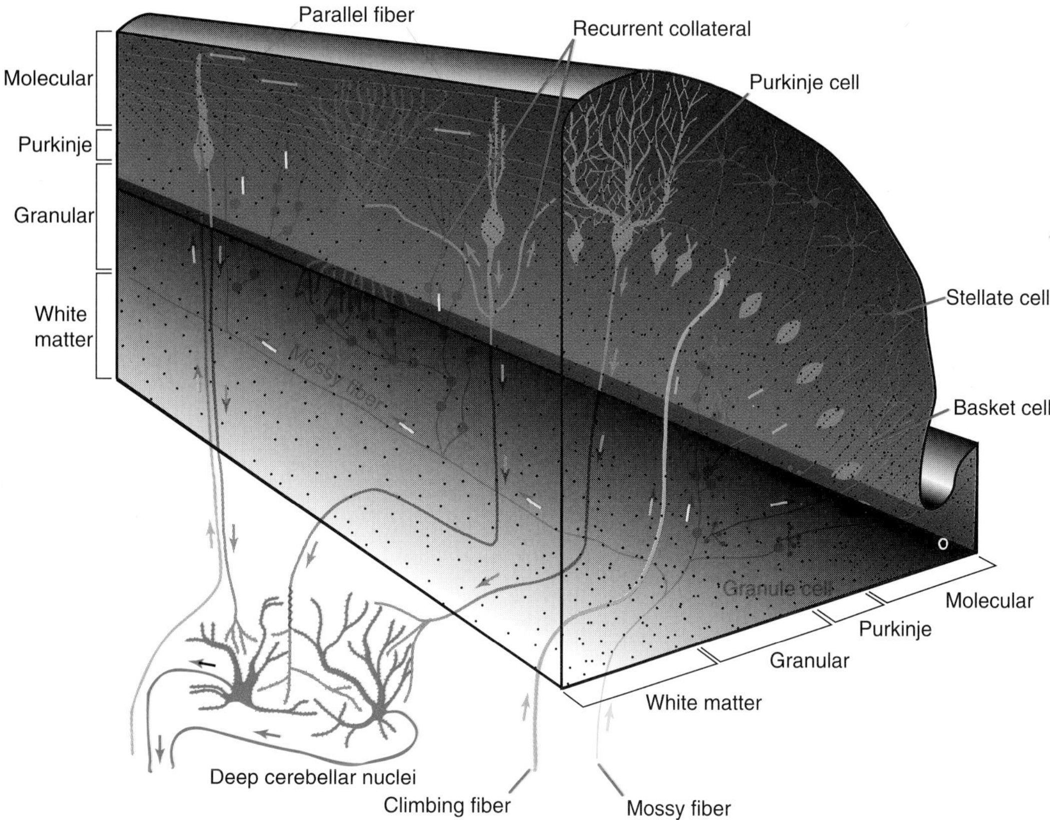

FIGURE 35.3 Schematic view of cerebellar cortex. This section shows the three-dimensional relationship between the different cell types—specifically, the medullary layer or white matter, granular layer, basket cells, stellate cells, Purkinje cells, Golgi cells, granular cells, parallel fibers, climbing fibers, mossy fibers, deep cerebellar nuclei, and recurrent collaterals. Adapted from Fox, C. A. (1962). The structure of the cerebellar cortex. In *Correlative Anatomy of the Nervous System*. New York, MacMillan. [Fig. 16.10A].

the dentate nucleus arise from the basal pontine nuclei. The basal pontine nuclei receive information from virtually the entire cerebral cortex but primarily from the premotor, supplementary motor area, sensorimotor, parietal association, and visual cortices.[33–37]

Another type of input to the cerebellum is the **climbing fiber,** which comes exclusively from the **inferior olive,** which is located in the brainstem.[28,31] Climbing fibers branch in the sagittal plane and make contact with up to 10 Purkinje cells in the molecular layer of the cortex. Each Purkinje cell receives input from only one climbing fiber, which contacts it many times on the soma and proximal dendrites in a very powerful excitatory synapse (glutamate). It fires at about 1 s^{-1}[38,39] and increases firing of these "complex spikes" (Fig. 35.4) as an animal encounters novel conditions or tries to adapt movements.[40–43] When Purkinje cell firing is coupled with that of the parallel fibers, the strength of the parallel fiber contact on the Purkinje cell is reduced.[44–47] This phenomenon, which is an example of

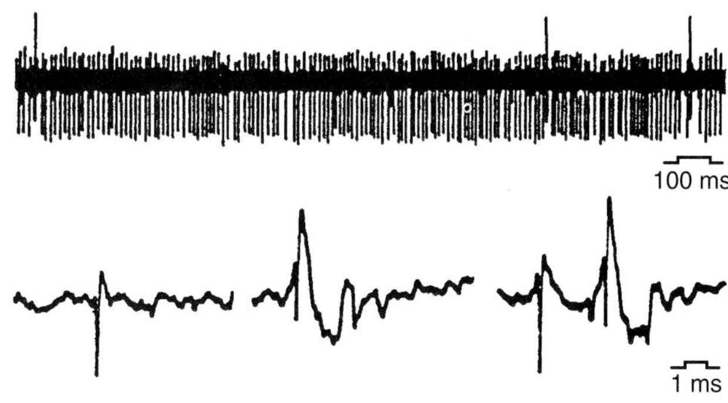

FIGURE 35.4 Maintained discharge of a Purkinje cell recorded extracellularly from an awake, behaving monkey. The "simple" and "complex" spikes are shown. The top trace shows the relationship between simple and complex spikes over a few seconds. The bottom traces show simple and complex spikes individually and together over smaller periods of time to demonstrate the different waveform patterns. Adapted from Thach.[38]

long-term depression (Chapter 58), is thought to be an important mechanism in **motor learning.**

Nonlaminar Afferents Are a Third Source of Cerebellar Inputs

A class of cerebellar afferents with nonlaminar distributions originates in the locus ceruleus, raphe nuclei, and other undefined brainstem nuclei. These afferents innervate the deep cerebellar nuclei and all cortical layers, with some preference for the molecular layer. Afferent fibers from the locus ceruleus release norepinephrine,[48–50] fibers from the raphe nuclei release serotonin (5HT), and fibers from the undefined brainstem nuclei release acetylcholine (ACh). All three nonlaminar fiber systems synapse on Purkinje cells, although they also target cortical neurons in all layers.

Synapses of nonlaminar afferents have been difficult to define at the electron microscopic level for several reasons.[50,51] The afferents are rather sparse and form terminal branches that mimic those of other cerebellar fibers. They may ascend radially from the granular layer and divide into two branches that run longitudinally in the folia, where they resemble parallel fibers; they may ascend into the molecular layer and branch along the dendritic arbors of Purkinje cells, resembling stunted climbing fibers; or they may form ascending and descending collaterals in the molecular layer, resembling stellate cell axons. In the granular layer, the branches of nonlaminar afferents intermingle with the axonal plexus of Golgi cells. With standard preparation methods, the synaptic vesicles contained in the varicosities of nonlaminar afferents are difficult to distinguish from the vesicles of granule cell axons. Some confusion also arises because certain mossy fiber endings in the caudal cerebellum have serotonin uptake properties similar to those of nonlaminar afferents from the raphe nuclei.[50,51] Distinct active zones and postsynaptic densities have been identified for all three nonlaminar afferent systems, although one can not exclude that these afferents may also release their transmitters at nonspecialized regions of their terminal branches.

The Cerebellar Cortex Contains Five Types of Neurons

The three-layered cerebellar cortex contains a highly regular arrangement of only five cell types.[29–32] Two types of inhibitory interneurons, called **stellate cells** and **basket cells,** are found in the outermost molecular layer. Also in the molecular layer are the excitatory **parallel fibers** of granule cells (so named because they run parallel to the folia) and the dendritic arbors of Purkinje cells and Golgi cells. The Purkinje cell layer contains only the somata of the large **Purkinje cells.** The granule cell layer contains an enormous number of small **granule cells** as well as other inhibitory neurons called **Golgi II cells.** Also found in the granule cell layer are numerous **glomeruli,** specialized synaptic clusters containing mossy fiber terminals, granule cell dendrites, and Golgi II cell axons and dendrites.

Each mossy fiber excites up to 30 granule cells, and each granule cell receives input from five to eight mossy fibers. Granule cell axons branch to form the parallel fibers, each of which extends 5–10 mm through the cortex and releases glutamate onto the dendritic spines of 2000–3000.[52] The parallel fibers in any one region of the cortex may come from granule cells in the medial, intermediate, and lateral zones of the cerebellum. Thus, each Purkinje cell may receive information about sensory conditions, internal states, external states, and the plans of the organism. Purkinje cells inhibit neurons in the deep cerebellar nuclei by releasing γ-aminobutyric acid (GABA). Since basket cells in one region of the cortex can inhibit Purkinje cells flanking that region, they effectively excite (through disinhibition) the deep nuclear neurons that receive input from those Purkinje cells.

Cerebellar Output Structures Develop First

Cerebellar cell types develop at different times and at different places.[53–55] The first cells to be formed are the neurons of the deep cerebellar nuclei. They are followed soon after by Purkinje cells, which originate in the ventricular epithelium and migrate to their ultimate location in the cortex. Golgi II cells, basket cells, stellate cells, astrocytes, and Bergmann glia also originate at the ventricular epithelium and migrate to their final positions after the migration of the Purkinje cells. The Bergmann glia later guide the descent of the granule cells from the external granule cell layer.

Cerebellar Input Structures Develop Next

Once the Purkinje, Golgi II, basket, and stellate cells have formed, climbing fibers enter the cerebellum from the inferior olive and begin to innervate the Purkinje cells. Much later, after the Purkinje cells have begun to receive synapses from parallel fibers, most of the climbing fiber contacts with Purkinje cells will be eliminated. Mossy fibers also enter the cerebellum and grow to the level just below the Purkinje cell layer. They will ultimately synapse on granule cells, which have yet to arrive.

The granule cells first develop at a very distant site, posterior and lateral in the anlagen at the rhombic lip. They then crawl over the Purkinje cells to form an

BOX 35.2

ANIMAL MODELS OF CEREBELLAR DEVELOPMENT

Several genetic mutations in mice perturb the normal development of the cerebellum. In the *weaver* mutation, granule cells (and thus parallel fibers) are absent, causing Purkinje cells to develop abnormally organized dendrites with an excessive number of spines.[126] The *reeler* mutation causes Purkinje cells to migrate abnormally, resulting in a large displacement of Purkinje cells within the central cerebellar mass.[127] In the *staggerer* mutation, most Purkinje cells are absent before granule cell migration,[128] while in the *nervous* mutation, Purkinje cells begin to develop normally but then degenerate after most synaptic connections with parallel fibers have been formed.[129] Studies of these and other mutations that cause specific cellular components to be deleted at different developmental stages are furthering our understanding of the complex cellular interactions that take place during normal synaptogenesis.

external granule cell layer. Some granule cells may cross the midline to the other side of the cerebellum as they make this migration. The granule cells extend their axons, which branch to form parallel fibers that run as coronal beams through the dendrites of the Purkinje cells. Only then do the granule cells descend, guided by the Bergmann glia, to form the internal granule cell layer. Each granule cell is connected by the proximal portion of its axon to the branch point of its parallel fibers, which remain in the external granule cell layer. In the internal granule cell layer, the cell's five to seven dendrites meet the terminals of the mossy fibers and gradually make connections with them. Connections are also made between granule cells and the intrinsic cortical inhibitory neurons—the Golgi II, stellate, and basket cells. It is interesting that the "motor" side of the cerebellar circuit (the deep nuclear cells and Purkinje cells) forms first, the "sensory" side (mossy fibers) then arrives in place, and the "matrix" that connects the two (the granule cells and intrinsic inhibitory neurons) is the last to develop.

Human Cerebellar Development Is Not Complete at Birth

In humans, the first cerebellar structures develop at approximately 32 days after fertilization, and development is not completed until after birth. The cerebellar cortex of the early embryo has six distinct layers, but this number is ultimately reduced to three. The cortex begins to differentiate slightly earlier in the vermis, flocculus, and median sections of the hemispheres than in the lateral hemispheres. By 7 months after fertilization, the deep cerebellar nuclei have attained the shape and location they will have in the adult. At birth, the cerebellar cortex consists of four uneven layers, and the Purkinje cells and basket cells are weakly developed. The fourth layer (the external granule cell layer) disappears within the first postnatal year. In humans, full myelination of cerebellar connections is not complete until the second year of life.[56]

Summary

The cerebellum is a discrete large structure in the nervous systems of all vertebrates. The cerebellum receives inputs from many parts of the nervous system but projects mainly to the motor and frontal lobe cognitive areas. Different regions correspond to different eras of phylogenetic motor development. This suggests that many different kinds of information are brought together to help control movement and certain cognitive functions. The intrinsic structure is relatively simple and very stereotyped throughout the cerebellum, very different from that of the cerebrum. The ontogenetic development is conspicuously late—cell migrations and fiber connections continue to occur after birth and the development of the rest of the motor nervous system.

ASSESSING CEREBELLAR FUNCTION

The Deep Nuclei Generate the Output of the Cerebellum

All of the cerebellum's output is produced by the deep cerebellar nuclei. Each deep nucleus has a separate somatotopic representation of the body in which the head, tail, trunk, and extremities are represented in the caudal, rostral, lateral, and medial regions of the nucleus, respectively.[5–8,13,14,28–30,57] The deep nuclei exert control over movement of ipsilateral parts of the body. Nearly every motor center in the CNS receives input from the deep nuclei, including the spinal cord, the vestibular, reticular, and red nuclei, the superior colliculus, and (via the thalamus) the primary motor and premotor cortices, the primary and secondary frontal eye fields, and even the prefrontal cortex, area 46. The projections from the deep nuclei to these centers are all glutamatergic and excitatory. However, a set of small neurons in the deep nuclei makes inhibitory projections to the inferior olivary complex.[50] All of these cerebellar target structures receive other excitatory inputs in addition to those from the cerebellum. There are no direct projections from the deep nuclei to the basal ganglia (Table 35.1). The deep nuclei differentially control the medial and lateral motor systems and their respective functions. The vestibular nucleus and the fastigius control equilibrium, upright stance, and gait; the interpositus controls the stretch, contact, placing, and other reflexes; and the dentate controls voluntary movements of the extremities, such as those involved in reaching and grasping for objects (Fig. 35.5).

In the absence of movement, the deep nuclear cells fire at maintained rates of approximately 40–50 Hz.[35,38,58–61] During movement, their firing rates increase and decrease above and below their baseline. Through these variations in firing rate, the cerebellum modulates the activity of motor pattern generators (MPGs), maintaining their sensitivity to other inputs. In addition, increases in cerebellar nuclear firing rate precede and help increase the discharge frequency in MPGs, thus contributing to the initiation of movement.[60,62–65] Deep cerebellar nuclear cells may also combine the functions resident in MPGs into new or novel combinations.[66–69] Thus, an MPG by itself could initiate movements that are within its repertoire, but only the cerebellum could initiate movements that are combinations of components within and across movement patterns.

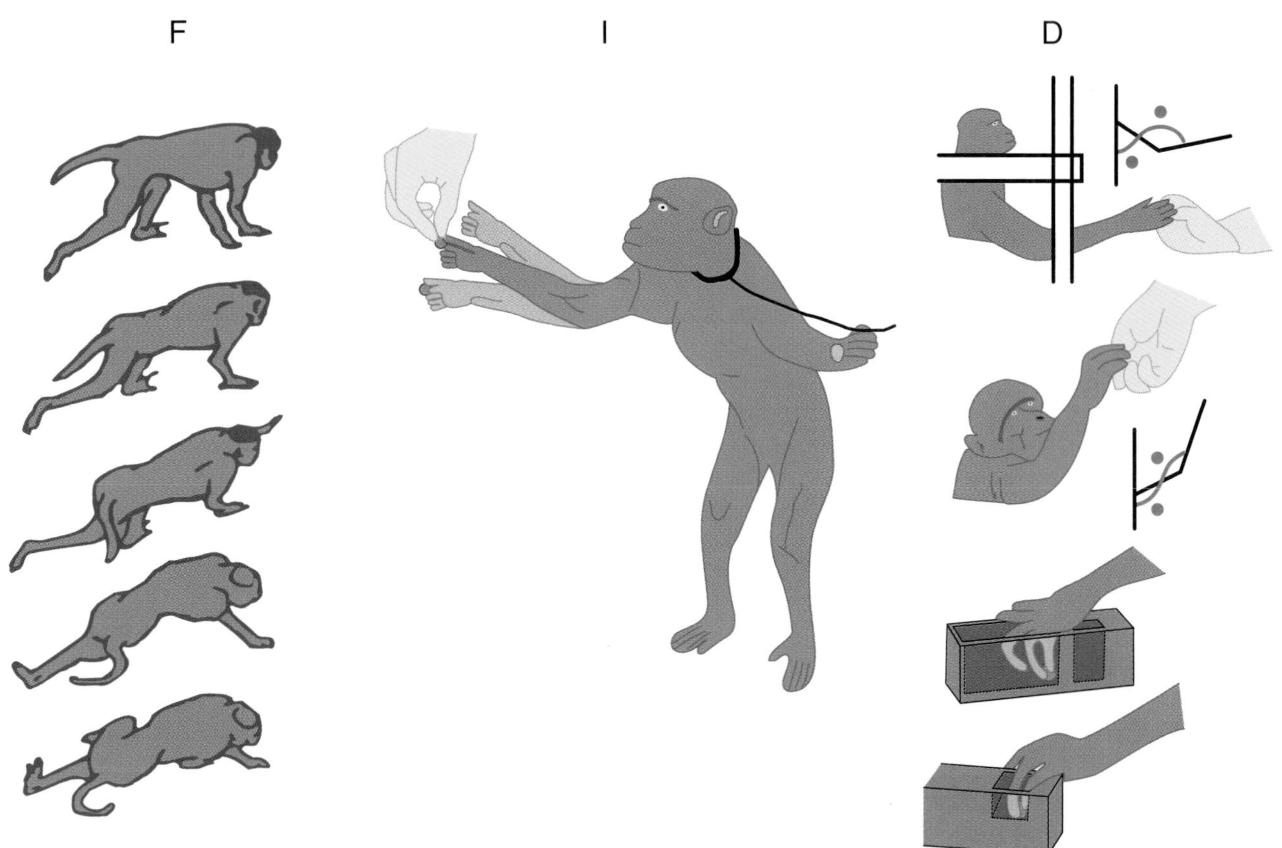

FIGURE 35.5 Major deficits produced by microinjection of muscimol and kainic acid into different regions of the cerebellum. F indicates the standing and walking deficit seen after muscimol injections into the fastigius. I indicates arm positon (tremor) during reaching after muscimol injection into the interpositus. D indicates the deficits in reaching and pinching after muscimol injection into the dentate. Adapted from Thach *et al.*[66]

Activity in Individual Deep Cerebellar Nuclei Correlates with Behavior

The fastigius controls all musculature involved in stance and gait.[35] It receives input from the vermal cortex, vestibular complex, lateral reticular nucleus, and (indirectly) spinocerebellar pathways. Single-unit recordings in the fastigius and vermal cortex of decerebrate cats have shown neural discharge that is correlated with both walking and scratching movements.[70,71] Discharge in the interpositus and dentate is not correlated with these behaviors.[72] These observations are consistent with the idea that the fastigius is specific for the control of stance and gait.

Single-unit recordings have also shown that interpositus neurons fire when the holding position of a limb is perturbed. In doing so, these neurons appear to control antagonist muscles that check the reflex movement of the limb to its prior hold position.[60,62,73–75] Interpositus neurons also modulate their activity in relation to sensory feedback, including that from tremor accompanying movement.[60,76,77] This finding is consistent with the idea that the interpositus is involved in somesthetic reflex behaviors, controlling the antagonist muscle to dampen the tremor.[73–75,78,79] Other evidence suggests that the interpositus is important in determining whether the pattern of activity in muscles acting at a joint represents reciprocal activation or cocontraction.[80–82] During behaviors that involve cocontraction, interpositus cells fire as if activating both agonist and antagonist muscles, and Purkinje cells are silent. In behaviors where agonists and antagonists are reciprocally active, both interpositus cells and Purkinje cells fire in similar patterns. One interpretation of these results is that alternating firing in Purkinje cells creates (through inhibition) a similar pattern of activity in the interpositus cells, which in turn produces the alternation between agonist and antagonist muscles. Other work suggests that the interpositus contributes to stretch reflex excitability by controlling the discharge of gamma motor neurons[76] (Fig. 35.6).

Neuronal activity in the dentate precedes the onset of movement and may also precede firing in the motor cortex.[60,63] Dentate cells fire preferentially at the onset of movements that are triggered by mental associations with either visual or auditory stimuli. In one study, single-unit recordings in the motor cortex, dentate, and interpositus were correlated with electromyograms as monkeys made wrist movements in response to stim-

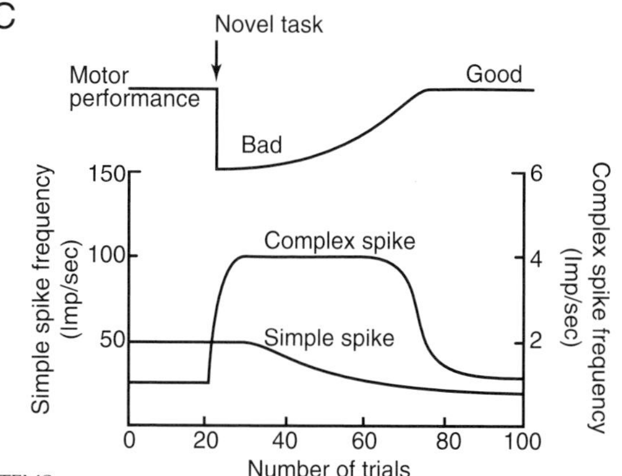

FIGURE 35.6 Simple and complex spikes recorded during motor learning task. Adapted from Ito; original reference Gilbert and Thach.[41]

uli. In tasks where movements were triggered by light, the order of activity was dentate, motor cortex, interpositus, and muscles. When a transient force perturbed the wrist, however, the firing order was muscles, interpositus, motor cortex, and dentate. These results suggest that the dentate helps initiate movements triggered by stimuli that are mentally associated with the movement, whereas the interpositus is more involved in compensatory or corrective movements initiated via feedback from the movement itself. In other studies, the dentate responded strongly when movements were triggered by either visual or auditory signals but not somesthetic signals.[63] Activity in both the dentate and the interpositus is thought to relate more to movements involving multiple joints than to those involving single joints. Neither nucleus codes for any specific parameter (e.g., velocity, amplitude, or duration) during single-jointed movements.[35,66,77–79,83] In sum, the dentate plays a role in initiating movements that require a mental interpretation of the visual or auditory signal, and both the dentate and the interpositus are increasingly active during multijointed movements.

Damage to the Cerebellar Nuclei Causes Unique Behavioral Deficits

Ablations of the **fastigius** in cat and monkey dramatically impair movements requiring control of equilibrium, such as unsupported sitting, stance, and gait.[19,22,28] Longitudinal splitting of the cerebellum along the midline also produces very significant and long-lasting disturbances of equilibrium. In humans, lesions in the vermal and intermediate zones of the anterior cerebellar lobe preferentially impair movements requiring equilibrium control.[84,85] These data suggest that the fastigius may be preferentially involved in movements like gait and stance.

Ablations of the interpositus in monkeys primarily cause tremor.[21] Temporary inactivation of both the interpositus and the dentate with cooling probes elicits tremor that is dependent on proprioceptive feedback but is uninfluenced by vision.[73] In monkeys, interpositus inactivation disturbs gait minimally but causes a large-amplitude, 3- to 5-Hz action tremor as the animals reach for food.[21] These studies support the idea that the interpositus in monkeys is most concerned with balancing the agonist–antagonist muscle activity of a limb as it moves. The interpositus may use the abundant afferent input it receives from the periphery to generate predictive signals that decrease alternating stretch reflexes capable of causing limb oscillation.

Ablations of the dentate nucleus in monkeys produce slight reaction time delays, poor endpoint control, and impaired multijointed movements far beyond any deficits found in single-jointed movements. In several studies, lesions of the dentate produced very slight delays in the onset of motor cortex cell activity.[28,64,65,86] These delays were due to the loss of phasic dentate activity rather than tonic support, because there was no change in the resting firing rate of motor cortical cells after dentate cooling.[64] Lesions of the dentate also produce a slight delay in the reaction time of movements triggered by light or sound.[65,86] In single-jointed movements, dentate ablation causes monkeys to overshoot very slightly[28] or moderately,[75] whereas in multijointed movements, it results in profoundly impaired reaching patterns with abnormally increased angulation of the shoulder and elbow and excessive overshoot of the target.[28] Dentate inactivation also causes monkeys to have difficulty pinching small bits of food out of a narrow well; instead, the animals use one finger as a scoop to retrieve the food[28] (Fig. 35.5). In sum, dentate ablation profoundly impairs movements requiring coordination of multiple joints but affects single-jointed movements only slightly. Dentate inactivation also slightly impairs the initiation of movements that are triggered by vision or mental percepts.

Damage to the cerebellar cortex causes disability similar to but less severe than that resulting from damage to the deep nuclei. Damage to the cortex and the inferior olive also prevents many kinds of motor adaptation, including the acquisition of new and novel muscle synergies.

Several Models Attempt to Explain the Fundamental Operation of the Cerebellum

Tonic Reinforcer Model

The cerebellum exerts a tonic reinforcing effect on other motor pattern generators in the vestibular and reticular nuclei and the motor cortex. Therefore, the cerebellum may be responsible for the tuning and fine adjustment of these structures so that they respond optimally to their noncerebellar driving inputs. This idea was first suggested by the observation that galvanic stimulation of the cerebellum increases movement. Luciani championed the idea of a reinforcing tone with his interpretation of the behavioral deficits produced by cerebellar ablation in animals, a principal component of which was "atonia." Holmes endorsed this interpretation based on his own analysis of behavioral deficits in human subjects with cerebellar lesions.[87–89] We now know that the output of the cerebellum is excitatory and that the cerebellum is tonically active even in the absence of movement.[31,38] Granit *et al.*[90] and Gilman[91] emphasized how tone could be controlled by the cerebellum's excitation of gamma motor neurons, which modulate stretch reflexes. However, because the cerebellum also projects to alpha motor neurons[21] and because cerebellar nuclear discharge changes tonically in relation to different held postures and phasically in relation to different movements, it is now clear that basic cerebellar function must be more complex than originally supposed. The lineal descendent of the tonic reinforcer model is the idea of sensorimotor "optimization," which maintains that the cerebellum contributes a constantly changing influence to provide "fine control" over posture and movement.[92]

Timer Model

A number of studies of the cerebellum have suggested that it performs a pure timing function. Braitenberg and colleagues[93] viewed the parallel fiber–Purkinje cell arrangement as a way of implementing a "tapped delay line." They proposed that a wave of activity propagated along a parallel fiber could be "tapped off" by successive Purkinje cells, each tap occurring at an incremental delay after the onset of the wave. This delay could be used to time movements for up to 50 ms or so. Llinas and Lamarre[94–96] independently proposed motor clock functions for the cerebellum on the basis of presumed periodic discharge in the inferior olive. This presumption was founded on the effects of the drug harmaline, which induced a whole-body, 10-Hz tremor in experimental animals[94] and a correlated synchronous discharge in inferior olive cells in slice preparations.[95] Since the tremor was abolished by ablation of the inferior olive, it was assumed to have been caused by the olivary discharge. A number of other findings seemed to uphold this interpretation, such as a tendency in undrugged animals for olivary neurons to fire periodically and in synchrony and the presence of gap junctions between olivary neurons, which might synchronize their discharge. However, this interpretation is contradicted by the finding that olivary discharge in the awake, performing monkey is not only nonperiodic but indeed random.[39]

Ivry *et al.*[97] proposed clock functions on still other evidence. Patients with lateral cerebellar injury are impaired in their ability to perceive differences in intervals between tone pairs of the order of half a second. This observation has been interpreted as indicative of a general clock not only for movement but also for perception. Additionally, Houk[98] suggested that motor programs are encoded as tonic reverberating activity within several closed-loop systems that make up the basic MPGs. In voluntary movement, the loops are excited by a higher cerebral input and continue to reverberate in a closed-loop fashion (all the while generating movement) until they are turned off. According to Houk's model, the function of the cerebellum is to turn them off—upon recognizing through trial-and-error learning of the context in which movement should stop, the bistable Purkinje cell output flipflops from a condition of no discharge to one of high maintained discharge. This change is hypothesized to stop reverberating activity in the MPG circuits. All of these formulations of the timer model maintain that the cerebellum (or the inferior olive) controls only the timing of muscle activity. Arguing against these ideas is the absence of any demonstrated clocklike periodicity in cerebellar nuclear cell discharge. Instead, these cells produce a graded, tonic discharge that correlates with muscle pattern and force, limb position, and movement direction.

Command–Feedback Comparator Model

Several models of cerebellar function incorporate linear systems principles.[33–35] According to these models the lateral cerebellum receives commands from the association cortex and feedback from the motor cortex, and it projects back to the motor cortex to help initiate and correct the commands. The intermediate cerebellum receives commands from the motor cortex and feedback from the spinal cord, and it projects to the red nucleus to help execute and correct errors in ongoing movements. These models are consistent with the early discharge of dentate neurons in the initiation of movement and the later discharge of interpositus neurons. However, the models do not specify how relatively slow neural feedback signals could make the same kind of error corrections that electronic feedback can.

Combiner–Coordinator Model

The combiner–coordinator model proposes that the role of the cerebellum is to coordinate movements.[67] This model is supported by the finding in cerebellar patients of a loss of coordination of compound movements without any impairment of force in simpler movements.[68,69] Mathematical descriptions of the model have been developed for translating one reference frame (such as body musculature) to another (such as movements in space), for both static and dynamic aspects of motor control.[99,100] The model has been modified to explain how parallel fibers might function in combining the activities of lower MPGs, motor neurons, and muscles to provide many unique patterns of coordinated movement.[66] A learning capability, as developed in the Marr–Albus–Ito hypothesis (discussed next), is another feature of the model.

Motor Learning Model

According to the Marr–Albus–Ito motor learning hypothesis,[66,101–106] the cerebellum controls movements that are made automatically, without conscious thought. The cerebellum gains this control through trial-and-error linking of a certain behavioral context to the movement response. When one initially tries to learn a new pattern of movements, such as those involved in playing a piece on a musical instrument, one must concentrate mentally, and each note is played one at a time and with great effort. With time, control of the process passes from the frontal cerebral cortex to the cerebellum. Repeated occurrence of the context in which the movement is made causes it to become linked to the response. Occurrence of the context alone may then trigger the movement. The context may be a very large and complex composition of signals representing intent and the status of the internal and external milieu at a given time. The response may involve a very large number of movement generators, muscles, and joints. Novel linkages define novel movements and their fine control and coordination. Because the learned movement is stereotyped, movement components may be triggered by contexts early in the performance to anticipate and prevent errors and to build sequences of movements. The cerebellar circuitry seems well suited to interpret the various aspects of the context, to implement the many components in a response, to formulate the context–response linkages that constitute our learned movement repertoire, and to carry out the process of learning them. Damage to the cerebellum abolishes the ability to make automatic, rapid, smoothly coordinated movements and to learn new complex movements. Patients with cerebellar damage can still move, by virtue of the activity of the frontal cerebral cortex and the actions of sensory inputs on each of the MPGs, but each component of a movement must be thought out; movements are slow and irregular, because the agonist, antagonist, synergist, and fixator muscles cannot be linked together in time, amplitude, and combination.

Parallel Fibers and Purkinje Cell Beams Act in the Coordination of Linked Nuclear Cells

The relationship between cerebellar somatotopic maps and parallel fiber morphology is consistent with a cerebellar role in movement coordination. In Fig. 35.2, in each body representation in the deep nuclei, the rostrocaudal axis of the body is mapped onto the sagittal axis of the nucleus. The hindlimbs are represented anteriorly, the head posteriorly, distal parts medially, and proximal parts laterally. This orientation would suggest that the myotomes, which are arranged orthogonal to the rostrocaudal axis of the body, are represented primarily in the coronal dimension of the cerebellum and thus roughly parallel to the trajectory of the parallel fibers. Because the parallel fibers are connected to the deep nuclear cells by Purkinje cells, a coronal "beam" of parallel fibers would control the nuclear cells that influence the synergistic muscles in a myotome. In this way, the parallel fiber would be a single neural element spanning and coordinating the activities of multiple synergistic muscles and joints.

Anatomical studies indicate that parallel fibers in the monkey are about 6 mm long.[52] In the macaque monkey, a 6-mm stretch of cerebellar cortex projects across the width of one nucleus. Thus, a strip of Purkinje cells under the influence of a set of parallel fibers of the same origin and length will control a strip of nuclear cells across an entire nucleus. Depending on which portion of the somatotopic map is involved, that nuclear strip may influence synergistic muscles across several joints in a limb or the muscles of the eyes, head, neck, and arm, for example.

Parallel fiber beams can also serve to link activity in different deep cerebellar nuclei. A link occurring across the two fastigial nuclei would effectively couple the two sides of the body in stance and gait. A link across the fastigius and interpositus would couple locomotion and reflex sensitivity. A link across the interpositus and dentate would couple reach and reflex sensitivity.

Support for the participation of the cerebellum in motor learning comes from both human and animal studies. Ablation of the cerebellar cortex prevents adaptation and learning and removes any previously established adaptation.[107–110] These adaptation and learning deficits can be independent of performance deficits. Neural recording during behavior has shown that the mossy fiber–granule cell–Purkinje cell–nuclear cell route through the cerebellum is the operational one.[38,58–63] Its high-frequency discharge correlates with and controls behavior. The climbing fiber–Purkinje cell route does not directly control moment-to-moment behavior. Its low-frequency discharge increases only when errors in motor performance occur and during adaptation or learning of movement[38–43] (Fig. 35.6). Conjoint electrical stimulation of mossy and climbing fibers depresses parallel fiber–Purkinje cell synapses that are concurrently active and spares those that are inactive.[44–47] Lisberger[111] has suggested that the cerebellum's role in motor learning is to recognize errors in behavior and compute correction factors, which are then sent to the vestibular nuclei in the brainstem.

The Cerebellum Contributes to Cognitive Processes

For many years, the cerebellum was thought to be involved only in the generation of movement. This belief was based on the fact that cerebellar projections had been traced only to motor areas and cerebellar lesions in humans seemed to cause only motor deficits. Recently, however, this view of the cerebellum has changed.[112] Sophisticated anatomical and brain imaging techniques, including positron emission tomography (PET) and magnetic resonance imaging (MRI), have provided evidence for cerebellar contributions to cognition (Box 35.3).

Initial suggestions that the cerebellum participates in cognition arose from anatomic connections that were thought to exist due to the parallel expansion of the frontal lobe, lateral cerebellum, and dentate.[113] Transneuronal transport of herpes simplex virus type 1

BOX 35.3

CEREBELLUM—THE TRUE THINKING MACHINE

It no longer seems reasonable to consider the function of the cerebellum as being confined to the control of voluntary movement, speech, and equilibrium. Considerable evidence suggests that the cerebellum is critical also for thought, behavior, and emotion. Anatomical studies demonstrate that the cerebellum is an important part of the distributed neural circuitry that subserves cognitive processing. The association and paralimbic cerebral cortices known to subserve higher order functions are linked with the cerebellum in a precisely organized system of feedforward and feedback loops, and physiological studies indicate that these pathways are functionally relevant. Cerebellar ablation and stimulation experiments in animals have demonstrated cerebellar influences on many nonmotor functions, including classical conditioning, navigational skills, cognitive flexibility, sham range, predatory attack, and aggression. Functional neuroimaging investigations of the morphologic correlates of cognitive processing using PET and fMRI in humans have revealed sites of activation in the cerebellum in a number of cognitive tasks. These include linguistic processing, verbal working memory, shifting attention, mental imagery, classical conditioning, motor learning, sensory processing, and modulation of emotion. Furthermore, there appears to be a topographic organization of the sites within the cerebellum activated by these different cognitive processes.

Clinical investigations of adults and children with diseases confined to the cerebellum have defined a cerebellar cognitive affective syndrome characterized by impairments of executive processing, working memory, visual spatial reasoning, language disturbances (ranging from mutism to agrammatism), and a flattened or inappropriate affect. The net effect of these deficits is a lowering of overall intellectual ability. The posterior lobe of the cerebellum appears particularly important in the generation of this syndrome, and the vermis is consistently involved when the affective component is pronounced. Elements of this clinical syndrome have also been noted in patients with developmental cerebellar anomalies, cerebellar degeneration, autism, and fragile X syndrome. In addition, cerebellar abnormalities, particularly in the vermis, have been observed in patients with schizophrenia.

The mechanisms whereby the cerebellum influences higher function are still debated. The organization of the cerebellar corticonuclear microcomplex and the interactions between the mossy and climbing fiber systems prompted the hypothesis that the cerebellum provides an error detection mechanism for the motor system. This mechanism may also be relevant for mental operations.

The relationship between the cerebellum and nonmotor function has been conceptualized as follows.

1. The cerebellum is able to subserve cognitive functions because it is anatomically interconnected with the associative and paralimbic cortices.
2. Cognitive and behavioral functions are organized topographically within the cerebellum.
3. The convergence of inputs from multiple associative cerebral regions to adjacent areas within the cerebellum facilitates cerebellar regulation of supramodal functions.
4. The cerebellar contribution to cognition is one of modulation rather than generation.
5. The cerebellum performs computations for cognitive functions similar to those for the sensorimotor system—but the information being modulated is different.
6. The disruption of the cerebellar influences on higher functions leads to dysmetria of thought, impairment of mental agility that manifests, at least in part, as the cerebellar cognitive affective syndrome.

The potential for further discovery in this field places the cerebellum, previously thought of as a motor control device, in the forefront of current behavioral neuroscience research.

Jeremy D. Schmahmann

(HSV1) has revealed these connections: injection of HSV1 into the principle sulcus (area 46) of the cerebral cortex in cebus monkeys retrogradely labels neurons in the dentate.[12] Area 46 lies in the prefrontal cortex, which is not thought to be directly involved in motor performance.

Human brain imaging studies indicate that the cerebellum participates in some types of cognitive functions. One study revealed cerebellar activation when subjects imagined or passively observed movement without moving themselves.[114] In another study, the lateral cerebellum was activated in a language task in which subjects were asked to generate appropriate verbs for visually presented nouns.[115] The cerebellum was not activated when the nouns were simply read, indicating that the cerebellum somehow contributed to the generation of the appropriate verb. Interestingly, once the verb generation task had been well practiced, cerebellar activation diminished.[116] A third study showed that the dentate was activated bilaterally when subjects worked to solve a pegboard puzzle, and this activation was three to four times greater in magnitude than during simple peg movements. Overall, these studies indicate that the lateral cerebellum and dentate are activated in ways that would not be expected to account for movement alone.

Behavioral observations of humans with cerebellar damage have also provided evidence that the cerebellum participates in nonmotor aspects of cognition. In one case study, a cerebellar patient showed impaired performance on the verb generation task described earlier: he was unable to detect errors in his performance of the task and did not exhibit normal practice-related learning. Interestingly, this patient performed normally on standard intelligence and memory tests.[117] In another study, cerebellar patients had deficits in both the production and the perception of a timing task. Lateral cerebellar lesions interfered with the perception of time intervals, while medial cerebellar lesions affected the timing of implemented responses.

The Cerebellum Exerts Oculomotor Control

Eye movements are also differentially controlled by specific parts of the cerebellum (see Chapter 36). The vestibular nuclei and the vestibulocerebellum control the vestibuloocular reflex (VOR). The cerebellar cortex is necessary for visual smooth-pursuit tracking, which requires VOR cancellation. The interpositus and intermediate cerebellar cortex participate in conditioned eyeblink. The dentate and lateral cerebellar cortex are involved in voluntary gaze, saccades, and eye–hand coordination (see Fig. 35.7 for a test).

Clinical Testing Can Reveal Cerebellar Damage

In the early 1900s, Gordon Holmes carefully described the movement deficits associated with discrete cerebellar lesions caused by gunshot wounds.[87–89] His descriptions provide the fundamental basis for our understanding of clinical cerebellar syndromes and a rationale for classifying the manifestations of cerebellar disease according to seven basic deficits. These deficits may be attributed to cerebellar disease only in patients who have normal strength and somesthesis, because similar symptoms may arise from damage to peripheral nerves, the corticospinal tract, and lemniscal–thalamocortical sensory systems (see Fig. 35.8).

1. **Ataxia** is a condition that involves incoordination between movements of body parts. The term is often used in reference to gait or movement of a specific body part, as in "ataxic arm movements."

2. **Dysmetria** is an inability to make a movement of the appropriate distance. **Hypometria** is undershooting a target, and **hypermetria** is overshooting a target. Patients with cerebellar damage tend to make hypermetric movements when they move rapidly and hypometric movements when they move more slowly and wish to be accurate.

3. **Dysdiadochokinesia** is an inability to make rapid, alternating movements of a limb. It appears to reflect abnormal agonist–antagonist control.

4. **Asynergia** is an inability to combine the movements of individual limb segments into a coordinated, multisegmental movement.

5. **Hypotonia** is an abnormally decreased muscle tone. It is manifest as a decreased resistance to passive movement, so that a limb swings freely upon external perturbation. Often, hypotonia is not present in cerebellar patients or is present only during the acute phase of cerebellar disease.

6. **Nystagmus** is an involuntary and rhythmic eye movement that usually consists of a slow and a fast phase. In an unilateral cerebellar lesion, the fast phase of nystagmus is toward the side of the lesion.

7. **Action tremor,** or **intention tremor,** is an involuntary oscillation that occurs during limb movement and disappears when the limb is at rest. Cerebellar action tremor is generally of high amplitude and low frequency (3–5 Hz). **Titubation** is a tremor of the entire trunk during stance and gait. Lesions of cerebellar target structures (e.g., the red nucleus and the thalamus) often result in cerebellar outflow tremor, or postural tremor. Most prominent when a limb is actively held in a static posture, postural tremor attenuates during limb movement and disappears when the limb is at rest.

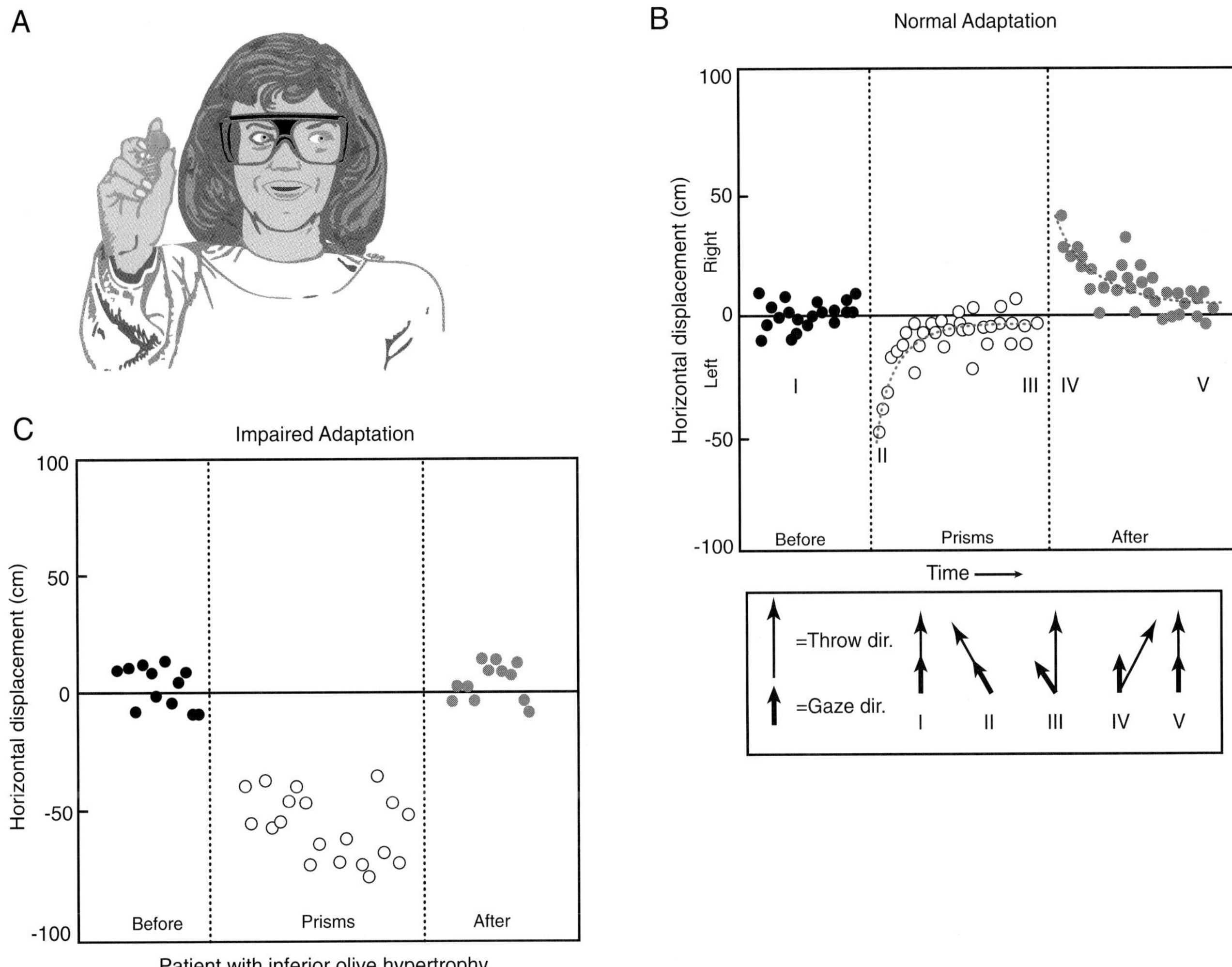

FIGURE 35.7 Prism adaptation test, control subject. (A) Eye–hand positions after adaptation to base-right prisms. The optic path is bent to the subject's right, giving a larger view of right side of her face. Her gaze is shifted left along the bent light path to foveate the target in front of her. Her hand position is ready for a throw at the target in front of her. (B) Horizontal locations of throw hits displayed sequentially by trial number. Deviations to the left are negative values; deviations to the right, positive. While the subject is wearing the prisms (gaze shifted to the left), the first hit is displaced 60 cm left of center. Thereafter, hits trend toward 0. After the prisms are removed, the first hit is 50 cm right of center. Thereafter, hits trend toward 0. Data during and after prism use have been fitted with exponential curves. The decay constant is a measure of the rate of adaptation. The standard deviation of the last eight preprism throws is a measure of performance. Gaze and throw directions are schematized with arrows. Inferred gaze (eye and head) direction assumes the subject is foveating the target. Roman numerals beneath the arrows indicate times during the prism adaptation experiment (see B). (C) Failure of adaptation in a patient with bilateral infarctions in the territory of the posterior inferior cerebellar artery. Adapted from Martin *et al.*[123]

Ataxia of stance and gait can result from a loss of equilibrium and vestibular reflexes produced by lesions of the vestibular nuclei and vestibulocerebellum. Abnormal synergies during standing and walking can also be produced by lesions of the fastigius and vermal cerebellar cortex. The fastigius ultimately influences muscles associated with posture and gait through the vestibulospinal and reticulospinal pathways. Finally, degeneration of the medial anterior lobe of the cerebellar cortex, which often results from thiamine deficiency in alcoholism,[118] can cause ataxic gait patterns.

Action tremor is probably caused by instability of stretch reflexes, due to an inability to adjust the gain and sensitivity of the reflexes. Dysdiadochokinesia may be due to a failure to coordinate the activation of a muscle with the inhibition of its antagonists and

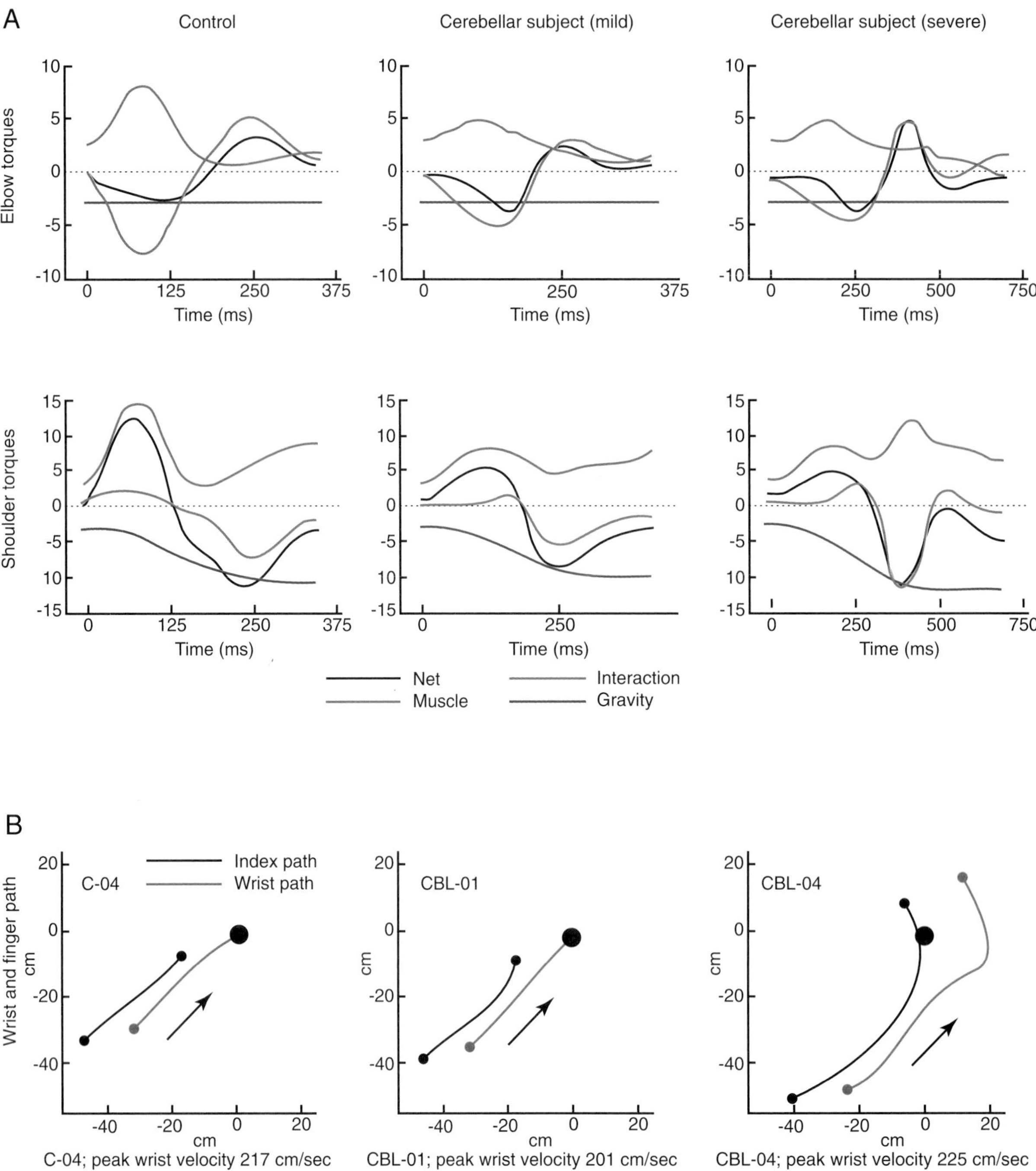

FIGURE 35.8 (A) Single trials of the torques produced by one control subject and two cerebellar subjects, all moving in the fast-accurate condition. One cerebellar subject (mild) produced mildly abnormal reaches by kinematic measures. The other cerebellar subject (severe) produced reaches that were profoundly abnormal by kinematic measures. The torques produced by the control subject and the mildly impaired cerebellar subject were similar, although the mildly impaired cerebellar subject's elbow and shoulder net torques (bold lines) more closely followed the dynamic interaction torque (small dotted lines). The severely impaired cerebellar subject produced torques that were abnormal, with the net elbow and shoulder torques (bold line) closely following the dynamic interaction torque at the respective joints (small dotted line). (B) The wrist and index finger paths are shown moving toward the target (large dot) for the same trials as in A. The control subject makes straight line wrist and index paths and stops right on the target (bold circle). One cerebellar subject (mild) produced slightly curved wrist and index paths and stopped on target. The other cerebellar subject (severe) produced curved wrist and index paths and overshot the target by a great extent. Adapted from Bastian *et al.*[121]

antagonistic stretch reflexes. Damage to the interpositus, alone or in combination with damage to the dentate, is speculated to cause this deficit.

Asynergy of voluntary movements is thought to result mostly from damage to the dentate and the lateral cerebellar cortex, because loss of the dentate significantly impairs the coordination of multijointed movements but has much less effect on single-jointed movements.[119,120] The increased number of degrees of freedom in multijointed movements adds greatly to the mechanical complexity of these movements. When multiple joints are moved together, the motor system must compensate for interaction torques, forces that are generated at one joint when a segment that is directly or indirectly linked to it moves. Cerebellar patients are unable to correct for interaction torques generated during multijointed movements[121] (Fig. 35.8). Therefore, their movements can become dominated by interaction torques, appearing ataxic and inaccurate. Thus, it has been proposed that a major function of the lateral cerebellum is to generate predictive and feedback corrections that are used to compensate for extraneous forces generated by one's own body movements. Lesions of the lateral cerebellum also produce modest increases in voluntary reaction time. This defect may reflect the loss of the early cerebellar signals that generate movements.

Cerebellar damage can also result in the loss of adjustability of movement. Studies of prism adaptation have shown that some patients with cerebellar damage are unable to adjust their hand–eye coordination appropriately[122,123] (Fig. 35.7).

Summary

The assessment of cerebellar function is routinely done by observing the subject perform a battery of movements. These movements have been selected empirically as those most sensitive in demonstrating cerebellar malfunction. For the most part, the movements involve many joints and many muscles. The examiner looks at the *coordination* across joints and muscles. Damage of the cerebellum impairs muscular coordination. Never is there paralysis and rarely ever any paresis (weakness).

The cerebellum is a part of the nervous systems of all vertebrates. It helps coordinate the actions of the many muscles that move the many segments of the skeleton. The cerebellum receives information from almost all parts of the nervous system but sends out control signals only to the motor parts and to certain regions of cognitive cerebral cortex. Its structure is simple and stereotyped; its ontogenetic development is late. The rest of the nervous system is in place and functioning before the cerebellum can begin to do its job. What precisely that job is still puzzles scientists, but it clearly helps to coordinate the many body parts unconsciously during movement, participates in adapting old and acquiring new movement patterns, and contributes in some poorly understood way to certain cognitive processes.

References

1. Jansen, J., and Brodal, A. (1954). *Aspects of cerebellar anatomy.* Oslo: Johan Grundt Tanum Forlag.
2. Larsell, O. (1967). *The comparative anatomy and histology of the cerebellum from myxinoids through birds.* (J. Jansen, ed.), University of Minnesota Press, Minneapolis.
3. Larsell, O. (1970). *The comparative anatomy and histology of the cerebellum from monotremes through apes.* (J. Jansen, ed.), University of Minnesota Press, Minneapolis.
4. Larsell, O. (1972). *The comparative anatomy and histology of the cerebellum: The human cerebellum, cerebellar connections, and cerebellar cortex.* (J. Jansen, ed.), University of Minnesota Press, Minneapolis.
5. Asanuma, C., Thach, W. T., and Jones, E. G. (1983). Cytoarchitectonic delineation of the ventral lateral thalamic region in the monkey. *Brain Res. Rev.* **5:** 219–235.
6. Asanuma, C., Thach, W. T., and Jones, E. G. (1983). Distribution of cerebellar terminations and their relation to other afferent terminations in the ventral lateral thalamic region of the monkey. *Brain Res Rev.* **5:** 237–265.
7. Asanuma, C., Thach, W. T., and Jones, E. G. (1983). Anatomical evidence for segregated focal groupings of efferent cells and their terminal ramifications in the cerebellothalamic pathway of the monkey. *Brain Res. Rev.* **5:** 267–299.
8. Asanuma, C., Thach, W. T., and Jones, E. G. (1983). Brainstem and spinal projections of the deep cerebellar nuclei in the monkey, with observations on the brainstem projections of the dorsal column nuclei. *Brain Res Rev.* **5:** 299–322.
9. Sasaki, K. S., Kawaguchi, S., Oka., H., Saki, M., and Mizuno, N. (1976). Electrophysiological studies on the cerebellocerebral projections in monkeys. *Exp. Brain Res.* **24:** 495–507.
10. Schell, G. R., and Strick, P. L. (1983). The origin of thalamic inputs to the arcuate premotor and supplementary motor areas. *J. Neurosci.* **4:** 539–560.
11. Orioli, P. J., and Strick, P. L. (1989). Cerebellar connections with the motor cortex and the arcuate premotor area: An analysis employing retrograde transneuronal transport of WGA-HRP. *J. Comp. Neurol.* **288:** 612–626.
12. Middleton, F. A., and Strick P. L. (1994). Anatomical evidence for cerebellar and basal ganglia involvement in higher cognitive function. *Science* **266:** 458–461.
13. Allen, G. I., Gilbert, P. F. C., Marini, R., Schultz, W., and Yin, T. C. T. (1977). Integration of cerebral and peripheral inputs by interpositus neurons in monkey. *Exp. Brain Res.* **27:** 81–99.
14. Allen, G. I., Gilbert, P. F. C., Yin, T. C. T. (1978). Convergence of cerebral inputs onto dentate neurons in monkey. *Exp. Brain Res.* **32:** 151–170.
15. Bloedel, J. R., and Courville, J. (1981). Cerebellar afferent systems. In: *Handbook of Physiology, The Nervous System,* Sect. 1, Vol. 2, (V. B. Brooks, ed.), pp. 735–831. Bethesda: *Am. Physiol. Soc.*
16. Voogd, J., and Bigaré, F. (1980). Topographical distribution of olivary and cortico nuclear fibers in the cerebellum: A review. In: *The inferior olivary nucleus: Anatomy and physiology* (J. Cour-

ville, C. de Montigny, and Y. Lamarre, eds.), pp. 207–234. New York: Raven Press.

17. Groenewegen, H. J., and Voogd, J. (1977). The parasagittal zonation within the olivocerebellar projection. I. Climbing fiber distribution in the vermis of cat cerebellum. *J. Comp. Neurol.* **174:** 417–488.
18. Groenewegen, H. J., Voogd, J., and Freedman, S. L. (1979). The parasagittal zonation within the olivocerebellar projection. II. Climbing fiber distribution in the intermediate and hemispheric parts of cat cerebellum. *J. Comp. Neurol.* **183:** 551–601.
19. Botterell E. H., and Fulton, J. F. (1938). Functional localization in the cerebellum of primates. II. Lesions of midline structures (vermis) and deep nuclei. *J. Comp. Neurol.* **69:** 47–62, 1938.
20. Botterell, E. H., and Fulton, J. F. (1938). Functional localization in the cerebellum of primates. III. Lesions of the hemispheres (neocerebellum). *J. Comp. Neurol.* **69:** 47–62.
21. Dow, R. S. (1938). Effect of lesions in the vestibular part of the cerebellum in primates. *Arch. Neurol. Psychiatry* **40:** 500–520.
22. Sprague, J. M., and Chambers, W. W. (1953). Regulation of posture in intact and decerebrate cat. I. Cerebellum, reticular formation, and vestibular nuclei. *J. Neurophysiol.* **16:** 451–463.
23. Chambers, W. W., and Sprague, J. M. (1955). Functional localization in the cerebellum. I. Organization in longitudinal corticonuclear zones and their contribution to the control of posture, both extrapyramidal and pyramidal. *J. Comp, Neurol.* **103:** 105–129.
24. Chambers, W. W., and Sprague, J. M. (1955). Functional localization in the cerebellum. II. Somatic organization in cortex and nuclei. *Arch. Neurol. Psychiat.* **74:** 653–680.
25. Adrian, E. D. (1943). Afferent areas in the cerebellum connected with the limbs. *Brain* **66:** 289–315.
26. Snider, R. S., and Eldred, E. (1952). Cerebro-cerebellar relationships in the monkey. *J. Neurophysiol.* **15:** 27–40.
27. Snider, R. S., and Stowell, A. (1944). Receiving areas of the tactile, auditory, and visual systems in the cerebellum. *J. Neurophysiol.* **7:** 331–357.
28. Thach, W. T., Kane, S. A., Mink, J. W., and Goodkin, H. P. (1992). Cerebellar output: Multiple maps and motor modes in movement coordination. In: *The cerebellum revisited* (R. Llinas and C. Sotelo, eds.), pp. 283–300. Springer-Verlag: New York.
29. Thach, W. T., Perry, J. G., Kane, S. A., and Goodkin, H. P. (1993). Cerebellar nuclei: rapid alternating movement, motor somatotopy, and a mechanism for the control of muscle synergy. *Rev. Neurol.* **149:** 607–628.
30. Ramón y Cajal, S. (1911). *Histologie du Systeme Nerveux.* Maloine, Paris.
31. Eccles, J. C., Ito, M., and Szentagothai, J. (1967). *The cerebellum as a neuronal machine.* New York, Springer-Verlag, Inc.
32. Llinas, R. (1981). Electrophysiology of cerebellar networks. In: *Handbook of Physiology,* Section 1, Volume II, Part 2, pp. 831–876. V. B. Brooks.
33. Evarts, E. V. and Thach, W. T. (1969). Motor mechanisms of the CNS: Cerebro-cerebellar interrelations. *Annu. Rev. Physiol.* **31:** 451–498.
34. Allen, G. I., and Tsukahara, N. (1974). Cerebro-cerebellar communication systems. *Physiol. Rev.* **54:** 957–1006.
35. Brooks, V. B., and Thach, W. T. (1981). Cerebellar control of posture and movement. In: *Handbook of Physiology, The Nervous System,* Sect. 1, Vol. II, (V. B. Brooks, ed.), pp. 877–946.
36. Glickstein, M., May, III, J. G., and Mercier, B. E. (1985). Corticopontine projection in the macaque: The distribution of labelled cortical cells after large injections of horseradish peroxidase in the pontine nuclei. *J. Comp. Neurol.* **253:** 343–359.
37. Brodal, P. (1978). The corticopontine projection in the rhesus monkey. Origin and principles of organisation. *Brain* **101:** 251–283.
38. Thach, W. T. (1968). Discharge of Purkinje and cerebellar nuclear neurons during rapidly alternating arm movements in the monkey. *J. Neurophysiol.* **31:** 785–797
39. Keating, J. G., and Thach, W. T. (1995). Nonclock behavior of inferior olive neurons: interspike interval of Purkinje cell complex spike discharge in the awake behaving monkey is random *J. Neurophysiol.* **73:** 1329–1340.
40. Simpson, J. I., and Alley, K. E. (1974). Visual climbing fiber input to rabbit vestibulocerebellum: a source of direction-specific information. *Brain Res.* **82:** 302–308.
41. Gilbert, P. F. C., and Thach, W. T. (1977). Purkinje cell activity during motor learning. *Brain Res.* **128:** 309–328.
42. Gellman, R., Gibson, A. R., and Houk, J. C. (1985). Inferior olivary neurons in the awake cat: Detection of contact and passive body displacement. *J. Neurophysiol.* **54:** 40–60.
43. Ojakangas, C. L., and Ebner, T. J. (1992). Purkinje cell complex and simple spike changes during a voluntary arm movement learning task in the monkey. *J. Neurophysiol.* **68:** 2222–2236.
44. Ito, M., Sakurai, M., and Tongroach, P. (1982). Climbing induced depression of both mossy fiber responsiveness and glutamate sensitivity of cerebellar Purkinje cells, *J. Physiol. (Lond.)* **324:** 113–134.
45. Ekerot, C.-F., and Kano, M. (1985). Long-term depression of parallel fibre synapses following stimulation of climbing fibres. *Brain Res.* **342:** 357–360.
46. Kano, M., and Kato, M. (1987). Quisqualate receptors are specifically involved in cerebellar synaptic plasticity. *Nature* **325:** 276–279.
47. Strata, P. (1985). Inferior olive: Functional aspects. In: *Cerebellar Functions,* (J. R. Bloedel, J. Dichgans, and W. Precht, eds.), pp. 231–246. Springer-Verlag, Berlin.
48. Hoffer, B. J., Siggins, G. R., Olive, A. P., and Bloom, F. E. (1973). Activation of the pathway from locus coeruleus to rat cerebellar Purkinje neurons: Pharmacologic evidence for noradrenergic central inhibition. *J. Pharm. Exp. Therap.* **184:** 553–569.
49. Hoffer, B. J., Siggins, G. R., Oliver, A. P., and Bloom, F. E. (1972). Cyclic AMP mediates adrenergic synapses to cerebellar Purkinje cells. *Adv. Cyclic Nucleotide Res.* **1:** 411–423.
50. Mugnaini, E. (1972). The comparative anatomy and histology of the cerebellum: The human cerebellum, cerebellar connections, and cerebellar cortex. In: *The Cerebellar Cortex,* Part II (J. Jansen, ed.), pp. 201–264. University of Minnesota Press, Minneapolis.
51. Palay, S. L., and Chan-Palay, V. (1974). *Cerebellar Cortex. Cytology and Organization.* Springer-Verlag, New York.
52. Mugnaini, E. (1983). The length of cerebellar parallel fibers in chicken and rhesus monkey. *J. Comp. Neurol.* **220:** 7–15.
53. Verbitskaya, L. B. (1969). Some aspects of the ontophylogenesis of the cerebellum. In: *Neurobiology of Cerebellar Evolution and Development* (R. Llinas, ed.), pp. 859–878. Chicago: American Medical Association.
54. Rakic, P. (1982). Early developmental events: Cell lineages, acquisition of neuronal positions, and areal and laminar development. *Neuro. Res. Prog. Bull.* **20:** 439–451.
55. Jacobson, M. (1985). Clonal analysis and cell lineages of the vertebrate central nervous system. *Ann. Rev. Neurosci.* **8:** 71–102.
56. Brody, A. B., Kinney, H. C., Kloman, A. S., and Gilles, F. H. (1987). Sequence of central nervous system myelination in human infancy. I. An autopsy study of myelination. *J. Neuropath. Exp. Neurol.* **46:** 283–301.
57. Rispal-Padel, L., Circirata, F., and Pons, C. (1982). Cerebellar nuclear topography of simple and synergistic movements in the alert baboon. *Exp. Brain Res.* **47:** 365–380

58. Thach, W. T. (1970). Discharge of cerebellar neurons related to two maintained postures and two prompt movements. I. Nuclear cell output. *J. Neurophysiol.* **33:** 527–536.
59. Thach, W. T. (1970). Discharge of cerebellar neurons related to two maintained postures and two prompt movements. II. Purkinje cell output and input. *J. Neurophysiol.* **33:** 537–547.
60. Thach, W. T. (1978). Correlation of neural discharge with pattern and force of muscular activity, joint position, and direction of intended next movement in motor cortex and cerebellum. *J. Neurophysiol.* **41:** 654–676.
61. Fortier, P. A., Kalaska, J. F., and Smith, A. M. (1989). Cerebellar neuronal activity related to whole-arm reaching movements in the monkey. *J. Neurophysiol.* **62:** 198–211.
62. Strick, P. L. (1983). The influence of motor preparation on the response of cerebellar neurons to limb displacements. *J. Neurosci.* **3:** 2007–2020.
63. Lamarre, Y., Spidalieri, G., and Chapman, C. E. (1983). A comparison of neuronal discharge recorded in the sensori-motor cortex, parietal cortex, and dentate nucleus of the monkey during arm movements triggered by light, sound or somesthetic stimuli. *Exp. Brain Res. Suppl.* **7:** 140–156.
64. Meyer-Lohman, J., Conrad, B., Matsunami, K., and Brooks, V. B. (1975). Effects of dentate cooling on precentral unit activity following torque pulse injections into elbow movements. *Brain Res.* **94:** 237–251.
65. Spidalieri, H. J., Busby, L., Lamarre, Y. (1983). Fast ballistic arm movements triggered by visual, auditory, and somesthetic stimuli in the monkey II. Effects of unilateral dentate lesion on discharge of precentral cortical neurons and reaction. *J. Neurophysiol.* **50:** 1359–1379.
66. Thach, W. T., Goodkin, H. G., and Keating, J. G. (1992). Cerebellum and the adaptive coordination of movement. *Ann. Rev. Neurosci.* **15:** 403–442.
67. Flourens, P. (1824). *Recherches esperimentales sur les proprietes et les fonctions du systeme nerveux, dans les animaux vertebres.* Crevot, Paris.
68. Babinski, J. (1899). De l'asynergie cerebelleuse. *Rev. Neurol.* **7:** 806–816.
69. Babinski, J. (1906). Asynergie et inertie cerebelleuses. *Rev. Neurol.* **14:** 685–686.
70. Antziferova, L. I., Arshavsky, Y. I., Orlovsky, G. N., and Pavlova, G. A. (1980). Activity of neurons of cerebellar nuclei during fictitious scratch reflex in the cat. I. Fastigial nucleus. *Brain Res.* **200:** 239–248.
71. Andersson, G., and Armstrong, D. M. (1987). Complex spikes in Purkinje cells in the lateral vermis (b zone) of the cat cerebellum during locomotion. *J. Physiol.* **385:** 107–134.
72. Arshavsky, Yu. I., Orlovsky, G. N., Pavlova, G. A., and Perret, C. (1980). Activity of neurons of cerebellar nuclei during fictitious scratch reflex in the cat. II. The interpositus and lateral nuclei. *Brain Res.* **200:** 249–258.
73. Vilis, T., and Hore, J. (1977). Effects of changes in mechanical state of limb on cerebellar intension tremor. *J. Neurophysiol.* **40:** 1214–1224.
74. Vilis, T., and Hore, J. (1980). Central neuronal mechanisms contributing to cerebellar tremor produced by limb perturbations. *J. Neurophysiol.* **43:** 279–291.
75. Flament, D., and Hore, J. (1986). Movement and electromyographic disorders associated with cerebellar dysmetria. *J. Neurophysiol.* **55:** 1221–1233.
76. Soechting, J. F., Burton, J. E., and Onoda, N. (1978). Relationships between sensory input, motor output and unit activity in interpositus and red nuclei during intentional movement. *Brain Res.* **152:** 65–79.
77. Schieber, M. H., and Thach, W. T. (1985). Trained slow tracking. II. Bidirectional discharge patterns of cerebellar nuclear, motor cortex, and spindle afferent neurons. *J. Neurophysiol.* **55:** 1228–1270.
78. Elble, R. J., Schieber, M. H., and Thach, W. T. Activity of muscle spindles, motor cortex, and cerebellar nuclei during action tremor. *Brain Res.* **323:** 330–334.
79. Mauritz, K. H., Schmidt, C., and Dichgans, J. (1981). Delayed and enhanced long latency reflexes as the possible cause of postural tremor in late cerebellar atrophy. *Brain* **104:** 97–116.
80. Smith, A. M., and Bourbonnais, D. (1981). Neuronal activity in cerebellar cortex related to control of prehensile force. *J. Neurophysiol.* **45:** 286–303.
81. Frysinger, R. C., Bourbonnais, D., Kalaska, J. F., and Smith, A. M. (1984). Cerebellar cortical activity during antagonist cocontraction and reciprocal inhibition of forearm muscles. *J. Neurophysiol.* **51:** 32–49.
82. Wetts, R., Kalaska, J. F., and Smith, A. M. (1985). Cerebellar nuclear cell activity during antagonist cocontraction and reciprocal inhibition of forearm muscles. *J. Neurophysiol.* **54:** 231–244.
83. Van Kan, P. L., Houk, J. C., and Gibson, A. R. (1993). Output organization of intermediate cerebellum of the monkey. *J. Neurophysiol.* **69:** 57–73.
84. Mauritz, K. H., Dichgans, J., and Hufschmidt, A. (1979). Quantitative analysis of stance in late cortical cerebellar atrophy of the anterior lobe and other forms of cerebellar ataxia. *Brain* **102:** 461–482.
85. Horak, F. B., and Diener, H. C. (1993). Cerebellar control of postural scaling and central set. *J. Neurophysiol.* **72:** 479–493.
86. Beaubaton, D., and Trouche, E. (1982). Participation of the cerebellar dentate nucleus in the control of a goal-directed movement in monkeys. Effects of reversible or permanent dentate lesion on the duration and accuracy of a pointing response. *Exp. Brain Res.* **46:** 127–138.
87. Holmes, G. (1939). The cerebellum of man. The Hughlings Jackson memorial lecture. *Brain* **62:** 1–30.
88. Dow, R. S., and Moruzzi, G. (1958). *The Physiology and Pathology of the Cerebellum.* Univ. of Minnesota Press, Minneapolis.
89. Dow, R. S. (1987). Cerebellum, pathology: symptoms and signs. In *The Encyclopedia of Neuroscience*, Vol. I, (G. Adelman, ed.), pp. 203–206. Boston: Birkhauser Boston, Inc.
90. Granit, R., Holmgren, B., and Merton, P. A. (1955). The two routes for excitation of muscle and their subservience to the cerebellum. *J. Physiol.* **130:** 213–224.
91. Gilman, S. (1969). The mechanism of cerebellar hypotonia. *Brain* **92:** 621–638.
92. Bloedel, J. R. (1992). Functional heterogeneity with structural homogeneity: How does the cerebellum operate? *Behav. Brain Sci.* **3:** 1–39.
93. Braitenberg, V. (1967). Is the cerebellar cortex a biological clock in the millisecond range? *Prog. Brain Res.* **25:** 2334–2346.
94. Lamarre, Y., and Mercier, L. A. (1971). Neurophysiological studies of harmaline-induced tremor in the cat. *Can. J. Physiol. Pharmacol.* **49:** 1049–1058.
95. Llinas, R., and Yarom, Y. (1986). Oscillatory properties of guinea-pig inferior olivary neurones and their pharmacological modulation: An *in vitro* study. *J. Physiol.* (*Lond.*) **376:** 163–182.
96. Lamarre, Y. (1984). Animal models of physiological, essential, and parkinsonian-like tremors. In: *Movement Disorders: Tremor,* (L. J. Findlay and R. Capildeo, eds.), pp. 183–194. Oxford University Press: New York.

97. Ivry, R. B., Keele, S. W., and Diener, H. C. (1988). Dissociation of the lateral and medial cerebellum in movement timing and movement execution. *Exp. Brain Res.* **73:** 167–180.
98. Houk, J. C. (1988). Cooperative control of limb movements by the motor cortex, brainstem and cerebellum. In: *Models of Brain Function,* (R. M. J. Cotterill, ed.), Cambridge University Press, Cambridge, U.K.
99. Fujita, M. (1982). Adaptive filter model of the cerebellum. *Biol. Cybern.* **45:** 195–206.
100. Pellionisz, A., and Llinas, R. (1980). Tensorial approach to the geometry of brain function: Cerebellar coordination via metric tensor. *Neurosci.* **2:** 1125–1136.
101. Ito, M. (1984). *The cerebellum and neural control.* New York: Appleton-Century-Crofts. Luciani, L. (1915). The hindbrain. In *Human Physiology,* (transl. F. A. Welby), Ch. 8, London, Macmillan.
102. Ito M. (1989). Long-term depression. *Ann. Rev. Neurosci.* **12:** 85–102.
103. Thompson, R. F. (1990). Neural mechanisms of classical conditioning in mammals. *Phil. Trans. R. Soc. Lond. Ser. B* **329:** 161–170.
104. Marr, D. (1969). A theory of cerebellar cortex. *J. Physiol.* **202:** 437–70.
105. Albus, J. S. (1971). A theory of cerebellar function. *Math. Biosci.* **10:** 25–61.
106. Ito, M. (1972). Neural design of the cerebellar control system. *Brain Res.* **40:** 80–82.
107. Robinson, D. A. (1976). Adaptive gain control of the vestibuloocular reflex by the cerebellum. **39:** 954–969.
108. McCormick, D. A., Lavond, D. G., Clark, G. A., Kettner, R. E., Rising, C. E., and Thompson, R. F. (1981). The engram found? Role of the cerebellum in classical conditioning of mictitating membrane and eyelid responses. *Bull. Psychon. Soc.* **18:** 103–105.
109. McCormick, D. A., and Thompson, R. F. (1984). Cerebellum: essential involvement in the classically conditioned eyelid response. *Science* **223:** 296–299.
110. Yeo, C. H., Hardiman, M. J., and Glickstein, M. (1984). Discrete lesions of the cerebellar cortex abolish the classically conditioned nictitating membrane response of the rabbit. *Behav. Brain Res.* **13:** 261–266.
111. Lisberger, S. G. (1988). The neural basis for learning of simple motor skills. *Science* **242:** 728–735.
112. Thach, W. T. (1996). On the specific role of the cerebellum in motor learning and cognition: Clues from pet activation and lesion studies in humans. *Behav. Brain Sci. (in press)*
113. Leiner, H. C., Leiner, A. L., and Dow, R. S. (1993). Cognitive and language functions of the human cerebellum. *Trends Neurosci.* **16:** 444–447.
114. Decety, J., Sjoholm, H., Ryding, E., Stenberg, G., and Ingvar, D. H. (1990). The cerebellum participates in mental activity: Tomographic measurements of regional cerebral blood flow. *Brain Res.* **535:** 313–317.
115. Petersen, S. E., Fox, P. T., Posner, M. I., Mitten, M., and Raichle, M. E. (1989). Positron emission tomographic studies of the processing of single words. *J. Cognitive Neurosci.* **1:** 153–170.
116. Raichle, M. E., Fiez, J. A., Videen, T. O., MacLeod, A.-M. K., Pardo, J. V., Fox, P. T., and Peterson, S. E. (1994). Practice-related changes in human brain functional anatomy during nonmotor learning. *Cerebral Cortex* **4:** 2–26.
117. Foiez, J. A., Petersen, S. E., Cheney, M. K., and Raichle, M. E. (1992). Impaired non-motor learning and error detection associated with cerebellar damage. *Brain* **115:** 155–178.
118. Victor, M., Adams, R. D., and Mancall, E. L. (1959). A restricted form of cerebellar cortical degeneration occurring in alcoholic patients. *Arch. Neurol.* **1:** 579–688.
119. Gilman, S., Carr, D., and Hollenberg, J. (1976). Kinematic effects of deafferentation and cerebellar ablation. *Brain* **99:** 311–330.
120. Goodkin, H. P., Keating, J. G., Martin, T. A., and Thach, W. T. (1993). Preserved simple and impaired compound movement after infarction in the territory of the superior cerebellar artery. *Can. J. Neurol. Sci.* **20**(suppl. **3**): S93–S104.
121. Bastian, A. J., Martin, T. A., Keating, J. G., and Thach, W. T. (1996). Cerebellar ataxia: Abnormal control of interaction torques across multiple joints. *J. Neurophysiol.* **76**(1): 492–509.
122. Weiner, M. J., Hallett, M., Funkenstein, H. H. (1983). Adaptation to lateral displacement of vision in patients with lesions of the central nervous system. *Neurology* **33:** 766–772.
123. Martin, T. A., Keating, J. G., Goodkin, H. P., Bastian, A. J., and Thach, W. T. (1966). Throwing while looking through prisms: I. Focal olivocerebellar lesions impair adaptation. *Brain* **119**(4): 1183–1198.
124. Bell, C. C., and Szabo, T. (1986). Electroreception in mormyrid fish: central anatomy. In *Electroreception* (T. H. Bullock and W. Heiligenberg, eds.), pp. 375–421. New York: Wiley.
125. Paulin, M. G. (1993). The role of the cerebellum in motor control and perception. *Brain Behav. Evol.* **41:** 39–50.
126. Rakic, P., and Sidman, R. (1973). Organization of cerebellar cortex secondary to deficit of granule cells in weaver mutant mouse. *J. Comp. Neurol.* **152:** 133–162.
127. Mariani, J., Crepel, F., Mikoshiba, K., Changeux, J. P., and Sotelo, C. (1977). Anatomical, physiological, and biochemical studies of the cerebellum from reeler mutant mouse. *Phil. Trans. R. Soc. Ser. B* **281:** 1–28.
128. Herrup, K., and Mullen, R. J. (1981). Roles of *staggerer* gene in determining Purkinje cells number in the cerebellar cortex of mouse chimeras. *Dev. Brain Res.* **1:** 475–485.
129. Landis, S. C. (1973). Ultrastructural changes in the mitochondria of cerebellar Purkinje cells of nervous mutant mice. *J. Cell. Biol.* **57:** 787–797.

CHAPTER

36

Eye Movements

Paul W. Glimcher

As we learned in Chapter 28, the photoreceptor mosaic of the vertebrate retina transduces light energy in the form of photons into neural activity, ultimately in the form of action potentials. The spatial resolution of this transduction system is limited by the resolution of the photoreceptor mosaic, but only if the eye can be kept stationary with regard to the objects in the external world that are the subjects of visual analysis. Thus, stabilizing the retina with regard to the outside world and aligning the retina with moving or stationary targets is a critical challenge to effective vision. Evolutionary pressures have shaped the eye movement systems of all animals to meet this challenge in ways that are tailored to the visual structures and environmental needs of each species. In this chapter we examine the neural and behavioral systems vertebrates use to achieve effective retinal stabilization. These systems employ two principal classes of mechanisms, one for **gaze stabilization** and one for **gaze shifting.** The former is found in all animals with visual systems, but the latter is found only in animals with retinal specializations, such as the primate fovea, that can be used to examine a limited region of visual space with higher acuity.

GAZE-STABILIZATION MECHANISMS

A completely stationary animal, whose photoreceptors were anchored to the earth, would always be able to resolve stationary stimuli at the resolution limits of its retina. When an animal moves, however, it risks degrading its visual acuity. Rotating the line of sight by moving the head, for example, will cause a point of light fixed in the environment to streak across the retina, appearing as a line or curve to the visual system. Gaze-stabilization mechanisms are movement systems that counteract this effect of self-motion on visual acuity. These mechanisms coordinate movements of the eye that precisely compenate for self-motion, thus stabilizing the visual world on the retina.

Gaze-stabilization mechanisms fall into two subclasses: the **vestibulo-ocular** system and the **optokinetic** system. The vestibulo-ocular system relies on the semicircular canals to determine the precise rate at which the head is rotated in any direction. The optokinetic system relies on information from the photoreceptors themselves to compute the speed and direction at which the visual world is shifting across the retina. The vestibulo-ocular system is most efficient at higher speeds of rotation, where the vestibular apparatus most accurately measures head velocity. In contrast, the optokinetic system operates most efficiently at low speeds of rotation, where the photoreceptors can be used to accurately determine the speed and direction of image motion. Both systems compensate for rotation by activating the **extraocular muscles** to produce a perfectly matched counterrotation of the eyes. The result is that the line of sight remains constant with respect to the environment, despite movements of the head. Thus, these sensorimotor systems use different types of sensory data to activate a common muscular system, stabilizing retinal images during self-motion over a wide range of speeds.

GAZE-SHIFTING MECHANISMS

Versional Movements Shift the Line of Gaze with Respect to the Visual World

While essentially all vertebrates have gaze-stabilization systems, several groups of vertebrates have evolved specialized retinas that can be effectively employed only if the direction of gaze can be shifted. Primates, for example, have a highly specialized central region of the retina known as the fovea. The fovea can gather visual information from only 1° of the visual world, but the photoreceptors in the fovea are packed at high density, permitting high resolution. High resolution would be useless, however, unless the fovea could be specifically directed to areas of interest in the visual world and stabilized with respect to those stimuli. To accomplish this, essentially all vertebrates with retinal subregions specialized for higher acuity have evolved gaze-shifting systems that employ the extraocular muscles and whose neural components are probably evolutionarily derived from gaze-stabilization mechanisms. Most gaze-shifting movements can be divided into two main groups: the **saccadic system,** which rapidly shifts gaze from one point to another, and the **smooth pursuit system,** which allows the fovea to track a moving target as it slides across a stationary background. The saccadic and smooth pursuit systems together are often referred to as **versional systems.** It should come as no surprise that the smooth pursuit system is believed to have evolved from the optokinetic system: both systems move the eyes to limit the velocity with which visual stimuli move across the retina. In a similar manner, the saccadic system appears to have evolved from a behavioral mechanism shared by the optokinetic and vestibulo-ocular systems.

Vergence Movements Shift the Lines of Gaze of the Two Eyes with Respect to Each Other

A third class of gaze-shifting eye movements has evolved in an even smaller subset of vertebrates, those with both fovealike retinal subregions and binocular vision. These animals have the ability to scrutinize a single visual target with both eyes and have evolved a special eye movement system to control the angle formed by the lines of gaze of the two eyes. When the eyes focus on an infinitely distant target, the lines of gaze projecting from the two foveas are parallel. As the target moves closer, however, the lines of gaze must converge. Thus, animals with binocular vision must have an eye movement system that can keep both eyes aligned with visual targets as those targets vary in distance from the eyes. Binocular convergence is accomplished by adding a gaze control signal, which is different for each eye, to the shared saccadic or pursuit signal. This mechanism of producing binocular convergence is known as **Hering's law of equal innervation.**

Summary

All eye movements belong to one or more of these five classes: the vestibulo-ocular, optokinetic, saccadic, smooth pursuit, and vergence systems. While each of these systems is a largely distinct neural entity, they all engage a common set of motor neurons and thus a common set of muscles. This shared motor circuitry imposes some interesting commonalities on the systems. For this reason, we first discuss the common muscular system before we examine the five eye movement systems.

THE OCULOMOTOR NUCLEI AND THE EXTRAOCULAR MUSCLES

The oculomotor system, in contrast to the somatomotor system, is said to be relatively simple. The motions of the single ball-in-socket eye joint do not face the complexities of coordinating somatic multiple joints. There are only six muscles that move each eye. The muscles are controlled by three cranial nerves, the actions of which are rather simply coordinated by the medial longitudinal fasciculus. Control mechanisms within the brainstem compute and mix together the dynamic and static signals to move and hold the eye.

Six Muscles Move Each Eye

In primates, all eye movements are produced by the contraction or relaxation of six extraocular muscles. These muscles surround each eye and can rotate the eye in any direction. As Fig. 36.1 illustrates, the muscles are arranged in three antagonistic pairs, much like the pairing that occurs in the skeletomuscular system. The **medial** and **lateral rectus** muscles form an antagonistic pair that controls the horizontal position of each eye. Contraction of the lateral rectus, coupled with commensurate relaxation of the medial rectus, causes the eye to rotate outward, shifting the direction of gaze laterally (Fig. 36.2). Because the two eyes move together, contraction of the medial rectus of one eye is accompanied by contraction of the lateral rectus of the other eye, thus similarly rotating both eyes. The **superior** and **inferior recti** control the up-and-down rotation of the eye, while the **superior** and **inferior oblique** muscles control torsion, the rotation of the eye about the line of sight. The obliques also make a small contribution to pulling the eye up or down. Because the superior and inferior recti also generate some torsion, the obliques are particularly important for guar-

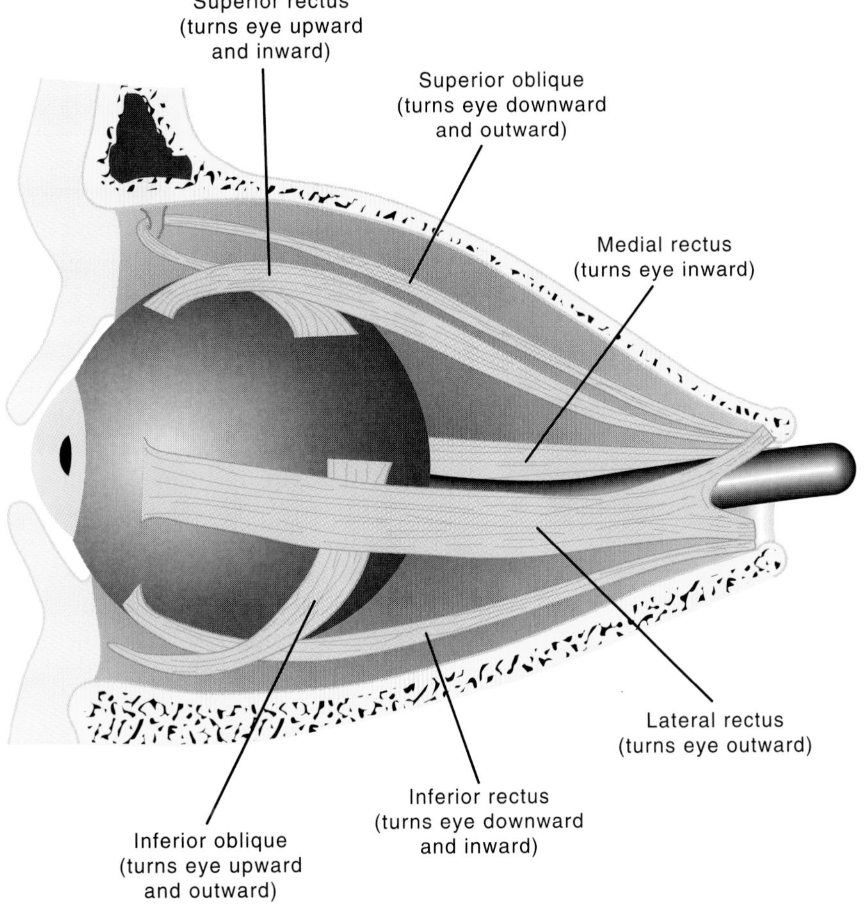

FIGURE 36.1 Muscles of the eye. Eye movements are controlled by six extraocular muscles arranged in three pairs, shown here in a cutaway view of the eye in its socket, or orbit.

anteeing that the eye maintains the same horizontal orientation as it moves around the orbit.

Three Cranial Nerves Control the Extraocular Muscles

The six extraocular muscles are innervated by three of the bilaterally paired cranial nerves discussed in Chapter 2. The oculomotor nerve (cranial nerve III) innervates the medial, superior, and inferior recti and the inferior oblique; the trochlear nerve (IV) innervates the superior oblique; and the abducens nerve (VI) innervates the lateral rectus. Thus, the somata of the oculomotor motor neurons are located in the third, fourth, and sixth cranial nuclei. These three nuclei are heavily interconnected by a pathway called the **medial longitudinal fasciculus.** This interconnection facilitates the coordination of extraocular muscle activity that is necessary for precise control of eye movements.

Eye Movements Are Produced by a Combination of Static and Dynamic Forces

To understand how muscle forces control the position and movement of the eyes, we must first understand how the tissues and muscles of the orbit produce resistance to movement. In its simplest form, the eye in the orbit can be thought of as a sphere held in place by a system of springs that tend to draw the eye into a central position. To hold the eye at an eccentric position, the muscles must produce a static force adequate to counteract the spring tensions. To move the eyes from one eccentric position to another requires an additional, dynamic, force that can overcome the resistance of the orbit to motion and accelerate the eye.[1] Whereas the static force must be maintained as long as the eye is stationary, the dynamic force need be applied only during the actual movement of the eye.

Oculomotor muscle force is controlled directly by

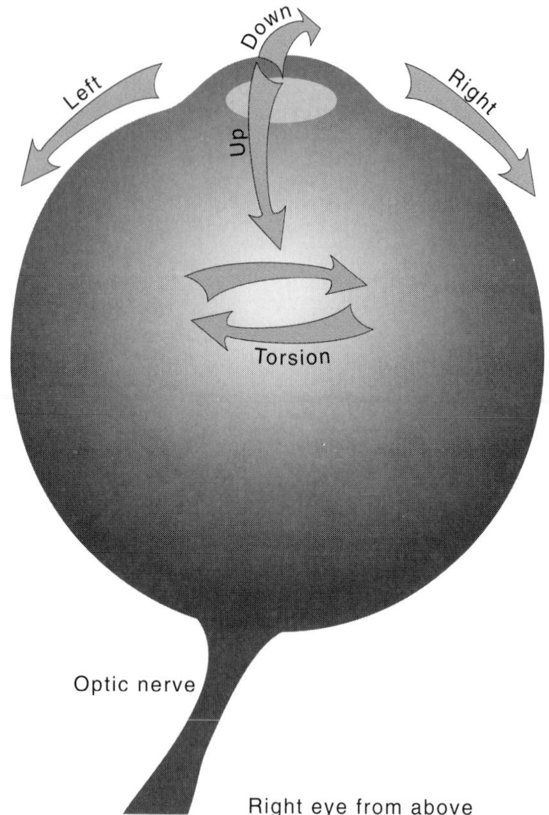

FIGURE 36.2 Axes of eye rotations. The extraocular muscles can rotate each eye along the horizontal, vertical, and torsional axes.

the firing rates of the oculomotor motor neurons. Therefore, when studying the oculomotor motor neurons, one can largely separate the static and dynamic forces by investigating motor neuron firing rates when the eye is either stationary or in motion.[2,3] Such investigations reveal that eye position is a linear function of firing rate while the eye is stationary (Fig. 36.3). Each motor neuron has a recruitment point (an eye position at which the neuron begins to fire) and a characteristic slope (change in firing frequency for a 1° shift of the eye toward the pulling direction of the innervated muscle). Oculomotor motor neurons also show a high-frequency pulse of activity during much of the high-velocity phase of eye movements. This pulse is followed by a sustained firing rate associated with the new static position of the eye. From these data we can conclude that the high-frequency pulse of activity generates the dynamic force produced during an eye movement, whereas the sustained firing generates the static force.

The preceding discussion describes the behavior of oculomotor motor neurons when their muscles are pulling the eye. For every eye movement, however, one muscle of each antagonistic pair must relax when the other contracts. During movements in which the muscle under study relaxes, the motor neurons innervating that muscle pause during the movement and then resume firing at a reduced rate appropriate for the new orbital position of the eye.

Perhaps the most interesting aspect of these observations is that all oculomotor motor neurons exhibit this pattern of behavior, encoding in their rate *both* the static and the dynamic components of the force structure of each movement.[4] This finding has two important implications. First, it means that all oculomotor muscle fibers contribute to both movement and position holding (because all oculomotor neurons do so.) Second, it means that the combined pulse/step structure of all eye movements is computed at or before the level of the oculomotor motor neurons. As we see in the following sections, a principal task of the oculomotor system is to compute these pulse/step muscle force patterns. The challenge faced by the system is to achieve either gaze stabilization or gaze shifting by converting sensory information from many

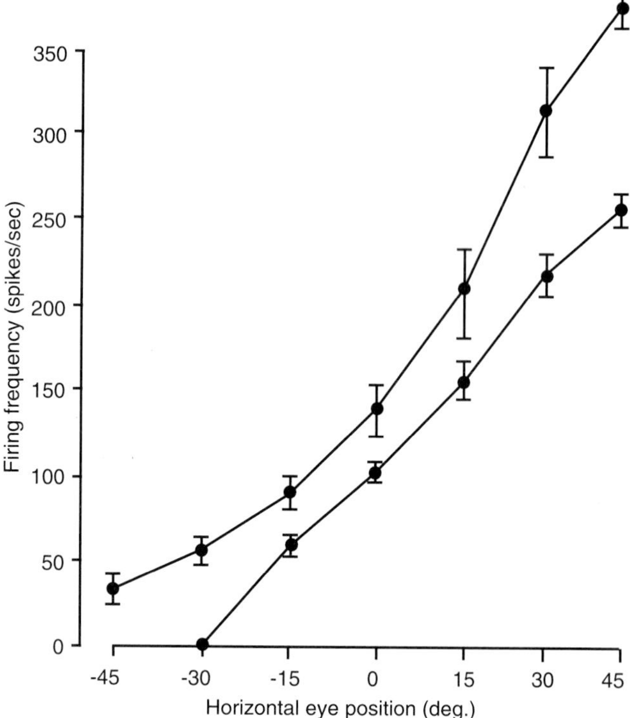

FIGURE 36.3 Rate-position curves for the abducens motor neurons. Such plots of motor neuron firing rate as a function of eye position when the eye is stationary demonstrate that motor neuron firing rate is linearly related to static eye position. From Fuchs and Lushei.[2]

modalities—visual, vestibular, auditory, and somatosensory—into the common language of pulse/step muscle forces.

Summary

The simplicity of the oculomotor system derives from the simplicity of its mechanics, the simplicity of its muscular and neural control, and the compactness of the brainstem circuitry that computes the fundamental neural signals required to drive it.

THE VESTIBULO-OCULAR REFLEX

The **vestibulo-ocular reflex** (VOR) is the neural system by which rotations of the head are detected by the semicircular canals of the vestibular organs, and the eyes are counterrotated in their sockets an equal amount in the opposite direction to stabilize the line of sight. This reflex is in constant use. Whenever you walk, for example, the VOR is engaged, compensating for the small visually disruptive movements of the head that are produced during locomotion. The VOR is also highly precise. If you rotate your head from left to right while reading this page, you will find that you can move your head quite quickly before the text becomes unreadable.

To compensate for head rotation, the VOR rotates the eyes. If the head continues to rotate, of course, the eyes cannot continue to counterrotate without being pointed backward in the orbit. To overcome this limitation, the eye is often reset to a central position in the orbit during a vestibular eye movement. After this resetting is complete, the compensatory counterrotation resumes (Fig. 36.4). The comparatively slow compensatory movements and the quick resetting movements constitute the two phases of the VOR. This characteristic pattern of alternating quick and slow phases during sustained rotation is called **nystagmus.** (A leftward nystagmus is one in which the quick phases shift gaze to the left.) Note that only the slow phase compensates for head rotation; the quick phase simply returns the eye to the center of the orbit. In the following discussion we focus on how inputs from the semicircular canals structure the compensatory slow phase of the VOR.

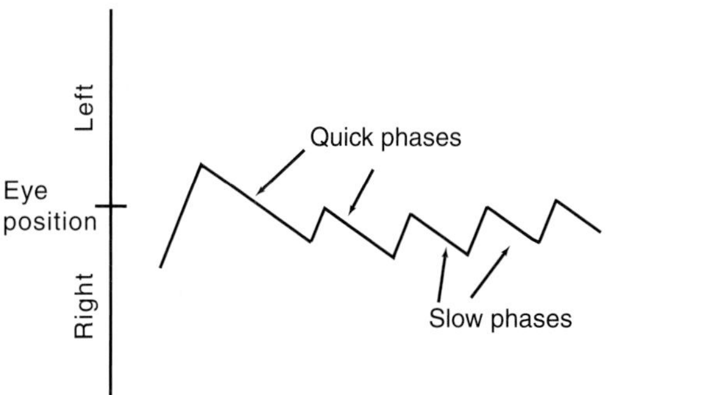

FIGURE 36.4 During a sustained rotation of the head, the eye moves slowly to the right (slow phase) and then abruptly shifts to the left (quick phase) before resuming its rightward movement. This pattern of movement is referred to as leftward nystagmus.

The Semicircular Canals Measure Angular Velocity of the Head in Space

Each member of the bilaterally symmetrical pair of vestibular organs contains three semicircular canals oriented at roughly 90° to one another (Fig. 36.5). Each canal consists of a very thin bony tube filled with fluid. As the tube rotates, the fluid inside lags behinds due to its inertia. The rotational motion of the tube can therefore be detected by comparing the relative rates at which the fluid and the tube move. In the vestibular organ, this comparison is performed by the **cupula,** a thin, elastic membrane that stretches across the canal. Rotation of a canal deflects the cupula, and this deflection is monitored by hair cells like those in the cochlea (Chapter 27). Recall that the neural output of a hair cell is proportional to the deflection of its kinocilium. In the semicircular canals, the kinocilia are mechanically coupled to the cupula, so that the output of the hair cell serves as an accurate measure of the angular velocity of canal rotation.[5]

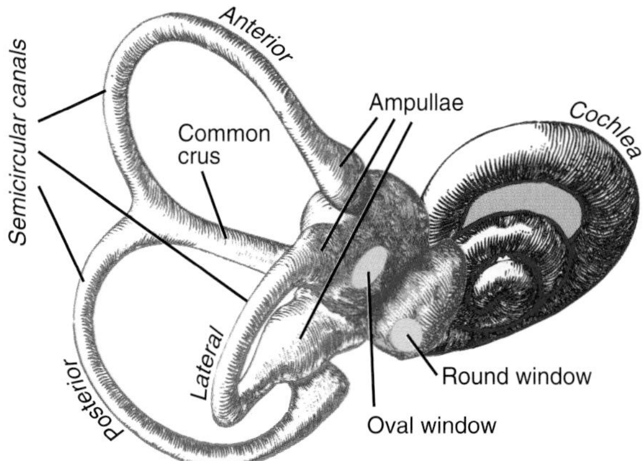

FIGURE 36.5 The semicircular canals in the labyrinth of the inner ear. These three bony tubes are oriented to detect rotational motion in any of the three dimensions of space.

Obviously, a system of this type is most sensitive to rotations aligned precisely in the plane of the canal. Put more exactly, a given canal can measure only that portion of the rotational velocity that lies in its plane. To completely measure the rotational velocity of the head in three dimensions, it is thus necessary to use three separate canals, each oriented in a different plane. In fact, vertebrates have six canals—three on each side—arranged in coplanar pairs. Rotation of the head to the left, for example, activates the two canals that lie in the horizontal plane. The hair cells in one of these canals will be depolarized by this rotation, as the cupula deflects their kinocilia in their preferred direction. The hair cells in the other canal will be hyperpolarized, as that canal's cupula, moving in the opposite direction, deflects their kinocilia in the opposite direction. Single-unit recordings from canal afferent fibers during rotations (Fig. 36.6) show that this system does accurately encode rotational velocity to the nervous system.[6,7]

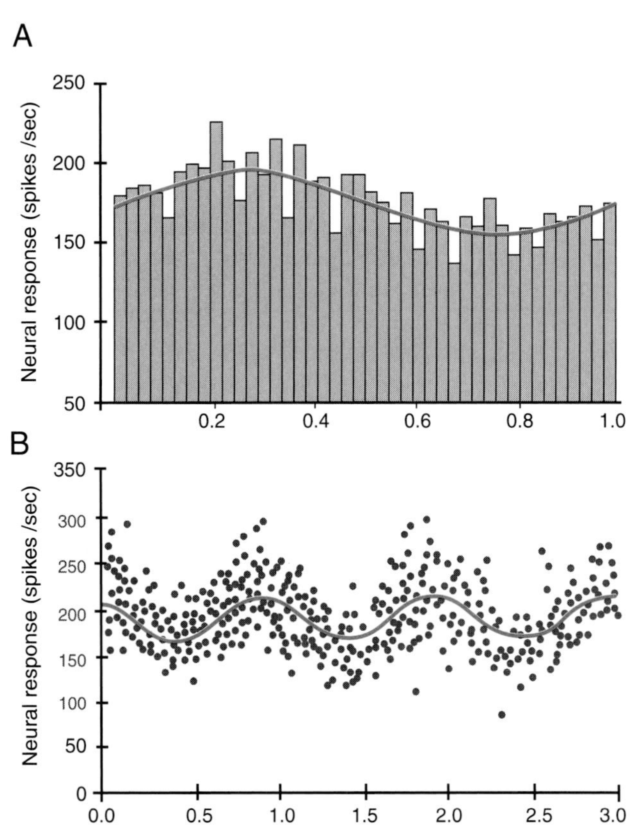

FIGURE 36.6 Response of a semicircular canal afferent to movement of the cupula. (A) The average firing frequency of the afferent nerve varies sinusoidally as the cupula is deflected in and then out in a single cycle. (B) The instantaneous firing frequency of the afferent is plotted over three consecutive cycles. From Dickman and Correia.[7]

The Vestibular Nuclei Add Static Eye-Holding Signals to the Dynamic Eye-Moving Signals

Canal afferents synapse on neurons of the vestibular nuclei, many of which have a firing rate that is proportional to rotational velocity in one of the canal planes (Fig. 36.7).[8] How is this sensory measure of the rotational velocity of each canal used to compute a matched velocity of eye rotation? Because each of the canal pairs is roughly aligned with one of the extraocular muscle pairs, the velocity signal associated with one canal pair could, in principle, be used to control the eye velocity governed by the aligned pair of muscles. The vestibular nuclei do make some direct projections to the oculomotor nuclei,[9] suggesting that head velocity signals could directly regulate eye velocity. The canal-derived velocity signal could therefore account for the velocity of vestibular eye movements, the *dynamic* component of the VOR.

Once the velocity of the head dropped to zero, we might expect the eye to return to its initial, pre-VOR position, because the static force necessary to hold the eye at a given position in the orbit must be changed each time the velocity of the eye carries it to a new position. As explained in the preceding section, it is the static, or step, force that must persist after each eye movement is complete. If the sensory signals in the vestibular nuclei are the source of the dynamic phase of each VOR eye movement, what is the source of the accompanying change in static force? Because velocity is the first derivative of position, the static force could be computed by taking the mathematical integral of the velocity signal supplied by the vestibular nuclei. One model proposed to explain this process is diagramed in Fig. 36.8.[10] In this model, signals proportional to velocity are generated by the semicircular canal afferents and transmitted to the vestibular nucleus. From there, the signal is relayed to the oculomotor nuclei and to a neural integrator that adds any change in step intensity to the pre-VOR step intensity. The output from the integrator is also passed to the oculomotor nuclei. In this way, a simple sensory signal encoding velocity could be transformed into a static and dynamic force pair tailored to the needs of the extraocular muscle system.

The VOR Is Plastic

In the preceding section, we described how the VOR appears to operate in general. To function well, this system must relate given levels of canal activation to given velocities of eye rotation. Changes in the strength or efficiency of the extraocular muscles, for example,

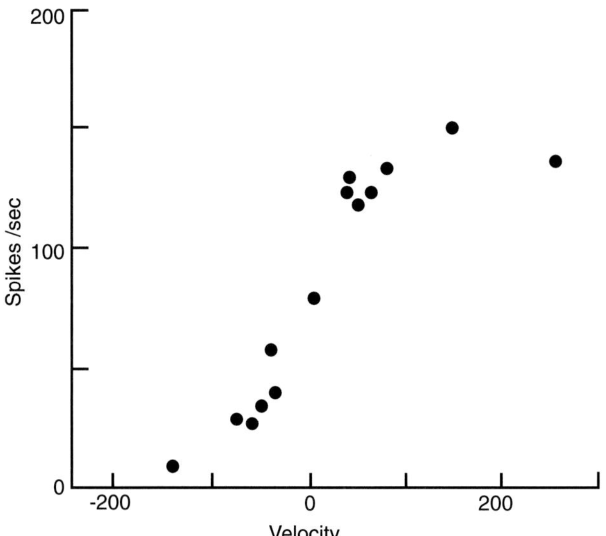

FIGURE 36.7 The firing rate of semicircular canal afferents codes rotational velocity. Over a range of almost 300%, firing rate is a linear function of velocity. From Groen *et al.*[8]

would require adjustments in the strength of the linkage between the vestibular signal and the muscle contraction. The strength of this linkage, usually referred to as its **gain**, is equal to the magnitude of the induced eye rotation divided by the magnitude of the vestibular rotation. Thus, a gain of 1 describes a situation in which eye and head rotations are perfectly matched, a gain of 0.5 describes one in which the eye undercompensates for head rotation by half, and a gain of 2 describes one in which the eye rotates twice as far as it should. To examine the flexibility, or **plasticity,** of VOR gain, investigators instructed human subjects to wear magnifying lenses. Such lenses expand the view of a small region of visual space, causing eye movements to produce smaller displacements of the retinal image. For example, 3× lenses would require a subject to make an eye movement three times as large to compensate for a given head rotation. In one experiment, a subject who wore 2× magnifying lenses had a VOR gain that changed to 1.8 after a few days.[11] This and similar experiments demonstrated that the VOR can adapt. Although the cerebellum is necessary for adaptation to occur, it can be removed after adaptation is complete without changing the gain of the VOR.[12–14] This observation led to a revision of the neural integrator model of the VOR. According to the revised model, the cerebellum uses visual information (the slippage of an image on the retina during head movement) to determine whether the current VOR gain effectively cancels out the effects of the head movement. If the effects are not canceled out, the cerebellum generates an **error signal** that can be used to increase or decrease the gain of the VOR.[15]

The VOR Is Frequency Limited

Many researchers studying the VOR have analyzed its gain during sinusoidal rotations of humans and animals. In these experiments, subjects are rotated back and forth at various frequencies. The gain of the VOR is calculated at each frequency and then plotted as a function of frequency. These rotations are performed in the dark so that the optokinetic system, which is discussed in the next section, cannot be responsible for eye movements. The rationale for this approach is that for some types of systems, those referred to as linear, it is possible to calculate the gain (or response) of the system to any stimulus the response of the system to

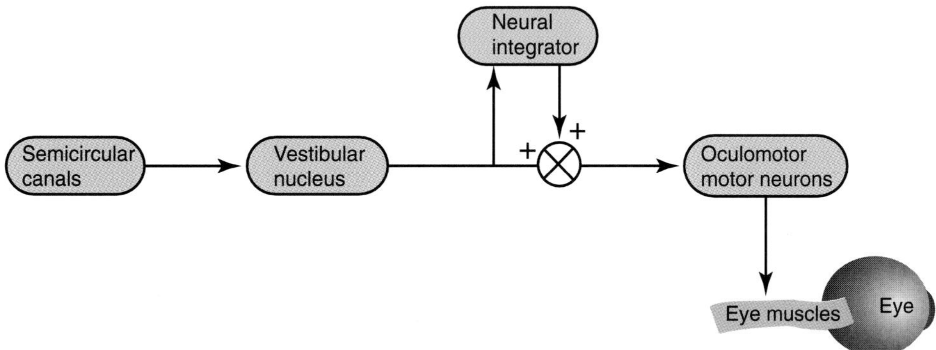

FIGURE 36.8 A model of the vestibulo-ocular reflex. The semicircular canals send a signal proportional to head velocity to the vestibular nuclei. This signal is then relayed to the oculomotor motor neurons where it controls eye velocity. A copy of the signal is also passed to a neural integrator, which computes a signal proportional to eye position that is also sent to the oculomotor motor neurons. The integrated signal is used to hold the eye stationary at its current position.

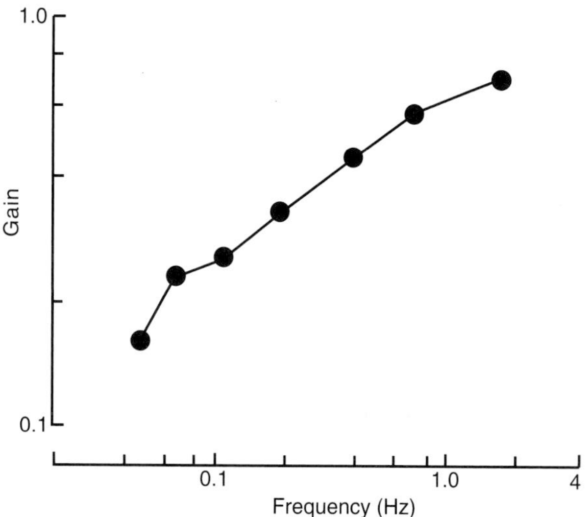

FIGURE 36.9 Gain of the vestibulo-ocular reflex as a function of rotation frequency. From Baarsma and Collewijn.[16]

all cases of single-frequency stimulation is known. As Fig. 36.9 indicates,[16] the VOR counterrotates the eye almost perfectly except at very low frequencies (around 0.1 Hz and lower). The lower limit on the VOR is of particular interest, because at low frequencies the visual system can be used to stabilize gaze. As we see in the next section, the optokinetic system does just that, efficiently compensating for very low speed movements of the head.

Summary

The vestibulo-ocular reflex is a good paradigm for understanding motor control in general. The behavioral goals are clear-cut, the mechanics of the movements and the neuromuscular controls are straightforward, and all of the computation needed for holding and moving the eye is performed by a compact and relatively well-described circuitry within the brainstem, all driven by input signals from the semicircular canals.

THE OPTOKINETIC SYSTEM

Like the VOR, the optokinetic system activates the oculomotor musculature to stabilize gaze during rotations of the head. Unlike the VOR, however, the optokinetic system uses visual information, extracting from the global pattern of visual stimulation a measure of how fast and in what direction the visual world is moving across the retina. This movement of the visual world, often called **retinal slip,** is used to generate an eye movement equal in speed and opposite in direction to the retinal slippage, thus stabilizing the visual world on the retina. Like the VOR, the optokinetic system produces nystagmus: a slow phase, during which the eyes compensate for movement of the visual world, is followed by a quick phase that moves the eyes back from the limits of their orbital rotation to a more central position. To study optokinetic nystagmus, scientists typically present subjects with a display of vertical stripes or randomly arranged dots that rotate uniformly around the center of the subject's head. Because the subjects are stationary, we know that the vestibular system cannot be responsible for generating the nystagmus, which must therefore be produced by the movement of the visual stimulus.

Midbrain Circuits Translate Visual Signals into Velocity Signals

In humans and most other vertebrates, the retina projects directly to a midbrain area just rostral to the superior colliculus called the **pretectum.** Many neurons in this area become active when the visual world slips in a particular direction, and their firing rate increases as the velocity of slippage increases (up to a point). Thus, pretectal neurons encode the velocity and direction of retinal slip.[17] They project directly to the vestibular nuclei via pontine and medullary relays. In fact, many vestibular neurons can be activated by both vestibular and visual stimuli,[18] suggesting that the two types of stimuli access a common circuitry for eye velocity control. This common motor circuitry may also integrate the optokinetic velocity signals to calculate the static force necessary to hold the eye at its new position.

The Optokinetic Response Has Gain

Like the VOR, the optokinetic response has a gain that can be measured. In this case, gain is the ratio of eye rotational speed to visual world rotational speed. A gain of 1 indicates that the eye rotates perfectly, completely stabilizing the visual world on the retina. A gain of less than 1 indicates that the eye lags behind the visual world, only partly compensating for retinal slip. Measurements of gain as a function of frequency have been made for the optokinetic response just as they have for the VOR. In one of these experiments, researchers rotated an animal back and forth in front of an illuminated and stationary visual environment after surgically removing the semicircular canals.[16] Notice in Fig. 36.10 that the gain of the optokinetic response falls off at higher frequencies of rotation. Comparison of Figs. 36.9 and 36.10 reveals that the vestibulo-ocular and optokinetic systems, which trans-

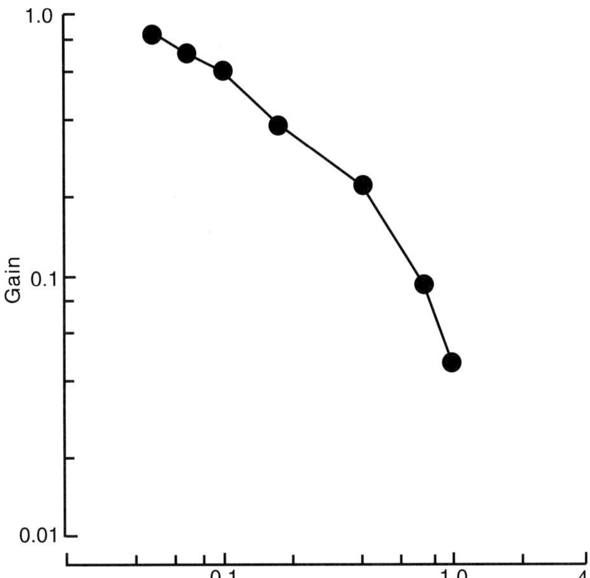

FIGURE 36.10 Gain of the optokinetic response as a function of rotation frequency. From Baarsma and Collewijn.[16]

late two types of sensory signals into a common motor framework, can effectively stabilize gaze over a very wide range of image/head velocities.

Summary

The optokinetic system complements the vestibulo-ocular reflex. Both maintain stability of gaze despite head movement, and both employ simple and shared control components. Although neither system working alone can completely stabilize vision, the combined vestibulo-ocular and optokinetic systems achieve nearly perfect stabilization across a broad range of head movement velocities.

THE SACCADIC SYSTEM

Saccades are gaze-shifting responses that can rotate the eyes as quickly as 800° s^{-1}. The circuitry that controls these movements is perhaps the most successfully studied voluntary movement in the mammalian motor system. Like the gaze-holding systems we have already examined, the saccadic system must generate a dynamic force pulse that accelerates the eye to a high velocity as well as an increment in the static force that keeps the eye at its new position. As we will see, the saccadic system uses visual, somatosensory, and auditory information to compute the eye rotation necessary to align the line of sight (often called the line of gaze) with a visual target. The magnitude and direction of the desired change in eye position—the motor error—are relayed to a set of brainstem control circuits that calculate the static and dynamic forces necessary for the selected eye rotation.

The Brainstem Contains Circuits That Control Saccades

As we learned in an earlier section, the extraocular muscles are controlled by three bilaterally symmetrical pairs of cranial nerve nuclei. Lying between these nuclei, straddling the midline of the brainstem, is the **paramedian pontine reticular formation** (PPRF). Recordings from the PPRF in awake, behaving monkeys demonstrated the existence of a class a neurons called **burst neurons,** which fire a vigorous burst of action potentials beginning about 8–12 ms before each eye movement.[19,20] Interestingly, the number of spikes in these bursts is linearly related to the horizontal amplitude of the saccade. A large upward movement that involves only a small rotation of the eyes to the left is preceded by a small burst in the left-preferring burst neurons, whereas a larger rotation directly to the left is preceded by a larger burst in the same neurons. These bursts, which code horizontal (in this case, leftward) motor error, could be used to generate the dynamic force pulse needed to accelerate the eye during a saccade. Supporting this hypothesis is the observation that these neurons often project directly into the oculomotor nuclei.[21,22] A group of neurons that seem to code vertical motor error has also been discovered just rostral to the oculomotor nuclei.

These findings suggest that the dynamic phase of a saccade is coded by pontine burst neuron activity. If the dynamic phase were generated alone, however, the viscoelastic "springs" that pull the eye back toward the center of the orbit would slowly return the eye to its presaccadic position. This is exactly what happens when a lesion is placed in the prepositus nucleus of the hypoglossal nerve,[23] suggesting that this nucleus may contain a neural integrator that calculates the static force needed to hold the eye at its new position.

Lying just rostral and ventral to the burst neurons is a group of tonically active neurons called omnipause neurons, which stop firing action potentials shortly before the burst neurons become active.[20] The duration of this pause in firing is tightly correlated with the duration of the saccade. Furthermore, electrical stimulation of the omnipause region prevents saccades from occurring. These observations suggest that the cessation of firing in omnipause neurons may be critical for triggering a saccade, whereas the amplitude and duration of the saccade would be specified by the particular motor error signals.

Where does the oculomotor brainstem receives the motor error signals that control saccades? Two principal structures appear to serve that role: the superior colliculus and the frontal eye fields. In fact, either structure seems to be capable of generating these signals, since lesions of one or the other can be compensated for but lesions of both abolish all saccades.[24] We begin our discussion of the generation of saccadic motor error signals by examining the superior colliculus.

The Superior Colliculus Is a Laminated Structure Lying above the Aqueduct in the Midbrain

At the end of the 19th century, researchers discovered that electrical stimulation of the superior colliculus produced high-velocity movements of the eyes similar to saccades. However, it was not until the early 1970s that researchers began to reexamine the superior colliculus and provide fundamental insights into how eye movements are controlled. In one series of experiments[25] an electrode was lowered into the colliculus and a small stimulating current was delivered through the electrode tip. About 20 ms after the onset of stimulation, a saccade began. The saccade had a characteristic amplitude and direction, and once the eye had moved that amount, it stopped. If the stimulation was maintained, a second saccade of identical amplitude and direction was eventually made from the end point of the first saccade. Moving the electrode to a new location in the colliculus yielded a similar pattern of results, but the movement amplitude and direction were different. These experiments allowed investigators to draw three important conclusions. First, stimulation of the colliculus does not simply cause the eye to move; rather, it specifies a precise eye movement specific for the location that is stimulated. Second, stimulation produces movements of a particular amplitude and direction regardless of the starting place of the eye in the orbit. Therefore, like pontine burst neurons, the colliculus appears to encode saccades with respect to a rotation of the eye, using what we have been referring to as motor error coordinates. Finally, the colliculus contains a topographic map of eye rotations: adjacent sites in the colliculus, when stimulated, produce saccades that shift gaze to adjacent points in visual space. The topographic map of the colliculus, which is now often referred to as a motor map, encodes movements in motor error coordinates much as visual area VI encodes visual stimuli with regard to their site of activation on the retina.

In another series of experiments, single-unit recordings were made in the superior colliculi of awake monkeys while the animals made saccades to fixate visual targets.[26] These recordings revealed a group of neurons, called collicular saccade-related burst neurons, that fire a high-frequency burst of impulses beginning about 20 ms before the saccade. Each neuron fires strongly before some saccades but only weakly or not at all before others. Although a given neuron is most active before a movement of a particular amplitude and direction (termed its **best movement**), it is also active for many similar movements. Thus, individual burst neurons are very broadly tuned. Collicular burst neurons are also arranged topographically, as cells with similar best movements are located near each other in the colliculus. These neurons encode motor error rather than information about the absolute position of the eye.

Vector Averaging across Collicular Neuron Populations May Code Saccadic Amplitude and Direction

The collicular stimulation and recording experiments gave rise to an obvious hypothesis: collicular burst neurons generate a motor error signal that is used by the pontine oculomotor circuitry to control saccades. One problem with this hypothesis is that collicular burst neurons are very broadly tuned, whereas saccades are highly precise. How could the amplitude and direction of a saccade be coded accurately by such inaccurate elements? One possible solution to this problem is that the output of the colliculus may be **vector averaged**.[27,28] According to this proposal, each collicular burst neuron "votes" for its best direction, but the strength of its vote is described by its rate of firing. Thus, a cell with a 10° upward best movement would vote strongly for a 10° upward movement and more weakly for movements 10° upward and slightly to the right or left. The vector average of these votes could specify the amplitude and direction of the movement with tremendous precision. As we saw in Chapter 33, the same proposal has been adopted to describe the way in which neurons in the motor cortex may code movement direction with precision.

The idea that vector averaging is used in the superior colliculus was tested by anesthetizing a small, circular portion of the colliculus with lidocaine injected from a micropipette.[29] Saccades corresponding to the best movements of the cells at the center of the anesthetized region were unaffected by the anesthesia, presumably because the cells around this region voted weakly, but equally, for movements in that direction. However, when the animal was directed to make a saccade that placed the anesthetized region to one side of the active region, its movements were systematically biased away from the direction specified by the anes-

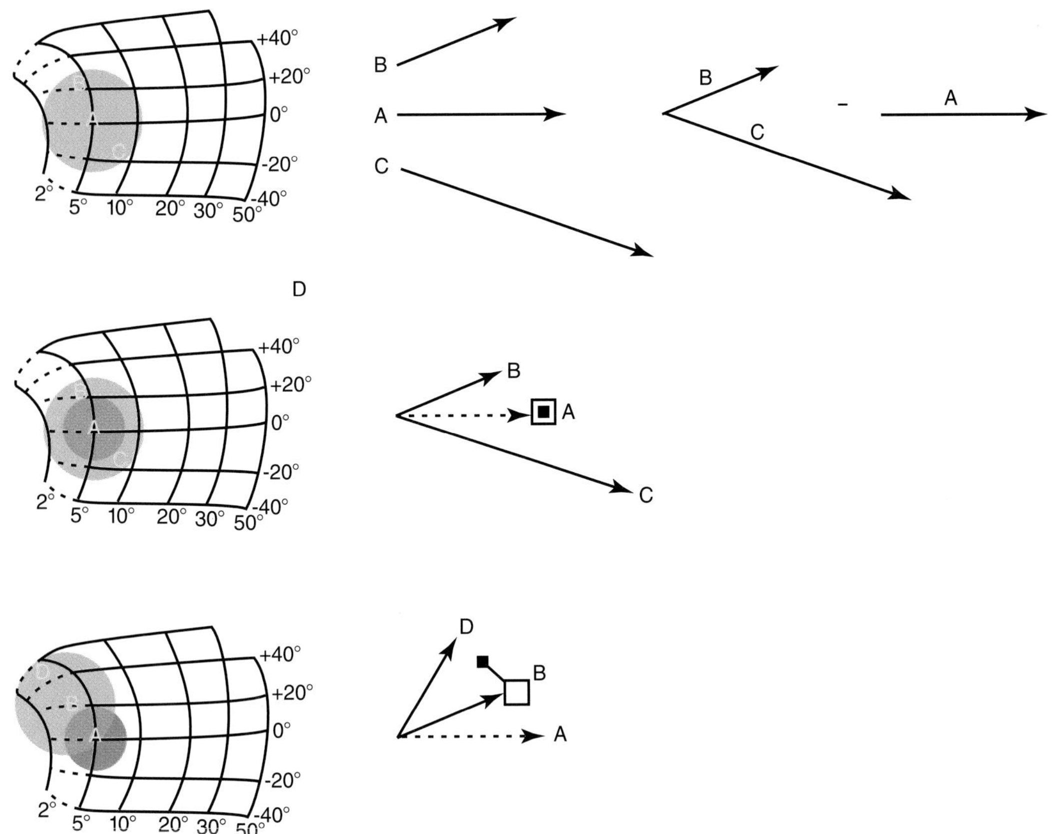

FIGURE 36.11 Vector averaging in the superior colliculus. Top left: The light purple area represents the location of neurons in the superior colliculus that are active before a 5° rightward saccade. Top middle: Cells at locations A, B, and C fire most vigorously for movements in the directions shown by the arrows. Top right: The weighted average of activity at points B and C yields the same movement as activity at A. Middle and bottom: The dark purple area represents a pharmacologically deactivated collicular region. The regions of the colliculus activated during saccades A and B are plotted in the middle and bottom panels, respectively. Saccades targeting A are normal, while saccades targeting B deviate toward D. From Lee *et al.*[29]

thetized region (Fig. 36.11). These experiments established that a vector average of a population code is used to specify the desired motor error for a saccade. They provided the first example of vector averaging in a mammalian motor system.

Sensory Signals from Many Modalities Guide Saccade Planning

So far, we have described how motor error is coded in the superior colliculus and how pontine circuitry uses that information to govern the rotation of the eye. We have not yet addressed the sources of those motor error signals. Primates and other foveate animals can shift their gaze to fixate visual, auditory, and somatosensory targets. This means that if a visual stimulus is presented in the peripheral visual field, the eye can be rotated to align the fovea with that stimulus. If a sound is presented or a point on the body surface is touched, the eye can be directed so that the line of gaze intersects with the sound source or that point on the body surface. Each of these events involves what is known as a sensorimotor transformation. Information encoded by each sensory system according to its own topographic map must be translated into motor error signals.

The simplest of these sensorimotor transformations involves the use of visual information to derive motor error. The simplicity is due to the fact that the retina, like the oculomotor muscles, is anchored to the eye. Thus, the location on the retina activated by a visual stimulus specifies the eye rotation required to foveate the stimulus. For example, if a visual stimulus activates the retina at a location 10° to the right of fixation, then a 10° rightward saccade will bring the fovea in line with the stimulus. In fact, the most superficial laminae of the superior colliculus receive a direct retinal projection that is topographically aligned with the collicular motor map.[30] Moreover, most of the extrastriate visual areas described in Chapter 28 also project directly to the colliculus, providing another route by which retinally sampled visual stimuli can be transformed into motor error signals.

The generation of saccades to auditory targets presents a larger problem for sensorimotor transformation. Auditory targets are localized by comparing information received from the two ears. However, knowing that the target lies straight ahead does not specify what rotation of the eye will fixate it. To solve that problem, the current line of gaze must also be known. If, for example, the eyes are directed leftward, then a straight-ahead target requires a rightward movement. If the eyes are directed rightward, a leftward eye movement is required. Recordings from collicular neurons have provided some insight into how the brain solves this problem.[31] These recordings show that collicular saccade-related burst neurons encode the motor error of impending saccades to auditory targets just as they do for visual targets, irrespective of where the eyes are directed before the saccades begin. Thus, the rotation required to foveate an auditory target—not the location of the target with respect to the ears—is supplied to the pontine saccadic circuitry by the collicular burst neurons (Fig. 36.12).[32] Another class of neurons found in the deepest laminae of the colliculus becomes active when an auditory target is presented in their receptive field. However, these neurons are activated only when the eyes are aligned so that the auditory target has the foveal motor error associated with each cell's location on the collicular motor map. This means that sensory stimuli received by the ears and used to compute the locations of targets relative to the ears must be transformed into motor error coordinates *before* they activate these collicular neurons. These studies helped establish that a **sensorimotor transformation** is a process by which stimuli from the many different sensory systems are translated into a common framework, one appropriate for activating the musculature.

Somatosensory stimuli are also transformed to guide saccadic eye movements. However, unlike auditory stimuli, for which only the position of the eyes in the orbit is necessary to transform location data,

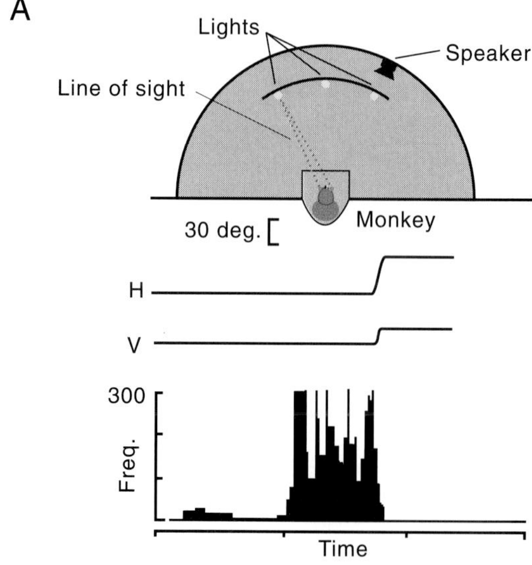

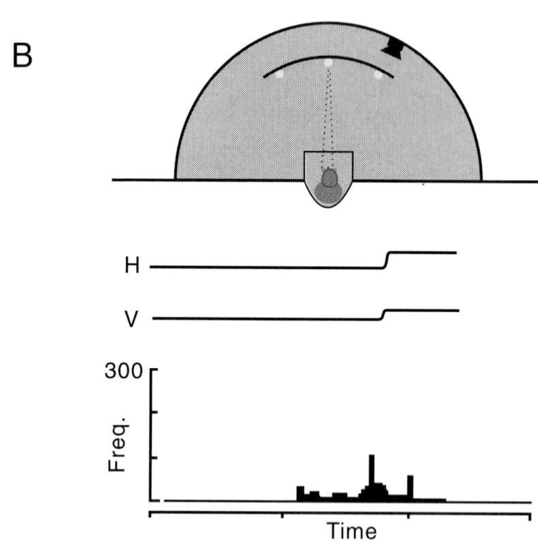

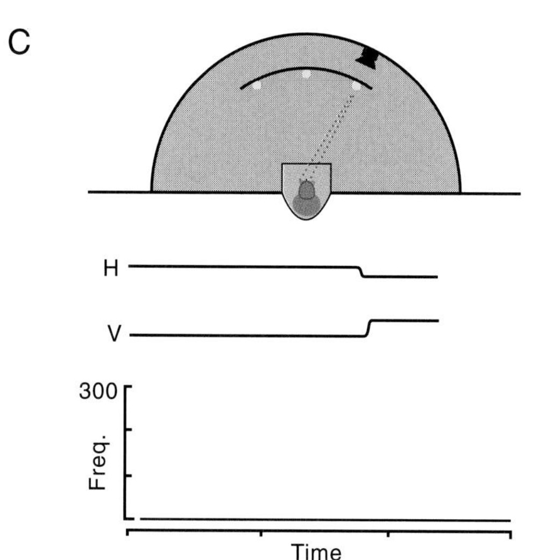

FIGURE 36.12 Shifts in auditory response fields produced by eye movements. All three panels plot the response of a single collicular neuron to an acoustic stimulus fixed 15° to the right of the monkey. (A) When the animal is fixating a leftward target, the neuron fires vigorously when the stimulus is presented. (B) When the animal fixates straight ahead, the neuron fires less vigorously. (C) When the animal fixates the speaker, the neuron is silent to the same acoustic stimulus. From Jay and Sparks.[32]

BOX 36.1

CLINICAL SYNDROMES OF THE FRONTAL EYE FIELDS

Damage to the frontal eye field in one hemisphere causes impairment in the ability to shift gaze to opposite side. At rest, gaze may be tonically shifted to the side damaged, due to unopposed normal tonic activity from the frontal eye field in the opposite hemisphere. In contrast, epileptic convulsive ("seizure") discharge in one frontal eye field causes forced gaze shift and/or saccades away from that hemisphere. Tests of even greater sensitivity depend on the fact that the frontal eye fields control voluntary gaze shifts and saccades. Thus, when a visual stimulus is presented in one visual field, the normal tendency is to look at it using visual targeting mechanisms in parietal lobes and superior colliculus in addition to those in the frontal eye fields. However, the frontal eye fields are exclusive in their ability of override voluntarily these visual attraction "reflexlike" mechanisms. Thus, the instruction to the subject is to "look away from the visual stimulus when it appears." An impaired ability to do this, for example, to look to the left away from a right visual field stimulus, indicates damage (e.g., tumor) of the right frontal eye field.

somatosensory stimuli of the limbs, for example, must be corrected both for the position of the eyes in the head and for the location of the stimulated limb with respect to the head. If neurons in the deeper layers of the colliculus code somatosensory stimuli in motor error coordinates, then their receptive fields on the body surface must depend on both eye position and body surface position. Recordings from these neurons confirm this prediction. In fact, if a monkey is made to shift its initial eye position, a collicular neuron's receptive field can be moved from one hand to the other! This remarkable demonstration of sensorimotor transformation makes it clear how important it is for the nervous system to take signals from disparate sensory systems and combine them in a single coordinate framework.

Higher-Level Saccadic Systems Include Cerebral Cortex and the Basal Ganglia

The sources of the collicular saccadic control signals are only vaguely understood. On anatomical and physiological grounds, we do know that collicular saccade-related information is provided by the frontal eye fields, the parietal cortex, and the basal ganglia. All of these areas project directly to the colliculus and have patterns of unit activity that indicate they play a role in activating collicular burst neurons. The most important of these areas is believed to be the frontal eye fields (see Box 36.1). Unlike the parietal cortex and the basal ganglia, the frontal eye fields project directly to the pontine eye movement control circuitry.[33] After lesions of the colliculus, the frontal eye fields alone can generate saccades.[24] This cortical area must therefore serve a role similar to that of the colliculus. Many of the collicular properties we have described above, like the transformation of auditory targets into saccadic motor error coordinates, are also evident in the frontal eye fields. Ongoing research seeks to understand how all of these antecedent structures give rise to the oculomotor control signals that guide collicular, pontine, and cortical eye movement control structures.

Summary

The saccadic system brings in higher brainstem and cerebral mechanisms to identify a target and shift gaze to it. The eye movements themselves are very fast (saccade means "jump") and they minimize the time lost in visual contact while gaze is shifting to a new target.

SMOOTH PURSUIT

The optokinetic system moves the eyes at a velocity that compensates for movement of the visual field. We considered this a gaze-stabilization mechanism and pointed out that essentially all animals have this phylogenetically ancient system. Animals with foveas can also use saccades to direct the fovea to scrutinize targets throughout visual space. However, these animals face a special challenge when they make a saccade to examine a moving target. The saccade may bring the fovea briefly into alignment with the target, but unless the eye can be made to move with the same velocity as the target, the target image will not be stabilized on the retina. Matching the velocity of the eye to that of the visual stimulus when the visual stimulus is the entire visual world is, of course, the optokinetic response. When the visual stimulus is only a tiny portion of the visual world, eye movements need to be driven by only a small portion of the retina. The eye movement system that minimizes the retinal slip of a small visual target while producing an increased retinal slip for the rest of the visual world is known as smooth pursuit. Although smooth pursuit might be viewed as a specialized form of the optokinetic response, these two systems involve at least partially distinct neural architectures.

Compared to what is known about the saccadic system, little is known about the brainstem circuits that compute the velocities of pursuit-related motor error. In general, neurobiologists have tended to view the pursuit system as similar to the optokinetic system: retinal slip, in this case restricted to a selected portion of the visual world, is minimized by adjusting eye velocity until slip is reduced or eliminated. Models of the pursuit system are thus quite similar to those of the optokinetic system. Knowledge about the speed and direction of the target's motion across the retina and the eye's current movement is used to compute a desired speed and direction of eye movement. The eye velocity signal is then passed via the brainstem oculomotor nuclei to the extraocular muscles to control the dynamic movement of the eye. This dynamic signal, like the dynamic signals for other eye movements, is presumed to be integrated to compute the static signal necessary to maintain the eye in a fixed position should the eye stop. This integrator is thought to reside in the prepositus nucleus of the hypoglossal nerve. Two hypotheses have been proposed to explain the source of the dynamic signal. One hypothesis states that the speed and direction of slip are the only visually derived inputs used by the smooth pursuit system.[34] The other hypothesis states that information about the position, speed, and acceleration of the target is combined to compute a dynamic force structure optimized for the properties of the visual stimulus.[35] The first hypothesis can thus be thought of as muscle-driven, in the sense that it uses a minimum of visual information and structures the dynamic force based entirely on the properties of the motor system. The second hypothesis can be thought of as sensory-driven, structuring the dynamic force by analyzing the visual target. As we examine the neural structures that generate pursuit movements, we see that these two hypotheses place the computational burden on different brain structures: the muscle-driven hypothesis places this burden in the oculomotor brainstem, where dynamic forces are structured for other types of eye movements, whereas the sensory-driven hypothesis places it in the largely cortical areas that compute information related to target motion.

The Cerebellum Plays a Key Role in Smooth Pursuit

The dorsolateral pontine nucleus (DLPN) is a critical link in the smooth pursuit system, bridging between the cortical motion-processing systems discussed in Chapter 33 and the oculomotor portions of the cerebellum and brainstem. The DLPN contains neurons that encode the direction and speed of pursuit, the direction and speed of target motion, or both.[36] Thus, the DLPN could, in principle, process information about both the sensory representations of targets and the motor error signals required to drive the eyes. The output of the DLPN passes to the cerebellum (the flocculus, paraflocculus, and vermis), where there are neurons whose firing rate is tightly coupled to the velocity of eye rotation specifically during smooth pursuit. These neurons in turn project to the vestibular nuclei, where their motor error signals are thought to be integrated into the vestibulopontine oculomotor systems.[37,38]

Cortical Areas MT and MST Are Sources of Visual Target Motion Signals

The identified brainstem pursuit pathways form a portion of the complete pursuit system. Signals that indicate target motion are critical to their function. This information appears to be provided to the pursuit system by the cortical motion system, which is composed in part of areas MT and MST (described in Chapter 33). These areas compute the direction and speed of moving stimuli throughout the visual field and pass this information to the DLPN, directly and via the posterior parietal cortex and the frontal eye fields.

Summary

The smooth pursuit system provides insights into both brainstem structures for oculomotor control and cortical structures for sensory processing. Pursuit thus may be unique; it combines high-level moving visual signals and pontine oculomotor circuits.

VERGENCE

The function of the vergence system is to converge or diverge the lines of gaze projecting from both eyes so that they meet at the target of foveal vision (Fig. 36.13). Of course, animals without binocular foveal vision do not need to align a single retinal region on both eyes with a single visual target. Therefore, only a limited number of vertebrates, including primates, generate vergence movements. The eye movements we

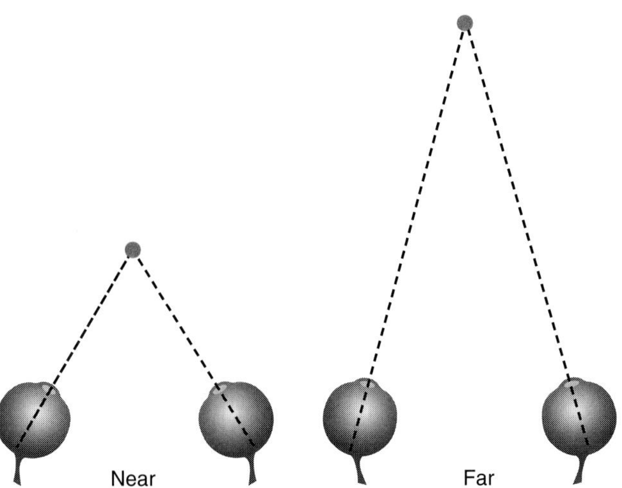

FIGURE 36.13 Convergence angle depends on target distance.

have considered so far produce shifts in gaze as if a single line of sight were being redirected. In fact, this is exactly how the saccadic and smooth pursuit systems appear to compute gaze shifts. How then are movements of the two eyes coordinated so that both eyes, which are separated by several centimeters, fixate a single target? The German physiologist Ewald Hering proposed that an entirely separate system computes the appropriate vergence "correction" for each eye during gaze shifts and adds that signal to the binocular saccadic or smooth pursuit motor error command. In this section we examine the sources of the vergence motor error signal and describe the physiological mechanisms that compute the dynamic and static muscle forces necessary to produce vergence movements.

There Are Four Sources of Vergence Motor Error Signals

The brains generates four experimentally separable classes of vergence motor error commands. The first and most obvious is related to **binocular disparity,** which occurs when a visual stimulus is presented to both eyes but appears at different locations on each retina. The second class deals with **accommodation**. Apparently, the accommodative state of both lenses is monitored, and this information is used to compute the distance to the target currently in focus. The third class, usually referred to as **tonic**, represents the default state of convergence for the animal in total darkness. In humans it is equal to about 3° of convergence. The final class of vergence motor error commands uses monocular (or cognitive) depth cues, such as linear perspective, to infer the distance to targets. This class is usually referred to as **proximal vergence.**

The Vergence Brainstem Is Similar to the Saccadic Brainstem

Physiological studies of the oculomotor brainstem[39] have revealed that a small group of neurons lying in the rostral midbrain reticular formation appear to form a control center for vergence much like the pontine horizontal gaze-control center for saccades. Two types of neurons have been identified in this area. **Vergence burst neurons** fire a high-frequency burst of impulses before the onset of a vergence movement, and their firing frequency is related to the velocity of the movement. Both convergence-specific and divergence-specific burst neurons have been identified. The number of impulses in a burst is related to the amplitude of the movement. **Vergence burst-tonic neurons** appear to combine the dynamic and static responses of the vergence system. By analogy with the saccadic system, it is tempting to presume that during a vergence eye movement, the output of the vergence burst neurons is integrated and reflected in the activity of the vergence burst-tonic neurons.

Most Gaze Shifts Involve Both Versional and Vergence Movements

As shown in Fig. 36.14, most gaze shifts for binocular, foveate animals involve both a coordinated movement of the two eyes together (version) and a separate movement of each eye to adjust for differences in the distance to the target (vergence). Thus, the point of gaze (the location at which the lines of gaze from each eye meet) must move both across and in or out. If we were to plot the location of the point of gaze during a saccade at successive 2-ms intervals, it would follow the trajectory plotted in green in Fig. 36.15. The observed eye movement has three phases. First, the eyes begin to converge quite slowly before the saccade begins. This constitutes the beginning of the vergence movement. After a delay, the high-velocity saccade begins; the point of gaze shifts across the visual field, but it also shifts in depth much more rapidly. Finally, the high-velocity saccade and the terminal, slow portion of the vergence movement are completed.

Simultaneous studies of the vergence and saccadic systems[40] suggest that the vergence burst neurons are normally inhibited by the saccadic omnipause neurons, and that this inhibition limits the frequency of the vergence burst neurons' firing rate and hence the velocity of the vergence movement. The omnipause neurons, which act as the saccade trigger, are silent during saccades, disinhibiting the vergence burst neurons and thereby accelerating vergence while the saccade is in progress. After the saccade is completed, the omni-

BOX 36.2

CLINICAL SYNDROMES OF THE MEDIAN LONGITUDINAL FASCICULUS

The median longitudinal fasciculus (MLF) carries signals that coordinate actions of the lateral rectus of one eye with the medial rectus of the other eye for lateral movement in the VOR, smooth pursuit, saccades, and maintained gaze. Thus, damage (typically a small infarct caused by occlusion of a small artery) of the right MLF (after crossing midline) will impair the coordinate adduction of the right eye that naturally accompanies abduction of the left eye on attempted left gaze. Right gaze (abduction of right eye, adduction of left) will be normal. Damage to the MLF on both sides (typically a bilateral lesion in multiple sclerosis) causes failure of adduction of both eyes—that is, the right eye on attempted left gaze, the left eye on attempted right gaze. To be sure that it is indeed the MLF that is involved and not the third nerve itself (diabetic infarct) or the neuromuscular junction (myasthenia gravis), the clinician must show that adduction is normal in *vergence,* which does not critically involve the MLF. In contrast, damage to the midbrain convergence center (tumor of the pineal body with pressure from above) will impair adduction of both eyes in attempted convergence, but not adduction or lateral gaze.

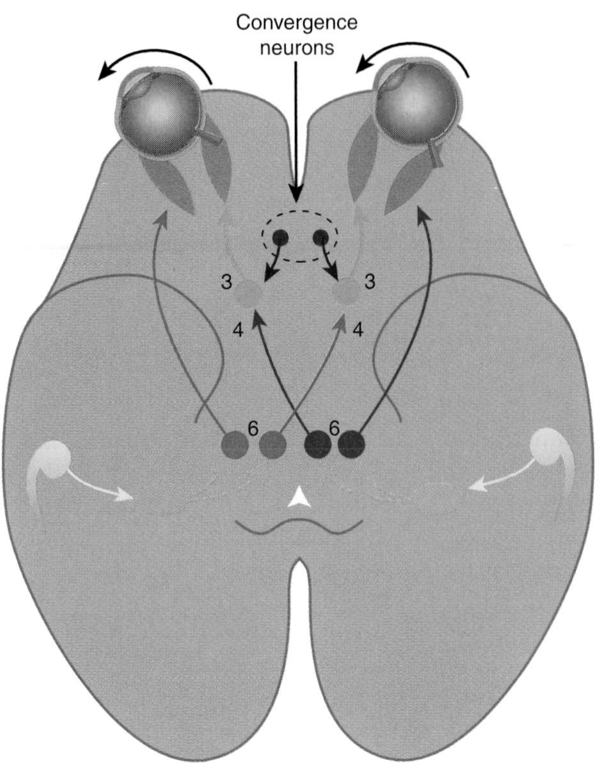

FIGURE 36.14 The 3, 4, and 6 refer to oculomotor, trochlear, and abducens nuclei and their respective cranial nerves.

pause neurons become active again, reinhibiting the vergence burst neurons and reducing the velocity of the remaining portion of the vergence movement. These studies reveal how the separate oculomotor systems interact during normal eye movements.

Summary

The effect of eye movements is twofold. First, eye movements stabilize the line of gaze while animals move in their environment. Unpredictable high-speed rotations of the head, which are produced whenever an animal moves, shift the line of gaze and smear the optical image, reducing the resolution of the visual system. These rotations are compensated for by counterrotations of the eyes generated by the vestibulo-ocular system. Working in tandem with the vestibulo-ocular system is the optokinetic system, which compensates for slower movements of the head. Second, in animals with retinas that have a small region of high resolution, a specialized set of eye movements—saccades, smooth pursuit, and vergence—align that region with visual targets of interest. Together, these sets of movements permit the efficient gathering of visual information by the retina.

As we have observed, eye movements involve generating at least two classes of signals: those involved in moving the eye to a new position and those involved in holding the eye at that position. The oculomotor system appears to combine these signals at or before the level of the motor neurons for all classes of movements. The oculomotor system also appears to employ a critical shortcut, computing explicitly only the dynamic signals and then integrating those signals to produce the static signals.

Many classes of sensory signals—vestibular, visual,

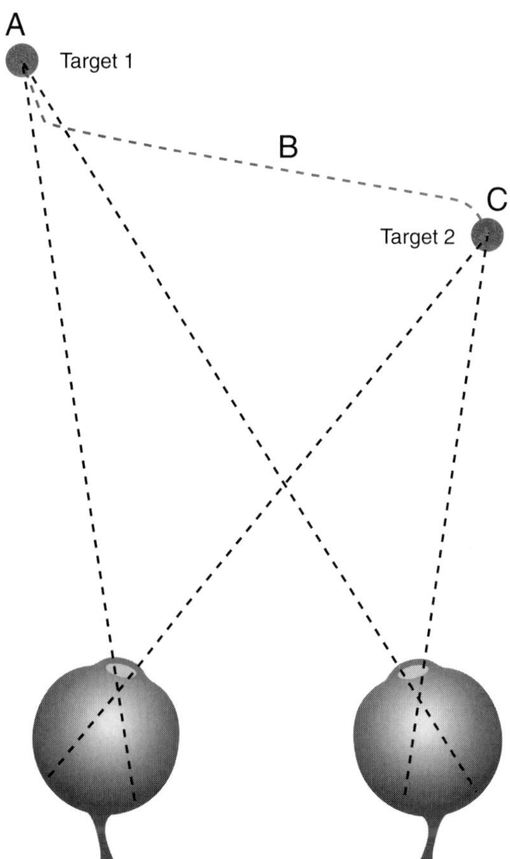

FIGURE 36.15 Trajectory of a saccade, viewed from above, that shifts the point of gaze laterally and in depth. (A) Vergence mechanisms begin to converge the eyes prior to the saccade. (B) The saccade then begins, and the rate of vergence accelerates. (C) After the saccade, the vergence mechanisms continue to converge the eyes until both foveas are aligned with the target.

auditory, and somatosensory—are used to guide eye movements. In order for a single common output pathway to make use of this wide variety of input signals, each of these inputs must be transformed into a motor error signal. This process of sensorimotor transformation, which has been studied so extensively in the oculomotor system, may well prove to be a general feature of all or most vertebrate motor systems.

Reviews/Selected Readings

General Eye Movement Sources

Carpenter, R. H. S. (1988). *Movements of the Eyes,* 2nd ed. Pion Limited, London.

Carpenter, R. H. S., ed. (1991). *Eye Movements. Vision and Visual Dysfunction,* Vol. 8. CRC Press, Boston.

Leigh, R. J., and Zee, D. S. (1991). *The Neurology of Eye Movements,* 2nd ed. Davis, Philadelphia.

Robinson, D. A. (1981). Control of eye movements. In *Handbook of Physiology* (V. B. Brooks, ed.), Sect. 1, Vol. II, Part 2, pp. 1275–1320. Williams & Wilkins, Baltimore.

Specific Reviews

Collewijn, H. (1981). *The Oculomotor System of the Rabbit and its Plasticity.* Springer, New York.

Fuchs, A. F., Kaneko, C. R. S., and Scudder, C. A. (1985). Brainstem control of saccadic eye movements. *Annu. Rev. Neurosci.* **8:** 307–337.

Lisberger, S. G., Morris, E. J., and Tychsen, L. (1987). Visual motion processing and sensory-motor integration for smooth pursuit eye movements. *Annu. Rev. Neurosci.* **10:** 97–129.

Melvill Jones, G. (1991). The vestibular contribution. In *Eye Movements* (R. H. S. Carpenter, ed.), pp. 13–44. CRC Press, Boston.

Raphan, T., and Cohen, B. (1978). Brainstem mechanisms for rapid and slow eye movements. *Annu. Rev. Physiol.* **40:** 527–552.

Sparks, D. L. (1986). Translation of sensory signals into commands for saccadic eye movements: Role of primate superior colliculus. *Physiol. Rev.* **66:** 118–171.

References

1. Robinson, D. A. (1964). The mechanics of human saccadic eye movements. *J. Physiol. (London)* **174:** 245–264.
2. Fuchs, A. F., and Lushei, E. S. (1970). Firing patterns of abducens neurons of alert monkeys in relationship to horizontal eye movements. *J. Neurophysiol.* **33:** 382–392.
3. Robinson, D. A. (1970). Oculomotor unit behavior in the monkey. *J. Neurophysiol.* **33:** 393–404.
4. Skavenski, A. A., and Robinson, D. A. (1973). Role of abducens nucleus in vestibulo-ocular reflex. *J. Neurophysiol.* **36:** 724–738.
5. Wilson, V. J., and Melvill Jones, G. (1979). *Mammalian Vestibular Physiology.* Plenum, London.
6. Dickman, J. D., and Correia, M. J. (1989). Responses of pigeon horizontal semicircular canal afferent fibers. I. Step, trapezoid and low-frequency sinusoidal mechanical and rotational stimulation. *J. Neurophysiol.* **62:** 1090–1101.
7. Dickman, J. D., and Correia, M. J. (1989). Responses of pigeon horizontal semicircular canal afferent fibers. II. High-frequency mechanical stimulation. *J. Neurophysiol.* **62:** 1102–1112.
8. Groen, J. J., Lowenstein, O., and Vendrik, A. (1952). The mechanical analysis of responses from the end organs of the horizontal semicircular canal in the isolated elasmobranch labyrinth. *J. Physiol. (London)* **117:** 329–346.
9. Melvill Jones, G., and Milsum, J. H. (1970). Characteristics of neural transmission from the semicircular canal to the vestibular nuclei of cats. *J. Physiol. (London)* **109:** 295–216.
10. Robinson, D. A. (1975). Oculomotor control signals. In *Basic Mechanisms of Ocular Motility and Their Clinical Implications* (P. Bach-y-Rita and G. Lennerstrand, eds.), pp. 337–374. Pergamon, Oxford.
11. Miles, F. A., and Eighmy, B. B. (1980). Long term adaptive changes in primate vestibulo-ocular reflex. I. Behavioral observations. *J. Neurophysiol.* **43:** 1406–1425.
12. Robinson, D. A. (1976). Adaptive gain control of the vestibulo-ocular reflex by the cerebellum. *J. Neurophysiol.* **39:** 954–969.
13. Miles, F. A., and Lisberger, S. G. (1981). Plasticity in the vestibulo-ocular reflex: A new hypothesis. *Annu. Rev. Neurosci.* **4:** 273–299.
14. Lisberger, S. G., and Pavelko, T. A. (1986). Vestibular signals

carried by pathways subserving plasticity of the vestibulo-ocular reflex in monkeys. *J. Neurosci.* **6:** 346–354.
15. Lisberger, S. G. (1986). Properties of pathways subserving long-term adaptive plasticity in the vestibulo-ocular reflex in monkeys. In *The Biology of Change in Otolaryngology* (R. W. Ruben *et al.*, eds.), pp. 171–183. Elsevier, Amsterdam.
16. Baarsma, E. A., and Collewijn, H. (1974). Vestibulo-ocular and optokinetic reactions to rotation and their interaction in the rabbit. *J. Physiol.* (*London*) **238:** 603–625.
17. Hoffman, K.-P., and Distler, C. (1989). Quantitative analysis of visual receptive fields in neurons in nucleus of the optic tract and dorsal terminal nucleus of the accessory optic tract in monkeys. *Exp. Brain Res.* **69:** 635–644.
18. Henn, V., Young, L. R., and Finley, C. (1974). Vestibular nucleus units in alert monkeys are also influenced by moving visual fields. *Brain Res.* **71:** 144–149.
19. Lushei, E. S., and Fuchs, A. F. (1972). Activity of brainstem neurons during eye movements of alert monkeys. *J. Neurophysiol.* **35:** 445–461.
20. Keller, E. L. (1974). Participation of the medial pontine reticular formation in eye movement generation in the monkey. *J. Neurophysiol.* **37:** 316–332.
21. Strassman, A., Highstein, S. M., and McCrea, R. A. (1986). Anatomy and physiology of saccadic burst neurons in the alert squirrel monkey: I. Excitatory burst neurons. *J. Comp. Neurol.* **249:** 337–357.
22. Strassman, A., Highstein, S. M., and McCrea, R. A. (1986). Anatomy and physiology of saccadic burst neurons in the alert squirrel monkey: II. Inhibitory burst neurons. *J. Comp. Neurol.* **249:** 358–380.
23. Cannon, S. C., and Robinson, D. A. (1987). Loss of the neural integrator of the oculomotor system from brainstem lesions in the monkey. *J. Neurophysiol.* **57:** 1383–1409.
24. Schiller, P. H., True, S. D., and Conway, J. L. (1980). Deficits in eye movements following frontal eye field and superior colliculus ablations. *J. Neurophysiol.* **44:** 1175–1189.
25. Robinson, D. A. (1972). Eye movements evoked by collicular stimulation in the alert monkey. *Vision Res.* **12:** 1795–1808.
26. Wurtz, R. H., and Goldberg, M. E. (1972). Activity of superior colliculus in the behaving monkey. III. Cells discharging before eye movements. *J. Neurophysiol.* **35:** 575–586.
27. McIlwain, J. T. (1976). Large receptive fields and spatial transformations in the visual system. *Int. Rev. Physiol.* **10:** 223–248.
28. Sparks, D. L., Holland, R., and Guthrie, B. L. (1976). Size and distribution of movement fields in the monkey superior colliculus. *Brain Res.* **113:** 21–00.
29. Lee, C., Rohrer, W. H., and Sparks, D. L. (1988). Population coding of saccadic eye movements by neurons in the superior colliculus. *Nature* (*London*) **332:** 357–360.
30. Goldberg, M. E., and Wurtz, R. H. (1972). Activity of superior colliculus in behaving monkey. I. Visual receptive fields of single neurons. *J. Neurophysiol.* **35:** 542–559.
31. Jay, M. F., and Sparks, D. L. (1987). Sensorimotor integration in the primate superior colliculus. II. Coordinates of auditory signals. *J. Neurophysiol.* **57:** 35–55.
32. Jay, M. F., and Sparks, D. L. (1984). Auditory receptive fields in primate superior colliculus shift with changes in eye position. *Nature* (*London*) **309:** 345–347.
33. Huerta, M. F., Krubitzer, L. A., and Kaas, J. H. (1986). Frontal eye field as defined by intracortical microstimulation in squirrel monkeys, owl monkeys, and macaque monkeys: I. Subcortical connections. *J. Comp. Neurol.* **253:** 415–439.
34. Robinson, D. A., Gordon, J. L., and Gordon, S. E. (1986). A model of the smooth pursuit eye movement system. *Biol. Cybernet.* **55:** 43–57.
35. Lisberger, S. G., Morris, E. J., and Tychsen, L. (1987). Visual motion processing and sensory-motor integration for smooth pursuit eye movements. *Annu. Rev. Neurosci.* **10:** 97–129.
36. Suzuki, D. A., and Keller, E. L. (1984). Visual signals in the dorsolateral pontine nucleus of the monkey: Their relationship to smooth pursuit eye movements. *Exp. Brain Res.* **53:** 473–478.
37. Langer, T., Fuchs, A. F., Chubb, M. C., Scudder, C. A., and Lisberger, S. G. (1985). Floccular efferents in the rhesus macaque as revealed by autoradiography and horseradish peroxidase. *J. Comp. Neurol.* **235:** 26–37.
38. Langer, T., Fuchs, A. F., Scudder, C. A., and Chubb, M. C. (1985). Afferents to the flocculus of the cerebellum in the rhesus macaque as revealed by retrograde transport of horseradish peroxidase. *J. Comp. Neurol.* **235:** 1–25.
39. Mays, L. E., Porter, J. D., Gamlin, P. D. R., and Tello, C. A. (1986). Neural control of vergence eye movements: Neurons encoding vergence velocity. *J. Neurophysiol.* **56:** 1007–1021.
40. Mays, L. E., and Gamlin, P. D. R. (1995). A neural mechanism subserving saccade-vergence interactions. In *Eye Movement Research: Mechanisms, Processes and Applications* (J. M. Findlay, R. Walker, and R. W. Kentridge, eds.), pp. 215–223. North-Holland Publ., New York.

SECTION VI

REGULATORY SYSTEMS

CHAPTER

37

The Hypothalamus: An Overview of Regulatory Systems

J. Patrick Card, Larry W. Swanson, and Robert Y. Moore

The hypothalamus is an integrative center essential for survival of an organism and reproduction of its species. Regulatory systems emerged as each organism adapted to its environment. The systems have evolved to control the complex interactions of physiology and behavior.

The regulatory role of the hypothalamus is reflected in its structural organization and connections. Almost every major subdivision of the neuraxis, or central nervous system, communicates with the hypothalamus and is subject to its influence. In addition, the hypothalamus communicates with peripheral organ systems by converting synaptic information to blood-borne humoral signals. In turn, the hypothalamus responds to input from the peripheral systems that it regulates. The chapters in this section discuss the processes by which the hypothalamus influences physiology and behavior. This introductory chapter provides an overview of the structural and functional organization of the hypothalamus.

HISTORICAL PERSPECTIVE

Research on the hypothalamus has a rich and storied history. Although depicted in early brain atlases, the hypothalamus was not recognized as a distinct division of the diencephalon until the work of Wilhelm His[1] a little over a century ago. Our understanding of the structure and function of the hypothalamus developed as basic and clinical neurosciences were integrated. One important early researcher was Harvey Cushing, a neurosurgeon who studied endocrine disorders from a neuroscience perspective. He described diabetes insipidus, a neuroendocrine dysfunction of uncontrolled urinary water excretion, and identified the importance of injury to the pituitary stalk in the condition. Cushing also studied other disorders of the endocrine system, including the syndrome that bears his name. In addition, he recognized that the hypothalamus and pituitary form a functional unit, and he pioneered pituitary surgery. Thus, he founded the fields of neurosurgery and endocrinology. In 1929, Cushing wrote about the hypothalamus, "Here in this well concealed spot, almost to be covered with a thumb nail, lies the very mainspring of primitive existence—vegetative, emotional, reproductive—on which, with more or less success, man has come to superimpose a cortex of inhibitions."

Since Cushing and others described dysfunctions associated with hypothalamic and pituitary pathology or experimental damage, technical advances have been allowing more and more sophisticated insights into the structural and functional organization of this region of the neuraxis. Gurdijian,[2] Kreig,[3] and Le Gros Clark *et al.*[4] used histological procedures to describe the organization of cells, cytoarchitecture and hypothalamic nuclei. These scientists' descriptions proved to be remarkably predictive of functional specialization within the hypothalamus. During the same period, Ranson, Hess, and others showed that lesions and localized stimulation of the hypothalamus could selectively affect appetite, weight control, water balance, autonomic control, reproductive function, and emotional behavior. This work progressed so well that in 1940 it could be summarized only in a large volume of the annual series of the Association for Research in Nervous and Mental Disease.[5]

In that volume, Ernst and Berta Scharrer[6] presented evidence for "neurosecretory neurons," providing the foundation for a fundamental tenet of hypothalamic function. That is, there were neurons—in the brain—that secrete hormones directly into the blood stream. In 1949, Wolfgang Bargmann published his studies about neurosecretory neurons with cell bodies that lay in the hypothalamus and axons that projected to the posterior lobe of the pituitary gland. Bargmann's work provided a framework for understanding neuroendocrine, or neurohumoral regulation. We now describe **neurohumoral regulation** as the release of hypothalamic peptides from the neurons into the peripheral circulation, where these peptides exert profound physiological influence on a variety of systems.

Neurohumoral regulation of the anterior lobe of the pituitary was defined by Harris and Green in the 1950s, when they identified the neurovascular link, the portal plexus, through which the hypothalamus regulates the anterior pituitary. In the 1960s, Guillemin and Schally independently isolated and characterized peptide hormones that act on the anterior pituitary, revealing the chemical basis of regulation. In subsequent years the field of neuroendocrinology built enormously on these observations, and the resulting literature documents a diverse family of hormones that are released into the portal plexus of the hypothalamus by neurons. The hypothalamic hormones stimulate or inhibit the release of other hormones from the anterior pituitary gland.

We have made great progress in improving our understanding of Cushing's "mainspring of primitive existence." Tremendous insights into CNS function have emerged from the analysis of hypothalamic structure and function, underscoring the importance of this small, complex region of the diencephalon. The hypothalamus controls diverse homeostatic and behavioral functions essential for survival of an organism.

HYPOTHALAMIC DEVELOPMENT

The hypothalamus develops from the diencephalic vesicle of the neural tube. Transverse sections through the vesicle reveal a prominent central cavity that will ultimately develop into the third ventricle. At this early stage, the walls of the vesicle are composed of germinal epithelium, which will generate the cells that ultimately develop into the thalamus and hypothalamus. The hypothalamic sulcus, a prominent groove in the luminal surface of the vesicle, marks the separation between the ventral thalamus and the hypothalamus. The diencephalic vesicle also gives rise to the optic vesicles, two prominent lateral evaginations that develop into the optic nerves and neural retina. A ventral evagination of the floor of the vesicle will develop into the infundibular stalk and posterior lobe of the pituitary gland, and a dorsal evagination of the roof plate will develop into the pineal gland.

Anatomists, particularly Herrick[7] and Kuhlenbeck,[8] showed that the diencephalon is composed of longitudinally organized cell columns that arise from distinct portions of the embryonic diencephalic germinal epithelium (Fig. 37.1). Differentiation of the walls of the vesicle ultimately defines three distinct regions, known as the epithalamus, thalamus (dorsal and ventral), and hypothalamus. The epithalamus is the anlage of the pineal gland (see Chapter 45) and arises from the dorsal and caudal extent of the diencephalon. The dorsal surface of the neural tube forms a thin roof plate. During development, the simple cuboidal epithelium of the roof plate proliferates in association with the vasculature and pia mater, the innermost membrane covering the brain. Together these form the highly invaginated choroid plexus along the roof of the third ventricle and in relation to the two intraventricular foramina.

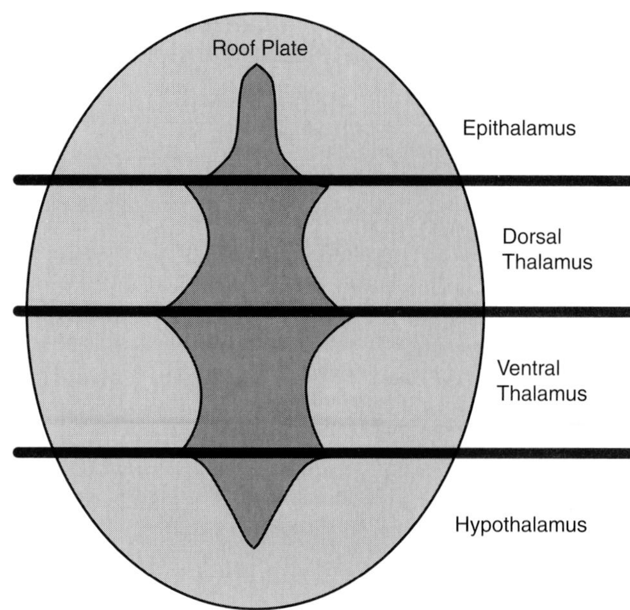

FIGURE 37.1 Organization of the diencephalic vesicle of the early neural tube of a typical vertebrate (transverse section). The locations of the four longitudinal diencephalic cell columns, modified from Herrick[7], are illustrated.

Differentiation of the ventral diencephalic germinal epithelium leads to the development of the hypothalamus in stages that generally proceed lateral to medial, or outside-in. The cells of the lateral hypothalamus are formed early and migrate toward the lateral diencephalic wall. The next cell groups are formed from the ventral diencephalic germinal epithelium and migrate to a position medial to the first group of cells, the lateral subdivision. The neurons generated in this wave of development form the major nuclei and fields of the medial hypothalamus. For example, the medial preoptic, anterior hypothalamic, and ventromedial hypothalamic nuclei and the mammillary complex develop from groups of cells that migrated from the ventral germinal epithelium. Periventricular cell groups are also formed from the germinal epithelium. They take a position adjacent to the wall of the third ventricle. This area is composed of the periventricular nucleus, a thin layer of cells immediately adjacent to the ependyma, and its major differentiations, the paraventricular and arcuate nuclei. Cells in this subdivision had been reported to be generated late in hypothalamic development, but later evidence indicates that essentially all neuroendocrine cells, both magnocellular and parvicellular, are generated at about the same time as the cells that migrate into the lateral zone.[9]

GENERAL ORGANIZATIONAL PRINCIPLES OF THE ADULT HYPOTHALAMUS

Studies of how the organization of the hypothalamus relates to its function have benefited enormously from the development of immunohistochemical and tract-tracing methods. Characterization of the chemoarchitecture of and connections among hypothalamic cell groups has helped explain how this small region of the brain exerts such a profound influence on physiology and behavior (Table 37.1). The following description is an overview of the cellular architecture and organizational principles that underlie the function of the hypothalamus. (For a comprehensive description of the cytoarchitecture, neurochemical phenotypes, and connectivity of hypothalamic neurons, see Swanson.[10]) Because most work was done using rodents, we have based our descriptions and illustrations on data derived from the rat. We have emphasized organizational principles that appear common to those found in primates.

TABLE 37.1 Major Nuclei Contributing to Preoptic, Chiasmatic (Anterior), Tuberal, and Mammillary Subdivisions

Hypothalamic subdivision	Nucleus
Preoptic	Vascular organ of the lamina terminalis
	Median preoptic nucleus
	Preoptic periventricular nucleus
	Anteroventral periventricular nucleus
	Medial preoptic nucleus
	Lateral preoptic area
Anterior	Suprachiasmatic nucleus
	Anterior periventricular nucleus
	Anterior hypothalamic nucleus
	Paraventricular nucleus
	Subparaventricular zone
	Supraoptic nucleus
	Retrochiasmatic area
	Lateral hypothalamic area
Tuberal	Intermediate periventricular nucleus
	Arcuate nucleus
	Ventromedial nucleus
	Dorsomedial nucleus
	Lateral hypothalamic area
	Ventral premammillary nucleus
Mammillary	Posterior periventricular nucleus
	Posterior hypothalamic nucleus
	Dorsal premammillary nucleus
	Mammillary nuclei
	Supramammillary nuclei
	Tuberomammillary nuclei
	Lateral hypothalamic area

Hypothalamic Boundaries Are Defined by Physical Landmarks

The boundaries of the hypothalamus are defined by landmarks that are apparent on the ventral surface of the brain, in medial exposures of the third ventricular wall (Fig. 37.2), and in Nissl-stained transverse sections through the diencephalon (Fig. 37.3). On the ventral surface of the brain are three prominent landmarks that define the floor of the hypothalamus. The most rostral of these is the **optic chiasm,** a myelinated fiber tract formed by the decussation of the optic nerves. Immediately caudal to the optic nerve is the **infundibular stalk,** an evagination emerging from a prominent oval protuberance, the **tuber cinereum,** located on the floor of the third ventricle. The infundibular stalk connects the ventral hypothalamus to the pituitary. Through it runs the **portal plexus,** connecting the hypothalamus to the anterior pituitary, and the axons of magnocellular neurosecretory neurons, which extend from the hypothalamus to the posterior pituitary. The caudal limit of the hypothalamus is defined by the mammillary nuclei. In rodents, these nuclei are found caudal to the tuber cinereum but exhibit no clear external landmark. In primates and humans, the mammillary nuclei are marked externally by paired spherical protrusions located immediately caudal to the infundibular stalk. All of the structures dorsal to these landmarks and ventral to the thalamus constitute the hypothalamus.

The Hypothalamus Is Composed of Three Longitudinally Oriented Cell Columns

Historically, the hypothalamus has been divided into subdivisions that can be distinguished in both the

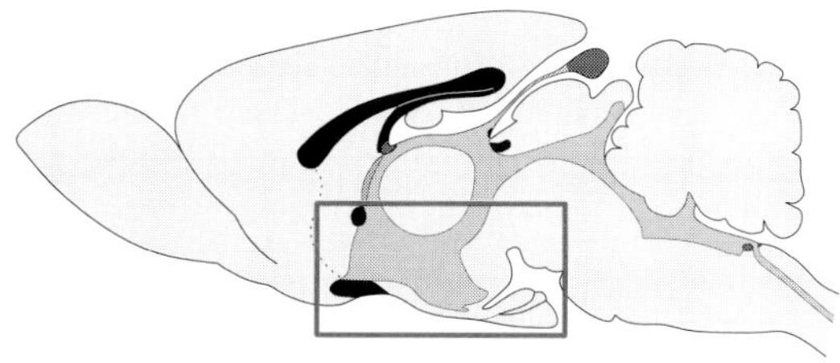

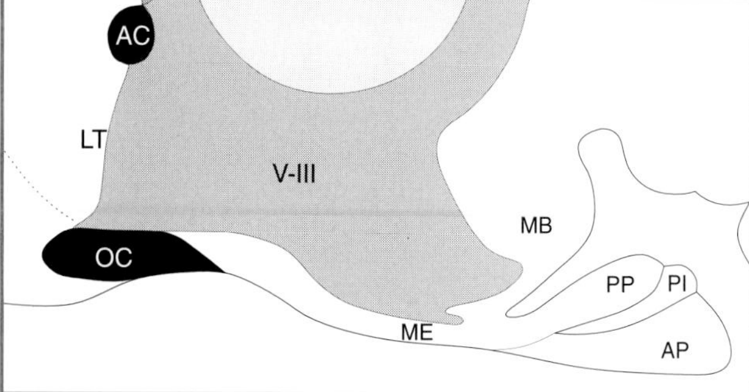

FIGURE 37.2 The boundaries of the hypothalamus of the rat (midsagittal section). The ventricular system is shaded. The boxed area shows the approximate location of the hypothalamus in the ventral quadrant of the diencephalon. The floor of the third ventricle (V-III), formed by the optic chiasm (OC), median eminence (ME) and rostral portion of the mammillary body (MB) defines a large portion of the rostrocaudal extent of the hypothalamus and is also distinguished by the infundibular stalk, which connects the pituitary to the ventral diencephalon. The rostral limit of the hypothalamus is the lamina terminalis (LT), a thin strip of tissue extending between the optic chasm and anterior commissure (AC) that also contributes to the rostral wall of the third ventricle. PP, posterior pituitary; AP, anterior pituitary, PI, pars intermedia of the pituitary.

longitudinal and the mediolateral axes of the diencephalon (Fig. 37.3 and Table 37.1). Current evidence favors three longitudinally organized zones that can be further divided into four levels, or nuclear groups, based on position in the rostrocaudal axis of the hypothalamus.

The longitudinal subdivisions are largely consistent with the initial descriptions of Gurdjian[2] and Krieg[3] and consist of periventricular, medial, and lateral zones. All three zones extend through the entire rostrocaudal length of the hypothalamus. The **periventricular zone,** as the name implies, lies adjacent to the ependymal lining of the third ventricle. Its neurons form well-defined nuclear groups involved in neuroendocrine regulation of a variety of behavioral and physiological processes, such as feeding. The **medial zone** lies immediately adjacent to the periventricular zone and contains a series of cytoarchitecturally distinct nuclei. The cell groups vary in size and cell morphology, but they are organized into nuclei, in contrast with the diffusely distributed neurons of the lateral zone. The **lateral zone,** a diffuse group of neurons in the ventrolateral hypothalamus, constitutes the major portion of the lateral subdivision and is traversed by the thin fibers of the medial forebrain bundle.

FUNCTIONAL ORGANIZATION OF THE HYPOTHALAMUS

To integrate a variety of physiological processes and behaviors, the hypothalamus must communicate with systems in the brain and its periphery. More than any other region of the nervous system, the hypothalamus depends on conversion of synaptic information to humoral signals. In addition, *the hypothalamus is subject to feedback regulation by the physiological processes that it controls.* In the following sections we consider the basic organization of functional systems governed by the hypothalamus as an introduction to material that will be presented in greater detail in subsequent chapters.

The Hypothalamus Integrates Selected Sensory and Nonsensory Information

Projections from several regions of the neuraxis terminate within the hypothalamus. In many instances, monosynaptic projections bring first-order sensory in-

FIGURE 37.3 The cytoarchitectural organization of the hypothalamus as viewed in six transverse Nissl stained sections is illustrated. Boundaries of the major hypothalamic nuclei and areas are designated by the dotted lines. Abbreviations: ac, anterior commissure; ADP, anterodorsal preoptic nucleus; AHA, anterior hypothalamic area; AHN, anterior hypothalamic nucleus; AMY, amygdala; ARC, arcutate nucleus; AVP, anteroventral preoptic nucleus; AVPV, anteroventral periventricular nucleus; BST, bed nucleus of the stria terminalis; CP, caudoputamen; cpd, cerebral peduncle; DMH, dorsomedial hypothalamic nucleus; FF, fields of Forel; fr, fasiculus retroflexus; fx, fornix; GP, globu pallidus; int, internal capsule; HF, hippocampal formation; LHA, lateral hypothalamic area; LM, lateral mammillary nucleus; LPO, lateral preoptic area; LS, lateral septum; MA, magnocellular preoptic nucleus; ME, median eminence; ml, medial lemniscus; mp, mammillary peduncle; MM, medial mammillary nucleus; MPN, medial preoptic nucleus; MPO, medial preoptic area; MRN, mesencephalic reticular nucleus; mtg, mammillotegmental tract; mtt, mammillothalamic tract; NDB, nucleus of the diagonal band; och, optic chiasm; opt, optic tract; PH, posterior hypothalamic nucleus; pm, principal mammillary tract; PMd, dorsal premammillary nucleus; PMv, ventral premammillary nucleus; PS, parastrial nucleus; PVH, paraventricular nucleus hypothalamus; Pvi, periventricular nucleus intermediate; PVT, paraventricular nucleus thalamus; RE, nucleus reuniens; SBPV, subparaventricular zone; SCN, suprachiasmatic nucleus; SI, substantia innoninata; SO, supraoptic nucleus; sm, stria medullaris; smd, supramammillary decussation; SN, substantia nigra; SPF, suparafascicular nucleus thalamus; STN, substalamic nucleus; SUM, supramammillary nucleus; sup, supraoptic commissure; TM, tuberomammillary nucleus; V3, third ventricle; VMH, ventromedial hypothalamic nucleus; VP, ventral posterior thalamic nucleus; VTA, ventral tegmental area; ZI, zona incerta.

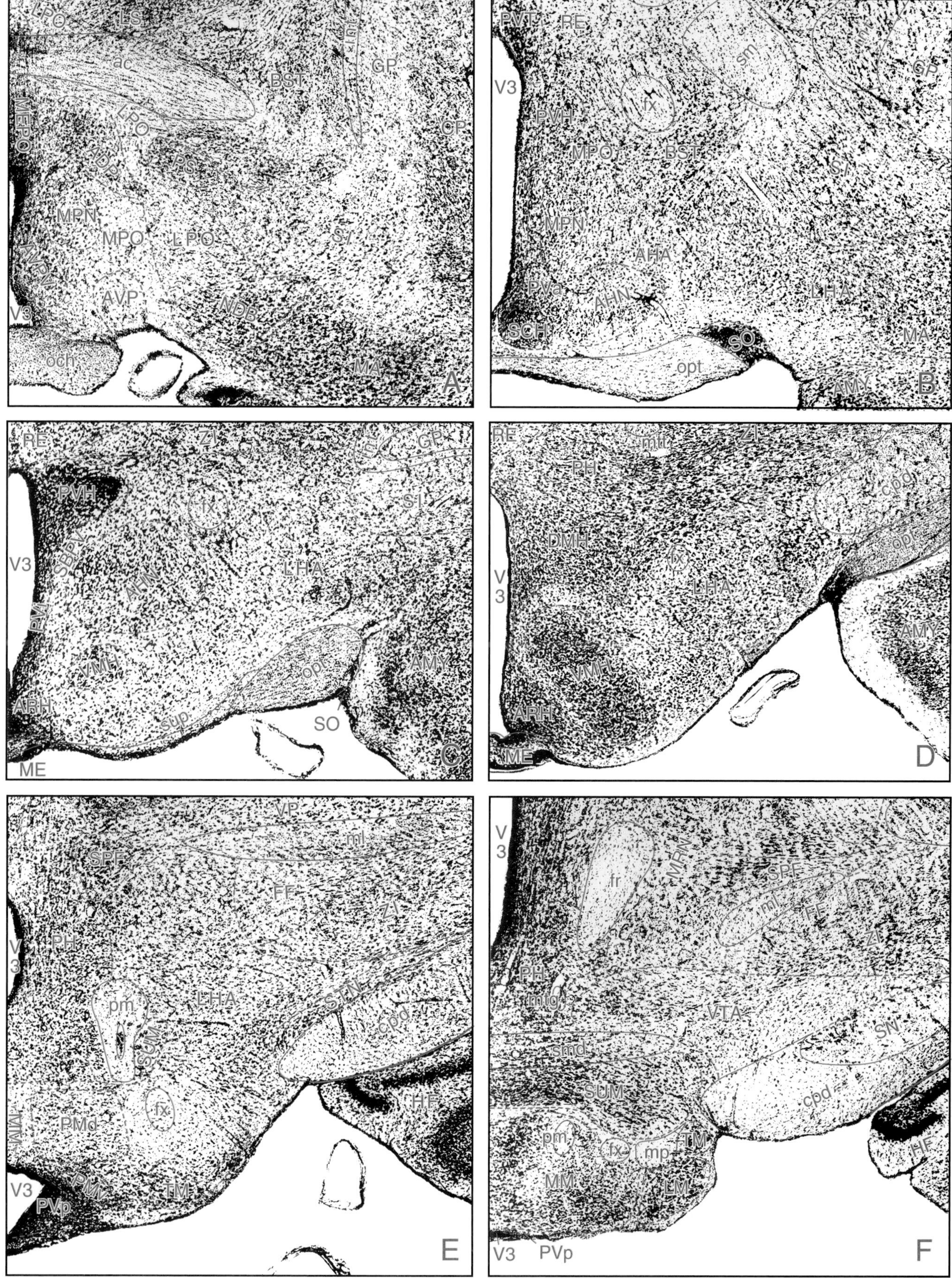
LPO
LS
ac
BST
GP
CP
MEPO
LPO
MPN
MPO
LPO
SI
AVPV
AVP
V3
NDB
och
MA
A
PVT
RE
sm
GP
V3
fx
PVH
MPO
BST
SI
MPN
AHA
PVa
AHN
LHA
SCH
SO
MA
opt
AMY
B
RE
ZI
GP
PVH
fx
SI
V3
AHN
LHA
VMH
opt
AMY
ARH
sup
SO
ME
C
RE
mtt
ZI
PH
cpd
DMH
fx
opt
LHA
AMY
VMH
ARH
ME
D
VP
ml
SPF
FF
ZI
PH
pm
LHA
STN
cpd
fx
HF
PMd
V3
PVp
PMv
TM
E
fr
SPF
ml
FF
ZI
PH
mtg
VTA
SN
smd
SUM
cpd
pm
fx
mp
TM
HF
MM
LM
V3
PVp
F

formation from the periphery directly to hypothalamic nuclei. In other cases, such as the limbic projections, multisynaptic pathways relay processed information to the hypothalamus. These overlapping systems are best understood by looking at the functions that they modulate.

Olfaction

Multisynaptic pathways allow the olfactory system to influence neurons in many parts of the hypothalamus. Direct olfactory projections to the olfactory tubercle, piriform cortex, and amygdala in turn project on the hypothalamus through the medial forebrain bundle (corticohypothalamic projections), stria terminalis, ventral amygdalofugal path, and fornix. These projection systems are essential to survival and reproductive functions, particularly in nocturnal animals that use olfaction as a primary sensory modality. In many vertebrates, olfaction is integral to behaviors involved in reproduction and feeding. The large amount of forebrain dedicated to processing of olfactory stimuli reflects the importance of these stimuli.

Visual Projections

A principal function of the hypothalamus is to temporally organize various hormonal and behavioral processes. Evidence strongly supports the conclusion that the timekeeping properties of the hypothalamus reside within the suprachiasmatic nuclei (SCN). The endogenous circadian activity of these compact cell masses imposes a temporal organization on physiological processes essential for successful adaptation and, in many instances, reproduction of the organism. For the SCN to impose this temporal organization, the activity of the biological clock must respond to environmental cues and the SCN must be able to transmit its temporal signal to other regions of the neuraxis. Light synchronizes the circadian activity of SCN neurons with the daily cycle of light and dark. The biological clock can also measure day length and thereby control reproduction in photoperiodic species. In the retina, the neural elements responsible for transduction and transmission of photoperiodic information are distinct from those involved in visual perception and reflex eye movement.

Surprisingly, the efferent projections of the SCN are relatively sparse and largely confined to the hypothalamus. Therefore, the SCN is probably part of a group of interconnected structures—the circadian timing system—that integrate a variety of sensory information important for the temporal organization of diverse functions regulated by the hypothalamus. A more detailed description of this system is presented in Chapter 45.

Visceral Sensation

Sensory information also reaches the hypothalamus through ascending projections arising in the nucleus of the solitary tract (NST) of the caudal brainstem. The NST is the principal visceral sensory nucleus that receives topographically organized input from the major organ systems of the body by way of cranial nerves X and XII, the vagus and glossopharyngeal nerves. As such, it is the first region in the CNS to process information about visceral, cardiovascular, and respiratory functions, as well as taste. The NST coordinates reflex modulation of peripheral organ function and sends processed sensory information to forebrain nuclei, where more complex physiological processes and behaviors are integrated.

The hypothalamus is a principal target of ascending NST projections. Neurons in the paraventricular hypothalamus (PVH) and the lateral hypothalamic area (LHA) receive direct projections from the NST and indirect projections through the ventrolateral medulla or the parabrachial nucleus in the pons. Many of these projections are bidirectional and are part of a larger system that includes the central nucleus of the amygdala, bed nuclei of the stria terminalis, and insular cortex. In addition, the NST and parabrachial nuclei relay splanchnic visceral sensory information ascending from the spinal cord.

Multimodal Brainstem Afferents

The medial forebrain bundle (mfb) is a group of thin fibers that traverse the lateral zone of the hypothalamus. This bidirectional fiber tract provides afferent projections to a number of hypothalamic nuclei. It also contains hypothalamic efferent projections and fibers that traverse the hypothalamus to end in other regions of the neuraxis. Early nonspecific stimulation and lesion experiments caused some confusion about the hypothalamus. Functions once incorrectly attributed to the lateral hypothalamus are actually associated with the stimulation or loss of fibers passing through the hypothalamus in the medial forebrain bundle rather than terminating within it.

Several distinct cell groups contribute to the medial forebrain bundle. Monoamine-containing axons are an especially prominent group of ascending fibers.[11] These axons arise from brainstem neurons, and many of them generate collaterals that terminate throughout the hypothalamus as they rostrally innervate other forebrain regions. The densely packed noradrenergic neurons of the locus ceruleus give rise to small-caliber axons that ascend through the mfb and terminate within hypothalamic nuclei. Larger caliber varicose axons, arising from the lateral tegmental noradrenergic cell groups, also terminate in the hypothalamus.

In addition, serotonergic neurons in the midbrain raphe nuclei give rise to prominent ascending projections that pass through the mfb to the hypothalamus and other areas of the forebrain. The midbrain raphe nuclei also generate a dense plexus of axons that enter the cerebral ventricles and arborize on the luminal surface of the ependyma. The precise function of this intraventricular plexus has not been established, but it has been postulated that serotonin may be released into the cerebrospinal fluid to modulate the neuraxis adjacent to the ventricular system. This mechanism is hormonal modulation by a neurotransmitter.

A number of systems not functionally associated with the hypothalamus also pass through the mfb in transit to other forebrain targets. Dopaminergic axons arising from the substantia nigra and ventral tegmental area (VTA) of the midbrain fall into this class. Dopaminergic neurons in the arcuate nuclei and zona incerta play an important role in hypothalamic functions. In contrast, fibers arising from midbrain dopaminergic neurons project rostrally through the mfb to innervate the striatum and cerebral cortex. Fiber systems arising in the brainstem reticular formation and telencephalon also pass through the mfb, but some of these fibers terminate within the hypothalamus.

Projections from Limbic Regions

The intimate association of the fornix, septum, stria terminalis, and diencephalon allows the limbic system to influence hypothalamic function. In the 1930s, Papez[12] suggested that these components form part of a multisynaptic pathway, classically known as Papez's circuit, that is responsible for the expression of emotion. This function has not been confirmed, although a number of studies have provided insight into the organization of this circuitry. It is considerably more complex than previously appreciated, in large part because the fornix arises from a number of different populations of neurons, and the projections of these neurons influence the activity of the hypothalamus through direct and indirect pathways. The long-recognized direct projection of the fornix to the mammillary bodies arises from neurons in the subicular complex of the hippocampal formation and constitutes the postcommissural bundle, which passes caudal to the anterior commissure. Precommissural fibers, which pass rostral to the anterior commissure, arise in the hippocampal formation. Risold and Swanson[13] showed that the precommissural fornix contains a dense, topographically organized projection to the lateral septum. The projection is part of a disynaptic circuit that innervates all three longitudinally organized columns of the hypothalamus, although not equally. The topography of hippocampal projections on the lateral septal nuclei is preserved in the second-order projections of lateral septal neurons to the hypothalamus. Thus, septal projections terminate differentially in areas that regulate neuroendocrine and autonomic function and ingestive behavior (periventricular zone), modulate motivated reproductive and agonistic behaviors (rostral medial zone), and project back to the hippocampus (mammillary complex).

The stria terminalis arises from neurons in the amygdala and follows a looping trajectory similar to the course of the fornix. Several cell groups in the amygdala are connected to the hypothalamus via this pathway or another pathway, the ventral amygdalofugal bundle, which passes directly over the optic tract to the hypothalamus.

The Circumventricular Organs

Not all sensory information reaching the hypothalamus is of synaptic origin. Some regions of the CNS are sensitive to chemosensory stimuli from plasma or cerebrospinal fluid. Such information about body fluids is used for homeostatis. Circumventricular organs (CVOs) are major chemosensitive areas, identified by Paul Ehrlich in the late 1800s, when he noted that vital dyes injected into the peripheral vasculature selectively accumulated within circumscribed regions of the brain surrounding the cerebral ventricles.[14] Later studies demonstrated that the accumulation of dye was due to the absence of a blood–brain barrier in CVOs. Unlike those in the brain parenchyma, capillaries in the CVOs are fenestrated, permitting relatively large molecules to leave the vascular lumen and enter the extracellular milieu of the CVO. Thus, neurons associated with CVOs are affected by blood-borne molecules that do not have access to other regions of the nervous system. The absence of a blood–brain barrier also allows CVOs to use neurohumoral mechanisms to influence peripheral function. Feedback regulatory mechanisms then modify CNS function via blood-borne signals from the periphery.

Eight CVOs surround the ventricular system in the diencephalon, midbrain, and brainstem[15]: the subfornical organ (SFO), the vascular organ of the lamina terminalis (OVLT), the median eminence (ME), the intermediate and posterior lobes of the pituitary gland, the pineal gland, the subcommissural organ (SCO), and the area postrema (AP) (Fig. 37.4). Two of these regions, the ME and OVLT, are located within the hypothalamus. Two other regions, the SFO and AP, have extensive connections with hypothalamic nuclei involved in neuroendocrine and homeostatic function. CVOs alter peripheral function by using humoral signals. Hormones also play an integral role in feedback regulation.

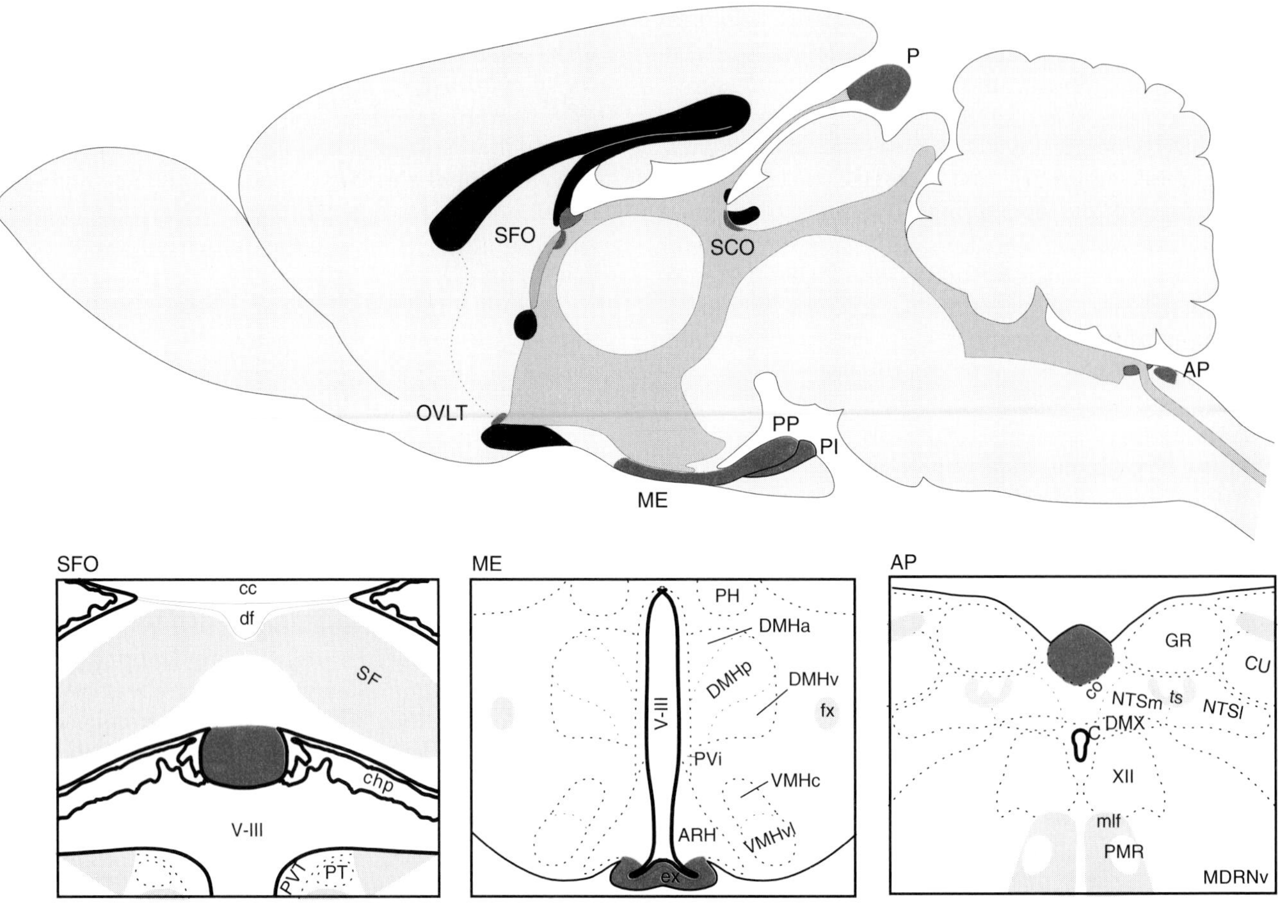

FIGURE 37.4 The location of the six circumventricular organs (shown in red) in the rat brain (midsaggital section). Three regions that have an intimate functional association with the hypothalamus are also illustrated in transverse section in the lower figures. AP, area postrema; ARH, arcuate nucleus; cc, corpus callosum; CU, cuneate nucleus; df, dorsal fornix; DMHa, anterior portion of the dorsomedial nucleus; DMHp, posterior portion of dorsomedial nucleus; DMHv, ventral portion of dorsomedial nucleus; DMX, dorsal motor vagal nucleus; GR, gracile nucleus; ME, median eminence; mlf, medial longitudinal fasiculus; co, commissural portion of the nucleus of the solitary tract; NTSl, lateral portion of the nucleus of the solitary tract; NTSm, medial portion of the nucleus of the solitary tract; OVLT, vascular organ of the lamina terminalis; PH, posterior hypothalamus; P, pineal gland; PMR, paramedian reticular nucleus; PVi, intermediate part of periventricular nucleus; SCO, subcommissural organ; SF, septofimbrial nucleus; SFO, subfornical organ; ts, tractus solitarius; V-III, third ventricle; VMHc, central part of ventromedial nucleus; VMHvl, ventrolateral part of ventromedial nucleus; XII, hypoglossal nucleus.

The functional organization of CVOs such as the median eminence that contribute to the effector limb of hypothalamic function will be considered in the following section and is also the subject of more in-depth consideration in individual chapters on regulatory functions. The purpose of the present discussion is to define the means through which sensory stimuli act at CVOs to influence the functional activity of hypothalamic nuclei. The area postrema and subfornical organ are two well-characterized examples of the pathways by which sensory stimuli act at CVOs and influence the activity of hypothalamic nuclei.

The area postrema is located adjacent to the nuclei of the solitary tracts, surrounding the caudal border of the fourth ventricle. Neurons in the AP give rise to axons that synapse on NST neurons, and dendrites of some NST neurons extend into the AP. Such intimate structural associations make it difficult to design experiments that can ascribe functions specifically to one region or the other. However, available data suggest the AP and NST function as a unit. Furthermore, the absence of a blood–brain barrier in the AP improves the ability of this unit to interact with the periphery. A variety of functions well-suited to a region lacking a blood–brain barrier have been ascribed to the AP, because it can thereby sample materials in the blood stream that neurons beyond (within) the blood–brain barrier cannot. These include regulation of food and water intake, cardiovascular function, and vomiting. The chemosensitive capacity of the AP seems to permit it to sense changes and convert that information to neural signals. The exact role of the AP in these processes is being investigated.

The subfornical organ is another CVO distinguished by chemosensitive capabilities and connections with other regions of the neuraxis. The subfornical organ lies beneath the columns of the fornix. It has dense projections to the supraoptic and paraventricular nuclei, to the region adjacent to the OVLT, and to the perifornical region of the lateral hypothalamic area. Such projections are consistent with postulated roles of the SFO in autonomic and homeostatic functions. The peptide hormone angiotensin II (AII) illustrates the way in which CVOs act as intermediaries between the brain and periphery. When blood pressure falls, the kidneys release renin into the bloodstream. Renin triggers a biochemical cascade that produces AII. Because of the absence of a blood–brain barrier in the SFO, circulating AII can enter the SFO and bind AII receptors on SFO neurons. Interestingly, SFO neurons appear to use AII as a neurotransmitter in projections to hypothalamic cells that are involved in the control of fluid dynamics. Fluid volume expands as a result of drinking, which partially restores blood pressure. The precise role of the SFO and the origin and site of action of AII in the brain are controversial, but available data support the conclusion that the SFO, like the AP, provides an important interface through which peripheral signals influence the activity of the CNS. (See Chapter 39.)

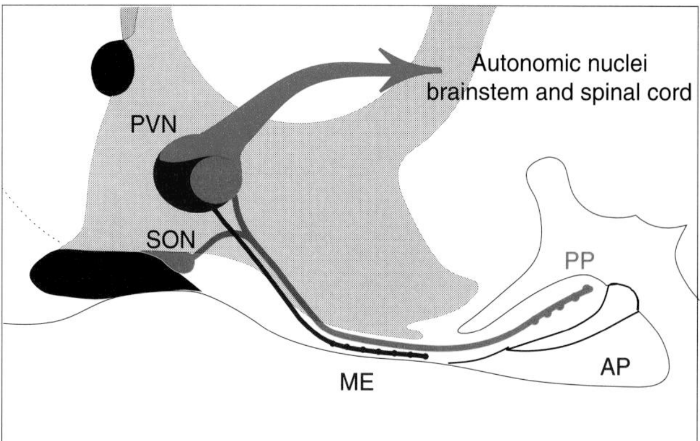

FIGURE 37.5 Functional associations of the paraventricular nucleus (PVN) and the endocrine and autonomic systems. Axons of magnocellular neurons in the PVN and supraoptic nuclei (SON) (shown in red) traverse the internal layer of the median eminence (ME) and the infundibular stalk to the posterior pituitary (PP). Parvicellular PVN neurons influence the functional activity of the anterior lobe of the pituitary (AP) through projections (shown in blue) that terminate on a fenestrated capillary plexus, the portal plexus, in the external zone of the median eminence. The terminal boutons of these axons release peptides and neurotransmitters into the portal vasculature, which carries the hormone to the anterior lobe of the pituitary. Parvicellular PVN neurons also give rise to descending projections (shown in turquoise) to autonomic nuclei in the brainstem and spinal cord. ac, anterior commissure; oc, optic chiasm.

Hypothalamic Projections Control Diverse Homeostatic, Neuroendocrine, and Behavioral Functions

The functional diversity of the hypothalamus is reflected in the way that it exerts its influence over the brain and periphery. The hypothalamus has projections to essentially every major subdivision of the CNS. Transfer of information is primarily synaptic. However, the hypothalamus also exerts an influence via control over pituitary function.

Communicating with the Pituitary Gland

Magnocellular neurons in the supraoptic and paraventricular nuclei give rise to axons that project through the internal layer of the median eminence and infundibular stalk and terminate within the posterior lobe of the pituitary (Fig. 37.5). This projection system, the **tuberohypophyseal tract,** is the only direct neural connection between the hypothalamus and pituitary. The tract regulates the release of peptide hormones from the posterior pituitary into the peripheral circulation. Vasopressin is involved in water homeostasis, and oxytocin causes milk letdown in lactating females. All other neural control of pituitary function is achieved through neurohumoral mechanisms via the portal plexus, which connects the median eminence to the anterior lobe of the pituitary. The fenestrated capillaries of this CVO loop through the median eminence and coalesce to form long portal vessels that travel along the infundibular stalk and terminate in vascular sinuses in the anterior pituitary. Axons from neurons in the PVH, arcuate nuclei, and other more widely disseminated hypothalamic cell groups terminate on this portal plexus, where they release peptides into its fenestrated vasculature. The peptide hormones travel through the portal plexus to the anterior pituitary, where they exert their regulatory effects.

Throughout the hypothalamus are neurosecretory neurons that project to the external zone of the median eminence. Table 37.2 summarizes the locations and chemical phenotypes of these neurons. Although a variety of hypothalamic nuclei contain neurons involved in this neurohumoral regulation, the PVH and arcuate nuclei are particularly prominent contributors. For example, neurons in the parvicellular subdivisions of the

PVH produce a variety of different peptides, such as corticotropin-releasing hormone and thyrotropin-releasing hormone. The peptides are released in the median eminence, where the neurons terminate. The peptides travel through the portal plexus to act on cells in the anterior pituitary. Similarly, neurons in the arcuate nucleus produce peptides, such as growth hormone-releasing hormone, and neurotransmitters, such as dopamine, that influence the secretory activity of the anterior pituitary. Thus, the synaptic activity of neurons projecting on these hypothalamic neurons is integrated, and the information is converted to a humoral signal that ultimately influences peripheral endocrine processes.

The output of the anterior pituitary depends on a balance of peptides and neurotransmitters that have opposite effects. For example, neurons in the arcuate nucleus release growth hormone-releasing hormone into the portal plexus to stimulate the release of growth hormone from somatotropic cells. On the other hand, somatostatinergic neurons in the periventricular nucleus release their peptide product, somatostatin (growth hormone-inhibiting factor), into the portal plexus to inhibit the release of growth hormone by somatotropes. At the level of the median eminence, the regulated release of such opposing peptides is complex and depends on feedback of pituitary hormones and the products of the metabolic pathways affected by their hormones.

Reproductive Function

The ability of mammals to reproduce depends on the function of the hypothalamus and its ability to communicate with the pituitary gland. This is especially true for the production of gametes, whose maturation and release in both males and females require a functionally intact hypothalamopituitary axis. In addition, the hypothalamus plays an essential role in the organization and expression of the complex behaviors that are necessary for copulation (see Chapter 50).

TABLE 37.2 Hormone Systems That Project to the Median Eminence and Act on the Pituitary

Peptide or neurotransmitter	Location of perikarya
Gonadotropin hormone-releasing hormone (GnRH)	Diffusely within preoptic region
Somatostatin (SS)	Periventricular nucleus
Growth hormone-releasing hormone (GRH)	Arcuate nucleus
Corticotropin-releasing hormone (CRH)	Paraventricular nucleus
Thyrotropin-releasing hormone (TRH)	Paraventricular nucleus
Dopamine (DA)	Arcuate nucleus

Experimental studies in rodents have demonstrated that the rostral medial zone of the hypothalamus plays an important role in orchestrating reproductive behaviors. The medial preoptic region participates in the control of masculine sexual behavior, such as erection, mounting, and ejaculation,[16] whereas the ventromedial nucleus of the hypothalamus plays a major role in the control of feminine sexual behaviors, such as the lordosis reflex.

A number of hypothalamic cell groups implicated in reproductive function are sexually dimorphic. For example, ultrastructural studies of a preoptic region in male and female rats[17] demonstrated differences in the patterns of synapses that developed in response to perinatal exposure to androgens. Also, differences in the size and serotonergic innervation of the medial preoptic nuclei of male and female rats have been demonstrated.[18,19] The possibility that similar dimorphisms are present in the human hypothalamus is supported by the identification of a region of the human preoptic area that is approximately twice as large in males as in females.[20,21] In addition, the cytoarchitecture of the rostral hypothalamus of homosexual men appears to be different from that of heterosexual men.[22] Although the functional significance of sexual dimorphism in the structure and connectivity of the hypothalamus remains to be established, the gender of the brain is clearly determined by the hormonal milieu present during a critical period of development.

Although evidence supports a role for the hypothalamus in sexual behavior, much more is known about the hypothalamic circuitry that influences the production of gametes. The production of ova and sperm is controlled by the release of gonadotropins from the anterior pituitary gland. The gonadotropins are in turn regulated by the hypothalamus. The response of the system to gonadotropins is gender-specific. For example, spermatogenesis occurs constantly in response to constant release of gonadotropins, whereas ovulation is a cyclic event initiated by a surge in gonadotropin release. In both cases hypothalamic neurons produce gonadotropin-releasing hormone (GnRH) to stimulate release of gonadotropin from the anterior lobe of the pituitary. Nevertheless, the gender-specific patterns of gonadotropin release imply that there are sexual differences in the functional organization of afferent systems that influence the activity of GnRH neurons. One postulated sexually dimorphic difference is a central pattern generator, which could be responsible for the cyclic release of GnRH in females. Dimorphism also probably exists in circuitry that integrates the sensory information underlying hormone secretion that leads to gamete production and mediates reproductive behaviors.

Central Integration of Autonomic Function

Projections descend directly from the hypothalamus to autonomic cell groups in the brainstem and spinal cord. These projections affect the sympathetic and parasympathetic subdivisions of the autonomic nervous system (ANS). Several cell groups of the hypothalamus also indirectly influence the ANS via projections to areas such as the central nucleus of the amygdala that project to autonomic nuclei. One of the more prominent and well-described components of the direct projection to the ANS arises in the PVH. This cell group contains a number of morphologically and neurochemically distinct subdivisions. The neurons that contribute to the direct projection to the ANS reside within the dorsal, medial, and lateral parvicellular subdivisions. Neurons within these subfields project to preganglionic neurons of the sympathetic and parasympathetic divisions of the ANS. The sympathetic preganglionic neurons are found within the intermediolateral cell columns of thoracic and upper lumbar spinal cord segments. In contrast, the parasympathetic neurons reside within distinct nuclei in the brainstem, such as the dorsal motor nucleus of the vagus nerve, as well as in the sacral spinal cord.

Immune Function

The activity of the immune system is influenced by the hypothalamus through neuroendocrine output and through the autonomic nervous system. Szentivanyi and colleagues[23,24] examined the effects of hypothalamic lesions and stimulation on anaphylactic responses and found that the diencephalon may influence immune function. Subsequent work by a number of investigators has provided compelling evidence that the nervous system exerts a direct effect on the immune system. Robert Ader wrote an excellent history of this literature.[25]

David Felten and colleagues demonstrated that the activity of immune cells of the spleen is directly influenced by "synaptic like" contacts of noradrenergic neurons of the sympathetic ANS.[26] This is but one of many examples of the hypothalamus influencing immune function through sympathetic outflow. Neuroendocrine influences have also been demonstrated by work pioneered by Hugo Besedovksy. Nevertheless, the mechanisms through which regulation is achieved remain unclear, and the extent to which the nervous system controls immune function remains to be established. This is an area ripe for insightful investigation in the coming years.

Behavioral State Control

The hypothalamus plays an important role in the timing of behaviors such as sleep. A number of regions of the neuraxis, particularly components of the brainstem reticular activating system and the thalamus, are involved in the regulation of sleep. Substantial evidence also implicates at least three regions of the hypothalamus in sleep regulation. For example, 50 years ago neuroanatomist Walle Nauta[27] demonstrated that lesions of the preoptic region produced insomnia in rats. Subsequently, researchers have shown that electrical stimulation of the preoptic region, or local injection of serotonin or prostaglandin D2, induces slow wave sleep. In contrast, lesions of the caudal hypothalamus produce somnolence, suggesting that this region is involved in arousal.

Until recently, little was known about the localization and connection of the rostral and caudal hypothalamic cell groups involved in sleep regulation. Using immunohistochemical localization of the protein product of the immediate-early gene *c-fos*, Clifford Saper and colleagues precisely defined the location of hypothalamic neurons that are active during sleep.[28] These cells, located in the ventrolateral preoptic region, project to the tuberomammillary nuclei in the caudal hypothalamus. In the tuberomammillary nuclei are histaminergic cell groups that diffusely innervate the cerebral cortex and most other parts of the brain and that have been implicated in arousal. In addition, preoptic neurons that project to the caudal hypothalamus contain the inhibitory neurotransmitter GABA (γ-aminobutyric acid). Thus, there is a monosynaptic connection between rostral and caudal hypothalamic cell groups that appears to regulate different aspects of the sleep–wake cycle.

Neurons of the rostral and caudal hypothalamic cell groups appear to be parts of a much larger circuitry. Serotonergic and noradrenergic neurons clearly play an important role in the regulation of the sleep–wake cycle, as do other brainstem and thalamic cell groups (Chapter 46). Furthermore, the temporal organization of the sleep–wake cycle indicates that the timekeeping function of the SCN is somehow involved in the regulation of sleep. The SCN projects to the preoptic region, but, as yet, no one has demonstrated that the fibers terminate on the ventrolateral preoptic neurons implicated in sleep–wake regulation. This area of investigation promises to advance our understanding of the neural regulation of sleep.

Thermoregulation

The preoptic region integrates complementary physiological and behavioral responses to thermal stress. Thermosensitive neurons identified within the preoptic region apparently provide integrative processes responsible for control of thermoregulation and sleep. Thermosensitive neurons appear to influence arousal mechanisms integral to regulation of the sleep–wake cycle. For example, Dennis McGinty and colleagues have shown that warming the preoptic region during waking suppresses arousal-related neuronal activity in the caudal hypothalamus and in magnocellular basal telencephalon neurons that have diffuse cortical projections.[29,30] The consequences of this experimental warming include decreased motor activity, reduced metabolic activity and respiratory rate, and enhanced peripheral heat loss. All these effects are similar to changes that characterize the onset of sleep. Thus, the response to thermal stress and the onset of sleep may be mediated through common circuitry. This conclusion is supported by the finding of single populations of preoptic neurons that increase their firing rate in response to warming or to onset of sleep.

To regulate temperature, the hypothalamus integrates input to the SCN and other hypothalamic nuclei. Circadian rhythm in body temperature, a well-characterized feature of mammalian physiology, and environmentally induced thermoregulation occur in large part through hypothalamic (particularly preoptic and anterior areas) control of autonomic function. The preoptic region of the hypothalamus also plays a role in producing fever.[31–33] Circulating cytokines may act at or near the OVLT to elicit fever, and a "pyrogenic zone" where prostaglandin injection induces fever has been identified in the region surrounding this CVO.[31,34] The precise pathways responsible for inducing fever are unknown, but a circumscribed population of neurons in central autonomic centers appears to participate.[34,35] Thus, thermoregulation is complex and requires the preoptic and anterior hypothalamus to integrate information about circadian rhythm, homeostasis, and microbial infection.

Fluid Homeostasis and Thirst

Insight into the regions of the brain involved in fluid homeostasis has come from observing the response of neurons to dehydration and other experimental changes in milieu. The hypothalamus is a prominent component of a set of CNS nuclei in which neurons respond to dehydration (an increase in fluid osmolarity) and changes in blood volume by increasing their metabolic activity. Activated neurons have been demonstrated in the subfornical organ, the paraventricular and supraoptic nuclei, and an area of the rostral hypothalamus known as the AV3V region, which includes the median preoptic nucleus and the OVLT. These regions interact with neurons in the area postrema, the nucleus of the solitary tract, the noradrenergic cell groups of the brainstem, and the parabrachial nucleus to integrate peripheral stimuli and elicit adaptive changes in the fluid environment of the organism.

Different populations of neurons elicit adaptive changes in fluid osmolarity and blood volume. For example, osmosensitive neurons are located primarily in the AV3V region, whereas central neurons responding to alterations in blood volume are found primarily within the NST and SFO. Despite this, these cell groups use common effector pathways to produce compensatory changes in the fluid milieu. The hypothalamus plays an essential role in the processes that lead to these adaptive changes. Adaptive alterations in water reabsorption and sodium excretion are regulated by magnocellular neurons of the supraoptic, paraventricular, and accessory magnocellular nuclei. These neurons give rise to tuberohypophyseal projections that release vasopressin or oxytocin into the peripheral vasculature in the posterior pituitary gland. These hormones act on the kidneys to change water absorption and sodium excretion. The other major adaptive response to increased fluid osmolarity and decreased blood volume is thirst. The neural circuitry that modulates this response is not fully understood but is known to involve input from the OVLT, SFO, and NST.

It is clear that the control of fluid homeostasis is a complex process involving a number of regions of the nervous system. The hypothalamus makes essential contributions to the neural regulation of fluid homeo-

CASE 6: A SUBJECT OF DISCUSSION

Keven Lewis feels fortunate that he was accepted into the laboratory of his choice for his graduate work. His advisor is Natalya Gorkin, a respected scientist working in the area of visual attention. For his first project, Mr. Lewis has been assigned a role on a project that involves recording from cat visual cortex. As an undergraduate he had routinely used rats as the subjects for his research project, but he is surprised by the emotional conflict he now feels about working with the cats. He mentions this to Dr. Gorkin, who suggests that if Mr. Lewis is going to worry about such matters he should seriously consider whether neuroscience is the right field for him. How should Mr. Lewis proceed?

See Appendix A for discussion questions.

stasis by detecting and processing sensory stimuli, as well as by providing effector pathways. In Chapter 42, these hypothalamic cell groups are considered in depth in the context of fluid homeostasis.

Food Intake

The consumption of food is another complex behavior that involves several regions of the brain. The hypothalamus integrates a variety of sensory stimuli, both synaptic and hormonal, and modulates autonomic outflow to the viscera. This view of neural regulation of food intake is a substantial modification of the concept of opposing centers for hunger and satiety. These centers were advanced by early studies that used hypothalamic lesions and stimulation. Chapter 41 contains a detailed discussion of more recent literature and understanding of the control of food intake. The following description summarizes the functional organization of hypothalamic nuclei that regulate food intake.

When food is consumed, hormones are released from the viscera, and sensory pathways innervating the alimentary tract are stimulated. These sensory pathways regulate neurons in the area postrema and NST that are bidirectionally connected with hypothalamic nuclei. Hypothalamic nuclei are also subject to feedback regulation from hormonal signals arising in the gut. At least four hypothalamic nuclei are involved in the control of feeding, and a prominent part of their influence is exerted via descending projections to autonomic nuclei in the brainstem and spinal cord. The paraventricular nuclei seem to provide the primary descending hypothalamic influence. In particular, parvicellular oxytocinergic neurons in the PVH provide an important descending projection to the dorsal vagal complex (including the NST) and the sympathetic preganglionic neurons of the thoracic spinal cord. At least some of this descending influence appears to be under the control of neuropeptide Y (NPY)-containing neurons that project from the arcuate nucleus to the PVH. In experiments, infusion of NPY into the PVH stimulates food intake. In addition, NPY-containing neurons in the arcuate nucleus are inhibited by insulin released into the peripheral circulation after a meal. Thus, hypothalamic nuclei regulate food intake through the autonomic nervous system, and a subset of these neurons is influenced by peripheral signals from the viscera.

Although recent work does not support the conclusion that the VMH functions as a satiety center, as was once thought, it remains possible that neurons in this nucleus are important for caloric homeostasis and, indirectly, for food intake. As discussed in detail in Chapter 41, evidence is consistent with neurons in this nucleus playing an important role in regulating the secretion of insulin. It is also clear that the SCN influences the temporal organization of feeding. For example, nocturnal rodents normally feed almost exclusively during the dark phase of the photoperiod, but rodents whose SCN has been ablated feed throughout the light–dark cycle.

Summary

The hypothalamus integrates the functions of several regulatory systems. The ventral diencephalic germinal epithelium develops into the hypothalamus in three waves of neuron migration. The neurons form the three longitudinal nuclear zones of the adult hypothalamus. The lateral zone of the hypothalamus contains the fibers of the medial forebrain bundle, a major tract connecting the hypothalamus, brainstem reticular formation, and limbic forebrain. The lateral hypothalamus also contains diffusely arranged neurons. The medial zone, on the other hand, is the principal nuclear region of the hypothalamus. The medial zone plays key roles in regulating the physiology and behavior of reproduction, the expression of agonistic behavior, and the memory of foraging events (via the mammillary complex). The periventricular zone is important for controlling the pituitary gland, regulating metabolism and feeding, maintaining body water, and timing physiology and behavior. The chapters that follow discuss in depth the neurobiology of these important regulatory roles of the hypothalamus.

References

General

Saper, C. B. (1990). Hypothalamus. In *The Human Nervous System* (G. Paxinos, ed.), pp. 389–414. Academic Press, San Diego, CA.

Swanson, L. W., and Cowan, W. M. (1975). Hippocampo-hypothalamic connections—origin in subicular cortex, not Ammons Horn. *Science* **189:** 303–304.

Cited

1. His, W. (1893). Vorschläge zur Einteilung des Gehirns. *Arch. Anat. Entwicklungs gesch.* (Leipzig) **17:** 157–171.
2. Gurdijian, E. S. (1927). The diencephalon of the albino rat. *J. Comp. Neurol.* **43:** 1–114. Harris, G. W. (1948). Neural control of the pituitary gland. *Physiol. Rev.* **28:** 139–179. Hess, W. R. (1957). *The Functional Organization of the Diencephalon.* Grune & Stratton, New York.
3. Krieg, W. J. S. (1932). The hypothalamus of the albino rat. *J. Comp. Neurol.* **55:** 19–89.
4. Le Gros Clark, W. E., Beattie, W. E., Riddoch, W. E., and Dott, N. M. (1938). *The Hypothalamus.* Oliver & Boyd, Edinburgh.
5. Fulton, J. F., Ranson, S. W., and Frantz, A. M., eds. (1940). *The Hypothalamus.* Williams & Wilkins, Baltimore, MD.
6. Scharrer, B., and Scharrer, E. (1940). Sensory cells within the hypothalamus. In *The Hypothalamus* (J. F. Fulton, S. W. Ranson, and A. M. Frantz, eds), pp. 170–194. Williams & Wilkins, Baltimore, MD.

7. Herrick, C. J. (1910). The morphology of the forebrain in Amphibia and Reptilia. *J. Comp. Neurol.* **20:** 413–547.
8. Kuhlenbeck, H. (1954). The human diencephalon. A summary of development, structure, function and pathology. *Confin. Neurol.* **14**(Suppl.): 1–230.
9. Markakis, E. A., and Swanson, L. W. (1997). Spatiotemporal patterns of secretomotor neuron generation in the parvicellular neuroendocrine system. *Brain Res. Revi.* **24:** 255–291.
10. Swanson, L. W. (1987). The hypothalamus. In *Handbook of Chemical Neuroanatomy* (A. Bjorklund, T. Hokfelt, and L. W. Swanson, eds.), Vol. 5, pp. 1–124. Elsevier, Amsterdam.
11. Moore, R. Y., and Bloom, F. E. (1979). Central catecholamine neuron systems: Anatomy and physiology of the norepinephrine and epinephrine systems. *Annu. Rev. Neurosci.* **2:** 113–168.
12. Papez, J. W. (1937). A proposed mechanism of emotion. *Arch. Neurol. Psychiatry* **38:** 725–743.
13. Risold, P. Y., and Swanson, L. W. (1996). Structural evidence for functional domains in the rat hippocampus. *Science* **272:** 1484–1486.
14. Ehrlich, P. (1956). Uber die methylenblaureaction der lebenden Nervensubstanz. In *The Collected Papers of Paul Ehrlich,* Vol. 1, *Histology, Biochemistry and Pathology* (F. Himmelweit, ed.), pp. 500–508. Pergamon Press, London.
15. Johnson, A. K., and Gross, P. M. (1993). Sensory circumventricular organs and brain homeostatic pathways. *FASEB J.* **7:** 678–686.
16. Larsson, K. (1979). Features of the neuroendocrine regulation of masculine sexual behavior. In *Endocrine Control of Sexual Behavior* (C. Beyer, ed.), pp. 77–163. Raven Press, New York.
17. Raisman, G., Field, P. M. (1973). Sexual dimorphism in the neuropil of the preoptic area of the rat and its dependence on neonatal androgen. *Brain Res.* **54:** 1–29.
18. Gorski, R. A., Harlan, R. E., Jacobson, C. D., Shryne, J. E. and Southan, A. M. (1980). Evidence for the existence of a sexually dimorphic nucleus in the preoptic area of the rat. *J. Comp. Neurol.* **193:** 529–539.
19. Simerly, R. B., Swanson, L. W., and Gorski, R. A. (1984). Demonstration of a sexual dimorphism in the distribution of serotonin-immunoreactive fibers in the medial preoptic nucleus of the rat. *J. Comp. Neurol.* **225:** 151–166.
20. Swaab, D. F., and Fliers, E. (1985). A sexually dimorphic nucleus in the human brain. *Science* **228:** 1112–1115.
21. Hofman, M. A., and Swaab, D. F. (1989). The sexually dimorphic nucleus of the preoptic area in the human brain: A comparative morphometric study. *J. Anat.* **164:** 55–72.
22. LeVay, S. (1991). A difference in hypothalamic structure between heterosexual and homosexual men. *Science* **253:** 1034–1037.
23. Szentivanyi, A., and Fillipp, G. (1958). Anaphylaxis and the nervous system. II. *Ann. Allergy* **16:** 143.
24. Szentivanyi, A., and Szekely, J. (1958). Anaphylaxis and the nervous system. IV. *Ann. Allergy* **16:** 389.
25. Ader, R. (1996). Historical perspectives on psychoneuroimmunology, In *Psychoneuroimmunology, Stress, and Infection* (H. Friedman, T. W. Klein, and A. L. Friedman, eds.), pp. 1–24. CRC Press, Boca Raton, FL.
26. Felten, D. L., Felten, S. Y., Bellinger, D. L., Carlson, S. L., Akerman, K. D., Madden, K. S., Olschowka, J. A., and Livnat, S. (1987). Noradrenergic sympathetic neural interactions with the immune system: Structure and function. *Immunol. Rev.* **100:** 225–260.
27. Nauta, W. J. H. (1946). Hypothalamic regulation of sleep in rats: An experimental study. *J. Neurophysiol.* **9:** 285.
28. Sherin, J. E., Shiromani, P. J., McCarley, R. W., and Saper, C. B. (1996). Activation of ventrolateral preoptic neurons during sleep. *Science* **217:** 216–219.
29. Krilowicz, B. L., Szymusiak, R., and McGinty, D. (1994). Regulation of posterior lateral hypothalamic arousal related neuronal discharge by preoptic anterior hypothalamic warming. *Brain Res.* **668:** 30–38.
30. Alam, M. N., Szymusiak, R., and McGinty, D. (1995). Local preoptic/anterior hypothalamic warming alters spontaneous and evoked neuronal activity in the magnocellular basal forebrain. *Brain Res.* **696:** 221–230.
31. Feldberg, W., and Saxena, P. N. (1971). Further studies on prostaglandin E1 fever in cats. *J. Physiol.* (*London*) **219:** 739–745.
32. Kluger, M. J. (1991). Fever: Role of pyrogens and cryogens. *Physiol. Rev.* **71:** 93–127.
33. Saper, C. B., and Breder, C. D. (1994). The neurologic basis of fever. *N. Engl. J. Med.* **330:** 1880–1886.
34. Scammell, T. E., Elmquist, J. K., Griffin, J. D., and Saper, C. B. (1996). Ventromedial preoptic prostanglandin E2 activates fever-producing autonomic pathways. *J. Neurosci.* **16:** 6246–6254.
35. Elmquist, J. L., Scammell, T. E., Jacobson, C. D., and Saper, C. B. (1996). Distribution of Fos-like immunoreactivity in the rat brain following intravenous lipopolysaccharide administration. *J. Comp. Neurol.* **371:** 85–103.

C H A P T E R

38

Central Control of Autonomic Functions

The Organization of the Autonomic Nervous System

Terry L. Powley

The **autonomic nervous system** (ANS) consists of the neural circuitry that controls many aspects of the body's physiology. Working in concert with the endocrine system, the ANS is the neural part of the functional system responsible for homeostasis. Unlike the somatic or skeletal motor system (described in Section V), which innervates striated muscles, the autonomic nervous system innervates the body's smooth muscle organs and tissues. The ANS projects to the hollow organs, or viscera, such as the heart and lungs in the thorax, and the gastrointestinal, genital, and urinary tracts in the abdomen. It also projects to the blood vessels, glands, and other target tissues in trunk muscles, limb muscles, and skin. Although endocrine and nonautonomic neural pathways couple the ANS to the sensory and skeletal motor systems to produce behavior, the autonomic nervous system is a morphologically, embryologically, functionally, and pharmacologically distinct division of the nervous system.

The autonomic nervous system is responsible for what Walter B. Cannon referred to as the "wisdom of the body." See Box 38.1.[1,2] In tandem with endocrine systems, the ANS orchestrates the continuous adjustments in blood chemistry, respiration, circulation, digestion, and immune system responses that protect the integrity of the internal milieu and enable the coordination of skeletal muscles and exteroceptive senses into what we know as behavior. For example, Cannon, in his seminal and defining physiological experiments on the ANS, found that selective surgical destruction of different autonomic pathways devastated the abilities of animals to regulate their body temperature, to respond to perturbations of their fluid and electrolyte balance, to control their blood sugar homeostasis adequately, or to mobilize in response to threats.[3] Autonomic adjustments are often fast and phasic responses that occur with the latencies and speeds typical of neural reflexes; in contrast, endocrine responses usually occur more slowly, taking anywhere from minutes to hours to seasons for full expression.

A commonplace example illustrates autonomic operations: Occasionally, when we have been lying down resting and then jump up suddenly,we may feel dizzy, our vision may become blurred, and we may momentarily have trouble maintaining our balance—let alone doing something active and coordinated. This phenomenon is known as **postural,** or **orthostatic**, **hypotension** and is caused by insufficient blood reaching the brain under the altered hemodynamic conditions produced by the rapid charge in posture. Most people experience postural hypotension only occasionally, although it can become a chronic medical problem for others. Indeed, it is a debilitating condition in people with pure autonomic failure, as well as a number of other forms of **dysautonomia.**[4,5] The problem is that something as mundane as a change in posture requires nearly instantaneous redistribution of blood flow throughout the body to protect the privileged flow of blood, and thus oxygen and glucose, to the brain. The demands of postural adjustments require unceasing monitoring and rebalancing of the circulatory loads. The fact that these adjustments happen routinely and automatically is testimony to the efficiency of the ANS in effecting homeostatic adjustments. This example also illustrates two other characteristics of many autonomic responses: (1) The responses often are either initiated in anticipation of the perturbation or implemented so rapidly that the individual does not experience a deficit, and (2) the activity of the autonomic nervous system is linked to and coordinated with activity of the somatic nervous system.

The ubiquity and immediacy of such autonomic re-

BOX 38.1

THE DISCOVERY OF THE AUTONOMIC NERVOUS SYSTEM

The study of the autonomic nervous system has a particularly long and interesting history, and the techniques available during the different periods of research have strongly shaped descriptions of the ANS. The gross morphology of the peripheral autonomic nerves has been studied since the time of Galen, but most microscopic anatomy and embryology of the ANS have been characterized only recently. Indeed, these topics remain the subject of ongoing research. In contrast, many of the early characterizations of the autonomic nervous system were functional studies. Still other early work, such as the studies of John Langley, defined the autonomic nervous system and its separate divisions in terms of their pharmacology. Some of the more recent techniques of molecular biology and cytochemistry are now forcing revisions of our descriptions and definitions.

The terminology used in autonomic neuroscience reflects this legacy of early structural, functional, and pharmacological descriptions.[1] The *vagus*, for example, takes its name from its wandering course of innervation. Using this nerve, Loewi demonstrated acetylcholinergic (or *Vagusstoff*) control of smooth muscle.

Prior to the foundations laid by Langley's work, the sympathetic and parasympathetic limbs of the ANS were not consistently or clearly distinguished, and the aggregate system was often called the sympathetic system. *Sympathetic* has a history that can be traced back to Galen's concept that "sympathy," or coordination between viscera, or organs, was accomplished by the nerves. Sympathetic also connoted that the visceral nervous system might subserve the "sympathies," or emotions, described in Homeric writing.

Autonomic, which means self-governing, was introduced by John Langley.[2] The ANS has also variously been called the *automatic* nervous system, the *involuntary* nervous system, the *visceral* nervous system, and the *animalic* nervous system. Langley is also responsible for clearly distinguishing—and naming—the *parasympathetic* division of the ANS.

sponses are hard to overemphasize. The example of circulatory adjustments illustrates two other functions and the range of autonomic operations. Differential activation of the cerebral cortex during cognitive activity, such as thinking, is associated with selective shunting of blood flow (see Chapter 59), changes achieved by autonomic adjustments of vascular tone. Similarly, autonomic regulation of blood flow in male genitalia makes mating (tumescence, erection, etc.) possible.

The autonomous nature of ANS function is a characteristic and essential element of autonomic control. We are rarely aware of the continuous reflex adjustments made to maintain cardiovascular and regulatory dynamics, fluid and electrolyte homeostasis, energy balance, immune system operations, and many other functions. Like the personal computer's disk operating system or batch files, which execute without normally intruding on the screen or requiring attention, the autonomic reflex adjustments run unceasingly in the "background," while other sensory events and functional decisions occupy the "foreground." In one of his delightful and trenchant essays, Lewis Thomas[6] underscores the adaptive advantage of the autonomous operations of the ANS. Thomas speculates on how disastrous and overwhelmingly confusing it would be for his cognitive processing if he were put in charge of his liver—if he had to consider all visceral inputs and make a conscious decision for all adjustments in liver function. The ANS takes care of such hepatic, as well as all other visceral, decisions automatically, allowing the individual to focus on the behavioral and cognitive functions that typically require awareness.

The hub of the autonomic nervous system is the **visceral motor outflow,** which is divided into the **sympathetic** (SNS) and **parasympathetic** (PNS) divisions. Each division is organized hierarchically into pre- and postganglionic levels (see Fig. 38.1). The cell bodies of the preganglionic neurons lie within the central nervous system, specifically in the spinal cord and medulla oblongata. Descending projections from more rostral levels of the neuraxis converge on these ANS preganglionic motor neurons in a pattern similar to that of the afferent projections to somatic motor neurons of the brainstem and spinal cord. However, unlike the outflow pattern of the skeletal motor system, in which the motor neurons of the ventral horn or the cranial nerve nuclei project directly to the effector or muscle target, autonomic preganglionic neurons project to ganglia located between the CNS and the target tissues. Compared with the one-neuron final common paths of the skeletal motor system, this extra synapse interrupting the autonomic outflows at peripheral gan-

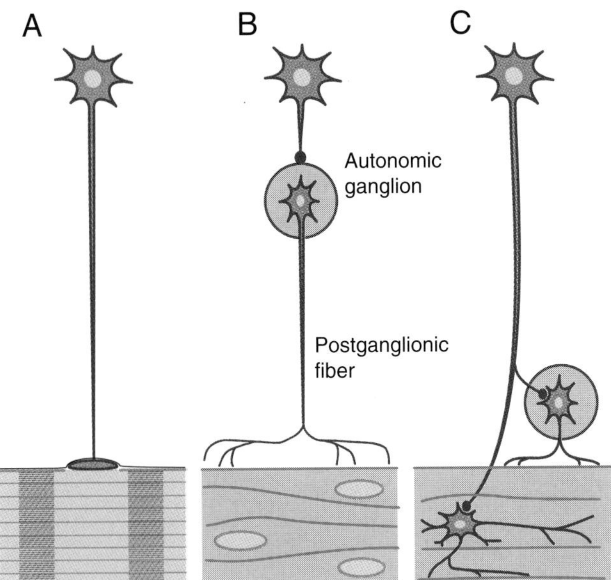

FIGURE 38.1 Somatic and autonomic styles of motor innervation are different. In the somatic motor pattern (A), motor neurons of the spinal cord or cranial nerve nuclei project directly to striated muscles to form neuromuscular junctions. In the autonomic or visceral pattern (B and C), in contrast, motor neurons in the central nervous system project to peripheral postganglionic neurons that in turn innervate smooth muscles. (B) The SNS has preganglionic neurons in the thoracic and lumbar spinal cord (intermediolateral cell column) that project to postganglionic motor neurons in para- and prevertebral autonomic ganglia. (C) The PNS consists of preganglionic neurons in the brainstem cranial nerve nuclei and in the sacral spinal cord (intermediomedial cell column) that project to postganglionic motor neurons in ganglia located near or inside the viscera. Source: Nauta and Feirtag.[44]

glia allows for more divergence, as well as the possibility of more local integrative circuitry to impinge on the outflow. These peripheral ganglia of the ANS contain the postganglionic motor neurons that project to the effector tissues. Different locations of the preganglionic motor neurons in the CNS and of the ganglia containing the somata of the postganglionic motor neurons in the periphery are distinguishing features of the two principal divisions of the autonomic nervous system (see Table 38.1).[7]

THE SYMPATHETIC DIVISION: ORGANIZED TO MOBILIZE THE BODY FOR ACTIVITY

Sympathetic Responses Predominately Produce Selective Energy Expenditure, Catabolic Functions, and Cardiopulmonary Adjustments for Intense Activity

Fight or flight, the prototypical example used extensively by Walter B. Cannon, epitomizes the function of the sympathetic division of the ANS: You are walking alone at night in an unfamiliar part of town. Although the area is considered somewhat unsafe, the night is quiet, and you are relaxed. After several minutes of walking, however, you hear a crisp, unfamiliar noise close by. In literally the time of a heart beat or two, your physiology moves into high gear. Your heart races; your blood pressure rises. Blood vessels in muscles dilate, increasing the flow of oxygen and energy. At the same time, blood vessels in the gastrointestinal tract and skin constrict, reducing flow through these organs and making more blood available to be shunted to skeletal muscle. Pupils dilate, improving vision. Digestion in the gastrointestinal tract is inhibited; release of glucose from the liver is facilitated. You begin to sweat, a response serving several functions, including reducing friction between limbs and trunk, improving traction, and perhaps promoting additional dissipation of heat so muscles can work efficiently if needed for defense or running. (Some speculate that sweat would also make an individual harder to catch or to hold.) Multiple other smooth and cardiac muscle adjustments occur automatically to increase your readiness to fight or flee, and almost all of them are effected by the sympathetic division of the ANS.

To reiterate, the fight-or-flight example illustrates

TABLE 38.1 Classical Comparisons of the Sympathetic and Parasympathetic Divisions of the ANS

	SNS	PNS
Location of preganglionic somata	Thoracolumbar cord	Cranial neuroaxis; sacral cord
Location of ganglia (& postgang. somata)	Distant from target organ	Near or in target organ
Postganglionic transmitter*	Norepinephrine	Acetylcholine
Length of preganglionic axon	Relatively short	Relatively long
Length of postganglionic axon	Relatively long	Relatively short
Divergence of preganglionic axonal projection*	One to many	One to few
Functions	Catabolic	Anabolic
Innervates trunk and limbs in addition to viscera	Yes	No

Note. Langley[7] stressed the contrasting and distinguishing traits of the two division of the ANS. Since his time, most texts have included several contrasting features. Most of these distinctions apply generally but not universally. Research since the time of Langley has suggested that those designated with * may be incorrect. Although many of these distinctions have blurred (e.g., transmitter) or may be completely unfounded (e.g., divergence), they are often discussed.

several important features of the autonomic nervous system, particularly its sympathetic division. First, the situation points out the need for the housekeeping functions of the autonomic nervous system. If the alarming noise turns out to be a threat and it is necessary to fight or flee, skeletal muscles must be optimally tuned and provisioned. Extra quantities of oxygen and energy are essential. Second, the synergy of adjustments indicates a coordinated and adaptive program of responses, which in this case happen immediately and without cognitive evaluation. Third, the short latency of the response is characteristic (and in such a case possibly critical). Some of the physiological adjustments could be effected more slowly by endocrine mechanisms, but such hormonal adjustments would be too slow to be of much immediate help if the noise turns out to signal a bona fide threat.

Not all sympathetic (or parasympathetic) responses happen on such short time scales. The operations of the autonomic nervous system also involve continuous, ongoing adjustments. Textbook accounts of the emergency functions of the ANS and of single, isolated reflex adjustments sometimes leave the incorrect impression that in the absence of a threat or specific stimulus, the ANS is quiescent. Instead, the autonomic nervous system, like the somatic nervous system, always maintains an operating tone. Even during periods of inactivity, the system maintains appropriate homeostatic balances and autonomic programs. The tonic control of heart rate and cardiac output maintained by both divisions of the ANS is a prototypic example of such maintenance. Or, in the case of sleep, for example, slow-wave sleep and REM sleep have characteristic autonomic profiles (see Chapter 46). SNS innervation of brown adipose tissue is important in controlling nonshivering thermogenesis, or heat production, over extended periods of time. Similarly, after a meal, even in a resting animal, the autonomic choreography of digestion and assimilation—anabolic functions—plays out.

Preganglionic Neurons of the Sympathetic Nervous System Lie in the Thoracic and Lumbar Spinal Cord

Sympathetic preganglionic neurons occupy the **intermediolateral nucleus,** a nearly continuous columnar grouping of cells running longitudinally through much of the spinal cord in the lateral horn of the spinal gray. In humans, these cells are found between the first thoracic spinal segment (T1) and the third lumbar segment (L3) (see Fig. 38.2A). The location of these preganglionic neurons and their axonal outflow gives the sympathetic nervous system another of its names,

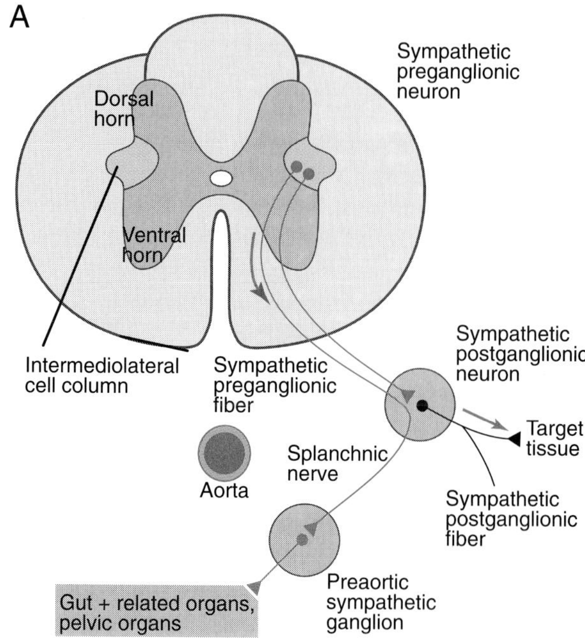

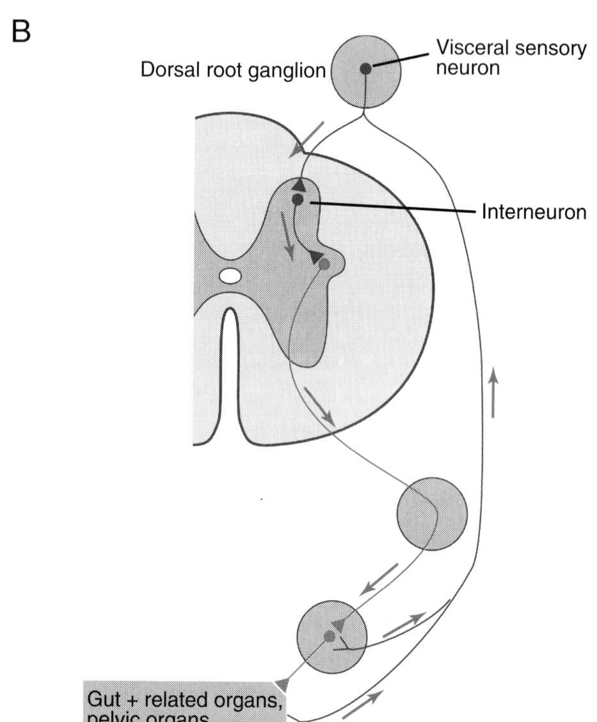

FIGURE 38.2 Details of the organization of the SNS and its sensory inputs. In thoracic and lumbar levels of the spinal cord, preganglionic cell bodies located in the intermediolateral cell column project through ventral roots to either the paravertebral chain ganglia or prevertebral ganglia, as illustrated for the splanchnic nerve (A). Visceral sensory neurons located in the dorsal root ganglia transmit information from innervated visceral organs to interneurons in the spinal cord to complete autonomic reflex arcs at the spinal level (B). Source: A. D. Loewy (1990). Anatomy of the autonomic nervous system. In *Central Regulation of Autonomic Functions* (A. D. Loewy and K. M. Spyer, eds.). Oxford University Press, New York.

the **thoracolumbar division.** The cells within the intermediolateral column show a tendency to segmental aggregation, and experiments in which retrograde tracers (e.g., horseradish peroxidase) have been injected into different target organs or ganglia, or in which the different nerve connectives have been cut and soaked with tracer, have established that the aggregations represent a **viscerotopy.**[8,9] There is a rostral-to-caudal viscerotopic organization to the distribution: Preganglionic neurons controlling the smooth muscle of the eye are most rostral (e.g., T1–2); cells controlling the heart and lungs are more caudal; and neurons controlling the gastrointestinal tract, bladder, and genitalia are most caudal. The column is found bilaterally, and the preganglionics on one side send their axons out the ipsilateral ventral root. The axon of a preganglionic neuron exits from the segment in which its soma is located. Many of the preganglionic axons are lightly myelinated, and, as they separate from the ventral root to project to the appropriate peripheral ganglion, they form a **white ramus,** a connective that takes its descriptive name from the myelinated fibers.

Sympathetic postganglionic neurons are found in two distinct types of ganglia, paravertebral and prevertebral ganglia. The **paravertebral ganglia,** as the name implies, are adjacent to the spinal cord bilaterally, in slightly ventral and lateral positions (see Figs. 38.3 and Fig. 38.4). Each ganglion receives a white ramus from the appropriate ventral root. The ganglia are also interconnected longitudinally into a **sympathetic chain** composed of axons from the preganglionic neurons that run rostrally or caudally to neighboring ganglia of the chain. The postganglionic neurons of the paravertebral ganglia course centrifugally out of the ganglion to join the peripheral nerves that will carry the individual axons to their targets. Most postganglionic axons in the sympathetic nervous system are unmyelinated, so these connectives joining the ventral roots are called **gray rami.**

The paravertebral ganglia of the sympathetic chain supply the postganglionic innervation of the head, trunk, and limbs. For the trunk and limbs, the postganglionic axons course both alongside and within the somatic peripheral nerve innervating the region. These

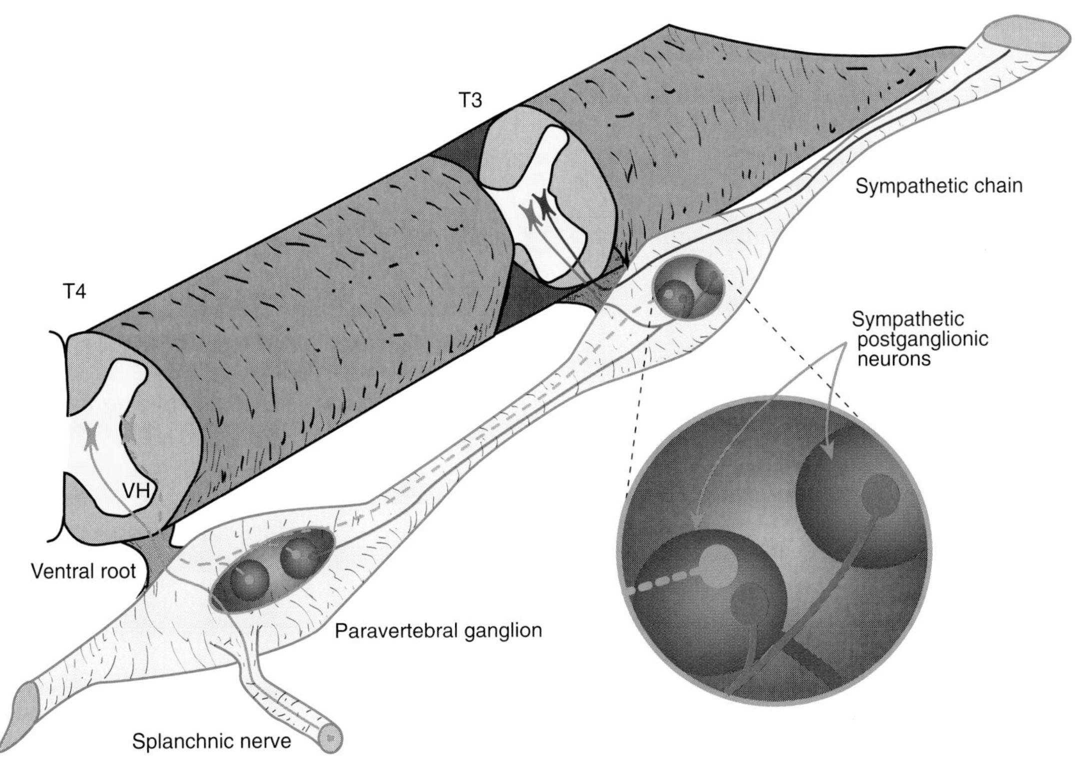

FIGURE 38.3 The SNS is segmentally organized. As illustrated here for segments T3 and T4 of the thoracic spinal cord, preganglionic axons exit through the ventral root of the segment in which the preganglionic cell body is located. These preganglionic axons can be myelinated (solid red lines) or unmyelinated (dashed red lines) and can project to the paravertebral ganglion associated with the segment, to neighboring paravertebral ganglia through the sympathetic chain, to postganglionic neurons located distally in the prevertebral ganglia, or through one of the autonomic nerves (splanchnic nerve is illustrated). T3 and T4, segments of the thoracic spinal cord; VH, ventral horn of spinal cord. Source: Cabot.[8]

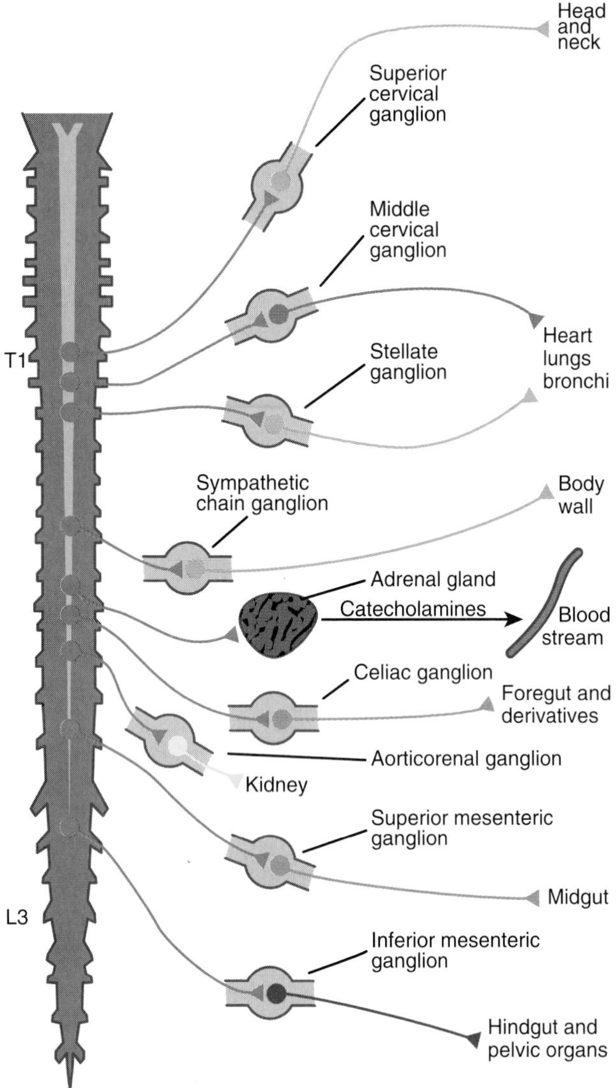

FIGURE 38.4 Summary of the major SNS ganglia and their target organs or tissues. Spinal cord is illustrated on the left. Source: A. D. Loewy (1990). Anatomy of the autonomic nervous system. In *Central Regulation of Autonomic Functions* (A. D. Loewy and K. M. Spyer, eds.). Oxford University Press, New York.

autonomic fibers innervate the blood vessels in the muscles (**vasoconstrictor fibers**), as well as different targets within the skin, including the sweat glands (**sudomotor fibers**) and erector pili muscles of erectile hairs (**pilomotor fibers**).

At the rostral end of the sympathetic chain, individual segmental ganglia are fused into aggregate ganglionic groupings. Thus, the sympathetic chain innervates the head and the thoracic viscera in a modification of the paravertebral chain pattern (Figs. 38.4 and 38.6). The most rostral group, the superior cervical ganglion (supplied from the first and second thoracic segments), supplies the head and neck. The targets of its projections are extensive, including the eyes, salivary glands, lacrimal glands, blood vessels of the cranial muscles, and even the blood vessels of the brain, targets that may influence cerebral functioning. The paravertebral ganglia just caudal to the superior cervical ganglion form the middle cervical ganglion and, moving caudally, the stellate ganglion. These latter ganglia supply the postganglionic sympathetic outflows that innervate the heart, lungs, and bronchi.

Unlike the trunk, limbs, head, heart, and lungs, the organs of the abdominal cavity are innervated by postganglionic neurons in ganglia situated distal to both the spinal cord and the paravertebral sympathetic chain, in locations closer to the target tissue. These sites give the ganglia their distinguishing name, the **prevertebral ganglia.** The preganglionic neurons innervating these sets of postganglionic neurons are located in the intermediolateral column of the spinal cord, like those innervating the paravertebral chain, but their axons pass through the white ramus, the chain ganglion, and the gray ramus without synapsing. They then make contact with the distally situated prevertebral ganglion cells (see Fig. 38-3).

Of the four major prevertebral postganglionic stations, the more rostral three are located at points where the major abdominal arteries separate from the descending aorta, and the ganglia take their names from the names of their associated arteries (see Fig. 38.5). Moving from more rostral to caudal, the **celiac, superior mesenteric,** and **inferior mesenteric ganglia** innervate the gastrointestinal tract. The celiac ganglion (also commonly called the solar plexus, because connectives radiate around or from it) projects predominantly to the stomach and rostralmost parts of the foregut and its derivatives, such as the liver and pancreas. Consistent with their progressively more caudal locations, the middle and inferior mesenteric ganglia innervate the mid- and hindgut tissue, respectively. The inferior mesenteric ganglion also supplies the postganglionic innervation to the pelvic organs. The fourth, and most caudal, prevertebral ganglion is the pelvic–hypogastric plexus, which innervates urinary and genital tissues.

The paravertebral ganglia comprising the sympathetic chain are structured largely as relay nuclei, whereas prevertebral ganglia have more complex organizations. Experiments injecting neural tracers into the target organs and electrophysiological analyses involving focal stimulation and recording have shown that prevertebral ganglia contain afferent neurons and postganglionic somata. These ganglia also receive afferent inputs from neurons located in the walls of the target organs. These ganglia may have more complex neural organization than paravertebral ganglia because prevertebral ganglia are located farther from the spinal cord and closer to the target organs, and they coordinate responses of visceral organs containing separate nerve networks (the enteric nervous system is described later).

Another specialization is found among the prevertebral ganglia: The **adrenal medulla** is a unique variant of the sympathetic postganglionic pattern. By several standard criteria, the adrenal medulla is a sympathetic prevertebral ganglion containing postganglionics. However, neurons of this medullary ganglion, rather than issuing axons to innervate target organs, function as an endocrine organ. The adrenal medulla secretes epinephrine and the classical postganglionic sympathetic transmitter norepinepherine directly into the blood stream. These catecholamines then circulate throughout the body as hormones, providing a humoral supplement to neural activation. Release of catecholamines from the adrenals during sympathetic activation provides powerful reinforcement and modulation of the more focal release of catecholamines at traditional—and local—effector sites. Although adrenal catecholamines provide dramatic amplification and divergence of sympathetic signals, these secretions from the adrenal medulla, like most hormones, are

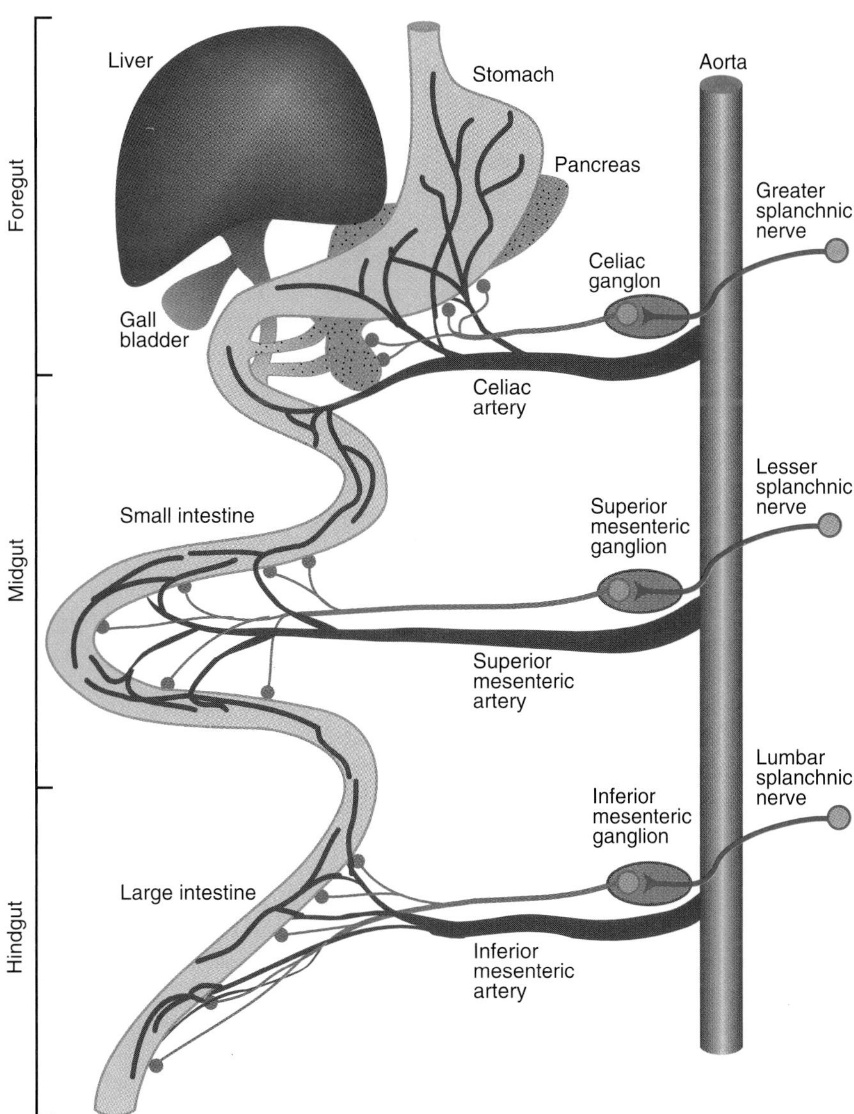

FIGURE 38.5 SNS innervation of the gastrointestinal tract. This more detailed schematic illustrates how separate segmental levels of the spinal cord and the associated paravertebral ganglia innervate targets in a topographic, specifically viscerotopic, pattern. A commonly observed association of autonomic pathways and vasculature is also shown. Source: A. D. Loewy (1990). Anatomy of the autonomic nervous system. In *Central Regulation of Autonomic Functions* (A. D. Loewy, and K. M. Spyer, eds.). Oxford University Press, New York.

slower to arrive at their targets and slower to dissipate. In addition, they lack the point-to-point specificity of other sympathetic projections.

Summary

Overall, the two major motor outflows, or divisions, of the ANS represent the neural mechanisms responsible for the maintenance of homeostasis, but the sympathetic nervous system is the branch specialized for the mobilization of energy. The SNS provides the vascular, glandular, metabolic, and other physiological adjustments that optimize behavioral responses, particularly in emergency situations and other conditions requiring activity. The SNS efferent outflow consists of preganglionic neurons, which are located in the intermediolateral column of the thoracic and lumbar spinal cord; their axons, which course to paravertebral and prevertebral ganglia containing the postganglionic neurons; and the axons of these postganglionic neurons, which project to the target tissues.

THE PARASYMPATHETIC DIVISION: ORGANIZED FOR ENERGY CONSERVATION

Parasympathetic Nervous System Functions Reduce Energy Expenditure and Increase Energy Stores

Functionally, the PNS and SNS usually mobilize opposite and antagonistic homeostatic adjustments (see Table 38.1). In particular, parasympathetic adjustments are often considered "rest and digest" responses, in contrast to the fight or flight sympathetic activation. The parasympathetic nervous system promotes anabolic processing, whereas the sympathetic nervous system augments catabolic activity. The PNS promotes the gastrointestinal processes required to digest and absorb nutrients, or energy, effectively. This branch of the ANS also augments the efficient use of energy and the storage of extra calories as fat and glycogen. The PNS, particularly the vagus nerve, plays a central role in controlling the dynamic flow of body reserves or energy between storage depots and the tissues that use the energy. The body's energy reserves are fat in adipose tissue and glycogen in liver and muscle. After a meal, the gastrointestinal tract serves as an additional reservoir of potential energy for the body. By mobilizing triglycerides from adipose tissue or glycogen from liver and muscle, the ANS can make reserves available for metabolism; similarly, by moving nutrient stores (for example, from the stomach) and promoting their digestion and absorption from the intestines into the blood stream, the ANS can supply energy to fuel metabolism or to restock triglyceride and glycogen stores, as needed. (See Chapter 41 for a more detailed discussion of autonomic influences on calorie storage.)

The antagonistic operation of the PNS and the SNS can be appreciated from an evolutionary perspective. Early in phylogeny, the ANS apparently consisted of a single, more-or-less undifferentiated autonomic division.[10,11] In more recent evolutionary history, the ANS separated into the predominantly catabolic SNS and the predominantly anabolic PNS, presumably because together the two opposing projection systems, which each have basal activity, provide better multivariate control of homeostasis than would be provided by the waxing or waning of activated responses in a single projection system. PNS facilitation of secretion, digestion, and absorption can be effectively antagonized by SNS activation, which inhibits motility in and reduces blood flow to the gastrointestinal tract. Conversely, PNS facilitation of digestive processes can be augmented by a coordinated ensemble of SNS adjustments, including an increase in blood flow to the alimentary canal (regional reduction of vasoconstriction) and a corresponding reduction in blood flow to skeletal muscle (regional increase in vasoconstriction). This pattern of dual autonomic innervation of individual viscera seems to be a principle of homeostasis [e.g., heart (Chapter 39), pancreas, and liver (Chapter 41)].

Preganglionic Neurons of the Parasympathetic Nervous System Lie in the Brainstem Cranial Nerve Nuclei and the Sacral Spinal Cord

One of the features distinguishing the PNS from the SNS is the location of preganglionic neurons. PNS preganglionic neurons are located in two broad longitudinal columns of neurons, one found in the brainstem and the other in the sacral spinal cord. These locations of the preganglionic neurons are responsible for the alternative name of this division of the ANS, the **craniosacral division** (or "bulbosacral" is also sometimes used). The longitudinal column of motor neurons in the brainstem is the general visceral cell column, which condenses into a number of more-or-less discrete nuclei just ventrolateral to the cerebral aqueduct system within the brain. These brainstem nuclei then project through their respective cranial nerves to targets in the head (cranial nerves III, VII, and IX) or thorax and abdomen (cranial nerve X). (See Fig. 38.6.) Cranial nerve III, the oculomotor nerve, carries the axons of the accessory, or autonomic, nucleus of the Edinger–Westphal complex, which participate

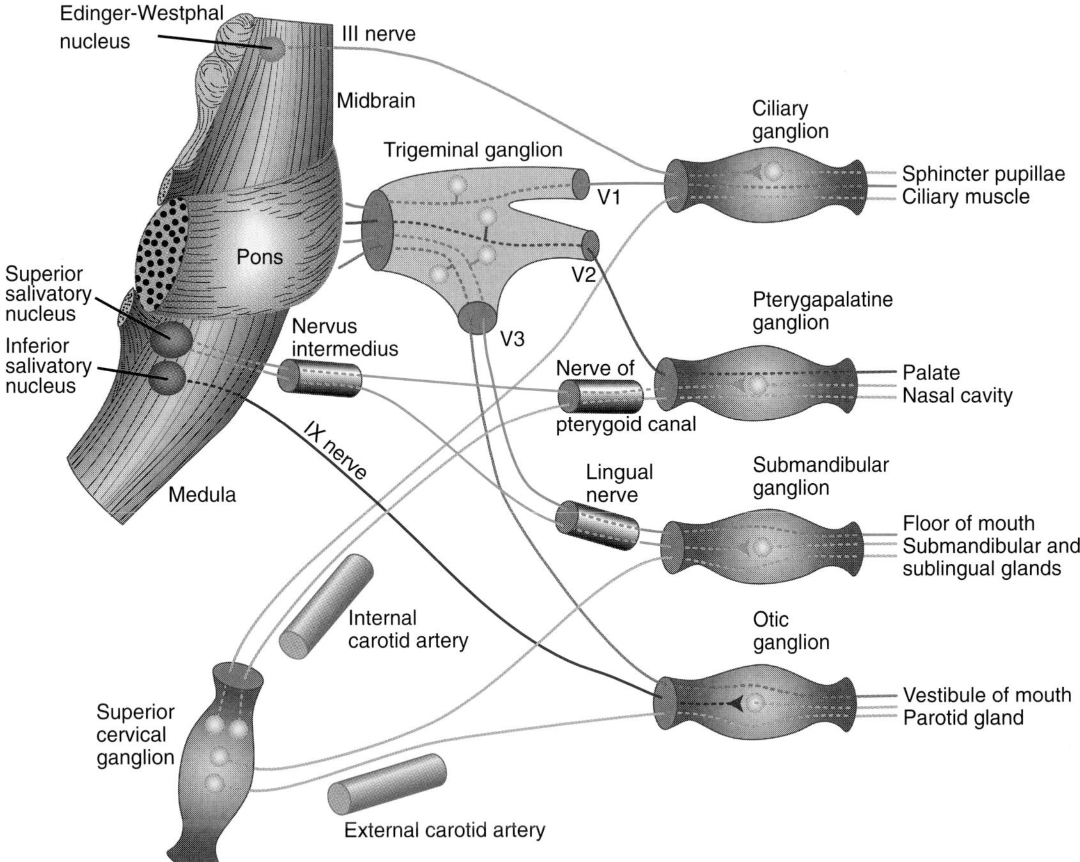

FIGURE 38.6 The autonomic innervation of the head by sympathetic (superior cervical ganglion) and parasympathetic (cranial nerve nuclei in the medulla and midbrain projecting to the several prevertebral ganglia) pathways. Visceral afferents associated with the autonomic nervous system are found in the trigeminal nerve (cranial nerve V) ganglion. Source: A. D. Loewy (1990). Anatomy of the autonomic nervous system. In *Central Regulation of Autonomic Functions* (A. D. Loewy and K. M. Spyer, eds.). Oxford University Press, New York. [After: Last, R. J. (1972). *Anatomy: Regional and Applied.* Churchill-Livingstone, Medical Publishers, New York.]

in the control of the pupillary sphincter and ciliary muscles. Cranial nerve VII, the facial nerve, carries preganglionic axons of the superior salivatory nucleus and controls the submaxillary and sublingual salivary glands as well as the lacrimal glands. Cranial nerve IX, the glossopharyngeal nerve, carries axons of the inferior salivatory nucleus, which control the parotid salivary glands and mucus secretion.

Preganglionic motor neurons of the Xth cranial nerve, the vagus nerve, control smooth muscles and glands throughout the entire digestive tract, from the pharynx to the distal colon, including viscera that are derived embryologically from the gut, such as the liver and pancreas. These Xth nerve neurons occupy a long fusiform nucleus in the medulla oblongata, the **dorsal motor nucleus of the vagus** (Fig. 38.7). They control numerous motor and secretomotor responses that participate in the ingestion and digestion of food, as well as in the assimilation of energy by the body. The vagus nerve also carries motor fibers of a special visceral nucleus, the **nucleus ambiguus** or ventral vagal nucleus, which controls the striated muscles of the pharynx, larynx, and esophagus and the cardiac muscle of the heart. Mapping experiments using neural tracers have demonstrated that, much like the case described for sympathetic neurons, the motor neurons of the dorsal motor nucleus of the vagus and the nucleus ambiguus are organized into viscerotopic subnuclei.[12–14]

The central representation of the much more caudal remainder of the PNS is found in the sacral spinal cord, in humans the second (S2) through fourth (S4) sacral segments (Fig. 38.8). The parasympathetic preganglionic somata occupy two longitudinal groupings, one column immediately dorsolateral to the central canal and the other in roughly the same transverse location

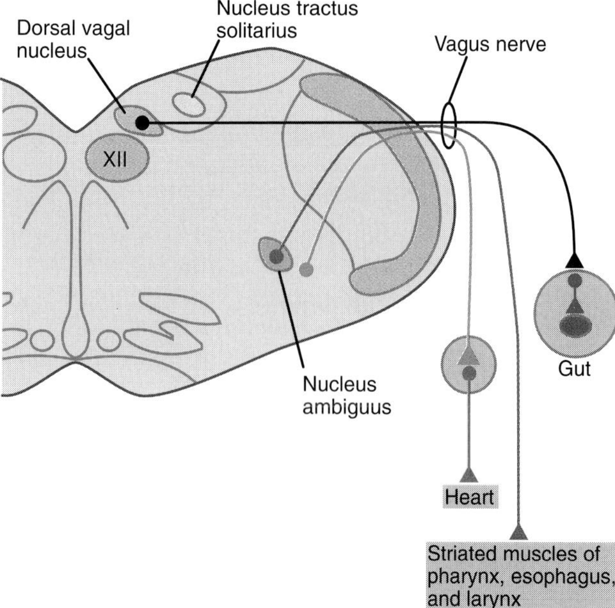

FIGURE 38.7 The parasympathetic projections of the vagal motor pathways, the most extensive of the PNS circuits, to the viscera of the thorax and abdomen. Source: A. D. Loewy (1990). Anatomy of the autonomic nervous system. In *Central Regulation of Autonomic Functions* (A. D. Loewy, and K. M. Spyer, eds.). Oxford University Press, New York.

as that of the intermediolateral column of cells, which sympathetic preganglionics occupy in the thoracic and lumbar cord. The axons of the sacral preganglionics exit the cord in the ventral roots, run in a sacral plexus, and project to the target organs. The sacral preganglionic cell columns control parasympathetic motor, vasomotor, and secretomotor functions of the kidneys, bladder, transverse and distal colon, and reproductive organs.

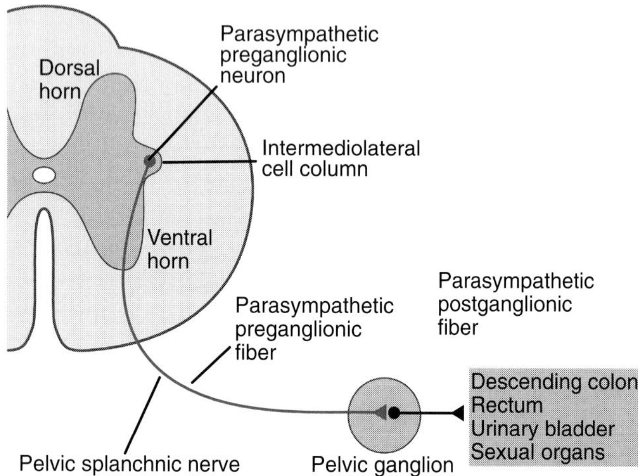

FIGURE 38.8 Spinal cord organization of the sacral division of the craniosacral, or parasympathetic, nervous system. Source: A. D. Loewy (1990). Anatomy of the autonomic nervous system. In *Central Regulation of Autonomic Functions* (A. D. Loewy and K. M. Spyer, eds.). Oxford University Press, New York.

The location of its postganglionic neurons is another feature that distinguishes the PNS from the SNS. The ganglia containing the PNS postganglionic neurons are juxtaposed to, on the surface of, or even in the target, in contrast to the para- and prevertebral locations of the SNS.[15] These juxta- and intramural stations are often called **plexuses,** rather than ganglia. Like the SNS prevertebral ganglia, the PNS postganglionic plexuses are complex integrative sites that typically receive inputs not only from preganglionic neurons but also from afferents within the plexuses or target tissues. Because the PNS postganglionic neurons are situated so near their targets, the parasympathetic division of the ANS has longer preganglionic axons and shorter postganglionic fibers than the sympathetic division. The relative lengths of the postganglionic fibers in the two divisions have been taken as evidence that individual axons of the SNS may diverge more extensively and innervate larger projection fields, whereas the PNS may exhibit less divergence and more localized projections (Box 38.2). (For counterarguments, see Wang *et al.*[16])

Summary

The second major outflow of the ANS, the parasympathetic nervous system or craniosacral division, is organized to digest, assimilate, and conserve energy. Its anabolic functions include not only those associated with the metabolism of nutrients but also numerous protective reflexes, such as those that limit heat loss, reduce energy expenditure, and slow the heart. The PNS outflow consists of preganglionic neurons located in brainstem cranial nerve nuclei or the autonomic columns of the sacral spinal cord. Their axons project to the postganglionic neurons located in ganglia situated near or in the target organs. The postganglionic neurons in turn project to the smooth muscle of the target viscera.

THE ENTERIC DIVISION OF THE ANS: THE NERVE NET FOUND IN THE WALLS OF VISCERAL ORGANS

When Langley articulated the modern definition of the ANS, he identified a third division of the ANS, the **enteric nervous system.** The alimentary canal, or "entrum," and the tissues derived from it, such as the pancreas and liver, contain extensive and well-formed

BOX 38.2

AUTONOMIC POSTGANGLIONIC NEURONS CAN CHANGE THEIR TRANSMITTER PHENOTYPES

Generally, the transmitter phenotype of autonomic neurons seems fixed, dictated by both intrinsic and extrinsic cues (see Chapter 17, particularly Fig. 17.26). One provocative observation in autonomic neurochemistry, made possible by the development of tissue culture techniques and immunocytochemistry, is the finding that ANS neurons can alter their phenotypes under appropriate environmental conditions. This conclusion was first reached when populations of postmitotic adrenergic and cholinergic neurons were cocultured *in vitro* in different culture media or in the presence of different tissues. Without overall changes in cell number, the percentages of adrenergic and cholinergic neurons in a given culture changed over time.[22] Even more compelling, when single postganglionic cells were grown in microculture wells, the presence of a medium conditioned by heart cells would allow these mature neurons to change from expressing an adrenergic phenotype to expressing a cholinergic one.[23]

This transition does not appear to be an artifact of cell culture situations; the change appears to occur normally in development *in vivo* to generate the specialized minority of sympathetic postganglionic neurons that are cholinergic (e.g., for innervation of sweat glands). Landis and co-workers have verified this hypothesis by using rat foot pad sweat gland innervation *in vivo* and characterizing the phenotype of the autonomic projections at different stages of development.[24] These investigators observed that the sympathetic postganglionic innervation of the sweat glands is initially adrenergic, as the axon grows toward its target. Once the sweat gland target is innervated, the tissue induces the change in neurotransmitter phenotype to a cholinergic one.

Such changes in transmitter are not unique to these examples. Perhaps reflecting pluripotential patterns seen earlier in phylogeny, at least some cholinergic neurons (e.g., avian ciliary ganglion cells) appear to remodel into an adrenergic phenotype. And other cells (e.g., developing neural crest cells in the developing gut wall) exhibit a transient catecholaminergic stage that is lost during ingrowth of extramural innervation.

Finally, autonomic postganglionic neurons also have been shown to alter their levels of transmitters and cotransmitters as a function of the activity of their preganglionic inputs.[25] For example, after preganglionic inputs are pharmacologically blocked or transected, postganglionic neurons of the superior cervical ganglion decrease their levels of tyrosine hydroxylase (the rate-limiting enzyme for norepinephrine production) while increasing their level of substance P.

---

neural networks. In particular, the gastrointestinal tract contains two well-organized major plexuses that have been estimated to contain as many neurons as the entire spinal cord (Fig. 38.9). Each plexus consists of an extensive sheet of small nodes of cells linked by connectives. One plexus, the **myenteric plexus,** is situated between the outer longitudinal and inner circular muscle layers of the viscus. The other plexus, the **submucosal** or **submucous plexus,** is located between the circular muscle layer and the lumenal mucosal layer of the viscera. As illustrated in Fig. 38.9, there are additional, less extensive, enteric networks as well. The number of neurons in the enteric plexuses, their extensive interconnections, and their capacity to support motility have led to proposals that the enteric nervous system serves as a "little brain" in the gut.[17]

Early descriptions emphasized the autonomy of the enteric nervous system by observing that the gastrointestinal tract could exhibit movement, peristalsis, even after all extrinsic connections to it were cut. However, more recent observations suggest that the many coordinated responses of the gastrointestinal tract, including motor responses other than peristalsis, as well as absorptive and secretory responses, involve extrinsic projections from the central nervous system to the enteric nervous system.

Because the preganglionic neurons of the vagus nerve project to the enteric ganglia rather than to independent postganglionic stations, the enteric nervous system serves as an extensive postganglionic station for the vagus.

Summary

The enteric nervous system, the third division of the ANS, consists of the intrinsic neurons that form ganglia and plexuses in the walls of the viscera associated with gastrointestinal tract. This nerve network contains intrinsic afferents, interneurons, and efferents that control local functions; it also receives extrinsic

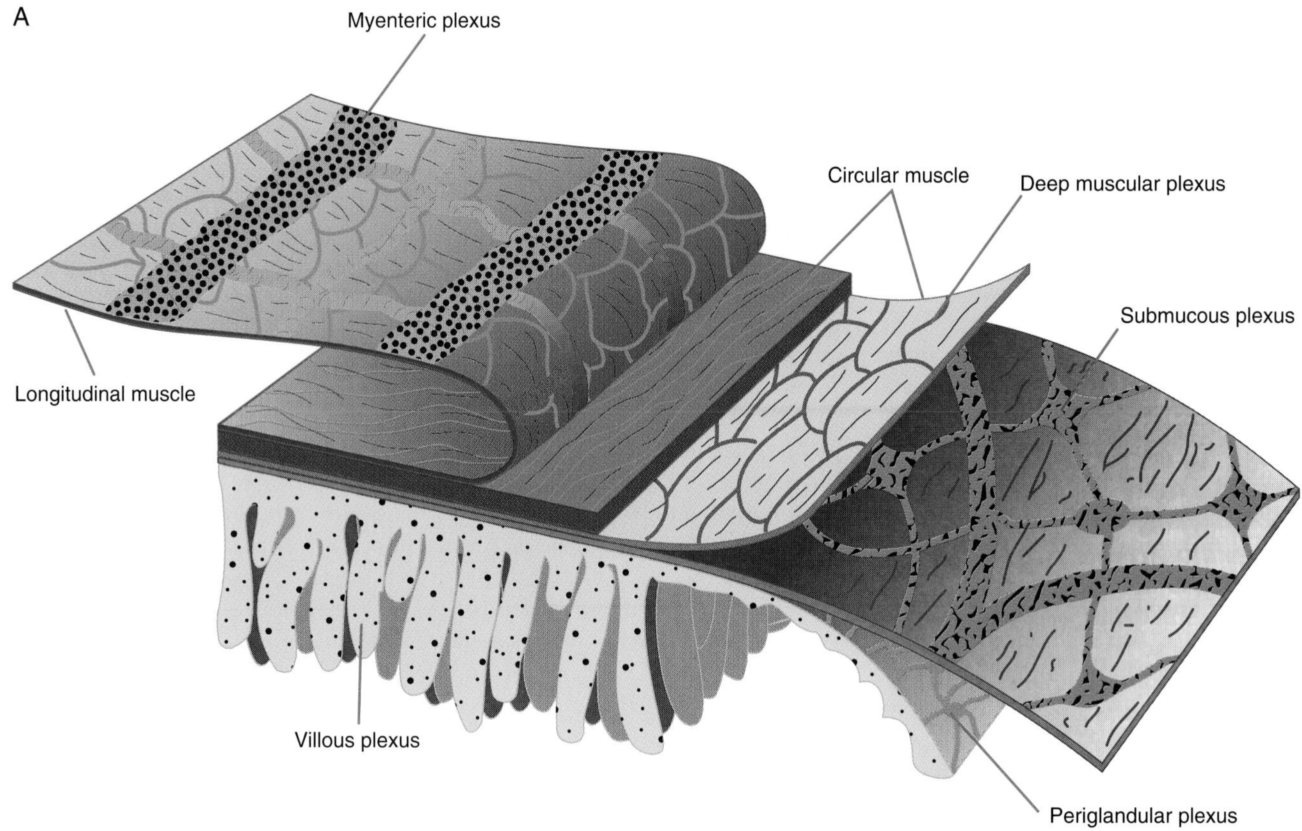

FIGURE 38.9 (A) The enteric nervous system plexuses in the wall of the intestine. The enteric neurons form two conspicuous and extensive networks, or plexuses, of ganglia and connectives located between the longitudinal and circular muscle layers of the wall (the myenteric plexus) and between the circular muscle layer and the inner mucosal layer (the submucous plexus). The deep muscular plexus, periglandular plexus, and villous plexus are additional networks of enteric neurons and their processes. Source: M. Costa, J. B. Furness, and I. J. Llewellyn-Smith (1987). Histochemistry of the enteric nervous system. In *Physiology of the Gastrointestinal Tract* (L. R. Johnson, ed.), Vol. 1. Raven Press, New York.

inputs from autonomic preganglionic efferents, particularly those coursing in the vagus nerve.

ANS PHARMACOLOGY: TRANSMITTER AND RECEPTOR CODING

Early in the 20th century, pharmacological studies performed with naturally occurring agonists and antagonists provided the basis for the original chemical differentiation of the autonomic nervous system into two major divisions—the SNS and PNS. Dale,[18,19] the contributor of "Dale's law" of neurotransmitters, Langley,[7] and a number of other early investigators applied muscarine (from a mushroom), nicotine (from tobacco), *d*-tubocurarine (the South American plant alkaloid used as an arrow poison), and other natural extracts to autonomic ganglia while measuring autonomic responses in order to infer the chemical taxonomy of the ANS. Subsequent experiments have replicated the basic distinctions made by these investigators, but this newer work, with access to an extensive pharmacopoeia of synthetic agonists and antagonists, as well as to immunocytochemistry for characterization of transmitter substances, has described a much richer and more complicated multiplicity of neurotransmitters and neuromodulators in autonomic nerves.[20,21]

Preganglionic Neurons Use Acetylcholine as a Transmitter

Most preganglionic neurons of both branches of the ANS have a cholinergic transmitter phenotype. In the peripheral ganglia of both branches of the ANS, most postganglionic neurons, which receive inputs from the preganglionics, express a predominance of the nicotinic form of the cholinergic receptor on their somata.

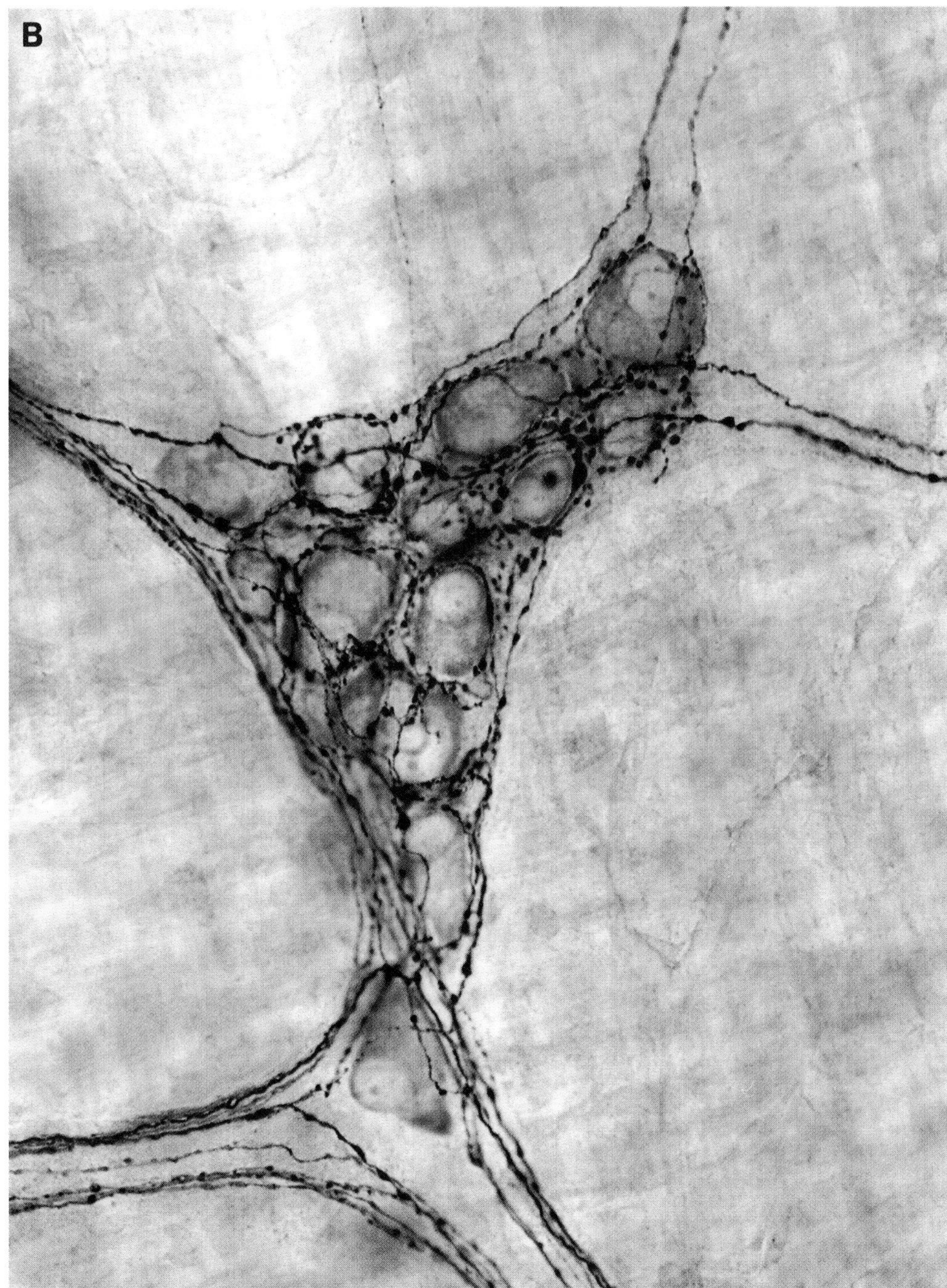

FIGURE 38.9 (*continued*) (B) Autonomic preganglionic terminals innervating postganglionic neurons. This example of vagal preganglionic projections (labeled with the tracer Phaseolus vulgaris) innervating myenteric ganglion neurons (stained with Cuprolinic blue) in the stomach wall illustrates that autonomic preganglionic axons can diverge widely to form extensive networks controlling postganglionics. M.-C. Holst, J. B. Kelly, and T. L. Powley (1997). Vagal preganglionic projections to the enteric nervous system characterized with PHA-L. *J. Comp. Neurol.* **381:** 81–100.

Only relatively small subpopulations of preganglionic neurons express other, e.g., dopaminergic or adrenergic, phenotypes. Specificity and response selectivity at the ganglionic level are normally maintained by the segregation of sympathetic and parasympathetic postganglionic neurons in separate ganglia, by the point-to-point axonal projections, and by the spatial separation of synapses within ganglia. As discovered by the early autonomic pharmacologists, nicotine can serve as a general "ganglionic blocker" to thwart transmission at these synapses.

Sympathetic and Parasympathetic Postganglionic Neurons Use Different Transmitters

One of the cardinal defining differences between the SNS and the PNS is the transmitter phenotype of the postganglionic neurons. The majority of sympathetic postganglionic neurons release the transmitter norepinephrine, whereas parasympathetic postganglionic neurons release primarily acetylcholine to control their targets. Such a two-transmitter chemical code makes it possible to have push–pull or positive bidirectional control of individual targets. The functional significance of this chemical code relates to the type of muscle, smooth or striated, the ANS controls. The biomechanics of smooth muscle are quite different from the biomechanics of striated muscle (Chapter 30). Consequently, important differences exist between the two motor systems.

To understand this point, a brief look at a few biomechanical features of striated muscle is helpful. For the most part, striated muscles are attached to the skeleton by tendons. These tendons attach the muscle so that it contracts across a joint to either flex or extend a limb or part of the body. Most striated muscles are organized into antagonistic pairs in which the flexor and extensor of the pair oppose each other's action across the hinge or joint. With such an organization, mechanical push–pull operations of a limb are achieved by graded activation of either the flexor or the extensor. In this striated muscle configuration, the single transmitter, namely, acetylcholine, serves both the flexion and the extension functions simply by the appropriate motor neuron activating the appropriate muscle.

In contrast, smooth muscle is not always organized into antagonistic pairs, with each member of the pair being innervated by a different motor neuron. Also, the smooth muscles forming the walls of the viscera are not differentially attached to a hard frame to provide mechanical leverage through opposal activity. Reciprocal motor programs of the viscera for the most part involve active, phased excitation and inhibition of the same muscle to achieve coordination. To produce these patterns of excitation and inhibition, the target organs and tissues express both adrenergic and cholinergic receptors and have different, often antagonistic or complementary, responses to selective activation of the different receptors.

Response patterns of smooth muscle are further differentiated by specializations of the receptors. Adrenergic receptors, influenced by the catecholaminergic transmitter released by sympathetic fibers, are differentiated into at least four different subtypes linked to different intracellular processes (see discussion of metabotropic receptors in Chapter 9). Similarly, the muscarinic acetylcholine receptor, influenced by the cholinergic transmitter released by parasympathetic postganglionic neurons, is differentiated into at least three subtypes with differential influences on intracellular transduction (see discussion of ionotropic receptors in Chapter 9). These heterogeneities of transmitter species and receptor types make it practical to mobilize multiple, different, and potentially highly differentiated responses from one effector tissue (see Box 38.2).[22–25]

Response selection may also be facilitated by neuropeptides that the postganglionic neurons also synthesize and release during activity. Somatostatin, neuropeptide Y, or both are found in many sympathetic neurons; vasoactive intestinal polypeptide and calcitonin gene-related peptide are often coexpressed in parasympathetic neurons. These peptides may serve as neuromodulators that vary postsynaptic responses to the conventional autonomic neurotransmitters. Experiments using different patterns and rates of electrical stimulation have established that the release of different neuropeptides and cotransmitters can vary with different rates or patterns of axonal firing and is not invariantly proportional to transmitter release. Thus, a heterogeneity of different cotransmitter and transmitter release patterns can be produced by a single fiber or fiber type, depending on firing pattern and other local factors at the synapse.[20,21]

Although dual innervation in an oppositional or push–pull pattern is presumed to yield faster, more responsive adjustments and to provide a mechanism that can adjust response gain, some tissues are innervated by only one arm of the ANS. The SNS has a wider distribution than the PNS. In particular, white and brown adipose tissue, peripheral blood vessels, and sweat glands are innervated by the SNS without complementary PNS projections. One possible explanation for this arrangement is that the functions of these particular effectors do not require the speed associated with push–pull projection patterns, particularly in terminating responses once activated. In the evolution of the autonomic nervous system, the SNS is thought to be the older, and correspondingly more extensive, network, whereas the PNS occurred more recently in phylogeny and therefore has less widespread projections.[10,11]

Finally, the enteric nervous system has an extensively varied set of transmitters, cotransmitters, and neuromodulators providing highly differentiated chemical coding of local functions.[15,20,21]

Summary

Both the SNS and the PNS use acetylcholine as a preganglionic transmitter, but they are distinguished by different postganglionic phenotypes: most SNS postganglionic neurons are catecholaminergic, whereas most PNS neurons are cholinergic. The different neurotransmitter and cotransmitter elements expressed in the postganglionic neurons, as well as numerous postsynaptic receptor subtypes, provide the chemical coding for responses of the PNS and SNS. This functional organization ensures varied, powerful, and dynamic push–pull operation of homeostatic systems.

AUTONOMIC CONTROLS OF HOMEOSTASIS

The "self-governing" or autonomic characteristic that gives its name to the ANS is based largely on reflexes. These reflexes involve afferent inputs and efferent outputs. Two major inflows of visceral, or autonomic, afferents (see Box 38.3) establish the basic reflex arcs. These visceral afferents provide critical cross-links between the sympathetic and the parasympathetic outflows, keeping them in balance. For example, sympathetic activity can increase heart rate (**tachycardia**) and produce constriction of vascular beds, thus leading to an increase in blood pressure. This increase in blood pressure, in turn, is detected by vagus nerve baroreceptors in the aortic arch and other sites. The visceral afferents in the vagus then can reflexively stimulate vagal parasympathetic efferents that slow heart rate (**bradycardia**). The visceral afferents monitoring the effects of autonomic activity produce positive, reciprocal, and dynamic regulation of physiological responses. When a more sustained adjustment in blood pressure is required (e.g., in the general arousal of the fight-or-flight response discussed before), these outflows are adjusted centrally, but unconsciously, so that sympathetic activation is not nullified by parasympathetic responses damping the needed activation.

Visceral Afferents Connect the Target Tissue and the CNS

Motor neurons of the sympathetic nervous system receive direct afferent input from most of the autonomic targets. The cell bodies of these primary affer-

BOX 38.3

AUTONOMIC REFLEXES: ACTIVATED BY VISCERAL AFFERENTS, AUTONOMIC AFFERENTS, OR JUST AFFERENTS?

A long-standing dispute about terminology still influences discussions of autonomic reflexes. Some authors (and textbooks) adhere to the original autonomic classification of Langley, who considered the ANS a motor system without an autonomic sensory inflow. This classic view acknowledges that autonomic effectors are influenced by afferents but considers somatic afferents and visceral afferents as independent of the ANS. Conversely, other scientists (and textbooks) consider afferents arising in and associated with the viscera as the necessary counterpart to autonomic efferents and label them autonomic afferents.

The controversy goes back to Langley's pharmacological definition of the ANS. In his initial studies, Langley speculated about the existence of autonomic afferents, but he was unable to find a neurochemical marker to distinguish visceral from somatic afferents. He sidelined the issue pending more information, focused his studies on efferents, and never returned to search for an afferent marker. Adherents to his original motor-only classification stress that somatic and visceral afferents can elicit autonomic responses and that both classes of afferents elicit somatic responses, as well. On the other hand, advocates for including visceral afferents within the autonomic schema argue that these afferents innervate the target tissues of the ANS efferents, share similar embryological histories with autonomic efferents, course in the same peripheral nerves as the autonomic efferents (e.g., the vagus), and form mono- and oligosynaptic reflex arcs influencing autonomic preganglionic neurons. These proponents for revising the autonomic terminology also point out that more recent analyses have identified neuropeptide markers shared by visceral afferents (but not somatic afferents) and autonomic motor neurons. This more inclusive view of the autonomic nervous system seems to be gaining ground. It works more naturally for the discussion of reflexes, and we have adopted it in this text.

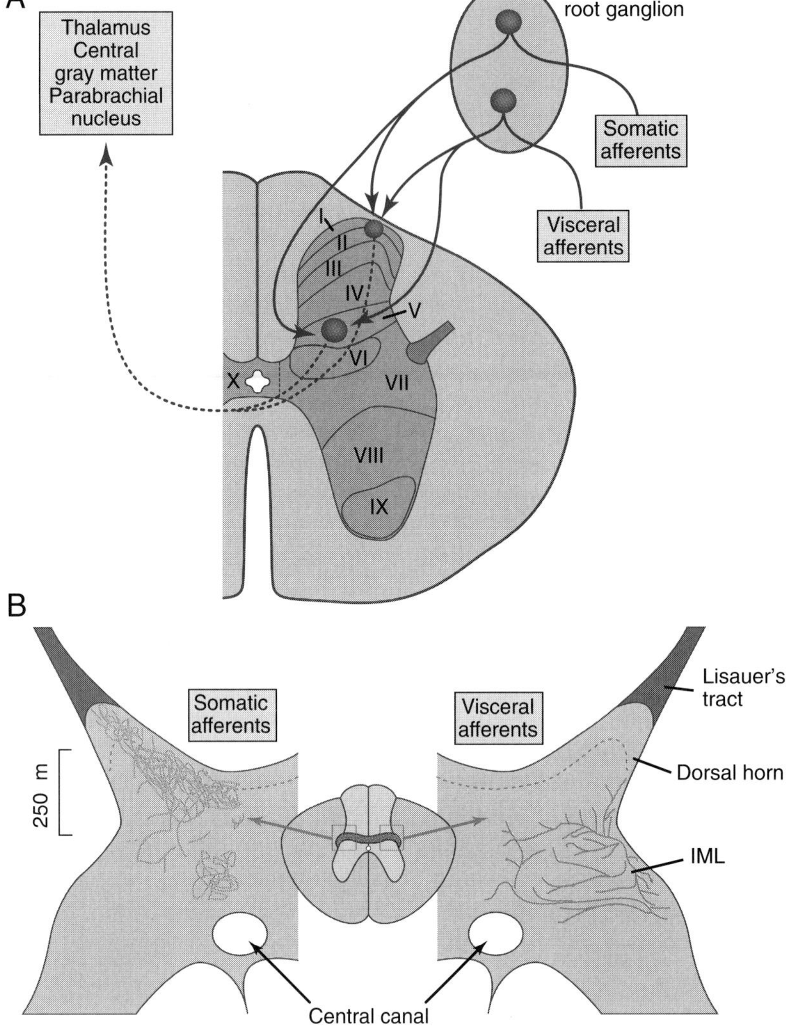

FIGURE 38.10 Visceral and somatic afferents follow parallel but distinct paths in the central nervous system. Visceral and somatic afferents consist of different populations of dorsal root ganglion neurons which project to laminae I and V of the dorsal horn of the spinal cord. These relay sites provide local spinal reflexes and also project to higher autonomic and somatic sites, respectively, in the brain (A). Although visceral and somatic afferents follow similar trajectories, more detailed tracer studies indicate the two types of afferents end in distinctly different distributions and densities within the spinal cord (B). IML, intermediolateral cell column. Source: Cervero and Foreman.[27]

ents are located in the dorsal root ganglia of the spinal cord segment(s) in which the corresponding preganglionic neurons are located (see Fig. 38.2B and Fig. 38.10). The afferent somata are similar to other dorsal root ganglion cells, although they frequently are distinguishable as small, dark neurons, or B afferents.[26] From endings in the innervated viscera or tissue, the centripetally directed peripheral processes of the afferents typically course in mixed nerves containing the motor outflow. These processes then reach the dorsal roots through the major peripheral nerves. The central processes of these visceral afferents enter the spinal cord in association with Lissauer's tract, ending in laminae I and V of the dorsal horn.[27]

Visceral afferent nerves relay sensory information about visceral volume, pressure or other stimuli to spinal centers, where automatic responses are interpreted and functional responses are generated.

For many of these visceral afferents, their endings in the periphery and in the spinal cord (particularly in lamina V, which neighbors the intermediolateral column containing the preganglionic motor neurons) contain substance P (SP) and other neuropeptides of the tachykinin family, such as neurokinin A (NKA) and neurokinin B (NKB). (See Chapter 8; also Lundberg.[21])

In the parasympathetic limb of the ANS are two major afferent inflows with different organization. In the cranial division, visceral afferents are most often found in the same cranial nerve as their corresponding motor counterparts. These mixed cranial nerves have sensory ganglia located outside the cranium, and the cell bodies of the afferents are found in these ganglia. Like other afferents, these neurons are typically pseudounipolar neurons with a peripheral process extending to the target tissue and a central process projecting to the central nervous system. The central terminals of these afferents end in a cranial nerve sensory nucleus. Visceral afferents associated with the outflow of cranial nerve III are complex and enter through different channels (e.g., cranial nerve V, the trigeminal nerve). Most of the visceral afferents associated with cranial nerve autonomic reflexes terminate in the extensive nucleus of the solitary tract, which is located immediately dorsal to the general visceral column of the brainstem. Afferents of VII, IX, and X all end in the nucleus of the solitary tract. These inputs form a broad viscerotopic map in the nucleus, with facial gustatory information projecting most rostrally and medially, the glossopharyngeal information somewhat more caudally, and the afferents of the different branches of the vagus nerve terminating most caudally in different subnuclei of the nucleus of the solitary tract. As the largest and most complex of the visceral afferent relays in the brain, the nucleus of the solitary tract also receives afferent inputs from the spinal division of the trigeminal nerve and second-order inputs from the dorsal column nuclei.

Like visceral afferents associated with the SNS, the visceral afferents associated with the PNS contain substance P and other tachykinins. In addition, several neuropeptides found in the gut also are found in some of these afferents. For example, the gut hormone and neuropeptide cholecystokinin (CCK) is found in vagal afferents relaying information from the gastrointestinal tract to the brain. CCK is also found in higher order ascending relays of vagal projections in the neuraxis, leading some to argue that CCK provides chemical coding for visceral afferents associated with the gastrointestinal tract.

The second major inflow of afferents to the parasympathetic limb of the ANS is associated with the sacral division. Visceral afferents in this division are organized much like the spinal afferents associated with the thoracolumbar or sympathetic division of the ANS.[28–30]

At the central relays of autonomic reflex arcs, the thoracolumbar circuitry of sympathetic reflexes and the craniosacral circuitry of parasympathetic responses have similar morphological elements. Their organization has been delineated with intracellular staining and axonal tracer techniques. Dembowsky and co-workers[31] injected horseradish peroxidase intracellularly to define the morphology of the sympathetic preganglionics (Fig. 38.11). The motor neurons preferentially distribute their dendrites within the long longitudinally oriented column that constitutes the intermediolateral nucleus of the spinal cord. The neurons also distribute a subset of their dendrites dorsolaterally in an arch that brings the dendrites into contact with the incoming visceral afferents. This characteristic dendroarchitecture is consistent with the ideas that local mono- or oligosynaptic reflexes are organized segmentally within the nucleus and that preganglionic neurons are heavily influenced by activity in the intermediolateral column immediately rostral and caudal to the cells' location. Parasympathetic preganglionics exhibit similar dendroarchitecture.[13,14]

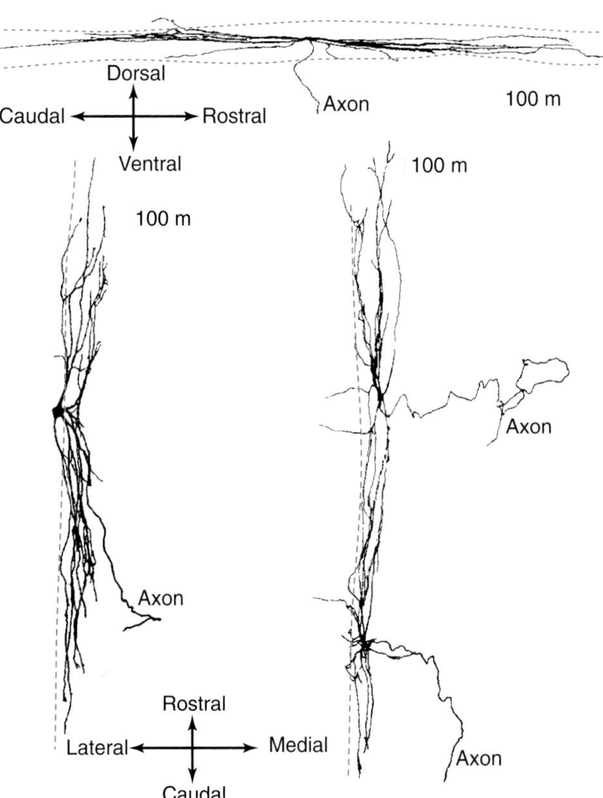

FIGURE 38.11 Examples of intracellularly labeled sympathetic neurons in the spinal cord. The preganglionics have extensive dendritic fields confined to the columnar pattern of the SNS intermediolateral cell column within the cord. Source: Cabot.[8] After Dembowsky *et al.*[31]

Visceral Afferents Also Organize Axon Reflexes and Signal Visceral Pain

In addition to forming conventional reflex circuits throughout the ANS, visceral afferents support a response known as an **axon reflex.** Unlike the conven-

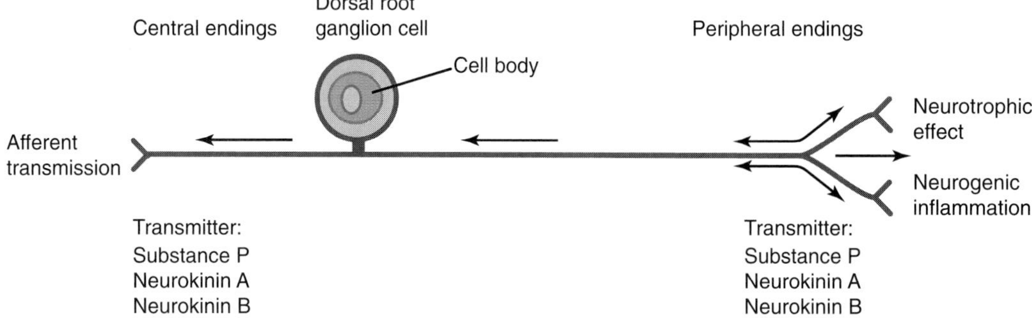

FIGURE 38.12 The architecture of visceral afferents that produces axon reflexes. Visceral and cutaneous afferents release transmitters from the tachykinin family. When action potentials (indicated by arrows) are generated peripherally, they are propagated centrally. Peripherally generated action potentials also produce a local release of tachykinins in the affected terminals and in terminals of the peripheral collaterals. Source: Cervero and Foreman.[27]

tional reflex, which involves an afferent neuron, at least one central nervous system synapse, and an efferent neuron, axon reflexes involve only the afferent neuron, and they occur in the target tissue—without a CNS relay. The phenomenon can be seen clearly in the type of experiment that was instrumental in establishing the existence of axon reflexes: If all motor axons projecting to a target tissue are eliminated by surgery or other appropriate means while sparing the afferent innervation of the site, the afferent axons can be stimulated selectively. When the afferent axons are stimulated such that their peripheral processes innervating the target are invaded by action potentials conducting in the direction opposite from normal, or "antidromically," one can measure an effector response or assay the release of a neuropeptide from the peripheral afferent neurite. Such experiments performed on a variety of different visceral (and cutaneous) afferent systems have demonstrated that axon reflexes produce a number of inflammatory and vascular effector responses.[21]

Presumably, when afferents are stimulated physiologically, or appropriately, axon reflexes are normally produced in peripheral collaterals contained in many and perhaps all visceral afferents (Fig. 38.12; also see the discussion of dendritic release of peptide transmitters in Chapter 9). When a peripheral ending of a visceral afferent transduces a stimulus, the resulting action potential can release extracellularly the neuropeptide contained in vesicles in that ending. The released compound then acts as a neuromodulator or neurotransmitter to effect local changes on smooth muscle—a local, or peripheral, axon reflex. The response is also relayed to neighboring tissues. When an action potential is transmitted centrally in an afferent axon, it can also be transmitted centrifugally in collaterals of the same fiber, and release of the neuromodulator from these collateral endings can propagate the reflex in the immediate area. The inflammatory responses and extravasation associated with the classic "wheal and flare" reaction to skin damage were the first axon reflexes analyzed and are a classic illustration of the phenomenon. Such local responses have been widely documented not only in the skin but also in the viscera. They are a repertoire of visceral effector responses that do not require a CNS relay.

Finally, visceral afferents, and in particular those associated with SNS pathways, are responsible for visceral pain.[32]

Summary

Visceral afferents innervate the target tissues of the ANS, and their axons frequently course in the same peripheral nerves as autonomic efferents. Also commonly called autonomic afferents, these sensory elements associated with the ANS constitute the afferent limbs of autonomic reflexes and carry the inputs recognized as visceral pain. Visceral afferents also mediate axon reflexes and are cross-linked with somatic, as well as autonomic, nervous system activity.

HIERARCHICALLY ORGANIZED CNS CIRCUITS

Homeostasis no more occurs through an isolated autonomic reflex (or set of reflexes) than posture is maintained, or movement is effected, through isolated somatic reflexes. Nevertheless, historical and methodological considerations have yielded a tendency to focus on individual autonomic reflexes. Historically, the ANS was conceptualized primarily as a motor branch of the peripheral nervous system, and many textbooks reflect this early emphasis. Methodologically, reductionistic requirements and the need for experimental control typically dictate that experiments isolate a reflex (or small set of reflexes) for examination.

Examination of the reflexes individually, however, tends to overlook the full capacity of the ANS to coordinate programs of motor response. The separate-reflex perspective shapes a view of the autonomic nervous system as a collection of individual motor responses, but autonomic activity typically involves finely coordinated, fully integrated adjustments of multiple outflows. Just as somatic posture and movement are coordinated by supraspinal CNS controls, autonomic integration is achieved by supraspinal controls. The preganglionic motor pools of the craniosacral and thoracolumbar outflows are *final common paths* for descending projections from the CNS. Similarly, the first- and second-order visceral afferent relays (e.g., the nucleus of the solitary tract and the spinal lamina V), which form short, mono- or oligosynaptic reflex arcs with these preganglionic motor pools, are targets of rostral CNS stations that coordinate the autonomic outflows.

The CNS coordination of autonomic activity provides a number of integrative functions: (1) Much like the suprasegmental organization of skeletal motor responses, the central ANS stations provide coordination and sequencing of different local autonomic reflexes. These stations provide, for example, the efferent choreography necessary to coordinate the autonomic responses in the mouth, stomach, intestines, and pancreas during and after a meal. Such programs coordinate brainstem and spinal cord efferents as well as reflexes within the SNS and PNS divisions of the autonomic outflow. (2) Central ANS circuitry also links autonomic activity and somatic motor activity. The earlier example of cardiovascular adjustments occurring in concert with postural adjustments illustrates such linkage between autonomic and somatic nervous system outflows. (3) The CNS stations of the autonomic nervous system also provide the information, as well as the organization and planning, that enables the individual to mobilize autonomic adjustments or responses in anticipation of environmental events. For example, both fluid and energy homeostases involve physiological adjustments in anticipation of major imbalances or deficits, responses that cannot be explained solely by reactive reflexes (see Chapter 42).

The autonomic controls of the cardiovascular system (discussed in Chapter 39) provide prototypic examples of these principles. The brainstem provides central coordination of autonomic reflexes controlling the cardiovascular system. For example, the brainstem integrates the sympathetic and parasympathetic feedback loops controlling vasomotor tone, baroreceptor reflexes, and cardiac rate. In addition to linking these separate homeostatic reflexes into an overall adaptive program, the brainstem also cross-couples the autonomic adjustments with complementary endocrine controls involving the hypothalamopituitary–adrenal axis. Furthermore, CNS neural circuitry also provides the linkages by which these cardiovascular adjustments are coordinated and integrated with other homeostatic loads and challenges that must be handled simultaneously (see, for example, the role of baroreceptor reflexes in volume regulation of fluid levels in Chapter 39).

The importance and the nature of central autonomic controls are underscored by clinical disorders that result from interruptions in the connections between the central autonomic circuitry and the preganglionic motor neurons. See Box 38.4. **Quadriplegia** and **paraplegia,** which result from injuries that divide the spinal cord and separate thoracic and lumbar sympathetic loops and sacral parasympathetic pathways from higher central regions, illustrate how essential these longitudinal connections are. Interruption of the longitudinal connections causes loss of voluntary bladder and bowel control. Disruption of the spinal cord also causes men to become impotent, because penile tumescence is a sympathetic response and ejaculation is a parasympathetic response. Although erections can occasionally be elicited as local reflexes caused by direct mechanical stimulation, ejaculations, which require suprasegmental coordination, almost universally disappear. In addition, numerous vascular and glandular reflexes are also disordered by interruption of long autonomic pathways connecting the brain and spinal cord.[4,5]

Early Physiological Experiments Suggested a Central Component of the ANS

Like the concept of the ANS itself, the corollary that the ANS includes a hierarchy of central mechanisms was first demonstrated by physiological experiments. Nineteenth- and early twentieth-century experiments manipulating the brain caused autonomic disturbances. In one classical experiment, for example, Claude Bernard demonstrated that localized mechanical lesions, or stab wounds, in the floor of the fourth ventricle near the dorsal vagal complex produced a "pîqure glycosurique," a disturbance of blood glucose homeostasis characterized by a diabetes-like condition in which glucose spills into the urine. Making similar observations, Flourens suggested the existence of respiratory "noeud vital" in the brainstem, and Schiff pointed to a "vasoconstrictor center" in the medulla. More modern lesion and stimulation studies have iden-

BOX 38.4

HEALTH AND DISEASE: THE WISDOM OF THE BODY

The importance of the autonomic nervous system to health often goes unnoticed. When ANS functions operate normally, they typically operate automatically, without the individual being aware of any adjustments.

Nevertheless, autonomic disorders can be debilitating.[4,5] In the classic example of adulthood ANS degeneration known as **multiple system atrophy and autonomic failure,** or the **Shy–Drager syndrome,** individuals may exhibit postural hypotension, urinary and fecal incontinence, sexual impotence, cranial nerve palsies, loss of sweating, and a movement disorder similar to Parkinson disease. Disconnection of the suprasegmental autonomic stations from the spinal cord can occur in neurological disorders, such as multiple sclerosis, and traumatic spinal cord injury. As a result, bowel and bladder control are lost, and impotence is caused by loss of autonomic genital reflexes.

Such deficits are clearly disabling, but some autonomic disorders are less conspicuous. In part, the apparently more subtle deficits may be ones that are less important in the carefully controlled environments found in industrialized countries. For example, impaired thermoregulatory responses may be tolerated well by a person living in a climate-controlled environment. Also, energy emergencies are unlikely to occur and need autonomic compensation if a person regularly eats enough food. Nevertheless, autonomic disorders occasion a number of serious, even life-threatening, health problems:

- Excess activation of the ANS is implicated in various stress-related disorders, including ulcers, colitis, high blood pressure, and heart attacks.
- Chronic failure of autonomic cardiovascular hemeostasis can cause debilitating postural hypotension.
- Developmental autonomic disorders, such as immature or anomalous medullary respiratory circuitry, are thought to contribute to **sudden infant death syndrome.** Some sleep disorders, such as sleep apnea, are also thought to have autonomic components.
- Widespread autonomic dysfunction resulting from autonomic neuropathies of diabetes, alcoholism, and Parkinson disease complicates the primary diseases.
- Autonomic disturbances can also underlie metabolic disorders, such as stress-induced diabetes and reactive hypoglycemia (see Chapter 41). Autonomic disturbances have also been hypothesized to be a cause of obesity in some people.

tified a number of "centers" for micturation, respiration (see Chapter 40), and other autonomic functions in the medulla oblongata and pons.

Other work has implicated the **hypothalamus** in even more extensively coordinated and crosslinked autonomic patterns. This work led to the concept of the hypothalamus as the "head ganglion" of the autonomic nervous system. Following an earlier application of electrical stimulation to the hypothalamus by Karplus and Kreidl, Walter Hess found that focal electrical stimulation of regions of the hypothalamus elicited coordinated patterns of sympathetic and parasympathetic adjustments (e.g., changes in pupil size, piloerection, and respiration) and affective responses that were appropriate to behavioral responses elicited from the same loci. Although Hess claimed that specific medial-to-lateral zones of the hypothalamus could be considered predominantly sympathetic or parasympathetic, most work has indicated that hypothalamic and other central sites influence autonomic outflows and coordinate synergy of the two limbs of the ANS. In fact, central manipulations that affect autonomic function seem invariably to produce adjustments of both SNS and PNS outputs, an observation that underscores the integrative role the brain plays in ANS function.

Brain lesions in virtually all limbic system regions, and notably in the septal area, amygdala, hippocampus, frontal cortex, cingulate cortex, and insular cortex, have been shown to exaggerate, dissociate, blunt, or in other ways distort autonomic responses to environmental situations.

Tracing Experiments and Anatomical Mapping Have Revealed Multiple Hierarchically Organized, Reciprocally Interconnected Stations of the Neuraxis That Control Autonomic Activity

As neuroscience tracing tools have become more powerful, they have revealed the extensive hierarchical autonomic circuitry linking visceral afferent inputs with autonomic efferent outflows, linking the SNS and PNS divisions of the ANS, and interconnecting the central autonomic stations with somatic and endocrine pathways in the brain See Box 38.5.[33–36] This central autonomic circuitry has been considered a "central visceromotor system"[37] or a "**central autonomic network.**"[38] This network was first revealed through application of selective brain lesions and early degeneration protocols, including the Glees and variations of the Nauta staining techniques. These degeneration studies revealed a network of multisynaptic relays descending from the hypothalamus and midbrain to preganglionic neurons in the brainstem and spinal cord. Similar projections, both direct and relayed through the hypothalamus, were also found for a number of limbic system nuclei, including most prominently the amygdala.[37] Neural tracers, immunocytochemical techniques, and electron microscopy have subsequently increased the resolution of the maps of this circuitry and its transmitters.[38]

For example, newer neuronal tracing techniques and immunocytochemistry have delineated a more extensive hierarchy of descending projections to the autonomic preganglionic nuclei of the lower brainstem and spinal cord. Such experiments have established that the paraventricular nucleus of the hypothalamus (see Chapter 37)[39] is a prototype of extensive and profound central autonomic coordination. Parvocellular neurons in the paraventricular nucleus project monosynaptically to vagal preganglionic neurons in the dorsal motor nucleus of the vagus and sympathetic preganglionics in the intermediolateral column of the spinal cord.[40–42] The paraventricular nucleus also projects to the visceral afferent relay nuclei associated with each of these efferent outflows (the nucleus of the solitary tract and spinal lamina V, respectively). These descending projections influence several cardiovascular

BOX 38.5

CENTRAL ANS CIRCUITS MAY INTEGRATE AUTONOMIC REFLEXES WITH AFFECTIVE OR EMOTIONAL RESPONSES, AS WELL AS WITH SOMATIC RESPONSES

In addition to its many other roles, the ANS has frequently been postulated to participate in emotion and motivation. Even the name of the first of the ANS division to be distinguished, i.e., the sympathetic, connotes an empathetic operation. More important, the central role that the limbic system plays in the hierarchical control of autonomic activity, as well as in affective responses, supports the hypothesis that the autonomic nervous system may have a pivotal role in emotional functions.

In one of the seminal early neurobiological explanations of emotion, the autonomic nervous system was proposed to be the substrate. Consider the fight-or-flight example that Cannon used in his characterizations of autonomic adjustments and that was discussed earlier in this chapter: The somatic and autonomic adjustments in a fight-or-flight situation contain elements we associate with anger or fear. The central relays, including the limbic circuitry just discussed, are important in organizing the autonomic components of these responses to external environmental stimuli and in coordinating them with the appropriate somatic responses. Thus, the central ANS circuitry may be involved in the *expression* of emotional reactions. Some have hypothesized that besides being involved in the expression of emotions, the ANS might be involved in the *experience* of emotions. The classic theory of this type was suggested independently by James[33] and Lange,[34] who speculated that afferent experience resulting from autonomic adjustments might be the basis of emotional experiences. For the fight-or-flight example, the James–Lange idea could be considered the proposition that "you do not run because you are afraid; you are afraid because you run." Cannon[35] offered an influential refutation of the James–Lange theory, but most of his argument was based on now outmoded ideas about the ANS.

In an experiment designed to examine the James–Lange idea, Hohmann[36] surveyed army veterans who had sustained spinal cord injuries at different levels. For self-reported experiences of both fear and anger, Hohmann found that the higher the spinal cord lesions (and thus the more of the visceral afferent inflow disconnected from the brain), the greater the reduction in affective experiences.

and gastrointestinal responses. Illustrating the extent of the central integration of responses, the additional neurons of the paraventricular nucleus control corticotropin-releasing factor and oxytocin neuron responses, which are often activated or modulated in association with autonomic functions.

Most mesencephalic, diencephalic, and telencephalic nuclei considered part of the limbic system affect visceral motor outflows and can be included in the concept of the central visceromotor system. In addition to the central gray and paramedian regions of the mesencephalon and the entire hypothalamus, including the preoptic hypothalamus, these limbic sites include the amygdala, bed nucleus of the stria terminalis, septal region, hippocampus, cingulate cortex, orbital frontal cortex, and insular and rhinal cortexes.

Summary

Although still autonomous and subconscious, multiple central structures of the subcortical and diencephalic hierarchies can impose special controls over the autonomic nervous system when required.

In addition to sending descending projections, the CNS sites constituting the hierarchy of autonomic circuitry receive, reciprocally, ascending visceral afferent inputs from the medullary (nucleus of the solitary tract) and spinal (lamina V) relays. For example, the second- and higher order neurons of the nucleus of the solitary tract project, by way of a relay in the pontine parabrachial nucleus (and in some cases monosynaptically), to the midbrain central gray, the lateral hypothalamus, the hypothalamic paraventricular nucleus, the amygdala, and the bed nucleus of the stria terminalis. Ascending connections from the spinal visceral afferents converge on many of these same stations.

A network of hierarchically organized central stations, many of them part of the limbic system, forms a central visceral neuroaxis that receives inputs from visceral afferents and issues descending projections to the ANS preganglionic neurons in the brainstem and spinal cord. This central autonomic circuitry organizes and sequences sets of separate autonomic reflexes, coordinates SNS and PNS responses so that they are synergistic, cross-links autonomic and skeletal responses, and integrates autonomic activity with ongoing and anticipated behavior of the individual.

PERSPECTIVE: FUTURE OF THE AUTONOMIC NERVOUS SYSTEM

Our understanding of the autonomic nervous system is still incomplete and evolving,[1,43] driven by the technological improvements in neuroscience. Modern techniques (e.g., molecular biology, immunocytochemistry, electron microscopy) are changing the definition of the autonomic nervous system initially derived with the techniques available to Langley and his contemporaries at the beginning of the 20th century (see Box 38.1). The distinction that sympathetic postganglionic neurons are noradrenergic whereas parasympathetic postganglionics are cholinergic has been blurred by the recognition of nonadrenergic noncholinergic (NANC) neurons, nitric oxide synthetase (NOS)-containing neurons, a large number of colocalized and coreleased neuropeptides, postganglionic neurons changing their neurotransmitter phenotypes, and other exceptions that broaden the view developed by Langley's pharmacological studies. The canon that the ANS is strictly a motor system without an afferent counterpart is challenged by many who argue on functional and molecular biological grounds that many "visceral afferents" belong to the ANS (see Box 38.3). The proposal that functional differences between the two limbs of the ANS can be attributed to their contrasting patterns of projection (the sympathetic system preganglionics projecting to postganglionics in a one-to-many pattern; the parasympathetic system projecting in a one-to-few pattern) has not been substantiated by modern analyses of divergence.[16] Continued application of modern technologies and the prospect of continuing developments promise to define an autonomic nervous system quite different from that of Langley.

The autonomic nervous system is the neural circuitry that maintains homeostasis and overall health. It is responsible for the neural components of Cannon's "wisdom of the body." With its sophisticated motor repertoire and complexes of reflexes—including local axon reflexes, segmental or oligosynaptic reflexes, and polysynaptic suprasegmental cascades—the ANS works continuously to adjust and defend the body's physiology. The importance of these processes was summarized succinctly by Nauta and Feirtag,[44] who wrote: "Life depends on the innervation of the viscera; in a way all the rest is biological luxury." The processes go on, for the most part, without awareness or cognitive representations. This automaticity is presumably crucial to the successful operation of the ANS and certainly frees the individual from bodily housekeeping tasks, thereby making it practical to focus on other activities and inputs from the environment.

The hub of the ANS consists of two separate motor outflows, each a hierarchical organization with preganglionic neurons stationed in the CNS and postganglionic neurons located in peripheral ganglia. The sympathetic, or thoracolumbar, division facilitates the mobilization of energy, increases catabolism, and promotes physiological responses that support activity, including emergency responses such as "fight" or "flight." The parasympathetic, or craniosacral, division facilitates conservation of energy, increases anabolism, and supports physiological responses that typically promote rest, digestion, and restoration of body reserves. The adrenergic phenotype of sympathetic postganglionic neurons, the cholinergic phenotype of parasympathetic neurons, and distinguishing complements of neuropeptides and receptor specializations provide neurochemical coding for the two divisions of the ANS.

The motor outflows of the ANS are efferent limbs of reflexes triggered by visceral and, in some cases, somatic afferents. These reflex circuits have second-order visceral afferent nuclei located adjacent to spinal and medullary nuclei of preganglionic motor neurons (laminae I and V and the nucleus of the solitary tract, respectively).

Higher order CNS circuitry, including the hypothalamus, limbic system, and a variety of cortical sites, provides hierarchical control and integration of autonomic reflexes. This hierarchy is responsible for coordinating different autonomic reflexes, integrating autonomic function with somatic activity, and executing response programs that anticipate needs and regulate physiology over more extended time scales than those represented by isolated reflexes.

References

General

Appenzeller, O. (1976). *The Autonomic Nervous System*, 2nd ed. North-Holland Publ./American Elsevier, New York.

Barraco, I. R. A., ed. (1994). *Nucleus of the Solitary Tract.* CRC Press, Boca Raton, FL.

Björklund, A., Hökfelt, T., and Owman, C., eds. (1988). *Handbook of Chemical Neuroanatomy,* Vol. 6. Elsevier Science Publishers, Amsterdam.

Burnstock, G., (1992–1997). *The Autonomic Nervous System*, Vols. 1–7. Harwood Academic Publishers, Chur, Switzerland.

Cannon, W. B. (1939). *The Wisdom of the Body,* 2nd ed. Norton, New York.

Gabella, G. (1976). *Structure of the Autonomic Nervous System.* Chapman & Hall, London.

Hockman, C. H., ed. (1972). *Limbic System Mechanisms and Autonomic Function.* Thomas, Springfield, IL.

Kuntz, A. (1953). *The Autonomic Nervous System,* 4th ed. Lea & Febiger, Philadelphia.

Loewy, A. D., and Spyer, K. M., eds. (1990). *Central Regulation of Autonomic Functions.* Oxford University Press, New York.

Pick, J. (1970). *The Autonomic Nervous System.* Lippincott, Philadelphia.

Ritter, S., Ritter, R. C., and Barnes, C. D., eds. (1992). *Neuroanatomy and Physiology of Abdominal Vagal Afferents.* CRC Press, Boca Raton, FL.

Willis, W. D., Jr., and Coggeshall, R. E. (1991). *Sensory Mechanisms of the Spinal Cord,* 2nd ed. Plenum, New York.

Cited

1. Sheehan, D. (1936). Discovery of the autonomic nervous system. *Arch. Neurol. Psychiatry* **35:** 1081–1115.
2. Langley, J. N. (1898). On the union of cranial autonomic (visceral) fibres with the nerve cells of the superior cervical ganglion. *J. Physiol. (London)* **23:** 240–270.
3. Cannon, W. B. (1939). *The Wisdom of the Body*, 2nd ed. Norton, New York.
4. Appenzeller, O. (1976). *The Autonomic Nervous System*, 2nd ed. North-Holland Publ./American Elsevier, New York.
5. Bannister, R. (1989). *Autonomic Failure. A Textbook of Clinical Disorders of the Autonomic Nervous System*, 2nd ed. Oxford Medical Publications, Oxford, UK.
6. Thomas, L. (1974). Autonomy. *The Lives of a Cell*, pp. 64–68. Viking Press, New York.
7. Langley, J. N. (1981). *The Autonomic Nervous System*, Part I. Heffer, Cambridge, UK.
8. Cabot, J. B. (1990). Sympathetic preganglionic neurons: Cytoarchitecture, ultrastructure, and biophysical properties. In *Central Regulation of Autonomic Functions* (A. D. Loewy and K. M. Spyer, eds.), pp. 44–67. Oxford University Press, New York.
9. Strack, A. M., Sawyer, W. B., Marubio, L. M., and Loewy, A. D. (1988). Spinal origin of sympathetic preganglionic neurons in the rat. *Brain Res.* **455:** 187–191.
10. Burnstock, G. (1969). Evolution of the autonomic innervation of visceral and cardiovascular systems in vertebrates. *Pharmacol. Rev.* **21:** 247–324.
11. Pick, J. (1970). *The Autonomic Nervous System.* Lippincott, Philadelphia.
12. Bieger, D., and Hopkins, D. A. (1987). Viscerotopic representation of the upper alimentary tract in the medulla oblongata in the rat: Nucleus ambiguus. *J. Comp. Neurol.* **262:** 546–562.
13. Fox, E. A., and Powley, T. L. (1992). Morphology of identified preganglionic neurons in the dorsal motor nucleus of the vagus. *J. Comp. Neurol.* **322:** 79–98.
14. Shapiro, R. E., and Miselis, R. R. (1985). The central organization of the vagus nerve innervating the stomach of the rat. *J. Comp. Neurol.* **238:** 473–488.
15. Karczmar, A. G., Koketsu, K., and Nishi, S., eds. (1986). *Autonomic and Enteric Ganglia: Transmission and its Pharmacology.* Plenum, New York.
16. Wang, F. B., Holst, M.-C., and Powley, T. L. (1995). The ratio of pre- to postganglionic neurons and related issues in the autonomic nervous system. *Brain Res. Rev.* **21:** 93–115.
17. Wood, J. D. (1987). Physiology of the enteric nervous system. In *Physiology of the Gastrointestinal Tract* (L. R. Johnson, J. Christensen, M. J. Jackson, E. D. Jacobson, and J. H. Walsh, eds.), 2nd ed., Vol. 1, pp. 67–110. Raven Press, New York.
18. Dale, H. H. (1914). The action of certain esters and ethers of choline, and their relation to muscarine. *J. Pharmacol. Exp. Ther.* **6:** 147–190.
19. Dale, H. H. (1935). Pharmacology and nerve endings. *Proc. R. Soc. London., Ser. B* **28:** 319–332.
20. Björklund, A., Hökfelt, T., and Owman, C., eds. (1988). *Handbook of Chemical Neuroanatomy,* Vol. 6. Elsevier Science Publishers, Amsterdam.
21. Lundberg, J. (1996). Pharmacology of cotransmission in the autonomic nervous system: Integrative aspects on amines, neuropeptides, adenosine triphosphate, amino acids and nitric oxide. *Pharmacol. Rev.* **48:** 113–178.
22. Patterson, P. H., and Chun, L. L. Y. (1977). The induction of acetylcholine synthesis in primary cultures of dissociated rat sympathetic neurons. I. Effects of conditioned medium. *Dev. Biol.* **56:** 263–280.

23. Potter, D. D., Landis, S. C., and Furshpan, E. J. (1980). Dual function during development of rat sympathetic neurones in culture. *J. Exp. Biol.* **89:** 57–71.
24. Landis, S. C., and Keefe, D. (1983). Evidence for transmitter plasticity *in vivo*: Developmental changes in properties of cholinergic sympathetic neurons. *Dev. Biol.* **98:** 349–372.
25. Black, I. B., Adler, J. E., and La Gamma, E. F. (1988). Neurotransmitter plasticity in the peripheral nervous system. In *Handbook of Chemical Neuroanatomy* (A. Björklund, T. Hökfelt, and C. Owman, eds.), Vol. 6, pp. 51–64. Elsevier Science Publishers, Amsterdam.
26. Prechtl, J. C., and Powley, T. L. (1990). B-afferents: A fundamental division of the nervous system mediating homeostasis? *Behav. Brain Sci.* **13:** 289–331.
27. Cervero, F., and Foreman, R. D. (1990). Sensory innervation of the viscera. In *Central Regulation of Autonomic Functions* (A. D. Loewy and K. M. Spyer, eds.), pp. 104–125. Oxford University Press, New York.
28. de Groat, W. C., and Steers, W. D. (1990). Autonomic regulation of the urinary bladder and sexual organs. In *Central Regulation of Autonomic Functions* (A. D. Loewy and K. M. Spyer, eds.). Oxford University Press, New York.
29. Morgan, C., Nadelhaft, I., and de Groat, W. C. (1981). The distribution of visceral primary afferents from the pelvic nerve within Lissaure's tract and the spinal gray matter and its relationship to the sacral parasympathetic nucleus. *J. Comp. Neurol.* **201:** 415–440.
30. Roppolo, J. R., Nadelhaft, I., and de Groat, W. C. (1985). The organization of pudendal motoneurons and primary afferent projections in the spinal cord of the rhesus monkey revealed by horseradish peroxidase. *J. Comp. Neurol.* **234:** 457–488.
31. Dembowsky, K., Czachurski, J., and Seller, H. (1985). Morphology of sympathetic preganglionic neurons in the thoracic spinal cord of the cat: An intracellular horseradish peroxidase study. *J. Comp. Neurol.* **238:** 453–465.
32. Jänig, W. (1996). Neurobiology of visceral afferent neurons: Neuroanatomy, functions, organ regulations and sensations. *Biol. Psychol.* **42:** 29–51.
33. James, W. (1884). What is an emotion? *Mind* **9:** 188–205.
34. Lange, C. (1885). *Ohne leudsbeveegelser* (I. A. Haupt, transl.). In *The Emotions* (K. Dunlap, ed). Williams & Wilkins, Baltimore, MD, 1922.
35. Cannon, W. B. (1927). The James-Lange theory of emotion: A critical examination and an alternative theory. *Am. J. Psychol.* **39:** 106–124.
36. Hohmann, G. W. (1962). Some effects of spinal cord lesions on experienced emotional feelings. *Psychophysiology* **3:** 143–156.
37. Nauta, W. J. H. (1972). The central visceromotor system: A general survey. In *Limbic System Mechanisms and Autonomic Function* (C. H. Hockman, ed.), pp. 21–40. Thomas, Springfield, IL.
38. Loewy, A. D. (1981). Descending pathways to sympathetic and parasympathetic preganglionic neurons. *J. Auton. Nerv. Syst.* **3:** 265–275.
39. Sawchenko, P. E. (1983). Central connections of the sensory and motor nuclei of the vagus nerve. *J. Auton. Nerv. Syst.* **9:** 13–26.
40. Sofroniew, M. V., and Schrell, U. (1981). Evidence for a direct projection from oxytocin and vasopressin neurons in the hypothalamic paraventricular nucleus to the medulla oblongata: Immunohistochemical visualization of both the horseradish peroxidase transported and the peptide produced by the same neurons. *Neurosci. Lett.* **22:** 211–217.
41. Sawchenko, P. E., and Swanson, L. W. (1982). Immunohistochemical identification of neurons in the paraventricular nucleus of the hypothalamus that project to the medulla or to the spinal cord in the rat. *J. Comp. Neurol.* **205:** 260–272.
42. Hornby, P. J., and Piekut, D. T. (1988). Anatomical evidence for interaction of $ACTH^{1-39}$ immunostained fibers and hypothalamic paraventricular neurons that project to the dorsal vagal complex. *Histochemistry* **90:** 201–206.
43. Brooks, C. McM. (1983). Newer concepts of the autonomic system's role derived from reductionist and behavioral studies of various animal species. *J. Auton. Nerv. Syst.* **7:** 199–212.
44. Nauta, W. J. H., and Feirtag, M. (1986). *Fundamental Neuroanatomy.* Freeman, New York.

CHAPTER

39

Cardiovascular System

Alan F. Sved

Several general principles of homeostatic or autonomic neural control systems are illustrated by the central and peripheral autonomic neural control of cardiovascular function. In this chapter, we describe the role of the nervous system in cardiovascular regulation, highlighting key points typical of neural control of homeostatic systems.

BASICS OF CARDIOVASCULAR PHYSIOLOGY

Pipes, Pumps, and Pressure Allow Perfusion of Tissues

The goal of the cardiovascular system is to adequately perfuse all tissues in the body with blood. To attain this goal the cardiovascular system must be able to adapt to a variety of circumstances ranging from rest, when blood flow is greatest to brain, kidneys, skin, and abdominal viscera; to exercise, when blood flow to the skeletal muscles is increased markedly; to hemorrhage, when blood volume is pooled in the central circulation at the expense of skeletal muscles, skin, and intestines.

The output of the pumping heart and the resistance of vessels to blood flow are the two factors that contribute to tissue perfusion, the supply of blood to the tissue per unit of time. **Cardiac output,** the amount of blood the heart pumps each minute, is influenced by the speed and force with which the heart beats and the pressure at which blood is supplied to the heart (cardiac filling pressure). The second factor, the resistance of vessels to blood flow, relates to the diameter of precapillary arterioles. Heart rate, cardiac filling pressure, and vascular resistance are all regulated by the nervous system.

The product of cardiac output and the resistance provided by the vasculature is arterial blood pressure. Arterial pressure fluctuates with each heart beat. It is lowest during filling of the heart's ventricles (**ventricular diastole**) and highest during ventricular contraction (**systole**). In humans, a normal systolic pressure is approximately 120 mm Hg, whereas a normal diastolic pressure is approximately 80 mm Hg. Throughout the day, blood pressure fluctuates according to the physiological and behavioral status of the organism. The importance of normal cardiovascular regulation is highlighted by the serious problems that can result from chronically elevated blood pressure (**hypertension**), for example, stroke, renal disease, and heart attack (see Box 39.1). Low blood pressure (**hypotension**) can also cause problems, such as fainting or light-headedness due to inadequate perfusion of the brain.

The pressure of blood on the venous side of the circulation is much lower than that on the arterial side. Venous and arterial pressures differ because the resistance to flow is much lower in veins than in arterioles. Veins are compliant, so they stretch to accommodate varying volumes of blood and provide little additional resistance to flow despite large volumes. Nevertheless, venous pressure is of critical importance in determining cardiac filling pressure, and therefore cardiac output. Although venous pressure largely reflects blood volume, neurally mediated changes in venous compliance also influence venous pressure.[1]

Outputs of the Brain Influence the Pipes and Pump

The nervous system affects the cardiovascular system by influencing cardiac output and vascular resistance. Control of the heart and blood vessels by the autonomic nervous system is especially powerful. As

BOX 39.1

HYPERTENSION AND THE CENTRAL NEURAL CONTROL OF CARDIOVASCULAR FUNCTION

Hypertension, or chronically elevated blood pressure, is an important risk factor for cardiovascular disease. Epidemiological data indicate that hypertension, typically defined as systolic pressure >140 mm Hg or diastolic pressure >90 mm Hg, increases the risk of myocardial infarction (heart attack), stroke, congestive heart failure, and renal disease. An estimated 43 million adults in the United States, or approximately a quarter of the adult population, has hypertension.

Despite the incidence of hypertension, the cause—or more appropriately, causes—of hypertension remains unknown. In less than 10% of cases, hypertension is clearly secondary to some other condition, such as kidney damage. In the remainder of the cases, no specific cause can be identified; this is primary, or essential, hypertension. Genetic and environmental factors certainly contribute to the development of hypertension, and given the redundancy of cardiovascular control mechanisms, the etiology of most hypertension is likely multifactorial.

Obviously, hypertension is a major health concern. Lowering blood pressure of hypertensive individuals reduces the risk of cardiovascular disease. Blood pressure can be lowered by a variety of nonpharmacological treatments (e.g., weight reduction, sodium restriction, regular exercise, smoking cessation), as well as by pharmacological intervention. Drugs used to treat hypertension target the systems that control blood pressure; thus, they include direct-acting vasodilators, inhibitors of the renin–angiotensin system, diuretics, and inhibitors of sympathetically mediated vasoconstriction.

Drugs that act in the CNS to inhibit sympathetic vasomotor outflow are also used to treat hypertension. Indeed, the appreciation that the antihypertensive drugs clonidine and α-methyl DOPA act in the CNS to lower blood pressure has been a major impetus for studies on the central neural control of cardiovascular function. This line of thought has also led to the hypothesis that hypertension, at least in some cases, may result from a central neural dysfunction. Inasmuch as the CNS is known to control skeletal muscle function, and movement disorders (e.g., Parkinson disease) have been related to specific CNS dysfunctions, some CNS abnormality might affect the control of vascular muscle tone and blood pressure.

Our understanding of the role of the CNS in hypertension has benefited greatly from studies of hypertensive animals. The CNS exerts powerful control over the cardiovascular system, and experimental manipulations within the CNS can produce profound increases in arterial pressure. For example, destruction of the NST or CVLM produce acute and severe hypertension in experimental animals. These responses can also be elicited by more selective pharmacological alteration of neurotransmitter mechanisms in these regions. In addition, certain forms of experimental hypertension are associated with changes in the synthesis, release, and receptor binding of specific neurotransmitters in specific CNS regions. For example, in rat models of hypertension, catecholamine synthesis is altered in several sites of the brain.

The most widely studied animal model of hypertension is the spontaneously hypertensive rat, a strain of rat that develops hypertension with age. This rat strain was developed by successively mating males and females with the highest blood pressures.[31] Although whether this model will shed light on the cause of hypertension in humans is not clear, this strain has been extremely useful in the study of antihypertensive drugs. Another inbred rat strain, the Dahl salt-sensitive rate, develops hypertension only when placed on a diet with a high salt content, and therefore provides a model of salt-sensitive hypertension.

---

described in Chapter 38, the heart is innervated by sympathetic and parasympathetic divisions of the autonomic nervous system. These two systems have antagonistic actions on cardiac function: Increased parasympathetic tone decreases heart rate and contractile force and thus decreases cardiac output. In contrast, increased sympathetic tone increases heart rate and contractile force and thus increases cardiac output.

In contrast to the dual innervation of the heart, blood vessels are innervated only by the sympathetic nervous system. This innervation is directed primarily at the precapillary arterioles, which are the main source of vascular resistance. Typically, the action of the sympathetic nervous system causes arterioles to constrict, thereby increasing resistance and central arterial blood pressure. Regional vascular resistances are adjusted by the selective regulation of sympathetic vasoconstrictor nerves that project to different tissues. Although in his classical formulation of the sympathetic nervous system Walter B. Cannon considered the sympathetic nervous system to be regulated as a unit, discrete and selective regulation seems to be more the rule.[2]

In certain tissues, most notably skeletal muscle, sympathetic nerves can promote vasodilation, with an accompanying increase in blood flow to that tissue, instead of the usual sympathetically mediated vasoconstriction. In some species (e.g., cat) this vasodilation is the result of sympathetic nerves that release acetylcholine instead of norepinephrine. However, these vasodilatory responses more often result from differences in the density of norepinephrine receptor subtypes on the vasculature: Stimulation of α-adrenergic receptors leads to vasoconstriction, and stimulation of β-adrenergic receptors leads to vasodilation.

In addition to direct innervation of the heart and vasculature, the sympathetic nervous system influences the cardiovascular system via a blood-borne, endocrine route. Chromaffin cells in the adrenal medulla in many ways can be considered sympathetic postganglionic neurons that release catecholamines into the circulation, rather than at a neuroeffector junction. Adrenal chromaffin cells are directly innervated by preganglionic sympathetic neurons, and this innervation controls the release of catecholamines from the adrenal gland into the blood stream. Catecholamines released into the circulation have access to sympathetic neuroeffector junctions and thus are capable of eliciting sympathetic-like responses. Because the adrenal chromaffin cells release more epinephrine than norepinephrine, and β-adrenergic receptors are more sensitive to epinephrine than to norepinephrine, sympathetically evoked responses that are mediated by β-adrenergic receptors are more sensitive than α-adrenergic receptor-mediated responses to adrenal regulation. Thus, because the heart and arterioles in skeletal muscle contain β-adrenergic receptors, whereas arterioles in other tissues have primarily α-adrenergic receptors, stimulation of the adrenal medulla increases heart rate and skeletal muscle vasodilation more potently than it does vasoconstriction.

The sympathetic nervous system also influences other endocrine systems that affect the cardiovascular system. For example, increased sympathetic outflow acts on β-adrenergic receptors in the kidney, causing the kidney to release **renin** into the blood stream. Renin is an enzyme that catalyzes the generation of **angiotensin,** a potent vasoactive peptide. Angiotensin produces vasoconstriction by direct action on angiotensin receptors located on blood vessels. Angiotensin also promotes vasoconstriction indirectly, by acting on postganglionic sympathetic nerve terminals to enhance norepinephrine release. In addition, circulating angiotensin acts at the area postrema and subfornical organ within the brain to increase sympathetic outflow. Thus, angiotensin increases arterial pressure in a variety of ways (Fig. 39.1).

The central nervous system can also influence the cardiovascular system independent of the autonomic nervous system. In the posterior pituitary, **vasopressin** is released into the circulation by the terminals of magnocellular hypothalamic neurons. This hormone acutely influences blood pressure by directly acting on arteriolar V_1 vasopressin receptors to elicit vasoconstriction. Circulating vasopressin also acts on the central nervous system (CNS) to potentiate the baroreceptor reflex (described later). In addition, this hormone acts on V_2 vasopressin receptors in the kidney to induce antidiuresis (see Chapter 42).

In addition to endocrine outputs of the CNS, behavioral responses must be considered. For example, water and salt intakes are essential in maintaining blood volume. In response to hypovolemia, water and salt are consumed to create fluid replacement (see Chapter 42). Lying down in response to feeling dizzy is behavioral compensation for inadequate blood flow to the head. Lying down decreases the pooling of venous flow in the lower limbs, thereby increasing cardiac filling and thus enhancing cardiac output and cerebral blood flow.

Summary

The nervous system clearly influences the cardiovascular system. Although the autonomic nervous system may play the major role in neural regulation of the cardiovascular system, other endocrine and behavioral responses arising from the central nervous system also contribute. Cardiovascular regulation should be considered an integrated response involving neural, endocrine, and behavioral outputs of the nervous system (Fig. 39.2). Thus, for example, the response to hypovolemic hypotension includes an increase in sympathetic neural activity to promote vasoconstriction and thereby increase blood pressure, an increase in the release of vasopressin to cause vasoconstriction and renal water conservation, and an increase in water and salt intake to restore the fluid deficit. This multiplicity of outputs provides backup mechanisms when one or more responses are compromised. Such redundancy of control mechanisms appears to be a general characteristic of the central neural regulation of homeostatic processes.

SYMPATHETIC VASOMOTOR TONE

Direct innervation of arterioles allows the sympathetic nervous system to substantially influence the

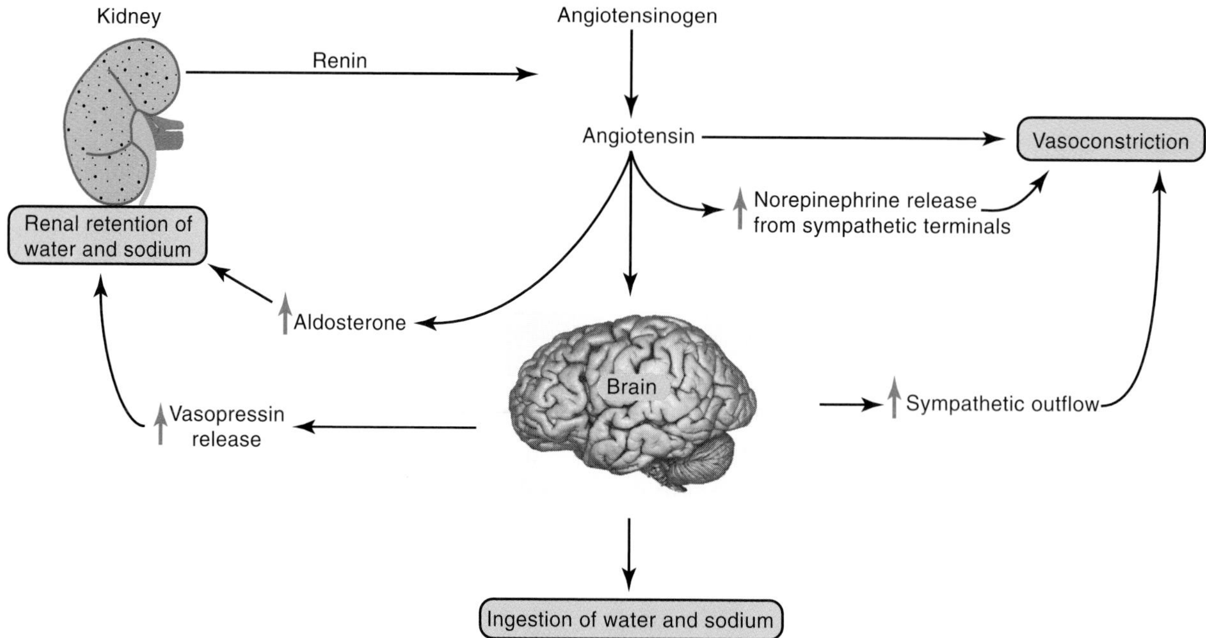

FIGURE 39.1 The renin–angiotensin system increases blood pressure by several mechanisms. Renin released by the kidneys catalyzes the production of angiotensin in the blood. Angiotensin increases blood pressure by constricting blood vessels and increasing blood volume: It acts on arterioles to cause vasoconstriction; promotes norepinephrine release from sympathetic nerve terminals and thereby potentiates sympathetically evoked vasoconstriction; and acts on the adrenal cortex to stimulate secretion of aldosterone and thereby promote retention of sodium. Angiotensin also acts on the brain to increase sympathetic neural activity, which causes vasoconstriction; to increase the secretion of vasopressin, which enhances water retention; and to increase the consumption of water and sodium chloride. These responses are adaptively coordinated because they are stimulated by the same signal.

cardiovascular system. Stimulation of sympathetic outflow can constrict blood vessels and increase arterial blood pressure to more than 200 mm Hg. Sympathetic nerves are normally active in the resting animal and therefore provide tonic vasoconstriction. This sympathetic vasomotor tone is demonstrated by pharmacologic blockade of the sympathetic nervous system: Vascular resistance decreases and arterial pressure rapidly falls from a mean of approximately 100 mm Hg to one of 60 mm Hg (see Fig. 39.3).[3] Basal vasomotor tone allows vascular resistance to be modulated up or down by changes in sympathetic activity.

The existence of basal sympathetic activity raises questions of where and how it is generated. Classically, the question of where this basal sympathetic drive is generated has been addressed by disrupting the sympathetic nervous system at successively higher levels of the neuraxis. Such experiments, originally performed in the middle of the 19th century by Claude Bernard, demonstrated that transection of the spinal cord near its junction with the brainstem results in the same decrease in arterial pressure that occurs with pharmacological inhibition of the sympathetic nerves, indicating that the source of basal sympathetic drive is supraspinal.

In experiments performed in Carl Ludwig's laboratory in the 1870s, blood pressure was maintained throughout increasingly caudal transections of the brain until the transections reached the medulla. These observations indicated that the neural circuitry necessary for maintenance of basal sympathetic vasomotor tone resides completely in the caudal brainstem. By making more discrete knife cuts through the rabbit medulla, Dittmar[4] identified an area in the ventral portion of the medulla just caudal to the facial nucleus that was necessary for the maintenance of normal resting blood pressure. Alexander[5] later showed that electrical stimulation of this region elicited increases in blood pressure and sympathetic nerve activity. However, the notion that a region of the rostral ventral medulla is essential for the maintenance of basal sympathetic vasomotor outflow received little attention until rediscovered by Feldberg and Guertzenstein[6] a century after Dittmar's experiments. These investigators found that when the neuroinhibitory amino acid glycine or the anesthetic pentobarbital was applied to a discrete site

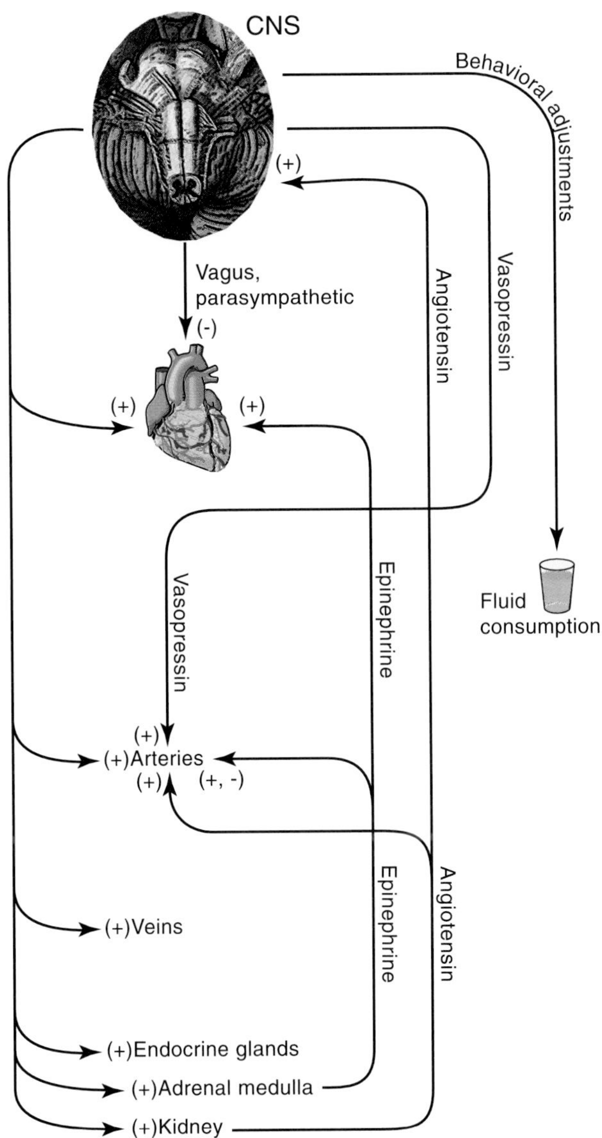

FIGURE 39.2 Neural, endocrine, and behavioral outputs of the brain influence the cardiovascular system. Sympathetic neural outflow increases heart rate, constricts blood vessels, and stimulates the release of epinephrine and renin into the blood; all these responses increase blood pressure. Circulating epinephrine increases heart rate and causes blood vessels to constrict or dilate, depending on the receptors present on the blood vessel. Angiotensin, generated by renin released from the kidney, causes vasoconstriction and acts on the brain to increase secretion of vasopressin and intake of fluid (see Fig. 39.1). The brain controls heart rate through parasympathetic output of the vagus nerve.

on the ventral surface of the cat rostral medulla, a large decrease in arterial pressure ensued.

More recent experiments aimed at precise localization of the source of supraspinal input providing basal tone to sympathetic vasomotor neurons have been guided by neuroanatomical studies of brainstem sites that project to regions of the spinal cord containing sympathetic preganglionic neurons. Such investigations have identified an area in the **rostral ventrolateral medulla** (RVLM) as the site responsible for basal drive of sympathetic vasomotor neurons.[7] As shown in Fig. 39.3, localized injection of glutamate and other excitative substances markedly increases blood pressure, whereas injection of inhibitory substances such as γ-aminobutyric acid (GABA) decreases arterial pressure to the same degree that spinal cord transection does.[3,8] Some investigators question whether all tonic supraspinal drive of sympathetic vasomotor tone emanates from this area,[9] because in some experiments, apparently total inhibition of the RVLM does not reduce arterial pressure to the same extent as total sympathetic blockade. Resolution of this issue requires a more complete understanding of the specific population of RVLM neurons involved in basal sympathetic vasomotor tone.

The initial observations concerning the RVLM sparked great interest in the role of this region in cardiovascular control. As mentioned earlier, neurons in this region project to the spinal cord; many neurons directly innervate sympathetic preganglionic neurons in the intermediolateral cell column of the thoracic spinal cord.[10] This group of neurons is composed of a heterogeneous population based on firing properties, axonal conductance rates, neurotransmitters, and cell morphology.[7] Which neurons in the RVLM are involved in the supraspinal drive of basal sympathetic vasomotor tone remains unclear. As described later in more detail, the RVLM appears to be a site where numerous and varied influences on sympathetic vasomotor tone are integrated.

Summary

Peripheral sympathetic vasomotor fibers are constantly active, providing basal tone to arterioles, from which vascular resistance is further mediated up or down, as environmental requirements demand. The constant activity arises from neurons in the rostral ventrolateral medulla. Neurons from this location directly innervate spinal intermediolateral column sympathetic preganglionic neurons.

NEURAL CONTROL OF THE HEART

Heart rate is established by spontaneously depolarizing cells in the sinoatrial node, and it is modulated by parasympathetic and sympathetic neural activity at these pacemaker cells. These two functionally antagonistic sources of innervation provide a powerful dual

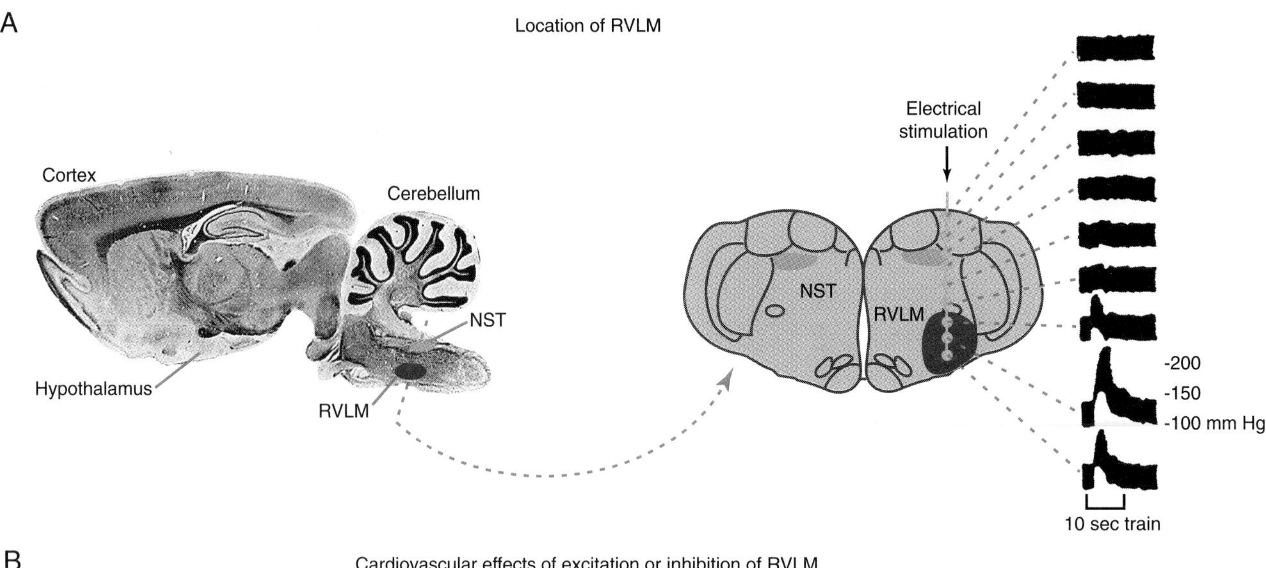

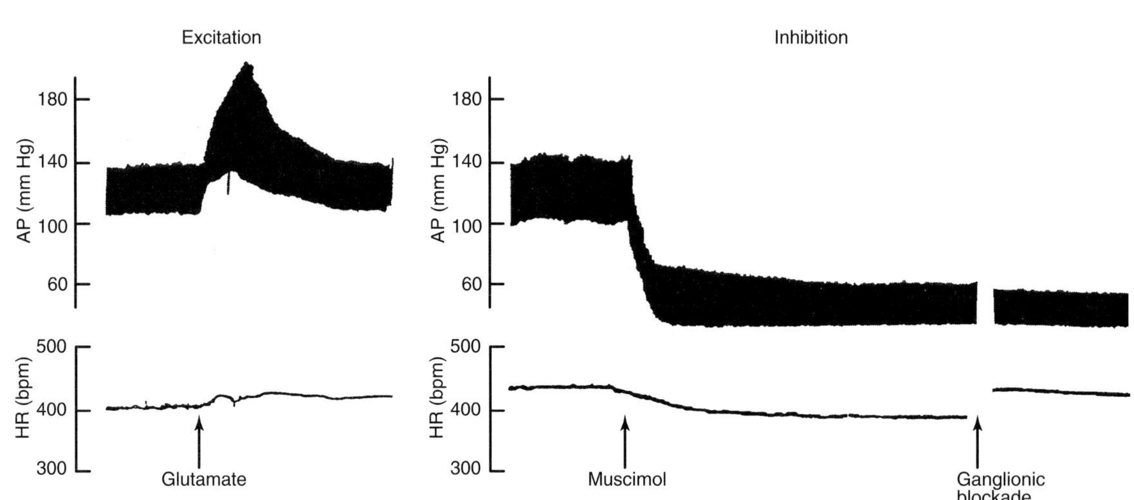

FIGURE 39.3 The rostral ventrolateral medulla (RVLM) plays a critical role in the maintenance of basal blood pressure. (A) The location of the region of the rostral ventral medulla in the rat that powerfully influences cardiovascular function. (B) The effects of specifically exciting or inhibiting the rostral ventrolateral medulla in an anesthetized rat. Note that inhibition decreases blood pressure to the same extent as total inhibition of the sympathetic nervous system. This figure is based on results of Ross *et al.*[3]

control system characteristic of most autonomically controlled systems (Chapter 38). Under basal resting conditions, parasympathetic tone predominates in the human heart, and therefore resting heart rate is lower than the intrinsic rate of the sinoatrial node. Heart rate can be increased either by reducing parasympathetic activity or by increasing sympathetic activity. Conversely, an increase in parasympathetic activity or a decrease in sympathetic activity will slow the heart. The functions of these divisions of the autonomic nervous system are integrated, and opposite changes in sympathetic and parasympathetic activity typically occur simultaneously to modulate heart rate.

Basal sympathetic drive to the heart, like sympathetic outflow to the vasculature, is known to emanate principally from the RVLM, although this tonic discharge of RVLM neurons is not fully understood. In the brainstem, parasympathetic preganglionic neurons that regulate the heart are tonically active *in vivo,* largely reflecting sensory afferent input from the cardiovascular and respiratory systems. Indeed, heart rate fluctuates in phase with breathing, as a result of changes in cardiac vagal activity.

Heart rate can also be powerfully influenced by higher levels of the neuraxis. Lethal cardiac arrhythmias can be elicited by stimulating certain diencephalic and telencephalic structures that influence autonomic nerves.[11]

Summary

Neural control of cardiac rate and contractility reflects continuous opposing effects of the sympathetic and parasympathetic innervation of the heart. Although parasympathetic tone generally predominates at rest, the rate of the cardiac cycle can be accelerated either by decreased parasympathetic or by increased sympathetic tone. Coordination of the cardiac cycle with respiration reflects central integration of cardiovascular and respiratory sensory information. Emotional conditions contribute higher level drive to central sympathetic centers.

CARDIOVASCULAR HOMEOSTASIS AND A NEGATIVE FEEDBACK REFLEX

Most homeostatic systems are mediated primarily by negative feedback reflexes. For the cardiovascular system, this negative feedback reflex is the **baroreceptor reflex.** As arterial blood pressure deviates from the set point, the baroreceptor reflex rapidly compensates for the change and thus maintains arterial pressure within a narrow normal range.

The afferent component of the baroreceptor reflex is derived from pressure-sensitive receptors associated with two major blood vessels: the **aortic arch** and the **carotid sinus** (Fig. 39.4). Blood pressures in these two vessels are critical, because they drive perfusion of the entire body and the brain, respectively. The afferents from the aortic arch baroreceptor form the aortic depressor nerve, which joins with the vagus nerve in the neck. The cell bodies of these afferents, as well as other vagal afferent fibers, are present in the **nodose ganglion.** The baroreceptor afferents from the carotid sinus, along with chemosensitive afferents from this region, form the carotid sinus nerve, which joins with the glossopharyngeal nerve. The cell bodies of these afferents, as well as other glossopharyngeal afferents, are present in the **petrosal ganglion.** These baroreceptor afferents all project to the dorsal medial medulla, where they terminate in a distinct region of the **nucleus of the solitary tract** (NST).

Baroreceptors are stretch receptors that are activated (and therefore fire more action potentials) when blood pressure increases and distends the walls of the blood vessels (Fig. 39.5).[12] As with other types of stretch receptors, the responses of these afferents adapt to prolonged stretch (Fig. 39.6). In the case of baroreceptors, this adaptation, or resetting, begins within minutes of a sustained change in blood pressure. Thus, baroreceptor afferents signal acute *changes* in pressure, rather than a specific pressure. Local and circulating factors, such as endothelin, also influence the firing rates of baroreceptor afferents.[13] These factors may be important in the role of the baroreceptor reflex in long-term regulation of arterial pressure.

The major efferents of the baroreceptor reflex are

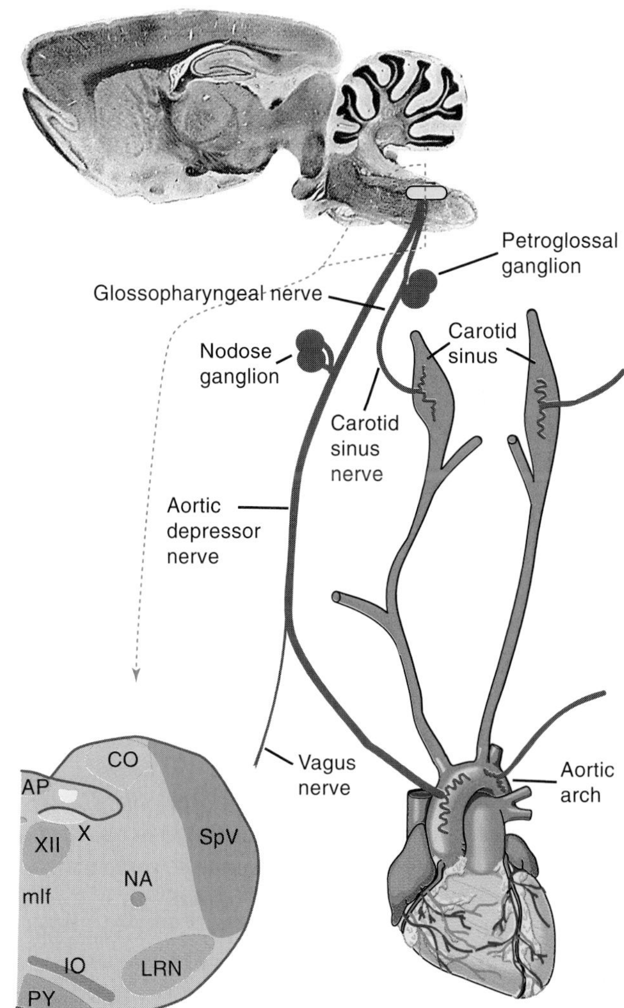

FIGURE 39.4 Baroreceptor afferents and their projection sites within the brainstem. Some baroreceptor afferent nerves sense stretch of the carotid sinus. The axons of these neurons, whose somata are in the nodose ganglion, form the carotid sinus nerve, which courses with the glossopharyngeal nerve and projects to a restricted region of the nucleus of the solitary tract (NST). Most of the afferent terminals are concentrated in the intermediate and dorsomedial subnuclei of the NST. Afferents from aortic arch baroreceptors, whose somata are in the petrosal ganglion, form the aortic depressor nerve, which joins the vagus nerve to enter the CNS and project to other regions of the NST that contain afferent projections from carotid sinus baroreceptors (yellow stippling).

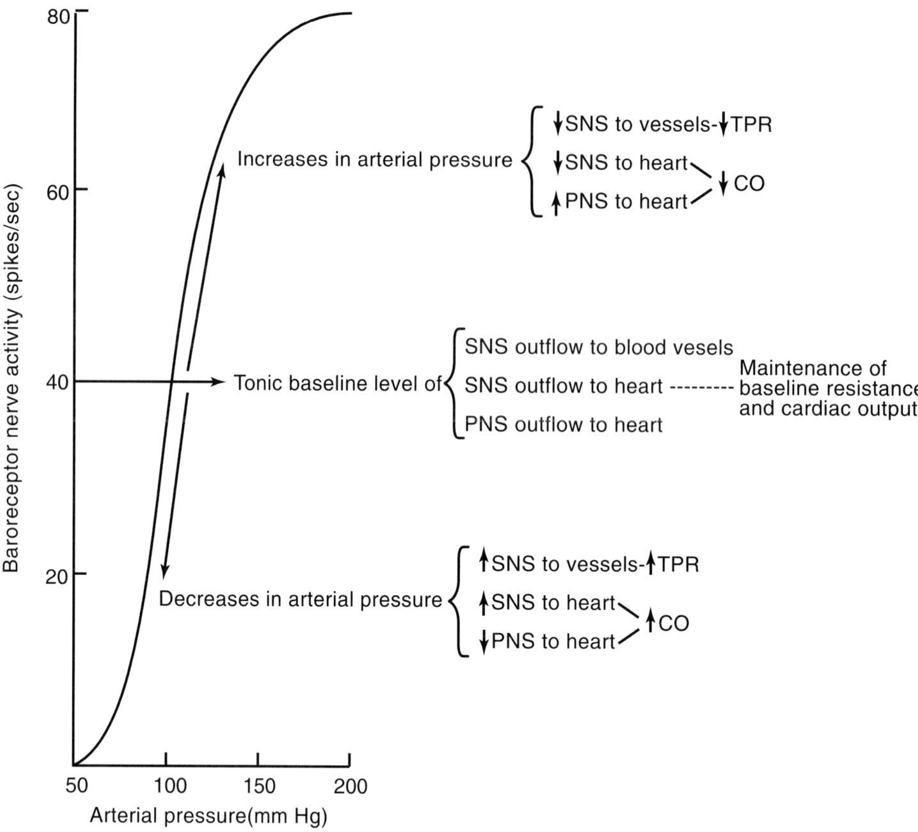

FIGURE 39.5 Baroreceptor afferent activity and the baroreceptor reflex. In the basal state, aortic arch and carotid sinus baroreceptors fire tonically. As blood pressure increases, baroreceptor firing rate increases, causing a decrease in cardiac and vasomotor sympathetic activity and an increase in cardiac parasympathetic activity. The opposite responses occur when blood pressure falls. These responses act to restore arterial pressure and baroreceptor afferent activity toward baseline. CO, cardiac output; TPR, total peripheral resistance (of the vasculature to blood flow).

parasympathetic innervation of the heart and sympathetic innervation of the heart and vasculature. As described in Chapter 38, sympathetic outflow arises from the intermediolateral cell column (IML) in the thoracic spinal cord, whereas parasympathetic innervation of the heart arises from the nucleus ambiguus and the dorsal motor nucleus of the vagus. Increased baroreceptor afferent activity stimulates parasympathetic activity to the heart and decreases sympathetic outflow to the heart and vasculature, responses that counteract an increase in arterial pressure (Fig. 39.5). Conversely, decreased baroreceptor afferent activity evokes the opposite responses. Sympathetic vasomotor outflow to different tissues responds nonuniformly to baroreceptor afferent activity.

Central neural pathways connect the baroreceptor afferent signal, which projects to the NST, to sympathetic preganglionic vasomotor neurons in the IML, and to parasympathetic (vagal) preganglionic cardiomotor neurons (Fig. 39.7). The pathway involves a projection from the NST to neurons in the **caudal ventrolateral medulla** (CVLM),[14] whose cells innervate neurons in the RVLM, which in turn innervate sympathetic preganglionic neurons. Thus, the RVLM is involved in maintenance of arterial pressure and in reflexive control of arterial pressure. The projection from the NST to the CVLM can be demonstrated anatomically,[15,16] and its importance in the baroreceptor reflex is demonstrated by the blockade of the reflex following inhibition of this region.[17,18] Although whether the NST neurons that project to the CVLM are secondary baroreceptor afferents or higher-order sensory neurons present in the NST is not clear, the short delay of baroreceptor afferent-evoked responses in CVLM neurons[14] suggests that few, if any, synapses intervene in the NST.

The NST probably innervates vagal cardiomotor neurons in the nucleus ambiguus and dorsal motor nucleus of the vagus, but whether other sites (e.g., the CVLM) are necessary for control of parasympathetic

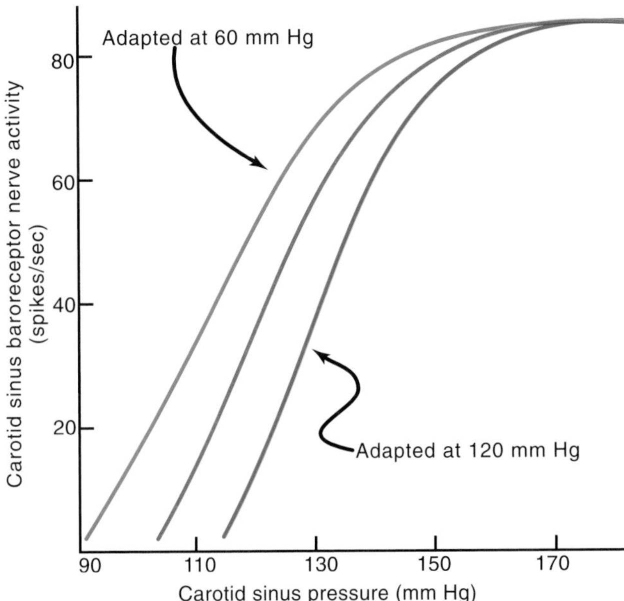

FIGURE 39.6 Resetting of baroreceptor afferent activity. The relationship between arterial pressure at the carotid sinus and firing rate of a single aortic depressor nerve baroreceptor fiber was determined after the aortic pressure had been held constant at 60, 100, or 120 mm Hg for 5 min. The baroreceptors rapidly reset to different resting pressures. From Munch *et al.*[12]

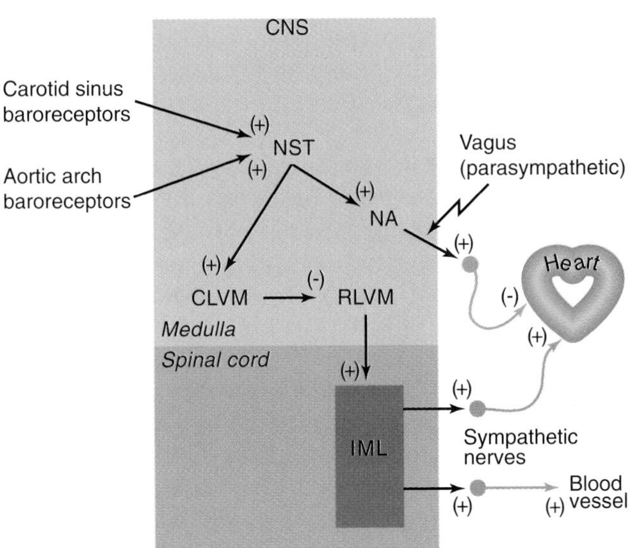

FIGURE 39.7 The baroreceptor reflex circuit. Baroreceptor afferent nerves terminate in the NST (see Fig. 39.4), where they excite secondary baroreceptor afferent neurons. In the NST, neurons involved in the baroreceptor reflex excite neurons in the CVLM, which in turn inhibit RVLM sympathoexcitatory neurons. The effect of the baroreceptor reflex on parasympathetic activity to the heart may be mediated via a direct projection from the NST to parasympathetic preganglionic neurons. (+) Excitatory; (−) inhibitory.

activity in the baroreceptor reflex remains unclear. The close proximity of the CVLM to the cardiomotor neurons in the nucleus ambiguus makes it difficult to determine whether neurons in the CVLM are critical for efferent parasympathetic activity to the heart, as they are known to be for the sympathetic vasomotor neurons of the baroreceptor reflex.

Evidence to date suggests that excitatory amino acids and GABA are dominant neurotransmitters in the baroreceptor reflex.[19] For example, excitatory amino acid antagonists administered directly into the NST, CVLM, or IML eliminate sympathetic vasomotor responses to baroreceptor input. GABA antagonists injected into the RVLM also block such responses.

In addition to the direct autonomic control of the heart and vasculature, afferent inputs from arterial baroreceptors influence other systems relevant to cardiovascular regulation, such as the renin–angiotensin system and vasopressin. Decreases in baroreceptor afferent activity, reflecting decreases in arterial pressure, stimulate the release of vasopressin and stimulate sympathoadrenal function, resulting in release of renin from the kidneys. Since each of these systems is capable of increasing arterial pressure, these responses again highlight the redundancy and complexity of central neural control of blood pressure. This issue is illustrated by the cardiovascular effects of inhibiting neural transmission in the NST. In rats, inhibition of neural transmission in the NST causes severe and lethal hypertension, due to release of vasopressin; an increase in sympathetic activity directly affecting the cardiovascular system; and a sympathetically mediated increase in the release of renin.[20]

Other Reflexes Influence Cardiovascular Homeostasis

Feedback from arterial pressure is not the only parameter involved in the short-term control of arterial pressure. Although maintaining arterial pressure at appropriate levels is certainly important, a variety of conditions require that blood pressure or regional blood flow change in an appropriate manner. For example, decreases in blood oxygen levels (hypoxemia) require circulatory adjustments to preserve oxygen delivery to the brain. Decreased blood oxygen content activates arterial chemoreceptors (Chapter 40), located primarily in the carotid sinus, which trigger reflex vasoconstriction in most tissues, redirecting blood flow to the brain. The regions of the brain involved in this chemoreceptor reflex include the NST, the site of termination of chemoreceptor afferent nerves, and the RVLM, the location of neurons that innervate sympathetic preganglionic neurons. Chemoreceptor and baroreceptor inputs typically do not influence the same NST neurons, but convergence of these inputs at the level of the RVLM is extensive.

Cardiovascular responses to changes in posture are another example of reflex cardiovascular compensations. During standing, vasoconstriction in the legs is required to counteract the effect of gravity on the circulatory system. This response is elicited, at least in part, by vestibular afferents that sense changes in posture.[21]

Skeletal muscle activity also places demands on the cardiovascular system. Exercise is accompanied by increased cardiac output and redistribution of blood flow toward the contracting muscles and away from the kidneys, gut, skin, and resting muscle. This response has been attributed to sensory feedback from the contracting muscles, a central neural command issued along with signals to contract the muscles, or, most likely, a complex combination of these two mechanisms.[22,23] Abundant data reveal the ability of muscle afferents innervating the spinal cord to elicit reflexive cardiovascular responses similar to the responses produced by exercise. For example, in an anesthetized cat when the ventral roots are stimulated to elicit isometric muscle contraction, blood pressure and heart rate increase in proportion to muscle contraction, and the response is eliminated by transection of the dorsal roots.[22] The muscle afferents involved in this response include unmyelinated fibers that are sensitive to chemicals produced by contracting muscle, as well as small myelinated fibers that respond to pressure. However, other experiments point to central neural drive initiating the cardiovascular response to voluntary muscle contraction. For example, in anesthetized cats stimulation of the subthalamic locomotor region elicits a pattern of skeletal muscle contraction similar to walking and also elicits cardiovascular responses similar to those accompanying muscle contraction, even when the muscles are pharmacologically paralyzed. In humans, when the perceived exertion is increased by partial paralysis of the muscle, blood pressure and heart rate increase in proportion to effort rather than to muscle contraction.[24] Such observations have led to the conclusions that under normal conditions, either central command or muscle feedback is capable of eliciting the appropriate cardiovascular response and that central drive predominates when the signals are mismatched.

Not all stimuli that evoke cardiovascular compensations are interoceptive. The behavioral alerting, or defense, reaction to a perceived threat or stressful stimulus is a good example of how cardiovascular compensations mediated by the CNS are integrated with other responses. When an organism is confronted with a threatening stimulus, the sympathetic nervous system is activated (the fight-or-flight response described by Cannon). This sympathetic activation is accompanied by activation of the hypothalamopituitary–adrenal axis and behavioral responses (e.g., a defensive posture) to produce an integrated and coordinated defense reaction. The entire collection of responses, including autonomic, behavioral, and endocrine aspects, can be evoked by stimulation of discrete sites in the brain, such as the perifornical hypothalamus.[25] The cardiovascular component of the defense reaction is patterned, including vasodilation in skeletal muscle, vasoconstriction of most other vascular beds, and tachycardia. Two aspects of the central mechanisms mediating this cardiovascular response deserve mention: First, the response includes inhibition of the baroreceptor reflex, mediated at least in part by inhibition of baroreceptor-sensitive neurons in the NST. This ensures that the evoked increase in arterial pressure will not be counteracted by the baroreceptor reflex. Second, the patterned cardiovascular response is mediated through the RVLM.[26] Thus, these reflex cardiovascular adjustments of the sympathetic nervous system are exerted via neurons in the RVLM that project to the spinal cord.

Summary

Cardiovascular homeostasis is the result of opposing controls between the tonically active sympathetic innervation and negative feedback to the RVLM provided by pressure receptors in the aortic arch and carotid sinus and converging on the nucleus of the solitary tract. These pressure receptors, or baroreceptors, fire when intra-arterial pressure changes and are further modulated by circulating hormones. When blood pressure rises, sensory information to the NTS activates central parasympathetic outflow from the nucleus ambiguus and the dorsal motor nucleus of the vagus and inhibits sympathetic vasomotor neurons via a pathway involving the CVLM and RVLM. When pressure falls, sensory information activates sympathetic outflow. Blood oxygen, motion, gravitational, and emotional signals can also modulate cardiovascular status.

THE NERVOUS SYSTEM AND THE LONG-TERM CONTROL OF THE CARDIOVASCULAR SYSTEM

In contrast to the established role of the CNS in controlling and coordinating cardiovascular responses to acute stimuli, the role of the CNS in the long-term control of blood pressure is less certain. Indeed, avail-

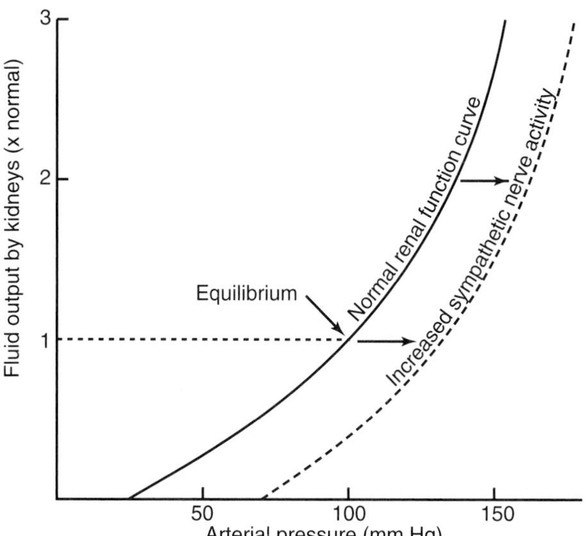

FIGURE 39.8 The effect of the sympathetic nervous system on renal function. In normal renal function, when arterial pressure changes, renal fluid output changes, and arterial pressure is ultimately restored to the equilibrium point set by the kidneys. However, in response to increased sympathetic output to the kidneys, the renal function curve shifts to the right, establishing a new, higher equilibrium blood pressure.

able evidence suggests that neural control is not essential for long-term control of blood pressure. The autonomic nervous system is not essential for life under controlled conditions, and resting arterial pressure is relatively normal in humans and animals devoid of autonomic nervous system function.[27] Furthermore, systems-level analyses of cardiovascular function highlight the blood volume-regulating capacity of the kidneys as the critical system involved in long-term cardiovascular control.[28] For example, when perfusion pressure rises, reflecting increased arterial pressure, the kidneys respond by increasing the excretion of water and sodium, thereby decreasing blood volume and therefore blood pressure. Conversely, when blood pressure falls, the reduction in renal blood flow helps to stabilize blood volume. Because this pressure–volume regulatory capacity of the kidney is an intrinsic property of the kidney, it can precisely (although not rapidly) compensate for any change in arterial pressure. Nevertheless, sympathetic neural innervation of the kidney modifies the pressure–volume regulatory capacity of the kidney by promoting sodium and water reabsorption (Fig. 39.8).[29,30] Thus, long-term control of arterial pressure may depend on sympathetic control of renal function.

Additional data implicate the brain in long-term control of arterial pressure. Even in the absence of baroreceptor reflexes, sympathetic vasomotor outflow is maintained at a level sufficient to provide normal basal arterial pressure. Thus, independent of baroreceptor feedback, the CNS is capable of chronically maintaining normal arterial pressure, although the responsible mechanisms are not yet known. Furthermore, data support a role of the brain in chronic hypertension (see Box 39.1), arguing that the central nervous system plays an important role in long-term regulation of blood pressure.

Summary

The cardiovascular system is precisely regulated and integrated with other systems in the body by the nervous system. The regulation is exerted primarily by the autonomic nervous system, but other redundant systems exist. Tonically, blood pressure is maintained within a narrow range by the baroreceptor reflex. Additional neural mechanisms, activated by stimuli both internal and external to the organism, elicit highly patterned and coordinated cardiovascular responses, with the goal of providing optimal perfusion of tissues under a variety of conditions.

References

General

Cowley, A. W. (1992). Long-term control of arterial pressure. *Physiol. Rev.* **72:** 231–300.

Dampney, R. A. L. (1994). Functional organization of central pathways regulating the cardiovascular system. *Physiol. Rev.* **74:** 323–364.

Jordan, D. (1990). Autonomic changes in affective behavior. In *Central Regulation of Autonomic Functions* (A. D. Loewy and K. M. Spyer, eds.), pp. 349–366. Oxford University Press, New York.

Rowell, L. B. (1993). *Human Cardiovascular Control.* Oxford University Press, New York.

Spyer, K. M. (1994). Central nervous mechanisms contributing to cardiovascular control. *J. Physiol. (London)* **474:** 1–19.

Wyss, J. M., Oparil, S., and Chen, S. (1990). The role of the central nervous system in hypertension. In *Hypertension: Pathophysiology, Diagnosis, and Management* (J. H. Laragh and B. M. Brenner, eds.), pp. 679–701. Raven Press, New York.

Cited

1. Hainsworth, R. (1986). Vascular capacitance: Its control and importance. *Rev. Physiol. Biochem. Pharmacol.* **105:** 101–173.
2. Janig, W., and McLachlan, E. M. (1992). Characteristics of function-specific pathways in the sympathetic nervous system. *Trends Neurosci.* **15:** 475–481.
3. Ross, C. A., Ruggiero, D. A., Park, D. H., Joh, T. H., Sved, A. F., Fernandez-Pardal, J., Saavedra, J. M., and Reis, D. J. (1984). Tonic vasomotor control by the rostral ventrolateral medulla: Effect of electrical or chemical stimulation of the area containing C1 adrenaline neurons on arterial pressure, heart rate and plasma catecholamines and vasopressin. *J. Neurosci.* **4:** 474–494.
4. Dittmar, C. (1873). Uber die lage des sogenannten gefasscentrums in der medulla oblongata. *Ber. Verh. Saech.* **25:** 449–469.

5. Alexander, R. S. (1946). Tonic and reflex functions of medullary sympathetic cardiovascular centers. *J. Neurophysiol.* **53:** 1551–1566.
6. Feldberg, W., and Guertzenstein, P. G. (1972). A vasodepressor effect of pentobarbitone sodium. *J. Physiol.* (*London*) **224:** 83–103.
7. Guyenet, P. G. (1990). Role of the ventral medulla oblongata in blood pressure regulation. In *Central Regulation of Autonomic Functions* (A. D. Loewy and K. M. Spyer, eds.), pp. 145–167. Oxford University Press, New York.
8. Willette, R. N., Krieger, A. J., Barcas, P. P., and Sapru, H. N. (1983). Medullary gamma-aminobutyric acid (GABA) receptors and the regulation of blood pressure in the rat. *J. Pharmacol. Exp. Ther.* **226:** 893–899.
9. Cochrane, K. L., and Nathan, M. A. (1989). Normotension in conscious rats after placement of bilateral electrolytic lesions in the rostral ventrolateral medulla. *J. Auton. Nerv. Syst.* **26:** 199–211.
10. Morrison, S. F., Callaway, J., Milner, T. A., and Reis, D. J. (1991). Rostral ventrolateral medulla: A source of glutamatergic innervation of the sympathetic intermediolateral nucleus. *Brain Res.* **562:** 126–135.
11. Oppemheimer, S. M., Wilson, J. X., Guiraudon, C., and Cechetto, D. F. (1991). Insular cortex stimulation produces lethal cardiac arrhymthias: A mechanism of sudden cardiac death. *Brain Res.* **550:** 115–121.
12. Munch, P. A., Andresen, M. C., and Brown, A. M. (1983). Rapid resetting of aortic baroreceptors in vitro. *Am. J. Physiol.* **244:** H672–H680.
13. Chapleau, M. W. (1992). Are arterial pressure and deformation the sole determinants of baroreceptor activity? Importance of humoral and endothelial modulation in normal and disease states. *Hypertension* (*Dallas*) **19:** 278–280.
14. Jeske, I., Morrison, S. F., Cravo, S. L., and Reis, D. J. (1993). Identification of baroreceptor reflex interneurons in the caudal ventrolateral medulla. *Am. J. Physiol.* **264:** R169-R178.
15. Somogyi, P., Minson, J. B., Morilak, D., Llewellyn-Smith, I., McIlhinney, J. R. A., and Chalmers, J. (1989). Evidence for an excitatory amino acid pathway in the brainstem and for its involvement in cardiovascular control. *Brain Res.* **496:** 401–407.
16. Aicher, S. A., Kurucz, O. S., Reis, D. J., and Milner, T. A. (1995). Nucleus tractus solitarius efferent terminals synapse on neurons in the caudal ventrolateral medulla that project to the rostral ventrolateral medulla. *Brain Res.* **693:** 51–63.
17. Willette, R. N., Punnen, S., Krieger, A. J., and Sapru, H. N. (1984). Interdependence of rostral and caudal ventrolateral medullary areas in the control of blood pressure. *Brain Res.* **321:** 169–174.
18. Gordon, F. J. (1987). Aortic baroreceptor reflexes are mediated by NMDA receptors in caudal ventrolateral medulla. *Am. J. Physiol.* **252:** R628–R633.
19. Sved, A. F., and Gordon, F. J. (1994). Amino acids as central neurotransmitters in the baroreceptor reflex pathway. *News Physiol. Sci.* **9:** 243–246.
20. Sved, A. F. (1986). Peripheral pressor systems in hypertension caused by nucleus tractus solitarius lesions. *Hypertension* (*Dallas*) **8:** 742–747.
21. Yates, B. J. (1992). Vestibular influences on the sympathetic nervous system. *Brain Res. Rev.* **17:** 51–59.
22. Coote, J. H., Hilton, S. M., and Perez-Gonzalez, J. F. (1971). The reflex nature of the pressor response to muscular exercise. *J. Physiol.* (*London*) **215:** 789–804.
23. Mitchell, J. H., Kaufman, M. P., and Iwamoto, G. A. (1983). The exercise pressor reflex: Its cardiovascular effects, afferent mechanisms and central pathways. *Annu. Rev. Physiol.* **45:** 229–242.
24. Leonard, B., Mitchell, J. H., Mizuno, M., Rube, N., Saltin, B., and Secher, N. H. (1985). Partial neuromuscular blockade and cardiovascular responses to static exercise in man. *J. Physiol.* (*London*) **359:** 365–379.
25. Hilton, S. M. (1982). The defence arousal system and its relevance for circulatory and respiratory control. *J. Exp. Biol.* **100**: 159–174.
26. Hilton, S. M., Marshall, J. M., and Timms, R. J. (1983). Ventral medullary relay neurones in the pathway from the defence areas of the cat and their effects on blood pressure. *J. Physiol.* (*London*) **345:** 149–166.
27. Mathias, C. J., and Frankel, H. J. (1988). Cardiovascular control in spinal man. *Annu. Rev. Physiol.* **50:** 577–592.
28. Guyton, A. C. (1991). Blood pressure control—special role of the kidneys and body fluids. *Science* **252:** 1813–1816.
29. DiBona, G. F. (1992). Sympathetic neural control of the kidney in hypertension. *Hypertension* (*Dallas*) **19:** I28–I35.
30. Osborn, J. L., Plato, C. F., and He, X. R. (1997). Long-term increases in renal sympathetic nerve activity and hypertension. *Clin. Exp. Physiol. Pharmacol.* **24:** 72–76.
31. Okamoto, K., and Aoki, K. (1963). Development of a strain of spontaneously hypertensive rats. *Jpn. Circ. J.* **27:** 282–293.

C H A P T E R

40

Neural Control of Breathing

Jack L. Feldman and Donald R. McCrimmon

Organisms must constantly exchange various substances with the environment to maintain homeostasis. A variety of physiological systems have evolved to handle solid, liquid, and gaseous metabolic precursors and by-products. For example, aerobic metabolism consumes O_2 and produces CO_2, the so-called blood gases. Organisms with large surface-to-volume ratios, such as bacteria, yeast, plants, and insects, rely on passive diffusion for exchange of these gases with the environment. However, more complex organisms, with low external surface-to-volume ratios and high metabolic rates, such as birds and mammals, actively pump gas using a reciprocating pump (respiratory muscles) to exchange air between the environment and the lungs and a circular pump (heart) to move blood through the pulmonary to systemic circulations. The brain controls breathing by generating the motor outflow driving the rhythmic contraction and relaxation of respiratory pump muscles and by modulating the tone of skeletal and smooth muscles in the upper airways and bronchi to control resistance to air flow.

Humans breathe continuously, because we need a constant supply of O_2 to support our high metabolism. Our brains drive our respiratory muscles to produce ventilation appropriate for the regulation of blood O_2 and CO_2 adaptable over an order of magnitude range in metabolic demand (in humans from 0.25 liter min^{-1} O_2 consumed at rest to ~3–6 liter min^{-1} O_2 consumed during extreme exercise). In controlling our breathing, our brains must also compensate for wide ranges of body posture and movement, which affect lung and musculoskeletal mechanics and compromise muscle or cardiopulmonary function. This control of ventilation must continue from birth until death without lapses of more than a few minutes. Respiratory muscles account for less than 5% of the body's metabolism at rest, but they need to be used efficiently, because the metabolic cost adds up over time. Moreover, serious respiratory muscle fatigue must be avoided. During exercise, energy costs of breathing must be kept low when possible (the respiratory pump moves up to 200 liters min^{-1} of air in world-class athletes) to maximize the amount of metabolic substrates available to other working muscles.

The drive for continuous ventilation is strong. Typically, breathing is the last consequential movement to disappear following generalized depression of higher function, such as during surgical anesthesia or following insults to the brain (e.g., hypoglycemic coma). Automatic, homeostatic breathing can remain in people who have lost cortical function, resulting in ethical and emotional dilemmas over people who are "brain dead."

In experimental animals, we take advantage of this robustness of breathing; we can study synaptic, neural, and network mechanisms in anesthetized or decerebrate animals who continue to breathe. The neural mechanisms underlying breathing are so robust and sufficiently self-contained that an *in vitro* tissue slice at an appropriate level in neonatal or late fetal rodent brainstem continues to generate respiratory-related patterns of motor nerve activity.[1]

EARLY NEUROSCIENCE AND THE BRAINSTEM

The persistent absence of breathing is the surest sign of death. Many ancient cultures associated life with breathing itself. *Animation,* to bring to life, and *animal* are derived from the Latin *anima,* which means to breathe (and also soul). Taoism holds breathing sacred, and proper breathing a key to enlightenment: immortality to the man who holds his breath for the time of 1000 respirations. Buddhists believe that special states of enlightenment can be attained through effective modulation of breathing.

Although the purpose of breathing—to move air into and out of the lungs—was not established until the end of the 18th century, the sites responsible for breathing movements have been a constant source of speculation in Western culture. Perhaps the earliest suggestion that the brain was involved came from Galen (ca. 131–201 AD), who observed that gladiators and animals injured below the neck continued to breathe, but those injured in the neck stopped.[2] Lorry,[3] who showed that cerebellectomized rabbits continued to breathe, concluded that the critical circuits lay within the brainstem and upper cervical spinal cord, essentially correct by our contemporary view. Legallois[4] "extracted" brain tissue to determine what was necessary

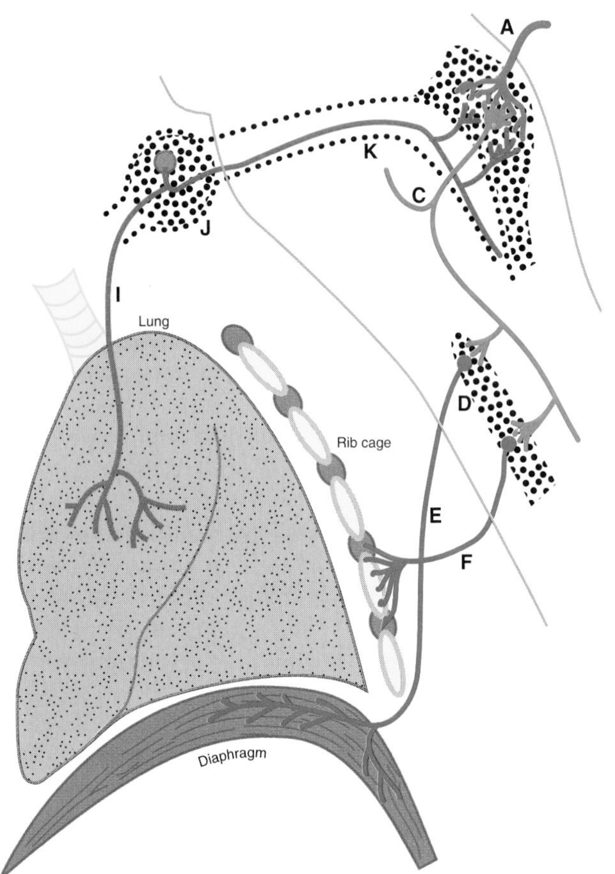

FIGURE 40.1 Ramón y Cajal's model for respiratory control. Respiratory neurons in solitary tract (C) process signals from pulmonary afferents (K; cell bodies in nodose ganglion (J)) and some blood factor present in local capillaries (A). Descending control signals go to spinal motor neurons (D), innervating the diaphragm (E) or intercostal muscles (F). From Ramón y Cajal.[8]

FIGURE 40.2 Oscillograph recordings of the gross electrical potential of an *en bloc in vitro* goldfish brainstem (top) compared to gill movement of an intact goldfish (bottom). From Adrian and Buytendijk.[9]

for breathing; he localized the critical sites to the rostral ventrolateral medulla, near the exit of the vagus nerve, close to the currently hypothesized site, the pre-Bötzinger complex. Later lesion-based work[5–7] was consistent with a critical role of various pontine and medullary sites. These lesion studies were at variance with studies that used electrical stimulation; this latter work is mostly of historical interest, given its rather high, and therefore nonphysiologic, stimulus parameters (1- to 30-V pulses delivered via low-resistance electrodes).

Ramón y Cajal,[8] among his many brilliant contributions to neuroscience, provided an anatomic rationale for medullary structures being central to the control of breathing. Examining the afferent and efferent projections of respiration-related nerves, he suggested that three brainstem nuclei are important: the nucleus of the solitary tract and commissural nuclei, primary targets of pulmonary afferents, and the nucleus ambiguus, which contains cranial motor neurons that innervate the upper airway muscles. His network model for breathing is prescient (Fig. 40.1): afferent signals, containing information about the status of the lungs and components of blood, combined with intrinsic properties of brainstem neurons to produce a rhythmic outflow to spinal and cranial respiratory motor neurons. Adrian and Buytendijk[9] recorded slow, rhythmic potentials in isolated *in vitro* goldfish brainstems. The periodicity of the potentials was similar to that of gill movements in intact goldfish (Fig. 40.2) and thus provided physiological evidence that the brainstem contained the critical circuits. Gesell and co-workers[10] subsequently recorded individual medullary neurons discharging bursts of activity in phase with the breathing rhythm. This finding initiated a concerted effort to identify neurons that generate respiratory rhythm.

BREATHING AND GAS EXCHANGE

The respiratory system exchanges gas between the bloodstream and the environment in order to supply O_2 to and remove CO_2 from mixed venous blood of the pulmonary circulation. Gas exchange occurs in ventilated and perfused alveoli of the lung. Adult human lungs have ~70 m^2 of gas-exchange surface in a volume of about 3 liters. Pulmonary gas exchange involves a number of distinct processes: **ventilation** to move air into and out of the lungs, **diffusion** to move gases across the alveolar and systemic capillary membranes, and **pulmonary** and **systemic circulations** to move blood between the gas-exchanging surfaces in the lungs and tissues. Of interest here is ventilation in mammals, which results from rhythmic contractions of the respiratory muscles.

The diaphragm is the most important inspiratory muscle. This dome-shaped muscle is attached to the ribs and separates the thorax (containing lungs and heart) from the abdomen (containing the stomach, liver, intestines, etc.). During contraction (inspiration), the dome descends, enlarging the thoracic cavity. The normal excursion of the dome during quiet breathing is ~1.5 cm in adult humans but ranges up to 6–7 cm during deep breathing. The inspiratory function of the diaphragm is supplemented by the external intercostal muscles, which connect the ribs pairwise; when these intercostal muscles contract, the ribs swing up and out, expanding the thorax. Expiration is usually a passive process that results from the elastic recoil of the lungs and thorax. However, active expiration can be produced by contraction of internal intercostals, which rotate the ribs down and in, and abdominal muscles, which displace the abdominal viscera upward, forcing the diaphragm to move upward, too. We actively expire when breathing at a high respiratory rate, when exhaling against a high resistance (in diseases such as asthma and emphysema), and when speaking or coughing.

Work must be done to inflate the lung. One component of this work generates air flow overcoming air viscosity and turbulence. Another component expands the lungs and chest wall. Stretching these elastic tissues during inspiration stores potential energy that is recovered when, during expiration, the lungs and chest wall recoil to their resting positions. Much like a stretched rubber band requires no energy input to return to its original length, the expanded chest cavity returns passively to its rest position.

CENTRAL NERVOUS SYSTEM AND BREATHING

Although conceptually simple and straightforward (air in, air out), breathing, from the brain's point of view, is much more than sine wave generation. Ventilation requires a patterned motor output with appropriate timing and magnitude of muscle contraction and relaxation and coordination of this activity among synergists and antagonists; that is, the muscles that move the rib cage in and out and the diaphragm up and down either pull together (synergistic muscles) or pull in opposite directions (opposing muscles). Ventilation is controlled by a complex and mutable regulatory system composed of many distinct components (Fig. 40.3). The brainstem and spinal cord contain the basic circuits for rhythm generation and pattern formation and are the targets of relevant sensory afferents. Suprapontine structures, including the cortex, hypothalamus, and cerebellum, affect ventilation but are not essential, because decerebrate mammals continue to breathe with appropriate blood gas regulation. Sensory afferents are essential for regulation, but also are not required for basic respiratory pattern formation. Following paralysis (or deafferentation), provided that blood gas homeostasis is maintained by artificial means (e.g., mechanical ventilation), rhythmic motor output continues in nerves innervating respiratory muscles.

Neuroscientists believe that a simple rhythm-generating system in the brainstem lies at the core of the neural circuits for breathing. Premotor circuits translate this rhythm into coordinated patterns of motor neuron activity. Motor neurons receive many inputs affecting their excitability and determine the pattern of motor output that drives ventilation. They are categorized into two functional groups: spinal motor neurons, which innervate muscles of the respiratory pump; and cranial motor neurons, which innervate muscles

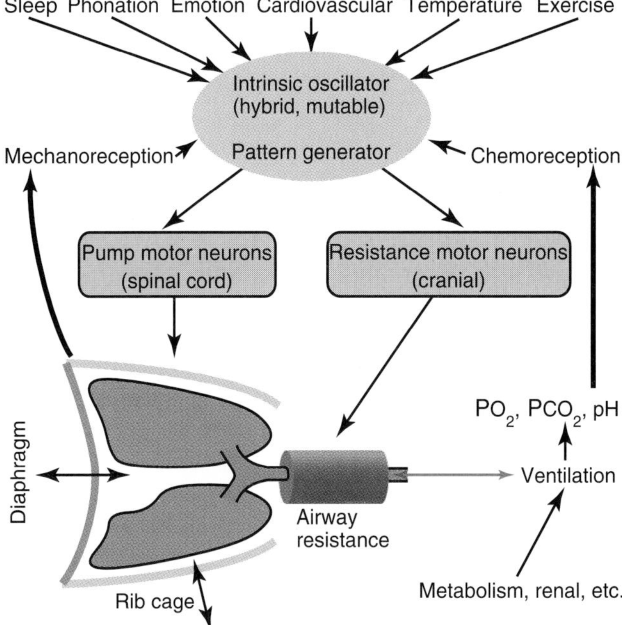

FIGURE 40.3 Functional organization of central nervous system control of breathing. Refer to text for details.

that modulate airway resistance (discussed later). Contraction and relaxation of the pump muscles changes the volume of the thorax, resulting in inflation and deflation of the lungs. The resultant ventilation, along with other factors such as metabolic load and renal function, affects the amounts of CO_2, O_2 (blood gases), and H^+ (pH) in the blood.

The brain mechanisms controlling breathing in intact mammals are subject to many influences, both chemoreceptive, including blood and brain O_2, CO_2, and pH, and behavioral, such as emotive, cognitive, or movement-related inputs. Signals reflecting these factors profoundly affect the performance of brainstem, bulbospinal, and spinal cord neurons, and perhaps even cause reorganization of the underlying neuronal circuits. Many of these modulatory signals arise in suprapontine regions, including the cortex and hypothalamus.[11–14]

Because inflation and deflation of the lung are essential to breathing, precise regulation of ventilation requires respiratory motor outflow to be modulated by information about lung volume. For example, the Breuer–Hering reflexes, activated by signals from pulmonary stretch receptors, ensure that breath-by-breath changes in lung volume are appropriate for exchange of gas. For example, if air flow is reduced (e.g., by airway congestion), inspiration is prolonged to ensure that the lungs fill to an appropriate volume, and expiration is prolonged to ensure that the tidal volume empties (see Mechanoreceptors in the Lungs Adjust Breathing Pattern and Initiate Protective Reflexes).

Although breathing is continuous in mammals, we cannot assume that the underlying neural mechanisms are fixed. The physical plant (lungs and muscles) changes *in utero,* during postnatal development, and throughout aging, requiring central adjustments.[15] Also, the pattern of breathing and the response to changes in blood gases and mechanical inputs change with the circadian sleep–wake cycle,[16] differ between species and even among strains of rats,[17] and change with procedures commonly used in experiments such as anesthesia, decerebration, deafferentation (e.g., vagotomy), and paralysis. The reader (and experimentalist) must keep in mind that data obtained under different conditions may not be comparable or even be an accurate reflection of the intact, undrugged human.

Complex Circuits Control Breathing

Neurons affecting and effecting respiratory patterns are found throughout the neuraxis. Breathing is a sensorimotor process, and the circuitry that processes afferent inputs and controls respiratory muscles has been studied with a variety of neuroanatomical tract tracing techniques. In this section, we examine the anatomy of motor neurons, sensory projections, and postsensory, premotor structures (Fig. 40.4).

Motor Neurons

The muscles of respiration, which expand and contract the thorax, are innervated by motor neurons in the midcervical and thoracolumbar spinal cord.[18,19] **Phrenic motor neurons** innervate the diaphragm and in humans are located in the most ventral part of the ventral horn of segments C3–C5.[20] Their periodic burst activity is the hallmark of inspiration. These neurons are uniquely organized in small clusters, with the intercluster space filled with the rostrocaudally extended dendrites of these neurons.[21–23] This bundling of dendrites may facilitate the collective modulation of their excitability by monoamines (e.g., serotonin and norepinephrine) and associated peptide transmitters (discussed later); terminals containing these transmitters are entwined with the bundles. The phrenic motor neuron pool has relatively few gamma motor neurons, reflecting sparse intrafusal fibers in the diaphragm, and few Renshaw cells.[24,25] The functional significance of the organization of these cells remains to be discovered. **Thoracic respiratory motor neurons,** which innervate intercostal and other rib cage and back muscles, are superficial in the ventral horn. Populations such as those innervating the external intercostals are active during phrenic motor neuron activity and are therefore inspiratory. Other populations, such as those innervating the internal intercostal, are active during the period between phrenic bursts and are considered expiratory.[18,19] **Abdominal motor neurons** are located in the upper lumbar and lower thoracic spinal cord and facilitate expiration. During other movements, such as defecation and emesis, they cocontract with the diaphragm to increase intra-abdominal pressure.

The striated muscles of the larynx and pharynx control airway resistance by dilating or constricting the airway. These muscles are innervated by cranial motor neurons that lie mainly in the nucleus ambiguus and project out the vagus nerve. The hypoglossal nucleus innervates striated muscles of the tongue, which is important in controlling upper airway patency. Mucus-secreting glands and the smooth muscle of the airways are innervated by postganglionic parasympathetic neurons, which increase mucus production and constrict the airways. Their preganglionic neurons are located in the nucleus ambiguus. Postganglionic sympathetic fibers are relatively sparse in the airways, despite the presence of β-adrenoceptors on airway smooth muscle. Activation of these β-adrenoreceptors causes airway dilation and reduces mucus produc-

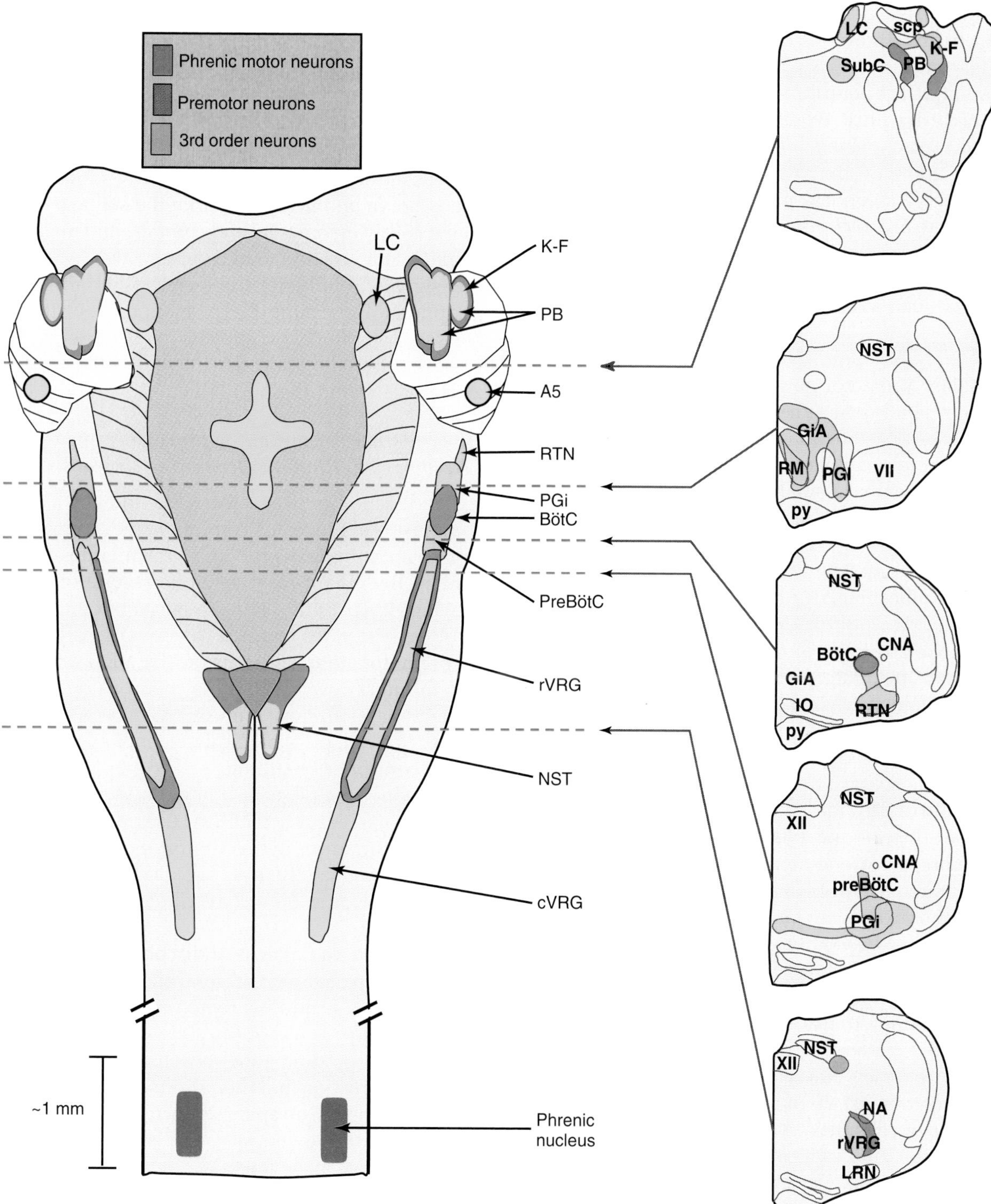

FIGURE 40.4 Respiratory neuroanatomy of the rat brainstem. Dorsal and transverse views. A5, catecholamine cell group; BötC, Bötzinger complex; CNA, caudal nucleus ambiguus; cVRG, caudal ventral respiratory group; GiA, pars alpha subdivision of the gigantocellular reticular nucleus; IO, inferior olive; K-F, Kölliker-Fuse nucleus; LC, locus ceruleus; LRN, lateral reticular nucleus; NA, nucleus ambiguus; NST, nucleus of the solitary tract; PB, parabrachial nucleus; PGi, paragigantocellular reticular nucleus; py, pyramidal tract; preBötC, pre-Bötzinger complex; RM, raphe magnus; RTN, retrotrapezoid nucleus; rVRG, rostral ventral respiratory group; scp, superior cerebellar peduncle; SubC, subceruleus; VII, facial nucleus; XII, hypoglossal nucleus. Adapted from Dobbins and Feldman.[22]

tion,[26] which is why β-adrenoreceptor agonists are used to treat asthma. Autonomic innervation of the lungs also includes a nonadrenergic–noncholinergic component, which contributes to airway dilation mediated mainly by nitric oxide and airway constriction mediated by tachykinins.[27,28]

Coordination of the motor neurons innervating these striated and smooth muscles is not fixed. Motor neurons that are reciprocally active during normal breathing—those that innervate inspiratory and expiratory pump muscles—may be coactive during other motor acts, such as coughing or vomiting.

Premotor Neurons

Medullary premotor neurons drive spinal respiratory motor neurons by synaptic excitation and inhibition (see Box 40.1).[19,29] The largest concentration of these bulbospinal premotor neurons is in a long rostrocaudal column in the ventrolateral medulla, the **ventral respiratory group** (VRG). The most caudal portion, extending rostrally from spinal cord segment C1 to the level of the obex (fourth ventricle), primarily contains expiratory bulbospinal neurons that provide excitatory drive to thoracolumbar expiratory motor neurons. From the obex rostrally to the retrofacial nucleus, the VRG contains inspiratory bulbospinal neurons, which provide excitatory drive to phrenic and thoracic inspiratory motor neurons. Additional inspiratory bulbospinal neurons are concentrated in the ventrolateral nucleus of the solitary tract (vlNST). The bulbospinal transmission of inspiratory and expiratory drive takes place along mono- and oligosynaptic pathways. Although there is a strong monosynaptic excitatory projection to phrenic motor neurons, the dominant projections to thoracolumbar respiratory motor neurons appear to be polysynaptic, via segmental and long propriospinal interneurons. Respiratory premotor neurons do not appear to participate in rhythm generation. Instead, they transform the rhythmic drive they receive into a pattern of output appropriate for the motor neurons they innervate.

At the rostralmost tip of the VRG column is a compact cluster of cells that have widespread projections throughout the VRG and the vlNST, as well as to spinal motor neurons. This cluster, the **Bötzinger complex,** appears to be a principal source of reciprocal inhibition (discussed later) in the respiratory network. Many Bötzinger complex neurons (probably GABAergic) inhibit premotor and motor neurons during their normally silent periods of the respiratory cycle. The Bötzinger complex also appears to be a major target of second-order pulmonary sensory neurons of the dorsomedial NST.

Sensory Projections

The principal peripheral sensory signals for breathing arise from lung mechanoreceptors and peripheral chemoreceptors. Pulmonary afferents, whose somata are in the **jugular** and **nodose** ganglia, provide information about lung volume, inflation rate, and pulmonary tissue status. These afferents travel mostly in the vagus nerve and synapse within the solitary tract nuclei, mostly dorsomedial and commissural nuclei.[30] Respiratory muscle and joint receptors also provide useful signals,[31] but not all sensory information is peripheral. For example, information about the acid–base status of the brain appears to arise from a variety of sites within the brainstem, including the retrotrapezoid nucleus and the NST.[32]

Higher-Order Sensorimotor Processing and (Presumptive) Rhythm-Generating Neurons

Sandwiched between the VRG and the Bötzinger complex is a cluster of respiratory neurons, the **pre-Bötzinger complex** (preBötC), which is postulated to contain the circuits that generate respiratory rhythm (see Fig. 40.4).[1] Little else is known about the functions of other structures coupled to populations of sensory or premotor neurons. Outside the VRG and vlNST, several nuclei project to motor neurons or to regions containing respiratory bulbospinal neurons. For many of these nuclei, physiological evidence supports a role in the control of breathing.

Lesions in the **parabrachial pons,** including the medial parabrachial and Kölliker-Fuse nuclei, lead to profound disturbances in the respiratory pattern of vagotomized mammals[33,34] (see Fig. 40.15). Neurons that modulate respiration are distributed throughout this region.

Neurons with patterns of discharge that are modulated by respiration are dispersed throughout the **raphe nuclei.** This midline region contains neurons that have excitatory or inhibitory effects on respiration. The neurons can modulate the response to carotid chemoreceptor activation, but their precise role is unknown.[35]

Finally, the **retrotrapezoid nucleus,** a thin lemniscal structure near the ventral medullary surface at about the level of the facial nucleus, appears to be important in central chemoreception.[36,37]

Synaptic Excitation and Inhibition Shape the Respiratory Pattern

The business end of breathing, which is the periodic contraction of skeletal muscles of the respiratory pump and of muscles (both skeletal and smooth) controlling

BOX 40.1

SPINAL CORD INJURY CAN DIMINISH VENTILATION[38]

Spinal injuries that affect the long axons of bulbospinal premotor neurons, which transmit respiratory drive to spinal motor neurons, can be life threatening. With respect to the control of breathing, the severity of the injury depends on the spinal cord level at which the injury occurs. Damage between T1 and S1, in addition to causing sensory and motor deficits in the legs (Chapter 31), can produce loss of control of intercostal muscles below the level of the injury, leading to a diminished ability to generate inspiratory or expiratory movements. The higher the level of functional spinal cord transection, the greater the respiratory impairment. Injury between C4 and C8 can cause quadriplegia and loss of control of all intercostal musculature. Although innervation of the diaphragm may remain (with low cervical damage), the lack of control of the chest wall means the diaphragm must do more work; these patients frequently experience an alarming sense of difficulty breathing (dyspnea). Injuries between the lower brainstem and C4 result in **pentaplegia**, in which there are motor and sensory losses to the legs, arms, diaphragm, and neck. Such injuries require immediate artificial support of ventilation to maintain life. This type of cervical injury is common following dives into shallow pools or unnoticed sandbars.

airway resistance, requires that brainstem neurons generate a rhythm that can then be sculpted into a precisely coordinated, efficient pattern of muscle contraction and relaxation (Fig. 40.5). Each muscle (or muscle group) must contract with the appropriate timing and burst pattern to produce the forces on the lung necessary to move the right amount of air. This requires precise patterns of motor neuron bursting and silence. Two factors determine the firing patterns of motor neurons: (rhythmic) synaptic drive, which is determined by impinging premotor neuronal circuits; and intrinsic excitability. In turn, the membrane potentials and firing patterns (see Fig. 40.8) of the premotor neurons and their predecessors leading back to rhythm-generating neurons are also determined by the impinging (rhythmic) synaptic drive and intrinsic excitability.

Typically, respiratory neurons fire when they receive phasic excitatory drive, and they are silent when they receive phasic inhibitory drive. The excitatory drive is periodic and underlies the rhythmic discharge of all neurons, with the possible exception of pacemaker neurons (discussed later). The inhibitory drive is a bit more complex than the excitatory drive: Three types of synaptically mediated inhibition must be considered (Fig. 40.6)[39]:

1. Reciprocal inhibition. Between phases of excitatory inputs, most respiratory motor neurons and premotor neurons are actively inhibited. Since these neurons are not spontaneously active and do not normally receive excitatory inputs between bursting phases, why is it necessary to inhibit them? Most likely, reciprocal inhibition prevents their spurious activation (leading to inappropriate muscle contraction) after unexpected afferent inputs. Except for motor neurons that signal opening of the jaws, which must be rapidly activated when a hard object is unexpectedly bitten during chewing, all motor and premotor neurons involved in periodic movements appear subject to reciprocal inhibition.
2. Recurrent inhibition. There is a push–pull control of neuronal firing during a burst—that is, excitation and inhibition are concurrent—with the net balance determining the firing pattern. Reduction of inhibition, for example, by administration of inhibitory receptor blockers to motor neurons, results in increased amplitudes of periodic bursts.
3. Phase-transition inhibition. Inhibition has been postulated to arrest the activity of neurons producing one phase, thereby allowing transition into the next phase, as the neurons of the next phase become active.

Excitatory and Inhibitory Amino Acids

The principal excitatory and inhibitory synaptic inputs that modulate membrane potentials of neurons occur on a millisecond time scale. As in the rest of the central nervous system, in the respiratory network, amino acids are the dominant transmitters, and they are functionally linked to ion pores. Glutamate is the primary excitatory agent, and GABA and glycine provide inhibition.

Pharmacology of Fast Excitatory Transmission

Fast excitatory drive is probably similar throughout the respiratory control system.[40–42] Application of an-

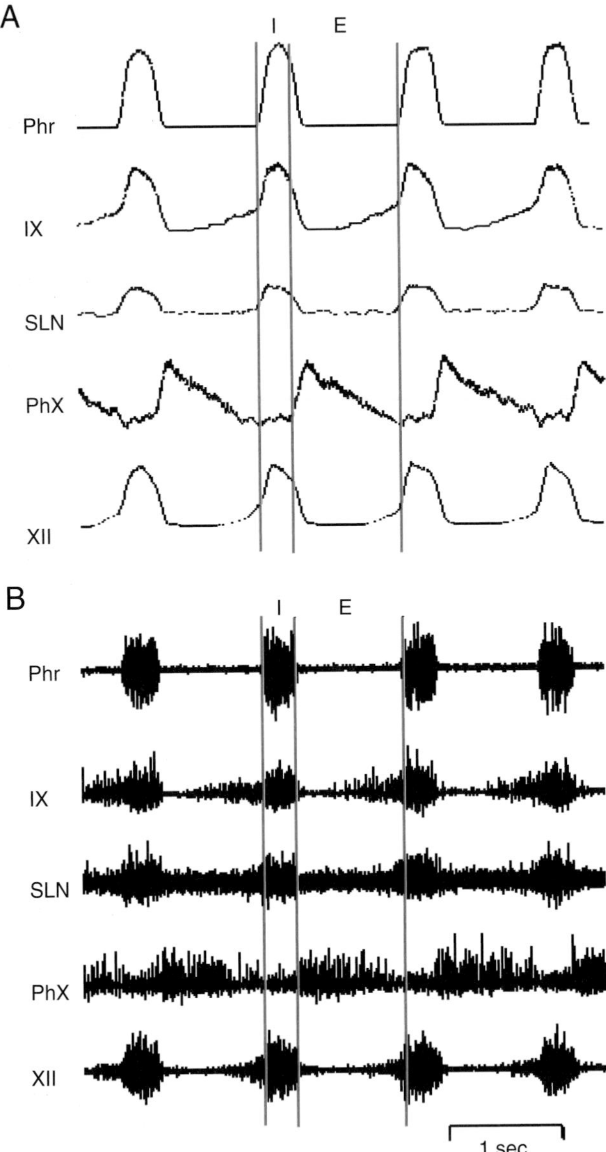

FIGURE 40.5 Patterns of respiratory motor activity on selected spinal (phrenic, Phr) and cranial nerves in an anesthetized rat. (A) Low pass filtered trace of activity showing overall pattern of discharge; (B) corresponding raw nerve recording. Red vertical lines indicate phase transitions between inspiration (I) and expiration (E). Note that the onset of inspiratory activity on cranial nerves precedes the onset of activity on the phrenic nerve. IX, glossopharyngeal nerve; PhX, pharyngeal branch of vagus nerve; SLN, superior laryngeal nerve XII, hypoglossal nerve. Adapted from Hayashi and McCrimmon, 1996.[38a]

tagonists of excitatory amino acid receptors reduces the activity of brainstem neurons.[43] This and similar observations confirm that almost all brainstem respiratory neurons receive at least part of their excitatory synaptic input via glutamatergic neurotransmission. Therefore, we can consider transmission at the synapse between bulbospinal premotor neurons and phrenic motor neurons as typical excitatory communication. The relatively long distance between the premotor neurons' somata in the medulla and their synapses onto phrenic motor neurons in the cervical spinal cord makes these synapses particularly amenable to pharmacologic manipulation without the complication of drugs affecting the distantly located somata of the premotor neurons.

Evidence supports an amino acid, almost certainly glutamate, as the primary excitatory transmitter at this synapse.[44,45] In phrenic and hypoglossal motor neurons, rhythmic inspiratory drive potentials and currents are reduced by local application of drugs that block α-amino-3-hydroxy-5-methyl-4-isoxazole propionic acid (AMPA), kainate, and metabotropic receptors (Fig. 40.7; see also Fig. 40.18).[44–46] Synaptically isolated motor neurons respond to exogenous glutamate, unless blocked by the appropriate receptor-selective antagonists. As further evidence, the concentration of glutamate, but not aspartate, in extracellular dialysates from the region of the phrenic nucleus is related to respiratory drive; for example, when respiratory drive decreases, glutamate in the dialysate also decreases.[47] In addition, bulbospinal respiratory premotor neurons are immunoreactive for glutamate.[48] Finally, unitary postsynaptic potentials (PSPs) underlying inspiratory drive are mediated by glutamate.[49]

Pharmacology of Fast Inhibitory Transmission

Fast synaptic inhibition in brainstem respiratory networks is associated with an increase in permeability to chloride ions. The principal mediators of this inhibition are GABA and glycine. In the network controlling breathing, the dominant mechanism appears to be GABA acting on postsynaptic $GABA_A$ receptors and contributes to shaping the discharge pattern of all re-

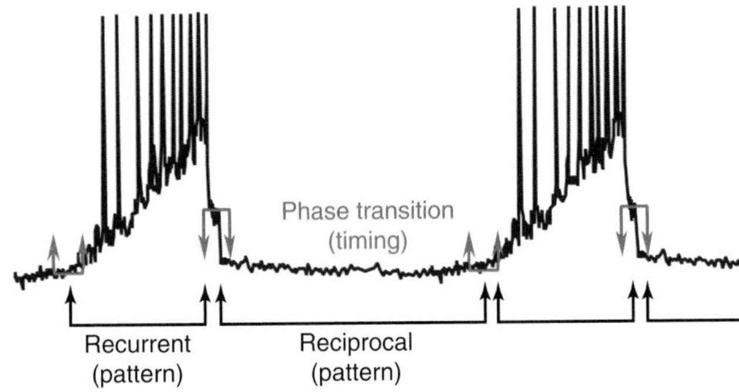

FIGURE 40.6 Membrane potential and discharge pattern of an augmenting inspiratory (or expiratory) neuron. The timing of three distinct types of inhibition is shown.

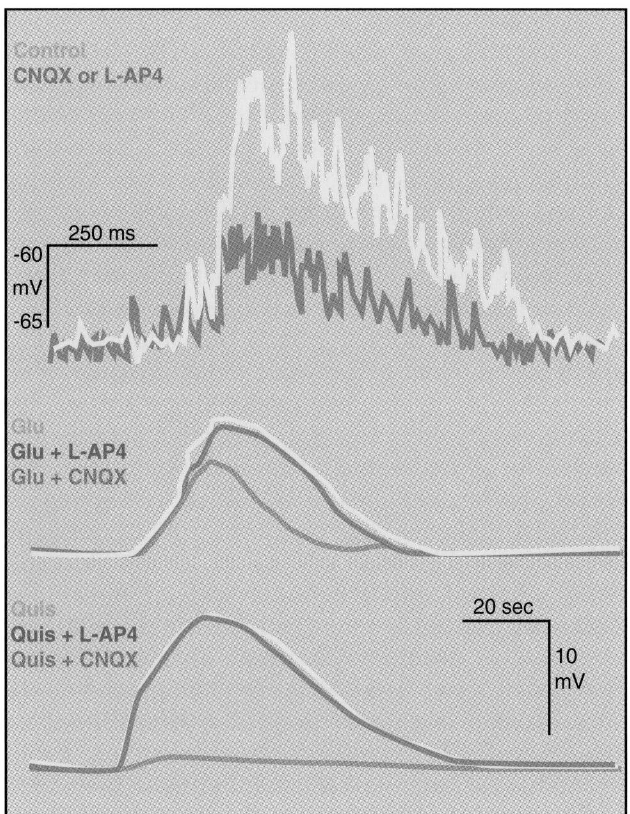

FIGURE 40.7 Glutamate excites phrenic motor neurons. Endogenous inspiratory drive to a phrenic motor neuron is attenuated by CNQX (6-cyano-7-nitroquinoxaline-2,3,dione) and AP4 (2-amino-4-phosphonobutyric acid). Following synaptic isolation of the neuron with tetrodotoxin, the exogenous application of glutamate or quisqualate, a non-NMDA agonist, is attenuated by CNQX but not by AP4. This suggests that CNQX affects postsynaptic non-NMDA receptors, whereas the action of AP4 is presynaptic. Further investigation suggests that AP4 is an agonist at a presynaptic metabotropic glutamate autoreceptor that acts to reduce transmitter release.

spiratory neurons.[40,42] Blocking $GABA_A$ receptors increases the discharge of all VRG neurons *in vivo.* GABA appears to participate in reciprocal and phase-transition inhibitions to help maintain appropriate timing of discharges in premotor networks.[50,51] Glycine also participates in sculpting the discharge patterns of respiratory neurons.[50,51] GABA and glycine inputs may be spatially segregated on respiratory neurons.[50] In inspiratory neurons, glycine-sensitive inhibitory PSPs appear to arise from synapses predominantly located on the somata, and they apparently mediate the rapid inhibition at the beginning of expiration. $GABA_A$ receptors appear to be concentrated on distal dendrites, and these receptors maintain synaptic inhibition in the latter part of expiration. Despite the clear role of synaptic inhibition in maintaining appropriate patterns of activity within the premotor circuitry, respiratory rhythms can be generated in the absence of phasic synaptic inhibition, at least in *in vitro* slices.

Respiratory Neurons

Within the brainstem regions that generate respiratory rhythm and pattern are neurons whose discharge patterns are related to the breathing rhythm (Fig. 40.8). At the simplest level, respiratory neurons fall into categories based on the respiratory phase in which their predominant discharge occurs. A **respiratory phase** is a segment of the respiratory cycle with definable beginning and end points and with an independently controlled duration (e.g., inspiration or expiration). Because experiments are often carried out on anesthetized, paralyzed mammals that are artificially ventilated, the discharge pattern of the phrenic nerve is used to define inspiration and expiration. Inspiratory onset is defined by the onset of a burst of phrenic nerve activity. The amplitude of phrenic nerve activity increases until an abrupt decline marks the end of inspiration. Expiration is the period between the abrupt decline in phrenic nerve activity and the onset of the next inspiratory burst. The pattern of inspiratory (diaphragm) and expiratory (e.g., internal intercostal) muscle activity has suggested to several investigators that mammals have two expiratory phases.[52,53] The onset of exhalation marks the onset of the first expiratory (E1), or postinspiratory, phase. During this phase, the diaphragm often exhibits a low level of activity, termed postinspiratory activity, that slows exhalation (Fig. 40.5). Postinspiratory activity declines, frequently ending by midexpiration. At this point an augmenting pattern of expiratory muscle activity begins, marking the onset of the second (E2) phase. Reflexes elicited by several different sensory afferent systems alter expiratory duration in a manner consistent with their independent control.[54] A concern with the concept of two expiratory phases is that the transition between the two phases is often ambiguous. For example, in Fig. 40.5, a declining postinspiratory output of the pharyngeal branch of the vagus nerve, which controls the diameter of the upper airway, overlaps with the E2 pattern of activity in other nerves that affect the diameter of the upper airway, such as the glossopharyngeal and hypoglossal nerves. Hence, even if two expiratory phases exist, the delineation between them is ill-defined. To further complicate matters, a comparative analysis of vertebrates suggests up to five respiratory phases (active inspiration, end-inspiratory pause, passive expiratory air flow, active expiration, and end-expiratory pause).[55]

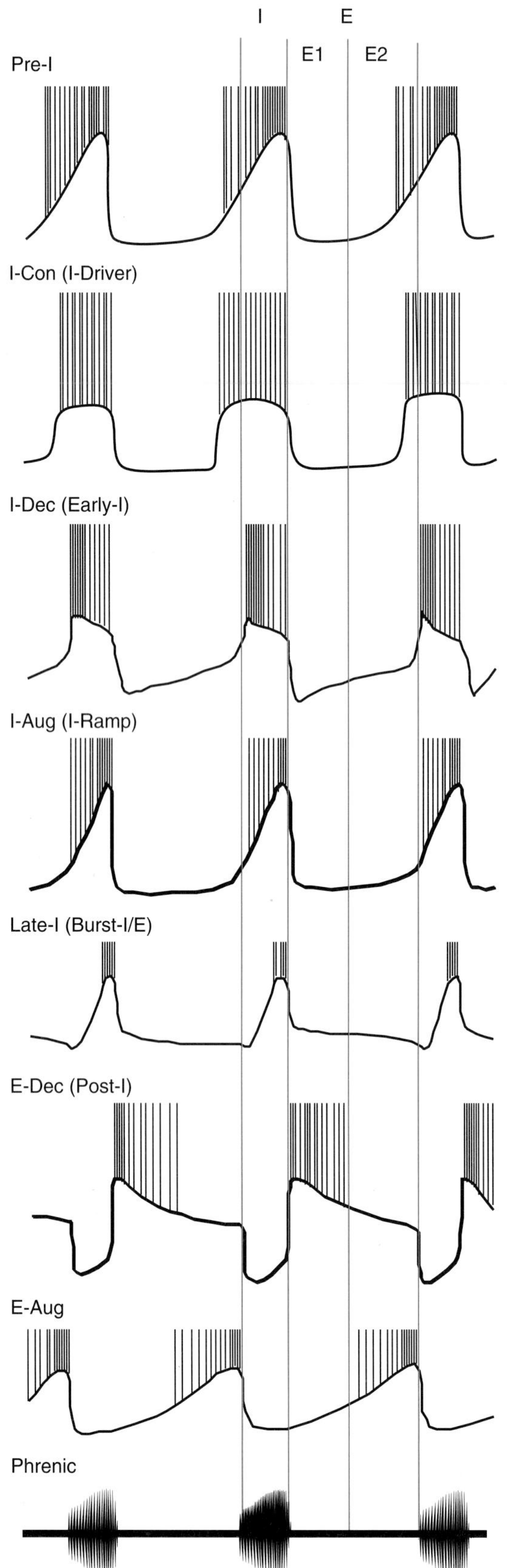

Even among neurons that discharge only during inspiration or only during expiration, different neurons can have distinctly different patterns of discharge. Investigators have interpreted these diverse patterns as evidence of the different roles of neurons in respiratory control and have used the discharge patterns to designate subgroups of respiratory neurons. While the total number of subgroups is relatively small, different investigators have measured neuronal activities under (slightly) different experimental conditions and have used (slightly) different criteria to name them. The result is a somewhat confusing array of names. The changes in membrane potential and patterns of discharge are shown in Fig. 40.8 with the most common names of the predominant neuronal subgroups.[29,40,56,57] Inspiratory augmenting (I-Aug or I-Ramp) neurons begin discharging near the onset of I, then progressively depolarize and increase their discharge rate during I. Pre-inspiratory (Pre-I) neurons have a similar discharge pattern but begin to depolarize and fire prior to the onset of I. Inspiratory-constant (I-Con or I-Driver) neurons discharge prior to inspiration, but these neurons maintain a constant level of depolarization and rate of firing. Inspiratory-decrementing (I-Dec) cells abruptly depolarize at the onset of inspiration and fire at a high rate. As inspiration progresses, these neurons slowly repolarize and decrease their rate of discharge. Late inspiratory (Late-I or Burst-I/E) neurons begin depolarizing late in inspiration and fire a burst just before the end of inspiration. Expiratory neurons are divided into two predominant groups. At the onset of expiration, expiratory-decrementing (E-Dec or Post-I) neurons begin to discharge at a high frequency. Throughout expiration, these cells then progressively repolarize and decrease their discharge rate. Some investigators distinguish between E-Dec neurons, which discharge at a declining rate throughout expiration, and Post-I neurons, which discharge only during the early portion of expiration (E1 or Post-I). Expiratory-augmenting (E-Aug) neurons typically begin discharging midway through expiration. Like I-Aug neurons,

FIGURE 40.8 Membrane potentials and discharge patterns of neuronal components of two- and three-phase models of respiratory rhythm generation. Two-phase models consist of an inspiratory phase (I) and an expiratory phase (E). In three-phase models, E is divided into E1, early expiration (or postinspiration), and E2, late expiration. The transition from inspiration to expiration is marked by a rapid decline in phrenic nerve activity. Residual, declining phrenic nerve activity (when present) and activity on postinspiratory neurons mark the E1 phase. Aug, augmenting neurons; Con, constant neurons; Dec, decrementing neurons. Alternative names in common usage are indicated in parentheses. E-Aug activity occurs largely in E2.

E-Aug neurons progressively depolarize resulting in a progressive increase in firing rate. For all cells receiving rhythmic drive, the patterns of synaptic input are constrained by the patterns of firing of their input neurons.

Summary

Periodic contractions of the diaphragm, chest, and abdominal muscles pump air in and out of the lung; skeletal and smooth muscles in the upper airway control the resistance to airflow. These movements require the brain to produce a precisely coordinated, continuous, rhythmic outflow to spinal and cranial motor neurons. The rhythm originates in the brainstem and is influenced by, but does not require, peripheral signals from chemoreceptors and mechanoreceptors and central signals from sites throughout the neuraxis. Specialized circuits within the brainstem and spinal cord, which are also modulated by peripheral and central input, transform the basic rhythm into patterns of motor output.

RESPIRATORY RHYTHM GENERATION

Rhythms with periods ranging from tens of milliseconds to annual are basic expressions of neural function. Several important movements, including breathing, chewing, locomotion in its various forms, and nystagmus, have periods of less than one to several seconds. The neural networks for these rhythms are genetically programmed and develop *in utero,* so that newborn mammals breathe, chew, and, in some cases, locomote. In this section, we look at how the brain generates the rhythms underlying one such movement, breathing.

Models of Respiratory Rhythm Generation Fall into Three Basic Categories

Models of generation of respiratory rhythm are divided into three categories (Fig. 40.9).[52,56,58,59] In **network models** rhythm is generated purely by inhibitory and excitatory interactions among mundane neurons using sodium and potassium currents. In **pacemaker models**, intrinsic membrane properties of single or coupled networks of pacemaker neurons cause rhythmic oscillations in membrane potential. Pattern-forming elements then shape and time the activity of various motor neuron pools. **Hybrid models** incorporate pacemaker neurons and synaptic interactions. Two- and three-phase hybrid models of rhythm generation have been developed.[52,56,58,59]

Network Models Depend on Connectivity to Produce Rhythm

Researchers have proposed network models for generating a two-phase (inspiration–expiration) breathing rhythm and a three-phase (inspiration–early expiration (E1)–late expiration (E2)) breathing rhythm.[52,56,58,59] The essential elements of the neural circuitry for respiratory rhythm generation in the adult mammal *in vivo* are clustered in the rostral VRG, and a growing consensus places the circuitry within (or centered on) the preBötC (see Fig. 40.4).[1,39,40,56] Network models of the circuitry underlying the generation of respiratory rhythm have been based on the patterns of activity and known (and hypothesized) synaptic connections of relatively few groups of respiratory neurons located within the VRG.

Examples of network models are shown in Fig. 40.9. In a two-phase model, two populations of decrementing neurons, one inspiratory (I-Dec; Early-I) and the other expiratory (E-Dec; Post-I), generate respiratory rhythm. These neurons receive a tonic excitatory drive from afferent input, such as that arising from peripheral and central chemoreceptors. Reciprocal inhibition between the two populations ensures that only one fires at a time. Phase transition between inspiration and expiration is achieved when activity in one population decreases sufficiently (due to the decrementing pattern of discharge) to reduce inhibition of the other group and allow its tonic excitatory input to bring it to threshold. Once these neurons start firing, they inhibit the first group. This basic timing circuitry is elaborated into a respiratory motor output, with an augmenting discharge pattern that is sensitive to afferent inputs.

Starting at the end of expiration, the declining level of inhibition arising from E-Dec neurons permits Pre-I (or I-Con or I-Driver) neurons to begin discharging at high rates, possibly triggered by postinhibitory rebound, (conditional) bursting pacemaker activity, or both. These Pre-I neurons provide a strong excitatory drive to premotor I-Aug and I-Dec neurons, which begin to fire. The initially high discharge rate of the inhibitory I-Dec neurons limits the initial firing frequency of I-Aug neurons, but as the discharge of I-Dec neurons slows, inhibition in I-Aug neurons progressively declines and the I-Aug neurons' firing frequency augments. Inspiration is terminated when the declining inhibition from I-Dec neurons permits a population of Late-I (or Burst-I/E) neurons to burst, inhibiting Pre-I and I-Aug neurons and thereby terminating I motor output. E-Dec neurons, now no longer inhibited, begin to discharge. The initially high rate of discharge in E-Dec neurons delays the onset of activity in E-Aug neurons.

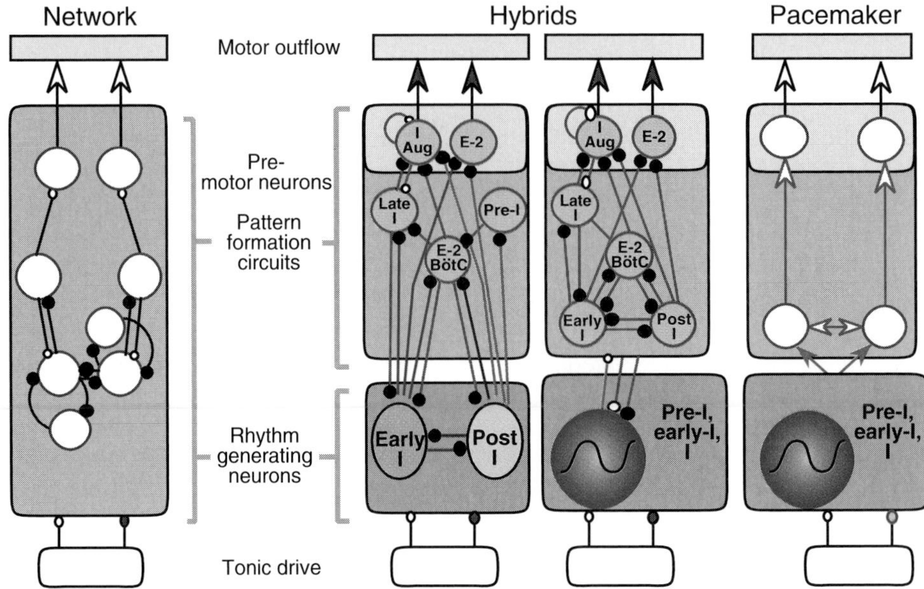

FIGURE 40.9 Models of rhythm generation (see text for details). I, inspiratory; E, expiratory; E-2 (BötC), inhibitory stage 2 expiratory neurons in the Bötzinger complex; E-2, stage 2 expiratory neurons (provide premotor drive to expiratory motor neurons); Aug, augmenting neurons. Filled circles, inhibitory; open circles, excitatory synapses.

As the discharge rate of E-Dec neurons declines, the inhibition of Pre-I neurons is reduced, permitting them to begin discharging and the cycle repeats.

The pattern of augmenting motor activity in pump muscle (e.g., diaphragm) motor neurons is a reflection of augmenting activity of I-Aug neurons. Several mechanisms (in addition to the declining inhibition from I-Dec neurons mentioned earlier) are likely to underlie this pattern of activity.[29,59,61,71,72] For example, mutual excitatory connections among I-Aug neurons provide positive feedback and augment excitatory drive. To prevent the positive feedback from generating explosive increases in discharge rate, the impact of the excitatory connections must be limited. Active membrane properties such as Ca^{2+}-activated K^+ channels could limit the increases in discharge rate. Recurrent inhibitory interneurons could also produce slower, more linear increases in activity.

It is likely that active, that is, nonmundane, membrane properties contribute to the full expression of respiratory rhythm even in network models. As indicated above, the kernel of network models is the mutual inhibitory interaction between I-Dec and E-Dec neurons. These two neuronal groups may have conductances that facilitate depolarization and bursting, but not pacemaker behavior. However, the conductances proposed to support bursting could produce endogenous oscillatory activity. I_h and $I_{Ca(LVA)}$ underlie burst depolarization; I_{CAN}, $I_{Na(p)}$, $I_{Na(HH)}$, $I_{K(HH)}$, and $I_{Ca(HVA)}$ sustain depolarization and generate action potential output; I_A and I_M modulate discharge; $I_{K(Ca)}$ contributes to repolarization (burst termination); and decay of $I_{K(Ca)}$ determines the interburst interval (expiratory period). A complete characterization of E-Dec and I-Dec conductances is required.

In the hybrid pacemaker–network model, the interaction between cellular and synaptic properties contribute to system behavior, but respiratory rhythm is derived from the endogenous oscillatory activity of a tightly synchronized group of pacemaker cells. Once initiated, the oscillation propagates through the pacemaker population, temporally dispersing the onset times of spiking within the population. Pattern-forming elements shape and time activity in various premotor and motor neuron pools and also synaptically modify cycle timing through tonic and phasic synaptic control of the membrane potentials of pacemaker cells. Respiratory neurons with voltage-dependent conductances have been identified *in vitro*, but the conductances underlying oscillatory behavior remain to be characterized. In addition, a causal relationship between pacemaker neurons and rhythm generation is lacking.

The key, and at present only, testable distinction between network and pacemaker models is the requirement for synaptic inhibition in phase transition in network models. This suggests a straightforward experiment: block inhibition in the central respiratory networks and see if rhythm remains. If so, then a compelling case is made for a pacemaker-generated rhythm. This experiment awaited development of a suitable experimental model (see Box 40.2),[63–66] a brainstem and spinal cord isolated *in vitro*.

BOX 40.2

EXPERIMENTAL ANALYSIS OF VENTILATION

Neuroscientists are constrained by what they can measure. Noninvasive experiments in humans reveal the phenomenology of breathing—for example, the relationship between ventilation and blood CO_2 levels. Brain imaging may reveal which regions are involved, but at present spatiotemporal resolution is too coarse to show networks, much less neurons or synapses. Respiration lends itself to study, because mammals suitable for experimental studies breathe much like humans. Breathing continues following anesthesia or decerebration, and the neural patterns remain following paralysis (and mechanical ventilation), making possible experimental procedures requiring highly invasive techniques, such as single neuron recording. Compared to studies of neurons in culture or in tissue slices, experiments in whole mammals have serious limitations. For example, movements of the heart and lungs make certain types of single neuron recording difficult in the brainstem and spinal cord. Also, in live animals the blood–brain barrier is intact, making precise control of brain extracellular fluid impossible. Finally, the experiments are expensive and often last 36 h or more, requiring the dedicated and concurrent efforts of several investigators. Fortunately, the robust features of breathing that allow it to persist when other behaviors are suppressed by anesthesia or decerebration permit further reduction in the experimental preparation that removes these limitations. For example, a respiratory-related rhythm persists in the brainstem and spinal cord that has been removed from a neonatal rat or mouse and transplanted to an *in vitro* chamber.[63,64] In addition, the rhythm persists in a particular slice of brainstem isolated from this preparation (Fig. 40.10).[1] Using such slices, one can correlate exquisite measures of a neuron's intrinsic and synaptic properties and projections with measures of endogenous behavior, for example, firing pattern. With some common and otherwise useful *in vitro* preparations, such as the hippocampal slice, such correlations cannot be made because no endogenous behavior *in vitro* relates to known behavior *in vivo.* In general, *en bloc in vitro*, or slice, preparations play an important role in the study of basic cellular, synaptic, and integrative mechanisms underlying motor behavior.

Another model of interest lacks a direct tie to mammalian behavior but has other considerable advantages. Syed and colleagues identified three neurons in the pulmonate mollusk *Lymnaea stagnalis* that are essential for generating muscle movements required for oxygen gas exchange.[65,66] They have isolated and cocultured these neurons to produce a three-neuron *in vitro* circuit that reproduces the repertoire of ventilatory behavior. With three large neurons *in vitro* that together have behaviorally relevant activity, the potential for analysis is virtually unlimited.

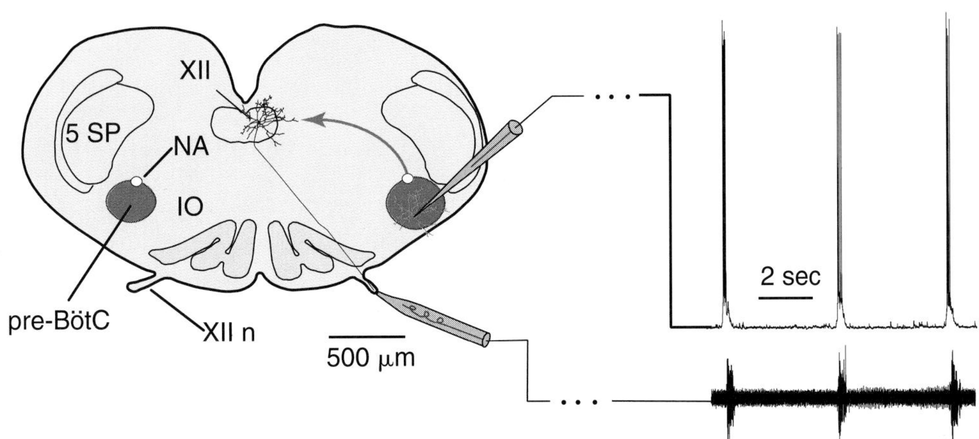

FIGURE 40.10 "Oscillating" slice preparation from rodent brainstem exhibits endogenous respiratory rhythm in XII with patch-clamp recordings from a preBötC neuron. Diagram of a transverse slice. Patch-clamp recordings can be made from XII or preBötC cells while drugs (or different solutions) are supplied in a bath or applied locally. Rhythm is generated in preBötC and transmitted to XII nucleus, so rhythm appears in motor axons (XII nerve). At right is a recording from a preBötC inspiratory neuron that shows periodic, inspiration-modulated depolarizations and associated action potentials (current-clamp) (upper tracing). Lower tracing is XII nerve recording; bursts of activity correspond to inspiration.

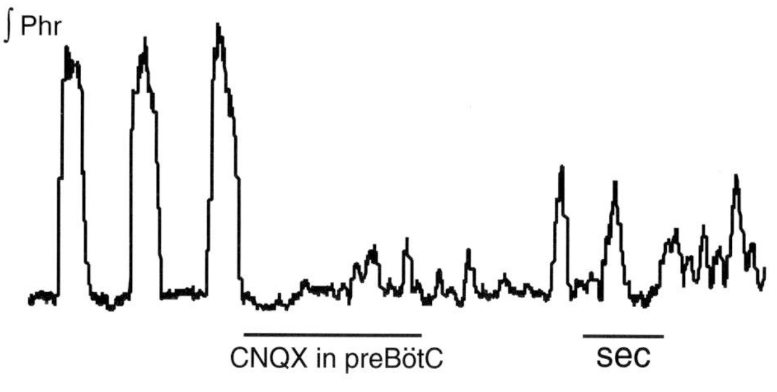

FIGURE 40.11 Systemic blockade of NMDA receptors with MK-801 in anesthetized adult rats does not perturb breathing rhythm. However, subsequent injection of CNQX into the preBötC blocks non-NMDA receptors and transiently abolishes respiratory rhythm.

The effect of blocking inhibition in the *en bloc in vitro* brainstem–spinal cord preparation from the neonatal rodent was unexpected: Neither antagonists of the known major inhibitory transmitter systems, GABA and glycine, nor ion substitution to interfere with inhibitory Cl^- or K^+ currents blocked rhythm.[67,68]

Pacemaker Models Require Special Neurons

Reducing the synaptic inhibition in neonatal respiratory networks *in vitro* does not block the generation of rhythm, and a parsimonious explanation of these results is that respiratory rhythm is generated by pacemaker neurons.[1,69] Localization of likely sites for rhythm generation made testing of this hypothesis feasible: Sectioning at different levels of the neuraxis revealed a brainstem segment that must remain intact for rhythm generation to occur. Physiological recordings from the slice, which could be cut so that hypoglossal (XIIth) nerve rootlets remain attached (Fig. 40.10), showed that the XIIth nerve exhibits periodic bursting quite like that of the *en bloc* brainstem. Within the slice, two nuclei contain neurons that fire rhythmically in relation to the motor output:

1. The XII nucleus, which is defined by the somata of motor neurons whose bursting is present in the XII nerve. This nucleus does not produce the rhythm; perturbing the cellular or synaptic properties in the XII nucleus affects the amplitude of motor output, but not the burst frequency (which is a function of the rhythm generator).[46]
2. The pre-Bötzinger complex, which is distinguished by several features: *in vivo* (Fig. 40.11) and *in vitro* perturbations of neuronal excitability in the preBötC affect respiratory rhythm.[46] Compared with adjacent BötC and VRG, the preBötC contains neurons with different impulse discharge patterns.[36,57,70] Also, the preBötC contains very few bulbospinal neurons, and many preBötC neurons project to regions containing premotor neurons, especially the VRG. Finally, in *in vitro* preparations, bursting pacemaker neurons are found in the preBötC.

Two hypotheses followed from these observations: (1) the preBötC is the source of respiratory rhythm, and (2) the preBötC contains pacemaker neurons (pacemaker hypothesis).

About 25% of the rhythmically active neurons in the preBötC have pacemaker properties such as those that follow.[1] Tonic injection of depolarizing current produces additional bursts of action potentials during the normally silent (expiratory) period. In response to a similar stimulus, follower cells simply increase their tonic discharge (Fig. 40.12). After abolition of respiratory rhythm in the slice, depolarizing currents produce

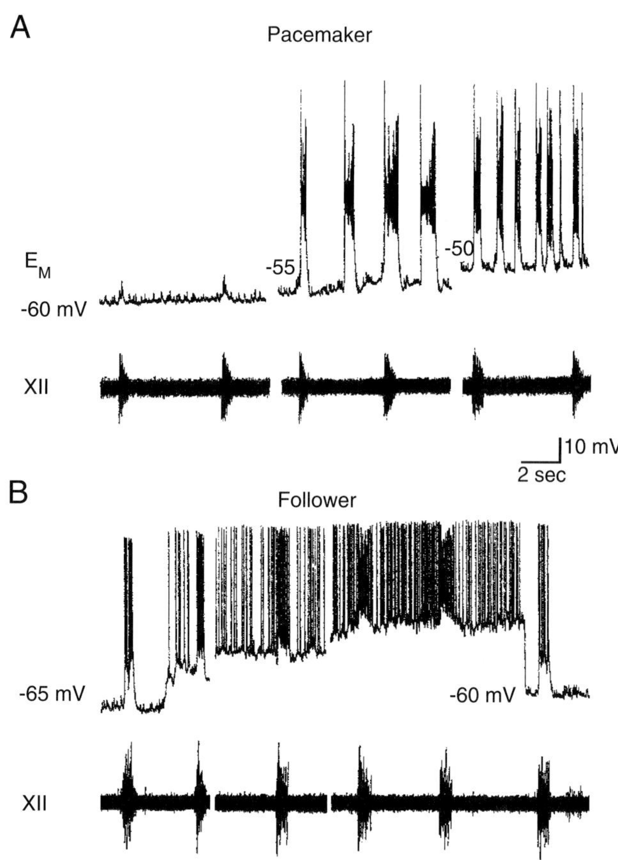

FIGURE 40.12 In an *in vitro* slice, pacemaker neurons in the preBötC (A) receive a rhythmic inspiratory synaptic drive. As the membrane is depolarized by current injection, additional distinct bursts of activity appear. This response is different from that of other follower cells (B). Periodic inspiratory activity is shown in recordings from XII. Depolarization of a follower neuron, for example, XII motor neuron, elicits tonic activity but does not increase it.

BOX 40.3

CNS LESIONS PRODUCE ABNORMAL BREATHING PATTERNS

Many brain injuries and diseases produce abnormal breathing patterns.[38,73–75] Because many brain regions provide afferent input to the neurons generating the breathing rhythm, pathology in regions not normally associated with the generation of breathing can produce abnormal breathing patterns. Despite the diffuse nature of many pathologies that give rise to abnormal breathing patterns, Fred Plum and colleagues have systematically characterized several breathing disorders (Fig. 40.13) arising from specific CNS pathologies.

Apneustic breathing is marked by prolonged inspiratory periods. In humans, the most frequent pattern is inspirations lasting 2–3 s alternating with prolonged expiratory pauses. In cats, the prolonged inspiratory periods are associated with plateaus in inspiratory drive that can last minutes (leading to death in the absence of mechanical ventilation). Apneusis is observed in people with lesions of the pons, including, or just ventral to, the pontine respiratory group. In experimental animals, apneusis requires not only lesions of the pontine respiratory group but also interruption of vagal afferent input.

Lesions of the corticobulbar or corticospinal tracts can lead to **Cheyne-Stokes respiration,** a rhythmic waxing and waning of the depth of breathing. Periods of no breathing (apnea) follow each period of waning inspiratory depth. Lesions of the corticobulbar and corticospinal tracts also can result in loss of voluntary control of breathing. In pseudobulbar palsy, for example, voluntary control of breathing and of cranial motor neuron function is lost secondary to a lesion often located dorsomedially in the base of the pons.

Extensive bilateral damage to the medullary respiratory groups can severely disrupt or abolish respiratory rhythm, resulting in death unless artificial ventilation is initiated immediately. Fortunately, unilateral damage does not appear to be sufficient to cause severe disruption of respiratory rhythm- and pattern-generating mechanisms. Two vertebral arteries supply blood to the medulla, so bilateral damage from an infarct or embolism is unlikely.

Less extensive damage to medullary respiratory structures can produce **ataxic breathing,** an irregular pattern of breathing with apparent randomly occurring large and small breaths and periods of apnea. Breathing frequency tends to be low.

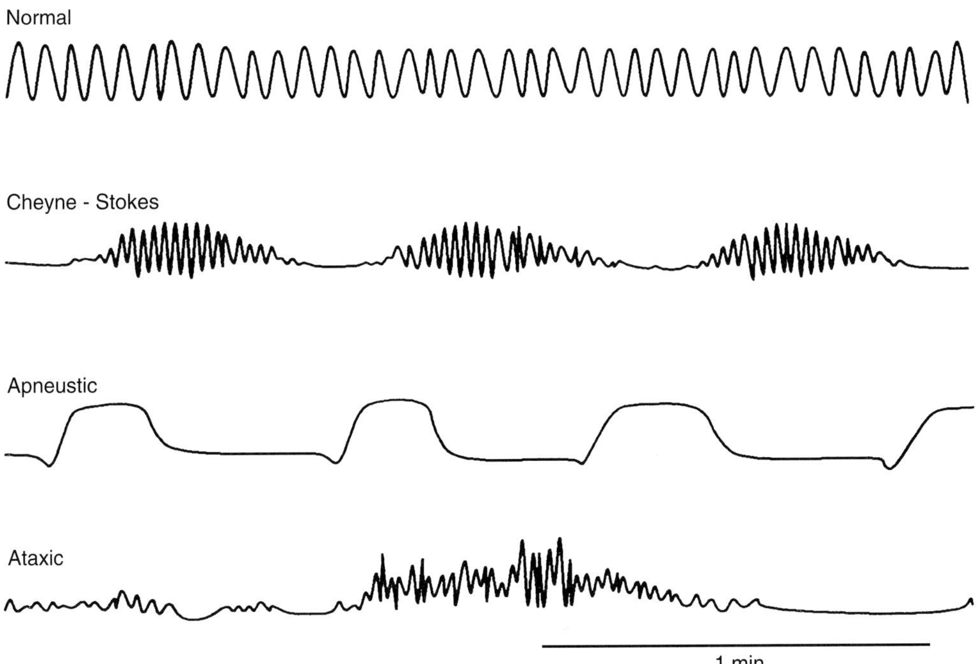

FIGURE 40.13 Abnormal breathing patterns resulting from CNS disorders. The ordinate is lung volume. Adapted from Plum and Posner.[75]

bursts, and the interval between bursts is sensitive to depolarization level. In response to hyperpolarizing pulses, rebound burst discharges develop when the current is removed. The current–voltage relationship of many pacemaker cells is nonlinear, whereas in follower cells, below the threshold for action potentials the current–voltage relationship is almost linear. Finally, many pacemaker neurons will generate periodic bursts when synaptic activity is blocked.

Regardless of whether the pacemaker hypothesis correctly explains rhythm generation *in vitro*, additional circuitry *in vivo* overlays the networks present *in vitro* and may alter the basic pattern-generating mechanisms. Perturbations affecting the pons or NMDA receptor activity incapacitate the central rhythm-generation circuitry in adult cats and rodents (but not in neonates) (e.g., as shown in Fig. 40.15); however, if a periodic pulmonary afferent input is present, the pattern appears normal. Marked derangements of breathing also occur in response to pathology within brain regions containing projections to respiratory rhythm generating neurons (see Box 40.3). Any model of rhythm generation must include a network of these various inputs, so a simple pacemaker model is, at best, incomplete. Moreover, embedded in a network in an intact mammal, a neuron that under reduced, experimental conditions can exhibit pacemaker properties may be constrained to play a more differentiated role in rhythmogenesis.

Excitatory Amino Acid Neurotransmission Is Required for Respiratory Rhythm Generation

As discussed earlier, excitatory amino acid neurotransmission, with glutamate the likely transmitter, is fundamental in the fast excitatory communication between respiratory neurons.[40–42] This excitatory transmission is essential for rhythm generation. Selective blockade of non-NMDA receptors in the preBötC abolishes respiratory rhythm in *in vitro* neonatal rat preparations. In the adult rat *in vivo*, blockade of excitatory amino acid neurotransmission in the same area also abolishes respiratory rhythm (Fig. 40.11), but because of the greater array of afferent inputs present *in vivo*, blockade of both NMDA and non-NMDA receptors is required. The precise role(s) excitatory amino acids play in generating respiratory rhythm is unknown, but could include providing the tonic background excitatory drive that is required to bring various populations of respiratory neurons to threshold. Excitatory amino acids also might contribute to recurrent excitatory connections that build up activity within the network. Alternatively, these amino acids might coordinate the periods of excitation in neurons contributing to rhythm generation, thereby providing the conditions necessary for the initiation of bursting in conditional pacemaker neurons.

Summary

At the heart of breathing is central rhythm generation. The site for automatic generation of this rhythm is within the brainstem. The consensus hypothesis is that the critical circuits lie within (but not necessarily restricted to) a small region of the rostral ventrolateral medulla, the pre-Bötzinger complex. The neural mechanisms undoubtedly require interactions among specialized classes of neurons and may include neurons with the burst properties of pacemakers.

SENSORY INPUTS AND ALTERED BREATHING

O_2 and CO_2 Are Measured by Chemoreceptors

The pathways and mechanisms for regulating O_2 and CO_2 are separate.[32,76,77] This distinction is probably because the consequences of acute shortfalls in O_2 are catastrophic, but the effects of modestly depressed or elevated P_{O_2} are benign. In contrast, cellular metabolism is strongly sensitive to small changes in P_{CO_2}. Thus, on a breath-by-breath basis at rest and in health, we control ventilation mostly to regulate CO_2 but not O_2; in the event of a marked drop in O_2, we ignore all else. For example, the exceptionally low ambient pressures at the top of Mount Everest ($P_{O_2} \approx 40$ mm Hg) result in such a strong ventilatory drive that blood P_{CO_2} in climbers without supplemental O_2 is exceptionally low ($\approx$7 mm Hg compared with normal $\approx$40 mm Hg). See Box 40.4.

O_2

The mammalian brain is extremely sensitive to O_2 deprivation. Several minutes of anoxia can initiate a cascade that leads to neuronal (and, if sufficiently widespread, brain) death. Brain hypoxia can cause loss of consciousness. Perhaps for these reasons, the principal O_2 sensors for the entire body are in the carotid bodies, at the bifurcation of the common carotid artery, through which most of the O_2 enters the brain. The mechanisms by which O_2 levels are transduced into afferent signals have been intensely studied since C. Heyman's discovery of the physiological function of the carotid bodies,[78] for which he was awarded the Nobel Prize in Physiology or Medicine in 1939. Carotid chemoreceptors do not exhibit a threshold for activation, different from most other sensory receptors, and chemoreceptor discharge is irregular, describable as a Poisson process.[79] O_2-related signals enter the brain

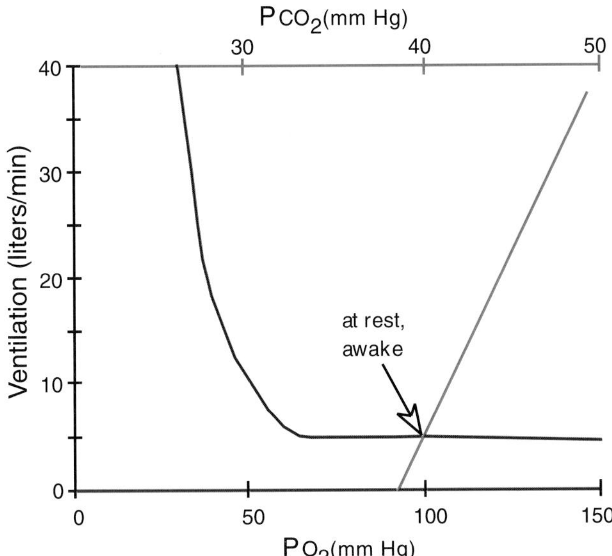

FIGURE 40.14 Changes in P_{O_2} cause a hyperbolic change in breathing that closely tracks the carotid chemoreceptor afferent activity. In contrast, the ventilatory response to changes in P_{CO_2} is linear and much more sensitive. A large part of the CO_2 response arises from activation of central chemoreceptors. These curves are representative of responses seen in healthy 20-year-old, 70-kg men.

via the glossopharyngeal nerve and synapse in the dorsomedial medulla in the NST.

Under normal conditions, O_2 sensors account for only a small part of the chemical drive to breathe. Removal of carotid body chemosensory input by breathing 100% O_2 reduces minute ventilation by about 15% in awake mammals.[80] Even when inspired air is 80% O_2 ($P_{O_2} \approx 600$ mm Hg), the carotid bodies still discharge. As P_{O_2} is lowered farther, chemoreceptor activity and ventilation increase relatively little until the P_{O_2} falls below about 60 mm Hg (Fig. 40.14). With further reductions in P_{O_2}, chemoreceptor discharge and ventilation increase exponentially.[81]

CO_2

Ventilation is very sensitive to small changes in P_{CO_2} (Fig. 40.14), which is normally about 40 mm Hg with ventilation of about 5 liters of air per minute. A 1 mm Hg increase in P_{CO_2} leads to a 2 liter min^{-1} increase in ventilation. In other words, a 2.5% increase in P_{CO_2} leads to a 40% increase in ventilation.

The sites and mechanisms of CO_2 chemoreception remain obscure. A robust CO_2 response is still seen in peripherally chemodenervated decerebrate mammals, suggesting that CO_2 or related variables (pH, HCO_3^-) have additional intracranial sensors. Most attention has focused on the ventral medulla. Researchers have demonstrated that significant alterations in pH at the ventral medullary surface alter breathing in anesthetized animals.[82,83] At pH 7.0 ventilation increases; and at pH 7.8, ventilation decreases (normal brain extracellular fluid pH is 7.3). These changes are in the appropriate directions, but relative to physiologically expected shifts in pH associated with significant changes in ventilation (e.g., a decrease of 0.05 unit in cerebrospinal fluid pH produces a three- to five-fold increase in ventilation) the experimental perturbations are extreme, like mapping touch receptors with a sledge hammer. More recently, experiments have delineated specific structures that appear to play a role in intracranial chemotransduction. The most convincing experiments have utilized small injections of the carbonic anhydrase inhibitor acetazolamide (AZ); carbonic anhydrase catalyzes the reaction $CO_2 + H_2O \leftrightarrow H^+ + HCO_3^-$. Injections of 1 nl of an AZ solution, which produce highly localized tissue acidosis, into various regions in cat or rat brainstem stimulated central structures sensitive to changes in CO_2 and pH and caused a consequent increase in ventilation.[32] These injections were centered at two distinct regions, including the retrotrapezoid nucleus and the NST; the raphe nuclei may also be involved (see Fig. 40.2). However, identification of neurons that act as sensors has proven elusive. Consequently, the cellular and synaptic mechanisms of CO_2 chemoreception remain unknown.

Mechanoreceptors in the Lungs Adjust Breathing Pattern and Initiate Protective Reflexes

Many patterns of muscle activity can produce alveolar ventilation appropriate for a given metabolic load; however, the chosen pattern must minimize energy expenditure. The efficiency of a pattern of respiratory muscle activity in turn depends on such factors as posture and lung and chest wall mechanics (e.g., a fibrotic lung is harder to inflate to a given tidal volume than a normal lung, and thus for this condition rapid, shallow breathing is more efficient). Feedback about the mechanical status of the lungs and chest wall is provided by mechanoreceptors.

For example, because the airways must be patent for air flow, airway receptors produce two of the most powerful and compelling reflexes, coughing and gagging.[91–94] Another example occurs at birth, when the transition from the liquid uterine environment to an air environment requires a powerful inspiratory effort (sigh) to overcome surface forces resisting the initial inflation of the lung. The necessary sigh is stimulated by pulmonary receptors. Additional reflex stimuli, typically mechanical or thermal, further facilitate the first inspiratory sighs. Special respiratory reflexes, such as sneezing and yawning, are also generated by pulmonary receptors.

Mechanosensory signals are critical in adapting, ad-

BOX 40.4

DISORDERS OF THE CHEMICAL CONTROL OF BREATHING ARE WIDESPREAD AND SERIOUS

Breathing is normally tightly controlled to maintain arterial P_{CO_2} within a narrow range close to 40 mm Hg. However, cardiopulmonary pathology can markedly increase P_{CO_2}. When P_{CO_2} exceeds 90–120 mm Hg, respiratory depression ensues.[84,85] With further increases in P_{CO_2}, central nervous system function can be severely impaired; a life-threatening positive feedback loop can develop, in which depression of breathing elevates P_{CO_2}, which further depresses breathing.[86] In some patients with advanced chronic lung disease, and consequently elevated P_{CO_2}, any acute lung disease, such as bronchitis or pneumonia, can cause a further increase in P_{CO_2} and exacerbate respiratory depression. In these patients, the drive to breathe comes from hypoxemia (low blood P_{O_2}), sensed by peripheral chemoreceptors. If these patients breathe O_2 without medical monitoring, the hypoxemia may disappear, and without this stimulus these patients' breathing may stop.

Drug abuse is another cause of respiratory depression sufficient to elevate P_{CO_2} to produce further respiratory depression. Narcotics, barbiturates, and most general anesthetics depress breathing and reduce the sensitivity of the chemoreceptors to elevations in P_{CO_2} or reductions in P_{O_2}. Therefore, at high doses these drugs can cause death by respiratory failure.

Sleep apnea. Sleep is associated with a modest decrease in ventilation and reduced responsiveness to deviations in P_{CO_2} and P_{O_2}.[16,87,88] As a result, during sleep arterial P_{CO_2} increases 2–7 mm Hg and P_{O_2} decreases 3–10 mm Hg. This change in respiratory control perhaps is associated with the loss of a wakefulness-related excitatory drive. The source of this wakefulness stimulus is not known, but it may derive from corollary activity originating in the brainstem reticular-activating system.

With the onset of sleep, the breathing pattern can become unstable, and apnea (defined as at least 10 s without breathing) can occur. Two major types of apnea have been defined. The most common, *obstructive sleep apnea,* occurs when inspiratory airflow reduces airway pressure (via the Bernoulli effect), pulling in on the walls of the upper airway and causing airway obstruction. During wakefulness, the activity of airway muscles counteracts this collapsing force. However, during sleep the reduction of airway muscle tone can result in vibration of the walls of the oropharynx (i.e., snoring). In more severe cases, the loss of activity in the glossopharyngeal nerve, which innervates the tongue, can cause the airway to become obstructed. Obstruction reduces or abolishes ventilation, raising CO_2 and lowering O_2. This in turn can cause arousal, or waking, and restoration of airway muscle tone and airway patency. In serious cases, the cycle of sleep, airway obstruction, and hypoxia-induced waking repeats hundreds of times every night. The marked disruption of sleep can cause debilitating hypersomnolesence, and severe obstructive sleep apnea can also have other sequelae, such as hypertension.

In *central sleep apnea,* a less common form of sleep apnea, pauses in breathing result from the failure of the central pattern generator for breathing to generate a rhythmic motor command. Mechanisms underlying central apneas are not understood, but the problem has been associated with a variety of neurologic disorders, including brainstem lesions, autonomic dysfunction, and encephalitis, which could impair brainstem function.

Sudden infant death syndrome (SIDS). SIDS is defined as the unexpected sudden death of an infant or young child that cannot be explained by a postmortem examination.[89,90] SIDS is the leading cause of death of infants between 1 month and 1 year of age in the United States. Although a number of etiologies are likely to contribute to SIDS, current hypotheses tend to focus on abnormalities of cardiorespiratory control. The apnea hypothesis of SIDS attributes apnea to disorders of both the chemical control of breathing and the arousal response to insufficient ventilation. Infants who later succumb to SIDS have been described as exhibiting irregular breathing patterns, including periods of apnea, and depressed arousal responses to hypoxia or hypercapnia. Epidemiologically, SIDS has been associated with infants sleeping face down, where pillows, blankets, and mattress can limit diffusion of expired air, resulting in elevated CO_2 and lower O_2 in inspired air and, consequently, in arterial blood. This in turn could depress breathing sufficiently to cause respiratory arrest and death.

justing, and integrating breathing with other acts of brain and body. Many movements impact directly on breathing, either by using the same muscles used for breathing (e.g., phonation, posture, defecation, and emesis) or through mechanical disturbances, such as locomotion.

Lung Afferents

Sensory receptors in the lungs and airways have important roles in the control of breathing and in pulmonary defense reflexes, such as cough. Three distinct groups of afferents, all with afferent fibers coursing in the vagus nerve and terminating in the nucleus of the solitary tract, have been identified (see Table 40.1). Two groups have large, myelinated A fibers, which are located in the airways and include slowly adapting and rapidly adapting pulmonary stretch receptors. The third group gives rise to small, unmyelinated C fibers and responds to inhaled irritants such as smoke. The relative inaccessibility of these stretch and irritant receptors has made it difficult to selectively activate a single type of receptor and precisely define the natural stimuli and reflex responses of each. Most natural stimuli (e.g., pulmonary edema or alveolar collapse) probably activate more than one category of receptor, and the CNS likely integrates these inputs to determine the nature of the appropriate response.

Slowly adapting pulmonary stretch receptors (SARs) Located in airway smooth muscle, SARs are activated when the airways stretch during lung inflation. Their activation leads to reflexes in which lung inflation prematurely terminates inspiration and prolongs expiration. This limitation in respiratory excursion is called the Breuer-Hering reflex and is important in respiratory timing. With the exception of humans, the activation of these receptors with each normal inspiration overrides the baseline rhythm of the respiratory pattern generator, shortening the inspiratory period and increasing the overall breathing frequency. In humans, normal breaths apparently do not activate the SAR receptors sufficiently to affect inspiratory timing. Activation of these receptors also relaxes airway smooth muscle. Asthma (caused by airway constriction) sufferers will often attempt to breathe such that their end-expiratory lung volume is larger than normal. This breathing activates slowly adapting pulmonary stretch receptors, producing compensatory bronchodilation.

The Breuer-Hering reflex has been exploited experimentally to explore the control of the timing of respiratory phases. If the lungs are prevented from emptying after normal inflation, the subsequent expiratory period is greatly lengthened.[95,96] In contrast, if the lungs are prevented from filling during an inspiratory period, the next inspiratory period is lengthened and the magnitude of inspiratory motor activity is greatly increased.[33,97] Less extreme limitations produce similar effects; that is, reduction of inspiratory air flow lengthens inspiration, and reduction of expiratory air flow lengthens expiration. The simplest way to study the Breuer-Hering reflex and the central circuitry generating respiratory rhythm is to paralyze an experimental animal and ventilate it with a ventilator while recording respiratory motor output on the phrenic nerve. If the respirator is turned off every few cycles so that lung inflation does not occur, inspiratory duration (defined by the duration of bursts on the phrenic nerve) increases. Lesions in the parabrachial nuclei and blockade of NMDA receptors each can markedly alter this response (Fig. 40.15). In either case, the pattern of activity looks normal when the lungs are inflated and deflated normally, but not when the lungs are kept static. The events associated with these reversible normal and apneustic states should provide key information about the central mechanisms underlying phase transition and rhythmicity.

Higher-order neurons in the Breuer-Hering reflex The Breuer-Hering reflex has been one of the more intensely studied vagal reflexes.[98–102] Because its activation changes the respiratory rhythm, an understanding of the underlying mechanisms will illuminate aspects of the central pattern generator for breathing. SAR afferents monosynaptically activate two groups of NST neurons. The I-β group is a subset of I-Aug neurons, many of which are bulbospinal premotor neurons. Ac-

A

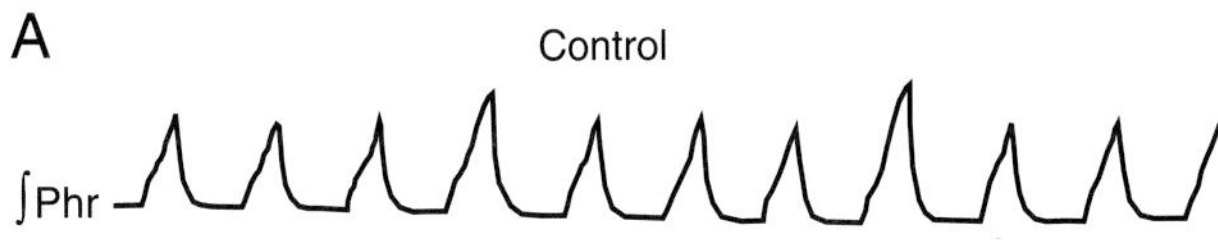

B

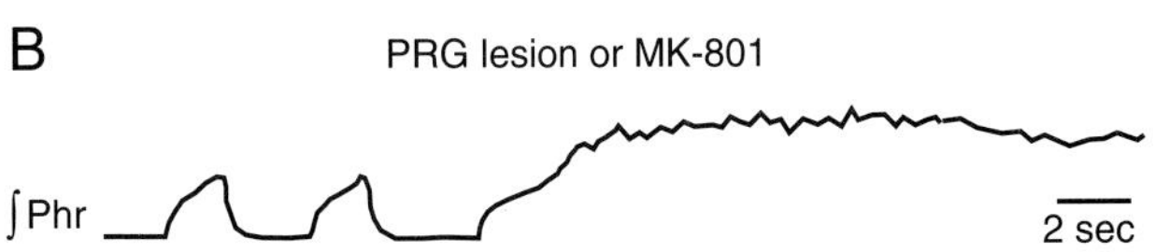

FIGURE 40.15 Breuer–Hering reflex. In an anesthetized, paralyzed cat or rodent, phrenic nerve activity (which would normally contract the diaphragm and produce lung inflation) drives a pump that inflates the lungs. (A) In cycles during which the pump is not activated, the inspiratory burst is longer, but still terminates (control). Following lesions in the pontine respiratory group (PRG) or block of NMDA receptor activity (B), the burst pattern during lung inflation is similar to that of the control; however, an apneusis develops if the lungs are not inflated, indicating that central mechanisms have been perturbed.

tivation of these neurons may increase the amplitude of phrenic motor output, but seems unlikely to change timing, because lesions of the vlNST (where I_β neurons are located) do not affect the Breuer-Hering reflex. The second group receiving SAR input is pump (P) cells, so named because in paralyzed, artificially ventilated animals SAR afferent input causes P cells to discharge in phase with the ventilator (pump)-induced lung inflations. P cells do not, however, receive a rhythmic input from the central respiratory rhythm generator; therefore, when the ventilator is turned off, they are silent. P cells receive oligosynaptic activation from vagus nerve afferent fibers (probably including SARs) and are depolarized during lung inflations that elicit the Breuer-Hering expiratory prolonging reflex. Figure 40.16 outlines a possible pathway for mediating the reflex prolongation of expiration. Lung inflation activates SARs and initiates sequential activation of several populations of neurons. SAR primary afferent fibers in the vagus nerve monosynaptically communicate lung volume information to P cells in the NST. These neurons then oligosynaptically activate E-Dec neurons, which, by virtue of their hypothesized connections, prolong expiratory duration. Note that not all pump cells appear to be involved in the Breuer-Hering reflex. The physiological roles of these P cells is not known, but could involve reflex changes in the pattern of motor output or control of airway smooth muscle tone. The neurons might even contribute to the ascending information that gives rise to respiratory sensations.

Rapidly adapting pulmonary stretch receptors (RARs) Located in airway epithelial and subepithelial layers, RARs initiate protective reflexes in response to a variety of stimuli, including large or rapid lung inflation or deflation, inhaled irritants, and, possibly, airway edema (see Table 40.1). Inhalation of irritants such as smoke activates RARs in the large airways and elicits a cough to rid the airway of the offending material. Activation of these receptors can also result in rapid breathing. In addition, these afferents have been proposed to elicit sighs in response to collapse of alveoli. As alveoli collapse, the lungs become stiffer. This change in pulmonary mechanics is sensed by RARs, and a larger than normal breath (a sigh) is elicited, inflating the lung and popping open the alveoli.

Bronchopulmonary C fibers C fiber afferents elicit apnea followed by rapid shallow breathing. Like RARs, C fibers are polymodal, activated by chemical and mechanical stimuli. Activation of these receptors enhances mucus secretion in the airways. Inhaled particles are trapped in the mucus and removed from the airways by the action of cilia, which continuously (in the non-

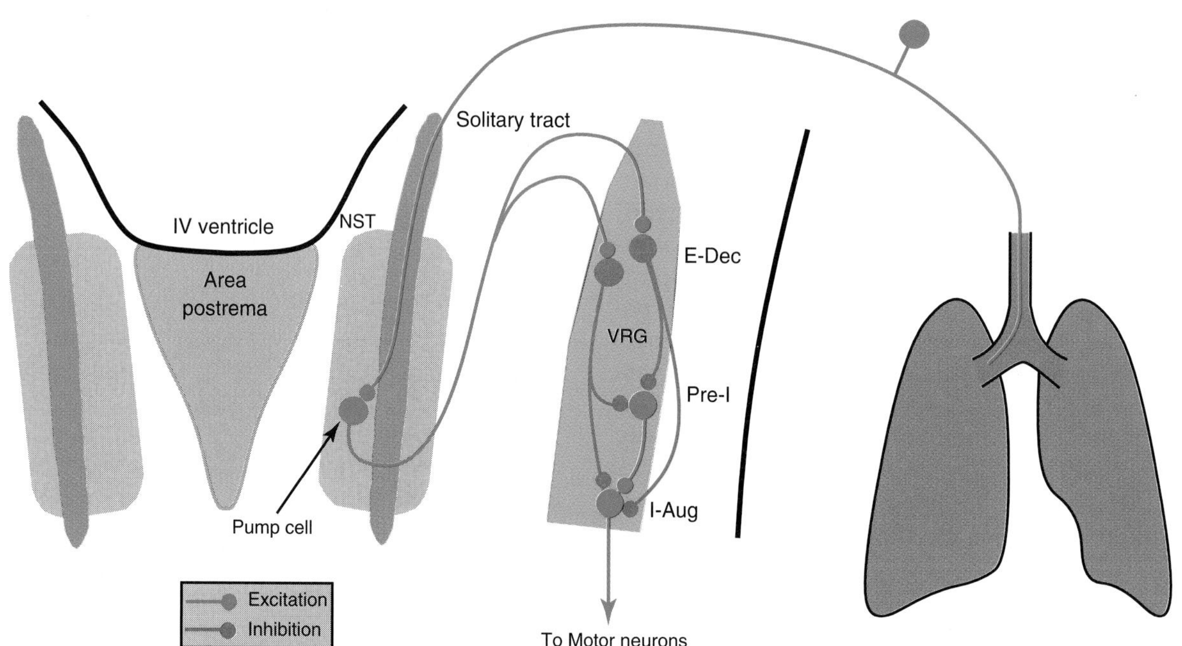

FIGURE 40.16 Dorsal view of rat brainstem showing hypothesized central pathway for producing reflex termination of inspiration and prolongation of expiration (the Breuer–Hering reflex). Slowly adapting pulmonary stretch receptor afferents activate pump cells in the nucleus of the solitary tract (NST). Subsequent activation of Late-I neurons terminates inspiration, while activation of E-Dec neurons prolongs expiration by inhibiting I-Dec and I-Aug neurons.

TABLE 40.1 Pulmonary Vagal Afferents and Their Associated Reflexes

Receptor (fiber type)	Location	Stimulus	Reflex response
Slowly adapting pulmonary stretch receptors (myelinated A fibers)	Airway smooth muscle	Lung inflation (distension of airways)	Breuer-Hering reflex: inspiratory termination and expiratory prolongation Airway dilation
Rapidly adapting pulmonary stretch receptors (myelinated A fibers)	Airway epithelium and subepithelial layers of mucosa	Rapid lung inflation or deflation Edema in walls of large airways Chemical irritants	Cough Augmented inspiration (sigh) Shortened expiration Airway constriction
Bronchopulmonary C fibers (unmyelinated C fibers)	Airways and aveolar wall	Chemical irritants; edema	Apnea (cessation of breathing) Rapid, shallow breathing Airway constriction Mucus secretion

smoker) move the mucus and trapped particles toward the mouth to be swallowed or expectorated.

Targets of Lung Afferents

Afferent fibers arising from the three groups of lung and airway receptors enter the medulla via the vagus nerve and course caudally in the solitary tract to terminate principally within the NST and area postrema. SAR afferents terminate in the ipsilateral NST in a region slightly rostral to the obex, while RAR fibers terminate bilaterally with a modest ipsilateral predominance in a region caudal to the obex.[103–106] C fiber afferents distribute to the dorsomedial aspects of the NST and adjacent area postrema, with distributions extending somewhat rostral and caudal to the obex.[107,108]

Summary

Chemoreceptors in the arterial system and in the brain provide sensory input to the central circuits controlling breathing to tightly regulate P_{CO_2} and P_{O_2} within narrow limits over a wide range of metabolic demand. Peripheral receptors in the carotid and aortic bodies are especially sensitive to decreases in arterial P_{O_2}, and they also sense increases in arterial P_{CO_2} and decreases in arterial pH. Central chemoreceptors in the brainstem are exquisitely sensitive to increases in tissue P_{CO_2} and decreases in pH, but central chemoreceptors respond little to changes in P_{O_2}. Mechanoreceptors, especially those in the lungs, are essential for the precise regulation of the timing and amplitude of breathing and participate in reflexes, such as cough, that protect the airways and lungs from compromises in airflow.

MODULATION OF RESPIRATORY MOTOR OUTPUT

As discussed earlier in this chapter, the generation of an appropriate motor output is not simply sine wave generation. A precise spatiotemporal pattern of motor outputs must be generated for a broad spectrum of activated muscles.[42,74,109–115] Reflex adjustments in pattern are made as body position changes. Other adjustments produce efficient breathing patterns during physical exercise and adapt to changes in lung and chest wall mechanics that accompany postnatal development and pulmonary disease.

How do we meet these challenges to appropriate control of breathing? Although the full answer is not yet apparent, it is clear that activation of sensory receptors often triggers changes in breathing that outlast the stimulus by seconds to hours. Electrical stimulation of carotid chemoreceptor afferents, for example, increases breathing over three distinct time frames: seconds, minutes, and hours (Fig. 40.17).[116] In an artificially ventilated cat or rat in which blood gases are maintained constant, a single 60- to 120-s period of stimulation produces an immediate increase in ventilation, followed by a smaller decrease when stimulation is terminated. Motor output remains elevated for several minutes, slowly decreasing back to the prestimulation level. This temporary increase in motor output is referred to as **short-term potentiation.** A long-lasting increase of several hours, called **long-term facilitation,** can be induced if the stimulation is repeated several times.

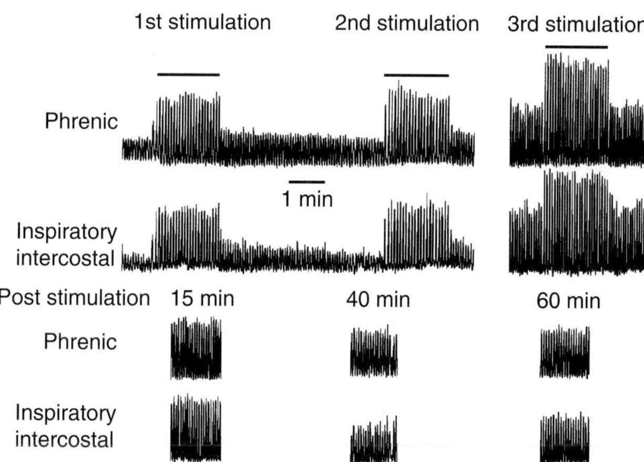

FIGURE 40.17 The increase in respiratory motor output of phrenic and inspiratory intercostal nerves in response to 25-Hz carotid sinus nerve stimulation falls into three distinct time frames. In the immediate response, respiratory motor output increases within seconds of beginning stimulation. Short-term potentiation follows a single 1- to 2-min period of stimulation, and respiratory motor output remains elevated for several minutes before slowly returning to prestimulation levels. Long-term facilitation follows five periods of stimulation, and a stable level of elevated respiratory motor output is maintained for at least 60 min. Redrawn from Fregosi and Mitchell.[116]

The short-term potentiation of ventilation likely involves mechanisms distributed at several stages between afferent input and motor output. NMDA receptors are probably activated in the region of afferent processing in the NST and within the phrenic nucleus. Long-term facilitation appears to involve activation of raphe serotonergic neurons, since electrical stimulation of the midline raphe produces long-term facilitation, while broad-spectrum serotonin antagonists prevent it.[110]

Short-term potentiation of breathing may be important in producing smoothly changing respiratory responses during rapid or large changes in afferent input. If breathing responded immediately and fully to changes in afferent signals, large swings in arterial blood gases would result, thereby causing further reflex changes in breathing and ultimately resulting in an unstable control system (e.g., Cheyne-Stokes respiration). Long-term facilitation could underlie adaptive changes to pathophysiological conditions that result in repeated peripheral chemoreceptor activation. For example, long-term facilitation may help restore stable respiration during sleep-disordered breathing in which repeated periods of sleep apnea result in episodic hypoxia.[42,114] During sleep, the activity of serotonergic raphe neurons is dramatically reduced. Repeated activation of these neurons secondary to apnea-induced chemoreceptor activation could result in arousal, which could increase ventilatory drive and reduce the probability of future apneas.

An example of unstable breathing is seen in patients in whom the central network controlling breathing responds to a change in activity of the chemoreceptors by causing too large or too rapid a change in breathing. The central circuitry controlling breathing is capable of rapidly (<200 ms) changing ventilation in response to changes in chemoreceptor activity, but the delay is much longer (several seconds) between the time ventilation changes and the detection of the resultant (corrective) changes in blood gases by peripheral and central chemoreceptors. This difference between the rapid response time and the much slower detection of the resultant change in blood gases is a potential source of instability[75]; such instability occurs in Cheyne-Stokes respiration (Fig. 40.13). A rapid response of the central controller to increased P_{CO_2} increases ventilation and lowers P_{CO_2} of blood leaving the lungs. However, because blood takes time to travel from the lungs to the carotid body chemoreceptors, ventilatory drive continues to increase. The increased ventilation lowers P_{CO_2} below optimal levels. When blood with this abnormally low P_{CO_2} arrives at the chemoreceptors, ventilation will be adjusted downward and respiration might stop. During apnea, CO_2 builds up in the lungs and the blood perfusing them. As this blood with a high P_{CO_2} reaches the chemoreceptors, breathing is restored and a progressive increase in ventilation will once again lower P_{CO_2} in the lungs, repeating the oscillation. A descending inhibitory system slows the respiratory response to chemoreceptor stimulation to prevent this type of instability. Instability can result from decreasing the inhibition, as may happen with a CNS lesion or injury, or from prolonging the delay between a change in ventilation (affecting P_{CO_2} in the lung) and the detection of the effects of the change by chemoreceptors (carotid body and brain). The latter prolonged delay may occur when blood flow decreases during heart failure, for example. Both changes can result in an exaggerated respiratory response. The source of descending inhibitory control has not been identified, but cortical and subcortical lesions of the cerebral hemispheres and bilateral interruption of descending pathways (corticobulbar pathways as far caudal as the pons) produce this breathing pattern.[75]

Neurotransmitters Contribute to the Modulation of Breathing

The waxing and waning membrane potential underlying the periodic bursting of motor neurons can be ascribed simply to the alternating release of glutamate, GABA, and glycine at their respective postsynaptic

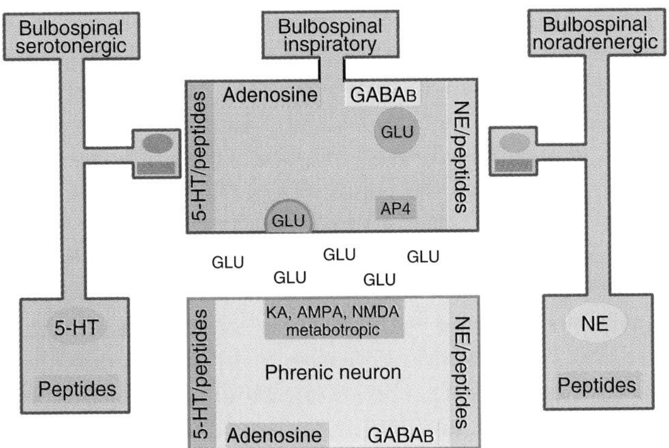

FIGURE 40.18 The diversity of synaptic control on phrenic motor neurons is essential for their proper functioning. The challenge is to understand how these mechanisms act in an integrated manner. Isolating and studying them one by one or out of context, for example, in culture, may fail to reveal key properties. AMPA (see text), AP4 (see Fig. 40.7), GLU, glutamate; 5-HT, serotonin; KA, kainate; NE, norepinephrine.

receptors. Given the straightforward task of these motor neurons, especially for muscle as specialized as the diaphragm, one might presume that little more is required to control their excitability. Yet the picture is richer, providing some insight into possible roles for diversity of transmitters.[39,40,42–45,50,51,109,117–122]

Regardless of the type of neuron considered, neurotransmitters transmit synaptic signals that shape its discharge pattern. A limited survey of possible neurotransmitters that alter respiratory rhythm and pattern includes excitatory amino acids (of which glutamate is the primary member), inhibitory amino acids, (principally GABA and glycine), the amine serotonin (5-HT), catecholamines (norepinephrine, epinephrine, and dopamine), acetylcholine, adenosine, and numerous peptides (typically colocalized with the amines), including substance P, neuropeptide Y, galanin, Met-enkephalin, cholecystokinin, and thyrotropin-releasing hormone (Fig. 40.18). We could look at each of these transmitters separately, but little detailed information about the roles of specific transmitters in respiratory rhythm generation is available, and this reductionist approach does not address why nature employs such a variety of neurotransmitters. Many of these transmitters have been identified in the phrenic nucleus, and researchers have asked why so many neurotransmitters are present at such a simple relay to a muscle with a limited repertoire of functions. Multiple transmitters and receptors may be necessary to control neuronal excitability over the broad time scales important in breathing, from the millisecond scale of synaptic currents of cycle-by-cycle respiratory drive, to the seconds required to alter ventilation in response to changes in blood gases, to the hours or days for acclimatization to altitude or adjustment to disease, development, and aging. Alternatively, multiple transmitters may allow coarse and fine control of P_{O_2}, P_{CO_2}, and pH. Multiple transmitters may also ensure that breathing is not compromised by changes in state, especially during sleep when global changes in amine levels can affect motor neuronal excitability. During rapid eye movement (REM) sleep, motor neuronal excitability produces a widespread muscle atonia, yet respiratory motor neurons must continue to drive respiratory muscles. The key to maintaining respiratory motor neuronal excitability may be related to 5-HT, which is drastically reduced during REM. Like most motor neurons, phrenic neurons depolarize in response to exogenously applied 5-HT (Fig. 40.19). In addition, 5-HT reduces inspiratory drive, apparently presynaptically. The combination of these two effects means that during the awake state 5-HT increases the excitability of phrenic motor neurons to all inputs and decreases inspiratory inputs. We propose that the drop in 5-HT release during REM sleep decreases the excitability of all motor neurons, but the inspiratory throughput of phrenic motor neurons to the diaphragm is maintained due to removal of 5-HT-mediated presynaptic inhibition of the bulbospinal inspiratory terminal (Fig. 40.20). Finally, multiple neurotransmitters may be needed to

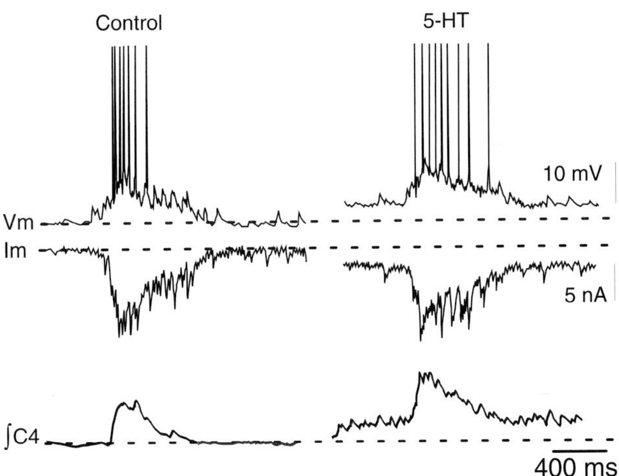

FIGURE 40.19 Effects of serotonin (5-HT) on motor neuron excitability. Left, control; right, 5-HT. Top, current-clamp recording from a phrenic motor neuron. Middle, voltage-clamp recording. Bottom, integrated respiratory activity recorded from a C4 ventral rootlet. Note that under current clamp, the net effect of 5-HT is excitatory, with no hint of inhibition. Under voltage clamp, however, two effects are seen: a decreased inspiratory drive and a tonic inward current (that produces a tonic depolarization). The balance of these two distinct effects determines the outcome of 5-HT application or withdrawal (see Fig. 40.20).

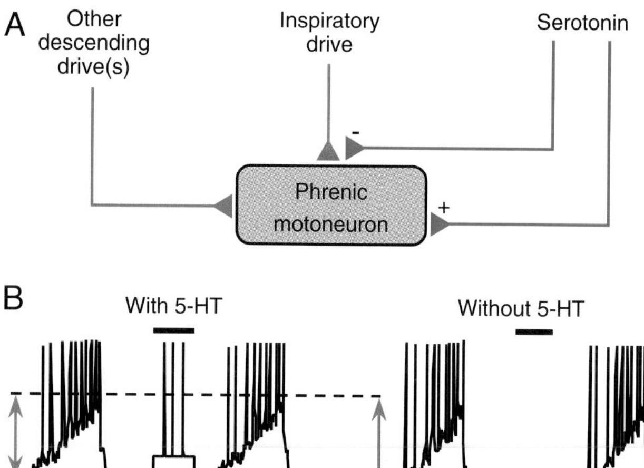

FIGURE 40.20 Differential control of phrenic motor neuron excitability may protect the diaphragm from sleep-induced depression of excitability. Serotonin (5-HT) receptors, which are located throughout the phrenic motor neuron pool, are present on motor neurons and presynaptic terminals transmitting inspiratory drive. The postsynaptic action is excitatory; the presynaptic action is inhibitory; that is, it reduces inspiratory drive. Reduction of 5-HT release, as occurs during REM sleep, reduces the response of phrenic motor neurons to all inputs; at the same time, the inhibition of the presynaptic terminals transmitting inspiratory drive is removed, increasing that input to the motor neurons. The net result is a relatively constant level of drive.

prevent respiratory muscle fatigue. Strong inspiratory drive will sufficiently elevate glutamate in the synaptic cleft to act via a presynaptic metabotropic receptor to reduce further release. This governor of maximal phrenic motor neuronal activity would limit the likelihood of diaphragmatic fatigue during periods of sustained high ventilatory demand (e.g., fleeing a predator).

Summary

As metabolism, posture, and sleep–wake state change, the breathing pattern must adjust rapidly to ensure appropriate and efficient ventilation. Development and disease, as well as changes in elevation, are processes that require slower adaptations in breathing. Amino acids, amines, peptides, and other neurotransmitters coordinate circuits generating and modulating respiratory pattern to ensure that adaptations proceed smoothly and precisely by mechanisms that remain to be determined.

SUPRAPONTINE STRUCTURES AND BREATHING

We have focused on the roles of the pons, medulla, and spinal cord in the control of breathing. These regions contain the minimum circuitry for generating respiratory rhythm, producing the motor output, and modifying its pattern in response to afferent input from the lungs, airways, and chest. Higher brain regions have fundamental roles in producing integrated responses in which the behaviors of multiple organ systems are coordinated to produce an appropriate output.[114,115,123–126] Speech, for example, requires the coordination of jaw and facial muscles, precise tongue, upper airway, and laryngeal control, and coordinated activity of breathing muscles to produce controlled subglottal pressure. The anterior limbic cortex (including the rostral anterior cingulate gyrus, the subcallosal gyrus, and gyrus rectus), midbrain periaqueductal gray, brainstem respiratory nuclei, and cranial and spinal motor neurons contribute to speech.[125,126]

Sustained or repetitive movement of large muscles involved in such basic behaviors as fleeing predators, chasing prey, and exercising also involves higher CNS functions. During exercise the metabolic production of CO_2 increases as a result of increased consumption of O_2. However, arterial P_{CO_2} and P_{O_2} change little during moderate exercise because of an increase in breathing proportional to the demand for gas exchange. This increase is believed to be produced by a feedforward descending command from higher brain systems and sensory input from joint and muscle receptors. The latter inputs provide feedback about limb and muscle mechanics but can be considered feedforward with respect to the control of arterial blood gases, because they may provide cues for adjusting the magnitude of the descending command. Any inadequacy in the feedforward mechanisms to produce appropriate ventilation is immediately met by chemoreceptor feedback (mostly P_{CO_2}, not P_{O_2}). Thus arterial blood gases are tightly regulated during moderate exercise.

The volitional initiation of exercise, signaled by suprapontine structures, likely involves parallel activation of spinal locomotor pathways and brainstem mechanisms controlling breathing and cardiovascular function so that pulmonary ventilation and gas transport change appropriately. We presume that the commands for activation of pulmonary and locomotor muscles arise in similar ways in the motor cortex, thalamus, and basal ganglia. Once the motor command has been initiated, respiratory and locomotor activities are believed to be coordinated at subcortical levels, including the hypothalamus. Electrical or chemical activation of the hypothalamus of an anesthetized, paralyzed cat elicits fictive locomotion paired with proportional increases in respiratory motor output (suggestive of exercise-related increases in ventilation or exercise hyperpnea) and redistribution of blood flow consistent with the induction of locomotion.[124] Because the animals were paralyzed, muscle activation did not occur, and thus the changes in breathing were the result of feedforward control rather than sensory feedback from joint or muscle receptors.

The exercise ventilatory response demonstrates the plasticity of the respiratory control system. An example of this modulation is evident in experiments in which goats were trained to stand or run on a treadmill.[109,113,114] Normally, ventilation increases in proportion to the exercise-induced increase in metabolic rate, and arterial blood gases remain close to resting values. When the animals breathed through a tube, which increased respiratory dead space, the response was markedly enhanced, and the enhancement occurred within one exercise trial. Normal response was restored when the dead space was removed. Application of serotonin receptor antagonists to the spinal cord attenuated or blocked this effect. When goats were repeatedly exercised with an increased dead space, additional mechanisms came into play to further alter the ventilatory response. For example, after 2 days of exercise with increased dead space, the response without the extra dead space was augmented for up to 6 h, resulting in hyperventilation and respiratory alkalosis (i.e., decreased blood P_{CO_2} and increased pH). This longer lasting effect, when prior experience alters ventilatory response, is a form of learning. These findings illustrate that ventilatory control is not a static, hard-wired reflex response but a complex integrative process capable of long-term adaptations to changing (patho)physiological or environmental conditions, such as onset of lung disease, acclimatization to high altitude, or scuba or firefighting equipment (which increase dead space).

Summary

Breathing is a basic physiologic function that must be vigilantly controlled by the brain. We have explored basic mechanisms underlying rhythm generation, sensory processing, and motor output. Given the broad range of experimental systems available to study these mechanisms, from *in vitro* rodent brainstem slices to intact awake and sleeping humans, all levels of neurobiological analysis have considerable potential to unravel integrative mechanisms that may be of general importance.

References

1. Smith, J. C., Ellenberger, H. H. Ballanyi, K., Richter, D. W., and Feldman, J. L. (1991). Pre-Bötzinger complex: A brainstem region that may generate respiratory rhythm in mammals. *Science* **254:** 726–729.
2. Galen. (1968). *Usefulness of the Parts of the Body* (M. T. May, ed.), Cornell University Press, Ithaca, NY.
3. Lorry, M. (1760). Les mouvements du cerveau. *Mem. Math. Phys. Pres. Acad. Roy. Sci. Div. Sav. Paris* **3:** 344–377.
4. Legallois, M. (1813). *Experiments on the Principle of Life.* Philadelphia: Thomas.
5. Lumsden, T. (1923). Observations on the respiratory centres in the cat. *J. Physiol. (London)* **57:** 153–160.
6. Hoff, H. E., and Breckenridge, C. G. (1949). The medullary origin of respiratory periodicity in the dog. *Am. J. Physiol.* **158:** 157–172.
7. Wang, S. C., Ngai, S. H., and Frumin, M. J. (1957). Organization of central respiratory mechanisms in the brain stem of the cat: Genesis of normal respiratory rhythmicity. *Am. J. Physiol.* **190:** 333–342.
8. Ramón y Cajal, S. (1909). *Histologie du système nerveux de l'homme et des vertèbres.* Maloine, Paris.
9. Adrian, E. D., and Buytendijk, F. J. J. (1931). Potential changes in the isolated brainstem of goldfish. *J. Physiol. (London)* **71:** 121–135.
10. Gesell, R., Bricker, J., and Magee, C. (1936). Structural and functional organization of the central mechanism controlling breathing. *Am. J. Physiol.* **117:** 423–452.
11. Aminoff, M. J., and Sears, T. A. (1971). Spinal integration of segmental, cortical and breathing inputs to thoracic respiratory motoneurons. *J. Physiol. (London)* **215:** 557–575.
12. Davenport, P. W., Shannon, R., Mercak, A., Reep, R. L., and Lindsey, B. G. (1993). Cerebral cortical evoked potentials elicited by cat intercostal muscle mechanoreceptors. *J. Appl. Physiol.* **74:** 799–804.
13. Pleschka, K., and Wang, S. C. (1975). The activity of respiratory neurons before and during panting in the cat. *Pflügers Arch. Gesamte Physiol. Menschen Tiere* **353:** 303–315.
14. Tenney, S. M., and Ou, L. C. (1977). Ventilatory response of decorticate and decerebrate cats to hypoxia and CO_2. *Respir. Physiol.* **29:** 81–92.
15. Haddad, G. G., Donnelly, D. F., and Bazzy-Asaad, A. R. (1995). Developmental control of respiration: neurobiological basis. *Lung Biol. Health Dis.* **79:** 743–796.
16. White, D. P. (1990). Ventilation and the control of respiration during sleep: Normal mechanisms, pathologic nocturnal hypoventilation, and central sleep apnea. In *Cardiorespiratory Disorders During Sleep* (R. J. Martin, ed.), pp. 53–108. Futura Publ. Co., Mount Kisco, NY.
17. Tenney, S. M., and Leiter, J. C. (1995). The control of breathing: An uninhibited survey from the perspective of comparative physiology. *Lung Biol. Health Dis.* **79:** 151–218.
18. Berger, A. J., and Bellingham, M. C. (1995). Mechanisms of respiratory motor output. In *Lung Biol. Health Dis.* **79:** 71–149.
19. Monteau, R., and Hilaire, G. (1991). Spinal respiratory motoneurons. *Prog. Neurobiol.* **37:** 83–144.
20. Keswani, N. H., and Hollinshead, W. H. (1956). Localization of the phrenic nucleus in the spinal cord of man. *Anat. Rec.* **125:** 683–699.
21. Berger, A. J., Cameron, W. E., Averill, D. B., Kramis, R. C., and Binder, M. D. (1984). Spatial distributions of phrenic and medial gastrocnemius motoneurons in the cat spinal cord. *Exp. Neurol.* **86:** 559–575.
22. Dobbins, E. G., and Feldman, J. L. (1994). Brainstem network controlling descending drive to phrenic motoneurons in rat. *J. Comp. Neurol.* **347:** 64–86.
23. Goshgarian, H. G., and Rafols, J. A. (1984). The ultrastructure and synaptic architecture of phrenic motor neurons in the spinal cord of the adult rat. *J. Neurocytol.* **13:** 85–109.
24. Duron, B., Jung-Caillol, M. C., and Marlot, D. (1978). Myelinated

nerve fiber supply and muscle spindles in the respiratory muscles of cat: Quantitative study. *Anat. Embryol.* **152:** 171–192.

25. Lipski, J., Fyffe, R. E. W., and Jodkowski, J. (1985). Recurrent inhibition of cat phrenic motoneurons. *J. Neurosci.* **5:** 1545–1555.
26. Verleden, G. M., Belvisi, M. G., Rabe, K. F., Miura, M., and Barnes, P. J. (1993). Beta 2-adrenoceptor agonists inhibit NANC neural bronchoconstrictor responses in vitro. *J. Appl. Physiol.* **74:** 1195–1199.
27. Belvisi, M. G., Ward, J. K., Mitchell, J. A., and Barnes, P. J. (1995). Nitric oxide as a neurotransmitter in human airways. *Arch. Int. Pharmacodyn. Ther.* **329:** 97–110.
28. Stretton, D., Belvisi, M. G., and Barnes, P. J. (1992). The effect of sensory nerve depletion on cholinergic neurotransmission in guinea pig airways. *J. Pharmacol. Exp. Ther.* **260:** 1073–1080.
29. Feldman, J. L. (1986). Neurophysiology of breathing in mammals. In *Handbook of Physiology* (F. E. Bloom, ed.), Sect. 1, Vol. IV, pp. 463–524. Am. Physiol. Soc., Bethesda, MD.
30. Kalia, M., and Mesulam, M. M. (1980). Brain stem projections of sensory and motor components of the vagus complex in the cat: II. Laryngeal, tracheobronchial, pulmonary, cardiac, and gastrointestinal branches. *J. Comp. Neurol.* **193:** 467–508.
31. Shannon, R. (1986). Reflexes from respiratory muscles and costovertebral joints. In *Handbook of Physiology* (A. P. Fishman, N. S. Cherniack, and J. G. Widdicombe, eds.), Sect. 3, Vol. II, Part I, pp. 431–448. Am. Physiol. Soc., Bethesda, MD.
32. Nattie, E. E. (1995). Central chemoreception. *Lung Biol. Health Dis.* **79:** 473–510.
33. Feldman, J. L., and Gautier, H. (1976). Interaction of pulmonary afferents and pneumotaxic center in control of respiratory pattern in cats. *J. Neurophysiol.* **39:** 31–44.
34. Knox, C. K., and King, G. W. (1977). Changes in the Breuer-Hering reflexes following rostral pontine lesion. *Respir. Physiol.* **28:** 189–206.
35. Lindsey, B. G., Hernandez, Y. M., Morris, K. F., and Shannon, R. (1992). Functional connectivity between brain stem midline neurons with respiratory-modulated firing rates. *J. Neurophysiol.* **67:** 890–904.
36. Connelly, C. A., Dobbins, E. G., and Feldman, J. L. (1992). Pre-Bötzinger complex in cats: Respiratory neuronal discharge patterns. *Brain Res.* **590:** 337–340.
37. Nattie, E. E., Li, A. H., and St. John, W. M. (1991). Lesions in retrotrapezoid nucleus decrease ventilatory output in anesthetized or decerebrate cats. *J. Appl. Physiol.* **71:** 1364–1375.
38. Prakash, U. B. S. (1989). Neurologic diseases. In *Textbook of Pulmonary Diseases* (G. L. Baum and E. Wolinsky, eds.), 4th ed., Vol. 2, pp. 1409–1436. Little, Brown, Boston.

38a. Hayashi, F., and McCrimmon, D. R. (1996). Respiratory motor responses to cranial afferent stimulation in rats. *Am. J. Physiol.* **271:** R1054–R1062.

39. Feldman, J. L., and Smith, J. C. (1995). Neural control of respiratory pattern in mammals: An overview. *Lung Biol. Health Dis.* **79:** 39–69.
40. Bianchi, A. L., Denavit-Saubié, M., and Champagnat, J. (1995). Central control of breathing in mammals: Neuronal circuitry, membrane properties, and neurotransmitters. *Physiol. Rev.* **75:** 1–45.
41. Bonham, A. C. (1995). Neurotransmitters in the CNS control of breathing. *Respir. Physiol.* **101:** 219–230.
42. McCrimmon, D. R., Mitchell, G. S., and Dekin, M. S. (1995). Glutamate, GABA, and serotonin in ventilatory control. *Lung Biol. Health Dis.* **79:** 151–218.
43. Pierrefiche, O., Schmid, K., Foutz, A. S., and Denavit-Saubié, M. (1991). Endogenous activation of NMDA and non-NMDA glutamate receptors on respiratory neurones in cat medulla. *Neuropharmacology* **30:** 429–440.
44. Liu, G., Feldman, J. L., and Smith, J. C. (1990). Excitatory amino acid-mediated transmission of inspiratory drive to phrenic motoneurons. *J. Neurophysiol.* **64:** 423–436.
45. McCrimmon, D. R., Smith, J. C., and Feldman, J. L. (1989). Involvement of excitatory amino acids in neurotransmission of inspiratory drive to spinal respiratory motoneurons. *J. Neurosci.* **9:** 1910–1921.
46. Funk, G. D., Smith, J. C., and Feldman, J. L. (1993). Generation and transmission of respiratory oscillations in medullary slices: Role of excitatory amino acids. *J. Neurophysiol.* **70:** 1497–1515.
47. Greer, J. J., Smith, J. C., and Feldman, J. L. (1992). Glutamate release and presynaptic action of AP4 during inspiratory drive to phrenic motoneurons. *Brain Res.* **576:** 355–357.
48. Saji, M., and Miura, M. (1990). Evidence that glutamate is the transmitter mediating respiratory drive from medullary premotor neurons to phrenic motoneurons: A double labeling study in the rat. *Neurosci. Lett.* **115:** 177–182.
49. Liu, G., and Feldman, J. L. (1992). Quantal synaptic transmission in phrenic motor nucleus. *J. Neurophysiol.* **68:** 1468–1471.
50. Champagnat, J., Denavit-Saubié, M., Moyanova, S., and Rondounin, G. (1982). Involvement of amino acids in periodic inhibitions of bulbar respiratory neurons. *Brain Res.* **237:** 351–365.
51. Haji, A., Takeda, R., and Remmers, J. E. (1992). Evidence that glycine and GABA mediate postsynaptic inhibition of bulbar respiratory neurons in the cat. *J. Appl. Physiol.* **73:** 2333–2342.
52. Botros, S. M., and Bruce, E. N. (1990). Neural network implementation of a three-phase model of respiratory rhythm generation. *Biol. Cybernet.* **63:** 143–153.
53. Richter, D. W., Ballantyne, D., and Remmers, J. E. (1986). How is the respiratory pattern generated? A model. *News Physiol. Sci.* **1:** 109–112.
54. Remmers, J. E., Richter, D. W., Ballantyne, D., Bainton, C. R., and Klein, J. P. (1986). Reflex prolongation of stage I of expiration. *Pflügers Arch.* **407:** 190–198.
55. Milsom, W. K. (1990). Mechanoreceptor modulation of endogenous respiratory rhythms in vertebrates. *Am. J. Physiol.* **259:** R898–R910.
56. Duffin, J., Ezure, K., and Lipski, J. (1995). Breathing rhythm generation: Focus on the rostral ventrolateral medulla. *News Physiol. Sci.* **10:** 133–140.
57. Ezure, K. (1990). Synaptic connections between medullary respiratory neurons and considerations on the genesis of respiratory rhythm. *Prog. Neurobiol.* **35:** 429–450.
58. Balis, U. J., Morris, K. F., Koleski, J., and Lindsey, B. G. (1994). Simulations of a ventrolateral medullary neural network for respiratory rhythmogenesis inferred from spike train cross-correlation. *Biol. Cybern.* **70:** 311–327.
59. Richter, D. W., Ballanyi, K., and Schwarzacher, S. (1992). Mechanisms of respiratory rhythm generation. *Curr. Opin. Neurobiol.* **2:** 788–793.
60. Cohen, M. I. (1970). How respiratory rhythm originates: Evidence from discharge patterns of brainstem respiratory neurones. In *Ciba Foundation Hering-Breuer Centenary Symposium; Breathing* (R. Porter, ed.), pp. 125–150. Churchill, London.
61. Feldman, J. L., and Cowan, J. D. (1975). Large-scale activity in neural nets II: A model for the brainstem respiratory oscillator. *Biol. Cybernet.* **17:** 39–51.
62. Feldman, J. L., and Cleland, C. L. (1982). Possible roles of pacemaker neurons in mammalian respiratory rhythmogenesis. In *Cellular Pacemakers II* (D. O. Carpenter, ed.), pp. 101–119. Wiley, New York.
63. Smith, J. C., and Feldman J. L. (1987). In vitro brainstem-spinal

cord preparations for study of motor systems for mammalian respiration and locomotion. *J. Neurosci. Methods* **21:** 321–333.

64. Suzue, T. (1984). Respiratory rhythm generation in the in vitro brain stem-spinal cord preparation of the neonatal rat. *J. Physiol. (London)* **354:** 173–183.
65. Syed, N. I., Bulloch, A. G. M., and Lukowiak, K. (1990). *In vitro* reconstruction of the respiratory central pattern generator of the mollusk *Lymnaea. Science* **250:** 282–285.
66. Syed, N. I., Ridgway, R. L., Lukowiak, K., and Bulloch, A. G. (1992). Transplantation and functional integration of an identified respiratory interneuron in *Lymnaea stagnalis. Neuron* **8:** 767–774.
67. Feldman, J. L., and Smith, J. C. (1989). Cellular mechanisms underlying modulation of breathing pattern in mammals. *Ann. N. Y. Acad. Sci.* **563:** 114–130.
68. Onimaru, H., Arata, A., and Homma, I. (1989). Firing properties of respiratory rhythm generating neurons in the absence of synaptic transmission in the rat medulla in vitro. *Exp. Brain Res.* **76:** 530–536.
69. Smith, J. C., Funk, G. D., Johnson, S. M., and Feldman, J. L. (1995). Cellular and synaptic mechanisms generating respiratory rhythms: Insights from in vitro and computational studies. In *Ventral Brainstem Mechanisms and Control of Respiration and Blood Pressure* (C. O. Trouth, R. M. Millis, eds.), pp. 463–496. Dekker, New York.
70. Schwarzacher, S. W., Smith, J. C., and Richter, D. W. (1995). Pre-Bötzinger complex in the cat. *J. Neurophysiol.* **73:** 1452–1461.
71. Champagnat, J., and Richter, D. W. (1994). The roles of K+ conductance in expiratory pattern generation in anaesthetized cats. *J. Physiol. (London)* **479:** 127–138.
72. Richter, D. W., Champagnat, J., Jacquin, T., and Benacka, R. (1993). Calcium currents and calcium-dependent potassium currents in mammalian medullary respiratory neurones. *J. Physiol. (London)* **470:** 23–33.
73. North, J. B., and Jennett, S. (1976). Response of ventilation and of intracranial pressure during rebreathing of carbon dioxide in patients with acute brain damage. *Brain* **99:** 169–182.
74. Plum, F., and Leigh, R. J. (1981). Abnormalities of central mechanisms. *Lung Biol. Health Dis.* **17** (Pt. 2): 989–1067.
75. Plum, F., and Posner, J. B. (1980). *The Diagnosis of Stupor and Coma,* 3rd ed., Contemp. Neurol. Ser. Vol. 19. Philadelphia: Davis.
76. Bisgard, G. E., and Neubauer, J. A. (1995). Peripheral and central effects of hypoxia. *Lung Biol. Health Dis.* **79:** 617–668.
77. Fitzgerald, R. S., and Lahiri, S. (1986). Reflex response to chemoreceptor stimulation. In *Handbook of Physiology* (A. P. Fishman, N. S. Cherniack, and J. G. Widdicombe, eds.), Sect. 3, Vol. II, Part 1, pp. 313–362. Am. Physiol. Soc., Bethesda, MD.
78. Heymans, C. (1967). Pharmacology in old and modern medicine. *Annu. Rev. Pharmacol.* **7:** 1–13.
79. Biscoe, T. J., and Taylor, A. (1963). The discharge pattern recorded in chemoreceptor afferent fibers from the cat carotid body with normal circulation and during perfusion. *J. Physiol. (London)* **168:** 332–344.
80. Cunningham, D. J. C. (1973). The control system regulating breathing in man. *Q. Rev. Biophys.* **6:** 433–483.
81. Weil, J. V., Byrne-Quinn, E., Sodal, I. E., Friesen, W. O., Underhill, B., Filley, G. F., and Grover, R. F., (1970) Hypoxic ventilatory drive in normal man. *J. Clin. Invest.* **49:** 1061–1072.
82. Mitchell, R. A., Loeschcke, H. H., Massion, W. H., and Severinghaus, J. W. (1963). Respiratory responses mediated through superficial chemosensitive areas on the medulla. *J. Appl. Physiol.* **18:** 523–533.
83. Mitchell, R. A., Loeschcke, H. H., Severinghaus, J. W., Richardson, B. W., and Massion, W. H. (1963). Regions of respiratory chemosensitivity on the surface of the medulla. *Ann. N.Y. Acad. Sci.* **109:** 661–681.
84. Eisele, J. H., Eger, E. I., and Muallem, M. (1967). Narcotic properties of carbon dioxide in the dog. *Anesthesiolgy* **28:** 856–865.
85. Nunn, J. F. (1987). *Applied Respiratory Physiology,* 3rd ed., pp. 460–470. Butterworth, Toronto.
86. Bone, R. C., Pierce, A. K., and Johnson, R. L., Jr. (1978). Controlled oxygen administration in acute respiratory failure in chronic obstructive pulmonary disease: A reappraisal. *Am. J. Med.* **65:** 896–902.
87. Ballard, D. P. (1990). The sleep apnea syndrome: Obstructive and mixed apneas. In *Cardiorespiratory Disorders During Sleep,* 2nd ed., pp. 109–140. Futura Publ. Co., Mount Kisco, NY.
88. Strohl, K. P. (1989). Sleep apnea syndrome and sleep-disordered breathing. In *Textbook of Pulmonary Diseases* (G. L. Baum and E. Wolinsky, eds.), 4th ed., Vol. 2, pp. 1019–1034. Little, Brown, Boston.
89. Hunt, C. E. (1992). Sudden infant death syndrome. In *Respiratory Control Disorders in Infants and Children* (R. C. Beckerman, R. T. Brouillette, and C. E. Hunt, eds.), pp. 190–211. Williams & Wilkins, Baltimore, MD.
90. Martin, R. J. (1990). Respiratory disorders during sleep in pediatrics. In *Cardiorespiratory Disorders During Sleep* (R. J. Martin, ed.), pp. 283–322. Futura Publ. Co., Mount Kisco, NY.
91. Coleridge, J. C. G., and Coleridge, H. M. (1984). Afferent vagal C fibre innervation of the lungs and airways and its functional significance. *Rev. Physiol. Biochem. Pharmacol.* **99:** 1–110.
92. Coleridge, H. M., and Coleridge, J. C. G. (1986). Reflexes evoked from tracheobronchial tree and lungs. In *Handbook of Physiology* (A. P. Fishman, N. S. Cherniack, and J. G. Widdicombe, eds.), Sect. 3, Vol. II, Part 1, pp. 395–429. Am. Physiol. Soc. Bethesda, MD.
93. Kubin, L., and Davies, R. O. (1995). Central pathways of pulmonary and airway vagal afferents. *Lung Biol. Health Dis.* **79:** 219–284.
94. Sant' Ambrogio, G. (1987). Nervous receptors of the tracheobronchial tree. *Annu. Rev. Physiol.* **49:** 611–627.
95. Clark, F. J., and von Euler, C. (1972). On the regulation of depth and rate of breathing. *J. Physiol. (London)* **222:** 267–295.
96. Mitchell, G. S., Cross, B. A., Hiramoto, T., and Scheid, P. (1980). Effects of intrapulmonary CO_2 and airway pressure on phrenic activity and pulmonary stretch receptor discharge in dogs. *Respir. Physiol.* **40:** 29–48.
97. Cohen, M. I., and Feldman, J. L. (1984). Discharge properties of dorsal medullary inspiratory neurons: Relation to pulmonary afferent and phrenic efferent discharge. *J. Neurophysiol.* **51:** 753–776.
98. Averill, D. B., Cameron, W. E., and Berger, A. J. (1984). Monosynaptic excitation of dorsal medullary respiratory neurons by slowly adapting pulmonary stretch receptors. *J. Neurophysiol.* **52:** 771–785.
99. Bonham, A. C., and McCrimmon, D. R. (1990). Neurones in a discrete region of the nucleus tractus solitarius are required for the Breuer-Hering reflex in rat. *J. Physiol. (London)* **427:** 261–280.
100. Davies, R. O., Kubin, L., and Pack, A. I. (1987). Pulmonary stretch receptor relay neurones of the cat: Localization and contralateral medullary projections. *J. Physiol. (London)* **383:** 571–585.
101. Hayashi, F., Coles, S. K., and McCrimmon, D. R. (1996). Respiratory neurons mediating the Breuer-Hering reflex prolongation of expiration in rat. *J. Neurosci.* **16:** 6526–6536.
102. Manabe, M., and Ezure, K. (1988). Decrementing expiratory

neurons of Bötzinger complex. I. Response to lung inflation and axonal projections. *Exp. Brain Res.* **72:** 150–158.

103. Davies, R. O., and Kubin, L. (1986). Projection of pulmonary rapidly adapting receptor neurones to the medulla of the cat: An antidromic mapping study. *J. Physiol.* (*London*) **373:** 63–86.
104. Donoghue, S., Garcia, M., Jordan, D., and Spyer, K. M. (1982). The brain-stem projections of pulmonary stretch afferent neurones in cats and rabbits. *J. Physiol.* (*London*) **322:** 353–363.
105. Berger, A. J., and Averill, D. B. (1983). Projection of single pulmonary stretch receptors to solitary tract region. *J. Neurophysiol.* **49:** 819–830.
106. Kalia, M., and Richter, D. (1985). Morphology of physiologically identified slowly adapting lung stretch receptor afferents stained with intra-axonal horseradish peroxidase in the nucleus of the tractus solitarius of the cat. I. A light microscopic analysis. *J. Comp. Neurol.* **241:** 503–520.
107. Bonham, A. C., and Joad, J. P. (1991). Neurones in commissural nucleus tractus solitarii required for full expression of the pulmonary C fibre reflex in rat. *J. Physiol.* (*London*) **441:** 95–112.
108. Kubin, L., Kimura, H., and Davies, R. O. (1991). The medullary projections of afferent bronchopulmonary C fibres in the cat as shown by antidromic mapping. *J. Physiol.* (*London*) **435:** 207–228.
109. Bach, K. B., Lutcavage, M., and Mitchell, G. S. (1993). Serotonin is necessary for short term modulation of the exercise ventilatory response. *Respir. Physiol.* **91:** 57–70.
110. Eldridge, F. L., and Millhorn, D. E. (1986). Oscillation, gating, and memory in the respiratory control system. In *Handbook of Physiology.* (A. P. Fishman, N. S. Cherniack, and J. G. Widdicombe, eds.), Sect. 3, Vol. II, Part 1, pp. 93–114. Am. Physiol. Soc., Bethesda, MD.
111. Hayashi, F., Coles, S. K., Bach, K. B., Mitchell, G. S., and McCrimmon, D. R. (1993). Time-dependent phrenic nerve responses to carotid afferent activation: Intact vs. decerebellate rats. *Am. J. Physiol.* **265:** R811–R819.
112. Ling, L., Olson, E. B., Vidruk, E. H., and Mitchell, G. S. (1996). Attenuation of the hypoxic ventilatory response in adult rats following one month of perinatal hyperoxia. *J. Physiol.* (*London*) **495:** 561–571.
113. Martin, P. A., and Mitchell, G. S. (1993). Long term modulation of the exercise ventilatory response. *J. Physiol.* (*London*) **470:** 601–617.
114. Mitchell, G. S. (1993). Modulation and plasticity of the exercise ventilatory response. *Funkts. Biol. Syst.* **23:** 269–277.
115. Waldrop, T. G., and Porter, J. P. (1995). Hypothalamic involvement in respiratory and cardiovascular regulation. *Lung Biol. Health Dis.* **79:** 315–364.
116. Fregosi, R. F., and Mitchell, G. S. (1994). Long-term facilitation of inspiratory intercostal nerve activity following carotid sinus nerve stimulation in cats. *J. Physiol.* (*London*) **477:** 469–479.
117. Berger, A. J., and Takahashi, T. (1990). Serotonin enhances a low-voltage-activated calcium current in rat spinal motoneurons. *J. Neurosci.* **10:** 1922–1928.
118. Bonham, A. C., Coles, S. K., and McCrimmon, D. R. (1993). Pulmonary stretch receptor afferents activate excitatory amino acid receptors in the nucleus tractus solitarii in rats. *J. Physiol.* (*London*) **464:** 725–745.
119. Dogas, Z., Stuth, E. A. E., Hopp, F. A., McCrimmon, D. R., and Zuperku, E. J. (1995). NMDA receptor-mediated transmission of carotid body chemoreceptor input to expiratory bulbospinal neurones in dogs. *J. Physiol.* (*London*) **487:** 639–651.
120. Dong, X.-W., and Feldman, J. L. (1995). Modulation of inspiratory drive to phrenic motoneurons by presynaptic adenosine A1 receptors. *J. Neurosci.* **15:** 3458–3467.
121. Fedorko, L., Connelly, C. A., and Remmers, J. E. (1987). Neurotransmitters mediating synaptic inhibition of phrenic motoneurons. In *Respiratory Muscles and Their Neuromotor Control* (G. C. Sieck, S. C. Gandevia, W. E. Cameron, eds.), pp. 167–173. Liss, New York.
122. Morin-Surun, M. P., Jordan, D., Champagnat, J., Spyer, K. M., and Denavit-Saubié, M. (1984). Excitatory effects of iontophoretically applied substance P on neurons in the nucleus tractus solitarius of the cat: Lack of interaction with opiates and opioids. *Brain Res.* **307:** 388–392.
123. Aritav, H., Kitav, I., and Sakamoto, M. (1995). Two distinct descending inputs to the cricothyroid motoneuron in the medulla originating from the amygdala and the lateral hypothalamic area. *Adv. Exp. Med. Biol.* **393:** 53–58.
124. Eldridge, F. L., Millhorn, D. E., and Waldrop, T. G. (1981). Exercise hyperpnea and locomotion: Parallel activation from the hypothalamus. *Science* **211:** 844–846.
125. Gonzalez-Lima, F., and Frysztak, R. J. (1991). Functional mapping of the rat brain during vocalizations: A 2-deoxyglucose study. *Neurosci. Lett.* **124:** 74–78.
126. Holstege, G. (1989). Anatomical study of the final common pathway for vocalization in the cat. *J. Comp. Neurol.* **284:** 242–252.

C H A P T E R

41

Food Intake and Metabolism

Stephen C. Woods and Edward M. Stricker

Eating is a familiar behavior. In humans, it is strongly influenced by cultural, social, and experiential factors. Consequently, eating has been a subject of considerable interest to social and behavioral scientists. In mammals, including humans, food intake is also a regulatory behavior with the primary function of supporting the continuous energy demands of body tissues. When considered from this perspective, food intake is influenced by hunger, satiety, and the biological mechanisms that couple eating with internal caloric supplies and a stable body weight. In this chapter, we discuss the signals important for the central nervous system to control food intake and also describe mechanisms thought to integrate those signals.

Despite decades of investigation, considerable differences of opinion about how food intake is controlled still exist. The multiple views follow one of two principles. The first principle considers eating to be a result of depleted energy stores in adipose tissue, reduced use of energy-rich **metabolic fuel** (glucose or lipid) in some critical tissue, or both. The purpose of eating is to restore energy reserves in adipose tissue or to increase fuel utilization to some desired level, and thereby eliminate the signal to eat. This traditional "depletion–repletion" model is not the approach we take in this chapter. Rather, we subscribe to the second principle—that is, the view that considers animals primed to eat unless influenced by inhibitory signals that are generated by meals. According to this view, the onset of eating does not result from acute needs, nor does its end result from a decrease in such needs. Instead, **caloric homeostasis** influences meals, albeit indirectly, and eating contributes to caloric homeostasis by providing nutrients. The storage and use of those nutrients are regulated independently by physiological mechanisms described later. We describe the properties of caloric homeostasis before we consider the control of food intake.

CALORIC HOMEOSTASIS

Homeostatic Mechanisms Provide a Continuous Supply of Metabolic Fuels to Cells

The purpose of caloric homeostasis is to preserve cellular metabolism. Cells oxidize metabolic fuels to drive all cellular processes; thus, the higher the cellular activity, the greater the demand for energy. Because most cells have limited amounts of stored energy, they rely on a steady supply of calories and oxygen from the blood stream. Oxygen is dependably and instantaneously available to the circulation via the respiratory system and is not stored in the body. In contrast, food calories can be scarce, and they require time after ingestion to become available to cells in significant quantities. One consequence of this arrangement is the capacity of mammals to store energy sufficient to bridge long intervals during which no food is eaten.

Three categories of macronutrients—carbohydrates, lipids, and proteins—provide usable energy, but the use of specific macronutrients by tissues of the body varies depending on the type of tissue. Most tissues can oxidize carbohydrates in the form of **glucose** or lipids in the form of **free fatty acids**, depending on the availability of these nutrients and the levels of certain hormones in the blood. Notable exceptions are the liver, which requires lipids for proper functioning, and the brain, which has a large, continuous need for glucose despite the ability to oxidize lipids in the form of **ketone bodies**. When the supply of glucose to the brain is compromised, neurons cease to function, and in a few minutes consciousness is lost. Death will ensue unless glucose delivery to the brain is restored. Therefore, maintenance of sufficient amounts of circulating glucose to support normal brain function is a critical goal of caloric homeostasis.

Two distinct metabolic states are defined by the availability of recently ingested food to cells. The **prandial**, or fed, state is characterized by an abundance of newly ingested and absorbed nutrients in the blood. These molecules are rapidly sequestered by tissues to prevent them from being wastefully excreted. The **postabsorptive**, or fasted, state is characterized by the absence of calories entering the circulation from the gastrointestinal tract and a consequent reliance on energy from metabolic fuels previously consumed and stored. These stores are gradually released into the blood during a fast. In both states, tissues take nutrients from the blood as needed for cellular metabolism.

Many tissues store carbohydrates in the form of **glycogen**, a polymer of glucose; the liver and skeletal muscles have the largest depots. Fat is stored mainly in adipose tissue as **triglyceride**, each molecule of which is glycerol with three attached fatty acids. During the prandial period, newly ingested energy is used immediately by the body or is stored as triglyceride or glycogen. Excess carbohydrate is converted to lipid (**lipogenesis**) since glycogen storage capacity is limited and triglyceride is a much more efficient form of stored energy. During the fasting period, liver glycogen is converted back to glucose (**glycogenolysis**), which enters the blood and is available to all tissues. Similarly, stored triglycerides are mobilized from adipose tissue (**lipolysis**) and enter the circulation as fatty acids and glycerol. The fatty acids are used by tissues as needed or are converted to ketone bodies (**ketogenesis**), whereas glycerol is converted to glucose (**gluconeogenesis**) (Fig. 41.1).

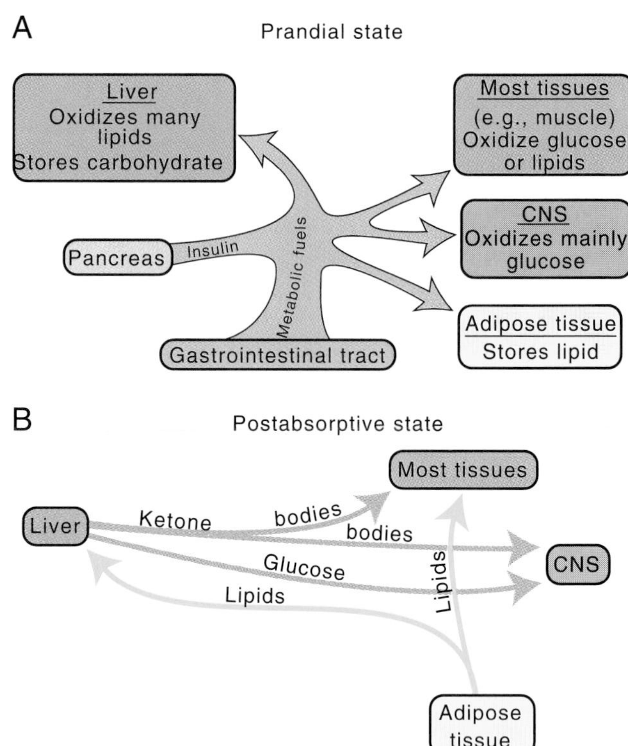

FIGURE 41.1 Schematic diagram of the fluxes of metabolic fuels in the (A) prandial and (B) postabsorptive states. Note the absence of insulin in the postabsorptive state, which greatly facilitates the mobilization of energy stores from the liver and adipose tissue. The adult human liver stores sufficient fuel to support metabolism during fasting for about 7 h, whereas the adipose mass has a far greater capacity.

The liver is a key organ in the traffic of energy. Lipogenesis (which also occurs in adipose tissue) and glycogen formation occur in the liver during the prandial period, and glycogenolysis, ketogenesis, and gluconeogenesis occur during the fasting period. These processes are regulated (discussed later), as are delivery of metabolic fuels (from the intestines into the circulation), storage of excess fuels, and mobilization of stored energy. The control system involves interplay among several hormones and the sympathetic and parasympathetic divisions of the autonomic nervous system.

Insulin Is the Key Hormone Affecting Caloric Homeostasis

Secretion of the peptide hormone **insulin** from the B cells of the pancreatic islets is influenced by several factors, among which interstitial glucose is critical. Insulin secretion increases in direct proportion to the concentration of glucose in the pancreas and does not occur in the absence of glucose. Other substrates, such as amino acids and ketone bodies, also stimulate insulin secretion. In addition, autonomic nerves innervate the pancreatic islets: Cholinergic parasympathetic activity stimulates secretion of insulin, and α-adrenergic sympathetic activity inhibits it.

When a hungry person anticipates a meal, the aroma and, subsequently, the taste of food initiate insulin secretion via neural activity. Signals descend from the cerebral cortex (where the smell and taste of food are recognized) through the hypothalamus to the dorsal motor nucleus of the vagus in the caudal brainstem and then to the pancreas by way of cholinergic fibers of the vagus nerve. This **cephalic phase** of insulin secretion helps to reverse the mobilization of fuels that occurs during fasting and to prepare the body for the entry of fuels from the gut (see Box 41.1). As ingested food enters the stomach and duodenum, several gastrointestinal hormones, which also are important in digestion, stimulate B cells to secrete more insulin. This **gastrointestinal phase** of insulin secretion ensures that

BOX 41.1

CLINICAL DISORDERS OF INSULIN SECRETION

Diabetes mellitus is a disorder characterized by abnormally high concentrations of blood glucose (**hyperglycemia**). Glucose concentrations may be so high that the kidneys cannot completely reabsorb the filtered glucose, resulting in measurable amounts of glucose in the urine. A chronically elevated concentration of glucose in the bloodstream suggests a lack of insulin, and, in fact, many diabetic people have a confirmed deficiency in the function of pancreatic B cells and an absence of insulin (Type 1 or insulin-dependent diabetes). The absence of insulin precludes fuel storage and the normal modulation of fuel mobilization. Therefore, in the postprandial period, metabolites of food accumulate in the circulation and are excreted, and individuals remain lean despite elevated food intake. Among humans with diabetes, however, the majority (85 to 90%) actually have substantial levels of circulating insulin but tend to be obese and resistant to the effects of insulin in promoting fuel storage (Type 2 or non-insulin-dependent diabetes). Their impaired ability to rapidly secrete insulin during a meal results in a pronounced hyperglycemia during and following meals.[62]

In people whose insulin production is compromised, inhibition of insulin secretion by the autonomic nervous system can mimic the symptoms of diabetes. During circumstances such as environmental stress, physical trauma, or pregnancy, an increase of sympathetic nervous activity inhibits insulin secretion sufficiently to allow the emergence of frank symptoms of diabetes, thereby revealing limited B cell function. The symptoms disappear when the stressor is removed but reappear when stress returns or as pancreatic disease progresses.

Just as salivary secretion can be conditioned to arbitrary stimuli that herald the onset of a meal,[63] classical conditioning similarly influences secretion of insulin at mealtimes. A parallel increase in stomach motility results in the familiar "growling" stomach. This learned reflex response provides a means for adapting the magnitude of insulin secretion to the food that is customarily eaten.[53] Patients with **reactive hypoglycemia** have an exaggerated cephalic phase of insulin secretion and consequent hypoglycemia, which in turn triggers a compensatory secretion of epinephrine from the adrenal medulla and feelings of faintness (due to hypoglycemia) and of anxiety and arousal (due to epinephrine). The most commonly prescribed treatment is a change to daily numerous, small, protein-rich meals, because such meals elicit relatively little secretion of insulin.[64]

the level of insulin in the circulation is high by the time digested nutrients first appear in the blood stream. Finally, nutrients absorbed from the intestine cause even greater stimulation of insulin secretion by their direct effect on the pancreas. This **substrate phase** of insulin secretion further increases the amount of insulin in the circulation. This effect lasts well beyond the cessation of eating. As a result of these coordinated meal-related events, prandial insulin secretion is rapid and appropriate to the caloric load, and ingested fuels are efficiently used and stored (Fig. 41.2).

An equilibrium of neural and endocrine factors controls the ebb and flow of metabolic fuels from body stores. Circulating insulin is the most important factor that promotes storage: Insulin enables most tissues to take up glucose from the blood for immediate oxidation or for storage during the prandial period. Conversely, the most important factor for fuel mobilization is disappearance of insulin from circulation during the postprandial, postabsorptive period, when fuel delivery from the intestines has ended and parasympathetic activity to the pancreas is no longer elevated. Insulin secretion at this time is greatly reduced, but it is not inhibited, and therefore can be stimulated immediately if necessary. For example, when more than the needed amount of stored fuels is mobilized, substrates directly stimulate the pancreas to secrete insulin, thereby slowing substrate mobilization to a rate appropriate for need. Thus, insulin is pivotal for storing calories in the fed state and for allowing stored calories to be mobilized in measured amounts during the postabsorptive state.

Superimposed on other factors that influence insulin secretion is the amount of body fat (adiposity). People with low adiposity have a large number of active insulin receptors on adipose tissue and skeletal muscle. Obese individuals have fewer active insulin receptors. Consequently, in response to a given stimulus, secretion of insulin is lower in people who are lean than in those who are obese. In healthy, nondiabetic people, this reciprocal relationship between the secretion of insulin and the sensitivity of most tissues to insulin ensures efficient storage and use of fuels independent of body weight. In these individuals, plasma insulin

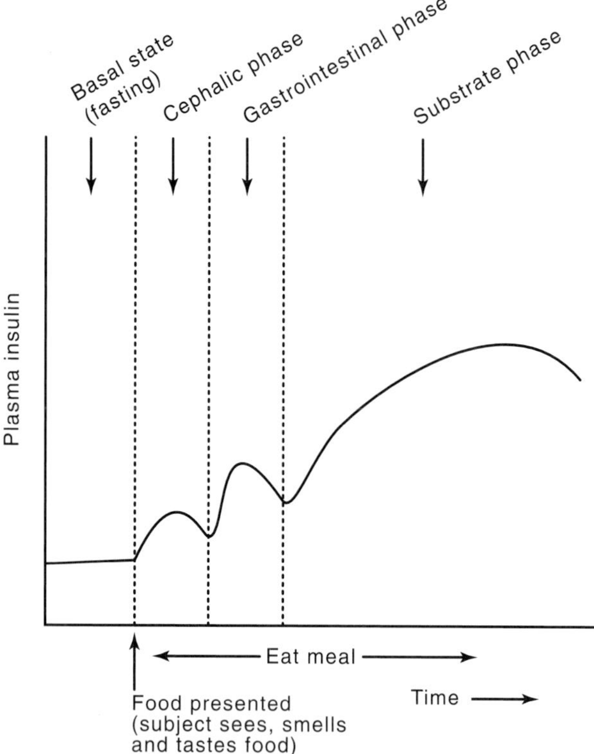

FIGURE 41.2 The three phases of meal-related insulin secretion. The cephalic phase, during which parasympathetic vagal activity stimulates the pancreas, is initiated when food is seen, smelled, and tasted. The gastrointestinal phase is mediated by the direct action of digestive hormones on the insulin-secreting B cells. The prolonged substrate phase is caused by metabolic fuels (mainly glucose) directly stimulating pancreatic B cells. When meals are prolonged, the three stimuli operate simultaneously and have additive effects.

levels in the prandial and the postprandial periods are reliable correlates of adiposity.

Summary

All cells require continuous supplies of metabolic fuels to support ongoing activity. The fuels enter the circulation from the intestines during the prandial period and from storage depots during fasting. The availability of fuels to tissues is primarily controlled by the liver and the hormone insulin. Hepatic function and insulin secretion are in turn controlled in large part by the autonomic nervous system.

THE ROLE OF CALORIC HOMEOSTASIS IN CONTROL OF FOOD INTAKE

Meals Generate Biological Satiety Signals

The traditional view of caloric homeostasis is that animals eat when they need calories. Yet as discussed earlier, the delivery of metabolic fuels to cells is continuous, and animals only periodically experience urgent needs for calories to support cellular metabolism. Instead, caloric homeostasis can be related to the control of food intake in ways that are unrelated to acute cellular needs.

Animals consume food in distinct bouts (i.e., meals); therefore, their daily food intake reflects the cumulative intake of multiple meals. Control factors influence the time when each meal is initiated and the amount of food consumed before the meal is terminated.

The first comprehensive study of meals was reported in 1966 by Le Magnen and Tallon.[1] They maintained laboratory rats in cages and allowed them to eat *ad libitum* for weeks, during which photosensors and electronic relays recorded intake. They obtained a full record of when meals were initiated, how much was eaten during each meal, how much time passed before the next meal, and so on. No relationship was found between how much a rat ate in a meal and how much time had passed since it had last eaten; in other words, meal sizes were unpredictable. However, the larger the meal, the longer the interval before the next meal, and the relationship was strongest during the night, when rats ate the largest meals. Thus, eating appeared to be inhibited by a satiety signal generated in proportion to the size of a meal, and eating resumed when that signal disappeared. Similar observations have since been made in many laboratories (Fig. 41.3).[2]

Gastric Distension and Calories Provide Satiety Signals

Several meal-related factors might plausibly provide satiety signals. These include factors based on the

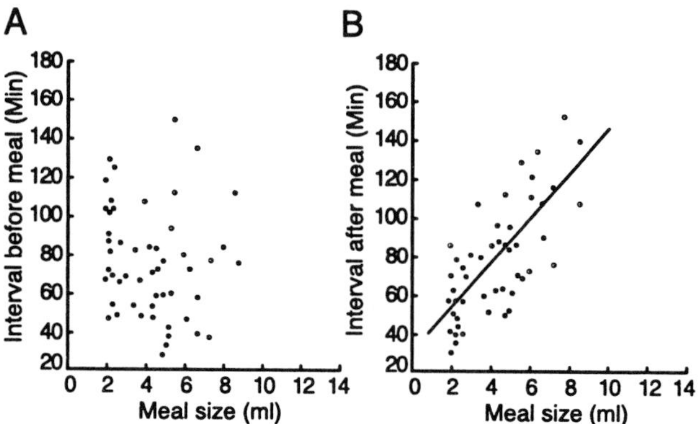

FIGURE 41.3 Meal sizes and intermeal intervals of a representative rat eating liquid food *ad libitum*. Shown are the sizes of 50 consecutive meals eaten by a neurologically normal control rat. Meal size is plotted against the intervals of time that separated each meal from the one preceding it (A) and the one following it (B). Note that the premeal intervals did not predict meal sizes, whereas meal sizes did predict postmeal intervals. From Thomas and Mayer.[2]

smell, taste, and texture of food. Factors arising from the stomach could also play a role. Finally, intestinal and postabsorptive factors could arise after ingested food has left the stomach. In studies of rats, pregastric factors have been ruled out, because little satiety is achieved when ingested food is immediately drained out through an esophageal or gastric fistula; these animals eat continuously, as if they had no satiety despite the passage of very large amounts of food through the oropharynx[3] (Fig. 41.4).[4] Because meals end long before significant digestion and absorption occur, gastric factors have been considered a likely source of satiety signals. Gastric volume is an obvious possibility, and, in fact, meals are known to end when substantial **gastric distension** occurs. The stomach wall is richly endowed with stretch receptors whose activity increases in proportion to the volume of the stomach. Those signals are communicated by way of the vagus nerve to the nucleus of the solitary tract (NST) and adjacent area postrema in the brainstem. The signals travel to the hypothalamus[5] and, ultimately, to the cortex, where gastric distension is perceived.

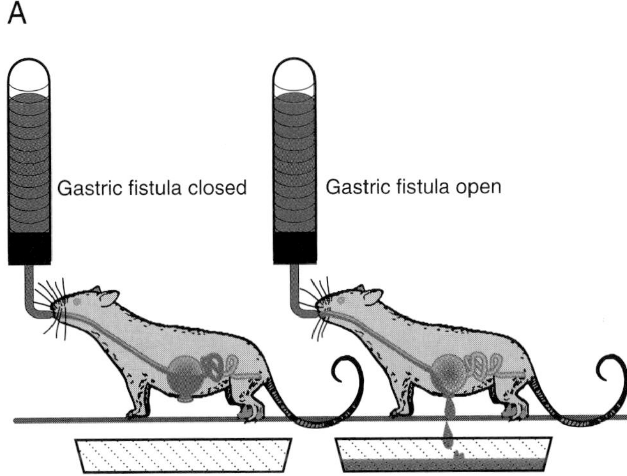

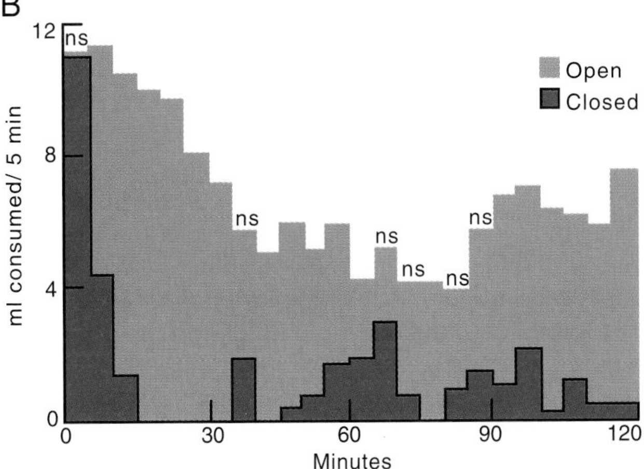

FIGURE 41.4 (A) Rats consuming liquid diet, with gastric fistula closed (real eating) or open ("sham eating"). When the gastric fistula is closed, food passes through the stomach and into the small intestine normally. When the gastric fistula is open, ingested food drains out the open fistula instead of accumulating in the stomach to distend it, and no food enters the small intestine. (B) Mean consumption of liquid diet (ml/5 min) by rats with a gastric fistula after 17 h of food deprivation. The rats consumed food in discrete meals when the fistula was closed. When the fistula was open, they ate continuously throughout the test period and never displayed satiety. Thus, rats consumed significantly more food during the 2-h test period when their fistulas were open than when they were closed. ns, intervals in which the amount of food consumed did not differ significantly between open and closed fistulas. From Smith *et al.*[4]

Gastric stretch that accompanies meals presumably interacts with other signals to produce satiety. For example, aside from directly affecting digestion, the intestinal peptide **cholecystokinin** (CCK), which is secreted during meals, appears to act on receptors located on vagal afferent fibers that carry gastric stretch signals from the pyloric region of the stomach to the brainstem. Thus, relatively small amounts of CCK can inhibit feeding in rats by acting synergistically with the effects of gastric distension.[6] When given in larger doses, CCK can inhibit food intake even when the stomach is empty.[7] As might be expected, total or selective gastric **vagotomy** (or ablation of brainstem areas to which the gastric vagus projects) decreases the ability of gastric volume and peripherally administered CCK to reduce meal size. Conversely, systemic administration of CCK receptor antagonists increases the size of meals (see Box 41.2).

Gastric distension is one of the factors that control suckling in neonatal rats. The dam controls the timing of meals, and at each meal pups consume as much milk as their stomachs allow; gastric volume, not caloric content, provides the signal to stop.[8] Consistent with the importance of gastric distension to suckling, pups are particularly sensitive to the inhibitory effects of CCK on food intake,[9] suggesting that a combination of gastric distension and CCK may be the principal signals that inhibit the initiation of spontaneous meals in suckling rats.

As rat pups mature, the importance of CCK and gastric distension as satiety signals diminishes, and the caloric content of food begins to participate in the complex control of meal size. This developmental change is important so that adults can ingest, assess, and respond to a variety of foods whose caloric density is not as constant as that of milk. For example, when liquid food is diluted with water, adult rats compensate by increasing the volume consumed in each meal, allowing daily caloric intake to remain stable.[10] This observation shows that gastric distension is but one of several possible satiety signals in adult rats and greater distension can be accommodated in circumstances in which the calorie-related satiety signals have diminished.

BOX 41.2

SATIETY FACTORS

Several metabolically important peptides, including CCK, insulin, **glucagon**, and **bombesin**, reduce food intake when administered systemically to laboratory animals. By themselves, these findings do not prove that the peptides normally function as endogenous satiety agents; blood levels of an administered agent must be shown to fall within physiological range. In addition, the behavioral effects of the agent must be specific to the inhibition of food intake and cannot merely reflect a secondary consequence of illness, behavioral depression, or motor incapacitation. Because investigators cannot be certain what animals sense, they must infer whether animals experience satiety in association with an observed reduction in food intake.

One common approach is to determine whether the agent can cause **learned flavor aversion** in animals. People readily learn to avoid food or drink that, when ingested, produces nausea due to the unsuspected presence of some toxic contaminant. Rats and other animals seem to respond in the same way; moreover, when a toxin is administered systemically soon after consumption of an uncontaminated, novelly flavored drink, the animals subsequently avoid fluids of that flavor and behave as if the drink had contained the toxic agent that made them sick. In addition, electrophysiological recording from the first gustatory relay nucleus in the brainstem, the nucleus of the solitary tract, shows that the response elicited by a taste that has been associated with a toxin is similar to the pattern of activity typical of naturally aversive flavor.[65] Nausea is critical to the process; damage to the "emetic center" in the area postrema eliminates the sensation of nausea and prevents the formation of the learned taste aversion.

Another approach to distinguishing nausea from satiety is to monitor biological variables that occur in association with nausea but not satiety, or vice versa. One such variable is neurohypophyseal hormone secretion. For example, administration of large doses of CCK causes nausea in humans and vomiting in monkeys and stimulates vasopressin secretion in both species.[66] In this example, because elevated plasma vasopressin does not itself cause nausea or vomiting, it can be considered a biological marker of nausea. Curiously, rats secrete the other neurohypophyseal peptide, oxytocin (and not vasopressin), in response to large doses of CCK and other nauseants.[67] Control experiments have shown that following an ordinary meal, vasopressin is not secreted in primates nor is oxytocin secreted in rats. Thus, when rats are administered a chemical agent that stimulates pituitary oxytocin secretion, nausea, rather than satiety, is the suspected basis of the reduction in food intake.

Such experiments help explain the anorexia that occurs when a hormone is administered exogenously, but insight into the normal effects of endogenously secreted hormones requires an alternative experimental approach: A drug that blocks the effect of a hormone on its receptors is administered. If the hormone functions to reduce food intake, then the blocking agent should increase the size of meals. Such drugs are not yet available for all hormones suspected of being satiety factors, but experiments using CCK receptor blockers showed an increase in meal size.[68] Food intake was also increased in similar experiments in which the action of insulin was inhibited within the brain and when the actions of bombesin and glucagon were blocked by selective antagonists. These observations strongly suggest that these four peptide hormones normally function as satiety factors.

The mechanism by which caloric signals are monitored remains unknown. Although early reports suggested that the stomach monitored caloric nutrients,[11] more recent findings have not supported this hypothesis. For example, when hungry rats were equipped with closed pyloric cuffs to prevent ingested food from entering their small intestines, the rats decreased their food intake in proportion to the volume, and not the caloric content, of intragastric infusions.[12] In contrast, when the cuff was open so that gastric contents could empty into the duodenum, caloric nutrients were much more effective in reducing food intake than calorie-free loads of equal volume. These observations suggest that the stomach does not detect caloric nutrients but instead contributes primarily inhibitory signals related to gastric distension.

Postgastric Effects of Meals Provide Other Satiety Signals

Normally, during a meal some ingested food enters the intestine and is absorbed, thus allowing postgastric signals to contribute to satiety. For example, small amounts of specific nutrients infused directly into the duodenum produce a robust suppression of eating that cannot be attributed to gastric factors.[13] Whether the upper small intestine or a postabsorptive site is responsible for detecting calories and generating the signals that limit meal size is not clear. For example, nutrients absorbed from the intestine circulate first to the liver. As discussed earlier, the liver plays a critical role in caloric homeostasis; the delivery of calories to the liver may be monitored to provide an important postgastric signal for the inhibition of food intake. Consistent with this hypothesis is the observation that infusion of glucose into the hepatic portal vein reduces food intake.[14] Researchers later found that such infusions increased the activity in hepatic vagal afferent fibers and that this signal increased gastric motility (via a vagovagal reflex).[15] Moreover, Friedman reported that infusion of fructose into the general circulation reduced food intake in normal rats but not in rats with hepatic vagotomy.[16] Collectively, these findings are consistent with the liver providing a satiety signal. This signal disappears as absorption slows, which is when satiety diminishes as well.[17]

Intravenously administered glucose reduces food intake but not by as much as the caloric content of the glucose. In contrast, when glucose solution is fed through a tube directly into the stomach, a compensatory reduction in food (calorie) intake is observed.[18] In this case, gastric signals might contribute to the increased satiety. For the same amount of glucose, more insulin is secreted in response to infusion into the stomach than into a vein; therefore, insulin also might contribute to the observed reduction in appetite. In fact, intravenously infused glucose reduces food intake by an equivalent caloric amount when insulin is added to the infusate.[19] Together, these observations suggest that insulin contributes to the satiety effect of glucose ingested during a meal. Consistent with this possibility, rats made diabetic by destruction of their pancreatic B cells eat discrete meals more frequently, as if they experienced less postprandial satiety.[20,21]

In addition to providing useful nutrients, consumption of food increases **plasma osmolality,** yet another factor influencing the size of a meal. Increased plasma osmolality stimulates thirst, and for this reason water intake usually accompanies eating. The important point, however, is that food intake is lower during meals without water. Similarly, increased osmolality caused by systemic injection of hypertonic saline reduces food intake in proportion to the administered osmotic load. The well-described osmoreceptors that cause thirst and influence vasopressin secretion (see Chapter 42) apparently do not mediate this inhibitory effect on food intake, which persists after those forebrain osmoreceptors have been surgically destroyed.[22] Instead, because the osmolality of blood in the hepatic portal vein affects the activity of visceral afferent fibers from the liver, hepatic osmoreceptors might mediate the inhibitory effect of increased osmolality on food intake.

Body Weight Influences Food Intake

Numerous investigations have shown that control of food intake is connected to maintenance of body weight. For example, after a period of deprivation and forced loss of body weight, animals (including humans) eat larger meals than normal until adiposity returns to pretreatment levels. Conversely, after a period of force-feeding, during which the increased daily intake of calories causes weight gain, animals eat smaller meals than normal (or no meals at all) until normal adiposity is restored. Long-term stability of adiposity in adult animals is attributed in part to these compensatory responses to weight fluctuations that are caused by acute changes in food intake or energy expenditure.

Adiposity may indirectly influence food intake by modulating how quickly food passes through the gastrointestinal tract, how long nutrients remain in the circulation, and how nutrients interact with the liver. For example, after fasting, less prolonged gastric distension or more rapid absorption and storage of ingested calories would diminish the duration of satiety signals and thereby increase the frequency of meals. These effects would promote the **hyperphagia** (overeating) associated with the restoration of body weight in animals that have fasted. Similarly, diversions of ingested food calories to the fetus (to support its growth) during pregnancy, to milk (to feed neonates) during lactation, and to skeletal muscle (to support shivering) during exposure to cold temperatures reduce the satiating properties of ingested food and thereby contribute to the hyperphagia associated with these conditions.

Alternatively adipose tissue may directly signal the brain to inhibit food intake. Because afferent nerves from adipose tissue to brain had not been described, such communication was hypothesized to be mediated by a humoral (circulating) factor. **Parabionts**, created by surgically joining two animals at the flank muscles and skin, were used to test the hypothesis. Vascular interconnection within a parabiont is demonstrated when a dye injected into one animal appears in the blood of its partner. Because the nervous systems of the two animals remain independent, any physiologic communication between the animals must occur through the vascular system. When two lean rats were parabiotically joined, each consumed its normal amount of food and maintained its usual body weight. Similar results were obtained when two obese rats with lesions in the ventromedial hypothalamus were joined together. However, when a lean animal was joined to an obese animal, the result was striking: The lean animal markedly reduced its food intake and consequently lost a considerable amount of weight.[23] These experiments have been interpreted to mean that a circulating factor, secreted in large amounts (proportional to adiposity) by the obese animal, enters the blood of the lean animal and somehow reduces food intake, as if the lean animal were receiving a signal that it was too fat.[24]

Investigations apparently have identified a key humoral agent in the regulation of food intake: When obese mice that are homozygous for a particular mutant gene (*obob* mice) were joined together with lean mice in parabiotic pairs, the *obob* mice reduced their food intake and lost body weight. In contrast, when other obese mice, homozygous for a different gene (*dbdb* mice), were joined with lean mice, they did not reduce their food intake or lose body weight (but the lean mice did). Moreover, when *obob* mice were joined with *dbdb* mice, the *obob* mice became lean but the *dbdb* mice did not change their body weight.[25] Thus, the *obob* mice may lack a circulating factor that reduces food intake, but they have receptors for the factor. Conversely, the *dbdb* mice apparently secrete this factor in abundance but have no receptors for it. Thus, the *obob* mice lose weight whether joined with lean animals or with *dbdb* mice, both of which can contribute the missing factor. The *dbdb* mice, on the other hand, are not affected by their parabiotic partners because they cannot respond to the factor.

The factor, called Ob protein (or **leptin**), is synthesized in adipose tissue, and its concentration in plasma is directly proportional to the adiposity of the person or animal. The leptin gene has been sequenced, and synthetic leptin is available for experiments. As expected from the studies described above, when given systemic leptin, *obob* mice reduce their food intake and lose body weight; *dbdb* mice, however, do not respond to the protein.[26] Interestingly, very low doses of leptin administered directly into the cerebral ventricles of *obob* mice reduce food intake and cause marked loss of body weight, suggesting that this protein acts in the brain to inhibit food intake.[27] Consistent with this possibility, the receptor for leptin has been identified and found to exist within the hypothalamus.[28] Moreover, administration of leptin to *obob* (but not *dbdb*) mice reduces synthesis of hypothalamic neuropeptide Y,[29] a neurotransmitter that stimulates appetite when injected in the hypothalamus. Leptin may be an important link between caloric homeostasis and the central control of food intake, and research on the mechanism of leptin function continues.

Finally, body weight may influence food intake in another way: Plasma levels of insulin are closely correlated with adiposity; thus, insulin may decrease food intake by acting in the brain, in addition to in the liver. Thus, body weight can influence food intake in three ways: by modifying how quickly food passes through the gastrointestinal tract, by affecting how long nutrients remain in the circulation, and by influencing plasma concentrations of insulin and leptin. These three possibilities are not mutually exclusive, and all may function to coordinate food intake with body weight maintenance.

Summary

Three effects of eating appear to limit the size of an ongoing meal: gastric distension (apparently potentiated by CCK), postgastric detection of calories (perhaps potentiated in the liver by insulin), and increased plasma osmolality. The signals reach the brain through visceral afferent fibers (especially those traveling with the vagus) and the circulatory system. Meal size invariably increases after inhibitory effects are experimentally removed by blocking the detection of gastric stretch or of CCK, diluting the food with noncaloric material, or rehydrating the animal. Inhibition appears to be integrated so that as one effect diminishes (e.g., the signal associated with gastric distension), another increases (e.g., the signal associated with the postabsorptive delivery of calories and insulin to the liver), thereby maintaining satiety and prolonging the interval between meals. When the satiety signals disappear hunger emerges and stimulates initiation of a meal.

Food intake is also normally linked closely with body weight. In experimental animals, periods of starvation or forced feeding will be followed by self-regulated eating patterns until prior body size is regained. Linkages between body weight and appetite can be mediated directly by gastrointestinal motility and absorption or by centrally active circulatory hormones such as leptin, released by adipocytes, or insulin.

CENTRAL CONTROL OF FOOD INTAKE

Early theories of the control of food intake focused on signals derived from stomach and blood. Peripheral markers, such as the concentration of glucose in the bloodstream, were plausibly associated with food intake and were accessible to experimentation. Theories involving the brain emerged after development of a

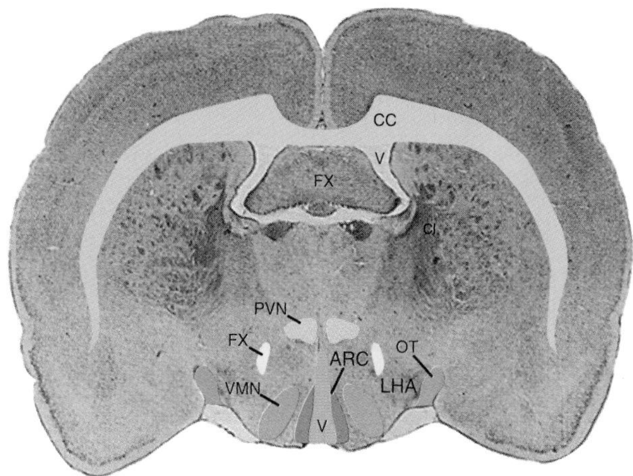

FIGURE 41.5 Coronal section through an adult rat brain at the level where the optic tract enters the two hemispheres. The lateral ventricle and third cerebral ventricle are shaded, and selected fiber tracts are outlined for reference (OT, optic tract; CC, corpus callosum; FX, fornix). Key hypothalamic sites important in caloric homeostasis, present in each hemisphere, are the paraventricular nuclei (PVN), the ventromedial nuclei (VMN), the arcuate nuclei (ARC), and the lateral hypothalamic area (LHA). Note that the dopaminergic fibers implicated in the lateral hypothalamic lesion syndrome pass just dorsolateral to the LHA.

stereotaxic instrument that enabled discrete lesions of the cerebrum to be made in laboratory animals, permitting evaluation of ideas about brain function (Fig. 41.5). The first findings from such experiments were striking: Bilateral electrolytic lesions of the ventromedial hypothalamus (VMH) caused marked hyperphagia and obesity in rats.[30] This observation was interpreted to mean that the animals had become less sensitive to incoming signals of satiety and that they therefore overate and became fat. Bilateral lesions in the adjacent ventrolateral hypothalamus (VLH) were later found to cause **aphagia** (absence of eating), which led to death by starvation.[31] This finding was interpreted to mean that these rats no longer detected hunger signals, and thus they starved to death while unaware of their internal state. Collectively, these results provided the foundation of a **dual center hypothesis**, in which a satiety center in the VMH was thought to suppress activity in a hunger center in the VLH.[32] Both the syndrome of hyperphagia and obesity and the syndrome of aphagia and weight loss that result from focal hypothalamic lesions have been reproduced in multiple laboratories and in multiple species. However, additional observations have caused reinterpretation of these familiar and reliable findings, and they now have a very different meaning. A striking example of the role of dual excitatory and inhibitory influences on feeding can be found in some invertebrates (see Box 41.3).

Food Intake Is Not Controlled by Hypothalamic Hunger and Satiety Centers

The strength of the traditional dual center model, in which one center mediates hunger and the other satiety, was that it provided a simple answer to the question of how the brain controls intake of food. The principal limitation of the model, however, was that it could not answer the next level of questions: What signals control individual meals? How are these signals integrated with physiological aspects of caloric homeostasis, including long-term maintenance of body weight? What is the influence of other neural sites and systems in the brain? How are excitatory and inhibitory influences on eating integrated? How are behaviors, such as motivation and reinforcement, explained? Investigators are addressing these and related questions, but they now usually take a perspective that does not presume the existence of brain centers mediating hunger and satiety.

In addition to causing hyperphagia, VMH lesions profoundly reduce sympathetic tone and increase parasympathetic tone and vagal reflexes. For example, the high concentration of insulin in animals with VMH lesions is not simply a secondary consequence of hyperphagia but occurs even when food intake is limited.[33] Because of the change in autonomic tone, caloric equilibrium in adipose tissue shifts away from lipolysis and toward lipogenesis, thereby allowing more rapid storage of ingested calories after a meal. Increased parasympathetic activity also allows faster gastric emptying.[34] Importantly, VMH lesions do not cause loss of satiety. Meal sizes continue to correlate with postmeal intervals, but the interval after a meal of any size is shorter in animals with VMH lesions than in control animals (Fig. 41.6).

Because the duration of their postprandial satiety signals is shorter than normal, rats with VMH lesions eat more frequent meals. They remain hyperphagic until the equilibrium between lipogenesis and lipolysis is reestablished in adipocytes.[35] For this to happen, triglyceride stores must accumulate in the cells to levels sufficient to create insulin resistance, whereupon lipogenesis subsides. Meals are eaten less frequently, and daily food intake is reduced. The animal maintains its obese state as if it had a new "set point" for body weight (Fig. 41.7). Thus, after obese rats with VMH lesions have been deprived of food and forced to lose weight, hyperphagia occurs until high adiposity is reattained.[36,37]

In sum, rats become hyperphagic after VMH lesions because accumulation of stored fat quickly increases, and the duration of satiety after meals decreases. This explanation contrasts with early hypotheses that body

BOX 41.3

FEEDING IN INVERTEBRATES: THE BLOWFLY AS A MODEL SYSTEM

The neural control of food intake in invertebrates is particularly well understood in the blowfly (*Phormia regina*). Its organization of neural controls, especially the central integration of excitatory and inhibitory signals, is surprisingly similar to key elements of the control of food intake in rats and other well-studied mammals.[69]

Briefly, flies usually require merely sugar and water for their sustenance. The excitatory signal to eat is provided solely by sweet taste, which is detected by sensory receptors located on hairs on blowflies' legs. This chemical signal causes the proboscis to extend into the sweet solution. Sucking commences and the liquid is drawn into the foregut and crop. Inhibitory signals are triggered by certain tastes (sodium chloride or acid solutions) and by distension of the crop and foregut during the meal. The flies ingest sugar until inhibition counterbalances excitation (from sweet taste), at which point consumption stops. Thus, more concentrated (i.e., sweeter) sugar solutions are consumed in larger meals. On the other hand, dilute (i.e., less sweet) sugar solutions require less gastric distension for inhibition to terminate ingestion. Inhibitory signals from the crop and foregut project to the brain via identified nerves from the abdomen. When those nerves are severed, ingestion of sugar solution cannot be inhibited, and the flies continue their intake until they literally burst.

The crop and foregut empty as absorption occurs, and the flies then become willing to feed again. Because concentrated solutions are absorbed relatively slowly, inhibitory signals generated by such fluids last longer than those generated by dilute solutions. Thus, flies ingest concentrated solutions in large meals taken infrequently, whereas dilute solutions are consumed in smaller but more frequent meals. In either case, the flies ingest the same amount of sugar over time. Remarkably, they do so despite their inability to detect calories. The fly is unable to monitor the metabolic consequences of feeding, but because sweet taste, sugar concentration, and caloric density correlate with one another, when the fly responds to sweet taste, it effectively tracks calories.

In sum, blowflies attend to signals of taste and gastric distension to find food and to eat enough to survive. The blowfly appears to eat reflexively, showing no evidence of experiencing hunger or of altering its eating on the basis of learning from past experience. In these respects, the flies are reminiscent of decerebrate rats. Thus, much of the control of eating in intact rats may be found in the brainstem, but forebrain function is required to mediate the separate but interrelated phenomena of motivation, sensation (e.g., hunger and satiety), caloric homeostasis, and cognitive functions (e.g., learning and memory).

weight increased after VMH lesions because animals became obligatorily hyperphagic. The primary phenomenon is now recognized as a change in autonomic tone to promote vagal reflexes. Because the change in autonomic tone is observed even when increased food intake is prevented, hyperphagia cannot be the primary phenomenon. The key element appears to be the chronic, neurally stimulated increase in insulin secretion. When this increase is prevented by denervating the pancreas, obesity does not develop and hyperphagia is greatly attenuated.[38]

In contrast to VMH lesions, bilateral VLH lesions reduce parasympathetic tone. As a result of blunted vagal reflexes, the rate of gastric emptying is reduced, and the secretion of insulin during meals is diminished. Longer intervals between meals might be expected because gastric distension is prolonged and absorbed calories are not cleared quickly. In fact, rats with relatively small VLH lesions have chronically reduced food intake and a lower body weight than normal.[39] A different phenomenon occurs in rats with large VLH lesions: The animals do not eat (to the point of starvation), and they also do not drink water when dehydrated (**adipsia**), move about in their cages (**akinesia**), or respond to diverse stimulation (**sensory neglect**).[40] The most prominent abnormalities in these rats are akinesia and sensory neglect. In this respect, rats with VLH lesions resemble human patients with **Parkinson disease**, a neurological disorder that has been attributed to degeneration of dopamine-containing neurons of the nigrostriatal bundle (see Chapters 8 and 34). Dopaminergic fibers course through the internal capsule just lateral to the VLH as they ascend from the ventral mesencephalon to the striatum along the medial forebrain bundle (Chapter 37). Large electrolytic lesions of the VLH area interrupt these dopaminergic fibers. More selective damage to the dopaminergic neurons by intracerebral administration of the neurotoxin 6-

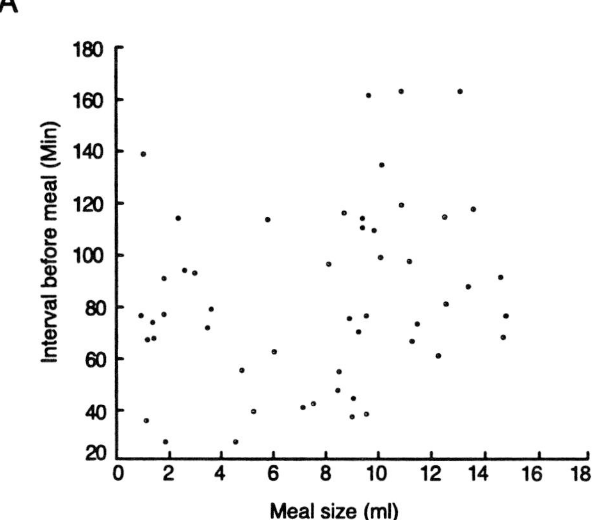

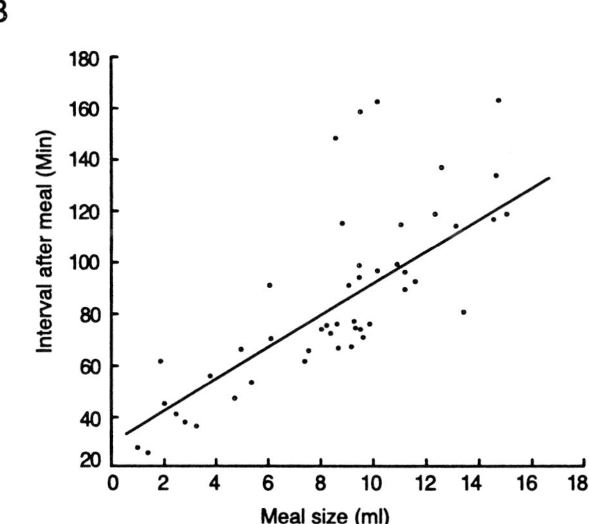

FIGURE 41.6 Meal sizes and intermeal intervals of a representative rat eating liquid food *ad libitum*. Shown are the sizes of 50 consecutive meals eaten by a rat that became hyperphagic after electrolytic lesions of the ventromedial hypothalamus. The volume of each meal is plotted against the intervals of time separating it from the preceding (A) and following (B) meals. As with control animals (see Fig. 41.3), premeal intervals did not predict meal sizes, whereas meal sizes did predict postmeal intervals. Note that after a meal of any given size, hyperphagic rats returned to eat sooner than neurologically normal control rats did. From Thomas and Mayer.[2]

hydroxydopamine also produces akinesia and sensory neglect in association with loss of food intake, and it does so without disturbing parasympathetic reflexes. Thus, the aphagia induced by large VLH lesions does not result from damage to a putative hunger center in the brain but instead reflects a more general disruption of movement and sensorimotor integration.[41]

Extensive studies of human parkinsonism and animals with dopamine-depleting brain lesions show that these dopaminergic fibers are critical for initiation of voluntary movement. The fibers appear to mediate a nonspecific component of arousal that is common to all motivated behaviors, and in its absence all behaviors are impaired—including eating. Rats with dopamine-depleting brain lesions (and patients with Parkinson disease) remain responsive to strong tastes and smells associated with food despite their lack of response to hunger. Thus, rats with VLH lesions might not eat laboratory food despite pronounced weight loss, but they will accept chocolate and other foods with an attractive taste and smell. These observations emphasize the important role of nonspecific activation as a component of behavior. They also emphasize the importance of exteroceptive signals in stimulating and guiding behavior in dopamine-depleted animals.

One of the interesting features of rats with large VLH lesions is that despite profound impairment, they can recover movement sufficient for eating that maintains body weight.[42] This recovery occurs if during the weeks or months while they are akinetic, the rats are sustained by multiple daily intragastric feedings of liquid food. However, even after apparent recovery of function, rats with VLH lesions do not behave normally. For example, initial studies indicated that these animals increased their food intake appropriately in response to a cold environment but not in response to insulin-induced hypoglycemia (see Box 41.4). Moreover, they drank water while eating dry food pellets but not in response to acute dehydration. Later studies found that the animals ate appropriate amounts when an induced hypoglycemia was less severe, but they did not eat when cold stress was enhanced.[43] It appears that the brain-damaged rats generally fail to respond to large amounts of stress, regardless of the nature of the stimulus, and the dysfunction occurs in association with akinesia and sensory neglect.[44] Sudden onset of akinesia also can be seen during acute stress in people with Parkinson disease.

The Brainstem Plays an Important Role in the Control of Food Intake

The NST and the adjacent area postrema in the brainstem receive sensory fibers from gustatory receptors in the mouth and throat (see Chapter 25), as well as afferent information from the stomach, intestines, pancreas, and liver. In the central control of food intake, these linked brainstem sites likely are where sensory input from the viscera is first integrated with input from tastebuds.

Evidence of the brainstem exerting some control over food intake comes from investigations of the de-

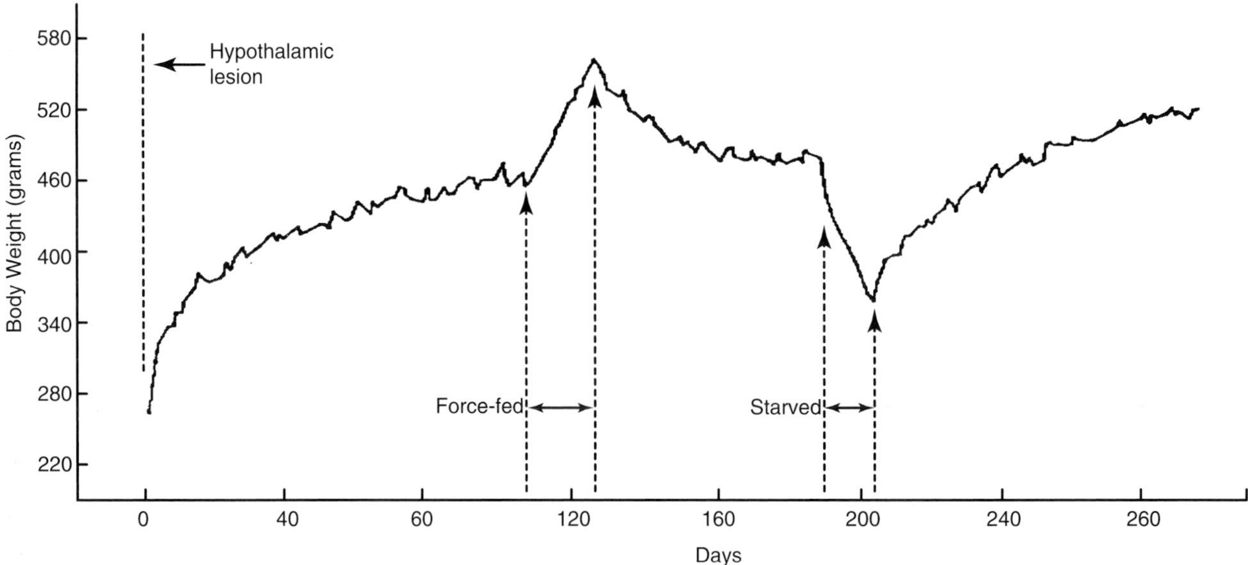

FIGURE 41.7 Changes in the body weight of rats with bilateral lesions of the ventromedial hypothalamus. After lesions are made on Day 0, rats rapidly gain weight and then defend that elevated body weight when challenged with periods of weight gain due to force-feeding and weight loss due to food restriction. Not shown are the associated food intakes, which increase subsequent to the lesion, decrease after the period of force-feeding, and increase after the period of food restriction. From Hoebel and Teitelbaum.[37]

cerebrate rat, in which all axonal connections between the caudal brainstem and the forebrain are severed at the midcollicular level of the midbrain.[45] This animal does not seek food or initiate spontaneous meals but, like an intact animal, will reflexively swallow liquid food put directly into its mouth. Thus, when investigators deliver sucrose solution through an oral fistula, the decerebrate rat will swallow the sweet fluid if its stomach is empty, such as after a period of food deprivation; however, it will not swallow water or saline when food-deprived, and it will not swallow sucrose solution (but instead lets the administered fluid passively drip from its mouth) when its stomach is full or if it has received a systemic injection of CCK or hypertonic saline. Therefore, sufficient control of food intake for such appropriate responses exists entirely within the caudal brainstem, but this animal is incapable of receiving input from forebrain sites that could modify intake based on learning or other experience.

Other observations provide additional support for an important role of the brainstem in the control of meal size. When the area postrema is ablated, rats eat much larger meals than normal, although total daily food intake is normal; that is, they compensate for their large meals by eating less frequently, indicating that long-term controls of food intake are not impaired. A similar effect is seen in rats pretreated with capsaicin, a neurotoxin that destroys most gastric afferent vagal axons, eliminating the food-intake-reducing effects of CCK and presumably damaging the signal of gastric distention.

The food-related sensory information that enters the brainstem is relayed along prominent neural projections to the hypothalamus, amygdala, and other portions of the limbic system, as well as to the thalamus and gustatory cortex. Reciprocal neural connections to the brainstem from these rostral sites allow emotion and cognitive function to influence the control of eating. Complementary and linked efferent elements participate in the central control of the gastrointestinal tract, the liver, and autonomic function generally.

Summary

The ability of brain circuitry to control food intake was initially based on the consequences of stereotaxic lesions of the ventromedial and ventrolateral hypothalamic nuclei leading to hyperphagia or aphagia, respectively. Subsequent studies revealed that each lesion also induces changes in gastrointestinal function and in the equilibrium between lipolysis and lipogenesis by adipocytes. In addition, these nuclei help regulate body weight through influences on spontaneous mobility and sensory responsivity to food-derived stimuli. The nucleus of the solitary tract also relays important visceral sensory cues on gastrointestinal fill that can further influence food intake.

BOX 41.4

THE GLUCOSTATIC HYPOTHESIS

Years ago, Mayer[17] proposed that onset and termination of meals were determined by changes in the amounts of glucose used by certain areas of the brain. Critical to Mayer's hypothesis was the observation that food intake was reliably increased by systemic injections of insulin, which reduced delivery of glucose to the brain. Another cornerstone of his theory was the observation that direct administration of the drug gold thioglucose (GTG) into the ventral hypothalamus destroyed local cells, after which the animals overate and became obese. Circulating insulin appeared necessary for this action because insulin-deficient (diabetic) animals were insensitive to the neurotoxic effects of GTG. Thus, Mayer hypothesized that food intake was controlled by a region of the ventral hypothalamus that, unlike the rest of the brain, was sensitive to insulin. In diabetic rats, the presence of hyperphagia despite elevated blood glucose emphasized the point that diminished glucose utilization in these insulin-dependent cells (as opposed to a reduction of blood glucose levels per se) was the critical factor in removing satiety and stimulating food intake.

At first widely accepted, the glucostatic theory fell into disfavor for several reasons. For one, although eating is induced by low availability of glucose to the brain, no evidence supports suppression of eating by high glucose availability. In addition, concentrations of blood glucose after administration of large doses of insulin are now known to be far lower than what occurs during a fast or at the normal onset of a meal. Thus, eating in response to insulin-induced hypoglycemia is now considered an "emergency" response that is not relevant to normal feeding. (A similar emergency response occurs after systemic injection of 2-deoxyglucose induces an acute decrease in cellular glycolysis.) Finally, the prevailing view of the ventromedial hypothalamus as a satiety center has changed considerably since the original formulation of the glucostatic hypothesis. This region of the brain is better regarded as a regulatory control center that influences many aspects of hormonal and autonomic function. Diabetic hyperphagia may therefore represent the loss of satiety promoted by insulin (in the liver or brain) that activates neural systems to inhibit food intake. In contrast, the earlier glucostatic hypothesis would have explained diabetic hyperphagia in terms of a special sensitivity to insulin of hypothalamic neurons that mediate satiety.

The glucostatic theory continues to evolve. In rats allowed to eat freely, Campfield and Smith[70] measured a decline in blood glucose that always began 15 to 20 min before an animal started to eat (Fig. 41.8). These investigators suggested that this small, transient episode of hypoglycemia causes initiation of a meal. Alternatively, this effect may result from a spurt of insulin secretion that reflects the animal's intention to begin a meal. Whether the transient decline of blood glucose is the cause or consequence of an inclination to eat remains unknown.

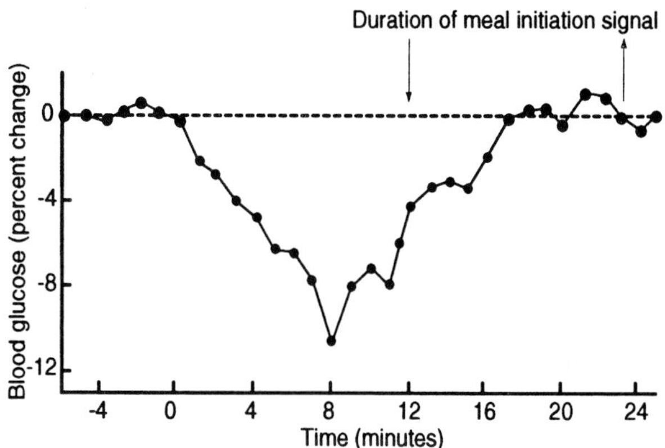

FIGURE 41.8 Transient decline of blood glucose in rats just prior to meal onset. Changes in the concentration of glucose are plotted as percent change from baseline against time. Values are from several experiments and normalized to the time of onset of the decline (0 min). On average, meals began at about 12 min (↓) and ended at about 23 min (↑). From Campfield and Smith.[70]

NEUROPEPTIDES AND THE CONTROL OF FOOD INTAKE

The complex arrangement of central control of food intake is incompletely understood, but it is known to involve neuropeptides. Although many neuropeptides have been implicated, we focus on oxytocin, insulin, and neuropeptide Y (NPY). Our focus on these three peptides is not intended to downplay the importance of other neuropeptides (e.g., the opioids, CCK, galanin, glucagon-like peptide-1), many of which may eventually be shown to have equally or more important roles in controlling food intake. Rather, we selected oxytocin, insulin, and NPY because each is known to provide a different kind of information to influence whether eating occurs. Oxytocin has been demonstrated to decrease food intake in rats for reasons unrelated to caloric homeostasis, whereas insulin has been demonstrated to decrease food intake, and NPY to increase food intake, for reasons that are related to caloric homeostasis.

Central Oxytocin Decreases Food Intake in Rats

Oxytocin is a peptide synthesized in the paraventricular nuclei (PVN) and supraoptic nuclei of the hypothalamus and secreted from the posterior lobe of the pituitary. In the systemic circulation of female mammals, this hormone is well known for stimulating uterine contractions for parturition and stimulating milk let down in mammary glands during lactation. However, the hypothalamus and pituitary of males contain as much oxytocin as those of females; therefore, the peptide has long been suspected of being secreted in other circumstances and having additional functions. In fact, research has revealed that gastric distension, CCK administration, and plasma hyperosmolality, treatments that decrease food intake in rats, elicit pituitary oxytocin secretion in male and female rats. In addition, increases in plasma concentrations of oxytocin correlate highly with observed decreases in food intake (Fig. 41.9).[46]

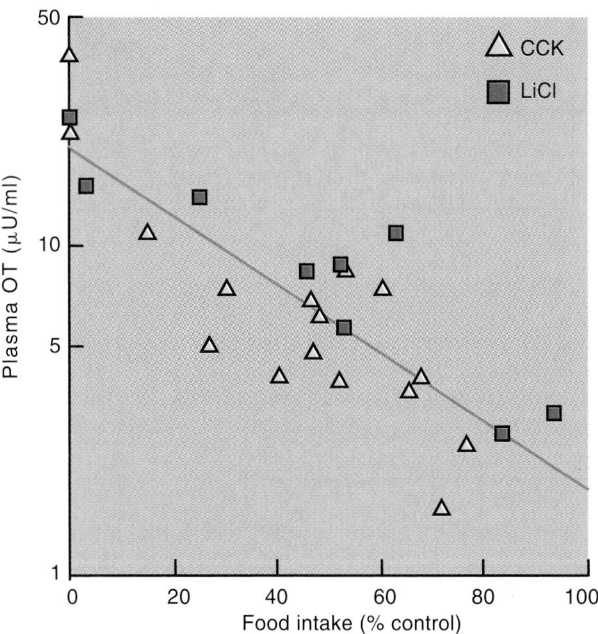

FIGURE 41.9 Relationship between plasma levels of oxytocin (OT) and inhibition of food intake by hungry rats pretreated with various doses of cholecystokinin (CCK) or lithium chloride (LiCl). Symbols represent individual rats. Food intake is expressed as a percentage of baseline for each rat. The same pattern was observed when hungry rats were pretreated with a hypertonic sodium chloride solution to induce hyperosmolality. Adapted from McCann *et al.*[46]

Although observations were consistent with oxytocin being an appetite suppressant, later experiments showed that this was not the case: Systemic administration of oxytocin does not affect food intake. Instead, the reduced food intake seen after treatment with CCK or hypertonic saline appears to be mediated by oxytocin secreted from neurons whose cell bodies are located in the hypothalamic PVN but whose axons project within the central nervous system rather than to the pituitary gland. Consistent with this hypothesis, central injection of oxytocin into the cerebral ventricles (icv) decreases food intake in rats, an effect that is blocked by icv pretreatment of the animals with an oxytocin receptor antagonist.[47] More to the point, the effects of exogenous CCK and hypertonic saline on food intake are blunted by icv pretreatment with an oxytocin receptor antagonist.[48]

Stress is also well known to decrease food intake in animals, and various stressors activate the hypothalamic–pituitary–adrenal axis. A key mediator of this effect is **corticotropin-releasing hormone** (CRH), which is synthesized and secreted from the PVN. CRH stimulates the secretion of adrenocorticotrophic hormone (ACTH) from the anterior pituitary, and ACTH in turn elicits steroid hormone secretion from the adrenal cortex (see Chapter 45). In rats, icv injection of CRH decreases food intake in the absence of stress and in association with oxytocin secretion from the posterior pituitary. In addition, icv pretreatment with an oxytocin receptor antagonist eliminates CRH-induced inhibition of food intake.[49] These findings are consistent with central oxytocinergic neurons mediating the inhibition of food intake that occurs during stress. Such inhibitory effects on eating would complement the known inhibitory effects of central oxytocin on gastric motility and emptying.[50]

Two additional features of these findings deserve note. First, central oxytocinergic pathways are not stimulated by suckling despite the prominent pituitary oxytocin secretion. Therefore, nursing does not inevitably reduce food intake in dams; in fact, lactating rats are hyperphagic in association with the substantial loss of calories through milk. Second, the various stimuli for oxytocin release are not related to caloric homeostasis, so oxytocin is not a factor in the termination of normal meals; in fact, oxytocin is not secreted by rats during meals taken *ad libitum.*

Insulin Stimulates Brain Neurons to Inhibit Food Intake

Although neurons do not require insulin for glucose transport and use, insulin does appear to have significant actions in the central control of food intake. Circulating insulin interacts with insulin receptors on the lumenal surface of brain capillaries. Bound insulin is then transported through the capillary endothelial cells into brain interstitial fluid, where insulin molecules have access to neurons and glial cells containing insulin receptors. The transport system from blood to brain is highly specific for the insulin molecule and does not respond to molecules of similar weight (e.g., inulin) or structure (e.g., proinsulin). Moreover, it is saturable and has kinetics similar to those of insulin receptor-mediated events in other tissues.[51]

Insulin penetration into the brain is proportional to blood insulin levels. Elevation of insulin within the brain usually occurs in association with increased body fat and appears to provide an adaptive signal to reduce food intake. Conversely, relatively low levels of insulin are found in the brain after a period of fasting, when pancreatic insulin secretion is low and food intake increases. More compelling than these correlations are observations that food intake and body weight are reduced in a dose-dependent manner by infusion of insulin into the ventral hypothalamus, which contains a high density of insulin receptors, or the adjacent third cerebral ventricle (Fig. 41.10).[52] This effect has been observed in several species, including nonhuman primates, and it does not appear to result from malaise. Furthermore, infusion of anti-insulin antibodies into the ventral hypothalamus increases food intake and body weight in rats. Finally, icv insulin has been shown to sensitize rats and nonhuman primates to the reduction of food intake by systemically administered CCK.

Together these results imply that insulin acts in the brain as a signal of satiety.[53] This signal is related to adiposity and likely is integrated with leptin, the other humoral signal related to adiposity, to sensitize the brain to neural signals from the stomach and liver in order to inhibit ongoing food ingestion.

Neuropeptide Y Acts in the Paraventricular Nucleus to Increase Food Intake

In the brain, icv insulin inhibits the synthesis of NPY, a peptide that causes food intake when given icv[54] or injected into the PVN.[55] This effect of NPY does not show tolerance, and chronic administration of NPY into the brain leads to obesity in rats (Fig. 41.11).[56] Among the numerous pathways containing NPY within the brain, one appears critical to the control of food intake. Axons of NPY-synthesizing neurons within the arcuate nucleus of the hypothalamus pass anteriorly to the PVN (see Fig. 41.5) to the same site at which NPY administration elicits eating. Endogenous levels of NPY in the arcuate–PVN system of rats peak when daylight ends and nocturnal activity begins,[57] which also is when rats typically eat their largest meal of the day. Food deprivation similarly increases the synthesis of NPY mRNA in the arcuate nucleus, increases the levels of NPY in axon terminals in the PVN, and increases secretion of NPY within the PVN. In addition, when antisense oligonucleotides to NPY receptors are given locally within the PVN, rats that had been deprived of food eat less than they usually would.[58] Finally, administration of insulin into the third cerebral ventricle reduces NPY mRNA in the arcuate nucleus and lowers the amount of food eaten by food-deprived rats in proportion to the decrease of NPY levels in the PVN.[59]

These findings are consistent with endogenous secretion of NPY into the PVN helping to mediate food intake, an effect that is blunted by the local presence of insulin. Consistent with this possibility, the elevated synthesis of NPY mRNA in the arcuate nucleus and high NPY levels in the PVN in insulin-deficient (i.e., diabetic) rats are normalized by systemic insulin treatments that also abolish the hyperglycemia and hyperphagia characteristic of diabetes. Small amounts of insulin administered immediately adjacent to the arcuate nucleus normalize local NPY mRNA synthesis and reduce food intake without ameliorating the hyperglycemia.[60] Thus, low insulin levels appear to stimulate hypothalamic NPY synthesis and increase food intake whereas high local insulin levels have the opposite effects.

In rats, the food intake elicited by icv NPY is greatly enhanced by systemic administration of ethanol in doses known to inhibit pituitary secretion of oxytocin.[61] This finding suggests that icv NPY actually has a mixed effect on food intake, both stimulatory and inhibitory. The stimulatory effect predominates so an additional inhibitory effect constraining intake, perhaps mediated by central oxytocinergic neurons, had not been suspected. If dual central peptidergic systems influence the control of food intake, an inhibitory system mediated by oxytocin often may be activated simultaneously with an excitatory system mediated by NPY, thereby limiting eating by hungry animals. The familiar appetite-enhancing effects of moderate amounts of ethanol are interesting to consider from this perspective.

Summary

To provide a biological context within which to consider the purpose of eating and the fate of ingested food, we began this chapter with a description of the physiology of caloric homeostasis. Two principles were emphasized. First, meal size is determined by the integrated effects of several acute stimuli. Delivery of calories to the stomach and intestines upon food consumption and postabsorptive delivery of nutrients to

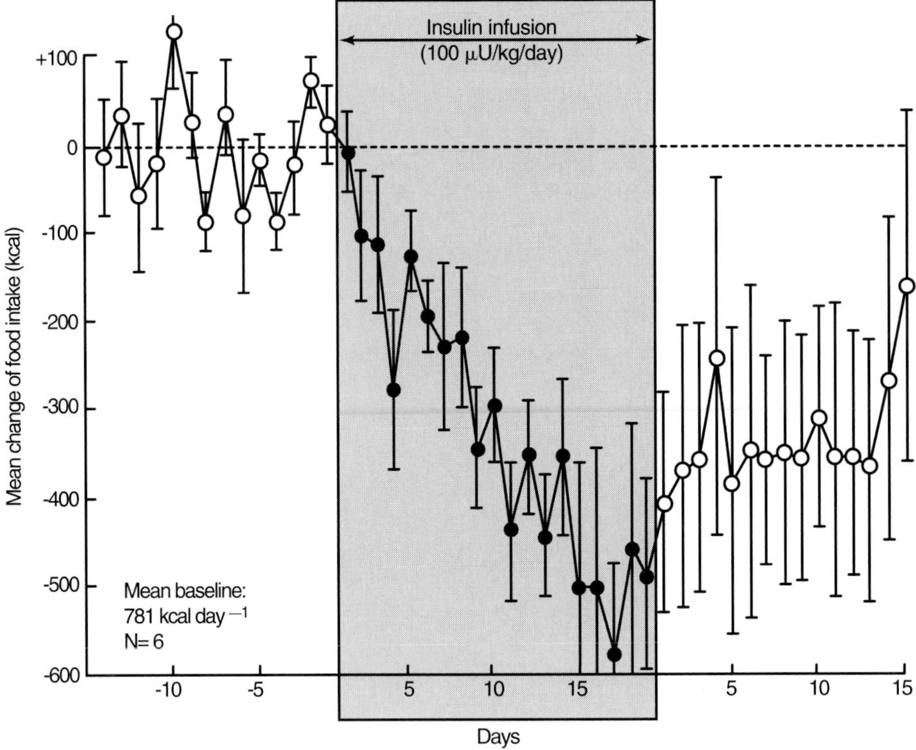

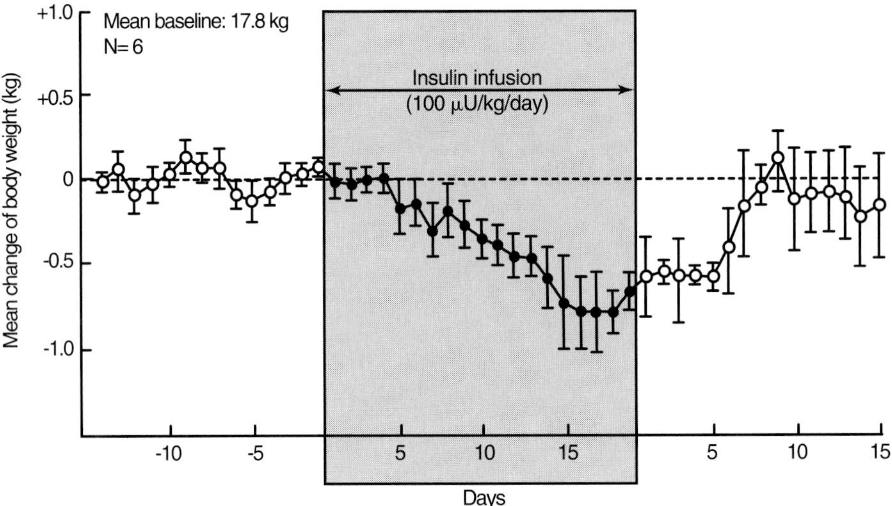

FIGURE 41.10 Mean change in food intake (top) and body weight (bottom) of six baboons during and after the infusion of insulin into the lateral cerebral ventricle. The reduction of food intake by insulin grew larger over days and the animals lost significant amounts of body weight. When the infusion of insulin was discontinued, body weight returned to baseline levels after 1 week and food intake returned to normal more slowly. The vehicle for the insulin (synthetic cerebrospinal fluid) was infused during the baseline period and after the infusion of insulin was discontinued. From Woods *et al.*[52]

A

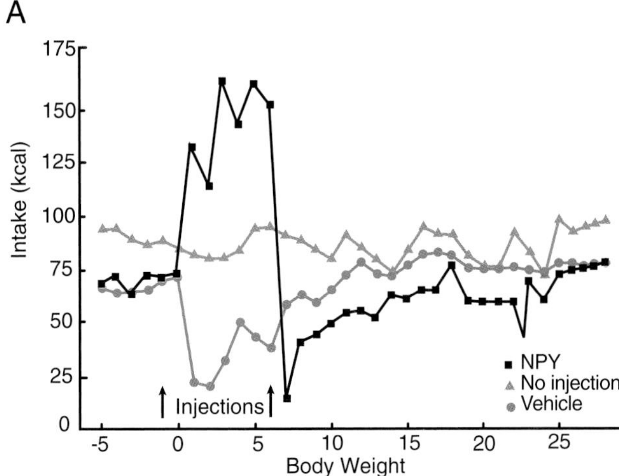

B

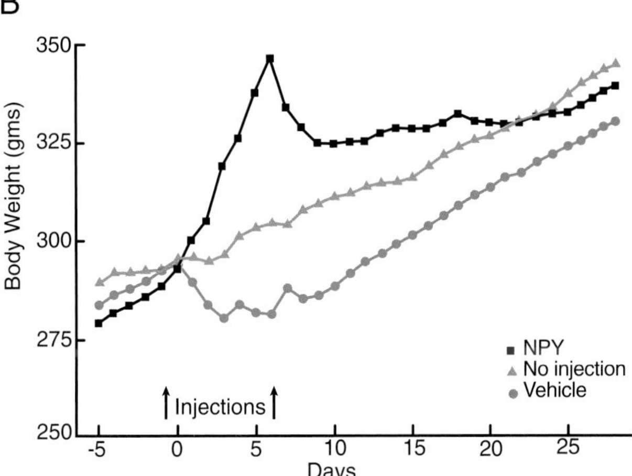

FIGURE 41.11 Mean food intake (A) and body weight (B) of rats receiving neuropeptide Y (NPY) or saline vehicle injected directly into the paraventricular nuclei every 8 h for 6 days. (Some rats received no treatment at all.) NPY markedly increased food intake and body weight, both of which returned to control levels 1–2 weeks after the injections of NPY were stopped. From Stanley *et al.*[56]

the liver elicit sensory neural signals from the stomach and the liver, respectively, to the brainstem. Second, food intake also is influenced by chronic signals associated with body adiposity. Adiposity indirectly affects gastric and hepatic signals of satiety. In addition, humoral signals proportionate to adiposity appear to affect food intake. One signal emanates from adipose tissue itself (i.e., leptin), and the other comes from the pancreas (i.e., insulin). These two peptides appear to be important in the central control of food intake; they might modulate the brain's response to the acute neural signals that affect food intake.

These neural and humoral signals are related to caloric homeostasis and are inhibitory in nature. During meals, they combine to stop ongoing ingestion; later, when these signals disappear in the postabsorptive state, new meals begin. Other inhibitory signals are unrelated to caloric homeostasis yet can have a pronounced effect on the cessation of eating. These signals include gastric distension, toxins (in the food or body), and dehydration.

The central nervous system exerts control over eating at many levels: The spinal cord and brainstem influence all aspects of caloric homeostasis via the autonomic nervous system. The hypothalamus and limbic forebrain receive signals about ingested food and body adiposity and integrate them with information about the taste of the food, the memory of that food, the experience of previous meals, the competition of other desires, and aspects of the environment. Thus, the central control of eating involves many areas of the central nervous system in the collective maintenance of caloric homeostasis. In short, food intake is a simple behavior influenced by a complex array of stimuli and situational variables, the details of which remain to be fully understood.

References

General

Bray, G. A., and York, D. A. (1979). Hypothalamic and genetic obesity in experimental animals: An autonomic and endocrine hypothesis. *Physiol. Rev.* **59:** 719–809.

Cahill, G. F., Jr. (1970). Starvation in man. *N. Engl. J. Med.* **282:** 668–675.

Friedman, M. I., and Stricker, E. M. (1976). The physiological psychology of hunger: A physiological perspective. *Psychol. Rev.* **83:** 409–431.

Garcia, J., Hankins, W. G., and Rusiniak, K. W. (1974). Behavioral regulation of the milieu interne in man and rat. *Science* **185:** 824–831.

Le Magnen, J. (1985). *Hunger*. Cambridge University Press, London.

McHugh, P. R., and Moran, T. H. (1985). The stomach: A conception of its dynamic role in satiety. *Prog. Psychobiol. Physiol. Psychol.* **11:** 197–232.

Newsholme, E. A., and Start, C. (1973). *Regulation in Metabolism*. Wiley, London.

Powley, T. L. (1977). The ventromedial hypothalamic syndrome, satiety, and a cephalic phase hypothesis. *Psychol. Rev.* **84:** 89–126.

Schwartz, M. W., Figlewicz, D. P., Baskin, D. G., Woods, S. C., and Porte, D., Jr. (1992). Insulin in the brain: A hormonal regulator of energy balance. *Endocr. Rev.* **13:** 387–414.

Smith, G. P., and Gibbs, J. (1992). The development and proof of the CCK hypothesis of satiety. *In Multiple Cholecystokinin Receptors in the CNS* (C. T. Dourish, S. J. Cooper, S. D. Iversen, and L. L. Iversen, eds.), pp. 166–182. Oxford University Press, London.

Stricker, E. M. (1984). Biological bases of hunger and satiety: Therapeutic implications. *Nutr. Rev.* **42:** 333–340.

Stricker, E. M., and Verbalis, J. G. (1990). Control of appetite and satiety: Insights from biologic and behavioral studies. *Nutr. Rev.* **48:** 49–56.

Stricker, E. M., and Zigmond, M. J. (1976). Recovery of function following damage to central catecholamine-containing neurons:

A neurochemical model for the lateral hypothalamic syndrome. *Progr. Psychobiol. Physiol. Psychol.* **6:** 121–188.

Woods, S. C., and Porte D., Jr. (1974). Autonomic control of the endocrine pancreas. *Physiol. Rev.* **54:** 596–619.

Cited

1. Le Magnen, J., and Tallon, S. (1966). La périodicité spontanée de la prise d'aliments *ad libitum* du rat blanc. *J. Physiol. (Paris)* **58:** 323–349.
2. Thomas, D. W., and Mayer, J. (1968). Meal taking and regulation of food intake by normal and hypothalamic hyperphagic rats. *J. Comp. Physiol. Psychol.* **66:** 642–653.
3. Young, R. C., Gibbs, J., Antin, J., Holt, J., and Smith, G. P. (1974). Absence of satiety during sham feeding in the rat. *J. Comp. Physiol. Psychol.* **87:** 795–800.
4. Smith, G. P., Gibbs, J., and Young, R. C. (1974). Cholecystokinin and intestinal satiety in the rat. *Fed. Proc., Fed. Am. Soc. Exp. Biol.* **33:** 1146–1150.
5. Olson, B. R., Freilino, M., Hoffman, G. E., Stricker, E. M., Sved, A. F., and Verbalis, J. G. (1993). C-fos expression in rat brain and brainstem nuclei in response to treatments that alter food intake and gastric motility. *Mol. Cell. Neurosci.* **4:** 93–106.
6. Schwartz, G. J., McHugh, P. R., and Moran, T. H. (1993). Gastric loads and cholecystokinin synergistically stimulate rat gastric vagal afferents. *Am. J. Physiol.* **265:** R872–R876.
7. Gibbs, J., Young, R. C., and Smith, G. P. (1973). Cholecystokinin decreases food intake in rats. *J. Comp. Physiol. Psychol.* **84:** 488–495.
8. Hall, W. G. (1990). The ontogeny of ingestive behavior: Changing control of components in the feeding sequence. In *Handbook of Behavioral Neurobiology* (E. M. Stricker, ed.), Vol. 10, pp. 77–123. Plenum, New York.
9. Weller, A., Smith, G. P., and Gibbs, J. (1991). Endogenous CCK reduces feeding in young rats. *Science* **247:** 1589–1591.
10. Adolph, E. F. (1947). Urges to eat and drink in rats. *Am. J. Physiol.* **151:** 110–125.
11. Deutsch, J. A. (1990). Food intake: Gastric factors. In *Handbook of Behavioral Neurobiology* (E. M. Stricker, ed.), Vol. 10, pp. 151–182. Plenum, New York.
12. Phillips, R. J., and Powley, T. L. (1996). Gastric volume rather than nutrient content inhibits food intake. *Am. J. Physiol.* **271:** R766–R779.
13. Yox, D. P., Stokesberry, H., and Ritter, R. C. (1991). Vagotomy attenuates suppression of sham feeding induced by intestinal nutrients. *Am. J. Physiol.* **260:** R503–R508.
14. Russek, M. (1963). Participation of hepatic glucoreceptors in the control of intake of food. *Nature (London)* **197:** 79–80.
15. Niijima, A. (1975). The effect of 2-deoxy-D-glucose and D-glucose on the efferent discharge rate of sympathetic nerves. *J. Physiol. (London)* **251:** 231–243.
16. Friedman, M. I. (1980). Hepatic-cerebral interactions in insulin-induced eating and gastric acid secretion. *Brain Res. Bull.* **5** (Suppl. 4): 63–68.
17. Mayer, J. (1955). Regulation of energy intake and the body weight: The glucostatic theory and the lipostatic hypothesis. *Ann. N. Y. Acad. Sci.* **63:** 15–43.
18. Booth, D. A. (1972). Satiety and behavioral caloric compensation following intragastric glucose loads in the rat. *J. Comp. Physiol. Psychol.* **78:** 412–432.
19. Nicolaidis, S., and Rowland, N. (1976). Metering of intravenous versus oral nutrients and regulation of energy balance. *Am. J. Physiol.* **231:** 661–668.
20. Booth, D. A. (1972). Some characteristics of feeding during streptozotocin-induced diabetes in the rat. *J. Comp. Physiol. Psychol.* **80:** 238–249.
21. Lindberg, N. O., Coburn, P. C., and Stricker, E. M. (1984). Increased feeding by rats after subdiabetogenic streptozotocin treatment: A role for insulin in satiety. *J. Comp. Physiol. Psychol.* **98:** 138–145.
22. Flanagan, L. M., Blackburn, R. E., Verbalis, J. G., and Stricker, E. M. (1992). Hypertonic NaCl inhibits gastric motility and food intake in rats with lesions in the rostral AV3V region. *Am. J. Physiol.* **263:** R9–R14.
23. Fleming, D. G. (1969). Food intake studies in parabiotic rats. *Ann. N. Y. Acad. Sci.* **157:** 985–1002.
24. Hervey, G. R. (1952). The effects of lesions in the hypothalamus in parabiotic rats. *J. Physiol. (London)* **145:** 336–352.
25. Coleman, D. L., and Hummel, K. P. (1969). Effects of parabiosis of normal with genetically diabetic mice. *Am. J. Physiol.* **217:** 1298–1304.
26. Weigle, D. S., Bukowski, T. R., Foster, D. C., Holderman, S., Kramer, J. M., Lasser, G., Lofton-Day, C. E., Prunkard, D. E., Raymond, C., and Kuijper, J. L. (1995). Recombinant *ob* protein reduces feeding and body weight in the *ob/ob* mouse. *J. Clin. Invest.* **96:** 2065–2070.
27. Campfield, L. A., Smith, F. J., Guisez, Y., Devos, R., and Burn, P. (1995). Recombinant mouse OB protein: Evidence for a peripheral signal linking adiposity to central neural networks. *Science* **269:** 546–549.
28. Tarataglia, L. A., Dembski, M., Weng, X., Deng, N., Culpepper, J., Devos, R., Richards, G. J., Campfield, L. A., Clark, F. T., Deeds, J., Muir, C., Sanker, S., Moriarity, A., Moore, K. J., Smutko, J. S., Mays, G. G., Woolf, E. A., Monroe, C. A., and Tepper, R. I. (1996). Identification and expression cloning of a leptin receptor OB-R. *Cell (Cambridge, Mass.)* **83:** 1–20.
29. Schwartz, M. W., Baskin, D. G., Bukowski, T. R., Kuijper, J. L., Foster, D., Lasser, G., Prunkard, D. E., Porte, D., Jr., Woods, S. C., Seeley, R. J., and Weigle, D. S. (1996). Specificity of leptin actin on elevated blood glucose levels and hypothalamic neuropeptide Y gene expression in *ob/ob* mice. *Diabetes* **45:** 531–535.
30. Hetherington, A. W., and Ranson, S. W. (1940). Hypothalamic lesions and adiposity in the rat. *Anat. Rec.* **78:** 149–172.
31. Anand, B. K., and Brobeck, J. R. (1951). Hypothalamic control of food intake in rats and cats. *Yale J. Biol. Med.* **24:** 123–140.
32. Stellar, E. (1954). The physiology of motivation. *Psychol. Rev.* **61:** 5–22.
33. Steffens, A. B. (1970). Plasma insulin content in relation to blood glucose level and meal pattern in the normal and hypothalamic hyperphagic rat. *Physiol. Behav.* **5:** 147–151.
34. Duggan, J. P., and Booth, D. A. (1986). Obesity, overeating, and rapid gastric emptying in rats with ventromedial hypothalamic lesions. *Science* **231:** 609–611.
35. Le Magnen, J., Devos, M., Gaudilliere, J.-P. Louis-Sylvestre, J., and Tallon, S. (1973). Role of a lipostatic mechanism in regulation by feeding of energy balance in rats. *J. Comp. Physiol. Psychol.* **84:** 1–23.
36. Brobeck, J. R., Tepperman, J., and Long, C. N. H. (1943). Experimental hypothalamic hyperphagia in the albino rat. *Yale J. Biol. Med.* **15:** 831–853.
37. Hoebel, B. G., and Teitelbaum, P. (1966). Weight regulation in normal and hypothalamic hyperphagic rats. *J. Comp. Physiol. Psychol.* **61:** 189–193.
38. Inoue, S., Bray, G. A., and Mullen, Y. S. (1978). Transplantation of pancreatic beta-cells prevents development of hypothalamic obesity in rats. *Am. J. Physiol.* **235:** E266–E271.
39. Powley, T. L., and Keesey, R. E. (1970). Relationship of body

weight to the lateral hypothalamic feeding syndrome. *J. Comp. Physiol. Psychol.* **70:** 25–36.

40. Marshall, J. F., Turner, B. H., and Teitelbaum, P. (1971). Sensory neglect produced by lateral hypothalamic damage. *Science* **174:** 523–525.
41. Ungerstedt, U. (1971). Adipsia and aphagia after 6-hydroxydopamine induced degeneration of the nigro-striatal dopamine system. *Acta Physiol. Scandin.*, Suppl. **367:** 95–122.
42. Teitelbaum, P., and Epstein, A. N. (1962). The lateral hypothalamic syndrome: Recovery of feeding and drinking after lateral hypothalamic lesions. *Psychol. Rev.* **69:** 74–90.
43. Stricker, E. M., Friedman, M. I., and Zigmond, M. J. (1975). Glucoregulatory feeding by rats after intraventricular 6-hydroxydopamine or lateral hypothalamic lesions. *Science* **189:** 895–897.
44. Stricker, E. M., Cooper, P. H., Marshall, J. F., and Zigmond, M. J. (1979). Acute homeostatic imbalances reinstate sensorimotor dysfunctions in rats with lateral hypothalamic lesions. *J. Comp. Physiol. Psychol.* **93:** 512–521.
45. Grill, H. J., and Kaplan, J. M. (1990). Caudal brainstem participants in the distributed neural control of feeding. In *Handbook of Behavioral Neurobiology* (E. M. Stricker, ed.), Vol. 10, pp. 125–149. Plenum, New York.
46. McCann, M. J., Verbalis, J. G., and Stricker, E. M. (1989). LiCl and CCK inhibit gastric emptying and feeding and stimulate OT secretion in rats. *Am. J. Physiol.* **256:** R463–R468.
47. Olson, B. R., Drutarosky, M. D., Chow, M. S., Hruby, V. J., Stricker, E. M., and Verbalis, J. G. (1991). Oxytocin and an oxytocin agonist administered centrally decrease food intake in rats. *Peptides (N.Y.)* **12:** 113–118.
48. Olson, B. R., Drutarosky, M. D., Stricker, E. M., and Verbalis, J. G. (1991). Brain oxytocin receptor antagonism blunts the effects of anorexigenic treatments in rats: Evidence for central oxytocin inhibition of food intake. *Endocrinology (Baltimore)* **129:** 785–791.
49. Olson, B. R., Drutarosky, M. D., Stricker, E. M., and Verbalis, J. G. (1991). Brain oxytocin receptors mediate corticotropin releasing hormone-induced anorexia. *Am. J. Physiol.* **260:** R448–R452.
50. Rogers, R. C., and Hermann, G. E. (1987). Oxytocin, oxytocin antagonist, TRH, and hypothalamic paraventricular nucleus stimulation effects on gastric motility. *Peptides (N.Y.)* **8:** 505–513.
51. Schwartz, M. W., Bergman, R. N., Kahn, S. E., Taborsky, G. J., Jr., Fisher, L. D., Sipols, A. J., Woods, S. C., Steil, G. M., and Porte, D., Jr. (1991). Evidence for entry of plasma insulin into cerebrospinal fluid through an intermediate compartment in dogs. *J. Clin. Invest.* **88:** 1271–1281.
52. Woods, S. E., Lotter, E. C., McKay, L. D., and Porte, D., Jr. (1979). Chronic intracerebroventricular infusion of insulin reduces food intake and body weight of baboons. *Nature (London)* **282:** 503–505.
53. Woods, S. C. (1995). Insulin and the brain: A mutual dependency. *Prog. Psychobiol. Physiol. Psychol.* **16:** 53–81.
54. Clark, J. T., Kalra, P. S., Crowley, W. R., and Kalra, S. P. (1984). Neuropeptide Y and human pancreatic polypeptide stimulate feeding behavior in rats. *Endocrinology (Baltimore)* **115:** 427–429.
55. Stanley, B. G., Kyrkouli, S. E., Lampert, S., and Leibowitz, S. F. (1986). Neuropeptide Y chronically injected into the hypothalamus: a powerful neurochemical inducer of hyperphagia and obesity. *Peptides (N.Y.)* **7:** 1189–1192.
56. Stanley, B. G., Anderson, K. C., Grayson, M. H., and Leibowitz, S. F. (1989). Repeated hypothalamic stimulation with neuropeptide Y increases daily carbohydrate and fat intake and body weight gain in female rats. *Physiol. Behav.* **46:** 173–177.
57. Leibowitz, S. F. (1990). Hypothalamic neuropeptide Y, galanin, and amines: Concepts of coexistence in relation to feeding behavior. *Ann. N. Y. Acad. Sci.* **611:** 221–235.
58. Akabayashi, A., Wahlestedt, C., Alexander, J. T., and Leibowitz, S. F. (1994). Specific inhibition of endogenous neuropeptide Y synthesis in arcuate nucleus by oligonucleotides suppresses feeding behavior and insulin secretion. *Mol. Brain Res.* **21:** 55–61.
59. Schwartz, M. W., Sipols, A. J., Marks, J. L., Sanacora, G., White, J. D., Scheurink, A. J. W., Kahn, S. E., Baskin, D. G., Woods, S. C., Figlewicz, D. P., and Porte, D., Jr. (1992). Inhibition of hypothalamic neuropeptide Y gene expression by insulin. *Endocrinology (Baltimore)* **130:** 3608–3616.
60. Sipols, A. J., Baskin, D. G., and Schwartz, M. W. (1995). Effect of intracerebroventricular insulin infusion on diabetic hyperphagia and hypothalamic neuropeptide Y gene expression. *Diabetes* **44:** 147–151.
61. Blackburn, R. E., Stricker, E. M., and Verbalis, J. G. (1994). Acute effects of ethanol on ingestive behavior in rats. *Alcoholism: Clin. Exp. Res.* **18:** 924–930.
62. Reaven, G. M. (1991). Insulin resistance, hyperinsulinemia, hypertriglyceridemia and hypertension: Parallels between human disease and rodent models. *Diabetes Care* **14:** 195–202.
63. Pavlov, I. P. (1927). *Conditioned Reflexes.* Oxford University Press, London.
64. Woods, S. C. (1991). The eating paradox. How we tolerate food. *Psychol. Rev.* **98:** 488–505.
65. Chang, F.-C. T., and Scott, T. P. (1984). Conditioned taste aversions modify neural responses in the rat nucleus tractus solitarius. *J. Neurosci.* **4:** 1850–1862.
66. Miaskiewicz, S. L., Stricker, E. M., and Verbalis, J. G. (1989). Neurohypophyseal secretion in response to cholecystokinin but not meal-induced gastric distention in humans. *J. Clin. Endocrinol. Metab.* **68:** 837–843.
67. Verbalis, J. G., McCann, M. J., McHale, C. M., and Stricker, E. M. (1986). Oxytocin secretion in response to cholecystokinin and food intake: Differentiation of nausea from satiety. *Science* **232:** 1417–1419.
68. Reidelberger, R. D., and O'Rourke, M. F. (1989). Potent cholecystokinin antagonist L364718 stimulates food intake in rats. *Am. J. Physiol.* **257:** R1512–R1518.
69. Dethier, V. G. (1976). *The Hungry Fly.* Harvard University Press, Cambridge, MA.
70. Campfield, L. A., and Smith, F. J. (1986). Functional coupling between transient declines in blood glucose and feeding behavior: Temporal relationships. *Brain Res. Bull.* **17:** 427–433.

CHAPTER

42

Water Intake and Body Fluids

Edward M. Stricker and Joseph G. Verbalis

Body fluids are the watery matrix in which the biochemical reactions of cellular metabolism occur. The concentration of substrates in cellular fluid is a key factor in determining the rate at which those reactions take place. All tissues depend on circulating blood to deliver the nutrients needed to support cellular metabolism and to carry away unwanted metabolites for excretion. Thus, the maintenance of solute concentrations or osmolalities—**osmotic homeostasis**—and the regulation of plasma volume—**volume homeostasis**—are essential functions in the physiology of animals.

When normal body fluid osmolality or plasma volume is threatened, various physiological and behavioral responses are stimulated to maintain or restore the basal state adaptively. For example, during water deprivation, animals decrease water lost to prevent dehydration from worsening, and they consume water to replace the fluid they have lost. Similarly, hemorrhage stimulates the urinary conservation of water and sodium as well as the ingestion of water and NaCl. Water retention and sodium retention are accomplished through actions of the antidiuretic hormone **arginine vasopressin** (AVP) and the antinatriuretic hormone **aldosterone**, while water ingestion and NaCl ingestion are motivated by **thirst** and **salt appetite**. These complementary responses are mediated and coordinated by the brain.

In this chapter, we describe the various mechanisms by which the cues for fluid homeostasis are detected and integrated by the central nervous system. However, we first present a brief overview of body fluid physiology to provide a context in which to consider the regulated functions.

BODY FLUID PHYSIOLOGY

Water is the largest constituent of the body. It contributes 55–65% of the body weight of animals, including humans, varying mostly in relation to the amount of body fat. Total body water is distributed between the **intracellular fluid** (ICF) and the **extracellular fluid** (ECF) **compartments**, with 55–65% in the former and 35–45% in the latter. The ECF can be further subdivided into the **interstitial fluid** surrounding the cells and the **intravascular fluid** within blood vessels. The intravascular fluid, the plasma (or serum) of blood, averages 7–8% of total body water, or approximately one-fifth of the ECF. Figure 42.1 summarizes the estimated body fluid spaces of an average adult human.

Fluid compartments differ not only in their volumes but also in the solutes that are dissolved in them. Specifically, membrane-bound Na^+–K^+ pumps move Na^+ outside the cells and K^+ inside. Despite the differences in solute composition, the **osmotic pressure**, which reflects the concentrations of all solutes in a fluid compartment, is equivalent between the ECF and ICF compartments because most biological membranes are freely permeable to water. Thus, water flows across the membranes by osmosis from a relatively dilute compartment into one with a higher solute concentration, until a steady state is reached. At steady state, the osmotic pressures are the same on both sides of the cell membrane.

Multiple Mechanisms Help Maintain Blood Volume and Pressure

The volume of intravascular fluid is especially important because it must always be sufficient to allow circulation of blood throughout the body. The distribution of fluid between the intravascular and the interstitial fluid compartments is determined by a balance between the **hydrostatic pressure** of the blood, which is maintained by cardiac output and arteriolar vasoconstriction, and the opposing osmotic pressure contributed by plasma proteins. Although those proteins contribute only 1–2% to overall plasma osmolality, the permeability of capillary membranes to such large molecules is low; therefore, the proteins exert a pressure differential (of approximately 15–20 mm Hg), called the **colloid osmotic (oncotic) pressure**, that tends to pull interstitial fluid into the circulation. Figure 42.2

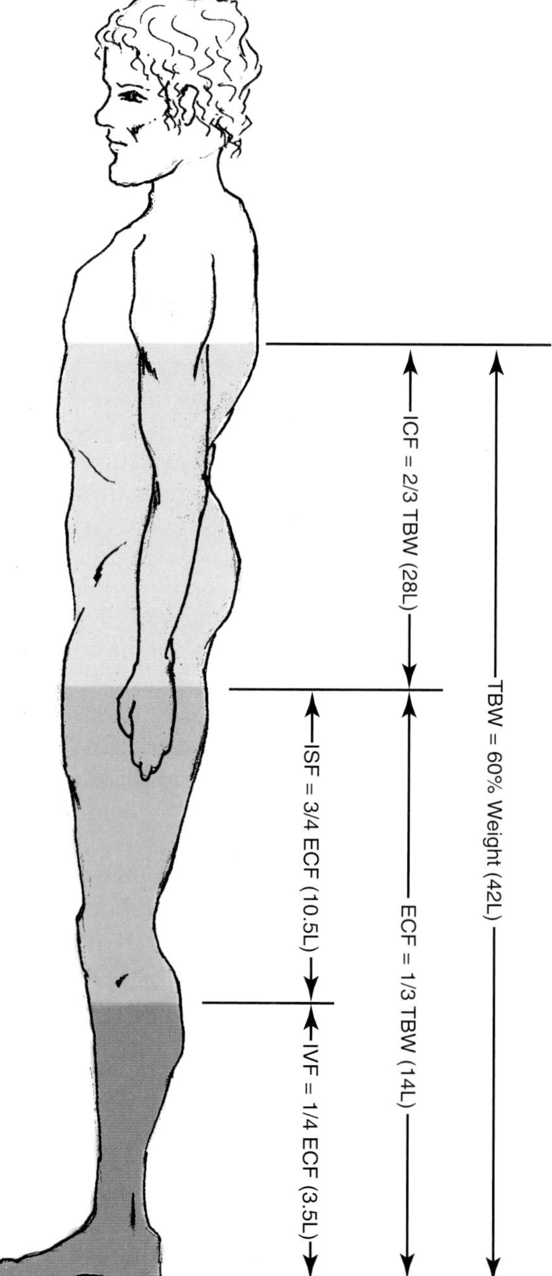

FIGURE 42.1 Schematic representation of body fluid compartments of humans. Shading shows approximately the portion of body weight contributed by each compartment. Approximate relative and absolute volumes of the fluid compartments are shown for a 70-kg adult. TBW, total body water; ICF, intracellular fluid; ECF, extracellular fluid; ISF, interstitial fluid; IVF, intravascular fluid.

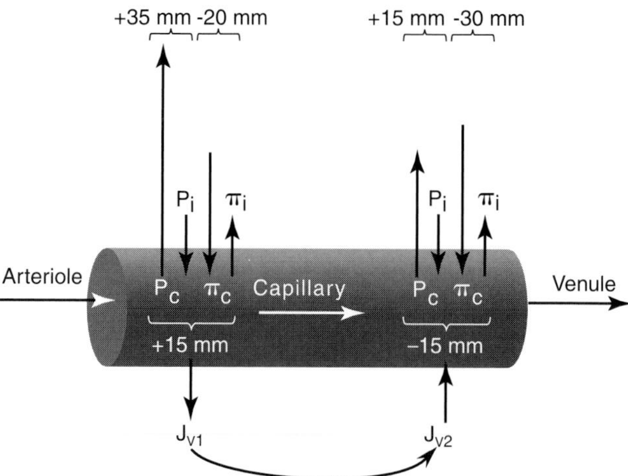

FIGURE 42.2 Starling forces governing transcapillary fluid transfer. At the arteriolar end of the capillary, the difference between the intravascular hydrostatic pressure (P_c) and the interstitial hydrostatic pressure (P_i) exceeds the oppositely oriented difference between the intravascular oncotic pressure (π_c) and the interstitial oncotic pressure (π_i); the resultant pressure gradient drives capillary fluid into the interstitial space (J_{v1}). As fluid leaves the capillary, P_c decreases due to fluid loss and π_c increases due to hemoconcentration. Consequently, at the venous end of the capillary, interstitial fluid is pulled back into the vascular space (J_{V2}). The numerical values indicate approximate net pressure differences (in mm Hg) between the intravascular and interstitial spaces. Relative sizes of P and π are indicated by arrow length. Note that fluid accumulating in the interstitial space ultimately returns to the blood via the lymphatic system (not shown).

summarizes the forces governing transcapillary fluid transfer between the two extracellular compartments, a phenomenon first described by the English physiologist Starling in 1896.[1] Note that according to this arrangement, the interstitial fluid acts as a reservoir for plasma. The Starling equilibrium is such that if blood pressure falls because of hemorrhage, interstitial fluid moves into the circulation, thereby helping to restore plasma volume. The reverse occurs when saline is added to the blood, because plasma proteins are then diluted and the oncotic pressure they provide diminishes, allowing fluid to flow into the interstitial space.

Blood pressure also is maintained by two other mechanisms intrinsic to the cardiovascular system. First, although the arteries that receive the cardiac output of blood have thick walls to preserve blood pressure, the veins are thin-walled, distensible vessels. After a moderate hemorrhage, veins collapse, redistributing blood to arteries, which cannot collapse and thus remain full. Consequently, arterial blood pressure is not compromised, and the blood is redistributed so that the deficit occurs primarily on the venous side of the circulation. Conversely, fluid accumulates in the veins when blood volume is expanded, again without much effect on arterial blood pressure. This property is called the **capacitance** or **compliance** of the vascular system. Second, the filtration of blood in the glomeruli of the kidneys is determined in large part by blood pressure in the renal arteries. A drop in blood pressure reduces the **glomerular filtration rate** (GFR) and decreases urine formation, whereas a rise in blood pressure elevates GFR and promotes urinary fluid loss. This normal function of the kidneys is so efficient that the development of hypertension always implicates renal dysfunction as a contributing factor, because the kidneys failed to adjust to the elevated blood pressure by increasing fluid excretion in urine.[2]

Summary

Body fluid homeostasis is directed at achieving stability in the osmolality of body fluids and the volume of plasma. Osmotic homeostasis prevents large shifts of water into and out of cells; such shifts would interfere with normal cell function. Volume homeostasis allows the normal circulatory function on which all tissues depend. Such homeostatic regulation is promoted by several mechanisms intrinsic to the physiology of body fluids and the cardiovascular system. For example, changes in the osmolality of ECF are buffered by rapid osmotic movement of water across cellular membranes. Similarly, acute changes in plasma volume are modulated by movement of fluid across capillary membranes (according to the Starling equilibrium), by venous compliance, and by compensatory alterations in GFR. Nevertheless, changes in body fluid osmolality and plasma volume may be so large that additional mechanisms must be recruited to maintain homeostasis. These other responses involve the central control of water and sodium excretion in urine through the actions of specific hormones and the central control of water and NaCl consumption motivated by thirst and salt appetite.

OSMOTIC HOMEOSTASIS

Osmolality is an expression of concentration—that is, a ratio of the total amount of solute dissolved in a given weight of water:

$$\frac{\text{solute (osmoles)}}{\text{water (kilograms)}}.$$

Dehydration and the consequent need for water occur whenever this ratio is elevated, whether by a decrease in its denominator or by an increase in its numerator. In fact, both changes occur naturally and often: Body water decreases as a result of water deprivation or the loss of dilute fluids to accomplish evaporative cooling (e.g., sweating) and increases as a result of solute load, primarily from the consumption of sodium as NaCl in foods.

The water loss associated with dehydration is borne by the ECF and the ICF in proportion to their sizes; the osmolality of fluid in the two compartments remains in equilibrium. In contrast, the increase in plasma osmolality that results from a sodium load results only in cellular dehydration, because the water leaving cells by osmosis expands ECF volume. Thus, a sodium load is a more abrupt, less complex treatment than water deprivation for stimulating AVP secretion and thirst, the two main osmoregulatory responses of the brain.

Arginine Vasopressin Is the Antidiuretic Hormone

AVP is a nine-amino-acid peptide that is synthesized in the magnocellular neurons in the supraoptic nucleus (SON) and the paraventricular nucleus (PVN) of the hypothalamus. The peptide is enzymatically cleaved from its prohormone (Fig. 42.3) and transported along axons projecting from the hypothalamus to the nearby posterior lobe of the pituitary gland (neurohypophysis). There, AVP is stored within neurosecretory granules until specific stimuli, such as an increase in the effective osmolality of body fluids, cause its secretion into the bloodstream. The importance of AVP in maintaining water balance is underscored by the fact that its stores in the pituitary are very large—more than a week's supply of hormone for maximal antidiuresis under conditions of sustained dehydration.

The circulating hormone acts on a subset of AVP receptors (termed V_2) in the kidney to increase water permeability of the distal convoluted tubules of nephrons through insertion of water channels into the apical membranes of tubular epithelial cells. Permeability of the collecting duct is also increased. Antidiuresis occurs when water moves out of the distal convoluted tubule and collecting duct by osmosis. As secondary responses to the increased net water reabsorption, urine flow decreases and urine osmolality increases.

With refinement of radioimmunoassays for AVP, the unique sensitivity of the hormone to small changes in osmolality has become apparent, as has the remarkable sensitivity of the kidney to small changes in plasma AVP levels. Circulating AVP is linearly related to plasma osmolality above a threshold of 1–2% pg ml^{-1} (Dunn *et al.*[3]) (Fig. 42.4).[4] The renal response to plasma AVP also is linear, with urinary osmolality

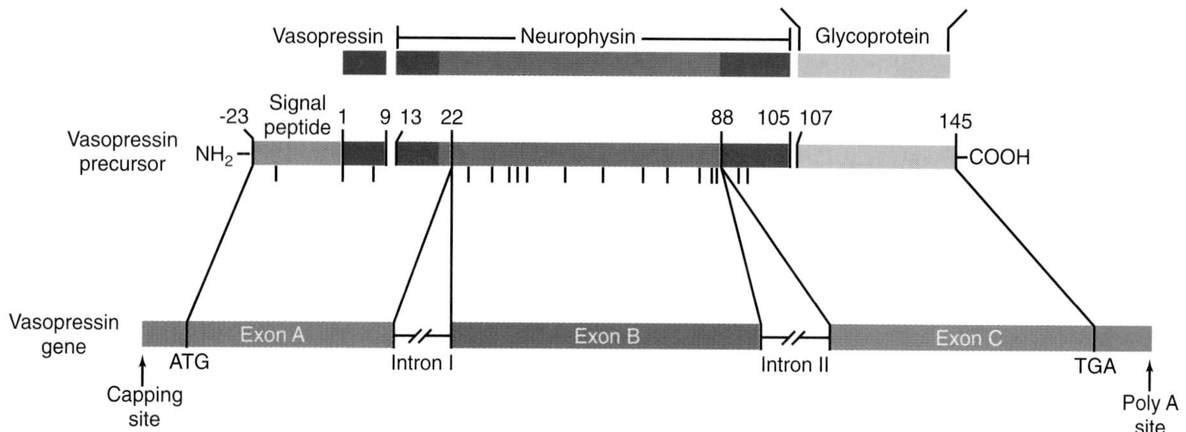

FIGURE 42.3 The vasopressin gene and its protein products. The three exons encode a 145-amino-acid prohormone with an amino-terminal signal peptide. The prohormone is packaged into neurosecretory granules of magnocellular neurons. During axonal transport of the granules from the hypothalamus to the posterior pituitary, enzymatic cleavage of the prohormone generates the final products: vasopressin, neurophysin, and a carboxy-terminal glycoprotein. When afferent stimulation depolarizes the vasopressin-containing neurons, the three products are released into capillaries of the posterior pituitary. Modified with permission from Richter and Schmale.[9]

increasing in proportion to AVP levels from 0.5 to 5–6 pg ml^{-1}, in association with increases in plasma osmolality to only 4% above the threshold for AVP secretion. Urine volume is inversely related to urine osmolality (Fig. 42.5).[5] Note that an increase in plasma AVP concentration from 0.5 to 2 pg ml^{-1} decreases urine flow much more than does a subsequent increase in AVP concentration from 2 to 5 pg ml^{-1}. This relationship emphasizes the physiological effects of small initial changes in plasma AVP levels. The net result of these relations among plasma osmolality, AVP secretion, urine volume, and urine osmolality is a finely tuned regulatory system that adjusts the rate of free water excretion according to plasma osmolality via changes in pituitary hormone secretion.

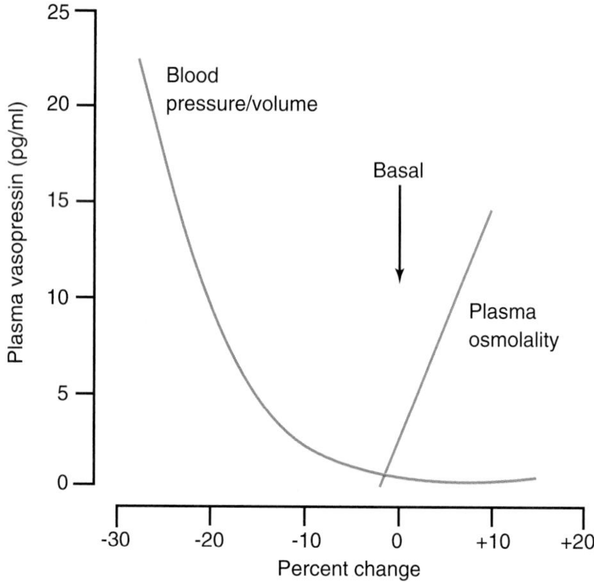

FIGURE 42.4 Plasma concentrations of AVP as a function of changes in plasma osmolality, blood volume, or blood pressure in humans. The arrow indicates the plasma AVP concentration at basal plasma osmolality, volume, and blood pressure. Modified with permission from Robertson.[4]

Thirst Is Another Effective Osmoregulatory Response to Dehydration

Accompanying the excretion of a concentrated urine is reabsorption of conserved water, which can considerably dilute remaining body fluids. Thirst, and the water intake it provokes, is a much more rapid and less limited response to dehydration than antidiuresis. Thirst may be defined as a strong motivation to seek, to obtain, and to consume water in response to deficits in body fluids. Like AVP secretion, thirst can be stimulated by cellular dehydration caused by increases in the effective osmolality of ECF.[6] Studies in animals consistently indicate that drinking behavior is elicited by 1–4% increases in plasma osmolality above basal levels, and analogous research in humans has revealed that similar thresholds must be reached to produce thirst.[4] This arrangement, in which the threshold for drinking is slightly higher than that for secretion of AVP (Fig. 42.5), ensures that ongoing behavior is not disrupted by thirst unless the buffering effects of osmosis and antidiuresis are insufficient to accomplish osmoregulation. It also ensures that dehydration does

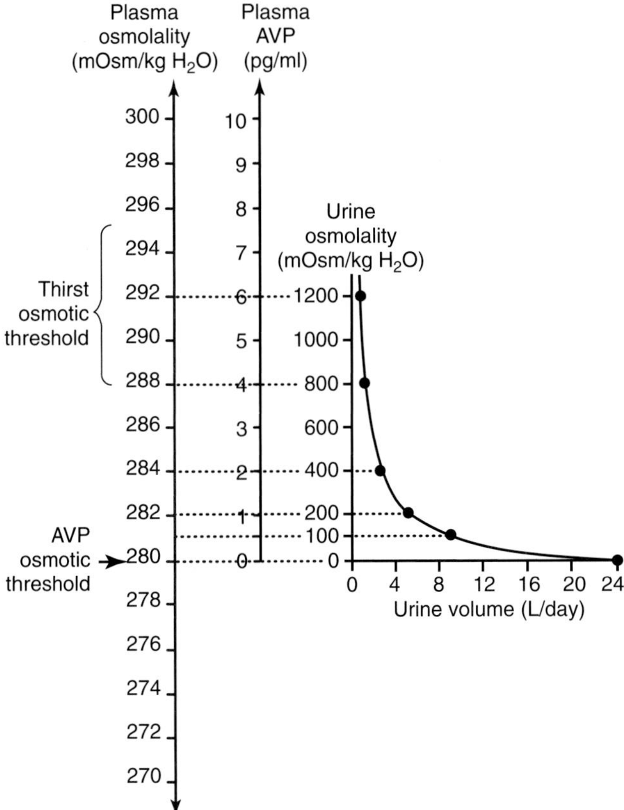

FIGURE 42.5 Relationship of plasma osmolality, plasma AVP concentrations, urine osmolality, and urine volume in humans. Note that small changes in plasma AVP concentrations have larger effects on urine volume at low plasma AVP concentrations than at high plasma AVP concentrations. Modified with permission from Robinson.[5]

not become severe before thirst is stimulated. See Box 42.1 for more on how the neurohypophysis controls the volume of water in the body.[7–11]

Also like AVP secretion, water intake increases linearly in proportion to increases in the effective osmolality of ECF.[12] The dilution of body fluids by ingested water complements the retention of water that occurs during antidiuresis, and both responses occur when drinking water is available. However, there may be marked individual differences in whether dehydrated subjects respond to their need for water promptly by drinking or more slowly by increasing renal water conservation.[13] AVP secretion and urine osmolality are more elevated when an induced increase in plasma osmolality is not compensated for by water intake (because drinking water is not available). Conversely, water intake in response to a sodium load increases in animals after their kidneys are removed or their capability to secrete AVP is compromised, thereby precluding rapid excretion of the load in urine. See Box 42.2 on the rapid inhibitory feedback control of drinking.[14–17]

Osmoreceptor Cells Stimulate AVP Secretion and Thirst

All bodily cells lose water by osmosis when the effective osmolality of ECF is increased. Thus, cells that provoke AVP secretion and thirst do not have unique osmosensitive properties, unlike retinal photoreceptor cells, which are specially responsive to light. Instead, the unique feature of osmoreceptor cells is thought to be their neural circuitry, which activates the central systems for AVP secretion and thirst when the cells are dehydrated.

Destruction of osmoreceptor neurons should eliminate detection of increased plasma osmolality and thus the AVP secretion and thirst responses that are elicited by dehydration. In fact, ample research has confirmed that certain brain lesions eliminate AVP secretion and thirst responses. Such studies also have revealed that the osmoreceptor cells[18,19] appear to be located in the vascular organ of the lamina terminalis (OVLT) and areas of the adjacent anterior hypothalamus, near the anterior wall of the third cerebral ventricle (Fig. 42.6).[20] Surgical destruction of that area of the brain abolishes the AVP secretion and thirst responses to hyperosmolality but not their responses to other stimuli. The same conclusion was drawn after study of people who were unable to osmoregulate when water-deprived or when given a NaCl load; these patients were found to have focal brain tumors that destroyed the region around the OVLT.

The location of osmoreceptor cells in the OVLT is consistent with the results of pioneering investigations in which hyperosmotic solutions injected into blood vessels perfusing the anterior hypothalamus stimulated AVP secretion in dogs.[21] The OVLT and surrounding areas of the anterior hypothalamus also have been implicated by studies in rats.[22] After systemic injections of hypertonic NaCl solution, modern immunocytochemical techniques were used to detect early gene products in cells associated with the production of new protein. Dense staining in the OVLT (and in the AVP-secreting cells in the hypothalamus) indicated that it had been strongly stimulated by the experimentally induced dehydration. See Box 42.3 on the use of cFos immunocytochemistry in studies of brain function.[23–25]

The neural pathways connecting the OVLT with the magnocellular AVP-secreting cells in the hypothalamic SON and PVN have been identified, whereas the neural circuits in the forebrain that control thirst are still unknown. Early reports identified the lateral hypothalamus as a "thirst center," because its destruction in rats eliminated the drinking response, but not the associated AVP secretion, to increased osmolality of body

BOX 42.1

DIABETES INSIPIDUS

The disease **diabetes insipidus** (DI), in which secretion of AVP is impaired or absent, illustrates the crucial role of AVP in controlling the volume of water in the body. Early Greeks named diabetes insipidus, or insipid urine, to distinguish it from **diabetes mellitus**, or sweet urine, in which abnormally high concentrations of glucose in the blood results in glucose appearing in the urine.

AVP is the only known antidiuretic substance in the body. In its absence, the kidney is unable to concentrate urine maximally to conserve water. The result is continued excretion of copious amounts of a very dilute watery urine. Patients with severe cases, in whom the ability to excrete AVP is completely lost, can excrete up to 25 liters of urine each day. Such patients urinate almost hourly, which renders the completion of even simple tasks and activities of daily living, including sleeping, exceedingly difficult.

In addition to the substantial disruption of normal lifestyle caused by DI, such patients can quickly become dehydrated if their urinary fluid losses are not replaced by drinking water. Fortunately, thirst remains intact in most patients with DI, because lesions that destroy the magnocellular neurons in the SON and PVN that synthesize AVP generally leave intact the osmoreceptors in the anterior hypothalamus as well as the higher brain centers that control thirst. Consequently, extreme thirst is one of the hallmarks of this disease, leading to the characteristic symptoms of **polydipsia** (excessive drinking) and **polyuria** (excessive urination). If drinking water is unavailable, or if a person with DI is unable to drink, then the unreplaced urinary water loss leads to dehydration and death in the absence of medical intervention.

DI can be caused by tumors and infiltrative diseases of the hypothalamus that destroy the AVP-producing magnocellular neurons that project to the posterior pituitary. Because four nuclei contain magnocellular neurons, and 10–20% of AVP-producing neurons are sufficient for normal urine concentration, lesions that cause DI are generally large.[7] Less commonly, DI is idiopathic (of unknown cause), perhaps with an autoimmune basis. DI can also be genetic, transmitted as an autosomal dominant trait. In families with congenital DI, point mutations have been found in the signal peptide region and the neurophysin part of the AVP prohormone (see Fig. 42.3).[8] Interestingly, none of these mutations is similar to the frameshift mutation responsible for the well-studied animal model of DI, the *Brattleboro rat*.[9] Some patients with DI do not have any defect in AVP secretion but rather have defects in the V_2 AVP receptors in the kidney that respond to circulating AVP.[10] These cases are called **nephrogenic** (of kidney origin), rather than central, DI. Finally, very rarely lesions of the anterior region of the hypothalamus, including the OVLT, destroy the osmoreceptors rather than the AVP-secreting neurons themselves. With such lesions, patients do not experience thirst despite severe dehydration. However, they can secrete AVP in response to stimuli from baroreceptors responding to volume status; the information is relayed to the hypothalamus via brainstem afferents (see Fig. 42.6).[11]

The treatment for DI, like that of other endocrine deficiency disorders, is replacement of the deficient hormone, in this case AVP. The short half-life of AVP in the circulation allows mammals minute-to-minute control of their urine output. However longer-acting synthetic analogs of AVP are more convenient for treatment, because they need not be taken as frequently as short-acting drugs.[5] These agents can restore urinary concentration and allow a person with DI to lead a normal life.

fluids. However, later investigations showed that the critical damage was not to hypothalamic cells but to dopamine-containing fibers that coursed through the area. The induced disruption of behavior was not specific to drinking but instead reflected a general inability of the brain-damaged animals to initiate movement.[26] Indeed, the syndrome of behavioral dysfunctions seen in these animals generally resembled that of Parkinson disease, which also has been attributed to the loss of dopaminergic fibers in the brain. (See Chapter 41 for the same reinterpretation of the inability of rats to eat normally after dopamine-depleting lesions of the lateral hypothalamus.)

Natriuresis and Inhibition of Solute Intake Also Promote Osmotic Homeostasis during Dehydration

When body fluid is hyperosmolal, adaptive behavior includes not only drinking and conserving water (thereby increasing the denominator in the ratio that represents body fluid osmolality) but also excreting the NaCl and avoiding consumption of additional osmoles (thereby decreasing the numerator of that ratio). Endogenous natriuretic agents promote urinary sodium loss after an administered NaCl load or a period of imposed water deprivation. One such agent is the hor-

BOX 42.2

RAPID INHIBITORY FEEDBACK CONTROL OF DRINKING

Osmotic dehydration, whether caused by water deprivation or by systemic administration of hypertonic saline, activates forebrain osmoreceptor cells responsive to increases in the effective osmolality of circulating plasma. Animals drink water, but 10–20 min pass before it is absorbed into the circulation and affects plasma osmolality. However, many species (e.g., dogs but not rats) drink water very quickly, stopping long before the ingested water actually rehydrates them. What are the biological mechanisms that mediate this anticipatory satiety?

One possibility is that a neural message is communicated from the oropharynx to the brain in association with the act of swallowing. Thus, the more animals drink and swallow, the greater the inhibition of thirst, even before the water is absorbed. In fact, evidence is consistent with metered fluid consumption providing a preliminary signal of satiety. The main experiments were done by implanting gastric fistulas into dogs.[14] When the fistula was closed, ingested water flowed normally from the stomach into the intestine and was absorbed; water-deprived dogs drank rapidly, stopped 15 min before their plasma osmolalities began to decrease, and did not resume drinking as their stomach emptied. In contrast, when the fistula was left open, ingested water drained out from the stomach, never entering the intestine and thus never being absorbed; the dogs drank normal amounts, stopped drinking, and after 10–20 min resumed drinking. When the dogs were not allowed to drink but water was introduced into the stomach through the fistula, thus bypassing the oropharynx, the gastric load did not affect water intake until it had been absorbed.

These observations are consistent with a temporary satiety being produced by the act of water consumption, with a more long-lasting satiety occurring only after absorption of the ingested water and rehydration of the dog. AVP secretion is affected in parallel, showing that physiological and behavioral components of osmoregulation are influenced similarly. Ingestion of concentrated NaCl solution instead of water produces the same temporary satiety and inhibition of AVP secretion, but after the saline is absorbed the increase in plasma osmolality stimulates more drinking and AVP secretion than occurred at first. In similar experiments, people respond the same way.

Animals drink appropriate amounts perhaps because they have learned from previous experiences how much to drink to relieve their thirst. After all, when we are thirsty we fill a glass to a volume that, based on previous experience, we think will be sufficient for satiety. No doubt animals behave equivalently. Alternatively, this drinking response may not be learned, and instead appropriate neural circuits linking the act of swallowing with satiety may be present at birth. Consistent with this possibility is the finding that the first drinking experience of newly hatched chickens is rapid and provides the correct amount of water needed for osmoregulation.[15]

Research[16] has also supported the hypothesis that gastric distension is important in short-term control of water intake by thirsty rats.[17] After destruction of gastric vagal afferent neurons or their projection sites in the caudal brainstem, rats drank excessive amounts of water in response to either elevated plasma osmolality or hypovolemia, and the extra drinking occurred during the first 15 min of the drinking test. These thirsty animals behaved as if they did not detect the gradual gastric distension caused by water ingestion and received no inhibitory feedback until the ingested water was absorbed and had reduced plasma osmolality. Thus, whether inhibitory signals arise from the oropharynx, the stomach, or both, preabsorptive messages modulate drinking.

mone **atrial natriuretic peptide** (ANP), which is synthesized in the atria of the heart and released when increased intravascular volume distends the atria. Another is the hormone oxytocin. Like AVP, oxytocin is synthesized in hypothalamic neurons in the PVN and SON and secreted from the posterior pituitary in proportion to induced hyperosmolality.[27] The kidney is as sensitive to the natriuretic effect of oxytocin as it is to the antidiuretic effects of AVP.[28]

Salt loads are also known to decrease the intake of osmoles, whether in the form of NaCl solution or food, complementing the stimulation of thirst and the secretion of AVP and oxytocin. However, because destruction of the OVLT eliminates the two latter effects but not the dehydration-induced reduction in sodium intake, osmoreceptors located outside the basal forebrain must mediate the inhibition of NaCl and food intake. One possible site for such cells is the liver, which has been suspected of having osmoreceptor functions.[29] Hepatic cells are well situated to detect the osmolality of ingested food and to modulate its intake accordingly.

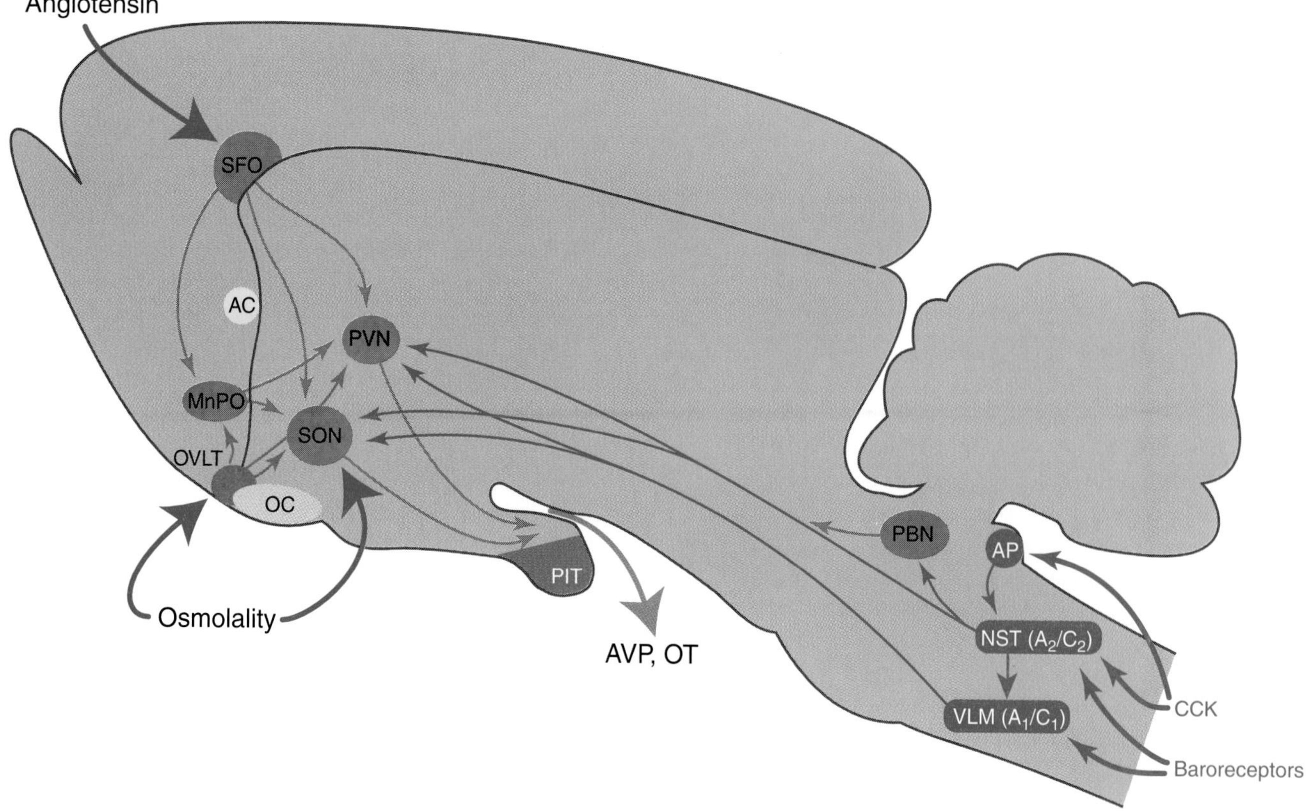

FIGURE 42.6 Summary of the main anterior hypothalamic pathways that mediate secretion of arginine vasopressin (AVP) and oxytocin (OT). The vascular organ of the lamina terminalis is especially sensitive to hyperosmolality. Hyperosmolality also activates other neurons in the anterior hypothalamus, such as those in the subfornical organ (SFO) and median preoptic nucleus (MnPO), and magnocellular neurons, which are intrinsically osmosensitive. Circulating angiotensin II (AII) activates neurons of the SFO, an essential site of AII action, as well as cells throughout the vascular organ of the lamina terminalis (OVLT) and MnPO. In response to hyperosmolality or AII, projections from the SFO and OVLT to the MnPO activate excitatory and inhibitory interneurons that project to the supraoptic nucleus (SON) and paraventricular nucleus (PVN) to modulate direct inputs to these areas from the circumventricular organs. Cholecystokinin (CCK) acts primarily on gastric vagal afferents that terminate in the nucleus of the solitary tract (NST), but at higher doses it can also act at the area postrema (AP). Although neurons apparently are activated in the ventrolateral medulla (VLM) and NST, most oxytocin secretion appears as a result of monosynaptic projections from A2/C2 cells, and possibly also noncatecholaminergic somatostatin/inhibin β cells, of the NST. Baroreceptor-mediated stimuli, such as hypovolemia and hypotension, are more complex. The major projection to magnocellular AVP neurons appears to arise from A1 cells of the VLM that are activated by excitatory interneurons from the NST. Other areas, such as the parabrachial nucleus (PBN), may contribute multisynaptic projections. Cranial nerves IX and X, which terminate in the NST, also contribute input to magnocellular AVP neurons. It is unclear whether baroreceptor-mediated secretion of oxytocin results from projections from VLM neurons or from NST neurons. AC, anterior commissure; OC, optic chiasm; PIT, anterior pituitary. Modified with permission from Verbalis *et al.*[20]

Diuresis and Inhibition of Water Intake Promote Osmotic Homeostasis during Overhydration

Osmoregulation is required not only under conditions of dehydration but also during periods of acute overhydration and hypoosmolality, as may result when beverages are consumed in excess of water needs. Such consumption occurs not because of thirst but, for example, because of the palatability of or chemical substances in the beverages (e.g., caffeine, alcohol). Unlike excess fuel, which is stored as triglycerides in adipose tissue, excess water is not stored for later use but instead is excreted in urine. When plasma osmolality is below normal, circulating levels of AVP are reduced, and in consequence, the kidneys make a dilute urine and thereby raise plasma osmolality. The major behavioral con-

BOX 42.3

USE OF cFOS IMMUNOCYTOCHEMISTRY IN STUDIES OF BRAIN FUNCTION

cFos was named for its homology to an **FBR o**steogenic **s**arcoma virus protein, v-fos. The cFos protein is the product of the *c-fos* gene, which belongs to a family of genes whose products are involved in regulation of gene transcription. The protein has a "leucine zipper" motif that promotes dimerization (pairing) with other regulatory proteins, most commonly with members of the Jun family. The genes encoding Jun and Fos are immediate-early genes (IEGs), the first genes expressed in response to activation of cells. Jun and Fos protein dimers bind specific DNA sequences (e.g., APS sites) to modulate expression of genes expressed later.[23]

The precise relationship between cFos expression and transcription of later gene products remains uncertain for most neural systems. However, many neurons are known to express cFos only upon synaptic activation; therefore, the mRNA or protein product (cFos) of the *c-fos* gene can be used as a marker of neuronal activation in the brain.[24] The protein product is especially useful because it is easily detected by antibodies directed against cFos. This immunohistochemical staining allows investigators to determine which neurons are activated in the brain in response to specific stimuli given to experimental animals.[25]

For example, the magnocellular neurons that produce AVP and oxytocin express cFos in response to a wide range of excitatory stimuli, including hyperosmolality, hypovolemia, hypotension, stress, systemic administration of cholecystokinin (CCK), and intracerebroventricular and systemic administration of AII.[20] Many of the initial studies of these stimuli simply localized the IEG expression to magnocellular neurons in the SON and PVN, but later studies used antibodies against proteins located in cytoplasm, along with antibody against IEG products, and showed that the IEG products were located in the nucleus.[25] Such studies have now confirmed that in response to these treatments IEG expression in AVP- and oxytocin-secreting neurons closely parallels pituitary AVP and oxytocin secretion. Thus, in rats, hyperosmolality, hypovolemia, and administration of AII stimulate secretion of AVP and oxytocin and activate cFos expression in AVP and OT neurons; CCK, which stimulates secretion of oxytocin but not AVP, causes expression of cFos only in neurons that secrete oxytocin. Similarly, although severe hemorrhage stimulates secretion of AVP and oxytocin and activates cFos expression in both types of neurons, lower intensity stimuli predominantly cause peptide secretion and cFos expression only in AVP neurons. During CCK administration and during hemorrhage, plasma AVP and oxytocin correlate well with cFos expression. Consequently, IEG expression is now considered a specific and sensitive marker of magnocellular secretory activity in response to most acute stimuli.

Immunocytochemical detection of cFos expression, phenotypic characterization of activated cells, and standard techniques of tract tracing together enable investigators to map brain circuits activated by specific stimuli.[22,25]

tribution of osmotic dilution to osmoregulation is inhibition of free water intake; the ingestion of osmoles in food and NaCl is not stimulated by osmotic dilution.

Summary

Osmoregulation in animals and humans is accomplished by a combination of physiological responses to dehydration, resulting in antidiuresis and natriuresis, and the behavioral response of increased water intake. Osmoreceptor cells critical for mediating these functions have been identified in the basal forebrain. These neurons are responsive to very small increases in plasma osmolality, and the effector systems they control rapidly correct any increase in plasma osmolality. When activated by hyperosmolality, these neurons respond by coordinating and stimulating three different effector systems with complementary functions. Other osmoreceptor cells appear to mediate the inhibition of NaCl and food intake, which also contributes to osmoregulation during dehydration. Conversely, osmoregulation during overhydration is promoted by diuresis and inhibition of water intake, but not by excitation of NaCl or food intake.

VOLUME HOMEOSTASIS

Like osmotic dehydration, loss of blood volume (**hypovolemia**) stimulates several adaptive compensatory responses appropriate for restoring circulatory volume. The physiological contributions to volume regulation have been studied extensively in laboratory animals subjected to controlled loss of blood. Because behavior is compromised by the anemia and hypotension that result from extensive hemorrhage, researchers studying thirst in rats often instead produce hypovolemia by subcutaneous injection of a colloidal solution.[30] Such treatment disrupts the Starling equilibrium in capillaries near the injection site, because the extravascular colloid opposes the oncotic effect of plasma proteins. Consequently, fluid leaches out of capillaries and remains in the interstitial space. Ingested fluid also is drawn into the interstitial space by the colloid, so the total fluid volume required to correct the plasma volume deficit may be substantial. Water does not move from the cells by osmosis, however, because the osmolality of the injected colloidal solutions actually is low relative to that of cells.

After colloid injections, rats conserve water and sodium in urine and increase their consumption of water and saline solution.[31] When given an isotonic NaCl solution to drink, these rats ingest volumes appropriate to their needs. When given separate bottles of water and concentrated NaCl solution, remarkably the rats drink appropriate amounts of each to create an isotonic fluid mixture. These observations raise several questions: How do the hypovolemic rats detect their plasma volume depletion? How are their thirst and salt appetite coordinated so that they consume the desired isotonic mixture of fluid? How are these two behavioral responses integrated with the complementary physiological responses of water and sodium conservation in urine, as well as with the vasoconstrictor responses needed to support blood pressure? Research has provided answers to these and related questions, which are discussed in the following sections.

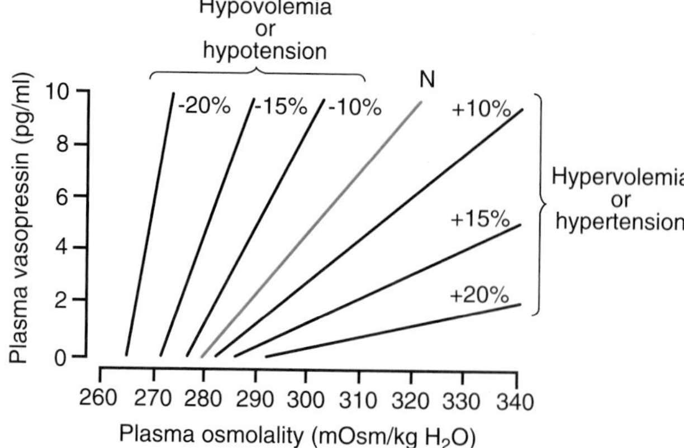

FIGURE 42.7 The relationship between the osmolality of plasma and the concentration of vasopressin (AVP) in plasma depends on blood volume and pressure. The line labeled N shows plasma vasopressin concentration across a range of plasma osmolality in an adult with normal intravascular volume (euvolemic) and normal blood pressure (normotensive). The lines to the left of N show the relationship between plasma vasopressin concentration and plasma osmolality in adults whose low intravascular volume (hypovolemia) or blood pressure (hypotension) is 10, 15, and 20% below normal. Lines to the right of N are for volumes and blood pressures 10, 15, and 20% above normal. Modified with permission from Robertson.[4]

Neural and Endocrine Signals of Hypovolemia Stimulate AVP Secretion

An appropriate physiological response to volume depletion should include water conservation and urine concentration. In fact, like plasma hyperosmolality, hypovolemia is an effective stimulus for AVP secretion.[3,27] However, AVP secretion does not occur until blood loss exceeds 10% of total blood volume, meaning AVP secretion is much less sensitive to hypovolemia than to increases in ECF osmolality (Fig. 42.4). The effects of hypovolemia and osmotic dehydration are additive; that is, a given increase in osmolality causes greater secretion of AVP when animals are hypovolemic than when they are euvolemic (Fig. 42.7).

Loss of blood volume is first detected by stretch receptors in the great veins entering the right atrium of the heart. These stretch receptors provide an afferent vagal signal to the nucleus of the solitary tract (NST) in the brainstem (see Chapter 39). Still larger decreases in blood volume also may lower arterial blood pressure and reduce the stretch of receptors in the walls of the carotid sinus and aortic arch. That information is integrated in the NST with neural messages from the low-pressure, venous side of the circulation. Note that these sensory neurons are not actually *baroreceptors* (literally, pressure receptors), although they are commonly referred to as such.

The ascending pathway between the NST in the brainstem and the SON and PVN in the hypothalamus includes noradrenergic fibers arising from A_1 cells in the ventrolateral medulla. Volume depletion stimulates AVP secretion via other pathways as well. In response to volume depletion, the kidneys secrete **renin**, a response mediated in part by sympathetic neural input to β-adrenergic receptors on cells that secrete renin. Renin is an enzyme that initiates a cascade of biochemical steps that result in the formation of **angiotensin II** (AII) (Fig. 42.8),[32] an extremely potent vasoconstrictor. AII stimulates AVP secretion by acting in the brain at the **subfornical organ** (SFO),[33] a small structure located in the dorsal portion of the third cerebral ventricle. Because this circumventricular organ lacks a blood–brain barrier, the AII receptors can detect very small increases in the blood levels of AII. Neural pathways from the SFO to the SON and PVN in the hypothalamus mediate AVP secretion and appear to use AII as a neurotransmitter. A branch of this pathway

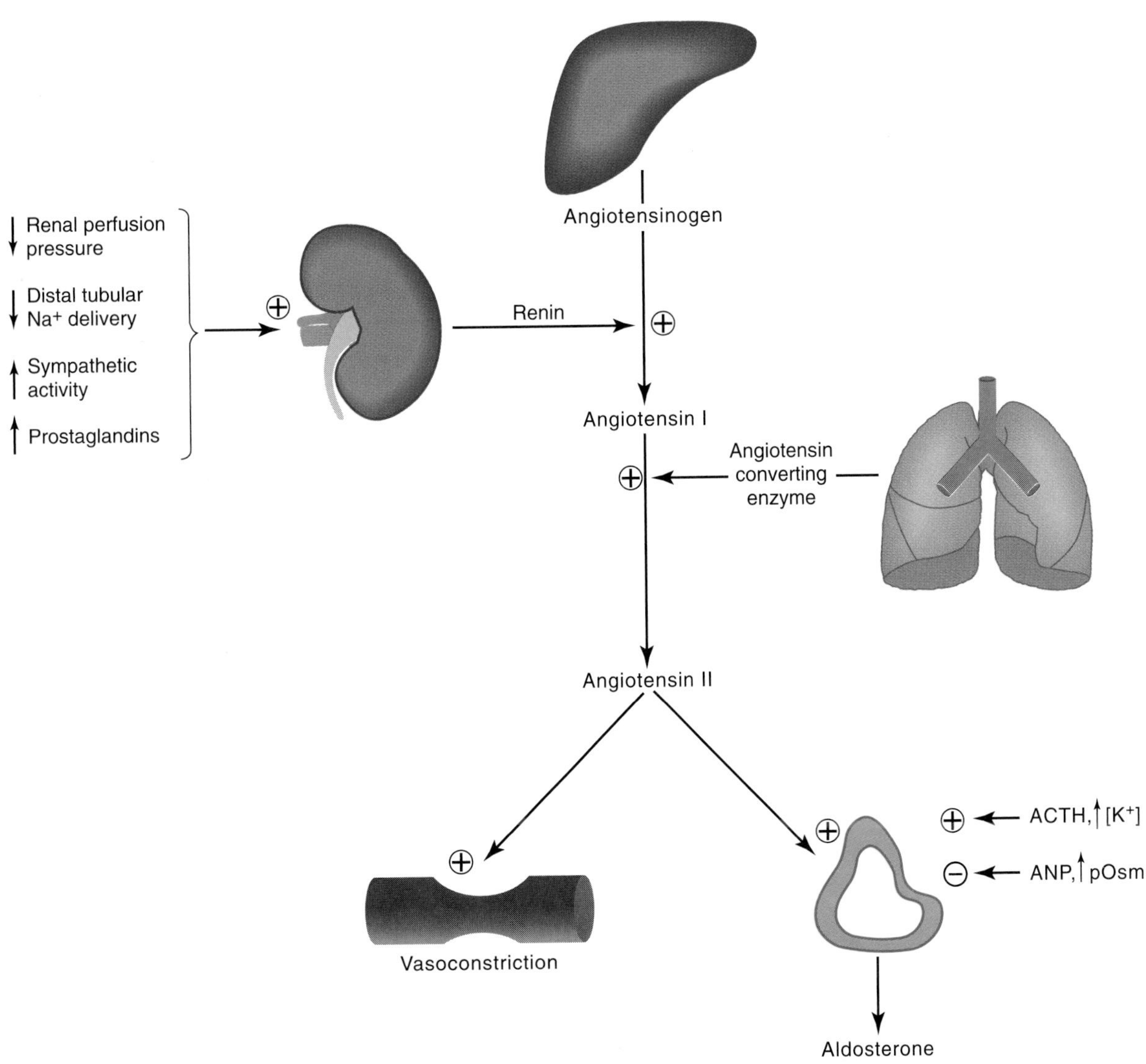

FIGURE 42.8 The renin–angiotensin cascade. Baroreceptors in the aortic arch, carotid sinus, and renal afferent arterioles sense hypovolemia and then cause the kidneys to secrete the enzyme renin. Renin cleaves angiotensinogen, which is synthesized by the liver, to produce angiotensin I. Angiotensin-converting enzyme, primarily in the lungs, cleaves angiotensin I to produce angiotensin II (AII), a peptide made of eight amino acid residues. AII is a potent vasoconstrictor and one of several stimulants of aldosterone secretion. Stimulation of aldosterone secretion from the adrenal cortex, along with possible direct intrarenal effects of AII, promotes renal conservation of sodium ions, complementing the pressor effect of AII in stabilizing arterial pressure and volume. ACTH, adrenocorticotropic hormone; ANP, atrial natriuretic peptide; pOsm, plasma osmolality. Modified with permission from Stricker and Verbalis.[32]

goes first to the OVLT, perhaps providing an opportunity for integration of information about volume states and osmotic concentration.

Neural and Endocrine Signals of Hypovolemia Also Stimulate Thirst

In addition to the antidiuresis and vasoconstriction produced by secretion of AVP and activation of the renin–angiotensin system, colloid treatment increases water intake in rats.[30,34] Once 5–10% of the normal plasma volume has been lost, the water intake elicited by hypovolemia increases linearly in relation to further deficits in plasma volume. This stimulus for water intake and the effect of a NaCl load on thirst are additive. The stimulus of thirst during hypovolemia appears to be the same as the signal for AVP secretion—that is, a combination of neural afferents from cardiovascular baroreceptors and endocrine stimulation by AII. Each signal can stimulate water intake in the absence of the other. Thus, for example, water intake by hypovolemic rats is not diminished by destruction of the NST and loss of neural input from baroreceptors, nor is it eliminated by the loss of AII resulting from bilateral removal of the kidneys or surgical destruction of the SFO. Presumably, colloid treatment would not elicit thirst in rats subjected concurrently to bilateral nephrectomy and NST lesions.

Intravenous infusion of AII strongly stimulates thirst in rats and most other animals studied in the laboratory (although, curiously, it does not in humans). AII adds to the thirst stimulated by an osmotic load when the two treatments are combined.[35] Nevertheless, considerable controversy remains about whether AII functions as a normal physiological stimulus of thirst, because the doses of AII required to stimulate significant water intake produce blood levels of AII well above the physiological range. Such doses also increase arterial blood pressure, and it has been argued that this hypertension inhibits thirst and limits the induced water intake.[36] Although this is a plausible hypothesis, no independent evidence has demonstrated that an increase in arterial blood pressure actually reduces water intake in any model of thirst.

Osmotic Dilution Inhibits Thirst and AVP Secretion during Hypovolemia

Hypovolemic (due to colloid injection) rats need isotonic saline, not water alone, to repair their plasma volume deficits. When the rats drink only water, about two-thirds of the ingested volume moves into cells by osmosis, and much of what remains extracellular is captured by the colloid. Thus, most of the water that is consumed does not remain in the vascular compartment, and the volume deficit within the vascular compartment persists. This situation contrasts with the negative feedback control of osmoregulatory thirst, in which dehydration of osmoreceptor cells causes thirst and ingested water repairs the dehydration, eliminating the stimulus for thirst.

Rather than repairing the volume deficit, the water ingested by hypovolemic rats causes a second serious challenge to body fluid homeostasis—osmotic dilution. The animals cannot readily eliminate this self-administered water load, because hypovolemia reduces GFR and thereby diminishes urinary excretion independent of AVP. Therefore, when water is the only drinking fluid available (and sodium is not provided in food), an appropriate response of colloid-treated rats would be to stop drinking and thereby limit the secondary problem of osmotic dilution. In experiments, rats actually do stop drinking water despite persistent hypovolemia, and the stimulus for the inhibition of thirst has been found to be osmotic dilution of body fluids.[37] A mere 4–7% decrease in osmolality is sufficient to stop drinking that has been motivated by a 30–40% loss of plasma volume. Thus, the osmoregulatory system appears dominant in the control of thirst. Comparable data demonstrate the same to be true of AVP secretion in colloid-treated rats: Osmotic dilution inhibits AVP secretion even in severely hypovolemic rats.[27]

Hypovolemia Also Stimulates Aldosterone Secretion and Salt Appetite

As mentioned, hypovolemic animals need to consume and retain water and NaCl, not just water. Appropriately, colloid-treated rats drink NaCl solution and conserve sodium in urine. Renal sodium retention is mediated largely by aldosterone secreted from the adrenal cortex, although sodium conservation also occurs in association with the decrease in GFR. The central nervous system does not innervate the adrenal cortex, as it does the adrenal medulla, but a neural influence on aldosterone secretion is provided indirectly because AII is a very potent stimulus of aldosterone secretion, and renin secretion from the kidneys during hypovolemia is stimulated in part by the sympathetic nervous system (Fig. 42.8). Moreover, the secretion of aldosterone also is stimulated by another peptide hormone, **adrenocorticotrophic hormone** (ACTH), which is secreted from the anterior lobe of the pituitary gland in response to corticotrophic releasing hormone (CRH). The release of CRH from the PVN is triggered by activated cardiovascular baroreceptors. Yet another stimulus of aldosterone secretion is increased plasma levels of potassium, which can develop as a consequence of reduced GFR and an associated decrease in urinary potassium excretion. The effects of these three independent stimuli of aldosterone secretion are additive. Note that aldosterone can eliminate sodium from urine, whereas AVP merely diminishes urinary water loss even during maximal antidiuresis. See Box 42.4 on salt appetite after adrenocortical dysfunction.[38,39]

The onset of salt appetite induced in rats by colloid treatment is curiously delayed relative to the appearance of thirst. That is, water intake increases within 1–2 h after colloid treatment, whereas the intake of NaCl solution does not increase until 5 h later.[31] Investigations showed that the delay is not caused by the gradual appearance of an excitatory stimulus of salt appetite but by the gradual disappearance of an inhibitory stimulus for NaCl intake. Recall that during the delay, hypovolemic rats drank water and thereby caused an osmotic dilution of body fluids, which in-

BOX 42.4

SALT APPETITE AFTER ADRENOCORTICAL DYSFUNCTION

Fifty years ago, a 4-year-old boy was brought by his parents to the Johns Hopkins University Hospital in Baltimore with the peculiar behavior of eating large amounts of table salt. The child heavily salted all his food, even juice, and often consumed salt directly from its container. His parents tried unsuccessfully to keep him from consuming salt and brought him to the hospital in the hope that his strange behavior could be understood and stopped. The physicians were able to prevent the boy from having access to NaCl, but they were shocked when he died a few days later.

Autopsy revealed that the child had bilateral tumors in his adrenal glands. In retrospect, it seems clear that he could not secrete aldosterone (which was discovered some years later) and therefore lost sodium in urine uncontrollably. Like patients with diabetes insipidus, who excrete a copious dilute urine and drink comparable volumes of water in compensation (see Box 42.1 on diabetes insipidus), this boy evidently was ingesting salt as an adaptive compensation to his recurrent need for sodium.[38] He died when that response was prevented.

After surgical removal of their adrenal glands, rats increase their consumption of NaCl by amounts proportional to the sodium loss in urine.[39] The stimulus for this salt appetite appears to be a combination of elevated circulating levels of AII and reduced activity in a central oxytocinergic inhibitory system. In humans, however, a comparable salt appetite is not common in patients with Addison disease, whose adrenocortical dysfunction causes them to lose salt in urine. Nor is salt appetite stimulated in people who lose excessive amounts of salt in perspiration. No explanation is available for why an adaptive salt appetite appears readily in laboratory animals but not in people.

hibit secretion of pituitary AVP and oxytocin. Either of these neurohypophyseal hormones might have provided an inhibitory stimulus for salt appetite that disappeared as the animals drank water. In other studies, however, rats showed a strong inverse relationship between intake of NaCl and plasma levels of oxytocin (but not AVP), suggesting that circulating oxytocin was an inhibitory stimulus of salt appetite.

Central Oxytocin Inhibits Salt Appetite

In tests of the hypothesis that circulating oxytocin inhibits salt appetite, intravenous infusion of physiological doses of oxytocin did not decrease NaCl intake in hypovolemic rats, nor did infusion of an oxytocin receptor blocker increase NaCl intake. These unexpected findings were clarified by the observation that, coincident with the secretion of oxytocin from magnocellular neurons, oxytocin was released from parvicellular neurons projecting centrally from the PVN. Thus, plasma oxytocin may have been a peripheral marker of the centrally acting oxytocin that mediated the inhibition of salt appetite in rats.[40] This revised hypothesis has been strongly supported by the results of a series of investigations.[41] For example, in colloid-treated rats, infusion of oxytocin into the cerebrospinal fluid inhibited NaCl intake but did not affect water intake. Similarly, salt appetite in hypovolemic rats was eliminated by systemic injection of naloxone, an opioid receptor antagonist that disinhibits oxytocin secretion, and this effect was blocked by the prior injection of an oxytocin receptor antagonist directly into the cerebrospinal fluid. Conversely, NaCl ingestion in response to hypovolemia or AII was potentiated by diverse treatments that inhibit secretion of oxytocin. In addition to osmotic dilution, these treatments included systemic injection of ethanol, maintenance on a sodium-deficient diet (instead of the standard laboratory diet rich in sodium), and peripheral administration of mineralocorticoid hormones such as aldosterone. Thus, excitatory and inhibitory components together regulate NaCl intake in a dual control system in the brain.

Two aspects of the preceding findings deserve emphasis. First, hypovolemia stimulates two endocrine effects in the central control of NaCl intake—acute stimulation of NaCl appetite by a peptide hormone (AII) and chronic disinhibition of NaCl intake by a steroid hormone (aldosterone). Second, hypovolemia and AII together provide a mixed stimulus, with excitatory and inhibitory components, for salt appetite. The coordination of thirst and salt appetite stimulated by colloid treatment in rats can be conceptualized as follows (Fig. 42.9)[42]: The combination of hypovolemia and AII stimulates thirst but provides a mixed stimulus of salt appetite. Thus, the animals at first drink water; however, by doing so, they dilute their body fluids.

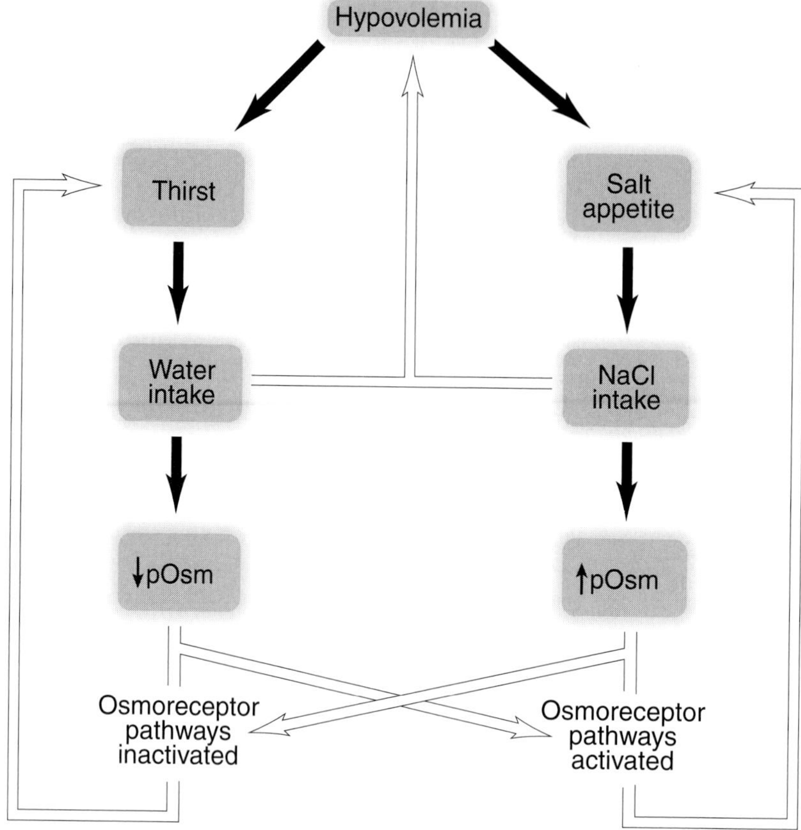

FIGURE 42.9 Schematic diagram of the mechanisms controlling thirst and salt appetite in hypovolemic rats. Solid arrows indicate stimulation, and unfilled arrows indicate inhibition. The combination of the effects of blood-borne AII on the brain and neural baroreceptor signals to the brainstem stimulates hypovolemic animals to drink water and concentrated saline solution. The rats alternately drink the two fluids in amounts that ultimately add up to a volume of isotonic saline sufficient to repair the volume deficit. When the animals have access to only one fluid, the water and salt intakes are limited by activation of the appropriate inhibitory osmoregulatory pathways. When rats drink isotonic saline (instead of water and concentrated saline), neither inhibitory pathway is activated, and consequently intake is continuous. Modified with permission from Stricker and Verbalis.[42]

The osmotic dilution eventually becomes large enough to inhibit thirst. Dilution has the additional effect of reducing central oxytocin secretion, which in turn disinhibits salt appetite, and the rats begin to drink concentrated NaCl solution. The NaCl raises plasma osmolality and thereby removes the dilution-induced inhibition of thirst and oxytocin secretion. Consequently, the rats stop drinking saline and resume drinking water. Osmotic dilution again develops, thirst is again inhibited, and salt appetite is again disinhibited. And thus the hypovolemic animals, stimulated by neural and endocrine signals of hypovolemia, alternate their intakes of the two fluids while maintaining body fluid near isotonic. Water and sodium are conserved in urine until the deficit in plasma volume is repaired. At that point the stimuli for adaptive physiological and behavioral responses disappear, and normal body fluid volume and tonicity are restored. Because the same neural and endocrine signals of hypovolemia stimulate thirst, salt appetite, and AVP and oxytocin secretion, these responses are integrated.

Central oxytocinergic neurons can inhibit salt intake and food intake (see Chapter 41). Both functions are a consequence of oxytocinergic neurons inhibiting the intake of osmoles to prevent hyperosmolality.[43] Thus, osmotic dehydration appropriately limits intake of food and salt. From this perspective, food is a source of osmoles (not just of calories) and NaCl solution provides osmoles without calories. Inhibition of intake of osmoles complements the natriuretic effect of pituitary oxytocin in supporting osmoregulation.

Salt Appetite Also Is Inhibited by Atrial Natriuretic Peptide

The role of oxytocin in osmoregulation has become apparent only during the last decade, and the identification of other peptide hormones as important factors in the homeostasis of body fluids may be anticipated. One likely candidate is atrial natriuretic peptide. Like oxytocin, ANP acts on the kidneys to promote sodium loss in urine. Also like oxytocin, ANP is secreted by neurons within the brain, and when administered directly into the cerebrospinal fluid it inhibits (an experimentally induced) salt appetite in rats.[44] Moreover, destruction of ANP receptors in the brain eliminates the inhibition of salt appetite caused by a NaCl load.[45] Further work will be needed to understand the role of ANP-containing neurons in the central control of salt intake and the relationship of the neurons with other systems that participate in the regulation of water and NaCl intake.

Summary

Regulation of blood volume, like osmoregulation, is accomplished by a combination of physiological responses to hypovolemia, resulting in antidiuresis and antinatriuresis, and the complementary behavioral responses of increased water and NaCl intake. Cardiovascular baroreceptor cells detect hypovolemia and send neural signals to the brainstem, which communicates to the hypothalamus and forebrain structures mediating AVP and oxytocin secretion as well as thirst and salt appetite. AII also appears to stimulate these responses while additionally supporting blood pressure as a potent vasoconstrictor.

Body fluid homeostasis is accomplished by separate but related regulations of fluid osmolality and plasma volume. Osmoregulation and volume regulation are directed at controlling the intake and urinary excretion of water, the principal constituent of the body, and sodium, the major electrolyte. Neural and endocrine signals act together with circulating substrates to stimulate behavioral and physiological responses. For example, stimulation of water intake and AVP secretion is provided by plasma substrates (osmoles) that are detected by cerebral osmoreceptors, the blood-borne hormone AII that is detected by cerebral AII receptors, and neural sensory signals that are generated by cardiovascular baroreceptors and project into the brainstem. Salt appetite is stimulated by these same neural and endocrine signals and is concurrently inhibited by them and by increased levels of plasma osmoles. Finally, aldosterone secretion is stimulated by AII, by another hormone (ACTH), and by another substrate (potassium), but not directly by the nervous system. Thus, AII participates in all aspects of body fluid homeostasis, whereas the other participants have more specific roles. The integration of these stimuli ensures that behavioral and physiological responses occur simultaneously, and their redundancy allows these vital regulatory processes to occur even when one or another stimulus is lost due to injury or disease. More generally, studies of water and NaCl ingestion provide insights into how the brain controls motivation and how peptide and steroid hormones interact with neural signals in the control of behavior.

References

General

Andersson, B. (1978). Regulation of water intake. *Physiol. Rev.* **58:** 582–603.

Denton, D. (1982). *The Hunger for Salt: An Anthropological, Physiological and Medical Analysis.* Springer-Verlag, Berlin.

Fitzsimons, J. T. (1979). *The Physiology of Thirst and Sodium Appetite.* Cambridge University Press, Cambridge, UK.

Gauer, O. H., and Henry, J. P. (1963). Circulatory basis of fluid volume control. *Physiol. Rev.* **43:** 423–481.

Guyton, A. C., Granger, H. J., and Taylor, A. E. (1971). Interstitial fluid pressure. *Physiol. Rev.* **51:** 527–563.

Ramsay, D. J., and Thrasher, T. N. (1990). Thirst and water balance. In *Handbook of Behavioral Neurobiology* (E. M. Stricker, ed.), Vol. 10, pp. 353–386. Plenum, New York.

Stricker, E. M., and Verbalis, J. G. (1990). Sodium appetite. In *Handbook of Behavioral Neurobiology* (E. M. Stricker, ed.), Vol. 10. pp. 387–419. Plenum, New York.

Verbalis, J. G. (1990). Clinical aspects of body fluid homeostasis in humans. In *Handbook of Behavioral Neurobiology* (E. M. Stricker, ed.), Vol. 10, pp. 421–462. Plenum, New York.

Verbalis, J. G. (1991). Satiety and inhibition of thirst. In *Thirst: Physiological and Psychological Aspects* (D. J. Ramsay and D. A. Booth, eds.), pp. 313–330. Springer-Verlag, Berlin.

Wolf, A. V. (1958). *Thirst: Physiology of the Urge to Drink and Problems of Water Lack.* Thomas, Springfield, IL.

Cited

1. Starling, E. H. (1896). On the absorption of fluids from the connective tissue spaces. *J. Physiol.* (*London*) **19:** 312–326.
2. Guyton, A. C., Hall, J. E., Lohmeier, T. E., Jackson, T. E., and Manning, R. D., Jr. (1981). The many roles of the kidney in arterial pressure control and hypertension. *Can. J. Physiol. Pharmacol.* **59:** 513–519.
3. Dunn, F. L., Brennan, T. J., Nelson, A. E., and Robertson, G. L. (1973). The role of blood osmolality and volume in regulating vasopressin secretion in the rat. *J. Clin. Invest.* **52:** 3212–3219.
4. Robertson, G. L. (1986). Posterior pituitary. In *Endocrinology and Metabolism* (P. Felig, J. Baxter, and L. A. Frohman, eds.), pp. 338–385. McGraw-Hill, New York.
5. Robinson, A. G. (1985). Disorders of antiduretic hormone secretion. *Clin. Endocrinol. Metab.* **14:** 55–88.
6. Gilman, A. (1937). The relation between blood osmotic pressure,

fluid distribution and voluntary water intake. *Am. J. Physiol.* **120:** 323–328.
7. Verbalis, J. G., Robinson, A. G., and Moses, A. M. (1984). Postoperative and post-traumatic diabetes insipidus. In *Diabetes Insipidus in Man* (P. Czernichow and A. G. Robinson, eds.), pp. 247–265. Karger, Basel.
8. Robertson, G. L. (1995). Diabetes insipidus. *Clin. Endocrinol. Metab.* **24:** 549–572.
9. Schmale, H., and Richter, D. (1984). Single base deletion in the vasopressin gene is the cause of diabetes insipidus in Brattleboro rats. *Nature (London)* **308:** 705–709.
10. Fugiwara, T. M., Morgan, K., and Bichet, D. G. (1995). Molecular biology of diabetes insipidus. *Annu. Rev. Med.* **46:** 331–343.
11. Baylis, P. H., and Thompson, C. J. (1988). Osmoregulation of vasopressin secretion and thirst in health and disease. *Clin. Endocrinol.* **29:** 549–576.
12. Fitzsimons, J. T. (1961). Drinking by nephrectromized rats injected with various substances. *J. Physiol. (London)* **155:** 563–579.
13. Kanter, G. S. (1953). Excretion and drinking after salt loading in dogs. *Am. J. Physiol.* **174:** 87–94.
14. Thrasher, T. N., Nistal-Herrera, J. F., Keil, L. C., and Ramsay, D. J. (1981). Satiety and inhibition of vasopressin secretion in dogs. *Am. J. Physiol.* **240:** E394–E401.
15. Stricker, E. M., and Sterritt, G. M. (1967). Osmoregulation in the newly hatched domestic chick. *Physiol. Behav.* **2:** 117–119.
16. Curtis, K. S., Verbalis, J. G., and Stricker, E. M. (1996). Area postrema lesions in rats appear to disrupt rapid feedback inhibition of fluid intake. *Brain Res.* **726:** 31–38.
17. Adolph, E. F. (1950). Thirst and its inhibition in the stomach. *Am. J. Physiol.* **161:** 374–386.
18. Johnson, A. K., and Buggy, J. (1978). Periventricular preoptic-hypothalamus is vital for thirst and normal water economy. *Am. J. Physiol.* **234:** R122–R125.
19. Thrasher, T. N., Keil, L. C., and Ramsay, D. J. (1982). Lesions of the laminar terminalis (OVLT) attenuate osmotically-induced drinking and vasopressin secretion in the dog. *Endocrinology (Baltimore)* **110:** 1837–1839.
20. Verbalis, J. G., Hoffman, G. E., and Sherman, T. G. (1995). Use of immediate early genes as markers of oxytocin and vasopressin neuronal function. *Curr. Opin. Endocrinol. Metab.* **2:** 157–168.
21. Jewell, P. A., and Verney, E. B. (1957). An experimental attempt to determine the site of the neurohypophysial osmoreceptors in the dog. *Philos. Trans. R. Soc. London Ser. B* **240:** 197–324.
22. Oldfield, B. J., Badoer, E., Hards, D. K., and McKinley, M. J. (1994). Fos production in retrogradely labeled neurons of the lamina terminalis following intravenous infusion of either hypertonic saline or angiotensin II. *Neuroscience* **60:** 255–262.
23. Curran, T. (1988). The fos oncogene. In *The Oncogene Handbook* (E. P. Reddy, A. M. Skalka, and T. Curran, eds.), pp. 307–354. Elsevier, Amsterdam.
24. Sagar, S. M., Sharp, F. R., and Curran, T. (1988). Expression of c-fos protein in brain: Metabolic mapping at the cellular level. *Science* **240:** 1328–1331.
25. Hoffman, G. E., Smith, M. S., and Verbalis, J. G. (1993). c-Fos and related immediate early gene products as markers of activity in neuroendocrine systems. *Front. Neuroendocrinol.* **14:** 173–213.
26. Stricker, E. M. (1976). Drinking by rats after lateral hypothalamic lesions: A new look at the lateral hypothalamic syndrome. *J. Comp. Physiol. Psychol.* **90:** 127–143.
27. Stricker, E. M., and Verbalis, J. G. (1986). Interaction of osmotic and volume stimuli in regulation of neurohypophyseal secretion in rats. *Am. J. Physiol.* **250:** R267–R275.
28. Verbalis, J. G., Mangione, M. P., and Stricker, E. M. (1991). Oxytocin produces natriuresis in rats at physiological plasma concentrations. *Endocrinology (Baltimore)* **128:** 1317–1322.
29. Baertschi, A. J., and Vallet, P. G. (1981). Osmosensitivity of the hepatic portal vein area and vasopressin release in rats. *J. Physiol. (London)* **315:** 217–230.
30. Stricker, E. M. (1968). Some physiological and motivational properties of the hypovolemic stimulus for thirst. *Physiol. Behav.* **3:** 379–385.
31. Stricker, E. M. (1981). Thirst and sodium appetite after colloid treatment in rats. *J. Comp. Physiol. Psychol.* **95:** 1–25.
32. Stricker, E. M., and Verbalis, J. G. (1992). Ingestive behaviors. In *Behavioral Endocrinology* (J. B. Becker, S. M. Breedlove, and D. Crews, eds.), pp. 451–472. MIT Press, Cambridge, MA.
33. Ferguson, A. V., and Renaud, L. P. (1986). Systemic angiotensin acts at subfornical organ to facilitate activity of neurohypophysial neurons. *Am. J. Physiol.* **251:** R712–R717.
34. Fitzsimons, J. T. (1961). Drinking by rats depleted of body fluid without increase in osmotic pressure. *J. Physiol. (London)* **159:** 297–309.
35. Fitzsimons, J. T., and Simons, B. J. (1969). The effect on drinking in the rat of intravenous infusion of angiotensin, given alone or in combination with other stimuli of thirst. *J. Physiol. (London)* **203:** 45–57.
36. Robinson, M. M., and Evered, M. D. (1987). Pressor action of intravenous angiotensin II reduces drinking response in rats. *Am. J. Physiol.* **252:** R754–R759.
37. Stricker, E. M. (1969). Osmoregulation and volume regulation in rats: Inhibition of hypovolemic thirst by water. *Am. J. Physiol.* **217:** 98–105.
38. Wilkins, L., and Richter, C. P. (1940). A great craving for salt by a child with cortico-adrenal insufficiency. *JAMA, J. Am. Med. Assoc.* **114:** 866–868.
39. Richter, C. P. (1936). Increased salt appetite in adrenalectomized rats. *Am. J. Physiol.* **115:** 155–161.
40. Stricker, E. M., and Verbalis, J. G. (1987). Central inhibitory control of sodium appetite in rats: Correlation with pituitary oxytocin secretion. *Behav. Neurosci.* **101:** 560–567.
41. Stricker, E. M., and Verbalis, J. G. (1996). Central inhibition of salt appetite by oxytocin in rats. *Regul. Pept.* **66:** 83–85.
42. Stricker, E. M., and Verbalis, J. G. (1988). Hormones and behavior: The biology of thirst and sodium appetite. *Am. Sci.* **76:** 261–267.
43. Verbalis, J. G., Blackburn, R. E., Olson, B. R., and Stricker, E. M. (1993). Central oxytocin inhibition of food and salt ingestion: A mechanism for intake regulation of solute homeostasis. *Regul. Pept.* **45:** 149–154.
44. Fitts, D. A., Thunhorst, R. L., and Simpson, J. B. (1985). Diuresis and reduction of salt appetite by lateral ventricular infusions of atriopeptin II. *Brain Res.* **348:**118–124.
45. Blackburn, R. E., Samson, W. K., Fulton, R. J., Stricker, E. M., and Verbalis, J. G. (1995). Central oxytocin and atrial natriuretic peptide receptors mediate osmotic inhibition of salt appetite in rats. *Am. J. Physiol.* **269:** R245–R251.

C H A P T E R

43

Neuroendocrine Systems I: Overview—Thyroid and Adrenal Axes

Huda Akil, Serge Campeau, William E. Cullinan, Ronald M. Lechan, Roberto Toni, Stanley J. Watson, and Robert Y. Moore

Neural communication typically requires the release of neuroactive substances at a synapse. A major exception to this principle occurs in neuroendocrine regulation of homeostasis, growth and development, stress responses, osmoregulation, and reproduction. In neuroendocrine regulation, peptides are released from neurons into the circulation to act at a distance as hormones, in this case neurohormones. In this chapter, and the one that follows, we discuss the systems that produce neurohormones to regulate the function of the anterior pituitary as part of a brain–pituitary–organ axis. A related topic, neuroendocrine regulation of fluid balance, was presented in Chapter 42.

The importance of the pituitary gland as a "master" gland was recognized by the end of the 19th century, and shortly thereafter it became clear that isolated damage to the hypothalamus could produce endocrine dysfunction equivalent to pituitary damage. The explanation for this remained a mystery for many years until Geoffrey Harris and his associates showed that a portal circulation flows from the hypothalamus to the pituitary, carrying factors that regulate the secretion of anterior pituitary hormones. In these chapters we analyze the five neuroendocrine networks that form regulatory axes controlling growth and development, cellular metabolism, stress responses, and reproductive function. These are critical aspects of adaptation; growth and development, fluid and metabolic homeostasis, and responses to stress are essential to individual survival, whereas reproduction is critical to survival of the species. These are the imperatives on which behavior is elaborated; the majority of behavior in most species is devoted to obtaining nutrients and water, avoiding environmental hazards, and to reproduction, including raising the young to independence. In this chapter, we begin with an overview of the major features common to these axes, followed by a discussion of the features of each axis in detail.

BRAIN–PITUITARY–ORGAN AXES

Hormones Are Secreted at Each Level of a Brain–Pituitary–Organ Axis

The five regulatory neuroendocrine axes are organized in a hierarchical fashion, with the control of function initiated in the brain, relayed through the anterior pituitary, and ending with the production of hormones in a visceral organ (Fig. 43.1). For each neuroendocrine axis, neural and hormonal feedback effects regulate the secretion of a **releasing hormone,** or an **inhibitory hormone,** from hypothalamic neurons into a specialized vasculature, the hypothalamopituitary portal system. The releasing and inhibitory hormones are secreted from the axon terminals of neurons located in several hypothalamic nuclei, particularly the paraventricular nucleus, preoptic area, arcuate nucleus, and periventricular nucleus. These axons terminate in a specialized structure, the **median eminence,** one of six, midline circumventricular organs (Fig. 43.2). The median eminence extends from the floor of the hypothalamus to the pituitary gland and has three zones. An ependymal zone surrounds the infundibular recess of the third ventricle. Surrounding the ependymal zone is an internal zone that contains axons of vasopressin- and oxytocin-producing neurons, located in the supraoptic and paraventricular nuclei, which traverse this **hypothalamohypophyseal system** to terminate in the posterior pituitary. The external zone of the median eminence contains axons and terminals of inhibitory

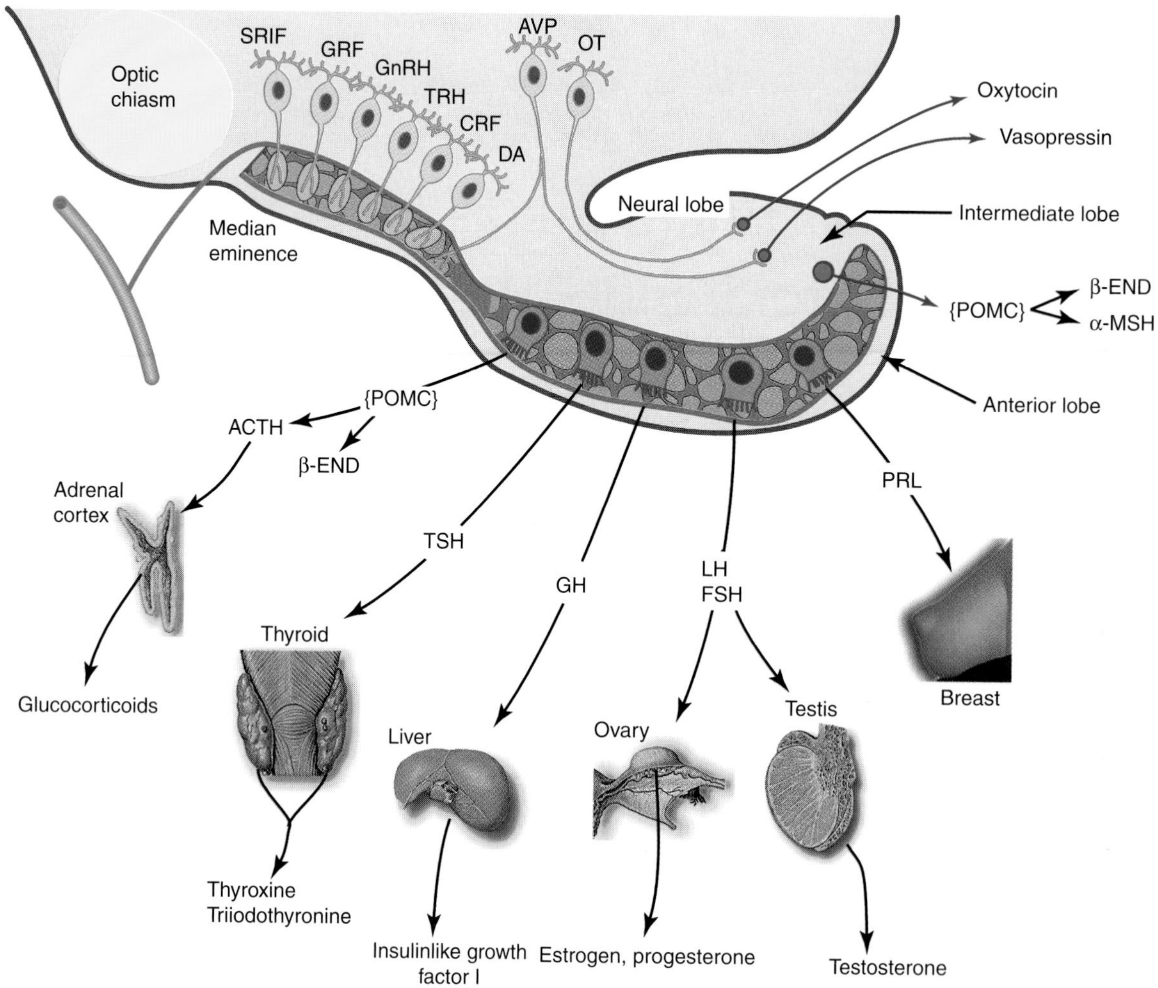

FIGURE 43.1 General organization of a brain–pituitary–organ axis.

and releasing hormone neurons and vessels of the portal plexus.

Because of the presence of the portal vessels, the external zone of the median eminence is highly vascular. Vessels arising from the superior hypophyseal artery (a branch of the internal carotid) break up into a complex array of capillaries and veins, the portal system. The releasing and inhibitory hormones are released from the axon terminals of the **tuberoinfundibular system** to enter the portal capillaries and long portal veins to reach venous sinusoids surrounding anterior pituitary cells (Fig. 43.3). Anterior pituitary cells are specialized and respond only to the appropriate releasing or inhibitory hormones by secreting **stimulating hormones.** For example, thyrotropes are anterior pituitary cells that respond to thyrotropin-releasing hormone (TRH) by secreting thyroid-stimulating hormone (TSH). Corticotrophs respond to corticotropin-releasing hormone (CRH) and secrete adrenocorticotropic hormone (ACTH). The secretion of growth hormone from somatotrophs is regulated both by a releasing hormone, growth hormone-releasing hormone, and an inhibitory hormone, somatostatin. Pituitary-stimulating hormones traverse the systemic circulation to interact with receptors on a series of visceral organs and glands.

The glandular, endocrine cells responding to the stimulating hormone from the pituitary secrete yet another hormone into the systemic circulation that has further actions that are a function of its structure and the receptors with which it interacts. Thus, the multiple levels of a brain–pituitary–organ axis permit very precise regulation of hormone secretion in response to homeostatic and environmental needs. Before describing components of each axis, we review some of the general neurobiology of hormone secretion.

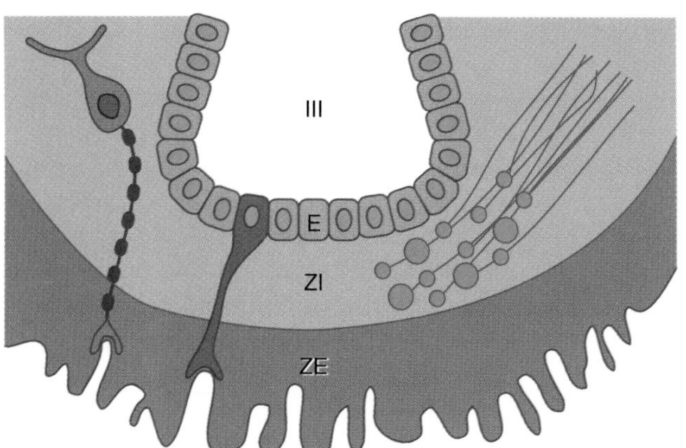

FIGURE 43.2 Diagram of the median eminence showing the organization of its three major zones. E, ependymal zone; ZI, internal zone; ZE, external zone; III, third ventricle. The ZE contains portal capillaries that are in close proximity to axon terminals of the tuberoinfundibular system and processes of specialized ependymal cells, the tanycytes.

Hypothalamic and Anterior Pituitary Hormone Secretion Is Pulsatile

The secretion of hypothalamic and pituitary hormones occurs in brief, ultradian pulses, often with a frequency of about one pulse every 60–180 min. Pulsatile secretion by hypothalamic neurons drives pulsatile anterior pituitary secretion and, at least in some axes (e.g., brain–pituitary–gonad), is necessary to maintain function. Disruption of pulsatile secretion typically results in a loss of proper regulatory function.

Circadian Control Is Also Important

Within each axis, the pulsatile secretion of hormone is under circadian as well as ultradian regulation. While most of these rhythms are truly circadian, independent of the light–dark cycle, others are associated with other events such as sleep. For example, there is a daily rhythm in secretion at all three levels of the brain–pituitary–adrenal axis, resulting in a peak of secretion of the adrenal hormone, cortisol, in the morning and a trough at night (see Chapter 45 for further details of circadian control), and this is maintained independent of the light–dark or rest–activity cycle. In contrast, growth hormone is secreted predominantly at night, but this apparently circadian pattern of secretion reflects an association of hormone secretion with non-REM sleep.

Secretion of Pituitary Hormones Is under Neural and Hormonal Control

The secretion of releasing and inhibitory hormones from tuberoinfundibular neurons occurs as a function of neuronal firing produced by the summation of inputs from other brain neurons. Specific aspects of this will be discussed in this and the following chapter. The secretion of releasing and inhibitory hormones and pituitary hormones is also regulated by the feedback of secreted hormones on upstream components of the axis. Hormones secreted by visceral organs act on the pituitary to decrease secretion of trophic hormones and some of these hormones feed back on the hypothalamus. For example, GHRH secretion is inhibited by TSH, and GH secretion is inhibited by insulinlike growth factor I. In the case of reproductive function, however, estradiol released by the ovaries can increase the release of the hypothalamic gonadotropin-releasing hormone. Thus, feedback regulation is not always negative.

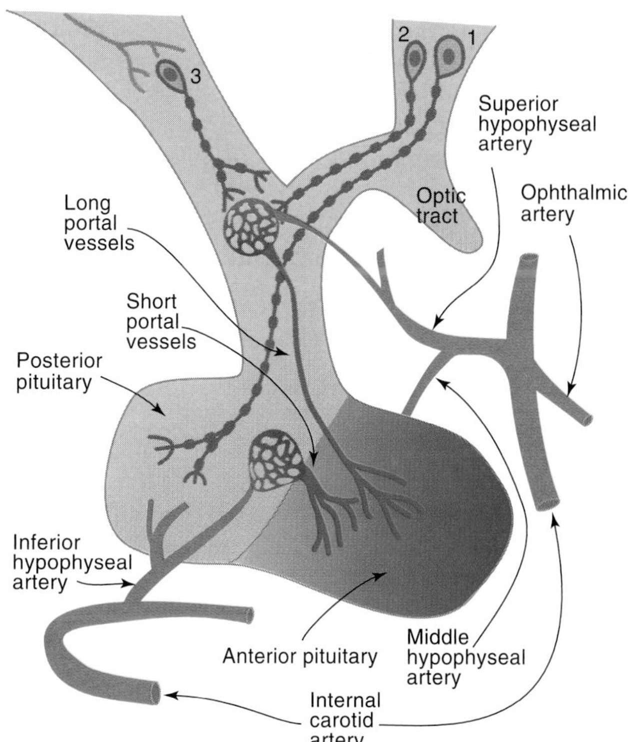

FIGURE 43.3 Neurovascular communication between the hypothalamus and the pituitary. In humans, the posterior pituitary is fed by the inferior hypophyseal artery and the hypothalamus by the superior hypophyseal artery, both branches of the internal carotid artery. A small portion of the anterior pituitary also receives arterial blood from the middle hypophyseal artery. Most of the blood supply to the anterior pituitary is venous by way of the long portal vessels that connect the portal capillary bed in the median eminence to the venous sinusoids in the anterior pituitary. The anterior pituitary also receives blood from short portal vessels draining the posterior pituitary. Neurons 2 and 3 terminate near portal capillaries in the external zone of the median eminence. Neuron 1 passes through the internal zone of the median eminence to terminate in the posterior pituitary. Adapted from Guy, V. L. (1972). The hypothalamus: physiology and clinical role of releasing factors. *Fertil Steril* **23:** 50.

Summary

Brain–pituitary–organ axes are crucial aspects of homeostatic regulation, growth, and reproduction. Hormones are secreted at each level of the axis, and secretion from the hypothalamus is both pulsatile and under circadian regulation. The control of hormone secretion is complex, but serves to provide high precision of regulation. Hormone secretion at the level of the brain is controlled by neural input, whereas secretion at the level of the pituitary and the visceral organ is controlled by a mixture of hypothalamic and trophic hormone stimulation and feedback inhibition.

METABOLIC ACTIVITY

In this and the following chapter, we discuss five brain–pituitary–organ axes, beginning with the brain–pituitary–thyroid and –adrenal axes. In the next chapter, we discuss regulation of somatotropin through a brain–pituitary axis that lacks a single target organ. We also discuss the brain–pituitary–adrenal axis. Finally, we examine how prolactin regulates lactation and other functions through an apparent brain–pituitary axis that has yet to be fully defined.

The Brain–Pituitary–Thyroid Axis Controls Metabolic Activity, Protein Synthesis, and Brain Development

The maintenance of normal thyroid function (euthyroidism) depends on complex interplay among hypothalamus, anterior pituitary, and thyroid gland, as well as other factors that influence the function of these organs (Fig. 43.4). The major hormone responsible for the secretion of **thyroid hormone** (**L-thyroxine,** or **T4,** and **triiodothyronine,** or **T3**) from the thyroid gland is **thyroid-stimulating hormone,** or **thyrotropin.** TSH is secreted from anterior pituitary **thyrotropes,** which constitute approximately 10% of the anterior pituitary cells. Secretion of TSH is positively regulated by **thyrotropin-releasing hormone,** originating in the hypothalamus. The fraction of free (vs protein-bound) thyroid hormone circulating in the bloodstream (<1% of all thyroid hormone) feeds back on the anterior pituitary to inhibit secretion of TSH and on the hypothalamus to inhibit secretion of TRH and thereby complete a classic **negative feedback loop** (Fig. 43.4).

In the control of thyroid function, the negative feedback system maintains a constant level of free thyroid hormone in the bloodstream. Free thyroid hormone affects protein synthesis, metabolic activity, or both in all organ systems and is necessary for normal development and function of the brain (see Box 43.1).

The concentration of free thyroid hormone in the bloodstream strongly influences secretion of TSH by the pituitary. When thyroid hormone levels fall below normal, an increase in TSH secretion restores thyroid hormone levels to normal; when thyroid hormone levels rise above normal, TSH secretion is suppressed. The inverse relationship between thyroid hormone levels and TSH secretion is extremely precise; slight increases or decreases in the concentration of free thyroid hormone circulating in the bloodstream, even within normal range, can have inhibitory or stimulatory effects on the secretion of TSH.[1,2] TRH influences the set point for TSH secretion; an increase or decrease in TRH secretion can alter the set point for feedback regulation of TSH secretion by thyroid hormone. In addition to TRH, TSH, and thyroid hormone, peptides, catecholamines, cytokines, steroid hormones, and nuclear regulatory factors, many originating in the brain, can be involved in the regulation of thyroid hormone secretion.

TRH Is Made in Neurons in the Paraventricular Nucleus

TRH, the tripeptide pyroGlu–His–ProNH2 (molecular mass 362 kDa) (Fig. 43.5A), was the first hypothalamic-releasing factor to be chemically identified and synthesized. It is the most important hypothalamic hormone involved in the regulation of anterior pituitary TSH.[3]

The C-terminal amide and the N-terminal cyclized glutamic acid are essential for biologic activity of TRH. The potency of this peptide in stimulating TSH release is demonstrated in humans by the abrupt rise in TSH beginning within 5 min of an intravenous injection of TRH and reaching a maximum 15 to 30 min after injection. Conversely, in animals, a marked decrease in basal TSH secretion follows the administration of anti-TRH antibodies.[4] Although TRH biosynthesis was long debated and hypothesized to be a nonribosomal mechanism,[4] subsequent experiments showed that, like most other hypothalamic-releasing factors, TRH synthesis is mRNA-directed and involves cleavage of a prohormone.

The complete sequence of the TRH prohormone has been deduced from its cDNA in frog, rat, mouse, and human (Fig. 43.5B). Common to the TRH prohormones of the four species are multiple copies of a progenitor sequence for TRH, Gln–His–Pro–Gly, flanked on each

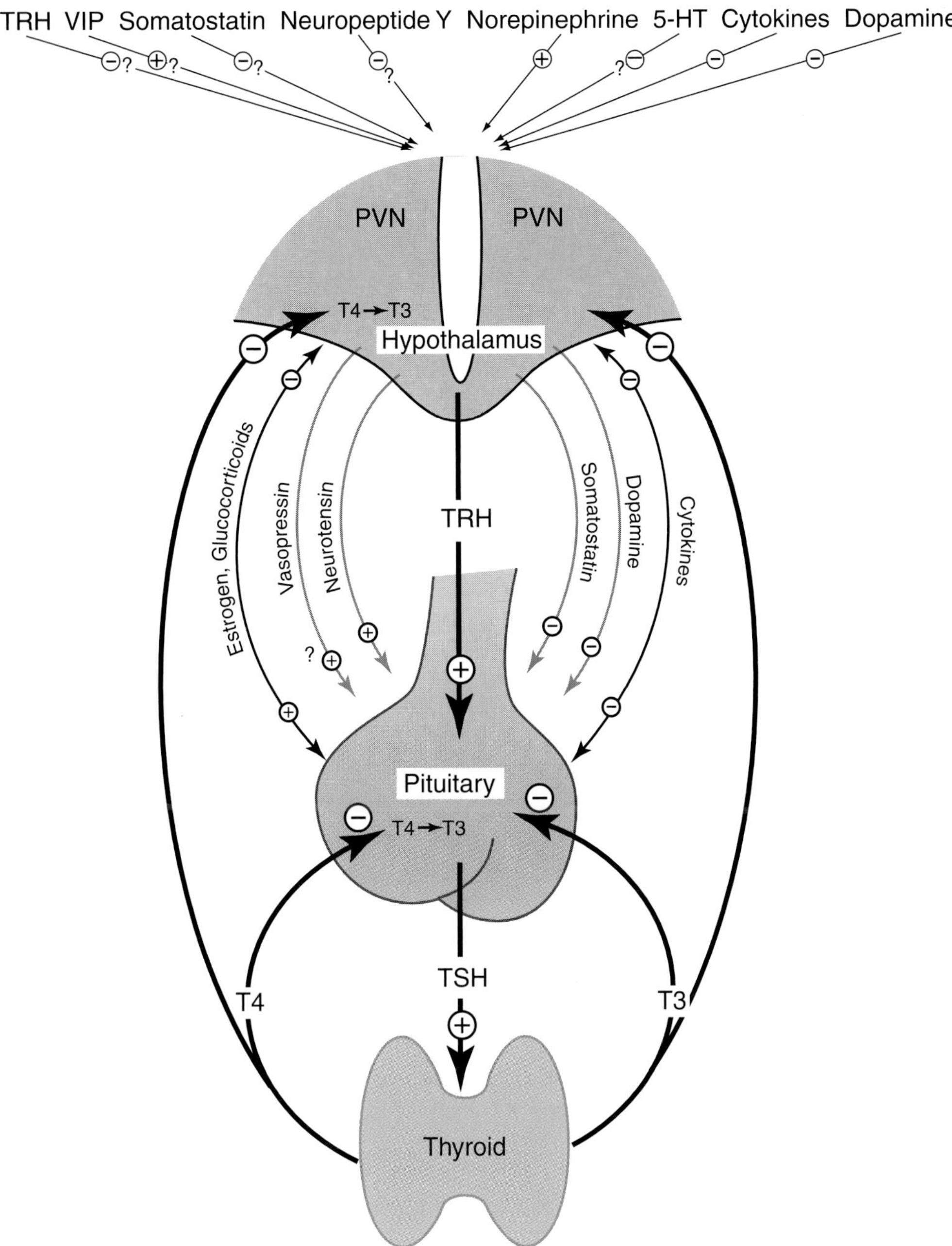

FIGURE 43.4 Schematic diagram of the brain–pituitary–thyroid axis, which regulates secretion of thyroid hormone. Bold lines denote the negative feedback of thyroid hormone on TRH secretion from the hypothalamus and TSH secretion from the anterior pituitary. Hypothalamic TRH neurons and anterior pituitary thyrotropes are affected by numerous other potential regulatory influences that are activated under specific physiological or pathological conditions. PVN, paraventricular nucleus.

side by paired basic amino acids, Lys–Arg or Arg–Arg, that are processing signals for carboxypeptidase B-like enzymes. The C-terminal glycine is a substrate for α-amidating enzymes that convert TRH–Gly to TRH, and the N-terminal glutamine residue is modified by glutaminyl cyclase to yield the fully mature and biologically active TRH.[5] Human preproTRH contains 242 amino acids and six copies of the TRH progenitor sequence.[6]

In experimental animals and in humans, TRH is present in great abundance in axons terminating in the external zone of the median eminence (Fig. 43.2B).[7–9] The origin of TRH-containing axons that terminate in the median eminence is the hypothalamic paraventric-

BOX 43.1

CRETINISM

Cretinism, characterized by deficits in mental, neurological, and physical development, can occur if thyroid hormone is not available during fetal and early neonatal development.[9a] In this syndrome, severe hypothyroidism gives rise to numerous structural and functional abnormalities in the brain, including poor neurite outgrowth, less synapse formation, decreased myelination, reduced microtubule formation, and delayed axonal transport, particularly in the cerebral cortex and cerebellum.[9b,9c] If thyroid hormone is not replaced within the critical 1–3 months (in humans) following birth, most of these abnormalities become permanent. Even transient hypothyroidism in preterm infants is associated with an increased risk of cerebral palsy and impaired mental development. In the mature brain, thyroid hormone insufficiency and excess can also have functional, neurological, and psychological manifestations, summarized in the accompanying table.

Roberto Toni and Ronald M. Lechan

Potential Clinical Manifestations of Thyroid Hormone Excess or Insufficiency on the Central and Peripheral Nervous Systems

Excess thyroid hormone	Insufficient thyroid hormone
Tremor	Cretinism
Nervousness	Mental deficiency, defects in hearing and speech, spastic or ataxic gait, impaired voluntary motor activity, clonus
Tremulousness	
Hyperkinesis, agitation, irritability	
Insomnia	Sleep apnea
Vivid dreams and nightmares	Dysarthria
Decreased memory	Hypothermia
Impaired concentration	Hypoventilation
Seizures	Cerebellar ataxia
Chorea	Coma
Coma	Neuropsychiatric syndromes
Neuropsychiatric syndromes	Myxedema madness (psychosis), dementia
Depression, anxiety, mania, dysphoria, emotional lability, attention deficit, delirium, paranoia	Peripheral neuropathy
	Carpal tunnel syndrome, facial weakness

ular nucleus (PVN), a region contained within the classic *thyrotropic area*.[10] This wing-shaped nucleus at the dorsal margin of the third ventricle can be divided into two major portions based on the size of neuron cell bodies: a *magnocellular division* of large neurons and a *parvicellular division* of small- to medium-sized neurons. The parvicellular portion is medial, adjacent to the ependymal wall of the third ventricle, and can be broken down into several smaller subdivisions (Fig. 43.6). As opposed to oxytocin and vasopressin, which originate primarily in the magnocellular PVN, TRH comes exclusively from neurons in the parvicellular PVN. Retrograde transport of marker substances injected into the external zone of the median eminence shows that these TRH neurons correspond precisely to a subpopulation of neurons in the PVN that contributes to the hypothalamic tuberoinfundibular system. TRH neurons have a symmetric, triangular distribution at the dorsal margin of the third ventricle in the medial and periventricular parts of the parvicellular PVN. The PVN is also recognized as a major source of other substances destined for transport to the median eminence, including corticotropin-releasing hormone, neurotensin, galanin, enkephalin, and vasoactive intestinal polypeptide.[7,8] TRH-containing neurons are also present in other areas inside and outside the hypothalamus, but these neurons probably do not contribute to the tuberoinfundibular tract. Instead, they participate in other neural functions, such as arousal, regulation of temperature, and control of respiration[11]; they are not involved directly in the regulation of TSH secretion.

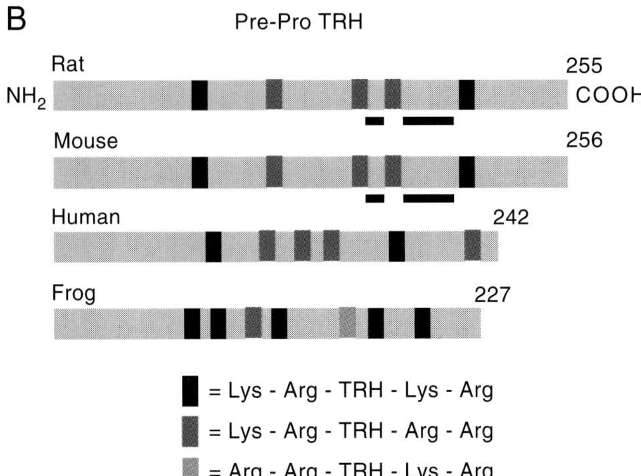

FIGURE 43.5 (A) Chemical structure of thyrotropin-releasing hormone (TRH). (B) Schematic representation of rat, mouse, frog, and human preproTRH. Each sequence contains multiple copies of a TRH progenitor sequence (Gln–His–Pro) preceded by Lys–Arg and followed by Lys–Arg or Arg–Arg. Unique to the frog is one TRH sequence that is preceded by Arg–Arg and followed by Lys–Arg. Non-TRH sequences preproTRH (160–169) and preproTRH (178–199) in the rat preprohormone are indicated by a bar below the sequences.

Thyroid Hormone Inhibits Synthesis and Secretion of TRH by Binding to Thyroid Hormone Receptors in the Nucleus of Hypophysiotropic TRH Neurons

Thyroid hormone receptors are part of a superfamily of steroid hormone receptors, which includes the estrogen, progesterone, and vitamin D receptors.[12] Steroid hormone receptors bind to specific regions in DNA referred to as response elements (REs). TRα1, TRβ1, and TRβ2 isoforms can be found in the nucleus of hypophysiotropic TRH neurons in the PVN. TRα1 and TRβ2 are the most abundant isoforms and are found in more than 80% of all TRH-producing neurons in the PVN.[13] A related protein, TRα2, can be found in the PVN but its colocalization with TRH neurons is only minimal. TRα2 can bind the same DNA sequences as TRα1 and TRβ but cannot bind to thyroid hormone because of differences in its C-terminal binding domain; therefore, TRα2 could act as a competitive antagonist of functional thyroid hormone receptors when present in the same cell. The relative paucity of TRα2 in hypophysiotropic TRH neurons[13] may explain the unique responsiveness of these neurons to circulating thyroid hormone in contrast to TRH-producing neurons in other regions of the brain that are not hypophysiotropic.

T3 presumably is the thyroid hormone that binds thyroid hormone receptors and mediates feedback on TRH gene expression. Although T4 is released preferentially from the thyroid gland, under most circumstances, T3, and not T4, is the biologically active form of thyroid hormone. T4, therefore, may be viewed as a prohormone that is converted to T3 by removal of an iodine from the outer phenolic ring of T4. Two enzymes catalyze the conversion of T4 to T3, Type I and Type II deiodinases.[14] Type I deiodinase is found in peripheral tissues and the pituitary gland, but Type II deiodinase is found only in the pituitary, brain, and brown fat. Type I deiodinase, therefore, is responsible for the majority of T3 in the bloodstream, whereas Type II deiodinase is responsible for intracellular conversion of T4 to T3 in the CNS before transport to the

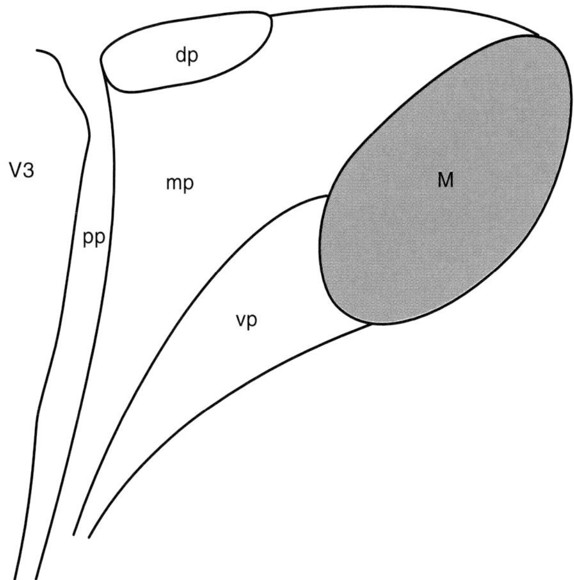

FIGURE 43.6 Schematic diagram of the paraventricular nucleus (PVN) illustrating the major and minor subdivisions. M, magnocellular division of the PVN; dp, dorsal parvicellular part; mp, medial parvicellular part; pp, periventricular parvicellular part; vp, ventral parvicellular part of the PVN; v3, third ventricle.

nucleus. The PVN, however, contains little or no Type II deiodinase,[15] indicating that neurons in this nucleus are not capable of converting T4 to biologically active T3. In the absence of T4, however, infusion of T3 into hypothyroid animals that restores its plasma levels to the euthyroid range does not suppress proTRH mRNA levels in the PVN to normal.[16] This finding indicates that feedback regulation of thyroid hormone on TRH neurons in the PVN requires circulating T4. Because the PVN lacks deiodinase, monodeiodination of T4 to T3 occurs at another locus within the brain, and the T3 is then transported to the PVN. Cerebrospinal fluid may be the alternative source of thyroid hormone for the PVN, because the choroid plexus can synthesize the T4-binding protein transthyretin and transport large amounts of T4 into the cerebrospinal fluid.[17]

In sum, the large number and variation of chemically coded neuronal inputs to TRH neurons in the hypothalamic PVN, the potential for axoaxonal interactions between TRH and other peptide- and amide-containing terminals in the median eminence, and the influence of circulating levels of thyroid hormone (and possibly steroids) suggest that regulation of hypophysiotropic TRH occurs at multiple levels. Feedback regulation by thyroid hormone on TRH neurons in the PVN is mediated by the action of circulating levels of T3 and T4 and are important for the moment-to-moment control over the biosynthesis and secretion of hypophyseotropic TRH. In contrast, the role of most afferent projections to TRH neurons in the PVN is not known precisely, but they are presumed to be called into play during specific physiologic conditions, including stress, fasting, infection, cold exposure, and suckling, to modulate the secretion of TRH and ultimately change the set point for feedback regulation of thyroid hormone on TSH secretion (see later).

TRH Modulates Feedback of Thyroid Hormone on TSH Secretion and Activates TSH Secretion by Thyrotropes

TSH secretion is regulated by feedback suppression of circulating thyroid hormone directly on anterior pituitary thyrotropes. In this system, the hypothalamus has an important role in determining the set point for thyroid hormone negative feedback on TSH secretion. Hypothalamic lesions reduce baseline levels of thyroid function and impair the TSH response to thyroid hormone deficiency.[18] TRH is the major hypothalamic peptide mediating control over the set point for anterior pituitary TSH secretion, but other substances originating in the brain also participate in the secretion of TSH either directly or by modulating the response of TSH to TRH.

TRH-Induced Secretion of TSH

TRH-induced secretion of TSH is primarily due to activation of transcription of the TSHβ and TSHα genes. The action of TRH requires binding to a G-protein-coupled membrane receptor that is immediately followed by activation of membrane-bound phospholipase C and hydrolysis of phosphatidylinositol 4,5-biphosphate (PIP_2) to inositol 1,4,5-triphosphate (IP_3) and diacylglycerol (DAG).[19] These actions ultimately result in the phosphorylation or increased concentration of nuclear proteins that interact with the TSHβ and TSHα genes and hence increase the transcription of these genes (Fig. 43.7). The continued presence of TRH over long intervals (24 h), however, downregulates the TRH receptor such that activation of the signaling pathway is reduced.[20]

The TRH Receptor

The TRH receptor is a member of the seven-transmembrane, G-protein-coupled receptor family.[21] The sex-related differences in TRH-induced TSH secretion in humans (greater in females) may be due to the stimulation of TRH receptor transcription by estrogen and a resultant increase in binding sites for TRH.[22] TRH-induced downregulation probably involves a decrease in the transcription of the TRH receptor gene, a secondary effect of TRH-induced stimulation of protein kinase C (PKC) and calcium mobilization.[23] Paradoxically, however, when thyroid hormone levels in the circulation fall and TRH increases in the portal capillary blood, there is an increase, rather than a decrease, in TRH receptors in the anterior pituitary.[24] This increase likely is due to overriding effects of T3 deficiency on stimulation of TRH receptor gene transcription.

Secretion of TSH and TRH Is Pulsatile and Follows a Circadian Rhythm

Secretion of TSH is pulsatile, with a frequency of one pulse every 90–180 min (or approximately 10–15 pulses per 24 h) in humans.[25] The frequency and amplitude of pulses tend to be greatest at night, but the pulse amplitude actually moves through three phases over a 24-h period: an evening rise until 4 A.M., a decline until noon, and then a resting phase in the afternoon. The evening rise in TSH is commonly referred to as the **nocturnal TSH surge.** Because the nocturnal surge begins 4–5 h prior to sleep, sleep is not believed to be an important mechanism for induction of the TSH peak. In addition, sleep deprivation does not interfere with the circadian rhythm of TSH.[26] In contrast, the rhythmic secretion of TSH can be phase-shifted by exposure to bright light, indicating that the

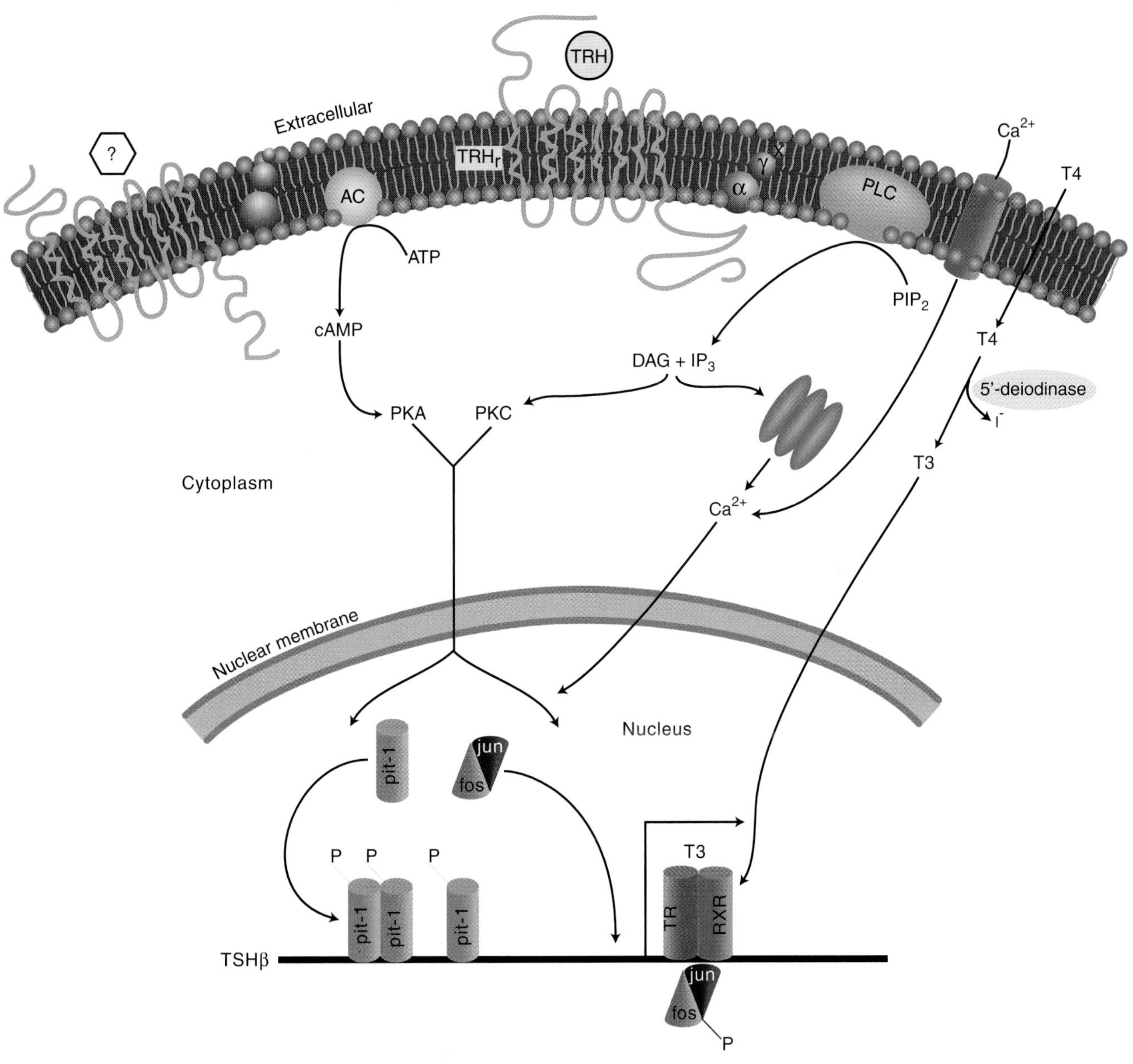

FIGURE 43.7 Simplified schema of the proposed regulation of TSHβ gene transcription by TRH and thyroid hormone. TRH binds to its receptor (TRH$_r$) on the cell membrane and activates phosphokinase C in the cytoplasm. Phosphokinase A may also be activated by an unknown ligand. This results in phosphorylation of Pit-1 and AP-1 (Fos–Jun) in the nucleus, enhancing their binding to TRH response regions in the TSHβ gene to activate the transcription of TSH. An increase in cytoplasmic free calcium (Ca^{2+}) also contributes to activation of the TSHβ gene by an unknown mechanism(s). Thyroid hormone is transported across the cell membrane, converted to T3 in the cytoplasm by 5-deiodinase, and then transported across the nuclear membrane. In the nucleus, T3 binds to its receptor (TR), which probably exists as a heterodimer together with the retinoid X receptor (RXR). T3 bound to its receptor may then compete with AP-1 for binding to the same site in the TSHβ gene, thereby inhibiting the transcription of TSH. AC, adenylate cyclase; DAG, diacylglycerol; IP$_3$, inositol triphosphate; PIP$_2$, phosphoinositol bisphosphate; PLC, phospholipase C.

suprachiasmatic nucleus—the major pacemaker in the hypothalamus—can influence the circadian timing of TSH secretion, as it does other rhythmic functions controlled by the CNS (see Chapter 49).

The pulse frequency of TSH is probably determined by the pulsatile secretion of hypothalamic TRH. The low, constant level of TSH in people who have large, destructive lesions of the hypothalamus (central or tertiary hypothyroidism) can be restored by pulsatile administration of exogenous TRH.[25] The frequency of

TRH pulsations from the hypothalamus is probably very rapid because a pulsatile TRH pattern can be established in experimental animals only if TRH is sampled at 2-min intervals.[27] As in other neuroendocrine control systems, pulsatile secretion from the hypothalamus is essential for the synthesis and activity of anterior pituitary hormones. In the case of TRH, pulsatile secretion is necessary to stimulate the synthesis of TSH β-subunit mRNA and influence the glycosylation of mature TSH.[28]

The Thyroid Gland Is Innervated by the Autonomic Nervous System

The idea that thyroid function can be influenced by neural activity other than hypothalamic control of TSH secretion arose from anatomical, physiological, and clinical observations that began with Galen's 2nd-century description of the inferior (recurrent) laryngeal nerve and its association with the thyroid gland. For example, near the turn of the 20th century Cannon and Fitz[29] observed that increased sympathetic input to the thyroid gland produces a hypermetabolic state. It is now well recognized that the peripheral nervous system, including autonomic and sensory branches, heavily innervates the thyroid gland and is particularly important in regulating blood flow to it.[30–32] This control system works in concert with or independent of TSH to contribute to regulation of thyroid hormone synthesis (and possibly secretion).

The thyroid gland is richly innervated by the sympathetic and parasympathetic divisions of the autonomic nervous system.[30,31] These fibers penetrate the thyroid parenchyma to terminate around arterioles, capillaries, and, less frequently, venules; these fibers also terminate near follicular cells. The sympathetic nerves derive from neuronal perikarya in the sympathetic cervical ganglia and reach the thyroid gland with the thyroid arteries and by joining the superior laryngeal nerve. The parasympathetic nerve fibers arise from neuronal perikarya located in ganglia juxtaposed or intrinsic to the thyroid gland (laryngeal and thyroid ganglia) or from perikarya in the jugular or nodose ganglia of the vagus nerve. The fibers reach the thyroid through the superior and inferior laryngeal nerves. Sensory fibers also arise from the dorsal root ganglia (C2–C5) and trigeminal ganglion (see Fig. 43.8).

Neuroendocrine Regulation of Thyroid Hormone Changes under Some Physiologic States

Under some conditions, feedback regulation of the hypothalamus–pituitary–thyroid axis does not function as expected. Such conditions include *cold exposure*, in which thyroid hormone is elevated but TSH and TRH are unexpectedly high; and, conversely, *severe infection* and *fasting*, in which thyroid hormone is low but TSH and TRH are unexpectedly low. These responses may be important for survival; during exposure to cold, elevated thyroid hormone levels contribute to thermogenesis, whereas during infection and fasting, low thyroid hormone levels may help reduce nitrogen losses. A number of mechanisms may contribute to these phenomena: neural projections to TRH neurons in the paraventricular nucleus, intrinsic factors within the anterior pituitary, and glucocorticoids circulating in the bloodstream may have important roles in mediating these responses (see Fig. 43.9).

Exposure to cold is associated with an increase in thyroid hormone and a rapid rise in TSH, occurring within 30 min of cold exposure.[33] This rise is due to increased transcription of the TRH gene[34] and, ultimately, increased secretion of TRH into portal capillaries.[35] This increased secretion of TRH into the portal system resets the setpoint for feedback regulation of TSH secretion by thyroid hormone, resulting in a sustained elevation in thyroid hormone levels over normal. TRH gene expression in paraventricular neurons is not as easily inhibited by circulating levels of thyroid hormone under these conditions, presumably because the TRH neurons are actively stimulated by catecholaminergic inputs from the brainstem.[33] In turn, brainstem catecholaminergic cell groups may be stimulated by thermosensitive neurons in the preoptic region. When these neurons are lesioned, the TSH response to cold exposure is abolished, but hypothyroidism does not ensue.[36]

The occurrence of low thyroid hormone levels with inappropriately low or normal TSH levels in the setting of severe illness has been called "sick euthyroid syndrome," or nonthyroidal illness, and is another example of a normal feedback regulatory mechanism of the thyroid axis being overridden. The inability of TSH to rise when thyroid hormone levels are low is at least partly due to increased elevation of cytokines, polypeptides that are important immune modulators. After systemic or intraventricular administration, cytokines interleukin-1 (IL-1) and tumor necrosis factor (TNF) reduce the content of TRH, TRH mRNA, or both,[37,38] suggesting that these cytokines inhibit TRH gene regulation. Because IL-1-containing axon terminals are located in the PVN,[39] cytokines intrinsic to the brain may directly affect TRH neurons, although synaptic contacts on TRH neurons have not yet been established.

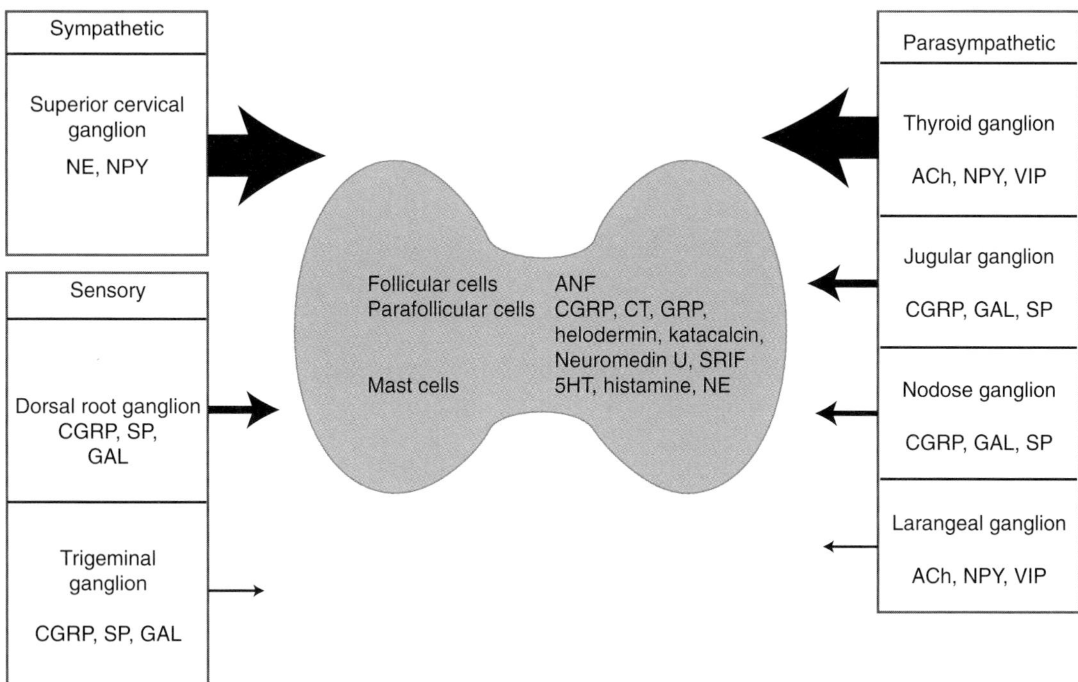

FIGURE 43.8 Summary of the anatomical sources of nerve fibers innervating the thyroid gland and of associated principal neurotransmitters and neuromediators. Peptides and amines intrinsic to thyroid follicular cells, parafollicular C cells, and mast cells are also shown. ACh, acetylcholine; ANF, atrial natriuretic factor; CGRP, calcitonin gene-related peptide; CT, calcitonin; DA, dopamine; GAL, galanin; GRP, gastrin-releasing peptide; 5HT, serotonin; NE, norepinephrine; NPY, neuropeptide Y; SP, substance P; SRIF, somatostatin; VIP, vasoactive intestinal polypeptide. Arrow size reflects the relative contribution of nerve fibers to the thyroid gland. Adapted from Grunditz *et al.*[31]

Summary

Through a brain–pituitary–thyroid axis, the central nervous system plays an important role in the regulation of thyroid hormone secretion. In the basal (euthyroid) state, an intricate feedback control system integrates signals from the hypothalamus, pituitary, and thyroid to maintain circulating levels of thyroid hormone in the normal range. Under conditions of thyroid hormone insufficiency or excess, the system is perturbed to increase or decrease the secretion of TRH into the portal capillary plexus, respectively, thereby raising or lowering the setpoint for feedback regulation of TSH by T3. Other factors assist in the feedback system to restore thyroid hormone levels to normal, including alterations in the glycosylation of TSH and activation of the autonomic nervous system to regulate blood flow to the thyroid gland. The normal operation of the thyroid control feedback system, however, can be overridden under certain physiological and pathological conditions, such as cold exposure, sepsis, and starvation. Under these circumstances, the feedback loop is reset to maintain thyroid hormone levels in an otherwise abnormal range. Resetting is accomplished by the activation of neural inputs to hypophyseotropic TRH neurons from brainstem catecholamine groups, intrinsic hypothalamic neurons, and perhaps limbic parts of the endbrain, which change the secretion pattern of other hypophyseotropic substances, such as somatostatin, into the portal system and change the concentration of glucocorticoids and cytokines circulating in the bloodstream. These changes allow an organism to adapt better to a wide variety of stimuli.

STRESS

The Brain–Pituitary–Adrenal Axis Mediates Response to Stress

In a variety of noxious situations—disease and fever, for example—animals show general responses such as enlargement of the adrenal cortex, involutions of the thymus and spleen, and formation of ulcers in the stomach and duodenum.[40] These general responses have been considered a call for the animal to fight injury. Seyle proposed that these responses to stress

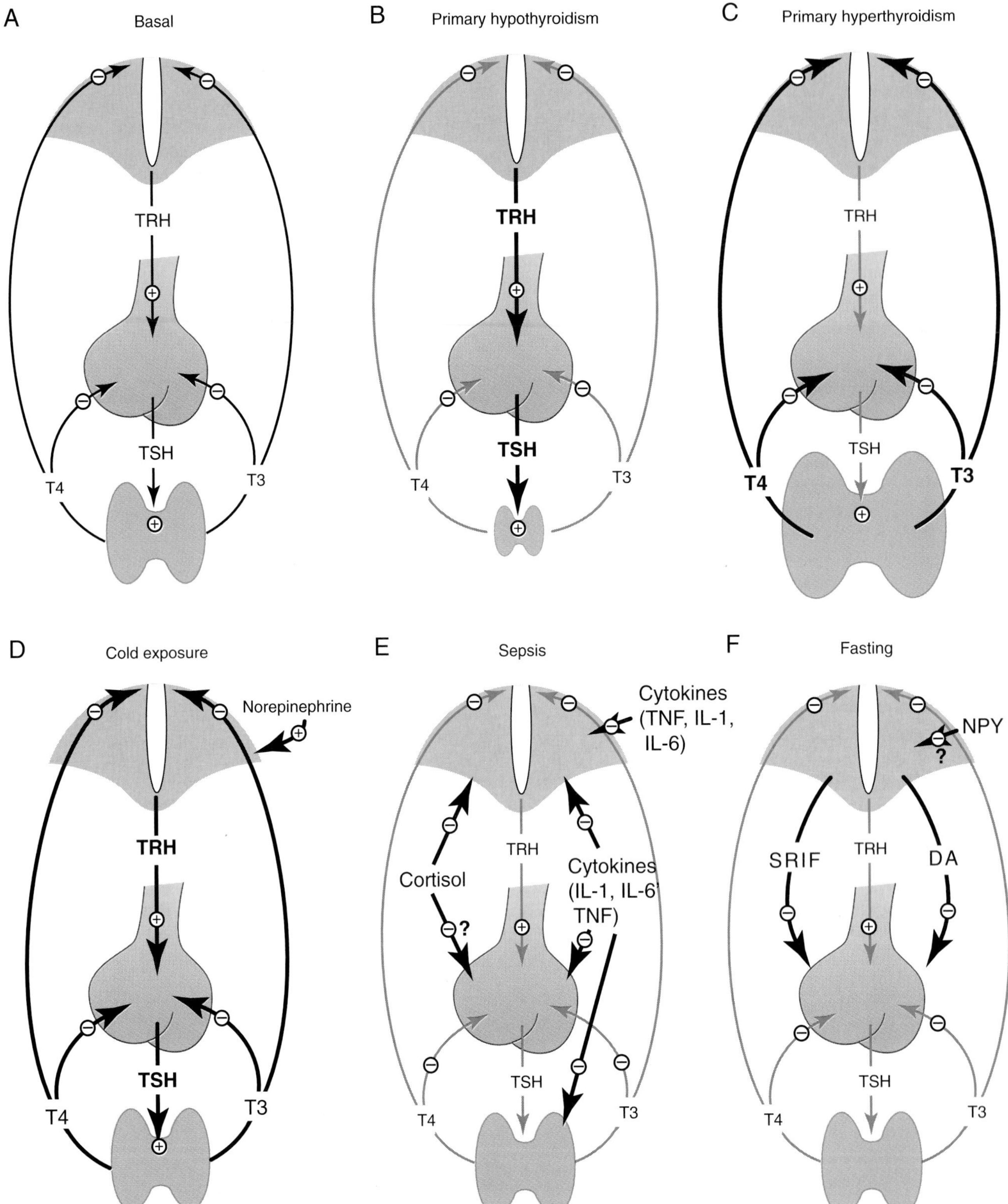

FIGURE 43.9 Schematic diagrams of the proposed factors involved in regulation of thyroid hormone secretion under varying physiological and pathological conditions. Thick arrows correspond to increased secretion of the factors shown in bold print. See text for details.

were based on known homeostasic processes, which correct the body's deviations from equilibrium.[41] Now, in addition to these automatic processes, homeostasis—and thus the response to stress—is understood to involve cognitive processes such as learning and memory, as well as physiologic responses.

The brain–pituitary–adrenal axis is a key player in an animal's response to stressful stimuli. Other participants are the adrenal medulla, which produces norepinephrine and epinephrine, and the autonomic nervous system, which modulates physiologic functions through neurotransmitters.

Corticotropin-releasing hormone is a 41-amino-acid peptide expressed in the hypothalamus.[42] The region with highest expression is the medial parvicellular part of the paraventricular nucleus (mpPVN).[43] CRH neurons in the mpPVN project to the external layer of the median eminence, where peptides are secreted into the portal bloodstream, through which they are transported to the anterior pituitary. In addition to CRH, CRH neurons express and release arginine vasopression (AVP), although most AVP is expressed in neighboring magnocellular elements of the PVN that project to the posterior pituitary. **Corticotropes** in the anterior pituitary express receptors for CRH and AVP. These receptors are members of the superfamily of G-protein-coupled receptors.[44,45] Because they activate different signal transduction pathways, peptides CRH and AVP have a synergistic effect on corticotropes.[46]

In response to stimulation, corticotropes synthesize and release **adrenocorticotropic hormone.** ACTH travels through the systemic circulation and binds and activates its receptor, which is expressed on the surface of cells of the adrenal cortex. The ACTH receptor was the first receptor described as coupled to activation of adenylate cyclase.[47] In response to receptor activation, adrenal cortical cells synthesize **glucocorticoids** from cholesterol through a series of enzymatic steps. Glucocorticoids are then rapidly secreted into the bloodstream. Adrenal cortical cells do not store glucocorticoids at rest.

ACTH Is Synthesized from a Precursor Molecule

ACTH is synthesized from a precursor, **proopiomelanocortin** (POMC), the first mammalian endocrine or neuronal precursor to be cloned.[48] ACTH and the potent opioid peptide ***β*-endorphin** derive from POMC (Fig. 43.10).[49,50] ACTH is encoded by the middle region of POMC, and *β*-endorphin by the C-terminal region; the function of the N-terminal region of POMC is unknown. In addition to the unusual finding of two active peptides deriving from a common precursor, POMC

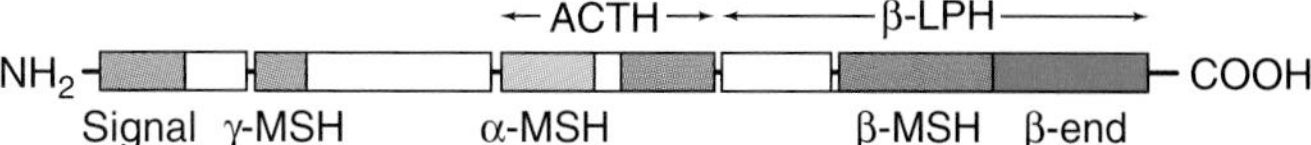

FIGURE 43.10 Proopiomelanocortin precursor peptide. Multiple processing enzymes in anterior pituitary corticotropes derive adrenocorticotropic hormone (ACTH) from the middle region of the precursor and *β*-endorphin (*β*-end) from the C-terminal region. The precursor can also be processed differently in the anterior and neurointermediate lobes of the pituitary to give the peptides shown. *β*-LPH, *β*-lipotropin; MSH, melanocyte-stimulating hormone.

has a single sequence within ACTH (ACTH amino acid residues 4–10) that is repeated elsewhere in the parent molecule. The sequence is present once in *β*-melanocyte-stimulating hormone (*β*-MSH) and once, with a slight modification, in a region called *γ*-MSH. Thus, the ACTH precursor is complex.[51] Additional information about the structure of the POMC gene,[52] its sites of expression,[53,54] and the enzymes involved in its maturation[55,56] have allowed thorough study of the biology and regulation of ACTH at the level of the pituitary.

The Brain Drives a Daily Rhythm of Secretion

The brain–pituitary–adrenal axis is not simply an alarm system activated by stress. Instead, the axis exhibits basal secretion with daily oscillations. Glucocorticoid levels are highest upon awakening and lowest at the end of the activity phase. Differences between nocturnal and diurnal animals show that this rhythmic variation in glucocorticoid levels is driven by activity, not light. In humans, glucocorticoid levels peak around 7 AM and decline steadily throughout the day. The nadir is reached in the late evening, 7 PM to midnight, after which glucocorticoid levels begin to rise. In rats, which are nocturnal, the highest levels of glucocorticoids are observed in evening, when the animals are awakening, and the lowest levels occur in morning.

Concentrations of circulating ACTH show similar, but less pronounced, fluctuations. The phase of the daily ACTH rhythm precedes that of glucocorticoids by about 1–2 h,[57,58] consistent with ACTH (from the pituitary) causing synthesis and release of glucocorticoids (from the adrenal cortex).

Like that of the hypothalmus–pituitary–thyroid axis, the daily rhythm of the hypothalamus–pituitary–adrenal axis appears to be driven by the hypothalamus. In rat parvicellular PVN, expression of CRH mRNA has a daily rhythm.[57,58] The rise in CRH message anticipates the glucocorticoid peak by several hours: In rats, the CRH mRNA pool begins to increase in the morning, when glucocorticoid levels are very low. The amount of CRH mRNA then shows a dramatic drop in late evening, as glucocorticoid levels peak. Although this relationship may suggest that the pattern of CRH mRNA expression is driven by negative feedback of glucocorticoid (discussed later), the pattern of CRH mRNA expression is rather complex and is likely controlled by intricate neuronal mechanisms. Indeed, removal of glucocorticoids by adrenalectomy dramatically changes the level of expression of CRH mRNA but does not lead to a substantial change in the pattern or shape of the CRH rhythm.

Lesion studies have shown that the suprachiasmatic nucleus, classically involved in circadian events, plays a role in the control of the CRH cycle[59]; however, it clearly is not the only important structure. In fact, food intake appears to be a major control factor in the timing of these daily rhythms. Secretions of ACTH and adrenal steroids occur around mealtime in response to and in anticipation of eating. Furthermore, sustained changes in the timing of meals shift the rhythm.[60]

In addition to affecting basal hormone levels along the brain–pituitary–adrenal axis, diurnal rhythms change the sensitivity and responsiveness of the axis to stress. At the nadir of the rhythm, an axis is exquisitely responsive to stress stimuli and shows clear activation. At that same time, the axis is also highly sensitive to inhibition and to negative feedback.[61] Thus, the initiation and termination of stress responses appear to be more efficient at the nadir than at the peak of the diurnal cycle.

Because glucocorticoids alter glucose metabolism and affect energy use throughout the body, it may not be surprising that their levels oscillate as a function of expected demands on the organism and are modulated by food intake. However, the fact that animals are more sensitive to stress when they are resting than when they are at the peak of activity shows that the system evaluates a stimulus as stressful in terms of not only its absolute magnitude but also its context and the organism's readiness to meet it. *Timing* and *context* are two central features of the responsiveness of this system that address the relative nature of stressful stimuli and will be discussed later.

Brain Pathways Activate the Response to Stress

Basal activity of the brain–pituitary–adrenal axis oscillates, but the system is activated under emergency conditions through neuronal input. In the hypothalamus, the PVN appears to sum and integrate input from numerous loci throughout the brain. The output of the PVN, release of CRH and AVP from CRH neurons, determines whether a stress response occurs.

Input to the PVN is divided into five broad classes,[62] depending on the source of the input. Inputs come from: (1) brainstem pathways, many of which are catecholaminergic, that appear involved in transmission of visceral information; (2) midbrain and pons cell groups that relay somatic and special sensory information; (3) the forebrain, from components traditionally classified as the "limbic system," which is thought to mediate cognition and emotion; (4) circumventricular organs, which convey information from blood-borne chemosensory signals; and (5) the hypothalamus itself, in connections that may provide information about an animal's motivational state or that may integrate stress-specific signals from other input classes.

Input from the Brainstem

Catecholaminergic inputs from brainstem pathways are perhaps the best studied inputs to the brain–pituitary–adrenal axis (see Fig. 43.11). Catecholaminergic activity increases in response to stress and is thought to stimulate activity in the axis. Catecholaminergic activity is also instrumental in early activation of

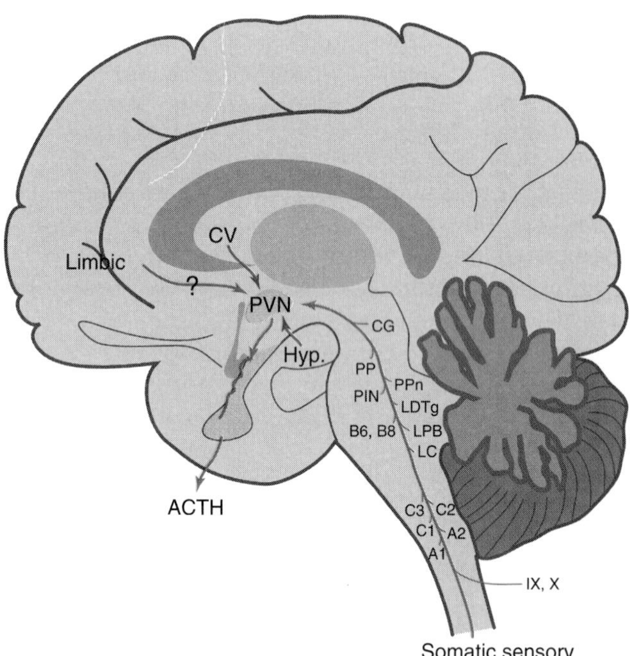

FIGURE 43.11 Afferent innervation of the paraventricular nucleus (PVN). Catecholaminergic inputs from brainstem A1, A2, C1, C2, C3, locus ceruleus (LC) regions convey visceral information. Other ascending inputs from tegmental nuclei (PPn, LDTg), serotonergic nuclei (B6, B7, B8), parabrachial nucleus (LPB), central gray (CG), and peripeduncular area (PP, PIN) provide somatic and specialized sensory information. Cognitive and emotional information is conveyed by limbic structures. Blood-borne chemosensory information is relayed via circumventricular organs (CV). Intrahypothalamic innervation (Hyp.) of the PVN provides motivational and integrative information from other systems.

the axis in response to stress. However, the precise site(s) of action and mechanism of receptor response remain unknown.

Noradrenergic projections originate in the caudal part of the nucleus of the solitary tract, or A2 cell group, and to some extent in the A1 cell group of the ventrolateral medulla. Noradrenergic projections also arise from the locus ceruleus. Adrenergic projections involve the C2 group of the NTS, the C1 group of the ventrolateral medulla, and the C3 group of the dorsomedial medulla. Because the cells of origin of many of these ascending projections appear to carry afferent information relayed through cranial nerves X and XI, such pathways are thought to convey visceral or interoceptive signals to the PVN. Several other neuropeptides, including galanin, substance P, and neuropeptide Y, colocalize with some of these projections, and their potential roles are likely important for regulation of the brain–pituitary–adrenal axis.

Because of morphologic evidence, serotonergic input to CRH neurons of the PVN is thought to originate from midbrain raphe cell groups. Several studies have suggested that these pathways stimulate activity in the brain–pituitary–adrenal axis, but the conclusion is controversial. Cell groups containing serotonin project diffusely throughout the neuraxis, but apparently the effect of serotonin in stress-induced activation of the brain–pituitary–adrenal axis may depend on the nature of the stressor. In turn, serotonergic systems, particularly specific subtypes of serotonin receptors, are exquisitely sensitive to glucocorticoid regulation.[63] Thus, there is constant interplay between activating and inhibitory mechanisms of this axis.

Other Ascending Inputs

Neural pathways by which sensory stimuli might affect the brain–pituitary–adrenal axis remain poorly understood, because the PVN apparently lacks direct inputs from cortical or thalamic regions associated with sensory functions. Portions of the midbrain periaqueductal gray and pontine central gray appear positioned to relay sensory, possibly including nociceptive, stimuli.[62] Some caudal thalamic sites (e.g., peripeduncular and posterior intralaminar nuclei) are similarly positioned to relay auditory stimuli. In addition, two largely cholinergic brainstem regions, the laterodorsal tegmental nucleus and the pedunculopontine nucleus, have been suggested to convey visual and auditory input to the PVN and somatosensory input from the spinal cord. Although the roles of many of these structures remain to be demonstrated, the results of activity-based mapping experiments are consistent with these structures mediating the responses to several forms of stress.

Limbic Inputs

Pathways by which portions of the prefrontal cortex, septum, amygdala, and hippocampus (all part of the traditional limbic system) may mediate cognitive, emotional, or affective influences on the brain–pituitary–adrenal axis remain unclear; anatomic studies suggest that these structures each lack significant direct projections to the PVN. A number of forebrain areas, most notably the bed nuclei of the stria terminalis and several sites in the hypothalamus, project directly to the PVN and have been proposed as relay sites for inputs from the limbic system. However, the extent to which such multisynaptic circuits might be involved in stress activation or in mediation of glucocorticoid negative feedback remains an important unresolved issue concerning the organization of stress-related pathways.

Circumventricular Organ Inputs

Circumventricular organs (e.g., subfornical organ and vascular organ of the lamina terminalis) sense blood-borne signals (e.g., angiotensin II) and transmit the information through neural projections to the PVN. The main targets within the PVN are magnocellular neurons involved in maintenance of water balance, although stress-related parvicellular neurons also appear affected. GABA and angiotensin II are prominent neurotransmitters in these projections.

Hypothalamic Inputs

Because of the anatomical complexity and numerous functional affiliations of the hypothalamus, hypothalamic afferents to the PVN are perhaps the least well understood of afferents affecting the brain–pituitary–adrenal axis. Based on retrograde tracing data, virtually all regions of the hypothalamus, except the medial and lateral mammillary nuclei and the supraoptic nucleus, contain some neurons that project to the PVN. Anterograde tracing has helped determine the relative contributions of various hypothalamic regions to innervation of the PVN, but the potential for direct or indirect regulation by the hypothalamus remains. For example, GABAergic innervation is thought to originate from the dorsomedial hypothalamic nucleus and from several hypothalamic sources adjacent to the PVN. Hypothalamic inputs are also likely to be involved in opioidergic input to the PVN. For example, the arcuate nucleus appears to be the source of a projection containing ACTH and β-endorphin and projections containing NPY and dopamine.

The functional roles of these pathways remain to be clarified. Whether different stressors engage completely different pathways that converge only at the PVN is not known; some brain structures might be shared by many stressors and help code a stimulus as stressful. In addition, whether there is a hierarchy among the many afferents to the PVN is not known. A visceral input activating catecholaminergic afferents might take precedence over a motivational input relayed locally from the hypothalamus. Also, how the severity of a stress, or the extent of deviation from equilibrium, is conveyed is unclear. Functional mapping (e.g., monitoring activation by following expression of immediate-early genes such as c-*fos*) combined with anatomical identification[64] reveals that some brain structures (e.g., cortex and PVN) are activated by most stressors, such as noise, pain, swimming, and immune challenges. Other structures are selectively activated to encode the sensory modality that has been challenged (e.g., auditory pathways for a startle response) or to encode subtle aspects of the stressor (e.g., the dominant or subordinate status of an animal in an aggressive interaction).

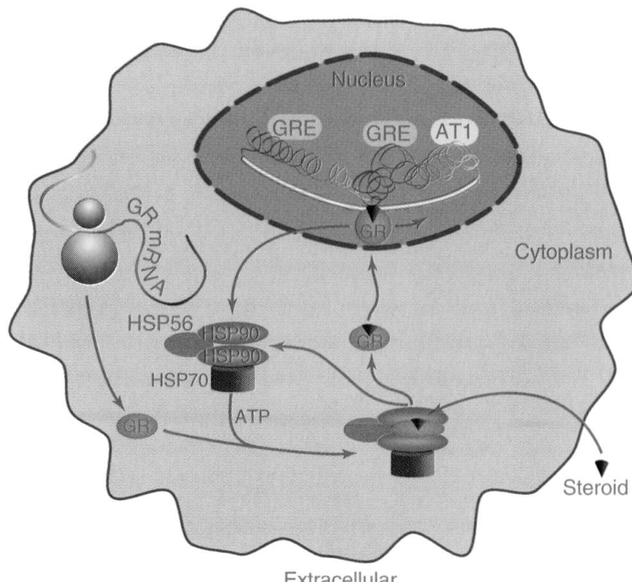

FIGURE 43.12 Model of glucocorticoid receptor (GR) function. Once translated in the cytoplasm, GR is quickly stabilized by a complex including many heat-shock protein (HSP) subtypes. Circulating steroids, including corticosteroids, easily cross cell membranes to access the cytoplasm from vasculature and bind to GR. Activation of GR by steroid binding induces its separation from the HSP complex and its translocation to the nucleus, where it interacts with DNA to activate or inhibit gene transcription.

Negative Feedback by Glucocorticoids Terminates the Stress Response

Feedback regulation of the brain–pituitary–adrenal axis is thought to occur mainly through negative feedback of glucocorticoids on pituitary, hypothalamic, and suprahypothalamic sites. In addition to differences in their sites of action, feedback through these loops differs in timing and mechanism.[65]

Removal of the adrenal, and hence of glucocorticoids, removes the negative feedback effects of these steroids. In this situation, with the brain–pituitary–adrenal axis unchecked by the restraining effects of glucocorticoids, concentrations of CRH and AVP mRNA in the mpPVN increase. In the neighboring magnocellular neurons of the PVN, concentrations of AVP mRNA are unchanged, demonstrating that normal glucocorticoid feedback is target-specific.[66] The increased expression of CRH and AVP leads to their increased release from the hypothalamus and thus to enhanced secretion of ACTH from the anterior pituitary. A 10-fold increase in POMC, the precursor of ACTH, is attributed to increased activation by CRH and to loss of direct negative feedback of glucocorticoids on the pituitary. These effects are due to lack of glucocorticoids, because treatment with exogenous corticosteroids, such as dexamethasone, can completely reverse the effects of adrenalectomy. In addition, administration of corticosteroids to intact animals leads to decreases in the expression (and secretion) of pituitary POMC and parvicellular AVP and CRH.

The mineralocorticoid receptor (MR) and the glucocorticoid receptor in the brain specifically recognize the adrenal corticosteroids (cortisol in human, corticosterone in rat). Both MR and GR are highly expressed in hippocampal pyramidal cells and in dentate gyrus granule cells.[67,68] In addition, GR is present throughout the neuraxis, including the CRH-expressing cells of the PVN.

The mineralocorticoid receptor, which in the kidneys recognizes aldosterone, also recognizes glucocorticoids in the brain. In fact, in the brain MR has an affinity for natural glucocorticoids higher than GR (The K_d of GR for corticosterone is approximately 5 n*M*, whereas the K_d of MR for corticosterone is about 0.5 n*M*). Beyond this difference in affinity, the two receptors have overlapping but distinguishable pharmacological profiles. Most notably, GR recognizes the synthetic glucocorticoid dexamethasone, and MR has a higher affinity for aldosterone.

MR and GR are members of a superfamily of receptors that act as ligand-regulated transacting factors. In each case, the receptor protein resides in the cytoplasm in a complex containing heat-shock proteins, which fold the receptor into the appropriate configuration for recognizing corticosteroid ligands (Fig. 43.12). Upon steroid binding, the receptor moves to the nucleus of the cell and interacts with specific hormone recognition (or response) elements (HRE) on the DNA, thereby changing transcription rates.

Our understanding of gene regulation by MR is considerably more limited than that for GR. MR is often seen as a low-threshold receptor, with high affinity but low capacity. One view is that MRs simply serve as more sensitive detectors of corticosteroid effects, but detectors with limited efficacy. According to this view, GR would take over where MR has left off, effecting much more profound changes in regulating transcription.[69] However, MR may act as an antagonist of GR in certain cases.[70,71]

Steroid receptors are thought to mediate negative feedback by inhibiting transcription of the relevant genes, CRH and POMC, in *genomic feedback*. This inhibitory mechanism is thought to involve protein–protein interactions, with complexes of transacting factors binding to complex DNA response elements. Some of these interactions would result in the prevention of activation induced by other transacting factors. For example, complexes could block the effects of the immediate-early genes c-*fos* and c-*jun*. The sequence of events appears to be important in determining whether GR will have stimulatory or inhibitory effects on a target gene; for example, genes previously interacting with c-*fos* and c-*jun* may be suppressed, whereas genes without such interactions may be activated.[72]

Although changes in transcription can occur promptly in response to stress or exogenous steroids,[52] the impact of these changes depends on the size of the mRNA pool. Thus, for POMC, which has a large mRNA pool, glucocorticoid-induced changes take hours to days for full effect.[73] Genomic feedback establishes the range of responsiveness to stress by altering the capacity of the brain–pituitary–adrenal axis.

Other, more rapid mechanisms of steroid negative feedback operate on a shorter time frame and regulate moment-to-moment activation and termination of stress responses. After the concentration of circulating glucocorticoids has risen in response to a stress, these mechanisms promptly terminate release of ACTH when the stressor is removed. This *fast feedback* establishes the magnitude and duration of the glucocorticoid response to stress. Fast feedback appears to depend on the rate of rise of circulating glucocorticoid concentration rather than on the absolute concentration.[61,65] Neuronal, rather than gene regulatory, events are thought to be involved in this feedback, but its mechanism remains unclear.

Intermediate feedback operates with a time course between that of genomic feedback and fast feedback and is thought to involve gene regulatory and other mechanisms.

Neuronal Circuits Participate in Negative Feedback

As discussed, CRH neurons of the PVN contain steroid receptors, and glucocorticoids inhibit transcription of CRH and AVP genes through genomic feedback. However, numerous other brain regions also express steroid receptors. These regions may exert negative feedback on the brain–pituitary–adrenal axis through projections to the PVN. Alternatively, or in addition, these regions could activate neuronal circuits that are ultimately inhibitory to the brain–pituitary–adrenal axis.

The hippocampus is the region of the brain richest in both types of corticosteroid receptors. Lesions of the hippocampus raise resting levels of glucocorticoids and stress-induced responses in glucocorticoid secretion.[74,75] In addition, hippocampal lesions prevent steroid-induced downregulation of the synthesis and release of CRH and AVP. They also lead to increases in the concentrations of CRH and AVP mRNAs and sustained increases in the levels of circulating glucocorticoids.[76,77] Thus, the hippocampus plays a role in lowering the basal tone of the hypothalamus–pituitary–adrenal axis. Furthermore, this control of basal tone is mediated by glucocorticoids.

Several hippocampal sites participate in controlling basal CRH expression, but only some hippocampal sites participate in terminating the stress response.[76] Lesion of these sites results in patterns of stress response in which activation is normal but termination is slowed. A similar pattern is seen in aged animals. Whether this effect is mediated by glucocorticoid receptors or by neurotransmitters and other modulators is not clear.

Anatomical studies suggest that multiple redundant pathways connect the hippocampus to the PVN through various relay points.[78] Some of these relays, such as the bed nuclei of the stria terminalis, are anatomically and functionally linked to the PVN. Studies of the hippocampus suggest that this structure plays a key role in inhibiting the basal tone of the brain–pituitary–adrenal axis. This inhibition occurs in part because the hippocampus is permissive for steroid negative feedback controlling expression of CRH. The hippocampus also appears to control termination of the stress response, but the roles of steroids and their receptors in this function are not known. All these effects mediated by the hippocampus may oscillate with the diurnal rhythm of the axis, with a greater impact occurring at the nadir than at the peak. We have focused on the hippocampus because of its rich endowment of glucocorticoid receptors, but several structures may play a role in controlling basal tone and termination of the stress response of the brain–pituitary–adrenal axis.

Chronic Glucocorticoid Excess Damages Some Neurons

The brain, especially the hippocampus, is exquisitely sensitive to circulating steroids. Chronic administration of corticosteroids changes the morphology of field CA3 cells' dendrites. These changes probably herald cell degeneration[79] and may result in cell death.[80] In addition, exposure to high concentrations of circulating steroids may increase loss of hippocampal neurons that have endured insults such as transient ischemia.[81] The mechanism of cell death has been proposed to involve inhibition of glucose transport[82] and, ultimately, failure to sequester calcium mobilized by excitatory amino acids. Interestingly, repeated stress can cause morphological changes in field CA3, and the effect can be blocked by phenytoin, which interferes with excitatory amino acid transmission.[83]

Although an excess of glucocorticoids damages some cells, other cells are damaged by a lack of glucocorticoids. Granule cells of the dentate gyrus appear to require glucocorticoids; there is dramatic loss of these cells after adrenalectomy.[84] In addition, in the rat dentate gyrus, unusual because neurogenesis occurs well into adulthood, adrenal steroids regulate the birth, death, and possibly migration of cells.[85] Thus, in adult rats, adrenalectomy increases the death of granule cells and the birth of neurons and glia.[86] Both effects can be reversed by exogenous steroids.[87]

Brain–Pituitary–Adrenal Function Changes Developmentally

In most mammals studied, the adrenal gland is the earliest maturing component of the brain–pituitary–adrenal axis. In humans, the primordium of the adrenal cortex appears at 20 to 25 days of gestation. POMC-containing cells of the anterior pituitary appear 7 to 8 weeks into gestation and begin to release ACTH almost immediately. Feedback inhibition of ACTH secretion by circulating glucocorticoids can be observed at midgestation. Structural signs of the interface between the pituitary and hypothalamus, via the median eminence and portal blood system, are evident at 7 to 8 weeks, functional by week 20, and resemble the adult interface after 7 months of gestation. At the level of the paraventricular nucleus of the hypothalamus, signs of CRH-containing neurons can be observed at the 16th gestational week. ACTH secretion is relatively independent of the hypothalamus prior to midgestation, but becomes dependent on hypothalamic factors thereafter. The neural pathways innervating the hypothalamus are much slower to develop, and they mature long after birth. Only after birth does the characteristic diurnal rhythm of plasma corticosterone appear. In humans, this rhythm reaches adultlike patterns at approximately 6 months of age.

Circulating corticosteroids play an important role in the developing fetus. However, because maternal corticosteroids easily cross the placenta, fetuses with abnormal endogenous corticosteroids usually develop relatively normally *in utero*. During fetal development, corticosteroids stimulate many enzymes in the liver, intestine, pancreas, lungs, and adrenal medulla. At birth, the brain–pituitary–adrenal axis undergoes a series of alterations. Corticosteroid levels are relatively high in the perinatal period of many mammals, including humans, presumably as a response to the stress of parturition.

Prenatal stress generally produces significant physical and behavioral alterations in later life, which may or may not be attributable to concomitant changes in brain–pituitary–adrenal axis functions. The impact of a stressor on offspring is a function of the degree of control that the mother has over a stressful situation. In some of the best controlled human studies, pregnant women undergoing uncontrollable stress have higher incidences of babies with physical, developmental, and behavioral problems (underweight, eczema, bronchitis and other respiratory problems, delay in ability to walk and speak, irritability, antisocial behavior). Prenatally stressed rats have increased basal levels of corticosterone and increased stress-induced corticosterone release. Sex is important in that the effects of prenatal stress are often greater in female offspring.

In contrast to prenatal stress, mild neonatal stress in rats (daily, short periods of separation from their mother) during the first 2 to 3 weeks after birth produces adult animals that generally present a cluster of behaviors characterized as less anxious, with reduced secretion of corticosterone to a variety of stress situations.[88] Interestingly, this type of neonatal stress reverses the behavioral effects induced by prenatal stress.

Although all elements of the brain–pituitary–adrenal axis are in place by midgestation, premature babies (less than 30-weeks gestation) show an abnormally low secretion of cortisol in response to stress. A similar hyporesponsive period is observed during the first 2 weeks of postnatal life in rats,[89,90] during the same developmental stage of the previously described premature human babies. The hyporesponsive period appears to be determined, in part, by the immaturity of afferent neural connections to the hypothalamus. In rats, adultlike brain–pituitary–adrenal axis responsiveness to stress emerges approximately 4 weeks after birth.

Changes occur in the aging brain–pituitary–adrenal axis, but there is a great deal of variation among individuals. In rats, the extent of brain–pituitary–adrenal dysregulation correlates with the extent of disruption in spatial memory. In some healthy aged humans, as well as in younger people with psychiatric disturbances such as major depression, corticosteroid dysregulation occurs and may be linked to changes in memory. A significant proportion of aged animals and humans (>75 years) have delayed recovery to basal corticosteroid levels after some stress situations.[91–94] Delayed return to basal levels suggests decreased sensitivity of corticosteroid feedback inhibition upon the brain–pituitary–adrenal axis. One suggested mechanism is based on the repeated finding of decreased corticoid receptor (both MR and GR) binding and mRNA levels in the hippocampus of aged animals,[95–98] with a corresponding loss of pyramidal cells in the hippocampus.[99,100] Because the hippocampus has been implicated in corticosteroid negative feedback, one hypothesis is that elevated circulating corticoids lead to hippocampal neurotoxicity,[80,101] generating a positive loop involving reduced feedback inhibition and higher corticosteroid release.[101]

Additional changes due to aging occur at almost every level of the brain–pituitary–adrenal axis; however, most of these changes are mutually compensatory, with upregulation of one element resulting in downregulation of the subsequent element. Thus, the net effect in many cases is that basal rhythm and stress responsiveness in aged animals (and humans) appears completely normal or shows dysregulation only in the rate of termination.[102]

Stress Influences Learning and Memory

A great deal of attention has focused on understanding the influence of stress on learning and memory. This interest may arise from the observation that the hippocampus, rich in corticosteroid receptors, plays a critical role in some spatial learning and memory tasks. Evidence of the simultaneous effect of aging on stress responsiveness and cognitive function has helped focus attention on this functional and anatomical connection. In addition, it is well known that learning requires arousal and attention, which stress clearly commands. Furthermore, a great deal of learning is motivated by negative, or aversive, stimuli, which are almost by definition stressful. Thus, stress is likely to play a role in the motivational aspects of learning and in its cognitive aspects.

Stress Hormones

The role of pituitary and adrenal hormones has been studied mainly in animals learning to make (active) or withhold (passive) specific responses to avoid punishment or gain reinforcement (instrumental conditioning). In general, hormones from the brain–pituitary–adrenal axis (ACTH, vasopressin) injected prior to or shortly after a learning experience strengthen the *memory* of instrumental responses.[103–106] Many hormonal influences are initiated peripherally, but some effects are mediated centrally.[103,107]

Acute Stress

A research strategy looking more broadly at the effects of stress on learning revealed that acute, inescapable stress interferes with the ability of animals and humans to learn subsequent instrumental responses.[108–112] Importantly, this effect is abolished when the subjects have some control over the duration or termination of the stressor. One cognitive function likely modified by inescapable stress is tied to attention.[111] When shifts in attention are minimized, inescapable stress no longer interferes with instrumental conditioning and can even improve learning.[113–115]

Chronic Stress

Interest in the effects of chronic stress on learning stemmed mainly from the correlation between reduced hippocampal activity and spatial learning deficits in aged rats.[100,116–118] Because aged animals and chronically stressed younger animals can display elevated corticosteroid levels, aging and chronic stress were suspected to lead to similar, hippocampus-dependent learning deficits, which have indeed been proven experimentally.[119–122] Some of the deficits in spatial learning can be mimicked by alteration of glucocorticoid receptor (GR), but not mineralocorticoid receptor (MR) functions in the hippocampus.[123,124] Hippocampal MRs affect the behavioral strategies used by animals to master spatial learning.[125] In general, although GR and MR work together in neuroendocrine regulation, they often differently and sometimes antagonistically modulate complex functions such as learning and memory.

The Brain–Pituitary–Adrenal Axis Is Part of the Stress Concept

In an effort to place the brain–pituitary–adrenal axis into an integrated view of brain function, in this section we speculate on the brain aspects of stress according to anatomical, behavioral, and clinical considerations.

Stress is typically operationally defined as the body's response to external stimuli that evoke a fight-

or-flight response. The central conceptual issue is: How is a psychological stimulus defined, neuronally, as stressful?

Psychologists agree that the perception of psychological stress is closely tied to control and coping. Thus, a stimulus will be perceived as a function of individuals' past experiences and their abilities to deal with the stressor, for example, controlling or viewing it as a challenge. Thus, we must view the neuronal process not only in terms of a throughput system that carries information to the CRH neurons of the PVN, but also as a comparator system that monitors the external and internal environments of the organism, compares them to past experience, and assigns an importance (**valence**) to them. Assigning valence is important for the organism to focus on the correct stimulus, discounting irrelevant stimuli and ending responses when the stimulus ceases to be important. The more complex an organism, the more it responds to stimuli with flexible, rather than preprogrammed, behavior and the more critical this comparator function becomes. For example, in bacteria a comparator function may consist of proteins that detect changes in temperature or nutrients. In mammals, however, a comparator function has a role in the decision-making process—what to attend to, what to ignore, and for how long.

If we broaden our view, we see that this monitoring system can encompass the detection not only of negative events but of positive events that require an organism's full attention and take precedence over other stimuli. Such positive events can, in fact, be associated with glucocorticoid secretion. In addition, we can conceive of the interplay of stress and learning and memory as truly fundamental to the nature of both stress and learning rather than as a secondary interaction. Viewed in this manner, the stress system is *an active monitoring system* that constantly compares current events to past experience, interprets the relevance (salience) of the events to the survival of the organism, assigns the events a valence (positive or negative), determines the organisms's ability to cope, and recruits physiological, endocrine, and motor mechanisms to respond as needed. Learning and memory are processes that are also aimed at coping by acquiring and storing key information for survival. Much of our learning is emotional, as opposed to the more "intellectual" learning of less emotionally laden material, such as calculus. We can conceive of stress mechanisms as fundamental to such emotional learning.

Our conceptualization requires inclusion of a number of neuronal elements that may not appear an obvious part of the brain–pituitary–adrenal axis in more hard-wired views of stress responsiveness. In addition to primary detectors of deviations from equilibrium (e.g., NST), we include higher structures involved in coding emotions (e.g., amygdala), interpreting stimuli (e.g., neocortex), and comparing current stimuli to past events (e.g., hippocampus and neocortex). In this ongoing monitoring process, the hippocampus determines the salience of stimuli and participates in the comparator function, according to its proposed role in mediating short-term memory and spatial learning. The hippocampus not only influences an organism's perception of stressors, but also monitors the current stress status of that organism. Thus, the glucocorticoid receptors within the hippocampus may have little to do with steroid feedback in the classical sense of terminating a stress response; instead, they may serve to keep the hippocampus apprised of stress conditions as it sorts and codes novel information.

What would happen if this system, involving the interplay of several circuits, is disrupted? One might imagine that stress responses might be initiated in response to the "wrong" stimulus. In other words, a stimulus might be coded as stressful despite not being perceived as such by most individuals or by that same individual at other times. One might also imagine that appropriate stress responses might not be terminated in a timely manner and that basic functions (e.g., eating, sleeping, sexual activity), which are often superseded by stress responses, become dysregulated. In fact, such phenomena are observed in major mood disorders. Mood disorders, particularly major depression, can lead to chronic dysregulation of the brain–pituitary–adrenal axis. In our view of stress, a disruption in the hippocampal and neocortical aspects of the axis can participate in precipitation and maintenance of depressive episodes. Possibly the most dramatic example of the powerful interplay among stress, memory, and emotions is posttraumatic stress syndrome (PTSD), in which a single, major, uncontrolled stressor produces extremely powerful emotional learning and can disrupt behavior for years thereafter.

The view we have put forward moves away from stress as something "bad" or unpleasant. It is more consistent with the idea that the system has a basal tone and a daily rhythm that is tied to energy expenditure. In other words, the brain–pituitary–adrenal axis is not simply an alarm system but a constant monitor keeping us functioning in the most optimal manner.

Summary

The brain–pituitary–adrenal axis mediates the organism's responses to the environmental requirements of daily living as well as the ability to adapt to unexpected stressful challenges. The axis consists of the paraventricular hypothalamic neurons, which secrete corticotropin-releasing hormone into the pituitary portal axis to activate secretion of adrenocorticotropin hormone from anterior pituitary corticotropes, and the corticosteroid-secreting cells of the adrenal cortex. In addition, hypothalamic vasopressin can synergize with CRH to drive corticotropes, and higher order afferents in emotion- and memory-related circuits can regulate the CRH neurons. The axis fluctuates in activity throughout the day, with the peak in activity just before arousal from sleep and the nadir in the evening. When steroid levels rise after axis activation, negative feedback is exerted at the pituitary, hypothalamic, and suprahypothalamic levels. Chronic elevation of corticosteroid secretion may be deleterious to hippocampal neurons. Stress can influence neuronal circuits underlying memory and learning, enabling an organism to profit from stressful experiences. The greater HPA stress axis serves as an important ongoing comparative monitor of the demands of the environment.

References

1. Snyder, P. J., and Utiger, R. D. (1973). Repetitive administration of thyrotropin-releasing hormone results in small elevations of serum thyroid hormones and in marked inhibition of thyrotropin response. *J Clin Invest* **52:** 2305–2312.
2. Saberi, M., and Utiger, R. D. (1975). Augmentation of thyrotropin responses to thyrotropin-releasing hormone following small decreases in serum thyroid hormone concentrations. *J. Clin. Endocrinol. Metabol.* **40:** 432–441.
3. Reichlin, S. (1989). TRH: Historical aspects. *Ann. N. Y. Acad. Sci.* **553:** 1–6.
4. Morley, J. E. (1981). Neuroendocrine control of thyrotropin secretion. *Endocr. Rev.* **2:** 396–436.
5. Jackson, I. M. D., Lechan, R. M., and Lee, S. L. (1990). TRH prohormone: Biosynthesis, anatomic distribution, and processing. *Front. Neuroendocrinol.* **11:** 267–312.
6. Yamada, M., Radovick, S., Wondisford, F. E., Nakayama, Y., Weintraub, B. D., and Wilber, J. F. (1990). Cloning and structure of human genomic DNA and hypothalamic cDNA encoding human preprothyrotropin-releasing hormone. *Mol. Endocrinol.* **4:** 551–556.
7. Lechan, R. M., and Toni, R. (1992). Thyrotropin-releasing hormone neuronal systems in the central nervous system. In *Neuroendocrinology* (C. B. Nemeroff, ed.) pp. 279–330. CRC Press, Boca Raton, FL.
8. Toni, T., and Lechan, R. M. (1993). Neuroendocrine regulation of thyrotropin-releasing hormone (TRH) in the tuberoinfundibular system. *J. Endocrinologic Investigation* **16:** 715–753.
9. Fliers, E., Noppen, N. W. A. M., Wiersinga, W. M., Visser, T. J., and Swaab, D. K. (1994). Distribution of thyrotropin-releasing hormone (TRH)-containing cells and fibers in the human hypothalamus. *J. Comp. Neurol.* **350:** 311–323.

9a. Dussault, J. H., and Ruel, J. (1987). Thyroid hormones and brain development. *Annual Review of Physiology* **49:** 321–334.

9b. Legrand, J. (1979). Morphogenetic action of thyroid hormones. *Trends Neurosci.* **2:** 234–236.

9c. Ruiz-Marcos, A., Salas, J., Sanchez-Toscano, F., Morreale de Escobar, F., and Morreale de Escobar G. (1983). Effect of neonatal and adult-onset hypothyroidism on pyramidal cells of the rat auditory cortex. *Brain Res.* **162:** 315–329.

10. Greer, M. A. (1957). Studies on the influence of the central nervous system on anterior pituitary function. *Rec. Prog. Horm. Res.* **13:** 67–104.
11. Reichlin, S. (1986). Neural functions of TRH. *Acta. Endocrinol.* **112**(Suppl. 276): 21–33.
12. Evans, R. M. (1988). The steroid and thyroid hormone receptor family. *Science* **240:** 889–895.
13. Lechan, R. M., Qi, Y., Jackson, I. M. D., and Mahdavi, V. (1994). Identification of thyroid hormone receptor isoforms in thyrotropin-releasing hormone neurons of the hypothalamic paraventricular nucleus. *Endocrinology* **135:** 92–100.
14. Berry, M. J., and Larsen, P. R. (1991). The molecular cloning of type I iodothyronine deiodinase: New insights into thyroid hormone action. *Thyroid Today* **XIV,** No. 4.
15. Riskind, P. N., Kolodny, J. M., and Larsen, P. R. (1987). The regional distribution of type II 5′-monodeiodinase in euthyroid and hypothyroid rats. *Brain Res.* **420:** 194–198.
16. Lechan, R. M., and Kakucska, I. (1992). Feedback regulation of thyrotropin-releasing hormone gene expression by thyroid hormone in the hypothalamic paraventricular nucleus. In *Functional Anatomy of the Neuroendocrine Hypothalamus,* pp. 144–164. Wiley, Chichester.
17. Schreiber, G., Aldred, A. R., Jaworowski, A., Nilsson, C., Achen, M. G., and Segal, M. B. (1990). Thyroxine transport from blood to brain via transthyrein synthesis in choroid plexus. *Am. J. Physiol.* **258:** R338–R345.
18. Reichlin, S. (1966). Control of thyrotropic hormone secretion. In *Neuroendocrinology,* (L. Martini and W. F. Ganong, eds.) pp. 445–536. Academic Press, NY.
19. Gershengorn, M. C. (1989). Mechanism of signal transduction by TRH, *Ann. N. Y. Acad. Sci.* **553:** 191–204.
20. Hinkle, P. M. (1989). Pituitary TRH receptors. *Ann. N. Y. Acad. Sci.* **553:** 176–187.
21. Straub, R. E., Frech, G. C., Joho, R. H., and Gershengorn, M. C. (1990). Expression cloning of a cDNA encoding the mouse pituitary thyrotropin-releasing hormone receptor. *Proc. Natl. Acad. Sci. U.S.A.* **87:** 9514–9518.
22. Kimura, N., Arai, K., Sahara, Y., Suzuki, H., and Kimura, N. (1994). Estradiol transcriptionally and posttranscriptionally upregulates thyrotropin-releasing hormone receptor messenger ribonucleic acid in rat pituitary cells. *Endocrinology* **134:** 432–440.
23. Han, B., and Tashjian, A. H., Jr. (1995). Identification of ASN289 in the thyrotropin-releasing hormone receptor as a binding site for pGlu of TRH as determined by complementary modifications in the ligand and receptor: A new model for TRH binding. *Abstracts of the 77th Annual Meeting of the Endocrine Society,* p. 77.
24. Yamada, M., Monden, T., Satoh, T., Iizuka, M., Murakami, M., Iriuchijima, T., and Mori, M. (1992). Differential regulation of thyrotropin-releasing hormone receptor mRNA levels by thyroid hormone *in vivo* and *in vitro* (GH3 cells). *Biochem. Biophys. Res. Commun.* **184:** 367–372.
25. Brabant, G., Prank, K., Ranft, U., Schuermeyer, T. H., Wagner, T. O. F., Hauser, H., Kummer, B., Feistner, H., Hesch, R. D., and von zur Muhlen, A. (1990). Physiological regulation of circadian and pulsatile thyrotropin secretion in normal man and woman. *J. Clin Endocrinol. Metabol.* **70:** 403–409.
26. Allan, J. S., and Czeisler, C. A. (1994). Persistence of the circadian thyrotropin rhythm under constant conditions and after light-induced shifts of circadian phase. *J. Clin. Endocrinol. and Metabol.* **79:** 508–512.
27. Dahl, G. E., Evans, N. P., Thrun, L. A., and Karsch, F. J. (1994). A central negative feedback action of thyroid hormones on

thyrotropin-releasing hormone secretion. *Endocrinology* **135:** 2392–2397.

28. Deleted.
29. Cannon, W. B., and Fitz, R. (1916). Further observations on over-activity of the cervical sympathetic. *Am. J. Physiol.* **40:** 126.
30. Ahren, B. (1986). Thyroid neuroendocrinology: Neural regulation of thyroid hormone secretion. *Endocr. Rev.* **7:** 149–155.
31. Grunditz, T., Hakanson, R., Sundler, F., and Uddman, R. (1988). Neuronal pathways to the rat thyroid revealed by retrograde tracing and immunocytochemistry. *Neuroscience* **24:** 321–335.
32. Melander, A., and Sundler, F. (1991). Autonomic nervous control: Adrenergic, cholinergic, and peptidergic regulation. In L. E. Braverman, R. D. Utiger, Werner's and Ingbar's *The Thyroid,* JB Lippincott Co, Philadelphia, pp. 313–321.
33. Krulich, L. (1982). Neurotransmitter control of thyrotropin secretion. *Neuroendocrinology* **35:** 139–147.
34. Zoeller, R. T., Kabeer, N., and Albers, E. (1990). Cold exposure elevates cellular levels of messenger ribonucleic acid encoding thyrotropin-releasing hormone in paraventricular nucleus despite elevated levels of thyroid hormones. *Endocrinology* **127:** 2955–2962.
35. Arancibia, S., Tapia-Arancibia, L., Assenmacher, I., and Astier, H. (1985). Direct evidence of short-term cold-induced TRH release in the median eminence of unanesthetized rats. *Neuroendocrinology* **37:** 225–228.
36. Scanlon, M. F., Weetman, A. P., Lewis, M., *et al.* (1980). Dopaminergic modulation of circadian thyrotropin rhythms and thyroid hormone levels in euthyroid subjects. *J. Clinical Endocrinology and Metabolism* **51:** 1251–1256.
37. Pang, X.-P., Hershman, J. M., Mirell, C. J., and Pekary, A. E. (1989). Impairment of hypothalamic-pituitary-thyroid function in rats treated with human recombinant tumor necrosis factor-α (Cachectin). *Endocrinology* **125:** 76–84.
38. Kakucska, I., Romero, L. I., Clark, B. D., Rondeel, J. M. M., Qi, Y., Alex, S., Emerson, C. H., and Lechan, R. M. (1994). Suppression of thyrotropin-releasing hormone gene expression by interleukin-1 beta in the rat: Implications for nonthyroidal illness. *Neuroendocrinology* **59:** 129–137.
39. Breeder, C. D., Dinarello, C. A., and Saper, C. B. (1988). Interleukin-1 immunoreactive innervation of the human hypothalamus. *Science* **240:** 321–324.
40. Seyle, H. (1936). A syndrome produced by diverse nocuous agents. *Nature* **138:** 22.
41. Seyle, H. (1956). *The Stress of Life.* McGraw-Hill, New York.
42. Vale, W., Spiess, J., Rivier, C., and Rivier, J. (1981). Characterization of a 41-residue ovine hypothalamic peptide that stimulates secretion of corticotropin and β-endorphin. *Science* **213:** 1394–1397.
43. Swanson, L. W., Sawchenko, P. E., Lind, R. W., and Rho, J.-H. (1988). The CRH motoneuron: Differential peptide regulation in neurons with possible synaptic, paracrine and endocrine outputs. *Ann. N.Y. Acad. Sci.* **512:** 12–23.
44. Chen, R., Lewis, K. A., Perrin, M. H., and Vale, W. W. (1993). Expression cloning of a human corticotropin-releasing factor receptor. *Proc. Natl. Acad. Sci. U.S.A* **90:** 8967–8970.
45. Morel, A., Lolait, S. J., and Brownstein, M. J. (1993). Molecular cloning and expression of V1a and V2 arginine vasopressin receptors. *Regul. Pep.* **45:** 53–59.
46. Antoni, F. A. (1986). Hypothalamic control of adrenocorticotropin secretion: Advances since the discovery of 41-residue CRF. *Endocr. Rev.* **7:** 351–378.
47. Haynes, R. C., and Berthet, L. (1957). Studies on the mechanisms of action of the adrenocorticotropic hormone. *J. Biol. Chem.* **225:** 115–124.
48. Nakanishi, S., Inoue, A., Kita, T., Nakamura, M., Chang, A. C. Y., Cohen, S. N., and Numa, S. (1979). Nucleotide sequence of cloned cDNA for bovine corticotropin-β-lipotropin precursor. *Nature* **278:** 423–427.
49. Eipper, B. A., and Mains, R. E. (1977). Peptide analysis of a glycoprotein form of adrenocorticotropic hormone. *J. Biol. Chem.* **252:** 8821–8832.
50. Roberts, J. L., and Herbert, E. (1977). Characterization of a common precursor to corticotropin and β-lipotropin: Cell-free synthesis of the precursor and identification of corticotropin peptides in the molecule. *Proc. Natl. Acad. Sci. U.S.A.* **74:** 4826–4830.
51. Akil, H., Watson, S. J., Young, E. A., Lewis, M. E., Kachaturian, H., and Walker, J. M. (1984). Endogenous opioids: Biology and function. *Annu. Rev. Neurosci.* **7:** 223–255.
52. Roberts, J. L., Lundbland, J. R., Eberwine, J. H., Fremeau, R. T., Salton, S. R., and Blum, M. (1987). Hormonal regulation of POMC expression in pituitary. *Ann. N.Y. Acad. Sci.* **512:** 275–285.
53. Bloom, F. E., Battenberg, E., Rossier, J., Ling, N., Leppaluoto, J., Vargo, T. M., and Guillemin, R. (1977). Endorphins are located in the intermediate and anterior lobes of the pituitary gland, not in the neurohypophysis. *Life Sci.* **20:** 43–48.
54. Watson, S. J., Akil, H., Richard, C. W., and Barchas, J. D. (1978). Evidence for two separate opiate peptide neuronal systems and the coexistence of beta-LPH, beta-endorphin and ACTH immunoreactivities in the same hypothalamic neurons. *Nature* **275:** 226–228.
55. Seidah, N. G., Gaspar, L., Mion, P., Marcinkiewicz, M., Mbikay, M., and Chretien, M. (1990). cDNA sequence of two distinct pituitary proteins homologous to Kex2 and furin gene products: tissue-specific mRNAs encoding candidates for pro-hormone processing proteinases. *DNA Cell Biol.* **9:** 415–424.
56. Smeekens, S. P., and Steiner, D. F. (1990). Identification of a human insulinoma cDNA encoding a novel mammalian protein structurally related to the yeast dibasic processing protease Kex2. *J. Biol. Chem.* **265:** 2997–3000.
57. Kwak, S. P., Morano, M. I., Young, E. A., Watson, S. J., and Akil, H. (1993). Diurnal CRH mRNA in the hypothalamus: Decreased expression in the evening is not dependent on endogenous glucocorticoids. *Neuroendocrinology* **57:** 96–105.
58. Kwak, S. P., Young, E. A., Morano, M. I., Watson, S. J., and Akil, H. (1992). Diurnal corticotropin-releasing hormone mRNA variation in the hypothalamus exhibits a rhythm distinct from that of plasma corticosterone. *Neuroendocrinology* **55:** 74–83.
59. Szafarczyk, A., Izart, G., Malaval, F., Nouguier-Soule, J., and Assenmacher, I. (1979). Effects of lesions of the suprachiasmatic nuclei and of p-chlorophenylalanine on the circadian rhythms of adrenocorticotrophic hormone and corticosterone in the plasma, and on locomotor activity of rats. *J. Endocrinol.* **83:** 1–16.
60. Krieger, D. T., and Hauser, H. (1978). Comparison of synchronization of circadian corticosteroid rhythms by photoperiod and food. *Proc. Natl. Acad. Sci. U.S.A.* **75:** 1577–1588.
61. Dallman, M. F., Akana, S. F., Scribner, K. A., Bradbury, M. J., Walker, C.-D., Strack, A. M., and Cascio, C. S. (1991). Stress, feedback and facilitation in the hypothalamo-pituitary-adrenal axis. *J. Neuroendocrinol.* **4,** 517–526.
62. Sawchenko, P. (1991). The final common path: Issues concerning the organization of central mechanisms controlling corticotropin secretion. In *Stress Neurobiology and Neuroendocrinology* (M. Brown, G. Koob, and C. Rivier, eds.), pp. 55–71. Marcel Dekker, New York.
63. Chalmers, D., Kwak, S., Mansour, A., Akil, H., and Watson, S. (1993). Corticosteroids regulate brain hippocampal 5-HT1A receptor mRNA expression. *J. Neurosci.* **13:** 914–923.
64. Cullinan, W. E., Herman, J. P., Battaglia, D. F., Akil, H., and

Watson, S. J. (1995). Pattern and time course of immediate early gene expression in rat following acute stress. *Neuroscience* **64:** 477–505.

65. Keller-Wood, M. E., and Dallman, M. F. (1984). Corticosteroid inhibition of ACTH secretion. *Endocr. Rev.* **5:** 1–24.
66. Sawchenko, P. R. (1987). Adrenalectomy-induced enhancement of CRF and vasopressin immunoreactivity in parvocellular neurosecretory neurons: Anatomic, peptide, and steroid specificity. *J. Neurosci.* **7:** 1093–1106.
67. Herman, J. P., Patel, P. D., Akil, H., and Watson, S. J. (1989). Localization and regulation of glucocorticoid and mineralocorticoid receptor messenger RNAs in the hippocampal formation of the rat. *Mol. Endocrinol.* **3:** 1886–1894.
68. Swanson, L. W., and Simmons, D. M. (1989). Differential steroid hormone and neural influences on peptide mRNA levels in CRH cells of the paraventricular nucleus: A hybridization histochemical study in the rat. *J. Comp. Neurol.* **285:** 413–435.
69. Ariza, J. L., Weinberger, C., Cerelli, G., Glaser, T. M., Handelin, B. M., Housman, D. E., and Evans, R. (1987). Cloning of the human mineralocorticoid receptor complementary DNA: Structural and functional kinship with the glucocorticoid receptor. *Science* **237:** 268–275.
70. Funder, J. W. (1993). Mineralocorticoids, glucocorticoids, receptors, and response elements. *Science* **259:** 1132–1133.
71. Pearce, D., and Yamamoto, K. R. (1993). Mineralocorticoid and glucocorticoid receptor activities distinguished by nonreceptor factors at a composite response element. *Science* **259:** 1161–1165.
72. Diamond, M. I., Miner, J. N., Yoshinaga, S. K., and Yamamoto, K. R. (1990). Transcription factor interactions: Selectors of positive or negative regulation from a single DNA element. *Science* **249:** 1266–1272.
73. Birnberg, N., Lissitsky, J., and Hinman, M. (1983). Glucocorticoids regulate proopiomelanocortin gene expression at the level of transcription and secretion. *Proc. Natl. Acad. Sci. U.S.A.* **80:** 6982–6986.
74. Feldman, S., and Conforti, N. (1980). Participation of the dorsal hippocampus in glucocorticoid negative feedback effect on adrenocortical activity. *Neuroendocrinology* **30:** 52–55.
75. Fischette, C. T., Komisaruk, B. R., and Edinger, H. M. (1980). Differential fornix ablations and the circadian rhythmicity of adrenal corticosteroid secretion. *Brain Res.* **195:** 373–387.
76. Herman, J. P., Cullinan, W. E., Young, E. A., Akil, H., and Watson, S. J. (1992). Selective forebrain fibertract lesions implicate ventral hippocampal structures in tonic regulation of paraventricular nucleus CRH and AVP mRNA expression. *Brain Res.* **592,** 228–238.
77. Herman, J. P., Schafer, M.K.-H., Young, E. A., Thompson, R., Douglass, J., Akil, H., and Watson, S. J. (1989). Evidence for hippocampal regulation of neuroendocrine neurons on the hypothalamo-pituitary-adrenocortical axis. *J. Neurosci.* **9:** 3072–3082.
78. Cullinan, W. E., Herman, J. P., and Watson, S. J. (1993). Ventral subicular interaction with the hypothalamic paraventricular nucleus: Evidence for a relay in the bed nucleus of the stria terminalis. *J. Comp. Neurol.* **332:** 1–20.
79. Woolley, C., Gould, E., and McEwen, B. (1990). Exposure to excess glucocorticoids alters dendritic morphology of adult hippocampal pyramidal neurons. *Brain Res.* **531:** 225–231.
80. Sapolsky, R. M., Krey, L. C., and McEwen, B. S. (1985). Prolonged glucocorticoid exposure reduces hippocampal neuron number: implications for aging. *J. Neurosci.* **5:** 1222–1227.
81. Sapolsky, R., and Pulsinelli, W. (1985). Glucocorticoids potentiate ischemic injury to neurons: therapeutic implications. *Science* **229:** 1397–1400.
82. Horner, H., and Sapolsky, R. (1988). Glucocorticoids decrease glucose transport in cultured hippocampal neurons. *Soc. Neurosci. Abstr.* **14:** 921.
83. Watanabe, Y., Gould, E., Cameron, H., Daniels, D., and McEwen, B. (1992). Phenytoin prevents stress- and corticosterone-induced atrophy of CA3 pyramidal neurons. *Hippocampus* **2**(4): 431–435.
84. Sloviter, R., Valiquette, G., Abrams, G., Ronk, E., Sollas, A., Paul, L., and Neubort, S. (1989). Selective loss of hippocampal granule cells in the mature rat brain after adrenalectomy. *Science* **243:** 535–538.
85. Gould, E. (1994). The effects of adrenal steroids and excitatory input on neuronal birth and survival. *Ann. N.Y. Acad. Sci.* **743:** 73–92.
86. Gould, E., Cameron, H., Daniels, D., Woolley, C., and McEwen, B. (1992). Adrenal hormones suppress cell division in the adult rat dentate gyrus. *J. Neurosci.* **12**(9): 3642–3650.
87. Cameron, H., and Gould, E. (1994). Adult neurogenesis is regulated by adrenal steroids in the dentate gyrus. *Neuroscience* **61**(2): 203–209.
88. Meaney, M., Bhatnagar, S., Larocque, S., McCormick, C., Shanks, N., Sharma, S., Smythe, J., Viau, V., and Plotsky, P. (1993). Individual differences in the hypothalamic-pituitary-adrenal stress response and the hypothalamic CRF system. *Ann. N.Y. Acad. Sci.* **697:** 70–85.
89. Meaney, M., Aitken, D., von Berkel, C., Bhatnagar, S., and Sapolsky, R. (1988). Effect of neonatal handling on age-related impairments associated with the hippocampus. *Science* **239:** 766–768.
90. Sapolsky, R., and Meaney, M. (1986). Maturation of the adrenocortical stress response: Neuroendocrine control mechanisms and the stress hyporesponsive period. *Brain Res. Rev.* **11:** 65–76.
91. Brett, L., Chong, G., Coyle, S., and Levine, S. (1981). The pituitary-adrenal response to novel stimulation and ether stress in young and aged rats. *Neurobiol. Aging* **4:** 133–138.
92. Morano, M., Vazquez, D., and Akil, H. (1994). The role of the hippocampal mineralocorticoid and glucocorticoid receptors in the hypothalamo-pituitary-adrenal axis of the aged Fisher rat. *Mol. Cell. Neurosci.* **5:** 400–412.
93. Odio, M., and Brodish, A. (1989). Age-related adaptation of pituitary-adrenocortical responses to stress. *Neuroendocrinology* **49:** 382–388.
94. Sapolsky, R. (1992). *Stress, the Aging Brain, and the Mechanisms of Neuron Death.* MIT Press, Cambridge, MA.
95. Meaney, M. J., Aitken, D. H., Bhatnagar, S., VanBerkel, C., and Sapolsky, R. M. (1988). Postnatal handling attenuates neuroendocrine, anatomical and cognitive impairments related to the aged hippocampus. *Science* **238:** 766–768.
96. Morano, M. I., and Akil, H. (1990). Age-related changes in the POMC stress axis in the rat. In *New Leads in Opioid Research* (J. M. VanRee, A. H. Mulder, V. M. Wiegant, and T. B. VanWimersma Greidanus, eds.), pp. 9–11. Excerpta Medica, Amsterdam.
97. Reul, J., Tonnaer, J., and De Kloet, E. (1988). Neurotrophic ACTH analogue promotes plasticity of type I corticosteroid receptor in brain of senescent male rats. *Neurobiol. Aging* **9:** 253–260.
98. Sapolsky, R. M., Krey, L. C., and McEwen, B. S. (1983). Corticosterone receptors decline in a site-specific manner in the aged rat. *Brain Res.* **289:** 235–240.
99. DeKlotsky, S., Scheff, S., and Cotman, C. (1984). Elevated corticosterone levels: A possible cause of reduced axon sprouting in aged animals. *Neuroendocrinology* **38:** 33–38.
100. Landfield, P., Waymire, J., and Lynch, G. (1978). Hippocampal aging and adrenocorticoids: Quantitative correlations. *Science* **202:** 1098–1102.
101. Sapolsky, R. M., Krey, L. C., and McEwen, B. S. (1986). The

neuroendocrinology of stress and aging: the glucocorticoid cascade hypothesis. *Endocr. Rev.* **7:** 284–301.

102. Akil, H., and Morano, M. I. (1995). Stress. In *Psychopharmacology: The Fourth Generation of Progress* (F. E. Bloom and D. J. Kupfer, eds.), pp. 773–785. Raven Press, New York.
103. De Wied, D. (1991). The effects of neurohypophyseal hormones and related peptides on learning and memory processes. In *Peripheral Signaling of the Brain: Role of Neural-Immune Interactions, Learning and Memory,* (R. Frederickson, J. McGaugh, and D. Felten, eds.), pp. 335–350. Hogrefe & Huber, New York.
104. Izquierdo, I., Medina, J., Netto, C., and Pereira, M. (1991). Peripheral and central effects on memory of peripherally and centrally administered opioids and benzodiazepines. In *Peripheral Signaling of the Brain: Role in Neural-Immune Interactions, Learning and Memory,* (R. Frederickson, J. McGaugh, and D. Felten, eds.), pp. 303–314. Hogrefe & Huber, New York.
105. McGaugh, J. (1992). Affect, neuromodulatory systems, and memory storage. In *The Handbook of Emotion and Memory: Research and Theory,* (S.-A. Christianson, ed.), pp. 245–268. Lawrence Erlbaum Associates, Hillsdale.
106. Ettenberg, A., Van der Kooy, D., LeMoal, M., Koob, G., and Bloom, F. (1983). Can aversive properties of (peripherally-injected) vasopressin account for its putative role in memory? *Behav. Brain Res.* **7:** 331–350.
107. Introini-Collison, I., and McGaugh, J. (1991). Interaction of hormones and neurotransmitter system in the modulation of memory storage. In *Peripheral Signaling of the Brain: Role of Neural-Immune Interactions, Learning and Memory,* (R. Frederickson, J. McGaugh, and D. Felten, eds.), pp. 275–301. Hogrefe & Huber, New York.
108. Brown, J., and Jacobs, A. (1949). The role of fear in the motivation and acquisition of responses. *J. Exp. Psychol.* **39:** 747–759.
109. Overmier, J., and Seligman, M. (1967). Effects of inescapable shock upon subsequent escape and avoidance responding. *J. Comp. Physiol. Psychol.* **63:** 28–33.
110. Anisman, H., Zalcman, S., Shanks, N., and Zacharko, R. (1991). Multisystem regulation of performance deficits induced by stressors. In *Neuromethods: Animal Models in Psychiatry II* (A. Boulton, G. Baker, and M. Martin-Iverson, eds.), Vol. 19, pp. 1–59. Humana Press, New York.
111. Maier, S. (1991). Stressor controllability, cognition and fear. In *Neurobiology of Learning, Emotion and Affect* (J. Madden IV, ed.), pp. 155–191. Raven Press, New York.
112. Nilsson, L.-G., and Archer, T. (1992). Biological aspects of memory and emotion: Affect and cognition. In *The Handbook of Emotion and Memory: Research and Theory* (S.-A. Christianson, ed.), pp. 289–306. Lawrence Erlbaum Associates, Hillsdale.
113. Lee, R., and Maier, S. (1988). Inescapable shock and attention to internal versus external cues in a water discrimination escape task. *J. Exp. Psychol. Anim. Behav.* **14:** 302–310.
114. Maier, S., Jackson, R., and Tomie, A. (1987). Potentiation, overshadowing, and prior exposure to inescapable shock. *J. Exp. Psychol. Anim. Behav.* **13:** 260–270.
115. Shors, T., Weiss, C., and Thompson, R. (1992). Stress-induced facilitation of classical conditioning. *Science* **257:** 537–539.
116. Gage, F., Kelly, P., and Bjorklund, A. (1984). Regional changes in brain glucose metabolism reflect cognitive impairments in aged rats. *J. Neurosci.* **4**(11): 2856–2865.
117. Issa, A. M., Rowe, W., Gauthier, S., and Meaney, M. J. (1990). Hypothalami-pituitary-adrenal activity in aged, cognitively impaired and cognitively unimpaired rats. *J. Neurosci.* **10:** 3247–3254.
118. Kadar, T., Silbermann, M., Brandeis, R., and Levy, A. (1990). Age-related structural changes in the rat hippocampus: Correlation with working memory deficiency. *Brain Res.* **512:** 113–120.
119. Bardgett, M., Taylor, G., Csernansky, J., Newcomer, J., and Nock, B. (1994). Chronic exposure treatment impairs spontaneous alternation behavior in rats. *Behav. Neural. Biol.* **61:** 186–190.
120. Bodnoff, S., Humphreys, A., Lehman, J., Diamond, D., Rose, G., and Meaney, M. (1995). Enduring effects of chronic corticosterone treatment on spatial learning, synaptic plasticity, and hippocampal neuropathology in young and mid-aged rats. *J. Neurosci.* **15:** 61–69.
121. Dachir, S., Kadar, T., Robinzon, B., and Levy, A. (1993). Cognitive deficits induced in young rats by long-term corticosterone administration. *Behav. Neural. Biol.* **60:** 103–109.
122. Luine, V., Villegas, M., Martinez, C., and McEwen, B. (1994). Repeated stress causes reversible impairments of spatial memory performance. *Brain Res.* **639:** 167–170.
123. De Kloet, E., De Kock, S., Schild, V., and Veldhuis, H. (1988). Antiglucocorticoid RU 38486 attenuates retention of a behaviour and disinhibits the hypothalamic-pituitary adrenal axis at different brain sites. *Neuroendocrinology* **47:** 109–115.
124. Oitzl, M., Sutanto, W., and De Kloet, E. (1990). Mineralo- and glucocorticoid receptor function in a spatial orientation task. *J. Steroid Biochem.* **36:** 72S.
125. De Kloet, E. (1991). Brain corticosteroid receptor balance and homeostatic control. *Front. Neuroendocrinol.* **12**(2): 95–164.

C H A P T E R

44

Neuroendocrine Systems II: Growth,* Reproduction,† and Lactation§

Lawrence Frohman, Judy Cameron,† and Phyllis Wise§*

The function of the nervous system is to integrate sensory information from both internal and external environments to provide a coordinated action of visceral and somatic effectors resulting in adaptive behavior that promotes the survival of the individual organism and the species. As introduced in Chapter 43, a fundamental component of this function is provided by neuroendocrine regulation, the process through which localized sets of hypothalamic neurons produce peptides to be released into a circulation and control reproduction, maternal function, growth and development, water balance, responses to stress, cellular metabolism, and other aspects of homeostasis.

Two different types of neuroendocrine regulatory systems have evolved in mammals. In the first, the classical neurosecretory system, hypothalamic neurons of the supraoptic and paraventricular nuclei produce the hormones oxytocin and vasopressin. These hormones are transported down the axons of the neurons through the hypothalamohypophyseal tract to be released from axon terminals into the systemic circulation in the posterior pituitary. The hormones act on peripheral organs involved in maternal function and osmoregulation, among others. The regulation of hormone production and release is by neural input onto the neurons of the supraoptic and paraventricular nuclei. Although this system is complex, it is much less so than the second neurosecretory systems.

The brain–pituitary–organ neuroendocrine systems each have three components. A separate set of hypothalamic nuclei each contains peptide-producing neurons whose axons project through the tuberoinfundibular tract to terminate on capillaries of the portal plexus in the median eminence. The hypothalamic neurons are under both neural control and feedback endocrine control. They produce either a releasing hormone or an inhibitory hormone, which is released from the presynaptic axon terminal to the portal circulation. These hormones pass through the portal circulation into sinusoids in the anterior pituitary, from which they act on receptors of the trophic hormone-producing cells of the anterior pituitary. For some of the pituitary hormones, ACTH, LH, FSH, TRH, there are only releasing hormones to regulate trophic hormone production and release. For others, such as prolactin and growth hormone (GH), the trophic hormone is controlled by both a releasing hormone and an inhibitory hormone. In all cases except prolactin, the nature of the releasing and inhibitory hormones is well understood. The release of both hypothalamic and pituitary hormones is pulsatile, with pulse frequency and amphitude variable and under regulation from several sources. The trophic hormones may act to stimulate the release of target gland hormones, as in the case of the adrenal, thyroid, and gonadal glands, or they may act through specific tissue receptors to stimulate cell proliferation and differentiation and a variety of other actions.

As we saw in Chapter 43, the function of neuroendocrine regulation is to provide the homeostatic adjustment on which adaptive behavior is elaborated and to provide the foundation for reproduction, maternal behavior, growth, and development. For many organisms, these functions, coupled with obtaining water and food, are their principal activities. For the human organism, for whom social interaction has removed much of the exigencies of obtaining food and water and avoiding environmental dangers, these activities are much reduced. Nevertheless, neuroendocrine regulation remains a critical aspect of human adaptation and the *sine qua non* of reproduction.

GROWTH AND DEVELOPMENT

Somatotropin, or **growth hormone** (GH), is the major growth-promoting hormone. It has a limited role in fetal growth but is important in the neonatal period (the highest plasma somatotropin levels occur immediately prior to birth and during the immediate postnatal period). It also plays a major role in the growth spurt of adolescence. The growth-promoting effects of somatotropin require numerous other factors, including nutritional effects (primarily protein), hormone regulators (e.g., insulin and thyroid hormone), tissue-specific factors, and genetic factors.

Somatotropin has anabolic activities critical for metabolic homeostasis. Administration of somatotropin enhances protein synthesis, reflected in a positive nitrogen balance and decreased urea production, and increases lipolysis, resulting in a decrease in body fat. In addition, somatotropin has complex effects on carbohydrate metabolism: somatotropin has insulinlike actions that enhance uptake and utilization of glucose and amino acids during eating. However, the insulin-antagonistic effects on somatotropin are of greater physiologic relevance. Somatotropin has potent lipolytic effects that oppose the lipogenic effects of insulin and mobilize fatty acids for use as a fuel source during fasting.

Somatotropin stimulates organ growth (e.g., cardiac and renal hypertrophy), hormone production, metabolism, skeletal growth and maturation, and immune function. These effects are most easily seen during treatment of somatotropin-deficient humans or animals with exogenous somatotropin. For maximal expression, many of these effects require intermittent, rather than continuous, exposure of tissues to somatotropin. A number of sexually dimorphic patterns of enzymes, receptors, and other proteins can be attributed to different patterns of somatotropin secretion in males and females, particularly rodents.

Somatotropin Release Is Controlled by a Separate Brain–Pituitary Axis

The axis that controls somatotropin differs from the two brain–pituitary axes previously discussed. First, in this axis, the hypothalamus produces two, rather than one, principal hormones: growth hormone-releasing hormone (GHRH) and somatostatin (SS; also known as somatotrope release-inhibiting hormone, SRIH). These hormones have opposing effects on the release of somatotropin: GHRH simulates release of somatotropin, whereas SS inhibits its release. Neural inputs to the hypothalamus allow the axis to respond to sleep and ultradian rhythms, physical and emotional stress, and increased and decreased eating. Secretion of these hypothalamic hormones also responds to other hormones, such as sex steroids, glucocorticoids, and thyroid hormone.

In response to GHRH, somatotropes in the anterior pituitary release somatotropin into the systemic circulation. In contrast to the brain–pituitary–thyroid and brain–pituitary–adrenal axes, each of which controls activity of one end-organ tissue (i.e., thyroid and adrenal cortex), the brain–pituitary axis that controls somatotropin lacks a single, major target organ. Instead, somatotropin released from the anterior pituitary directly affects a number of tissues. Cells of a variety of tissues express receptors for somatotropin (GH receptors) on their surface. Somatotropin binds these receptors to play its essential role in growth, tissue regeneration, and metabolic homeostasis. As with other brain–pituitary axes, negative feedback is necessary for proper regulation of the axis: somatotropin feeds back on the hypothalamus to inhibit its own release.

Growth Hormone-Releasing Hormone Is Synthesized from a Precursor

The 10-kb human GHRH gene is located on chromosome 20 and contains five exons (Fig. 44.1). Its 0.75-kb mRNA codes for a 108-amino-acid precursor (prepro-

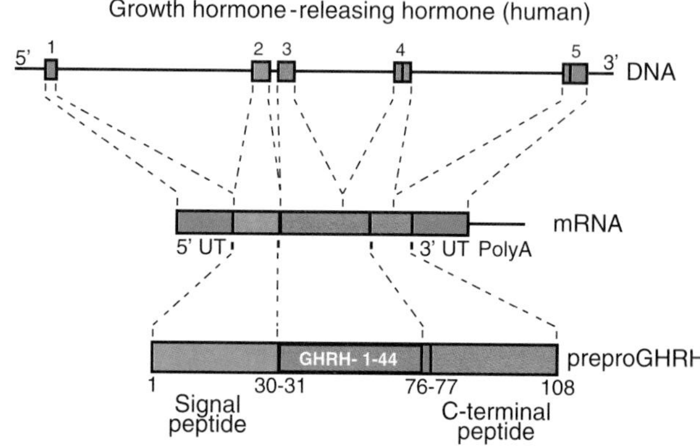

FIGURE 44.1 Schematic representation of the human GHRH gene, mRNA, and precursor, prepro-GHRH. The precursor undergoes endopeptidase cleavage and carboxyl-terminal amidation to generate the mature peptide, GHRH-44-NH_2. Subsequent removal of four amino acids from its C terminus produces GHRH-40-OH.

GHRH) consisting of a 30-residue N-terminal signal peptide, the 44-residue GHRH peptide, an amidation signal, and a 31-residue C-terminal peptide (GCTP). After removal of the signal peptide, GCTP is cleaved from pro-GHRH by endopeptidases and the resulting GHRH-45 is converted to GHRH-44-NH_2. Some GHRH-44-NH_2 is subsequently cleaved to GHRH-40-OH; the two GHRH forms have comparable biologic activity. The full biological activity of GHRH is contained within its first 29 amino acids. The N-terminal region is critically important for binding to GHRH receptor.

Other mammals have only a single form of GHRH. In large mammals, GHRH consists of 44 amino acid residues and exhibits close sequence similarity with human GHRH. In contrast, mouse and rat GHRH are slightly shorter (42 and 43 residues, respectively); they are not amidated, and they have up to 30% sequence variation from human GHRH.

The major site of GHRH production is the basomedial hypothalamus, where the perikarya of GHRH-secreting neurons are centered in the arcuate nucleus, just lateral to the floor of the third ventricle. The axon terminals of these neurons end in the external zone of the median eminence, from which GHRH is released into the hypothalamopituitary portal system, to travel to the anterior pituitary (see Figs. 43.2A and 43.3). Other GHRH-containing cells in and near the arcuate nucleus send axons to other hypothalamic regions, where GHRH appears to influence feeding behavior.

GHRH Is Negatively Regulated by Somatotropin

Somatotropin is the most important regulator of GHRH gene expression. GHRH mRNA levels in rats and mice are markedly increased as a consequence of hypophysectomy[1] or genetic disorders with isolated GH deficiency.[2] When exogenous somatotropin is given to these animals, GHRH mRNA levels decrease. Also, in animals with somatotropin-secreting tumors, GHRH mRNA is suppressed below the normal range. Thyroid hormone deficiency also decreases GHRH mRNA levels, although this effect is a consequence of the profound suppression of GH gene expression that occurs.[3]

Other hormones also affect GHRH mRNA level. Testosterone causes levels of GHRH mRNA to be greater in male than in female rats and mice.[4] Also, administration of insulinlike growth factor I (IGF-I) directly into the CNS, but not peripherally, suppresses GHRH mRNA levels.[5]

Metabolic Signals Are Important in GHRH Gene Regulation

Four metabolic disturbances have been associated with changes in steady-state levels of GHRH mRNA: (1) diabetes, (2) genetic obesity, (3) ethanol toxicity, and (4) protein deprivation. In diabetic rats, GHRH mRNA levels are decreased and can be restored to normal by treatment with insulin at doses sufficient to permit weight regain, though not to restore euglycemia or to normalize the elevated level of SS mRNA. In rats with genetic obesity, GHRH mRNA levels are also decreased, but because GH mRNA levels are also decreased, this change is independent of negative regulation by somatotropin. Similar changes in GHRH and GH mRNA levels are seen in ethanol-treated rats.[6] Protein deficiency and, more selectively, deficiency of a single amino acid, histidine, lead to a decrease in GHRH mRNA levels.[7] In rodents, each of these perturbations is associated with a decreased secretion of somatotropin. However, in humans, diabetes and protein–calorie malnutrition result in increased somatotropin secretion; thus, metabolic regulation is species dependent.

Neurotransmitters Stimulate Secretion of GHRH

GHRH secretion has been measured directly in incubated hypothalamic fragments from mice and rats and in portal blood of rats and sheep. The secretion of GHRH is pulsatile and is suppressed (as is GH secretion) by insulin-induced hypoglycemia and by protein deprivation. GHRH secretion is stimulated by α-adrenergic, dopaminergic, serotonergic, and enkephalinergic systems. Other neurotransmitter systems and metabolically active agents stimulate (e.g., amino acids) or inhibit (e.g., glucose, fatty acids) secretion of somatotropin, although whether these effects occur through changes in the secretion of GHRH, SS, or both is not clear.

In vitro studies also have revealed an inhibitory effect of IGF-I and SS. This latter effect is thought to be direct, because SS receptors colocalize with GHRH immunoreactivity in neurons of the rat arcuate nucleus.[8] Although an α-noradrenergic stimulatory effect has also been seen, other tested neurotransmitters and neuropeptides have not had an effect. However, glucocytopenia stimulates release of GHRH, an effect mediated through NMDA receptors.[9]

Because of the multiple influences of GHRH-secreting neurons, the study of isolated tissues devoid of neural inputs and in artificial environments provides only limited information. The most informative model in which GHRH secretion has been measured directly *in vivo* is the unanesthetized sheep, where portal blood is collected by means of an implanted cannula.[10] Studies in humans are indirect (measurements of somatotropin, rather than GHRH, levels) because access to portal blood is not feasible and peripheral GHRH immunoreactivity reflects, at least in part, extrahypothalamic sources of GHRH (primarily the gastrointestinal tract). With maximally effective doses of GHRH, the effects of different agents on GHRH and SS secretion can be assessed, because under these conditions, commonly used agents ([e.g., insulin (to induce hypoglycemia), arginine, and nicotinic cholinergic agonist pyridostigmine)] are believed to stimulate somatotropin secretion independent of GHRH.

GHRH Acts on Somatotropes through a Signal Transduction System

GHRH binds to a specific receptor on somatotropes. The GHRH receptor (GHRH-R) is a member of a large family of G-protein-coupled receptors. The GHRH-R binds to a single species of G proteins, G_s, and triggers a cascade of events with cyclic AMP (cAMP) serving as a second messenger. They result in phosphorylation of proteins involved in the synthesis and release of GH and in somatotrope mitogenesis. A second signaling system, initiated by binding of a yet unidentified hypothalamic GH secretagogue to its specific receptor, is linked through a separate G protein, G_q, and uses diacylglycerol and inositol triphosphate as second messengers. The two pathways are linked to one another and result in translocation of intracellular Ca^{++}, membrane depolarization, and releases of GH secretory granules.

Independent of its effects on somatotropin release, GHRH stimulates somatotropin synthesis. This effect occurs through cAMP, which stimulates phosphorylation of nuclear transcription protein CREB (cAMP response element-binding protein), which in turn binds to an enhancer element in the regulatory portion of the somatotropin gene. In somatotropes, GHRH stimulates expression of c-*fos*, increases thymidine incorporation, and enhances cellular proliferation.

Mutations in the GHRH signal transduction system are implicated in human pituitary disease. Forty percent of patients with somatotropin-secreting pituitary tumors and acromegaly have a point mutation in the G_s protein that leads to a constitutively activated state, which in turn produces not only somatotropin hypersecretion but somatotrope proliferation and neoplastic transformation.[11] The most common type of somatotropin deficiency in childhood (idiopathic GH deficiency) is attributed to a defect in hypothalamic GHRH secretion (the basis of which is not understood). Injections of synthetic GHRH increase somatotropin secretion and enhance linear growth in most patients with this disorder.[12]

Somatostatin Neurons Are Distributed throughout the CNS

The human SS gene is located on chromosome 3 and contains two exons (Fig. 44.2). Its mRNA is 0.85 kb and codes for a 116-amino-acid precursor (prepro-SS). Cleavage of the precursor is accomplished by endopeptidases and varies depending on the tissue. The hypothalamus has two biologically active forms of SS, SS-14 and SS-28. SS-28 has an N-terminal extension compared with SS-14. SS is rapidly degraded in the plasma by endo- and exopeptidases and has a half-life of less than 2 min.

SS neurons, in contrast to GHRH neurons, are located throughout the CNS and participate in many pathways unrelated to GH. The perikarya of those neurons affecting somatotropin secretion are located primarily in the periventricular region of the anterior hypothalamus. The axon terminals of these neurons end in the external zone of the median eminence. Other somatostatin-containing neurons in the hypothalamus send axons to GHRH-containing neurons in the nearby arcuate nucleus, where the SS neurons are believed to exert inhibitory effects.

Somatostatin Expression and Secretion Are Affected by Multiple Physiologic Signals

Because of the widespread distribution of SS, both within and outside the CNS, extensive studies of SS gene expression have been possible. The SS gene has a cAMP response element (CRE); thus, a wide variety of stimuli can act through G proteins to enhance expression of SS.[13] However, the stimuli that regulate hypothalamic SS gene expression (specifically in those neurons participating in somatotropin regulation) are poorly understood. The primary regulator of SS in periventricular neurons is somatotropin itself. Steady-state SS mRNA levels are decreased in hypophysectomized rats and are increased after somatotropin treatment.[14] As with GHRH, SS mRNA levels are higher in male than in female rats and are increased by testosterone. Also, IGF-I administered directly into the CNS, though not peripherally, increases SS mRNA levels.[5]

Metabolic signals also regulate SS gene expression. Hypoglycemia and hyperglycemia increase SS mRNA levels.[15] In animals with diabetes, SS mRNA levels are increased. The extent to which blood glucose control

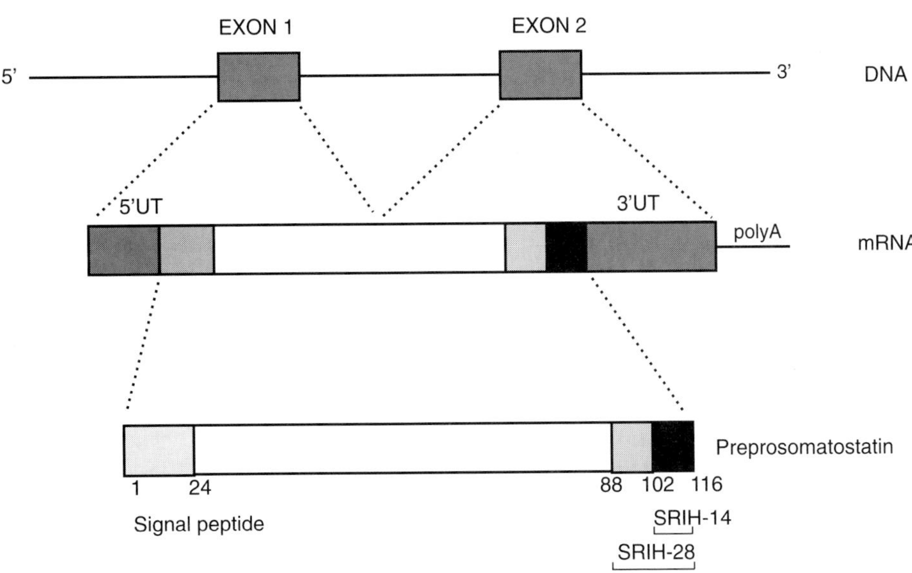

FIGURE 44.2 Schematic representation of the somatostatin (SS) gene, mRNA, and precursor, preprosomatostatin. SS-14 and SS-28 are formed by differential processing of the same precursor.

must be restored for normalization of SS mRNA levels is greater than that for GHRH levels.

Measurements in sheep portal plasma have shown[10] that SS is secreted in a pulsatile manner with a pulse frequency similar to that of GHRH. SS release is enhanced *in vitro* by Ca^{2+}-dependent, K^+-induced membrane depolarization and by cAMP, dopamine, and norepinephrine. Stimulation and suppression have been reported for the cholinergic system. In humans, SS release is suppressed by cholinergic stimuli. Glucocytopenia, GH, IGF-I, and GHRH have each been reported to stimulate SS release. Many neuropeptides, including thyrotropin-releasing hormone, corticotropin-releasing hormone, GHRH, secretin, glucagon, and neurotensin stimulate SS secretion when administered directly into the CNS. Insulin-induced hypoglycemia is also a potent stimulus for the release of SS,[10] although starvation impairs SS release.

SS Action Is Mediated through Inhibitory G Proteins

Somatostatin action is initiated when SS binds to an SS receptor (SS-R). To date, five different SS-Rs have been cloned. Each receptor is the product of a separate gene and is present on cell membranes in the pituitary.[16] Relative affinities for different forms of SS and for SS analogs differ among the five receptors. However, when SS binds any of the SS-Rs, the SS-R works through an inhibitory G protein (G_i) to reduce cAMP generation and hyperpolarize the cell membrane, diminishing Ca^{2+} influx into cells.

The inhibitory effects of SS on somatotropin synthesis and somatotrope proliferation apparently are due to modulation of GHRH action. SS might influence normal GH synthesis and body growth: Animals expressing a SS transgene grow at a normal rate despite very high SS concentrations in the pituitary[17]; however, rats with diminished SS production as a consequence of anterolateral hypothalamic deafferentiation grow more quickly than normal.[18]

Secretion of Somatotropin Is Affected by Peptides Other Than GHRH and SS

Several other transmitters participate in the regulation of somatotropin secretion, although their roles appear to be less important than those of GHRH and SS, and are only partially understood. They include peptides structurally related to GHRH (e.g., vasoactive intestinal peptide and pituitary adenylate cyclase-activating peptide) and structurally distinct from GHRH (e.g., TRH, galanin, neuropeptide Y, motilin, and a separate hypothalamic GH secretagogue). Interleukins-1 and -2 also regulate GHRH/GH secretion.

Classical Neurotransmitters

Although several monoamine neurotransmitters affect somatotropin secretion, their sites of action are at the hypothalamic rather than the pituitary level. One exception is dopamine, which can exert effects at both levels. The central effects of dopamine are stimulatory, as already described, and occur at the level of the hypothalamus. The inhibitory effects of dopamine are mediated through D_2 receptors on somatotropes. Dopamine inhibits forskolin-stimulated GH secretion without impairing cAMP formation, implying an action at a step distal to the generation of cAMP.

Somatotropes Express Somatotropin

The first demonstration of a growth-promoting substance in the anterior pituitary was reported in 1921[19] and was followed a few years later by a report that pituitary extracts could restore growth of hypophysectomized rats.[20] Another 15 years elapsed before GH was isolated.[21] Although human GH has been synthesized by classical chemical means, recombinant techniques are currently used for the production of both human and bovine somatotropin.

Growth hormone is a single chain protein of 191 amino acids (21.8 kDa). Two disulfide bonds confer its three-dimensional conformation essential for biological activity. The human somatotropin gene is a member of a five-member family of genes on chromosome 17 that also includes a somatotropin variant gene (GH-V) and three chorionic somatomammotropin genes that are expressed only in the placenta (Fig. 44.3). The human somatotropin gene contains five exons, and its mRNA is alternatively spliced to yield two mRNA species that code for 22-kDa (major) and 20-kDa (minor) forms of the hormone. After it is synthesized in the endoplasmic reticulum, somatotropin is transported to storage granules that are released from the somatotrope, primarily on stimulation. The 20-kDa hormone accounts for about 5–10% of total pituitary GH and has biologic activity similar to that of 22-kDa somatotropin. No evidence of multiple forms of somatotropin has been reported for other mammalian species. Moderate species variation exists among mammalian somatotropins: Although human somatotropin is biologically active in nearly all mammalian species, only primate somatotropins are active in humans.

The GH Gene Is Expressed Only in Pituitary Somatotropes

Within the pituitary, somatotropes are the most numerous cell type. In rats, somatotropes constitute 30–40% of pituitary cells in males and 20–30% in females. Although present throughout the anterior pituitary, the cells are concentrated in lateral regions.

Expression of the somatotropin gene requires the pituitary-specific transcription factor Pit-1 (also known as GHF-1).[22] Mutations of the Pit-1 gene, as in the Snell dwarf mouse, are associated with the absence of somatotropin mRNA and protein, and somatotropes.[23] Pit-1 is also required for lactotrope and thyrotrope development and for prolactin and TSH gene expression. Mutations of the Pit-1 gene in humans are associated with combined somatotropin, prolactin, and TSH deficiency, an exact counterpart of the Snell mouse.[24]

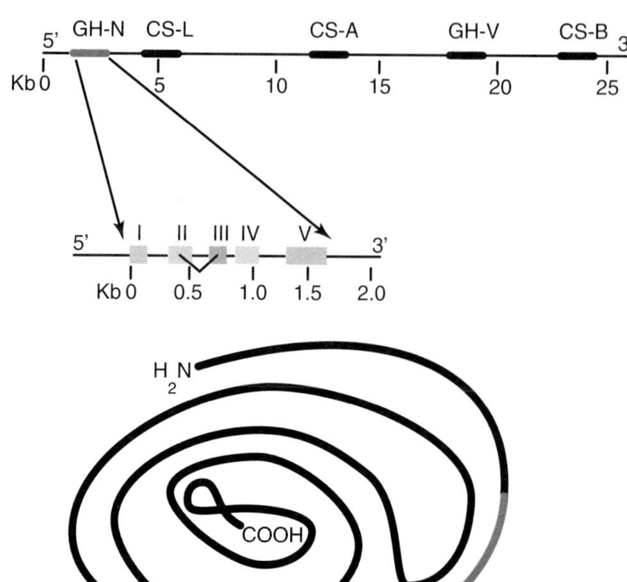

FIGURE 44.3 The human growth hormone (somatotropin)–somatomammotropin gene family. The GH-N gene is expressed in pituitary somatotropes. Alternative splicing of the second intron gives rise to two mRNAs that generate a full-length (22 kDa) somatotropin protein and the shorter form (20 kDa), which lacks the 15-amino-acid sequence indicated by the shaded region.

Biologic Effects of Somatotropin Are Direct and Indirect

About half of the secreted somatotropin is transported through the circulation in association with a binding protein (GHBP) that is the same as the extracellular domain of the somatotropin receptor (GH-R). In humans and most other mammalian species, alternative splicing of the GH-R provides two distinct mRNAs, one for GHBP and one for GH-R.

All somatotropin-sensitive tissues have GH-R on their cells' membranes. A single hormone molecule binds sequentially to the extracellular parts of two GH-R molecules; this complex is required for biologic effects.[25] The activated receptor initiates a cascade of intermediary protein phosphorylations that eventually lead to activation of nuclear transcription factors and stimulatory effects on somatotropin-regulated genes.

Among its many effects, somatotropin stimulates the production of insulinlike growth factor I (IGF-I) in peripheral tissues. Together, the two hormones act at the cellular level and lead to lineage commitment (maturation) and clonal expansion of cells. At the level of whole animals, most effects of somatotropin can be reproduced by IGF-I, although not as efficiently as when the two hormones act in combination.

Somatotropin and IGF-I Feed Back on the Hypothalamus and Pituitary

The ability of somatotropin to feed back on its secretion was first recognized in humans in whom treatment with exogenous somatotropin resulted in decreased somatotropin responses to stimulation. With the development of techniques for measuring pituitary and hypothalamic hormones in experimental animals, the mechanism of these effects has been extensively studied. At the pituitary level, feedback is mediated primarily by IGF-I and minimally or not at all by GH (Fig. 44.4). Somatotropes contain IGF-I receptors, and IGF-I inhibits somatotropin gene expression and somatotropin secretion in basal and GHRH-stimulated states.[26,27] IGF-I may come from peripheral tissues via the circulation or from the pituitary itself, which is also a site of IGF-I synthesis. Effects mediated through circulating IGF-I are likely to be tonic because serum levels do not vary greatly during a 24-h period. However, IGF-I circulates in bound and free states. Because the free form is believed to be more active biologically, changes in the concentration of the major IGF-I serum-binding protein, IGFBP-3, could modulate the effect of the IGF-I in circulation. Serum IGFBP-3 levels are suppressed by hyperglycemia, resulting in a greater concentration of free (more biologically active) circulating IGF-I, which could lead to suppression of SS secretion.

Within the hypothalamus, the role of IGF-I feedback is less well defined. IGF-I crosses the blood–brain barrier to a limited extent and is synthesized within the basomedial hypothalamus, where IGF-I receptors are also present. Thus, locally generated IGF-I could influence feedback. IGF-I suppresses hypothalamic GHRH secretion *in vitro*,[28] and weakly suppresses GHRH mRNA levels after intracerebroventricular (ICV) injection.[5] IGF-I stimulates the release of SS *in vitro*[26] and, at high concentrations, increases hypothalamic SS mRNA levels after ICV injection.[5] Because IGF-I effects on GHRH mRNA levels occur at doses that do not affect

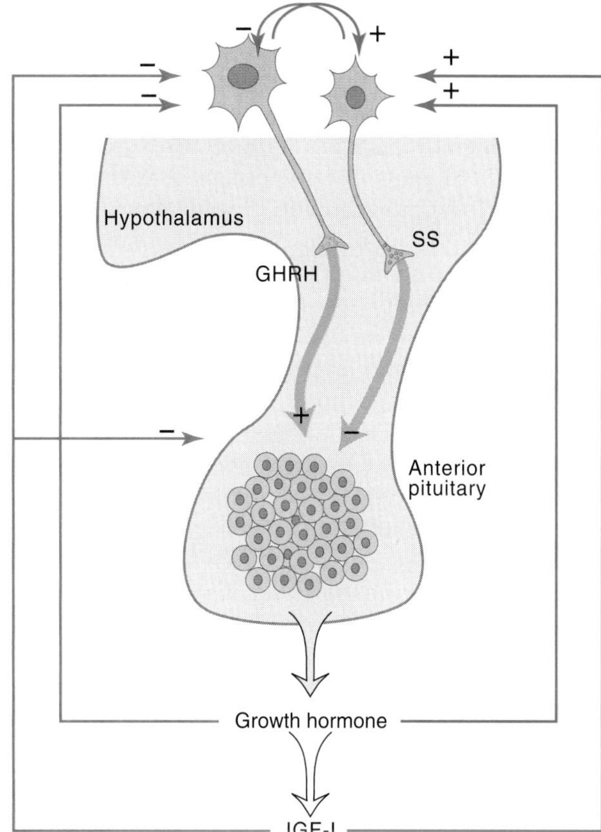

FIGURE 44.4 Model of somatotropin feedback regulation. Somatotropin feeds back on the hypothalamus, and IGF-I feeds back to the hypothalamus and the pituitary. In addition, GHRH and SS affect one another reciprocally.

SS mRNA levels, the major effects of IGF-I are more likely to be mediated by GHRH rather than by SS. Whether these effects are direct or are mediated through other interneurons is not known. IGF-II has not been implicated as a major regulator of somatotropin secretion but may participate in feedback regulation. Combined administration of IGF-I and IGF-II synergistically inhibits GH secretion through unknown mechanisms. However, unless hypothalamic IGFs are regulated differently from peripheral IGFs, their effects are more likely to be long-term modulatory influences rather than short-term regulatory factors.

Hypothalamic feedback effects of somatotropin occur through GHRH and SS. Somatotropin receptors are present in the basomedial hypothalamus, implying some penetration of somatotropin through the blood–brain barrier in this region. Somatotropin stimulates SS secretion *in vitro*,[29] increases periventricular SS mRNA levels,[14] and suppresses GHRH mRNA levels.[1] Whether these effects occur directly or are mediated through IGF-I or other factors is not known. The only known acute effect of somatotropin on the hypothalamus is an increase in c-Fos protein.[30] Localization of this effect to arcuate neurons containing SS and NPY[31] suggests that these peptides may help mediate the inhibitory feedback of somatotropin on GHRH.

Somatostatin feedback inhibition is sexually dimorphic in rats. Infusion of exogenous somatotropin suppresses endogenous secretion of somatotropin in both sexes. However, in males the endogenous somatotropin response to GHRH is also inhibited, implying a stimulation of endogenous SS secretion, whereas in females the endogenous somatotropin response to GHRH remains intact, suggesting an inhibition of endogenous GHRH secretion.[32]

The redundancy of the somatotropin feedback system and the multiple sites at which feedback occurs allow for multifaceted regulation of somatotropin secretion. Although numerous neuropeptides and nonpeptide transmitters have been shown to affect somatotropin secretion, GHRH and SS exert the most important regulatory effects. The neural regulation of somatotropin occurs primarily within the basomedial hypothalamus and the median eminence, although there are inputs from numerous other structures, permitting integration of various factors, including emotional and physical stress, sleep, circadian rhythmicity, and nutrients.

Other Hormones and Metabolic Substrates Affect Somatotropin Secretion

Thyroid hormone, glucocorticoids, androgens and estrogens, and metabolic fuels influence somatotropin secretion. The major effects of thyroid hormone on somatotropin secretion occur within the pituitary. Activated thyroid hormone receptor binds to thyroid response elements on the somatotropin gene, resulting in enhanced gene expression and somatotropin synthesis.

Glucocorticoid hormones contribute to the regulation of somatotropin secretion at the pituitary and hypothalamic levels. In the pituitary, glucocorticoids enhance somatotropin gene expression through a glucocorticoid response element in the somatotropin gene, to which activated glucocorticoid receptor binds.

In addition, growth hormone secretion is markedly influenced by sex steroids in many species, including humans. The effects are complex, and demonstration is sometimes dependent on the experimental model. In the pituitary, androgens increase somatotropin gene expression, although specific enhancer elements have not yet been identified. Estrogens, in contrast, reduce somatotropin expression. Thus, females have lower concentrations of pituitary somatotropin than males.

Metabolic fuels exert major effects on hypothalamic regulation of somatotropin secretion.[33] Protein deprivation has long been recognized to impair somatotropin secretion. In rats this effect has been attributed to histidine, a deficiency of which leads to a decreased GHRH mRNA level.[7]

Alterations in glucose metabolism also profoundly influence somatotropin secretion; hyperglycemia suppresses and insulin-induced hypoglycemia enhances somatotropin secretion in humans and other large mammals. Changes in serum concentrations of nonesterified (free) fatty acid (NEFA) can affect somatotropin secretion. Increases in serum NEFA suppress somatotropin release, and decreases in serum NEFA enchance somatotropin secretion. Elevations in serum NEFA block the effects of GHRH on somatotropin secretion *in vivo,* implying a mediating role for SS.[34]

Extrahypothalamic regions of the CNS also participate in the control of somatotropin secretion, although, with a few exceptions, the pathways are not well characterized. Entrainment of somatotropin secretory bursts to stages III and IV of sleep implies the presence of pathways from sleep-associated centers to the arcuate nucleus, although this remains to be confirmed. The amygdala also participates in the control of somatotropin secretion.[35]

Somatotropin Secretion Is Pulsatile

Spontaneous somatotropin secretion is pulsatile and has pulse-to-trough ratios of up to 100:1. Intervals between pulses vary with species and are ~2 h in humans, ~1 h in sheep, and ~3 h in rats (Fig. 44.5). The GH secretory pattern depends on the precisely regulated interaction of GHRH and SS on the somatotrope. Both GHRH and SS are required for pulsatile GH secretion; pulsatility is abolished by either anti-GHRH serum or anti-SS serum or by anteromedial hypothalmic lesions or anterolateral hypothalamic deafferentation, each of which eliminates SS tone. The persistence of pulsatile somatotropin secretion during infusion of supraphysiologic concentrations of GHRH underscores the important role of SS in maintaining rhythmic secretion.[36]

The pulsatile pattern of somatotropin secretion was originally proposed to be caused by asynchronous pulses of GHRH and SS secretion, in which GHRH pulses and SS troughs produced somatotropin pulses, and GHRH troughs and SS pulses produced somatotropin troughs.[37] Measurement of GHRH and SS in portal blood of sheep, however, suggested a more complex regulation. In sheep, GHRH secretion and SS secretion are pulsatile. About 70% of somatotropin pulses can be attributed to pulses of GHRH. These GHRH pulses are not necessarily asynchronous with pulses of SS. Thus, GHRH appears to have a dominant role in

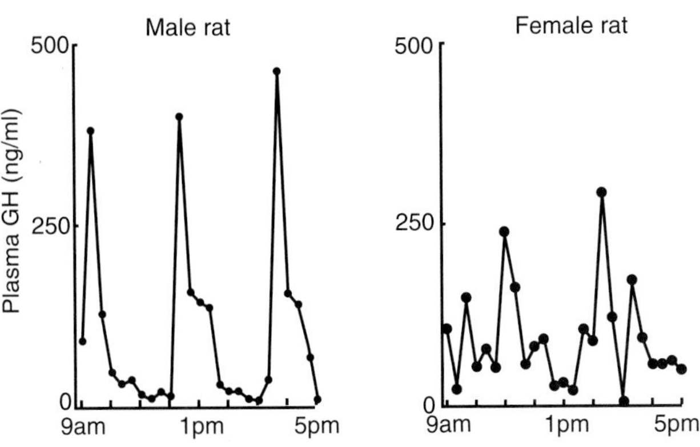

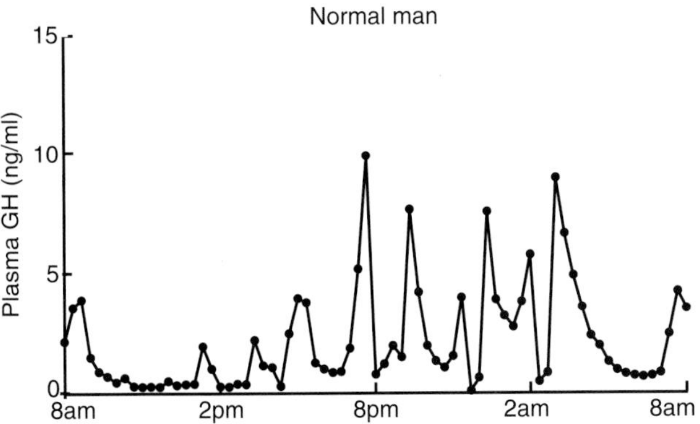

FIGURE 44.5 Examples of the pulsatile pattern of somatotropin secretion in rats and humans. The pattern of pulses is sexually dimorphic in rats, with more regular and higher peaked somatotropin pulses occurring in males. In humans, pulses are larger during the nocturnal period.

timing pulses of somatotrophin. Hypothalamic GHRH and SS mRNA levels also fluctuate, with the highest GHRH mRNA levels occurring at the time of somatotropin troughs and the highest SS mRNA levels occurring at the time of somatotropin peaks, suggesting a delayed response of gene expression to previous periods of secretory activity.[10]

The secretory pattern of somatotropin is sexually dimorphic; males exhibit higher pulses and lower troughs and, in rats, a more regular pulsatile pattern than females.[38] The pattern is influenced by androgens and estrogens, with androgens regulating pulse amplitude and estrogens regulating basal secretion.[39] Although androgen and estrogens can affect pituitary somatotropin gene expression, their effects on the ultradian rhythm of somatotropin secretion indicate that they have an influence on GHRH and / or SS secretion, as previously discussed.

In humans, a burst of somatotropin secretion is also observed in association with deep (stages III and IV) sleep, but this association does not appear to be tightly linked with neural processes required for slow-wave sleep. Nearly 70% of all somatotropin secretion occurs at night.[40,41]

Summary

Regulation of somatotropin (growth hormone) is a complex process that evolved to control a hormone essential for growth, tissue regeneration, and metabolic homeostasis. Neural inputs are funneled through two principal hypothalamic hormones, GHRH and SS, that have the most important roles in controlling somatotropin secretion. The sources of input to this brain–pituitary axis include external inputs (e.g., physical and emotional stress), metabolic environment (e.g., feeding and fasting), hormones (e.g., sex steroids, glucocorticoids, and thyroid hormone), and inherent ultradian and sleep-associated CNS rhythms. Feedback regulation occurs through somatotropin and somatotropin-dependent IGFs at the levels of the pituitary and hypothalamus.

REPRODUCTION

The Brain–Pituitary–Gonad Axis Controls Reproductive Function

Reproduction in mammals involves finely tuned coordination of the brain, pituitary, and gonads to bring about production of mature male and female gametes, coordinate sexual interactions between the male and female so that joining of the gametes occurs, and provide an appropriate uterine environment within the female for growth and maturation of the developing conceptus.[42] For both sexes, **gonadotropin-releasing hormone** (GnRH) neurons in the hypothalamic region of the brain provide the central neural drive that directs all aspects of these reproductive processes. GnRH neurons are neuroendocrine cells whose axons terminate on blood vessels of the hypothalamus–pituitary portal vasculature within the median eminence and release bursts of GnRH into this bloodstream each time they fire. Released GnRH travels a short distance to the anterior pituitary, where it binds to specific membrane receptors on the pituitary cells that produce two gonadotropic glycoprotein hormones, **luteinizing hormone** (LH) and **follicle-stimulating hormone** (FSH), together referred to as **gonadotropins.** LH and FSH are released from the pituitary into the systemic circulation in response to GnRH, and they travel to the gonads, where they direct gamete production, as well as gonadal hormone production.

In males, LH stimulates **testosterone** production in the Leydig cells of the testes. FSH and testosterone then act in coordination to stimulate spermatogenesis in the testicular seminiferous tubules. In addition, testosterone supports the secondary sexual organs of the male, including the penis, prostate, and seminal vesicles. Testosterone also acts on other tissues of the body to increase muscle mass, increase facial and body hair, and enlarge the epiglottis, which leads to deepening of the voice.

In females, these same pituitary hormones act at the ovary. FSH stimulates ovarian follicle development at the beginning of each ovarian cycle, and FSH and LH together stimulate ovulation in the middle of each cycle. FSH and LH also stimulate the production of the ovarian steroid hormones, estrogen and progesterone. These ovarian hormones, in turn, support the secondary sexual organs of the female, including the uterus, cervix, and fallopian tubes. Estrogen, in particular, also acts on other body tissues to cause breast development and increase subcutaneous deposition of fat.

GnRH Neurons Are Born outside the Brain and Migrate to Their Final Positions during Embryonic Development

GnRH neurons are one of the few types of neurons born outside the brain. In the early stages of embryonic development, cells containing immunoreactive GnRH can first be detected in the **olfactory placode.** Soon after they are first detectable, primordial GnRH neurons begin to emerge from the olfactory placode to form cords of migrating cells along the nasal septum, following the route of the developing olfactory, vomeronasal, and terminal nerves into the medial ventral forebrain. GnRH neurons then migrate caudally to their final positions in the septal, preoptic, and anterior hypothalamic areas. In the initial phases of migration from the olfactory placode to the medial ventral forebrain, GnRH neurons appear to follow a pathway formed by a population of nonneuronal progenitor cells that migrate out of the olfactory epithelium at about the same time. These cells appear to form physical channels that guide the early stages of GnRH neuronal migration. Interestingly, the fascicles formed by these progenitor cells are coated with **neural cell adhesion molecule** (NCAM), which likely helps guide GnRH neurons along the migratory pathway. Injection of anti-NCAM antibodies into the olfactory placode at the time of GnRH neuronal migration can significantly disrupt the migratory process.[43] After the GnRH neurons enter the forebrain, they are no longer associated with this physical guidance pathway or with NCAM containing fibers, and the signals guiding GnRH neuronal migration to their final locations within the medial ventral forebrain are unknown. (See Box 44.1.)

GnRH Neurons Form a Diffuse Network, Not Discrete Nuclei, within the Hypothalamus

After embryonic migration, GnRH neurons are not localized in discrete hypothalamic nuclei. Instead, they are scattered diffusely throughout much of the hypothalamus (Fig. 44.6). In most mammals GnRH neurons are found in the rostral hypothalamus, the preoptic area, and the basal forebrain, including the diagonal band of Broca and septal nuclei. The degree to which GnRH neurons are found in the caudal regions of the hypothalamus is considerably more variable. In rats

BOX 44.1

KALLMANN SYNDROME

Failure of GnRH neurons to migrate properly during embryonic development is one aspect of the congenital disease Kallmann syndrome. Patients with Kallmann syndrome never enter puberty and are thus infertile and eunuchoid, being generally tall with little muscle mass, a high voice, and sparse pubic and axillary hair. In these patients, the olfactory, vomeronasal, and terminal nerves fail to enter the forebrain, and thus GnRH neurons appear to have no route to follow out of the olfactory placode, and they accumulate above the cribriform plate or in the anterior fossa.[43a] Without migration of GnRH neurons into the hypothalamus and GnRH release into the hypophyseal portal vasculature, there is no central drive to the pituitary–gonadal axis. Thus, these individuals are completely devoid of gonadal function. Recognition of this defect has led to the treatment of Kallmann syndrome with exogenous GnRH provided by a portable pump, such as those worn by diabetic patients needing insulin infusions. With such treatment, secretion of pituitary gonadotropin increases and maturation of gonadal function occurs, leading to the induction of normal secondary sexual characteristics and fertility.

Judy L. Cameron

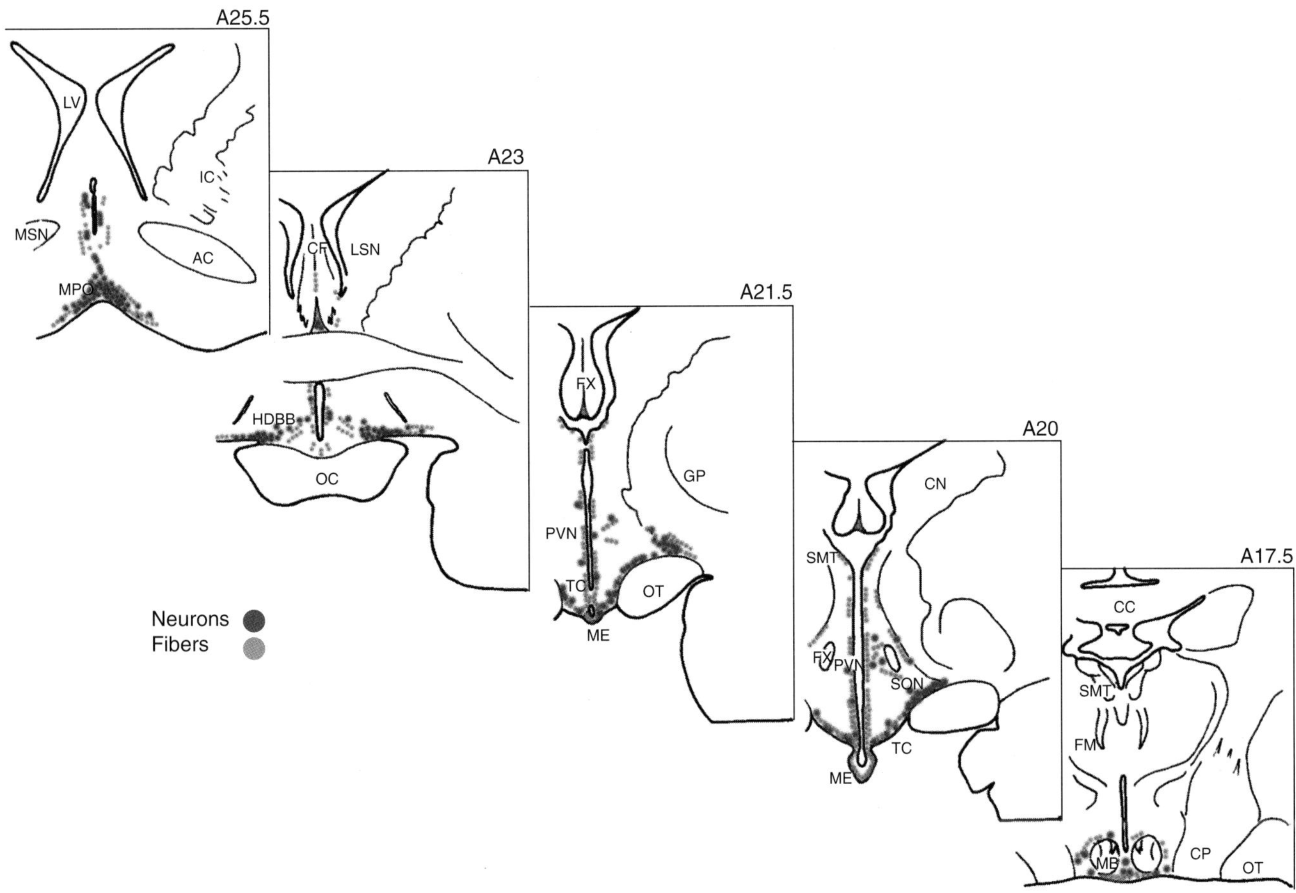

FIGURE 44.6 GnRH neuronal distribution in the primate brain. The relative densities of neurons and fibers are shown in frontal sections through the preoptic region and hypothalamus. AC, anterior commissure; CC, corpus callosum; CN, caudate nucleus; CP, cerebellar peduncle; FM, mammillary fasciculus; FX, fornix; GP, globus pallidus; HDBB, horizontal limb of the diagonal band of Broca; IC, internal capsule: LSN, lateral septal nucleus; LV, lateral ventricle; MB, mammillary body; ME, median eminence; MPO, medial preoptic area; MSN, medial septal nucleus; OC, optic chiasm; OT, optic tract; PVN, paraventricular nucleus; SMT, stria medullaris of the thalamus.

and mice, many GnRH neurons can be found in the medial preoptic area, but no GnRH cell bodies are found as far caudal as the arcuate nucleus. In contrast, in humans and nonhuman primates, as well as in a number of other species, GnRH neurons are found in significant numbers in the arcuate nucleus, the lateral hypothalamus, the periventricular nuclei, and the ventral hypothalamic tract.

GnRH Release into the Portal Bloodstream Occurs in a Pulsatile Pattern

GnRH release into the portal bloodstream occurs in a coordinated fashion, with distinct pulses of GnRH secretion followed by periods of virtually no GnRH secretion.[44] The pulsatile stimulation of the anterior pituitary by GnRH leads, in turn, to pulsatile release of LH and FSH from the pituitary gonadotropes into the peripheral bloodstream (Fig. 44.7). Studies in species such as sheep, in which it is technically feasible to collect portal and peripheral blood simultaneously, indicate that there is often a one to one correspondence between GnRH pulses and LH pulses, although examples of small GnRH pulses that are not followed by LH pulses have been reported. In general, there is less concordance between GnRH pulses and FSH pulses than between GnRH pulses and LH pulses, probably because FSH secretion is coregulated by GnRH and the gonadal peptide **inhibin** (discussed in more detail later). Also, the clearance of FSH from the bloodstream is slower than LH clearance, so acute changes in secretory rate have less impact on blood levels of FSH than of LH.

Multiple-unit recording electrodes placed in the medial basal hypothalamus of rhesus monkeys, rats, and goats have measured spikes of electrical activity that

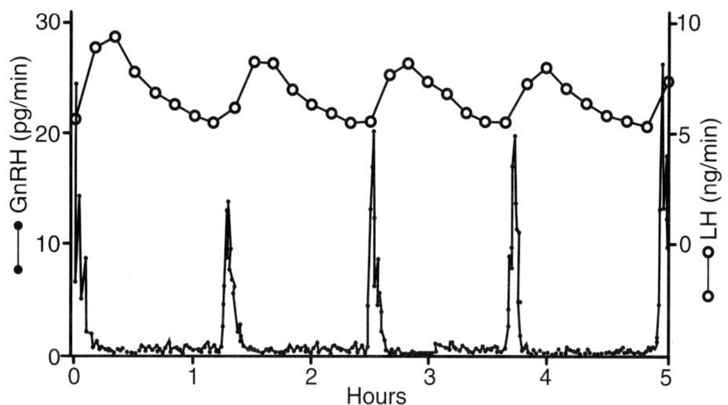

FIGURE 44.7 Correlation of pulses of LH in the general circulation (○) and pulses of GnRH in the hypothalamopituitary–portal circulation (●) in a female sheep. After Moenter *et al.*[44a]

correspond in time to pulses of LH release (Fig. 44.8).[45] These bursts of electrical activity may come from GnRH neurons themselves or from neurons that impinge on the GnRH neural system and thereby govern its firing pattern. The circuit, which is not yet fully understood, that underlies the pulsatile neural drive to the reproductive axis is commonly referred to as the **pulse generator.** The pulse generator may reside within GnRH neurons: there are several reports of a clonal cell line derived from GnRH neurons (i.e., GT-1 cells) that shows pulsatile release of GnRH.[46] However, the possibility remains that in the brain some as yet unidentified neural system with endogenous

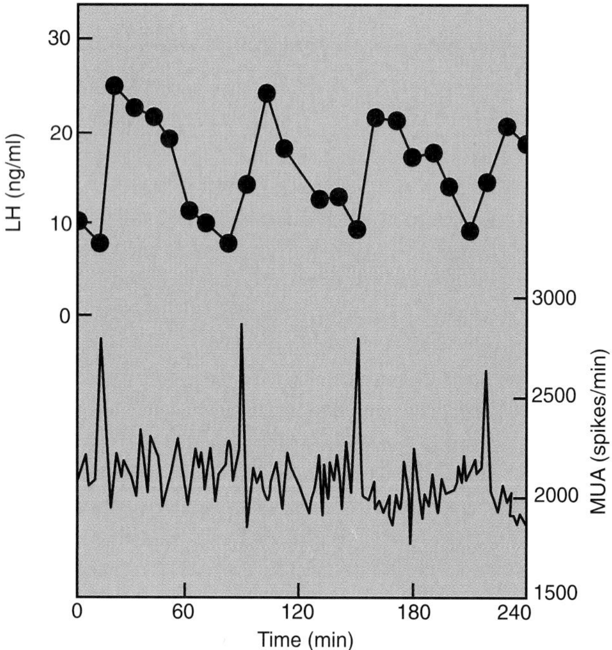

FIGURE 44.8 Correlation of pulses of LH in the general circulation and increases in spikes of electrical activity, multiple-unit activity (MUA), measured by an electrode placed in the medial basal hypothalamus of a female monkey. After Wilson *et al.*[45]

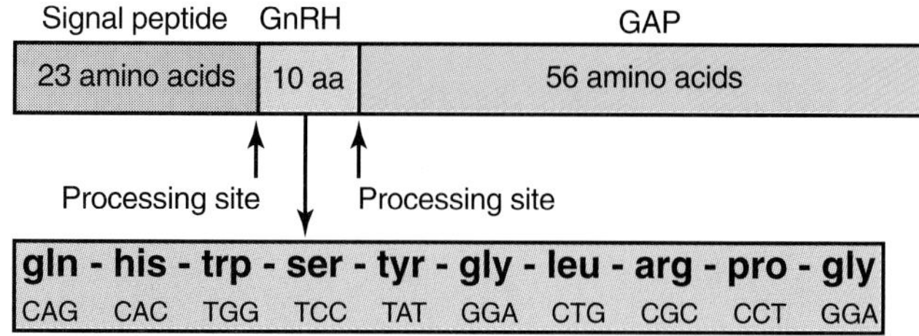

FIGURE 44.9 Schematic illustration of the precursor of GnRH (prepro-GnRH) and the amino acid sequence of GnRH.

rhythmic activity is the pulse generator and provides the central drive to the brain–pituitary–gonad axis.

The interesting question of how GnRH neurons, distributed diffusely throughout the hypothalamus, coordinate the release of discrete pulses of GnRH into the portal bloodstream remains unanswered. GnRH neurons might actually form an interconnected network. Anatomical studies showing synapses between GnRH neurons, and perhaps cytoplasmic bridges between adjacent GnRH neurons, support this possibility. It is further supported by receptor autoradiographic studies showing that GnRH neurons have GnRH receptors and by physiological studies showing that administration of GnRH, *in vivo* and to clonal GnRH neurons (i.e., GT-1 cells) *in vitro,* can modulate GnRH release.[47] Another possibility is GnRH release is coordinated, by GnRH neurons or by some other neural system, at the level of the median eminence, where GnRH axon terminals come in close proximity to each other as they terminate on the portal vasculature.

GnRH Is Synthesized as Part of a Large Precursor Molecule in GnRH Neurons

GnRH is a 10-amino-acid peptide that is synthesized as part of a larger precursor molecule of 92 amino acids (Fig. 44.9). The GnRH sequence is preceded by a 23-amino-acid signal peptide, which is enzymatically cleaved after a Gly–Lys–Arg sequence. Following the GnRH peptide is a 56-amino-acid peptide, referred to as GnRH-associated peptide, or GAP. GAP is secreted with GnRH into the portal vasculature and appears to weakly stimulate pituitary release of LH and FSH; GAP also appears to inhibit prolactin secretion. However, the physiological importance of GAP's actions at the pituitary remains to be determined.

Lower vertebrate species appear to have two distinct genes encoding the GnRH precursor; however, higher vertebrates have a single GnRH–GAP gene. The cDNA sequences of the precursor for rat and human show a high degree of interspecies homology. Since the gene was cloned, *in situ* hybridization has been used to quantitate changes in expression of the GnRH gene in individual neurons under various physiological conditions. Surprisingly, under a variety of physiological conditions in which there appear to be large changes in the release of GnRH, little to no change in the level of GnRH gene expression is seen.[48] For example, few changes in GnRH gene expression have been reported in either males or females after castration, a time when GnRH secretion is believed to increase dramatically. Furthermore, during the prepubertal period, when the GnRH neuronal system is believed to be quiescent, accounting for prepubertal infertility, GnRH gene expression appears to be similar to that in adults. These studies strongly support that GnRH drive to the reproductive axis is controlled primarily by regulation of GnRH release, rather than regulation of GnRH synthesis.

Depending on the species, 40–80% of hypothalamic GnRH neurons send axons to the median eminence, and these neurons are thus believed to play an integral role in regulating **gonadotropes,** gonadotropin-releasing cells in the anterior pituitary. GnRH neurons that project to the median eminence do not tend to be located in any specific area of the hypothalamus and, interestingly, are often found adjacent to GnRH neurons that do not project to the median eminence. These latter GnRH neurons project to areas within the hypothalamus, as well as to extrahypothalamic areas, including the habenula, interpeduncular nucleus, medial amygdala, ventral tegmental area of the midbrain, and periaqueductal region. These nonneuroendocrine GnRH neurons may play a role in regulating various reproductive behaviors.[49]

Although the majority of GnRH neurons appear to participate in neuroendocrine regulation, only a small subset of the total GnRH population is necessary for normal function of the brain–pituitary–gonad axis.[50] In monkeys, isolation of the mediobasal hypothalamus by knife cuts does not prevent either pulsatile LH release or estradiol-induced gonadotropin surges, even though many GnRH neurons no longer are connected to the median eminence. Similar lesions in the guinea pig remove the majority of GnRH input to the median eminence without affecting pulsatile LH release or surges. Most dramatically, transplants of normal fetal or neonatal hypothalamus containing small numbers (as few as 5–10) of GnRH neurons into the third ventricle of a hypogonadal (hpg) mouse can restore the pulsatile release of gonadotropins and gonadal function in both sexes.[51] The hpg mouse has a genetic defect in GnRH production and lacks physiologically active GnRH. Thus, the GnRH neuronal system appears to be very redundant, such that many fewer GnRH neurons than normally participate in the regulation of pituitary gonadotropin secretion are actually needed to maintain gonadotropin secretion.

GnRH Neurons Can Be Regulated by Direct Neural Input

GnRH neurons are very simple in structure: they have an oval or fusiform-shaped cell body and simple dendrites, with relatively little branching, that extend from one or both poles of the cell body. The axon arises either from the cell body or from one of the dendrites. GnRH neurons have a large nucleus, and their cytoplasm contains large quantities of rough endoplasmic reticulum, Golgi, and neurosecretory granules. Neurosecretory granules are also found in quantity within the axon terminals. GnRH neurons are known to contain at least two other neuropeptides, galanin and delta-sleep-inducing peptide; however, the physiological actions of these two peptides released from GnRH neurons remain to be defined.

The density of innervation on GnRH neurons is markedly lower than the density of innervation on most other neurons in the hypothalamus. Ultrastructural analysis of various hypothalamic neurons has shown that only 0.38% of the GnRH dendritic membrane is covered by synaptic apposition, whereas 6.6% of the dendritic membrane in non-GnRH neurons is covered by synaptic apposition.[52] Although the number of synaptic inputs to GnRH neurons is small, synaptic input from a variety of neural types has been reported, including other GnRH neurons; dopaminergic, noradrenergic, and serotonergic neurons; and neurons containing β-endorphin, corticotropin-releasing hormone (CRH), GABA, vasopressin, neurotensin, substance P, and glutamate.[53] Thus, GnRH neurons can be regulated by direct input from a number of different neural systems. They also can be regulated indirectly by the numerous systems that in turn modulate the neural systems having direct synaptic connections to GnRH neurons.

GnRH neurons also appear to have interactions that do not fit the classification of typical synaptic contacts. Specifically, between some pairs of GnRH neurons are cytoplasmic bridges that were identified by tracing pairs of immunocytochemically identified GnRH neurons lying near each other through many ultrathin histological section.[54]

Steroid Hormones Affect GnRH Release

The interaction of GnRH neurons with other neurons can be dramatically altered by the presence or absence of gonadal steroid hormones. Gonadal steroid hormones appear to be important in influencing neural input onto GnRH neurons and sheathing of GnRH neurons by glia.[55] In monkeys, ovariectomy results in decreased synaptic input onto the cell bodies of GnRH neurons. This decrease perhaps results from a simulta-

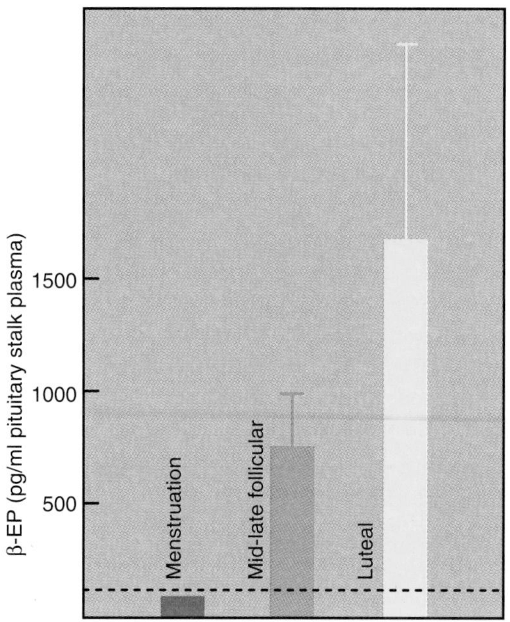

FIGURE 44.10 β-Endorphin concentrations measured in portal blood samples collected from rhesus monkeys at various times during the menstrual cycle. After Ferin *et al.*[56]

neous increase in the percentage of the cell bodies' membrane sheathed by glial processes. Ovarian steroid hormones also alter the glial sheathing of GnRH neuronal processes at the median eminence: with ovariectomy, glial processes retract so that GnRH terminals are closer to the basal lamina of blood vessels into which they put GnRH. These responses to ovarian steroid hormones likely play an important role in regulating the dramatic changes in the quantity of gonadotropins secreted from the pituitary across the course of the menstrual cycle, as well as in the postmenopausal state.

Evidence that steroid hormones act at the level of the hypothalamus to suppress pulsatile LH secretion has been provided by direct measurement of GnRH release into the portal bloodstream after treatment with steroid hormones. In addition, small amounts of crystalline steroid hormone placed within discrete areas of the hypothalamus modulate pulsatile LH secretion without concordant changes in levels of steroid hormone in the peripheral bloodstream. Steroid hormone negative feedback at the hypothalamus decreases the frequency of pulsatile GnRH stimulation of the pituitary and thus results in decreased frequency of pulsatile LH secretion. A good example of hypothalamic steroid hormone negative feedback action occurs during the luteal phase, when progesterone, in the presence of estrogen, leads to a marked decrease in the frequency of LH pulses with no decrease in LH pulse amplitude. Interestingly, LH pulses during the luteal phase are very large; the slow rate of LH pulses is thought to allow greater buildup within gonadotropes of releasable LH between pulses.

At the level of the hypothalamus, steroid hormones likely modulate the firing rate of GnRH neurons by acting indirectly to modulate neural systems that impinge on GnRH neurons. This conclusion is based on the inability of virtually all investigations to detect receptors for gonadal steroid hormones within GnRH neurons. In contrast, receptors for gonodal steroid hormones have been found on many of the neural systems that are known to make synaptic contact with GnRH neurons and to be capable of modulating GnRH neuronal firing rate. These systems include, among others, opioidergic, GABAergic, catecholaminergic, and NPY neurons. In females, there is strong evidence that the dramatic slowing of pulsatile LH secretion by progesterone in the luteal phase of the menstrual cycle is mediated by an increase in opioidergic inhibition of GnRH neuronal activity.[56] Direct measurement of the endogenous opioid peptide β-endorphin in the portal bloodstream of rhesus monkeys has shown that β-endorphin levels are lowest in the early follicular phase and greatest in the luteal phase of the menstrual cycle (Fig. 44.10). Moreover, when the opiate receptor antagonist **naloxone** is administered to monkeys or humans during the luteal phase of the menstrual cycle, LH pulse frequency increases to a rate similar to that occurring during the follicular phase (Fig. 44.11).

Pulsatile Stimulation of Pituitary Gonadotropes Is Necessary to Maintain Normal LH and FSH Secretion

Pulsatile stimulation of the pituitary by GnRH is necessary to maintain the normal function of pituitary gonadotropes. Exposure of the pituitary to continuous GnRH rapidly leads to a downregulation of GnRH

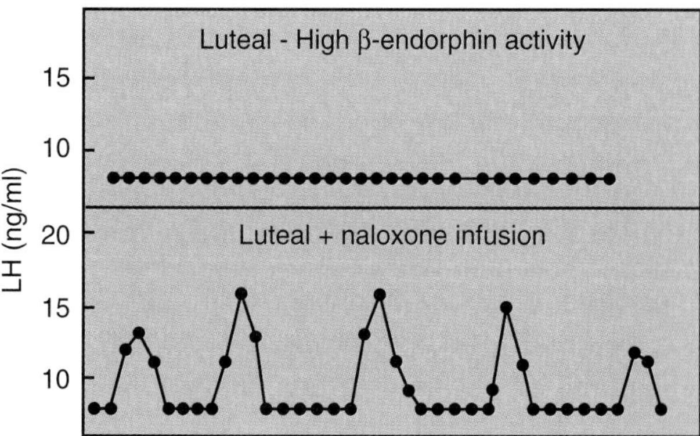

FIGURE 44.11 LH secretion in a female monkey during the luteal phase of the menstrual cycle and during a subsequent luteal phase when the animal received treatment with the opiate receptor antagonist naloxone. After Ferin *et al.*[56]

BOX 44.2

IDIOPATHIC CENTRAL PRECOCIOUS PUBERTY

If GnRH stimulates the pituitary in a continuous, rather than pulsatile, pattern, the pituitary rapidly downregulates its GnRH receptors. As a result, secretion of pituitary gonadotropins ceases. This finding is applied clinically to reverse pubertal development in children with idiopathic central precocious puberty, which results from an increase, of unknown origin, in GnRH drive to the pituitary prior to the normal onset time of puberty. Oral treatment with long-acting GnRH agonists, which provide a continuous GnRH stimulus to the pituitary, leads to GnRH receptor downregulation and effectively reverses pubertal development.[57a] These children are maintained on GnRH agonists until the time of normal puberty; this widely accepted method for treating precocious puberty has few side effects. When continuous exposure to GnRH is terminated, endogenous pulsatile GnRH stimulation of the pituitary occurs and onset of puberty and then normal adult reproductive function ensue.

Judy L. Cameron

receptors and an accompanying complete inhibition of pituitary gonadotropin secretion (Fig. 44.7).[57] This response can be used to treat precocious puberty (see Box 44.2).

At physiological frequencies of pulsatile GnRH release, GnRH upregulates its own receptors on pituitary gonadotropes. Thus, during periods of little GnRH neuron activity, such as the prepubertal period, periods of lactation, and states of chronic undernutrition, the number of GnRH receptors on gonadotropes decreases. Transition from a quiescent state to a state of normal adult activity is accompanied by an increase in the number of GnRH receptors and thus an increase in responsiveness of the pituitary to stimulation by GnRH.

There is a fairly narrow window of acceptable frequencies for stimulation of the pituitary by GnRH to achieve normal gonadotropin secretion. Pulse frequencies faster than once per hour lead to an inhibition of gonadotropin secretion and thus appear somewhat analogous to continuous GnRH stimulation of the pituitary. On the other hand, a GnRH pulse frequency of one every three hours in ovariectomized rhesus monkeys leads to a decrease in normal circulating levels of LH. Paradoxically, such slow frequencies of pulsatile GnRH lead to increased circulating levels of FSH. Whether this is a function of the longer half-life of FSH than of LH or is related to the ability of slow rates of GnRH stimulation of gonadotropes to preferentially release FSH is not well understood.

Negative Feedback by Gonadal Steroid Hormones Slows Pulsatile LH Secretion and Decreases LH Pulse Amplitude

The gonadal steroid hormones estradiol and testosterone can negatively feedback at the levels of the hypothalamus and pituitary to decrease the frequency of pulsatile gonadotropin secretion and decrease the amplitude of LH pulses.[58] The degree to which negative feedback occurs at the hypothalamus versus the pituitary appears to depend on species and sex. Progesterone appears to provide negative feedback exclusively at the level of the hypothalamus. The negative feedback action of gonadal steroids determines to a great extent the frequency of pulsatile gonadotropin secretion, which varies with the state of gonadal activity (Fig. 44.12).[59] For example, in women, pulsatile LH secretion in the early follicular phase of the menstrual cycle, when circulating concentrations of ovarian steroid hormones are quite low, occurs at a frequency of approximately one pulse per hour. As the follicular phase

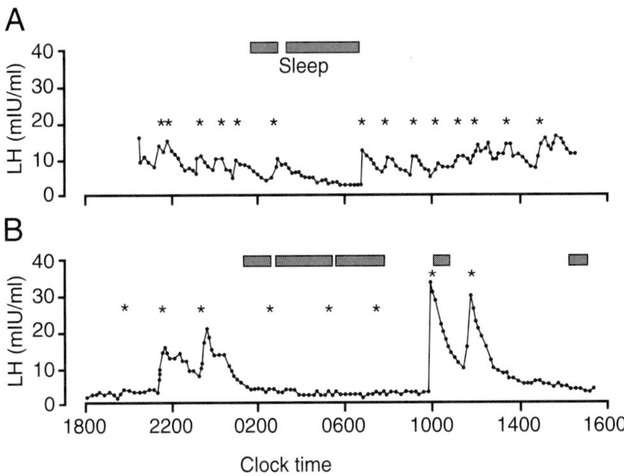

FIGURE 44.12 Rapid LH pulses in a woman during the early follicular phase of the menstrual cycle (top) and slow-frequency, large-amplitude LH pulses in a woman during the late luteal phase. Slowing of pulsatile LH secretion is apparent during sleep (indicated by the black bars). After Filicori *et al.*[59a]

progresses, and the developing ovarian follicles begin to secrete increasing amounts of estradiol, the frequency of pulsatile LH secretion slows to one pulse every 90 min. In the luteal phase of the menstrual cycle, when the ovary is secreting large quantities of progesterone, as well as estrodiol, LH pulses occur at a frequency of once every 6–12 h. In contrast, in men, LH pulse frequency remains rather stable throughout adulthood, at approximately one pulse every 2–3 h. However, testosterone levels play a large part in determining this frequency, as seen by the effects of castration (see Fig. 44.13).

Negative feedback of steroid hormones at the level of the pituitary decreases the sensitivity of pituitary gonadotropes to GnRH and thus results in a decrease in the amplitude of LH pulses but not in the frquency of LH pulses. In female primates, where estradiol negative feedback appears to be predominately at the level of the pituitary, LH secretion during the late follicular phase occurs as small, rapid pulses. Evidence that estradiol can act at the level of the pituitary comes from studies showing that the pituitary contains estradiol receptors, that estradiol can decrease the release of LH from pituitaries studied *in vitro*, and that estradiol can suppress secretion of gonadotropins in animals whose GnRH input to the pituitary is held constant by the intravenous infusion of exogenous GnRH.

Gonadal steroid hormones also provide negative feedback action that governs FSH secretion. The control of FSH secretion, however, is not as well understood as the control of LH secretion. In females, FSH secretion decreases over the course of the follicular phase, remains low throughout most of the luteal phase, and increases at the luteal–follicular phase transition at the beginning of each ovarian cycle. Studies in the monkey indicate that both the decrease in FSH secretion during the follicular phase and the increase in FSH secretion in the perimenstrual period can be accounted for by changes in estradiol negative feedback.[60] However, follicles and corpora lutea produce a

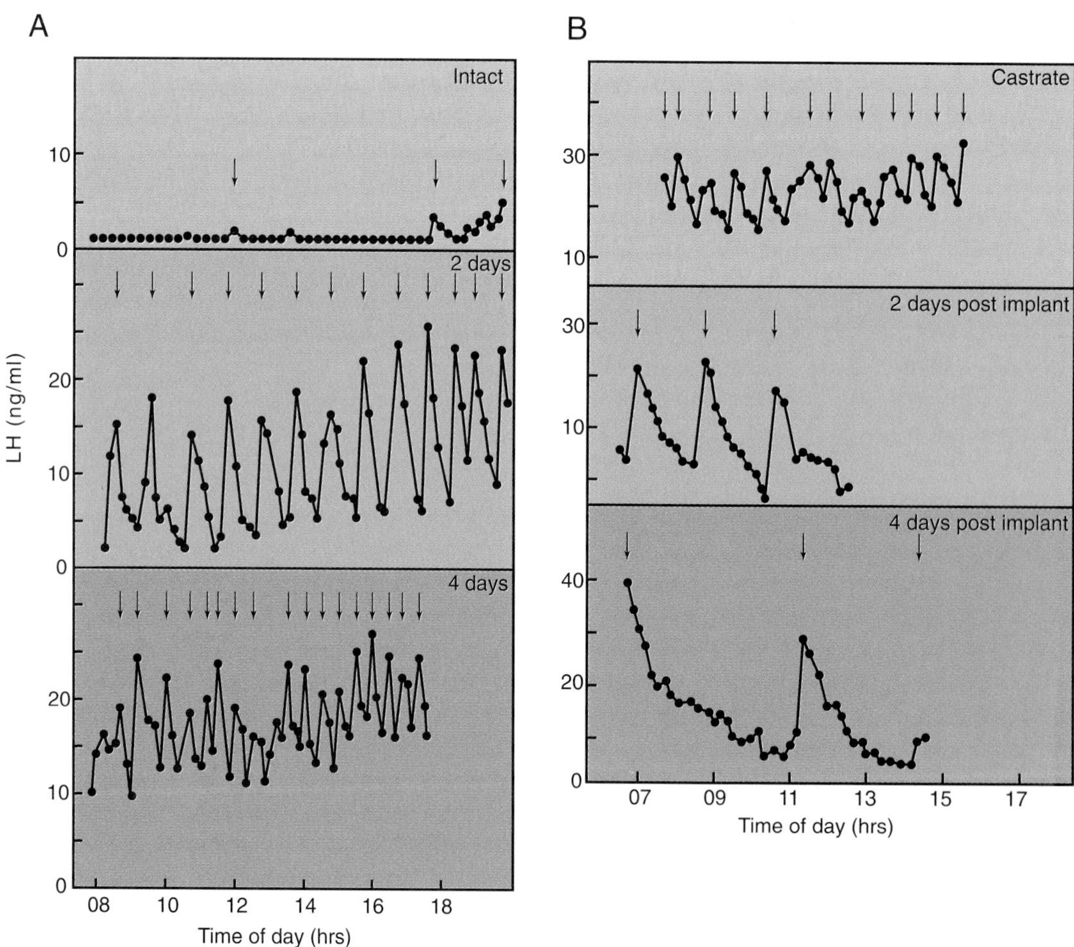

FIGURE 44.13 LH pulses in a male monkey before (A) and after (B) castration with replacement of physiological levels of testosterone (lower right). After Plant.[59b]

glycoprotein hormone, **inhibin,** that can selectively act at the pituitary to suppress FSH secretion.[61] The relative roles of estradiol and inhibin in providing negative feedback to FSH secretion over the course of the ovarian cycle remain to be determined. Differences in the actions of inhibin in the female may also vary by species. A role for inhibin in providing negative feedback to FSH secretion is more firmly established in the male, at least in some species. In monkeys, testosterone replacement after castration cannot suppress the high, postcastration levels of FSH to normal physiological range, but replacement with testosterone plus inhibin reestablishes normal levels of FSH.[62]

Positive Feedback by Estradiol Causes the Midcycle Gonadotropin Surge in Females and Regulates Ovarian Cyclicity

Ovarian function is cyclic. In women, the first half of the menstrual cycle is characterized by the growth and development of a cohort of follicles, culminating with selection and ovulation of the ovum from a single dominant follicle at about 14 days from the beginning of the cycle. After ovulation, the cells of the collapsed follicle are reorganized into a transiently functional, steroid-producing gland, the **corpus luteum,** that secretes progesterone and estrogen. Should fertilization of the ovulated ovum occur, these ovarian hormones play a critical role in preparing the uterus for implantation of the developing embryo. If a pregnancy does not occur, the corpus luteum spontaneously becomes dysfunctional after approximately 14 days. Withdrawal of gonadal steroid hormone support to the uterus leads to sloughing of the endometrial lining (i.e., menses), and the period of follicular development is reinitiated. In women, and other primates with menstrual bleeding, Day 1 of the menstrual cycle is designated the first day of menstrual bleeding. Species in which the endometrium is reabsorbed, rather than sloughed, show a behavioral predisposition to mating during the time of ovulation. Cycles in these species are referred to as **estrous cycles,** and the first day of the cycle is designated the day of ovulation, the time when estrus is maximal. Females of all mammalian species show cyclic ovarian activity; however, the duration of the follicular and luteal phases of the cycle differs among species. In all species, the cyclic events within ovaries are regulated by finely tuned interplay between gonadal steroid hormones and the hypothalamic and pituitary systems that provide the central drive to the reproductive axis.

A key event in the regulation of cyclic ovarian function is the midcycle gonadotropin surge. This surge triggers the final maturation of the ovum inside the ripe preovulatory follicle; it is also responsible for ovulation and the development of the corpus luteum. During the follicular phase of the cycle, the developing follicles begin to secrete estradiol in response to FSH from the pituitary. As estradiol (and perhaps inhibin) levels increase, they provide negative feedback that decreases gonadotrophic support to the follicle. However, simultaneously, the most developed follicle (or follicles, in species that ovulate multiple follicles each cycle) develops receptors for LH and FSH, and thus it receives enough gonadotrophic support to continue developing. Less developed follicles, with inadequate numbers of LH receptors, lose gonadotrophic support and undergo a degenerative process called **atresia.** The dominant follicle(s) responds to FSH and LH by greatly increasing estradiol synthesis in the last few days of the follicular phase. The sustained high levels of estradiol act at the hypothalamus and pituitary to cause a positive feedback effect such that a large outpouring of LH and FSH is released from the pituitary (i.e., the midcycle gonadotropin surge). The very high levels of LH and FSH released during the surge trigger the final maturation of the ovum within the dominant follicle and trigger ovulation of that follicle. The gonadotropin surge also initiates the development of the corpus luteum, and LH provides essential trophic support to the corpus luteum throughout the luteal phase. As the corpus luteum develops and secretes increasing amounts of progesterone and estrogen, the negative feedback to the hypothalamus is increased, and LH pulse frequency slows dramatically. If fertilization and implantation do not occur, the corpus luteum spontaneously regresses. The ensuing decline in circulating levels of progesterone and estrogen allow an increase in gonadotropin secretion, which plays an important role in supporting follicular development in the following cycle.

In women, estradiol positive feedback occurs when estradiol levels reach approximately 150 pg ml^{-1} for at least 36 h. Both the magnitude and the duration of elevated estradiol are critical for the induction of the gonadotropin surge. Estradiol elicits positive feedback by acting at the level of the hypothalamus to increase GnRH release and at the level of the pituitary to increase gonadtrope sensitivity to GnRH. In primates, the dual sites of estradiol positive feedback ensure the release of a large gonadotropin surge, but experiments have shown that positive feedback at the pituitary alone can effectively elicit a gonadotropin surge. In no species is the mechanism underlying the estradiol positive feedback action known. However, measurement of GnRH in the portal bloodstream of sheep indicates that GnRH release during the surge is not pulsatile, suggesting that the surge may involve a GnRH release mechanism that is distinctly different from the normal, pulsatile GnRH release mechanism.

Although the hypothalamopituitary branch of the reproductive axis plays a critical role in producing the midcycle gonadotropin surge, the timing of events in the ovarian cycle clearly is regulated by the ovaries. The pace of follicular development determines the timing of the preovulatory rise in estradiol, which in turn determines the timing of the midcycle gonadotropin surge. The gonadotropin surge triggers ovulation and development of the corpus luteum; however, the duration of the luteal phase does not appear to be governed by the central neural drive to the reproductive axis. This has been very clearly established by studies in monkeys with hypothalamic lesions: when the monkeys receive pulses of exogenous GnRH, the life span of the corpus luteum is normal despite unchanging pituitary gonadotrophic support to the corpus luteum. The concept that events within the ovary provide the timing mechanism for ovarian cycles has led to the ovary being called the *zeitgeber* (i.e., timekeeper) of cyclic reproductive function within the female.

Estrous Cycles Represent a Different Female Reproductive Pattern

Many studies in the field of neuroscience use the rat as an experimental model. The regulation of ovarian cyclicity in the female rat differs from that in primates in several important aspects. First, the rat has 4- to 5-day estrous cycles rather than 28-day menstrual cycles. During a 4-day estrous cycle, the day of ovulation and behavioral receptivity to the male is denoted as the day of estrus. The next days are metestrus and diestrus, and the 4th day is proestrous, the day of the gonadotropin surge. Five-day estrous cycles have an extra day of diestrus. As in primates, the pattern of gonadotropin secretion changes over the course of the cycle. Gonadotropin levels are markedly suppressed on the day of estrus; they increase on metestrus and diestrus, when high-frequency LH pulses are present; and the gonadotropin surge occurs on proestrous (Fig. 44.14). Despite a short cycle length, the duration of follicular development is not shortened: individual ovarian follicles develop over multiple ovarian cycles in the rat. The follicles that are selected for ovulation are those that reach the final developmental stages at the time of the midcycle gonadotropin surge. In rodents, multiple follicles ovulate during each cycle, in contrast to ovulation of a single follicle in primates. On the day of proestrous, positive feedback of estradiol at the level of the hypothalamus is necessary to trigger a gonadotropin surge. The rostral hypothalamus appears to play a critical role in mediating estradiol-induced gonadotropin surges in this species. Implantation of small amounts of estradiol into this region will evoke a gonadotropin surge, and destruction of the rostral hypothalamus will not interfere with estradiol-induced negative feedback but will prevent estradiol-induced positive feedback. In rodents, CNS timekeeping mechanisms also play a role in regulating the timing of the gonadotropin surge so that the gonadotropin surge occurs only at a particular time of day with reference to the light–dark cycle. Another important difference between the primate menstrual cycle and the rat estrous cycle is that in the rat the corpus luteum produces progesterone for only a very short period of time (i.e., on the day of estrus) during a nonfertile cycle. This lack of a true luteal phase in the rat cycle is what allows the cycle length to be very short. A short estrous cycle is advantageous for this relatively short-lived species, because it increases the frequency with which the rat enters periods of fertility (i.e., estrus). If pregnancy occurs, the life span of the corpus luteum is extended to provide steroid hormone support to the uterine lining. The life span of the corpus luteum is also extended during

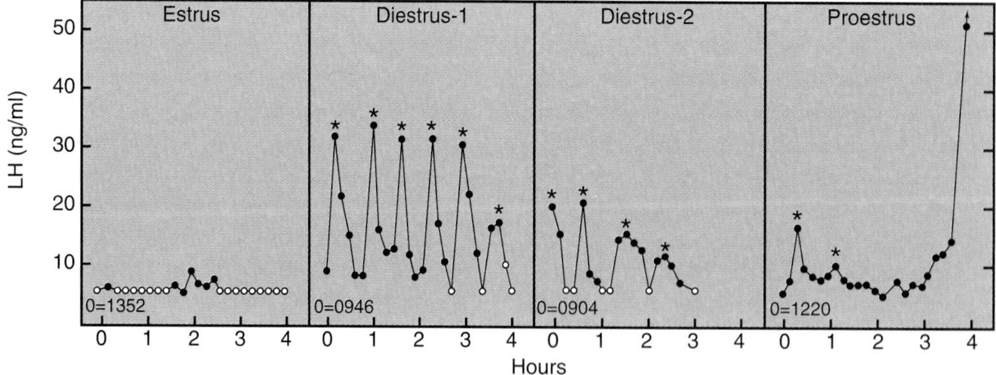

FIGURE 44.14 Pattern of pulsatile LH secretion in female rats during each day of the estrous cycle. After Fox and Smith.[59]

pseudopregnancy, which is brought about by stimulating the rat's vaginal area. In the rat the pituitary hormone **prolactin** provides critical support to the corpus luteum; this role is played by LH in primates and many other species.

The Activity of GnRH Neurons Changes during a Lifetime

Reproductive function is not static throughout life. Instead, it matures developmentally,[63] and in adulthood it can be influenced by a number of environmental mediators.[64] In general, shifts in the activity of the reproductive axis are directed by shifts in the activity of GnRH neurons, which provide the central drive to the reproductive axis. During childhood, the reproductive axis is quiescent, with virtually no LH or FSH production by the pituitary and minimal activity within the ovaries and testes. At puberty, an increase in activity of GnRH neurons directs the awakening of the reproductive axis and initiates the period of adult fertility. Fertility in adulthood can be interrupted, however, by periods of low energy availability caused by undernutrition or by high energy utilization resulting from exercise or thermogenesis, by a variety of stresses, and in seasonally breeding species by environmental cues such as day length. Interestingly, all of these cues appear to modulate the activity of the reproductive axis by acting at the level of the brain to decrease the activity of the GnRH neuronal system. Thus, the GnRH neuronal system serves as the central coordination site that tailors the reproductive capacity of an individual to a level appropriate for the environment in which it lives.

Functional GnRH Neurons in the Fetal Hypothalamus

Soon after migrating to their final destinations within the hypothalamus, GnRH neurons are active and provide stimulatory drive to the anterior pituitary gonadotropes. In primates, gonadotropin secretion then declines during the late stages of gestation, likely as a result of increased negative feedback from placental steroid hormones. In humans and nonhuman primates, a second period of increased activity of the reproductive axis occurs in the early postnatal period. In males, the neonatal period of reproductive axis activation is characterized by elevated circulating concentrations of LH, FSH, and testosterone. In females, LH and FSH levels are elevated, but follicular development and consequent gonadal steroid hormone production do not proceed as in the adult female. Evidence that the neonatal period of reproductive axis activation results from increased activity of the GnRH neuronal system comes from studies showing that treatment with a GnRH agonist in the neonatal period (which downregulates GnRH receptors on the pituitary gonadotropes) can suppress reproductive hormone secretion during this developmental stage. After the period of neonatal activation of the reproductive axis, gonadotropin and gonadal steroid hormone levels fall to concentrations at or below those detectable for most assays. This juvenile period of reproductive axis quiescence occurs in humans from the latter half of the first year of life to the time of puberty, which usually occurs between the ages of 8 and 11 in girls and from 11 to 14 in boys.

Childhood Reproductive Quiescence and Decreased Activity of the GnRH Neuronal System

In primate species, the juvenile period of reproductive quiescence is not a result of increased negative feedback from gonadal steroid hormones: a similar decrease in circulating gonadotropin concentrations is observed in neonatally castrated monkeys and in humans with gonadal dysgenesis. Rather, the juvenile period of reproductive quiescence appears to be central in origin, resulting from decreased activity of the GnRH neuronal system. Other mammals also show developmental changes in reproductive capacity and have an early period of reproductive axis inactivity. However, in all other species studied, removal of the gonads results in an elevation of gonadotropin secretion, indicating that the quiescence emanates from increased sensitivity of the central neural axis to gonadal steroid hormone negative feedback.

Decreased GnRH neural drive to the pituitary during the prepubertal period does not result from a failure of GnRH neurons to produce GnRH. Prior to puberty, GnRH neurons contain levels of GnRH mRNA and peptide that are equivalent or nearly equivalent to those measured in adulthood. Moreover, prior to puberty GnRH neurons stimulated by electrical depolarization or an excitatory neurotransmitter are capable of releasing GnRH, and the released GnRH is able to enter the portal vasculature and travel to the pituitary to stimulate pituitary gonadotropin secretion. These findings are consistent with the prepubertal period having either an increase in inhibitory neural input to the GnRH neuronal system or a decrease in stimulatory drive to the GnRH neuronal system. Increased GABAergic inhibition of GnRH release may play a role in the prepubertal inhibition of GnRH neuronal activity: Studies have shown a decrease in GABA secretion at the level of the median eminence in monkeys during the pubertal transition. Moreover, administration of an antiserum to GABA can increase GnRH release in prepubertal, but not peripubertal, monkeys, suggesting that GABAergic tone on the GnRH system decreases as puberty progresses. Another possibility is that multiple mechanisms contribute to the inhibition of GnRH neuronal activity during the prepubertal period, such that developmental changes in inhibitory and stimulatory input to GnRH neuronal system trigger puberty.

Species- and Sex-Specific Timing and Pattern of GnRH Neuronal Activation at Puberty

The mechanism that governs the timing of puberty is not well understood. One possibility is that an intrinsic timing mechanism exists in whatever neural system is responsible for stimulating the GnRH neuronal system at puberty. Alternatively, a great deal of evidence suggests that the timing of the onset of puberty is linked to growth of an individual, so that in many species reproductive capacity is attained when an individual has attained adult body proportions. The concept that some aspect of body growth or size modulates GnRH neuronal activity is appealing because it provides a means for coordinating the development of reproductive capacity and the capability of females to carry a pregnancy to term and the capability of males to compete for a mate and for mating territory. This hypothesis is consistent with the finding that puberty is delayed in chronically undernourished individuals who display impaired growth. However, currently no conclusive evidence supports the hypothesis that some aspect of body growth or size cues the activation of the GnRH neuronal system at puberty.

Activation of the GnRH neuronal system occurs in a distinctive pattern. During the early stages of puberty, there is a marked nighttime increase in LH pulsatility in both girls and boys. This nighttime increase can be quite dramatic, with virtually no LH pulses occurring in the daytime hours and a number of large LH pulses occurring at night. The diurnal rhythm appears to be sleep-associated; that is, it can be reversed in individuals who are kept awake during the night and allowed to sleep during the day (Fig. 44.15). Interestingly, after the central drive to the reproductive axis is suppressed in adulthood, such as by chronic undernutrition or vigorous exercise training, when normal metabolic status is reinstated, the reawakening of the reproductive axis is accompanied by this same nighttime increase in pulsatile LH secretion. Thus, the initiation of pulsatile LH secretion at any time in life appears to involve neural input to the GnRH pulse generator, which receives information about day–night rhythms.

Effects of Pregnancy and Lactation on Activity of the Adult Female Reproductive Axis

If fertilization occurs and pregnancy ensues, the normal activity of the reproductive axis is disrupted for the duration of the pregnancy and the period of lactation. During pregnancy the placenta takes over many of the functions of the pituitary and the ovaries. In women, the placenta produces a glycoprotein hormone, **human chorionic gonadotropin** (hCG), that binds to LH receptors and extends the life span of the corpus luteum. hCG plays a critical role in providing adequate progesterone to support the uterine lining during early pregnancy. As the placenta develops, it produces massive quantities (compared with the amounts produced during normal ovarian cycle) of estrogen and progesterone. Interestingly, the placenta synthesizes and secretes GnRH, and placental GnRH appears at least partially responsible for stimulating the placental production of hCG. The mechanisms governing placental GnRH production and release are not well understood; however, a number of hormones and neurotransmitters (i.e., prostaglandins, epinephrine, insulin, and vasoactive intestinal peptide) may modulate placental GnRH release.

After parturition, female mammals lactate, wholly or partially providing nutritional support to their young. In many species, cyclic ovarian activity is suppressed during the period of intense lactation. This acyclicity is associated with suppressed pituitary LH and FSH secretion, which results from a decrease in GnRH stimulation to the pituitary. Suppression of the central neural drive to the reproductive axis lessens as the frequency and duration of lactation diminish and the young increase their intake of other food sources. The mechanism by which lactation suppresses GnRH neuronal activity is not well understood; however, it appears to be multifactorial, because several neural and hormonal changes that occur during lactation appear to contribute to the suppression of GnRH secretion. One aspect of the inhibition is increased production of the pituitary hormone prolactin (discussed in detail later) during the period of lactation. Prolactin acts primarily at the breast but has also been shown to inhibit GnRH neuronal activity.

Menopause and a Decline in Ovarian Function

Male and female mammals show changes in fertility and reproductive function with aging; however, the changes in males are subtle, whereas dramatic changes occur in females. In males, fertility decreases with age, apparently as a consequence of cumulative physical, physiological, and behavioral changes. However, despite a statistical decrease in fertility with age, many males remain fertile and reproductively competent well into old age. In contrast, reproductive senescence in females is essentially universal in mammalian species and results from a depletion of ovarian follicles. Females are born with all ovarian follicles that they

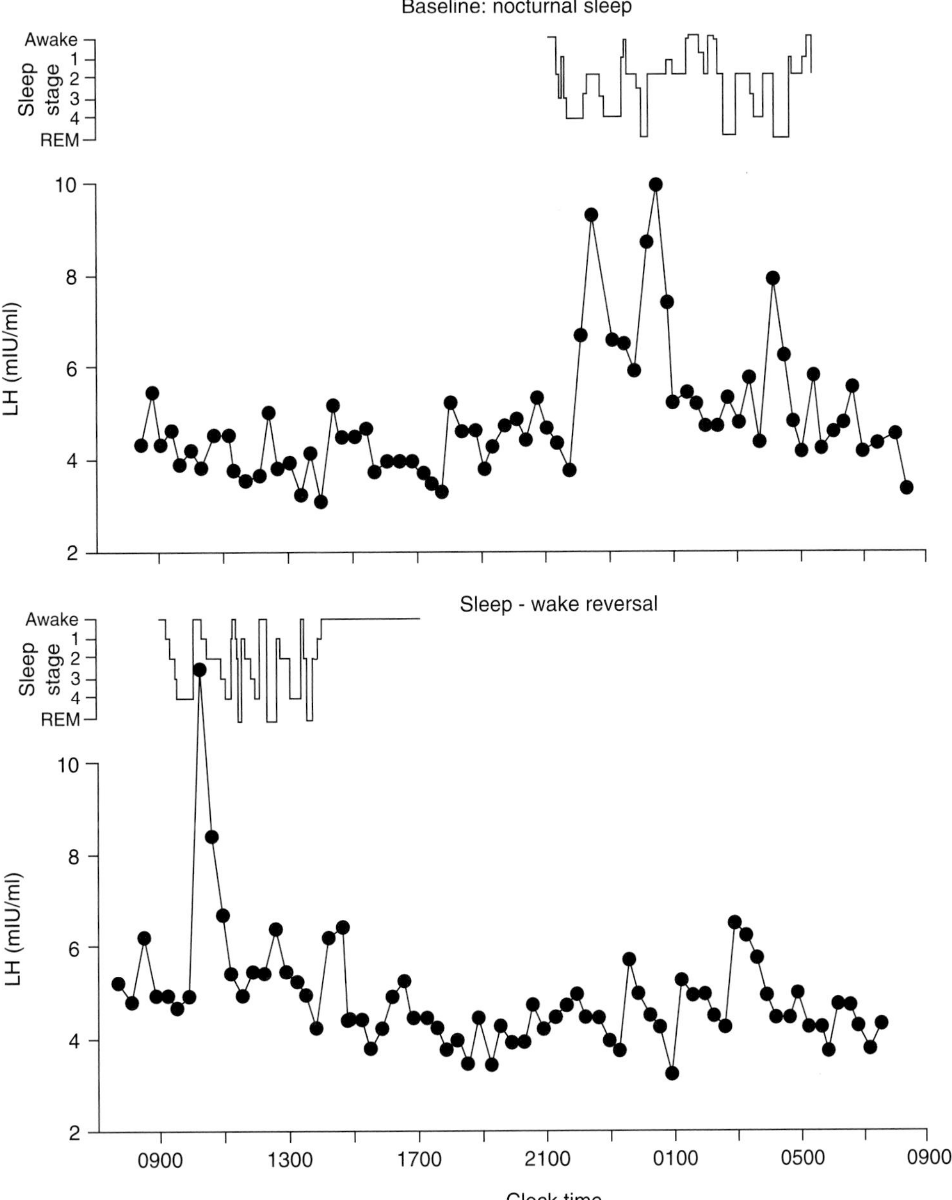

FIGURE 44.15 (Top) Nocturnal sleep. (Bottom) Sleep–wake reversal.

will have during their life span. Females do not produce new primordial follicles at the beginning of each ovarian cycle. Instead, during each cycle a cohort of existing primordial follicles begins to develop and mature. Within each cohort only one or several follicles (depending on the species) will fully develop and ovulate, while the other follicles that began development undergo the degenerative process of atresia. With increasing age, the ovaries have fewer and fewer primordial follicles, until eventually the ovarian supply of follicles is depleted. As follicular depletion occurs, follicular estrogen production decreases, leading to a loss of estrogen support to estrogen-responsive tissues in the body, such as the uterine lining, the breasts, and the vaginal epithelium. Loss of estrogen support to the uterus results in decreased development of the uterine lining during each ovarian cycle, which eventually leads to a loss of menstrual shedding of the uterine lining in species that show menses. The term **menopause** refers to the cessation of menstrual cycles. Menopause is a late event in the process of reproductive aging, and it is preceded by a period of variable ovarian function, characterized by irregular cycle lengths, decreased estrogen production, anovulation, and reduced fertility. In addition to providing less estrogen support to secondary reproductive tissues, diminishing ovarian estrogen production leads to a decline in negative feedback to the hypothalamic and pituitary components of the reproductive axis. Thus, the pituitary secretion of LH and FSH increases during the period of declining ovarian function and is very high in the postmenopausal period. Loss of fertility at menopause results from a decline in ovarian function, not a decrease in GnRH stimulation of the reproductive axis. In women, ovarian depletion of follicles occurs at about 50 years of age, regardless of reproductive history (the age at which onset of puberty occurred, the number of pregnancies, etc.). Thus, women generally live 20 to 30 years beyond the cessation of reproductive function. During these years, many women experience pathologies associated with the cessation of ovarian hormone production, such as osteoporosis and cardiovascular disease.

The decline in circulating levels of estrogen is also associated with the occurrence of *hot flashes*, sudden, uncomfortable sensations of warmth sweeping over the upper body and face, usually accompanied by sweating. Hot flashes also occur in younger women who undergo ovariectomy and in men who undergo castration—conditions in which circulating estrogen levels decrease dramatically. The etiology of hot flashes is not well understood, but they appear to result from a disturbance in the hypothalamic center that regulates body temperature, an area that expresses a high density of estrogen receptors. Hot flashes, like many symptoms resulting from the postmenopausal decrease in circulating estrogen levels, can be alleviated by low doses of estrogen. More importantly, estrogen treatment is used to decrease the risk of cardiovascular disease and to slow the rate of bone loss (i.e., osteoporosis) in postmenopausal women. Estrogen replacement therapy is often supplemented with a progesteronelike compound, because estrogen replacement, alone, is linked to an increased incidence of endometrial carcinoma.

Environmental Regulation of GnRH Neuronal Activity

Reproductive function can be regulated by many environmental cues. For the most part, environmental cues modulate the central neural drive to the reproductive axis. GnRH neurons are ideally located to receive information from several of the brain's sensory systems, such as the visual and olfactory systems. However, with their axons extending into the hypothalamic median eminence, which is outside the blood–brain barrier, GnRH neurons are also in a position to detect homeostatic changes within the body, such as changes in circulating levels of metabolic fuels and hormones.

Diurnal Rhythms Occur in a Number of Reproductive Processes, and Many of the Rhythms Can Be Entrained to the 24-Hour Day–Night Cycle

Examples of diurnal rhythms can be found in most reproductive processes, including the secretion of reproductive hormones, the timing of ovulation, and even the timing of parturition. However, some species demonstrate much greater entrainment to the 24-h day–night cycle than others. Rodents show marked diurnal rhythms both in the secretion of reproductive hormones and in the timing of ovulation. For example, a female rat maintained on a regular light–dark cycle will experience the midcycle LH–FSH surge and ovulation on a specific day of the ovarian cycle and at a specific time of day. Moreover, if the normally occurring gonadotropin surge is blocked by anesthetizing the rat during the normal period of the surge, it will not experience the surge until the appropriate time in the 24-h light cycle on the following day. In other species, the midcycle LH surge and ovulation are less tightly linked to the 24-h light–dark cycle, but in many species, diurnal rhythms are evident in the secretion of reproductive hormones. For example, men have an increased secretion of testosterone at night. In contrast, in women LH secretion slows at night, particularly during the follicular phase of the menstrual cycle. Humans also display a transient, but marked, diurnal pattern of reproductive hormone secretion during the onset of puberty, as discussed earlier. During early pubertal awakening of the reproductive axis, gonadotropin and gonadal steroid hormone secretion occurs almost exclusively at night. As puberty progresses, more reproductive hormone secretion occurs during the daylight hours. Little is known about the central neural mechanisms regulating circadian rhythms of reproductive processes.

Many Species Have Seasonal Rhythms in Reproductive Processes

Most species living in temperate zones show seasonal rhythms in reproductive processes. Reproductive capacity is optimal during the time of year that results in the birth of young during periods when the likelihood of their survival is highest. In many such species, reproductive hormone levels and gonadal function are markedly suppressed during the period of the year when reproductive function is minimal. Suppression of the reproductive axis usually results from decreased central neural drive to the pituitary. Suppression is characterized by low, noncyclic release of pituitary gonadotropins, a decrease in pituitary responsiveness to GnRH, and a cessation of ovulation. In these species seasonal increases in reproductive capacity are stimulated by a pubertal-like activation of the central neural drive to the reproductive axis. No single strategy is used to adapt reproductive function to variability of the environment; different species use day length, food availability, temperature, and social cues independently or together to time annual periodicity in reproductive capacity.

In many species, seasonal fluxes in reproductive capacity are governed by seasonal changes in day length. Day length is detected and transduced into a signal governing GnRH neuronal activity via the pathway from the optic tracts to the suprachiasmatic nucleus to the pineal body, as discussed in Chapter 45. The duration of the daily production of melatonin by the pineal body, which occurs almost exclusively during darkness, is the critical cue that transmits information about the relative lengths of day and night to the GnRH neuronal system. Depending on the species, melatonin can be either inhibitory or stimulatory to the central neural drive to the reproductive axis. For example, short nights, with a brief duration of melatonin secretion, provide a stimulatory signal to the reproductive axis of some species, such as the hamster. The same short nights provide an inhibitory signal to the reproductive axis of other species, such as sheep. As a consequence of the influence of melatonin in these species, hamsters breed during the time of year when the days are long, and sheep breed during the time of year when days are short. Interestingly, in a number of species in which day length does not modulate seasonal breeding, such as the laboratory rat, melatonin secretion remains sensitive to the daily photoperiod, but the reproductive axis does not react to the pattern of melatonin secretion. Although melatonin is a powerful regulator of the reproductive axis, the neural route by which melatonin modulates GnRH neuronal activity is unknown, as is the mechanism that determines whether melatonin provides stimulatory or inhibitory input to the reproductive axis.

Food availability, combined with demands on energy resources, also provides cues used by many species to time reproductive function to specific periods of the years. As discussed later, dietary energy intake can profoundly affect the level of central neural drive to the reproductive axis. Also, the reproductive axis of some species is more sensitive to levels of energy availability than that of others. Energy need, either for thermogenesis or for foraging, also plays a role in determining energy availability, and in some species energy requirements regulate seasonal changes in reproductive function. Moreover, some species use a combined signal integrating food availability and energy requirements to regulate reproductive function. For example, female mice reproduce in cool ambient temperatures when they are allowed to increase their food intake, but their reproductive function is suppressed if increased food intake is not permitted.

Many species also use social cues to regulate the timing of reproductive function. Such social cues are frequently mediated by chemicals (i.e., pheromones) released by one individual that affect the reproductive capacity of other individuals. In many species the presence of pheromones is detected by a specialized sensory organ, the vomeronasal organ, located behind the olfactory lobe (see Chapter 25).

The Availability of Adequate Nutrition Plays an Important Role in Modulating the Central Neural Drive to the Reproductive Axis[37]

In most species studied to date, nutritional intake can profoundly affect the central neural drive to the reproductive axis. Chronically undernourished animals and humans generally have a decline in gonadal function and reproductive hormone secretion. A particularly striking example of this relationship between the level of food intake and reproductive function is found in individuals with anorexia nervosa, a disease in which individuals see themselves as too fat and severely restrict their food intake, often leading to a profound loss of body weight. In anorexic women and in females of many species, undernutrition leads to a loss of ovarian cyclicity, an absence of ovulation, and a regression of breasts and other secondary sexual characteristics that are supported by ovarian steroid hormones. In males, undernutrition leads to a decrease in testosterone production and spermatogenesis, and again a regression of secondary sexual characteristics. Circulating levels of the gonadotropins LH and FSH are also markedly suppressed in undernourished states. If the period of undernutrition has been extensive, administration of exogenous GnRH may cause little gonadotropin release, because pituitary gonadotropes may have lost GnRH receptors. However, treatment with a pulsatile regimen of GnRH can restore gonadotropin secretion and full gonadal function if the treatment is of long enough duration. This finding provides strong evidence that the primary locus of dysfunction within the reproductive axis in undernourished states is at the level of the GnRH neurons. And in fact, in sheep, from which blood can be directly sampled from the hypothalamopituitary portal system, chronic undernutrition leads to a decrease in GnRH concentrations in portal blood.

Chronic undernutrition can also delay the onset of puberty. If undernutrition is severe, puberty can be delayed for many months or years, until a time when adequate nutrition is provided. In some species that are seasonal breeders, nutritional variation among adequately nourished animals can play an important role in determining the year in which puberty onset will occur. For example, large, well-nourished lambs will generally enter puberty in the first breeding season after birth, whereas relatively small, poorly nourished lambs will often not enter puberty until the second breeding season. Similar effects of nutrition as a natural modulator of puberty onset have been documented in rhesus monkeys. A similar relationship is suspected in humans, because the age of onset of puberty correlates with body fat mass.

Although it is well documented that chronic states of undernutrition can suppress the central neural drive to the reproductive axis, as well as delay the pubertal awakening of the GnRH pulse generator, studies indicate that very brief changes in nutritional intake can also modulate GnRH stimulation of the reproductive axis. In hamsters, fasting on the day of the midcycle gonadotropin surge can delay the surge until the following day. In rats, fasting for 2 days can significantly decrease the rate of pulsatile LH secretion, and similar findings have been documented in men after 2 days of fasting and in monkeys within hours after a single meal is missed. In each of these species, normal pulsatile gonadotropin secretion is rapidly restored when adequate nutritional intake is restored. These findings suggest that nutritional signals are part of the normal physiological mechanism governing the central neural drive to the reproductive axis and are not signals that influence GnRH neuronal activity only in severe undernutrition.

The mechanism by which nutritional signals modulate GnRH neuronal activity is unknown. However, the signal does not appear to be dependent on the level of a specific nutrient, nor do nutrients need to enter the body via the gastrointestinal tract to serve as effective modulators of reproductive hormone secretion. Cumulative data from several species suggest that cellular energy availability may be a key regulator of the central neural drive to the reproductive axis, but which cells sense the level of available energy remains to be determined.

Modulation of Energy Availability by Exercise Can Also Alter the Central Neural Drive to the Reproductive Axis

Thermogenesis and exercise also can change energy availability and modulate the central drive to the reproductive axis. Exercise-induced reproductive dysfunction, best characterized in women athletes, is associated with very high levels of aerobic exercise in individuals who characteristically maintain low body weights (i.e., runners, ballet dancers). Exercise-induced reproductive dysfunction in adulthood, like undernutrition-induced reproductive dysfunction, is associated with a loss of normal ovarian cyclicity, a decrease in circulating levels of ovarian hormones, and a suppression of pulsatile LH secretion. Chronic, strenuous exercise in the prepubertal period can also delay onset of puberty. Longitudinal studies of female teenage ballet dancers have shown that pubertal onset can occur very rapidly (in a matter of weeks) in prepubertal ballet dancers when their training level decreases due to injury or vacation. Secondary reproductive dysfunction recurs when strenuous training is reinitiated. Studies in female monkeys trained to exercise vigorously on a treadmill have shown that exercise suppresses the central drive to the reproductive axis via the decrease in energy availability caused by increased energy utilization. This finding helps explain why exercise-induced reproductive dysfunction is more prevalent in thin individuals and can be induced only in some species, such as rats, when accompanied by the restriction of food intake. Again, as in undernutrition-induced reproductive dysfunction, the mechanism by which changes in energy availability modulate GnRH neuronal activity remains unknown.

Many Types of Stress Can Suppress the Activity of GnRH Neurons

In addition to the metabolic stresses discussed earlier, many other types of stress are known to impair the activity of GnRH neurons. Stresses able to suppress reproductive function range from physical stresses, such as experimentally induced footshock and activation of the immune system, to psychological stresses, such as fright and social stress. Acute and chronic exposures to various stresses have been shown to suppress pulsatile LH secretion. For example, secretion is suppressed within minutes to hours of footshock or a single dose of exogenously administered interleukin-1. In contrast, chronic social stress can impair reproductive function for months to years. Despite their heterogeneity, all stressors that can suppress the reproductive axis appear to act primarily by decreasing the central drive to the reproductive axis, demonstrated by a suppression of gonadotropin secretion. Although some stressors may act at the level of the pituitary to decrease pituitary responsiveness to GnRH, evidence suggests that stress acts primarily within the central nervous system to decrease GnRH stimulation of the pituitary.

Various stressors probably suppress GnRH neuronal activity via different mechanisms. For several specific types of stress, evidence indicates that the mechanism for suppressing the GnRH neuronal system differs among species. Therefore, generalizations are difficult to make about the routes by which stress impairs GnRH neuronal activity. Nevertheless, two afferent neuronal systems activated by a variety of stresses are known to synapse onto GnRH neurons and to inhibit GnRH neuronal activity. These systems have received much attention in the field of stress-induced reproductive dysfunction; they are β-endorphin- and CRH-containing neuronal systems.

β-Endorphin-containing neurons have been shown to synapse onto GnRH neurons in the rat, sheep, and monkey. Moreover, agonists of this opioid peptide rapidly and profoundly suppress gonadotropin secretion, and antagonists can often stimulate basal gonadotropin secretion, as well as reverse the effects of some forms of stress-induced reproductive dysfunction. For example, footshock-induced suppression of LH secretion in the rat can be prevented by the prior administration of the opioid antagonist naloxone. In contrast, undernutrition-induced suppression of LH secretion cannot be restored by the administration of naloxone. In fact, measurement of β-endorphin levels in the median eminence of undernourished animals has indicated that activity of β-endorphin-containing neurons may be suppressed rather than activated by nutritional stress.

As discussed earlier, CRH neurons provide the central hypothalamic drive to the brain–pituitary–adrenal axis. Although many CRH neurons are neuroendocrine in nature and have axons that terminate on portal vessels within the median eminence, CRH neurons also synapse onto GnRH neurons in several species. CRH administration into the cerebral ventricular system can suppress gonadotropin secretion, and administration of a CRH antagonist can prevent several forms of stress-induced suppression of reproductive hormone secretion. For example, in monkeys, a CRH antagonist can prevent the suppression of LH secretion caused by interleukin-1 administration. However, the mechanism of interleukin-1 suppression of LH secretion appears to differ in the rat, where administration of a CRH antagonist cannot prevent the suppression of LH secretion. Findings such as these illustrate the need for further research into the mechanisms underlying stress-induced suppression of the reproductive axis. They also highlight the need to consider each form of stress, as well as each species, individually.

In the mechanisms underlying stress-induced suppression of the central neural drive to the reproductive axis, the level of gonadal steroid hormones in the circulation is critical in determining the impact of stresses and many stress-induced neuropeptides on GnRH neuronal activity. A variety of stresses, such as nutritional stress, suppress LH secretion when gonadal steroid hormones are present but are much less effective in suppressing gonadotropin secretion in agonadal animals. These effects of gonadal steroid hormones are unlikely to be mediated directly at the level of GnRH neurons, because GnRH neurons lack estorgen and androgen receptors. Instead, such effects of gonadal steroid hormones more likely are mediated by afferent neural projections onto GnRH neurons; many such projection systems have receptors for gonadal steroid hormones.

Summary

GnRH neurons provide the central neural drive that directs all aspects of reproductive function. GnRH neurons are a diffuse population of specialized neuroendocrine cells in the medial basal hypothalamus that release coordinated pulses of GnRH into the hypothalamopituitary portal bloodstream. GnRH stimulates both the production and the secretion of the gonadotropins LH and FSH from the pituitary gonadotropes. LH and FSH, in turn, govern ovarian and testicular function and the production of the gonadal hormones, estradiol, progesterone, and testosterone. A pulsatile pattern of GnRH is critical for the stimulation of the gonadotropes. Pulse frequency is modulated by negative and positive feedback of circulating gonadal steroid hormones and changes dramatically during the course of the ovarian cycle in females. There is remarkable species variation in the female ovarian cycle, including differences in the length of the cycle, the pattern of hormone secretion, the duration of luteal function, and the sensitivity of the reproductive axis to regulation by the circadian timing system.

GnRH neuronal activity fluctuates over a lifetime and in response to environmental mediators. Developmental and environmental modulation of reproductive function results primarily from modulation of GnRH drive to the rest of the reproductive axis. GnRH neurons are born outside the brain, in the olfactory placode, and migrate caudally during embryonic development to the hypothalamus and basal forebrain. GnRH neurons become active during fetal development, but late in gestation their activity appears to be suppressed by high levels of placental steroid hormones. In humans and nonhuman primates, a second transient period of increased activity of the reproductive axis occurs during the first few months after birth. This is followed by a prolonged childhood period of quiescence in the GnRH drive to the pituitary. At puberty the GnRH neuronal system reawakens by mechanisms that are not well understood at this time. The pubertal awakening and adult functioning of the GnRH neuronal system can be modulated by a number of environmental cues, including day length, seasonal cues, nutritional and metabolic factors, and various stresses. All of these environmental mediators of reproductive function act at the level of the central nervous system to modulate GnRH drive to the reproductive axis.

LACTATION

Prolactin Regulates Lactation and Other Functions through an Apparent Brain–Pituitary Axis

The prolactin gene is a member of the family of genes that includes somatotropin. Like somatotropin, prolactin is secreted from the anterior pituitary and affects many rather than one target organ. Also similar to somatotropin, secretion of prolactin follows a pulsatile, diurnal rhythm and is regulated mainly by the hypothalamus. In addition, the brain inhibits secretion of prolactin from the pituitary, like SS inhibits secretion of somatotropin; the hypothalamus secretes **prolactin-inhibiting factor** (PIF). However, in contrast to hormones controlled through other brain–pituitary–organ axes, prolactin lacks a major releasing hormone. Because prolactin is related to somatotropin, which is controlled by an inhibiting factor (SS) and a releasing factor (GHRH) from the hypothalamus, researchers suspect that in addition to PIF, a prolactin-releasing factor exists but has not been found.

Patterns of Prolactin Secretion Depend on Age, Sex, Time of Day, and Reproductive State

Prolactin, like other hormones that are regulated by the hypothalamus, exhibits a pulsatile,[65,66] diurnal[67,68] rhythm in laboratory animals and humans. Secretory patterns vary with time of day, sex, stage of the reproductive cycle, pregnancy, lactation, and age. Prolactin concentrations are higher in females than in males as

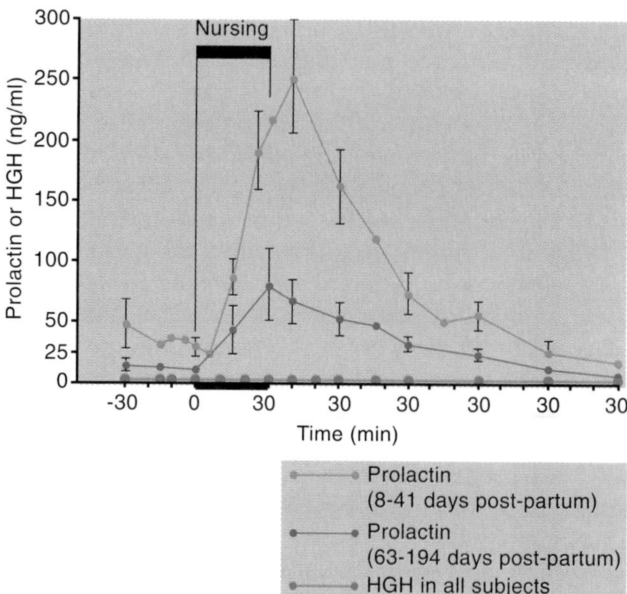

FIGURE 44.16 Plasma prolactin and somatotropin concentrations during nursing in postpartum women. Twelve studies were performed on eight women between 8 and 41 days postpartum, and six studies were performed on six women between 63 and 194 days postpartum. Vertical lines indicate standard error of the mean. Somatotropin (HGH) did not rise with suckling. Reprinted with permission from Noel *et al.*[73]

a result of estrogens. During the menstrual cycle in women, the diurnal peak of prolactin is more pronounced during the luteal than the follicular phase.[69] In rats, a preovulatory surge of prolactin precedes the surge of LH by approximately one hour and depends on the presence of the ovary.[70] During pregnancy in humans, maternal serum prolactin rises dramatically during the first trimester and increases steadily throughout pregnancy, resulting in about a 10-fold increase near term.[71] Levels decrease to a nadir just before birth and then rise again immediately after delivery. The suckling-induced rise in prolactin during lactation remains the most dramatic physiological change in prolactin secretion, the only universal response of prolactin in mammals. The response is a neuroendocrine reflex that is apparent within minutes of the suckling stimulus and diminishes with increasing time since parturition.[72,73] The role of prolactin in lactation is the best studied function of prolactin (Fig. 44.16).

The Hypothalamus Is the Major Determinant of Prolactin Secretion

Many factors regulate the pattern of secretion and the amount of circulating prolactin,[74] but the hypothalamus is dominant. Prolactin is unique among pituitary hormones in that it is the only one under predominantly inhibitory control of the brain. Experimental separation of the pituitary gland from the hypothalamus resulted in a major increase in basal prolactin secretion; therefore a factor in the hypothalamus was postulated to be normally released into the hypophyseal portal blood to inhibit prolactin secretion.[74] Subsequently, a PIF, which is different from other hypothalamic factors, was found.[75] Investigators were slow to accept the possibility that a catecholamine, classically thought of as a neurotransmitter, could act as a neuroendocrine hormone. Nevertheless, an overwhelming body of data support the conclusion that dopamine (DA) is the major endogenous factor that inhibits prolactin release from the pituitary gland.

The conclusion that DA is the major inhibitor of prolactin release is supported by the following experimental findings: (1) drugs that decrease catecholamine synthesis and surgical manipulations that decrease DA in the hypophyseal portal blood increase prolactin secretion[76,77]; (2) DA is present in the median eminence in high concentration[78] and exists in the hypophyseal portal plasma in sufficient concentration to suppress prolactin secretion[79]; (3) spontaneous prolactin secretion is inhibited by small amounts of DA[80]; (4) DA receptors are present on lactotropes,[81] and hormone suppression is proportional to receptor occupancy[82]; and (5) DA concentrations in the hypophyseal portal blood and/or turnover rates in the basomedial hypothalamus decrease immediately before large increases in prolactin release, such as on the last day of pregnancy,[83] during the proestrous or estradiol-induced prolactin surge,[84] during lactation in response to suckling,[85] or following electrical stimulation of the mammary nerve,[85,86] a procedure that simulates suckling. Interestingly, evidence suggests that DA can also *stimulate* prolactin release[87,88]: A high dose of DA (>100 n*M*) consistently blocks prolactin release, whereas lower doses augment prolactin secretion under experimental conditions. In addition, acute withdrawal of DA potentiates the stimulatory actions of some, but not all, prolactin-releasing factors.[89]

The population of dopaminergic neurons that control prolactin resides within the hypothalamus. The perikarya of these tuberoinfundibular neurons, the so-called A12 cell group, lie in the arcuate nuclei and their axons terminals are located in the median eminence, where they constitute as much as a third of all terminals in the external zone. Some of the terminals contact the basement membrane of perivascular spaces, enabling direct release of DA into portal blood.

Only dopamine receptors of the D2 subtype have been found on the membranes of lactotropes. Activation of these receptors decreases cAMP concentrations in enriched populations of lactotrophes.[89] These effects are mimicked by D2 agonists and blocked by D2 antagonists. A cAMP-responsive element and a Pit-1-binding site[90,91] have been found in the rat prolactin gene. The Pit-1-binding site confers some DA inhibition, possibly because DA inhibits transcription of the Pit-1 gene, which encodes the protein that binds Pit-1 sites.[91] Together, these findings suggest that two distinct signaling pathways initiated at D2 receptors may be involved in the transcriptional regulation of the prolactin gene and that one of these pathways may be indirect, through the Pit-1 gene. The action of DA may also be mediated through another pathway, the Ca^{2+}/phosphokinase C system.[92] Whether another, yet to be detected, DA receptor subtype exists on lactotropes or whether the interaction of Pit-1 with DA explains the role of the Ca^{2+}/phosphokinase C system as a signaling pathway is not known.

The presence of a prolactin-inhibiting factor and the close relationship of prolactin and somatotropin, which is controlled by both a releasing factor and a release-inhibiting factor, suggest that there should be a prolactin-releasing factor (PRF). The existence of one or more PRF(s) is supported by the following evidence: (1) hypothalamic extracts and plasma contain prolactin-releasing activity[93]; (2) prolactin secretion can be increased by stress, even when DA receptors are blocked[94]; (3) prolactin surges can be abolished by removal of the posterior pituitary and, conversely, extracts of the posterior pituitary gland can stimulate prolactin release *in vivo* and *in vitro*.[95]

As discussed earlier, TRH is a tripeptide synthesized in the hypothalamus and associated with regulation of thyrotropin-stimulating hormone. It has also been found to stimulate prolactin release *in vivo* and *in vitro*[96] under a variety of physiological conditions. Membrane receptors for TRH have been identified in non-prolactin-secreting and prolactin-secreting cell lines.[97,98] However, the importance of the role of TRH is not universally accepted because there are inconsistent findings regarding its levels in portal blood at times when prolactin secretion is high, such as in the afternoon of proestrus,[99] during suckling,[100] or after treatment with estradiol.[101] TRH stimulates prolactin via the Ca^{2+}/phosphokinase C system: TRH-stimulated increases in intracellular Ca^{2+} rapidly stimulate prolactin gene transcription.[102] A TRH response element and a calcium response element have been mapped to the area of the Pit-1-binding site of the rat prolactin promoter region, suggesting that TRH and calcium effects may be mediated via Pit-1.[103]

VIP is another neuropeptide that stimulates release of prolactin *in vivo* and *in vitro*.[104] The peptide is present in active concentrations in the portal blood,[105] and antisera to VIP inhibit basal prolactin secretion *in vitro*.[106,107]

However, it is not uniformly agreed that VIP is a major physiologically important PRF, because VIP concentrations do not always correlate with prolactin concentrations.[108] Nevertheless, the secretory response of prolactin to VIP has been examined. Compared to the effects of TRH, VIP-induced prolactin secretion is delayed; the response is substantially smaller; and the response is progressive, that is, increases with successive exposures to VIP.[109,110] The actions of these two secretagogues are additive, suggesting separate signaling pathways for the two hormones. VIP stimulates production of cAMP and increases intracellular Ca^{2+},[117] thereby increasing prolactin mRNA levels.[112]

Considerable evidence suggests that substances in the posterior pituitary gland may play an important stimulatory role in prolactin release. These factors are thought to reach the anterior pituitary via short portal vessels traversing the avascular cleft of the pars intermedia.[113,114] Unfortunately, because it is impossible to cannulate these minute vessels of the posterior pituitary, studies to determine whether concentrations of putative PRFs are higher in this component of the hypophyseal portal vasculature than in the peripheral circulation are not possible. Oxytocin, which is synthesized in the hypothalamus and transported to the posterior pituitary gland, is thought to exert a stimulatory effect on prolactin secretion[115,116]; however, other substances thought to be synthesized within the intermediate and posterior lobes of the pituitary itself have been partially purified and observed to have dramatic stimulatory effects on prolactin secretion.

That cells within these parts of the pituitary synthesize one or more PRF(s) was first suggested by work demonstrating that removal of the intermediate lobe of the pituitary blocks the suckling-induced release of prolactin, suppresses the peak preovulatory prolactin surge, and attenuates the mating-induced nocturnal prolactin surge.[95] Extracts of the intermediate-posterior pituitary stimulate prolactin secretion in a rapid, dose-dependent, and hormone-specific manner *in vitro* and *in vivo*[117] (Fig. 44.17). Microdissection of this tissue demonstrated that a PRF is localized in the intermediate lobe.[118] In addition, tumors of the intermediate lobe, induced by targeted tumorigenesis using a proopiomelanocortin gene promoter ligated to the simian virus 40 large T antigen, resulted in mice with massive tumors of the intermediate lobe and prolactin levels that were five- to sixfold higher than in control mice.[119] Also, lactotrophe-derived tumor cells exhibit an increase in prolactin mRNA when cocultured with intermediate-posterior pituitary cells.[120] Finally, the PRF(s) produced by the intermediate lobe appear to increase prolactin by acting at the distal enhancer region of the prolactin promoter.[121]

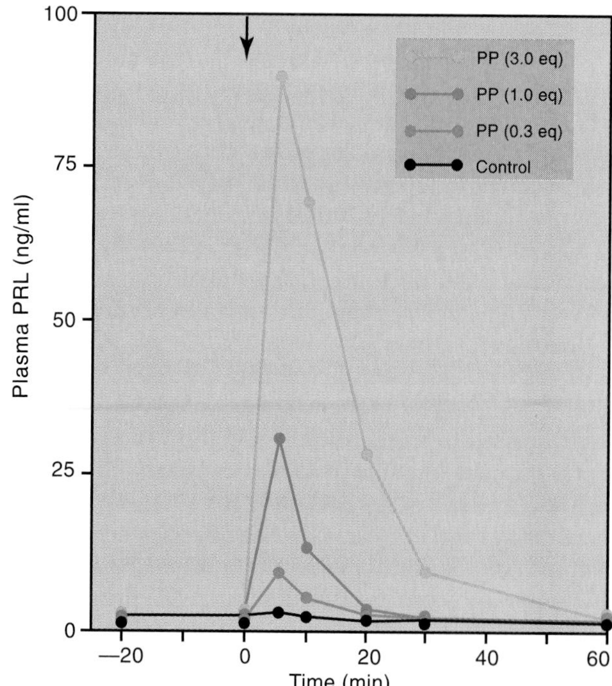

FIGURE 44.17 Dose-dependent increase in plasma prolactin (PRL) in ovariectomized rats injected (intracarotid) with intermediate–posterior pituitary extract (0.3, 1.0, 3.0 eq) or cerebellar extract (Control). Injection occurred at time zero (arrow). Each value is the mean ± SEM of seven to nine determinations. Reprinted with permission from Hyde and Ben-Jonathan.[117]

Estradiol plays an important stimulatory role in prolactin synthesis, storage, and secretion. Its effects on prolactin depend on dose, duration of exposure, and sex. Estradiol acts directly on pituitary lactotrophes to stimulate synthesis and storage of prolactin,[122,123] enhance the size and number of lactotrophes,[124,125] and stimulate transcription of the prolactin gene.[126–128] In addition, estradiol alters pituitary responsiveness to hypothalamic factors by changing the density of receptors for some hypothalamic factors.[129–131] Finally, estradiol induces the preovulatory surge of prolactin[70] by modulating the rhythm of synthesis and release of hypothalamic regulatory factors.[132] The effects of estradiol on the prolactin gene occur through direct binding of the estradiol receptor to promoter regions or through interaction with another transcription factor that binds directly to the promoter.

A summary of the factors that regulate prolactin synthesis and secretion is depicted in Fig. 44.18. As can be seen clearly from this diagram, the number and the tissue sources of relevant factors are diverse. This may explain how prolactin secretion is regulated differentially under a wide variety of physiological and pathological circumstances (see Box 44.3).

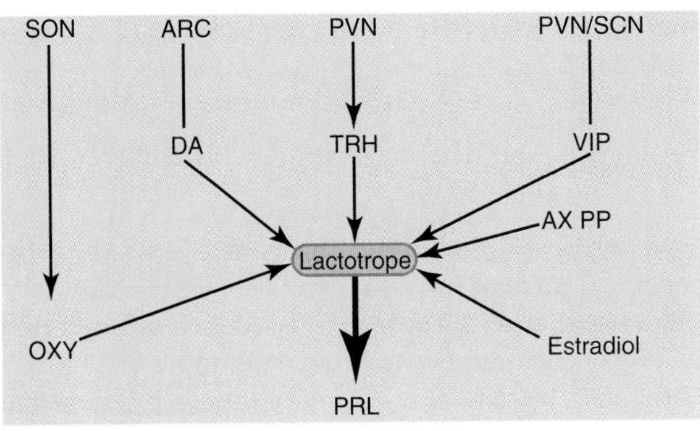

FIGURE 44.18 Control of prolactin secretion by anterior pituitary lactotropes. Prolactin secretion is inhibited by dopamine synthesized in the arcuate nucleus and released in the median eminence into the hypophyseal portal circulation. Prolactin is stimulated by a number of factors, including (1) TRH from the paraventricular nucleus (PVN); (2) VIP from neurons that originate in the suprachiasmatic nucleus (SCN), PVN, and anterior pituitary; (3) a factor(s) that has not yet been purified (X) that is synthesized in the intermediate–posterior pituitary (PP) gland and reaches the anterior pituitary via short portal vessels; (4) oxytocin that is synthesized in the supraoptic nucleus (SON) and released from the posterior pituitary; and (5) circulating estradiol.

The Prolactin Gene Is Part of a Larger Family

The rat prolactin gene was cloned in 1980.[133] Speculation that prolactin, somatotropin, and chorionic somatomammotropin evolved from a common ancestor was based on the large number of common amino acid sequences shared by these hormones.[134] The concept gained even greater acceptance when the genes were cloned, revealing that somatotropin and prolactin shared an even higher degree of nucleotide than amino acid sequence identity.[135] Because all of the exon–intron boundaries in the rat prolactin gene contain more than one potential splicing site,[136] multiple prolactin variants with differing functions and biological activities may be possible.

Originally, it was thought that the prolactin gene is expressed only in the pituitary gland; however, more recent findings have clearly established that prolactin or prolactinlike genes are expressed in multiple diverse tissues, including the decidua,[137] mammary gland,[138] brain,[139] and cells of the immune system.[140,141]

The major protein translated from the prolactin gene has a molecular mass of 23–24 kDa.[74] It was first discovered in the pituitary gland[142] and is secreted by a class of acidophilic staining cells known as lactotropes.[143] In most mammalian species, the hormone consists of 197–199 amino acids and contains three disulfide bridges. As for most protein hormones, it is synthesized as a prohormone (227 amino acid residues[134]) and is processed to the mature hormone by proteolytic cleavage of the signal peptide on ribosomes of the rough endoplasmic reticulum. Biologically active prolactin exists in several forms, varying primarily in their degree of glycosylation, but their functional differences are not known.

BOX 44.3

INAPPROPRIATE PROLACTIN SECRETION

Hyperprolactinemia, the elevated secretion of prolactin (more than 20 ng ml^{-1}) over a prolonged period of time, is the most common human hypothalamopituitary disorder. It has multiple causes. For example, hypothalamic hyperprolactinemia can be caused by interruption of dopamine delivery due to stalk transection or tumors that block the connection between the basal hypothalamus and the pituitary stalk. Prolactin-secreting adenomas are a cause of pituitary hyperprolactinemia. (Most of these tumors contain DA receptors and can be treated with dopamine agonists, such as bromoergocryptine.) Many drugs that interfere with DA synthesis, reuptake, or binding lead to hypersecretion of prolactin. Thus, hyperprolactinemia and inappropriate lactation are common complications of treatment with neuroleptics, dopamine receptor blockers, antidepressants, antihypertensives, or oral contraceptives, which in various ways reduce dopaminergic suppression of prolactin secretion. The syndrome hyperprolactinemia–amenorrhea illustrates the importance of interactions between regulated prolactin secretion and the brain–pituitary–gonad axis.

In men and women, hyperprolactinemia can cause gonadal dysfunction, headaches, and visual field disturbances. Several routes of therapy have been used to restore normal prolactin levels, reduce tumor mass, reinstate normal vision, and allow normal reproductive function. Surgical resection, pituitary radiation, and dopamine agonists have been used with considerable success.

Phyllis M. Wise

Prolactin and Growth Hormone-Secreting Cells May Differentiate from a Common Precursor

The fetal pituitary gland synthesizes prolactin and GH prior to histological differentiation of the pituitary cells into mammotropes (prolactin-secreting cells) and somatotrophes (somatotropin-secreting cells). During embryonic and early postnatal development, somatotropin secretion can be detected before prolactin levels are detectable.[144] These findings have led investigators to hypothesize that somatotrophes give rise to mammotrophes by way of a bipotential mammosomatotrophe precursor cell.[143] Studies in transgenic mice led to similar conclusions[145,146]; dwarf mice produced by ablation of somatotropin-expressing cells lose both somatotrophes and mammotrophes from their pituitaries and have a markedly decreased secretion of somatotropin and prolactin.

Prolactin Acts through Specific Receptors and Signaling Pathways

With the cloning of the prolactin receptor, it has become clear that multiple forms of the receptor exist (Fig. 44.19) and that it is expressed in a wide variety of tissues, including the mammary gland, liver, kidney, adrenals, ovaries, uterus, placenta, testis, prostate, seminal vesicles, hypothalamus, choroid plexus, pancreas, lymphoid tissues, intestine, and others.[147,148] The diversity of prolactin receptor isoforms (varying from 329 to 591 amino acids[148]), its structural overlap with receptors in the large family of cytokines, and its wide distribution in tissues that are known targets for pro-

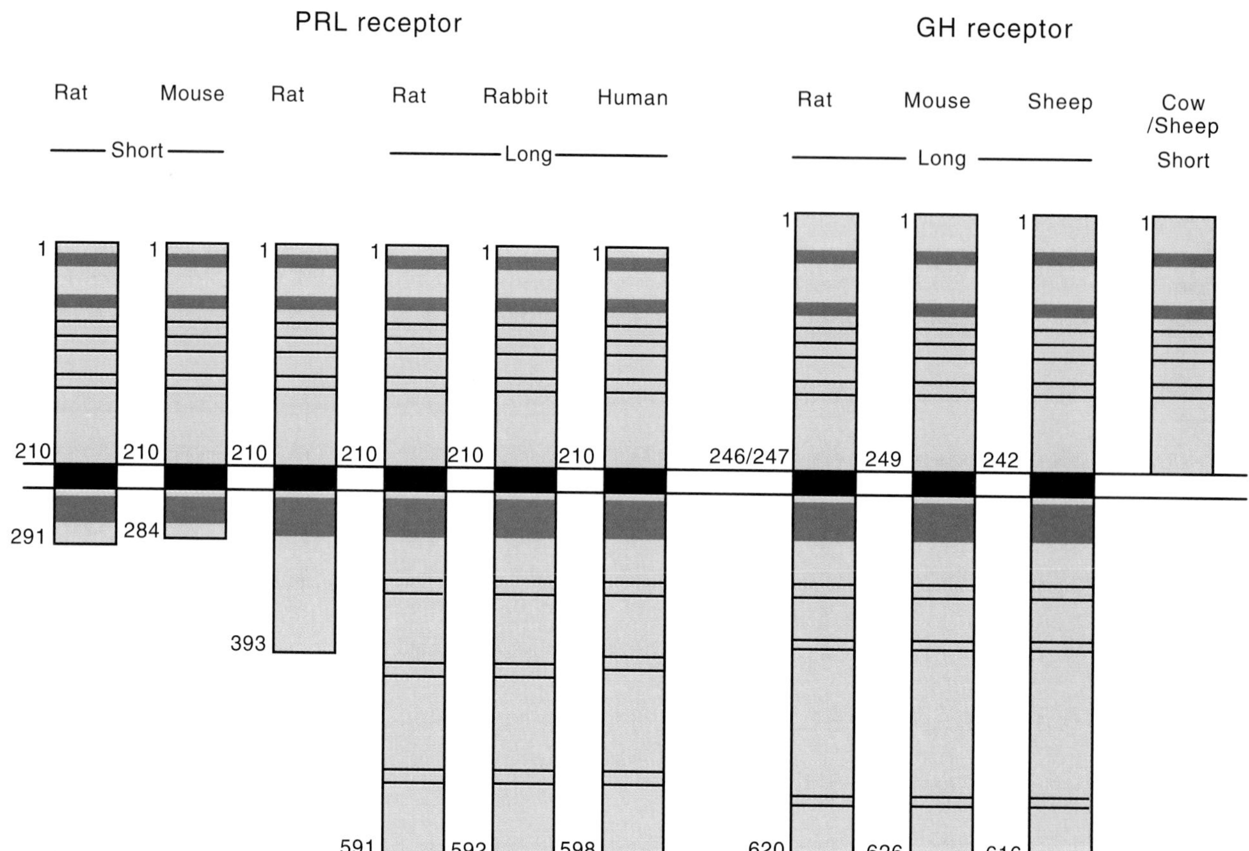

FIGURE 44.19 The prolactin–somatotropin (GH) receptor family. The short form of the prolactin receptor from rat and mouse, the intermediate form from Nb2 cells, and the long form of rat, rabbit, and human are compared to long and short (binding protein) forms of the somatotropin receptor in human, rabbit, cow, sheep, mouse, and rat. The first and last amino acids of the mature proteins are indicated, as well as the last amino acid of the extracellular domain. The transmembrane domains are shown in black. Regions of high (>68%) amino acid identity are cross-hatched; regions with moderate (40–60%) identity are stippled. Reprinted with permission from Kelly *et al.*[148]

lactin action (and some that are not) may partially explain prolactin's bewildering array of biological actions.[148]

Prolactin Has Diverse Functions and Sites of Action

Prolactin receptors are found in multiple tissues, where the hormone exerts diverse functions. We will review only a few of the major functions.

Prolactin exerts several actions on the ovary by influencing the effects of gonadotropins: prolactin increases (1) the number of LH receptors in the corpus luteum, (2) the synthesis of progesterone by the corpus luteum, and (3) high-density lipoprotein and low-density lipoprotein binding in membranes of the corpus luteum. These actions are clear in studies performed in rats, but not in humans. They lead to rescue of the corpus luteum, which is necessary for uterine endometrial development and implantation of the blastocyst.

In all mammalian species, prolactin action on the mammary gland is essential for preparation, maintenance, and secretory activity of the mammary gland. Prolactin appears to cause primarily ductal and lobuloaveolar growth. Prolactin also increases mRNA levels of the milk protein casein and increases the rate of translation of casein mRNA into protein.

The principal role of suckling-induced prolactin secretion is to stimulate the synthesis of milk; however, in many species it also plays a role in reproductive functions.[149] For example, in rats, suckling causes a delay in implantation if conception occurs during postpartum estrus. In humans and some other primates, suckling can induce prolonged periods of anovulation and infertility, presumably to allow time for maternal care of the young. Suckling inhibits the amplitude and frequency of pulsatile LH secretion[150] (Fig. 44.20), and can be mimicked by exogenously administered prolactin.[151]

Maternal behavior in mammals is controlled by multiple biochemical, neural, and environmental factors.[152] Maternal behavior can be elicited in nulliparious rats by administration of a pregnancy-like hormone regimen. When this behavioral response was prevented (e.g., by removal of the anterior pituitary), treatment with bovine prolactin reinstated the behavior. However, in higher animals, including humans, the role of the endocrine system, and prolactin in particular, is less clear.

Prolactin influences osmoregulation in a wide variety of species. It is involved in the migration from salt to fresh water in fish and in the migration from land to water to lay eggs in amphibians. Prolactin receptors have been found in the kidney, gut, urinary bladder, and skin[148] and therefore may act at all of these sites. Evidence suggests that prolactin stimulates activity in lymphocytes and is involved in cell-mediated immunity.

Summary

Prolactin is produced by a subpopulation of anterior pituitary cells, the lactotrophes. Like other anterior pituitary hormones, it is produced initially as a prohormone and several alternatively processed forms are known. Prolactin belongs to the somatogropin–chorionic somatomammotropin family of hormones. In normal males and females, prolactin is secreted in a diurnal pattern, with the greatest secretion associated with sleep. The best understood functions of prolactin are in reproduction, where prolactin is involved in lactation, postpartum suppression of reproductive cycling, and maternal behavior. Prolactin has diverse functions, however, and is involved in immune function and, in lower vertebrates, in osmoregulation. The production and secretion of prolactin are controlled principally by the hypothalamus: A PIF, dopamine, and a series of PRFs, including TRH, VIP, oxytocin, estradiol, and factors from the pituitary intermediate lobe, together control prolactin production and selection. Prolactin acts on a receptor that belongs to the cytokine receptor family and is expressed in multiple isoforms in multiple tissues. Although much is understood about prolactin, much is yet to be learned about its regulation and diverse functions.

Growth and development, cellular metabolism, stress response, and reproductive function, all hugely variable and critically inportant for survival, are controlled through networks of hormones organized in brain–pituitary–organ axes. Hormones are secreted at each level of an axis. Secretion by the pituitary and hypothalamus is pulsatile, and pulse frequency and amplitude vary in daily rhythms. Secretion is controlled by neural input (positive control) and by feedback of hormones released by the axis (negative control). For a single axis, neural input to the hypothalamus can come from several regions of the brain.

In several axes, hormones are synthesized through the processing of precursor peptides. A hormone can activate a cell that has appropriate hormone receptors on its surface. Binding of hormone activates a receptor and initiates a chain of events. Some hormone receptors trigger cascades that use second messengers (e.g., cAMP) to eventually cause, for example, release of secretory granules. Other receptors work without a

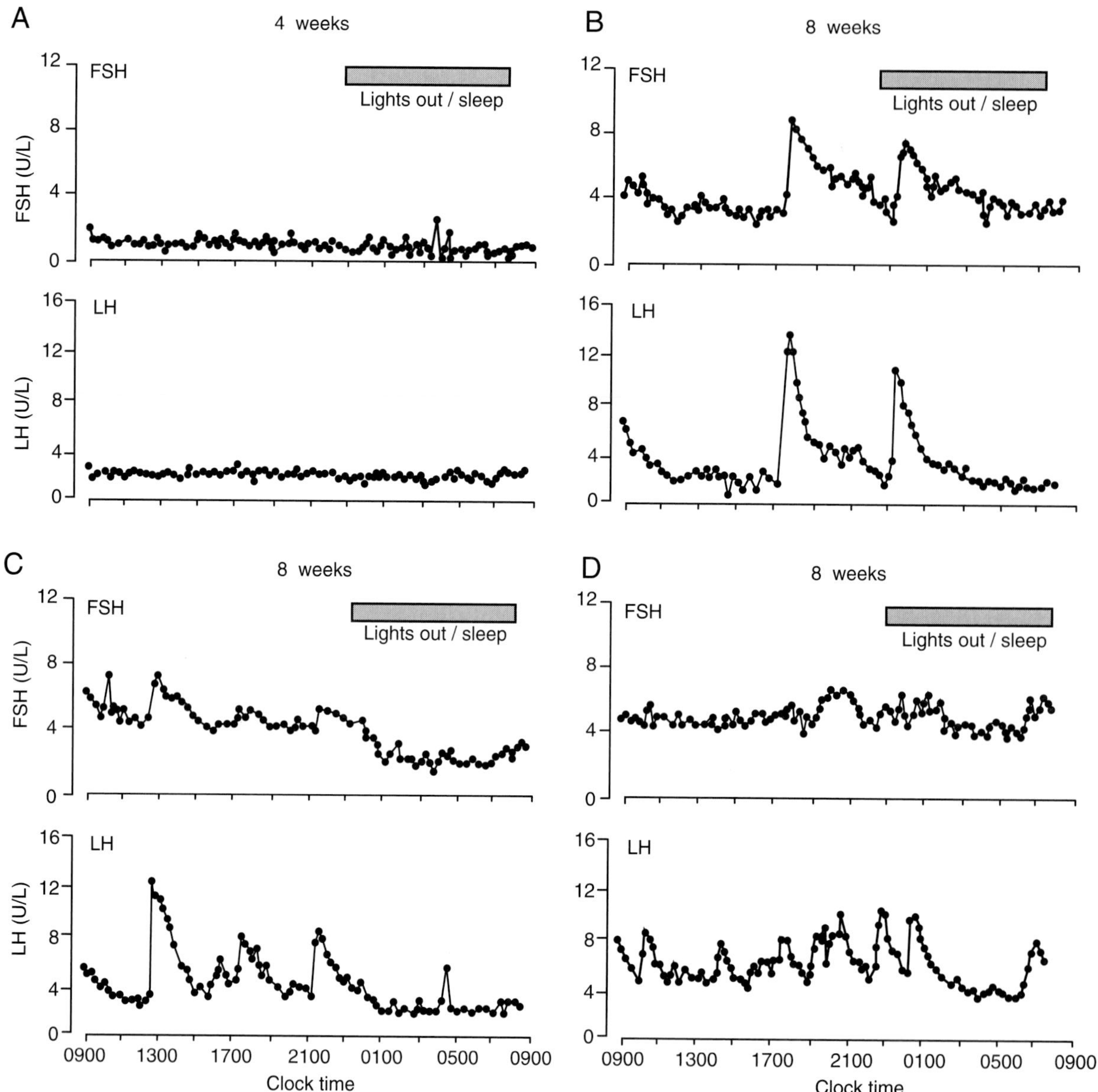

FIGURE 44.20 Pattern of resumption of pulsatile secretion of LH and FSH over a 24-h period in breast-feeding women at (A) 4 weeks and (B–D) 8 weeks postpartum. Note that FSH and LH pulses coincide only at low LH (and therefore GnRH) pulse frequencies. Pulsatile LH secretion resumes at a variable frequency and at random over the 24-h period, with pulses occurring at night, when prolactin response to suckling was maximal. All women remained amenorrheic for at least 20 weeks after sampling. Reprinted with permission from McNeilly.[149]

second messenger to change the transcription rate, for example.

References

1. Chomczynski, P., Downs, T. R., and Frohman, L. A. (1988). Feedback regulation of growth hormone releasing hormone gene expression by growth hormone in rat hypothalamus. *Mol. Endocrinol.* **2:** 236–241.
2. Frohman, M. A., Downs, T. R., Chomczynski, P., and Frohman, L. A. (1989). Cloning and characterization of mouse growth hormone-releasing hormone (GRH) cDNA: Increased GRH mRNA levels in the growth hormone deficient lit/lit mouse. *Mol. Endocrinol.* **3:** 1529–1536.
3. Downs, T. R., Chomczynski, P., and Frohman, L. A. (1990). Effects of thyroid hormone deficiency and replacement on rat hypothalamic growth hormone-releasing hormone (GRH) gene expression in vivo are mediated by growth hormone (GH). *Mol. Endocrinol.* **4:** 402–408.
4. Hasegawa, O., Sugihara, H., Minami, S., and Wakabayashi, I. (1992). Masculinization of growth hormone (GH) secretory pattern by dihydrotestosterone is associated with augmentation of hypothalamic somatostatin and GH-releasing hormone

mRNA levels in ovariectomized adult rats. *Peptides* **13:** 475–481.

5. Sato, M., and Frohman, L. A. (1993). Differential effects of central and peripheral administration of growth hormone (GH) and insulin-like growth factor on hypothalamic GH-releasing hormone (GRH) and somatostatin gene expression in GH-deficient dwarf rats. *Endocrinology* **133:** 793–799.
6. Soszynski, P., and Frohman, L. A. (1992). Inhibitory effects of ethanol on the growth hormone (GH)-releasing hormone-GH-insulin-like growth factor I axis in the rat. *Endocrinology* **131:** 2603–2608.
7. Bruno, J. F., Song, J., Xu, Y., and Berelowitz, M. (1993). Regulation of hypothalamic preprogrowth hormone-releasing factor messenger ribonucleic acid expression in food-deprived rats: A role for histaminergic neurotransmission. *Endocrinology* **133:** 1377–1381.
8. McCarthy, G. F., Beaudet, A., and Tannenbaum, G. S. (1992). Colocalization of somatostatin receptors and growth hormone-releasing factor immunoreactivity in neurons of the rat arcuate nucleus. *Neuroendocrinology* **56:** 18–24.
9. Sato, M., and Frohman, L. A. (1993). Differential sensitivity of growth hormone-releasing hormone and somatostatin release from perifused mouse hypothalamic fragments in response to glucose deficiency. *Neuroendocrinology* **57:** 1097–1105.
10. Frohman, L. A., Downs, T. R., Clarke, I. J., and Thomas, G. B. (1990). Measurement of growth hormone-releasing hormone and somatostatin in hypothalamic-portal plasma of unanesthetized sheep: Spontaneous secretion and response to insulin-induced hypoglycemia. *J. Clin. Invest.* **86:** 17–24.
11. Landis, C. A., Masters, S. B., Spada, A., Pace, A. M., Bourne, H. R., and Vallar, L. (1989). GTPase inhibiting mutations activate the alpha chain of G_s and stimulate adenylyl cyclase in human pituitary tumours. *Nature* **340:** 692–696.
12. Schriock, E. A., Lustig, R. H., Rosenthal, S. M., Kaplan, S. L., and Grumbach, M. M. (1984). Effect of growth hormone (GH)-releasing hormone (GRH) on plasma GH in relation to magnitude and duration of GH deficiency in 26 children and adults with isolated GH deficiency or multiple pituitary hormone deficiencies: Evidence for hypothalamic GRH deficiency. *J. Clin. Endocrinol. Metab.* **58:** 1043–1049.
13. Montminy, M. R., Sevarino, K. A., and Wagner, J. A., *et al.* (1986). Identification of a cyclic AMP-responsive element within the rat somatostatin gene. *Proc. Natl. Acad. Sci. USA* **83:** 6682–6686.
14. Rogers, K. V., Vician, L., Steiner, R. A., and Clifton, D. K. (1988). The effects of hypophysectomy and growth hormone administration on pre-prosomatostatin messenger ribonucleic acid in the periventricular nucleus of the rat hypothalamus. *Endocrinology* **122:** 586–591.
15. Murao, K., Sato, M., Mizobuchi, M., Nimi, M., Ishida, T., and Takahara, J. (1994). Acute effects of hypoglycemia and hyperglycemia on hypothalamic growth hormone-releasing hormone and somatostatin gene expression in the rat. *Endocrinology* **134:** 418–423.
16. Bruno, J. F., Xu, Y., Song, J., and Berelowitz, M. (1993). Tissue distribution of somatostatin receptor subtype messenger ribonucleic acid in the rat. *Endocrinology* **133:** 2561–2567.
17. Low, M. J., Hammer, R. E., Goodman, R. H., Habener, J. F., Palmiter, R. D., and Brinster, R. L. (1985). Tissue-specific post-translational processing of pre-prosomatostatin encoded by a metallothionein-somatostatin fusion gene in transgenic mice. *Cell* **41:** 211–219.
18. Mitchell, J. A., Hutchins, M., Schindler, W. J., and Critchlow, V. (1973). Increases in plasma growth hormone and naso-anal length in rats following isolation of the medial basal hypothalamus. *Neuroendocrinology* **12:** 161–173.
19. Evans, H. M., and Long, J. A. (1921). The effect of the anterior lobe administered intraperitoneally upon growth, maturity and oestrus cycles of the rat. *Anat. Rec.* **21:** 62–63.
20. Smith, P. E. (1930). Hypophysectomy and replacement therapy in the rat. *Am. J. Anat.* **45:** 207–274.
21. Li, C. H., Evans, H. M., and Simpson, M. E. (1945). Isolation and properties of the anterior hypophyseal growth hormone. *J. Biol. Chem.* **159:** 353–366.
22. Li, S., Crenshaw, E. B., III, Rawson, E. J., Simmons, D. M., Swanson, L. W., and Rosenfeld, M. G. (1990). Dwarf locus mutants lacking three pituitary cell types result from mutations in the POU-domain gene pit-1. *Nature* **347:** 528–533.
23. Mangalam, H. J., Albert, V. R., Ingraham, H. A., Kapiloff, M., Wilson, L., Nelson, C., Elsholtz, H., and Rosenfeld, M. G. (1989). A pituitary POU domain protein, Pit-1, activates both growth hormone and prolactin promoters transcriptionally. *Genes Dev.* **3:** 946–958.
24. Tatsumi, K., Miyai, K., Notomi, T., Kaibe, K., Amino, N., Mizuno, Y., and Kohno, H. (1992). Cretinism with combined hormone deficiency caused by a mutation in the PIT1 gene. *Nat. Genet.* **1:** 56–58.
25. de Vos, A. M., Ultsch, M., and Kossiakoff, A. A. (1992). Human growth hormone and extracellular domain of its receptor: Crystal structure of the complex. *Science* **255:** 306–312.
26. Berelowitz, M., Szabo, M., Frohman, L. A., Firestone, S., Chu, L., and Hintz, R. L. (1981). Somatomedin-C mediates growth hormone negative feedback by effects on both the hypothalamus and the pituitary. *Science* **212:** 1279–1281.
27. Yamashita, S., and Melmed, S. (1987). Insulinlike growth factor I regulation of growth hormone gene transcription in primary rat pituitary cells. *J. Clin. Invest.* **79:** 449–452.
28. Shibasaki, T., Yamauchi, N., Hotta, M., Masuda, A., Imaki, T., Demura, H., Ling, N., and Shizume, K. (1986). In vitro release of growth hormone-releasing factor from rat hypothalamus: Effect of insulin-like growth factor-1. *Regul. Pept.* **15:** 47–53.
29. Berelowitz, M., Firestone, S. L., and Frohman, L. A. (1981a). Effects of growth hormone excess and deficiency on hypothalamic somatostatin content and release and on tissue somatostatin distribution. *Endocrinology* **109:** 714–719.
30. Dickson, S. L., Leng, G., and Robinson, I. C. A. F. (1993). Systemic administration of growth hormone-releasing peptide activates hypothalamic arcuate neurons. *Neuroscience* **53:** 303–306.
31. Kamegai, J., Minami, S., Sugihara, H., Higuchi, H., and Wakabayashi, I. (1994). GH induces expression of c-*fos* gene on hypothalamic neuropeptide-Y and somatostatin neurons in hypophysectomized rats. *Endocrinology* **135:** 2765–2771, 1994.
32. Carlsson, L. M., Clark, R. G., and Robinson, I. C. (1990). Sex difference in growth hormone feedback in the rat. *J. Endocrinol.* **126:** 27–35.
33. Abrams, R. L., Parker, M. L., Blanco, S., Reichlin, S., and Daughaday, W. H. (1966). Hypothalamic regulation of growth hormone secretion. *Endocrinology* **78:** 605–613.
34. Imaki, T., Shibasaki, T., Shizume, K., Masuda, A., Hotta, M., Kiyosawa, Y., Jibiki, K., Demura, H., Tsushima, T., and Ling, N. (1985). The effect of free fatty acids on growth hormone (GH)-releasing hormone-mediated GH secretion in man. *J. Clin. Endocrinol. Metab.* **60:** 290–293.
35. Martin, J. B. (1972). Plasma growth hormone (GH) responses to hypothalamic or extrahypothalamic electrical stimulation. *Endocrinology* **91:** 107–115.
36. Vance, M. L., Kaiser, D. L., Evans, W. S., Thorner, M. O., Furlanetto, R., Rivier, J., Vale, W., Perisutti, G., and Frohman, L. A.

(1985). Evidence for a limited GRF-releasable quantity of GH: Effects of 6 hour infusions of GRF on growth hormone secretion in normal man. *J. Clin. Endocrinol. Metab.* **60:** 370–375.

37. Tannenbaum, G. S., and Ling, N. (1984). The interrelationship of growth hormone (GH)-releasing factor and somatostatin in generation of the ultradian rhythm of GH secretion. *Endocrinology* **115:** 1952–1957.
38. Zeitler, P., Tannenbaum, G. S., Clifton, D. K., and Steiner, R. A. (1991). Ultradian oscillations in somatostatin and growth hormone-releasing hormone mRNAs in the brains of adult male rats. *Proc. Natl. Acad. Sci. USA* **88:** 8920–8924.
39. Jansson, J., Eden, S., and Isaksson, O. (1985). Sexual dimorphism in the control of growth hormone secretion. *Endocr. Rev.* **6:** 128–150.
40. Jansson, J., and Frohman, L. A. (1987). Differential effects of neonatal and adult androgen exposure on the growth hormone secretory pattern in male rats. *Endocrinology* **120:** 1551–1557.
41. Jansson, J., and Frohman, L. A. (1987). Inhibitory effect of the ovaries on neonatal androgen imprinting of growth hormone secretion in female rats. *Endocrinology* **121:** 1417–1423.
42. Johnson, M. H., and Everitt, B. J. (1984). *Essential Reproduction.* Second Edition. Blackwell, Boston.
43. Pfaff, D. W., and Schwanzel-Fukuda, M. (1995). Development of GnRH neurons important for the onset of reproductive endocrine and behavioral functions. In *The Neurobiology of Puberty* (T. M. Plant and P. A. Lee, eds.), pp. 3–13. *Journal of Endocrinology Limited,* Bristol.

43a. Schwanzel-Fukuda, M., Bick, D., and Pfaff, D. W. (1989). Luteinizing hormone-releasing hormone (LHRH)-expressing cells do not migrate normally in an inherited hypogonadal (Kallman) syndrome. *Mol. Brain. Res.* **6:** 311–326.

44. Dierschke, D. J., Bhattacharya, A. N., Atkinson, I. E., and Knobil, E. (1970). Circhoral oscillations of plasma LH levels in the ovariectomized rhesus monkey. *Endocrinology* **87:** 850–853.

44a. Moenter, S. M., Brand, R. C., and Karsch, F. J. (1992). Dynamics of GnRH release during a pulse. *Endocrinology* **130:** 503–510.

45. Wilson, R. C., Kesner, J. S., Kaufman, J. M., Uemura, T., Akema, T., and Knobil, E. (1984). Central electrophysiological correlates of pulsatile luteinizing hormone secretion in the rhesus monkey. *Neuroendocrinology* **39:** 256–260.
46. Weiner, R. L., and Martinez de la Escalera, G. (1993). Pulsatile release of gonadotrophin releasing hormone (GnRH) is an intrinsic property of GT1 GnRH neuronal cell lines. *Hum. Reprod.* **8**(Suppl. 2): 13–17.
47. Leranth, C., Segura, L. M. G., Palkovits, M., MacLusky, N. J., Shanabrough, M., and Naftolin, F. (1985). The GnRH-containing neuronal network in the preoptic area of the rat: Demonstration of GnRH-containing nerve terminals in synaptic contact with GnRH neurons. *Brain Res.* **345:** 332–336.
48. Pfaff, D. W. (1986). Gene expression in hypothalamic neurons: Luteinizing hormone releasing hormone. *J. Neurosci. Res.* **16:** 109–115.
49. Pfaff, D. W., Schwanzel-Fukuda, M., Parhar, I. S., Lauber, A. H., McCarthy, M. M., and Kow, L.-M. (1994). GnRH neurons and other cellular and molecular mechanisms for simple mammalian reproductive behaviors. *Rec. Prog. Horm. Res.* **49:** 1–25.
50. Krey, L. C., Butler, W. R., and Knobil, E. (1975). Surgical disconnection of the medial basal hypothalamus and pituitary function in the rhesus monkey. I. Gonadotropin secretion. *Endocrinology* **96:** 1073–1087.
51. Krieger, D. T., Perlow, M. J., Gibson, M. J., Davies, T. F., Zimmerman, E. A., Ferin, M., and Charlton, H. M. (1982). Brain grafts reverse hypogonadism of gonadotropin releasing hormone deficiency. *Nature* **298:** 1–3.
52. Witkin, J. W. (1987). Aging changes in synaptology of LHRH neurons in male rat preoptic area. *Neuroscience* **22:** 1003–1013.
53. Leranth, C., Naftolin, F., Shanabrough, M., and Horvath, T. L. (1995). Neuronal circuits regulating gonadotropin release in the rat. In *The Neurobiology of Puberty* (T. M. Plant and P. A. Lee, eds.), pp. 55–72. *Journal of Endocrinology Limited,* Bristol.
54. Witkin, J. W., O'Sullivan, H., and Silverman, A-J. (1995). Novel associations among gonadotropin-releasing hormone neurons. *Endocrinology* **136:** 4323–4330.
55. Witkin, J. W., Ferin, M., Popilskis, S. J., and Silverman, A. J. (1991). Effects of gonadal steroids on the ultrastructure of GnRH neurons in the rhesus monkey: Synaptic input and glial apposition. *Endocrinology* **129:** 1083–1092.
56. Ferin, M., Van Vugt, D., and Wardlaw, S. (1984). The hypothalamic control of the menstrual cycle and the role of endogenous opioid peptides. *Rec. Prog. Horm. Res.* **39:** 599–635.
57. Belchetz, P. E., Plant, T. M., Nakai, Y., Keogh, E. J., and Knobil, E. (1978). Hypophysial responses to continuous and intermittent delivery of hypothalamic gonadotropin-releasing hormone. *Science* **202:** 631–633.

57a. Kulin, H. E., and Bourguignon, J. P. (1994). True central precocious puberty. *Current Therapy in Endocrinology and Metabolism* **5:** 7–11.

58. Nakai, Y., Plant, T. M., Hess, D. L., Keogh, E. J., and Knobil, E. (1978). On the sites of the negative and positive feedback actions of estradiol in the control of gonadotropin secretion in the rhesus monkey. *Endocrinology* **102:** 1008–1014.
59. Fox, S. R., and Smith, M. S. (1985). Changes in the pulsatile pattern of luteinizing hormone secretion during the rat estrus cycle. *Endocrinology* **116:** 1485–1492.

59a. Filicori, M., Santoro, N., Merriam, G. R., and Crowley, W. F., Jr. (1986). Characterization of the physiological pattern of episodic gonadotropin secretion throughout the human menstrual cycle. *J. Clin. Endocrinol. Metab.* **62:** 1136–1144.

59b. Plant, T. M. (1982). Effects of orchidectomy and testosterone replacement treatment on pulsatile luteinizing hormone secretion in the adult rhesus monkey (*Macaca mulatta*). *Endocrinology* **110:** 1905.

60. Zeleznik, A. J., Hutchison, J. S., and Schuler, H. M. (1985). Interference with the gonadotropin suppressing actions of estradiol in macaques overrides the selection of a single preovulatory follicle. *Endocrinology* **117:** 991–999.
61. Ying, S-Y. (1988). Inhibins, activins and follistatins: Gonadal proteins modulating the secretion of follicle stimulating hormone. *Endocr. Rev.* **9:** 267–293.
62. Majumdar, S. S., Mikuma, N., Ishwad, P. C., Winters, S. J., Attardi, B. J., Perera, A. D., and Plant, T. M. (1995). Replacement with recombinant human inhibin immediately after orchidectomy in the hypophysiotropically clamped male rhesus monkey (*Macaca mulatta*) maintains follicle-stimulating hormone (FSH) secretion and FSHb messenger ribonucleic acid levels at precastration values. *Endocrinology* **136:** 1969–1977.
63. Plant, T. M., and Lee, P. A., eds. (1995). *The Neurobiology of Puberty. Journal of Endocrinology Limited,* Bristol.
64. Negus, N. C., and Berger, P. J. (1987). Mammalian reproductive physiology: Adaptive responses to changing environments. In *Current Mammalogy* (H. H. Genoways, ed.), pp. 149–173. Plenum Press, New York.
65. Lopez, F. J., Dominguez, J. R., Sanchez-Criado, J. E., and Negro-Vilar, A. (1989). Distinct pulsatile prolactin secretory patterns during the estrous cycle: Possible encoding for diverse physiological responses. *Endocrinology* **124:** 536–542.
66. Van Cauter, E., L'Hermite, M., and Copinschi, G. (1981). Quanti-

tative analysis of spontaneous variations of plasma prolactin in normal man. *Am. J. Physiol.* **241:** E355–E363.

67. Mattheij, J. A. M., and Swarts, J. J. M. (1978). Circadian variations in the plasma concentration of prolactin in the adult male rat. *J. Endocrinol.* **79:** 85–89.
68. Sassin, J. F., Frantz, A. G., Kapen, S., and Weitzman, E. D. (1973). The nocturnal rise of human prolactin is dependent on sleep. *J. Clin. Endocrinol. Metab.* **37:** 436–440.
69. Tennekoon, K. H., and Lenton, E. A. (1985). Early evening prolactin rise in women with regular cycles. *J. Reprod. Fertil.* **73:** 523–527.
70. Neill, J. D., Freeman, M. E., and Tillson, S. A. (1971). Control of the proestrus surge of prolactin and luteinizing hormone secretion by estrogens in the rat. *Endocrinology* **89:** 1448–1453.
71. Rigg, L. A., Lein, A., and Yen, S. S. C. (1977). Pattern of increase in circulating prolactin levels during human gestation. *Am. J. Obstet. Gynecol.* **129:** 454–456.
72. Selmanoff, M., and Wise, P. M. (1981). Decreased dopamine turnover in the median eminence in response to suckling in the lactating rat. *Brain Res.* **212:** 101–115.
73. Noel, G. L., Suh, H. K., and Frantz, A. G. (1974). Prolactin release during nursing and breast stimulation in postpartum and nonpostpartum subjects. *J. Clin. Endocrinol. Metab.* **38:** 413–423.
74. Neill, J. D., and Nagy, G. M. (1994). Prolactin secretion and its control. In *The Physiology of Reproduction* (E. Knobil and J. D. Neill, eds.), Vol. 2, pp. 1833–1860. Raven Press, New York.
75. Talwalker, P. K., Ratner, A., and Meites, J. (1963). In vitro inhibition of pituitary prolactin synthesis and release by hypothalamic extract. *Am. J. Physiol.* **205:** 213–218.
76. Murai, I., Garris, P. A., and Ben-Jonathan, N. (1989). Time-dependent increase in plasma prolactin after pituitary stalk section: Role of posterior pituitary dopamine. *Endocrinology* **124:** 2343–2349.
77. Barraclough, C. A., and Sawyer, C. H. (1959). Induction of pseudopregnancy in the rat by reserpine and chlorpromazine. *Endocrinology* **65:** 563–571.
78. Bjorklund, A., and Lindvall, O. (1984). Dopamine-containing systems in the CNS. In *Handbook of Chemical Neuroanatomy* (A Bjorklund and T. Hokfelt, eds.), Vol. 2, pp. 55–112. Elsevier Science Publishers.
79. Gibbs, D. M., and Neill, J. D. (1978). Dopamine levels in hypophysial stalk blood in the rat are sufficient to inhibit prolactin secretion in vivo. *Endocrinology* **102:** 1895–1990.
80. Takahara, J., Arimura, A., and Schally, A. V. (1974). Suppression of prolactin release by a purified porcine PIF preparation and catecholamines infused into a rat hypophysial portal vessel. *Endocrinology* **95:** 462–465.
81. Goldsmith, P. C., Cronin, M. J., and Weiner, R. I. (1979). Dopamine receptor sites in the anterior pituitary. *J. Histochem. Cytochem.* **27:** 1205–1207, 1979.
82. Caron, M. G., Beaulieu, M., Raymond, V., Gagne, B., Drouin, J., Lefkowitz, R. J., and Labrie, F. (1978). Dopaminergic receptors in the anterior pituitary gland. Correlation of [3H]dihydroergocryptine binding with the dopaminergic control of prolactin release. *J. Biol. Chem.* **253:** 2244–2253.
83. Ben-Jonathan, N., Neill, M. A., Arbogast, L. A., Peters, L. L., and Hoefer, M. T. (1980). Dopamine in hypophysial portal blood: Relationship to circulating prolactin in pregnant and lactating rats. *Endocrinology* **106:** 690–696.
84. Rance, N., Wise, P. M., Selmanoff, M. K., and Barraclough, C. A. (1981). Catecholamine turnover rates in discrete hypothalamic areas and associated changes in median eminence luteinizing hormone-releasing hormone and serum gonadotropins on proestrus and diestrous day 1. *Endocrinology* **108:** 1795–1802.
85. de Greef, W. J., Plotsky, P. M., and Neill, J. D. (1981). Dopamine levels in hypophysial stalk plasma and prolactin levels in peripheral plasma of the lactating rat: Effects of a simulated suckling stimulus. *Neuroendocrinology* **32:** 229–233.
86. Plotsky, P. M., and Neill, J. D. (1982). Interactions of dopamine and thyrotropin-releasing hormone in the regulation of prolactin release in lactating rats. *Endocrinology* **111:** 168–173.
87. Denef, C., Manet, D., and Dewals, R. (1980). Dopaminergic stimulation of prolactin release. *Nature* **285:** 243–246.
88. Burris, T. P., Nguyen, D. N., Smith, S. G., and Freeman, M. E. (1992). The stimulatory and inhibitory effects of dopamine on prolactin secretion involve different G-proteins. *Endocrinology* **130:** 926–932.
89. Martinez de la Escalera, G., and Weiner, R. I. (1992). Dissociation of dopamine from its receptor as a signal in the pleiotropic hypothalamic regulation of prolactin secretion. *Endocr. Rev.* **13:** 241–255.
90. Keech, C. A., and Gutierrez-Hartmann, A. (1989). Analysis of rat prolactin promoter sequences that mediate pituitary-specific and 3′,5′-cyclic adenosine monophosphate-regulated gene expression in vivo. *Mol. Endocrinol.* **3:** 832–839.
91. Elsholtz, H. P., Lew, A. M., Albert, P. R., and Sundmark, V. C. (1991). Inhibitory control of prolactin and pit-1 gene promoters by dopamine. *J. Biol. Chem.* **266:** 22919–22925.
92. Delbeke, D., Scammell, J. G., Martinez-Campos, A., and Dannies, P. S. (1986). Dopamine inhibits prolactin release when cyclic adenosine 3′,5′-monophosphate levels are elevated. *Endocrinology* **118:** 1271–1277.
93. Boyd, A. E., III, Spencer, E., Jackson, I. M. D., and Reichlin, S. (1976). Prolactin-releasing factor (PRF) in porcine hypothalamic extract distinct from TRH. *Endocrinology* **99:** 861–871.
94. Shin, S. H. (1980). Physiological evidence for the existence of prolactin releasing factor: stress-induced prolactin secretion is not linked to dopaminergic receptors. *Neuroendocrinology* **31:** 375–379.
95. Ben-Jonathan, N., Arbogast, L. A., and Hyde, J. F. (1989). Neuroendocrine regulation of prolactin release. *Prog. Neurobiol.* **33:** 399–447.
96. Grosvenor, C. E., and Mena, F. (1980). Evidence that thyrotropin-releasing hormone and a hypothalamic prolactin-releasing factor may function in the release of prolactin in the lactating rat. *Endocrinology* **107:** 863–868.
97. Labrie, F., Barden, N., Poirier, G., and DeLean, A. (1972). Binding of TRH to plasma membranes of bovine anterior pituitary gland. *Proc. Natl. Acad. Sci. USA* **69:** 283–288.
98. Hinkle, P. M., and Tashjian, A. H., Jr. (1973). Receptors for thyrotropin-releasing hormone in prolactin-producing rat pituitary cells in culture. *J. Biol. Chem.* **248:** 6180–6186.
99. Fink, G., Koch, Y., and Aroya, N. B. (1982). Release of thyrotropin releasing hormone into hypophysial portal blood is high relative to other neuropeptides and may be related to prolactin secretion. *Brain Res.* **243:** 186–189.
100. de Greef, W. J., and Visser, T. J. (1981). Evidence for the involvement of hypothalamic dopamine and thyrotrophin-releasing hormone in suckling-induced release of prolactin. *J. Endocrinol.* **91:** 213–223.
101. de Greef, W. J., Klootwijk, W., Karels, B., and Visser, T. J. (1985). Levels of dopamine and thyrotrophin-releasing hormone in hypophysial stalk blood during an estrogen-stimulated surge of prolactin in the ovariectomized rat. *J. Endocrinol.* **105:** 107–112.
102. White, B. A., and Bancroft, F. C. (1983). Epidermal growth factor and thyrotropin-releasing hormone interact synergistically

with calcium to regulate prolactin mRNA levels. *J. Biol. Chem.* **258:** 4618–4622.

103. Yan, G.-z., and Bancroft, C. (1991). Mediation by calcium of thyrotropin-releasing hormone action on the prolactin promoter via transcription factor pit-1. *Mol. Endocrinol.* **5:** 1488–1497.
104. Kato, Y., Iwasaki, Y., Iwasaki, J., Abe, H., Yanaihara, N., and Imura, H. (1978). Prolactin release by vasoactive intestinal peptide in rats. *Endocrinology* **103:** 554–558.
105. Shimatsu, A., Kato, Y., Matsushita, N., Katakami, H., Ohta, H., Yanaihara, N., and Imura, H. (1983). Effect of prostaglandin E1 on vasoactive intestinal polypeptide release from the hypothalamus and on prolactin secretion from the pituitary in rats. *Endocrinology* **113:** 2059–2064.
106. Kaji, H., Chihara, K., Abe, H., Kita, T., Kashio, Y., Okimura, Y., and Fujita, T. (1985). Effect of passive immunization with antisera to vasoactive intestinal polypeptide and peptide histidine isoleucine amide on 5-hydroxy-L-tryptophan-induced prolactin release in rats. *Endocrinology* **117:** 1914–1919.
107. Kaji, H., Chihara, K., Kita, T., Kashio, Y., Okimura, Y., and Fujita, T. (1985). Administration of antisera to vasoactive intestinal polypeptide and peptide histidine isoleucine attenuates ether-induced prolactin secretion in rats. *Neuroendocrinology* **41:** 529–531.
108. Brar, A. K., Fink, G., Maletti, M., and Rostene, W. (1985). Vasoactive intestinal peptide in rat hypophysial portal blood: Effects of electrical stimulation of various brain areas, the estrous cycle and anaesthetics. *J. Endocrinol.* **106:** 275–280.
109. Bjoro, T., Sand, O., Ostberg, B. C., Gordeladze, J. O., Torjesen, P., Gautvik, K. M., and Haug, E. (1990). The mechanisms by which vasoactive intestinal peptide (VIP) and thyrotropin releasing hormone (TRH) stimulate prolactin release from pituitary cells. *Biosci. Rep.* **10:** 189–199.
110. Martinez de la Escalera, G., Guthrie, J., and Weiner, R. I. (1988). Transient removal of dopamine potentiates the stimulation of prolactin release by TRH but not VIP: Stimulation via Ca^{2+}/protein kinase C pathway. *Neuroendocrinology* **47:** 38–45.
111. Bethea, C. L. (1990). Effect of vasoactive intestinal peptide on monkey prolactin secretion and cyclic AMP in culture: Interaction with estradiol and phenol red. *Neuroendocrinology* **51:** 576–585.
112. Carrillo, A. J., Pool, T. B., and Sharp, Z. D. (1985). Vasoactive intestinal peptide increases prolactin messenger ribonucleic acid content in GH3 cells. *Endocrinology* **116:** 202–206.
113. Bergland, R. M., and Page, R. B. (1979). Pituitary-brain vascular relations: A new paradigm. *Science* **204:** 18–24.
114. Daniel, P. M., and Prichard, M. M. L. (1975). Studies on the hypothalamus and the pituitary gland. *Acta Endocrinol.* **201:** 27–54.
115. Gibbs, D. M. (1984). High concentrations of oxytocin in hypophyseal portal plasma. *Endocrinology* **114:** 1216–1218.
116. Lumpkin, M. D., Samson, W. K., and McCann, S. M. (1983). Hypothalamic and pituitary sites of oxytocin to alter prolactin secretion in the rat. *Endocrinology* **112:** 1711–1717.
117. Hyde, J. F., and Ben-Jonathan, N. (1989). The posterior pituitary contains a potent prolactin-releasing factor: *In vivo* studies. *Endocrinology* **125:** 736–741.
118. Laudon, M., Grossman, D. A., and Ben-Jonathan, N. (1990). Prolactin-releasing factor: Cellular origin in the intermediate lobe of the pituitary. *Endocrinology* **126:** 3185–3192.
119. Allen, D. L., Low, M. J., Allen, R. G., Ben-Jonathan, N. (1995). Identification of two classes of prolactin-releasing factors in intermediate lobe tumors from transgenic mice. *Endocrinology* **136:** 3093–3099.
120. Corcia, A., Steinmetz, R., Liu, J. W., and Ben-Jonathan, N. (1993). Coculturing posterior pituitary cells and GH_3 cells: Dramatic stimulation of prolactin gene expression. *Endocrinology* **131:** 80–85.
121. Steinmetz, R., Gutierrez-Hartmann, A., Bigsby, R. M., and Ben-Jonathan, N. (1994). Activation of the prolactin promoter in transfected GH_3 cells by posterior pituitary cells. *Endocrinology* **135:** 2737–2741.
122. Maurer, R. A., and Gorski, J. (1977). Effects of estradiol-17beta and pimozide on prolactin synthesis in male and female rats. *Endocrinology* **101:** 76–84.
123. Vician, L., Shupnik, M. A., and Gorski, J. (1979). Effects of estrogen on primary ovine pituitary cell cultures: Stimulation of prolactin secretion, synthesis, and preprolactin messenger ribonucleic acid activity. *Endocrinology* **104:** 736–743.
124. Boockfor, F. R., Hoeffler, J. P., and Frawley, L. S. (1986). Estradiol induces a shift in cultured cells that release prolactin or growth hormone. *Am. J. Physiol.* **250:** E103–E105.
125. Amara, J. F., Van Itallie, C., and Dannies, P. S. (1987). Regulation of prolactin production and cell growth by estradiol: Difference in sensitivity to estradiol occurs at level of messenger ribonucleic acid accumulation. *Endocrinology* **120:** 264–271.
126. Seyfred, M. A., Kladde, M. P., and Gorski, J. (1989). Transcriptional regulation by estrogen of episomal prolactin gene regulatory elements. *Mol. Endocrinol.* **3:** 305–314.
127. Maurer, R. A., and Notides, A. C. (1987). Identification of an estrogen-responsive element from the 5′-flanking region of the rat prolactin gene. *Mol. Cell. Biol.* **7:** 4247–4254.
128. Seyfred, M. A., and Gorski, J. (1990). An interaction between the 5′ flanking distal and proximal regulatory domains of the rat prolactin gene is required for transcriptional activation by estrogens. *Mol. Endocrinol.* **4:** 1226–1234.
129. De Lean, A., Ferland, L., Drouin, J., Kelly, P. A., and Labrie, F. (1977). Modulation of pituitary thyrotropin releasing hormone receptor levels by estrogens and thyroid hormones. *Endocrinology* **100:** 1496–1504.
130. Gershengorn, M. C., Marcus-Samuels, B. E., and Geras, E. (1979). Estrogens increase the number of thyrotropin-releasing hormone receptors on mammotropic cells in culture. *Endocrinology* **105:** 171–176.
131. Pasqualini, C., Bojda, F., and Kerdelhue, B. (1986). Direct effect of estradiol on the number of dopamine receptors in the anterior pituitary of ovariectomized rats. *Endocrinology* **119:** 2484–2489.
132. Wise, P. M., Rance, N., and Barraclough, C. A. (1981). Effects of estradiol and progesterone on catecholamine turnover rates in discrete hypothalamic regions in ovariectomized rats. *Endocrinology* **108:** 2186–2193.
133. Gubbins, E. J., Maurer, R. A., Lagrimini, M., Erwin, C. R., and Donelson, J. E. (1980). Structure of the rat prolactin gene. *J. Biol. Chem.* **255:** 8655–8662.
134. Miller, W. L., and Eberhardt, N. L. (1983). Structure and evolution of the growth hormone gene family. *Endocr. Rev.* **4:** 97–130.
135. Cooke, N. E., Coit, D., and Shine, J. (1981). Human prolactin: cDNA structural analysis and evolutionary comparisons. *J. Biol. Chem.* **256:** 4007–4016.
136. Maurer, R. A., Erwin, C. R., and Donelson, J. E. (1981). Analysis of 5′ flanking sequences and intron-exon boundaries of the rat prolactin gene. *J. Biol. Chem.* **256:** 10524–10528.
137. Gellersen, B., DiMattia, G. E., Friesen, H. G., and Bohnet, H. G. (1989). Prolactin (PRL) mRNA from human decidua differs from pituitary PRL mRNA but resembles the IM-9-P3 lymphoblast PRL transcript. *Mol. Cell Endocrinol.* **64:** 127–130.
138. Kurtz, A., Bristol, L. A., Toth, B. E., Lazar-Wesley, E., Takacs,

L., and Kacsoh, B. (1993). Mammary epithelial cells of lactating rats express prolactin messenger ribonucleic acid. *Biol. Reprod.* **48:** 1095–1103.

139. Emanuele, N. V., Jurgens, J. K., Halloran, M. M., Tentler, J. J., Lawrence, A. M., and Kelley, M. R. (1992). The rat prolactin gene is expressed in brain tissue: Detection of normal and alternatively spliced prolactin messenger RNA. *Mol. Endocrinol.* **6:** 35–42.
140. Pellegrini, I., Lebrun, J.-J., Ali, S., and Kelly, P. A. (1992). Expression of prolactin and its receptor in human lymphoid cells. *Mol. Endocrinol.* **6:** 1023–1031.
141. O'Neal, K. D., Schwarz, L. A., and Yu-Lee, L. (1991). Prolactin receptor gene expression in lymphoid cells. *Mol. Cell Endocrinol.* **82:** 127–135.
142. Stricker, P., and Grueter, R. (1928). Action du lobe anterieur de l'hypophyse sur la montee laiteuse. *C. R. Soc. Biol. (Paris)* **99:** 1978–1980.
143. Frawley, L. S., and Boockfor, F. R. (1991). Mammosomatotropes: Presence and functions in normal and neoplastic pituitary tissue. *Endocr. Rev.* **12:** 337–355.
144. Hoeffler, J. P., Boockfor, F. R., and Frawley, L. S. (1985). Ontogeny of prolactin cells in neonatal rats: Initial prolactin secretors also release growth hormone. *Endocrinology* **117:** 187–195.
145. Behringer, R. R., Mathews, L. S., Palmiter, R. D., and Brinster, R. L. (1988). Dwarf mice produced by genetic ablation of growth hormone-expressing cells. *Genes Dev.* **2:** 453–460.
146. Borelli, E., Heyman, R. A., and Arias, C. (1989). Transgenic mice with inducible dwarfism. *Nature* **339:** 538–541.
147. Cooke, N. E. (1995). Prolactin: Basic physiology. In *Endocrinology.* (L. J. DeGroot, ed.), Vol. 3, pp. 368–393. Saunders, Philadelphia.
148. Kelly, P. A., Djiane, J., Postel-Vinay, M.-C., and Edery, M. (1991). The prolactin/growth hormone receptor family. *Endocr. Rev.* **12:** 235–251.
149. McNeilly, A. S. (1994). Suckling and the control of gonadotropin secretion. In *The Physiology of Reproduction* (E. Knobil and J. D. Neill, eds.), Vol. 2, pp. 1179–1212. Raven Press, New York.
150. Wright, P. J., Stelmasiak, T., and Chamley, W. A. (1980). Pituitary responsiveness to LH-RH in post-partum ewes treated with oestradiol-17beta and failing to show a plasma LH surge. *Aust. J. Biol. Sci.* **33:** 465–469.
151. Cohen-Becker, I. R., Selmanoff, M., and Wise, P. M. (1986). Hyperprolactinemia alters the frequency and amplitude of pulsatile luteinizing hormone secretion in the ovariectomized rat. *Neuroendocrinology* **42:** 328–333.
152. Numan, M. (1994). Maternal behavior. In *The Physiology of Reproduction* (E. Knobil and J. D. Neill, eds.), Vol. 2, pp. 221–302. Raven Press, New York.

C H A P T E R

45

Circadian Timing

Robert Y. Moore

In its elliptic course around the sun, the earth revolves on its axis, such that at any given moment, half the earth is in light and half in dark. This inexorable progress of light and dark, day and night, is the most pervasive recurring stimulus in the environment and is the basis for a fundamental adaptation of living organisms—**circadian rhythms.** (Circadian is derived from *circa*—about—and *diem*—day.) These rhythms are expressed in nearly all living organisms, from bacteria to humans, and they have been recognized since the earliest recorded observations by humans. They were generally assumed to represent a passive response to the solar light–dark cycle, but we now know that circadian rhythms are genetically determined, endogenously generated adaptations. The French geologist deMairan provided the first clear description of the persistence of rhythmic events under constant conditions in 1729. Observing a plant kept in a dark room, deMairan recorded rhythmic leaf movements that persisted with a daily periodicity in the absence of a light–dark cycle. This persistence in the absence of exogenous stimuli is now known to be a fundamental property of circadian rhythms.

CIRCADIAN RHYTHMS: A FUNDAMENTAL ADAPTATION OF LIVING ORGANISMS

Circadian rhythms probably are the most common adaptation of living organisms. These rhythms are observed in virtually all eukaryotic organisms, and growing evidence indicates that they occur in prokaryotes as well. In mammals, circadian rhythms affect a wide variety of behavioral and physiological functions (Fig. 45.1),[1] such as the cycle of rest–activity, variations in psychomotor performance and sensory perception, secretion of hormones, and regulation of core body temperature. Circadian rhythms are normally entrained to the light–dark cycle such that the phase relationship is stable. In addition, as noted earlier, in the absence of a light–dark cycle, the rhythm persists. Generation of circadian rhythms is a regulatory function of the nervous system. This function is mediated by the circadian timing system (CTS), a set of specific neural structures that establish a temporal organization of physiological processes and behaviors into precise patterns. The fundamental properties of circadian rhythms, endogenous generation and entrainment, require that the CTS have at least three components: (1) photoreceptors and visual pathways that transduce photic entraining information, (2) pacemakers that generate a circadian signal, and (3) output pathways that couple the pacemaker to effector systems (Fig. 45.2).

Animals have evolved two different patterns of circadian timing for organizing behavior into cycles of rest and activity. In animals in which vision has evolved as the primary sense, activity typically occurs during the day, when vision best serves adaptation, and rest occurs at night. Such animals are called **diurnal.** In animals in which audition and olfaction dominate perception of the environment, activity typically occurs at night and rest occurs during the day, a pattern called **nocturnal.** In each case, the temporal order of behavior has evolved so that activity and rest occur when the dominant senses can best aid feeding and reproducing, as well as avoidance of predators. These patterns of behavior are integrated with a number of temporally organized physiological processes that fur-

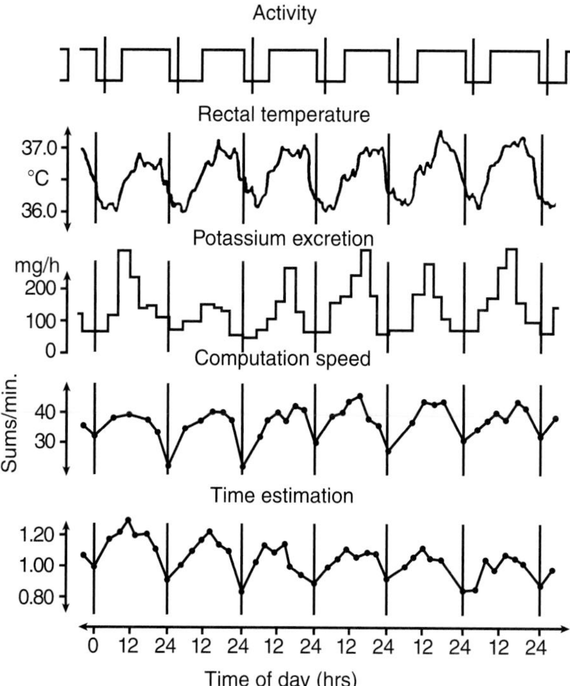

FIGURE 45.1 Daily rhythms in rest–activity, body temperature, potassium excretion, computation speed (number of computations performed per minute), and time estimation (accuracy with which short intervals of time are assessed). From Wever[1] with permission.

ther promote successful adaptive behavior. For example, circadian timing provides the basis for successful reproduction in many mammals.

Circadian Timing Depends on the Nervous System

The systematic study of circadian rhythms began in the first half of this century with observations of a wide variety of rhythms in diverse organisms. Studies in the 1950s and 1960s describing fundamental features of animal rhythms firmly established that the rhythms are generated by endogenous pacemakers, or clocks. This work led to the discovery of neural clocks and to the elucidation and analysis of a CTS. Many individuals contributed to these advances in our understanding of circadian rhythms. For example, the work of Colin Pittendrigh[2] and Jurgen Aschoff[3] provided fundamental insights in both animals and humans. After circadian regulation was identified as a CNS function in mammals, Curt Richter, another early investigator of circadian function, concluded that a circadian pacemaker controlling rest–activity cycles was likely to be located in the anterior hypothalamus.

Another important line of investigation in this era was initiated by the identification and characterization of the pineal hormone **melatonin** by Aaron Lerner and the demonstration of melatonin synthetic pathways by Julius Axelrod.[4] Melatonin is synthesized and secreted in a circadian pattern. To identify the visual pathways that controlled synthesis of pineal melatonin and the fluctuating pineal content of the melatonin precursor serotonin, Moore and collaborators selectively ablated visual pathways until all known pathways had been transected, leaving the optic chiasm.[5] Surprisingly, although after ablation animals were blind and had no pupillary reflex response to light, they retained circadian entrainment. This failure to identify an entrainment pathway among the known visual pathways led to experiments that demonstrated a direct projection from the retina to the **suprachiasmatic nucleus** (SCN) of the hypothalamus. Because entrainment requires the lateral eyes in mammals, and ablation of visual pathways distal to the optic chiasm does not affect entrainment,[6] this **retinohypothalamic tract** (RHT) terminat-

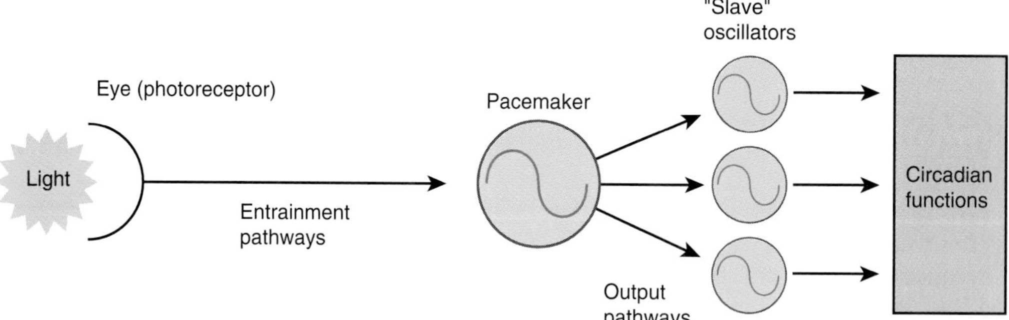

FIGURE 45.2 Overview of the basic organization of the circadian timing system (CTS). The control feature of the CTS is the circadian pacemaker. Information from photoreceptors is conveyed by entrainment pathways to the pacemaker. The pacemaker has a rhythmic output that drives "slave" oscillators, which control functions that exhibit circadian regulation.

ing in the SCN is sufficient to maintain entrainment. Transection of the RHT at its entry into the SCN abolishes entrainment without affecting other visual functions, indicating that the RHT is necessary for entrainment. Identification of the SCN as the site of RHT termination led directly to a test of the hypothesis that the SCN is the circadian pacemaker. Researchers showed that ablation of the SCN results in a loss of circadian rhythms (Fig. 45.3)[7] and established the role of the SCN in circadian function.

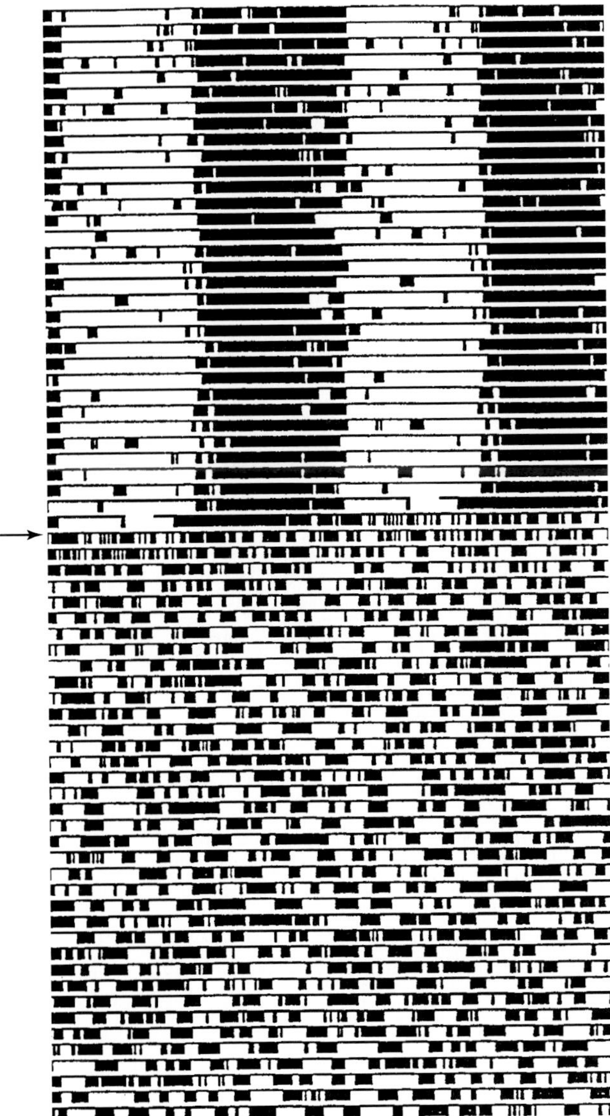

FIGURE 45.3 SCN ablation results in loss of circadian function. This is a record of activity of an albino rat maintained in a light–dark cycle. From the top of the record to the arrow, the animal exhibits a normal rhythm of activity, indicated by dark areas. The record is double-plotted, which means that each line shows the preceding day and the new day to ease evaluation of the record. At the arrow, a bilateral SCN lesion was performed. Activity is randomly distributed thereafter, meaning circadian organization of rest–activity has been lost.

The demonstration of the RHT and the dramatic effects of SCN ablation were the introductory events to a remarkable period of intense investigation of the mammalian circadian timing system. There also have been striking advances in our understanding of the organization of the circadian timing system in invertebrates and nonmammalian vertebrates and of the molecular mechanisms of pacemaker function. In the sections that follow we consider the neural mechanisms of pacemaker organization, function, and entrainment, as well as coupling to effector systems.

Summary

The circadian timing system is composed of central and peripheral neural elements and the attendent sensory and motor performances they regulate. Critical components include photoreceptors and visual pathways (e.g., retinohypothalamic tract), circadian "clocks" or pacemakers (such as the suprachiasmatic nucleus), and output pathways (such as the pineal gland and its hormone melatonin) to couple pacemakers to effectors.

THE SUPRACHIASMATIC NUCLEUS

In mammals, the SCN is a paired nucleus of small neurons lying above the optic chiasm on each side of the ventral third ventricle (Fig. 45.4). Four lines of evidence support the view that the SCN is the dominant mammalian circadian pacemaker. First, as mentioned earlier, the SCN is the site of termination of an entraining pathway—the RHT—and SCN ablation abolishes circadian rhythms. Second, lesions of the SCN only alter the temporal organization of a function; the function itself is not changed. For example, with SCN lesions, the sleep–wake rhythm is eliminated, but the amount of time spent asleep and awake and the amount of REM and nonREM sleep are unaffected.[8] Third, isolation of the SCN, either *in vivo* or *in vitro*, does not alter its ability to generate a circadian signal.[9] Finally, transplantation of a fetal SCN into the third ventricle of arrhythmic hosts with SCN lesions restores circadian rhythm[10] with a period that reflects donor, not host, rhythm.[11]

The SCN Has Two Distinct Divisions

In Golgi material, neurons in the dorsomedial region of the SCN are quite small and have sparse dendritic arbors, whereas neurons in the ventral and lateral por-

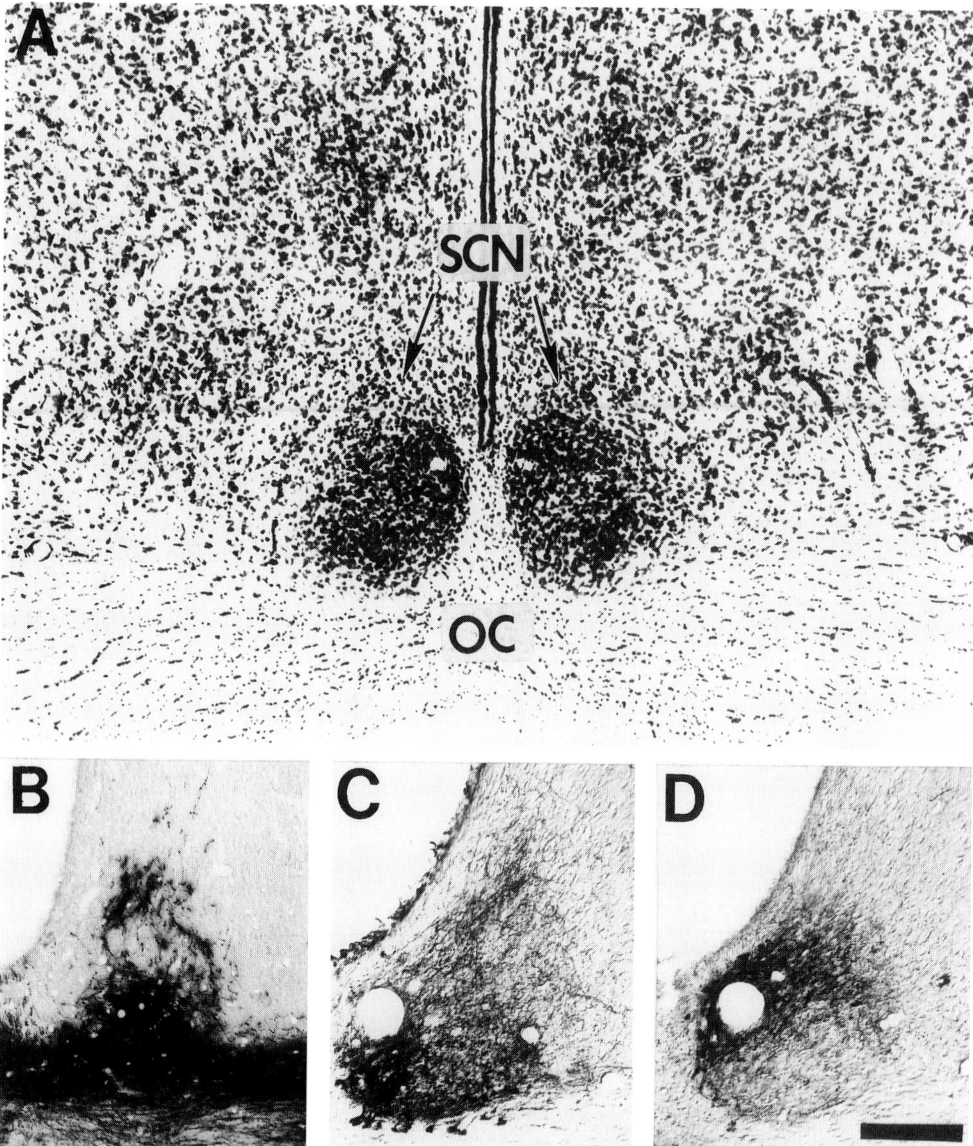

FIGURE 45.4 Mammalian suprachiasmatic nucleus (SCN). (A) Nissl-stained, coronal section through the anterior hypothalamus and optic chiasm (oc) of the rat. The SCN is two compact cell groups lying above the optic chiasm and lateral to the third ventricle, the slitlike structure in the center of the figure. (B) Photomicrograph through the same level of the SCN showing the distribution of the retinohypothalamic tract, the darkly stained material. (C) Photomicrograph showing vasoactive intestinal polypeptide-containing neurons in the ventrolateral SCN. (D) Vasopressin-containing neurons in the dorsomedial SCN.

tions of the nucleus are larger and have more extensive dendritic arbors, which often extend beyond the apparent boundary of the SCN. Dorsomedial SCN neurons contain either arginine vasopressin (AVP) or angiotensin II (AII) and GABA. Afferents to the dorsomedial SCN arise from hypothalamus, basal forebrain, and the limbic cortex. Ventrolateral SCN neurons, on the other hand, typically contain vasoactive intestinal polypeptide (VIP), gastrin-releasing peptide (GRP), and GABA. Visual afferents, the primary retinal input from the RHT and secondary visual projections from the **intergeniculate leaflet (IGL)** of the lateral geniculate complex, terminate in the ventrolateral subdivision. Another important input to this area is from the serotoninergic neurons of the midbrain raphe nuclei. Because the ventrolateral SCN receives the primary entraining afferents and because data indicate that it contains a set of pacemaker neurons,[12] this subdivision of the SCN is designated the "core" (Fig. 45.5). The dorsomedial subdivision is the

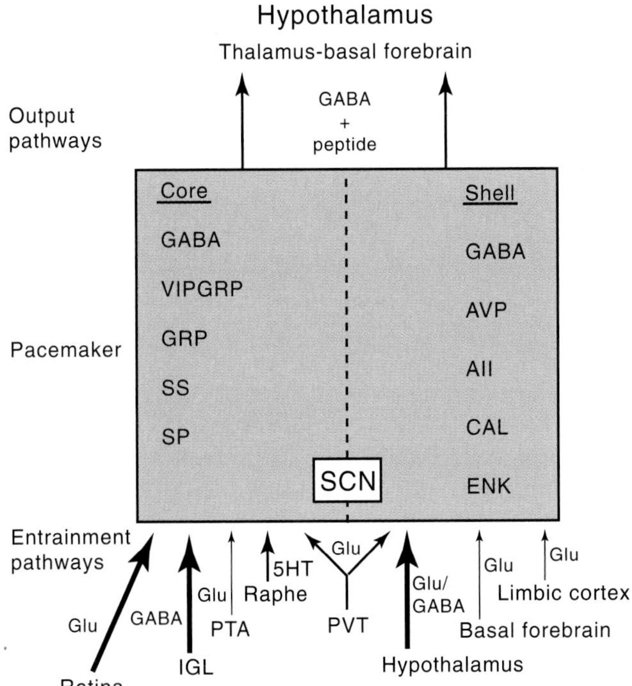

FIGURE 45.5 Organization of the SCN in mammals. The SCN has two subdivisions: a core, which contains neurons in which vasoactive intestinal polypeptide (VIP), gastrin-releasing peptide (GRP), calretinin (CAL), somatostatin (SS), or substance P (SP) is colocalized with GABA, and a shell, in which arginine vasopressin (AVP), angiotensin II (AII), or enkephalin (ENK) is colocalized with GABA. The bottom of the figure shows the pattern of distribution of entrainment pathways to core and shell. Transmitters are shown for each pathway. SCN output is summarized at the top of the figure. Glu, glutamate; 5HT, serotonin; IGL, intergeniculate leaflet; PTA, pretectal area; PVT, thalamic paraventricular nucleus.

SCN "shell." These subdivisions are found in all mammals.

SCN Neurons Are Circadian Oscillators

At least two possible patterns of organization exist for the SCN pacemaker: Individual neurons could be born as oscillators and subsequently coupled by neural connections to form a pacemaker. Alternatively, pacemaker function could emerge from the interaction of neurons that have rhythms with periods of less than a day (ultradian rhythm). Data strongly support the view that individual SCN neurons are circadian oscillators that are coupled to make a pacemaker. For example, tetrodotoxin, which blocks sodium-dependent action potentials, does not alter timekeeping in the SCN.[13] Also, circadian function develops in the fetal SCN before synapses appear. Finally, individual SCN neurons maintained in cell culture each have a rhythmic firing rate.[14] Similar findings are seen in another neuronal preparation, the isolated *Bulla* basal retinal neuron (see Fig. 45.6). Whether only one subdivision of the SCN, the core, contains oscillator neurons or whether neurons in both subdivisions express this phenotype is not clear.

In Fetal Life the SCN Pacemaker Is Entrained to Maternal Rhythms

Overt circadian rhythms are typically expressed in mammals after birth. The SCN in the rat is formed in late gestation, between embryonic days 14 and 17 (E14–17; gestation in the rat is 21 days). Circadian function in the SCN first occurs at E19 and is expressed as a rhythm in glucose utilization. The rhythmic glucose utilization is entrained to maternal rhythms; how-

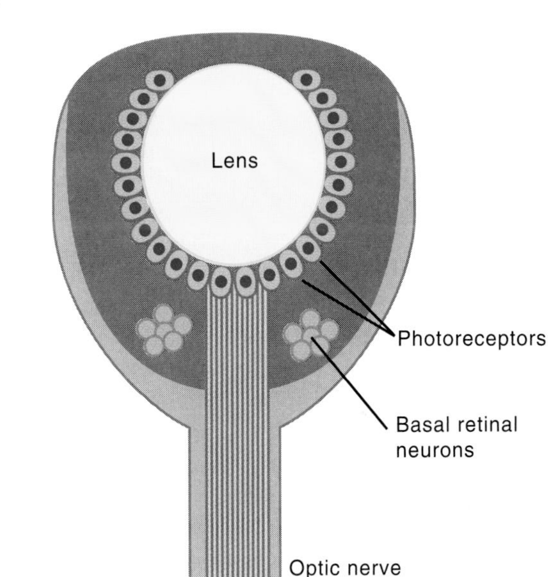

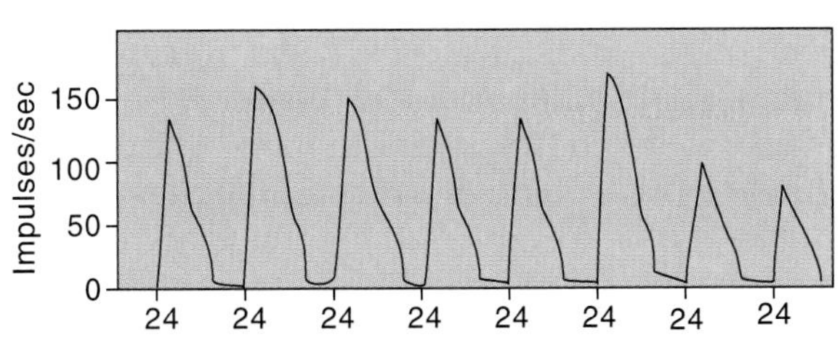

FIGURE 45.6 (A) Drawing of a *Bulla* eye showing locations of photoreceptors around the lens and basal retinal neurons at the origin of the optic nerve. (B) Compound action potential circadian rhythm recorded from the *Bulla* optic nerve *in vitro*. Individual neurons also are rhythmic. Modified from Block *et al.* (*Int. Rev. Cytol.* **146:** 83–144, 1993) with permission.

ever, the maternal rhythms are not necessary for development of SCN function. When the SCN of pregnant females is ablated early in gestation, development of fetuses, including development of the SCN glucose utilization rhythm, progresses normally. In this situation, however, individual pups develop rhythms independent of one another and of their environment. The signal for entrainment to maternal rhythms is not known with certainty, but melatonin appears to play a role.

The Mammalian Eye Contains an Independent Circadian Pacemaker

As we discuss in a later section, the avian circadian system is more complex than that of mammals, and in some birds, the SCN, pineal gland, and eye may be primary pacemakers controlling circadian function. The evidence for non-SCN pacemakers in mammals, however, had been quite limited until the first indication that the eye contains an independent pacemaker came from studies showing that circadian rhythm in visual sensitivity persists after ablation of the SCN. Subsequent work showed that in animals with SCN lesions, the shedding of rod outer segments continues to be rhythmic.[15] A problem with studies such as these, however, is that the lesions might have been too small, for example, to abolish rhythm. This problem was resolved by a study[16] that showed a circadian rhythm in the production of melatonin by cultured neural retina of the golden hamster. This study provided definitive evidence that the mammalian eye contains a circadian pacemaker. Presumably, this pacemaker maintains the circadian rhythm of visual sensitivity.

Evidence suggests the presence of additional non-SCN oscillators. In one study, when the feeding of animals with SCN lesions was restricted to 1 h daily, the animals developed bouts of activity that regularly preceded food availability. The timing of the activity reflected the function of a circadian clock. In another study of animals with SCN lesions, administration of methamphetamine in drinking water restored circadian rhythm to locomotor activity. In both of these studies, the function of the oscillator did not persist beyond the period of administration of the entraining stimulus; that is, with cessation of food restriction or methamphetamine administration, animals rapidly become arrhythmic. The mechanisms responsible for these rhythms must be fundamentally different from the SCN pacemaker; in these experiments, rhythms did not "free-run" in the absence of environmental cues (the entraining stimuli). The locations of these oscillators are unknown.

Summary

The suprachiasmatic nucleus is the dominant mammalian pacemaker. This paired anterior hypothalamic nucleus has a parvicellular dorsomedial division with AVP or AII GABA neurons and a ventrolateral division containing VIP or GRP GABA neurons that receive the retinal input and afferents from the intergeniculate leaflet of the lateral geniculate. SCN neurons are spontaneously active circadian oscillators even when deprived of the afferent signals.

LIGHT AS THE DOMINANT STIMULUS

Light establishes both the phase and period of the pacemaker, and thus is the dominant entraining stimulus, or *Zeitgeber* (time-giver), of the circadian system. The pacemaker can be viewed as a somewhat inaccurate clock, which must be repeatedly reset. It free-runs with a period that is slightly off 24 h in the absence of a light–dark cycle. The light–dark cycle sets the exact timing of the pacemaker and is best understood by looking at the pacemaker's **phase response curve** (PRC) to light (Fig. 45.7). The PRC shows that the pacemaker responds differently to light at different times of day.

Entrainment Is Mediated by a Specific Photoreceptive System

The circadian system is not responsive to specialized aspects of visual stimuli. It responds to changes in luminance, the total amount of light, but not to color, shape, movement, or other visual parameters. The system is maximally responsive at wavelengths of about 500 nm but has a wide range of sensitivity. The responsiveness of the circadian system is not altered in mutant mice with retinal degeneration and nearly complete loss of rods.[17] This evidence suggests that cones are likely to be the crucial photoreceptor. It is not clear, however, whether there is a special subset of cones and specific retinal pathways that transmit photic information to the circadian system.

The Circadian Retina

Neurotropic viruses have been used as tools to determine whether specific retinal ganglion cells give rise to the RHT and the specific retinal pathways that lead to these ganglion cells. When a wild-type pseudorabies virus (a swine herpesvirus) is injected into the vitreous of the eye, retinal ganglion cells take up the virus.

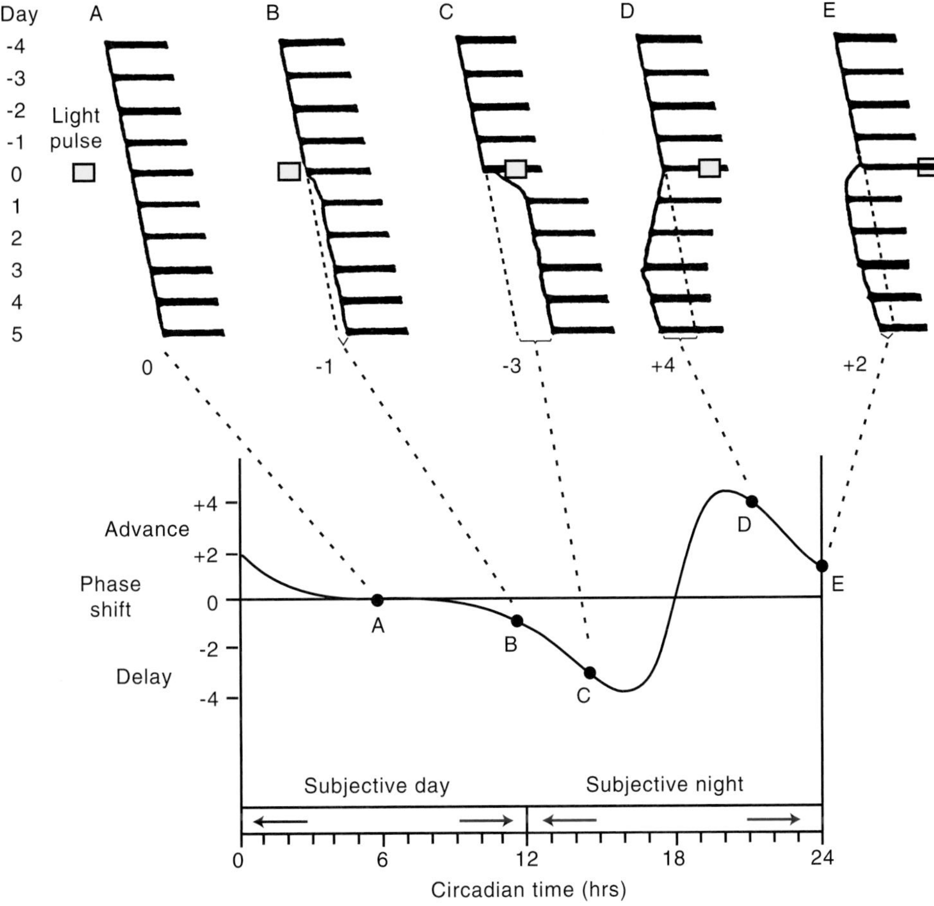

FIGURE 45.7 The phase response curve (PRC). With animals maintained in constant dark, activity is recorded (horizontal bars) and light pulses are given as indicated. The effects of light are determined and then the PRC is constructed as shown.

The virus is replicated in the ganglion cells and then transported along axons to be released at synaptic terminals. Postsynaptic neurons take up and replicate the virus, thus allowing functional mapping of brain circuitry. In contrast, a mutant virus that lacks some of the protein parts of its glycoprotein envelope protein is taken up, replicated, and transported only by retinal ganglion cells that project to the circadian system, accessory optic nuclei, and pretectal area.[18] This selective invasiveness and transport allowed identification of a specific subset of retinal ganglion cells that gives rise to the RHT. The virus labels a homogeneous population of small retinal ganglion cells with sparse, but widely spread, dendrites. These ganglion cells project only to the SCN and **intergeniculate leaflet** (IGL), a thalamic component of the CTS, and appear to be a homolog of feline W cells.

The mutant pseudorabies virus can also be used to identify retinal elements that process visual input for entrainment. After infection of retinal ganglion cells, viral infection progresses by transynaptic transport through the retina. The first elements infected are wide-field amacrine cells and cone bipolar cells, indicating that transduction of photic information takes place through a cone pathway, as suggested by the retinal degeneration studies mentioned earlier.[17] The cones and cone pathway in the retina probably are not dedicated components of the CTS, in contrast to the ganglion cells that project to the SCN and IGL. Instead, it seems likely that any cone can provide input to RHT ganglion cells.

Glutamate

Glutamate has long been recognized as a neurotransmitter produced by most retinal ganglion cells, and glutamate is now known to mediate action of the ganglion cells of the RHT projecting to the SCN and IGL. For establishment as a transmitter, substances must meet three criteria (see Chapter 9). First, the substance must be present in the axon terminals of the neurons for which it is the putative transmitter. Glutamate is present in all neurons as part of a normal metabolic pool of amino acids, which is difficult to distinguish from a transmitter pool. Second, the substance must be released from axon terminals when the neuron is stimulated; glutamate has met this criterion. The third criterion, identity of action, is most stringent: Exogenously applied glutamate must have the same postsynaptic effect as stimulation of the RHT. Stimulation of the RHT produces a PRC essentially identical to the PRC obtained with light. In *in vivo* experiments glutamate produces the same phase changes.[19,20] Thus, glutamate meets the criteria for a transmitter in the RHT.

The Intergeniculate Leaflet (IGL) Mediates Nonphotic Input

The flow diagram shown in Fig. 45.2 implies that visual input should suffice for entrainment of the circadian system. Although this is probably correct, evidence indicates that the regulation of the SCN pacemaker is quite complex in the intact mammal. As mentioned earlier, the SCN has multiple inputs in addition to the RHT, two of which are from the lateral geniculate complex and the midbrain raphe.

The IGL is a subdivision of the lateral geniculate complex of all mammals.[21] This small, ventral derivative of the thalamas contains a population of NPY- and GABA-containing neurons that project to the SCN core. Perfusion of NPY into the SCN region produces a PRC with phase advances during subjective day and phase delays during subjective night. A similar PRC is obtained by stimulating the IGL or by applying NPY to slices of SCN *in vitro*.[22] However, the physiological significance of the phase shifts was unknown until stimuli that produce vigorous locomotor activity were shown to cause phase advances during subject day. The phase shifts are a function of activity; when activity is prevented, no phase change occurs.[23,24] Furthermore, lesions that ablate the IGL eliminate activity-induced phase changes, indicating that the effects of activity on phase are mediated by the IGL–SCN projection. Thus, the IGL modulates entrainment by transmitting information about nonphotic events to the SCN. As described earlier, the IGL receives dense retinal input from the retinal ganglion cells that give rise to the RHT, so it seems likely that the IGL integrates photic and nonphotic information for the CTS to affect pacemaker function (Fig. 45.8).

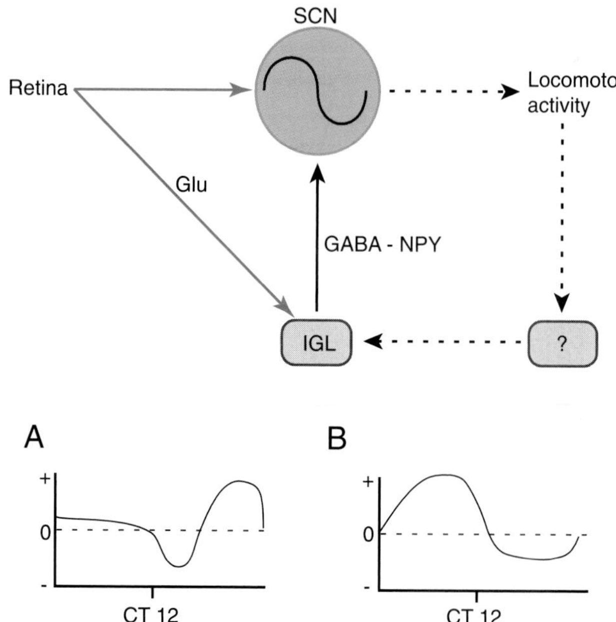

FIGURE 45.8 The actions of two entrainment pathways. The RHT projects to the SCN and IGL. The SCN controls the rest–activity cycle, and locomotor activity feeds back through the IGL projection to the SCN to affect SCN pacemaker function. The effect of RHT activation is shown by the light phase response curve (PRC) (A), and the effect of IGL–RHT activation is shown by the nonphotic PRC (B).

Raphe Modulates Photic Entrainment through Serotonergic Innervation of the SCN

Serotonergic neurons of the midbrain raphe densely innervate the core of the SCN to modulate its responses to light.[25] Raphe neurons are usually state dependent; they fire regularly during waking, slowly during slow-wave sleep, and not at all during rapid eye movement sleep. During waking, visual stimulation acutely increases the activity of the neurons. Serotonin inhibits the responses of the SCN to light and optic nerve stimulation *in vivo* and *in vitro*. Data suggest that serotonin acts between the RHT and pacemaker mechanisms, on the entrainment mechanisms within SCN neurons. In addition, many effects of entraining stimuli other than light may occur through altered responses to light.

Summary

Entrainment is mediated by specific photoreceptors and their efferent circuitry. Cones, perhaps a subset, provide the initial required photic detection. Circuitry arising from their targeted ganglion cells projects to the SCN, accessory optic nuclei, and the pretectal area independent of classical retinal efferent circuits to geniculate and colliculus. The ganglion cell–SCN circuit uses Glu as neurotransmitter, while the intergeniculate–SCN afferent provides nonphotic input whose cotransmitters are GABA and NPY. A 5HT-mediated projection from the raphe nuclei can regulate SCN oscillator rhythm.

PACEMAKER OUTPUT

Efferent projections of the SCN[26] are largely to the hypothalamus, with the densest projections going to a region intercalated between the dorsal border of the SCN and the ventral border of the paraventricular nucleus, the **subparaventricular zone.** This zone has projections that largely overlap projections of the SCN, leading to the view that its function is to reinforce SCN control of effector systems. The SCN also projects to other hypothalamic areas, the medial preoptic area, lateral hypothalamic area, retrochiasmatic area, paraventricular nucleus, dorsomedial nucleus, and posterior hypothalamic area. Outside the hypothalamus, the SCN projects to the basal forebrain (bed nucleus of the stria terminalis (BNST) and lateral septal nucleus), midline thalamus (nucleus reuniens and paraventricular nucleus), and IGL. Figure 45.9 shows one possibility of how the SCN might control a myriad of functions using only these restricted projections.

What is the signal that SCN projections deliver to the innervated areas? SCN projections have peak daytime firing rates that are about twice as fast as trough rates, which occur at night. The rhythm has a simple, nearly sinusoidal waveform; the output of the SCN is a gradually changing frequency of neuronal firing. Firing occurs at high frequency during subjective day and low frequency during subjective night. This pattern appears to be the same in diurnal and nocturnal animals. However, simple neuronal firing with transmitter release may not be the only means by which the SCN communicates with the areas it controls. In animals in which SCN transplants restore rhythmicity that was lost due to SCN lesions, direct connections into the host brain from the transplant, typically in the third ventricle, appear unnecessary for functional recovery. This suggests that a humoral mechanism may play a role in rhythm regulation.

Summary

The SCN projects to the subparaventricular zone and other hypothalamic neurons and several other nonhypothalamic structures of the diencephalon (BNST, lateral septal nucleus, nucleus reuniens, the thalamic paraventricular nucleus, and the IGL). Direct activation of these efferent circuits controls the expression of circadian rhythmicity.

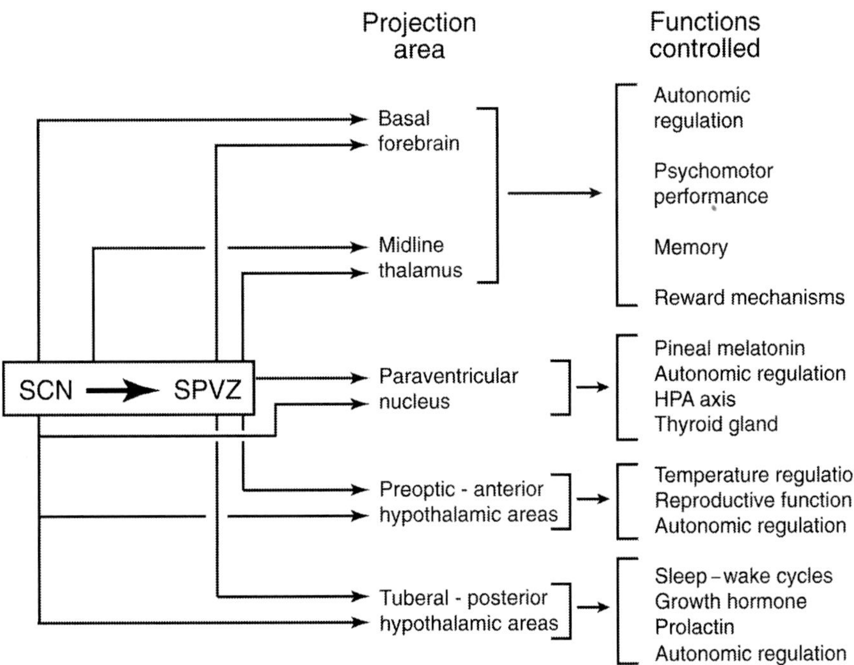

FIGURE 45.9 Projections of the SCN–subparaventricular zone (SPVZ) complex and functions likely controlled by these pathways.

CIRCADIAN TIMING AND REPRODUCTION

The CTS Controls Estrus in Some Mammals

In many female mammals, reproductive events occur in cycles called estrous cycles. The estrous cycle in the rat is 4 days long and culminates on the day of proestrus in a midafternoon surge of release of luteinizing hormone (LH). The timing of the LH surge is precise and results in ovulation followed by receptivity to males the subsequent night. SCN ablation results in loss of estrous cycles and reproductive capacity. The surge in LH production and release results from release of gonadotropin-releasing hormone (GnRH) from the median eminence into the portal circulation.[27] (GnRH neurons are located in the preoptic anterior hypothalamic area and have axons projecting to the median eminence (see Chapter 43).) The precise timing of the release of GnRH to produce the LH surge is a function of a series of endocrine and neural events that lead to proestrus, with the SCN providing the crucial temporal signal. Although the exact pathways and mechanisms of this timing are not known, circadian mechanisms clearly are an essential aspect of the process. This is an example of the CTS providing precise temporal organization to physiological processes and behavior, in this case reproductive physiology and behavior.

The CTS Also Regulates Seasonal Reproduction

In habitats with marked seasonal variation of temperature and food supply, survival of species requires seasonal regulation of reproduction. The CTS of these animals uses production of the pineal hormone melatonin to measure day length as a means of predicting seasonal changes.

The pineal body is a neural structure derived from the caudal portion of the dorsal diencephalic germinal epithelium. It begins as an evagination from the third ventricle and develops into a solid structure connected with the caudal thalamus by the pineal stalk (Fig. 45.10). The pineal body contains two types of cells: pinealocytes, which are a modified neuronal element, and glia. In primates and most carnivores, the pineal stalk is short, and the pineal body lies immediately caudal to the diencephalon above the tectum. In many rodents, however, the pineal stalk is quite long, and the pineal body lies at the top of the interhemispheric fissure, below the confluence of venous sinuses. The pineal typically has two types of innervation, a sympathetic input from the superior cervical ganglion and a direct central innervation from diencephalic nuclei.

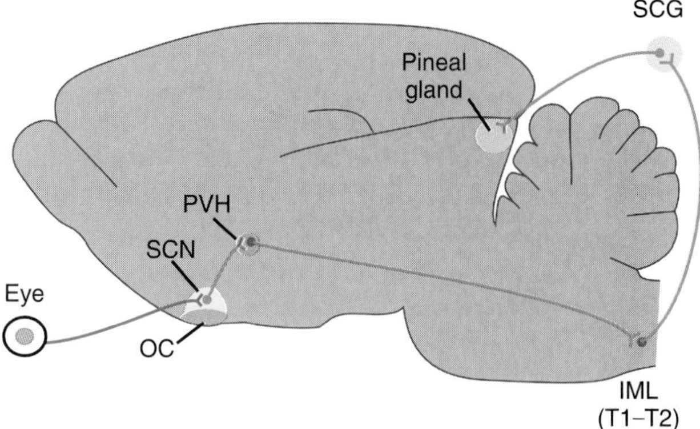

FIGURE 45.10 Diagram of a sagittal view of the rat brain showing the pathways controlling pineal melatonin production. The RHT runs from the retina to the SCN, which in turn projects to the paraventricular nucleus of the hypothalamus (PVH). The PVH projects to the intermediolateral cell column of the upper thoracic cord (IML, T1–T2), which provides preganglionic input to sympathetic neurons in the superior cervical ganglion (SCG) innervating the pineal gland.

Only the sympathetic innervation is known to function in regulating melatonin production. In all mammals, the activity of superior cervical sympathetic neurons innervating the pineal increases at night. The release of norepinephrine from axon terminals acts through β-adrenergic receptors to stimulate melatonin synthesis and release. At night, exposure to light acts through the RHT to inhibit cervical sympathetic activity and thereby quickly stop production of melatonin.

Melatonin is synthesized from the amino acid tryptophan in a series of steps, one of which involves the enzyme serotonin *N*-acetyltransferase. The synthesis of serotonin *N*-acetyltransferase, in turn, follows a circadian rhythm. Thus, regulation of melatonin production depends on sympathetic input to the pineal to affect synthesis of serotonin *N*-acetyltransferase in a rhythm dependent on the SCN (Fig. 45.11).[6] The RHT entrains the SCN and, in addition, mediates the effect of bright light in suppressing melatonin production at night. The pathway for pineal control is from the SCN to the autonomic subdivision of the paraventricular nucleus, which projects directly to the intermediolateral cell column of the upper thoracic cord. These preganglionic neurons innervate the superior cervical ganglion, which then innervates the pineal.[12]

The pineal was tied to seasonal reproduction in a remarkable series of experiments[28] in which male hamsters were shown to change their reproductive function in response to changes in day length (photoperiod). Hamsters are long-day breeders; they breed and bear young in spring and summer. The gestation period is short, as is the period required for young to develop to independence. As days shorten in the fall to a photoperiod less than about 12.5 h, the male hamsters' testes shrink, and spermatogenesis stops. Thus, male hamsters are incapable of reproducing at a time of year when survival of young would be jeopardized by cold weather and limited food. In the spring, as days lengthen, the testes recover to full function in time for the normal mating season. Pinealectomy blocks the response to short days; even in constant darkness gonadal size and function remain unaffected in an animal from which the pineal has been removed. In these animals, the response to short photoperiods can be mimicked by administration of melatonin. The response is dependent on the timing and duration of melatonin administration. It is now clear that the SCN controls this photoperiodic response by controlling the duration of melatonin secretion by the pineal. In short days, melatonin is secreted over a long period and produces a decrease in gonadal function, whereas in long days gonadal function is maintained with a short period of melatonin secretion (Fig. 45.12). In essence, the duration of nocturnal melatonin production is a measure of day length.

The mechanism by which melatonin alters reproductive function is unclear. The situation is quite complex, however, as demonstrated by the pattern of reproductive function in short-day breeders, such as sheep. In contrast to hamsters, sheep predominantly exhibit estrous cycles in the fall and early winter; the sheep also mate at that time. Lambs are born in the spring, which gives them a long period of warm weather and plentiful food to grow and become independent. The reproductive cycle in sheep is generated by endogenous mechanisms that are regulated by melatonin.[29] The photoperiodic control of melatonin secretion synchronizes the endogenous year-long cycle, but in this case, the effect of melatonin is the reverse of that in the hamster. Long photoperiods inhibit the endogenous promotion of reproductive function, whereas short photoperiods promote it. Every day, the SCN–pineal axis provides a pulse of melatonin secretion that faithfully mirrors the lengths of day and night. Thus, the duration of the melatonin signal allows the animals to track time on an annual basis.

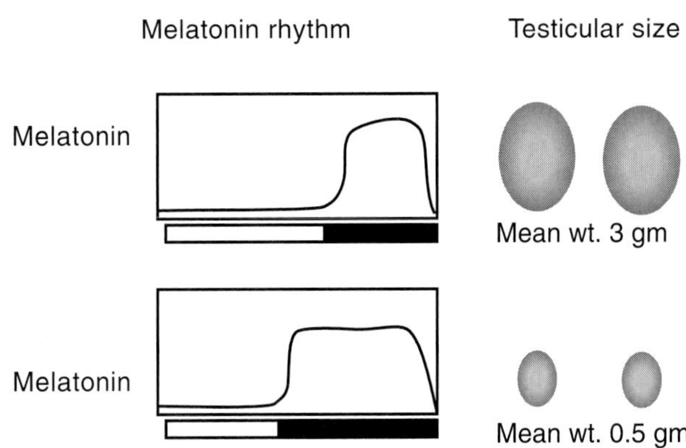

FIGURE 45.12 Melatonin rhythm and testicular size in male hamsters in different day lengths. In 14 h of light alternating with 10 h of dark (LD 14 : 10), the duration of melatonin secretion is short, and testes are large. In contrast, with 10 h of light and 14 h of dark (LD 10 : 14), the duration of melatonin secretion is long, and testes are small.

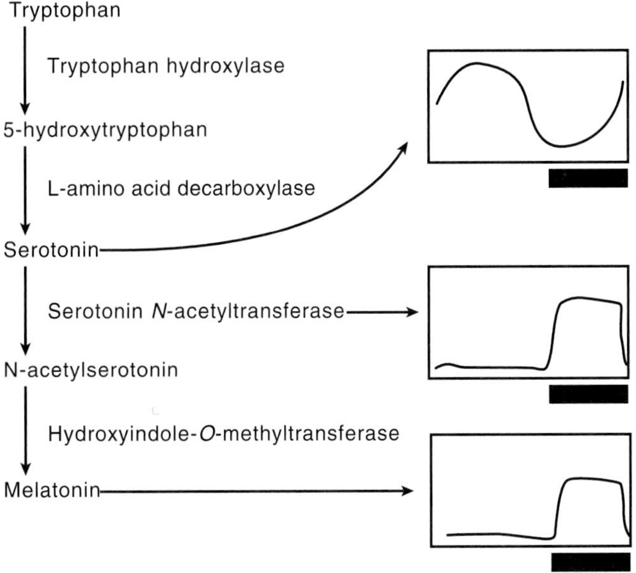

FIGURE 45.11 Metabolic pathway for the production of melatonin from tryptophan in the pineal gland. The circadian rhythms of serotonin, serotonin *N*-acetyltransferase, and melatonin are shown on the right.

The Action of Melatonin Is Mediated by a Specific G-Protein-Coupled Receptor

Melatonin receptors were identified through the use of a radioactive iodine analog of melatonin, iodomelatonin as a ligand in experiments.[30] In the mammalian brain, melatonin receptors have a very limited distribution; they are consistently present only in the SCN and midline thalamic nuclei and in the pars tuberalis of the anterior pituitary. The gene for the melatonin receptor has been cloned, and the receptor is a member of the family of receptors coupled to G proteins.[31] SCN melatonin receptors are thought to mediate feedback of melatonin on the CTS, and the melatonin receptors in the pars tuberalis are thought to mediate reproductive effects.

Substantial evidence indicates that melatonin can affect pacemaker function.[32,33] For example, melatonin can lessen the symptoms of jet lag[34] and, in elderly people, the disruptions of sleep that occur as a consequence of alterations of pacemaker function (see Box 45.1). Thus, melatonin is important not only for seasonal reproduction but for feedback regulation of pacemaker function.

Summary

The circadian timing system can control reproductive cycles in female mammals by regulating estrus. In mammals with seasonal reproductive control, the pineal and melatonin secretions mediate the reproductive regulation in some cases by control of spermotogenesis.

COMPLEXITY OF THE AVIAN CTS

Studies of birds have provided remarkable insight into the organization of the vertebrate CTS. Birds typically have a highly developed visual system and a diurnal pattern of rest–activity. The circadian system of birds has been studied for many years in the common house sparrow, *Passer domesticus.* The locomotor activity of these small birds is readily recorded, and they exhibit a robust circadian rhythm with high levels of activity during the day and low levels at night. The rhythm free-runs under constant lighting conditions. The pineal appears to be a primary pacemaker in these birds. Early work showed that pinealectomy leads to a loss of the circadian activity rhythm in constant darkness.[35] Rhythm persists in a light–dark cycle, but it is driven by the light–dark cycle and mediated by extraretinal photoreceptors[36] and, hence, is not a true circadian rhythm. (This response is quite different from that in mammals, in which no functional extraretinal photoreceptors are known.) The conclusive demonstration that the pineal is a circadian pacemaker in the sparrow was provided in experiments[37] in which pineals from intact animals were transplanted into the anterior chamber of the eyes of animals that were arrhythmic due to pinealectomy. Rhythm was immediately restored in the transplant recipients, with the phase of the restored rhythms identical to that of the sparrows from which the pineals were obtained.

Communication between the pineal and brain appears to be mediated by melatonin. Continuous infusion of melatonin abolishes locomotor rhythm in intact animals, whereas administration of melatonin for 12 h each day to arrhythmic, pinealectomized sparrows restores rhythm. If melatonin is the signal for rhythm, where does it act? An avian homolog of the mammalian SCN receives direct retinal input. Ablation of the SCN in the sparrow abolishes the rhythm of locomotor activity in constant illumination even when the pineal is intact.[38] In animals with SCN lesions, rhythm continues in the presence of a light–dark cycle, as in animals with pinealectomy. The rhythm could be caused by direct action of light on extraretinal photoreceptors, which in turn activate locomotor centers. The loss of rhythm in SCN-ablated animals indicates that melatonin acts through the SCN, which is known to have melatonin receptors.[32]

BOX 45.1

DISORDERS OF CIRCADIAN TIMING

The passenger of an aircraft flying across several time zones will experience the most common of circadian disorders, the jet lag, or rapid time-zone change syndrome. Like most other disorders of circadian timing, jet lag manifests primarily as a sleep disorder. Afflicted individuals typically report nighttime insomnia and daytime sleepiness. Jet lag reflects the delay in readjustment of the circadian pacemaker to the new time zone; it is a disorder of entrainment. It is self-limited, rarely lasting more than a few days. Consistently, even seasoned travelers report the symptoms rarely occur with travel over fewer than five time zones, and travel from west to east is usually more troublesome than travel from east to west perhaps because a long day is much less onerous than an early day after a short night. Recently, treatment of jet lag with melatonin has been reported to be effective.[34]

Non-24-hour sleep–wake disorder occurs most frequently in blind people whose circadian rhythms, lacking visual input, typically free-run with a period of about 25 hours. For many years the human circadian system was erronously believed to be insensitive to light and entrained to social cues. Blind individuals show quite clearly that this is not the case. Their pacemakers are not entrained to social cues and they suffer symptoms very similar to jet lag when they attempt to maintain a regular schedule temporally synchronized with the environment. Some people are entrained to the light–dark cycle despite being totally blind.[59] Apparently, the RHT is intact because their nocturnal rise in pineal melatonin secretion is blocked by light. Conversely, some people with normal sight exhibit a free-running sleep–wake cycle, indicating an absence of RHT function despite normal function of other central retinal projections.

Delayed sleep phase syndrome is another disorder of entrainment, common in adolescence and sometimes continuing into adult life. Affected individuals shift their sleep–wake cycle toward going to bed late and getting up late. Such a change in the phase of the rest–activity cycle typically begins around the time of puberty. Apparently a change in the sensitivity of the pacemaker to phase-advancing stimuli disrupts the normal balance between phase advances and phase delays (Fig. 45.13). This balance is disrupted differently in the **advanced sleep phase syndrome**, in which people (typically elderly) go to sleep early in the evening and awaken early in the morning. This sleep–wake cycle appears to represent a change in sensitivity in the phase delay portion of the PRC (Fig. 45.13).

Disorders of pacemaker function and output appear to be less common than disorders of entrainment. Occasionally tumors disrupt the pacemaker and result in loss of rhythm similar to that seen in animals with SCN lesions.[60] Also, elderly people frequently show a decrease in the amplitude of circadian rhythms, but whether this represents an abnormality in pacemaker function, in output amplitude, or in the capacity of effector systems to respond to pacemaker output is unclear. Without a method for measuring pacemaker output in humans, these alternatives are not easily distinguished.

Seasonal affective disorder also may fall into this category of circadian rhythm disorders. Symptoms typically begin in autumn and remit in spring. Affected individuals experience changes in mood, sleep pattern, appetite, libido, memory, and cognition. Treatment with bright light that extends the length of the day has been successful in treating this disorder.[61] At the simplest level, seasonal affective disorder reflects a disturbance in the measurement of the length of photoperiods.

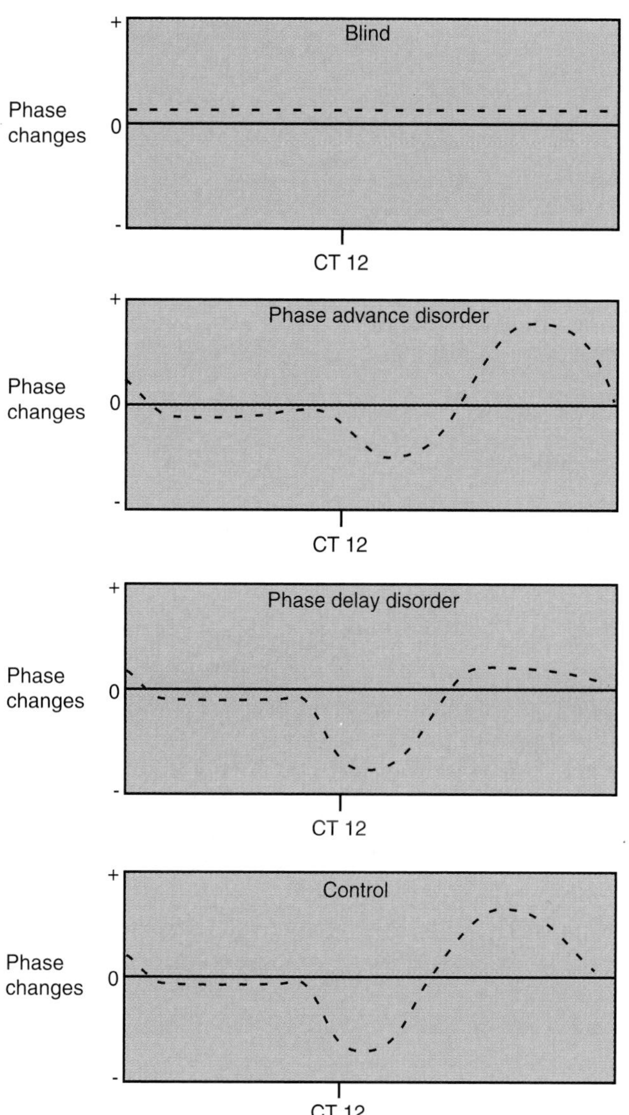

FIGURE 45.13 Phase response curves in three disorders of circadian timing: non-24-hour sleep–wake disorder, phase advance disorder, phase delay disorder.

Investigators initially thought that in all birds the control of circadian rhythm would be like that of the sparrow, but four patterns of pacemaker organization are now recognized in birds. One pattern is expressed by passerine birds, such as sparrows. A second pattern was demonstrated in the Japanese quail, *Coturnix coturnix*.[39] In this species, ablation of the pineal has no effect on the rhythm of locomotor activity. However, removal of the eyes results in a complete loss of rhythm under conditions of constant lighting, indicating that the eye contains the circadian pacemaker that organizes the rest–activity cycle in these birds. The eye pacemaker requires direct neural connections to the brain to generate the rhythm for locomotor activity; transection of the optic nerves is as effective as removal of the eyes in abolishing the activity rhythm.

A third pattern of pineal and ocular pacemakers is seen in the pigeon *Columbia livia*.[40,41] When these birds are kept in constant, dim light, neither pinealectomy nor enucleation alters their activity, but together the

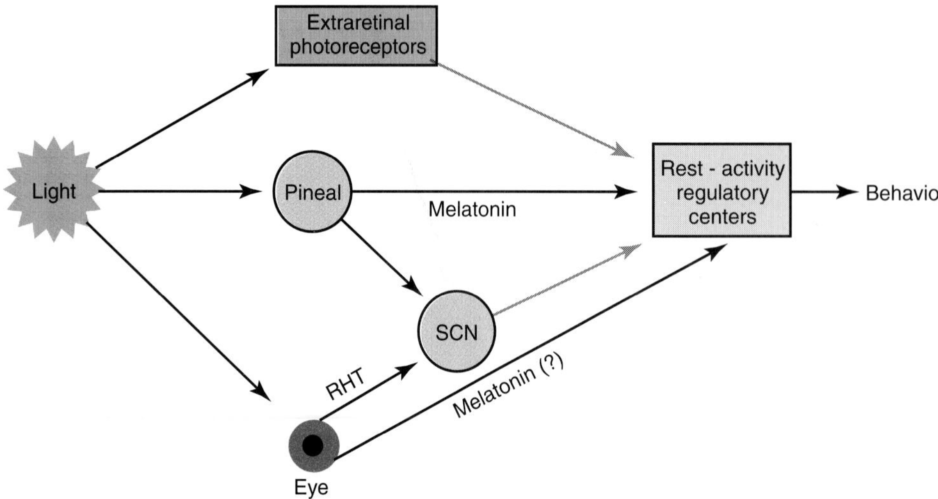

FIGURE 45.14 Organization of avian circadian systems. Depending on the type of bird, the pineal, eye, or SCN may be a circadian pacemaker driving the rest–activity rhythm. The interactions of these structures is shown diagrammatically.

lesions result in an altered rhythm that degrades over days to arrhythmicity. This observation indicates that both the pineal and the eye contribute to generation of the rest–activity rhythm, presumably through their production of melatonin.[42]

The final variant in avian generation of circadian rhythm is exhibited by the chicken *Gallus domesticus.* Singly or together, pinealectomy and enucleation do not abolish circadian function in the chicken; however, SCN ablation does. Thus, the chicken is an avian species that appears similar to mammals with respect to organization of the circadian system. Some reptilian species are also organized this way.

In addition to its importance in studies of circadian function in intact birds, the avian pineal is an important object of studies *in vitro.* The avian pineal culture system lends itself to interesting experiments because the pineal, and presumably individual pineal cells, contain an entire circadian pacemaker, from photoreceptors through pacemaker and output. In culture, the pineals of most birds show entrainment to a light–dark cycle and free-running rhythm of melatonin secretion.[43,44] In constant, dim light or darkness the rhythm persists for several days but usually damps out. At this point, returning the culture to a light–dark cycle restores robust rhythmicity.

In sum, the avian and mammalian circadian systems share many characteristics, such as localization of function, but they also differ in significant ways, such as the presence of extraretinal photoreceptors (Fig. 45.14). In addition, the avian system shows much more variation than the mammalian system. In mammals, the SCN is the primary pacemaker and the eye a secondary one. Although this is true in some birds, the eye and the pineal gland are the dominant pacemakers in most avian species. Mammals and birds express melatonin receptors in the SCN, but the receptors are also expressed in other areas of the avian brain, such as the visual centers.[32] Vincent Cassone proposed a model in which circadian rhythm is the result of interactions among the SCN, pineal, and eye. In this model the SCN and pineal oscillators are maintained in opposite states (so called out of phase) by mutual inhibition,[36] and the eye has the same phase as the pineal.

Summary

The avian circadian timing system is more complex than that of mammals. Extraretinal photic information also arises in some but not all birds in the pineal gland and is transmitted through melatonin secretion to the SCN via the cerebrospinal fluid. In other birds, ocular pacemakers have been detected without pineal participation, and combined ocular–pineal pacemakers have been observed in pigeons. In the chicken, the system more strongly resembles the mammalian timing system, with the SCN taking on the primary pacemaker role.

HERITABILITY OF CIRCADIAN TIMING

Circadian timing in plants and animals is an inherited adaptation and, as such, is genetically determined. Clock mutants in *Drosophila* (fruit fly)[45] and *Neurospora* (bread mold)[46] have provided most of our understanding of the molecular mechanisms of circadian function.

In *Drosophila* and *Neurospora*, the principal mutants express altered free-running periods. For example, in *Drosophila* the affected flies are called *per* mutants (*per* for period). One mutant, *per*^{s}, has a short (less than 24 h) period of free-running; a second mutant, *per*^{l}, has a long period of free-running; and yet another, *per*^{0}, is arrhythmic. The *Neurospora* mutants are designated *frq* mutants (*frq* for frequency) and also express a variety of free-run phenotypes. Our advanced understanding of *Drosophila* and *Neurospora* genetics has enabled rapid progress in understanding the molecular mechanisms of circadian function,[47,48] and although some differences exist between the organisms, the fundamental mechanism appears similar. Three proteins, FRQ in *Neurospora* and PER and TIM in *Drosophila*, have been identified as candidate clock components and tested against the criteria for clock components: (1) the amount, or activity, of the component should cycle with an appropriate period; (2) the phase of the component's rhythm must be reset by the light–dark cycle, and experimentally induced changes in the amount of the component should reset overt rhythms; (3) loss or prevention of the component's rhythm should result in loss of overt rhythms; and (4) mutations affecting the component should affect canonical clock properties, free-run period (*Tau*) and temperature compensation, and a null mutation should abolish rhythm. FRQ, PER, and TIM meet these criteria. We describe the current understanding of molecular mechanisms of clock function in *Drosophila* as an example.

The Drosophila Clock Is Probably Neural

The *per* gene was the first potential clock component to be identified and cloned.[48] PER protein and *per* mRNA both show a circadian oscillation (Fig. 45.15A). The peak in *per* mRNA precedes that in PER protein. PER is a nuclear protein believed to provide negative feedback regulation of *per* gene expression. Overexpression of PER protein eliminates *per* mRNA cycling.[49] The mutations causing the *per*^{s} and *per*^{l} phenotypes are single amino acid substitutions, whereas the *per*^{0} phenotype is a consequence of a null mutation.[48] The *per* gene normally is expressed in a number of tissues, the eye, brain (in neurons and glia), gut, and reproductive system.[48] However, the *per* gene restores rhythmic behavior to *per*^{0} flies when the gene is expressed rhythmically only in head neurons.[50] Thus, rhythmic behaviors in *Drosophila* appear to depend on rhythmic expression of the *per* gene in neurons of the fly brain. The discovery of another mutant, *timeless*, has added additional detail to the clock.[51] Like *per*^{0} flies, *tim* flies are behaviorally arrhythmic and have no rhythmic *per* gene expression. In *tim* flies the PER protein fails to localize to the nucleus, suggesting that the *tim* mutation blocks the entry of the PER protein into the nucleus and thus blocks the feedback regulation of *per*.[52]

PER and TIM Interact to Provide Feedback Regulation of Clock Function

The *tim* gene encodes a 1122-amino-acid protein that has no homology to *per*.[53] Both *per* and *tim* lack a recognizable DNA-binding motif. However, PER contains a PAS dimerization domain through which PER interacts with TIM, and researchers have concluded that the PER–TIM heterodimer enters the nucleus to affect *per* and *tim* transcription (Fig. 45.15).[54] (The *per* gene is on the X chromosome; *tim* is on chromosome 2.) The molecular basis of entrainment may lie in the rapid degradation of TIM caused by light (Fig. 45.16).[55] When flies are kept in a constant environment, a light pulse between hours 2 and 10 of the circadian day (CT2 and CT10) has no effect on rhythm, because TIM is absent during these hours. Because *per* and *tim* are transcribed during this time, PER and TIM normally are produced late in subjective day. Light, however, rapidly degrades TIM, and the protein must reaccumulate after translation from abundant *tim* RNA. Consequently, production of the PER–TIM heterodimer is delayed. Thus, no heterodimer enters the nucleus to suppress *per* and *tim* transcription, and a phase delay results. Later in the circadian day, CT18–CT0, a pulse of light will decrease peak TIM levels, resulting in an advance of transcription of *per* and *tim* and, hence, a phase advance. Thus, light causes a unidirectional biochemical effect beginning with degradation of TIM that results in phase delay, phase advance, or in the "dead zone" of the PRC no phase change.

The *tim* and *per* genes are involved in feedback loops in which entry of PER–TIM heterodimers into the nucleus is an essential feature. The PER–TIM association may depend on posttranslational modifications of the proteins, and the regulatory loops of *per* and *tim* may be coordinated with other elements that have not yet been identified. However, we have a basic understanding of the molecular biology of circadian clocks, and mutants in mammalian, bacterial, and plant systems[56–58] will doubtless add to our understanding.

Summary

Circadian rhythms are fundamental adaptations of living organisms to their environment. In mammals, the circadian timing system establishes the temporal organization of behavior into cycles of sleep and wakefulness, maximizing the adaptive success of sleep and waking behaviors. The CTS has three components: (1) photoreceptors and entrainment pathways, which determine the precise period and phase of the circadian pacemakers and, therefore, the rhythms that they generate; (2) circadian pacemakers; and (3) pacemaker output to effector systems. Light is the dominant stimulus for the CTS, and the major photic entrainment pathway is the retinolypothalamic tract. The RHT terminates densely in the principal circadian pacemaker, the suprachiasmatic nucleus. The SCN produces a simple circadian signal, which is conveyed to hypothalamic, thalamic, and basal forebrain areas that regulate circadian function. The CTS not only provides temporal organization for behavior but also regulates aspects of reproductive function, particularly in animals that reproduce seasonally. Circadian function is genetically controlled, and data indicate that function is maintained by the expression of clock genes that code for specific proteins that feed back on the nucleus to control their own production. Finally, disorders of circadian function are common, but research on the neurobiology of circadian timing has facilitated our understanding of the disorders and led to further insights into pathophysiology treatments.

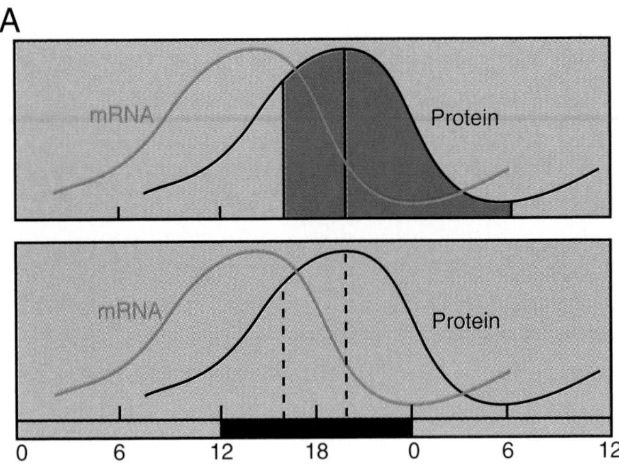

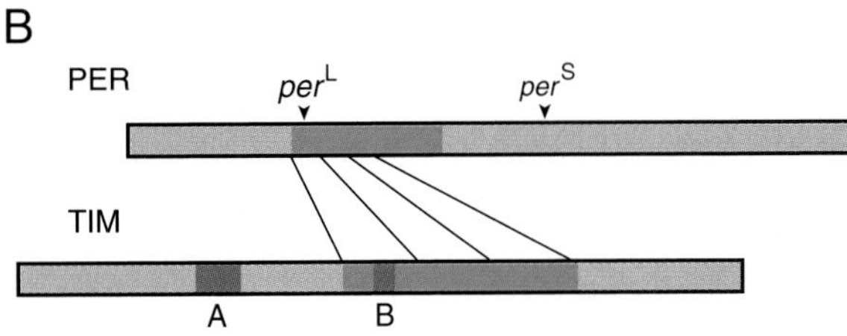

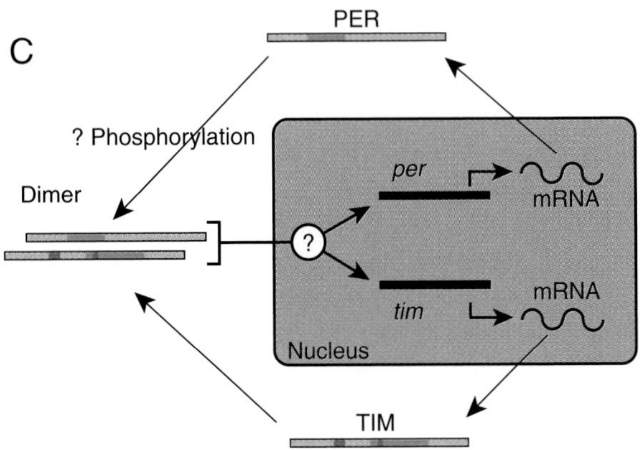

FIGURE 45.15 Features of *per–tim* interactions. (A) Profiles of PER and TIM mRNA and protein levels across a light (open bar)–dark (filled bar) cycle. The shaded area shows when PER–TIM heterodimers are present in the nucleus. (B) Structures of PER and TIM proteins. The connecting lines indicate areas of each protein thought to be involved in PER–TIM dimerization. A, acidic region; B, basic region. (C) Interdependent negative feedback control loops of *per* and *tim*. From Reppert and Sauman,[54] with permission.

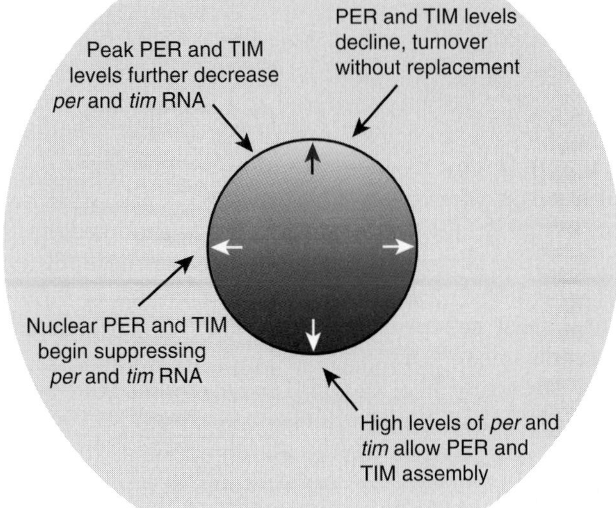

FIGURE 45.16 Diagrammatic representation of the effect of light on the PER–TIM cycle. From Myers *et al.*,[55] with permission.

References

1. Wever, R. A. (1974). *The Circadian System of Man*. Springer-Verlag, New York.
2. Pittindrigh, C. S. (1993). Temporal organization: Reflections of a Darwinian clock-watcher. *Annu. Rev. Physiol.* **55:** 17–54.

3. Aschoff, J. (1965). Circadian rhythms in man. *Science* **148:** 1427–1432.
4. Axelrod, J. (1974). The pineal gland: A neuroendocrine transducer. *Science* **184:** 1341–1348.
5. Moore, R. Y. (1996). Neural control of the pineal gland. *Behav. Brain Res.* **73:** 125–130.
6. Klein, D. C., and Moore, R. Y. (1979). Pineal N-acetyltransferase and hydroxyindole-o-methyltransferase: Control by the retinohypothalamic tract and the suprachiasmatic nucleus. *Brain Res.* **174:** 245–262.
7. Stephan, F. K., and Zucker, I. (1972). Circadian rhythms in drinking behavior and locomotor activity of rats are eliminated by hypothalamic lesions. *Proc. Natl. Acad. Sci. U.S.A.* **69:** 1583–1586.
8. Ibuka, M., Inouye, S.-I., and Kawanura, H. (1977). Analysis of sleep-wakefulness rhythms in male rats after suprachaismatic lesions and ocular enucleation. *Brain Res.* **122:** 33–47.
9. Inouye, S. I. T., and Kawamura, H. (1979). Persistence of circadian rhythmicity in a mammalian hypothalamic "island" containing the suprachiasmatic nucleus. *Proc. Natl. Acad. Sci. U.S.A.* **76:** 5962–5966.
10. Lehman, M. N., Silver, R., Gladstone, W. R., Kahn, M. R., Gibson, M., and Brittman, E. L. (1987). Circadian rhythmicity restored by neural transplant. Immunocytochemical characterization of the graft and its integration with the host brain. *J. Neurosci.* **7:** 1626–1638.
11. Ralph, M. R., Foster, R. G., Davis, F. C., and Menaker, M. (1990). Transplanted suprachiasmatic nucleus determines circadian rhythms. *Science* **247:** 975–978.
12. Moore, R. Y. (1996). Entrainment pathways and the functional organization of the circadian system. *Prog. Brain Res.* **111:** 103–119.
13. Schwartz, W. J., Gross, R. A., and Morton, M. T. (1987). The suprachiasmatic nuclei contain a tetrodotoxin-resistant circadian pacemaker. *Proc. Natl. Acad. Sci. U.S.A.* **84:** 1694–1698.
14. Welch, D. K., Logothetis, D. E., Meister, M., and Reppert, S. M. (1995). Individual neurons dissociated from rat suprachiasmatic nucleus express independently phased circadian firing patterns. *Neuron* **14:** 697–706.
15. Reme, C. E., Wirz-Justice, A., and Terman, M. (1991). The visual input stage of the mammalian circadian pacemaking system. I. Is there a clock in the mammalian eye. *J. Biol. Rhythms* **6:** 5–29.
16. Tosini, G., and Menaker, M. (1996). Circadian rhythms in cultured mammalian retina. *Science* **272:** 419–421.
17. Foster, R. G., Provencio, I., Hudson, D., Fiske, S., DeGrip, W., and Menaker, M. (1991). Circadian photoreception in the retinally degenerate mouse (rd/rd). *J. Comp. Physiol. A* **169:** 39–50.
18. Card, J. P., Whealy, M. E., Robbins, A. K., Moore, R. Y., and Enquist, L. W. (1991). Two alpha herpes virus strains are transported differentially in the rodent visual system. *Neuron* **6:** 957–969.
19. Shirakawa, T., and Moore, R. Y. (1994). Responses of rat suprachiasmatic nucleus neurons to substance P and glutamate in vitro. *Brain Res.* **642:** 213–220.
20. Ding, J. M., Chen, D., Weber, E. T., Faiman, L. E., Rea, M. A., and Gillette, M. U. (1994). Resetting the biological clock: Mediation of nocturnal circadian shifts by glutamate and NO. *Science* **266:** 1713–1717.
21. Moore, R. Y., and Card, J. P. (1994). The intergeniculate leaflet: An anatomically and functionally distinct subdivision of the lateral geniculate complex. *J. Comp. Neurol.* **344:** 403–430.
22. Shibata, S., and Moore, R. Y. (1993). Tetradoxin does not affect circadian neuronal activity or metabolic rhythms in suprachiasmatic nucleus in vitro. *Brain Res.* **606:** 259–266.
23. Reebs, S. G., and Mrosovsky, N. (1989). Effects of induced wheel running on the circadian activity rhythms of Syrian hamsters: Entrainment and phase response curve. *J. Biol. Rhythms* **4:** 39–48.
24. Turek, F. W. (1989). The effects of stimulated physical activity on the circadian pacemaker of mammals. *J. Biol. Rhythms* **4:** 135–148.
25. Rea, M. A., Glass, J. D., and Colwell, C. S. (1994). Serotonin modulates photic responses in the hamster suprachiasmatic nuclei. *J. Neurosci.* **14:** 3635–3642.
26. Watts, A. G. (1991). The efferent projections of the suprachiasmatic nucleus: Anatomical insights into the control of circadian rhythms. In *The Suprachiasmatic Nucleus—The Mind's Clock* (D. C. Klein, R. Y. Moore, and S. M. Reppert, eds.), pp. 77–106. Oxford University Press, New York.
27. Kalra, S. P. (1993). Mandatory neuropeptide-steroid signaling for the preovulatory luteinizing hormone-releasing hormone discharge. *Endocr. Rev.* **14:** 507–538.
28. Reiter, R. J. (1980). The pineal and its hormones in the control of reproduction in mammals. *Endocr. Rev.* **1:** 109–131.
29. Karsh, F. J., Woodfill, C. J., Malpaux, B., Robinson, J. E., and Wayne, N. L. (1991). Melatonin and mammalian photoperiodism: Synchronization of annual reproductive cycle. In *The Suprachiasmatic Nuclei—The Mind's Clock* (D. C. Klein, R. Y. Moore, and S. M. Reppert, eds.), pp. 217–231. Oxford University Press, New York.
30. Morgan, P. J., Barrett, P., Howell, H. E., and Helliwell, R. (1994). Melatonin receptors: Localization, molecular pharmacology and physiological significance. *Neurochem. Int.* **24:** 101–146.
31. Reppert, S. M., Weaver, D. R., and Ebisawa, T. (1994). Cloning and characterization of a mammalian melatonin receptor that mediates reproductive and circadian responses. *Neuron* **13:** 1177–1185.
32. Cassone, V. M. (1990). Effects of melatonin on vertebrate circadian systems. *Trends Neurosci.* **13:** 457–464.
33. Warren, W. S., and Cassone, V. M. (1995). The pineal gland: Photoreception and coupling of behavioral, metabolic and cardiovascular circadian outputs. *J. Biol. Rhythms* **10:** 64–79.
34. Arendt, J. (1995). *Melatonin and the Mammalian Pineal Gland.* Chapman & Hall, London.
35. Gaston, S., and Menaker, M. (1968). Pineal function: The biological clock in the sparrow? *Science* **160:** 1125–1127.
36. Cassone, V. M., and Menaker, M. (1984). Is the avian circadian system a neuroendocrine loop? *J. Exp. Zool.* **232:** 539–549.
37. Zimmerman, N. H., and Menaker, M. (1979). The pineal gland: A pacemaker within the circadian system of the house sparrow. *Proc. Natl. Acad. Sci. U.S.A.* **76:** 999–1003.
38. Takahashi, J. S., and Menaker, M. (1982). Role of the suprachiasmatic nuclei in the circadian system of the house sparrow, *Passer domesticus. J. Neurosci.* **2:** 815–828.
39. Underwood, H. (1994). The circadian rhythm of thermoregulation in Japanese quail. I. Role of the eyes and pineal. *J. Comp. Physiol. A* **175:** 639–653.
40. Ebihara, S., Uchiyama, K., and Oshima, I. (1984). Circadian organization in the pigeon, *Columbia livia:* The role of the pineal organ and the eye. *J. Comp. Physiol. A.* **154:** 59–69.
41. Oshima, I., Yamada, N., Goto, M., Sato, K., and Ebihara, S. (1989). Pineal and retinal melatonin is involved in the control of circadian locomotor activity and body temperature rhythms in the pigeon. *J. Comp. Physiol. A* **166:** 217–266.
42. Chabot, C. L., and Menaker, M. (1992). Effects of cycles of infused melatonin on circadian rhythmicity in pigeons. *J. Comp. Physiol. A* **170:** 615–622.
43. Zatz, M., Mullen, D. A., and Moskal, J. R. (1988). Photoendocrine transduction in cultured chick pineal cells: Effects of light, dark and potassium on the melatonin rhythm. *Brain Res.* **438:** 199–215.

44. Murakami, N., Nakamura, N., Nishi, R., Marumoto, N., and Nasu, T. (1994). Comparison of circadian oscillation of melatonin release in pineal cells of house sparrow, pigeon and Japanese quail using cell perfusion systems. *Brain Res.* **651:** 208–214.
45. Konopka, R. J., and Benzer, S. (1971). Clock mutants of *Drosophila melanogaster. Proc. Natl. Acad. Sci. U.S.A.* **68:** 2112–2116.
46. Feldman, J. F., and Hoyle, M. (1973). Isolation of circadian clock mutants of *Neurospora crassa. Genetics* **75:** 605–613.
47. Aronson, B. D., Johnson, K. A., Loros, J. J., and Dunlap, J. C. (1994). Negative feedback defining a circadian clock: Autoregulation of the clock gene, *frequency. Science* **263:** 1578–1584.
48. Hall, J. D. (1995). Tripping along the trail to the molecular mechanisms of biological clocks. *Trends Neurosci.* **18:** 230–240.
49. Zeng, H., Hardin, P. E., and Rosbash, M. (1994). Constitutive overexpression of the *Drosophila period* protein inhibits *period* mRNA cycling. *EMBO J.* **13:** 3590–3598.
50. Frisch, B., Hardin, P. E., Hambleu-Coyle, M. J., Rosbash, M., and Hall, J. C. (1994). A promotorless *period* gene mediates behavioral rhythmicity and cyclical *per* expression in a restricted subset of the *Drosophila* nervous system. *Neuron* **12:** 555–570.
51. Sehgal, A., Rothenfluh-Hilfiker, A., Hunter-Ensor, M., Chen, Y., Myers, M. P., and Young, M. W. (1995). Rhythmic expression of *timeless:* A basis for promoting circadian cycles in *period* gene autoregulation. *Science* **270:** 808–810.
52. Vosshall, L. B., Price, J. L., Sehgal, A., Saez, L., and Young, M. W. (1994). Specific block in nuclear organization of period protein by a second clock mutation, *timeless. Science* **263:** 1606–1609.
53. Myers, M. P., Wager-Smith, K., Wesley, C. S., Young, M. W., and Sehgal, A. (1995). Positional cloning and sequence analysis of the *Drosophila* clock gene, *timeless. Science* **270:** 805–808.
54. Reppert, S. M., and Sauman, I. (1995). *Period* and *timeless* tango: A dance of two clock genes. *Neuron* **15:** 983–986.
55. Myers, M. P., Wager-Smith, K., Rothenfluh-Hilfiker, A., and Young, M. W. (1996). Light-induced degradation of TIMELESS and entrainment of the *Drosophila* circadian clock. *Science* **271:** 1736–1740.
56. Vitaterna, M. H., King, D. P., Chang, A.-M., Kornhauser, J. M., Lowrey, P. L., McDonald, J. D., Dove, W. F., Pinto, L. H., Turek, F. W., and Takahashi, J. S. (1994). Mutagenesis and mapping of a mouse gene, *clock,* essential for circadian behavior. *Science* **264:** 719–725.
57. Kondo, T., Tsinoremas, F., Golden, S. S., Johnson, C. H., Kutsuna, S., and Ishinora, M. (1994). Circadian clock mutants of cyanobacteria. *Science* **266:** 1233–1236.
58. Miller, A. J., Carre, I. A., Strayer, C. A., Chua, N.-H., and Kay, S. A. (1995). Circadian clock mutants in *Arabidopsis* identified by luciferase imaging. *Science* **267:** 1161–1163.
59. Czeisler, C. A., Shanahan, T. L., Klerman, E. R., *et al.* (1995). Suppression of melatonin secretion in some blind patients by exposure to bright light. *N. Engl. J. Med.* **332:** 6–11.
60. Cohen, R. A., and Albers, H. E. (1991). Disruption of human circadian and cognitive function following a discrete hypothalamic lesion. *Neurology* **41:** 726–728.
61. Wehr, T. A., and Rosenthal, N. E. (1989). Seasonality and affective illness. *Am. J. Psychiatry* **146:** 829–839.

CHAPTER

46

Sleep and Dreaming

J. Allan Hobson

Sleep is a behavioral state that alternates with waking. Sleep is characterized by a recumbent posture, a raised threshold to sensory stimulation, a low level of motor output, and a unique behavior—dreaming. The complex neurobiology of these behavioral features of sleep has been explored at the systemic, cellular, and molecular levels for more than 35 years. Although these studies have provided substantial insight into the physiology and pathology of sleep, we have yet to obtain definitive answers to the adaptive significance of sleep, the behavioral state that takes up one-third of our lives.

In contrast to sleep, the conscious behavior of waking is characterized by an active and deliberate sensorimotor discourse with the environment. For maintenance of waking behavior, neural gates must remain open for sensory input and motor output, the brain must be tuned and activated, and the chemical microclimate must be appropriate for processing and recording of information. Wakefulness is accompanied by conscious experience that reaches its highest level of complexity in adult humans. Waking behavior includes a number of components, such as sensation, perception, attention, memory, instinct, emotion, volition, cognition, and language, that make up our awareness of the world and self and form the basis of an adaptive interaction with our environment. In this chapter, we focus on the mechanisms of behavioral state control that make such interactions possible, with an emphasis on sleep as a component of adaptive behavior. Because evidence so strongly favors an integration of psychological and physiological features, we refer to the substrate of conscious experience as the brain–mind.

THE TWO STATES OF SLEEP: SLOW WAVE AND RAPID EYE MOVEMENT

The behavioral signs of sleep vary regularly during every period of sleep; posture, arousal, threshold and motor output change in a stereotyped, cyclic manner. Although these changes can be directly observed, their study is facilitated by placing electrodes on the scalp to measure the electrical activity of the brain. From these **electroencephalograms** (EEGs) (Fig. 46.1),[1] two distinct substates of sleep—slow wave and rapid eye movement (REM)—can be discerned. Both show interesting contrasts with waking, and these contrasts improve our understanding of states of consciousness.

At the onset of sleep, the brain deactivates, and awareness of the outside world is lost. A well-described sequence of thalamocortical events causes the progressive slowing of brain waves, seen on EEG during this phase of sleep. The threshold for arousal rises in proportion to the degree of EEG slowing, and at the greatest depth of sleep, awakenings are often difficult, incomplete, and brief. This sleep state is designated **slow wave**, or **non-REM** (NREM), **sleep**. People have little or no recall of conscious experience in deep NREM sleep. Many autonomic and regulatory functions, such as heart rate, blood pressure, and respiration rate, diminish in NREM sleep, but neuroendocrine activity increases. The pulsatile release of growth hormone and sexual maturation hormones from the pituitary is maximal during sleep, with over 95% of the daily output occurring in NREM sleep.

At regular intervals during sleep, the brain reactivates into a state characterized by fast, low-voltage

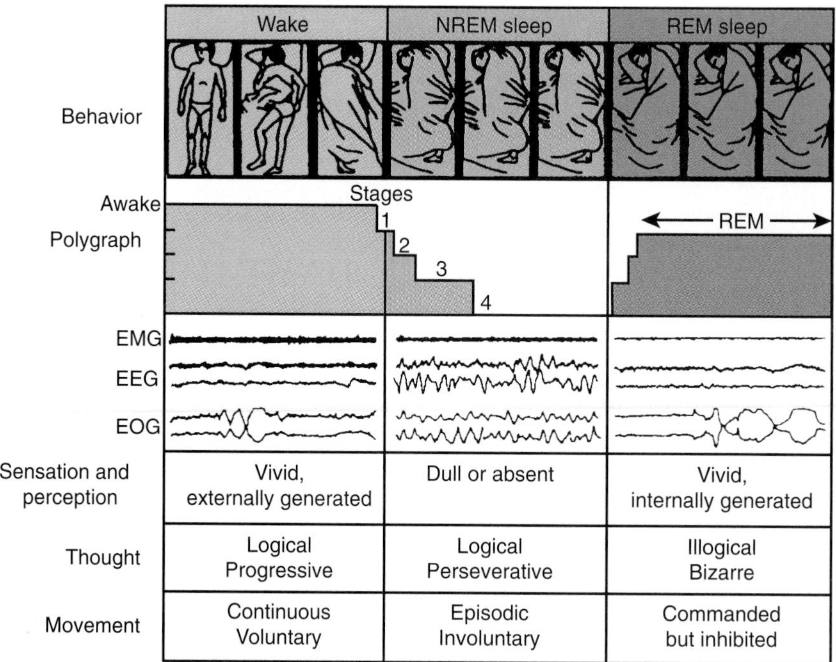

FIGURE 46.1 Behavioral states in humans. Body position changes during waking and at the time of phase changes in the sleep cycle. Removal of facilitation (during stages 1–4 of NREM sleep) and addition of inhibition (during REM sleep) account for immobility during sleep. In dreams, we imagine that we move, but no movement occurs. Tracings of electrical activity are shown in ~20-s sample records. The amplitude of the electromyogram (EMG) is highest in waking, intermediate in NREM sleep, and lowest in REM sleep. The electroencephalogram (EEG) and electrooculogram (EOG) are activated in waking and REM sleep and inactivated in NREM sleep. Reprint with permission from Hobson and Steriade.[1]

activity characterized by muscle atonia and rapid eye movements. This sleep state, termed **rapid eye movement** (REM) **sleep**, because of the prominent eye movements differs from waking by an inhibition of sensory input and motor output. Postural shifts precede and follow REM sleep; eye movements, intermittent small muscle twitching, and penile erection occur during REM sleep. The presence (or absence) of REM sleep erection is used clinically to distinguish between psychological and physiological male impotence. In REM sleep many autonomic functions change; control of temperature and cardiopulmonary function is lost.

People aroused from NREM sleep, especially early in the night, are confused, have difficulty reporting conscious experience, and return to sleep rapidly. Subjects aroused from REM sleep, especially during periods with frequent eye movements, give detailed reports of dreams characterized by vivid hallucinations, bizarre thinking, and intense emotion. These observations indicate that dreaming is the behavior associated with activation of the brain in REM sleep.

The NREM and REM Phases Alternate throughout Sleep

The two sleep states alternate at intervals of 90 minutes in adult humans. The NREM phases are deeper and longer early in the night (Fig. 46.2A). Together with the regularity of the periods (see Fig. 46.2B), this property has suggested that a damped oscillator is the underlying neural mechanism for NREM–REM cycles. The portion of the 24-h day devoted to NREM and REM sleep varies within and across species (Fig. 46.3 and Table 46.1).

Sleep Appears to Have Multiple Functions

As a quiescent and ecologically protected behavior, sleep fosters conservation of energy, repair of injury, and defense from predation. The anabolic character of NREM sleep (e.g., brain and body inactivity and hormone release) suggests a rest and restoration function. In contrast, the high proportion of REM sleep in the developing brain, the high level of forebrain activity, and the stereotyped movements in REM sleep suggest a role of REM sleep in brain development and plasticity. In fact, many studies indicate a role for REM sleep in memory consolidation. The crucial role of sleep is illustrated by studies showing that sleep deprivation results in disruption of metabolic and caloric homeostasis and, if prolonged, death.

Summary

Sleep and waking are distinct, alternate behavioral states that are mutually exclusive, but interrelated. Within sleep, two substates of behavior are readily distinguishable by electroencephalographic recordings, termed slow wave sleep and rapid eye movement

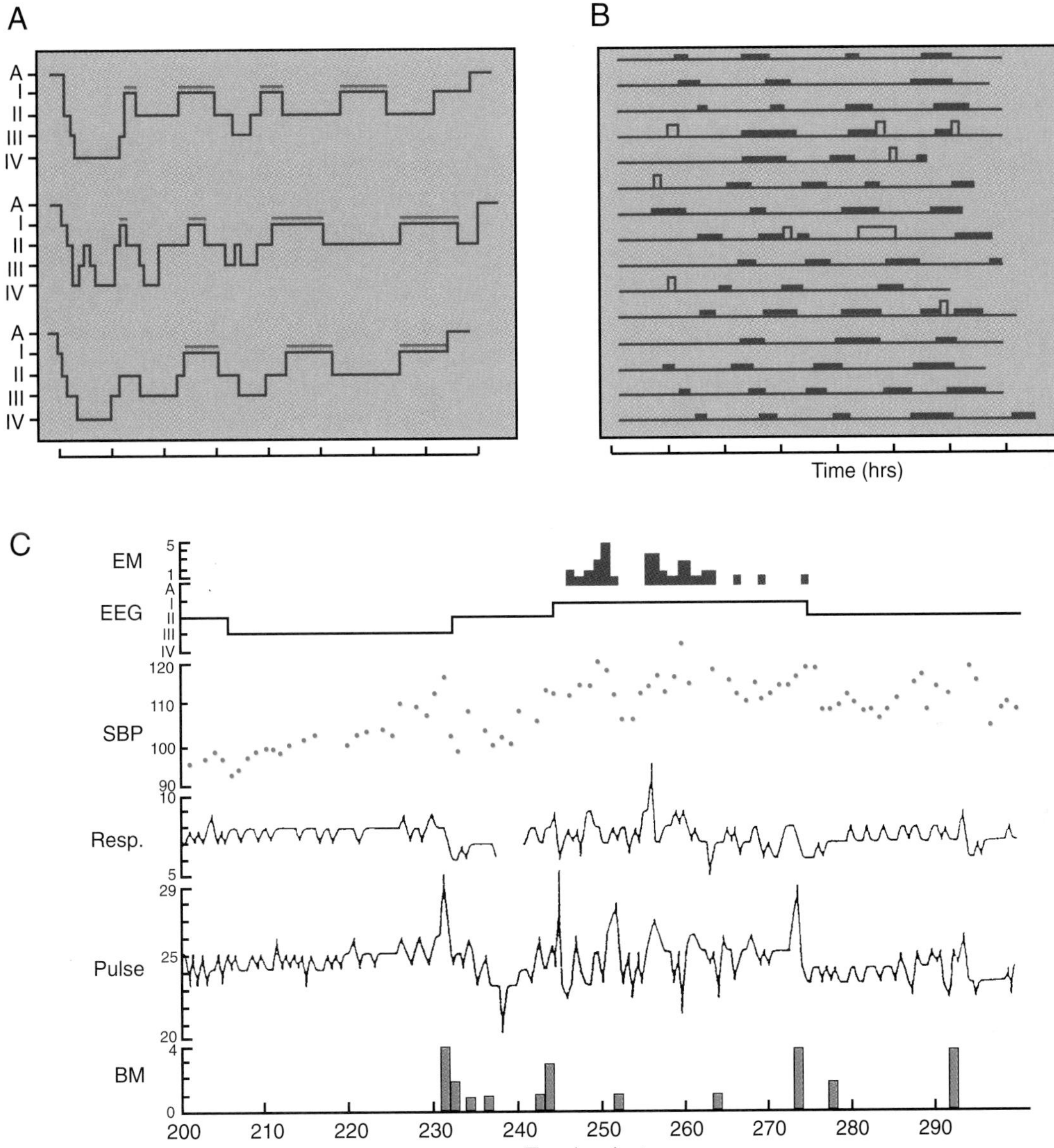

FIGURE 46.2 Periodic activation in sleep cycles. (A) The sleep stages of three people are graphed. The first two or three cycles of the night are dominated by deep stages (3 and 4) of NREM sleep, and REM sleep (indicated by red bars) is brief or nonexistent. During the last two cycles of the night, NREM sleep is lighter (stage 2), and REM episodes are longer, sometimes more than an hour. (B) Records begin at the onset of sleep. The amount of time before the first episode of REM varies, but once REM has begun, the interval between episodes is fairly constant. (C) Eye movements (EM), EEG, systolic blood pressure (SBP), respiration (Resp.), pulse, and body movement (BM) over 100 minutes of uninterrupted sleep. The interval from 242 to 273 minutes is considered the REM period, although eye movements are not continuous during that interval.

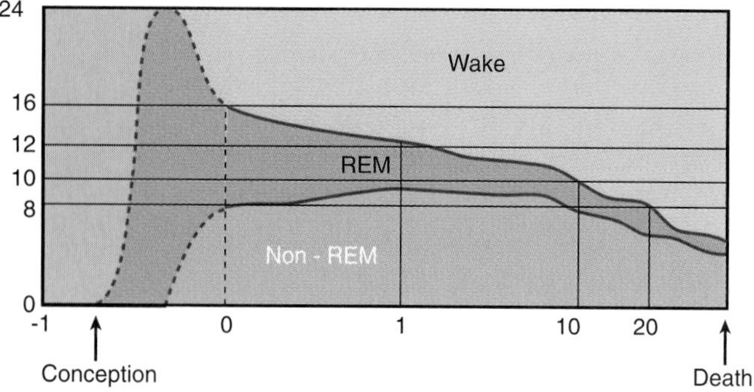

FIGURE 46.3 The portions of a 24-h day that are devoted to waking, REM sleep, and non-REM (NREM) sleep change over a lifetime. Although the timing of these changes *in utero* is not known with certainty (dotted lines), data from premature infants are consistent with REM sleep occupying most of life at a gestational age of 26 weeks. After 26 weeks, the time spent in waking increases until death.

(REM) sleep. The characteristic behaviors of sleep include relaxed posture, elevated thresholds for sensory arousal, and diminished motor activity. The slow wave and REM sleep phases alternate throughout the sleep period in cycles. Although the precise function of sleep remains unknown, much scientific evidence favors the sleep period being for rest and restoration.

SLEEP IN THE MODERN ERA OF NEUROSCIENCE

Philosophical speculation about the nature of sleep and conscious behavior is as old as recorded history, and many philosophers, including the Ionian Greeks, anticipated the physicalistic models that have only recently been articulated in modern neuroscience.[2] The signal event of the modern era of neuroscience was the discovery of the electrical nature of nervous activity and, more specifically, the 1928 discovery of the human electroencephalogram by the German psychiatrist Adolf Berger.

The state-dependent nature of the EEG helped Berger convince his skeptical critics that the rhythmic oscillations he recorded across the human scalp with his galvanometer originated in the brain and were not artifacts of movement or of scalp muscle activity. When his subjects relaxed, closed their eyes, or dozed off, the low-voltage brain waves associated with alertness gave way to higher voltage, lower frequency patterns (Fig. 46.4). These patterns stopped rapidly when the subjects were aroused.

Waking and Sleep Initially Were Viewed as Activated and Nonactivated States

Following Berger's discovery, a flurry of descriptive and experimental studies aimed at understanding the EEG itself, the full range of its state-dependent variability, and the control of that variability by the brain were performed. Loomis and Harvey[3] were the first to describe the tendency of the EEG to show systematic changes in activity as subjects fell asleep at night (tracings 3–5 of Fig. 46.4).

Because mammals shared the same correlation between arousal level and EEG, the Belgian physiologist Frederick Bremer[4] made experimental transections of the mammalian brain to determine the nature and source of EEG activation (the low-voltage, fast pattern of waking) and deactivation (the high-voltage, slow pattern of sleep). Thinking the activity level probably depended on sensory input, Bremer transected the brain at the level of the first cervical spinal cord segment, producing a preparation called the *encephale isolé*. He was surprised to find that the isolated forebrain was activated and alert despite such transection of a major portion of its sensory input. When he then produced the *cerveau isolé* preparation, by transecting the midbrain at the intercollicular level, he observed persistent EEG slowing and unresponsiveness. Interpreting this observation, Bremer incorrectly inferred that removal of the trigeminal nerve afferents (which entered the brainstem between the level of the two cuts) accounted for the sleeplike state of the *cerveau isolé*.

Sleep Can Be Induced Electrically

That sleep might be an active brain process—and not simply the absence of waking as Bremer sup-

TABLE 46.1 Phylogeny of Rest and Sleep

Organism	Rest	Sleep	REM sleep
Mammals			
Adults	+	+	+
Neonates	+	+	+, −
Birds			
Adults	+	+	−
Neonates	+	+	+
Reptiles	+	+	−
Amphibians	+	−	−
Fish	+	+, −	−

Note. REM, rapid eye movement; +, present; +, −, ambiguously or inconsistently present; −, absent.

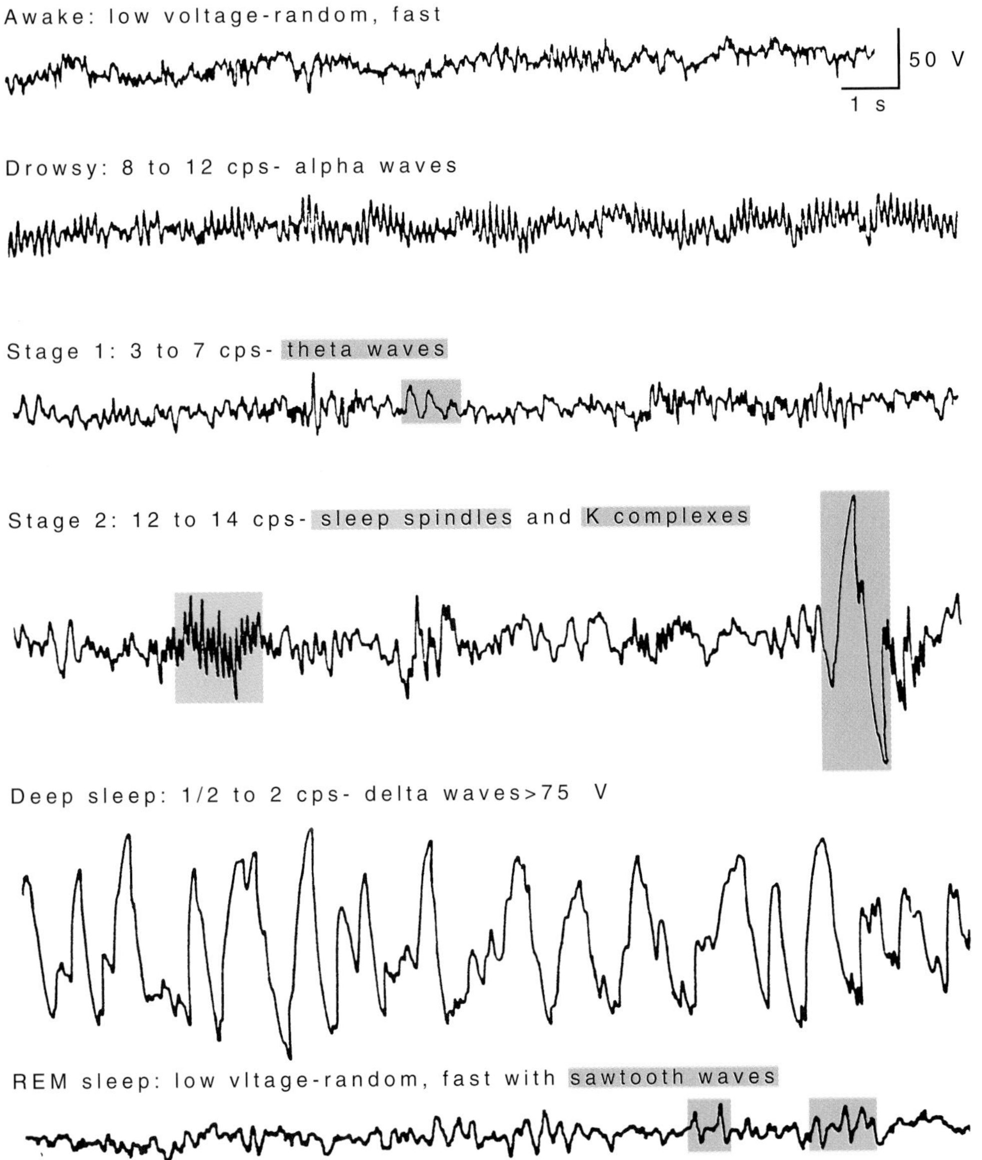

FIGURE 46.4 Electroencephalograms (EEGs) showing electrical activity of the human brain during different stages of sleep.

posed—was first experimentally suggested by the work of the Swiss Nobel laureate W. R. Hess.[5] Hess was involved in a broad program investigating the effects of electrical stimulation of the subcortical regions mediating autonomic control (especially the hypothalamus). He discovered that by driving the thalamocortical system at the frequencies of intrinsic EEG spindles (short series of waves) and slow waves, he could induce the behavioral and electrographic signs of sleeping in unanesthetized cats.[5] This discovery opened the door to the idea that sleep and waking might be active processes, each with its own specific cellular and metabolic mechanisms and functional consequences. This paradigm has since born abundant scientific fruit: The precise details of spindle and slow wave elaboration have been worked out.[1,6] In addition, the paradigm correctly anticipated the finding that central homologs of sympathetic neurons mediate waking, whereas central cholinergic neurons mediate REM sleep. In his concept of arousal as energy consuming and sleep as energy conserving, Hess anticipated much of our present understanding of sleep.

The intrinsic nature of brain activation was clearly demonstrated in 1949 when Giuseppe Moruzzi and Horace Magoun[7] discovered that EEG desynchronization and behavioral arousal could be produced by high-frequency electrical stimulation of the midbrain. To explain their observation, Moruzzi and Magoun suggested that the nonspecific (i.e., nonsensory) reticular activating system operates in series and in parallel with the ascending sensory pathways. This concept allowed for the translation of afferent stimuli into central activation (Bremer's idea) and opened the door to the more radical idea that not only waking but also adaptive behavior could be autoactivated by brainstem mechanisms.

Now that we accept the idea that spontaneous activity of neurons determines the substages of sleep, it is difficult for us to appreciate the strength and persistence of its predecessor, the reflex concept of sleep. Scientific giants such as Ivan Pavlov[8] and Charles Sherrington[9] were so inspired by the reflex doctrine that they were convinced that brain activity simply ceased in the absence of sensory input.

The Brain–Mind Is Activated during REM Sleep

In 1953, Eugene Aserinsky and Nathaniel Kleitman,[10] working in Chicago, discovered that the brain–mind did indeed self-activate during sleep. They observed regularly timed, spontaneous desynchronization of the EEG, accompanied by clusters of rapid, saccadic eye movements (or REMs) and acute accelerations of heart and respiration rates. Working with Kleitman, William Dement[11,12] then showed that these periods of spontaneous autoactivation of the brain–mind were associated with dreaming and that this autoactivation process was also found in another mammal, the cat[13] (see Fig. 46.1 and tracing number 6 of Fig. 46.4).

In adult humans, the intrinsic cycle of inactivation (NREM sleep) and activation (REM sleep) recurs with a period length of 90–100 minutes (see Fig. 46.2). REM sleep occupies 20–25% of the recording time and NREM the remainder (75–80%). The NREM phases of the first two cycles are deep and long, whereas REM phases, during which sleep lightens, occupy more of the last two or three cycles.

Input–Output Gating Occurs during Sleep

The paradoxical preservation of sleep in the face of dreaming in REM sleep began to be explained when Francois Michel and Michel Jouvet, working in Lyon in 1959, demonstrated that inhibition of muscle activity was a component of REM sleep in cats. Using transection, lesion, and stimulation techniques, the Jouvet team also discovered that the control system for REM sleep was located in the pontine brainstem. The pons is the source of EEG activation and REMs. Muscle inhibition is also mediated by pontine signals, but these are relayed via the bulbar inhibitory reticular formation to the spinal cord.[14] Synchronous with each flurry of REMs, periodic activation signals, or pontine–geniculate–occipital (PGO) waves, are sent from the pons up to the forebrain (and down to the spinal cord). The PGO waves trigger bursts of firing by geniculate and cortical neurons, and other signals originating in the brainstem damp sensory input (via presynaptic inhibition) and motor output (via postsynaptic inhibition).[15] Thus, in REM sleep the brain–mind is effectively off-line with respect to external inputs and outputs and internally generated signals.

The cellular and molecular bases of these dramatic changes in input–output gating have been detailed using Sherrington's reflex paradigm together with extracellular and intracellular recording techniques.[16] For example, such techniques revealed that during REM sleep, each motor neuron was subject to a 10-mV hyperpolarization, which blocked all but a few of the activation signals generated by the REM–PGO system. Furthermore, the studies showed that this inhibition was mediated by glycine.[17,18] When this motor inhibition was experimentally disrupted by lesions in the pons, the cats, still in a REM-like sleep state but without the atonia, showed stereotyped behaviors (such as defense and attack postures). These behaviors reflected the activation, in REM, of the generators that produce the motor patterns for these instinctual, fixed acts.[19,20]

These studies indicated that in normal REM sleep, motor inhibition prevents the motor commands of the generators of instinctual behavior patterns from being acted out. As a result, during REM these patterns are unexpressed in the outside world and fictive in the internal world of the brain–mind. One strong significance of these findings for a theory of dream consciousness lies in their ability to explain the ubiquity of imagined movement in dreams.[21] From a sensorimotor point of view, the highly patterned (and hence nonrandom) organization of autoactivation in REM sleep may be important.

Summary

The scientific history of sleep began with the application of electroencephalography in 1928, demonstrating that the brain's electrical activity changed but did not cease during sleep. Subsequent refinements revealed the necessary role of the reticular formation for arousal and the association of arousal with desynchronized cortical activity. In addition, emulating the oscillatory EEG spindles of thalamic projections to cortex allowed sleep to be induced by direct thalamic electrical stimulation in experimental animals. Sleep analysis in the 1950s showed REM sleep to be a "paradoxical" state in which sleep was at its deepest, yet accompanied by rapid eye movements and sympathetic signs of arousal, interpreted as dreaming, and accompanied by still further reductions of postural muscle tone. During REM sleep, pontine waves of activity arise with each flurry of eye movements, during which motor activity is deeply depressed.

ANATOMY AND PHYSIOLOGY OF BRAINSTEM REGULATORY SYSTEMS

The Brainstem Reticular Formation Contains Specific Neuronal Groups Involved in Behavioral State Regulation

Moruzzi and Magoun's original concept of a nonspecific reticular activating system has been greatly elaborated and modified by subsequent anatomical and physiological studies. Two general principles have emerged. One is that most of the classic reticular core neurons have very specific afferent inputs and highly organized outputs. The other is that the reticular formation contains small groups of neurons that send widely branching axons to distant parts of the brain, where the neurons' neurotransmitters modulate brain function.

The input–output characteristics of each of the reticular formation's multiple subsystems reflect specific sensorimotor function, modulatory function, or both. For example, many neurons of the reticular formation are involved in the integration of eye, head, and trunk positions as these change to accommodate specific behavioral challenges and tasks. These reticular neurons receive inputs from skin, muscle, bone, and joint receptors in the periphery, which they integrate and link to the vestibular and cerebellar circuits that determine posture and movement. This information must also be integrated by higher brain structures in the visual, somatosensory, and motor systems to develop the complex motor patterns of adaptive behavior.

A series of chemically specified neuronal groups also lies in the reticular formation; they have different patterns of connections that differ from those of the previously discussed neurons of the reticular formation. Dahlstrom and Fuxe[22] were the first to identify neuronal populations in brain that produced norepinephrine (NE) and serotonin (5HT).

The norepinephrine neurons (designated A1–A7 by Dahlstrom and Fuxe) are located in the pons and medulla in two major groups. One group consists of scattered neurons largely located in the ventral and lateral reticular formation (Fig. 46.5A). The most caudal neurons (A1–A3) project rostrally to the brainstem, hypothalamus, and basal forebrain, whereas the rostral groups (A5 and A7) project caudally to the brainstem and spinal cord. These neuronal groups, together called the **lateral tegmental neuron group**,[23] appear to be involved in hypothalamic regulation and motor control.

The major norepinephrine cell group is the **locus ceruleus** (A4 and A6). This compact cell group is located in the rostral pontine reticular formation and central gray matter. The neurons of the locus ceruleus project widely but in a highly specific pattern. One group of locus ceruleus neurons appears to project largely caudally to sensory regions of the brainstem and spinal cord. Other neurons of the locus ceruleus project widely to cerebellar cortex, dorsal thalamus, and cerebral cortex.[23] Thus, the projection patterns of the locus ceruleus appear to be primarily to sensory structures and to cortical structures involved in integration. From this we could expect the locus ceruleus to be involved in regulating sensory input and cortical activation. As we shall see, this expectation is in accord with the available information on function.

Two additional subsets of chemically identified neurons appear critically involved in behavioral state regulation. The first subset to be discovered contained the serotonin neurons of the brainstem raphe[22] (B1–B9 in their nomenclature, Fig. 46.5B). These neurons extend from caudal medulla to midbrain and are located predominantly in the raphe nuclei, a set of neuronal groups located in the midline of the brainstem reticular formation. The largest numbers of serotonin neurons are found in the midbrain nuclei, the dorsal raphe nuclei, and the median raphe nuclei (B8 and B9). These groups project rostrally, innervating nearly the entire forebrain[24] in a pattern that also suggests a role in regulation of behavioral state.

The other important set of reticular formation nuclei involved in behavioral state control produces acetylcholine as its neurotransmitter. Acetylcholine (ACh) was well known as the transmitter of motor neurons, and early work indicated that acetylcholine is found in nonmotor brain areas. Two sets of cholinergic neurons are involved in control of behavioral state. The first set is two pontine nuclei, the laterodorsal tegmental nucleus and the pedunculopontine nucleus. Cholinergic neurons in these nuclei project to the brainstem reticular formation, hypothalamus, thalamus, and basal forebrain. The projection to the forebrain involves the second set of cholinergic neurons, those in the medial septum, the nucleus of the diagonal band, and the substantia innominata–nucleus basalis complex (Fig.

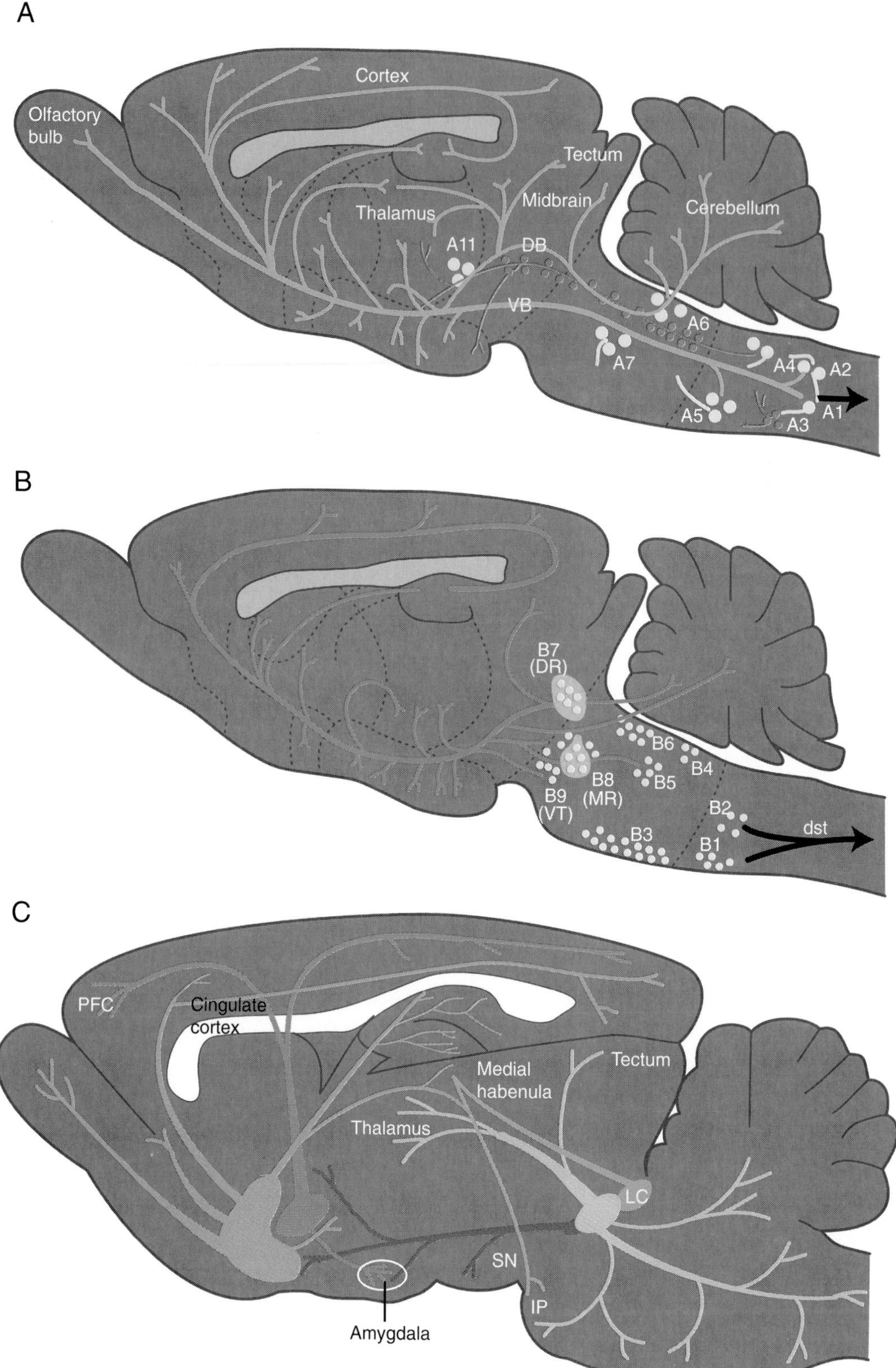

FIGURE 46.5 Origin and distribution of the primary modulatory systems containing norepinephrine (A), serotonin (B), and acetylcholine (C). Cells groups are named according to the nomenclature of Dahlstrom and Fuxe. DB, dorsal bundle; dst, descending spinal tract; IP, interpeduncular nucleus; LC, locus ceruleus; DR, dorsal raphe nucleus; MR, median raphe nucleus; PFC, prefrontal cortex; SN, substantia nigra; VB, ventral bundle; VT, ventral tegmentum.

46.5C). This set projects to limbic forebrain, including the hippocampus, and to the neocortex.

In contrast to the modulatory neurons, which are characterized by their production of norepinephrine, serotonin, and acetylcholine, the neurons in reticular formation nuclei that are involved in sensorimotor integration typically produce either the excitatory transmitter glutamate or the inhibitory transmitter GABA.

Sensorimotor and Modulatory Reticular Neurons Differ Functionally

Sensorimotor and modulatory neurons of the reticular formation differ markedly in their firing properties. Sensorimotor neurons, approximately 50 to 75 μm in diameter, can fire continuously at high rates of up to 50 Hz and can generate bursts of up to 500 Hz. Their larger axons, especially those projecting to the spinal cord, have conduction velocities in excess of 100 m s^{-1}, making these neurons well suited to rapid posture adjustment and motor control.

Modulatory neurons are smaller (10–25 μm in diameter) than sensorimotor neurons, and even those with long axons conduct their signals very slowly (1 m s^{-1}). They fire wider spikes (2 ms in duration) at much slower tonic frequencies (1–10 Hz) than do sensorimotor neurons. In addition, they often show a very regular, metronomelike firing pattern, a reflection of the pacemaker properties they share with the Purkinje cells of the heart. As their leaky membranes spontaneously and slowly depolarize, they reach threshold, fire, and then self-inhibit, becoming refractory even to exogenous excitatory inputs. Modulatory neurons are much less likely than sensorimotor neurons to fire in clusters or bursts unless powerfully excited; even then, they rapidly adapt. Thus, modulatory neurons are well suited to detect novel input. Because of their vast postsynaptic domain, they also can help set behavioral and mental states.

The contrasting features of sensorimotor and modulatory neurons confer functionally important distinctions on their neuronal populations. The high rate of discharge of the sensorimotor neurons, acting through extensive interconnections that tie together sensorimotor neurons, causes exponential recruitment. This amplification occurs in response to novel stimuli requiring analysis and directed action (in the wake state) and in the generation of REM sleep a state of sustained activation (when the system is off-line with respect to its inputs and outputs).

In contrast, the feedback inhibition and pacemaker potentials of modulatory neurons allow production of highly synchronized output during waking and sleeping. These features also somehow cause an exponential decline in the rate of these neurons' firing during REM sleep, until firing stops. Studies suggest that this REM sleep inhibition may involve a GABAergic action that arises in the hypothalamus at sleep onset and spreads through the brainstem as NREM sleep progresses to REM (see Fig. 46.6). These contrasting properties of sensorimotor and modulatory neurons of the reticular formation are the physical basis for the reciprocal interaction that causes NREM–REM sleep cycles.

Waking Requires Active Maintenance

Moruzzi and Magoun demonstrated that the reticular formation is necessary to maintain the waking con-

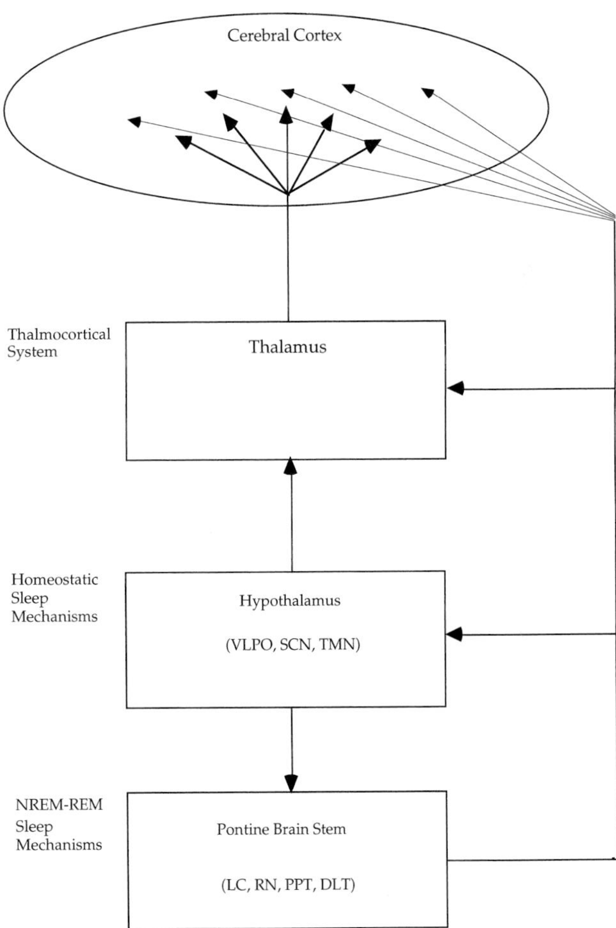

FIGURE 46.6 The state of the thalamocortical systems of the brain changes as a function of two subcortical systems. Homeostatic sleep mechanisms residing in the hypothalamus synchronize the NREM–REM sleep cycle by gating the neuromodulatory systems of the pontine brain stem. The neuromodulatory systems project widely and diffusely to the cerebral cortex where they interact with the modular thalamo-cortical system to determine behavioral and conscious states. VLPO, veutrolateral pre-optic area; SCN, suprachiasmatic nucleus; TMN, tubero-mammillary nucleus; LC, locus coeruleus; RN, raphe nuclei; PPT, pedunculo pontine tegmental nucleus; DLT, dorsolateral tegmental nucleus.

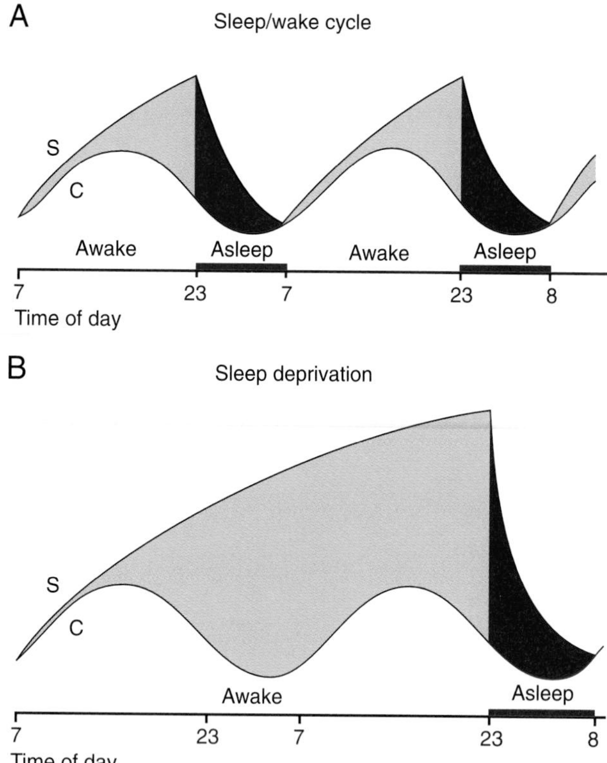

FIGURE 46.7 The Borbely and Daan model of sleep regulation. Sleep is assumed to result from the actions of process C and process S. Process C follows a circadian rhythm and is independent of sleeping and waking. Process S, on the other hand, depends on sleep–wake behavior; S declines during sleep and rises continuously during sleep deprivation. The period of recovery sleep that follows sleep deprivation is more intensive but only slightly longer than normal. If curve C represents the threshold for waking up, then at any time, "sleep pressure" is the (vertical) distance between the S and C curves. The greater the distance, the greater the pressure to fall asleep. Reprinted with permission from Daan *et al.*[25]

scious state. Lesions in the midbrain reticular formation, sparing the lemniscal sensory pathways, result in a state that resembles NREM sleep. Although maintenance of the waking state often seems effortless, it requires brain mechanisms that compete with other active mechanisms that promote and mediate sleep.

Later, Borbely and Dann proposed that two mechanisms interact to regulate sleep–wake cycles.[25] One of these, outlined in detail in Chapter 45, is a circadian rhythm in the propensity to fall asleep (curve C in the model of Borbely and Daan, Fig. 46.7). The tendency to fall asleep is normally lowest early in the day, peaks at about late afternoon, and then declines in the evening. This sleepiness cycles independent of sleeping and waking. That is, if a subject is deprived of sleep, sleepiness will continue to follow a circadian rhythm. The second mechanism is a homeostatic property, designated S in Fig. 46.7. It increases as a function of the amount of time since the last sleep episode. S can be viewed as the equivalent of a sleep-promoting substance that accumulates during waking and dissipates during sleep. Although a large amount of work has been devoted to identifying a "sleep substance," whether one or more such substances is normally involved in sleep regulation remains unclear.[26,27] Many factors likely contribute to the homeostatic regulation of sleep.

Waking is a complex state. Its fundamental features are the maintenance of sensory input from multiple receptors, the capacity for directing attention and accessing memory, the constant readjustments of posture, the maintenance of forebrain activation, and an array of motor output. The mechanisms of many specific behaviors will be discussed in Chapters 50 through 59. It is worth noting here, however, that the reticular formation plays a crucial role in the initiation and maintenance of both wakefulness and sleep. We now focus on the active control of sleep.

The onset of sleep occurs when S and C factors coincide and the environmental milieu is conducive to sleep. At this point, the brainstem and cortical mechanisms of waking are relaxed: vigilance lapses, muscle tone declines, eyelids close, and the EEG slows. Because the cortex is still active, removal of ascending influences often results in sudden unresponsiveness, which may be associated with dreamlike imagery. This sleep onset mentation is usually quickly abolished by the thalamocortical oscillation of NREM sleep. As NREM sleep begins, the incomplete relaxation of the mechanisms maintaining muscle tone may result in paroxysmal twitching, a form of myoclonus often affecting the legs.

The Hypothalmus Participates in Sleep–Wake Regulation

During World War I and the following decade, an epidemic of encephalitis often resulted in a prolonged sleeplike state of unresponsiveness. The pathology of this encephalitis, called Von Economo encephalitis lethargica, included lesions in the posterior hypothalamus, and subsequent experimental animal work showed that large, posterior hypothalamic lesions produced a prolonged sleeplike state,[28] whereas lesions in the preoptic area–anterior hypothalamus markedly suppressed sleep.[29] These and similar observations led to the hypothesis of a sleep center in the posterior hypothalamus.

We now know that during NREM sleep a small nucleus in the **ventrolateral preoptic area** (VLPO) activates the immediate-early gene c-*fos*,[30] indicating an increase in metabolic activity in NREM sleep. The VLPO apparently contains GABA neurons that project to the posterior hypothalamus, particularly the tuberomammillary nucleus, which contains histamine-producing neurons and projects widely to the thalamus and cortex. Thus, one could conceive of a hypothalamic network in which the homeostatic and circadian regulatory processes of sleep interact at least in part at the VLPO, which in turn inhibits histaminergic activation of the thalamus and cerebral cortex by the tuberomammillary nucleus. Such a mechanism would allow complex thalamocortical interactions to result in NREM sleep, as described in the next section.

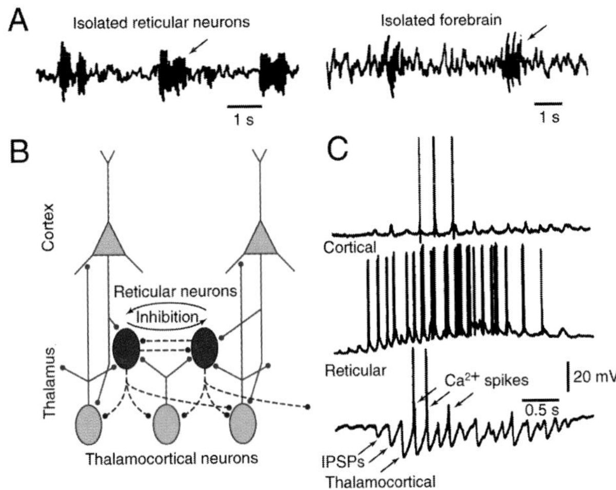

FIGURE 46.8 Thalamocortical oscillations *in vivo*. Sleep spindle oscillations are generated by synapses in the thalamus. (A, left) Potentials recorded through a microelectrode inserted in the deafferented reticular thalamic nucleus of a cat. The arrow points to one spindle sequence. (A, right) Spindle oscillations recorded from the thalamus of a cat with an upper brainstem transection that created an isolated forebrain preparation. The figure shows two spindle sequences (the second marked by an arrow) and, between them, lower frequency (delta) waves. (B) Neuronal connections involved in the generation of spindle oscillations. (C) Intracellular recordings of one spindle sequence (see A) in three types of neurons (cortical, reticular thalamic, and thalamocortical). Ca^{2+}, calcium ions; IPSP, inhibitory postsynaptic potential.

NREM Sleep Requires a Thalamocortical Interaction

About 75% of sleep time is spent in the NREM phase. Detailed studies of cellular activity in thalamocortical circuits[31,32] have led to important, unifying concepts, such as that the forebrain, and particularly the cortex, tends toward oscillation and unconsciousness unless activated by the brainstem.

The initiation of NREM sleep is gradual and is characterized by slowing of the frequency of brain waves seen on EEG. This initial slowing is **stage 1 sleep**. It is succeeded by **stage 2 sleep**, characterized by a further decrease in frequency of brain waves and the presence of intermittent, high-frequency clusters of spikes of electrical activity, sleep spindles. Sleep spindles decrease in **stage 3 sleep**, and the amplitude of slow waves increases. Very high amplitude delta waves occur in deepest sleep, **stage 4** (Fig. 46.4).

The critical circuitry (Fig. 46.8B) consists of reciprocally interconnected thalamic and cortical neurons that oscillate to produce the NREM sleep spindle waves (Fig. 46.8A) of stages 2 and 3 of NREM sleep. The thalamocortical and thalamic reticular neurons regulating this state are shifted into the burst firing mode by deactivation and demodulation from the hypothalamus and brainstem. During waking, these circuits are modulated by neurons that produce acetylcholine, norepinephrine, serotonin, or glutamate, whereas the principal modulator released during REM sleep is acetylcholine. Thus, the net brainstem and hypothalamic drive on the thalamocortical system sustains consciousness in the activated brain. In addition, the different modulatory inputs to the thalamocortical circuitry produce the different kinds of consciousness seen in waking and dreaming.

As sleep becomes deeper and spindling diminishes (in NREM stages 3 and 4), thalamocortical cells become progressively hyperpolarized. Cortical neurons then generate their own spontaneous delta (1–4 Hz) and slow (1 Hz) oscillations. When these high-voltage slow waves are present, people are difficult to arouse, and after waking they are confused, may confabulate, and cannot perform cognitive tests. Thalamocortical and cortical neurons may use the oscillations in NREM sleep to balance ionic currents and intracellular regulatory mechanisms in such a way that experience from previous waking episodes is incorporated into memory. NREM sleep is a quiescent state for the brain, in which blood flow and glucose use are decreased by more than 40%. A positron emission tomography (PET) study showed that decreases in blood flow in NREM sleep are particularly marked in the brainstem and diencephalon.[33]

REM Sleep Is Initiated in the Brainstem

Extracellular and intracellular recording techniques allowed detailed study of the cellular and molecular bases of the changes in input–output gating in REM sleep.[16]

Edward Evarts[34] used the movable microelectrode system of David Hubel[35] to record the activity of indi-

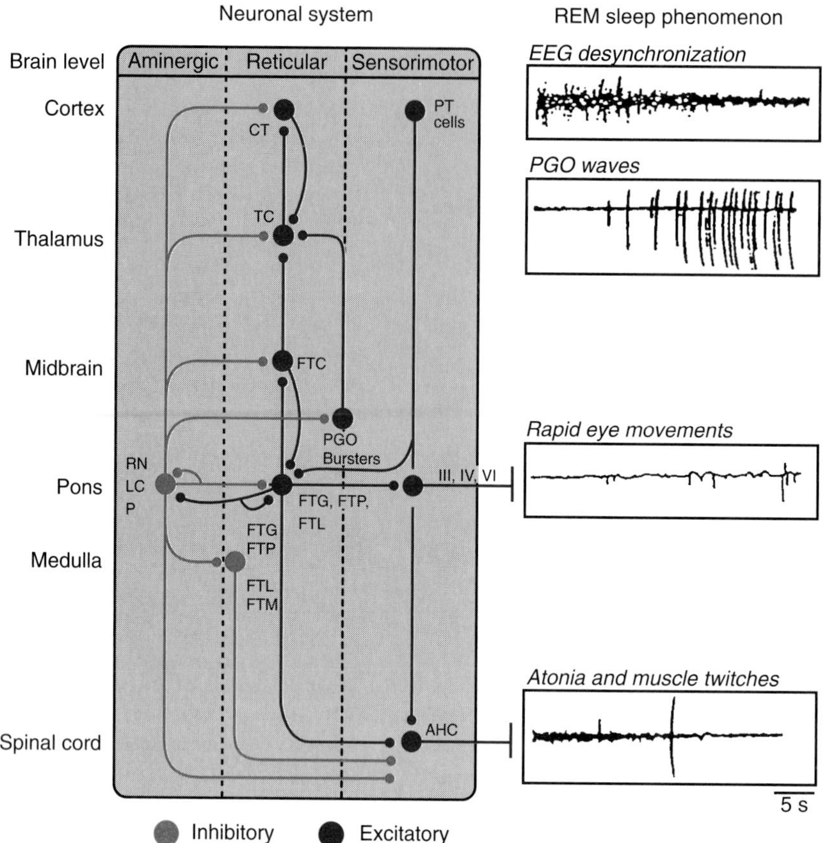

FIGURE 46.9 Schematic representation of the neuronal basis of REM sleep. The network of neurons responsible for generating REM sleep is distributed over many levels of the brain (left). The network is shown as three systems of neurons (center) that mediate the electrographic phemonena of REM sleep (right). Postulated inhibitory connections are shown as red circles; postulated excitatory connections as green circles. In many places (e.g., the thalamus and cortex), the architecture of the systems is known to be far more complex than indicated here. An increase in the firing of reticular, thalamocortical, and cortical neurons desynchronized the EEG. Tonic disinhibition and phasic excitation of burst cells results in pontine–geniculate–occipital (PGO) waves. Phasic firing by reticular and vestibular cells causes rapid eye movements; vestibular cells directly excite oculomotor neurons. Tonic postsynaptic inhibition of spinal anterior horn cells by the pontomedullary reticular formation causes muscle atonia. Muscle twitches occur when excitation by reticular and pyramidal tract motor neurons occasionally overcomes the inhibition of the anterior horn cells. AHC, anterior horn cell; CT, cortical; FT, reticular tegmental nuclei; LC, locus ceruleus; P, peribrachial region; PT cells, pyramidal cells; RN, raphe nucleus; TC, thalamocortical; III, oculomotor nucleus; IV, trochlear nucleas; V, trigeminal motor nucleus.

vidual brain neurons in animals. He showed that the generalized activity and the periodic PGO wave activation seen on EEG during REM sleep reflects the excitation of neurons throughout the forebrain, including the visual, motor, and association cortices[36] and the thalamic nuclei reciprocally connected to them[37,38] (Fig. 46.9). It may come as a surprise that we now know more about the neurophysiology of REM sleep and dreaming than we know about waking. REM sleep naturally favors neurophysiological studies because during REM sleep the normal modulation of motor and sensory systems paralyzes and partially anesthetizes animals.

REM sleep is a period of global but specific changes in the activation of neurons and flow of information throughout the brain. This picture of REM sleep is relevant to understanding the features that distinguish the conscious state of waking from those of NREM sleep and REM sleep, which is accompanied by dreaming (see Table 46.2). In waking, the activated brain–mind prefer-

TABLE 46.2 Physiological Basis of Changes That Occur during Dreaming

Function	Change (compared with waking)	Hypothesized cause
Sensory input	Blocked	Presynaptic inhibition
Perception (external)	Diminished	Blockade of sensory input
Perception (internal)	Enhanced	Removal of inhibition from networks that store sensory representations
Attention	Lost	Aminergic modulation decreases, causing a decrease in the ratio of signal to noise
Memory (recent)	Diminished	Because of a decrease in aminergic activity, activated representations are not stored in memory
Memory (remote)	Enhanced	Removal of inhibition from networks that store memory representations
Orientation	Unstable	Internally inconsistent signals are generated by cholinergic systems
Thought	Poor reasoning, processing hyper-associative	Loss of attention, memory, and volition leads to failure of sequencing and rule inconstancy; analogy replaces analysis
Insight	Self-reflection lost	Failures of attention, logic, and memory weaken second- (and third-) order representations
Language (internal)	Confabulatory	Aminergic demodulation frees the use of language from the restraint of logic
Emotion	Episodically strong	Cholinergic hyperstimulation of the amygdala and related structures of the temporal lobe triggers emotional storms, which are not modulated by aminergic activity
Instinct	Episodically strong	Cholinergic hyperstimulation of the hypothalamus and limbic forebrain triggers fixed motor programs, which are experienced fictively but not enacted
Volition	Weak	Cortical motor control cannot compete with disinhibited subcortical networks
Output	Blocked	Postsynaptic inhibition

entially processes data from the outside world and responds by directing actions. In NREM sleep, the system is taken off-line via deactivation and therefore does not process information about the outside world. In REM sleep, in contrast to waking, the internal representations of the outside world become inputs, and the action summoned (but not executed) in response to those inputs itself becomes one of those inputs.[39]

The modulatory neuron system of the brainstem, particularly the noradrenergic locus ceruleus and the serotonergic pontine raphe neurons, mediates these changes in brain–mind state.[40] As we have seen, these aminergic populations contain pacemaker neurons that fire spontaneously throughout waking. The neurons also respond to stimuli by increasing their output. Output decreases during lulls between stimuli and at the onset of sleep.[41–43] The cholinergic neurons of the pedunculopontine nucleus also respond to stimuli, but these cells are not pacemakers and tend to be otherwise quiescent in waking. Thus, the waking brain is bathed in constant levels of norepinephrine and serotonin and receives pulsatile boosts of these two chemicals and of acetylcholine when novel input data call for them. Because histaminergic neurons of the hypothalamus also are selectively active in waking and in REM sleep, these observations suggest that the attentive, memory-forming awake state is chemically characterized as an aminergic–cholinergic collaboration.

At the onset of sleep, the activity of these subcortical modulatory neurons decreases, and the neurons contribute to the development of EEG spindles and slow waves. As NREM sleep deepens, the activity of the two pontine aminergic systems gradually and spontaneously declines,[43–45] while the activity of the cholinergic neurons gradually and spontaneously increases.[44] At the onset of REM sleep, the aminergic system is completely quiet and the cholinergic system is fully active. The net effect, confirmed by measurements of transmitter release,[46] is a shift from an aminergic microclimate in waking to a cholinergic microclimate in REM.

These physiological findings are supported by experiments showing that antiaminergic and procholinergic drugs tend to increase REM, while proaminergic and anticholinergic agents suppress it. In addition, these drugs have reciprocal effects on waking and NREM sleep. Among the wealth of pharmacological studies,[1] two are particularly impressive and reveal dramatic REM sleep enhancement.

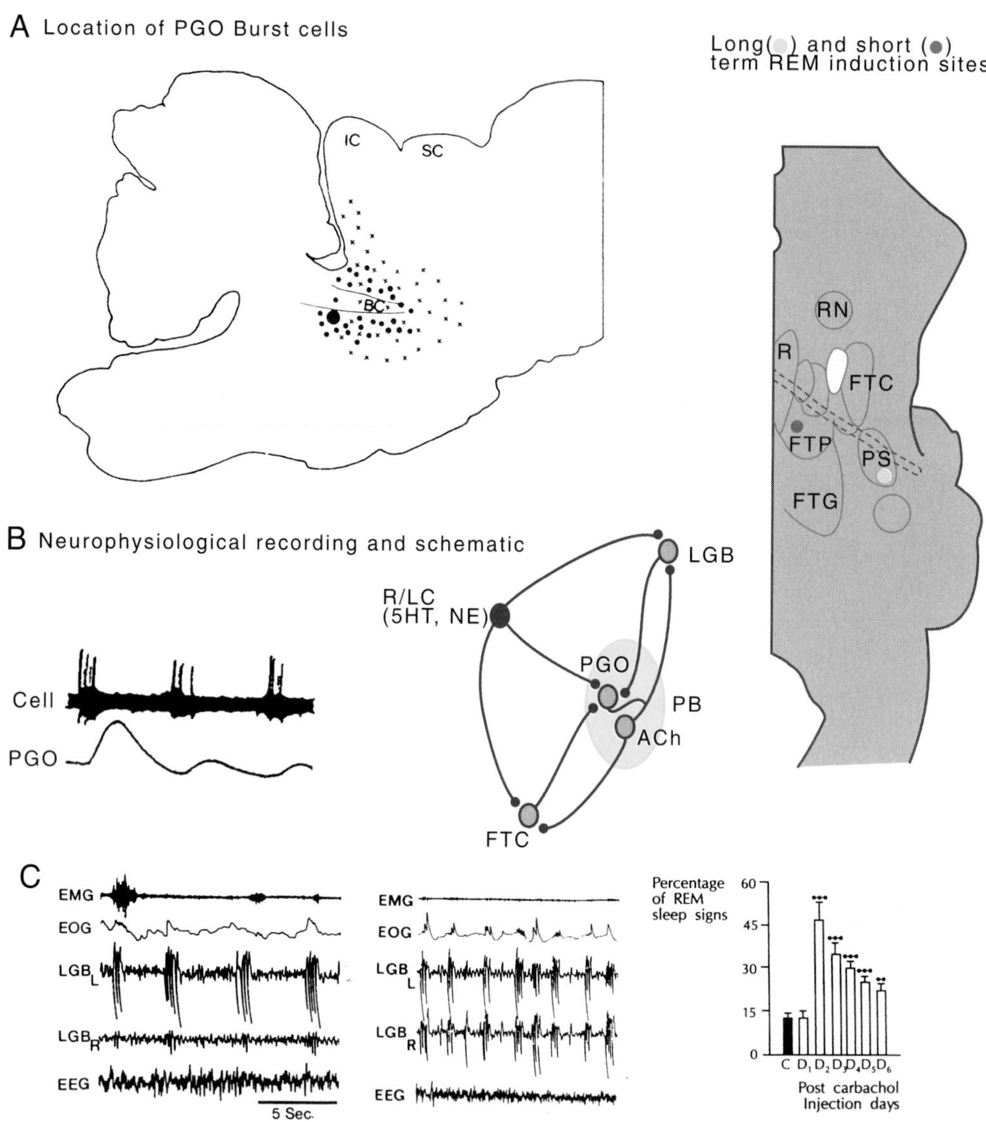

FIGURE 46.10 Sites of REM induction. (A, left) Filled circle indicates site of injection of carbachol into peribrachial pons. Small dots indicate location of cholinergic cells and crosses location of PGO burst cells. (A, right) Injection of carbachol, an acetylcholine agonist, in the perimedian pons (magenta dot) causes short-term induction of REM sleep. Injection of the peribrachial pons (yellow dot) causes long-term induction of REM sleep. After injection of a cholinergic agonist into the peribrachial pons, pontine–geniculate–occipital (PGO) burst cell activity and PGO waves can immediately be measured in the lateral geniculate body (LGB) on the same side (ipsilateral) of the brain as the injections (B, left). Hypothesized connections among the PGO trigger zone (PB), modulatory aminergic raphe (R), locus ceruleus (LC), and paramedian pontine reticular cells (FTC) are shown in (B, left). (C, left) Injections of carbachol at the PB site shown in (A) produce immediate PGO waves in the ipsilateral LGB. After 24 h, REM sleep intensifies (C, middle) and remains so for 6 days (C, right). FTC, FTG, and FTP are reticular tegmented nuclei. C5 and C6 are cholinergic nuclei. RN, red nucleus; V, trigeminal motor nucleus.

When the cholinergic agonist carbachol or the anticholinesterase (blocker of the enzyme cholinesterase, which breaks down acetylcholine) neostigmine is injected into the paramedian pontine brainstem, an immediate, intense, and prolonged episode of REM sleep results.[47–49] This effect, which disappears in about 6 h, is called short-term REM sleep enhancement. When injected into the far lateral peribrachial pons, the cholinergic agonist and acetylcholinesterase antagonist immediately but only unilaterally enhance PGO waves and, 24–48 h later, enhance activity in REM sleep episodes for 6–10 days; this is long-term REM sleep enhancement,[50,51] and some of its features are illustrated in Fig. 46.10.

Summary

Specific neuronal groups within the hypothalamus, pons, and medulla are responsible for the regulation of behavioral states of sleep and wakefulness. Because some of these neuronal groups often lack distinct neuronal boundaries, they are a part of the so-called reticular core of the brainstem. These neuronal systems have very distinct afferent and efferent connections and very specific chemical specifications, containing norepinephrine (NE), serotonin (5HT), and acetylcholine (ACh). These neurons are small or modest in size with extensive and elaborate axonal projections to hypothalmus, midbrain, and forebrain and include descending projections to the spinal cord. In addition, the three sets of neurons are heavily interconnected, such that the NE and 5HT neurons fire slowly in quiet waking and are reduced further as the ACh neurons activate during slow wave and REM sleep. NE neurons are actively suppressed, but with the end of REM sleep show activation by novel sensory events. 5HT neurons fire most rapidly during continuous motor activity, such as walking or running. Both systems must be active for maintenance of the waking state. A posterior hypothalamic projection to thalamus and cortex may serve to integrate thermal and circadian aspects of sleep and waking. Reciprocal connections between the cortex and thalamus organized into synchronized oscillations underlie the EEG manifestations of slow wave sleep, diminishing as sleep deepens. In REM sleep, when NE and 5HT neurons are silent, autoactivation of the ACh neurons or pharmacological enhancement of cholinergic transmission within the reticular formation enhances REM sleep duration.

MODELING THE CONTROL OF BEHAVIORAL STATE

Two linked models—one neurobiological[53] and the other psychophysiological[52]—have been advanced to organize experimental findings and their implications for a theory of consciousness. According to the neurobiological model (Fig. 46.11), in waking, brain activation and open input–output gates result from a combination of continual aminergic activity and phasic (waxing and waning) aminergic and cholinergic activities. In contrast, in REM sleep the continually low level of aminergic activity and the periodic increases in cholinergic activity close input–output gates, activate the brain, and periodically stimulate the brain.

Waking, NREM sleep, and REM sleep can tentatively be linked to their accompanying changes in physiology (Table 46.2). Sensation and perception progressively decline during the cortical deactivation that occurs at the onset of sleep; responsiveness declines further as NREM sleep deepens. During REM sleep the brain reactivates, but presynaptic inhibition blocks sensory signals. REMs and their associated PGO waves act as internal stimuli, which take the place of stimuli from external sources. The brainstem sends information about eye movements to the thalamocortical visual system, possibly accounting for the intense visual hallucination of dreams. Furthermore, these PGO signals also drive the amygdala, perhaps accounting for such emotions as anxiety and surprise in dreams. Interestingly, PET studies of regional cerebral blood flow show an increase in the flow of blood in limbic structures, including the amygdala.

In the early days of the EEG, brain waves with frequencies greater than 25 Hz were either ignored or filtered out because of the problem of interference by

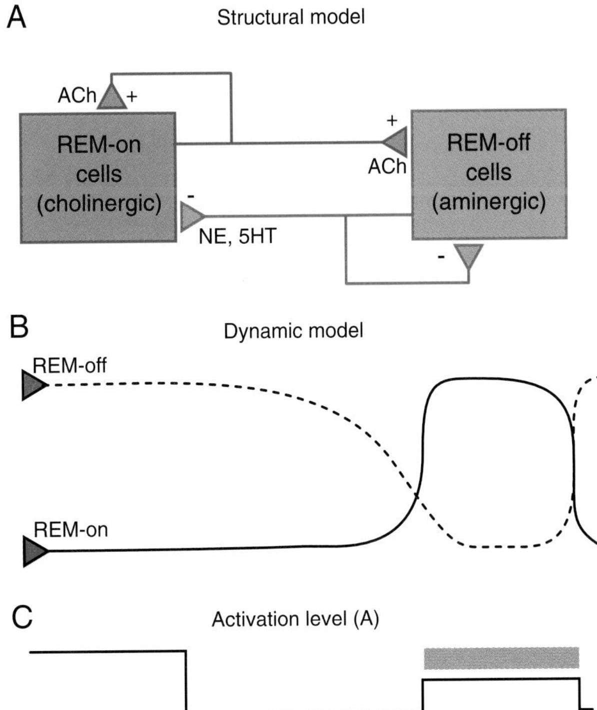

FIGURE 46.11 Structural and dynamic models of activation in REM sleep. (A) In the structural model, REM-on cells of the pontine reticular formation are excited by acetylcholine (ACh), or they produce excitatory signals using ACh in their synaptic terminals (or they do both). REM-off cells respond to or use norepinephrine (NE) or serotonin (5HT) as inhibitory neurotransmitters (or they do both). (B) In the dynamic model, during waking the pontine aminergic system (dashed line) is continuously active and inhibits the pontine cholinergic system (solid line). During NREM sleep, aminergic activity decreases, allowing cholinergic activity to rise. By the time REM sleep begins, the aminergic system is off and cholinergic excitation has peaked. (C) As a result of the neuronal systems modeled in (A) and (B).

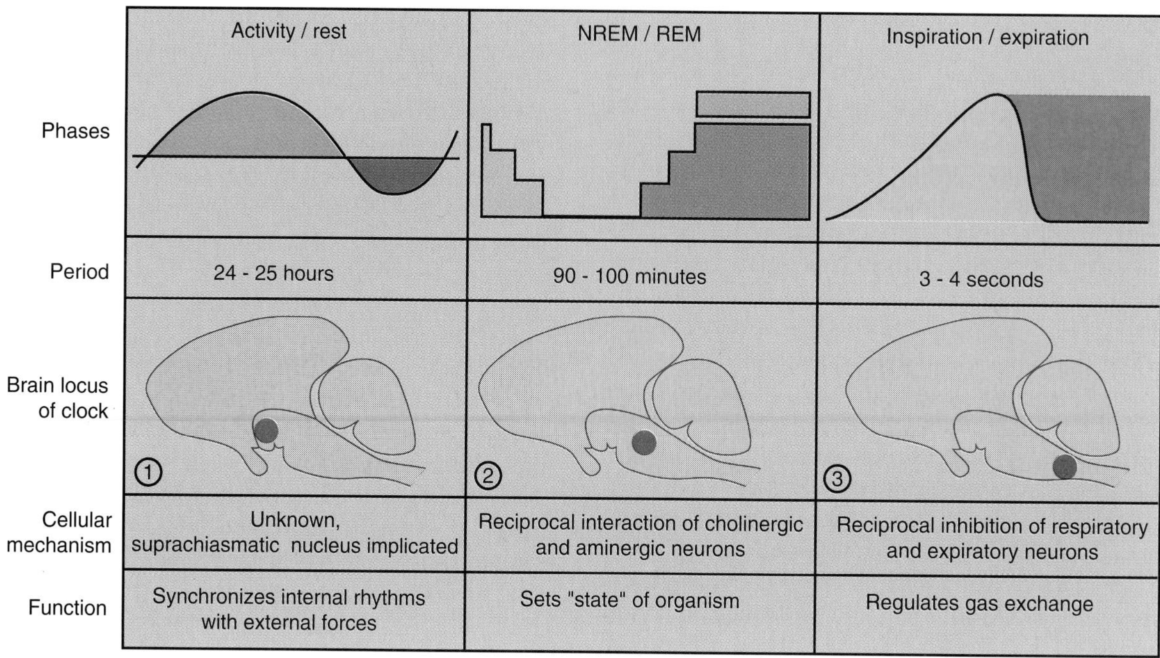

FIGURE 46.12 Biological rhythms and brainstem clocks. Three rhythms interact during sleep. Circadian rhythms have a period of about 24 hours and control many cycles, including the rest–activity cycle. The circadian clock appears to be located in the suprachiasmatic nucleus of the hypothalamus. The 90–100 minute period of NREM–REM sleep cycles is controlled by cholinergic and aminergic neurons of the pontine reticular formation. These neurons oscillate out of phase from each other to determine behavioral state (waking, NREM sleep, or REM sleep). The circadian clock sets the threshold of the sleep cycle clock by an unknown mechanism. The respiratory oscillator is similar in neuronal design to the sleep cycle clock but has a shorter period (3 seconds), which is controlled by reciprocal inhibition of expiratory and inspiratory neurons in the medulla.

50- or 60-Hz artifacts from electrical power sources. Later, researchers were able to focus on the possibility that 40-Hz EEG activity synchronizes processing in cortical areas.

Rodolfo Llinas proposed that as the cortex is scanned by the thalamus, 40-Hz waves propagate from the frontal to the occipital poles. Noting that 40-Hz activity is observed in REM sleep as well as in waking, he suggested that intrinsic neuronal oscillations are important in the genesis of both states of consciousness and that the main difference between waking and dreaming arises from differences in input–output gating.[39] In addition to being without temporal or spatial input, in REM sleep the brain has little background aminergic activity; this lack may contribute to the declines in attention, orientation, memory, and logic that characterize dreaming and make dreams difficult to remember.[53–57]

The Brainstem Has Three Clocks

An important question is how the circadian clock (or clocks), located in the suprachiasmatic nucleus of the hypothalamus,[58] interacts with the NREM–REM sleep clock in the pons so that full-amplitude oscillation of the sleep clock is confined to the rest phase of the rest–activity cycle (see Fig. 46.12). The suprachiasmatic nucleus receives input from the serotonergic raphe nuclei, but no other connections between the two centers have been demonstrated. As mentioned earlier, the NREM–REM cycle free-runs when the connections between pons and hypothalamus are cut or when the hypothalamus is removed. However, we do not understand exactly how the synchronizing signals are transmitted and what their cellular and molecular basis may be.[59] (See Chapter 45.)

During waking, the damping of the NREM–REM oscillator is incomplete. Numerous studies have revealed a weak but significant periodicity of behavior during the activity phase of the rest–activity cycle. The period is about 90–100 minutes, suggesting the pontine clock may be timing at low amplitude throughout the day and thus causing the normal waxing and waning of attention and motor activity during waking. A better understanding of the interaction of this clock with the circadian clock is an important issue for research (Fig. 46.12).

Central Autonomic Control Systems Are State-Dependent

Cognitive and vegetative functions are linked to changes in central modulatory systems during sleep. For example, active hypothalamic temperature control is diminished or abandoned in REM sleep,[60,61] and the sensitivity of the respiratory control system is likewise diminished. As a result, a neuron that during waking is sensitive to temperature or pO_2 loses that responsiveness during REM sleep.[61,62] Sleep, then, involves significant changes in reflex control of autonomic function. Our understanding of changes in the control of vegetative and sensorimotor functions during waking and sleep can be applied to understand sleep-related dysfunctions such as insomnia (inability to sleep), hypersomnia (excessive sleepiness), and parasomnia (sleep with reflex responses to stimuli).[63,64]

Sleep Disorders Result from Disrupted Control of Behavioral State

When CNS aminergic activity increases, the brain is shifted in the direction of hyperarousal, and insomnia and sometimes stress result. If stress and insomnia are prolonged, the chronic sympathetic overdrive can harm an animal's cardiovascular, cognitive, and behavioral functions. Behavioral and pharmacologic interventions that decrease sympathetic output may be understood as reversals of the peripheral and central excitatory stimuli that prevent the locus ceruleus and raphe systems from the periodic respite of sleep; insomnia is a form of sleep deprivation that prevents the cholinergic system from exerting its restorative effects.

The decrease in CNS aminergic activity (as in depression or narcolepsy) has opposite effects on cardiovascular, cognitive, and behavioral systems. With sleepiness, attention and cognition decline, and motor activity is impaired. Under these conditions the cholinergic system is disinhibited, and the REM generator is triggered abnormally easily. The result is unwanted sleepiness or frank REM sleep attacks. These symptoms are decreased by aminergic agonists, such as blockers of amine reuptake, and anticholinergics, both of which boost sympathetic activity. Indeed, the best drugs for treating hypersomnia have both proaminergic and anticholinergic actins.

Respiratory Dysfunction Is Common in Sleep

One of the more dramatic problems associated with sleep is an exaggeration, at sleep onset, of the normal decline in respiratory drive. Also, respiratory irregularity may be provoked by the altered brainstem activity of REM sleep. This sleep-dependent disruption of respiratory function is **central sleep apnea**, a decrease in respiratory drive during NREM sleep (Fig. 46.13). In addition, especially in obese people, mechanical collapse or compression of the airway can result in **peripheral sleep apnea**, in which ventilation decreases because of a mechanical problem in the oropharynx. In peripheral sleep apnea, central respiratory drive causes continued respiratory effort. Eventually, arousal results in increased muscle tone in the oropharynx, and the airway opens. As the person falls into deeper sleep again, the oropharynx relaxes and the airway becomes obstructed until arousal recurs. This cycle can repeat.

People with sleep apnea usually feel excessively sleepy during daytime, because frequent arousal prevents deep, sustained sleep. They are often unaware of their sleep-dependent breathing pattern because they are never fully aroused from sleep. Instead, observant friends or family often describe seeing these signs of respiratory dysfunction. In a sleep laboratory, EEG, respiratory effort, and cardiovascular parameters (e.g., heart rate and blood pressure) are measured to quantify the problem. Sleep apnea can be treated by having the person wear a mask through which air is gently forced, helping to keep the airway open. The pressure of the air fluctuates to allow regular exhalation. People with sleep apnea are treated not only to alleviate their constant drowsiness but to prevent long-term effects of sleep apnea, such as cardiopulmonary complications.[64]

Motor Disturbances Occur during Sleep

Parasomnias that affect the skeletal motor system (e.g., sleep walking, sleep talking, tooth grinding, and night terrors) result from activation, in NREM sleep, of the response to central motor pattern generators. Normally, the responses to these generators are disinhibited at sleep onset and later inhibited, so no motor commands are enacted during REM sleep. Unlike NREM sleep phenomena, which affect mainly young people, **REM sleep behavior disorder** can be a sign of degenerative brain disease in the elderly. Because of a failure to inhibit the expression of motor acts in REM, people may literally enact their dream scenarios in their bedrooms.

A syndrome strikingly similar to REM sleep behavior disorder can be experimentally induced by bilateral lesions of the pontine tegmentum in cats. When in REM sleep, these animals perform stereotyped behavior sequences, such as hissing, piloerection, pouncing, and jumping. Jouvet[59] called these "hallucinatory behaviors," and Morrison called the phenomenon "REM sleep without atonia." The cats' ability to inhibit motor pattern commands during REM sleep is impaired by

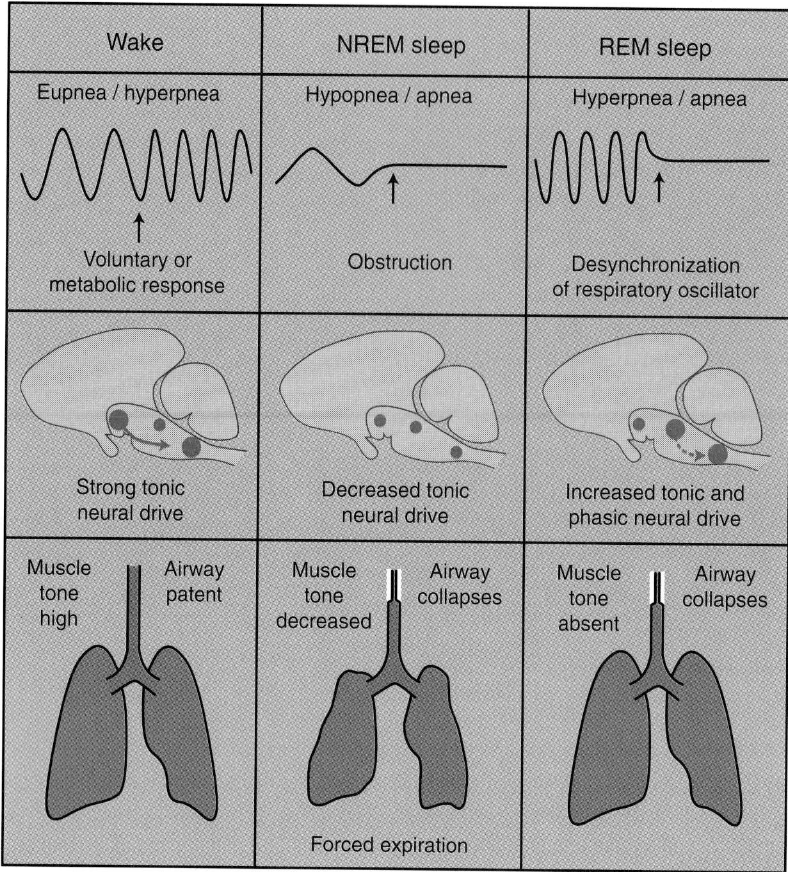

FIGURE 46.13 Central sleep apnea. During waking, the respiratory oscillator of the medulla receives tonic drive from other neural structures and can respond to voluntary and metabolic signals to change breathing pattern. Muscle tone keeps the oropharynx open to the flow of air. In NREM sleep, central drive decreases, and the rate and depth of ventilation fall. If the airway collapses, prolonged apnea (lack of breathing) may result. During REM sleep, activation of pontine generator neurons drives the respiratory oscillator, and desynchronization may lead to breathing efforts that are too frequent or strong (hyperpnea) or that stop. During REM sleep the oscillator also becomes unresponsive to metabolic signals.

the lesions, so they act out the commands. The instinctual aspect of these released behaviors is relevant to the psychophysiology of dreaming and has important implications for the hypothesis that REM sleep serves an active maintenance function.

Sleep Has a Function

Although it is easy to conceptualize the function of waking and to understand the adaptive value of consciousness, it has been difficult to move beyond the subjectively compelling but scientifically unsatisfactory notion of sleep as rest. Evidence strongly suggests that sleep has an anabolic and actively conservative function that is related to the complexity of the mammalian brain (see Table 46.1). In fact, Bennington and Heller[65] propose that an important function of NREM sleep is to restore brain glycogen stores.

The most dramatic evidence of this homeostatic function comes from sleep deprivation studies in rats in which sleep deprivation was fatal when it persisted for 4 to 6 weeks. Early in the deprivation period, the rats began to eat more but could not maintain their body weight. Later, they lost their ability to maintain body temperature and developed strong heat-seeking behavior. Finally, they died of overwhelming sepsis because of immunodeficiency. The study implied that metabolic caloric balance, thermal equilibrium, and immune competence are preserved by sleep.[66,67]

Additional evidence links immune function and sleep. Pappenheimer[68] found that in rabbits NREM sleep was enhanced by dimuramyl peptides of bacterial cell wall origin. NREM sleep is also enhanced by the cytokines interleukin-1 and interleukin-2, both of which are released during NREM sleep.

Contributing to the notion that sleep has an anabolic function is the abundance of sleep in early life. REM sleep predominates *in utero*, where its stereotypic pattern of motor activation and its chemical microenvironment could promote CNS development.[69] Such a function would be expected to decline in childhood, just as REM does. Also, growth and development could be enhanced by the release of growth hormone and gonadotropins in NREM sleep. Such hormone release declines, as does NREM sleep, after growth and sexual maturation are complete, around 30 years of age.

The theory of sleep as rest is supported by recognition that sleep is an energy- and heat-saving behavior that tends to occur at night, when ambient temperatures are low.[2] In addition, sleeping with other members of the species may provide safety from predators and supply warmth.

Not only energy but also information may be conserved in sleep. Numerous studies show that animals have more REM sleep when learning a task and that REM deprivation interferes with learning.[70–74] Neurotransmitters needed to form recent memories (e.g., norepinephrine and serotonin) could be conserved and their receptors could be regulated or sensitized during REM sleep if their neurons stop firing. At that time, the cholinergic environment of the brain could help consolidate memories already in the system. Finally, cognition and emotion, which most people agree benefit from sleep, could be mediated by the reversal of wake state neuromodulation in REM.[2]

Summary

Two models attempt to explain sleep and wakefulness. In the neurobiological model, sleep and waking are the result of reciprocal, phasic interactions between the NE and 5HT neurons and the ACh neurons. In the alternative psychophysical model, the influences of external and internal sensations are emphasized. During slow wave sleep, thalamocortical synchronous activity diminishes responsiveness to the external world. During REM sleep, under the influence of forebrain cholinergic projections, internal representations of visual information predominate. In addition to changes in levels of sensory arousal and cognitive performance during sleeping, vegetative functions such as circadian rhythm recognition, body temperature, and autonomic activity are also regulated coordinately. Disorders of sleep adversely influence emotional and cognitive functions. Prolonged sleep deprivation is lethal, ending in a septic state of immunodeficiency, strongly suggesting that sleep serves an important but uncertainly mediated restorative function.

The brain undergoes daily, complex, systematic changes that profoundly alter the nature of our consciousness, behavior, autonomic control, and physiologic homeostasis. At the root of these changes is the circadian clock. Located in the hypothalamus, this clock programs rest–activity and body temperature cycles. It also gates the NREM–REM sleep cycle control system in the pons.

Some cellular and molecular details of the pontine system are clear: For the awake state, the noradrenergic locus ceruleus and the serotonergic raphe neurons must fire regularly to support alertness, attentiveness, memory, orientation, logical thought, and emotional stability. When the output of these two chemical systems diminishs, drowsiness occurs. When sleep begins, the output of these two systems further declines, and the brain–mind enters NREM sleep, a phase of lowered consciousness. During NREM sleep, cholinergic activity gradually increases. At the NREM–REM transition, the activity of the two aminergic systems is at its nadir, and the output of the cholinergic system increases exponentially. This chemical switch results in the cholinergic activation and autostimulation of REM sleep. Combined with the lack of aminergic stimulation, this cholinergic overdrive accounts for the characteristic hallucination, delusion, disorientation, memory loss, and emotional intensity of dreaming.

Although the details of these daily changes in brain chemistry remain to be specified, consequences of their dysfunction are becoming more clearly understood through the study of insomnias, hypersomnias, and parasomnias. Integration of data from basic neurobiology, cognitive psychology, and clinical science enables construction of specific, testable models of how waking and sleep affect our conscious experience. These models, in turn, constitute the building blocks of a scientific theory of consciousness.

References

General

Hobson, J. A. (1988). *The Dreaming Brain.* Basic Books, New York.

Kryger, M. H., Roth, T., and Dement, W. C. (1994). *Principles and Practice of Sleep Medicine*, 2nd ed. Saunders, Philadelphia.

Steriade, M., and McCarley, R. W. (1990). *Brainstem Control of Wakefulness and Sleep.* Plenum, New York.

Cited

1. Hobson, J. A., and Steriade, M. (1986). The neuronal basis of behavioral state control. In *Handbook of Physiology* (F. E. Bloom, ed.), Sect. 1, Vol. 4, pp. 701–823. American Physiological Society, Bethesda, MD.
2. Hobson, J. A. (1988). *The Dreaming Brain.* Basic Books, New York.

3. Loomis, A. L., Harvey, E. N., and Hobart, G. A. (1937). Cerebral states during sleep as studied by human brain potentials. *J. Exp. Psychol.* **21:** 127.
4. Bremer, F. (1937). L'activité cérébrale au cours du sommeil et de la narcose. Contribution à l'étude du mécanisme du sommeil. *Bull. Acad. R. Med. Belg.* **4:** 68–86.
5. Hess, W. R. (1954). *Diencephalon: Autonomic and Extrapyramidal Functions.* Grune & Stratton, New York.
6. Steriade, M., and McCarley, R. W. (1990). *Brainstem Control of Wakefulness and Sleep.* Plenum, New York.
7. Moruzzi, G., and Magoun, H. W. (1949). Brainstem reticular formation and activation of the EEG. *Electroencephalogr. Clin. Neurophysiol.* **1:** 455–473.
8. Pavlov, I. P. (1960). *Conditioned Reflexes: An Investigation of the Physiological Activity of the Cerebral Cortex* (G. V. Anrep, transl.). Dover, New York.
9. Sherrington, C. (1955). *Man on His Nature.* Doubleday, New York.
10. Aserinsky, E., and Kleitman, N. (1963). Regularly occurring periods of ocular mobility and concomitant phenomena during sleep. *Science* **118:** 361–375.
11. Dement, W., and Kleitman, N. (1955). Cyclic variations in EEG during sleep and their relation to eye movements, body mobility and dreaming. *Electroencephalogr. Clin. Neurophysiol.* **9:** 673–690.
12. Dement, W., and Kleitman, N. (1957). The relation of eye movements during sleep to dream activity: An objective method for the study of dreaming. *J. Exp. Psychol.* **53:** 89–97.
13. Dement, W. (1958). The occurrence of low voltage, fast, electroencephalogram patterns during behavioral sleep in the cat. *Electroencephalogr. Clin. Neurophysiol.* **10:** 291–296.
14. Jouvet, M. (1962). Recherche sur les structures nerveuses et les mécanismes responsables des différentes phases du sommeil physiologique. *Arch. Ital. Biol.* **100:** 125–206.
15. Callaway, C. W., Lydic, R., Baghdoyan, H. A., and Hobson, J. A. (1987). Ponto-geniculo-occipital waves: Spontaneous visual system activation occurring in REM sleep. *Cell. Mol. Neurobiol.* **7:** 105–149.
16. Pompeiano, O. (1967). The neurophysiological mechanisms of the postural and motor events during desynchronized sleep. *Proc. Assoc. Res. Nerv. Ment. Dis.* **45:** 351–423.
17. Morales, F. R., and Chase, M. H. (1981). Postsynaptic control of lumbar motoneuron excitability during active sleep in the chronic rat. *Brain Res.* **225:** 279–295.
18. Soja, P. J., Finch, D. M., and Chase, M. H. (1987). Effect of inhibitory amino acid antagonists on masseteric reflex suppression during active sleep. *Exp. Neurol.* **96**(1): 178–193.
19. Jouvet, M., and Delorme, F. (1965). Locus coeruleus et sommeil paradoxal. *Soc. Biol.* **159:** 895.
20. Henley, K., and Morrison, A. R. (1974). A re-evaluation of the effects of lesions of the pontine tegmentum and locus coeruleus on phenomena of paradoxical sleep in the cat. *Acta Neurobiol. Exp.* **34:** 251–232.
21. Porte, H. S., and Hobson, J. A. (1996). Physical motion in dreams: One measure of three theories. *J. Abnormal Psychol.* **105:** 329–335.
22. Dahlstrom, A., and Fuxe, K. (1964). Evidence for the existence of monoamine neurons in the central nervous system. I. Demonstration of monoamines in the cell bodies of brain stem neurons. *Acta Physiol. Scand.* **62**(S232): 1–55.
23. Moore, R. Y., and Card, J. P., eds. (1984). *Noradrenaline-Containing Neuron Systems.* Elsevier, Amsterdam.
24. Jacobs, B. L., and Azmitia, E. C. (1992). Structure and function of the brain serotonin system. *Physiol. Rev.* **72:** 165–229.
25. Daan, S., Beersma, D. G. M., and Borbely, A. A. (1984). Timing of human sleep: Recovery process gated by a circadian pacemaker. *Am. J. Physiol.* **246:** R161–R178.
26. Jones, B. E. (1994). Basic mechanisms of sleep-wake states. In *The Principles and Practice of Sleep Medicine* (M. H. Kryger, T. Roth, and W. C. Dement, eds.), 2nd ed., pp. 145–162. Saunders, Philadelphia.
27. Cravatt, B. F., Prospero-Garcia, O., Siuzdak, G., Gilula, N. B., Henricksen, S. J., Boger, D. L., and Lerner, R. A. (1995). Chemical characterization of a family of brain lipids that induce sleep. *Science* **268:** 1506–1509.
28. Nauta, W. J. H. (1946). Hypothalamic regulation of sleep in rats. *J. Neurophysiol.* **9:** 285–316.
29. McGinty, D. J., and Sterman, M. B. (1968). Sleep suppression after basal forebrain lesions in the cat. *Science* **160:** 1253–1255.
30. Sherin, J. E., Shiromani, P. J., McCarley, R. W., and Saper, C. B. (1996). Activation of ventrolateral preoptic neurons during sleep. *Science* **27:** 216–219.
31. Steriade, M., Contrera, D., and Aronzica, F. (1994). Synchronized sleep oscillations and their paroxysmal developments. *Trends Neurosci.* **17:** 199–208.
32. McCormick, D. A., and Bal, T. (1997). Sleep and arousal: Thalamocortical mechanisms. *Annu. Rev. Neurosci.* **20:** 185–215.
33. Maquet, P., Dequeldre, C., Delfiure, G., Aerts, J., Peters, J.-M., Luxen, A., and Franck, G. (1997). Functional neuroanatomy of human slow wave sleep. *J. Neurosci.* **17:** 2807–2812.
34. Evarts, E. V. (1960). Effects of sleep and waking on spontaneous and evoked discharge of single units in visual cortex. *Fed. Proc. Fed. Am. Soc. Exp. Biol., Suppl.* **4:** 828–837.
35. Hubel, D. H. (1959). Single unit activity in striate cortex of unrestrained cats. *J. Physiol.* (*London*) **147:** 226–238.
36. Adey, W. R., Kado, R. T., and Rhodes, J. M. (1963). Sleep: Cortical and subcortical recordings in the chimpanzee. *Science* **141:** 932.
37. Steriade, M., Pare, D., Parent, A., and Smith, Y. (1988). Projections of cholinergic and noncholinergic neurons of the brainstem core to relay and associational thalamic nuclei in the cat and macaque monkey. *Neuroscience* **25:** 47–67.
38. Bizzi, E., and Brooks, D. C. (1963). Functional connections between pontine reticular formation and lateral geniculate nucleus during deep sleep. *Arch. Ital. Biol.* **101:** 666–680.
39. Llinas, R. R., and Pare, D. (1991). Of dreaming and wakefulness. *Neuroscience* **44:** 521–535.
40. Jouvet, M. (1972). The role of monoamines and acetylcholine-containing neurons in the regulation of the sleep-waking cycle. *Ergeb. Physiol., Biol. Chem. Exp. Pharmakol.* **64:** 166–307.
41. Aston-Jones, G., and Bloom, F. E. (1981). Activity of norepinephrine-containing locus coeruleus neurons in behaving rats anticipates fluctuations in the sleep-waking cycle. *J. Neurosci.* **1:** 876–886.
42. Aston-Jones, G., and Bloom, F. E. (1981). Norepinephrine-containing locus coeruleus neurons in behaving rats exhibit pronounced responses to nonnoxious environmental stimuli. *J. Neurosci.* **1:** 887–900.
43. Chu, N. S., and Bloom, F. E. (1974). Activity patterns of catecholamine-containing pontine neurons in the dorsolateral tegmentum of unrestrained rats. *J. Neurobiol.* **5:** 527–544.
44. Hobson, J. A., McCarley, R. W., and Qyzinki, P. W. (1975). Sleep cycle oscillation: Reciprocal discharge by two brainstem neuronal groups. *Science* **189:** 55–58.
45. McGinty, D. J., and Harper, R. M. (1976). Dorsal raphe neurons: Depression of firing during sleep in cats. *Brain Res.* **101:** 569–575.
46. Lydic, R., Baghdoyan, H. A., and Lorinc, Z. (1991). Microdialysis of cat pons reveals enhanced acetylcholine release during state-dependent respiratory depression. *Am. J. Physiol.* **261:** 766–770.
47. Baghdoyan, H. A., Monaco, A. P., Rodrigo-Angulo, M. L., Assens, F., McCarley, R. W., and Hobson, J. A. (1984). Microinjection of neostigmine into the pontine reticular formation of cats en-

hances desynchronized sleep signs. *J. Pharmacol. Exp. Ther.* **231:** 173–180.

48. Baghdoyan, H. A., Rodrigo-Angulo, M. L., McCarley, R. W., and Hobson, J. A. (1984). Site-specific enhancement and suppression of desynchronized sleep signs following cholinergic stimulation of three brainstem regions. *Brain Res.* **306:** 39–52.
49. Baghdoyan, H. A., Rodrigo-Angulo, M. L., McCarley, R. W., and Hobson, J. A. (1987). A neuroanatomical gradient in the pontine tegmentum for the cholinoceptive induction of desynchronized sleep signs. *Brain Res.* **414:** 245–261.
50. Calvo, J., Datta, S., Quattrochi, J. J., and Hobson, J. A. (1992). Cholinergic microstimulation of the peribrachial nucleus in the cat. II. Delayed and prolonged increases in REM sleep. *Arch. Ital. Biol.* **130:** 285–301.
51. Datta, S., Calvo, J., Quattrochi, J. J., and Hobson, J. A. (1992). Cholinergic microstimulation of the peribrachial nucleus in the cat. I. Immediate and prolonged increases in ponto-geniculo-occipital waves. *Arch. Ital. Biol.* **130:** 263–284.
52. Hobson, J. A., and McCarley, R. (1977). The brain as a dream state generator: An activation-synthesis hypothesis of the dream process. *Am. J. Psychiatry* **134:** 1335–1348.
53. McCarley, R. W., and Hobson, J. A. (1975). Neuronal excitability modulation over the sleep cycle: A structural and mathematical model. *Science* **189:** 58–60.
54. Deleted at proof.
55. Hobson, J. A. (1994). Consciousness as a state-dependent phenomenon. In *Scientific Approaches to the Question of Consciousness* (J. Cohen and J. Schooler, eds.), pp. 379–396. Lawrence Erlbaum.
56. Hobson, J. A. (1994). Consciousness: Lessons for anesthesia from sleep research. In *Textbook Anaesthesia: Biologic Foundations* (J. F. Biebuyck, ed.), pp. 423–431. Raven Press, New York.
57. Hobson, J. A., and Stickgold, R. (1994). The Conscious State Paradigm: A neurocognitive approach to waking, sleeping and dreaming. In *The Cognitive Neurosciences* (M. Gazzaniga, ed.), pp. 1373–1389. MIT Press, Cambridge, MA.
58. Moore, R. Y. (1996). Entrainment pathways and the functional organization of the circadian system. *Prog. Brain Res.* **111:** 103–119.
59. Jouvet, M., Buda, L., Denges, M., Kitahama, K., Sallanon, M., and Sastre, J. (1988). Hypothalamic regulation of paradoxical sleep. In *Neurogiology of Sleep-Wakefulness Cycle* (T. Onian, ed.), pp. 1–17. Georgian Academy of Sciences, Metsniereba, Tbilisi.
60. Heller, C. S., Glotzbach, S., Grahn, D., and Radehe, C. (1988). Sleep dependent changes in the thermo-regulatory system. In *Clinical Physiology of Sleep* (R. Lydic and J. F. Biebuyck, eds.), pp. 145–158. American Physiological Society, Bethesda, MD.
61. Parmeggiani, P. L. (1988). Thermoregulation during sleep from the viewpoint of homeostasis. In *Clinical Physiology of Sleep* (R. Lydic and J. F. Biebuyck, eds.), pp. 159–170. American Physiological Society, Bethesda, MD.
62. Phillipson, E. A. (1978). Control of breathing during sleep. *Am. Rev. Respir. Dis.* **118:** 909–939.
63. Hobson, J. A. (1982). *Sleep and Its Disorders*. pp. 1930–1935. Cecil Textbook of Medicine.
64. Kryger, M. H., Roth, T., and Dement, W. C., eds. (1994). *The Principles and Practice of Sleep Medicine*, 2nd ed. Saunders, Philadelphia.
65. Bennington, J., and Heller, H. C. (1995). Restoration of brain energy metabolism as the function of sleep. *Prog. Neurobiol.* **45:** 347–360.
66. Rechtschaffen, A., Bergmann, B. M., Everson, C. A., Kushida, C. A., and Gilliland, M. A. (1989). Sleep deprivation in the rat: I. Conceptual issues. *Sleep* **12:** 1–4.
67. Rechtschaffen, A., Bergmann, B. M., Everson, C. A., Kushida, C. A., and Gilliland, M. A. (1989). Sleep deprivation in the rat: X. Integration and discussion of the findings. *Sleep* **12:** 68–87.
68. Pappenheimer, J. R., Koski, G., Fenci, V., Karnovsky, M. L., and Krueger, J. (1975). Extraction of sleep-promoting factor S from cerebrospinal fluid and from brain of sleep-deprived animals. *J. Neurophysiol.* **38:** 1299–1311.
69. Roffwarg, J. P., Muzio, J. M., and Dement, W. C. (1966). Ontogenetic development of the human sleep-dream cycle. *Science* **152:** 604–619.
70. Fishbein, W. C., Kastaniotis, C., and Chattman, D. (1974). Paradoxical sleep: Prolonged augmentation following learning. *Brain Res.* **79:** 61–77.
71. Smith, C., Kitahama, K., Valatx, J. L., and Jouvet, M. (1974). Increased paradoxical sleep in mice during acquisition of a shock avoidance task. *Brain Res.* **77:** 221–230.
72. Smith, C., Young, J., and Young, W. (1980). Prolonged increases in paradoxical sleep during and after avoidance-task acquisition. *Sleep* **3**(1): 67–81.
73. Karni, A., Tanne, D., Rubenstein, B. S., Askenasy, J. J. M., and Sagi, D. (1994). Dependence on REM sleep of overnight improvement of a perceptual skill. *Science* **265:** 679–682.
74. Pavlides, C., and Winson, J. (1989). Influences of hippocampal place cell firing in the awake state on the activity of these cells during subsequent sleep episodes. *J. Neurosci.* **9:** 2907–2918.

CHAPTER

47

Psychosexual Development

Michael J. Baum

Behaviors can be placed, simplistically, into two categories: those promoting survival of the individual and those ensuring survival of the species. The latter behaviors include selecting and courting mates, mating per se, and rearing offspring. The neurobiology of mammalian psychosexual development, which promotes survival of the species, encompasses sex differences in numerous facets of social behavior and neuroendocrine function.

Functions in which male and female animals differ but overlap are referred to as **sexually allomorphic traits.** For example, female mammals typically are more responsive than males to newborn offspring, whereas males are more likely to establish and defend a home territory. These differences in parental responsiveness and territoriality, however, are not discontinuous between males and females. Hence, they are called sexually allomorphic traits.[1] The motivation of male and female mammals to seek out, mate with, and, in many cases, stay with a partner in a heterosexual pair bond (and display parenting behavior) is also sexually allomorphic. In contrast, traits for which the sexes do not overlap are referred to as **sexually dimorphic.** For example, in many rodent species females show a preovulatory surge in pituitary secretion of luteinizing hormone (LH) in response to ovarian steroids, but no such effect occurs in males (see Chapter 44).[2]

The existence of sexually allomorphic and dimorphic behavioral and neuroendocrine traits reflects sex differences in the structure and function of the nervous system. In the 1940s and 1950s William Young, Frank Beach, Geoffrey Harris, and their students initiated this field of study. These workers showed that **testosterone** of testicular origin acts in the male mammal during critical, species-specific perinatal periods to organize male-typical patterns of psychosexual and neuroendocrine function. Sex steroids activate species-specific reproductive behaviors that differ depending on sex. Evidence for hormone-dependent sex differences in reproductive behaviors of rats led to the hypothesis that rats must also have steroid-dependent sexual allomorphisms in hypothalamic morphology.[3,4] Indeed, investigators found clear instances of sexually allomorphic brain structure. A different but equally important discovery linked the sexually allomorphic singing behavior of canaries and zebra finches to sexual dimorphism in the size of different nuclei of the telencephalic song-control circuit.[5]

In this chapter we focus on mammalian models that illustrate the developmental effects of sex steroids, acting perinatally in the males, to establish sexually allomorphic or dimorphic patterns of psychosexual function. In some instances, the effects of perinatal steroid hormone exposure on male-typical behavior have been linked to long-term, steroid-dependent changes in male brain morphology.

EXPRESSION OF THE SRY GENE

In female mammals, the default pattern of development of indifferent gonads results in differentiation of ovaries. During perinatal life the ovaries remain functionally quiescent, while the primordial Müllerian ducts develop into oviducts, uterus, and upper vagina. In females external genitals also differentiate without an endocrine stimulus. At puberty, ovarian secretions of **estradiol,** produced in granulosa cells via aromatization of testosterone from thecal cells, and **progesterone,** produced by thecal cells, establish adult female neuroendocrine function.

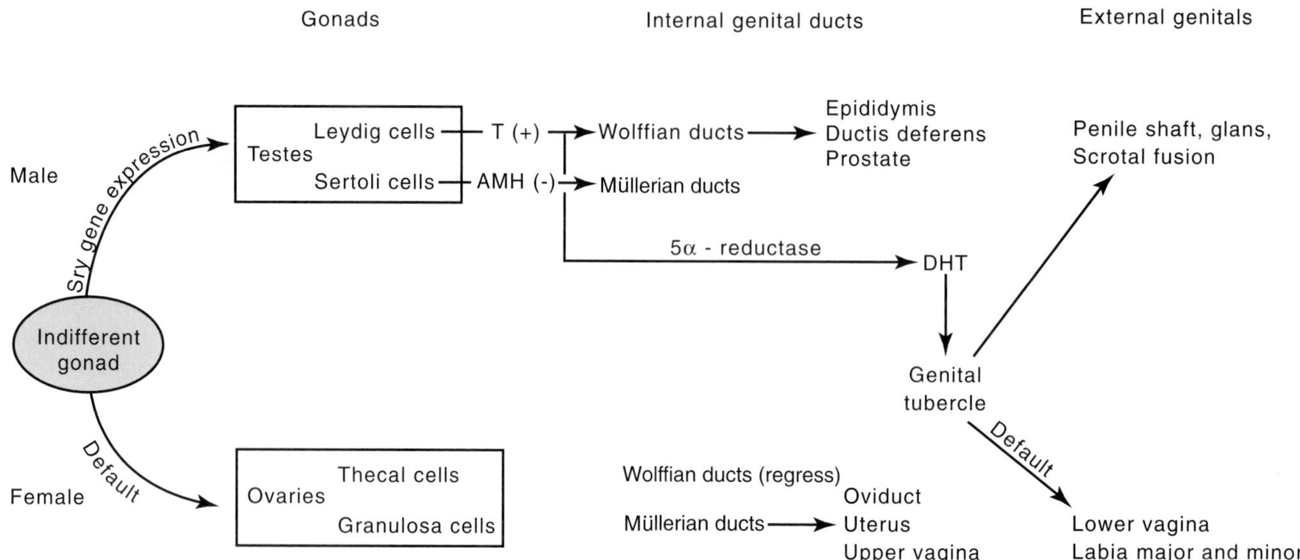

FIGURE 47.1 Genetic and endocrine factors controlling gonadal differentiation and genital development in male and female mammals. T, testosterone; DHT, dihydrotestosterone; AMH, anti-Müllerian hormone; +, activates; −, inhibits.

The fundamental event of male sexual differentiation is expression of the **SRY gene,** whose protein product, **testis-determining factor,** promotes differentiation of testes in fetal males[6] (Fig. 47.1). Leydig cells of the testes produce testosterone, which promotes growth and development of the primordial Wolffian ducts into the epididymis, vas deferens, and prostate.[7] In the external genital tubercle, 5α-reductase converts testosterone into **5α-dihydrotestosterone** (DHT), which is required for differentiation of the penis and scrotum.[8] At the same time, testicular Sertolic cells produce a peptide hormone, **anti-Müllerian duct hormone** (AMH), that promotes regression of the Müllerian ducts, precluding further differentiation of female-type internal genital structures.[9]

Hundreds of experiments suggest that testosterone and its neural metabolite estradiol organize various aspects of male psychosexual potential. In addition, experiments have shown that testosterone and estradiol act perinatally to affect the morphology of the developing male nervous system. SRY gene expression, which occurs perinatally in the brain and testes, may also act directly to promote neuronal sexual differentiation in males.[10] This is a minority view, however, as most, if not all, aspects of differentiation of masculine brain and behavior in mammals can be accounted for by the actions of testosterone or estradiol in the developing male nervous system.

Interim Summary

The Y chromosome of male mammals carries the SRY gene. When expressed, its protein product, testis-determining factor, promotes differentiation of the indifferent gonad into testes. Testes in turn produce testosterone, which directly and indirectly (through DHT) promotes development of male genitalia. AMH, also produced by the testes, halts development of female reproductive structures. Female mammals do not have an SRY gene; thus, their indifferent gonads develop into ovaries. Without AMH, female reproductive structures develop, and because of the absence of testosterone, no male structures develop.

SEX HORMONES

The Testicular Hormone Testosterone Acts Perinatally to Defeminize Psychosexual Function in Males

The default developmental program in mammals produces female sexual behavior. In rodents, such as rat and guinea pig, the female's response to a male's mount is a rigid, immobile stance with an arched back (lordosis). Numerous experiments show that activation of this reflex in female rodents depends at least in part on the sequential actions of estradiol and progesterone in the ventromedial nucleus of the hypothalamus (VMH) over the 2 days leading up to the preovulatory surge in pituitary LH secretion.[11–14] First, estradiol secreted by the ovaries is bound by estrogen receptors in the nuclei of neurons in the ventrolateral subdivision of the VMH. This estradiol–receptor complex promotes transcription of several genes, one of which encodes the progesterone receptor. Within 24 h the quantity of progesterone receptor protein rises dramatically in VMH neurons. When plasma concentrations of progesterone rise just prior to ovulation, progesterone receptors in VMH neurons bind the hormone. The female becomes very active, seeks out male conspecifics, and displays lordosis reflexes when mounted during a 10-h period around the time of ovulation. This effect of steroid hormones on behavior ensures transmission of sperm and induction of endocrine events (e.g., continuous ovarian production of progesterone) needed to initiate and sustain pregnancy.[15]

Researchers[16] have shown that adult guinea pigs will exhibit lordosis in response to manual palpation of the flanks by an investigator. In one experiment, after removal of their gonads and injections of estradiol benzoate, followed 36–48 h later by progesterone, female and male guinea pigs showed different lordosis behavior (Fig. 47.2). The response of female lordotic behavior to ovarian hormones was reduced by exposure to testosterone *in utero*. When pregnant females were injected with testosterone propionate (TP) beginning on gestational day 10 and continuing intermittently until gestational day 68 (just prior to birth), the effect on lordosis behavior of female offspring was dose-dependent: Slight reductions in the frequency of lordosis occurred in females receiving a TP dose insufficient to masculinize the external genital organs, and a greater reduction in the frequency of lordotic behavior occurred after higher doses of TP, which masculinized the external genitals. This experiment has been repeated with several mammalian species, including rat, mouse, hamster, gerbil, and dog,[17] and receptive female responses have been found to vary with species. For example, in the ferret, the female's receptive response is passive acceptance of the male's neck grip (see Fig. 47.3). In rhesus monkeys, the receptive response to a male is immobile posture. In these species perinatal exposure to testosterone does not reduce female receptive responses. However, perinatal testosterone reduces the motivation of adult female ferrets and monkeys primed with ovarian hormones to seek out male conspecifics.[18,19] Thus, in all mammalian species studied, perinatal administration of testosterone—shown to act via its neural metabolism to estradiol—decreases some aspect of female psychosexual function. In males, this process of psychosexual defeminization occurs naturally in response to perinatal secretion of testosterone by the testes (Box 47.1).

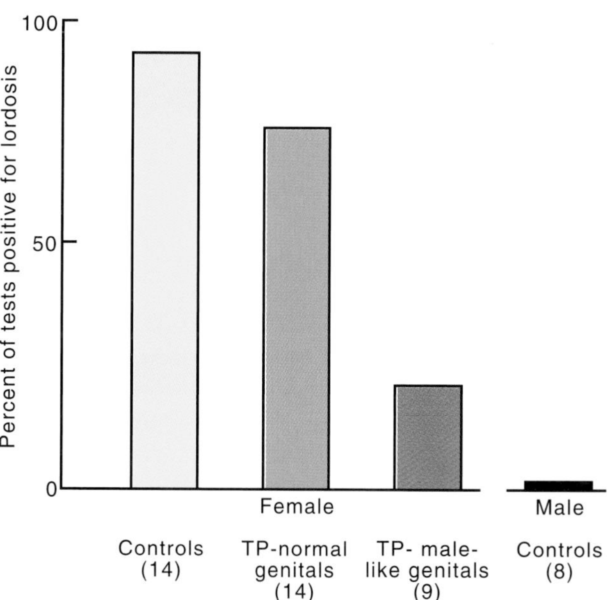

FIGURE 47.2 Prenatal exposure to testosterone propionate (TP) decreases lordosis behavior in female guinea pigs. Lordosis behavior, elicited by manual palpation of the flanks, was studied in female guinea pigs that had been exposed *in utero* to TP administered to their pregnant mothers. The mothers of male and female control subjects received no treatment during gestation. Gonads were removed from all animals during adulthood. Animals were injected with estradiol benzoate followed 36 h later by progesterone and then given behavioral tests hourly over the next 12 h. Adapted from Phoenix *et al.*[16]

Perinatal Exposure to Testosterone Masculinizes Sexual Behavior and Sexual Partner Preference

Perinatal exposure of mammals to testosterone promotes differentiation of species-typical patterns of male sexual behavior (e.g., neck grip of the male ferret; see Fig. 47.3). When female guinea pigs are exposed *in utero* to enough TP to masculinize external genitalia, after ovariectomy they display significantly more mounting behavior than do control females in tests with estrous females.[16] Results from several species, including rat, ferret, and rhesus monkey,[20–22] suggest that full masculinization of sexual behavior and partner preference requires an extended period of exposure to testosterone. Testosterone is required during fetal life. It is also required immediately after birth, when testicular output of testosterone surges dramatically, and over several postnatal weeks (rat and ferret) or months (rhesus monkey), when the testes continue to secrete testosterone prior to becoming quiescent during an extended prepubertal period.

In ferrets, masculinization of partner preference by testosterone is completed about 3 weeks after birth. In one experiment, females were exposed to testosterone (or vehicle control) *in utero* (embryonic days 27–39 of a 41-day gestation), within minutes after birth, or both

FIGURE 47.3 Mating in the ferret. A male neck-grips and mounts an estrous female, in which a receptive response includes passivity and tail deviation.

in utero and immediately after birth. All females received testosterone between postnatal days 5 and 20 and were ovariectomized on postnatal day 20. As a control, a group of males was exposed to vehicle prior to castration on postnatal day 20. When subjects reached adulthood, they were injected daily with estradiol benzoate and tested daily in a T-maze, in which they could choose to approach either an estrous female or a sexually active male. As shown in Fig. 47.4, females exposed only to vehicle prenatally and at birth and females exposed to testosterone at birth and neonatally preferred to approach and interact with a sexually active male. In contrast, males given vehicle perinatally preferred to approach and interact with an estrous female. Females that received testosterone over a prolonged perinatal period, beginning embryonic day 27 and ending on postnatal day 20, approach an estrous female, showing a male-typical preference.

Two explanations have been offered for masculinizing and defeminizing effects of prenatal testosterone on sexual behavior of female guinea pigs. Phoenix *et al.*[16] attributed the effect changes in the neural tissues that control these behaviors. In contrast, workers led by Frank Beach[23] argued that the effects of perinatal testosterone on behavior resulted from the masculinizing effect of this androgen on external genital organs, as opposed to the developing nervous system. The overlap in the perinatal actions of testosterone in masculinizing genital development and sexual behavior supported Beach's view. Most contemporary researchers in this field agree, however, that organizational effects of testosterone on psychosexual development cannot be attributed solely to the actions of this androgen on genitals. There are examples of dissociation in the timing of masculinization of external genitals and of sexual behavior. Castration of male ferrets on postnatal day 5 reduced their adult male-typical behavior when they were given TP and tested with estrous females. Development of the external genitals had already been completed by the time these males were

BOX 47.1

SEXUAL DIFFERENTIATION OF MATING, PAIR BONDING, AND SONG IN BIRDS

In mammals the female is the homogametic (XX) sex. Most aspects of female genital and CNS development are generally thought to occur perinatally without an active endocrine stimulus, although a minority view[62] holds that estradiol contributes actively to differentiation of aspects of neural development in females. In avian species the male is the homogametic sex (ZZ), and, as in the case of female mammals, evidence suggests that many aspects of psychosexual differentiation occur without an endocrine stimulus. In female quail the capacity to display mounting behavior with a receptive female conspecific is normally eliminated (feminized) by the prehatching action of estradiol, presumably of ovarian origin.[63] When given estradiol as adults, male quail readily mount receptive females and display receptive responses to mounts by other males. Administration of estradiol to quail prior to hatching or to zebra finches after hatching[64] feminizes mounting capacity in males, whereas administration of an aromatase inhibitor to female quail prior to hatching enhances their later mounting behavior.[65] These results are predicted by analogy to the mammalian situation, in which psychosexual differentiation occurs in the homogametic sex (i.e., females) without an active perinatal steroid signal.

An additional body of literature suggests that in male birds (which are homogametic), as in male mammals (which are heterogametic), estradiol acts shortly before or after hatching to organize male-typical patterns of mate choice (including pair bonding) and courtship song. Thus, in zebra finches administration of estradiol (but not testosterone or DHT) to females in the weeks after hatching permanently enhances their potential to learn and perform courtship song.[66] Females treated with estradiol early in life also are much more likely than normal females to form long-lasting pair bonds with other (stimulus) females.[64] The effects of early estradiol treatment on singing behavior in female zebra finches correlated with an increase in the number of neurons in several parts of the telencephalic circuit that controls song learning and production.[5,66]

Several puzzling questions remain, however, about the normal role of estradiol in the development of neural mechanisms controlling singing and pair bonding in male song birds.[67,68] In the case of the song-control system, it has been difficult to duplicate the male phenotype (e.g., number of neurons in song-control nuclei) by administering estradiol to females after they have hatched. Even more puzzling is the inability of blockers of estrogen or aromatase to interfere with song-system development in male zebra finches.[69,70] Likewise, such drugs failed to disrupt development of female-oriented pair bonding in male finches. Considerable uncertainty exists about the perinatal role of sex steroids in sexual differentiation of brain mechanisms controlling song and pair-bonding in male birds.

castrated; thus, this behavioral outcome is not easily attributed to removal of testosterone during development of male genitals.[24] Estrogenic metabolites of testosterone also have been implicated in many of the masculinizing and defeminizing actions of perinatal exposure to testosterone (see following). Estrogens normally play no role in male genital development. Instead, their contribution to male psychosexual differentiation likely reflects their action in the developing male nervous system.

Estradiol Formed Perinatally in the Brain Mediates Many of the Effects of Testosterone on Male Psychosexual Differentiation

Testosterone is the principal steroid secreted by mammalian testes during development and in adulthood. Testosterone is metabolized by **aromatase** into estradiol and by **5α-reductase** into DHT (Fig. 47.5) in a variety of tissues, including the brain. Studies of species representing almost every vertebrate class show that aromatase is present in subcortical brain, including the preoptic region, bed nuclei of the stria terminalis (BST), and medial amygdala.[25–27] Circulating testosterone readily passes into the extracellular space of the brain and then into neurons in these regions of the brain, where the hormone binds to aromatase and is converted to estradiol.

In mammals, high levels of neuronal aromatase activity occur perinatally in medial terencephalic ("limbic") and hypothalamic regions at the time of psychosexual and brain sexual differentiation. The activity of this enzyme is reduced 10-fold in adulthood. Neurons in these brain regions expressing aromatase also express androgen receptors (which bind testosterone or DHT) and estrogen receptors (which bind estradiol)

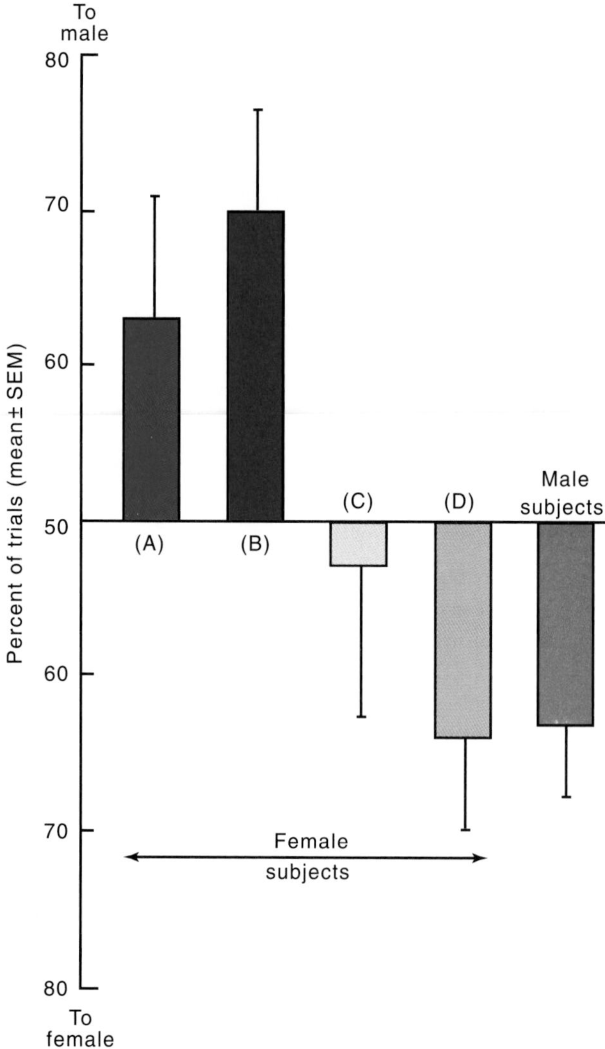

FIGURE 47.4 Prolonged prenatal and neonatal administration of testosterone (T) masculinizes sexual partner preference in female ferrets. Groups of female ferrets were treated with vehicle prenatally and within minutes after birth (A), with vehicle prenatally followed by T within minutes after birth (B), with T prenatally followed by vehicle within minutes after birth (C), and with T prenatally and within minutes after birth (D). The ovaries of all female subjects were removed on postnatal day 5, and the animals were treated with T between postnatal days 5 and 20. Male subjects received vehicle prenatally and within minutes after birth; they were castrated on postnatal day 20. In adulthood all subjects were treated with estradiol benzoate and tested in a T-maze for their preference to approach and interact with an estrous female (To female) versus a stud male (To male). Adapted from Baum *et al.*[4]

perinatally, when circulating testosterone masculinizes psychosexual function. The estradiol formed intraneuronally binds estrogen receptors in the same neurons where the estradiol was produced or, via a paracrine action, in adjacent neurons.

Several aspects of male psychosexual differentiation depend in part on the actions of estrogenic metabolites of circulating testosterone in the developing male nervous system. The earliest supportive studies[28,29] showed that neonatal administration of estradiol to female rats mimicked the defeminizing effects of neonatal testosterone treatment on lordosis. In addition, neonatal administration of either the synthetic steroid androstatrienedione (ATD), which blocks neural aromatase activity,[30,31] or antiestrogenic drugs[32] to male rats greatly enhanced the response of their later lordotic behavior to ovarian steroids. Also, neonatal infusion of antisense oligonucleotide to estrogen receptor mRNA (presumably decreasing synthesis of neuronal estrogen receptor for many hours) into the cerebral

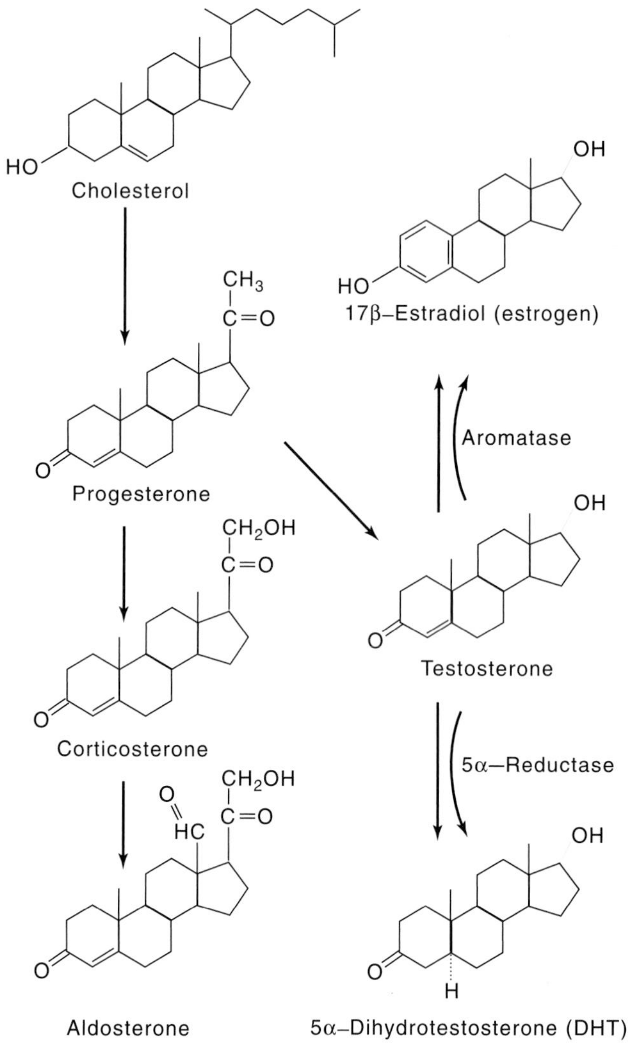

HO
Cholesterol
OH
HO
17β–Estradiol (estrogen)
CH_3
C=O
O
Progesterone
Aromatase
OH
CH_2OH
C=O
O
Testosterone
O
Corticosterone
5α–Reductase
CH_2OH
O
HC
C=O
OH
O
O
H
Aldosterone
5α–Dihydrotestosterone (DHT)

FIGURE 47.5 Synthesis and metabolism of steroid hormones. The number of arrows represents the number of enzymatic conversions between any two structures. Testosterone is synthesized from progesterone and, in turn, is metabolized in the fetal and adult nervous system into estradiol (through aromatization of the steroid A-ring) or dihydrotestosterone (DHT; through reduction of the steroid A-ring). DHT is also formed in the genital tubercle of male fetuses, where it promotes differentiation of external genital organs.

ventricles of female rats blocked the reduction in lordotic behavior otherwise induced by neonatal TP treatment.[33] These results suggest that estradiol, formed from circulating testosterone in the brain, is normally responsible for psychosexual defeminization of male rats.

Perinatal inhibition (with ATD) of the brain's production of estradiol also decreased male rats' later preference for approaching and mounting an estrous female (as opposed to another male) in an operant choice apparatus.[34] This finding suggests that estrogenic metabolites of testosterone contribute to development of male-typical partner preference in male rats. Evidence of a role for estradiol in controlling male coital function comes from the observation[35] that male mice in which estrogen receptor synthesis was disrupted by gene targeting[36] rarely ejaculated despite displaying mounting and intromission behaviors. A similar decrease in frequency of ejaculation was seen in male rats treated perinatally with ATD.[37]

In ferrets the effects of prenatal testosterone on coital performance require aromatization of the hormone.[38] Ovaries were removed from pregnant ferrets on gestational day 30, and progesterone capsules were implanted subcutaneously into the animals to maintain their pregnancies. Groups of females were given no additional treatment (control), were treated with the aromatase inhibitor ATD (gestational days 30–41), or were given ATD plus estradiol in an attempt to reverse the expected drug-induced inhibition of neural aromatase activity. Pups were delivered by caesarian section and raised by other lactating dams. Other pregnant females were treated with the androgen receptor antagonist flutamide, which disrupted external genital organ development in male offspring. Male pups were castrated on postnatal day 5 and later (at 5 months of age) injected daily with TP and tested for male-typical mating behavior. Male offspring of mothers that received ATD showed very low fetal hypothalamic aromatase activity and, as adults, displayed significantly less male-typical masculine mating behavior (neck gripping, see Fig. 47.3) than controls (Fig. 47.6). Prenatal androgen receptor blockade by flutamide did not reduce adult male mating behavior.

Concurrent administration of a low dose of estradiol failed to reverse the disruptive effect of fetal ATD exposure on male ferrets' mating behavior (Fig. 47.6). Administration of higher doses of estradiol to pregnant ferrets had toxic effects on the offspring (most died before or within a few days after birth). Despite this difficulty, one male survived into adulthood after prenatal exposure to ATD plus a high dose of estradiol. This male displayed a higher level of male-typical mating behavior than any other subject in this study. This observation suggests that the localized aromatization of circulating testosterone into estradiol in the nervous system of male fetuses has evolved as a mechanism for supplying specific populations of neurons (e.g., in the medial preoptic nucleus, bed nuclei of the stria terminalis, medial amygdala) with high concentrations of estradiol at critical periods of development without burdening the rest of the brain with high levels of

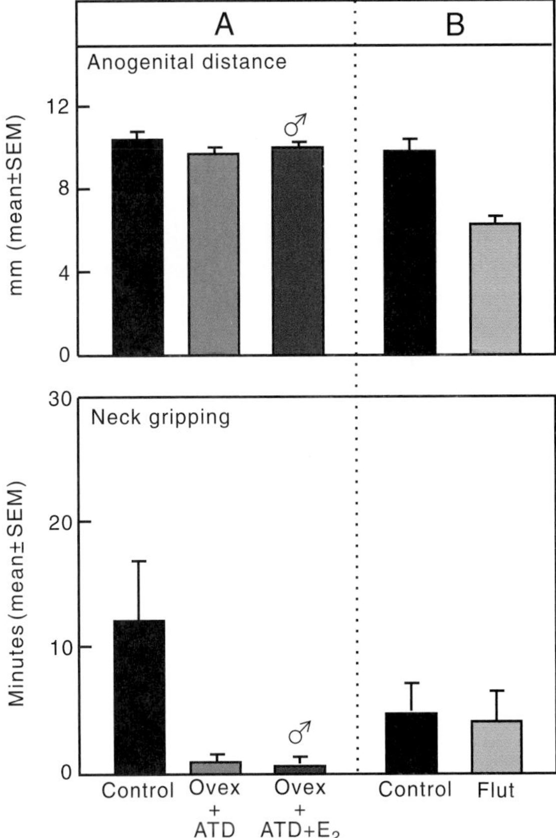

FIGURE 47.6 Prenatal blockage of estrogen biosynthesis in male ferrets reduces their later coital responsiveness. Masculine sexual behavior (neck gripping of an estrous female) was studied in males that were castrated on postnatal day 5 and tested in adulthood while receiving testosterone propionate. Each group of 6–7 males was deprived of estrogenic or androgenic stimulation on days 30–41 of gestation by treating their mothers as follows: (A) ovaries were removed and mothers were implanted with Silastic capsules containing the aromatase inhibitor androstatrienedione (ATD) or ATD and a low dosage of estradiol (E_2). Control mothers were sham-operated; all mothers received progesterone to maintain pregnancy. Males deprived of prenatal estrogenic stimulation displayed significantly less neck gripping behavior than controls. Administration of a low dose of estradiol concurrently with ATD did not reverse this deficit. A high dose of estradiol was generally fatal, but data are shown for one male (♂) that survived despite his mother receiving a high dose of estradiol and that showed more neck gripping than any other male subject. (B) Mothers were injected twice daily with the androgen receptor antagonist flutamide (Flut) or with vehicle (Control). Flutamide disrupted development of male external genitalia (reflected in shorter anogenital distances) but did not affect mating. Adapted from Tobet and Baum.[38]

estradiol. In some species (e.g., rat and mouse), the fetal liver produces a form of α-fetoprotein that binds estradiol with high affinity.[39] In these species this blood-borne estrogen-binding protein may further protect the developing female (and perhaps even males) from the potential masculinizing and defeminizing actions of circulating estradiol.[31] However, many mammalian species (including ferret and primates) lack significant levels of plasma estrogen-binding proteins during fetal development. In these species, males apparently rely solely on the regional localization of aromatase in the developing nervous system to avoid high circulating levels of estradiol and the potential for neural toxicity.[40]

Testosterone itself, acting through neural androgen receptors, also contributes to psychosexual differentiation in male ferrets. Neonatal administration of testosterone, but not estradiol or DHT, to female ferrets enhanced their neck gripping of an estrous female following removal of ovaries and treatment with testosterone in adulthood (Fig. 47.7).[41] In contrast to its prenatal effects (Fig. 47.6), the aromatase inhibitor ATD given neonatally caused no decrease in neck gripping in male ferrets (Fig. 47.7).[42] These results suggest that

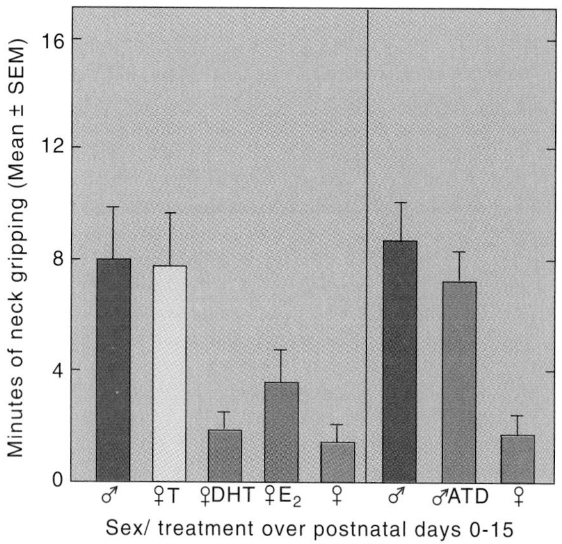

FIGURE 47.7 Testosterone itself acts neonatally in male ferrets to complete differentiation of male mating behavior. Male mating behavior (neck gripping of an estrous female) was studied in male and female ferrets that were gonadectomized in adulthood and implanted subcutaneously with Silastic capsules containing steroid hormone. Female subjects were implanted over postnatal days 0–15 with Silastic capsules containing testosterone (♀T), dihydrotestosterone (♀DHT), or estradiol (♀E_2). Only T significantly increased neck gripping behavior in females. Males received the aromatase inhibitor ATD over postnatal days 0–15 (♂ATD). No reduction in neck gripping was seen, suggesting that neonatal estrogenic metabolites of T make no contribution to differentiation of mating behavior in male ferrets. Adapted from Baum *et al.*[41,42]

testosterone itself acts neonatally in the male ferret to complete the process of psychosexual differentiation, initiated prenatally by estrogenic metabolites of testosterone (Box 47.2).

Summary

Without exposure to gonadal or external sources of testosterone, rodent brains will develop to express female sexual behavior and lordosis: a rigid immobile stance with arched back and tilted pelvis. If exposed to testosterone by embryonic day 10, male external genitalia will emerge with greatly decreased lordotic responses in genetic females. Prenatal exposure to testosterone in males promotes male sexual behaviors, including gender preference in partners. Castration after birth reduces typical male behavior patterns without changes in genitalia. Within the male brain, testosterone is converted to estradiol to regulate gender-specific sexual behavior, through the regionally selective expression of the steroid-converting enzyme aromatase.

THE VOMERONASAL (ACCESSORY) OLFACTORY PATHWAY

Nonvolatile molecules secreted by specialized epithelial glands in the urogenital tract and on the body's ventral surface provide signals between males and females of numerous rodents and carnivores. These pheromones serve a variety of social functions, including the attraction of conspecifics prior to mating, delineation of territories, and communication between mother and young. Pheromones are detected by receptors in the vomeronasal organ, whose axons project to the glomerulae of the accessory olfactory bulbs[43] (Fig. 47.8).[44] These projections are the first synapses in a system that then projects to the medial and cortical amygdalar nuclei and the bed nuclei of the stria terminalis which in turn project to the medial hypothalamus.

Structural allomorphisms in the vomeronasal pathway develop as a result of perinatal actions of estrogen in males. For example, male rats possess more vomeronasal receptors and neurons than females.[45] The most extensively studied portion of this circuit is located at one of its terminations, in the central part of the medial preoptic nucleus near the border with the anterior hypothalamus. This sexually dimorphic nucleus of the preoptic area–anterior hypothalamus (SDN) is three to four times larger in male than in female rats.[4] Sexual allomorphisms in morphology of the preoptic region have also been described in other mammalian species, including mouse, gerbil, and ferret.[46] Perinatal administration of TP or the synthetic estrogen diethylstilbes-

BOX 47.2

PSYCHOSEXUAL DIFFERENTIATION (GENDER IDENTITY AND SEXUAL ORIENTATION) IN HUMANS

Nature sometimes varies the exposure of human fetuses to sex hormones. The resultant clinical syndromes suggest that in humans, as in animals, psychosexual differentiation is organized by perinatal exposure to sex steroids. Two clinical syndromes provide parallels with animal studies showing that perinatal exposure to testosterone, which acts in part through neural conversion to estradiol, contributes to development of male-typical patterns of sex partner preference and coital behavior.

Congenital adrenal hyperplasia usually is caused by a mutation in the gene encoding 21-hydroxylase, the enzyme that catalyzes the conversion of progesterone to cortisol in the fetal adrenal cortex.[71] Lack of glucocorticoid and mineralocorticoid secretion leads to diagnosis soon after birth. These symptoms are treated with continuous administration of adrenal steroids. In addition to underproduction of glucocorticoids and mineralocorticoids, congenital adrenal hyperplasia involves overproduction of androgens, including testosterone, which in females causes varying degrees of genital virilization. In early childhood, many of these girls have surgical reconstruction of their external genitals and are assigned a female gender role. As adults, most of these women express satisfaction with their core sexual identity and report exclusively heterosexual choices of romantic partners. Still, when compared with women matched for age and experience, women with congenital adrenal hyperplasia more often reported homosexual or bisexual romantic experience or interest.[72–74]

Another clinical syndrome suggests that estrogenic metabolites of androgens may mediate some effects of fetal exposure to testosterone on sexual orientation. The synthetic estrogen diethylstilbestrol (DES) was prescribed to thousands of pregnant American women between 1947 and 1971 in the mistaken belief that it would reduce the incidence of spontaneous abortion. The psychosexual profile of young women exposed prenatally to DES is remarkably similar to that of women with congenital adrenal hyperplasia[75,76]: Core sexual identity is typically female, and although the majority report exclusively heterosexual orientation, significantly more of these women report homosexual or bisexual orientation than matched controls.

Testicular feminizing syndrome, caused by androgen insensitivity in genetic males, is another relevant clinical syndrome. The SRY gene is normally expressed in these individuals during fetal life, leading to the differentiation of testes. In this syndrome, the Tfm gene, which encodes the androgen receptor, is mutated. Thus, testosterone and DHT cause less or none of their usual somatic and CNS effects. As a result, despite normal fetal expression of SRY and subsequent differentiation of testes, boys with Tfm mutations have female-typical external genitalia and are assigned a female gender role at birth. Breasts develop at puberty in response to estrogens formed through peripheral aromatization of testosterone secreted by testes (which typically remain undescended in the body cavity). Typically, core sexual identity is female, and as adults genetic males with Tfm mutations are attracted sexually to men. Presumably, estradiol is normally synthesized from circulating testosterone in the developing nervous system of fetuses with Tfm mutations, and estrogen receptors are present in their brains. Yet male psychosexual differentiation does not occur.[77,78] Nevertheless, estradiol may play a role in male psychosexual differentiation. Perhaps like ferrets and monkeys (discussed earlier), humans require testosterone to act through androgen receptors in the nervous system shortly after birth to complete male psychosexual differentiation begun prenatally by the action of estrogens. Absence of functional androgen receptors in individuals with Tfm gene mutations would preclude this event, leaving the Tfm male able to assume a female core identity. Also, in the absence of functional androgen receptors, female external genitalia cannot be masculinized by exogenous testosterone. This female body image is incompatible with psychosexual functioning as a male and thus may contribute to the female core identity and sexual orientation that characterizes Tfm individuals. More study of nonhuman primate models is needed to assess contributions of androgen and estrogen to psychosexual differentiation and CNS development.

trol (DES) increased the volume of the SDN in female rats.[47] The effect of neonatal TP treatment on the size of the SDN in female rats was blocked by intracerebral infusion of antisense oligonucleotide to the estrogen receptor.[33] In ferrets, prenatal administration of testosterone to females stimulated differentiation of a male-typical nucleus (which normally is absent in females) in the dorsomedial preoptic region. In addition, prenatal exposure of males to the aromatase inhibitor ATD completely blocked differentiation of this sexually dimor-

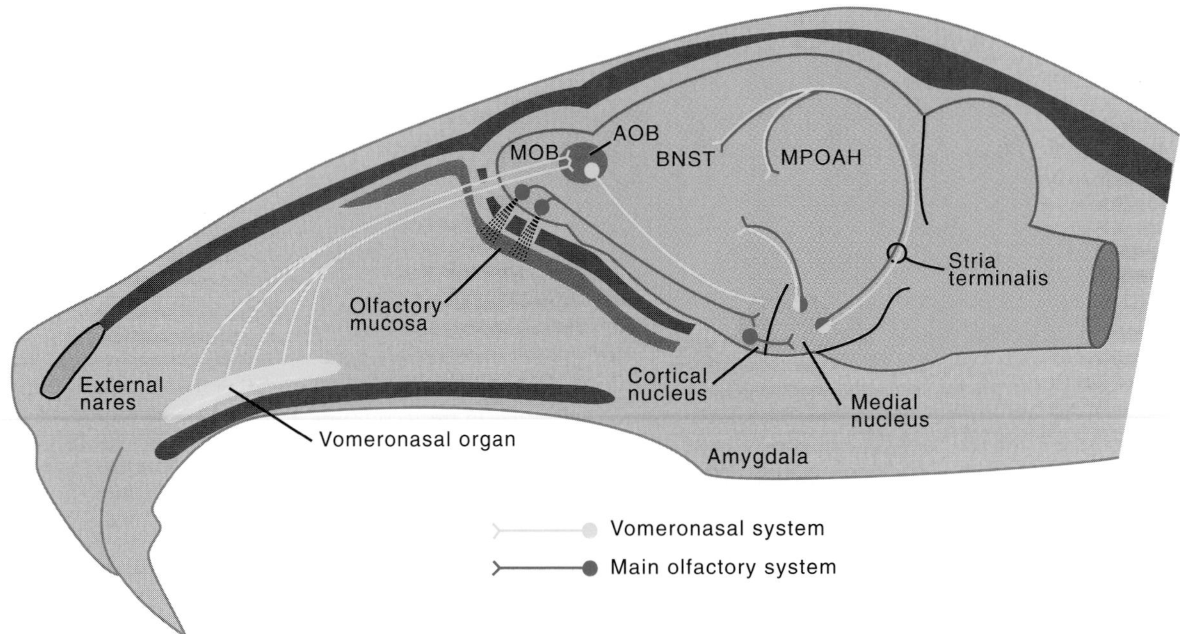

FIGURE 47.8 The main olfactory and accessory olfactory (vomeronasal) pathways that project to the medial hypothalamus (MHY) in rodents. MOB, main olfactory bulb; AOB, accessory olfactory bulb; BNST, bed nuclei of the stria terminalis; VP, ventral pathway from the medial amygdala to the BST and MHY. Adapted from Winans *et al.*[44] Drawing courtesy of Sarah Newman.

phic dorsomedial preoptic nucleus.[48,49] These data establish the critical perinatal role of estrogenic metabolites of testosterone, produced locally in the developing nervous system, in organizing male-typical structure and function in the preoptic region of the vomeronasal pathway. Other components of the vomeronasal pathway also require these estrogenic metabolites for male-typical development.

The Function of the Vomeronasal Pathway Is Sexually Allomorphic

The discovery of steroid-dependent sexual allomorphisms in psychosexual function led to the discovery of sex differences in the structure of the vomeronasal pathway. Likewise, the observation that in most species of song bird only the male sings preceded the discovery that telencephalic song-control nuclei are larger in males than in females.[5] Consistent, causal links between sexually allomorphic structures of the vomeronasal pathway and specific aspects of psychosexual function have been difficult to establish in mammals. One approach to this problem has been to monitor expression of immediate-early genes in neurons after exposure to relevant stimuli. For example, the protein product of the immediate-early gene *c-fos* can be visualized by immunocytochemistry. In neurons located throughout the vomeronasal pathway of male and female rats, the amount of cFos protein increased within 1 h after mating.[50–52] In contrast, sexually dimorphic expression of cFos protein was observed at different levels of this pathway in gonadectomized male and female rats that had been primed with estradiol and then exposed for 1 h to pheromones in bedding on which an adult male rat had urinated.[53] In more distal parts of the vomeronasal pathway (i.e., accessory olfactory bulb and medial amygdalar nucleus) of males and females, exposure to male bedding significantly increased the number of neurons containing cFos protein. This increase was also seen in males in which masculinization of this pathway had been attenuated by neonatal treatment with the aromatase blocker ATD. These observations suggest that males and females can detect pheromonal cues from male conspecifics. However, in more central parts of the vomeronasal pathway (e.g., bed nuclei of the stria terminalis and medial preoptic region) neuronal cFos protein increased only in females and in males treated neonatally with ATD (Fig. 47.9).

Thus, in females, and in males in which neonatal inhibition of estrogen biosynthesis had affected development of the vomeronasal pathway, pheromonal cues in urine-soiled bedding of male rats increased cFos in neurons throughout the vomeronasal pathway. However, in males this stimulus was detected and responded to by neurons in distal parts of the pathway

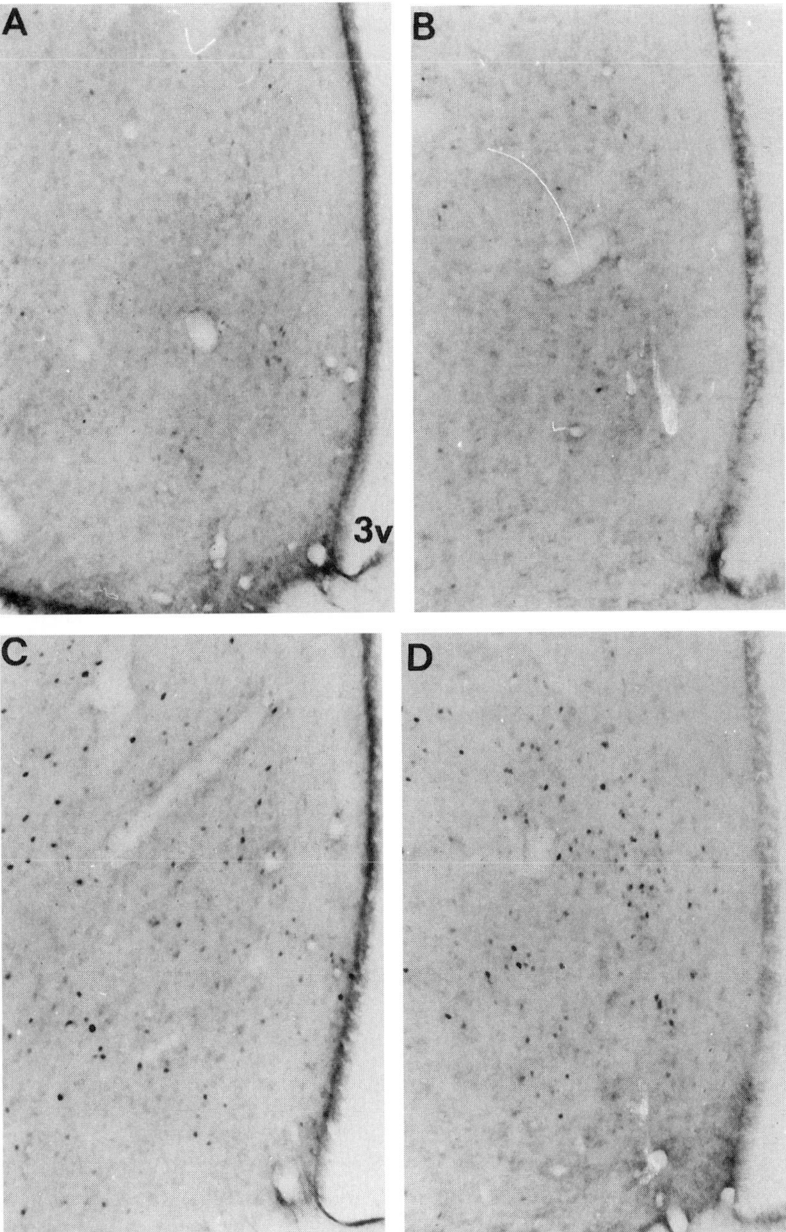

FIGURE 47.9 Immediate early genes are expressed in rat brain after exposure to phereomones. The protein product of the immediate early gene c-fos, cFos, can be detected using antibodies to the protein. Few cFos-immunoreactive neurons (black nuclei) were present in the medial preoptic area of (A) a male rat exposed to clean bedding for 1.5 h or (B) a male rat exposed to bedding soiled by another sexually active male. In contrast, exposure to bedding soiled by a male increased the number of cFos-immunoreactive neurons in (C) a male treated neonatally with the aromatase inhibitor ATD, and (D) a female. Thus, the response of medial preoptic neurons to pheromones produced by a sexually active male is higher in females than in males. This response to male pheromones is unusually high in males deprived neonatally of estrogen, suggesting that estogenic metabolites of circulating testosterone normally act neonatally to defeminize males. 3v, third ventricle. Adapted from Bakker *et al.*[9] Photo courtesy of Julie Bakker.

but not centrally in the bed nuclei or medial preoptic region. This sexual allomorphism in the response of neurons in central parts of the vomeronasal system correlates with the behavioral response of different groups of rats to stimuli derived from male conspecifics. Thus, when given free access to a sexually active male and an estrous female, estrogen-primed females, as well as males treated neonatally with ATD, preferred to approach and interact with the male stimulus, whereas normal male rats preferred the estrous female.[34] These data establish a correlation between sexual allomorphism in the response of neurons (reflected by increased cFos) in central parts of the vomeronasal system and rats' motivation to approach and interact with conspecifics of a particular sex.

Studies of ferrets[54] point to a similar relationship between sexual partner preference and sexually allomorphic function in the medial preoptic region. As shown in Fig. 47.4, when ferrets are gonadectomized and later treated with estradiol, they show a sexually allomorphic pattern of partner preference when allowed to choose between a sexually active male and an estrous female. In a separate experiment, medial preoptic neurons were destroyed in adult male ferrets by infusing the NMDA receptor agonist quinolinic acid. Males with bilateral lesions of the medial preoptic region were significantly more likely than sham-operated controls or males with unilateral or no detectible damage to the medial preoptic region (despite bilateral infusions of quinolinic acid) to approach and interact with a stud male (Fig. 47.10). That is, males with bilateral medial preoptic lesions more closely resembled females in their preference for a male conspecific. Bilateral excitotoxic lesions in the medial preoptic region of female ferrets did not disrupt their preference for male conspecifics. The lesions produced in these experiments were centered dorsally in the SDN. In males, the activation of these sexually dimorphic medial preoptic neurons may normally inhibit circuits that mediate the female-typical pattern of sexual partner preference (Box 47.3).

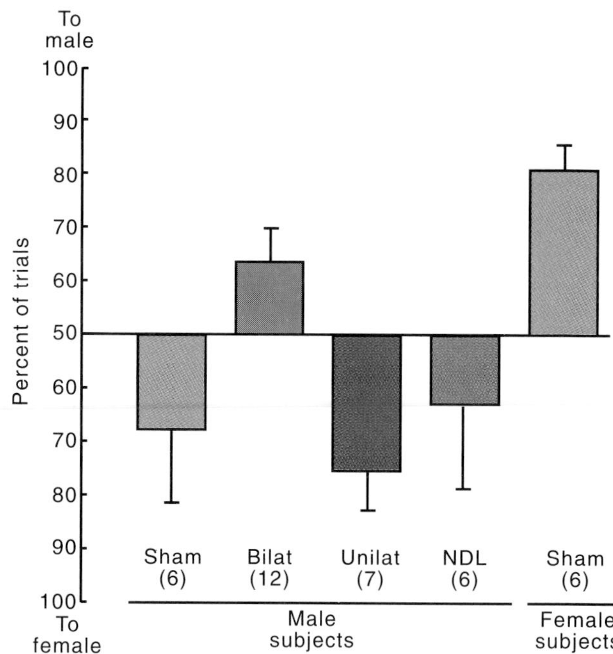

FIGURE 47.10 Bilateral excitotoxic lesions of the medial preoptic region caused male ferrets to prefer to approach and interact with a sexually active male (To male) instead of an estrous female (To female). After removal of their gonads, ferrets were treated with estradiol benzoate and given T-maze tests of sexual partner preference. Sham, bilateral infusions of saline into the dorsomedial preoptic region, Bilat and Unilat, histologically confirmed bilateral or unilateral excitotoxic lesions of the medial preoptic region; NDL, no detectable excitotoxic lesion despite bilateral infusion of quinolinic acid into the medial preoptic region. From Paredes and Baum.[54]

MATERNAL STIMULATION AND MALE PSYCHOSEXUAL DEVELOPMENT

Evidence already summarized establishes that neurons convert testosterone to estradiol, which acts on the fetal male nervous system to promote structural changes in the medial preoptic region and other parts of the vomeronasal system. These changes are probably caused by a combination of steroid actions and involve male-specific patterns of cell migration from proliferative zones lining the third and lateral ventricles, as well as changes in programmed cell death and specification of neuronal phenotypes.[55] Studies of rats, gerbils, and ferrets show that mothers provide more anogenital stimulation to male offspring than to female offspring in the first several postnatal weeks.[56–58] Such stimulation is critical in both sexes for development of urination and fecal elimination. In addition, anogenital stimulation provided by mothers to male offspring may finalize the development of brain mechanisms controlling aspects of male coital function.

Testosterone acts neonatally in male rats to promote the secretion of a preputial gland pheromone into the urine.[59] Mothers prefer ingesting urine containing this pheromone—thus leading them to provide more anogenital stimulation to male than to female pups. Mothers that were made anosmic shortly after delivering their young provided less anogenital licking to their offspring than control mothers.[60] When tested with estrous females as adults, the male offspring of anosmic mothers mounted more slowly and took more time to achieve ejaculation than control males. Such male rats

BOX 47.3

SEXUAL ALLOMORPHISMS IN HUMAN BRAIN STRUCTURE: CORRELATIONS BETWEEN SEXUAL ORIENTATION AND GENDER IDENTITY

Animal studies linking male psychosexual function to the integrity of medial preoptic neurons and neuronal inputs to them led several researchers to examine whether the human preoptic region also contains sexual allomorphisms. Despite considerable controversy about the number and nature of sex differences in the human brain,[46,79,80] there is some agreement about the existence of a series of nuclei (interstitial nuclei 1–4 of the anterior hypothalamus; INAH) in the human hypothalamus. One of these nuclei (INAH-3) appears to be larger in heterosexual men than women. LeVay[81] also reported that INAH-3 was significantly smaller (similar to that of heterosexual women) in homosexual men than in heterosexual men (Fig. 47.11).

This report generated considerable controversy because many of the homosexual subjects included in the study had died of AIDS; thus, their neuronal morphology might have been affected by HIV infection. Controversy also arose regarding the openly political agenda of the author, who seeks legal sanctioning of same-sex relationships. Another report[82] links core gender identity with the volume of a central region of the bed nuclei of the stria terminalis. In this study of the bed nuclei, volume shown with immunohistological staining for vasoactive intestinal polypeptide (VIP), was significantly greater in heterosexual men than in women. Furthermore, bed nuclei volume was significantly smaller (similar to women) in male to female transsexuals. These men had assumed female gender identity, usually with the aid of genital reconstructive surgery and estrogen therapy, at some point well prior to death and autopsy. Interestingly, bed nuclei volume was similar in hetero- and homosexual men whose gender identity was male.

Replication is critical to all scientific endeavors; however, replication is particularly difficult when postmortem human tissue is involved. Even if these studies were replicated, they could only correlate psychosexual orientation and sexually allomorphic morphology of the human hypothalamus. Imaging methods with high anatomic resolution will make it easier to rigorously address the question of how brain morphology and function differ between sexes and among people with different gender identities and sexual partner preferences.

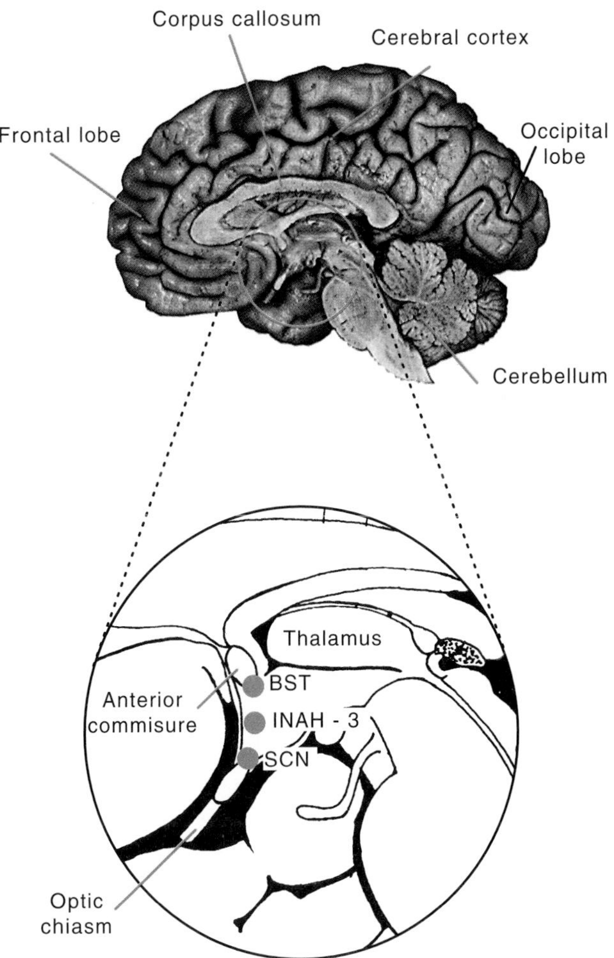

FIGURE 47.11 Brain structures for which published data suggest that volume is sexually allomorphic (e.g., anterior commissure, central region of the bed nuclei of the stria terminalis (BST), and third interstitial nucleus of the anterior hypothalamus (INAH-3)), differs in heterosexual versus homosexual men (anterior commissure, INAH-3, suprachiasmatic nucleus (SCN)), or differs in men with male versus female gender identities (BST).

also had significantly fewer lumbar spinal motor neurons innervating the striated bulbocavernosus muscles of the penis (SNB neurons). Other research[61] suggests that perinatal exposure to testosterone, acting via androgen receptors in the striated bulbocavernosus muscles, promotes survival of these motor neurons, whereas these motor neurons die in females because they have no testosterone. The results of Moore and co-workers suggest that at least some of the actions of testosterone on the developing male SNB neurons are indirect and reflect the large amount of anogenital stimulation received by males.[60] Naturally occurring variations in the number of sexually allomorphic SNB neurons in male rats may reflect variation in the neonatal secretion of testosterone by the testes and in the amount of anogenital stimulation given by the dam.

Summary

In response to pheromone produced by male neonates, mother rats provide more anogenital stimulation to male than female pups. Such stimulation appears necessary for testosterone to fully promote survival of SNB neurons and development of male sexual function.

In male mammals fetal expression of the SRY gene causes differentiation of the testes, which produce several hormones, including testosterone. Acting via androgen receptors, testosterone stimulates growth of the internal Wolffian ducts, and its primary androgenic metabolite, DHT, masculinizes external genitalia. Testosterone and estradiol, produced in the developing nervous system through aromatization of circulating testosterone, contribute to psychosexual differentiation of male mammals. Female psychosexual development generally occurs without neural action of sex steroids, although in some species females are typically exposed to substantial levels of perinatal testosterone. Behavioral experiments using a variety of animals show that testosterone and estradiol act during critical, species-specific, perinatal periods to organize male-typical features of psychosexual function. One effect is to decrease receptive or proceptive sexual behavior, usually displayed by females in response to ovarian steroid hormones. Another is to masculinize motivational (partner preference) and coital (mounting, ejaculation) components of psychosexual function.

Early experiments inspired neuroscientists to search for steroid-dependent sexual allomorphisms in brain structure that might account for hormone-dependent sexual allomorphisms in psychosexual function. Although many details remain unexplained, data specify hormone-dependent sexual allomorphisms in several subcortical regions of the brain implicated in reproductive function. In rodents these regions include numerous nuclei of the vomeronasal projection system to the medial hypothalamus, which processes socially relevant pheromonal cues.

References

General

Balthazart, J., and Ball, G. F. (1995). Sexual differentiation of brain and behavior in birds. *Trends Endocrinol. Metab.* **6:** 21–29.

Baum, M. J., Carroll, R. S., Cherry, J. A., and Tobet, S. A. (1990). Steroidal control of behavioral, neuroendocrine and brain sexual differentiation: Studies in a carnivore, the ferret. *J. Neuroendocrinol.* **2:** 401–418.

Collaer, M. L., and Hines, M. (1995). Human behavioral sex differences: A role for gonadal hormones during early development? *Psychol. Bull.* **118:** 55–107.

Gerall, A. A., Moltz, H., and Ward, I. L., eds. (1992). *Sexual Differentiation: Handbook of Behavioral Neurobiology*, Vol. 11. Plenum, New York.

Goy, R. W., and McEwen, B. S. (1980). *Sexual Differentiation of the Brain.* MIT Press, Cambridge, MA.

Meisel, R. L., and Sachs, B. D. (1994). The physiology of male sexual behavior. In *The Physiology of Reproduction* (E. Knobil and J. D. Neill, eds.), 2nd ed., pp. 3–105. Raven Press, New York.

Ulibarri, C., and Yahr, P. (1996). Effects of androgens and estrogens on sexual differentiation of sex behavior, scent marking and the sexually dimorphic area of the gerbil hypothalamus. *Horm. Behav.* **30:** 107–130.

Cited

1. Fox, T. O., Tobet, S. A., and Baum, M. J. (1997). Sex differences in human brain and behavior. In *Encyclopedia of Neuroscience* (G. Adelman and B. Smith, eds.). Elsevier, Amsterdam.
2. Neill, J. D. (1972). Sexual differences in the hypothalamic regulation of prolactin secretion. *Endocrinology* (*Baltimore*) **90:** 1154–1159.
3. Raisman, G., and Field, P. M. (1971). Sexual dimorphism in the preoptic area of the rat. *Science* **173:** 731–733.
4. Gorski, R. A., Gordon, J. H., Shryne, J. E., and Southam, A. M. (1978). Evidence for a morphological sex difference within the medial preoptic area of the rat brain. *Brain Res.* **148:** 333–346.
5. Nottebohm, F., and Arnold, A. P. (1976). Sexual dimorphism in vocal control areas of the songbird brain. *Science* **194:** 211–213.
6. Koopman, P., Gubbay, J., Vivian, N., Goodfellow, P., and Lovell-Badge, R. (1991). Male development of chromosomally female mice transgenic for Sry. *Nature* (*London*) **351:** 117–121.
7. Jost, A., Vigier, B., Prepin, J., and Perchellet, J. P. (1973). Studies on sex differentiation in mammals. *Recent Prog. Horm. Res.* **29:** 1–41.
8. Wilson, J. D., Griffin, J. E., and Russell, D. W. (1993). Steroid 5a-reductase 2 deficiency. *Endocr. Rev.* **14:** 577–593.
9. Lee, M. M., and Donahoe, P. K. (1993). Mullerian inhibiting substance: A gonadal hormone with multiple functions. *Endocr. Rev.* **14:** 152–164.
10. Pilgrim, C., and Hutchison, J. B. (1994). Developmental regulation of sex differences in the brain: Can the role of gonadal steroids be redefined? *Neuroscience* **60:** 843–855.

11. Pfaff, D. W. (1980). *Estrogens and Brain Function.* Springer-Verlag, New York.
12. Parsons, B., MacLusky, N. J., Krey, L., Pfaff, D. W., and McEwen, B. S. (1980). The temporal relationship between estrogen-inducible progestin receptors in the female rat brain and the time course of estrogen activation of mating behavior. *Endocrinology (Baltimore)* **107:** 774–779.
13. Rubin, B. S., and Barfield, R. J. (1980). Priming estrous responsiveness by implants of 17B-estradiol in the ventromedial hypothalamic nucleus of female rats. *Endocrinology (Baltimore)* **106:** 504–509.
14. Mani, S. K., Blaustein, J. D., Allen, J. M. C., Law, S. W., O'Malley, B. W., and Clark, J. H. (1994). Inhibition of rat sexual behavior by antisense oligonucleotides to the progesterone receptor. *Endocrinology (Baltimore)* **135:** 1409–1414.
15. Erskine, M. S. (1995). Prolactin release after mating and genitosensory stimulation in females. *Endocr. Rev.* **16:** 508–528.
16. Phoenix, C. H., Goy, R. W., Gerall, A. A., and Young, W. C. (1959). Organizing actions of prenatally administered testosterone propionate on the tissues mediating mating behavior in the female guinea pig. *Endocrinology (Baltimore)* **65:** 369–382.
17. Baum, M. J. (1979). Differentiation of coital behavior in mammals: A comparative analysis. *Neurosci. Biobehav. Rev.* **3:** 265–284.
18. Baum, M. J., Stockman, E. R., and Lundell, L. A. (1985). Evidence of proceptive without receptive defeminization. *Behav. Neurosci.* **99:** 742–750.
19. Pomerantz, S. M., Roy, M. M., Thornton, J. E., and Goy, R. W. (1985). Expression of adult female patterns of sexual behavior by male, female, and pseudohermaphroditic female rhesus monkeys. *Biol. Reprod.* **33:** 878–889.
20. Hoepfner, B. A., and Ward, I. L. (1988). Prenatal and neonatal androgen exposure interact to affect sexual differentiation in female rats. *Behav. Neurosci.* **102:** 61–65.
21. Baum, M. J., Erskine, M. S., Kornberg, E., and Weaver, C. E. (1990). Prenatal and neonatal testosterone exposure interact to affect differentiation of sexual behavior and partner preference in female ferrets. *Behav. Neurosci.* **10:** 183–198.
22. Wallen, K., Maestripieri, D., and Mann, D. R. (1995). Effects of neonatal testicular suppression with GnRH antagonist on social behavior in group-living juvenile rhesus monkeys. *Horm. Behav.* **29:** 322–337.
23. Beach, F. A. (1971). Hormonal factors controlling the differentiation, development, and display of copulatory behavior in the ramstergig and related species. In *The Biopsychology of Development* (E. Tobach, L. R. Aronson, and E. Shaw, eds.), pp. 249–296. Academic Press, New York.
24. Baum, M. J., and Erskine, M. S. (1984). Effect of neonatal gonadectomy and administration of testosterone on coital masculinization in the ferret. *Endocrinology (Baltimore)* **115:** 2440–2444.
25. Naftolin, F., Ryan, K. J., Davies, I. J., Reddy, V. V., Flores, F., Petro, Z., Kuhn, M., White, R. J., Takoaka, Y., and Wolin, L. (1975). The formation of estrogens by central neuroendocrine tissues. *Recent Prog. Horm. Res.* **31:** 295–315.
26. Roselli, C. E., and Resko, J. A. (1986). Effects of gonadectomy and androgen treatment on aromatase activity in the fetal monkey brain. *Biol. Reprod.* **35:** 106–112.
27. Weaver, C. E., and Baum, M. J. (1991). Differential regulation of brain aromatase by androgen in adult and fetal ferrets. *Endocrinology (Baltimore)* **128:** 1247–1254.
28. Whalen, R. E., and Nadler, R. D. (1963). Suppression of the development of female mating behavior by estrogen administered in infancy. *Science* **141:** 273–274.
29. Levine, S., and Mullins, Jr. (1964). Estrogen administered neonatally affects adult sexual behavior in male and female rats. *Science* **144:** 185–187.
30. Vreeburg, J. T. M., van der Vaart, P., and van der Schoot, P. (1977). Prevention of central defeminization but not masculinization in male rats by inhibition neonatally of oestrogen biosynthesis. *J. Endocrinol.* **74:** 375–382.
31. McEwen, B. S., Lieberburg, I., Chaptal, C., and Krey, L. C. (1977). Aromatization: Important for sexual differentiation of the neonatal rat brain. *Horm. Behav.* **9:** 249–263.
32. Sodersten, P. (1978). Effects of anti-oestrogen treatment of neonatal rats on lordosis behaviour and mounting behaviour in the adult. *J. Endocrinol.* **76:** 241–249.
33. McCarthy, M. M., Schlenker, E. H., and Pfaff, D. W. (1993). Enduring consequences of neonatal treatment with antisense oligodeoxynucleotides to estrogen receptor messenger ribonucleic acid on sexual differentiation of rat brain. *Endocrinology (Baltimore)* **133:** 433–439.
34. Bakker, J., Brand, T., van Ophemert, J., and Slob, A. K. (1993). Hormonal regulation of adult partner preference behavior in neonatally ATD-treated male rats. *Behav. Neurosci.* **107:** 481–487.
35. Ogawa, S., Lubahn, D. B., Korach, K. S., and Pfaff, D. W. (1995). Behavioral characteristics of transgenic estrogen receptor knockout male mice: Sexual, aggressive and open-field behaviors. *Endocrinol. Soc. Abstr.* **77:** 133.
36. Lubahn, D. B., Moyer, J. S., Golding, T. S., Couse, J. F., Korach, K. S., and Smithies, O. (1993). Alteration of reproductive function but not prenatal sexual development after insertional disruption of the mouse estrogen receptor gene. *Proc. Natl. Acad. Sci. U.S.A.* **90:** 11162–11166.
37. Bakker, J., van Ophemert, J., and Slob, A. K. (1993). Organization of partner preference and sexual behavior and its nocturnal rhythmicity in male rats. *Behav. Neurosci.* **107:** 1049–1058.
38. Tobet, S. A., and Baum, M. J. (1987). Role for prenatal estrogen in the development of masculine sexual behavior in the male ferret. *Horm. Behav.* **21:** 419–429.
39. Raynaud, J.-P., Mercier-Bodard, C., and Baulieu, E. E. (1971). Rat estradiol-binding protein. *Steroids* **18:** 767–788.
40. Brawer, J. R., Beaudet, A., Desjardins, G. C., and Schipper, H. M. (1993). Pathologic effect of estradiol on the hypothalamus. *Biol. Reprod.* **49:** 647–652.
41. Baum, M. J., Gallagher, C. A., Martin, J. T., and Damassa, D. A. (1982). Effects of testosterone, dihydrotestosterone, or estradiol administered neonatally on sexual behavior of female ferrets. *Endocrinology (Baltimore)* **111:** 773–780.
42. Baum, M. J., Canick, J. A., Erskine, M. S., Gallagher, C. A., and Shim, J. H. (1983). Normal differentiation of masculine sexual behavior in male ferrets despite neonatal inhibition of brain aromatase or 5-alpha-reductase activity. *Neuroendocrinology* **36:** 277–284.
43. Scalia, F., and Winans, S. S. (1975). The differential projections of the olfactory bulb and accessory olfactory bulb in mammals. *J. Comp. Neurol.* **161:** 31–56.
44. Winans, S. S., Lehman, M. N., and Powers, J. B. (1982). Vomeronasal and olfactory CNS pathways that control male hamster mating behavior. In *Olfaction and Endocrine Regulation.* (W. Breipohl, ed.), pp. 23–34. IRL Press, Oxford.
45. Segovia, S., and Guillamon, A. (1993). Sexual dimorphism in the vomeronasal pathway and sex differences in reproductive behaviors. *Brain Res. Rev.* **18:** 51–74.
46. Tobet, S. A., and Fox, T. O. (1992). Sex differences in neuronal morphology influenced hormonally throughout life. In *Sexual Differentiation: Handbook of Behavioral Neurobiology* (A. A. Gerall, H. Moltz, and I. L. Ward, eds.), Vol. 11, pp. 41–83. Plenum, New York.

47. Dohler, K.-D., Srivastava, S. S, Shryne, J. E., Jarzab, B., Sipos, A., and Gorski, R. A. (1984). Differentiation of the sexually dimorphic nucleus in the preoptic area of the rat brain is inhibited by postnatal treatment with an estrogen antagonist. *Neuroendocrinology* **38:** 297–301.
48. Tobet, S. A., Zahniser, D. J., and Baum, M. J. (1986). Differentiation in male ferrets of a sexually dimorphic nucleus of the preoptic / anterior hypothalamic area requires prenatal estrogen. *Neuroendocrinology* **44:** 299–308.
49. Cherry, J. A., Basham, M. E., Weaver, C. E., Krohmer, R. W., and Baum, M. J. (1990). Ontogeny of the sexually dimorphic male nucleus in the preoptic / anterior hypothalamus of ferrets and its manipulation by gonadal steroids. *J. Neurobiol.* **21:** 844–857.
50. Baum, M. J., and Everitt, B. J. (1992). Increased expression of c-fos in the medial preoptic area after mating in male rats: Role of afferent inputs from the medial amygdala and midbrain central tegmental field. *Neuroscience* **50:** 627–646.
51. Pfaus, J. G., Kleopoulos, S. P., Mobbs, C. V., Gibbs, R. B., and Pfaff, D. W. (1993). Sexual stimulation activates c-fos within estrogen-concentrating regions of the female rat forebrain. *Brain Res.* **624:** 253–267.
52. Dudley, C. A., Rajendren, G., and Moss, R. L. (1992). Induction of Fos imunoreactivity in central accessory olfactory structures of the female rat following exposure to conspecific males. *Mol. Cell. Neurosci.* **3:** 360–369.
53. Bakker, J., Baum, M. J., and Slob, A. K. (1996). Neonatal inhibition of brain estrogen synthesis alters adult neural Fos responses to mating and pheromonal stimulation in the male rat. *Neuroscience* **74:** 251–260.
54. Paredes, R. G., and Baum, M. J. (1995). Altered sexual partner preference in male ferrets given excitotoxic lesions of the preoptic area / anterior hypothalamus. *J. Neurosci.* **15:** 6619–6630.
55. Arnold, A. P., and Gorski, R. A. (1984). Gonadal steroid induction of structural sex differences in the central nervous system. *Annu. Rev. Neurosci.* **7:** 413–442.
56. Moore, C. L., and Morelli, G. A. (1979). Mother rats interact differently with male and female offspring. *J. Comp. Physiol. Psychol.* **93:** 677–684.
57. Clark, M. M., Bone, S., and Galef, B. G., Jr. (1989). Uterine positions and schedules of urination: Correlates of differential maternal anogenital stimulation. *Dev. Psychobiol.* **22:** 389–400.
58. Baum, M. J., Bressler, S. C., Daum, M. C., Veiga, C. A., and McNamee, C. S. (1996). Ferret mothers provide more anogenital licking to male offspring: Possible contribution to psychosexual differentiation. *Physiol. Behav.* **60:** 353–359.
59. Moore, C. L., and Samonte, B. R. (1986). Preputial glands of infant rats provide chemosignals for maternal discrimination of sex. *J. Comp. Psychol.* **100:** 76–80.
60. Moore, C. L., Dou, H., and Juraska, J. M. (1992). Maternal stimulation affects the number of motor neurons in a sexually dimorphic nucleus of the lumbar spinal cord. *Brain Res.* **572:** 52–56.
61. Breedlove, S. M. (1992). Sexual dimorphism in the vertebrate nervous system. *J. Neurosci.* **12:** 4133–4142.
62. Toran-Allerand, C. D. (1984). On the genesis of sexual differentiation of the central nervous system: Morphogenetic consequences of steroidal exposure and possible role of alpha-fetoprotein. *Prog. Brain Res.* **61:** 63–98.
63. Adkins, E. K. (1975). Hormonal basis of sexual differentiation in the Japanese quail. *J. Comp. Physiol. Psychol.* **89:** 61–71.
64. Adkins-Regan, E., and Ascenzi, M. (1987). Social and sexual behaviour of male and female zebra finches treated with oestradiol during the nestling period. *Anim. Behav.* **35:** 1100–1112.
65. Balthazart, J., DeClerk, A., and Foidart, A. (1992). Behavioral demasculinization of female quail is induced by estrogens: Studies with a new aromatase inhibitor, R76713. *Horm. Behav.* **26:** 179–203.
66. Gurney, M. E., and Konishi, M. (1980). Hormone-induced sexual differentiation of brain and behavior in zebra finches. *Science* **208:** 1380–1383.
67. Arnold, A. P., and Schlinger, B. A. (1993). Sexual differentiation of brain and behavior: The zebra finch is not just a flying rat. *Brain Behav. Evol.* **42:** 231–241.
68. Balthazart, J., and Ball, G. F. (1995). Sexual differentiation of brain and behavior in birds. *Trends Endocrinol. Metab.* **6:** 21–29.
69. Balthazart, J., Absil, P., Fiasse, V., and Ball, G. F. (1995). Effects of the aromatase inhibitor R76713 on sexual differentiation of brain and behavior in zebra finches. *Behaviour* **131:** 225–260.
70. Adkins-Regan, E., Mausukhani, V., Thompson, R., and Yang, S. (1997). Organizational actions of sex hormones on sexual partner preference. *Brain Res. Bull.* **44:** 497–502.
71. Pang, S., Levine, L. S., Cederqvist, L. L., Fuentes, M., Riccardi, V. M., Holcombe, J. H., Nitowsky, H. M., Sachs, G., Anderson, C. E., Cuchon, C. E., Owens, R., Merkatz, I., and New, M. I. (1980). Amniotic fluid concentrations of steroids in fetuses with congenital adrenal hyperplasia due to 21-hydroxylase deficiency and in anencephalic fetuses. *J. Clin. Endocrinol. Metab.* **51:** 223–229.
72. Money, J., and Schwartz, M. (1977). Dating, romantic and nonromantic friendships, and sexuality in 17 early-treated adrenogenital females, aged 16–25. In *Congenital Adrenal Hyperplasia* (P. A. Lee, L. P. Plotnick, A. A. Kowarski, and C. J. Migeon, eds.), pp. 419–431. University Park Press, Baltimore, MD.
73. Money, J., Schwartz, M., and Lewis, V. G. (1984). Adult erotosexual status and fetal hormonal masculinization and demasculinization: 46,XX congenital virilizing adrenal hyperplasia and 46,XY androgen-insensitivity syndrome compared. *Psychoneuroendocrinology* **9:** 405–414.
74. Dittmann, R. W., Kappes, M. E., and Kappes, M. H. (1992). Sexual behavior in adolescent and adult females with congenital adrenal hyperplasia. *Psychoneuroendocrinology* **17:** 153–170.
75. Ehrhardt, A. A., Meyer-Bahlburg, H. F. L., Rosen, L. R., Feldman, J. F., Veridiano, N. P., Zimmerman, I., and McEwen, B. S. (1985). Sexual orientation after prenatal exposure to exogenous estrogen. *Arch. Sex. Behav.* **14:** 57–77.
76. Meyer-Bahlburg, H. F. L., Ehrhardt, A. A., Rosen, L. R., Gruen, R. S., Veridiano, N. P., Vann, F. H., and Neuwalder, H. F. (1995). Prenatal estrogens and the development of homosexual orientation. *Dev. Psychol.* **31:** 12–21.
77. Masica, D. N., Money, J., and Ehrhardt, A. A. (1971). Fetal feminization and female gender identity in the testicular feminizing syndrome of androgen insensitivity. *Arch. Sex. Behav.* **1:** 131–142.
78. Money, J., and Ogunro, C. (1974). Behavioral sexology: Ten cases of genetic male intersexuality with impaired prenatal and pubertal androgenization. *Arch. Sex. Behav.* **3:** 181–205.
79. Swaab, D. F., and Hofman, M. A. (1995). Sexual differentiation of the human hypothalamus in relation to gender and sexual orientation. *Trends Neurosci.* **18:** 264–270.
80. Allen, L. S., Hines, M., Shryne, J. E., and Gorski, R. A. (1989). Two sexually dimorphic cell groups in the human brain. *J. Neurosci.* **9:** 497–506.
81. LeVay, S. (1991). A difference in hypothalamic structure between heterosexual and homosexual men. *Science* **253:** 1034–1037.
82. Zhou, J.-N., Hofman, M. A., Gooren, L. J. G., and Swaab, D. F (1995). A sex difference in the human brain and its relation to transsexuality. *Nature (London)* **378:** 68–70.

CHAPTER

48

Motivation and Reward

T. W. Robbins and B. J. Everitt

Animals adapt to change, whether external or internal, through motivated behavior. Such adjustments to change may integrate endocrine, autonomic, and behavioral responses. Some adjustments are part of the regulatory process of homeostasis, and act through negative feedback loops to correct an internal change. Indeed, motivation used to be explained largely in terms of reductions of needs, or "drives," such as that for sodium chloride or water. Although this purely homeostatic explanation of motivation could plausibly account for ingestive and thermoregulatory behaviors, it fails to satisfactorily explain behavior such as aggression, mating, or exploration, for which there is no identifiable deficit state but for which there are obvious external triggering stimuli. It also fails to explain what happens when homeostatic mechanisms are apparently overridden by powerful external incentives, as occurs during drug binges and during overingestion of delicious food. Instead, such behavior often is explained by attraction to external stimuli that have appetitive or rewarding properties **(incentive–motivation).**

In many cases, goals such as food or a sexual partner are not available, and an animal must search or forage for them. Therefore, motivated behavior is more than simple control of **consummatory** responses, such as eating, drinking, and sexual mounting or lordosis, which end sequences of motivated behavior. Consummatory behavior tends to be stereotyped and reflexive and is acquired early in an animal's life. In sequences of motivated behavior, however, consummatory behavior is usually preceded by adaptive, flexible forms of **appetitive** behavior (e.g., foraging for food), which enables an animal to come into physical contact with its goal. This appetitive behavior may be simple locomotor approach responses to the goal or may include exploratory behavior and complex response sequences. In addition, appetitive behavior may occur in parallel with endocrine and autonomic responses (e.g., secretion of saliva and insulin; see Chapter 41) that prepare the animal for efficient interaction with the goal.

In the absence of immediate goals, an animal usually must use past experience to predict the likelihood of an occurrence. This learning may involve **classically conditioned** (i.e., **Pavlovian**) **reflexes** and **goal-directed instrumental** (or **operant**) **behaviors.** With the latter behaviors, an outcome that increases occurrence of a preceding behavior is a **positive reinforcer.** This term is often used interchangeably with the more colloquial term *reward,* which connotes pleasure. However, accurately inferring such subjective states in animals is difficult, if not impossible. Thus, to avoid ambiguity, most behavioral neuroscientists prefer to use operational definitions of motivated behavior, such as incentive and positive reinforcement. Identification of neural structures that mediate subjective phenomena, such as pleasure, may have to depend on functional neuroimaging of humans. *Incentive,* on the other hand, generally refers to the attractiveness of a goal, and *positive reinforcement* strengthens specific responses by the presenting stimuli contingent on performance. For example, rats can learn arbitrary instrumental actions, such as a lever press, to gain access to positive reinforcers, such as food or drugs—**self-administration behavior** (see Chapter 49)—or to stimuli associated with these primary reinforcers—**conditioned reinforcers. Schedules of reinforcement** vary the relationship between activity and positive reinforcement. Thus, an animal's degree of motivation can be assessed by its capacity to work for a goal.

The complexity of motivated behavior (see Fig. 48.1), from selection of voluntary actions based on past

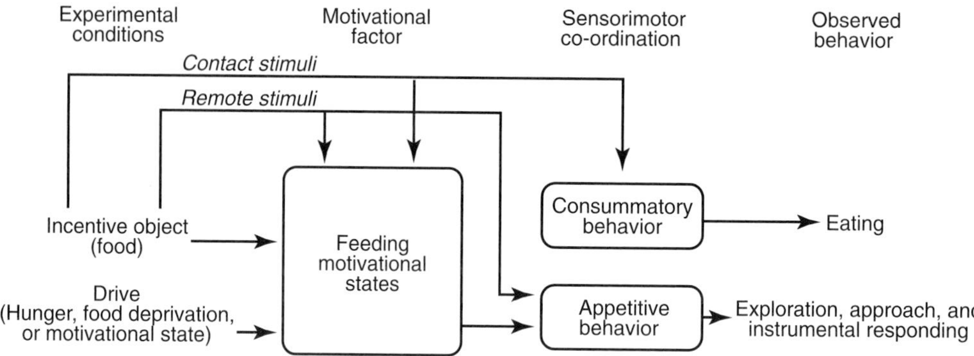

FIGURE 48.1 Theory of incentive–motivation, as applied to feeding. Note that drive (internal stimuli) and food (external stimuli) separately affect central motivation to feed. Also, incentive (i.e., food) and discriminative (i.e., sensorimotor) influences exert their effects separately to control consummatory behavior (when food is contacted) and appetitive behavior (when food remains remote). Modified after T. W. Robbins, Hunger. In *Neuroendocrinology* (S. L. Lightman and B. J. Everitt, eds.), pp. 252–303. Blackwell, Oxford, 1986, with permission.

experience to reflexive control of consummatory behavior, involves coordination of several levels of neural control, including the neocortex, limbic system, integrative centers (e.g., hypothalamus), and the basic executive mechanisms (e.g., brainstem).

NEURAL MECHANISMS OF MOTIVATION

The Hypothalamus Plays a Role in Motivation

Guided by the concept of homeostatic centers, many investigators approached motivation as a search for specific neural or hormonal signals that could trigger a center to initiate the appropriate behavioral responses. Thus, hypothetical motivational centers were based on early concepts of brainstem centers for fundamental processes, such as respiration. Such models could explain the efficient integration of many different signals to produce coordinated sequences of behavior. The hypothalamus is an ideal structure for such integrative functions, given its exposure to cerebrospinal fluid, control over the pituitary, and connections (through brainstem and spinal centers) with visceral afferent information (e.g., taste and olfaction) and autonomic outflow. The concept of mutually inhibitory centers for the initiation (hunger) and suppression (satiety) of feeding arose from such a view (see Chapter 41).

Criteria for Motivational Centers

Theorists defined principles for identifying motivational centers.[1] For example, designation of the lateral hypothalamic region (LH) as a "feeding center" was based on the following: (1) Electrolytic lesions produced profound aphagia (abstention from eating).[2] (2) Electrical stimulation of the brain (ESB) through electrodes implanted in the LH induced eating in sated rats.[3] (3) Infusions of the neurotransmitter noradrenaline into the hypothalamus also induced eating in sated rats.[4,5] (4) Finally, electrophysiological recording showed that when monkeys were deprived of food, individual neurons in the LH were sensitive to the sight and taste of food.[6]

Hypothalamic Centers for Other Forms of Motivation

On the basis of the criteria described above, the list of hypothalamic motivational centers can be extended to include behaviors as diverse as drinking (see Chapter 42), thermoregulation, aggression, and sex. Thermoregulatory behavior, such as reflexive shivering, panting, and grooming, is impaired by lesions of the preoptic region of the hypothalamus and is elicited by cooling or warming of this region.[7] Defensive (affective) aggression and accompanying autonomic changes, such as piloerection, are produced by electrical stimulation of the ventromedial hypothalamus (VMH). In contrast, in the rat, cat, and opossum, predatory ("quiet") aggression is produced by electrical stimulation of the lateral hypothalamus.[8]

Relevant to sexual motivation, hypothalamic nuclei contain high concentrations of steroid receptors (e.g., for estradiol and testosterone), especially in the medial preoptic region and the VMH. In rats, male copulatory behavior is abolished by medial preoptic lesions,[9] whereas electrical stimulation of this region elicits copulation. In female rats, lordosis is blocked (and aggression toward males increased) by lesions of the ventromedial nucleus of the hypothalamus. Lordosis is also induced by electrical stimulation of this region. Most of these responses are hormone-dependent: In females from which ovaries have been removed, **proceptive** (ear-wiggling, hopping, and darting) and **receptive** (lordosis) behaviors can be elicited by implanting estradiol into the VMH.[10] Similarly, sexual behavior of castrated males can be restored by implanting testosterone into the preoptic area.[11] This hormone dependence underlines the interaction between external state (environmental) and internal state (plasma steroids) in inducing motivated responses. Also, sex hormones influence the organization of sexually dimorphic brain development—for example, development of the sexually dimorphic nuclei in the preoptic region—and sexually dimorphic behavior (see Chapter 47). Maternal behavior also is dependent on hormones and is impaired by lesions of the medial preoptic area (see Chapter 44).

The intermingling of hypothalamic neural mechanisms controlling thermoregulation, maternal behavior, feeding, and mating suggests that these behaviors share controls in many circumstances. In summary, a wide variety of motivational states expressed as easily elicited complex behaviors are represented within the hypothalamus and related structures.

Critique of the Hypothalamic "Drive Center" Hypothesis

Despite this considerable evidence, the importance of the hypothalamus in motivation remains unclear. For example, lesions of the LH do not reduce only eating and drinking but virtually all motivated behaviors, as well as basic sensorimotor processes. Animals can recover from many of the eating deficits caused by lateral hypothalamic lesions, but residual deficits remain in the control of drinking and the response to changes in body fluids[12] (see Chapter 41). Recovery probably occurs by two main processes: **reorganization** of the rest of the brain to compensate behaviorally and **intrinsic recovery** of the damaged neurotransmitter systems. The phenomenon of recovery is important because it suggests that hypothalamic centers are not necessary for control of motivation and that motivation can be affected by plastic neural systems.

Furthermore, the effects of experimental brain stimulation can be misinterpreted. Although in nondeprived animals ESB produces behavior that resembles naturally motivated behavior, the behaviors also differ depending on the nature of the goal–object. In addition, expression of a consummatory response often gradually evolves over a number of experiences with ESB, suggesting involvement of learning mechanisms instead of or in addition to local activation of a hypothetical motivational center.[13] Behavior elicited by ESB could also reflect abnormal functions, such as a coping response to the stress of ESB itself. For example, sated rats will resume eating in response to sustained pinching of their tails![14] These results point to possible nonspecific "arousing" or "activating" effects of stimulation, which can lead to specific motivational responses based on present context and previous experience of the animal.

Measuring Consummatory Rather Than Instrumental Behavior

Many studies of the role of the hypothalamus in motivation have measured consummatory rather than learned instrumental behavior. For example, rats with preoptic lesions will not respond to thermal stress with reflex mechanisms such as shivering, adjustment of food intake, nest-building, or changes in locomotion. However, they *will* learn to press a lever for hot or cool air and can achieve thermoregulation by this means.[15] Similarly, male monkeys with preoptic lesions still show motivated behavior such as masturbation, but they are unable to copulate with females. Moreover, male rats with preoptic lesions still show displacement behaviors and locomotor excitement in the presence of a receptive female, as well as lever-pressing to gain access to her, but do not copulate.[16] This dissociation is important because damage to a component of the limbic system, the amygdala, is known to produce the opposite pattern of effects—unimpaired mounting but reduced instrumental behavior.[16] These examples show that hypothalamic mechanisms operate mainly at the level of controlling consummatory rather than learned instrumental behavior leading to a goal. Behavioral flexibility illustrated by learning appears to require recruitment of additional neural systems, including the amygdala (see following).

Motivation Can Be Controlled at Other Levels of the Neuraxis

Below the Level of the Hypothalamus

The hypothalamus is not necessary for the fundamental reflexive elements of consummatory behavior. For example, researchers[17] showed that cats with midbrain transections (below the hypothalamus) could still perform complete responses, such as chewing, swallowing, growling, and piloerection ("sham rage"). Only when the transection was *above* the hypothalamus, however, did the responses look like integrated, motivated behavior. Thus, the hypothalamus appeared to coordinate and sequence motivated responses (which probably include autonomic and endocrine responses, as well as behavior). The circuitry is now known to descend from the hypothalamus to the midbrain and then to integrative centers in the brainstem and spinal cord.

Crude regulation of body temperature persists after the brain is transected below the hypothalamus (midbrain preparation). In addition, decerebrate rats show normal acceptance and rejection behaviors in response to pleasant and unpleasant foods. They also show a normal rise in insulin secretion in anticipation of eating, as well as a decrease in response to satiety.[18] Thus, glucoreceptors in the hindbrain can be sufficient to complete this response.[19] However, decerebrate rats cannot learn taste aversion or search for food.

The pathway mediating lordosis in female rats maps to the level of the spinal cord, where vertebral dorsiflexion is reflexly executed in response to appropriate cutaneous stimulation by a male.[10] The hormone-dependent influence of the hypothalamus appears to allow integration of this lordosis response into an appropriate sequence of behavior. Thus, the hypothalamus again apparently plays an integrative role, but one that is limited to simple, often consummatory, behaviors.

Above the Level of the Hypothalamus

Structures above the level of the hypothalamus—for example, the neocortex and limbic system—modulate motivated behavior. For instance, stimulation of the amygdala *inhibits* the rage elicited by stimulation of the hypothalamus. Also, inhibition of the neocortex (using potassium chloride) *disinhibits* lordosis. Many such descending influences are *learned,* such as responses to novel and familiar foods, conditioned taste aversion, and control of instrumental behavior (see preceding). Inhibition of motivation is not restricted to neocortex and limbic system; for example, inhibitory mechanisms (of food intake) apparently are located in the paraventricular nucleus and ventromedial region of the hypothalamus (see Chapter 41).

Summary

Gallistel[20] has provided a scheme that helps to summarize the findings described so far about neural control of motivation (Fig. 48.2). According to this model, motivated behavior is organized at several levels of the brain. These levels operate somewhat autonomously but with progressively less sophistication from the top levels down. Whereas upper levels participate in learning new sequences of behavior (e.g., lever-pressing), lower levels represent simple responses, such as reflexes. Higher levels tend to select or deselect the operation of lower levels, rather than exerting outright excitation or inhibition. Such a **lattice hierarchy** allows flexibility of control, including top-down control of instrumental behavior and recruitment of similar motor responses for different purposes (e.g., the licking response, expressed in maternal behavior, grooming, and eating). However, this model does not explain how learning affects motivation or incorporate a role for nonspecific processes, such as arousal and activation (see following).

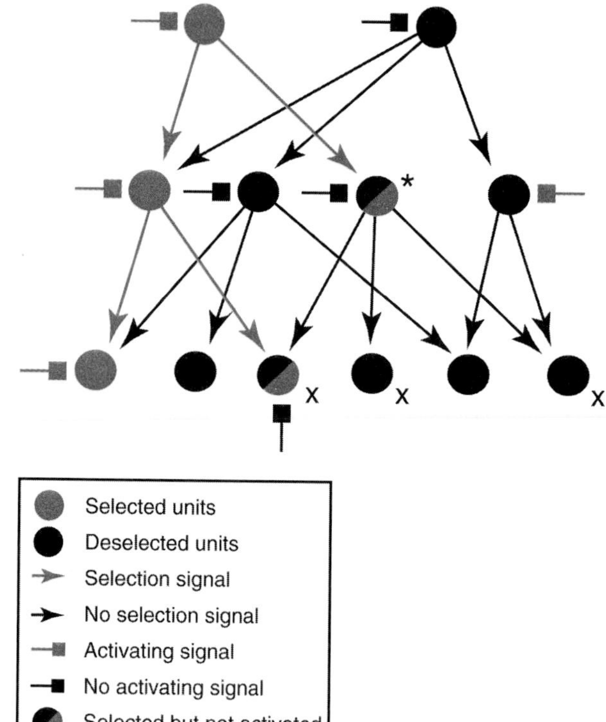

FIGURE 48.2 Lattice hierarchy model for the control of motivation. Signals selecting behavioral responses progress from higher, learned control to lower, reflexive control levels of this hierarchy. Selected units represent individual response elements, such as approach, licking, etc., that are activated by combinations of external (i.e., learned) and internal (e.g., hormonal) influences. Activation causes a selected unit to be performed. In the case of elementary (lowest level) units, outputs go directly to muscles. In the case of higher units, outputs select and deselect lower units. For example, if activating conditions arose for the unit marked with an asterisk (*), the lower units it controls (x) would be selected. Modified after C. R. Gallistel,[20] with permission.

DOPAMINE AND THE LATERAL HYPOTHALAMIC SYNDROME

Electrolytic lesions of the LH destroy far more than the LH region itself, mainly by interrupting ascending and descending fibers in the medial forebrain bundle (Fig. 48.3). Thus, the effects of LH lesions on eating were unlikely all to be caused by damage to an LH "feeding" center. For example, the nigrostriatal dopamine pathway courses through the LH without synapsing there.[21] Injection of a catecholamine-selective neu-

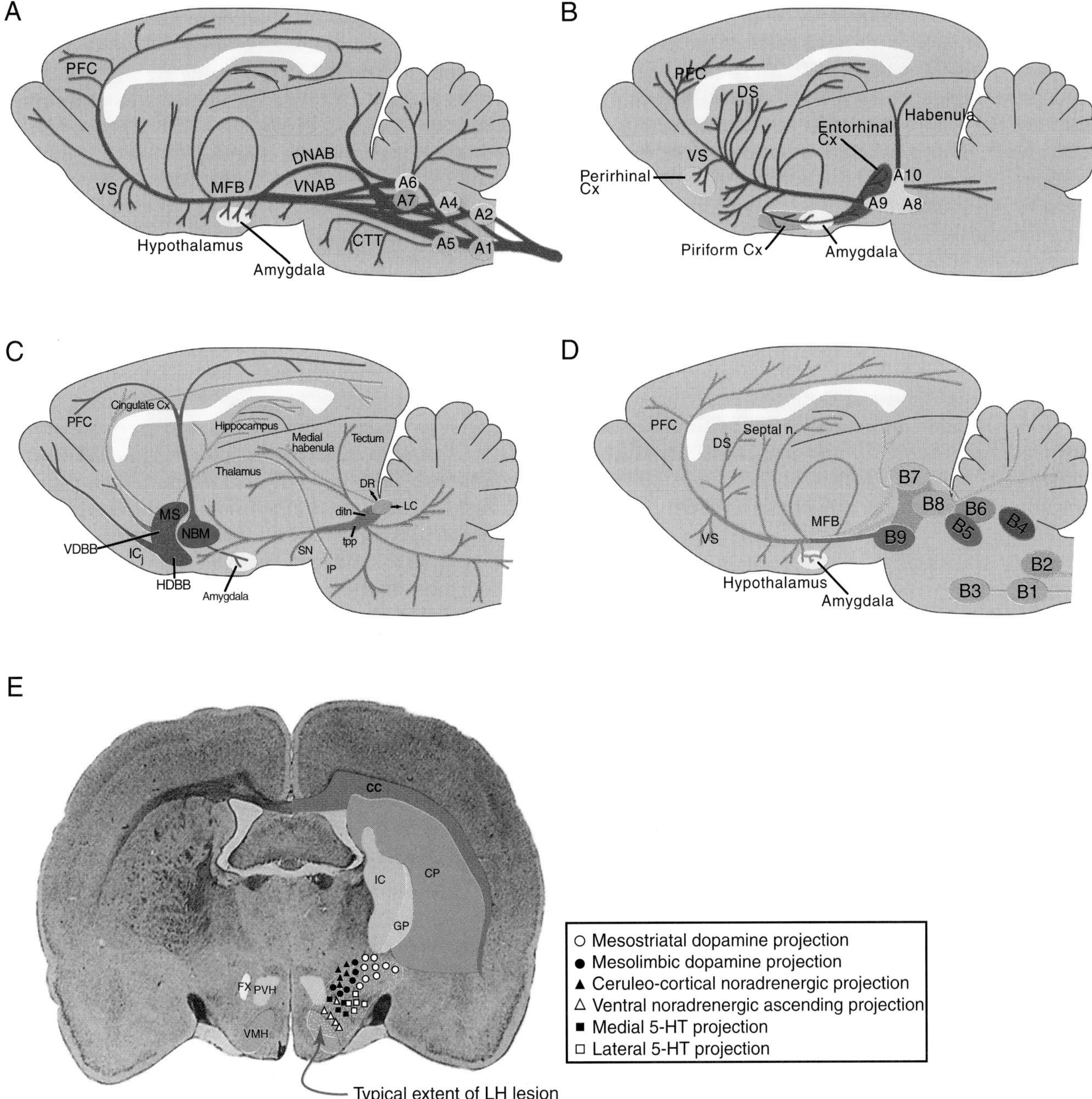

FIGURE 48.3 Ascending monoamine neurotransmitter systems. Figure shows schematic sagittal (A–D) and coronal (E) sections through the lateral hypothalamus of a rat brain. (A) Origin and distribution of central noradrenergic pathways. Note noradrenergic cell groups A1–A7, including the locus ceruleus (A6). DNAB, dorsal noradrenergic ascending bundle; VNAB, ventral noradrenergic ascending bundle. (B) Origin and distribution of central dopamine pathways. Note dopaminergic cell groups A8–A10. (C) Origin and distribution of central cholinergic pathways. Note rostral cell groups. NBM, nucleus basalis magnocellularis (Meynert in primates); MS, medial septum; VDBB, vertical limb nucleus of the diagonal band of Broca; HDBB, horizontal limb nucleus of the diagonal band of Broca. (D) Origin and distribution of central serotoninergic pathways. Note cell groups in the raphe nucleus, B4–B9. MFB, medial forebrain bundle; PFC, prefrontal cortex; VS, ventral striatum; DS, dorsal striatum. Based on T. W. Robbins and B. J. Everitt, in *The Cognitive Neurosciences*. MIT Press, Cambridge MA, 1995; reproduced with permission. (E) Schematic coronal section through the rat brain at the level of the ventromedial hypothalamus. LH lesions could disrupt various ascending monoaminergic fibers. CC, corpus callosum; CP, caudate–putamen; IC, internal capsule; GP, globus pallidus; PVH, paraventricular hypothalamus; LH, lateral hypothalamus; FX, fornix; VMH, ventromedial hypothalamus. Modified from T. W. Robbins, Hunger. In *Neuroendocrinology* (S. L. Lightman and B. J. Everitt, eds.). Blackwell, Oxford, 1986, with permission.

rotoxin, 6-hydroxydopamine (6-DHDA), into the vicinity of the LH reproduced most of the classic LH syndrome (see also Chapter 41): The injected rats suffered large depletions (>90%) of dopamine from the striatum. They were cataleptic and had difficulty initiating head, limb, axial, and oral movements. Further experiments showed that the syndrome could be produced by injection of 6-OHDA at any of several points along the nigrostriatal dopamine pathway between its origin in the substantia nigra and its termination in the caudate–putamen. Thus, dopamine depletion at sites well away from the LH reproduced much of the LH syndrome. 6-Hydroxydopamine lesions of the mesolimbic rather than the mesostriatal pathway minimally affect ingestion but do affect other behaviors, such as locomotion and exploration, that may accompany feeding.[22] Therefore, both consummatory and appetitive behaviors are affected by dopamine depletion, probably in different regions of the forebrain.

LH Syndrome Is Similar and Dissimilar to the Syndrome Produced by 6-Hydroxydopamine

Recovery from the LH syndrome and the syndrome produced by 6-hydroxydopamine is similar[23]: Early, animals show adipsia (absence of drinking), aphagia (absence of eating), sensorimotor neglect (lack of response to stimuli), and akinesia (dearth of movements). Recovery from sensorimotor neglect parallels recovery from aphagia in both syndromes. (Recovered rats do not respond normally to physiological challenges, such as hyperosmolality.) Stricker and Zigmond[12] explain this recovery as intrinsic recovery of function in dopaminergic systems. They propose that changes in dopamine turnover and reuptake, as well as increases in the number of DA receptors, combine to minimize the impact of a lesion (see Chapter 41). In fact, in animals recovered from 6-OHDA lesions, aphagia and adipsia can be reinstated by drugs that block synthesis of catecholamines or that block DA receptors. These studies led to the hypothesis that the entire LH syndrome is caused by a deficit in activation and results from depletion of brain DA rather than damage to LH cells.

Despite these similarities, subtle differences between the two syndromes cannot be explained by this DA hypothesis. For example, 6-OHDA-lesioned rats, unlike animals with LH lesions, are not somnolent (drowsy). 6-OHDA-lesioned rats also are less finicky about food and have fewer deficits in thermoregulation, taste aversion, learning, and oral motor performance. However, the most compelling difference is that rats with LH lesions and the full syndrome have only 50% depletion of striatal DA, whereas 6-OHDA-lesioned rats (even with less than the full syndrome) have greater than 90% depletion of striatal DA. Therefore, damage to the LH itself or to fibers of passage in addition to those of the ascending DA system apparently contributes to LH syndrome.[12] Somnolence, for example, might be related to damage to other fibers of passage (e.g., noradrenergic or cholinergic) in the medial forebrain bundle (see Fig. 48.3B).

Cell Body Lesions in the Hypothalamus Produce a Less Severe LH Syndrome

The neurotoxins kainic, ibotenic, and quisqualic acids are structurally related to the excitatory neurotransmitter glutamate. They bind to various subtypes of glutamate receptor and essentially stimulate the neuron to death (see Chapter 9). These acids can be used to produce lesions of cell bodies while *sparing fibers of passage.* Electrolytic and mechanical lesions, in contrast, damage soma and fibers. Despite sparing striatal DA, such cell body lesions lead to severe problems with eating, followed by long-lasting deficits in homeostasis.[24] However, there are no signs of akinesia or sensorimotor neglect. Hence, at least two factors are required to explain the LH syndrome: damage to the LH disrupts homeostasis, and striatal DA loss disrupts initiation and execution of feeding and related behaviors.

Animals with Dopamine Denervation Syndrome Show Rotation and Sensorimotor Neglect

A central question for research in this area is what is the precise nature of the dopaminergic contribution to motivation? Some clues to answering this question were provided by experiments[25] in which rats received unilateral 6-OHDA lesions of the nigrostriatal system. The rats rotated toward the side of the lesion following treatment with a DA-releasing drug, such as *d*-amphetamine (Ungerstedt, 1971b). Presumably, this rotation occurred because more DA is released on the intact side than the lesioned side of the brain, and because any output pathway from the striatum crosses to the opposite side of the body. Of even greater interest, the direct DA receptor agonist apomorphine caused the rat to turn away from the side of the lesion This rotation could be explained by supersensitive DA receptors on the lesioned side. These studies of drug-induced movement have helped to identify mechanisms of receptor regulation that might contribute to recovery from motivational deficits of dopamine denervation.

Unilateral lesions of the LH or nigrostriatal DA system also produce polymodal sensorimotor neglect, measured by responses to contralateral somatic, auditory, and olfactory stimuli, initially attributed to *sensory inattention.*[23] A more detailed analysis suggests

BOX 48.1

SEPARATION OF SENSORY AND RESPONSE FACTORS IN THE DOPAMINERGIC SYNDROME OF NEGLECT

Sensory and motor aspects of the neglect syndrome were separated in the following way.[26] Rats were trained to detect brief flashes of light presented to either side of the head. In one case, they were trained to respond where the light was. In the alternate case, rats were trained to respond in a location away from the side of the light (see Fig. 48.4). Rats with DA depleted from one side of the striatum could not properly respond toward the contralateral side, whether or not the stimulus was presented on that side. Measurement of reaction time showed that the problem was in initiation, rather than completion, of the movement. Consistent with these data, DA-depleted rats could detect a contralateral stimulus and respond to it with an unlateralized response. Thus, their deficit was in initiation of movement in response to stimuli rather than in detection of the stimuli.

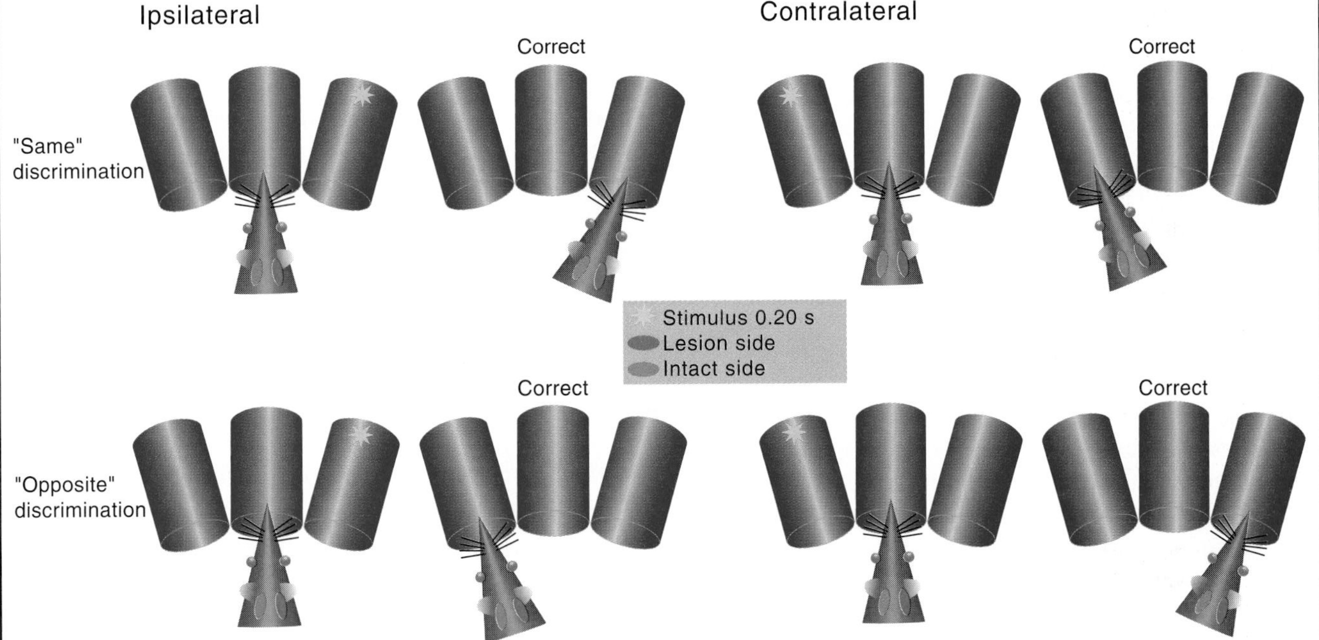

FIGURE 48.4 Distinguishing between sensory and response factors. Rats were trained to move toward the *Same* or *Opposite* side on which a brief (0.2 s) visual stimulus was presented. If a rat did not respond to stimulus, it remained in a central location. After training, unilateral striatal lesions (oval) were made. Rats were then observed for their ability to respond to stimuli presented ipsilateral or contralateral to their lesions. Based on the responses of lesioned rats to stimuli, conclusions were drawn about the sensory and motor nature of the deficits caused by striatal lesions.

that the fundamental deficit is a failure in activation of the responses (Box 48.1).[26]

Mesencephalic Dopamine Mediates Activation of Behavior

The general role of the nigrostriatal DA system is **activation,** modulating the vigor of behavioral output. Animals with lesions of the system retain the *capacity* for movement; they do not have an irreversible motor deficit. However, they cannot start that movement without an intact DA system.

To identify the circumstances in which the DA system normally becomes active, researchers have examined the firing of DA cells in response to particular stimuli.[27] In addition, *in vivo* neurochemical techniques, such as microdialysis and voltammetry,[28] have been used to monitor release of DA in animals exhibiting particular behaviors.

Such techniques show that different DA systems (i.e., mesocortical, mesolimbic, and mesostriatal; see Chapter 9) probably have different roles in activation of behavior, depending on the target structures they innervate. Two broad generalizations can be made. (1) Nigrostriatal DA projections to the caudate–putamen participate in activation of behavior triggered by stimuli of endogenous origin (e.g., as in anticipation of movement). (2) The mesolimbic DA system is involved in activation of responses to external stimuli with incentive–motivational properties. However, determining whether motivational or motor functions are being monitored is sometimes difficult. For example, a failure to approach an incentive stimulus may be due to a deficit in locomotion or in motivation. One way to resolve the issue is to investigate whether animals will learn new responses that change dopaminergic activity in the mesolimbic system. Such changes could be considered positive reinforcement, and newly learned behaviors the result of motivated behavior.

Summary

Because ascending projections of the dopamine neurons travel through the lateral hypothalamus, selective lesions of the dopamine axons with 6-hydroxydopamine revealed a significant contribution of this system to the classical experimental condition of the lateral hypothalamic lesion with severe appetitive and sensory neglect. However, animals with only dopamine axon lesions show fewer deficits in thermoregulation, taste aversion, and motor performance and are less alert than classical LH-lesioned animals. Selective lesion of neurons, but not axons, in the LH produce a more subtle behavioral deficit pattern. Part of the result of dopamine denervation and recovery from it depend on adaptive responses in residual dopamine fibers and postsynaptic receptors.

REINFORCEMENT SYSTEMS

Electrical Stimulation of the Brain Can Be a Positive Reinforcer

In 1954 Olds and Milner[29] discovered that rats learned new responses when their learning was positively reinforced by electrical stimulation of the brain. That finding affirmed the importance of incentive factors in instrumental behavior. The best natural parallel appeared to be behavior in response to large incentives in low states of drive (e.g., chocolate milk in undeprived rats).[30] However, equating rewarding brain stimulation with subjective feelings of pleasure and hedonism seemed inappropriate when literature on human intracranial self-stimulation (ICSS) was considered because the subjects, often people with schizophrenia or intractable pain, frequently had difficulty verbalizing their responses.[13] Measurement of the strength of reinforcers in microamperes (Box 48.2)[31,32] promised a pragmatic, as well as objective, new approach to the psychophysics of an operational hedonism. However, its greatest contribution was to enable the anatomical mapping of the central reward or reinforcement mechanisms of the brain.

Reward and Punishment Regions

Using the rate of responses that elicited rewarding brain stimulation, researchers mapped sites of ICSS in the rat and other species to the medial forebrain bundle.[33] Response rates were high and often accompanied by stimulus-bound behavior, such as eating whenever food was present or locomotion despite absence of a goal object.[3,13] At first, theorists assumed that the consummatory behavior was caused by ESB mimicking the effect of natural rewards within hypothalamic centers. This response contrasted with that seen at other, often limbic, sites (e.g., septum, amygdala, hippocampus, and prefrontal cortex). At these sites, response rates were lower and behavioral activation was less evident.[31,34] When ESB occurred in negatively reinforcing regions of the brain, rats' new responses would allow them to escape from or avoid the stimulation (see section on Aversion Systems).

Catecholamine Hypothesis of Rewarding Brain Stimulation

Later work showed that animals will also learn behaviors to stimulate other sites through ICSS (e.g., the locus ceruleus, central gray, cerebellum, trigeminal motor nucleus, substantia nigra, caudate nucleus, and nucleus accumbens).[31] The diversity of these sites has not been explained, but many of them are known to lie along the trajectory of catecholamine-containing neurons.[33] However, noradrenaline is not currently postulated to participate in reinforcement, because most pharmacologic data can be interpreted in terms of dopaminergic mechanisms (Box 48.2). In particular, very high rates of responding for ICSS were found in the ventral tegmental area, ventral striatum (including the nucleus accumbens to which DA neurons project), and limbic system. On the other hand, of several, possibly independent neural systems that may subserve rewarding brain stimulation, only some depend on dopamine.[31] The difficulty in interpreting the role of striatal DA in ICSS lies in distinguishing motor from reward effects (see Box 48.2). The phenomenon of human drug dependence and the discovery in the early 1960s of drug self-administration in animals opened the way

BOX 48.2

THE PSYCHOPHYSICS OF HEDONISM AS MEASURED BY BRAIN STIMULATION REWARD

Electrical stimulation of the brain can be used as positive reinforcement of learned behaviors. An apparatus is set up so that when an animal presses a lever, its brain is stimulated. An advantage of using stimulation to measure motivation is that the strength of the reward can easily be titrated by adjusting the amount of current delivered for each lever press. If the current is adjusted too low (i.e., below the threshold for reinforcement), then the animals will not press the lever. As current is increased, the relationship between rate of lever pressing and strength of current typically follows a sigmoidal curve called termed a rate–intensity function.[31] Pharmacologic manipulation of catecholamine neurotransmitter systems can shift the function to the left (e.g., treatment with amphetamine or cocaine) or to the right (e.g., treatment with α-methyl-p-tyrosine, reserpine, or the dopamine receptor antagonist pimozide) (Fig. 48.5). Such shifts mean the amount of current required to support lever presses varies while maximal response rate is unchanged. Thus, these drugs affect reward processes, rather than motor function. The threshold of reinforcement can also be measured by allowing rats to adjust the strength of the current. In this setup, a process is employed in which rats press lever one to produce ICSS, but each lever-one press also reduces the intensity of the current. To reset current intensity, rats must press lever two. Such "self-titration" experiments yield conclusions similar to those based on rate–intensity functions.[32]

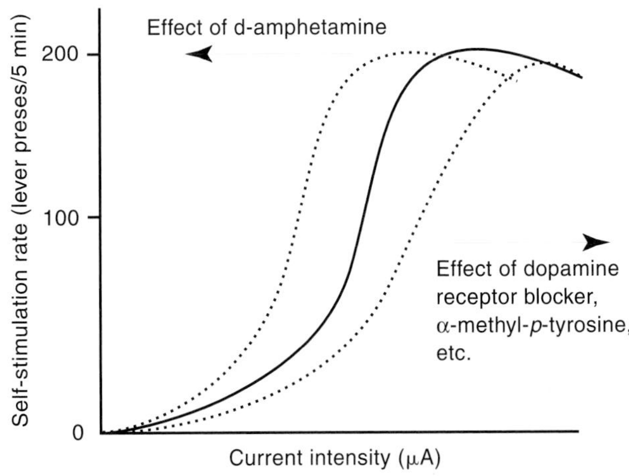

FIGURE 48.5 Rate–intensity function for electrical self-stimulation of the brain. Pharmacologic agents shift the curve left (e.g., amphetamine or cocaine) or right (e.g., catecholamine-depleting agents, such as α-methyl-p-tyrosine and reserpine, and catecholamine receptor blockers, such as chlorpromazine and pimozide).

to an analysis of reward effects, the neurochemical basis of reinforcement (see Chapter 52).

The Role of the Mesolimbic Dopamine System in Natural Rewards

Wise[35] proposed that drugs and natural reinforcers are perceived as rewards because they increase activity of the mesolimbic DA system (see Chapter 9). If Wise's hypothesis is correct, the mesolimbic DA system should mediate natural rewards, such as food and sex. In fact, depletion of dopamine in the nucleus accumbens does not impair consummatory behavior in rats (unlike DA depletion from the caudate–putamen), but it may reduce incentive–motivational responses. For example, proceptive behavior is reduced in female rats (in the presence of males). Also, depletion of dopamine from the nucleus accumbens decreases locomotor excitement of hungry rats in the presence of food.[22]

Mesolimbic DA may also control behavior motivated by reward. For example, when a previously neutral light became a predictor of the occurrence of a primary reinforcer, water, rats learned a new behavior to turn on the light. Injection of amphetamine into the nucleus accumbens (but not the caudate) increased the frequency of the behavior. This increased frequency of response suggested that amphetamine enhanced the motivational properties of this reward-related stimulus (i.e., the light, which was related to the reward, water). Amphetamine itself was well known to suppress eating and drinking; thus, the increased frequency of behavior was not due to increased thirst, for example. Furthermore, amphetamine did not increase the frequency of response for a randomly paired stimulus. Finally, amphetamine-induced facilitation was completely blocked by depletion of dopamine in the nucleus accumbens (but not by depletion in the caudate). These results indicated that increased activity in the mesolimbic dopamine system could enhance the motivational properties of stimuli predictive of natural rewards. Excessive activation of this and other systems may result in emotional diseases such as mania (see Box 48.3).

BOX 48.3

MANIA

Mania is a clinical syndrome characterized by a persistently euphoric, labile, or irritable mood along with motor restlessness, insomnia, racing thoughts, and impairment of insight and judgment.[1,14] Although this syndrome may arise secondarily to the effects of certain pharmacological agents (e.g., prednisone) or medical conditions (e.g., stroke or Huntington disease), it is most commonly seen in the primary, idiopathic condition of bipolar disorder (BD; "manic–depressive illness"). In BD, both manic and depressive episodes generally alternate with the normal, or "euthymic," state.

Mania and depression reflect phenomenological antitheses of one another, being characterized by increases and decreases, respectively, in mood, motivation, energy, psychomotor activity, self-esteem, libido, and hedonia[1,11,14] The hedonic state of mania reflects an increased capacity for deriving pleasure and reward from social, work-related, or creative activities.[7,13,14] Patients consequently increase their engagement in such activities, often continuing them throughout the night.[11] This "hypermotivational" state is fueled by a sense of having boundless energy and needing less sleep (patients may sleep very little, yet deny feeling fatigued).[14] The euphoria also interrelates with grandiose ideas of having special talents, prowess, or religious significance, and in some cases with delusions of having supernatural powers, possessing great wealth, or being a famous political or religious figure. While productivity may increase in the initial stages, as mania worsens the work performance deteriorates and thought processes become disorganized.[14] In addition, the increased engagement in pleasurable activities and the impairment of judgment may lead to ruinous buying sprees, sexual indiscretions, or alcohol abuse.[11,14]

Psychomotor activity is also increased in mania, which may be manifested by agitation, pacing, or restlessness.[1] Patients report that their thoughts race, which is clinically apparent as rapid speech, reduced attention, and frequent, tangential shifts in the topic of conversation ("flight of ideas").[13] Agitation commonly coincides with irritability and anger, which typically alternate with euphoria during the manic state and may lead to violent behavior.[14]

The age of onset for BD is usually in adolescence or the early twenties, and the lifetime prevalence is about 1%.[11,14] While the first manic episode is commonly preceded by multiple depressive episodes, once the bipolar course is established each manic episode is typically followed by depression.[11,13] Untreated episodes typically last several months. Treatment with lithium, valproate, or antipsychotic drugs decreases episode length and severity, and maintenance treatment with these agents can reduce episode frequency.[4,11,14] Ten to 15% of bipolar patients have more than three episodes per year ("rapid cycling") and at least 20% continue to manifest mood instability and occupational impairment between episodes.[11]

Adult twin and adoption studies indicate that the transmission of bipolar disorder is largely due to genetic factors.[11] Earlier age of onset appears to increase the transmissibility of bipolar disorder. While there have been several claims of linkage of particular genetic loci to bipolar disorder, at present none of the putative linkage locations or associations are widely accepted and positive studies have generally not been replicated.[11]

Relatively little is known about the pathophysiology of mania. Since the dopaminergic projections from the ventral tegmental area and the substantia nigra into the ventral striatum and the medial prefrontal cortex (PFC) appear to play a role in mediating hedonia, motivation, behavioral reinforcement, and psychomotor activity, this system may compose a neural substrate where dysfunction results in the emotional and behavioral features of BD.[11,13,21] Specifically, increased mesolimbic dopaminergic function is hypothesized to produce the euphoria, motor restlessness, and hypermotivational state of mania, and decreased function to account for the anhedonia, psychomotor slowing, and amotivation of depression.[7,13,21,24] Pharmacological data are compatible with this hypothesis, as manic symptoms are reduced by DA receptor antagonists or DA synthesis inhibitors and can be precipitated in euthymic or depressed bipolar patients by DA receptor agonist or precursor administration.[2,5,13] Conversely, DA depletion during reserpine administration or Parkinson disease is associated with depression, antidepressant drugs enhance DA receptor function in limbic structures, and CSF concentrations of the DA metabolite homovanillic acid are reduced in nondelusional depressives.[11,14,24] Moreover, the bipolar course of manic episodes followed by depressive episodes resembles that of cocaine dependence, in which cocaine-mediated DA reuptake inhibition produces euphoria, restlessness, insomnia, and behavioral reinforcement, while the transient, functional DA deficiency state of cocaine withdrawal is associated with depressed mood and anhedonia.[13,23] Nevertheless, the preliminary data from DA receptor imaging studies in BD, the observations that psychotic symptoms in either mania or depression respond to DA receptor antagonists (i.e., antipsychotic drugs), and the existence of mixed episodes characterized by both manic and depressive features suggest that if DA dysfunction exists in BD, it likely differs across brain regions and involves complex interactions with other neurotransmitter systems.[1,10,13]

Recently, elucidation of lithium's biochemical effects has given rise to hypotheses that BD results from dysregulation of the second messenger cascades mediating signal transduction, which could potentially account not only for disturbances of dopaminergic function, but also for the abnormalities in noradrenergic, serotonergic, and peptidergic (e.g., CRF) function which have been reported in BD.[2,7,14] Lithium inhibits adenylate cyclase, alters certain types of protein phosphorylation, affects expression of some G-protein and adenylate cyclase subtypes, and alters the coupling between neurotransmitter receptors and G proteins.[2] Lithium's inhibitory effects on the phosphoinositide cascade (via inhibition of several inositol phosphatases), in particular, would dampen or alter the cellular responses to the large number of neurotransmitters whose actions are mediated by polyphosphoinositide turnover.[2] An abnormality at one step in these second messenger cascades could thus alter cellular processes in a variety of brain systems.

Finally, a neuroimaging abnormality evident in the ventral anterior cingulate cortex may also relate to mesolimbic DA dysfunction in BD.[12] In the prefrontal cortex lying ventral to the genu of the corpus callosum, MRI-based measures of gray matter volume are decreased in familial cases of BD relative to controls.[12] In addition, preliminary PET imaging studies indicate that glucose metabolism in this region is abnormally decreased in the depressed phase and increased in the manic phase of BD. This area is among the medial PFC structures that are extensively and reciprocally connected to DA neurons in the ventral tegmental area and the substantia nigra (as well as to serotonergic neurons in the raphe).[12,19] In rats, electrical or glutamatergic stimulation of medial PFC areas that include the subgenual PFC elicits burst firing patterns of DA cells in the ventral tegmental area and/or increases the release of DA from neuron terminals in the nucleus accumbens.[8,15,18,22] These data, along with the observation that metabolic activity in the subgenual PFC increases and decreases, respectively, in mania and depression, suggest that the function of this region could conceivably relate to dopaminergic dysfunction in BD.[12]

Structural imaging studies have shown morphometric abnormalities in other brain regions as well in BD. For example, the left amygdala volume is abnormally reduced and the third ventricle enlarged in BD.[10,17] Since the subgenual PFC shares substantial, predominantly ipsilateral connections with the amygdala and the medial thalamic nuclei lining the third ventricle, the volumetric abnormalities in these structures may involve a common neuropathological process.[6] The same circuitry is implicated by lesion analysis studies in the pathophysiology of BD, as cerebrovascular or traumatic lesions which have been associated with induced manic or bipolar syndromes also involve the ventral PFC, the thalamus, the basotemporal cortex (which includes the amygdala), and the striatum.[20] Furthermore, humans with lesions involving the ventromedial PFC area that includes the subgenual PFC fail to comprehend the adverse consequences of inappropriate social behaviors and demonstrate abnormal autonomic responses to emotional experiences, show an inability to experience emotion related to concepts that ordinarily evoke emotion, and have impaired comprehension of the adverse consequences of pernicious social behaviors.[3,9,16] *Postmortem* histopathological studies within the neural circuits formed by these structures are now in progress and may further elucidate the neurobiology of BD.

Wayne C. Drevets

References

1. American Psychiatric Association (1987). *Diagnostic and Statistical Manual of Mental Disorders (DSM-III-R)*, Washington, DC.
2. Barchas, J. D., Hamblin, M. W., and Malenka, R. C. (1994). Biochemical hypotheses of mood and anxiety disorders. In *Basic Neurochemistry*, 5th ed. (G. J. Siegel, *et al.*, eds.). Raven, New York.
3. Bechara, A., Tranel, D., Damasio, H., and Damasio, A. R. (1996). Failure to respond autonomically to anticipated future outcomes following damage to the prefrontal cortex. *Cerebral Cortex* **6:** 215–225.
4. Bowden, C. L., *et al.* (1994). Efficacy of divalproex vs lithium and placebo in the treatment of mania, The Depakote Mania Study Group. *JAMA* **271:** 918–924.
5. Bunney, W. E. Jr, Goodwin, F. K., Murphy, D. L., *et al.* (1972). The "switch process' in manic-depressive illness: II: Relationship to catecholamines, REM sleep, and drugs. *Arch. Gen. Psychiatry* **27:** 304–309.
6. Carmichael, S. T., and Price, J. L. (1995). Limbic connections of the orbital and medial prefrontal cortex in macaque monkeys. *J. Comp. Neurol.* **363:** 615–641.
7. Carroll, B. J. (1994). Brain mechanisms in manic depression. *Clin. Chem.* **40:** 303–308.
8. Chergui, K., Charlety, P. J., Akaoka, H., *et al.* (1993). Tonic activation of NMDA receptors causes spontaneous burst discharge of rat midbrain dopamine neurons in vivo. *Eur. J. Neurosci.* **5:** 137–144.
9. Damasio, A. R. (1995). *Descarte's Error: Emotion, Reason, and the Human Brain.* Grosset/Putnam, New York, 1994; Picador MacMillan, London.
10. Drevets, W. C., and Botteron, K. (1997). Neuroimaging in psychiatry. In *Adult Psychiatry* (Guze, S. B., ed.), pp. 53–82. Mosby, St. Louis, MO.
11. Drevets, W. C., and Todd, R. D. (1997). Depression, mania and related disorders. In *Adult Psychiatry* (S. B. Guze, ed.), Vol. 8, pp. 99–141. Mosby, St. Louis, MO.

12. Drevets, W. C., Price, J. L., Simpson, J. R., *et al.* (1997). Subgenual prefrontal cortex abnormalities in mood disorders. *Nature* **386:** 824–827.
13. Fibiger, H. C. (1991). The dopamine hypotheses of schizophrenia and mood disorders. In *The Mesolimbic Dopamine System: From Motivation to Action* (P. Willner and J. Scheel-Kruger, eds.), pp. 615–638. Wiley, New York.
14. Goodwin, F. K., Jamison, K. R. (1990). *Manic-Depressive Illness*, Oxford, New York.
15. Murase, S., Grenhoff, J., Chouvet, G., *et al.* (1993). Prefrontal cortex regulates burst firing and transmitter release in rat mesolimbic dopamine neurons. *Neurosci. Lett.* **157:** 53–56.
16. Neafsey, E. J., Terreberry, R. R., Hurley, K. M., *et al.* (1993). Anterior cingulate cortex in rodents: connections, visceral control functions, and implications for emotion. In *Neurobiology of Cingulate Cortex and Limbic Thalamus* (B. A. Vogt and M. Gabriel, eds.). Birkhauser, Boston.
17. Pearlson, G. D., Barta, P. E., Powers, R. E., Menon, R. R., Richards, S. S., Aylward, E. H., Federman, E. B., Chase, G. A., Petty, R. G., and Tien, A. Y. Medial and superior temporal gyral volumes and cerebral asymmetry in schizophrenia versus bipolar disorder. *Biol. Psychiatry*, in press.
18. Roth, R. H., and and Elsworth, J. D. (1995). Biochemical pharmacology of midbrain dopamine neurons. In *Psychopharmacology: The Fourth Generation of Progress* (F. E. Bloom and D. J. Kupfer, eds.), Chapter 21, pp. 227–243. Raven Press, New York.
19. Sesack, S. R., and Pickel, V. M. (1992). Prefrontal cortical efferents in the rat synapse on unlabeled neuronal targets of catecholamine terminals in the nucleus accumbens septi and on dopamine neurons in the ventral tegmental area. *J. Comp. Neurol.* **320:** 145–160.
20. Starkstein, S. E., Fedoroff, P., Berthier, M. L., and Robinson, R. G. (1991). Manic-depressive and pure manic states after brain lesions. *Biol. Psychiatry* **29:** 149–158.
21. Swerdlow, N. R., and Koob, G. F. (1987). Dopamine, schizophrenia, mania and depression: Toward a unified hypothesis of cortico-striato-pallido-thalamic function. *Behav. Brain Sci.* **10:** 197–245.
22. Taber, M. T., and Fibiger, H. C. (1993). Electrical stimulation of the medial prefrontal cortex increases dopamine release in the striatum. *Neuropsychopharmacology* **9:** 271–275.
23. Volkow, N. D., *et al.* (1990). Effects of chronic cocaine abuse on postsynaptic dopamine receptors. *Am. J. Psychiatry* **147:** 719–724.
24. Willner, P. (1995). Dopaminergic mechanisms in depression and mania. In *Psychopharmacology: The Fourth Generation of Progress* (F. E. Bloom and D. J. Kupfer, eds.), Chapter 80, pp. 921–932. Raven Press, New York.

The Amygdala Has a Role in Appetitive Conditioning and Motivation

Less is known about the role of the amygdala in positive affective functions than its role in aversive functions (see Chapter 58). However, monkeys with lesions of the temporal pole, including the amygdala, poorly learn new stimulus–reward associations, suggesting an altered emotional response to reward.[36] In rats, excitotoxic, axon-sparing lesions of the amygdala diminish the capacity of stimuli associated with reward to motivate behavior.[37] Such lesions also impair responses that are rewarded with access to female rats. However, mating per se is unaffected, in contrast with the effect of preoptic lesions.[38] This separation of control of consummatory and learned aspects of sexual behavior indicates that motivated sequences of behavior are constructed through coordination of neural systems that are at least partly independent. Lesions of the basolateral amygdala also impair the phenomenon of place preference,[39] in which experimental animals will consistently return to locations—generally in a well-defined environmental enclosure—where they were previously given reward (see Chapter 52). Overall, portions of the amygdala clearly function in associative processes that contribute to appetitive behavior.

Learned Control of Motivated Behavior

The ventral striatum (see Chapter 52) is part of a system that receives afferents from several limbic cortical structures, including the basolateral amygdala, the hippocampal formation, and the prefrontal cortex, and that projects to structures such as the lateral hypothalamus and ventral pallidum (Fig. 48.6). Output from the pallidum is routed in several different ways, including to brainstem motor regions and looping back to the prefrontal cortex through the mediodorsal thalamus. This circuit (limbic system–ventral striatum–pallidum) could in principle, provide "a neural mechanism by which motivation gets translated into action."[40] To understand the function of this circuit, Mogenson and his colleagues[40] used electrophysiological experiments to demonstrate interactions among its components, for example, between the amygdala and the nucleus accumbens. The researchers also looked at the effects of specific drugs on locomotor activity in rats.

As described earlier, the basolateral and lateral amygdala convey associative information about stimuli that predict the occurrence of reinforcers. The recipients of this information are systems that select responses. A link between the amygdala and the ventral striatum is important in the translation of emotion (and motivational effects of stimuli) to behavioral output, or action.[39] In some circumstances, therefore, reinforcement involves glutamatergic inputs from these limbic afferents to the striatum. These inputs interact with the ascending dopamine system, and together they determine the output of the ventral striatal GABAergic medium spiny neurons that project to the globus pallidus (ventral pallidum).

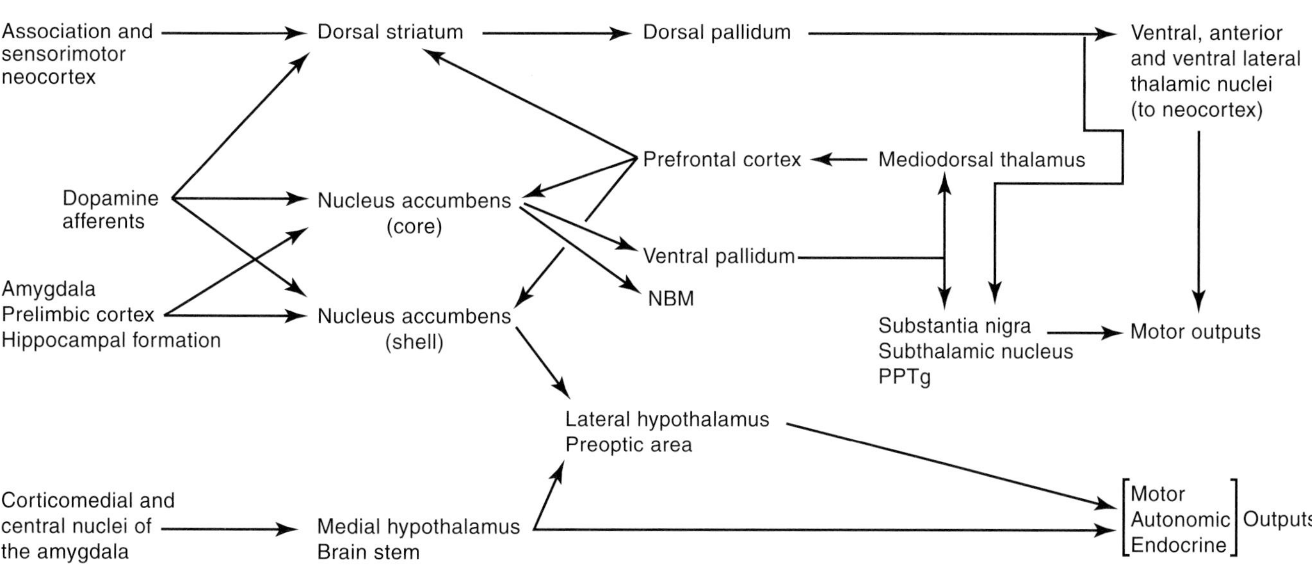

FIGURE 48.6 Schematic of limbic–striatal–pallidal–brainstem circuitry. Processing of motivational and emotional information occurs in limbic and cortical regions of the brain, which interact with dopamine-dependent functions of the nucleus accumbens. The shell and core of this structure act as interfaces with motor (behavioral), endocrine, and autonomic outputs to the hypothalamus and brainstem. The tegmental pedunculopontine (PPTg) nuclei are major components of the midbrain locomotor region. Cortical projections of the dopaminergic and cholinergic neurons of the nucleus basalis magnocellaris (NBM) are not shown. Reproduced with permission from T. W. Robbins and B. J. Everitt, Neurobehavioural mechanisms of reward and motivation. *Curr. Opin. Neurobiol.* **6:** 228–236, 1996.

The nucleus accumbens has turned out to be a heterogeneous structure. Its medial "shell" and lateral "core" can be distinguished anatomically, neurochemically, and functionally. The shell region may be considered part of an extended amygdala encompassing the central nucleus of the amygdala and the bed nucleus of the stria terminalis.[41]

Summary

Appetitive motivational systems organize responses to regulatory and incentive (external sensory) influences and integrate these responses with higher order controls dictated by learning. These controls probably require coordination of several levels of the central nervous system, including limbic, hypothalamic, and brainstem structures. Integration of the activity of these structures appears to be modulated by ascending monoaminergic neurotransmitter systems, such as the mesencephalic dopamine neurons. This modulation probably optimizes the vigor of behavioral responses and enables the reward process to contribute to learning of behavioral sequences (through associative functions of the limbic system).

BRAIN AVERSION SYSTEMS

The affective component of pain is mediated through densely branching collaterals of the somatosensory projections that innervate the reticular formation, especially the nucleus gigantocellularis, the dorsal periaqueductal gray, and the "periventricular punishment system." The system that mediates aversion was identified by a combination of anatomical and behavioral data. For example, mapping studies identified sites eliciting escape from brain stimulation,[34] sites at which ESB elicits defensive responses, and sites at which fear or pain naturally evokes aggressive responses. Many of these pathways are like central reflex pathways, with both ascending and descending components modulated by descending influences from the central nucleus of the amygdala.

Some ESB sites (e.g., VMH) produced markedly ambivalent reinforcing effects, which were interpreted as an interaction between positive reinforcement and aversion systems. ESB itself has been suggested to have both appetitive and aversive properties, as have drugs of abuse and, in some situations, electric shock. In fact, animal learning theory has led to the concept of **opponent motivational processes** (one appetitive, one aversive) (see Chapter 49).

Aversion May Be Mediated by Opponent Motivational Processes

Many reinforcers are said to produce affective and hedonic effects (A processes) that are opposed by B

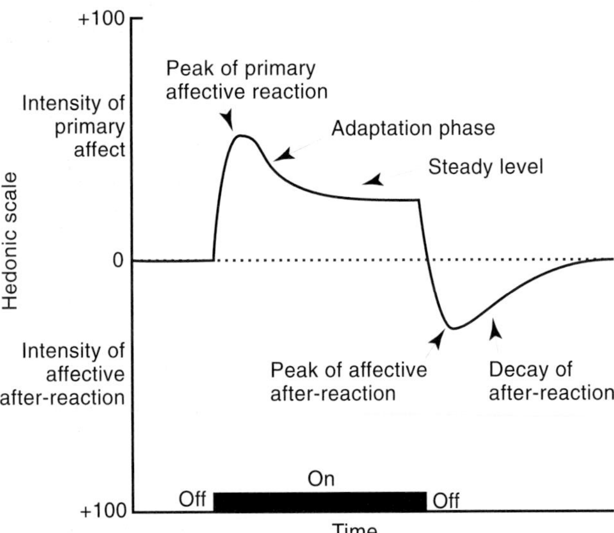

FIGURE 48.7 Opponent motivational system. The graph shows the standard time course of dynamic control of affect. Five distinctive features of affect result from a typical, square-wave input (black bar). The B process becomes apparent after the A process ends. Modified with permission from R. L. Solomon and J. D. Corbit, An opponent-process theory of motivation. *Psychol. Rev.* **81:** 119–145, 1974.

processes of opposite affective sign in a simple, dynamic control system for affect (Fig. 48.7).[42] The A processes follow the reinforcing event with short latency and then decay. The size of the A processes decreases with repeated presentation of the reinforcer. The B processes have longer latency of onset, reach their maximum only after repeated trials, and decay very slowly. These components of emotional responses are exhibited in response to many reinforcers, including not only drugs such as heroin (see Chapter 49), but also natural rewards that also may lead to different forms of "dependence," such as attachment of offspring to a mother.[42] The opponent process can also work in reverse. For example, if tolerance develops for an initially aversive experience, a rebound hedonic response can occur when this experience stops (e.g., as may explain the "pleasure" of jogging).

How might these opponent processes by represented in the brain? Evidence of functional antagonism between systems using noradrenaline and serotonin led researchers[43] to postulate a noradrenergic reinforcing system balanced by a serotoninergic punishment system. Although this particular interaction is now in doubt, the general idea of opposed chemical systems remains feasible. For example, opposing interactions may occur between central dopaminergic and serotoninergic systems. (See Chapter 49 for hypotheses based on studies of drug withdrawal.) Another consideration for research is that the same limbic–striatal interactions that mediate conditioning of appetitive behavior may also affect learning aversive behavior, particularly when this behavior has an operant, or instrumental, as distinct from simple reflexive, component.

Summary

Neural systems controlling aversive motivation are probably distinct from those controlling appetitive motivation. However, opponent relationships involving mutual inhibition have been theorized to exist between the two systems. These interactions are hypothetically subserved by brain regions where appetitive and aversive systems overlap and may underline complex forms of motivation, such as dependence.

Motivation is thus a complex behavioral process that depends on controls provided both by internal stimuli (homeostasis) and by external incentives, the latter often dependent on learning. These stimuli together enable state-dependent selection and coordination of different sequences of behavior that have flexible anticipatory elements and more stereotyped terminal elements. Neural control of these processes is distributed throughout the brain and is powerfully modulated by the activity of neurotransmitter systems such as dopamine. Appetitive motivation may be opposed by aversive processes through mechanisms mediated by neural systems that have overlapping, as well as distinct, components.

References

General

Blackburn, J. R., Pfaus, J. G., and Phillips, A. G. (1992). Dopamine functions in appetitive and defensive behaviors. *Prog. Neurobiol.* **39:** 247–279.

Dickinson, A., and Balleine, B. (1994). Motivational control of goal-directed action. *Anim. Learn. Behav.* **22:** 1–18.

Everitt, B. J., and Robbins, T. W. (1992). Behavioural functions of the Amygdala-ventral striatal interactions and reward-related processes. In *The Amygdala* (J. Aggleton, ed.), pp. 401–429. Wiley, Chichester.

Pfaff, D. W., ed. (1982). *The Physiological Mechanisms of Motivation*, pp. 217–251. Springer-Verlag, New York.

Robbins, T. W., Taylor, J. R., Cador, M., and Everitt, B. J. (1989). Limbic-striatal interactions and reward-related processes. *Neurosci. Biobehav. Rev.* **13:** 155–162.

Sachs, B. D., and Meisel, R. L. (1988). The physiology of male sexual behavior. In *The Physiology of Reproduction* (E. Knobil and J. Neill, eds.), pp. 1393–1485. Raven Press, New York.

Stellar, J. R., and Stellar, E. (1985). *The Neurobiology of Motivation and Reward.* Springer-Verlag, New York.

Toates, F. (1980). *Animal Behaviour: A Systems Approach.* Wiley, Chichester.

Cited

1. Stellar, E. (1954). The psychology of motivation. *Psychol. Rev.* **61:** 5–22.
2. Anand, B. K., and Brobeck, J. R. (1951). Localization of a feeding centre in the hypothalamus of the rat. *Proc. Soc. Exp. Biol. Med.* **77:** 323–324.
3. Hoebel, B. G. (1974). Brain reward and aversion systems in the control of feeding and sexual behavior. In *Nebraska Symposium on Motivation* (J. Cole and T. Sonderegger, eds.), pp. 49–112. University of Nebraska Press, Lincoln.
4. Grossman, S. P. (1960). Eating or drinking elicited by direct adrenergic or cholinergic stimulation of hypothalamus. *Science* **132:** 301–302.
5. Leibowitz, S. F. (1980). Neurochemical systems of the hypothalamus: Control of feeding and drinking behaviour and water-electrolyte excretion. In *Handbook of the Hypothalamus* (P. J. Morgan and J. Panksepp, eds.), Vol. 3, Part A, pp. 299–437. Raven Press, New York.
6. Rolls, E. T. (1985). The neurophysiology of feeding. In *Psychopharmacology and Food* (M. Sandler and T. Silverstone, eds.), pp. 1–16. Oxford University Press, Oxford.
7. Satinoff, E. (1982). Are there similarities between thermoregulation and sexual behaviour? In *The Physiological Mechanisms of Motivation* (D. W. Pfaff, ed.), pp. 217–251. Springer-Verlag, New York.
8. Flynn, J. P., Vanegas, H., Foote,W., and Edwards, S. (1970). Neural mechanisms involved in a cat's attack on a rat. In *The Neural Control of Behaviour* (R. Whalen, R. F. Thompson, M. Verzeano, and N. M. Weinberger, eds.), pp. 135–173. Academic Press, New York.
9. Heimer, L., and Larsson, K. (1966–1967). Impairment of mating behaviour in male rats following lesions in the preoptic-anterior hypothalamic contimuum. *Brain Res.* **3:** 248–263.
10. Pfaff, D. W. (1982). Neurobiological mechanisms of sexual motivation. In *The Physiological Mechanisms of Motivation* (D. W. Paff, ed.), pp. 287–317. Springer-Verlag, New York.
11. Davidson, J. M. (1966). Activation of male rat's sexual behaviour by intracerebral implantation of androgen. *Endocrinology (Baltimore)* **79:** 783–794.
12. Stricker, E. M., and Zigmond, M. J. (1976). Recovery of function after damage to central catecholamine-containing neurons: A neurochemical model for the lateral hypothalamic syndrome. *Prog. Psychol. Physiol. Psychol.* **6:** 121–188.
13. Valenstein, E. T. (1973). *Brain Control.* Wiley, New York.
14. Antelman, S. M., and Szechtman, H. (1975). Tail-pinch induces eating in hungry rats which appears to depend on nigrostriatal dopamine. *Science* **189:** 731–733.
15. Carlisle, H. J. (1969). The effects of preoptic and anterior hypothalamic lesions on behavioral thermoregulation in the cold. *J. Comp. Physiol. Psychol.* **69:** 391–402.
16. Everitt, B. J. (1990). Sexual motivation: A neural and behavioral analysis of the mechanisms underlying appetitive copulatory responses of male rats. *Neurosci. Biobehav. Rev.* **14:** 217–232.
17. Bard, P., and Mountcastle, V. B. (1947). Some forebrain mechanisms involved in expression of rage with special reference to the suppression of angry behavior. *Res. Publ. Assoc. Nerv. Ment. Dis.* **27:** 362–404.
18. Norgren, R., and Grill, H. (1982). Brain-stem control of ingestive behavior. In *The Physiological Mechanisms of Motivation* (D. W. Pfaff, ed.), Vol. 4, pp. 99–131. Springer-Verlag, New York.
19. Ritter, R., Slusser, P. G., and Stone, S. (1981). Glucoreceptors controlling feeding and blood glucose: Location in the hindbrain. *Science* **213:** 451–453.
20. Gallistel, C. R. (1980). *The Organization of Action: A New Synthesis.* Erlbaum, Hillsdale, NJ.
21. Ungerstedt, U. (1971). Adipsia and aphagia after 6-hydroxydopamine induced degeneration of the nigrostriatal dopamine system. *Acta Physiol. Scand. Suppl.* **367:** 95–122.
22. Koob, G. F., Riley, S., Smith, S. C., and Robbins, T. W. (1978). Effects of 6-hydroxydopamine lesions to nucleus accumbens septi and olfactory tubercle on food intake, locomotor activity and amphetamine anorexia in the rat. *J. Comp. Physiol. Psychol.* **92:** 917–927.
23. Marshall, J. F., and Teitelbaum, P. (1977). New considerations in the neuropsychology of motivated behaviors. In *Handbook of Psychopharmacology* (L. L. Iversen, S. D. Iversen, and S. H. Snyder, eds.), Vol. 7, pp. 201–229. Plenum, New York.
24. Winn, P., Tarbuck, A., and Dunnett, S. B. (1984). Ibotenic acid lesions of the lateral hypothalamus: Comparison with the electrolytic lesion syndrome. *Neuroscience* **12:** 225–240.
25. Ungerstedt, U. (1971). Striatal dopamine release after amphetamine or nerve degeneration revealed by rotational behavior. *Acta Physiol. Scand. Suppl.* **367:** 49–68.
26. Carli, M., Evenden, J. L., and Robbins, T. W. (1985). Depletion of unilateral striatal dopamine impairs initiation of contralateral actions and not sensory attention. *Nature (London)* **313:** 679–682.
27. Schultz, W., Romo, R., Ljungberg, T., Mirenowicz, J., Hollerman, J. R., and Dickinson, A. (1995). Reward-related signals carried by dopamine neurons. In *Models of Information Processing in the Basal Ganglia* (J. R. Houk, J. L. Davis, and D. Beiser, eds.), pp. 233–248. MIT Press, Cambridge, MA.
28. Phillips, A. G., Pfaus, J. G., and Blaha, D. C. (1991). Dopamine and motivated behavior. In *The Mesolimbic Dopamine System: From Motivation to Action* (P. Willner and J. Scheel-Kruger, eds.), pp. 199–224. Wiley, Chichester.
29. Olds, J., and Milner, P. (1954). Positive reinforcement produced by electrical stimulation of the septal area and other regions of the rat brain. *J. Comp. Physiol. Psychol.* **47:** 419–427.
30. Trowill, J. A., Panksepp, J. E., and Gandelman, R. (1969). An incentive model of rewarding brain stimulation. *Psychol. Rev.* **76:** 264–281.
31. Phillips, A. G. (1984). Brain reward circuitry: A case for separate systems. *Brain Res. Bull.* **12:** 195–201.
32. Zaravecs, P., and Setler, P. E. (1979). Simultaneous rate-independent and rate-dependent assessment of intracranial self-stimulation: Evidence for the direct involvement of dopamine in brain reinforcement mechanisms. *Brain Res.* **169:** 499–512.
33. German, D. C., and Bowden, D. M. (1974). Catecholamine systems as the neural substrate for intracranial self-stimulation: A hypothesis. *Brain Res.* **73:** 381–419.
34. Olds, J., and Olds, M. (1965). Drives rewards, and the brain. In *New Directions in Psychology*, Vol. 2, pp. 327–410. Holt, Rinehart & Winston, New York.
35. Wise, R. (1982). Neuroleptics and operant behavior: The anhedonia hypothesis. *Behav. Brain Sci.* **5:** 39–87.
36. Jones, B., and Mishkin, M. (1972). Limbic lesions and the problem of stimulus reward associations. *Exp. Neurol.* **36:** 362–377.
37. Cador, M., Everitt, B. J., and Robbins, T. W. (1989). Effects of excitotoxic lesions of the amygdala on the acquisition of new behaviour controlled by conditioned reinforcement: Interaction with the ventral striatum. *Neuroscience* **30:** 77–86.
38. Everitt, B. J., Cador, M., and Robbins, T. W. (1989). Interactions between the amygdala and ventral striatum in stimulus-reward association: Studies using a second-order schedule of sexual reinforcement. *Neuroscience* **30:** 63–75.
39. Everitt, B. J., Morris, K., O'Brien, A., and Robbins, T. W. (1991). The amygdala-ventral striatal system: Role in reward-related processes. *Neuroscience* **42:** 1–18.

40. Mogenson, G. J., Jones, D. L., and Yim, C. Y. (1980). From motivation to action: Functional interface between the limbic system and the motor system. *Prog. Neurobiol.* **14:** 69–97.
41. Heimer, L., Zahm, D. S., and Alheid, G. F. (1995). Basal ganglia. In *The Rat Nervous System* (G. Paxinos, ed.), 2nd ed., pp. 579–614. Academic Press, Sydney.
42. Solomon, R. L., and Corbit, J. D. (1974). An opponent-process theory of motivation: I. Temporal dynamics of affect. *Psychol. Rev.* **81:** 119–145.
43. Stein, L. (1980). The chemistry of reward. In *Biology of Reinforcement: Facets of Brain Stimulation Reward* (A. Routtenberg, ed.), pp. 109–130. Academic Press, New York.

CHAPTER

49

Drug Reward and Addiction

George F. Koob

A common characteristic of most definitions of drug dependence and addiction is a *compulsion to take a drug* with a loss of control in limiting intake (WHO, DSM-IV). The criteria used to diagnose drug dependence incorporate changes in behavior that, when present in a person's daily repertoire, are likely to reflect drug dependence or addiction (Table 49.1). In this chapter, **drug addiction** will be equated with substance dependence as defined by the American Psychiatric Association (DSM-IV).[1] **Drug abuse,** in contrast, will be defined as the harmful use of a drug; it is important to distinguish among drug use, abuse, and dependence. Reinforcement and motivation are crucial parts of substance dependence. Reinforcement has been defined operationally in psychology as a theoretical construct, namely, the process by which stimuli increase the probability of a subjects' responding (see Box 49.1). The term motivation can be defined as the tendency to produce organized activity.

Most views of substance dependence also involve development of tolerance and withdrawal. **Tolerance** is the loss of an effect of a drug with repeated administration. **Withdrawal** is defined as the appearance of symptoms associated with termination of chronic drug use. The concepts of tolerance and withdrawal are key elements supporting the idea that neuroadaptive processes are initiated to counter acute effects of a drug, and our understanding of this subject emphasizes tolerance and withdrawal associated with affective measures, not physical signs.[1a] Another neuroadaptive process that has been proposed as a key element in the development of drug dependence is **sensitization**—the increased response to a drug that follows its repeated, intermittent presentation.[2] These neuroadaptive processes can persist long after a drug has left the brain, and they have been explored at all levels of drug dependence research from the behavioral to the molecular.[3] Motivational hypotheses involving central nervous system counteradaptive changes[4] have particular relevance to dependence phenomena.[4]

ADDICTION: DEFINITIONS AND ANIMAL MODELS

Reinforcement is the process by which stimuli increase the probability of a response. In the context of drug addiction, many sources of reinforcement contribute to compulsive drug use during the course of substance dependence. A drug can directly increase the probability that it will be self-administered through positive reinforcement or through negative reinforcement (e.g., self-medication and/or relief from aversive symptoms of abstinence).[4] A drug also can have indirect motivating properties because of the drug's ability to produce conditioned positive reinforcement. In other words, previously neutral stimuli can come to have druglike positive reinforcing effects; for example, people can actually get "high" simply from the ritual of injection. Further, a drug can produce conditioned negative reinforcement (e.g., conditioned abstinence syndrome) (see Table 49.2 and Box 49.1). Using this framework, we can begin to explore the neurobiological bases of acute positive reinforcing effects of drugs, negative reinforcing effects of the dependent state, and conditioned reinforcing effects associated with protracted abstinence and relapse.[5]

TABLE 49.1 Diagnostic Criteria for Substance Abuse and Substance Dependence (DSM-IV, the American Psychiatric Association)[1]

Substance abuse	Substance dependence
A maladaptive pattern of substance use leading to clinically significant impairment or distress, as manifested by one or more of the following occurring over the same 12-month period.	1. Tolerance.
1. Recurrent substance use resulting in a failure to fulfill major role obligations at work, school, or home.	2. Withdrawal.
2. Recurrent substance use in situations in which it is physically hazardous.	3. The substance is often taken in larger amounts over a longer period than was intended.
3. Recurrent substance-related legal problems.	4. Any unsuccessful effort or a persistent desire to cut down or control substance use.
4. Continued substance use despite having persistent or recurrent social or interpersonal problems caused by substance.	5. A great deal of time is spent in activities necessary to obtain the substance or recover from its effects.
	6. Important social, occupational, or recreational activities given up or reduced because of substance use.
	7. Continued substance use despite knowledge of or having had a persistent or recurrent physical or psychological problem that is likely to be caused or exacerbated by the substance.
	8. Three or more symptoms occurring during the last year.

TABLE 49.2 Relationship of Addictive Components and Behavioral Constructs

Addictive component	Behavioral construct
Pleasure	Positive reinforcement
Self-medication	Negative reinforcement
Habit	Conditioned positive reinforcement
Habit	Conditioned negative reinforcement

BEHAVIORAL PHARMACOLOGICAL PROCEDURES FOR ASSESSING THE REINFORCING ACTIONS OF DRUGS

Animals will self-administer drugs orally and intravenously. In general, drugs that are self-administered correspond to those that have high abuse potential.[6] This relationship is so strong that animal models of drug self-administration are considered to have predictive value for abuse potential in humans, and these models have been suggested for use in batteries of the preclinical assessment of the abuse liability of new pharmaceutical agents.

Animals equipped with long-term intravenous catheters readily learn to intravenously self-administer cocaine or heroin. A typical pattern of cocaine self-administration in a rat maintained on a simple fixed-ratio schedule is shown in Fig. 49.1 (see Box 49.2).[7–10] Note the relationship between dose of the self-administered

BOX 49.1

REINFORCEMENT AND CONDITIONING

The terms describing reinforcement can be confusing and difficult, and it is often best to return to basic definitions taken from experimental psychology. A *reinforcer* is the stimulus or thing that increases the probability of reoccurrence of a response that produces it or strengthens the response that produces it. Generally, the terms reinforcer and *reward* have shared the same meaning; however, reward is often perceived to have some positive emotional content associated with it. *Positive reinforcement* has been defined as the process by which presentation of a stimulus increases the probability of a response, and *negative reinforcement* is the process by which termination of an aversive stimulus increases the probability of a response. *Conditioned reinforcement* is the process by which reinforcing properties are acquired by previously neutral stimuli.

Classical, or *Pavlovian, conditioning* refers to learning that results from presentation of a conditioned stimulus (previously neutral) with an unconditioned stimulus (a biologically significant event) independent of the animal's activities. *Instrumental,* or *operant, conditioning,* in contrast, is learning that results from the relationship between a behavior and its consequences; a behavior occurs because it produces a particular consequence, or reinforcer.

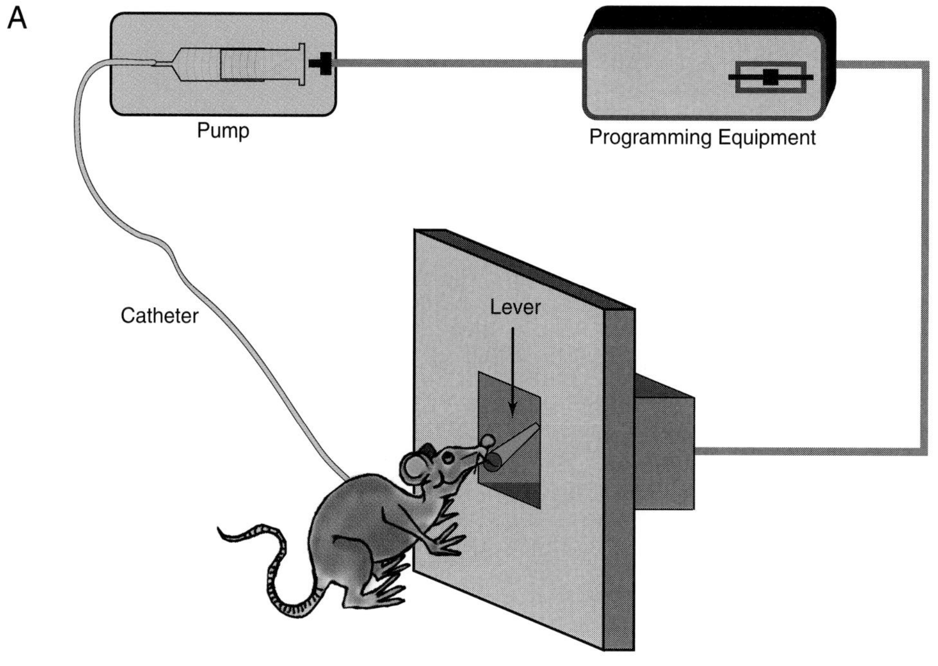

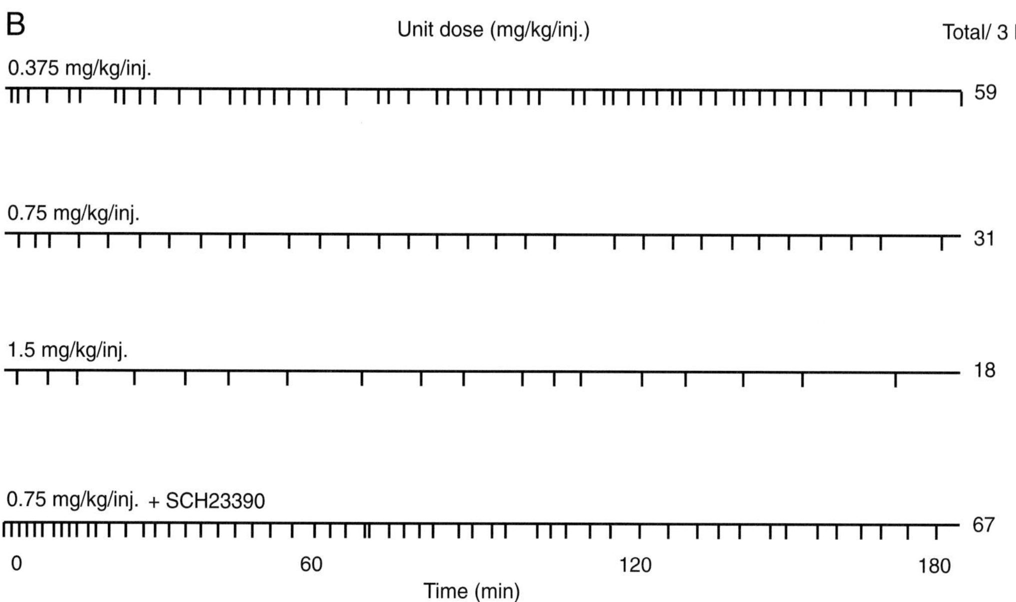

FIGURE 49.1 Intravenous self-administration by rats. (Top) Drawing illustrating the set-up for intravenous self-administration of cocaine by rats. (Bottom) Event records for different unit doses of cocaine show a dose–response relationship relating dose of cocaine to number of infusions. Rats implanted with intravenous catheters and trained to self-administer cocaine with limited access (3 h day^{-1}) show stable and regular drug intake over each daily session. No obvious tolerance or dependence develops. Rats are generally maintained on a fixed-ratio (FR) schedule of drug infusion, such as FR-1 or FR-5. In an FR-1 schedule, one lever press is required to deliver an intravenous infusion of cocaine; in an FR-5 situation, five lever presses are required to deliver an infusion of cocaine. With an FR schedule, rats appear to regulate the amount of drug self-administered. Lowering the dose from the training level of 0.75 mg kg^{-1} $injection^{-1}$ increases the number of self-administered infusions, and raising the unit dose decreases the number of infusions. Pretreatment with dopamine antagonist SCH23390 also increases the number of self-administered infusions. Reprinted from Caine[80] by permission of Oxford University Press.

drug and number of self-administered infusions (termed a *dose–response* or dose–effect function). Within the range of doses that maintain stable responding, as the dose received per self-injection increases, animals increase the interval between injections. Said differently, animals decrease their rates of self-administration, apparently compensating for the increased dose received with each self-injection. Conversely, when dose per self-injection decreases, animals reduce the interval between injections, or increase their rate of self-administration.

In pharmacology, competitive antagonists shift a dose–effect function to the right, as more drug is required to overcome antagonism (see Box 49.2 and Figs. 49.2 and 49.3). With drug self-administration, pharmacologic antagonists of cocaine shift the dose–effect function to the right (representing a decrease in the reinforcing potency of cocaine) and cause increases in self-administered infusions of cocaine (see following). For oral self-administration of drugs such as ethanol, the relationship between dose and number of deliveries of the liquid reinforcer is more of a monotonic function, with higher doses producing higher intake of drug.[11]

Another behavioral test that has been used extensively to measure positive reinforcing effects of drugs of abuse is **rewarding brain stimulation,** or **intracranial self-stimulation** (ICSS). Electrical self-stimulation

BOX 49.2

DRUG DOSE AND RESPONSE

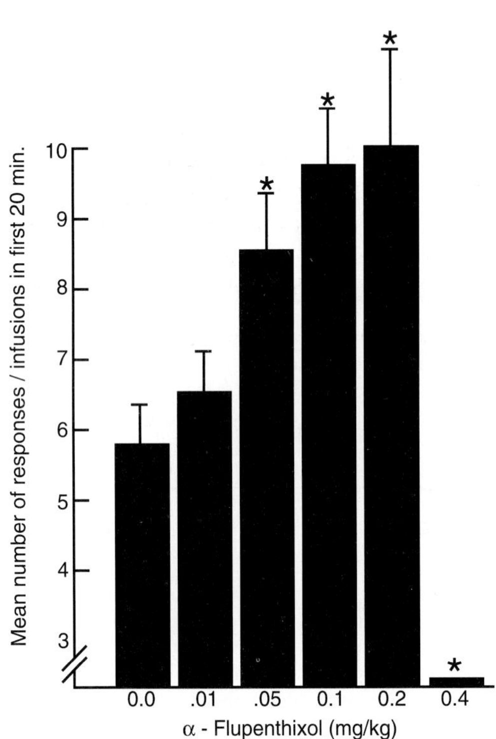

FIGURE 49.2 Effects of pretreatment with the dopamine antagonist α-flupenthixol on cocaine self-administration in rats. α-Flupenthixol, a long-acting, mixed D-1 and D-2 antagonist, was injected 2.5 h before the session. The data represent the effects of α-flupenthixol on the loading dose (infusions during the first 20 min of 3-h test sessions) of cocaine self-administering animals. Asterisks reflect differences between each treatment dose and the appropriate no-drug control ($P < 0.05$, Newman–Keuls test). Asterisks indicate responses that differed reliably between treatment (drug) and control (saline) ($P < 0.05$, Newman–Keuls test). Reprinted with permission from Ettenberg *et al.*[7]

With the intravenous self-administration technique, the relationship between drug dose and an animal's responding for drugs is complex and is usually described by an inverted U-shaped function. As the dose of drug increases, the number of injections increases on the ascending limb. However, at the higher doses in the range often studied in rodent experiments, as dose increases, the number of infusions decreases, and the interval between infusions grows. Administration of dopamine antagonists produces effects similar to those of *decreasing* the dose of cocaine. The number of infusions actually increases in these studies, but the interval between injections decreases, as occurs when the dose of cocaine decreases (see Fig. 49.1). Animals appear to compensate for decreases in the magnitude of reinforcement by increasing cocaine self-administration; however, high doses of a dopamine antagonist abolish responding (see Fig. 49.2).[7] Confirmation that these dopamine antagonists are blocking the reinforcing effects of cocaine comes from dose–effect studies in which the antagonists shift the cocaine dose–effect function to the right (see Fig. 49.3).[8,9] In general, experiments investigating the effects of antagonists selective for subtypes of dopamine receptors reveal that antagonists of D-1, D-2 (74), and D-3 receptors decrease the reinforcing properties of cocaine.[10]

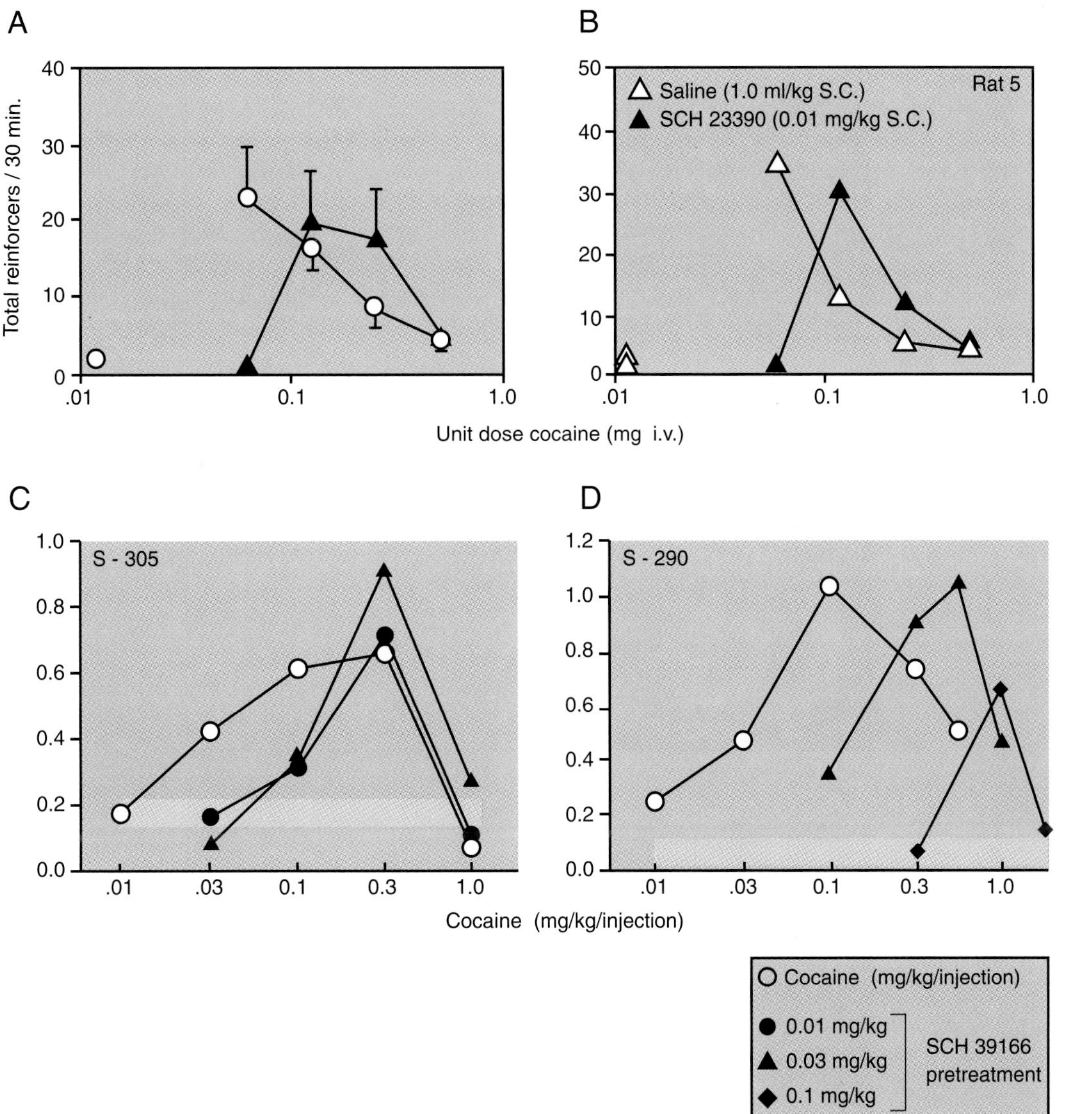

FIGURE 49.3 The cocaine dose–effect function shifts to the right following pretreatment with the dopamine D-1 antagonists SCH23390 and SCH39166. (A) Effects of pretreatment with SCH23390 (0.01 mg kg^{-1} subcutaneous) on the dose–effect function of intravenously self-administered cocaine (0.06–0.50 mg) measured using the within-session dose–effect paradigm (n = 4). (B) Same as (A) but for an individual rat. Reprinted with permission from Caine and Koob.[8] (C and D) Effects of pretreatment with SCH39166 on cocaine self-administration in two squirrel monkeys. Points are means based on the last three sessions at each dose of drug. Reprinted with permission from Bergman *et al.*[9]

of certain brain areas is rewarding for animals and humans, as demonstrated by subjects that readily self-administer such stimulation.[12,13] The high reward value of ICSS has led to the hypothesis that ICSS directly activates neuronal reward circuits. Because ICSS bypasses much of the input side of these neuronal circuit(s), it provides a unique tool in neuropharmacological research with which to study the influence of various substances on reward and reinforcement processes. ICSS differs significantly from drug self-administration in that animals work to directly stimulate presumed reinforcement circuits in the brain that are activated by conventional reinforcers (e.g., food, water, sex). Drugs of abuse appear to make ICSS *more* re-

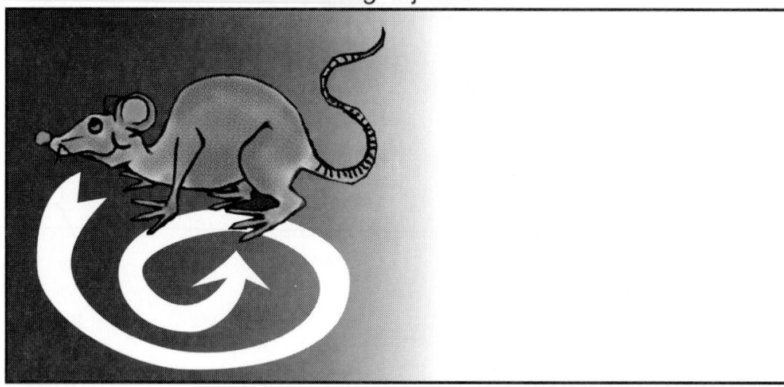

FIGURE 49.4 The place conditioning procedure in a rat. See text for details. Reprinted with permission from N. R. Swerdlow, D. Gilbert, and G. F. Koob (1989). In *Neuromethods* (A. A. Boulton, G. B. Baker, and A. J. Greenshaw, eds.), Vol. 13, pp. 399–446, Humana Press, Clifton, NJ.

warding or decrease thresholds for ICSS, and there is a good correlation between the ability of drugs to decrease ICSS thresholds and their potential for abuse.[14]

The third major behavioral test used to measure reinforcing actions of drugs of abuse is a procedure called **place conditioning.** In effect, this is a Pavlovian conditioning procedure in which a drug state is paired with experience in a particular environment. In a simple version of the *place preference* paradigm, animals experience two distinct neutral environments that are subsequently paired spatially and temporally with distinct drug states, the unconditioned stimuli (UCS). The animal is then given an opportunity to choose to enter and explore either environment in the absence of the drug. Positive reinforcing effects of the drug are reflected in the choice of the animal to spend more time in the environment that was paired with the drug (see Fig. 49.4). Of course, the opposite also can occur—an aversive experience becomes a negative reinforcer (see following). One of the earlier demonstrations of place preference was the observation by Olds and Milner[12] that rats stimulated through an intracranial electrode would return to the location in which they received the stimulation.

Summary

Compulsive drug-seeking behaviors are the result of positive and negative reinforcement associated with chronic drug taking, with varying degrees of residual drug-induced rewards. These multiple sources of reinforcement serve to strengthen the power of drugs in the abuser's life.

NEUROBIOLOGICAL SUBSTRATES OF DRUG REWARD

Positive Reinforcing Effects of Drugs Are Mediated by Multiple Systems Converging on Common Targets in the Basal Forebrain

The midbrain and forebrain long have been hypothesized to be involved in motivated behavior through connections of the medial forebrain bundle, which is composed of both ascending and descending connections including most of the brain monoamine systems.[12,15,16] The medial forebrain bundle is involved in brain stimulation reward[12,17,18] and natural rewards.[19] Work in the neurobiology of addiction has led to an understanding of the neurochemical and neuroanatomical components of this system. The principal components of this system include the ventral tegmental area, the basal forebrain (the nucleus accumbens, olfactory tubercle, frontal cortex, and amygdala), and the dopamine connection between the ventral tegmental area and the basal forebrain, called the mesolimbic dopamine system. Additional components are the opioid peptide systems, GABA systems, and serotonin systems that interact with the ventral tegmental area and the basal forebrain[20] (see Fig. 49.5). The functional role of each component of this mesolimbic system will be discussed in the following sections, and a concept called the extended amygdala will be introduced to provide insight into the relationship between drug reward and natural reward systems.

The Positive Reinforcing Effects of Cocaine and Other Indirect Sympathomimetics Depend Critically on the Mesolimbic Dopamine System

Amphetamine and **cocaine** are psychomotor stimulants and as such have behavioral effects such as suppressing hunger and fatigue and inducing euphoria in humans. In animals, these drugs increase motor activity, decrease food intake, stimulate operant behavior (psychomotor stimulation), enhance conditioned responding, and produce place preferences.[21] They also decrease thresholds for reinforcing brain stimulation (see Fig. 49.6)[22] and act as reinforcers for drug self-administration[23] (see Fig. 49.1).

Psychomotor stimulants with high potential for abuse have effects that lead to increases in the availability of monoamine neurotransmitters at synapses. Cocaine and amphetamine increase the synaptic availability of dopamine, norepinephrine, and serotonin, mainly by blocking reuptake of these monoamines. However, the acute reinforcing effects of these drugs depend critically on dopamine.[7,24] Studies of intravenous self-administration (see Fig. 49.2) have provided the most direct evidence implicating dopamine, and more specifically the mesolimbic dopamine system, in the reinforcing actions of cocaine. Low doses of dopamine receptor antagonists injected systemically and centrally reliably block the reinforcing effects of cocaine and amphetamine self-administration in rats.[7,24] A specific role for the mesolimbic dopamine system in the reinforcing properties of cocaine and amphetamine was deduced from the observation that, over days, neurotoxin-induced lesions of the terminal regions of the mesolimbic dopamine system in the nucleus accumbens produce extinctionlike responding and a significant and long-lasting decrease in self-administration of cocaine and amphetamine.[1] The neurotoxin, an analog of dopamine called 6-hydroxydopamine, was directly injected into the brain; it is taken up by presynaptic dopamine nerve terminals and destroys

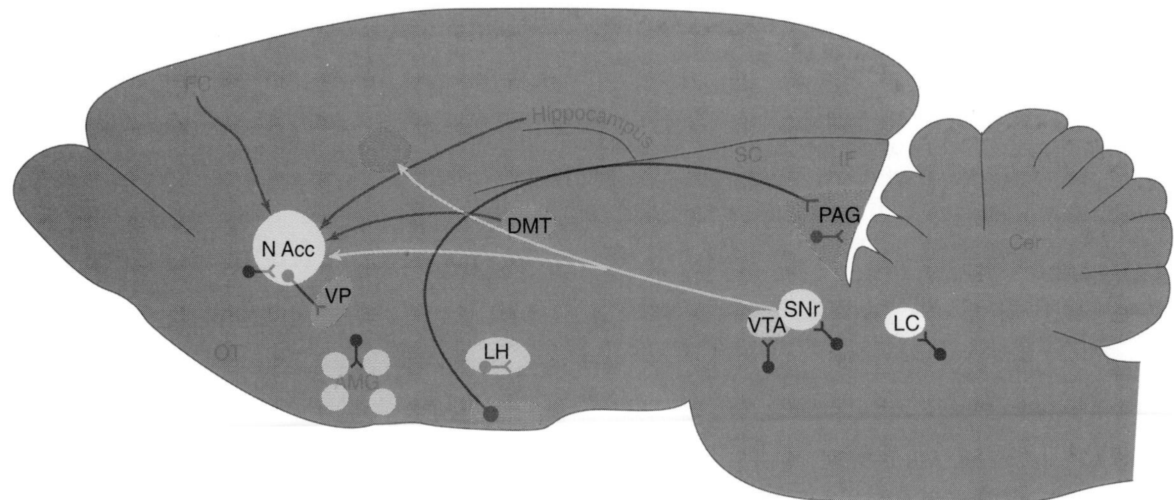

FIGURE 49.5 Sagittal section through the brain of a rat depicting the neurochemical systems implicated in the reinforcing effects of drugs of abuse. Yellow indicates limbic afferents to the nucleus accumbens (N. Acc.). Orange represents efferents from the nucleus accumbens thought to be involved in psychomotor stimulant reward. Red indicates the projection of the mesocorticolimbic dopamine system thought to be a critical substrate for psychomotor stimulant reward. This system originates in the A10 cell group of the ventral tegmental area (VTA) and projects to the N. Acc., olfactory tubercle, and ventral striatal domains of the caudate–putamen (CP). Green indicates opioid peptide-containing neurons that may be involved in opiate and ethanol reward. These opioid peptide systems include the local enkephalin circuits (short segments) and the hypothalamic midbrain β-endorphin circuit (long segment). Blue shows the approximate distribution of $GABA_A$ receptor complexes, some of which may mediate sedative–hypnotic (ethanol) reward (determined by binding of tritiated (i.e., radioactively labeled) flumazenil to GABA receptors and by expression of the α, β, and γ subunits of the $GABA_A$ receptor). VP, ventral pallidum; LH, lateral hypothalamus; SN, substantia nigra pars reticulata; DMT, dorsomedial thalamus; PG, periaqueductal gray; OT, olfactory tract; AC, anterior commissure; LC, locus ceruleus; AMG, amygdala; Hippo, hippocampus; FC, frontal cortex. Modified with permission from Koob.[20]

them. These decreases in cocaine self-administration have been observed in a variety of tests and conditions, including situations in which animals decreased the amount of work they would perform for cocaine and situations in which other reinforcers, such as food, were unaffected but cocaine self-administration was abolished. The specific sites within the mesolimbic dopamine system that appear important for the reinforcing actions of cocaine correspond with specific subregions, such as the shell (medial part) of the nucleus accumbens and the central nucleus of the amygdala.

Neurobiological Substrates for the Acute Reinforcing Effects of Opiates Involve Opioid Peptide Systems

Much like psychostimulants, opiate drugs such as **heroin** are readily self-administered intravenously by animals. When provided an opiate in limited-access situations, rats and primates[6] will maintain stable daily opiate intake without major signs of physical dependence. Advances in opiate pharmacology, such as identification of high specific binding for opiates in the brain and discovery of endogenous opioid peptides, provided insight into the brain systems responsible for the reinforcing effects of these drugs (see Box 49.3).[25] Both systemic administration and central administration of competitive opiate antagonists decrease intravenous opiate self-administration.[26] The reinforcing actions of heroin and morphine appear to be mediated largely by the mu opiate receptor subtype. Mu opioid antagonists produce dose-dependent decreases in heroin reinforcement, and intracerebral opioid antagonists dose-dependently block heroin self-administration in nondependent rats when these drugs are injected into the ventral tegmental area or the region of the nucleus accumbens. Microinjections of opioids into the ventral tegmental area also lower thresholds of brain stimulation reward and produce robust place preferences.[27] Rats also will self-administer opioid peptides in the region of the nucleus accumbens. Furthermore, heroin self-administration is not blocked by DA antagonists given in doses that block cocaine self-administration (cocaine-blocking doses of dopamine antagonists)[7] nor by large neurotoxin-induced lesions of the mesolimbic dopamine system. These results demonstrate that neu-

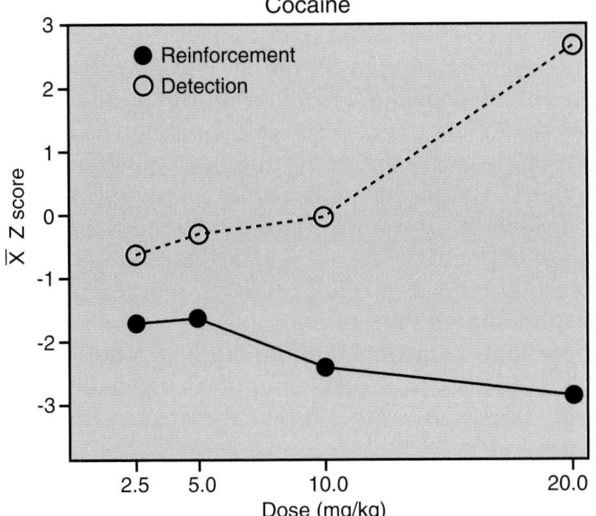

FIGURE 49.6 Effects of cocaine on thresholds of brain stimulation reward and brain stimulation detection. For measurement of detection threshold, the initial, noncontingent stimulus varied in intensity (at subreward levels), while the second, or response-contingent, stimulus was held constant at a rewarding intensity to maintain responding. Each point is the mean z score ± SEM, the difference between the means of the thresholds after administration of vehicle and drug, divided by the standard deviation of all thresholds after vehicle administration. A z score of 2 indicates significant difference from vehicle treatment sessions. These results show that acute administration of cocaine can lower thresholds of brain stimulation (e.g., facilitate central reward). The cocaine treatment does not affect the ability of the rat to discriminate because detection of a nonrewarding stimulus is not altered (detection threshold). (Error bars not shown indicate SEM less than the diameter of the symbols in this illustration.) Reprinted with permission from Kornetsky and Bain.[2]

ral elements in the regions of the ventral tegmental area *and* the nucleus accumbens are responsible for the reinforcing properties of opiates, suggesting both dopamine-dependent and dopamine-independent opiate action.[20,27]

Nicotine Activates Mesolimbic Dopamine and Opioid Peptide Systems

Nicotine has antifatigue, stimulantlike actions and antistress effects and appears to improve cognitive performance in animals and humans. It has direct reinforcing actions, as measured by intravenous self-administration in animals and humans. Smoking 1–2 packs of cigarettes per day leads to nicotine dependence (addiction), characterized by tolerance, withdrawal, craving, and continued use despite repeated efforts to stop use.

Nicotine is a direct agonist at nicotinic acetylcholine receptors of the brain and appears to activate the mesolimbic dopamine system and endogenous opioid peptide systems. Antagonism of dopaminergic systems also can block nicotine self-administration.[28,29] Administration of nicotinic acetylcholine antagonists and the opiate antagonist naloxone can precipitate nicotine withdrawal in rodents.[29,30]

Alcohol Has Multiple Neurochemical Substrates within Brain Reinforcement Systems

Ethanol, barbiturates, and **benzodiazepines** all have measurable sedative–hypnotic actions, including euphoria, disinhibition, anxiety reduction, sedation, and hypnosis. All of these drugs also have antianxiety

BOX 49.3

OPIATE RECEPTORS

In 1978, Professors Solomon H. Snyder, John Hughes, and Hans W. Kosterlitz were awarded the Lasker Award for their combined discovery of opiate receptors in the brain and for the even more amazing discovery of the existence of endogenous ligands for the opiate receptors.[25] The endogenous brain compounds were peptides, called enkephalins and endorphins, that shared all the physiologic properties of opiates. These observations opened a rich field of inquiry into the mechanism of action of opiate drugs, and these findings began a new outlook on neuropeptide neurotransmitters, an area of intense research. First, other drugs for which no specific neurotransmitter mediators were known were now subjected to the possibility of other undiscovered "peptides" whose receptors provided receptors, such as barbiturates, benzodiazepines, and anticonvulsants. Second, because neuropeptides are contained within neurons that also are more conventional amino acid or amine transmitters, the possibility of multiple mediators for any specific synapse had now to be considered.

effects, reflected in conflict situations as a reduction of behavior suppressed by punishment. The anticonflict effect of sedative–hypnotics correlates well with their ability to act as anxiolytics in clinical settings[31] and may be a major component of the reinforcing actions of these drugs. These effects of sedative–hypnotics correlate well with their ability to modulate the receptors of the major inhibitory neurotransmitter in the brain—GABA.[32] At the electrophysiological level GABA produces postsynaptic inhibition, and at the molecular level GABA increases chloride ion (Cl^-) flux in synaptic neurosomal preparations. This increase in ion flux produced by GABA is potentiated by benzodiazepines, barbiturates, and ethanol.[33]

The neurobiological basis of the anxiolytic properties of these sedative–hypnotic drugs has provided clues to their reinforcing properties and their abuse potential.[23,31,34] For example, GABAergic antagonists reverse many of the behavioral effects of ethanol, an observation that has led to the hypothesis that GABA has a role in the intoxicating effects of ethanol. Further support for a role of brain GABA in ethanol reinforcement is the observation that potent antagonists of GABA receptor function decrease ethanol reinforcement; one particularly affected brain site is the central nucleus of the amygdala.[35,36]

Several studies also have suggested that brain dopamine systems may be involved in the reinforcing properties of ethanol. Dopamine receptor antagonists reduce lever-pressing for ethanol in nondeprived rats,[23] and extracellular dopamine levels increase in nondependent rats orally self-administering low doses of ethanol.[23] However, virtually complete destruction of dopamine terminals in the nucleus accumbens by the neurotoxin 6-hydroxydopamine failed to alter voluntary responding for alcohol.[23] Combined with the pharmacologic data discussed earlier, these results suggest that although mesolimbic dopamine transmission may be associated with important aspects of ethanol reinforcement, it is not critical for the reinforcing properties of ethanol; other neurochemical systems may participate in the mediation of ethanol's reinforcing actions. In fact, the view is emerging that multiple neurotransmitters combine to orchestrate the reward profile of alcohol.[23,37]

For example, alcohol in a physiologic dose range may antagonize the actions of glutamate.[38,39] Also, increases in synaptic availability of serotonin (accomplished through precursor loading), blockade of serotonin reuptake, and central injection of serotonin all reduce voluntary intake of alcohol.[40] Consistent with a serotonergic role in ethanol abuse, serotonin reuptake inhibitors have produced mild to moderate decreases in alcohol consumption in humans in several double-blind, placebo-controlled clinical studies.[41]

Activation of opioid peptide systems has been implicated in alcohol reinforcement by numerous reports that the opiate antagonists **naloxone** and **naltrexone** reduce alcohol self-administration in several animal models.[42] Consistent with a role for opioid peptides in alcohol reinforcement, two double-blind, placebo-controlled clinical trials showed that naltrexone significantly reduces alcohol consumption, frequency of relapse, and craving for alcohol in humans.[43,44] Thus, interactions of alcohol with opioid neurotransmission may contribute to alcohol reinforcement and be particularly important in the development or maintenance of dependence.

The Extended Amygdala May Be a Common Substrate for Drug Reward and Natural Rewards

Neuroanatomic and functional data have provided the basis for an interesting hypothesis that neuroanatomical substrates for the reinforcing actions of drugs may involve neural circuitry that forms a separate entity within the basal forebrain, termed the **extended amygdala**.[45] The concept of an extended amygdala represents a macrostructure, originally described by Johnston,[46] composed of several basal forebrain structures: the bed nucleus of the stria terminalis, the centromedial amygdala and medial part of the nucleus accumbens (i.e., shell),[45] and continuous cell columns in the sublenticular substantia innominata. The functional entity called the extended amygdala is based on similarities in morphology, immunohistochemistry, and connectivity among these structures.[45] Afferent connections to this complex include frontal, entorhinal, and olfactory cortices and the hippocampal formation, basolateral amygdala, thalamic nuclei, ventral tegmental area, ventral pallidum, lateral hypothalamus, and lateral septum. Efferent connections from this complex include the posterior medial (sublenticular) ventral pallidum, medial ventral tegmental area, reticular formation, and central gray. Also included are a small projection to the raphe nuclei and, perhaps most intriguing from a functional point of view, a considerable projection to the lateral hypothalamus. There also are numerous connections among the components of the extended amygdala, particularly between the central nucleus of the amygdala and the bed nucleus of the stria terminalis.[45]

The concept of the extended amygdala essentially links extensive developments in the neurobiology of drug reward with knowledge of the substrates for natural rewards, essentially bridging what have been largely independent research pursuits in the neurosciences. For many years in the search for the neurochemical components that are the basis of brain reward circuits, the neuroanatomical focus has been the medial forebrain bundle (see preceding). Neurobiological studies showing important neurochemical links to drug reward within the extended amygdala and important neuroanatomical connections from the extended amygdala to the hypothalamus may provide not only the substrates of drug rewards but the neurochemical key to natural reward mechanisms.

Summary

The positive reinforcing effects of drugs are mediated by multiple systems converging on common targets in the basal forebrain. The positive reinforcing effects of cocaine and other psychostimulants (indirect sympathomimetics) depend on the mesolimbic dopamine circuits. Within these forebrain reward systems, the acute reinforcing effects of opiates involve opioid peptide-mediated circuits. Nicotine activates both ascending dopamine and, possibly, intrinsic opioid peptide-mediated circuits. Within this complex array of targets, ethanol-induced effects rely on dopamine, opioid, and probably other transmitter systems. The outer boundaries of the drug-sensitive forebrain roughly resemble the extended boundaries of the amygdala complex.

NEUROBIOLOGICAL SUBSTRATES FOR MOTIVATIONAL EFFECTS OF DRUG DEPENDENCE

Negative Affect Is a Common Result of Withdrawal from Chronic Administration of Drugs of Abuse

Withdrawal signs associated with cessation of chronic drug administration are usually characterized by responses opposite to the acute initial actions of the drug; however, few if any physical signs have ever been observed with cocaine and other indirect sympathomimetics. In contrast, subjective symptoms of dysphoria, negative affect, and anxiety are common to all three classes of drugs (see Table 49.3). Cocaine withdrawal in humans in the outpatient setting is characterized by severe depressive symptoms combined with irritability, anxiety, and anhedonia, lasting several hours to several days (i.e., the "crash") and may be a motivating factor in the maintenance of the cocaine dependence cycle.[47] Opiate withdrawal in humans is characterized by physical signs and subjective symptoms of extreme discomfort (DSM-IV). The physical signs include pupillary dilation, hot and cold flashes, goose bumps, and a flulike state. Subjective symptoms include dysphoria, anxiety, craving (for drugs), and muscle aches. Signs of alcohol withdrawal in humans include tremor and increases in heartbeat rate, blood pressure, and body temperature. Symptoms include anxiety, hallucinations, and malaise (DSM-IV).

TABLE 49.3 Diagnostic Criteria for Drug Withdrawal (DSM-IV)[1]

Opioid	Alcohol	Cocaine	Nicotine
Dysphoric mood	Autonomic hyperactivity	Dysphoric mood	Dysphoric or depressed mood
Nausea or vomiting	Hand tremor	Fatigue	Insomnia
Muscle aches	Insomnia	Unpleasant dreams	Irritability
Lacrimation	Nausea or vomiting	Insomnia or hypersomnia	Anxiety
Rhinorrhea	Hallucinations	Increased appetite	Difficulty concentrating
Pupillary dilation	Illusions	Psychomotor retardation or agitation	Restlessness
Piloerection	Psychomotor agitation	Anxiety	Decreased heart rate
Sweating	Anxiety		Increased appetite
Diarrhea	Seizures		Weight gain
Yawning			
Fever			
Insomnia			
Anxiety			

TABLE 49.4 Drug Effects on Thresholds of Rewarding Brain Stimulation

Drug class	Acute administration	Withdrawal from chronic treatment
Psychostimulants (cocaine, amphetamines)	↓	↑
Opiates (morphine, heroin)	↓	↑
Nicotine	↓	↑
Sedative–hypnotics (ethanol)	↓	↑

Chronic Drug Administration Compromises the Brain Reward Systems

In animal studies, withdrawal from chronic administration of stimulants has been studied using repeated administration of cocaine or amphetamines over days and weeks or, alternatively, prolonged periods (12–48 h) of self-administration. Withdrawal from prolonged self-administration of cocaine in rats increases ICSS reward thresholds. The increase in threshold is dose- and time-dependent[48] and is an effect opposite to that of acute cocaine use (see Table 49.4).[5] Similar effects have been observed in withdrawal from chronic amphetamine administration. Opiate withdrawal induced by administration of low doses of the opiate antagonist naloxone also elevates brain stimulation thresholds, as does spontaneous withdrawal from ethanol.[49]

Summary

Negative affect is a common consequence of withdrawal from the continuous use of abusable drugs. This chronic use compromises the effectiveness of the brain reward systems on which drugs of abuse impose their effects.

NEUROCHEMICAL ADAPTATION IN REWARD NEUROTRANSMITTERS

Dopamine and Serotonin Neurochemical Systems Show Neuroadaptive Changes with Substance Dependence

Dopamine in the mesolimbic dopamine system has been implicated in the reinforcing actions of stimulants, opiates, nicotine, and ethanol. One way of assessing the prolonged effects of drug self-administration is to measure extracellular levels of a neurotransmitter during ongoing behaviors such as intravenous self-administration of a drug or withdrawal from the drug after a period of chronic self-administration. Such measurements can be made by using the neuropharmacological technique of *in vivo* microdialysis. *In vivo* microdialysis involves implanting into the brain a guide tube through which a probe with a semipermeable membrane at the tip perfuses and collects neurotransmitter in cerebrospinal fluid at a specific site in the brain. Several studies have shown that extracellular dopamine levels in the nucleus accumbens, measured by *in vivo* microdialysis, decrease during acute withdrawal from cocaine, opiates, and alcohol,[27,50] an effect opposite to that of acute drug administration. For example, following a session of cocaine self-administration, extracellular dopamine levels in the nucleus accumbens decreased significantly during cocaine withdrawal compared to presession levels.[51] This dopamine decrease correlated with the amount of cocaine consumed during the preceding binge and was maximal at the time of maximal elevation in ICSS threshold.[48] Perhaps more interesting was that extracellular serotonin levels decreased even more dramatically during cocaine withdrawal (see Fig. 49.7).[52] The duration of the serotonin decrease and the time course of recovery are unknown.

Signal Transduction Level Shows Neuroadaptive Changes with Substance Dependence

Not only can functional activity of neurotransmitters increase due to increased presynaptic activity of chronic drug use, but these increases can be translated to postsynaptic signal transduction. These changes in signal transduction can be long-lasting and may result in long-term changes in receptor function. Whereas chronic opiate use has minimal effect on the binding of opiate receptors by opioid peptides, it dramatically changes signal transduction in the terminal regions of the mesolimbic dopamine system, such as the nucleus accumbens.[53] Chronic opiates increase adenylate cyclase activity, its state of protein phosphorylation, and intermediate-early gene expression. These changes can result in expression of novel proteins and, consequently, changes in neuronal function that could explain clinical phenomena, such as protracted abstinence and vulnerability to relapse, in people formerly addicted to drugs.

Brain Corticotropin-Releasing Factor Systems Show Neuroadaptive Changes with Substance Dependence

Anxiety and stress are common elements of substance dependence and acute withdrawal from drugs

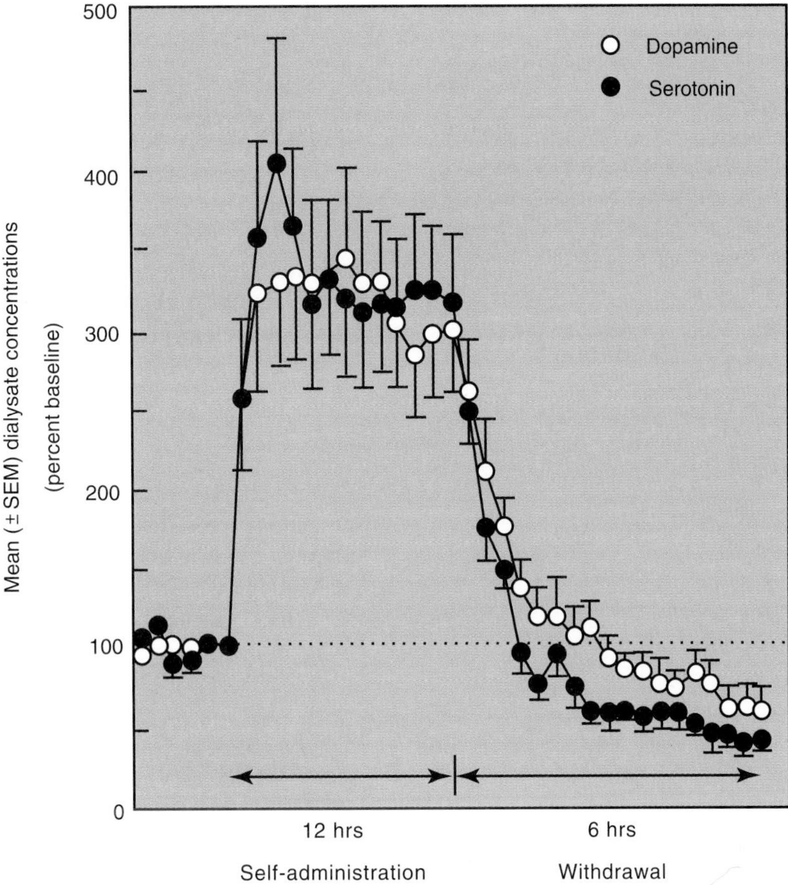

FIGURE 49.7 Extracellular dopamine and serotonin levels in the nucleus accumbens during and following a 12 h binge of cocaine self-administration in rats (A). For 12 h, rats had unlimited access to cocaine self-administration. The mean (± SEM) presession baseline dialysate (see text) concentrations of dopamine and serotonin were 5.3 ± 0.5 and 1.0 ± 0.1 n*M*, respectively ($n = 7$). Reprinted with permission from Parsons *et al.*[52]

of abuse (see Table 49.3). Drug withdrawal in humans is characterized by anxiety (DSM-IV), and withdrawal from repeated cocaine, opiate, or alcohol administration produces stresslike behavior in animal tests.[31,54,55]

Animal studies exploring the role of corticotropin-releasing factor (CRF) in the actions of alcohol, opiates, and cocaine have provided evidence of a neurochemical basis for the stress associated with abstinence following chronic drug administration. CRF not only is a major hypothalamic releasing factor controlling the classic stress response but also appears to have a neurotropic role in the central nervous system modulating behavioral responses to stress.[55] CRF itself produces stress behaviors, and CRF antagonists reverse a number of behavioral responses to stress.[55] Rats treated repeatedly with drugs such as alcohol, opiates, and cocaine show significant stresslike responses in behavioral tests that follow cessation of drug administration, and the responses are reversed by administration of a CRF antagonist directly into the brain. Injection of a CRF antagonist into the central nucleus of the amygdala reverses the stresslike effects of ethanol withdrawal in rats.[23] Furthermore, withdrawal from ethanol is associated with an increase in the release of CRF into the amygdala, suggesting that ethanol withdrawal can activate CRF systems previously implicated in behavioral responses to stress[56] (see Fig. 49.8).

The Locus Ceruleus Norepinephrine System Shows Neuroadaptive Changes with Substance Dependence

Norepinephrine in the limbic forebrain has long been implicated in the physical and motivational signs of opiate withdrawal. The primary source of noradrenergic innervation of the limbic system is the locus ceru-

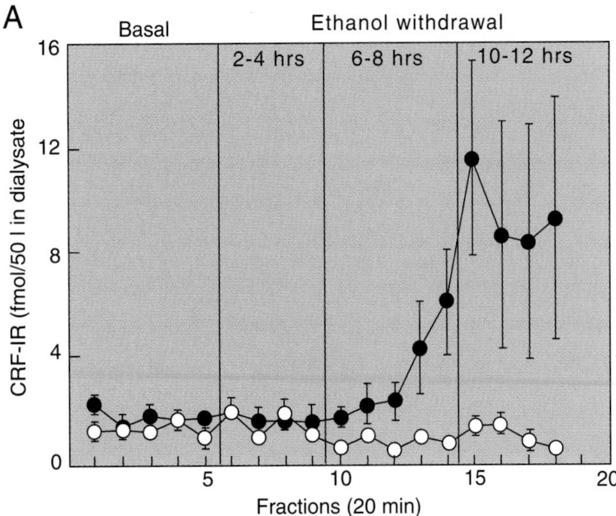

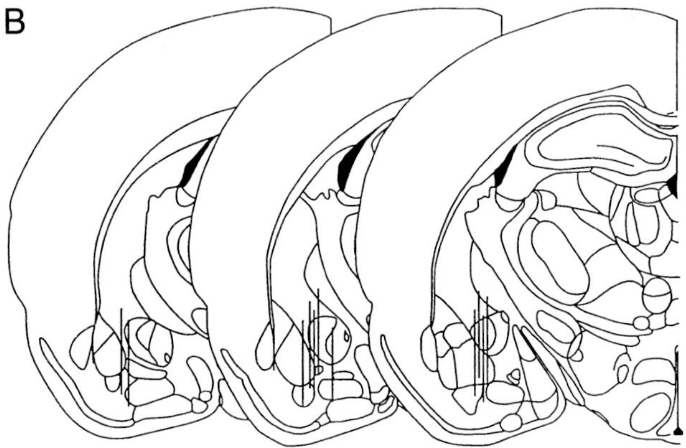

FIGURE 49.8 Extracellular levels of corticotropin-releasing factor (CRF) in the amygdala during withdrawal from chronic ethanol administration. (A) Dialysate was collected over four 2-h periods, which alternated with nonsampling 2-h periods. The four sampling periods correspond to the basal collection (before removal of ethanol) and 2–4 h, 6–8 h, and 10–12 h after withdrawal of ethanol. Fractions were collected every 20 min. Data are represented as means ± SEM (n = 5/group). ANOVA confirmed significant differences between the two groups over time ($P < 0.05$). (B) Anatomical analysis identified these locations (vertical lines) as sites where changes in CRF concentration were detected in the ethanol experiment (n = 10) as being within the amygdaloid complex. Reprinted with permission from Pich *et al.*[56]

leus, a large cluster of noradrenergic neurons in the pons.[57] The first evidence of a role for the locus ceruleus in opiate withdrawal was the observation that opiate withdrawal produced an increase in the firing rate of the locus ceruleus.[58] Now, several neuropharmacological lines of evidence support a role for the locus ceruleus in opiate withdrawal: Electrical stimulation of the locus ceruleus causes signs that mimic opiate withdrawal.[58a] Microinjection of very low doses of opiate antagonists into the locus ceruleus induces opiate withdrawal. Even more compelling is evidence that lesions of the locus ceruleus block various signs of opiate withdrawal, and that systemic and central administration of clonidine, an α-adrenergic agonist that suppresses locus ceruleus firing, decreases both physical and motivational signs of withdrawal.[59,60] Extensive work has shown that changes in the locus ceruleus system associated with opiate dependence are mediated by changes in the function of opiate receptors in the locus ceruleus,[53] as well as changes in glutamatergic input to the locus ceruleus.[61]

Summary

With chronic exposure, dopamine and serotonin circuits adapt to the actions of drugs of abuse. These changes include adaptation in the signal transduction molecular mediators, including dopamine, corticotropin-releasing factor, and the noradrenergic locus ceruleus forebrain circuits.

NEUROADAPTATION, PROLONGED ABSTINENCE, AND RELAPSE

The Neurobiological Basis for Neuroadaptation to Chronic Drugs of Abuse Can Be Modeled as an Opponent Process

Drug tolerance and withdrawal have long been hypothesized to involve neuroadaptation,[62] and changes in reward threshold in the medial forebrain bundle reflect such adaptations, as do accompanying neurochemical changes.[3] A number of hypotheses have been developed to explain drug-induced neuroadaptations, but the opponent process model was developed specifically to explain changes in hedonic state.[70] Here, initial hedonic response to a drug (the A process) is followed by a negative affective state (the B process). Theoretically, the A process becomes smaller and smaller with repeated drug administration (tolerance), and the B process becomes larger and larger (affective withdrawal). Neurochemical changes associated with drug withdrawal might produce the B process and can take on one of two forms, a within-system or a between-system neuroadaptation.[3] In within-system adaptation, changes occur within the neurochemical system directly affected by a drug. Here, the primary cellular activities involved in the acute hedonic effects of a drug adapt to oppose and neutralize the drug's effects; persistence of this opposition after the drug has disappeared produces a motivational withdrawal response. A between-system adaptation is one in

TABLE 49.5 Neurotransmitters Implicated in the Motivational Effects of Withdrawal from Drugs of Abuse

Change in neurotransmitter	Effect
↓ Dopamine	Dysphoria
↓ Opioid peptides	Pain, dysphoria
↓ Serotonin	Pain, dysphoria, depression
↓ GABA	Anxiety, panic attacks
↑ Corticotropin-releasing factor	Stress

which changes occur in a separate neurochemical system different from that directly affected by a drug. Here, different cellular and molecular systems are triggered by changes in the primary neurons responsible for the acute hedonic effects of a drug. These different systems then contribute to or produce the motivational effects of withdrawal after drug removal.

Thus, in the framework of within- and between-system adaptations, neurochemical alterations in dopamine, and possibly serotonin, neurotransmission during drug withdrawal could be considered within-system adaptations.[51,63,64] Changes in function of opiate receptors associated with signal transduction also have been described and could contribute to the motivational effects of drug withdrawal[53] (Table 49.5). Thus, the same neurotransmitter system, presumably with an important, if not essential, role in the acute hedonic action of drugs, may contribute to the motivational effects of cocaine withdrawal. Neurotransmitters possibly involved in a between-system adaptation of the extended amygdala include CRF, because CRF in the brain appears to be an important contributor to the stress associated with drug withdrawal.[55]

Neural Substrates of Sensitization Involve Changes in the Mesolimbic Dopamine System and Activation of Brain Stress Systems

Repeated administration of stimulants and opiates results in increasingly larger activating effects. This sensitization to the activating effects of stimulants and opiates appears to involve activation of the mesolimbic dopamine system.[65] For example, injections of opiates directly into the ventral tegmental area produce sensitization. Also, repeated microinjections of amphetamine into the somatodendritic region of the ventral tegmental area dopamine cells, at doses that do not cause behavioral activation, are sufficient to sensitize the dopamine cells to later systemic injections of amphetamine or morphine. Thus, changes in the activity of these dopamine cells are sufficient to produce sensitization.

Multiple mechanisms for sensitization have been proposed. However, a common theme is a time-dependent chain of adaptations that ultimately lead to long-lasting changes in the function of the mesolimbic dopamine system.[66] Repeated administration of cocaine produces a decrease in the sensitivity of impulse-regulating somatodendritic dopamine D-2 receptors on dopamine neurons (so-called "autoreceptors" because the neuron is responding to the transmitter it releases). This change in sensitivity could translate into enhanced dopaminergic function with subsequent injections of cocaine.[66] However, the decrease in dopaminergic sensitivity lasts only 4–8 days, and behavioral sensitization can persist for weeks.

The CRF–stress axis also may have an important role in sensitization. Stressors can cause sensitization to stimulant drugs, and the hypothalamo pituitary–adrenal stress axis and extrahypothalamic CRF system appear to be important in stress-induced sensitization. Finally, *N*-methyl-D-aspartate glutamate receptor antagonists selectively block development of sensitization to psychomotor stimulants, suggesting a role for brain glutamate systems and specific Glu receptors in sensitization.[67,68]

Neuroadaptive Processes Define the Neurobiological Basis of Substance Dependence

Compulsive, uncontrollable drug use defines substance dependence; however, the basis or etiology of that compulsive use continues to be controversial. One position is the argument that positive reinforcing effects of a drug are critical for addiction.[68] Partially as a result of this concept, alleviation of withdrawal symptoms fell out of favor as an explanation for compulsive drug use. However, although simple positive reinforcement clearly is necessary for the development of drug use, it falls short in explaining the development of compulsive use. Indeed, this issue raises the question of what factors distinguish drug use from abuse from dependence (in this sense, addiction). Sensitization theory addresses this issue by invoking a shift to a state of **incentive salience,** defined as a hypersensitive neural state that produces the experience of craving. This state of incentive salience is hypothesized to be produced by drug-induced sensitization of the mesolimbic dopamine system.[69] Thus, the pathologically strong craving or yearning encountered during protracted abstinence would be hypothesized as due, in large part, to an overactive mesolimbic dopamine system.

In contrast, neuroadaptation theories, such as opponent–process theory, postulate that the processes of

BOX 49.4

NON-DRUG ADDICTIONS

While many substances that humans consume to produce chemical dependency act to achieve a common end event—namely, enhanced release of dopamine at key sites in the extended amygdala—as described in the text, each class of drugs does so in a unique way (see Fig. 49.9). In fact, life events that may be reinforcing to a given individual's behaviors may have the same end result. Specific recurrent behaviors that escaped from the individual's ability to control have been termed "impulse control disorders" and share common clusters of symptoms with the chemical dependencies: (a) anticipation and obsession with performing the act; (b) repeated performance of the act leading to binges of action and "intoxication"; (c) and the withdrawal phase accompanied by severe unpleasant feelings ("dysphoria"). Behaviors that can be qualified as impulse control disorders include gambling, shopping, eating, exercise, and sex.

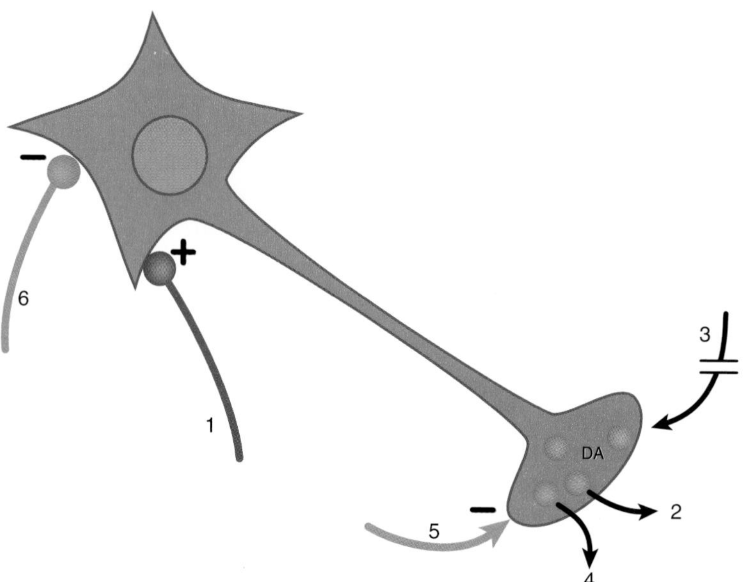

FIGURE 49.9 Drugs and other reinforcing events can release dopamine from the synaptic terminals of dopaminergic neurons, each acting in selective means: (1) Dopamine neurons can be activated by reinforcing events, which directly activate these neurons; such activations also have been reported after exposure to nicotine, opiates, and THC. (2) Dopamine can be displaced from presynatic terminals by amphetamine or methamphetamine. (3) Dopamine reuptake can be blocked by cocaine, amphetamine, and methamphetamine. (4) Vesicular storage of dopamine can be blocked by methylphenidate. (5) Caffeine and other drugs may directly inhibit DA feedback, limiting presynaptic release. (6) Drugs may act at distant neurons to disinhibit DA neurons and allow them to fire more easily.

tolerance to the positive affective state (hedonic tolerance) and subsequent development of the negative affective state (affective withdrawal) play important roles in the transition of drug use to drug dependence.[70] Thus, whereas initial drug use may be motivated by the positive affective state produced by a drug, continued use leads to neuroadaptation to the presence of drug, to development of a negative affective state, and ultimately to self-medication of that affective state. Indeed, some theorists have gone so far as to argue that the presence of a negative affective state is the defining feature of addiction.[71] However, regardless of whether the neuroadaptation-induced motivational state during protracted abstinence is caused by an opponent process, sensitization, or some combination of the two phenomena, other factors must be considered in explaining the chronic relapsing nature of the addictive process.

Conditioning Has an Important Role in Sustaining Substance Dependence

One explanation for the chronic relapsing nature of drug addiction is that reinforcement can be derived from secondary sources that motivate continued drug use. Both the positive and negative affective states can become associated with stimuli in the drug-taking environment through classical conditioning processes. When the drug taker is reexposed to these conditioned stimuli, compulsive drug use is reestablished.

Conditioning to the positive affective states induced by drugs has been demonstrated in animals. Stimuli associated with drugs of abuse, including psychomotor stimulants, opiates, nicotine, ethanol, and barbiturates, can maintain responding in rats and monkeys when presented without the drug.[72,73] In conditioned withdrawal, previously neutral stimuli are paired with naloxone-induced withdrawal and themselves elicit signs of opiate withdrawal; conditioned withdrawal has been observed in opiate-dependent animals and humans.[5,74] However, there is little evidence of conditioned withdrawal with cocaine or amphetamines. Furthermore, it is not clear whether stimuli paired with the negative affective state of cocaine withdrawal can acquire aversive properties, as occurs with opiates.

Neurobiological Elements That Project to the Extended Amygdala May Mediate Conditioned Drug Effects

Neurobiological substrates for conditioned drug effects have only begun to be explored. The enhancement of conditioned reinforcement produced by psychomotor stimulants (e.g., cocaine) appears to involve activation of the mesolimbic dopamine system[75] and the basolateral amygdala, a main projection to the extended amygdala.[76,77] The neurobiological substrates for conditioned withdrawal are largely unexplored, although there is evidence that conditioned opiate withdrawal, measured by place aversion in rats, can be reversed by administration of clonidine.[78] Clonidine is a norepinephrine α-2 agonist that has been shown to decrease firing of the locus ceruleus norepinephrine system and has been used clinically for opiate detoxification.[79]

Summary

Much is known about the neurobiological substrates for the acute reinforcing actions of drugs of abuse. The mesolimbic dopamine system is critical for the reinforcing actions of psychomotor stimulants and plays an important role in opiate, nicotine, and alcohol reinforcement. Opioid peptide systems have important roles in opiate, nicotine, and alcohol reinforcement. Other neurotransmitter systems, such as GABA, serotonin, and glutamate, localized within the extended amygdala area of the basal forebrain appear to have an important role in ethanol reinforcement. However, much less is known about the neurobiological substrates for the reinforcement associated with chronic drug use. Compulsive use that characterizes substance dependence produces neuroadaptive changes in these neurotransmitter systems, resulting in a compromised reward system. Acute abstinence is characterized by functional decreases within motivational systems mediating acute drug reinforcement, (e.g., the dopamine system) and increases in stress systems recruited during development of dependence (e.g., CRF and locus ceruleus). Protracted abstinence and the propensity for relapse are probably the keys to maintenance of addiction, but only a little is known about the neurobiology of protracted abstinence. Sensitization probably involves development of a hypersensitive dopamine system and activation of brain stress mechanisms. Conditioned drug effects are only beginning to be explored but may involve limbic elements that project to the extended amygdala. Study of the changes in the central nervous system that are associated with such homeostatic dysregulation may provide the key not only to drug addiction but also to the etiology of psychopathologies associated with mood and anxiety disorders.

References

1. American Psychiatric Association (1994). *Diagnostic and Statistical Manual of Mental Disorders,* 4th ed., American Psychiatric Press, Washington, DC.

1a. Koob, G. F. (1992). Dopamine, addiction and reward. *Semin. Neurosci.* **4:** 139–148.

2. Stewart, J., and Badiani, A. (1993). Tolerance and sensitization to the behavioral effects of drugs. *Behav. Pharmacol.* **4:** 289–312.

3. Koob, G. F., and Bloom, F. E. (1988). Cellular and molecular mechanisms of drug dependence. *Science* **242:** 715–723.

4. Wikler, A. (1973). Dynamics of drug dependence: Implications of a conditioning theory of research and treatment. *Arch. Gen. Psychiatry* **28:** 611–616.

5. Koob, G. F., Markou, A., Weiss, F., and Schulteis, G. (1993). Opponent process and drug dependence: Neurobiological mechanisms. *Semin. Neurosci.* **5:** 351–358.

6. Schuster, C. R., and Thompson, T. (1969). Self administration and behavioral dependence on drugs. *Annu. Rev. Pharmacol. Toxicol.* **9:** 483–502.

7. Ettenberg, A., Pettit, H. O., Bloom, F. E., and Koob, G. F. (1982). Heroin and cocaine intravenous self-administration in rats: Mediation by separate neural systems. *Psychopharmacology (Berlin)* **78:** 204–209.

8. Caine, S. B., and Koob, G. F. (1995). Pretreatment with the dopamine agonist 7-OH-DPAT shifts the cocaine self-administration dose–effect function to the left under different schedules in the rat. *Behav. Pharmacol.* **6:** 333–347.
9. Bergman, J., Kamien, J. B., and Spealman, R. D. (1990). Antagonism of cocaine self-administration by selective dopamine D1 and D2 antagonist. *Behav. Pharmacol.* **1:** 355–363.
10. Caine, S. B., and Koob, G. F. (1993). Modulation of cocaine self-administration in the rat through D-3 dopamine receptors. *Science* **260:** 1814–1816.
11. Samson, H. H. (1986). Initiation of ethanol reinforcement using a sucrose-substitution procedure in food- and water-sated rats. *Alcohol: Clin. Exp. Res.* **10:** 436–442.
12. Olds, J., and Milner, P. (1954). Positive reinforcement produced by electrical stimulation of septal area and other regions of rat brain. *J. Comp. Physiol. Psychol.* **47:** 419–427.
13. Gallistel, C. R. (1983). Self-stimulation. In *The Physiological Basis of Memory* (J. A. Deutsch, ed.), 2nd ed., pp. 73–77. Academic Press, New York.
14. Kornetsky, C., and Esposito, R. U. (1979). Euphorigenic drugs: Effects on reward pathways of the brain. *Fed. Proc., Fed. Am. Soc. Exp. Biol.* **38:** 2473–2476.
15. Stein, L. (1968). Chemistry of reward and punishment. In *Psychopharmacology: A Review of Progress (1957–1967)*, Publ. Health Serv. Publ. No. 1836 (D. H. Efron, ed.), pp. 105–123. U.S. Government Printing Office, Washington, D.C.
16. Nauta, J. H., and Haymaker, W. (1969). Hypothalamic nuclei and fiber connections. In *The Hypothalamus* (W. Haymaker, E. Anderson, and W. J. H. Nauta, eds.), pp. 136–209. Thomas, Springfield, IL.
17. Valenstein, E. S., and Campbell, J. F. (1966). Medial forebrain bundle-lateral hypothalmic area and reinforcing brain stimulation. *Am. J. Physiol.* **210:** 270–274.
18. Liebman, J. M., and Cooper, S. J. (1989). *The Neuropharmacological Basis of Reward.* Clarendon Press, Oxford.
19. Keesey, R. E., and Powley, T. L. (1973). Self-stimulation and body weight in rats with lateral hypothalmic lesions. *Am. J. Physiol.* **224:** 970–978.
20. Koob, G. F. (1992). Drugs of abuse: Anatomy, pharmacology, and function of reward pathways. *Trends Pharmacol. Sci.* **13:** 177–184.
21. Mucha, R. F., van der Kooy, D., O'Shaughnessy, M., and Bucenieks, P. (1982). Drug reinforcement studied by the use of place conditioning in rat. *Brain Res.* **243:** 91–105.
22. Kornetsky, C., and Bain, G. (1982). Biobehavioral bases of the reinforcing properties of opiate drugs. *Ann. N.Y. Acad. Sci.* **398:** 240–259.
23. Koob, G. F., Vaccarino, F. J., Amalric, M., and Bloom, F. E. (1987). Positive reinforcement properties of drugs: Search for neural substrates. In *Brain Reward Systems and Abuse* (J. Engel and L. Oreland, eds.), pp. 35–50. Raven Press, New York.
24. Yokel, R. A., and Wise, R. A. (1975). Increased lever pressing for amphetamine after pimozide in rats: Implications for a dopamine theory of reward. *Science* **187:** 547–549.
25. Thomas, L. (1986). *The Lasker Awards: Four Decades of Scientific Medical Progress*, pp. 43–44. Raven Press, New York.
26. Engel, G. (1980). The clinical application of the biopsychosocial model. *Am. J. Psychiatry* **137:** 535–544.
27. Di Chiara, G., and North, R. A. (1992). Neurobiology of opiate abuse. *Trends Pharmacol. Sci.* **13:** 185–193.
28. Corrigall, W. A., Franklin, K. B. J., Coen, K. M., and Clarke, P. B. S. (1992). The mesolimbic dopaminergic system is implicated in the reinforcing effects of nicotine. *Psychopharmacology (Berlin)* **107:** 285–289.
29. Malin, D. H., Lake, J. R., Carter, V. A., Cunningham, J. S., and Wilson, O. B. (1993). Naloxone precipitates abstinence syndrome in the rat. *Psychopharmacology (Berlin)* **112:** 339–342.
30. Malin, D. H., Lake, J. R., Carter, V. A., Cunningham, J. S., Hebert, K. M., Conrad, D. L., and Wilson, O. B. (1994). The nicotine antagonist mecamylamine precipitates nicotine abstinence syndrome in the rat. *Psychopharmacology (Berlin)* **115:** 180–184.
31. Koob, G. F., and Britton, K. T. (1996). Neurobiological substrates for the anti-anxiety effects of ethanol. In *The Pharmacology of Alcohol and Alcohol Dependence* (H. Begleiter and B. Kissin, eds.), Vol. 2, pp. 477–506. Oxford University Press, New York.
32. Richards, G., Schoch, P., and Haefely, W. (1991). Benzodiazepine receptors: New vistas. *Semin. Neurosci.* **3:** 191–203.
33. Suzdak, P. D., Glowa, J. R., Crawley, J. N., Schwartz, R. D., Skolnick, P., and Paul, S. M. (1986). A selective imidazobenzodiazepine antagonist of ethanol in the rat. *Science* **236:** 1243–1247.
34. Tabakoff, B., and Hoffman, P. L. (1992). Alcohol: Neurobiology. In *Substance Abuse. A Comprehensive Textbook* (J. H. Lowenstein, P. Ruiz, and R. B. Millman, eds.), 2nd ed., pp. 152–185. Williams & Wilkins, Baltimore, MD.
35. Samson, H. H., Tolliver, G. A., Pfeffer, A. O., Sadeghi, K. G., and Mills, F. G. (1987). Oral ethanol reinforcement in the rat: Effect of the partial inverse benzodiazepine agonist R015–4513. *Pharmacol. Biochem. Behav.* **27:** 517–519.
36. Hyytia, P., and Koob, G. F. (1995). $GABA_A$ receptor antagonism in the extended amygdala decreases ethanol self-administration in rats. *Eur. J. Pharmacol.* **283:** 151–159.
37. Engel, J. A., Enerback, C., Fahlke, C., Hulthe, P., Hard, E., Johannessen, K., Svensson, L., and Soderpalm, B. (1992). Serotonergic and dopaminergic involvement in ethanol intake. In *Novel Pharmacological Interventions for Alcoholism* (C. A. Naranjo and E. M. Sellers, eds.), pp. 68–82. Springer, New York.
38. Hoffman, P. L., Rabe, C., Moses, F., and Tabakoff, B. (1989). *N*-methyl-D-aspartate receptors and ethanol: Inhibition of calcium flux and cyclic GMP production. *J. Neurochem.* **52:** 1937–1940.
39. Lovinger, D. M., White, G., and Weight, F. F. (1989). Ethanol inhibits NMDA-activated ion currents in hippocampal neurons. *Science* **243:** 1721–1724.
40. Sellers, E. M., Higgins, G. A., and Sobell, M. B. (1992). 5-HT and alcohol abuse trends. *Trends Pharmacol. Sci.* **13:** 69–75.
41. Naranjo, C., Kadlec, K., Sanhueza, P., Woodley-Remus, D., and Sellers, E. M. (1990). Fluoxetine differentially alters alcohol intake and other consummatory behaviors in problem drinkers. *Clin. Pharmacol. Ther.* **47:** 490–498.
42. Hubbell, C. L., Marglin, S. H., Spitalnic, S. J., Abelson, M. L., Wild, K. D., and Reid, L. D. (1991). Opioidergic, serotonergic and dopaminergic manipulations and rats' intake of a sweetened alcoholic beverage. *Alcohol* **8:** 355–367.
43. Volpicelli, J. R., Alterman, A. I., Hayashida, M., and O'Brien, C. P. (1992). Naltrexone in the treatment of alcohol dependence. *Arch. Gen. Psychiatry* **49:** 876–880.
44. O'Malley, S. S., Jaffe, A. J., Chang, G., Schottenfeld, R. S., Meyer, R. E., and Rounsaville, B., (1992). Naltrexone and coping skills therapy for alcohol dependence: A controlled study. *Arch. Gen. Psychiatry* **49:** 881–887.
45. Heimer, L., and Alheid, G. (1991). Piecing together the puzzle of basal forebrain anatomy. In *Advances in Experimental Medicine and Biology* (T. C. Napier, P. Kalivas, and I. Hanin, eds.), Vol. 295, pp. 1–42. Plenum, New York.
46. Johnston, J. B. (1923). Further contributions to the study of the evolution of the forebrain. *J. Comp. Neurol.* **35:** 337–481.

47. Gawin, F. H., and Kleber, H. D. (1986). Abstinence symptomatology and psychiatric diagnosis in cocaine abusers: Clinical observations. *Arch. Gen. Psychiatry* **43:** 107–113.
48. Markou, A., and Koob, G. F. (1991). Postcocaine anhedonia. An animal model of cocaine withdrawal. *Neuropsychopharmacology* **4:** 17–26.
49. Schulteis, G., Markou, A., Cole, M., and Koob, G. F. (1995). Decreased brain reward produced by ethanol withdrawal. *Proc. Natl. Acad. Sci. U.S.A.* **92:** 5880–5884.
50. Rossetti, Z. L., Hmaidan, Y., and Gessa, G. L. (1992). Marked inhibition of mesolimbic dopamine release: A common feature of ethanol, morphine, cocaine and amphetamine abstinence in rats. *Eur. J. Pharmacol.* **221:** 227–234.
51. Weiss, F., Markou, A., Lorang, M. T., and Koob, G. F. (1992). Basal extracellular dopamine levels in the nucleus accumbens are decreased during cocaine withdrawal after unlimited-access self-administration. *Brain Res.* **593:** 314–318.
52. Parsons, L. H., Koob, G. F., and Weiss, F. (1995). Serotonin dysfunction in the nucleus accumbens of rats during withdrawal after unlimited access to intravenous cocaine. *J. Pharmacol. Exp. Ther.* **274:** 1182–1191.
53. Nestler, E. J. (1992). Molecular mechanisms of drug addiction. *J. Neurosci.* **12:** 2439–2450.
54. Wood, D. M., and Lal, H., (1987). Anxiogenic properties of cocaine withdrawal. *Life Sci.* **41:** 1431–1436.
55. Koob, G. F., Heinrichs, S. C., Menzaghi, F., Pich, E. M., and Britton, K. T. (1994). Corticotropin-releasing factor, stress and behavior. *Semin. Neurosci.* **7:** 221–229.
56. Pich, E. M., Lorang, M., Yeganeh, M., Rodriguez de Fonseca, F., Koob, G. F., and Weiss, F. (1995). Increase of extracellular corticotropin-releasing factor-like immunoreactivity levels in the amygdala of awake rats during restraint stress and ethanol withdrawal as measured by microdialysis. *J. Neurosci.* **15:** 5439–5447.
57. Moore, R. Y., and Bloom, F. E. (1978). Central catecholamine neuron systems: Anatomy and physiology of the dopamine systems. *Annu. Rev. Neurosci.* **1:** 129–169.
58. Aghajanian, G. K. (1978). Tolerance of locus coeruleus neurones to morphine and suppression of withdrawal response by clonidine. *Nature (London)* **276:** 186–188.
58a. Koob, G. F., Maldonado, R., and Stinus, L. (1992). Neural substrates of opiate withdrawal. *Trends Neurosci.* **15:** 186–191.
59. Taylor, J. R., Elsworth, J. D., Garcia, E. J., Grant, S. J., Roth, R. H., and Redmond, D. E., Jr. (1988). Clonidine infusions into the locus coeruleus attenuate behavioral and neurochemical changes associated with naloxone-precipitated withdrawal. *Psychopharmacology (Berlin)* **96:** 121–134.
60. Tseng, L. F., Loh, H. H., and Wei, E. T. (1975). Effects of clonidine on morphine withdrawal signs in the rat. *Eur. J. Pharmacol.* **30:** 93–99.
61. Akaoka, H., and Aston-Jones, G. (1991). Opiate withdrawal-induced hyperactivity of locus coeruleus neurons is substantially mediated by augmented excitatory amino acid input. *J. Neurosci.* **11:** 3830–3839.
62. Himmelsbach, C. K. (1943). Symposium: Can the euphoric, analgetic, and physical dependence effects of drugs be separated? IV. With reference to physical dependence. *Fed. Proc., Fed. Am. Soc. Exp. Biol.* **2:** 201–203.
63. Parsons, L. H., Smith, A. D., and Justice, J. B., Jr. (1991). Basal extracellular dopamine is decreased in the rat nucleus accumbens during abstinence from chronic cocaine. *Synapse* **9:** 60–65.
64. Rossetti, Z. L., Hmaidan, Y., and Gessa, G. L. (1992). Marked inhibition of mesolimbic dopamine release: A common feature of ethanol, morphine, cocaine and amphetamine abstinence in rats. *Eur. J. Pharmacol.* **221:** 227–234.
65. Wise, R. A., and Leeb, K. (1993). Psychomotor-stimulant sensitization: A unitary phenomenon? *Behav. Pharmacol.* **4:** 339–349.
66. White, E. J., and Wolf, M. E. (1991). Psychomotor stimulants. In *The Biological Bases of Drug Tolerance and Dependence* (J. A. Pratt, ed.), pp. 153–197. Academic Press, London.
67. Karler, R., Calder, L. D., Chaudhry, I. A., and Turkanis, S. A. (1989). Blockade of "reverse tolerance" to cocaine and amphetamine by MK-801. *Life Sci.* **45:** 599–606.
68. Wise, R. A. (1988). The neurobiology of craving: Implications for the understanding and treatment of addiction. *J. Abnorm. Psychol.* **97:** 118–132.
69. Robinson, T. E., and Berridge, K. C. (1993). The neural basis of drug craving: An incentive-sensitization theory of addiction. *Brain Res. Rev.* **18:** 247–291.
70. Solomon, R. L. (1977). The opponent-process theory of acquired motivation: The affective dynamics of addiction. In *Psychopathology: Experimental Models* (J. D. Maser and M. E. P. Seligman, eds.), pp. 124–145. Freeman, San Francisco.
71. Russell, M. A. H. (1976). What is dependence? In *Drugs and Drug Dependence* (G. Edwards, M. A. H. Russell, D. Hawks, and M. MacCafferty, eds.), pp. 182–187. Lexington Books, Lexington, MA.
72. Markou, A., Weiss, F., Gold, L. H., Caine, S. B., Schulteis, G., and Koob, G. F. (1993). Animal models of drug craving. *Psychopharmacology (Berlin)* **112:** 163–182.
73. Davis, W. M., and Smith, S. G. (1987). Conditioned reinforcement as a measure of the rewarding properties of drugs. In *Methods of Assessing the Reinforcing Properties of Abused Drugs* (M. A. Bozarth, ed.), pp. 199–210. Springer-Verlag, New York.
74. O'Brien, C. P., Testa, T., O'Brien, T. J., Brady, J. P., and Wells, B. (1977). Conditioned narcotic withdrawal in humans. *Science* **195:** 1000–1002.
75. Taylor, J. R., and Robbins, T. W. (1984). Enhanced behavioural control by conditioned reinforcers following microinjections of d-amphetamine into the nucleus accumbens. *Psychopharmacology (Berlin)* **84:** 405–412.
76. Cador, M., Robbins, T. W., and Everitt, B. J. (1989). Involvement of the amygdala in stimulus-reward associations: Interaction with the ventral striatum. *Neuroscience* **30:** 77–86.
77. Everitt, B. J., Morris, K. A., O'Brien, A., and Robbins, T. W. (1991). The basolateral amygdala-ventral striatal system and conditioned place preference: Further evidence of limbic-striatal interactions underlying reward-related processes. *Neuroscience* **42:** 1–18.
78. Kosten, T. A. (1994). Clonidine attenuates conditioned aversion produced by naloxone-precipitated opiate withdrawal. *Eur. J. Pharmacol.* **254:** 59–63.
79. Washton, A. M., and Resnick, R. B. (1982). Outpatient opiate detoxification with clonidine. *J. Clin. Psychiatry* **43:** 39–41.
80. Caine, S. B., Lintz, R., and Koob, G. F. (1993). Intravenous drug self-administration techniques in animals. In *Behavioral Neurosciences: A Practical Approach* (A. Sahgal, ed.), Vol. 2, pp. 117–143, Oxford University Press, New York.

SECTION VII

BEHAVIORAL AND COGNITIVE NEUROSCIENCE

C H A P T E R

50

Human Brain Evolution

Todd M. Preuss and John H. Kaas

Much of the allure of the neurosciences stems from the common conviction that there is something unusual about the human brain and its behavioral capacities. Nevertheless, modern neuroscientists have paid rather little attention to the study of brain evolution, and so our understanding of how the human brain differs from that of other animals is very rudimentary. In part, this neglect is due to a widely held belief that mammalian brains are all essentially similar in their internal structure and that species differ mainly in the size of the brain.

In this chapter, we review the modern evidence concerning brain evolution, and see that brain structure, far from being uniform across species, exhibits some remarkable variations. The subject is vast, so the discussion will necessarily be selective. After a brief review of evolutionary principles, we discuss the evolutionary history of three groups of vertebrates that are of special interest to people: mammals, primates, and humans themselves. Also, we focus primarily on the evolution of the cerebral cortex, because this structure has been studied in a wide variety of mammalian species and because the cortex is critically involved in psychological phenomena that we think of as being distinctively human.

EVOLUTIONARY AND COMPARATIVE PRINCIPLES

The Evolution of Species Is Better Portrayed by a Tree Than by a Ladder

It is very common to hear people—even scientists—refer to the "phylogenetic scale," and to most people, it seems obvious that humans reside at the pinnacle of this scale. In fact, the idea that living species can be arranged along a scale from lower to higher forms is a philosophical and religious concept, the so-called Great Chain of Being,[1] that long predates the biological theory of evolution. The view that the history of life is like a scale or ladder also reflects the popular idea that evolution (phylogeny) is primarily a process of progressive improvement. Beginning with Darwin,[2] however, evolutionary biologists have come to understand that the history of life is fundamentally a chronicle of diversification, which (using Darwin's metaphor) can be likened to a branching tree (Fig. 50.1). As the tree of life grows, parent species divide to form daughter species, with each species becoming adapted to its particular environment through natural selection.

Only recently have biologists fully appreciated the profound difference between viewing the history of life as ladder-like and viewing it as treelike. Consider that every branch of the tree of life—every species or lineage—has undergone a unique history of modification, evolving characteristics that distinguish it from other species. The very diversity of life, the variety of forms, bedevils any attempt to array species along a single dimension of evolutionary change. How can we say that bats, so exquisitely equipped for flying, are lower forms of life than human beings? We can do so only if we arbitrarily decree that the peculiarities of human beings are somehow higher or better than the peculiarities of bats. The concept that life is like a branching tree is fundamentally very difficult to reconcile with the idea of a general, progressive scale of being. For this reason, evolutionary biologists have almost entirely abandoned the phylogenetic scale.

Even if we replace the scale with the tree, there is still a place for progress in evolution. Natural selection may act in a given lineage to make animals larger,

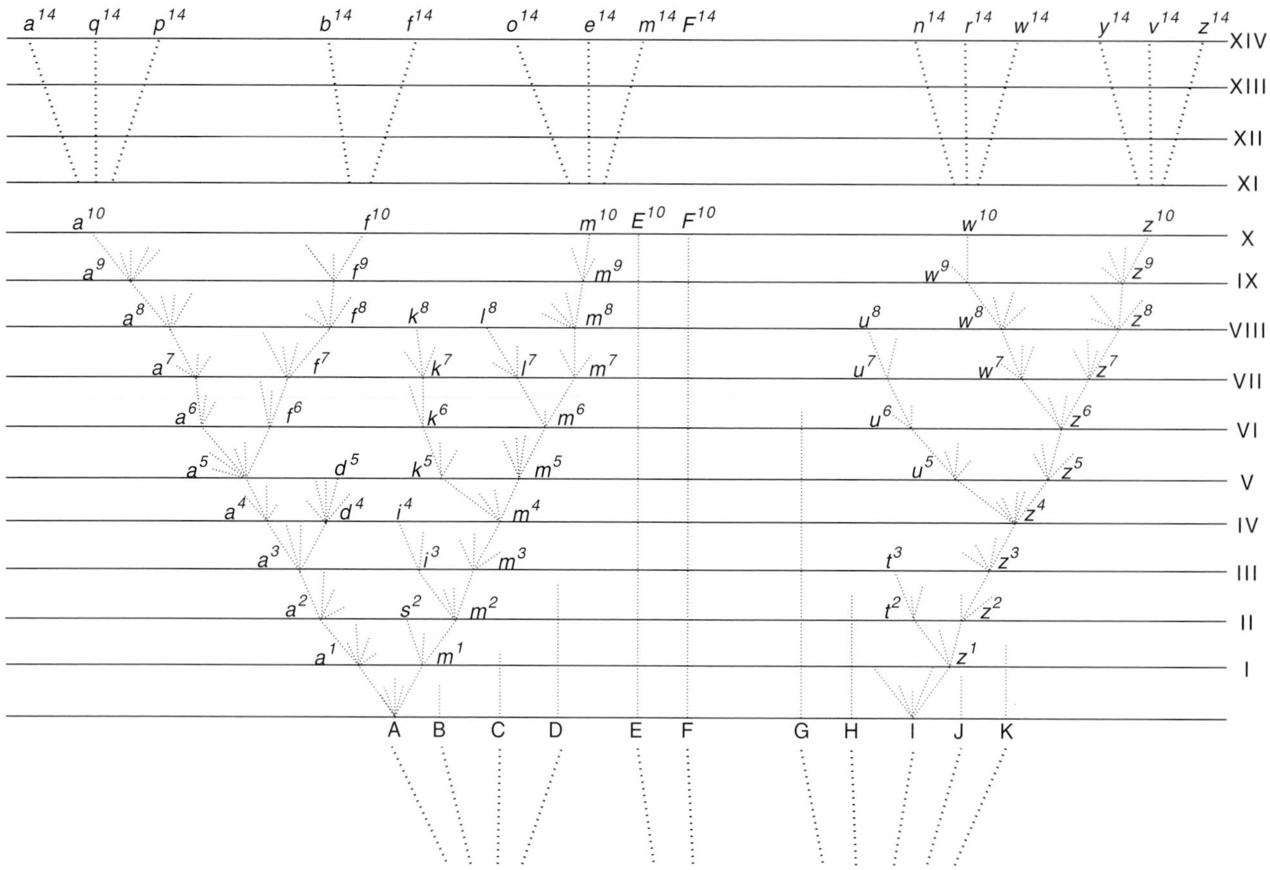

FIGURE 50.1 The sole figure in Charles Darwin's *On the Origin of Species*[2] likened the evolutionary process to the branching of a tree.

faster, more complex, and so forth. The problem with the idea of progress is that there is no single, universal, objective standard of progress: the particular combination of characteristics that promotes survival and reproduction will usually be different in different species. Furthermore, evolution commonly promotes the reduction or simplification of form, so there is no universal trend toward increased complexity. Evolutionary biologists do make a distinction between characteristics that are *primitive* (or ancestral) and those that are *derived* (or specialized), but these terms merely indicate whether the characteristics were present in the last common ancestor of the group under consideration (primitive) or have evolved in the descendants of the ancestor (derived).

Living species typically possess combinations of primitive and derived characteristics. This is particularly true of animals that have existed as long as mammals. The processes of extinction and adaptation tend to ensure that no living mammal species will have retained all the characteristics of ancestral mammals; some, perhaps, but not all. In general, it is advisable to view each species as a mosaic of features, some acquired recently, some retained from earlier (ancestral) species.

There is a tradition in the neurosciences of regarding some of the living insectivores (hedgehogs and shrews, specifically) as "stand-ins" for the earliest mammals, because they have very small brains and are thought to be similar to ancestral mammals in other aspects of their anatomy. Nonetheless, these so-called basal insectivores are known to have specializations of brain organization. For example, corticospinal projections in at least some insectivore species are mainly uncrossed,[3] and some insectivores appear to have a large number of crossed projections from the thalamus to the cortex;[4] in both respects, insectivores are very different from other mammals. Similarly, we should be cautious about thinking of rodents as "prototypical" mammals: their bodies certainly are not prototypical—the continuously growing incisors of rodents are unquestionably an evolutionary specialization—and their brains are not prototypical, either. For instance, the division of somatosensory cortex into discrete "barrels," each representing a different vibrissa, is a feature found in rats, mice, and some (but not all) other rodents, but is not a feature of mammalian cortex generally, nor is it likely to be a primitive mammalian characteristic.[5]

The mosaic character of species has important implications for the study of brain evolution. It has sometimes been argued that the way to reconstruct the evolutionary history of the brain is to study a set of species that approximate an evolutionary lineage. For example, if we want to trace the evolution of some feature of the human cortex, we should compare the so-called "basal" insectivores (as models of ancestral mammals), tree shrews (thought to resemble the ancestors of primates), bushbabies (prosimian primates, often considered to be representative of primitive primates), and monkeys (thought to resemble ancestral anthropoid primates, the group to which humans belong). The problem with this approach is that none of the animals listed above are really "living fossils"; they all have their own peculiar, recently evolved, specializations. To reconstruct brain evolution, we need only to be able to distinguish ancestral and derived *characters,* rather than ancestral and derived *species.* As discussed below, modern phylogenetic techniques provide the means for making these distinctions.

Brain Evolution Is Better Studied by Comparing the Brains of Living Species Than by Studying Fossils

Information about brain evolution comes primarily from comparative studies of living species, rather than from the study of fossils, for the simple reason that brain tissue (like other soft tissues) does not fossilize. While it would certainly be valuable to be able to study the brain organization of extinct species, the absence of fossil brains by no means renders the study of brain evolution impossible. It is important to remember that much of what we know about the history of life comes from the comparative study of living species. Indeed,

BOX 50.1

HOMOLOGY AND ANALOGY

Homology and **analogy** are among the more important concepts in biology. Both terms refer to similarity, but to similarity arising from different sources. When species possess similar characteristics because they have inherited them from a common ancestor, those characteristics are said to be **homologous.** When species have independently evolved similar characteristics, rather than retaining them from a common ancestor, the characteristics are said to be **analogous.** (The terms homoplastic or homoplaseous are sometimes used as synonyms for analogous.) The process by which analogous similarities emerge is referred to as **convergent** or **parallel** evolution. In the neuroscientific literature, one often sees the term analogy applied to any similarity, even a homologous similarity. But homology and analogy are mutually exclusive categories: similarities due to common ancestry are homologous and, by definition, are not analogous.

Both homology and analogy can be applied to structures or to specific features of structures. The forelimbs of bats and birds are homologous as forelimbs, because both bats and birds inherited forelimbs from their common ancestor. The common ancestor of bats and birds did not fly, however, and the modifications that have transformed the forelimbs of bats and birds into wings evolved independently; these winglike characteristics are therefore analogous.

Identifying homologous similarities and distinguishing homologies from analogies are a large part of comparative biology. The process of recognizing homologies begins with identifying similarities in structures. Any similarity is grist for the mill, although it has long been recognized that some kinds of similarities are particularly informative—for example, the position of an anatomical structure relative to other structures. Nevertheless, similarity is not an infallible guide to homology. Because evolution usually results in a divergence of form, the homologous structures of related animals—the forelimbs of bats and whales, for instance—may differ considerably in appearance. On the other hand, analogous structures may be remarkably similar. Ultimately, the degree of similarity and dissimilarity is not decisive in distinguishing homologies and analogies. Rather, the key lies in the phyletic distribution of similarities. Consider that primates and cats both have forward-facing eyes. It this an analogous or a homologous similarity? The answer can be gleaned from the fact that most carnivores do not have forward-facing eyes, nor do the animals most closely related to primates (bats and tree shrews). It is likely, then, that both cats and primates evolved forward-facing eyes independently, which means it is an analogous similarity. An example of a similarity in the visual cortex of cats and primates that is probably analogous (the cytochrome-oxidase "blobs" of area V1) is discused in the text.

by comparing living forms, the outline of the relationships among the major vertebrate classes was worked out before there was any substantial fossil record of those groups, and molecular biologists have been able to reconstruct many aspects of nucleic acid and protein evolution without the benefit of fossil molecules.

The formal theory of comparative biology and phylogenetic reconstruction has undergone remarkable development during the past 20 years, and a thorough exposition is beyond the scope of this chapter.[6] These methods provide the basis for determining whether the similarities observed between two animals are due to shared evolutionary history (homologous similarity) or due to independent evolutionary development (analogous similarity; for more details, see Box 50.1). These methods also provide the means for identifying the ancestral and derived characteristics of a particular group, by comparing members of the group in question to members of closely related groups (known as sister groups or outgroups). Of special importance is the set of characteristics that are inferred to have been present in the last common ancestor of the reference group, but to be absent in closely related groups. These are the so-called **shared-derived characteristics** of the reference group, characteristics that provide important clues to the early history of the group. For example, as will be discussed in more detail later, the forward-facing eyes of primates have been taken as evidence that ancestral primates were nocturnal predators.

The comparative method is of course essential for reconstructing the evolution of soft tissues, such as brains. In fact, fossils do provide us with some information about brain evolution. Given a reasonably intact skull, one can make a cast of the impression of the brain left on the inner surface of the skull; these are called **endocasts.** In very rare instances, natural endocasts are formed during fossilization, when the brain tissue is gradually replaced by mineral deposits. Endocasts, whether natural or artificial, provide information about the size of the brain and the pattern of sulci and gyri on the cortical surface. Unfortunately, we can infer little about the internal organization and functions of brains from their size and sulcal patterns. To reconstruct the evolution of these and other aspects of the internal organization of brains, we must carry out comparative studies of living forms.

Summary

In evolutionary biology, the popular view that the history of life can be depicted as a scale or ladder of progress, with humans at the top, has been supplanted by Darwin's metaphor of evolution as a branching tree. Evolutionary biologists stress that each group of animals has evolved its own distinctive set of specialized characteristics. Powerful new methods have been developed to identify the evolutionary specializations of particular animal groups that entail comparisons with closely related groups. Using these methods, we can reconstruct the evolutionary history of the brain in considerable detail from comparative studies of brain organization in living species.

MAMMALIAN EVOLUTION

Present Day Mammals Evolved from Reptilelike Ancestors and Are Divided into Three Main Groups

The early evolutionary history of mammals is fairly well known, thanks to an extensive fossil record.[7,8] The split between mammals and their closest vertebrate relatives, reptiles and birds, is a very ancient one: it occurred about 300 million years ago (myr), over 100 million years before the rise of the dinosaurs. From the time of this split until the time that modern mammalian groups appeared (during the era when dinosaurs flourished), early mammals underwent a succession of adaptive radiations. Compared with the wealth of available fossils documenting the origin of mammals, however, there are relatively few mammalian fossils from the age of dinosaurs (the middle and late parts of the Mesozoic era). Even so, it is clear that during this time the three main living groups of mammals appeared—the monotremes (or Prototheria), marsupials (or Metatheria), and placentals (or Eutheria) (see Fig. 50.2). Monotremes are represented today only by the duck-billed platypus and spiny echidnas, which live in Australia and New Guinea. Like reptiles, the monotremes lay eggs, rather than giving live birth like other mammals. While primitive in this respect, however, they have evolved many distinctive characteristics, including a horny, toothless beak and quite large and convoluted brains. The marsupials are found today in the New World, where they are represented by a variety of opossums, and of course in Australia. Although it is conventional to regard the marsupials as a single mammalian order, they are a diverse lot: in Australia, where marsupials existed in virtual isolation from placentals until recently, they evolved into a remarkable variety of forms, including small opossumlike creatures, gliders resembling flying squirrels, wolflike carnivores, and large, bipedal herbivores (kangaroos and wallabies). As the name indicates, the placental (or eutherian) mammals are distinguished by the presence of the placenta, an organ that mediates the exchange of nutrients and gasses between mother

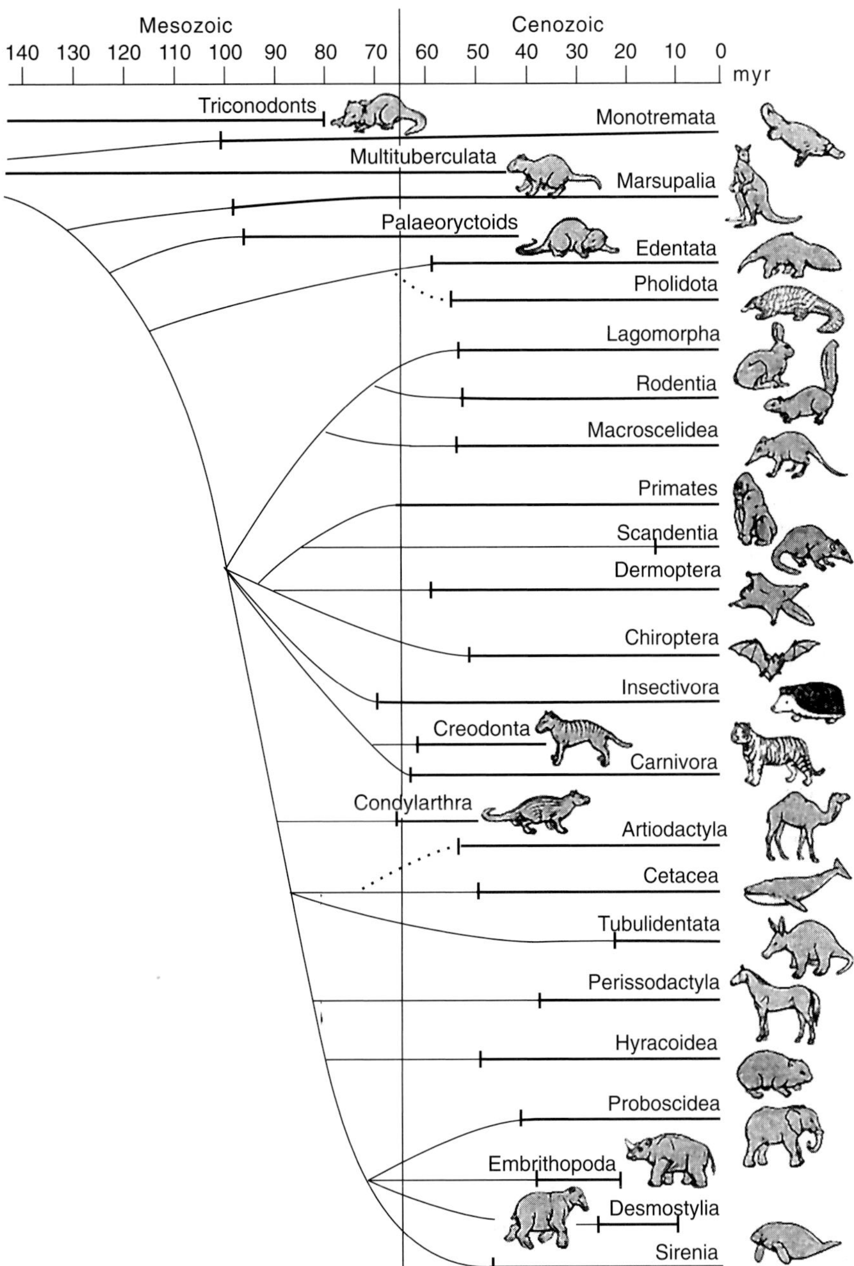

FIGURE 50.2 The relationships among mammalian orders, as currently understood. With the exception of the first four branches of the mammalian tree (triconodonts, monotremes, multituberculates, and marsupials), all other mammals are placed in the placental (eutherian) group. Based on Novacek.[7]

and fetus. The placental mammals form the most numerous and diversive group of mammals today, comprising about 20 orders, which include such familiar animals as bats, carnivores, hoofed animals (ungulates), whales and dolphins (cetaceans), sloths, armadillos, elephants, and primates. Our understanding of the relationships among the different orders of living eutherian mammals is at present quite incomplete.

The evolution of mammals from reptilelike ancestors was marked by the gradual accretion of a large number of distinctive characteristics.[8] Mammalian innovations include the evolution of hair; the appearance of sweat glands; the development of mammary glands and suckling; the differentiation of the relatively uniform teeth of reptiles into forms specialized for slicing, piercing, and grinding (incisors, canines, and premolars and molars); and the appearance of physiological mechanisms for maintaining relatively constant body temperature (endothermy or homeothermy). All these changes are related to energetics or metabolism, and they suggest that early mammals were adapted for an active, predatory lifestyle. The brain, too, underwent a remarkable transformation.

The Distinctive Isocortex of Mammalian Brains Was Probably Developed by Modification of the Cortex of Nonmammals

Mammals are distinguished from other vertebrates by their possession of a multilayered telencephalic covering, the **isocortex** or **neocortex** (Fig. 50.3). Although reptiles and birds possess a cortex, it has a relatively simple histological appearance and is usually described as having three layers: a very thick, fibrous outer stratum containing few cells; a thin, cell-dense deeper stratum, which constitutes the main cell layer; and a thin stratum below the main cell layer that contains a mixture of cells and fibers. In most mammals, the largest part of the telencephalic mantle is composed of isocortex, which is richer in cells and more highly stratified than reptilian cortex. Following the lead of the great neuroanatomist Korbinian Brodmann,[9] workers today generally recognize six layers in isocortex: a thin, fibrous, cell-sparse outer band (layer I) and five deeper layers that are densely packed with cells (layers II–VI). Mammalian cortex does not consist entirely of isocortex, however; as it approaches the lateral and medial margins of the hemisphere, the laminar structure of the cortex goes through a series of changes, culminating in a three-layered structure somewhat similar to reptilian cortex. Nonisocortical portions of the cortical mantle are referred to collectively as **allocortex.** The allocortices located at the extreme lateral and medial margins of the cortical mantle correspond to the olfactory cortex and hippocampus, respectively. (The expansion of the isocortex in some mammalian groups has resulted in the hippocampus shifting secondarily to a more lateral location in the hemisphere.) Homologs of the mammalian olfactory cortex and hippocampus are thought to exist in nonmammalian vertebrates.

How did the isocortex arise in mammalian evolution? One possibility is that the isocortex is an entirely neomorphic structure, having no homolog in nonmammals (as indeed the term "*neo*cortex" suggests). Most comparative neuroanatomists believe, however, that the isocortex represents a modification of the cortex of nonmammals, at least in part. One interpretation, suggested by comparative studies of cellular biochemistry, is that the deep layers of the mammalian cortex correspond to the cellular parts of reptilian cortex, whereas the cells of the superficial layers are neomorphic, having been added to cortical mantle early in mammalian evolution.[10] Another interpretation is that the isocortex (or at least some portion of the isocortex) is a composite of cells derived from reptilian cortex and cells that are present in deeper telencephalic structures of reptiles. Most reptiles and birds possess a **dorsal ventricular ridge** (or DVR), a large structure located immediately beneath the cortex. The DVR appears to be the main target of sensory afferents from the thalamus in these animals, and like the isocortex, it contains a number of anatomically and functionally distinct divisions. The similarities between the isocortex and the DVR have led some workers to suggest that the isocortex evolved when cells that made up the DVR in the common ancestor of reptiles and mammals came to migrate into a more superficial, cortical location in mammals.[11]

If important questions of *how* the isocortex evolved remain unanswered, we have even less understanding of *why* it evolved. We would like to know what selection pressures favored the initial development of the features of laminar and cellular organization that are peculiar to the isocortex. It is tempting to suppose that the evolution of the isocortex is somehow related to the evolution of an active, predatory lifestyle, if only because so many features of mammalian biology are plausibly explained in this fashion. Unfortunately, because brains do not fossilize and because there are no living species that preserve the early stages in the evolution of the isocortex, we cannot reconstruct with much confidence the steps through which the cortex passed as it was being transformed into isocortex.

Evolution Has Given Rise to Mammalian Brains That Vary Considerably in Size and Degree of Folding

How does brain structure vary among the 20 or so orders of mammals? The most obvious differences are in the size of the brain and the degree of folding of the cortex. Brain size increases with body size, of course, but even among mammals of similar body size, brain size varies by nearly 10-fold.[12] Animals with larger brains (relative to body size) are said to be more **encephalized** than animals with smaller brains. Most of the differences in brain size among mammals are due to differences in the amount of cortex. As brain size increases, the extent to which the cortex folds (forming sulci and gyri) also increases. Animals with smooth-surfaced brains are said to be **lissencephalic,** while animals with folded or convoluted brains are said to be **gyrencephalic.** It is important to recognize that the

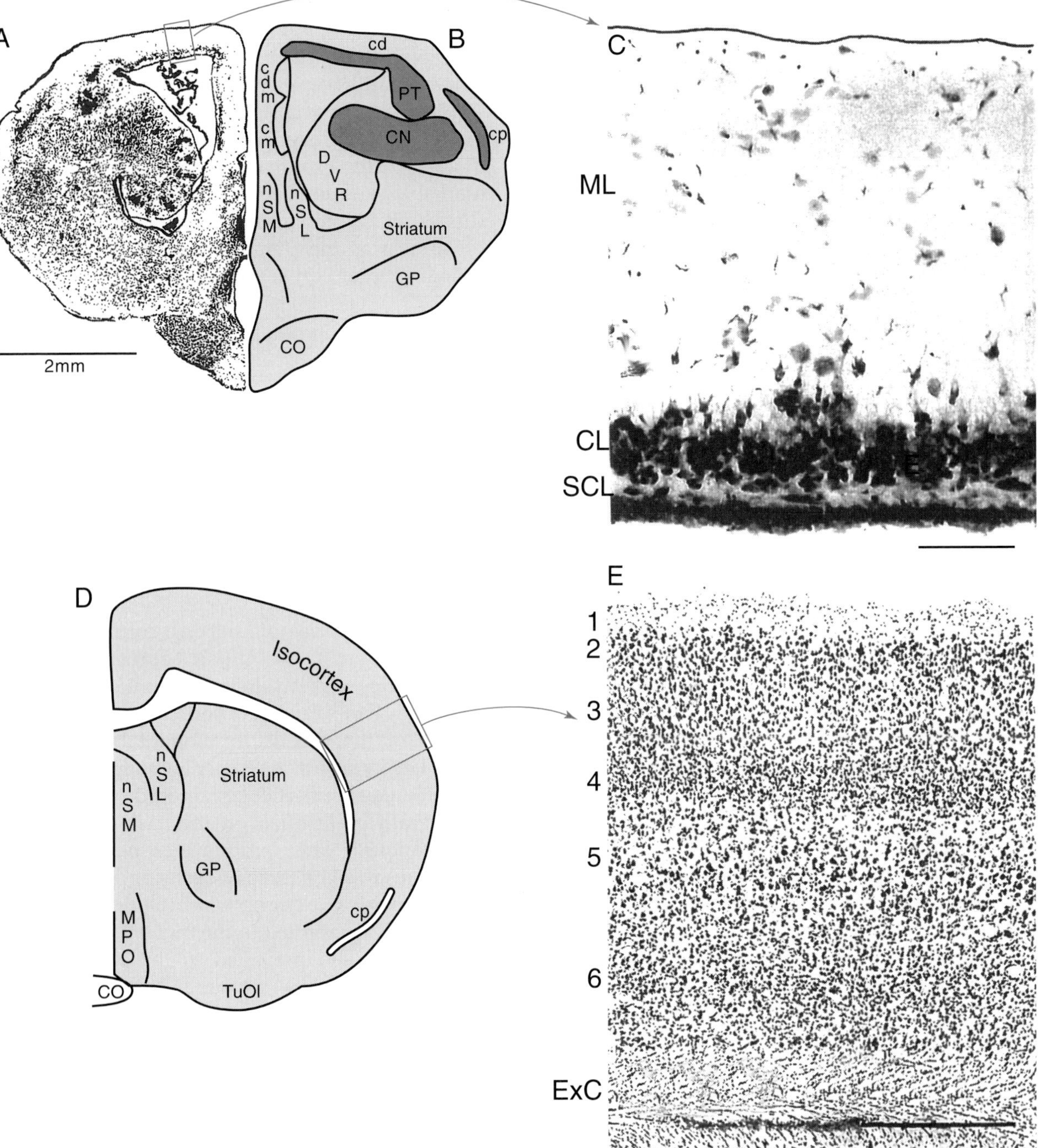

FIGURE 50.3 The telencephalon of a reptile (turtle) and a mammal (rat). In turtles, the cortical mantle of the telencephalon has a three-layered form. In contrast, six layers are usually recognized in mammalian cortex. Based on Reiner.[10] (A) High-contrast photomicrograph of a cresyl violet-stained transverse section through the telencephalon of a painted turtle at the level of the anterior commissure juxtaposed to a line drawing (B) of this same section. The major telencephalic subdivisions are identified. The dorsal cortex constitutes a thin piece of tissue overlying the lateral ventricle and grades into the pallial thickening laterally. (C) High-power photomicrograph of turtle dorsal cortex showing its cytoarchitectonic and laminar organization. A line has been drawn along the pial surface to accentuate its location. The scale bar equals 100 μm. (D) Line drawing of a transverse section of rat telencephalon through the level of the anterior commissure, presented for comparison to the turtle telencephalic section shown in A and B. (E) High-power photomicrograph of rat cortex, with the individual layers indicated. Note the much greater laminar and cytoarchitectonic complexity, compared to the turtle cortex shown in C. The scale bar equals 500 μm. Abbreviations: CL, cellular layer of cortex; CN, core nucleus of the DVR; CO, optic chiasm; cd, dorsal cortex; cdm, dorsomedial cortex; cm, medial cortex; cp, pyriform cortex; DVR, dorsal ventricular ridge; ExC, external capsule; GP, globus pallidus; ML, molecular layer of cortex; MPO, medial preoptic area; nPH, periventricular hypothalamic nucleus; nSL, lateral septal nucleus; nSM, medial septal nucleus; PT, pallial thickening; SCL, subcellular layer of cortex; TuOl, olfactory tubercle.

degree of folding is a consequence of the absolute size of the brain and does not reflect the size of the brain relative to body size (encephalization). Thus, large animals will tend to be more gyrencephalic, even if they are not highly encephalized. Whereas the *degree* of folding seems to be a consequence of size, however, the *pattern* of folding varies among mammalian groups, each having their own distinctive set of gyri and sulci.

Clearly, the large variation in brain size among mammals is important, but how one views the significance of this variation depends on one's view of brain organization. Researchers who believe that the structure of the cortex (which accounts for the largest part of brain variation) is very similar across mammalian species have suggested that brain size provides an index of the functional capacity or intelligence of a species.[12] This view has considerable appeal, given that *Homo sapiens* is among the most encephalized, if not *the* most encephalized, of mammals. On the other hand, if cortical structure varies substantially among mammals, then a straightforward relationship between brain size and brain function is unlikely.[13] We need to consider, then, the extent of variation in brain structure, and particularly in cortical organization, among mammals.

Neuroanatomists Have Attempted To Study the Diversification of the Mammalian Cortex by Mapping Brain Areas in Various Species

Early neuroanatomists recognized both similarities and differences in cortical organization among mammals. The influential work of Brodmann[9] is particularly noteworthy in this regard. Brodmann found that cortex exhibits considerable regional variation in its appearance in cell stains (cytoarchitecture), and he divided the cortex into a number of distinct areas. Furthermore, based on comparative studies of a wide range of mammalian orders, Brodmann argued that the number of areas varies among mammals, a belief that is reflected in the well-known cytoarchitectonic maps he drew for several species (Fig. 50.4). Brodmann believed it possible to identify a set of areas that mammals possess in common (such as the primary visual, somatosensory, and motor areas, and several allocortical areas), but that individual mammalian groups also possess areas that are unique. In general, Brodmann thought that mammals with larger brains have more areas than those with smaller brains. New areas can be isocortical or allocortical. Furthermore, although Brodmann was a staunch believer in the idea that the isocortex of all mammalian species passed through a six-layered phase at some point in its development, he also recognized that the adult pattern of lamination could vary considerably between species. He noted, for example, that there are several different patterns of lamination in the primary visual cortex (Brodmann's area 17) among mammals, and even different patterns among primates. Finally, Brodmann observed that there was remarkable variation between mammalian groups in the shapes, sizes, and clustering of specific classes of neurons, such as the pyramidal cells in layer V of the primary motor cortex (area 4).

The Cortex Is Composed of Many Areal Subdivisions

Many of Brodmann's contemporaries shared his goal of dividing the cortex into discrete structural regions to better understand cortical evolution and the localization of function. During the first half of the 20th century there was a proliferation of cortical maps derived from the examination of cell-stained (cytoarchitectonic) and fiber-stained (myeloarchitectonic) tissue in a wide variety of species. By midcentury, however, the enterprise of charting cortical areas began to meet with disfavor, in part because workers using similar cyto- and myeloarchitectonic methods could not agree on the number of cortical areas in a particular species or the precise location of borders between areas. Critics such as Karl Lashley suggested that Brodmann's maps, in particular, showed many more areas than could be justified on the basis of reproducible observations.[14] This critique was part of a broader challenge by some psychologists and neurologists to the concept of strong cortical localizationism—particularly as applied to the higher-order association cortex—that had prevailed in the early part of the century. In response to these criticisms, those who studied the organization of cortical areas moderated their views, and in maps drawn in the 1940s and 1950s the number of subdivisions within the association cortex was greatly reduced from the number appearing in maps drawn earlier in the century. During this period, there seems to have been a consensus that the human cortex is composed of something on the order of a dozen areas and that there is little variation in the number of cortical areas among mammals.

Modern studies have confirmed many of Brodmann's general conclusions about areal organization, and there has been a rebirth of localizationism. This rebirth has been spurred by the introduction of new methods for studying cortical organization, particularly techniques for recording and stimulating neural activity from microelectrodes inserted into the depth of the cortex that began to be applied in the 1960s. Workers using intracortical microelectrodes were able to map neural activity in much finer detail than was

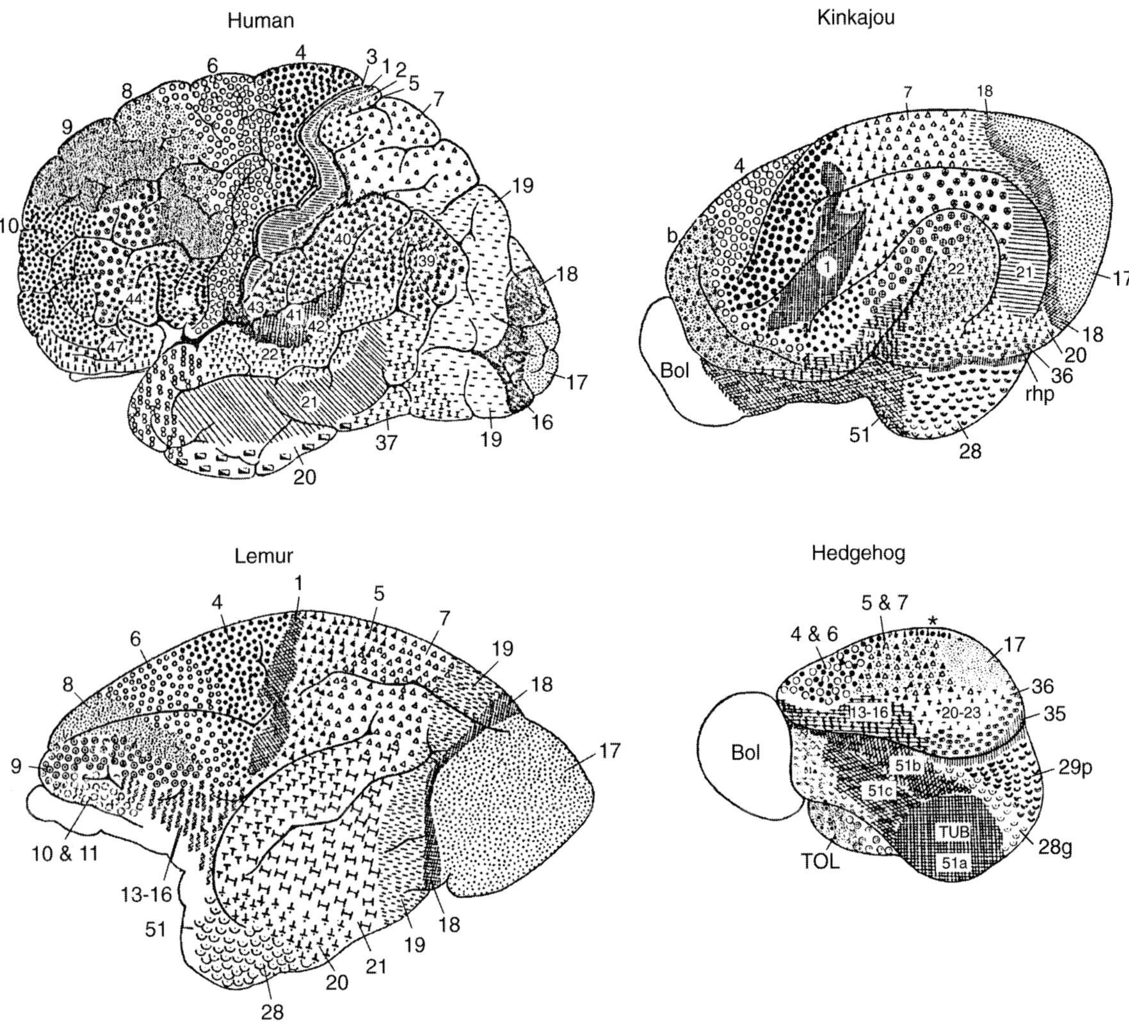

FIGURE 50.4 Four cytoarchitectonic maps from the comparative studies of cortical organization by Brodmann.[9] Humans and lemurs are primates, kinkajous are small carnivores, hedgehogs are insectivores. The numbers denote different cortical areas. BOL and TOL denote the olfactory bulb and olfactory tubercle, respectively. Figures are not to scale: numbering of areas follows Brodmann.

possible using earlier techniques that involved placing relatively large electrodes on the surface of the cortex. One important result of this was the discovery that, although the cortex contains a large number of separate areas,[15] much of the so-called association cortex of the parietal and temporal lobes of primates—cortex classically thought to integrate sensory information from multiple modalities—actually represents visual information only.[16] Most secondary or higher-order visual areas appear to contain separate "maps" of the contralateral visual field, as does the primary visual area (V1) (see Chapter 28). However, the response properties of neurons in each area differ to some extent, suggesting that each area makes a distinctive contribution to visual processing. In addition to the visual fields, multiple divisions of somatosensory, auditory, and motor cortex have been described. Similar results have been obtained in studies of carnivores, rodents, and other mammals. These studies indicate that large portions of cortex process information from a single modality and that the cortical representation of vision, somatosensation, audition, and movement each involve multiple areas (although it is not yet clear to what extent these principles apply to the olfactory, gustatory, and vestibular systems). Multimodal areas have been identified as well, although these appear to occupy relatively small portions of the parietal and temporal cortex along the borders of the visual, somatosensory, and auditory cortices.

Mapping cortical areas has once again become a major preoccupation of neuroscientists, and these efforts have been enhanced by the development of improved anatomical techniques. Beginning in the 1970s and continuing up to the present, new and powerful methods for tracing neural connections have been introduced. By using the enzyme horseradish peroxidase (HRP) and tritiated amino acids as tracer substances, neuroscientists can determine the full set of afferent and efferent connections of a given region of cortex. Differences in connectivity between regions serve as one line of evidence that the regions should be regarded as different areas. In addition, thanks to the development of immunocytochemistry and other techniques for locating specific molecules in the nervous system, it is now possible to examine the distribution of particular transmitters, enzymes, and structural molecules in the cortex. Locating these molecules enables us to investigate the areal organization of the cortex, because the distribution of molecules may differ from area to area. Thus, to augment the classical cyto- and myeloarchitectonic methods (which remain valuable tools), neuroscientists can now bring a number of different techniques to bear on the question of how to subdivide the cortex. In postulating the existence of a cortical area, it is possible—and indeed desirable—to identify multiple characteristics that distinguish the proposed area from other areas. The availability of multiple techniques for parceling the cortex does not mean that all the controversies surrounding the number of areas and the location of borders have been resolved, but much progress has been made, and it seems likely that the major controversies will ultimately be settled.

Modern Studies Indicate That the Number of Cortical Areas Varies among Mammals

Although we are far from having a complete accounting of cortical areas in mammals, it appears that animals with relatively large brains, such as primates and carnivores, have more cortical areas than animals with relatively small brains, such as rodents and insectivores.[17] This is consistent with Brodmann's claim, although it is important to recognize that modern studies recognize many areas that Brodmann missed and often draw the borders of areas differently from the way Brodmann drew them. The shortcomings of Brodmann's maps should be borne in mind, as they are still widely used as guides to cortical localization, especially in human studies.

Given that the number of cortical areas varies among mammalian groups, it follows that some mammalian groups possess cortical areas that have no homologs in other groups. According to the definition of homology, a structure is homologous in two groups only if the structure was inherited from the common ancestor of those groups. Thus, when a new area evolves in a given species, homologs of that area may be present in the descendants of that species, but, by definition, a homolog cannot be present in any other animals. The importance of this principle in understanding cortical variation can be illustrated by the following example. Both primates and carnivores possess a large number of cortical visual areas (perhaps 15–20 or more), and it has been suggested that many or most of the areas present in primates have homologs in carnivores, based on similarities in the connections of areas, their receptive field properties, and so forth.[18] The ultimate test, however, is whether the visual areas thought to be homologous in carnivores and primates were present in the common ancestry of primates and carnivores. Although we cannot completely resolve this issue at present, owing mainly to the lack of comprehensive comparative studies, it seems likely that many of the visual areas present in carnivores and primates evolved independently and are therefore not homologous. The reason for this is that the animals most closely related to primates—bats and tree shrews—appear to have relatively few visual areas (despite the fact that tree shrews and some bats have very well developed visual systems.) Presumably, the last common ancestor of primates, tree shrews, and bats had relatively few visual areas, which implies that many of visual areas present in primates evolved after the divergence of primates from other mammalian lineages and are primate specializations.

Theories Differ about Which Cortical Areas Were Present in Ancestral Mammals

Despite the variation in mammalian areal organization, a number of areas appear to be common to many mammalian groups. If we cast the net wide enough, comparing members of each of the major branches of mammalian evolution—monotremes, marsupials, and placentals—we can begin to reconstruct the areal organization of the last common ancestor of the living mammals.

What cortical regions and areas were present in ancestral mammals?[19] Comparative studies suggest the presence of a relatively small number of isocortical and allocortical divisions. Perhaps three or four visual areas were present in ancestral mammals, including the primary visual area (V1) and second visual area (V2). Somatosensory areas probably included the primary sensory area (S1) and an area located lateral to S1 termed the parietal ventral (PV) area.[20] An additional somatosensory field, area S2, is present in marsupials and placentals, but apparently not in monotremes. Ancestral mammals probably possessed a primary auditory area (A1) and a few additional auditory areas, but because the homologies of auditory areas in living mammals are poorly understood, it is not possible to make strong inferences about ancestral organization. Comparative studies of the motor cortex suggest that ancestral mammals may have possessed one or two motor areas. In addition to these sensory and motor areas, ancestral mammals probably possessed regions of orbital and cingulate cortex, as well as divisions of the allocortex, including retrosplenial and entorhinal cortices, hippocampus, and olfactory (piriform) cortex. Because the parcellation of some of these "limbic" regions in modern mammals is poorly understood, we can say little about the number of divisions of limbic cortex that were present in ancestral mammals.

In the preceding presentation, the evaluation of areal organization in ancestral mammals is remarkably similar to the one published by Brodmann in 1909.[9] It represents a major challenge to an alternative theory of cortical evolution that has achieved a considerable following. That theory holds that the cortical areas present in ancestral mammals correspond to the limbic and association cortex of later mammals and that the primary sensory and motor areas are late-evolving specializations.[21] The principal evidence offered is that the primary areas show the most elaborate development of lamination and cellular differentiation, as typified, for example, by the development of a thick layer of tiny granular cells in the primary visual, somatosensory, and auditory areas of primates. Proponents of this view contrast the architecture of these areas with the less elaborately stratified cortex of the association regions and also with the relatively unstratified cortex of insectivores and other mammals held to be living models of ancestral forms. From this viewpoint, however, it is very difficult to explain why so many different and distantly related groups of mammals (including monotremes and marsupials) possess areas that resemble the primary sensory areas of primates in their physiology, connectivity, and, in some cases, cytoarchitecture. The most reasonable explanation of these similarities is that ancestral mammals also possessed primary sensory areas. The variability observed in the architectonic appearance of cortex in different groups of mammals is, nevertheless, an important aspect of mammalian biology that deserves further consideration.

There Is Abundant Variation in the Cellular, Laminar, and Connectional Organization of the Cortex

The areal organization of cortex varies among mammals, but are there variations in other aspects of cortical organization? It seems reasonable that variations in the cellular composition of the cortex, in the laminar distribution of its cell types, and in its intrinsic and extrinsic connectivity should also exist. As discussed earlier, Brodmann[9] documented many phyletic differences in the microscopic appearance of the cortex in different species. Nevertheless, many neuroscientists have believed that there is a "basic uniformity" in the cellular makeup and intrinsic circuitry of cell "columns" in the cortex.[22–24] In this view, the computations performed by columns on incoming information are held to be fundamentally similar across areas and across species.

It now seems likely that claims of phyletic invariance in the structure and function of local cortical circuitry have been overstated. Evidence now indicates that the number of cells in a cortical column, at one time considered to be fairly constant between areas and species, actually varies substantially.[25,26] Moreover, comparative studies indicate that the expression of metabolic and structural proteins by cells in specific areas of the cortex differs among species.[27–30] Comparative studies of the intrinsic connections of the primary visual area indicate that there are differences even between closely related species. In addition, there are marked variations in the distributions of neurotransmitters and receptors within homologous areas of different mammalian groups. For example, the primary motor area (M1) of macaque monkeys and humans receives a very dense innervation from dopamine-containing fibers originating in the midbrain, whereas the M1 of rats receives very few dopaminergic fibers[31] (Fig. 50.5). There are even differences in the laminar distribution of transmitters and receptors between homologous areas within the primate order.[32–34] Finally, the long, extrinsic connections of the cortex, including connections with other areas, are known to vary as well.

With such an abundance of differences in cortical organization, the existence of a single computational design common to all cortical areas and to all species is very unlikely. This does not mean that some features of organization present in the last common ancestor of mammals were not retained in many of its living descendants. To identify these features, however, we must compare cortical structure in a broad sample of mammalian groups and reconstruct ancestral organization in the same fashion that workers have reconstructed the ancestral areal organization of mammals. We must remember, too, that if we are to understand how particular groups of animals use their brains to cope with the challenges of life, identifying how these animals differ from other mammals is every bit as important as understanding the common features of mammalian organization.

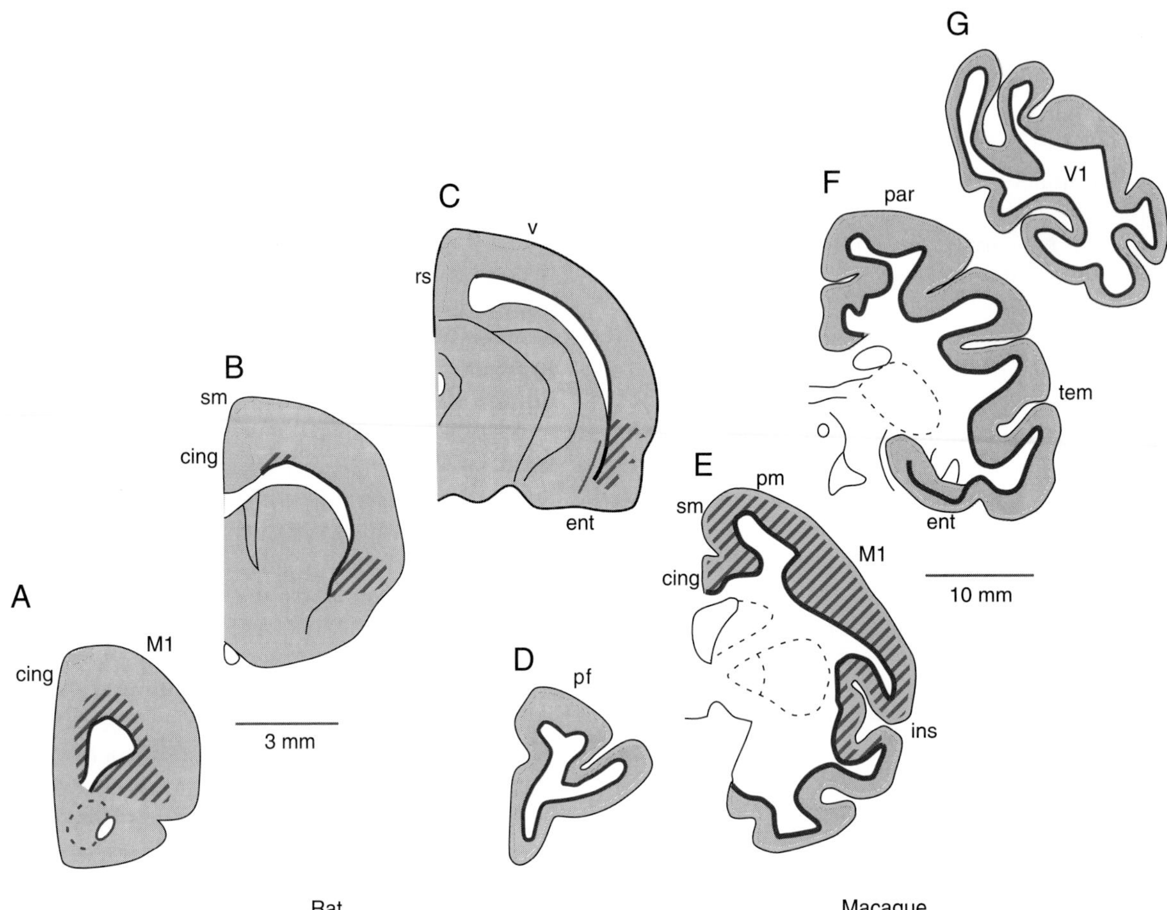

FIGURE 50.5 Dopaminergic innervation of the cortex in rats and macaque monkeys is shown in blue. Note that the motor cortex of macaques, including the primary motor area (M1), premotor cortex (PM), and supplementary motor area (SM), receives dense dopaminergic inputs that extend throughout the layers of the cortex, whereas in rats, the dopaminergic inputs to motor cortex are minimal. Other abbreviations: cing, cingulate cortex; ent, entorhinal cortex; ins, insular cortex; par, parietal cortex; pf, prefrontal cortex; rs, retrosplenial cortex; tem, temporal cortex; v, visual cortex; V1, primary visual area. Modified from Berger *et al.*[31]

Summary

Mammals are a diverse group of animals, composed of approximately 20 different orders. As a group, mammals have evolved many distinctive biological characteristics, including a unique forebrain structure: the six-layer isocortex (or neocortex). Mammals vary greatly in the amount of cortex they possess, but also vary in the way cortex is organized. Cortex is composed of multiple subdivisions (areas). Comparisons among living mammals suggest that early mammals had relatively few areas and that new areas evolved independently in several different mammalian orders. Also, there is evidence that the connections within and between areas varies among mammals, as does the distribution of neurotransmitters and receptors within the cortex.

PRIMATE EVOLUTION

Evolution has produced distinctive specializations in each group of mammals. What are the particular specializations of brain organization that evolved in primates? Before addressing this question, let us consider some basic information about the order Primates.

Primates Are a Diverse Group, but Characteristics That Are Widely Shared among Primates May Provide Clues to Their Ancestral Adaptations

Although one sometimes hears scientists refer to "the primate," there are in fact nearly 200 species of living primates and they exhibit a variety of behaviors and social organizations.[8,35] Primates are classified into two main groups, prosimians and anthropoids (Fig. 50.6). The prosimians consist of bushbabies, lorises, lemurs, and tarsiers and are found today in Asia, in Africa, and on the island of Madagascar. Prosimians have often been regarded as primitive primates, and while they do retain a number of primitive characteristics, they have nevertheless evolved a variety of specializations as well. The anthropoids are composed of a New World group (the New World monkeys), and an Old World group (the Old World monkeys, apes, and humans). Humans are actually a branch of the ape radiation, and apes and humans are referred to collectively as "hominoids." Old World monkeys include the familiar rhesus monkeys and other members of the genus *Macaca,* which have been widely used in research. Some New World monkeys, such as squirrel monkeys (genus *Saimiri*) and owl monkeys (*Aotus*), have also been intensively studied by neuroscientists, as have the promisian bushbabies (genus *Galago*). It is noteworthy, however, that most neurobiological research in primates has concentrated on a very small sample of the nearly 200 primate species.

It is sometimes supposed that primates are distinctive in being more "social" than other mammals. This is not the case. Some primate species live in small social groups, while others are quite solitary. Other primate species, notably some of the Old World monkeys and chimpanzees, live in large groups; but then so do many species of other mammalian orders, such as cetaceans and ungulates. Most primate species are tropical or subtropical in distribution and subsist on some combination of fruit, leaves, sap, insects, and small vertebrates. Anthropoid primates are active in the day (diurnal), with a single exception, the New World owl monkey (genus *Aotus*). Among prosimians, the smaller species (those with body weights less than 1 kg) are mostly active at night (nocturnal), while some of the larger species are diurnal. Most primate species are arboreal, although some Old World monkey and hominoid species spend considerable time on the ground.

Primates are a diverse group of mammals; yet there are a number of characteristics that are widely shared by living species, and these provide clues to the ancestral adaptations of primates. Among these characteristics are close-set, forward-facing eyes with broadly overlapping visual fields, grasping big toes (and in some species, grasping thumbs as well), and broad digit tips that are capped, on at least some digits, with flattened nails (rather than claws, as in most mammals). Many additional characteristics are commonly associated with primates, such as the reduction of the olfactory apparatus and brain enlargement, but these are actually specializations found in anthropoid primates rather than in primates generally.

Ancestral Primates Probably Were Small Nocturnal Animals That Lived in the Terminal Branches of Trees

Let us assume that the ancestors of living primates had forward-facing eyes, grasping big toes, and digits

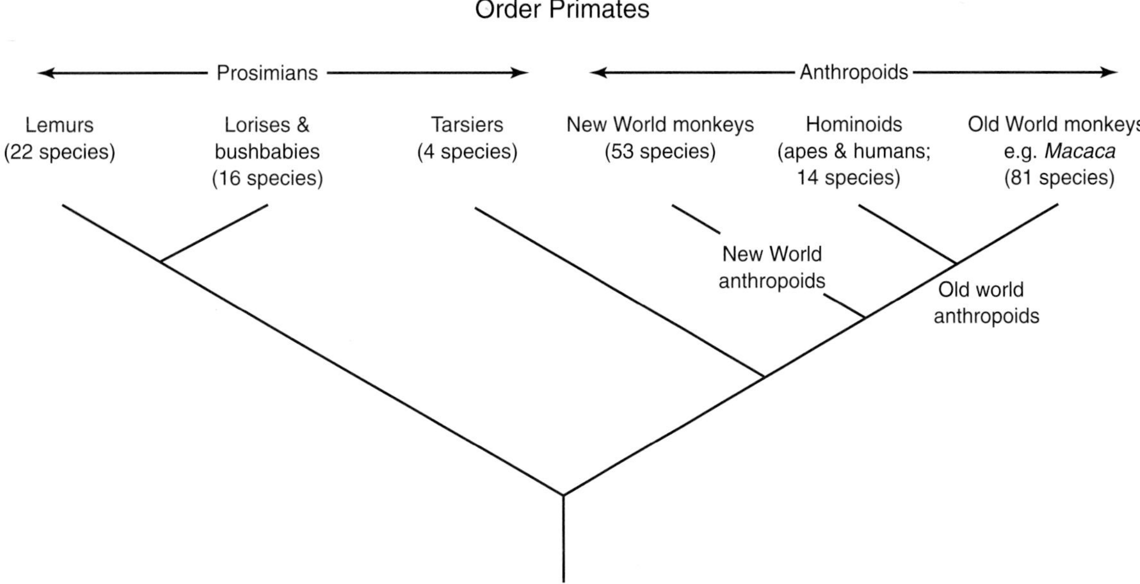

FIGURE 50.6 Phyletic relationships of the living primates. Based primarily on Fleagle.[35]

tipped with nails, all characteristics consistent with both the comparative and the paleontological evidence. Let us assume further that they were nocturnal, which is suggested by the very large orbits of early fossil primates. What sort of lifestyle shaped the evolution of these early primates? One very influential view, developed early in this century, is that the distinctive features of primates are adaptations for an arboreal existence.[36,37] For example, primates were thought to need stereoscopic vision, and consequently the overlapping visual fields that made stereoscopic vision possible, to judge the distance between branches when leaping from limb to limb. Moreover, life in the trees was held to promote visual acuity, manual dexterity, and physical agility, which were thought to foster in turn the development of the brain and intelligence. Modern primatologists have noted, however, that plenty of animals with clawed digits and eyes on the side of the head—squirrels, for instance—manage to get around very well in trees without falling into the abyss. While ancestral primates may indeed have lived in trees, primate specializations cannot be explained as adaptations to arboreality per se.

Perhaps we can identify specific behaviors that are associated with primate characteristics by looking at the behavior of other animals that have evolved similar characteristics.[38] For example, forward-facing eyes[8,35] have evolved independently in a number of nocturnal, visually oriented predators, such as owls and cats. The fact that the smaller living prosimians feed heavily on insects, seizing them with the hands and mouth under visual guidance, is consistent with the view that ancestral primates were visual predators. It seems likely that the original functional significance of forward-facing eyes was related more to visual acuity than to stereopsis: forward-facing placement of the eyes minimizes distortion of the visual scene immediately in front of an animal because the light travels a relatively straight path to the retinal fovea.[39] This advantage is greatest under low-light conditions, nocturnal activity. Another primate characteristic, grasping hands and feet with broad digit tips, has evolved in several groups of small vertebrates that navigate in the fine terminal branches of trees, where nonprehensile, squirrel-like appendages provide poor support. If we look at behaviors associated with forward-facing eyes and grasping hands and feet in other animals, the picture of ancestral primates that emerges is one of small, nocturnal animals that lived in the terminal branches of trees, where they made their living (at least in part) by visually guided foraging on insects and other small prey.[38]

To Reconstruct Primate Brain Evolution We Need to Identify Changes in Specific Neural Structures and Systems

Classical accounts of primate brain evolution stressed the large size of the primate brain and enlargement of the central visual system.[36,37] These accounts leave much to be desired. For one thing, among primates, only anthropoids have brains that are markedly larger (at a given body size) than those of most other mammals; prosimians have brains more nearly average in size. It is also true that primates have well-developed central visual systems, but so do some of their close relatives, such as tree shrews and some bats. Primates may simply have inherited their large central visual structures from their nonprimate ancestors. We would like to identify changes in the structure of *specific* neural structures and systems that occurred in the ancestry of primates and during the subsequent evolution of particular primate groups. With the advent of modern techniques for elucidating brain structure, we can begin to identify these changes.

The Complex Structure and Connectional Pathways of the Primate Visual System Have Been Studied Extensively

The visual system is the most intensively studied part of the nervous system in primates, and information about its organization in a relatively large number of prosimian and anthropoid species is available (see Chapter 28). As explained elsewhere in this volume, visual information originating in the retina reaches the paired lateral geniculate nuclei (LGN) in the thalamus, and the superior colliculi (SC) in the midbrain. The superior colliculus controls orienting movements of the eyes, ears, and head. It projects caudally, to brainstem motor nuclei, and rostrally, to the LGN and to other thalamic nuclei. The LGN serves to relay visual information from the retina and superior colliculus to the primary visual cortical area (V1), also known as the striate cortex or area 17. From V1, visual information is passed on to a dozen or more higher-order, extrastriate visual areas[40,41,42] (see Chapters 28 and 52 and Fig. 50.7).

In Primates, Unlike Other Vertebrates, Visual Inputs to the Superior Colliculi from the Contralateral and Ipsilateral Eyes Are Nearly Equal

In almost all vertebrates that have been studied, including fish, amphibians, reptiles, and most mammals, each of the paired SC receives a large projection from the contralateral eye and a smaller (and phyletically variable) projection from the ipsilateral eye. As a result, the SC represents the entire visual field seen by the contralateral eye, along with a small region of binocular representation.[43] Primates are an exception to the general vertebrate pattern. In all primates that have been examined, each SC receives nearly equal inputs from the contralateral and ipsilateral eyes,[44] and each SC represents only the contralateral visual hemifield, rather than both hemifields.[45]

Among the mammals thought to be closely related to primates, tree shrews and the echolocating (microchiropteran) bats possess the primitive pattern of SC organization.[46,47] Recently, it has been suggested that one group of bats, the fruit bats (megachiropterans), possesses the derived primate pattern of SC, and therefore that this group of bats is more closely related to primates than are any other group of mammals.[47] This is referred to as the "flying primate" hypothesis. Subsequently, however, at least some fruit bats were found to possess the nonprimate pattern of SC organization.[48] For this and other reasons, the "flying primate" hypothesis has not yet won wide acceptance.

The Visual Systems of Primates and Other Mammals Differ in Morphology

Mammalian LGNs typically are composed of several cellular laminae; however, the number of laminae and the kinds of visual information represented in different laminae vary between mammalian groups.[49,50] In most mammals, each LGN receives a large input from the contralateral eye and a smaller projection from the ipsilateral eye. When the visual fields of both eyes overlap extensively, as in primates, the contra- and ipsilateral projections tend to be more nearly equal. In primates, the LGN consists of four main cellular lamina: a pair of large-celled or magnocellular (M) layers and a pair of small-celled or parvocellular (P) layers (Fig. 50.7). Each retina projects to one M layer and one P layer in each of the paired LGNs. The M and P layers receive different types of visual information from the retina: the M layers receive inputs from cells sensitive to stimulus change, such as that produced by movement, but insensitive to spatial detail; the P layers receive inputs from cells with high spatial resolution and color sensitivity (in diurnal species). The P layers are well developed in Old World anthropoid primates, including humans, and in these species each P layer splits into leaflets, giving the LGN a six-layered, rather than a four-layered, appearance.[51]

The koniocellular (K) cells constitute an additional class of neurons in the LGN. Compared with the properties of M and P cells, the functional properties of K cells have received little attention from physiologists and are rather poorly understood.[52] This is unfortunate, as modifications of K-cell circuitry would seem to be at the heart of primate visual system evolution. Specifically, K cells receive projections from the superior colliculus, which as we have noted has a derived organization in primates, and K cells project directly to a specialized compartment of primate primary visual cortex (the "blobs"), as described below. One reason the K cells have received little attention from neuroscientists is that they do not form very conspicuous laminae in anthropoid primates. In most prosimian primates, by contrast, the K cells form a pair of distinct layers, located between the P layers.

The LGN relays visual information to the primary visual area (V1). V1 evinces a number of specializations in primates. Perhaps the most striking feature of primate V1 is that it is a mosaic of small, repeating tissue compartments or modules, called **blobs** and **interblobs.** The term blob describes the appearance of small, roundish territories of V1 tissue that stain intensely for the metabolic enzyme cytochrome oxidase (CO) and are surrounded by more lightly stained (interblob) territories. Blobs and interblobs have different connections and presumably make different contributions to visual function. Blobs receive direct inputs from the K cells of the LGN and indirect inputs from M and P cells. In squirrel monkeys and macaque monkeys, which are diurnal primates, blobs contain many color-selective cells, and blobs may constitute part of a color-processing network.[53] Yet this cannot be the whole story, as blobs are present in nocturnal primates, which presumably have poor color discrimination. Casagrande[52] suggests that the blobs and other components of the K-cell system are involved in the control of visual attention.

We have an unusually large amount of information about the phyletic distribution of blobs, because they can be revealed in fresh tissue using a simple histochemical stain for cytochrome oxidase. To date, blobs have been demonstrated in all anthropoid primates that have been examined and in most, if not all, prosimian primates.[54,55] Thus, it is likely that the segregation of V1 into blobs and interblobs was present in the last common ancestor of living primates. Moreover, blobs are absent in bats and tree shrews and in most other mammals studied. Relatively faint, bloblike structures are evident in carnivores,[56] but given the absence of blobs in the animals closely related to primates, it is likely that carnivore blobs evolved independently and are therefore not homologous to primate blobs.[55]

The second visual area, V2 (or area 18), which bor-

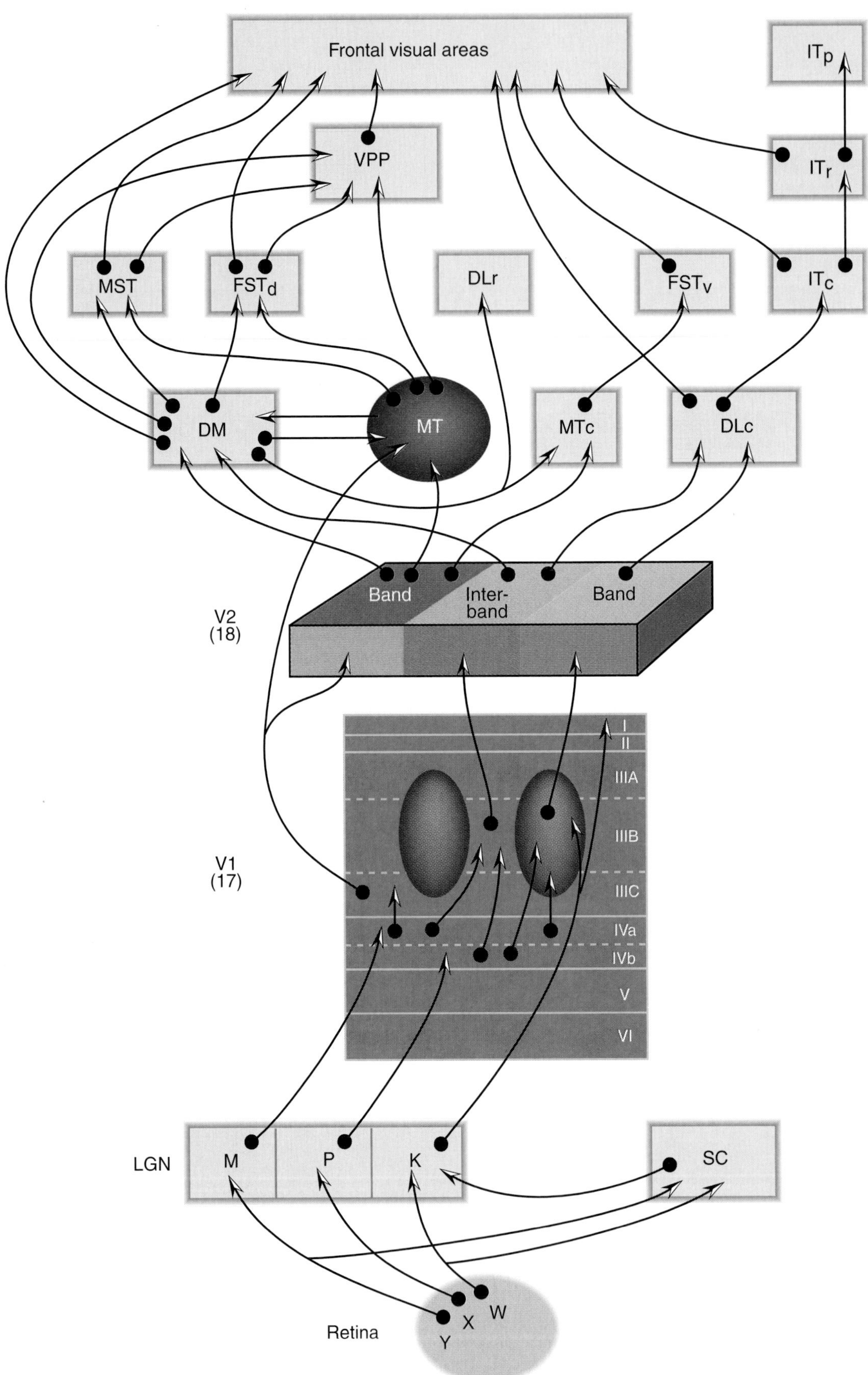

Frontal visual areas
ITp
VPP
ITr
MST
FSTd
DLr
FSTv
ITc
MT
DM
MTc
DLc
V2
(18)
Band
Inter-
band
Band
I
II
IIIA
IIIB
V1
(17)
IIIC
IVa
IVb
V
VI
LGN
M
P
K
SC
Retina
X
Y
W

ders V1 anteriorly, is a major target of projections from V1 (Fig. 50.7). In anthropoid primates, V2 has a patchy structure, composed of three types of repeating, band-like compartments (see Chapter 28). Two sets of stripes stain intensely for CO; the other stains lightly. The three classes of bands receive inputs from different compartments of V1 and project to different regions of higher-order visual cortex.[53] Among mammals, only anthropoid primates have been reported to have three types of repeating compartments in V2. The compartmentation of V2 into CO-dark and CO-light bands is much more apparent in anthropoids than in prosimians.[55]

In Primates, Information from the Primary and Secondary Visual Areas Is Analyzed by over a Dozen Higher-Order Areas, Many of Which Have No Homologs in Other Mammals

Primates possess a large number of higher-order areas devoted exclusively to the analysis of visual information. Although there is still much debate over how many visual areas exist in primates, there are at least 15 well-characterized areas in New World and Old World monkeys.[40,41] Many of the areas identified in anthropoids have been identified in prosimians as well. As discussed in a preceding section, there is reason to believe that many of the higher-order visual areas of primates have no homologs in other mammals. Some of the strongest candidates for primate-specific visual areas are located in the posterior parietal and inferior temporal lobes. Portions of the inferotemporal cortex of macaques, particularly the region lying within the superior temporal sulcus, have been shown to contain cells that respond selectively to the sight of natural stimuli, including hands and faces.[57,58] Moreover, some classes of cells in this region are reported to respond selectively when an animal views other members of its species performing particular behavioral acts.[59] This region of cortex could thus be of great importance in social cognition.

The parietal and temporal cortices of nonprimates differ in a number of respects from those of primates. Although carnivores and rodents both possess regions that have been likened to the primate posterior parietal cortex, and which could be homologous to a portion of it, for neither group is there evidence of a large number of distinct connectional and architectonic subdivisions, as there is in primates.[60] Furthermore, although the cortical visual system is well developed in carnivores, these animals evidently do not possess a region of temporal cortex where neurons respond selectively to faces. On these and other grounds, neither carnivores nor rodents appear to possess homologs of the inferotemporal visual cortex. Interestingly, however, sheep reportedly have face-selective cells in the visual cortex.[61] Evidently this constitutes an instance of convergent evolution between ungulates and primates.

FIGURE 50.7 A highly simplified schematic diagram showing organization of the visual system in New World monkeys; other primate groups share many of the same structures and connections. The visual system is composed of three partly separate pathways that traverse multiple structures. The segregation of visual information begins in the retina, which has three types of output cells: W, X, and Y cells. These cells project to the K, P, and M layers, respectively, of the lateral geniculate nucleus (LGN). The W and Y cells also form an indirect connection to the K layers via projections to the superior colliculus, which in turn projects to the LGN. Each of the LGN layers projects to different layers of the primary visual area, V1, also known as the striate cortex. Inputs and outputs are segregated in different layers and sublayers within V1. V1 is also divided into "blob" and "interblob" regions, which differ connectionally. V2 is divided into three striplike compartments, each with a distinctive set of connections. From V1 and V2, visual information reaches the extrastriate visual areas. Extrastriate areas include DLc and DLr, the dorsolateral visual area, caudal and rostral divisions; DM, the dorsomedial area; MST, the middle superior temporal visual area; FSTd and FSTv, the visual area of the fundus of the superior temporal sulcus (dorsal and ventral divisions); ITc, ITr, and ITp, the inferotemporal visual cortex (caudal, rostral, and polar divisions); MT, the middle temporal area; MTc, the "crescent" around MT; VPP, ventral posterior parietal cortex. Modified from Casagrande and Kaas.[42]

The Brains of Primates Possess Somatosensory and Motor Areas Not Found in Other Mammals

In marsupial and placental mammals, two somatosensory areas receive input predominantly from cutaneous (tactile) receptors; these are the first (S1) and second (S2) somatosensory areas (see Chapter 26). (Other areas receive input from muscle, joint, and other deep receptors.) Prosimian primates retain this pattern, whereas most anthropoid primates possess an additional cutaneous area immediately caudal to S1.[62] There is also evidence that anthropoids have a "rewired" cortical network for processing cutaneous information (Fig. 50.8). Comparative studies indicate that in a wide variety of mammals, including the prosimian *Galago*, area S2 receives direct cutaneous inputs from the ventroposterior (VP) thalamic nucleus, as does area S1. Thus, lesions of S1 have a minimal effect on the cutaneous responsiveness of S2. By contrast, anthropoid S2 receives its cutaneous input through a cortical relay in S1, rather than directly from VP, as indicated by the finding that lesions of S1 leave S2 largely unresponsive to cutaneous stimulation.[63]

In primates, the motor cortex consists of a large primary motor area (M1) and a number of "premotor"

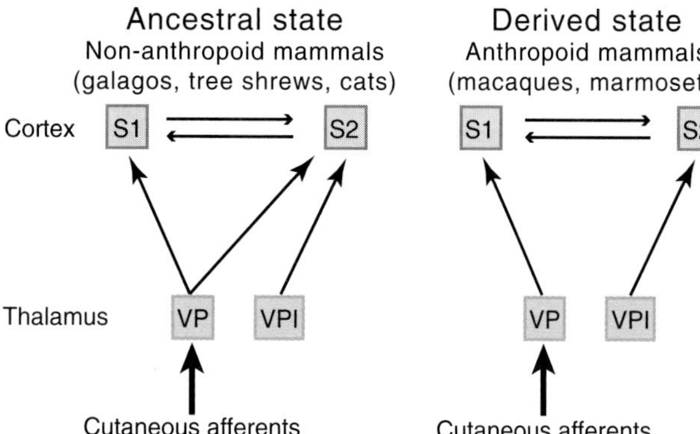

FIGURE 50.8 The distribution of cutaneous (tactile) information in the first and second somatosensory areas (S1, S2) of different mammals. In most mammals investigated, cutaneous inputs reach S1 and S2 directly via projections from the ventroposterior (VP) nucleus of the thalamus. In anthropoid primates, VP does not project directly to S2; instead, cutaneous information reaches S2 via a relay through S1. The ventroposterior inferior nucleus (VPI) is a division of the thalamus that relays noncutaneous information to the cortex. Modified from reference 63.

areas. M1 is highly responsive to electrical stimulation, which evokes bodily movements in a somatotopically organized fashion. It has long been understood that the control of the fractionated, independent digit movements so characteristic of anthropoid primates (and especially Old World anthropoids) depends on M1 and its projections to the spinal cord, and for this reason it has been argued that primate phylogeny was marked by the progressive elaboration of the corticospinal system.[64] Although a relationship between fine motor control and corticospinal connectivity exists, such a linear evolutionary scheme is too simplistic to account for the diversity of corticospinal organization and motor abilities found in primates.[65] Moreover, comparative studies indicate that some prosimian primates have extraordinarily dense populations of corticospinal neurons, exceeding even the density of corticospinal neurons in anthropoid primates.[3]

The premotor region, located anteriorly and medially to M1, is usually thought to be involved in higher-order aspects of motor control, including the selection and serial organization of movements and the integration of limb and body segments during movements. Although the organization of this region has long been a subject of dispute, it is now apparent that anthropoid primates possess at least six premotor areas.[66,67] In rodents and carnivores, the most intensively studied non-primate mammals, present evidence indicates the existence of only one or two premotor areas.[68] It is likely, therefore, that some of the divisions of primate premotor cortex are unique to primates. One area that deserves particular attention is the ventral premotor area, or PMV. This area is found in both prosimians and anthropoids, but may be absent in other mammals.[3] PMV represents movements of the mouth and forelimb[67,69] and evidence indicates its involvement in visually guided reaching and grasping movements of the hands and mouth.[69] These results are particularly interesting in view of the importance ascribed to this class of movements in modern interpretations of primate origins, as discussed earlier. It is noteworthy that forelimb movements are prominently represented in several other parts of premotor cortex and that eye movements are represented in multiple divisions of premotor and prefrontal cortex.[67]

A Large Region of Prefrontal Cortex Is Characteristic of Primates, and Portions of This Region Appear To Be Unique to the Order

The term prefrontal cortex is usually used to describe all the frontal cortex that lies anterior and medial to the motor and premotor cortex. However, the cingulate cortex and orbital cortex, which occupy part of this region, are sometimes considered territories distinct from the prefrontal cortex. The evolutionary status of the prefrontal cortex, and in particular the part of the prefrontal cortex that occupies the dorsolateral surface of the frontal lobe of primates, has long been the subject of controversy among neuroscientists.

The prefrontal cortex is greatly enlarged in primates compared with most other mammals;[70] this is indicated by the fact that the motor cortex is found near the frontal pole in most mammals, whereas in primates it lies near the center of the cerebrum. The pioneering primatologist and neuroanatomist Elliot Smith[36] thought that enlargement of the prefrontal cortex was responsible for the quickness of thought and action that he believed distinguished primates from other mammals. In primates, the dorsolateral prefrontal cortex is marked microscopically by the presence of a distinct lamina IV, densely packed with tiny granular cells. Brodmann[9] argued that the granular prefrontal cortex was well developed only in primates. He also believed that the size and number of areas of prefrontal cortex increased in primate evolution, culminating in humans. The idea that the prefrontal cortex is greatly modified in primate evolution is particularly interesting in light of the substantial body of evidence implicating the prefrontal cortex in higher-order cognitive functions (see Chapters 51 and 59).

Claims for the uniqueness of primate dorsolateral cortex have met vigorous opposition, in keeping with the general resistance of neuroscientists to suggestions of major phyletic differences in cerebral organization.

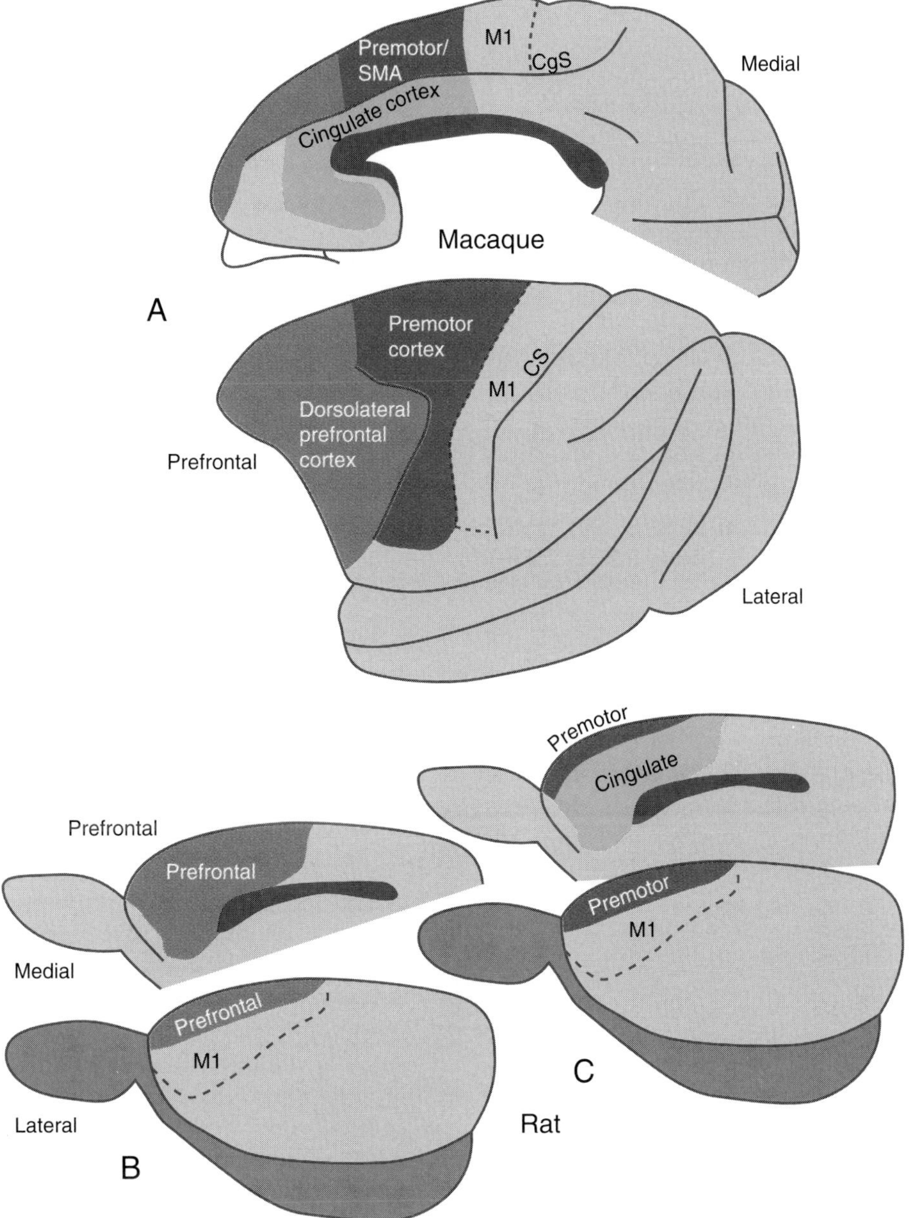

FIGURE 50.9 Alternative interpretations of frontal lobe in macaque monkeys (A) and rats (B, C). In the usual interpretation of homologies, the dorsal and medial frontal cortex of rats is considered homologous to the dorsolateral prefrontal cortex of primates (gray). Recent findings suggest that the dorsal and medial frontal cortex of rats is actually homologous to the cingulate cortex (blue) and premotor cortex (purple) of primates. Abbreviations: CS, central sulcus; CgS, cingulate sulcus; M1, primary motor area. Modified from Preuss.[76]

This opposition rests on the observation that although the frontal cortex of most nonprimates lacks a well-developed granular layer, it does possess other anatomical and functional characteristics similar to those of the primate dorsolateral prefrontal cortex. In particular, neuroscientists have argued that homologs of the dorsolateral cortex can be identified on the basis of inputs from the thalamic mediodorsal nucleus (MD), dense innervation by dopamine-containing fibers, and involvement in working memory (delayed response and delayed alternation) tasks.[71–74]

Recent findings challenge the view that nonprimates possess homologs of the dorsolateral prefrontal cortex. The connectional and functional characteristics thought to be specific to the dorsolateral prefrontal cortex in primates turn out to be attributes of other parts of the frontal cortex as well.[75,76] For example, in primates, the thalamic nucleus MD and the midbrain dopaminergic nuclei project to the premotor, cingulate, and orbital cortices as well as to the dorsolateral prefrontal cortex; in addition, the cingulate cortices evidently contribute to performance on working memory tasks. In fact, the regions traditionally considered prefrontal in rodents resemble the premotor, cingulate, and orbital areas of primates more closely than they do the dorsolateral prefrontal cortex, and it seems likely that traditional interpretations of rodent–primate homologies are mistaken (Fig. 50.9). The presumed dorsolateral prefrontal cortex of carnivores also differs in many respects from that of primates, and it is not clear that the two regions are homologous. Thus, although detailed information about frontal lobe organization is limited to only three mammalian orders (primates, rodents, and carnivores), current evidence is consistent with the possibility that the dorsolateral prefrontal cortex is a primate specialization.[76] There is also evidence of significant variation in prefrontal organization among primates. A comparison of cortical connections and architectonics in prosimian bushbabies and anthropoid macaque monkeys suggests that macaques possess several dorsolateral prefrontal areas in addition to those found in bushbabies.[77] This is in agreement with Brodmann's[9] general claim that anthropoids possess more prefrontal subdivisions that do prosimians.

Summary

The first primates were probably small, nocturnal creatures that preyed on insects and small vertebrates in the fine terminal branches of trees. This is inferred from such distinctive features of primate anatomy as forward-facing eyes and grasping fingers and toes. Primates also display many neurobiological specializations. Specializations of the visual system have been extensively documented and involve both subcortical and cortical structures. Primates have a large number of visual cortical areas, many of which are probably unique to primates. Primates also have specializations of cortical regions involved in somatosensation, motor control, and cognition. In particular, comparative studies indicate that the dorsolateral prefrontal cortex, a region implicated in higher-order cognitive functions, was extensively modified during primate evolution and may contain areas not found in other mammals.

HUMAN EVOLUTION

We have seen that mammals possess brain specializations that distinguish them from other vertebrates and that different groups of mammals have also evolved distinctive brain specializations. We are developing an especially detailed picture of the evolutionary specializations of primates. When we turn to humans, however, we find that although we know a great deal about the evolution of the human body, we know very little about the human brain and its capacities. There are a number of reasons for this, some of which involve limitations of neuroscientific methodology and the history of ideas about human evolution. However, our prospects for making progress in this field have recently improved greatly.

Human Characteristics Evolved in a More Piecemeal Fashion Than Darwin Envisioned

The closest relatives of humans are the apes, specifically the African great apes, the chimpanzees and gorilla (Fig. 50.10). The relationship between humans and African apes is now very well established on the basis of paleontological, comparative anatomical, and comparative biochemical evidence.[78] For example, the oldest fossils in the human lineage have been found in Africa, and these show close anatomical resemblances to the African apes. Furthermore, human DNA sequences are remarkably similar to those of African apes. Some workers have suggested that humans may be more closely related to chimpanzees than to gorillas, but this conclusion is controversial, and the exact branching relationship between humans, chimpanzees, and gorillas remains unresolved. Comparative molecular evidence suggests that humans shared a common ancestor with African apes very recently in terms of geological time, approximately 5 to 7 million years ago (myr).

Human evolution is often depicted as a simple, linear transformation from ape to human through a series of increasingly human "ape-men." The reality of human evolution is much more complex.[79] Paleoanthropological research has revealed a remarkably variety of extinct humanlike forms, or "hominids"—so many that the total numbers of species and genera, and the exact branching relationships between species, are still far from completely understood (Fig. 50.11). Paleoanthropologists usually recognize two subfamilies of hominids, the australopithecines and the hominines. The australopithecines are further divided into three genera, *Australopithecus, Paranthropus,* and *Ardipithecus.* The genus *Homo* (the only genus of hominines) is a relatively late branch of the hominid radiation, the oldest known representatives of *Homo* being about 2 million years old. The oldest australopithecines, the recently described *Australopithecus anamensis* and *Ardipithecus ramidus*, extend the known range of hominids

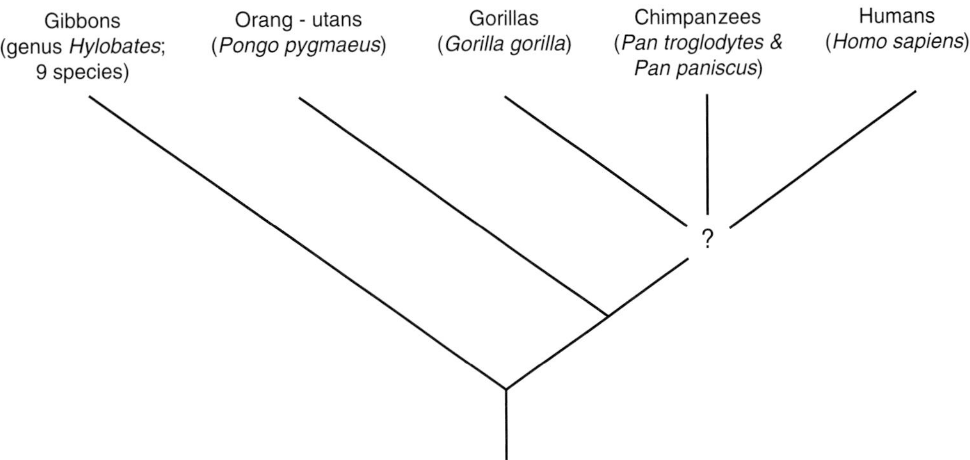

FIGURE 50.10 Phylogenetic relationships among the hominoid primates (apes and humans). The closest relatives of humans are chimpanzees and gorillas. The branching relationship between humans, chimpanzees, and gorillas is currently unsettled.

back to nearly 5 myr, very close to the postulated splitting time of humans and African apes. Not surprisingly, the early australopithecines preserved some very apelike characteristics, including relatively large canines, long, curved fingers and toes, and legs that were short compared to trunk and arm length. Nevertheless, upright, bipedal locomotion appears to have evolved early in the hominid lineage, evidence of which comes from both the study of australopithecine anatomy and the discovery of humanlike footprints, left in volcanic ash in East Africa some 3.7 myr.

How did the distinctive features of human biology evolve? Charles Darwin suggested an explanation in *The Descent of Man*, published in 1871.[80] Darwin pictured early humans as feeble creatures with few natural defenses. To compensate, he proposed, humans

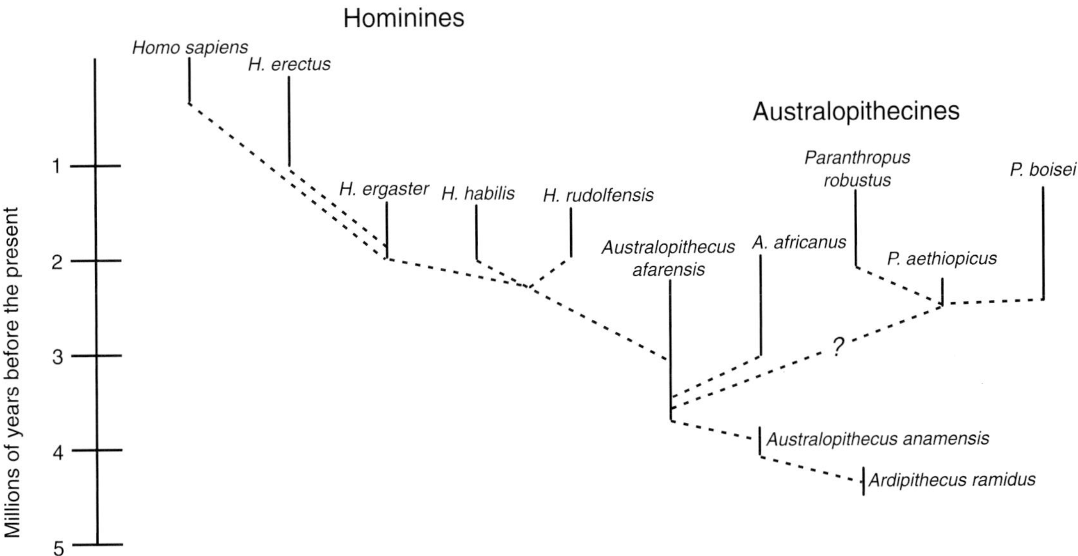

FIGURE 50.11 One interpretation of the phyletic relationships among the hominid primates, based on paleontological investigations. Currently, there is evidence for as many as 11 extinct species of hominids, in addition to the one living species (*Homo sapiens*). The branching relationships among these species are not fully understood. This interpretation is based on that of Wood,[79] with the addition of information about the recently described *Australopithecus anamensis* and *Ardipithecus ramidus*. Comparative molecular evidence suggests that hominids and African great apes (chimpanzess and gorillas) diverged between 5 and 7 myr.

came to rely on artificial weapons and tools for survival, and on the cooperative activities of individuals in social groups. According to Darwin, the use of tools and weapons fostered the evolution of bipedalism, which freed the arms and hands to become better adapted for throwing stones and making tools. Tool making, along with cooperative defense and hunting, promoted canine reduction as well as intellectual development and brain enlargement, which resulted in further technological and social advances. According to Darwin, then, there was a synergistic, feedback relationship among the evolution of tool use, bipedalism, intelligence, and brain size.

It now appears that human characteristics evolved in a more piecemeal fashion than Darwin envisioned. Although bipedalism in known to have evolved very early in human history, there is no evidence that the earliest hominids used stone tools or relied on cooperative hunting to obtain a significant portion of their dietary needs. Moreover, the earliest hominids had relatively small brains, little larger than those of modern apes (discussed later in this chapter). The oldest, extremely simple, stone tools have been dated to about 2.5 myr, about the time when the first members of the genus *Homo* appeared. The first evidence of meat-eating on a significant scale comes from about 2 myr, in the form of marks left by stone tools on meat-bearing animal bones.[81] In view of the importance placed on hunting in many accounts of human evolution, it should be noted that the archeological evidence suggests that early hominids may have been obtaining at least as much meat by scavenging as by hunting. Furthermore, it is by no means clear that scavenging or hunting involved the cooperative efforts of many individuals.

We Should Expect That Humans Differ from Other Animals in Brain Structure and Function Just as They Do in Bodily Form

When we inquire about the evolutionary specializations of the human brain and its functional capacities, we encounter some very well entrenched views. Darwin, writing in the *Descent of Man*,[80] expressed strong opinions on this subject: With the possible exception of language, Darwin wrote, all the capabilities of humans are present in at least rudimentary form in apes and other primates. Thus, he concluded, the difference between humans and related mammals, "great as it is, is certainly one of degree and not of kind." Darwin's contemporary, T. H. Huxley, extended this conclusion to the brain. Huxley claimed that there are no essential differences in the structure of human brains and ape brains, despite the fact that human brains are remarkably large compared to those of other primates. (Human brain volume averages about 1350 cubic centimeters (cc) compared to about 385 cc in chimpanzees, animals that are closely related and similar to us in body size.) Huxley's view has become known as the **doctrine of continuity** in comparative psychology and neuroscience, and it has dominated thinking in these fields for 100 years. Clearly, it has a close kinship to the idea of the basic uniformity of cortical organization. Under the doctrine of continuity, the study of human brain evolution became mainly the study of brain size, and discussions of behavioral differences between humans and related primates have been couched in terms of differences in general intelligence, rather than in terms of differences in specific cognitive or intellectual abilities.

Although the doctrine of continuity continues to influence ideas about the evolution of the brain and cognition, evolutionary biologists long ago abandoned the doctrine of continuity when dealing with other parts of the body. We can list a host of ways in which humans differ in bodily form from other animals, ways that are not simply matters of degree. These differences extend literally from our heads to our toes. For example, the human foot is radically restructured from its ancestral condition: the big toe has been transformed from a mobile, prehensile organ to a stout, relatively rigid appendage, and we have developed a longitudinal arch (which puts the spring in our step). Human hands are notably modified, too, with new muscles that provide extraordinarily precise control over thumb movements. In a similar vein, we have seen that many variations in cortical organization among mammals are not simply matters of degree. Evolutionary considerations therefore lead us to expect that in addition to its unusually large size, the human brain possesses unique functional and structural characteristics.

With the Exception of Language, There Is Little Agreement Regarding Evolutionary Specializations in Human Cognition and Behavior

Language is probably the cognitive or behavioral characteristic most widely accepted as a human evolutionary specialization[82] (see Chapter 57). Even this has been questioned: Apes, while unable to convey language through speech, can in some cases be taught to communicate with manual signs or with artificial symbols. Yet even the most accomplished of ape signers, with many years of intensive interactions with human signers, has a smaller vocabulary and far less grammatical sophistication than a 3-year-old child.

Humans learn language by exposure, without explicit training, and seem to be born with a predisposition to communicate linguistically. For example, some deaf children who are raised without exposure to sign language will spontaneously develop their own systems of hand gestures, and their gestures are organized in specifically languagelike ways.[83]

Humans, as a species, exhibit a right-hand dominance in most activities involving the hands. Individual humans, of course, may be right-handed or left-handed, and some individuals can and do use both hands with nearly equal facility. What seems to be unusual about humans, among primates, is that a large majority of individual humans, about 90%, show a right-hand preference for many different tasks; other primates do not show such a consistent right-hand bias. Since control of the right hand is exerted mainly by the left hemisphere, which is the hemisphere dominant for most aspects of language, it is commonly thought there is a relationship between hand dominance and language.

Humans are also said to possess a "theory of mind"[84]; that is, our behavior toward others is based on our inferences about what others know about us and about the present situation. Do individuals of nonhuman species make inferences about the knowledge others possess? Although early work indicated that chimpanzees also possess a theory of mind,[84] more recent research in apes and in monkeys suggests that this capacity is restricted to humans.[85,86] These results are quite surprising, given the many close similarities in the overt behavior of humans and apes. However, behavioral similarities can mask differences in underlying cognitive processes. It is well known that chimpanzees make tools, which they use to acquire food items that would otherwise be inaccessible to them, and that young chimpanzees learn to use tools by watching their mother. Yet there is little good evidence that adult chimpanzees intentionally teach tool use, or other skills, to their offspring. If they lack a theory of mind, this is not surprising; we would not expect chimpanzees to be very good teachers if they were unable to assess what their offspring had come to know as a result of their teaching.

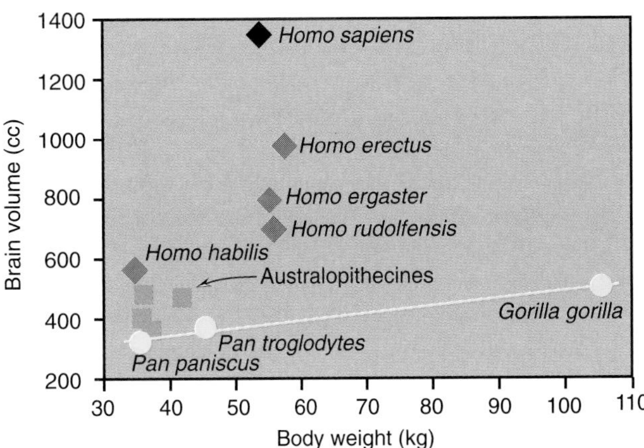

FIGURE 50.12 The relationship between body weight and brain volume in African apes, extinct hominid species, and modern *Homo sapiens*. *Pan paniscus* and *Pan troglodytes* are the pygmy chimpanzee (bonobo) and common chimpanzee, respectively. Dramatic increases in brain size occurred in the evolution of the genus *Homo*, with relatively little change in body size. Body weights are the mean of the adult male and adult female means for each species. Body weights for extinct species are estimated from the dimensions of recovered skeletal materials. Data are from McHenry.[78]

It Is Difficult to Gauge the Development of Human Neural and Psychological Specializations from Paleontological Evidence

How were differences in the psychological characteristics of humans and apes—whether differences of degree or of kind—reflected in the evolution of the brain? We can say a good deal about the evolutionary history of brain size, based on the information from the fossil record. Most of the increase in brain size occurred relatively late in hominid history.[78] Early australopithecines had brain volumes of about 400 cc, perhaps 10–25% larger than the brains of African apes when body size is taken into account (Fig. 50.12). By contrast, early members of *Homo*, about 2 myr, had brain volumes in the range of about 600–800 cc. The species *Homo erectus*, about 500,000 years ago, had brain volumes close to 1000 cc, and shortly thereafter, the brain volumes of hominids fell mainly within the range found in modern *Homo sapiens*.

It is interesting that the dramatic increase in brain size in hominids began at about the same time that the archeological evidence indicates hominids began using stone tools to remove meat from animal bones (as discussed earlier). There may be a causal relationship between the use of meat by hominids and the evolution of larger brains.[87] Compared with other primates, *Homo sapiens* has a relatively large brain and a relatively small gut. Brain and gut tissue are very expensive metabolically, so that plant-eating animals must pay a very steep price for even small increases in brain size in terms of increased food requirements. Animal tissue is very high in calories and relatively easy to digest, so that by increasing the amount of animal tissue in their diets and by reducing their gut size, early members of the genus *Homo* may have been able to obtain the calories necessary to support larger brains.

Although the earliest hominids, the australopithe-

CASE 7: COTTER'S QUANDARY

Andrea Cotter just started her residency at a clinic for senior citizens under the advice of Raj Sharma, a well-known psychiatrist involved in the development of treatments for Alzheimer disease. During their first meeting, Dr. Sharma informed Dr. Cotter that she and the other residents are each expected to enroll at least 20 patients in a research project. That project, which has been approved by the university's Institutional Review Board (IRB), requires that patients undergo a spinal tap every 6 months for 2 years so that cerebrospinal fluid can be assayed for a presumptive marker of Alzheimer disease. The patients will be given $250 each time a spinal tap is performed, and they will be informed of their test results.

Dr. Cotter is uncomfortable with Dr. Sharma's request: Even though all of the patients will be told about the test and its associated risks before being asked to sign a consent form, she is not sure that they will understand the information. Moreover, she questions what the patients will gain by learning that they can anticipate developing a disease for which she feels there is no good treatment. She is concerned that by encouraging patients to participate she is violating the trust they have placed in her as their physician. What should Dr. Cotter do?

See Appendix for discussion questions.

cines, had brains only slightly larger than those of African apes, it has been suggested that their brains were reorganized along human lines. The first fossil australopithecine ever recovered, from the cave at Taung in South Africa in 1924, includes a remarkable natural endocast, which has been the source of controversy since nearly the day of its discovery. Some workers, including the neuroanatomist Raymond Dart, who published the first description of the fossil, and later the paleoanthropologist Ralph Holloway, argued that the sulcal pattern of the Taung fossil was more humanlike than apelike in some respects. In particular, it was suggested that the lunate sulcus, which marks the border between the primary visual area and the higher-order visual areas in many primates, is located more posteriorly in Taung than in apes, thus occupying a more humanlike position. Others, however, such as the paleoanthropologist Dean Falk, have argued that the configuration of the lunate and other sulci is actually apelike in Taung and in australopithecines generally. According to Falk, humanlike sulcal configurations appear in the fossil record for the first time with the appearance of the genus *Homo*. In particular, Falk notes that some early members of *Homo* showed a sulcal configuration in the inferior frontal cortex (which includes Broca's language area) that was very similar to that seen in modern humans.

Do similarities in size and sulcal configuration imply that australopithecine brains were essentially similar in their internal organization to ape brains? Can we conclude that language had evolved by the time the earliest members of *Homo* appeared? Here we have to face that fundamental, frustrating limitations of paleoneurology. First, we have no reason to suppose that significant evolutionary changes in the internal organization and functional capacities of the brain were necessarily accompanied by changes in brain size and cortical folding patterns. Furthermore, the changes in size and folding that did occur cannot be readily related to changes in internal organization. Given our current state of neuroscientific knowledge, we can say very little about the behavioral or cognitive capacities of extinct hominids based on the size or sulcal configurations of their brains. We must admit, in particular, that we do not know when language evolved. At present, the best evidence of the behavioral characteristics of extinct hominids comes from the archeological record. Interestingly, the patterns of work on some of the oldest known stone tools have been interpreted as evidence that right-hand dominance was established by the time stone tools first appeared.[88] In addition, the archeological evidence suggests that the flowering of human cognitive capacities, as reflected in the appearance of art, ritual, finely crafted tools, and complex patterns of social organization, occurred very late in human history, within about the last 100 thousand years and long after human brain size had reached modern levels.

Comparing Human and Nonhuman Brains Is Complicated Because Our Knowledge of Each Is Based on the Use of Different Techniques

Given the limitations of paleoneurology, our understanding of how human brains differ from those of other animals must depend largely on comparative studies of living species. As we have seen, comparative studies have provided us with much insight into mammalian and primate brain evolution. In the case of human evolution, however, scientists face a number of difficulties. Perhaps the most daunting limitation is that, for ethical reasons, some of the most valuable techniques used to study brain organization in other animals cannot be used in humans.[89] For example, most methods for tracing neuronal connections, recording brain activity, and stimulating brain tissue involve invasive surgical procedures and require that the animal be killed at the end of the experiment so that the distribution of tracer substances or the location of electrode placements can be determined. Obviously, such procedures cannot be used with humans. Nevertheless, neuroscientists now have marvelous tools for mapping the functional activity of the human brain noninvasively, such as positron emission tomography (PET) scanning and functional magnetic resonance imaging (MRI) (see Chapter 14). As valuable as these techniques are for studying humans, however, they are of limited utility at present for studying other species. For one thing, the brains of most nonhuman species are so small that even the best scanners achieve relatively poor resolution. In addition, substantial practical problems arise in working with awake, behaving animals in expensive and delicate scanners. The upshot is that while we know a great deal about the brain organization in humans and in nonhumans, for the most part our knowledge comes from the use of different techniques. This makes the task of evaluating claims of similarities and differences between humans and nonhumans more difficult than one might suppose.

Lack of information about ape brains is another serious obstacle to understanding human brain specializations. Because apes are increasingly rare in nature, and because of their close relationship to humans, apes are very rarely used today in neuroscientific research. Again, this poses a problem in evaluating claims of human specialization. Suppose we identified a feature of brain organization that is present in humans, but lacking in Old World monkeys, New World monkeys, and prosimians. Would we be justified in claiming that this feature is a human specialization? No, because we have not shown that the feature is lacking in apes. Humans are much more closely related to apes than they are to other primates, and owing to their long period of common ancestry, apes and humans share many molecular and anatomical characteristics that distinguish them from other primates. Presumably, humans and apes also share characteristics of brain organization that other primates lack. Unless we study ape brains, we cannot distinguish features that humans share with apes from those that are human specializations.

All is not lost, however. There are techniques for studying brain structure that do not require invasive procedures or PET scanners, and which therefore can be used to study and compare humans, apes, and other primates.

New Analytical Techniques Offer the Possibility of Comparing the Brains of Humans and Other Species

New techniques include methods studying cortical histology and gross brain morphology. These techniques can be used to test and refine specific hypotheses of human brain specialization.

Histological procedures include modern immunocytochemical techniques, as well as traditional cell and fiber stains. The advantage of these techniques is that they can be used to study autopsied tissue; therefore, they can be used to study humans as well as rare and endangered species not normally examined by neuroscientists. As discussed in a previous section, classical architectonic techniques, using cell and fiber stains, are not very reliable guides to phyletic differences in brain organization by themselves. Immunocytochemistry offers great promise, however, thanks to the remarkable growth in the family of available antibodies that recognize specific transmitters, receptors, and structural and metabolic proteins. Using immunocytochemistry and other methods for studying the distribution of specific molecules in the cortex, along with classical architectonic techniques, neuroscientists should be better able to map cortical areas in different species, identify homologous areas across species, and determine whether humans possess cortical areas not found in other primates. Moreover, these techniques may identify evolutionary changes in the intrinsic organization of the cortex. Already, the literature contains reports of differences between humans and Old World monkeys in the distribution of certain classes of cortical interneurons.[90,91]

It may also be that human specializations of brain organization are reflected in the size and folding patterns of specific cortical regions. The study of human cerebral morphology has undergone something of a renaissance of late. For example, it is now clear that individual differences in language representation, handedness, and other features of behavior and cognition are reflected in differences in the sulcal patterns.[92,93] This renaissance has been spurred by the development of magnetic resonance imaging for imaging brain morphology in living humans. However, information about the size and folding patterns of cortical regions can be obtained with a variety of anatomical techniques, including those that can be readily used with nonhuman species, so it should be possible to obtain comparable morphological information for both humans and nonhumans. By studying the relationship between cortical morphology and cognitive function in living species, we may be able to make better inferences about the cognitive capacities of extinct species from the paleoneurological evidence.

Specifically Human Brain Functions May Have Evolved by the Development of New Brain Areas or by Modification of Preexisting Areas or Systems

In our search for human brain specializations, we can be guided by ideas about the evolution of human cognition and behavior, by specific theories of human brain evolution, and by our general understanding of brain evolution. The fact that human brains are about three times the volume of ape brains, and that larger-brained mammals tend to have more areas than smaller-brained mammals, has suggested to some workers that humans probably have more areas than other primates. Assuming that language is unique to humans, it is natural to support that language-related areas, such as Wernicke's area in the temporoparietal region of cortex and Broca's area in the frontal lobe, are also unique to humans.[89] In a similar vein, if we assume that "theory of mind" is a human psychological specialization, we might infer that cortical regions involved in this function are also unique to humans. Several lines of evidence suggest that theory of mind is primarily a function of frontal cortex.[94,95] In view of its involvement in theory of mind, in language, and in other higher-order cognitive functions, there are particularly good reasons to suspect that the frontal lobe underwent extensive modification in human evolution.

What might be the nature of evolutionary changes in frontal-lobe organization? One obvious possibility is that humans possess more frontal-lobe areas than other primates. This possibility is reinforced by comparative evidence suggesting that the frontal cortex was disproportionately enlarged in human evolution.[70] At present, however, there is no clear evidence that humans possess new frontal lobe areas. Furthermore, evidence from both functional and architectonic studies indicates that homologs of Broca's area, or at least portions of it, exist in nonhuman primates, as claimed by some earlier workers.[96] In functional imaging studies, Broca's area is activated during both language tasks and tasks involving nonlinguistic movements of the mouth and forelimb; in nonhuman primates, an area that resembles Broca's area in location and in architecture—the ventral premotor area—represents mouth and forelimb movements.[67] It has also been asserted that homologs of Wernicke's area are present in nonhuman primates.[97] Thus, as an alternative to the hypothesis that evolution of language and other human-specific functions proceeded through addition of new areas, the evolution of new functions may have been brought about by modifying preexisting areas and systems, old areas being "recruited" into the network of cortical language areas.[90] This hypothesis implies that the evolution of new functions involved changes in the intrinsic organization of areas, the connections between areas, or both. Changes at these levels of organization may have led to increases in the size of the areas involved. Of course, changes in the intrinsic and connectional organization of the cortex do not preclude the possibility that new areas appeared as well.

At present, therefore, we do not know what changes in human brain organization accompanied evolutionary changes in human psychology. If there is no strong evidence for new areas in human cortex, it must be said that the evidence against new areas is also weak, being based primarily on cytoarchitecture. We can improve our understanding of the evolution of human cortical areas by using a wider range of techniques to map areas and by using these techniques to compare humans to apes and to other primates.

Summary

Neuroanatomists since the 19th century have known that the physical architecture of the brain must provide clues to the workings of mental processes. Since then, enormous progress has been made in understanding both the structure and the functions of the brains of humans and other mammals. Also, we have learned a great deal about the evolutionary history of mammals, including the sequence of changes in bodily form that occurred in the human lineage since the divergence of humans from apes. It is remarkable, then, that beyond the fact that human brain volume is about three times that of apes, we know very little about what is distinctively human in the structure and function of the human brain. Our lack of understanding of the distinctively human brain characteristics can be attributed in part to the widespread belief that there are, in fact, no important differences in brain organization among mammals and in part to the lack (until recently) of powerful techniques for studying how human brains vary in many aspects of organization. We now have techniques for studying the brains of humans and of nonhuman species in great detail. There is good reason to believe, therefore, that we are on the verge of making important discoveries about the neurobiological foundations of human nature.

References

1. Lovejoy, A. O. (1936). *The Great Chain of Being*. Harvard University Press, Cambridge, MA.
2. Darwin, C. (1859). *On the Origin of Species*. John Murray, London. [Facsimile of the first edition: Harvard University Press, Cambridge, MA, 1984].
3. Nudo, R. J., and Masterton, R. B. (1990). Descending pathways to the spinal cord, III: Sites of origin of the corticospinal tract. *J. Comp. Neurol.* **296:** 559–583.
4. Regidor, J., and Divac, I. (1992). Bilateral thalamocortical projection in hedgehogs: Evolutionary implications. *Brain Behav. Evol.* **39:** 265–269.
5. Johnston, J. I., Switzer, R. C. III, and Kirsch, J. A. W. (1982). Phylogeny through brain traits: The distribution of categorizing characters in contemporary mammals. *Brain. Behav. Evol.* **20:** 97–117.
6. Harvey, P. H., and Pagel, M. D. (1991). *The Comparative Method in Evolutionary Biology*. Oxford University Press, Oxford.
7. Novacek, M. J. (1992). Mammalian phylogeny: Shaking the tree. *Nature* **356:** 121–125.
8. Martin, R. D. (1990). *Primate Origins and Evolution*. Princeton University Press, Princeton.
9. Brodmann, K. (1909). *Vergleichende Lokalisationslehre der Grosshirnrhinde*. Barth, Leipzig. [Reprinted as Brodmann's 'Localisation in the Cerebral Cortex,' translated and edited by L. J. Garey, Smith-Gordon, London, 1994.]
10. Reiner, A. (1993). Neurotransmitter organization and connections of turtle cortex: Implications for the evolution of mammalian isocortex. *Comp. Biochem. Physiol.* **104A:** 735–748.
11. Karten, H. J., and Shimazu, T. (1989). The origins of neocortex: Connections and lamination as distinct events in evolution. *J. Cogn. Neurosci.* **1:** 291–301.
12. Jerison, H. J. (1973). *Evolution of the Brain and Intelligence*. Academic Press, New York.
13. Holloway, R. L. Jr. (1966). Cranial capacity, neural reorganization, and hominid evolution: A search for more suitable parameters. *Am. Anthrop.* **68:** 103–121.
14. Lashley, K. S., and Clark, G. (1946). The cytoarchitecture of the cerebral cortex of Ateles: A critical examination of architectonic studies. *J. Comp. Neurol.* **85:** 223–306.
15. Kaas, J. H. (1977). Sensory representations in mammals. In *Function and Formation of Neural Systems* (G. S. Stent, ed.), pp. 65–80. Dahlem Konferenzen, Berlin.
16. Allman, J. M., and Kaas, J. H. (1971). A representation of the visual field in the caudal third of the middle temporal gyrus of the owl monkey (*Aotus trivirgatus*). *Brain Res.* **31:** 85–105.
17. Kaas, J. H. (1987). The organization and evolution of neocortex. In Higher Brain Function: Recent Explorations of the Brain's Emergent Properties (S. P. Wise, ed.), pp. 347–378. John Wiley, New York.
18. Payne, B. R. (1993). Evidence for visual cortical area homologs in cat and macaque monkey. *Cereb. Cortex* **3:** 1–25.
19. Northcutt, R. G., and Kaas, J. H. (1995). The emergence and evolution of mammalian neocortex. *Trends Neurosci.* **18:** 373–379.
20. Krubitzer, L,. Manger, P., Pettigrew, J., and Calford, M. (1994). Organization of somatosensory cortex in monotremes: In search of the prototypical pain. *J. Comp. Neurol* **351:** 261–306.
21. Sanides, F. (1970). Functional architecture of motor and sensory cortices in primates in the light of a new concept of neocortex evolution. In *The Primate Brain* (C. R. Woback and W. Montagna, eds.), pp. 137–208. Appleton-Century-Crofts, New York.
22. Creutzfeldt, O. D. (1977). Generality of functional structure of the neocortex. *Naturwissenschaften* **64:** 507–517.
23. Mountcastle, V. B. (1978). An organizating principle for cerebral function: The unit module and the distributed sytem. In *The Mindful Brain*, (G. M. Edelman, ed.), pp. 7–50. MIT Press, Cambridge, MA.
24. Rockel, A. J., Hiorns, R. W., and Powell, T. P. S. (1980). The basic uniformity of structure of the neocortex. *Brain* **103:** 221–224.
25. Haug, H. (1987). Brain sizes, surfaces, and neuronal sizes of the cortex cerebri: A stereological investigation of man and his variability and a comparison with some mammals (primates, whales, marsupials, insectivores, and one elephant). *Am. J. Anat.* **180:** 126–142.
26. Skoglund, T. S., Pascher, R., and Berthold, C. H. (1996). Heterogeneity in the columnar number of neurons in different neocortical areas in the rat. *Neurosci. Lett.* **208:** 97–100.
27. Hof, P. R., Glezer, I. I., Archin, N., Janssen, W. G., Morgane, P. J., and Morrison, J. H. (1992). The primary auditory cortex in cetacean and human brain: A comparative analysis of neurofilament protein-containing pyramidal neurons. *Neurosci. Lett.* **146:** 91–95.
28. Glezer, I. I., Hof, P. R., Leranth, C., and Morgane, P. J. (1993). Calcium-binding protein-containing neuronal populations in mammalian visual cortex: A comparative study in whales, insectivores, bats, rodents, and primates. *Cereb. Cortex* **3:** 249–72.
29. Hendry, S. H., and Carder, R. K. (1993). Neurochemical compartmentation of monkey and human visual cortex: Similarities and variations in calbindin immunoreactivity across species. *Vis. Neurosci.* **10:** 1109–1120.
30. Jain, N., Preuss, T. M., and Kaas, J. H. (1994). Subdivisions of the visual system labeled with the Cat-301 antibody in tree shrews. *Vis. Neurosci.* **11:** 731–741.
31. Berger, B., Gaspar, P., and Verney, C. (1991). Dopaminergic innervation of the cerebral cortex: Unexpected differences between rodent and primate. *Trends Neurosci.* **14:** 21–27.
32. Kosofsky, B. E., Molliver, M. E., Morrison, J. H., and Foote, S. L. (1984). The serotonin and norepinephrine innervation of primary visual cortex in the cynomolgus monkey (*Macaca fascicularis*). *J. Comp. Neurol.* **230:** 168–178.
33. Lewis, D. A., and Lund, J. S. (1990). Heterogeneity of chandelier neurons in monkey neocortex: Corticotropin-releasing factor- and parvalbumin-immunoreactive populations. *J. Comp. Neurol.* **293:** 599–615.
34. Gebhard, R., Zilles, K., Schleicher, A., Everitt, B. J., Robbins, T. W., and Divac, I. (1995). Parcellation of the frontal cortex of the New World monkey *Callithrix jacchus* by eight neurotransmitter-binding sites. *Anat. Embryol.* **191:** 509–517.
35. Fleagle, J. G. (1988). *Primate Adaptation and Evolution*. Academic Press, San Diego.
36. Elliot Smith, G. (1924). *The Evolution of Man. Essays*. Oxford University Press, London.
37. Le Gros Clark, W. E. (1959). *The Antecedents of Man*. Edinburgh University Press, Edinburgh.
38. Cartmill, M. (1992). New views on primate origins. *Evol. Anthropol.* **1:** 105–111.
39. Allman, J. M. (1977). Evolution of the visual system in the early primates. In *Progress in Psychology and Physiological Psychology* (J. M. Sprague and A. N. Epstein, eds.), pp. 1–53. Academic Press, New York.
40. Felleman, D. J., and Van Essen, D. C. (1991). Distributed hierarchical processing in the primate cerebral cortex. *Cerebral Cortex* **1:** 1–47.
41. Kaas, J. H., and Krubitzer, L. A. (1991). The organization of extrastriate cortex. In *Neuroanatomy of the Visual Pathways and their Development* (B. Dreher and S. R. Robinson, eds.), pp. 302–323. Macmillan Press, London.

42. Casagrande, V. A., and Kaas, J. H. (1994). The afferent, intrinsic, and efferent connections of primary visual cortex in primates. In *Cerebral Cortex,* Vol. 10, *Primary Visual Cortex in Primates* (A. Peters and K. Rockland, eds.), pp. 201–259. Plenum, New York.
43. Kaas, J. H., Harting, J. K., and Guillery, R. W. (1973). Representation of the complete retina in the contralateral superior colliculus of some mammals. *Brain Res.* **65:** 343–346.
44. Huerta, M. F., and Harting, J. K. (1984). The mammalian superior colliculus: Studies of its morphology and connections. In *Comparative Neurology of the Optic Tectum* (H. Vanegas, ed.), pp. 687–773. Plenum, New York.
45. Lane, R. H., Allman, J. M., Kaas, J. H., and Miezin, F. M. (1973). The visuotopic organization of the superior colliculus of the owl monkey (*Aotus trivigatus*) and the bush baby (*Galago senegalensis*). *Brain Res.* **60:** 335–349.
46. Lane, R. H., Allman, J. M., and Kaas, J. H. (1971). Representation of the visual field in the superior colliculus of the grey squirrel (*Sciurius carolinensis*) and the tree show (*Tupaia glis*). *Brain Res.* **26:** 277–292.
47. Pettigrew, J. P. (1986). Flying primates? Megabats have the advanced pathway from eye to midbrain. *Science* **231:** 1304–1306.
48. Thiele, A., Vogelsang, M., and Hoffman, K.-P. (1991). Pattern of retinotectal projection in the megachiropteran bat *Rousettus aegyptiacus. J. Comp. Neurol.* **314:** 671–683.
49. Kaas, J. H., Guillery, R. W., and Allman, J. M. (1972). Some principles of organization in the dorsal lateral geniculate nucleus. *Brain Behav. Evol.* **6:** 253–299.
50. Sanderson, K. J. (1986). Evolution of the lateral geniculate nucleus. In *Visual Neuroscience* (J. D. Pettigrew, K. J. Sanderson, and W. R. Levick, eds.), pp. 183–195. Cambridge University Press, Cambridge.
51. Kaas, J. H., and Huerta, M. F. (1988). The subcortical visual system of primates. In *Comparative Primate Biology,* Volume 4: *Neurosciences* (H. D. Steklis and J. Erwin, eds.), pp. 327–391. Alan R. Liss, New York.
52. Casagrande, V. A. (1994). A third parallel visual pathway to primate V1. *Trends Neurosci.* **17:** 305–310.
53. Livingstone, M. S., and Hubel, D. H. (1988). Segregation of form, color, movement and depth: Anatomy, physiology and perception. *Science* **240:** 740–749.
54. Horton, J. C. (1984). Cytochrome oxidase patches: A new cytoarchitectonic feature of monkey visual cortex. *Philos. Trans. R. Soc. Lond. Biol.* **304:** 199–253.
55. Preuss, T. M., and Kaas, J. H. (1996). Cytochrome oxidase "blobs" and other characteristics of primary visual cortex in a lemuroid primate, *Cheirogaleus medius. Brain Behav. Evol.* **47:** 103–112.
56. Murphy, K. M., Jones, D. G., and Van Sluyter, R. C. (1995). Cytochrome-oxidase blobs in cat primary visual cortex. *J. Neurosci.* **15:** 4196–4208.
57. Perrett, D. I., Mistlin, A. J., and Chitty, A. J. (1987). Visual neurones responsive to faces. *Trends Neurosci.* **10:** 358–364.
58. Perrett, D. I., Mistlin, A. J., Harries, M. H., and Chitty, A. J. (1990). Understanding the visual appearance and consequence of hand actions. In *Vision and Action: The Control of Grasping* (M. A. Goodale, ed.), pp. 163–180. Ablex Publishing, Norwood, NJ.
59. Brothers, L., and Ring, B. (1992). A neuroethological framework for the representation of minds. *J. Cog. Neurosci.* **4:** 107–118.
60. Preuss, T. M., and Goldman-Rakic, P. S. (1991). Architectonics of the parietal and temporal association cortex in the strepsirhine primate *Galago,* compared to the anthropoid primate *Macaca. J. Comp. Neurol.* **310:** 475–506.
61. Kendrick, K. M., and Baldwin, B. A. (1987). Cells in temporal cortex of conscious sheep can respond preferentially to the sight of faces. *Science* **236:** 448–450.
62. Kaas, J. H. (1983). What, if anything, is SI? Organization of the first somatosensory area in mammals. *Physiol. Rev.* **63:** 206–231.
63. Garraghty, P. E., Florence, S. L., Tenhula, W. N., and Kaas, J. H. (1991). Parallel thalamic activation of the first and second somatosensory areas in prosimian primates and tree shrews. *J. Comp. Neurol.* **311:** 289–299.
64. Kuypers, H. G. J. M. (1981). Anatomy of the descending projections. In *Handbook of Physiology, Section I: The Nervous System,* Volume II: *Motor Control,* Part 2, (V. B. Brooks, ed.), pp. 597–666. American Physiological Society, Bethesda, MD.
65. Bortoff, G. A., and Strick, P. L. (1993). Corticospinal terminations in two New-World primates: Further evidence that corticomotoneuronal connections provide part of the neural substrate for manual dexterity. *J. Neurosci.* **13:** 5105–5118.
66. Wiesendanger, M., and Wise, S. P. (1992). Current issues concerning the functional organization of motor cortical areas in nonhuman primates. In *Frontal Lobe Seizures and Epilepsy, Advances in Neurology,* Volume 57, (P. Chauvel, A. V. Delgado-Escueta, E. Halgren, and J. Bancaud, eds.), pp. 117–134. Raven, New York.
67. Preuss, T. M., Stepniewska, I., and Kaas, J. H. (1996). Movement representation in the dorsal and ventral premotor areas of owl monkeys: A microstimulation study. *J. Comp. Neurol.* **371:** 649–676.
68. Wise, S. P. (1996). Evolutionary and comparative neurobiology of the supplementary sensorimotor cortex. In *The Supplementary Sensorimotor Cortex, Advances in Neurology,* Volume 70, pp. 71–83. Raven Press, New York.
69. Rizzolatti, G., and Gentilucci, M. (1988). Motor and visual-motor functions of the premotor cortex. In *Neurobiology of Neocortex* (P. Rakic and W. Singer, eds.), pp. 269–295. John Wiley, Chichester.
70. Brodmann, K. (1912). Neue Ergibnisse uber die vergleichende histologische Lokalisation der Grosshirnrinde mit besonderer Berucksichtigung des Stirnhirns. *Anat. Anz.* (Suppl.) **41:** 157–216.
71. Akert, K. (1964). Comparative anatomy of frontal cortex and thalamofrontal connections. In *The Frontal Granular Cortex and Behavior* (J. M. Warren and K. Akert, eds.), pp. 372–396. McGraw-Hill, New York.
72. Leonard, C. M. (1972). The connections of the dorsomedial nucleus. *Brain Behav. Evol.* **6:** 524–541.
73. Divac, I., Björklund, A., Lindvall, O., and Passingham, R. E. (1978). Converging projections from the mediodorsal thalamic nucleus and mesencephalic dopaminergic neurons to the neocortex in three species. *J. Comp. Neurol.* **180:** 59–72.
74. Kolb, B. (1990). Organization of the neocortex of the rat. In *The Cerebral Cortex of the Rat* (B. Kolb and R. C. Tees, eds.), pp. 21–33. MIT Press, Cambridge, MA.
75. Markowitsch, H. J., and Pritzel, M. (1979). The prefrontal cortex: Projection area of the thalamic mediodorsal nucleus? *Physiol. Psychol.* **7:** 1–6.
76. Preuss, T. M. (1995). Do rats have prefrontal cortex? The Rose-Woolsey-Akert program reconsidered. *J. Cogn. Neurosci.* **7:** 1–24.
77. Preuss, T. M., and Goldman-Rakic, P. S. (1991). Ipsilateral cortical corrections of granular frontal cortex and surrounding regions in the strepsirhine primate *Galago* and the anthropoid primate *Macaca. J. Comp. Neurol.* **310:** 429–474.
78. McHenry, H. M. (1994). Tempo and mode in human evolution. *Proc. Natl. Acad. Sci. U.S.A.* **91:** 6780–6786.
79. Wood, B. (1992). Origin and evolution of the genus *Homo. Nature* **355:** 783–790.
80. Darwin, C. (1871). *The Descent of Man, and Selection in Relation to Sex.* John Murray, London. [Facsimile edition: Princeton University Press, Princeton, NJ, 1981.]

81. Potts, R. (1988). *Early Hominid Activities at Olduvai.* Aldine de Gruyter, New York.
82. Tomasello, M., and Call, J. (1997). *Primate Cognition.* Oxford University Press, New York.
83. Goldin-Meadow, S., and Mylander, C. (1991). Levels of structure in a communication system developed without a language model. In *Brain Maturation and Cognitive Development* (K. R. Gibson and A. C. Petersen, eds.), pp. 315–344. Aldine de Gruyter, New York.
84. Premack, D., and Woodruff, G. (1978). Does the chimpanzee have a theory of mind? *Behav. Brain Sci.* **1:** 515–526.
85. Povinelli, D. J., and Preuss, T. M. (1995). Theory of mind: Evolutionary history of a cognitive specialization. *Trends Neurosci.* **18:** 418–424.
86. Cheney, D. L., and Seyfarth, R. M. (1990). *How Monkeys See the World.* University of Chicago Press, Chicago.
87. Aeillo, L. C., and Wheeler, P. (1995). The expensive-tissue hypothesis. *Curr. Anthropol.* **36:** 199–221.
88. Toth, N. (1985). Archeological evidence for preferential right-handedness in the Lower and Middle Peleistocene, and its possible implications. *J. Human Evol.* **14:** 607–614.
89. Crick, F., and Jones, E. G. (1993). Backwardness of human neuroanatomy. *Nature* **361:** 109–110.
90. Hayes, T. L., Cameron, J. L., Fernstrom, J. D., and Lewis, D. A. (1991). A comparative analysis of the distribution of prosomatostatin-derived peptides in human and monkey neocortex. *J. Comp. Neurol.* **303:** 584–599.
91. Del Rio, M. R., and DeFelipe, J. (1996). Colocalization of calbindin D-28k, calretinin, and GABA immunoreactivities in neurons of the human temporal cortex. *J. Comp. Neurol.* **369:** 472–482.
92. Foundas, A. L., Leonard, C. M., and Heilman, K. M. (1995). Morphologic cerebral asymmetries and handedness: The pars triangularis and planum temporale. *Arch. Neurol.* **52:** 501–508.
93. Leonard, C. M. (1996). Structural variation in developing and mature cerebral cortex: Noise or signal? In *Developmental Neuroimaging* (R. Thatcher, G. R. Lyon, N. Krasnegor, and J. Rumsey, eds.), pp. 207–231. Academic Press, San Diego, CA.
94. Ozonoff, S., Pennington, B. F., Rogers, S. F. (1991). Executive function deficits in high-functioning autistic individuals: Relationship to theory of mind. *J. Child Psychol. Psychiatr.* **32:** 1081–1105.
95. Frith, C. (1996). Brain mechanisms for 'having a theory of mind.' *J. Psychopharm.* **10:** 9–15.
96. Bonin, G. von. (1944). The architecture. In *The Precentral Motor Cortex* (P. C. Bucy, ed.), pp. 7–82. University of Illinois Press, Urbana, IL.
97. Galaburda, A. M., and Pandya, D. N. (1982). Role of architectonics and connections in the study of brain evolution. In *Primate Brain Evolution* (E. Armstrong and D. Falk, eds.), pp. 203–216. Plenum, New York.

C H A P T E R

51

Cognitive Development

Marilyn S. Albert, Adele D. Diamond, Roslyn Holly Fitch, Helen J. Neville, Peter R. Rapp, and Paula A. Tallal

The human brain has evolved over a very extensive period (Chapter 50), but an individual human brain develops swiftly over the first few years of life, allowing the nearly helpless human infant to gain control of locomotion, language, and thought. The story of the unfolding of brain development in the early years of infancy occupies the first part of this chapter. Later, we consider abnormalities that arise in this developmental process. In the final parts of the chapter, we consider brain changes that occur late in life and that can be accompanied by a reduction in mental ability.

POSTNATAL DEVELOPMENT OF BRAIN STRUCTURE AND PHYSIOLOGY

Many Processes Show Postnatal Development

Recent studies of the anatomy and physiology of the developing human cerebral cortex provide evidence of a postnatal development that is very protracted, highly dynamic, and variable from region to region. Figure 51.1 shows a gross overview of changes in the size and shape of the brain from conception through the first 9 months of life.

More detailed examination of brain growth shows that different components of the neuropil display different developmental time courses. Whereas most morphometric data have been obtained from studies of the primary visual cortex (area 17 or V1), the limited data from other brain regions, such as the frontal cortex, show considerable variability in the timing of maturation of different brain regions. Measures of cerebral metabolism and electrophysiological activity, like structural studies, indicate a long and variable time course of brain development.

The human brain displays many of the progressive and regressive structural events that have been described for nonhuman brains (see Section III). Distinctive features of the development of the human brain are its very prolonged postnatal time course, a lack of evidence for postnatal loss of neurons, a large number of redundant synapses, and the persistence of copious (*exuberant*) connectivity until the late teens.

The Cortex Thickens during Development

The classic studies of Conel and Rabinowicz documented the increasing cortical thickness during maturation of the human brain.[1,2] The primary visual cortex increases in thickness until around the 6th postnatal month, when it attains values observed in adults. Cell densities and overall structure are also mature by this time. In contrast, other cortical areas, including visual association areas, display a long and variable increase in cortical thickness that approaches maturity around 10 years after birth.

Formation of the gyri of the brain is basically complete by birth. Thus includes the superior temporal and middle temporal gyri, pre- and postcentral gyri, the superior and middle frontal gyri, and the superior and inferior occipital gyri. The primary gyri become well defined between 26 and 28 weeks of gestation. Development of secondary and tertiary gyri occurs later in gestation, and in the last trimester the sulci become deeply enfolded. Several left–right asymmetries have been observed in the fetal brain. The superior frontal and temporal gyri are present 1–2 weeks earlier on the right hemisphere than on the left. As in adults, more transverse gyri are present in the right hemisphere, and a larger temporal planum is present on

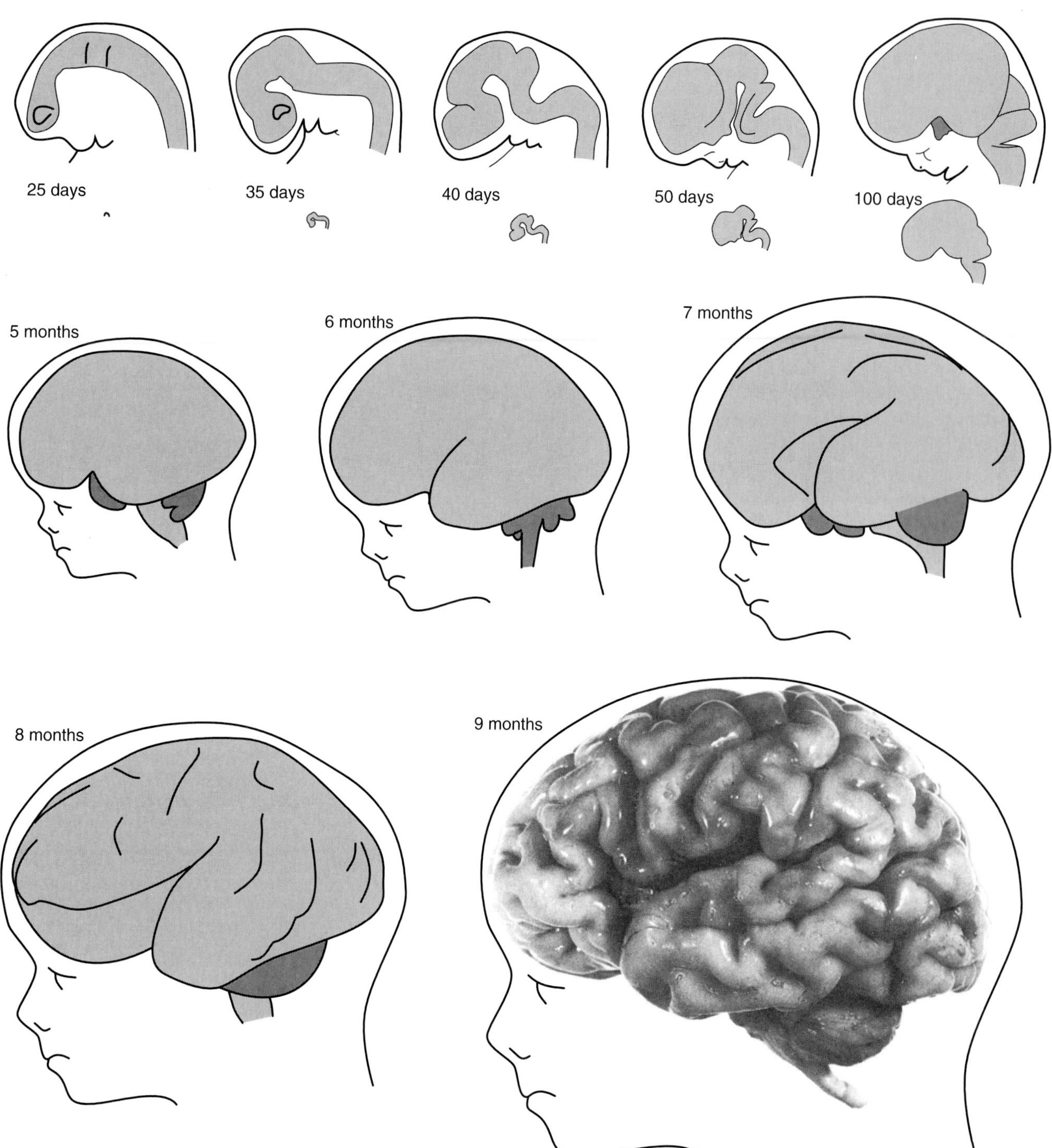

FIGURE 51.1 The size and form of the human brain as it develops through gestation and early infancy.

the left temporal cortex than on the right.[3–5] (See also Chapter 52.)

Axons Myelinate during Development

The time course of myelination varies widely in different brain regions and systems.[6] Sensory and motor systems display mature myelination within the first 2 years of life. However, the nonspecific thalamic radiations do not reach mature levels until 5–7 years of age, and intracortical connections display increasing myelination well into the third decade of life.

The Volume of the Cortex Increases

The volume of the immature brain expands considerably. Quantification of the total volume of a given area is necessary to estimate densities of neuronal structures; however, measurements of the volume of most cortical areas are not possible because of the difficulty in identifying clear structural changes between areas. The notable exception is V1, which is clearly bounded by the **stria of Gennari,** the large granular layer transected by a fiber bundle. Studies[7,8] show that there is rapid expansion of the volume of V1 throughout gestation and the first 4 months of postnatal life, by which time the adult volume is attained. This expansion is in marked contrast to remaining brain areas, which have attained only about 50% of the adult volume at that time.

The density of neurons in V1 decreases rapidly until birth, and then slowly decreases until it stabilizes around 4–5 months after birth; however, there is no evidence for neuronal loss during development, and the total neuronal number remains constant from 28 weeks of gestation until 70 years. This decrease in neuronal density in VI appears to be related to the expanding cortical volume due to the growth of axons, dendrites, and glia.

The Number of Dendritic Spines Increases

The formation of dendritic spines and the time course of development of the length and branching patterns of dendrites have been described for visual and frontal cortical areas in humans. Within the visual cortex the maximum density of spines is present around 5 months of age; this number then decreases until adult values are obtained around 21 months of age.[9] Progressive elongation of dendrites occurs up to 24 months, so that there may be a decrease in spine density during this period rather than a loss of spines[10] from 5 to 24 months. Dendritic development within the visual cortex reaches mature levels earlier in the lower than in the upper cortical layers and thus displays the "inside-out" pattern of cortical development that is characteristic of neurogenesis and migration.[11]

Development within the frontal cortex proceeds more slowly. Whereas neuronal density in the primary visual cortex reaches adult levels by 4–5 months, neuronal density in the frontal cortex has still not reached adult levels by 7 years of age.[12] Additionally, by 2 years of age, dendritic length (which is mature by 18–24 months in V1) is only half that found in adults, an observation suggesting a longer developmental time course in frontal cortex.[12] Left–right asymmetries exist in the dendritic branching patterns of pyramidal neurons within layer V of the inferior frontal and anterior precentral cortex.[13] Within the first year, growth is more advanced on the right side, but by 6–8 years of age the maturation of distal dendrites on the left exceeds that of the right.

Synapses First Increase and Then Decrease in Number

As in the brains of other animals (see Chapter 19), the immature human brain contains many more synapses than the mature brain. Within the primary visual cortex, synaptic density increases gradually during late gestation and early postnatal life; it then displays a steep increase from 2 to 4 months of age, during which period the density doubles. After 1 year of age, however, there is a decline in synaptic density until adult values (50–60% of the maximum) are attained at about 11 years of age (see Fig. 51.2).[14,15] The time course of the decrease in synaptic density varies within different cortical layers. The decrease does not display the "inside-out" pattern of development; rather, there is a considerable decrease, over time, in the number of synapses in every layer.[7]

The other cortical area for which data on synaptogenesis are available in humans is the middle frontal gyrus (layer III).[17] This area also shows a postnatal increase in synaptic density followed by a decrease, but these changes occur along a longer time course in the frontal cortex than in the primary visual cortex. The maximum density of synapses occurs around 1 year of age (compared to 4 months in the visual cortex). Adult values are not obtained until around 16 years of age (compared to 7–11 years for the visual cortex). Overall synaptic density in humans is greater in the frontal and motor cortex than in the visual cortex.[7,17,18]

In summary, these quantitative anatomical measures suggest that in humans there appears to be little role for programmed cell death. In animal studies this is not the case (see Chapter 20). On the other hand,

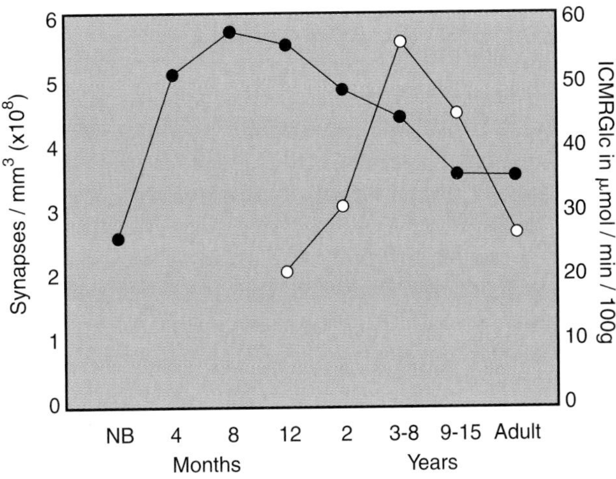

FIGURE 51.2 Variations in cortex with age: Density of synapses in human primary visual cortex (black circles)[14] and resting glucose uptake in occipital cortex (white circles).[15] Adapted with permission from M. Johnson.

synapse elimination in humans and other primates exceeds that in other animals, and perhaps this elimination is more important in the development of more complex systems. These results are consistent with a role for incoming afferent input in selectively stabilizing functional synapses and in eliminating or suppressing inactive contacts.[19–21] The redundancy of connections (synapses) may also make it possible to adjust cerebral organization following damage or altered input.

After Birth Cerebral Metabolic Rate First Increases and Then Decreases

Increases in neuronal activity have been linked to increases in cerebral metabolism, as measured by positron emission tomography (PET), and changes in cerebral metabolism in neurologically at-risk infants and children from 5 days to 15 years of age have been described. These data show substantial subcortical activation in newborns but little activation of cerebral cortex. However, over the first 3–4 years of life, the cortical metabolic rate increases until it reaches levels twice those observed in adults (see Fig. 51.3). After 4 years of age metabolic activity gradually decreases until adult levels are reached, around 15 years of age. The time course of the rise and decline of PET data parallels the rise and decline in the number of synapses in human frontal cortex, and suggests that the exuberant synapses there are metabolically active.

Electrophysiological Activity Also Undergoes Development

Averaged scalp recordings (ERPs or event-related potentials) largely reflect postsynaptic potentials of apical dendrites. These recordings show a highly variable and protracted course of brain development in their responses to sensory and cognitive information. Measures of brainstem and thalamic electrical activity (e.g., the auditory brainstem responses) reveal rapid decreases in *latency* from 30 weeks of gestation onward and then attainment of adult values by 2 years of age.[23] In contrast, the early cortical sensory responses (the N100-P200 vertex potential or N1-P2) do not appear mature in form until around 13–15 years of age[24–26] (Fig. 51.3). In addition, several later ERP events linked to cognitive functions that include attention and language do not display a mature pattern until even later, at 15–20 years of age.[25,27]

A

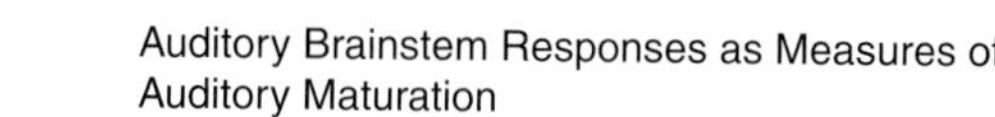

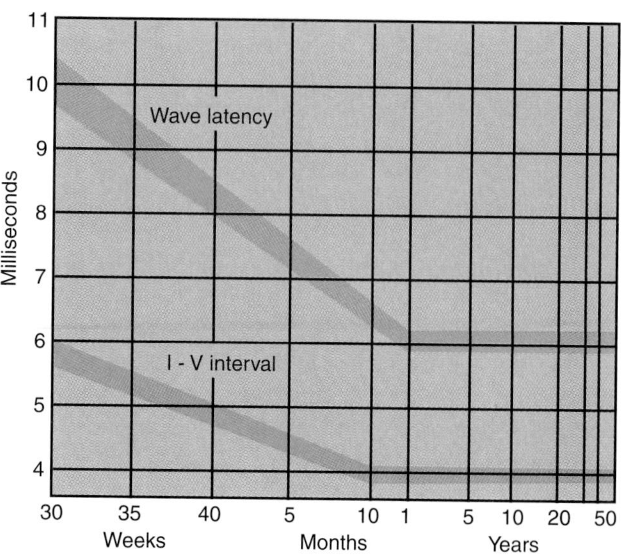

B

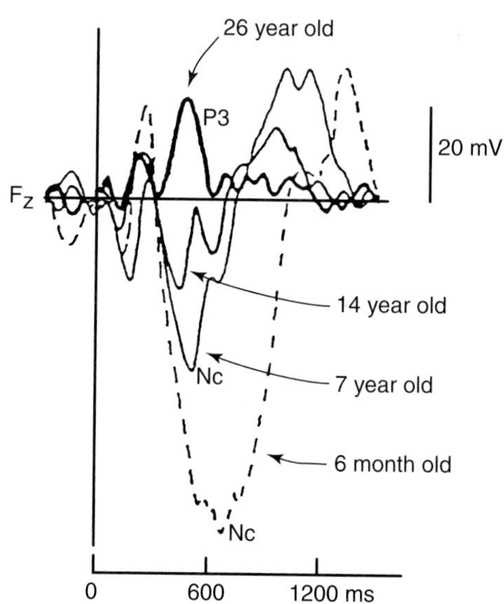

FIGURE 51.3 Changes in electrophysiological activity of the brain. (A) Declines over the first year of life in the latency of components of the auditory ERP that are generated by subcortical structures. (B) Changes in the ERP waveform at varying ages. The later components generated by cortical structures change dramatically as development progresses (for a discussion of the ERP method see Chapter 54, Box 54.1).

Summary

Structural, metabolic, and physiological indices of human brain development all point to a long time course that displays considerable variability from region to region and from system to system.

THE FUNCTIONAL DEVELOPMENT OF NORMAL HUMAN BRAIN

Investigators are now attempting to link the types of evidence described in the preceding section to sensory and cognitive functions in infants and children. At present, such studies are limited in number. Central tasks are identifying factors that drive the dynamic and extensive changes observed in human brain development and assessing the relative contributions of intrinsic and extrinsic variables in the functional differentiation of different brain systems. Until recently, the predominant view was that postnatal development of the cortex is largely intrinsically determined. However, new studies of both animals and humans have revealed a central role for extrinsic factors in shaping the organization of neural systems and in permitting recovery from brain damage. Indeed, calculations showing that the information in the genome is not sufficient to specify the connectivity of the brain, together with evidence for the long-lasting existence of transient, redundant connections in primates, suggest that regressive phenomena under the influence of environmental input play a significant and persistent role in the development of the functional specificity of the human brain.

Anatomical Development of the Visual System in Infants Can Be Linked to Functional Development

Several parallels between anatomical changes and the emergence of function in human visual systems have been noted. Looking preferences are used to examine visual functions in infancy. To study acuity, infants are given a choice between two displays that differ in some way, for example, in spatial frequency, which is usually varied by the thickness of stripes.[28] Preferences for one of the two patterns indicates the limits in the infant's ability to discriminate between the two patterns.

The visual abilities of the newborn have been linked to subcortical structures that show mature anatomy and high metabolic rates during this period.[7,15,29,30] The limited visual abilities of the newborn are augmented by the appearance of smooth pursuit tracking around 6–8 weeks. This development may be accounted for by the maturation of cortical layers 4, 5, and 6 in V1. These layers connect magnocellular afferents from the lateral geniculate nucleus and the middle temporal (MT) region, a pathway important for visual attention.[31] Visual acuity and visual alertness increase dramatically around 4 months of age, when the volume of visual cortex reaches adult levels and the highest density of synapses is present. Around the same age of 4–5 months, binocular interactions that are clearly dependent on cortical function become apparent. These interactions, which include stereoacuity, binocular summation of the light reflex, and stereopsis, appear in the same time frame as maturation of the middle cortical layers and a rapid synaptogenesis in V1.[7,28,32,33] This period of rapid growth appears to be a time of increased vulnerability to altered afferent input. Strabismic amblyopia and amblyopia due to the absence of patterned input are reported to occur at this age unless corrected early.

The time period when visual impairments can be corrected is different for different visual functions. Correction for an absent lens (*aphakia*) due to cataracts may be completely effective only when performed prior to 2 months of age,[34] i.e., just prior to the onset of exuberant synaptogenesis in V1. On the other hand, very high synaptic density persists to at least the age of 4 years in V1. The presence of these unspecified synapses may account for the ability to recover from amblyopia (with forced use of the strabismic eye) during this time.

Recent studies suggest that the ability to see sterescopically may not develop if the disruption of binocular convergence by strabismus is not corrected within the first year of life.[35] In contrast, these same children develop normal acuity and contrast sensitivity in the corrected strabismic eye even when the correction occurs after the first year of life. These results suggest there may be separate critical periods for the development of resolution acuity and stereopsis. Because the parvocellular system is thought to underlie acuity, whereas disparity detection is mediated by the magnocellular system, the magnocellular system may be more modifiable by environmental input than the parvocellular system, both in humans and in other animals.[26,33,36–38] This differential sensitivity may be due to the slower maturation of the magnocellular system[33,37–39] and/or to differences in the number of exuberant synapses within the systems.[26,40]

Studies of individuals born deaf and blind suggest that in humans, as in other animals,[41–44] there is a time period when cortical areas that normally process information from the deprived modality may become reorganized to process information from remaining modalities.[26,45–49] From the alteration of visual functions seen in individuals born deaf, it appears that areas of auditory cortex have been recruited for visual function (see Fig. 51.4). Deaf subjects show abnormally strong electrical responses to peripheral visual stimuli. These responses are not found in normally hearing individuals, even those exposed to sign language by deaf parents.

The prolonged persistence of exuberant cortico–

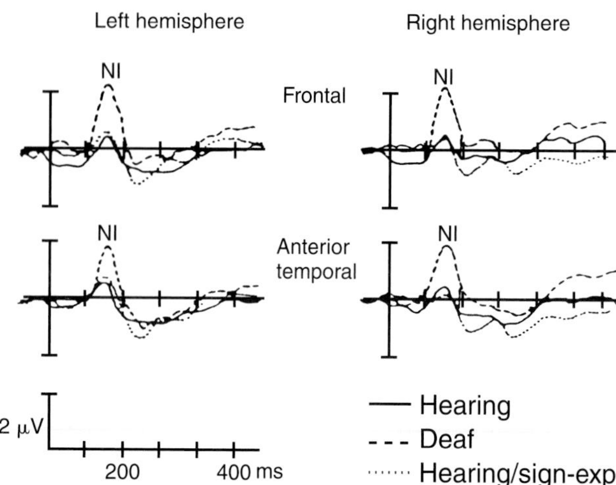

FIGURE 51.4 Visual evoked potentials to peripheral stimuli recorded from congenitally deaf subjects and from hearing subjects who had early exposure to sign language (hearing/sign-exposed) and those who did not. Only deaf subjects showed enhanced ERPs over temporal areas.

cortico connections may provide the substrate for such cortical reorganization.

Toward the End of the First Year of Life Infants Show Changes in Visual Search

Infants younger than 7 or 8 months of age will not uncover a hidden object. If a cloth is thrown over a toy while an infant of 5 or 6 months is reaching for it, the infant will withdraw his or her hand and stop reaching. By 7 or 8 months, most infants who watch an object being hidden can retrieve it. However, if the infant then watches as the object is hidden at a second location, most infants of 7–8 months search for the object at its first hiding location, which is now empty.

Jean Piaget called this the A-not-B error, because the infant is correct at the first hiding place (A) but not at the second (B). It is rare to see this error when there is no delay between when the object is hidden and when the infant is allowed to reach, but a delay as brief as 1, 2, or 3 s is sufficient to produce the error in infants 7–8 months of age. As infants grow older, the error is still seen if the delay between hiding and retrieval is increased. The delay at which the A-not-B error is produced increases by about 2 s per month from 7 to 12 months of age, although there is considerable individual variation among infants. The A-not-B error is a robust phenomenon that has been observed all over the world in children from diverse cultures, physical environments, socioeconomic backgrounds, and household and daycare arrangements and has been observed in dozens of laboratories using diverse procedures.

For Piaget, achieving the ability to retrieve a hidden object was a landmark accomplishment. A younger infant reaching for a visible toy might simply have been reacting almost reflexively to the sight of the object. However, reasoned Piaget, an older infant who reaches for something he cannot see and who must execute a sequence of actions (first removing the cloth and then reaching for the toy) to obtain it, must have had the goal of retrieving the toy in mind from the outset. For Piaget this marked the first clear appearance of intentionality, planning, and foresight. The A-not-B error reflected the fragility of these abilities and infants' poor understanding of the laws governing the location of objects in space. Either infants were not yet able to hold a representation of the object's location in mind for a few seconds or they did not yet quite understand the relationship of (a) their previous action of retrieving the object, (b) the subsequent hiding of the object in a different location (even though they observed the hiding), and (c) the object's present whereabouts.

The A-Not-B Task and the Delayed Response Test Depend on Frontal Lobe Function

The functions of dorsolateral prefrontal cortex in nonhuman primates have been studied extensively using "delayed response," a task that is virtually the same as the A-not-B task described above. Dorsolateral prefrontal cortex is one of the last regions of the brain to develop phylogenetically and ontogenetically. During primate evolution it has exploded in size, and is thought to be responsible for "executive" functions such as planning and foresight. Dorsolateral prefrontal cortex is defined in the macaque brain as that area of frontal cortex between the arcuate sulcus and the frontal pole on the dorsolateral surface. The most critical portion of this region for delayed response and A-not-B performance in macaques is the principal sulcus (roughly Walker's area 46). The entire region consists of Brodmann's area 9 and much of areas 8 and 10, as well as area 46. The homologous region in humans is thought to lie within the middle frontal gyrus.

When dorsolateral prefrontal cortex is ablated or inactivated, subjects fail the delayed response task. Subjects succeed on trials where cells within the principal sulcal region sustain their firing during the delay period, and fail on trials where this neuronal firing is not sustained. Judging by their firing patterns, some of these neurons encode the spatial location of the cue, while others encode the location where the animal should respond at the end of the delay.

Human infants improve on the delayed response task over the same age range and at the same rate as they do on the A-not-B task. Infants find both tasks easier, and succeed at a younger age, when the memory requirements of the task are reduced (by reducing the delay or by permitting subjects to orient toward the correct hiding place during the delay).

Primate Behavior Is the Result of Multiple Cortical Functions

Infant monkeys improve on the delayed response task over the same ages ($1\frac{1}{2}$ to 4 months) and at the same rate as they do on the A-not-B task. Ablation of dorsolateral prefrontal cortex impairs performance on both the delayed response and the A-not-B tasks. This is true in infant monkeys lesioned at $4\frac{1}{2}$ months and retested at 5 months and in adult monkeys. Ablation of posterior parietal cortex (Brodmann's area 7) or of much of the medial temporal lobe (including the hippocampus, subiculum), and much of the entorhinal and parahippocampal cortices) does not affect performance on either task if the delays are the same as those used with human infants.

Prefrontal cortex may be important for the memory of temporal order information (before and after), although it is not yet clear which region(s) within prefrontal cortex are responsible for carrying out this function. Instead of conceiving of A-not-B and delayed response as presenting the problem of holding spatial information in mind ("Was the reward hidden on the right or the left?"), one might think of these tasks as requiring the memory of temporal order information ("Where was the reward hidden last?"). All subjects perform correctly on the initial trials at the first hiding place (where temporal order information is irrelevant); it is only when the second location comes into play that errors appear in infants (humans or macaques) or in macaques (infant or adult) in whom dorsolateral prefrontal cortex has been inactivated or removed. Perhaps dorsolateral prefrontal cortex is important for holding in mind the spatial–temporal context of stimuli; or for holding relational information in general in mind (nothing is "left" or "right," "before" or "after," except in relationship to something else; if this is true then dorsolateral prefrontal cortex might also be important for holding in mind "louder," "softer," "brighter," "dimmer," etc.); or when more than one piece of information must be held in mind at the same time (a relationship, after all, consists of at least two items). Further investigation is needed to determine which, if any, of these alternative interpretations is correct.

One hypothesis, however, is that the need to hold information in mind is not in itself sufficient for a task to require activity by dorsolateral prefrontal cortex. According to this hypothesis, the task must also require the subject to inhibit an action that he or she was predisposed to make; that is, tasks that require dorsolateral prefrontal cortex involvement must require the subject to keep information in mind and to act other than is the subject's first inclination. On A-not-B and delayed response tasks, rewarding subjects for reaching toward the first hiding place may strengthen the response to reach there, in essence conditioning subjects to repeat that response. If this is true, the conditioned response must be inhibited if subjects are to succeed when the reward is hidden in a different place, where a different response is required. Evidence indicates that even when subjects appear to know where the reward is, they have trouble resisting the tendency to reach back to the old location where they found the reward previously. If this hypothesis is correct, the more times a subject is rewarded for retrieving the object at the first hiding place, the more difficult it should become for the subject to change that response when the object is hidden at the other location. There is evidence that increasing the number of reinforced trials in the first location increases the errors that infants make when the second location is rewarded. Distractibility (being pulled by irrelevent stimuli during the delay) or sensitivity to "proactive interference" (being influenced by earlier trials when it is the present trial that is relevant) can also be looked at from two viewpoints: as problems on the A-not-B and delayed response tasks and as problems in the inhibitory control of behavior. Both prefrontal cortex and motor cortex are part of the frontal cortex. All areas of frontal cortex are probably concerned with action and with the control of our actions. It is possible that maturation of the prefrontal neural system is centrally involved with the development of self-control in children and with the development of children's ability to exercise choice and control over their actions.

Language Undergoes Rapid but Prolonged Development

In humans, the prolonged structural, metabolic, and neurophysiological maturation of "association" cortical areas, which continues well into the teens, provides the substrate for the panoply of higher cognitive functions that continue to develop during this time. Attempts have been made to link the very rapid development of speech and language skills over the first 3 years of life to these general changes. In general, this goal has remained elusive, probably because so many aspects of the brain and behavior are changing together. Moreover, key elements of language appear to be processed within systems organized at the cellular and synaptic levels, where functional observations by researchers are not possible at present.

There is wide agreement that language is strongly dependent on structures within the left perisylvian region (see Chapter 58). Very early on (by 28 weeks of gestation), structural asymmetries appear between the temporal lobes; these may provide the substrate for the functional asymmetries that appear later.[4] The rapid and early acquisition of phonological information and speech production and comprehension and the subsequent vocabulary burst may be linked to the rapid rise in the number of synapses and the marked increases in cortical metabolism that occur during the second year of life. Also, the persistence of large numbers of exuberant synapses through adolescence may provide the anatomical substrate for prolonged neural plasticity and recovery of language skills following cortical damage in the first decade of life. It is well established that language skills can display considerable recovery following large lesions to the left hemisphere during the first 7–10 years of life.[50–57] The impressive recovery of language skills in children in whom the left hemisphere has been removed is even more striking in light of the enduring language impairment of specifically language-impaired children in whom macroscopic aspects of brain structure are basically normal, as discussed later in this chapter. These findings underscore the importance of characterizing microscopic structural aspects of the brain and the functional organization of the brain in relation to processing.

The prolonged time course of development that may confer plasticity on the immature brain appears to be characterized by optimal or critical periods (see Chapter 22) for language acquisition. Several studies report that both first and second language acquisitions are impaired and cerebral organization is altered when language is acquired after the first decade of life.[58–61] Moreover, as has been observed for vision, different aspects of language appear to display different critical periods. Vocabulary items can be acquired long past the first decade of life, but the grammatical rules of a language appear to be most readily acquired before the age of 10.[26,58,59,62] Along with other evidence, this pattern suggests that different neural systems, with differing developmental time courses, mediate these various aspects of language.[25,26]

Studies of changes in cerebral organization during childhood suggest that both maturational factors and individual differences in levels of language skills predict the time course of the increasing specialization of the language systems of the brain.[26,63] Additionally, when language is acquired through visual–manual modalities, as in the case of deaf individuals acquiring American Sign Language (ASL), language-relevant brain systems display similarities to those that are active during the processing of oral–aural language, leading to the conclusion that there are intrinsic constraints on language-relevant aspects of brain organization.[64] In addition, however, when ASL is acquired, significant departures from the typical pattern of cerebral organization take place. These departures allow us to evaluate the role of external input in specifying the final pattern of cerebral organization for language.[65]

Summary

Elements of normal brain development have been summarized within this section. These include the development of the sensory systems within the first year of life and development of frontal control systems and of language late in the first year and through the second year of life.

In the future, it will be possible to analyze the neural basis of cognition in more detail, by using the new high-resolution methods for imaging brain structure and function to study normally developing children and children with specific structural or functional deficits.

ABNORMALITIES IN THE DEVELOPMENTAL PROCESS

Developmental disabilities are typically defined by performance on specific psychological tests and are frequently classified as mental disorders, distinct from other physically characterized disorders of childhood such as cerebral palsy, muscular dystrophy, spina bifida, and congenital malformations. This classification suggests that developmental or childhood disorders can be neatly divided into categories of *physical* and *mental* disability. However, this is not necessarily the case. Developmental disabilities such as mental retardation can, for example, co-occur with physical disorders such as neural tube defect. Moreover, an increasing body of research demonstrates that there are physical (e.g., neural, genetic, and biochemical) anomalies associated with specific developmental (mental) disabilities.

Research in this field employs behavioral data to make the evaluation or clinical diagnosis. The neural features of behaviorally identified subjects are then studied for differences from normal controls. In other words, developmental problems, as expressed by behavior, bring a child to clinical attention, and then researchers work to understand the underlying organic causes of the disorder. Some day, however, specific reading disorders like dyslexia may be confirmed or even diagnosed with a magnetic resonance imaging (MRI) scan. Quite possibly, neurological diagnosis of mental disorders may alter their very definitions, which are currently primarily behavioral. For example, it may be possible to diagnose neural anomalies associated with dyslexia prior to behavioral expression of the disorder (i.e., in a child who has not yet learned to read). With current technology, however, we continue to approach developmental disabilities from the perspective of mental disorders, in hopes that we will one day understand their physical basis.

The next section addresses how behavior and cognition are measured and how "disability" is defined.

Disabilities Are Defined in Relation to Normal Function

In studying human development, it is sometimes difficult to define what is normal. Most people would agree that human beings have two arms and legs, two eyes and ears, a nose, and a mouth. When it comes to human behavior and cognition, however, defining normal becomes increasingly complicated. One way in which human behavior and intellect can be assessed is via comparison with the **norm.** That is, researchers construct a test designed to measure a certain ability or characteristic. The test is then given to large, representative groups of people of both genders and a wide range of ages. Based on this sample population data, researchers derive an average score for certain age ranges, for boys and girls, for men and women. Measures of variation or **standard deviation** from the norm, which reflect the magnitude of individual differences, are also calculated. Typically, such normative data produce a **bell curve,** or a concentrated grouping of scores around the mean, and decreasing numbers of people with scores 1, 2, or more standard deviations above or below the mean (Fig. 51.5). Using such a standard curve, researchers can compare scores for individual subjects against "what is normal." Certain criteria, such as "a score of *X* or below," can then be set to define when an individual is significantly impaired for a specific function.

Because the process of standardized testing and evaluation is critical to the study of developmental disabilities, it is important to understand that commonly used psychological tests are only as valid and useful as the degree to which the populations used in standardization represent the real-world population for whom these tests are later used. For example,

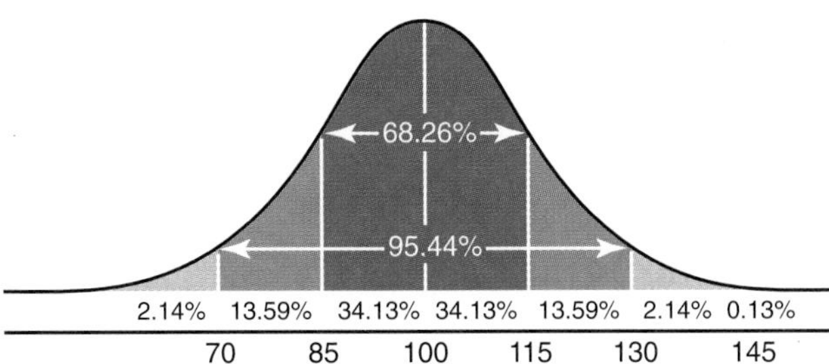

FIGURE 51.5 Intelligence tests are designed to have a mean of 100 and a normal distribution of scores around the mean with a standard deviation of 15. Each score can then be associated with a percentile, indicating the percentage of the population that would achieve that score or a score below it.

a language test standardized 25 to 50 years ago on a select sample of middle-class, Caucasian, native English-speaking children would not be representative of the current culturally diverse U.S. population. Hence, norms established for these tests could produce misleading evaluations of children from families with a low socioeconomic status or from families whose native language is not English. These issues are a source of political and educational controversy.

Efforts Are Being Made to Develop Biological Correlates of Disabilities

Recent advances in neuroimaging and gene linkage technology have vastly expanded research possibilities for noninvasive clinical studies. Even with a new arsenal of research technology, however, it has not been possible to isolate and define characteristics of each developmental disability. There are several reasons for these limitations:

1. Disagreement regarding criteria for subject selection. Because different researchers often use differing behavioral criteria, cross-study comparisons frequently show inconsistencies in results.

2. Heterogeneity of disorders. Even when consistent behavioral criteria are carefully applied, different underlying etiologies can result in the same behavioral profile.

3. Difficulties inherent to the study of children. Although modern MRI techniques are considered noninvasive, they are stressful and time-consuming, and parents will not always allow their affected children to participate in such studies. Although studies can be conducted using adults who have been affected since childhood, the data obtained from such studies may not accurately reflect anomalies that characterize early disruption of brain development, because brains change over time. Moreover, retrospective diagnoses

of childhood disorders frequently rely on memory (e.g., a patient is asked "Did you have difficulty reading as a young child?"), and hence can be unreliable.

Despite these difficulties, ongoing research has uncovered important neurological and genetic features that seem to be associated with specific developmental disorders. For instance, neurological studies have shown that developmentally disabled children do not simply exhibit focal lesions specifically in "reading" or "language" or "attention" areas of the brain, while all other systems and functions are intact. Although such localized damage can indeed occur in an older child (e.g., due to localized hemorrhage, trauma, or tumor), such neurological disorders are typically not classified as developmental disabilities. On the other hand, focal damage that occurs in the prenatal and early postnatal period, particularly during critical neural events such as neuromigration, does not remain focal. In this case, focal damage can result in developmental disability.

Although the neurophysiological basis of developmental disabilities cannot be characterized by discrete and localized lesions of specific functional areas, neural anomalies underlying specific disorders may be most evident in localized regions (e.g., atypical symmetry and cellular anomalies in left-hemisphere language regions) and may be expressed in relatively discrete cognitive deficits (e.g., reading impairment with normal oral language and nonverbal IQ). It may also be characterized by more pervasive anomalies (e.g., diffuse volumetric reductions and anomalies throughout the cerebral cortex and cerebellum) and be expressed as more pervasive behavioral deficits (e.g., autism with retardation).

In the following sections we will discuss what is known about how specific injuries or anomalies in development of the brain may result in specific patterns of cognitive and behavioral impairment. We begin by considering two specific contrasting forms of mental disability. The first is a specific language impairment that arises in development and produces a profound effect on this basic human skill. The second, Williams syndrome, spares the language system in many ways, but produces devastating losses in other forms of behavior.

Specific Language Impairment Is Defined Behaviorally

In the absence of peripheral disorders or general cognitive deficits, a child is classified as language-impaired (or dysphasic) if there is significant delay in acquiring language skills at the level predicted for his/her age.[66] Many children exhibit delays in language development, and there are many different reasons this can occur. The most common are hearing impairment or deafness, mental retardation, autism, and anomalies in development or use of the oral musculature (resulting from malformation of the vocal apparatus or paralysis of speech musculature). Severe environmental deprivation or abuse can also result in impaired language development. A diagnosis of specific language impairment (SLI) entails exclusion of all of these underlying causes for language delay and typically requires diagnosis by a team of professionals, including a speech–language pathologist, psychologist, and pediatric neurologist. Only about one-third of children who exhibit language delays are ultimately diagnosed as having SLI. Some children exhibit specific difficulty in articulating the sounds of speech (e.g., lisp, stutter), but otherwise display normal language development. These children are diagnosed with speech articulation disorder, which is distinct from the cognitive disorder SLI. However, many children with SLI also exhibit concomitant speech-articulation disorders. Consequently, it is important that speech and/or language difficulties be carefully diagnosed by a speech–language pathologist.

In assessing this disorder, the diagnostician compares language scores against other cognitive measures such as nonverbal IQ, as well as motor skills and hearing levels. Specific language impairment is revealed by lowered language scores when intelligence and development otherwise fall in the normal range. By definition, SLI excludes other pervasive cognitive disorders such as mental retardation and autism that might be expected to cause depressed language scores. Children with SLI appear to be developing normally in all areas except for language.

Behavioral studies of children with SLI have demonstrated a broad range of linguistic disabilities. These children appear to exhibit difficulties with many components of language, from identifying and discriminating the building blocks that make up words (phonology), to syntactic (grammatical) and semantic (conceptual) aspects of language. Children with SLI can be divided into two groups based on a breakdown of deficits seen on standardized behavioral tests. The first group is characterized primarily by expressive (speech production) deficits with near-normal comprehension, and the second group is characterized by more pervasive language deficits affecting both expression and comprehension. Longitudinal studies have shown that outcomes are considerably better for children whose language disorders are primarily expressive than for children with both expressive and comprehension deficits.

There Are Symptomatic Biological Correlates of Specific Language Impairment

It is estimated that 7–8% of preschool children have SLI. Longitudinal studies show that a large majority of these children overcome the most noticeable aspects of preschool language delays and learn to talk. However, their disability does not disappear. Instead, it changes form, because children with SLI must use poorly established phonological systems to learn to read. Not surprisingly, children with SLI are highly likely to develop reading disabilities or dyslexia. For this reason, SLI and dyslexia are difficult to differentiate at a research level in studies of school age children, adolescents, and adults. This returns us to an issue raised earlier (see *Efforts Are Being Made to Develop Biological Correlates of Disabilities*). Specifically, neurophysiological studies of SLI reflect significant variance due to being from studies of adults screened on the basis of reading disability and unreliable retrospective reports of childhood language deficits. Variance also comes from studies that include older children with both SLI and dyslexia, as well as studies that include younger children with SLI but who *will develop* dyslexia. Finally, evidence strongly suggests the existence of persistent auditory rate processing deficits among adult dyslexics, but the difficulties inherent in retrospective clinical classification (i.e., trying to make a clinical diagnosis from childhood memories) limit the ability to determine whether adult dyslexics with auditory and phonological processing deficits also had SLI as children. For all these reasons, neuroscientists still do not know whether SLI and dyslexia are expressions of (1) different, (2) related and overlapping, or (3) identical underlying neurophysiological anomalies. At the behavioral level at least, evidence obtained from longitudinal studies strongly supports the existence of significant overlap between these two clinical populations.

There Is a Genetic Contribution to Language Impairment

One method of assessing the genetic contribution to developmental disabilities is to conduct family studies, in which evidence of the transgenerational incidence of disability is compared against known genetic models of inheritance. From such studies, SLI appears to be inherited by an autosomal dominant mechanism with full penetrance.[67,68] Other studies have examined the family history of specific individuals diagnosed with SLI, and again found an elevated incidence of SLI or related disorders among parents, siblings, and other biological relatives of the **proband**—the impaired individual bringing the family to clinical attention.[68,69] Studies of twins, for example, have demonstrated close to 100% concordance in language disability for monozygotic twins and, as expected, approximately half that for dizygotic twins.[70] Although these findings support genetic mechanisms of familial transmission of SLI, we should note that some SLI cases show no known family history of language-related disorders; thus, other factors may also be involved in the underlying etiology of SLI.

Brain Regions Can Be Abnormal in Specific Language Impairment

Studies of both receptive and expressive language impairment have focused heavily on regions of the brain known to be involved in language processing, particularly left-hemisphere regions of the temporal, parietal, and frontal cortex, such as **Wernicke's area**—a temporal cortical region involved in language comprehension—and **Broca's area**—a frontal region involved in speech perception and expressive language (see Chapter 57 for details). In most normal subjects studied, the planum temporale, which lies on the superior surface of the temporal lobe and encompasses a portion of Wernicke's area, is larger on the left side of the brain than on the right[3,4,71–73] (see also Chapter 59, Fig. 59.4). This structural difference is consistent with the left-hemisphere specialization for language processing found in behavioral studies, with neuroimaging studies, and with studies of the behavioral effects of lateralized lesions.

In one of the few studies of neuropathology underlying specific language impairment, researchers used MRI techniques to examine the cerebrum of 20 SLI and 12 matched control children. Results showed that the volume of the posterior perisylvian region (which includes the planum temporale) was reduced bilaterally in language-impaired children, most markedly in the left hemisphere. Although language-impaired children showed greater variability in the asymmetry of cortical volume for this region, the degree of asymmetry did not differ significantly between the impaired and control groups. However, asymmetries in the inferoanterior and superoposterior cerebral regions were significantly different in control and impaired children. In addition, bilateral reductions in the overall volume were found subcortically in the caudate, putamen, and diencephalic structures.

Associations between Neuropathology and Behavior Are Being Explored

The anomalies described in the preceding section provide a possible explanation for a paradox in the field of developmental disabilities: Children with SLI appear to have relatively subtle neural anomalies, with the differences reported by Jernigan *et al.*[73a] evident only when groups of SLI and control children were compared. Examination of an individual MRI from a child with SLI generally shows nothing grossly atypical. Nevertheless, this same child can show remarkably severe behavioral deficits that are evident even to an untrained person. In contrast, another child may lose the entire left hemisphere through surgery to treat intractable epilepsy, and yet will still develop language skills in the normal range. How is it possible that subtle neurological anomalies can underlie massive behavioral deficits, when massive lesions produce relatively minor behavioral effects? One possible answer to this paradox may be found in the MRI data showing that cortical anomalies in children with SLI are bilateral; this may reduce chances for recovery via reorganization in homologous regions of the right hemisphere when left hemisphere language areas are damaged. Another explanation may involve the volumetric anomalies seen subcortically, because subcortical damage has particularly profound and lasting effects on language development. Finally, cellular evidence from postmortem analyses of dyslexic brains is discussed below. This evidence suggests that cellular anomalies not visible by MRI may exist in the brains of individuals with SLI and that such anomalies may result in subtle but dysfunctional organization of sensory neural systems critical to normal language development.

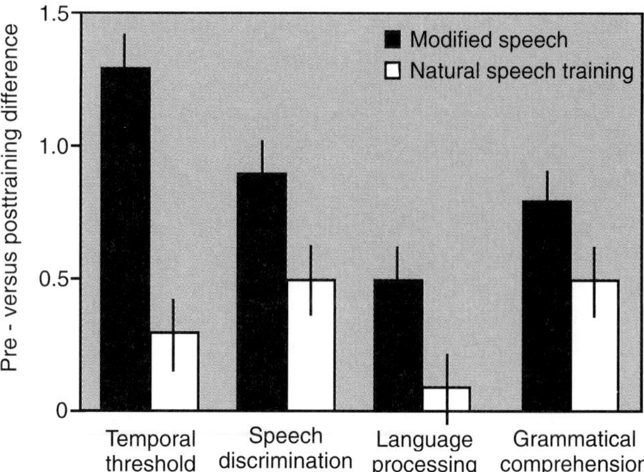

FIGURE 51.6 Human speech can be modified to lengthen or emphasize the rapid transients. Difference Z scores (posttraining minus pretraining) are shown for SLI subjects who received speech and language training with either acoustically modified or natural speech. Difference Z scores are presented for measures of temporal threshold (Tallal Repetition Test), speech discrimination (Goldman, Fristoe, Woodcock Diagnostic Auditory Discrimination Test), language processing (sentences of increasing length and grammatical complexity; Token Test for Children), and grammatical comprehension (Curtiss and Yamada Comprehensive Language Evaluation Receptive). Temporal threshold Z scores were converted to positive values for display purposes. Figure from Tallal *et al.*, 1996, *Science*, **271,** p. 82. When children with specific language impairment are trained with these modified sounds (black bars), their speech discrimination and other language functions improve more than when they are trained with normal speech sounds (white bars).

Behavioral evidence supports the view that cognitive deficits in children with SLI arise from deficits in rate of neural processing for sensory information presented in rapid succession. In fact, children with SLI exhibit severe deficits in the ability to perform auditory discriminations of information that changes rapidly within a brief time window (350 ms or less). Although this deficit is profoundly evident when children with SLI are asked to discriminate speech stimuli characterized by brief and rapidly changing acoustic spectra (e.g., consonant–vowel syllables such as /ba/ and /da/), the presented material need not be linguistic for the deficit to be observed. While normal children are able to discriminate two 75-ms tones separated by as little as 8 ms, language-impaired children require an interval of at least 150 ms to perform this same discrimination.[74] Such auditory temporal processing deficits may significantly disrupt phonological processing, and consequently speech perception, leading to developmental impairment of language skills.[75]

In this regard, it is significant that training SLI children with computer-controlled acoustically modified speech leads to dramatic improvement in a number of acoustic processing and language skills. These studies were theoretically based on evidence that sensory maps in adult primate cortex are highly plastic and can be dramatically altered by intensive and adaptive sensory training, as well as on extensive research demonstrating fundamental auditory rate processing deficits in children with SLI.[75] In these training studies, Tallal and Merzenich developed a computer algorithm to alter the acoustics within speech syllables. Specifically, the rapidly successive acoustic cues that occur within speech syllables such as /ba/ and /da/, and which have been shown to be particularly difficult for children with SLI to discriminate, were artifically amplitude-enhanced and extended in time. A group of children with SLI then underwent extensive training using the modified speech. These novel computer exercises allowed children with SLI to speed up their rate of auditory processing and to improve their language abilities to more age-appropriate levels (Fig. 51.6). Ongoing results from this line of research have led to a wide availability of this therapy to children in clinics and classrooms.

Although the neurophysiological basis for deficits in processing auditory information at rapid rates has not been pinpointed, evidence strongly suggests a relationship to anomalies seen in postmortem analyses of the brains of dyslexics. Such analyses have shown cellular anomalies in the cortex of dyslexics, in the form of atypical clusters of cells that have migrated improperly (specifically, ectopias and microgyric lesions). Interestingly, these anomalies are seen most often in left perisylvian (language) regions.

Anomalies have also been seen subcortically, in magnocellular regions of the lateral geniculate nucleus and medial geniculate nucleus (LGN and MGN). In the visual system, the magnocellular portion of the LGN is thought to specifically carry low-frequency, transient visual information (as opposed to high-frequency detail and color, which are transmitted in the parvocellular system). At the behavioral level, anomalies in magnocellular cells of the LGN of dyslexics are consistent with delayed neural response (as measured by evoked potential) to transient visual information.[76] More recent evidence has also shown anomalies in magnocellular cells of the MGN of dyslexics.[77] Although these latter anomalies have not been directly tied to behavior, it seems highly likely that they may relate to the deficits seen in processing transient (or rapidly changing) auditory information for individuals with SLI. Finally, these anomalies have been seen only in the postmortem brains of adults identified as dyslexic, and we do not know if they occur in individuals with SLI. Because the cortical anomalies (ectopias and microgyric lesions) are too small to be easily detected within the current limits of live neuroimaging, and because cellular anomalies in subcortical structures are also difficult to detect by MRI, we have not yet studied the brains of living children with SLI at this level. Nevertheless, data from postmortem analyses of brains from adults with dyslexia are suggestive because many children with SLI go on to develop dyslexia and because evidence shows that adults with dyslexia also exhibit the auditory rate processing deficits seen in children with SLI. Thus, it seems very likely that the neurological etiologies of dyslexia and SLI are related.

Tests with an Animal Model Suggest That Neuromigrational Anomalies and Auditory Processing Deficits Are Related

To further test the validity of a link between anomalous neurobiological development seen in dyslexics and aberrant auditory processing seen in SLI, auditory processing studies were performed on adult male rats with neuropathological anomalies like those seen in human dyslexics. Specifically, newborn rats received focal freezing lesions that resulted in microgyric cortical lesions. These rats were tested on an auditory discrimination task based on a two-tone sequence discrimination task used with control and SLI children. This task had revealed severe deficits in children with SLI for discriminating a two-tone sequence when that sequence occurred in a window of 350 ms or less.[74] In that study, control children were able to discriminate sequences that occurred in as little as 158 ms total (thus differing significantly from children with SLI). The experiment with rats showed that subjects with neocortical anomalies, like children with SLI, also exhibited significant impairments in discriminating auditory information presented at rapid rates (or conversely, within a brief time window of 350 ms or less[78]) (see Fig. 51.7). The parallel between the results of this experiment performed on rats with microgyric lesions and those of prior studies on

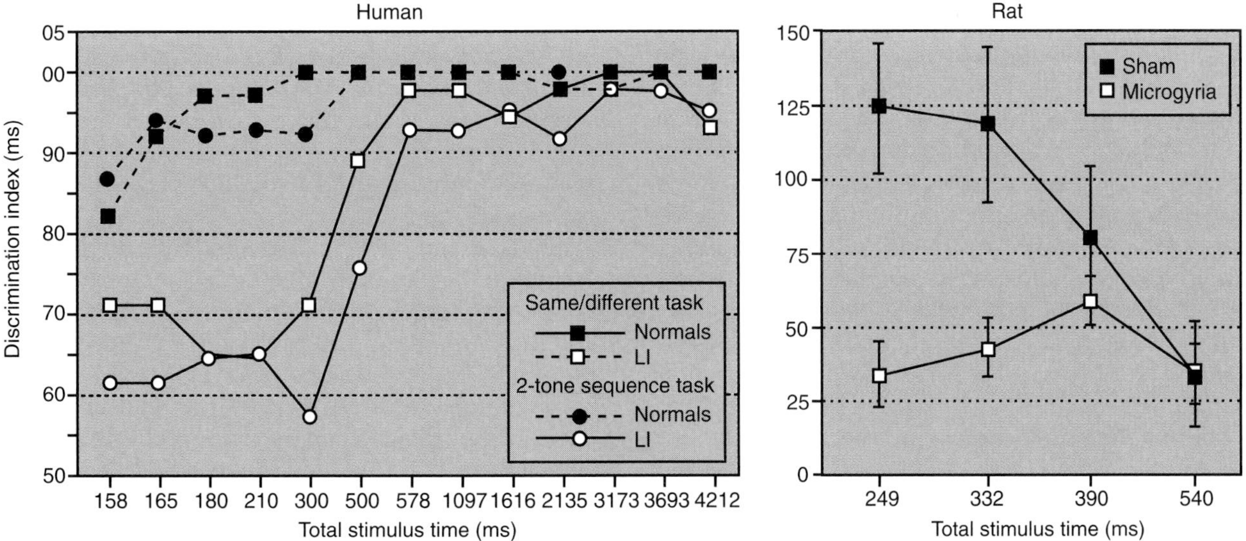

FIGURE 51.7 Left: Differences between normal and language-impaired (L1) children in their ability to report small tonal differences between tone pairs. Right: Similar differences in a rodent model.

children with SLI is compelling, and supports the view that the neuroanatomical anomalies seen in dyslexia are related to the auditory rate processing deficits seen in SLI.

These results suggested that neuropathological anomalies such as ectopias and microgyric lesions may be associated with subtle but pervasive reorganization of neural connectivity patterns. The notion of subtle but pervasive changes in the brains of language and reading impaired individuals is consistent with the fact that SLI and dyslexic individuals do not have large lesions or otherwise grossly atypical brains, but they do have profound behavioral deficits. The idea of pervasive reorganization caused by focal but cascading damage early in development (i.e., during periods of neuronal migration) is also consistent with evidence of subtle changes throughout the cortex and subcortex of these individuals, as well as the fact that sensory rate processing deficits are seen not only in the auditory but also in the visual, tactile, and motor modalities.[79–82]

In conclusion, individuals with SLI exhibit significant delays in language development and frequently display later reading disorders (or dyslexia) as well. Research has shown that both groups (SLI children and adult dyslexics) exhibit impaired or anomalous processing of rapidly changing auditory and visual information. Animal studies strongly suggest a link between the focal developmental anomalies seen in dyslexic brains and the auditory processing deficits seen in individuals with SLI. Thus, at least one theory that links behavioral and neural evidence from affected individuals is as follows. Focal cortical damage during early development (i.e., during periods of neural migration) may cause cellular anomalies in neocortex and may also adversely affect development of subcortical structures, including lateral and medial geniculate nuclei. These anomalies in critical sensory systems may be reflected in deficits in discriminating rapidly changing auditory and visual information, which in turn cause severe difficulties in understanding speech, in learning to speak, and in associating written letters with phonemic (sound) representations. Although this model is at present speculative, it provides a scenario linking high-level cognitive disorders such as language and reading impairment to pervasive deficits in neural organization and function in impaired individuals. Finally, it is worth noting the possibility that detrimental environmental factors in early development (e.g., sensory deprivation from chronic ear infections) may also produce pervasive neurophysiological changes in the brain. As with many other developmental disabilities, it appears that focal damage to the brain at the "wrong" time in early development may cause pervasive and dysfunctional reorganization of neural systems, with devastating consequences on behavioral outcome.

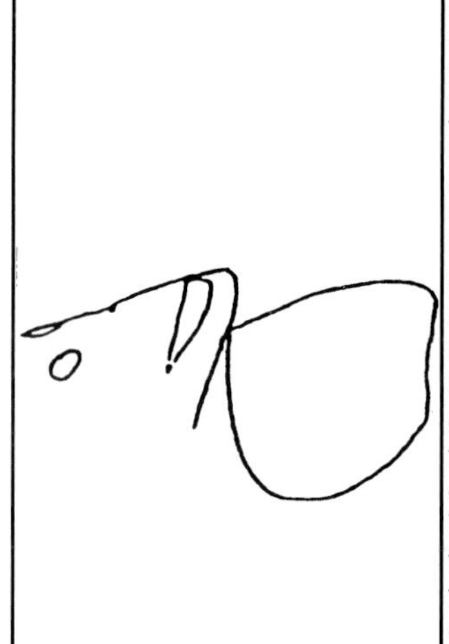

And what an elephant is, it is one of the animals. And what the elephant does, it lives in the jungle. It can also live in the zoo. And what it has, it has long gray ears, fan ears, ears that can blow in the wind. It has a long trunk that can pick up grass, or pick up hay...If the elephant gets mad it could stomp; it could charge. Sometimes elephants can charge. They have big long tusks. They can damage a car...It could be dangerous. When they're in a pinch, when they're in a bad mood it can be terrible. You don't want an elephant as a pet. You want a cat or a dog or a bird..

FIGURE 51.8 Left: Drawing of an elephant by an 18-year-old person with Williams syndrome (IQ = 49). Right: Verbal description by the same person. The figure illustrates the dramatic dissociation between spatial and language performance in this syndrome.

Williams Syndrome Is Inherited as an Autosomal Dominant and Is Associated with Characteristic Behavioral, Anatomical, and Physiological Anomalies

Williams syndrome (WS) is a relatively rare disorder, occurring in 1 in 50,000 children (an incidence of 0.002%). Behaviorally, it is characterized by severely depressed nonverbal IQ and visuospatial ability, along with paradoxical sparing of verbal fluency and grammar, an effect referred to as cognitive "fractionation."[84] This disparity is illustrated in Fig. 51.8. Individuals with this syndrome are typically classified as mentally retarded on the basis of overall subnormal scores on intelligence tests.[84]

Physically, a child with WS is characterized by an "elfinlike" facial appearance, cardiac anomalies (including supravalvular aortic stenosis), hypercalcemia, and malformations in musculoskeletal, endocrine, and renal systems (see Bellugi *et al.*[84] or Bellugi *et al.*[85] for review). In all cases of WS examined, genetic analyses have shown a deletion on the long arm of chromosome 7, including the elastin gene.[86] WS appears to be inherited by an *autosomal dominant mode.*[87]

Morphometric analysis of the brains of individuals with WS has shown reduced cerebral volume, with preservation in the size of the anterior cerebral and temperolimbic regions, as well as preservation of cerebellar volume.[88–90] These anomalies are consistent with the behavioral observation of spared verbal fluency, despite otherwise retarded cognitive functioning. The aberrant cerebrum–cerebellum ratio may distinguish this syndrome from other clinical disorders such as Down syndrome. Down syndrome represents another genetic disorder characterized by mental retardation, but in this case effects are pervasive (or nonspecific), with across-the-board reductions in intelligence scores. Bellugi and colleagues[84] postulate that the differing behavioral and neural profile of Down and Williams syndromes may provide a clue as to the developmental pathogenesis of these disorders. In individuals with WS, the cerebellum matures earlier than the cerebral cortex. In developmental terms, Down syndrome may be distinguished by factors that appear earlier in the developmental process and affect both cerebellum and cerebrum, while later processes selectively affecting cerebral cell populations may be characteristic of Williams syndrome. This view is supported by the results of postmortem cytoarchitectural analyses of an individual with WS. These analyses revealed evidence of aberrant neural migration, including ectopic neurons. Interestingly, such anomalies were previously described in dyslexic brains.

At the neurophysiological level, WS subjects appear to be hypersensitive to auditory stimulation and, following the presentation of tone sequences, show abnormally fast neural recovery as measured by event-related potentials. Spoken words were also found to elicit anomalous ERPs, although these differences were not seen for visually presented linguistic material. Individuals with SLI show basic auditory and visual processing deficits. Basic anomalies in sensory processing may thus affect systemic development of higher-order functions processing that sensory information. In the case of WS, hypersensitive auditory processing may actually facilitate sparing of language functions, whereas in SLI, the opposite auditory anomaly, a deficit in auditory processing, is associated with language impairment.

In Williams Syndrome Behavioral Abnormality Can Be Associated with Neuropathology

As with behavioral and neurological studies of individuals with SLI and dyslexia, we can find some association between neural and behavioral anomalies in WS. Recall that in dyslexics, cellular anomalies are seen in subcortical sensory areas critical to language development and also in cortical regions involved in language processing. MRI analyses of SLI individuals also showed volumetric reductions in cortical areas critical to language. In individuals with WS, we see a different pattern of behavioral deficits, with some verbal sparing but severely affected spatial processing. Accordingly, we see volumetric sparing of frontal and temporal cortical regions associated with language in WS, and preservation or even facilitation of auditory processing systems associated with language. Moreover, because individuals with SLI failed to show grossly atypical morphology in language-related areas of the brain, individuals with WS also fail to show grossly atypical morphology of right hemisphere regions associated with spatial processing. Instead, the mechanism underlying the expression of aberrant behavior in WS appears to be more subtle and pervasive. Indeed, postmortem analysis of the brain of a WS individual revealed cellular neuromigrational anomalies in the cortex (as seen in dyslexics), supporting the notion that early focal damage followed by pervasive and dysfunctional reorganization of neural systems is a hallmark of developmental disabilities. In the case of WS, it is not known which precise neural systems are affected, and the mechanism by which developmental changes in these system(s) are expressed in depressed spatial processing is not known. Nevertheless, this remains a fascinating area for future research, with enormous potential for understanding relationships between the development of complex neural systems and the expression of complex behavior including cognition.

Sex Hormones May Influence Neurodevelopmental Disorders

There are gender differences in the occurrence of neurodevelopmental disorders. The gender ratio of incidence is skewed toward boys for a variety of developmental disabilities, including severe mental retardation (1.3 boys/1 girl), speech and language disorders (2.6/1), learning difficulties (2.2/1), dyslexia (4.3/1), and autism (4/1). Why? Although the existence of sex differences in the area of language and learning disorders has been hotly contested on the basis that it is a result of teacher and clinician bias,[91] recent studies have supported the existence of a significant gender difference in the incidence of these disorders (e.g., see Liederman and Flannery[92]). Moreover, gender differences are also seen in clear-cut phenomena such as complications of pregnancy and birth,[93] where they cannot be easily explained as a reflection of investigator or clinician bias.

One theory to account for this phenomenon is that male but not female fetuses invoke a form of "antigenic" response from the mother during pregnancy, being recognized by the immune system as "foreign." The hostile environment thus created for the male fetus *in utero* would explain not only a higher incidence of developmental disorder among boys but also the finding that later-born sons are increasingly likely to be adversely affected (consistent with increased immune responsiveness on repeated exposure).[93]

Another theory to account for uneven gender ratios in developmental disorders was put forth by Galaburda and co-workers.[94] These researchers reviewed a vast literature on the relations among hormonal exposure, gender, cerebral laterality, immune disorder, and developmental disorders. They concluded that exposure to some "male factor" (possibly androgen) during the last trimester of fetal development acts to slow cortical maturation in male fetuses, particularly in the left hemisphere, rendering them more susceptible to perturbation from the normal course of development. This exposure would explain the higher incidence of developmental disorders among boys. Conversely, faster CNS development in female fetuses would enable them to better withstand insult during late pregnancy and birth. This assertion is supported by evidence that female infants appear to show better cognitive recovery than male infants from intracranial hemorrhage resulting from prematurity. Such an assertion is also consistent with recently published data showing that induced microgyric lesions do not lead to anomalies in cell structure of the medial geniculate nucleus or to auditory rate processing deficits in female rats, although severe effects are seen in males.[95]

The Geschwind theory, as it came to be known, is generally consistent with evidence of sex differences in cerebral organization, particularly for language. For example, women exhibit significantly better verbal recovery after focal left hemisphere damage (via tumor, stroke, etc.) compared to men, and significantly less functional lateralization for processing verbal material (see Kimura and Harshman[96]). Studies have also revealed sex differences in the pattern of cerebral blood flow during the performance of verbal tasks, in asymmetry as measured by functional MRI during verbal tasks,[97] and in structural asymmetry, as measured by size of the right and left plenum temporale of men and women.[72] These results all point to sex differences in the pattern of cerebral organization of language (and language-related functions), particularly with regard to the degree of left-hemisphere specialization for language.

In summary, evidence supports the existence of sex differences in brain development and organization. These differences may in turn affect the response of the brain to injury as a function of sex, and hence be reflected in differing numbers of boys and girls affected by developmental disability.

Summary

In this section we have examined two forms of developmental abnormalities, SLI and WS. In both cases it has been possible to link the behavioral manifestations of the disorder to anomalies in neurobiological systems. In both cases, too, there appears to be a genetic component. In both SLI and WS, affected individuals do not show localized damage in circumscribed brain regions, but show evidence of cellular disturbance early in brain development (i.e., during neuromigration), which has given rise to pervasive and dysfunctional reorganization of critical neural systems underlying complex behaviors. Evidence suggests that this phenomenon may characterize other developmental disabilities, including autism, retardation, and attention deficit disorder.

In the case of specific language impairment, training based on neurological findings has shown some success in remediating the deficit. The success of this approach shows the subtle interplay of nature and nurture in fostering healthy development.

NORMAL AGING OF THE BRAIN

People born in the United States in 1900 could expect to live an average of only 50 years. Advances in health care and preventative medicine in the intervening years have led to dramatic increases in life expectancy, and current estimates suggest that mean life span in most industrialized countries will exceed 80 years early in the next century. A substantial segment of the population can expect to enjoy the benefits of increased longevity while remaining free of dementing illness and other debilitating disease. The process of normal aging is not always benign, however, and many otherwise healthy aged individuals experience declining cognitive function that substantially compromises the quality of later life. Because of these demographic trends, substantial efforts have been made to identify changes in the structure and function of the brain that might account for the cognitive deficits associated with normal aging. Modern experimental approaches and analytic strategies, once a large descriptive enterprise, have opened new horizons for exploring the neurobiology of normal brain aging. In the process, many of our most entrenched assumptions about the effects of aging have been called into question.

Memory Serves as a Model Neuropsychological Framework for Exploring Normal Brain Aging

As discussed in Chapter 56, memory is not a unitary function, but encompasses a variety of dissociable processes mediated by distinct brain systems. Explicit or declarative memory refers to the conscious recollection of facts and events and is known to depend critically on a system of anatomically related structures in the medial temporal lobe, including the hippocampal formation and adjacent cortical regions. Although many important details about the cognitive structure and neurobiological organization of multiple memory systems remain to be clarified, information already available has guided research on the neural basis of age-related cognitive decline and provides a useful framework for reviewing current perspectives on normal brain aging.

Brain Structure Is Preserved in Normal Aging

Traditionally, moderate neuron death, distributed diffusely across multiple brain regions, was assumed to be an inevitable consequence of normal aging. Seminal studies conducted by Brody[98] provided support for this view, by indicating that neuron loss occurs throughout life, with more than 50% loss of cells in many neocortical areas by age 95[98] (see Brody[99] for historical review). While not all regions of the brain seemed to be affected to the same degree, significant age-related neuron loss was reported in every region examined, including both primary sensory and association areas of cortex. Thus, the concept emerged from early observations that diffusely distributed neuron death might account for many of the cognitive deficits associated with normal aging (reviewed in Coleman and Flood[100]).

Advances in Stereology Show That the Number of Cortical Neurons Is Largely Preserved during Normal Aging

Improved methods for quantifying cell number have led to a significant revision in traditional views on age-related neuron loss (see West[101] for a detailed discussion). Until recently, most investigators had focused their attention primarily on neuron density, defined as the number of neurons present in a fixed area or volume of tissue. Neuron density is measured experimentally by counting the number of neurons in a fixed volume of tissue within a brain region of interest. Typically, this is accomplished using standard histological staining procedures to visualize cells microscopically, and counting stained profiles of cell bodies, nuclei, or nucleoli, either manually or with automated image detection routines. A significant limitation of this approach, however, is that density can vary widely in the absence of any difference in cell number. For example, assume that the total numbers of neurons are identical in a region of interest in two brains, but that the sizes of the brains differ due to gliosis, white matter abnormalities, or other neuropil alterations. Under these conditions, average neuron density will necessarily be lower in a fixed volume of the larger brain. Therefore, volumetric differences between young and aged brains (either real or as an artifact of differential shrinkage during histological processing) could substantially influence measures of cell density in the absence of any actual loss of neurons. Other limitations of traditional cell counting methods have also been recognized (see West[101] for a recent discussion).

In contrast to measures of cell density, new methods in stereology are specifically designed to estimate total neuron number in a brain region of interest, providing an unequivocal measure for examining potential neuron loss during normal aging (see Box 51.1). Modern stereological tools have been widely used in recent years to reexamine neuron number in the aged hippocampus. In addition to the known importance of this structure for normal explicit memory, early studies based on cell density measurements suggested that the hippocampus is especially susceptible to age-related cell death and that this effect is most pronounced among aged subjects with documented deficits in hippocampal-dependent learning and memory.[102,103] The surprising outcome of investigations using newer stereological methods was that the total number of principal neurons (i.e., the granule cells of the dentate gyrus and pyramidal neurons in fields CA2, CA3, and CA1) is entirely preserved in the aged hippocampus. Similar results have been observed in all species examined, including rats, monkeys, and humans.[104–107] Data from animal models of cognitive aging have been particularly compelling, demonstrating that hippocampal neuron number remains normal even among aged individuals with pronounced learning and memory deficits indicative of hippocampal dysfunction[104–106]

BOX 51.1

THE OPTICAL FRACTIONATOR STEREOLOGICAL METHOD

Figure 51.9 shows the key features of a new stereological technique designed to provide accurate and efficient estimates of total neuron number in a brain region of interest. The hippocampal formation of the rhesus monkey brain is used as an example. The method consists of counting the number of neurons in a known and representative fraction of a neuroanatomically defined structure in such a way that each cell has an equal probability of being counted. The sum of the neurons counted, multiplied by the reciprocal of the fraction of the structure that was sampled, provides an estimate of total neuron number.

Serial histological sections are prepared through the entire rostrocaudal extent of the hippocampus and stained by routine methods for visualizing neurons microscopically. An evenly spaced series of the sections is then chosen for analysis (schematically represented by dotted lines at top left). This first level of sampling, the "section fraction," is therefore defined as the fraction of the total number of sections examined. For example, if every tenth section through the hippocampus is analyzed, the section fraction equals 1/10.

The appropriate sections are then surveyed according to a systematic sampling scheme, typically carried out

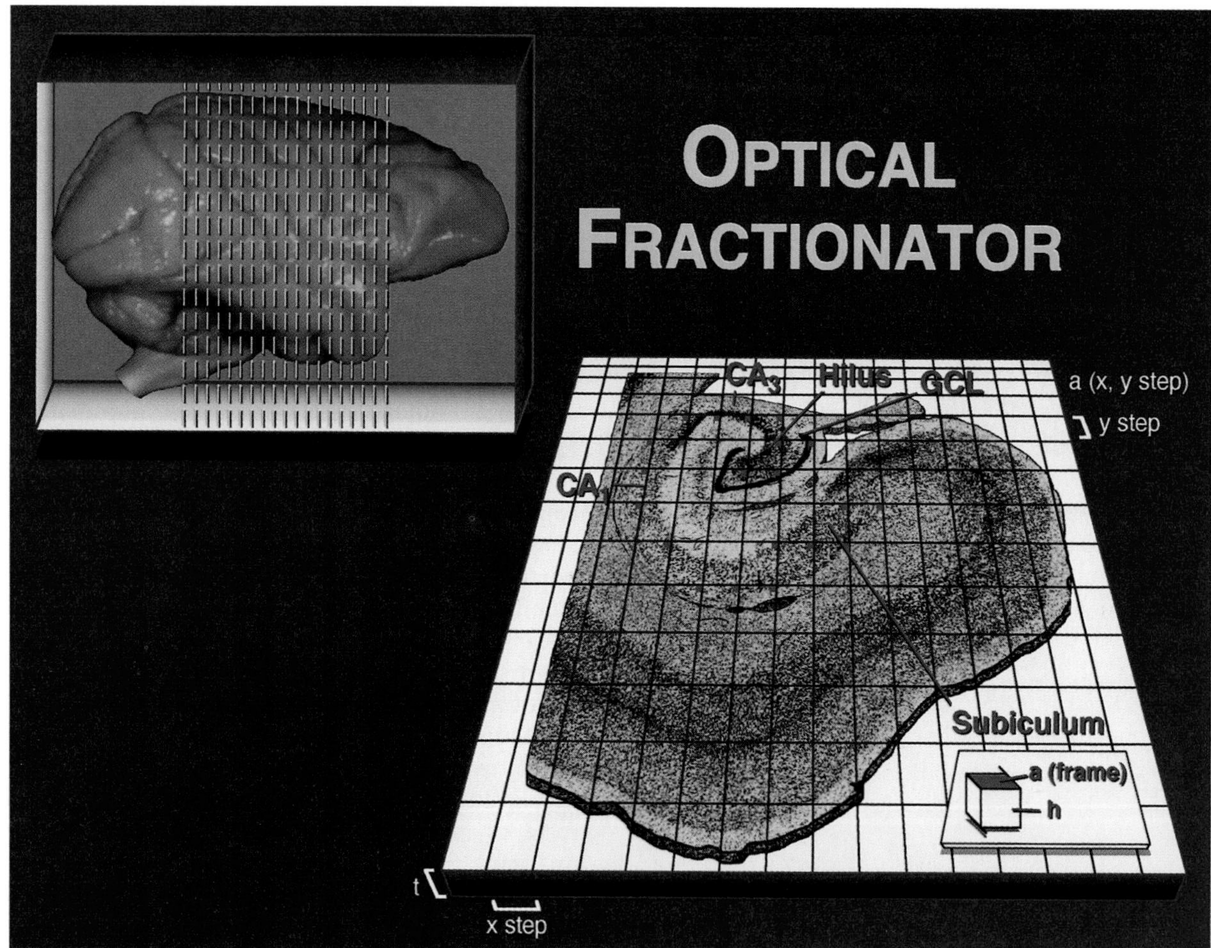

FIGURE 51.9 Illustration of optical fractionator. Original illustration design by P. R. Rapp and J. P. Stanisic.

on a microscope with a motorized, computer-controlled stage. The lower right panel illustrates this design in which the microscope stage is moved in even X and Y intervals, and neurons are counted within the areas defined by the small red squares. The second level of the fractionator sampling scheme is therefore the "area fraction," or the fraction of the XY step (XY_{area}) from which the cell counts are derived ("a" in the inset).

The last level of sampling is counting cells only within a known fraction of the total section thickness, avoiding a variety of known errors introduced by including the cut surfaces of the histological preparations in the analysis. This is accomplished using a high-magnification microscope objective (usually 100×) with a shallow focal depth. In the illustration provided, the "thickness fraction" is defined as h/t. Neurons are counted as they first come into focus, according to an unbiased counting rule, called the "optical disector," that eliminates the possibility of counting a given cell more than once.

Finally, the total neuron number in the region of interest (N) is estimated as the sum of the neurons counted (ΣQ^-), multiplied by the reciprocal of the three sampling fractions; the "section fraction," "area fraction," and the "thickness fraction." For the present example, total estimated neuron number is given by the formula

$$N = (\Sigma Q^-) \cdot (10/1) \cdot (XY_{area}/a) \cdot (t/h).$$

(Fig. 51.10). In a recent experiment, for example, young and aged rats were tested on a spatial learning task that is known to require the functional integrity of the hippocampus. As illustrated in Fig. 51.10, subsequent stereological analysis revealed that the numbers of principal hippocampal neurons were comparable in young subjects and in aged rats with or without spatial learning and memory deficits. These findings indicate that hippocampal neuron loss is not inevitable, as was traditionally assumed, and that neuron death in the hippocampus fails to account for age-related learning and memory impairment.

Age-Related Neuron Loss Preferentially Targets Subcortical Brain Systems

Quantitative data relating neuron number and aging are not yet available for all brain systems. Nevertheless, like the hippocampus, a variety of other cortical regions also appear to be relatively spared from significant age-related neuron loss. These regions include the dorsolateral aspects of the prefrontal cortex and unimodal visual areas. Aging does result in substantial *subcortical* cell loss, however, particularly among neurochemically specific classes of neurons that send ascending projections to widespread cortical regions. The loss of cholinergic neurons in the basal forebrain has been studied intensively because this system is the site of profound degeneration in pathological disorders of aging such as Alzheimer disease.[108] A smaller loss of these acetylcholine-containing neurons, affecting cell groups that project to the hippocampus, amygdala, and neocortex, is also observed during normal aging.[109–112] Cholinergic cell loss might disrupt the information-processing functions of these target regions, and significant correlations between the magnitude of loss and behavioral impairment have been documented in aged individuals.[111] Although cholinergic abnormalities alone are unlikely to account for the full profile of age-related cognitive decline,[113,114] combined with changes in other neurochemically specific projection systems,[115,116] subcortical contributions to normal cognitive aging may be substantial. These findings also highlight the concept that neuron loss during normal aging preferentially affects subcortical brain structures. Defining the cell biological mechanisms that confer this regionally selective vulnerability or protection remains a significant challenge.

Electrophysiological Markers Correlate with Functional Alteration in the Aged Hippocampus

To complement research on the structural integrity of the aged brain, physiological studies in rodent models have looked for changes in the functional and computational properties of neurons that might contribute to cognitive decline. These studies have focused prominently on the hippocampus, because of the known role of this structure in normal learning and memory and because forms of memory dependent on the hippocampus are frequently compromised during normal aging. In addition, cellular models of learning-related plasticity [e.g., long-term potentiation (LTP)] have been particularly well characterized in the hippocampus, so that there is a useful background against which to examine the effects of aging (see Chapter 55 for a discussion of LTP). A prominent theme emerging from this area of research is that age-related changes in hippocampal physiology are highly selective. Significant parameters generally unaffected by aging include the resting potential, input resistance, and the amplitude

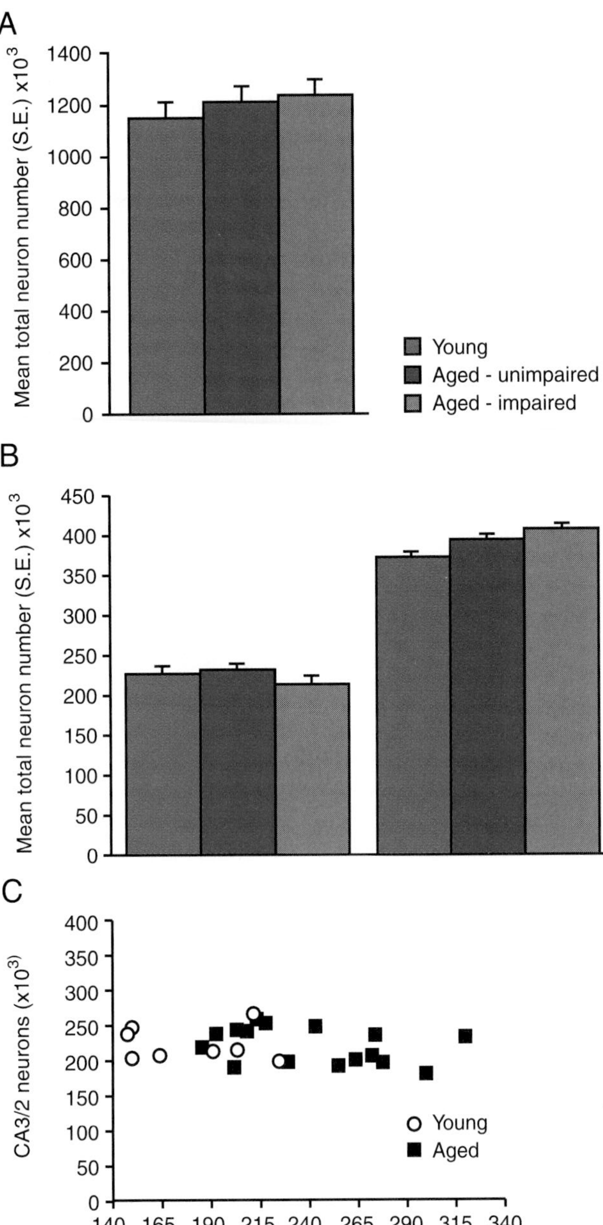

FIGURE 51.10 Estimated total neuron number in the principal cell layers of the hippocampus for behaviorally characterized young and aged rats. The total neuron number values illustrated are for one hippocampus from each brain. Prior to histological evaluation, subjects were tested on the spatial, hippocampal-dependent version of the Morris water maze. Half of the aged rats exhibited substantial learning deficits (aged-impaired); the other half performed within the range of learning scores for the young group (aged-unimpaired). (A) Mean estimated total neuron number (±standard error) in the granule cell layer for young, aged-unimpaired, and aged-impaired rats. Average granule cell number is comparable across the groups. (B) Mean estimated total neuron number (±SE) in the CA3/2 (left) and CA1 (right) pyramidal cell fields of the hippocampus for behaviorally characterized young and aged rats. Neuron number does not differ with age or cognitive status. (C) Scatter plot of total neuron number in the CA3/2 hippocampal field for individual rats plotted as a function of spatial learning scores (lower values indicate better learning). Neuron number is stable with age and across a broad range of learning capacities. Adapted from Rapp and Gallagher.[104]

and duration of evoked action potentials among principal hippocampal neurons (reviewed in Barnes;[117] Barnes *et al.*[118]).

Although many functions of the hippocampus are preserved, several aspects of its physiology and plasticity are compromised. For example, although the stimulus intensity necessary to induce maximal LTP is comparable in the young and aged hippocampus, and while the peak magnitude of the potentiated response remains normal, LTP decays to prepotentiated baseline levels more rapidly in aged subjects. This enhanced rate of decay is significantly correlated with the rapid forgetting that aged subjects exhibit on a test of spatial memory requiring the functional integrity of the hippocampus.[119] The aged hippocampus also shows alterations in location-specific firing[120,121] and abnormally inflexible coding of the relationships between task-relevant stimuli.[122]

Thus, although many aspects of hippocampal physiology are preserved, the functional organization of the hippocampus is substantially altered during normal aging. Future study is needed to determine whether these features of hippocampal aging originate intrinsically or occur as a result of disrupted information processing in other brain systems that project to the hippocampus. Research focusing on the connectional characteristics of the hippocampus provide a basis for addressing this issue.

Hippocampal Connectivity Is Prominently Affected during Normal Aging

The entorhinal cortex originates a major source of cortical input to the hippocampus, projecting via the perforant path to synapse on the distal dendrites of the dentate gyrus granule cells, in outer portions of the molecular layer. Proximal dendrites of the granule cells, in contrast, receive an intrinsic hippocampal input arising from neurons in the hilar region of the dentate gyrus. This strict laminar segregation, where there are two nonoverlapping inputs of known origin, provides a useful model for exploring potential age-related changes in hippocampal connectivity. Ultrastructural studies have demonstrated that the number of a morphologically distinct subset of synapses is depleted in both inner and outer portions of the molecular layer during aging in the rat.[123] Importantly, the magnitude of this loss in the termination zone of the entorhinal cortex is greatest among aged subjects with documented deficits on tasks sensitive to hippocampal damage and in older animals that display impaired LTP and deficits in other physiological measures of hippocampal cellular plasticity.[124]

The same circuitry has been examined in the aged monkey using confocal laser microscopy to quantify the density of different glutamate receptor subtypes in the molecular layer.[125] Aged subjects display a substantial reduction in labeling for the NMDA receptor subtype, and this effect is anatomically restricted to outer portions of the molecular layer that receive entorhinal cortical input. The density of non-NMDA glutamate receptors is largely preserved. Although the relationship of this change to the status of hippocampal information processing has not been directly evaluated, these findings are potentially significant because NMDA receptor activity is known to play a critical role in mechanisms of plasticity that are thought to constitute the cellular basis of learning and memory. This background leads to the testable prediction that the magnitude of NMDA receptor alteration in aged individuals might correlate with the degree of age-related impairment in learning and memory supported by the hippocampus. Studies of this sort, combining behavioral and neurobiological assessment in the same subjects, are an increasingly prominent focus of research on normal aging.

Summary

The traditional view of normal brain aging is that cognitive decline is a consequence of mild and diffusely distributed neuron death. Recent evidence demonstrates that neuron loss is more anatomically selective and smaller in magnitude than previously assumed, and many cortical regions implicated in normal cognitive function display little or no significant neuron loss during aging. Prominent cell death occurs among a number of neurochemically specific subcortical systems, however, and information processing in cortical target regions could be substantially compromised as a consequence. Electrophysiological investigations confirm that neuronal coding and plasticity are altered in the aged hippocampus, and in some cases, these changes are tightly coupled to behavioral measures of hippocampal function. Although the neurobiological basis of these effects remains to be defined in detail, alterations in the normal connectivity of memory-related brain systems are likely to play a significant role.

We now have a solid foundation of descriptive information on the nature, severity, and distribution of neural alterations in the aged brain. The fundamental mechanisms responsible for the known behavioral and neurobiological signatures of normal aging, however, remain to be defined. Molecular biological techniques are revealing an increasingly broad profile of age-related changes with significant implications for cell structure and function.[126] Although it has sometimes proved challenging to incorporate these findings within a neural systems analysis, molecular, neurobiological, and behavioral approaches may soon converge on a more unified understanding of normal cognitive aging.

DEMENTIAS: PATHOLOGIES OF AGING

Dementia is a general term used to describe a chronic and substantial decline in two or more areas of cognitive function. This decline is in contrast to amnesia or aphasia, for example, where a patient shows a severe and striking deficit in only one area of function (memory and language, respectively). Approximately 50 disorders are known to cause dementia.[127] Most dementias are progressive, but some dementias are nonprogressive (e.g., alcoholic dementia).

The onset and progression of the patient's difficulties differ greatly among the major dementing disorders. Most of the dementias have an insidious onset and develop slowly and gradually; these include Alzheimer disease, Huntington disease, and frontotemporal dementia. The most virulent dementing disorder, Creutzfeldt–Jakob disease, develops insidiously, but is known for its rapid rate of progression from onset to death (often only 1 year). In vascular dementia, the initial symptoms develop acutely, but because multiple cerebral infarcts (large or small) are the cause of the cognitive decline, the ultimate clinical picture can take many years to develop, in a stepwise and stuttering fashion. The pattern of spared and impaired function in the early stages of each disorder is directly related to the neuropathological abnormalities that underlie it.

Alzheimer Disease Is the Most Widely Occurring and Widely Studied Form of Dementia

First described in 1907 by Alois Alzheimer, Alzheimer disease was originally thought to be a rare disorder affecting only people in the presenile age range (i.e., under the age of 65). It is now recognized as the most common cause of dementia, and alone is responsible for about 50% of all dementias; an additional 15–20% of dementias have combined Alzheimer and vascular pathology. The prevalence of the disease is directly related to age. It can occur in the fourth decade of life but is extraordinarily rare at this age. The prevalence then increases logarithmically with each succeeding decade, and over the age of 85 at least 1 person in 4 is afflicted.[128] Because persons over 85 form the most rapidly growing portion of the population, Alzheimer disease represents a major health problem.

The pathological hallmarks of Alzheimer disease are the senile plaques and neurofibrillary tangles that Alzheimer first reported. Senile plaques are spherical and usually many times larger than a single neuron. They typically contain a central core of amyloid surrounded by degenerating neuronal processes. Neurofibrillary tangles are twisted abnormal filaments composed of the protein tau and other cytoskeletal proteins. The accumulation of plaques and tangles, and the progression of other pathological processes, leads to extensive neuronal loss, which is usually preceded by synapse loss.

In the early stages of disease, pathological changes are most evident in the perforant pathway of the hippocampal formation.[129] For example, in mildly impaired patients, layers 2 and 4 of the entorhinal cortex have a 60 and 40% loss of neurons, respectively.[130] These losses are entirely consistent with the fact that a memory problem, consisting of difficulty retaining new information over brief delays, is the most common symptom in mildly impaired patients. Problems with planning and set shifting (i.e., difficulties with "executive function" abilities) also occur early in the course of disease. This situation may be the result of the loss of neocortical synapses and long cortico–cortical projection systems[131] seen in Alzheimer disease; the partial degeneration of an intracortical projection system could produce difficulties in tasks that require the rapid and simultaneous integration of multiple types of information.

Following neuronal loss in specific cortical and subcortical regions, a number of neurochemical abnormalities become evident in Alzheimer disease. These abnormalities are related to the cholinergic system, the noradrenergic system, and the serotonergic system and arise from loss of cells in the basal forebrain, the locus coeruleus, and the dorsal raphe nucleus, respectively. As these abnormalities accumulate and spread throughout the brain, the patient shows increasing difficulty with cognitive function and ultimately a loss of all major cognitive abilities, including memory, language, spatial ability, and executive function.

Genetics Plays a Role in Alzheimer Disease

Genetics plays an important but complex role in the development of Alzheimer disease. To date, four genes

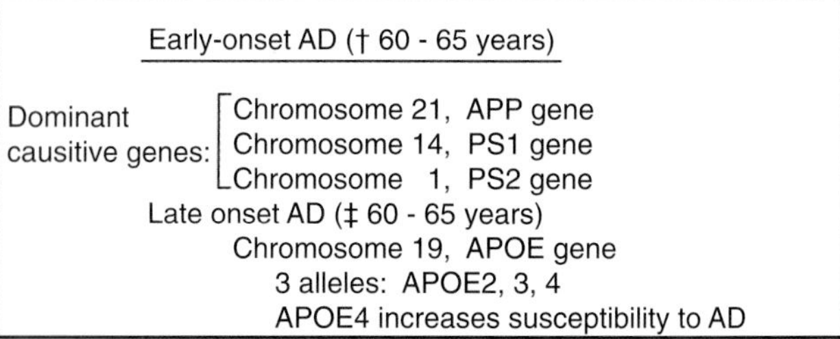

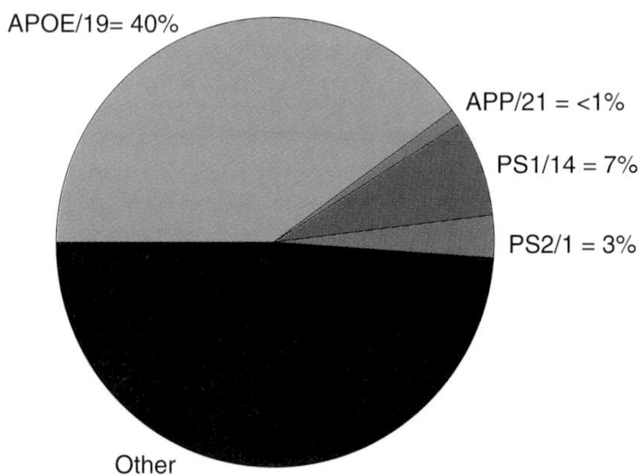

FIGURE 51.11 Percentage of cases of Alzheimer disease in which a specific genetic abnormality is implicated.

have been associated with the development of the disease (Fig. 51.11). Three of these (on chromosomes 21, 14, and 1[132–134]) pertain to the development of early-onset AD (onset prior to age 60 or 65). Each of these three early-onset genes acts as a dominant, causative gene. Only one gene, the apolipoprotein E gene (*APOE*, on chromosome 19), has been associated primarily with the much more common late-onset form of Alzheimer disease (onset after age 60 to 65).[135,136] The apolipoprotein E gene has three alleles, designated 2, 3, and 4. Allele 4 has been shown in numerous studies to be associated with Alzheimer disease. The general consensus is that *APOE4* is acting as a risk factor for Alzheimer disease, rather than as an etiologic gene, and that several more genes related to the development of Alzheimer disease will be identified.

Important clues to the cellular and molecular basis of Alzheimer disease are being provided by genetic, pathological, and biochemical studies. Currently, various lines of evidence point to an important role for amyloid precursor protein (β-APP), the precursor of the β-amyloid in senile plaques. It is possible that the β-amyloid protein is directly responsible for the abnormal accumulation of the fibrillar material that kills neurons, or conversely that β-amyloid is important in protecting neurons from the accumulated effects of injury (as a result of aging, environmental insults, etc.).

Summary

This chapter has examined efforts to relate development over the life span to changes in the nervous system. In early development, profound changes in sensory systems, frontal areas, and language areas underlie many new achievements of the infant. These functions are clearly subject to developmental pathologies that may delay the emergence of complex functions such as language and organization rather than the number of neurons in many brain areas. Changes in the hippocampus may underlie difficulties in memory in normal aging. In pathologies such as Alzheimer disease, more profound changes in behavior emerge, probably first due to damage to the temporal lobe, but later throughout the cortex. These findings all indicate the relation between specific brain changes and differences found in development.

References

1. Conel, J. L. (1939–1963). *The Postnatal Development of the Human Cerebral Cortex,* Vols. I–VI. Harvard University Press, Cambridge, MA.
2. Rabinowicz, T. (1979). The differentiate maturation of the human cerebral cortex. In *Human Growth 3 Neurobiology and Nutrition* (F. Falkner and J. M. Tanner, eds.), pp. 97–123. Plenum Press, New York.
3. Witelson, S. F., and Pallie, W. (1973). Left hemisphere specialization for language in the newborn: Neuroanatomical evidence of asymmetry. *Brain* **96:** 641–646.
4. Wada, J. A., Clarke, R., and Hamm, A. (1975). Cerebral hemispheric asymmetry in humans. *Arch. Neurol.* **32:** 239–246.
5. Dooling, E. C., Chi, J. G., and Gilles, F. H. (1983). Telencephalic development: Changing gyral patterns. In *The Developing Human Brain* (F. H. Gilles, A. Leviton and E. C. Dooling, eds.), pp. 94–104. John Wright, Boston.
6. Yakovlev, P. I., and Lecours, A. R. (1967). The myelogenetic cycles of regional maturation of the brain. In *Regional Development of the Brain in Early Life* (A. Minkowsky, ed.), pp. 3–70. Blackwells, Oxford.
7. Huttenlocher, P. R., Courten, C., Garey, L., and Van Der Loos, D. (1982). Synaptogenesis in human visual cortex-evidence for synapse elimination during normal development. *Neurosci. Lett.* **33:** 247–252.
8. Sauer, N., Kammaradt, G., Krauthausen, I., Kretschmann, H. T., Lange, H. W., and Wingert, F. (1983). Qualitative and quantitative development of the visual cortex in man. *J. Comp. Neurol.* **214:** 441–450.
9. Michel, A. E., and Garey, L. J. (1984). The development of dendritic spines in the human visual cortex. *Human Neurobiol.* **3:** 223–227.
10. Becker, L. E., Armstrong, D. L., Chan, F., and Wood, M. M. (1984). Dendritic development in human occipital cortical neurons. *Dev. Brain Res.* **13:** 117–124.
11. Sidman, R. L., and Rakic, P. (1973). Neuronal migration with special reference to developing human brain: A review. *Brain Res.* **62:** 1–35.
12. Schade, J. P., and Van Groenigen, W. B. (1961). Structural organization of the human cerebral cortex. 1: Maturation of the middle frontal gyrus. *Acta Anat.* **47:** 74–111.
13. Scheibel, A. B. (1993). Dendritic structure and language development. In *Developmental Neurocognition: Speech and Face Processing in the First Year of Life* (B. Deboysson-Bardies, S. de Schonen, P. Jusczyk, P. McNeilage, and J. Morton, eds.), pp. 51–62. Kluwer Academic, Boston.
14. Huttenlocher, P. R. (1990). Morphometric study of human cerebral cortex development. *Neuropsychologia* **28:** 517–527.
15. Chugani, H. T., Phelps, M. E., and Mazziotta, J. C. (1987). Positron emission tomography study of human brain functional development. *Ann. Neurol.* **22:** 487–497.
16. Deleted.
17. Huttenlocher, P. R. (1979). Synaptic density in human frontal cortex-developmental changes and effects of aging. *Brain Res.* **163:** 195–205.
18. Cragg, B. G. (1967). The density of synapses and neurons in the motor and visual areas of the cerebral cortex. *J. Anat.* **101:** 639–654.
19. Maudsley, H. (1876). *The Physiology and Pathology of Mind.* Macmillan, London.
20. Changeux, J. P., and Danchin, A. (1976). Selective stabilisation of developing synapses as a mechanism for the specification of neuronal networks. *Nature* **264:** 705–712.
21. Jacobson, M., and Abrahams, R. M. (1978). *Developmental Neurobiology,* 2nd ed., pp. 302–307. Plenum, New York.
22. Deleted.
23. Galambos, R. (1982). Maturation of auditory evoked potentials. In *Clinical Application of Cerebral Evoked Potentials in Pediatric Medicine* (G. A. Chiarenza and D. Papakostopoulos, eds.), pp. 323–343. Excerpta Medica, Amsterdam.
24. Courchesne, E. (1978). Neurophysiological correlates of cognitive development: Changes in long-latency event-related potentials from childhood to adulthood. *Electroencephalog. Clin. Neurophysiol.* **45:** 468–482.
25. Holcomb, P. J., Coffey, S. A., and Neville, H. J. (1992). Visual and auditory sentence processing: A development analysis using event-related brain potentials. *Dev. Neuropsychol.* **8:** 203–241.
26. Neville, H. J. (1995). Developmental specificity in neurocognitive development in humans. In *The Cognitive Neuroscience* (M. Gazzaniga, ed.), pp. 219–231. MIT Press, Cambridge, MA.
27. Courchesne, E. (1990). Chronology of postnatal human brain development: Event-related potential, positron emission tomography, myelinogenesis, and synaptogenesis studies. In *Event-Related Brain Potentials* (J. Rohrbaugh, R. Parasuraman and R. Johnson, eds.), Chap. 14, pp. 210–214. Oxford University Press, New York.
28. Held, R., Birch, E., and Gwiazda, J. (1980). Steroacuity of human infants. *Proc. Natl. Acad. Sci. USA* **77:** 5572–5774.
29. Posner, M. I., and Rothbart, M. K. (1980). The development of attentional mechanisms. *Nebraska Symp. Motivation* **28:** 1–52.
30. Leuba, G., and Gary (1987). Evolution of neuronal numerical density in the developing and aging human visual cortex. *Human Neurobiol.* **6:** 11–18.
31. Johnson, M. H. (1990). Cortical maturation and the development of visual attention in early infancy. *J. Cognit. Neurosci.* **2:** 81–94.
32. Teller, D. Y. (1983). Scotopic vision, color vision and stereopsis in infants. *Curr. Eye Res.* **2:** 199–210.
33. Atkinson, J. (1992). Early visual development: Differential functioning of parvocellular and magnocellular pathways. *Eye* **6:** 129–135.
34. Gelbart, S. S., Hoty, C. S., Jastrebski, G., and Marg, E. (1982). Long-term visual results in bilateral congenital cataracts. *Am. J. Ophthamol.* **93:** 615–621.
35. Atkinson, J. (1993). The Cambridge assessment and screening

of vision in 'high risk' infants and young children. In *At-Risk Infants: Interventions, Families, and Research* (S. Harel and N. J. Anastasiow, eds.). Paul H. Brookes Publishing Co.

36. Sherman, S. M., and Spear, P. D. (1982). Organization of visual pathways in normal and visually deprived cats. *Physiol. Rev.* **62:** 738–855.
37. Garraghty, P. E., and Sur, M. (1993). Competitive interactions influencing the development of retinal exonal arbors in cat lateral geniculate nucleus. *Psychol. Rev.* **73:** 529–545.
38. Garraghty, P. E., Frost, D. O., and Sur, M. (1987). The morphology of retinogeniculate X- and Y-cell axonal arbors in dark-reared cats. *Exp. Brain Res.* **66:** 115–127.
39. Hickey, T. L. (1981). The developing visual system. *Trends Neurosci.* **Feb.,** 41–44.
40. Chalupa, L. M., and Dreher, B. (1991). High precision systems require high precision "Blueprints": A new view regarding the formation of connections in the mammalian visual system. *J. Cognit. Neurosci.* **3**(3): 209–219.
41. Sur, M., Pallas, S., and Roe, A. (1990). Cross-modal plasticity in cortical development: Differentiation and specification of sensory neocortex. *Trends Neurosci.* **13:** 227–233.
42. Frost, D. (1989). Transitory neuronal connections in normal development and disease. In *Brain and Reading* (C. Von Eula, ed.). MacMillan, London.
43. Frost, D. (1990). Sensory processing by novel, experimentally induced cross-modal circuits. In *The Development and Neural Bases of Higher Cognitive Function* (A. Diamond, ed.), pp. 92–112. New York Academy of Sciences, New York.
44. Rauschecker, J. (1995). Compensatory plasticity and sensory substitution in the cerebral cortex. *Trends Neurosci.* **18:** 36–43.
45. Neville, H. J., Schmidt, A., and Kutas, M. (1983). Altered visual evoked potentials in congenitally deaf adults. *Brain Res.* **266:** 127–132.
46. Veraart, C., DeVolder, A. G., Wanet-Defalque, M. C., Bol, A., Michel, C., and Goffinet, A. M. (1990). Glucose utilization in human visual cortex is abnormally elevated in blindness of early onset but decreased in blindness of late onset. *Brain Res.* **510:** 114–121.
47. Uhl, F., Franzen, P., Lindinger, G., Lang, W., and Deccke, L. (1991). On the functionality of the visually deprived occipital cortex in early blind persons. *Neurosci. Lett.* **124:** 256–259.
48. Kujala, T., Alho, K., Paavilaninen, P., Summala, H., and Näätänen, R. (1992). Neural plasticity in processing of sound locations by the early blind: An event-related potential study. *Electroencephalogr. Clin. Neurophysiol.* **84:** 469–472.
49. Kujala, T., Huotilainen, M., Sinkkonen, J., Ahonen, A., Alho, K., Hämäläinen, M. Ilmoniemi, R., Kajola, M., Knuutila, J., Lavikainen, J., Salonen, O., Simola, J., Standerskjöld-Nordenstam, C., Tiitinen, H., Tissari, S., and Näätänen, R. (1995). Visual cortex activation in blind humans during sound discrimination. *Neurosci. Lett.* **183:** 143–146.
50. Gutterman, E. (1942). Aphasia in children. *Brain* **65:** 205–219.
51. Smith, A. (1966). Speech and other functions after left dominant hemispherectomy. *J. Neurol. Neurosurg. Psych.* **29:** 467–471.
52. Lenneberg, E. H. (1967). *Biological Foundations of Language.* Wiley, New York.
53. Woods, B. T., and Teuber, H. L. (1978). Changing patterns of childhood aphasia. *Ann. Neurol.* **3:** 273–280.
54. Bishop, D. V. M. (1983). Linguistic impairment after left hemidecortication for infantile hemiplegia: A reappraisal. *Q. J. Exp. Psychol.* **35A:** 199–207.
55. Aram, D. B., Ekelman, B. L., Rose, D. F., and Whitaker, H. A. (1985). Verbal and cognitive sequelae of unilateral lesions acquired in early childhood. *J. Clin. Exp. Neuropsychol.* **7:** 55–78.
56. Thal, D. J., Marchman, J., Stiles, D., Aram, D., Trauner, D., Nass, R., and Bates, E. (1991). Early lexical development in children with focal brain injury. *Brain Language* **40:** 491–527.
57. Stromswold, K. (1995). The cognitive and neural bases of language acquisition. In *The Cognitive Neurosciences* (M. Gazzaniga, ed.), pp. 855–870. MIT Press, Cambridge, MA.
58. Curtiss, S. (1977). *Genie: A Psycholinguistic Study of a Modern-Day "Wild Child".* Academic Press, New York.
59. Curtiss, S., (1989). The independence and task-specificity of language. In *Interaction in Human Development* (A. Bornstein and J. Bruner, eds.). Erlbaum, Hillsdale, NJ.
60. Johnson, J. S., and Newport, E. L. (1991). Critical period effects on universal properties of language: The status of subjacency in the acquisition of a second language. *Cognition* **39:** 215–258.
61. Weber-Fox, C. M., and Neville, H. J. (1996). Maturational constraints on functional specializations for language processing: ERP and behavioral evidence in bilingual speakers. *J. Cognit. Neurosci.* **8**(3): 231–256.
62. Neville, H. J., Mills, D. L., and Lawson, D. S. (1992). Fractionating language: Different neural subsystems with different sensitive periods. *Cereb. Cortex* **2:** 244–258.
63. Mills, D. L., Coffey, S. A., and Neville, H. J. (1993). Language acquisition and cerebral specialization in 20-month-old infants. *J. Cognit. Neurosci.* **5:** 317–334.
64. Poizner, H., Klima, E. S., and Bellugi, U. (1987). *What the Hands Reveal About the Brain.* MIT Press, Cambridge, MA.
65. Neville, H. J., Coffey, S. A., Lawson, D. Fischer, A., Emmorey, K., and Bellugi, U. (1997). Neural systems mediating American Sign Language: Effects of sensory experiment and age of acquisition. *Brain Language* **57:** 285–308.
66. Tallal, P. (1987). Dysphasia, developmental. In *Encyclopedia of Neuroscience* (G. Adelman, ed.), pp. 351–353, Vol. I. Birkhauser Press, Boston.
67. Hurst, J. A., Baraitser, M., Auger, E., Graham, F., and Norell, S. (1990). An extended family with a dominantly inherited speech disorder. *Dev. Med. Child. Neurol.* **32:** 352–355.
68. Tallal, P., Ross, R., and Curtiss, S. (1989). Familial aggregation in specific language impairment. *J. Speech Hear. Disord.* **54:** 173–176.
69. Robinson (1987). Introduction and overview. In *Proceedings of the First International Symposium on Specific Speech and Language Disorders in Children.* AFASIC, London.
70. Bishop, D. V. M. (1994). Is specific language impairment a valid diagnostic category? Genetic and psycholinguistic evidence. *Philos. Trans. R. Soc.* **346:** 1315–1326.
71. Geschwind, N., and Levitsky, W. (1968). Human brain: Left-right asymmetries in temporal speech region. *Science* **161:** 186–187.
72. Kulynych, J. J., Vladar, K., Jones, D. W., and Weinberger, D. R. (1994). Gender differences in the normal lateralization of the supratemporal cortex: MRI surface-rendering morphometry of Heschl's gyrus and the planum temproale. *Cerebral Cortex* **4:** 107–118.
73. Teszner, D., Tzavaras, A., Gruner, J., and Hécaen, H. (1972). L'asymmétrie droite-gauche du planum temporale: A propos de l'étude anatomique de 100 cervaeux. *Rev. Neurol.* **126:** 444–449.

73a. Jernigan, T. L., Hesselink, J. R., Sowell, E., and Tallal, P. (1991). Cerebral structure on magnetic resonance imaging in language- and learning-impaired children. *Arch. Neurol.* **48:** 539–545.

74. Tallal, P., and Piercy, M. (1973). Defects of non-verbal auditory perception in children with developmental asphasia. *Nature* **241:** 468–469.
75. Tallal, P., Miller, S., and Fitch, R. H. (1993). Neurobiological

basis of speech: A case for the preeminence of temporal processing. In *Temporal Information Processing in the Nervous System, with Special Reference to Dyslexia and Dysphasia* (P. Tallal, A. M. Galaburda, R. Llinas, and C. von Euler, eds.), pp. 27–47. New York Academy of Sciences, New York.
76. Livingstone, M. S., Rosen, G. D., Drislane, F. W., and Galaburda, A. M. (1991). Physiological and anatomical evidence for a magnocellular defect in developmental dyslexia. *Proc. Natl. Acad. Sci., USA* **88:** 7943–7947.
77. Galaburda, A. M., Menard, M. T., Rosen, G. D., and Livingstone, M. S. (1994). Evidence for aberrant auditory anatomy in developmental dyslexia. *Proc. Natl. Acad. Sci. USA* **91:** 8010–8013.
78. Fitch, R. H., Tallal, P., Brown, C., Galaburda, A., and Rosen, G. (1994). Induced microgyria and auditory temporal processing in rats: A model for language impairment? *Cereb. Cortex* **4:** 260–270.
79. Johnston, R. B., Stark, R. E., Mellits, E. D., and Tallal, P. (1981). Neurological status of language-impaired and normal children. *Ann. Neurol.* **10:** 159–163.
80. Katz, W. F., Curtiss, S., and Tallal, P. (1992). Rapid automatized naming and gesture by normal and language-impaired children. *Brain Lang.* **43:** 623–641.
81. Tallal, P. l., Stark, R., Kallman, C., and Mellits, D. (1981). A reexamination of some nonverbal perceptual abilities of language-impaired and normal children as a function of age and sensory modality. *J. Speech Hearing Res.* **24:** 351–357.
82. Tallal, P. l., Stark, R. E.,, and Mellits, D. (1985). Identification of language-impaired children on the basis of rapid perception and production skills. *Brain Language* **25:** 314–322.
83. Wang, P. P., and Bellugi, U. (1993). Williams syndrome, Down syndrome, and cognitive neuroscience. *Am. J. Dis. Child.* **147:** 1246–1251.
84. Bellugi, U., Bihrle, A., Tauner, D., Jernigan, T., and Doherty, S. (1990). Neuropsychological, neurological, and neuroanatomical profile of Williams Syndrome children. *Am. J. Med. Genet. Supp.* **6:** 115–125.
85. Bellugi, U., Sabo, H., and Vaid, J. (1988). Spatial deficits in children with Williams Syndrome. In *Spatial Cognition: Brain Bases and Development* (J. Stiles-Davis, M. Kritchevsky, and U. Bellugi, eds.), pp. 273–298. Erlbaum, Hillsdale, NJ.
86. Ewart, A. K., Morris, C. A., Atkinson, D., *et al.* (1993). *Nature Genet.* **5:** 11–16.
87. Morris, C. A., Thomas, I. T., and Greenberg, F. (1993). Williams syndrome: Autosomal dominant inheritance. *Am. J. Med. Genet.* **47:** 478–481.
88. Jernigan, T. L., and Bellugi, U. (1990). Anomalous brain morphology on magnetic resonance images in Williams Syndrome. *Arch. Neurol.* **47:** 529–533.
89. Jernigan, T. L., Bellugi, U., Sowell, E., Doherty, S., and Hesselingk, J. R. (1993). Cerebral morphological distinctions between Williams and Down syndromes. *Arch. Neurol.* **50:** 186–191.
90. Wang, P. P., Hesselink, J. R., Jernigan, T. L., Doherty, S., and Bellugi, U. (1992). Specific neurobehavioral profile of Williams' syndrome is associated with neocerebellar hemispheric preservation. *Neurology* **42:** 199–2002.
91. Shaywitz, S. E., Escobar, M. D., Shaywitz, B. A., Fletcher, J. M., and Makuch, R. (1992). Evidence that dyslexia may represent the lower tail of a normal distribution of reading ability. *N. Engl. J. Med.* **326:** 145–150.
92. Liederman, J., and Flannery, K. (1994). Male prevalence for reading disability is found in a large sample free from ascertainment bias. *Pediatric News.*
93. Gualetieri, T., and Hicks, R. (1985). An immunoreactive theory of selective male affliction. *Behav. Brain Sci.* **8:** 427–441.
94. Galaburda, A. M., Sherman, G. F., Rosen, G. D., Aboitiz, F., and Geschwind, N. (1985). Development dyslexia: Four consecutive cases with cortical anomalies. *Ann. Neurol.* **18:** 222–233.
95. Fitch, R. H., Brown, C. P., Tallal, P., and Rosen, G. (1997). Effects of sex and MK-801 on auditory-processing deficits associated with developmental microgyric lesions in rats. *Behav. Neurosci.* **111:** 404–412.
96. Kimura, D., and Harshman, R. (1984). Sex differences in brain organization for verbal and non-verbal functions. In *Progress in Brain Research* (G. J. DeVries, *et al.*, eds.), Vol. 61. Elsevier Science, Amsterdam.
97. Shaywitz, B. A., Shaywitz, S. E., Pugh, K. R., Constable, R. T., Skudlarski, P., Fulbright, R. K., Bronen, R. A., Fletcher, J. M., Shankweilier, D. P., Katz, L., and Gore, J. C. (1995). Sex differences in the functional organization of the brain for language. *Nature* **373:** 607–609.
98. Brody, H. (1955). Organization of the cerebral cortex III. A study of aging in the human cerebral cortex. *J. Comp. Neurol.* **102:** 511–556.
99. Brody, H. (1970). Structural changes in the aging nervous system. *Interdiscipl. Topics Gerontol.* **7:** 9–21.
100. Coleman, P. D., and Flood, D. G. (1987). Neuron numbers and dendritic extent in normal aging and Alzheimer's disease. *Neurobiol. Aging* **8:** 521–545.
101. West, M. J. (1993). New stereological methods for counting neurons. *Neurobiol. Aging* **14:** 275–285.
102. Issa, A. M., Rowe, W., Gauthier, S., and Meaney, M. J. (1990). Hypothalamic-pituitary-adrenal activity in aged, cognitively impaired and cognitively unimpaired rats. *J. Neurosci.* **10:** 2347–2354.
103. Meaney, M. J., Aitken, D. H., van Berkel, C., Bhatnager, S., and Sapolsky, R. M. (1988). Effect of neonatal handling on age-related impairments associated with the hippocampus. *Science* **239:** 766–768.
104. Rapp, P. R., and Gallagher, M. (1996). Preserved neuron number in the hippocampus of aged rats with spatial learning deficits. *Proc. Natl. Acad. Sci USA* **93:** 9926–9930.
105. Rapp, P. R. (1995). Cognitive neuroscience perspectives on aging in nonhuman primates. In *Emotion, Memory and Behavior* (T. Nakajima and T. Ono, eds.), pp. 197–211. Japan Scientific Societies Press, Tokyo.
106. Rasmussen, T., Schliemann, T., Sorensen, J. C., Zimmer, J., and West, M. J. (1996). Memory impaired aged rats: No loss of principal hippocampal and subicular neurons. *Neurobiol. Aging* **17:** 143–147.
107. West, M. J. (1993). Regionally specific loss of neurons in the aging human hippocampus. *Neurobiol. Aging* **14:** 287–293.
108. Whitehouse, P. J., Price, D. L., Clark, A. W., Coyle, J. T., and DeLong, M. R. (1981). Alzheimer disease: Evidence for selective loss of cholinergic neurons in the nucleus basalis. *Ann. Neurol.* **10:** 122–126.
109. Armstrong, D. M., Sheffield, R., Buzsaki, G., Chen, K. S., Hersh, L. B., Nearing, B., and Gage, F. H. (1993). Morphologic alterations of choline acetyltransferase-positive neurons in the basal forebrain of aged behaviorally characterized Fisher 344 rats. *Neurobiol. Aging* **14:** 457–470.
110. de Lacalle, S., Iraizoz, I., and Gonzalo, L. M. (1991). Differential changes in cell size and number in topographic subdivisions of human basal nucleus in normal aging. *Neuroscience* **43:** 445–456.
111. Fischer, W., Chen, K. S., Gage, F. H., and Björklund, A. (1991). Progressive decline in spatial learning and integrity of forebrain cholinergic neurons in rats during aging. *Neurobiol. Aging* **13:** 9–23.

112. Stroessner-Johnson, H. M., Rapp, P. R., and Amaral, D. G. (1992). Cholinergic cell loss and hypertrophy in the medial septal nucleus of the behaviorally characterized aged rhesus monkey. *J. Neurosci.* **12:** 1936–1944.
113. Baxter, M. G., Bucci, D. J., Gorman, L. K., Wiley, R. G., and Gallagher, M. (1995). Selective immunotoxic lesions of basal forebrain cholinergic cells: Effects on learning and memory in rats. *Behav. Neurosci.* **109:** 714–722.
114. Gallagher, M., and Colombo, P. (1995). Aging: The cholinergic hypothesis of cognitive decline. *Curr. Opin. Neurobiol.* **5:** 161–168.
115. Gallagher, M., Burwell, R. D., Kodsi, M. H., McKinney, M., Southerland, S., Vella-Rountree, L., and Lewis, M. H. (1990). Markers for biogenic amines in the aged rat brain: Relationship to decline in spatial learning ability. *Neurobiol. Aging* **11:** 507–514.
116. Goldman-Rakic, P. S., and Brown, R. M. (1981). Regional changes of monoamines in cerebral cortex and subcortical structures of aging in rhesus monkey. *Neuroscience* **6:** 177–187.
117. Barnes, C. A. (1994). Normal aging: Regionally specific changes in hippocampal synaptic transmission. *Trends Neurol. Sci.* **17:** 13–18.
118. Barnes, C. A., Treves, A., Rao, G., and Shen, J. (1994). Electrophysiological markers of cognitive aging: Region specificity and computational consequences. *Sem. Neurosci.* **6:** 359–367.
119. Barnes, C. A., and McNaughton, B. L. (1985). An age comparison of rates of acquisition and forgetting of spatial information in relation to long-term enhancement of hippocampal synapses. *Behav. Neurosci.* **99:** 1040–1048.
120. Barnes, C. A., Suster, M. S., Shen, J., and McNaughton, B. L. (1997). Multistability of cognitive maps in the hippocampus of old rats. *Nature* **388:** 272–275.
121. Mizumori, S. J. Y., Lavoie, A. M., and Kalyani, A. (1996). Redistribution of spatial representation in the hippocampus of aged rats performing a spatial memory task. *Behav. Neurosci.* **110,** 1006–1016.
122. Tanila, H., Sipila, P., Shapiro, M., and Eichenbaum, H. (1997). Brain aging: changes in the nature of information coding by the hippocampus. *J. Neurosci.* **17:** 5155–5166.
123. Geinisman, Y., de Toledo-Morrell, L., Morrell, F., Persina, I. S., and Rossi, M. (1992). Age-related loss of axospinous synapses formed by two afferent systems in the rat dentate gyrus as revealed by the unbiased stereological disector technique. *Hippocampus* **2:** 347–444.
124. de Toledo-Morrell, L., Geinisman, Y. , and Morrell, F. (1988). Individual differences in hippocampal synaptic plasticity as a function of aging: Behavioral, electrophysiological and morphological evidence. In *Neural Plasticity: A Lifespan Approach* (T. Petit and G. Ivy, eds.), pp. 283–328. A. R. Liss, New York.
125. Gazzaley, A. H., Siegel, S. J., Kordower, J. H., Mufson, E. J., and Morrison, J. H. (1996). Circuit-specific alterations of N-methyl-D-aspartate receptor subunit 1 in the dentate gyrus of aged monkeys. *Proc. Natl. Acad. Sci. USA* **93:** 3121–3125.
126. Sugaya, K., Chouinard, M., Greene, R., Robbins, M., Personett, D., Kent, D., Gallagher, M., and McKinney, M. (1996). Molecular indices of neuronal and glial plasticity in the hippocampal formation in a rodent model of age-induced spatial learning impairment. *J. Neurosci.* **16:** 3427–3443.
127. Haase, E. (1977). Diseases presenting as dementia. In *Dementia* (C. Wells, ed.), pp. 27–68. Davis, Philadelphia.
128. Katzman, R., and Kawas, C. (1994). The epidemiology of dementia and Alzheimer disease. In *Alzheimer Disease* (R. Terry, R. Katzman, and K. Bick, eds.), pp. 105–122. Raven, New York.
129. Hyman, G., Van Hoesen, G., Kromer, C., and Damasio, A. (1985). Alzheimer's disease: Cell specific pathology isolates the hippocampal formation. *Science* **255:** 1168–1170.
130. Gomez-Isla, T., Price, J., McKeel, D., *et al.* (in press). Profound loss of entrohinal cortex occurs in very mild Alzheimer's disease. *J. Neurosci.*
131. Morrison, J., Scherr, S., Lewis, D., Campbell, M., Bloom, F., Rogers, J., and Benoit, R. (1986). The laminar and regional distribution of neocortical somatostatin and neuritic plaques: Implications for Alzheimer's disease as a global neocortical disconnection syndrome. In *Biological Substrates of Alzheimer's Disease* (A. Scheibel and A. Weschler, eds.), pp. 115–131. Academic Press, New York.
132. Goate, A., Chartier-Harlin, M. C., Mullan, M., *et al.* (1991). Segregation of a missensen mutation of the amyloid precursor protein gene with familial Alzheimer's disease. *Nature* **349:** 704–706.
133. Sherrington, R., Rogaev, E., Liang, Y., *et al.* (1995). Cloning of a novel gene bearing missense mutation in early familial Alzheimer disease. *Nature* **375:** 754–760.
134. Levy-Lehad, E., Wasco, W., Poorkaj, P., *et al.* (1995). Candidate gene for the chromosome 1 familial Alzheimer's disease locus. *Science* **269:** 973–977.
135. Strittmatter, W. J., Saunders, A. M., Schmechel, D., *et al.* (1993). Apolipoprotein E: High avidity binding to -amyloid and increased frequency of type 4 allele in late-onset familial Alzheimer's disease. *Proc. Natl. Acad. Sci. USA* **190:** 1977–1981.
136. Saunders, A., Strittmater, W., Schmechel, D., *et al.* (1993). Apolipoprotein E: High avidity binding to B-Amyloid and increased frequency of type 4 allele in late-onset familial Alzheimer's disease. *Proc. Natl. Acad. Sci. USA* **190:** 1977–1981.

C H A P T E R

52

Object and Face Recognition

Martha Farah, G.W. Humphreys, and Hillary R. Rodman

As objects and viewers move with respect to one another, the images cast by objects on the viewer's retinas can change radically. Not only will image position and size change, but object surfaces may be foreshortened, occluded, or newly revealed. Similarly, changes in lighting conditions can reveal new surfaces, hide old ones in shadow, and introduce spurious edges where light ends and shadow begins. Yet the visual system is able to extract some reasonably constant representation of the shapes of objects and faces across these transformations. Image processing by the retina, lateral geniculate nucleus of the thalamus, and occipital visual areas makes some headway toward stable object representations by extracting features and representing them over increasingly large receptive fields (see Chapter 28). However, in going from the occipital to the temporal visual cortex, the stimulus representation undergoes its most radical transformation away from image properties and toward intrinsic object shape properties. In this chapter, we examine the role of the temporal cortex in object and face recognition.

EVIDENCE FOR VISUAL AREAS BEYOND THE OCCIPITAL LOBE

The earliest clues about the neural bases of object recognition came from the study of patients with visual agnosia. Visual agnosia is a blanket term for a wide array of visual disorders affecting object recognition, in which elementary visual functions such as acuity and visual fields are grossly intact or at least adequate to allow recognition (see Farah[1] for a taxonomy and detailed review). Lissauer[2] is usually credited with the first detailed discussion of visual agnosia, and early attempts to generalize about the lesions in such cases are found mainly in the German neurology literature of the early decades of this century.[3] Writers as early as Potzl[4] recognized the importance of inferior temporal regions in visual agnosia, including the lingual and fusiform gyri, as well as adjacent occipital regions. Lesions in patients with visual agnosia are typically bilateral or right-sided; left-sided lesions are found primarily in those who retain face recognition ability.[5,6]

Object Recognition in Monkeys Depends on the Inferior Temporal Cortex

One of the earliest experimental studies in animals on the role of the temporal cortex in visual recognition was that of Klüver and Bucy,[7] on what is now known as the *Klüver–Bucy syndrome.* When these researchers removed the temporal lobes of monkeys bilaterally, the monkeys demonstrated complex changes in visual, social, sexual, and eating behavior. These changes appeared to result from a combination of perceptual, mnemonic, and motivational impairments. Later researchers attempted to identify the areas of the temporal lobe responsible for the visual functions disrupted in these monkeys, eventually identifying the inferior temporal gyrus, also known as **inferior temporal** (IT) cortex, as the critical area for producing the visual deficits.[8–10] Monkeys with IT lesions were impaired with respect to learning visual discriminations among different patterns or objects and retaining previously acquired visual discriminations.[11] Figure 52.1 shows the location of this area in the macaque brain.[12]

What type of stimulus representation is impaired after IT lesions? Much research has been aimed at answering this question. The general approach has been to infer which stimulus properties are normally encoded (or not encoded) in IT representations by show-

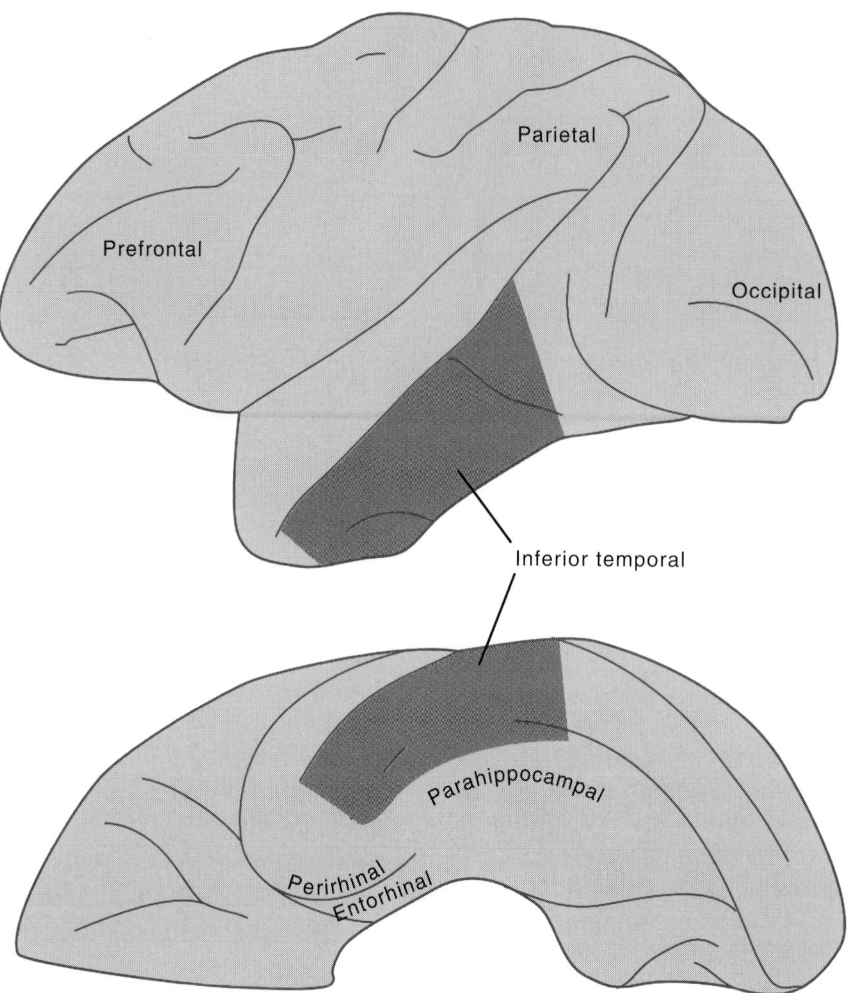

FIGURE 52.1 The inferior temporal region in a rhesus monkey. (Top) Lateral view. (Bottom) Ventral view. Adapted from Dean.[12]

ing which stimulus properties monkeys with IT lesions are impaired at using (or not impaired at using) as a basis for discrimination. On the basis of our current knowledge, a reasonable short answer might be that IT cortex represents aspects of the intrinsic shape of the stimulus that are useful for recognition (e.g., the salient features in a face and their relative positions) and omits most aspects of stimulus appearance that depend on viewing conditions (e.g., absolute size and luminance). We present a few representative studies here.

Position in the visual field is one visual property that is clearly not necessary for objective recognition, and normal monkeys will easily generalize a visual discrimination learned in one hemifield to the other. In other words, if monkeys learn to tell apart stimuli in one half of visual space, they will easily transfer this discrimination when the same stimuli are switched to the other half. The fact that monkeys with bilateral IT lesions are impaired at this generalization implies that they have lost representations that are invariant across visual field locations.[13,14] The retinal image size of the stimulus is another visual property that depends on viewing conditions and not just intrinsic object geometry, and this is another property that monkeys with IT lesions have trouble ignoring. For example, in one experiment, monkeys were trained to discriminate between two disks of different absolute sizes, varying their distance and hence their retinal image size.[15] Monkeys with IT lesions were unable to relearn the discrimination, responding instead on the basis of retinal size or distance. This result implies that representations within the IT cortex normally encode the absolute size of an object, an intrinsic object property useful for recognition, rather than its distance per se or its retinal image size.

Monkeys with IT lesions are also typically impaired at generalizing across views of the same stimulus in a different orientation,[16] implying that orientation is yet another of the incidental image properties that has been discarded from representations within IT cortex. Finally, variations in illumination prevent monkeys with IT lesions from seeing the equivalence of objects,[16] implying that representations in IT cortex are unaffected by patterns of shadow and light falling on object surfaces.

Damage to Object Representations in Humans Causes Associative Visual Agnosia

Agnosias are commonly divided into **apperceptive** and **associative** varieties.[2] Agnosic patients whose perception is obviously impaired, despite intact or at least adequate visual sensory function, are classified as apperceptive agnosics on the basis that their impairment is a perceptual one, that is, in the stage of apperception. Agnosic patients whose perception seems grossly intact are classified as associative agnosics on the basis that their impairment is in the stage of association of percept and memory. The apperceptive and associative distinction is valid in the sense that there are agnosic patients with and without obvious perceptual impairments, and their underlying problems do appear to be different. However, it is probably not true that the underlying problem in associative agnosia is one of association, as opposed to perception. In fact, whereas apperceptive agnosia is thought to result from relatively early impairments in image processing, associative agnosia can be conceptualized as an impairment of perceptual object representation *per se*.

To be considered an associative agnosic, a patient must demonstrate the following features: First, he or she must have difficulty recognizing visually presented objects, as measured by both naming and nonverbal tests of recognition, such as sorting objects by category (e.g., putting kitchen utensils together, separate from sports equipment) or pantomiming the objects' functions. Second, the patient must demonstrate that knowledge of the objects is available through modalities other than vision, for example, by tactile or auditory recognition or by verbal questioning (e.g., "What is an egg beater?"). Third, the patient must be able to see the object clearly enough to describe its appearance, draw it, or answer whether it is the same as or different in appearance from a second stimulus. A good illustrative case of associative visual agnosia has been described by Rubens and Benson[17] and is summarized in Box 52.1. Figure 52.2 shows some copies made by their patient, who did not recognize the pictures he copied.

Summary

How can someone be of sound mind, see pictures clearly enough to produce the copies shown in Fig. 52.2, and yet not recognize the pictures? This constellation of abilities and impairments seems almost paradoxical, and perhaps for this reason the very existence of visual agnosia has been doubted.[18,19] The resolution of this paradox lies in the realization that copying, matching, and so forth can be accomplished using representations based on the specific appearance of the image. In contrast, as discussed at the beginning of this chapter, such representations are too changeable to suffice for object recognition. Indeed, closer examination of the manner in which agnosics copy and match pictures suggests that they are abnormally tied to the local structure of the image rather than guided by the shape of the object itself: their copies are executed in a slow and slavish manner, and they may classify two pictures as different because of a small flaw in the printing of one (see Farah[1] for a review of these and other sources of evidence for perceptual impairment in associative agnosia). Unfortunately, the effects of transformations in size, orientation, lighting, and so forth have not been studied systematically in associative agnosics, as they have been in monkeys with IT lesions and in recordings from single IT neurons. Nevertheless, the evidence available from copying, matching, and other tasks is consistent with an impairment in representing the intrinsic shapes of objects and a consequent overreliance on structural image representations.

VISUAL PATHWAYS FOR OBJECT RECOGNITION

The Visual Cortex of Primates Can Be Divided into Dorsal and Ventral Streams

A major portion of the neocortex of primates is devoted to the processing of visual information. This expanse of visual cortex has been differentiated into a large number of separate regions, which can be thought of as organized in a hierarchical fashion. Visual cortical areas of primates can be divided roughly into a **dorsal stream,** concerned with the analysis of the locations of objects and their movements in space, and a **ventral stream,** responsible for the processing and storage of information about their identity—their shape, color, and other salient physical features. Although the two cortical streams are not completely segregated anatomically or functionally, this formulation, first put forth in 1982 by Ungerleider and Mishkin[20] (Fig. 52.3A)[21]

BOX 52.1

CASE STUDY OF ASSOCIATIVE OBJECT AGNOSIA

The subject was a 47-year-old man who had suffered an acute loss of blood pressure with resulting brain damage. His mental status and language abilities were normal, and his visual acuity was 20/30, with a right homonymous hemianopia (blindness in the right visual hemifield). His one severe impairment was an inability to recognize most visual stimuli.

For the first 3 weeks in the hospital, the patient could not identify common objects presented visually and did not know what was on his plate until he tasted it. He identified objects immediately on touching them.

When shown a stethoscope, he described it as "a long cord with a round thing at the end" and asked if it could be a watch. He identified a can opener as a key. Asked to name a cigarette lighter, he said, "I don't know" but named it after the examiner lit it. He said he was "not sure" when shown a toothbrush.

He was never able to describe or demonstrate the use of an object if he could not name it. If he misnamed an object, his demonstration of use would correspond to the mistaken identification. Identification improved very slightly when given the category of the object (e.g., something to eat) or when asked to point to a named object instead of being required to give the name. When told the correct name of an object, he usually responded with a quick nod and often said, "Yes, I see it now." Then, often he could point out various parts of the previously unrecognized item as readily as a normal subject (e.g., the stem and bowl of a pipe and the laces, sole, and heel of a shoe). However, if asked by the examiner, "Suppose I told you that the last object was not really a pipe, what would you say?" He would reply, "I would take your word for it. Perhaps it's not a pipe." Similar vacillation never occurred with tactilely or aurally identified objects.

After he had spent 3 weeks on the ward, his object-naming ability improved so that he could name many common objects, but this was variable; he might correctly name an object at one time and misname it later. Performance deteriorated severely when any part of the object was covered by the examiner. He could match identical objects but could not group objects by categories (clothing, food). He could draw the outlines of objects (key, spoon, etc.) that he could not identify.

He was unable to recognize members of his family, the hospital staff, or even his own face in the mirror. Sometimes he had difficulty distinguishing a line drawing of an animal face from a man's face but always recognized it as a face.

The ability to recognize pictures of objects was greatly impaired, and after repeated testing he could name only 1 or 2 of 10 line drawings. He was always able to name geometrical forms (circle, square, triangle, cube). Remarkably, he could make excellent copies of line drawings and still fail to name the subject. He easily matched drawings of objects that he could not identify and had no difficulty discriminating between complex nonrepresentational patterns, differing from each other only subtly. He occasionally failed in discriminating because he included imperfections in the paper or in the printer's ink. He could never group drawings of objects by class unless he could first name the subject.

Reading, both aloud and for comprehension, was greatly limited. He could read, hesitantly, most printed letters but often misread "K" as "R," and "L" as "T" and vice versa. He was able to read words slowly by spelling them aloud. (Excerpted from Rubens and Benson.[17])

and subsequently elaborated by these authors and other workers,[22,23] remains one of the most valuable principles in our understanding of the visual cortex. The following section deals with the organization of the ventral stream and how cells in areas within it represent objects in terms of their distinguishing individual features and the configurations of these features, which together make up coherent wholes.

The Ventral Stream of Monkeys Consists of an Interconnected Set of Visual Cortical Areas

Most of our detailed knowledge of the organization of primate visual cortex, including that of pathways specialized for object recognition, comes from studies of Old World monkeys of the genus *Macaca*. Similar areas and connections appear to exist in New World

FIGURE 52.2 Pictures that a patient with associative visual agnosia did not recognize but was able to copy. Asterisks indicate the patient's copies. From Rubens and Benson.[17]

monkeys. Figures 52.3B and 52.3C illustrate the locations of areas and overall flow of information within the ventral stream of the macaque monkey. Analysis of objects begins in V1, where information about edges and about the color and brightness of stimuli is extracted from visual inputs from the dorsal lateral geniculate nucleus (Chapter 28). This information is then sent on to certain subdivisions of area V2. From V2, the object recognition pathway takes a largely ventral, occipitotemporal course. Visual information about objects is sent from V2 to area V4 on the lateral and ventromedial surfaces of the hemisphere and to a posterior inferior temporal area, TEO, just anterior to V4. From these regions, information proceeds forward to area TE, located in the anterior inferior temporal cortex. Together, areas TEO and TE constitute IT cortex as described in the previous section. From there, visual information is sent to the most ventral and anterior reaches of temporal lobe neocortex, namely, temporal polar areas TG and perirhinal area 36. These areas and adjacent parahippocampal (areas TF and TH) and entorhinal (area 28) cortices are interconnected with medial temporal lobe structures, most notably, the hippocampus, which are crucial for forming memories of visual objects.

At all stages of the pathway, connections tend to be reciprocal, so that an area receiving feedforward projections from an area earlier in the ventral hierarchy provides feedback projections to that area. Long-range nonreciprocal connections, such as those from area TE back to V1, also exist. In addition, the ventral object recognition pathway involves interconnections of temporal areas, such as TEO and TE, with ventral portions of the frontal lobe neocortex and with portions of the superior temporal polysensory area (STP), which appears to contribute to both object and motion analyses on the basis of converging projections from both dorsal and ventral streams.[24] Further, all areas in the ventral stream are interconnected with subcortical visual structures, most notably with the pulvinar and portions of the amygdala, claustrum, and basal ganglia. Finally, all areas in the ventral stream are interconnected with their counterparts and other ventral stream areas of the opposite hemisphere through the corpus callosum or, in the anterior and ventral regions, through the anterior commissure.

Trends in Anatomical Features Are Evident along the Ventral Stream

Paralleling the flow of information just described, several trends in anatomical features are evident as one progresses forward along the ventral stream of monkeys.[23,25,26] First, at successive stages, patterns of cortical connectivity become successively less topographic or "point-to-point." Inputs to area TE from V4 and TEO, for example, have no obvious retinotopic organization. Similarly, connections with subcortical structures, both visual and nonvisual, become progressively more diffuse at successive levels of this pathway. For example, whereas areas V2 and V4 are topographically interconnected with portions of the pulvinar that themselves show retinotopic organization, areas such as TE and STP have nontopographic connections with nonretinotopic pulvinar subdivisions. Third, commissural pathways interconnecting areas of the ventral stream on the two sides of the brain tend to be restricted to the representation of the midline of visual space early in the pathway, but their representation becomes more widespread at higher levels in the pathway. Other physical gradients are also present. The concentration of opiate receptors increases in a graded fashion along the ventral stream, perhaps reflecting an increasing role for affect-based attentional processes at successive levels of the system.[27] Successive levels of the ventral stream also show increasing levels of activation of several proteins that have been implicated in synaptic plasticity and long-term storage of information in the brain.[28]

A

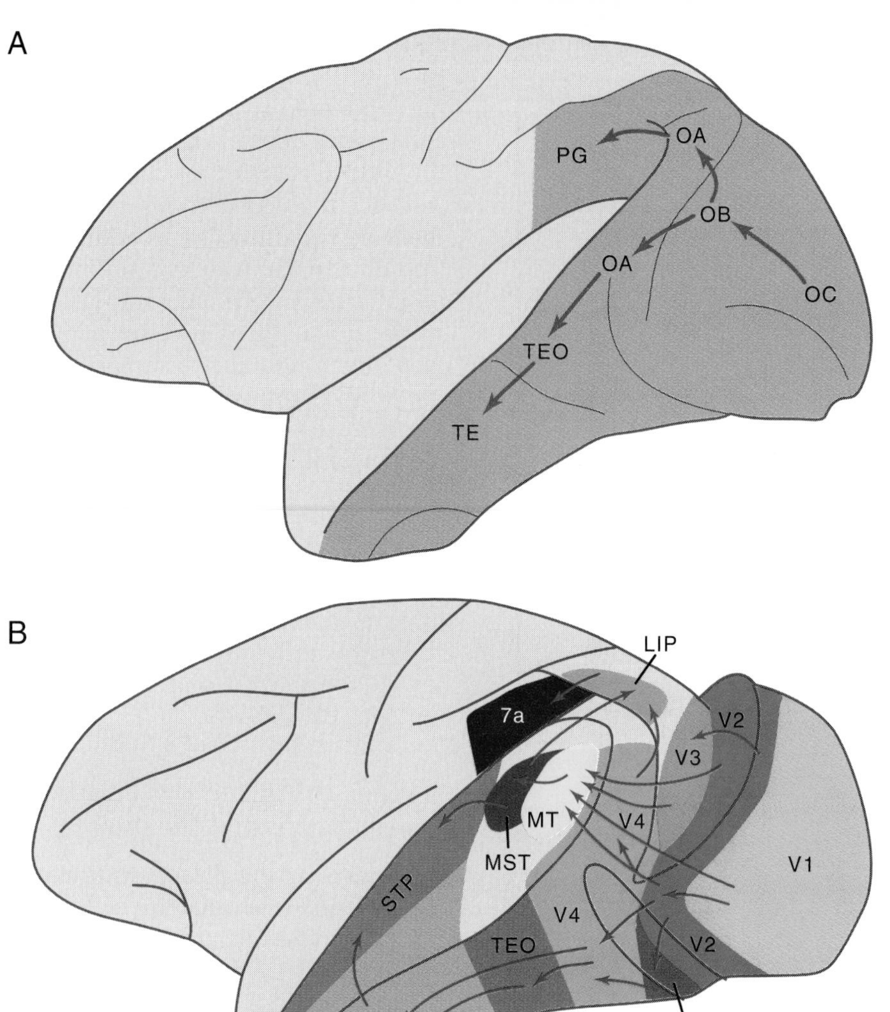

C

A	amygdala
ER	entorhinal cortex
H	hippocampus
LIP	lateral intraparietal area
MST	medial superior temporal area
MT	middle temporal area
PH	parahippocampal cortex
PR	perirhinal cortex
STP	superior temporal polysensory area
TE	ant. inferior temporal cortex
TEO	post. inferior temporal cortex
V1	first visual area
V2	second visual area
V3	third visual area
V4	fourth visual area
VP	ventral posterior area

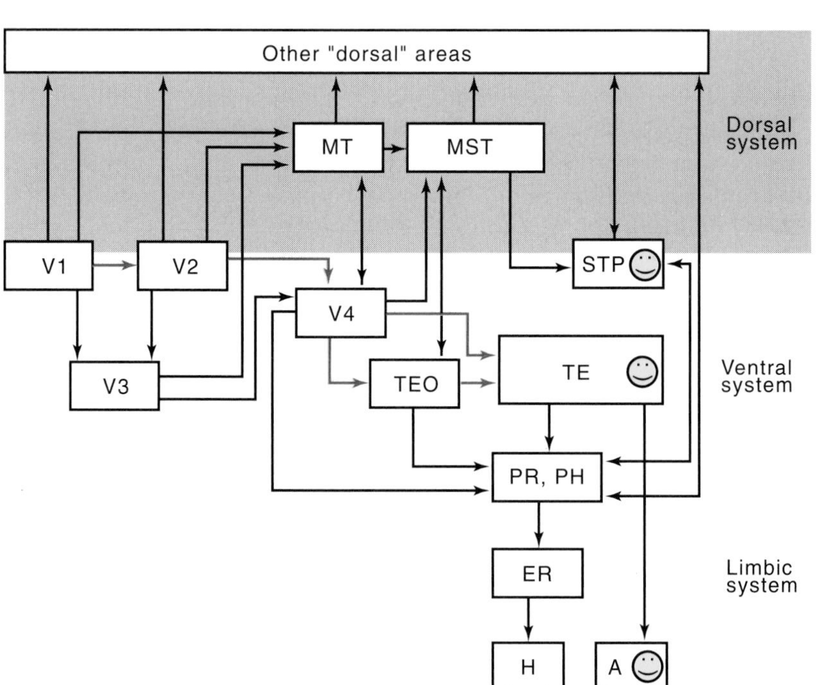

Trends in Neuronal Response Properties Are Also Evident along the Ventral Stream

In monkeys, the different cortical areas in the ventral stream share a number of physiological characteristics. Consistent with their role in object recognition, all areas in the pathway contain populations of cells sensitive to the shape, color, or texture (regular pattern of detail) of visual stimuli or some combination of these features.[23,29] Four major physiological trends are evident as one moves forward along the pathway. First, the nature of the visual field representation changes from a precise map of the contralateral visual field to a more diffuse mapping of overall visual space. For example, moving from V1 to V2 to V4 and then to areas TEO and TE, neuronal receptive fields (i.e., the portions of visual space from which a stimulus can evoke a neuronal response) become larger (Fig. 52.4)[30–33] and their organization into a map less precise, reflecting changes in anatomical connectivity patterns, so that by area TE no clear retinotopic organization is present. The amount of the ipsilateral visual field represented in the receptive fields (RFs) in a given area also increases at successive levels of the pathway, which is again consistent with anatomical trends; RFs vary from 1 or 2 degrees of the visual field in areas V1 and V2 to the large, bilateral RFs found in areas TE and STP. The second trend is an increase in the degree to which particular stimulus features, such as an appropriately oriented edge, are signaled regardless of their exact retinal location; in other words, there is an increase in the extent of invariance of neuronal responses, progressing from a degree or two of such tolerance in the RFs of complex cells in V1 to the maintained stimulus

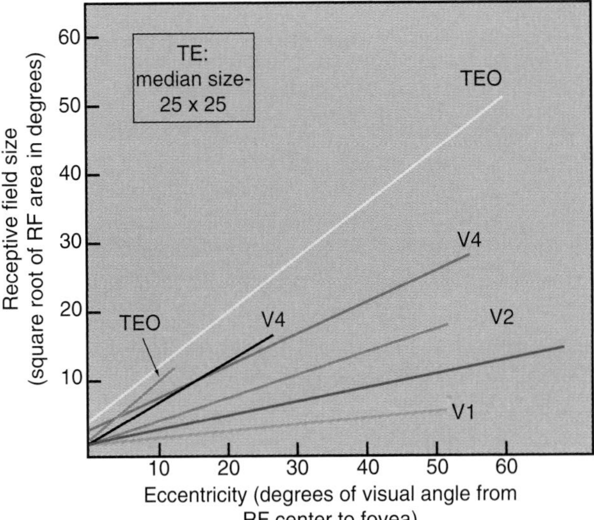

FIGURE 52.4 Regression lines relating multiunit receptive field size (square root of receptive field area) to receptive field eccentricity in various areas along the ventral stream. The two lines for V2 (red and blue) show data separately for two different animals. Adapted from Boussaoud *et al.*,[30] Fenstemaker *et al.*,[31] Gattass *et al.*,[32,33] and Gross *et al.*[23]

selectivity across wide expanses of visual space exhibited by cells in TE and STP.[34] The third trend is toward selectivity for increasingly complex stimulus features or combinations of features, progressing from the selectivity for simple dimensions such as the orientation of edges and wavelength in V1 to the preference for complex objects, including biologically meaningful stimuli, such as faces and body movements, shown by many neurons in late stages of the ventral pathway. Finally, progressing along the ventral stream and continuing into the frontal lobe, there is an increase in the extent to which cells contribute information related to the recentness and familiarity of visual objects (visual memory traces).[35]

FIGURE 52.3 (A) Schematic diagram of the monkey brain illustrating the two cortical visual system model of Ungerleider and Mishkin.[20] According to this model, there are two major processing pathways, or "streams," in the visual cortex, both originating in the primary visual cortex: a ventral stream, directed into the temporal lobe and crucial for the identification of objects, and a dorsal stream, directed into the parietal lobe and crucial for spatial perception and visuomotor performance. The shaded region indicates the extent of visual cortex in the monkey, and the labels on the figure (OC, OB, OA, TEO, TE, PG) indicate cytoarchitectonic areas according to the nomenclature of von Bonin and Bailey.[21] Adapted from Mishkin *et al.*[22] (B) A lateral view of the monkey brain illustrating the multiplicity of functional areas within the visual cortex and the connections between them. For simplicity, only projections from lower-order to higher-order areas are shown, but each of these feedforward projections is reciprocated by a feedback projection. (C) Some of the pertinent connections of inferior temporal cortex with other cortical areas and medial temporal lobe structures. Red lines indicate the main afferent pathway to area TE, which includes areas V1, V2, V4, and TEO. Faces indicate areas in which neurons selectively responsive to faces have been found. Adapted from Gross *et al.*[23]

Novel Neuronal Response Properties Emerge in Successive Areas in the Ventral Stream

There is considerable variation in the degree to which different components of the ventral stream have been explored physiologically in monkeys. Overall, areas V2, V4, and TE have received the most attention. Neuronal activity related to object recognition in areas STP, and in areas 36 and TG (sometimes considered the most anterior-ventral portion of IT cortex), has also become a recent focus of research. Less is currently known about the object-related visual response properties of neurons in area TEO, parahippocampal areas TF and TH, and the ventral frontal cortical regions to which ventral temporal visual areas project.

Area V2

Like cells in V1, individual neurons in area V2 respond in a selective fashion to length, width, orientation, or wavelength of a bar of light or to the spatial frequency of a grating.[36,37] However, some cells in V2 are jointly selective for wavelength and small dimensions of stimuli throughout their RFs; such **spot cells** represent an early stage of integration of stimulus features.[36] Moreover, some neurons in V2 (but not V1) respond to **illusory contours** of appropriate orientation generated by the stimulation of regions surrounding the classical receptive field.[38]

Area V4

A number of fundamental elaborations become evident in area V4. First, many neurons in V4 are conjointly tuned for both the length and the width of a bar stimulus[39] and maintain such selectivity over a considerably wider RF than at earlier stages of the visual pathway. Second, many cells in V4 show a combination of varied shape selectivity with wavelength selectivity. Third, beginning in V4, a small number of cells are found with optimal stimuli clearly more complex than oriented edges or spots, consisting instead of features such as edge conjunctions, irregular borders, and concentrically organized areas of contrast (Fig. 52.5).[40,41] A fourth and critical elaboration in V4 is the appearance of large, **silent surrounds** adjacent to the excitatory or classical RF.[29] These surrounds presumably reflect the increase seen at the level of V4 in commissural inputs and feedback projections from more anterior areas with large RFs. Stimulation of the surrounds typically influences activity of the cell only when carried out in concert with stimulation of the classical RF, and the selectivities of the surround and classical RF for form, wavelength, spatial frequency, and so on are usually antagonistic. Accordingly, such cells tend to respond maximally only when the stimulus stands out from its background on the basis of a difference in such features. These antagonistic surrounds may represent an important step in figure-ground separation—that is, the breakdown of scenes into objects to be analyzed.

A fifth development at the level of V4 has to do with the perception of color. Originally, V4 had been thought of as an area specialized for color processing, but it now appears that the percentage of cells in V4 tuned for wavelength (and the sharpness of their tuning) does not differ significantly from that in other areas in the ventral stream. Moreover, both the physiological studies described previously and the effects of lesions underscore the crucial role of this area in form perception. Nevertheless, many cells in monkey V4 have been shown to exhibit color constancy.[42] In other words, like human observers, they perceive (i.e., respond maximally) to the apparent color of an object defined by the relative reflectances of the object and its surround, independent of the actual wavelengths reflected by the object itself. The complementary wavelength selectivities of the classical RF and of the surround of V4 cells have been suggested to form the basis for the behavior of these cells.

A final noteworthy development at the level of V4 is the sensitivity of neuronal firing patterns to several

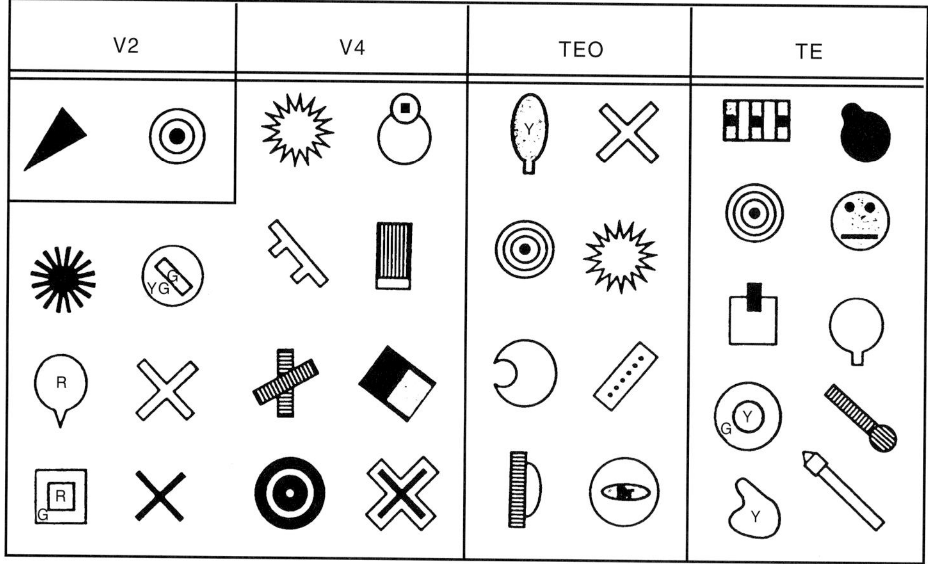

FIGURE 52.5 Examples of the complex object features preferred for four ventral stream areas. Y, yellow; R, red; G, green; YG, yellow green; Br, brown. Adapted from Kobatake and Tanaka.[41]

types of nonvisual signals. For example, whether or not an animal pays attention to a particular visual stimulus located in the RF of a V4 neuron can dramatically affect the strength of a cell's response to the stimulus.[43] There is also some evidence that requiring an animal to generate a visual mental image of a cell's preferred stimulus, based on input in other sensory modalities, can actually activate V4 neurons.[44]

Inferior Temporal Cortex

An additional set of crucial elaborations in the response properties of ventral stream neurons takes place as one moves forward into the IT cortex. First, moving successively into area TEO and then into posterior and anterior portions of area TE, there is a progressive increase in both the complexity of the critical features needed to activate the neurons in each area and the proportion of neurons that are selectively driven by some type of complex pattern or object. Although some proportion of cells selectively responsive to simple stimulus parameters of length, width, orientation, wavelength, and spatial frequency remain in each of these regions, by the level of anterior area TE many neurons respond only to relatively complicated stimuli or classes of stimuli, often three-dimensional stimuli with particular patterns of internal detail.[45] Among cells selective for particular classes of complex patterns or objects, cells that respond selectively to faces are particularly common and have been studied extensively (see following section). Attempts by various workers[45,46] to determine whether simpler critical features within complex objects are crucial for eliciting the response have shown that this is true for only some of those TE neurons that respond maximally to complex stimuli.

Second, while some TE cells respond only to particular complex stimuli or stimulus classes, other TE neurons fire equally well to a great variety of stimuli, albeit with a varying response strength. Still others show what has been called **paradoxical selectivity:** they fire best or only in response to a small number of complex stimuli with few obvious common features.[23] For the first time in the ventral pathway, the critical stimulus dimension for a majority of neurons remains unspecified. All of these observations suggest that TE neurons do not code objects either by serving as complex feature detectors or by responding to any shape primitives thus far tested (an exception to this may be *face-selective* neurons described later). Rather, most workers in the field believe that by the level of area TE, visual stimuli are represented by a pattern of activity across a population or ensemble of cells, each member of which may participate in representing several different objects. Despite this cooperative activity across cell types, cells in area TE with similar types of selectivity tend to cluster into clumps or modules, possibly organized into vertical columns like the ocular dominance and orientation columns demonstrated in V1. (See Chapter 28.)

A third critical development that appears by the level of TE is the considerable response invariance achieved by many neurons. Many neurons throughout the ventral pathway tend to prefer a given stimulus type or parameter independent of the size or exact position of the stimulus within their RFs. However, in area TE, RFs can be very large—20 degrees on a side or more—and extend far into the ipsilateral visual field, such that a proportion of cells in area TE respond to relatively complex objects over a wide expanse of the visual world and do so despite changes in location in depth, which alter retinal image size. A fairly precise characterization of the information represented by individual area TE cells can be obtained from experiments in which responses from a cell are recorded while specific properties of a stimulus are varied. The results of these experiments are generally consonant with the conclusions of the lesion studies reviewed earlier and with the general view that area TE represents intrinsic aspects of object shape and not incidental aspects of appearance that are determined by viewing conditions. For example, the position,[45] retinal image size,[47] and picture plane orientation[45] have relatively small effects on a cell's response to an optimal shape. Moreover, neurons that are selective for a particular shape defined by luminosity differences (e.g., a white star on a black background) are selective for the same shape defined by texture cues and motion cues [e.g., a star-shaped region of speckles with the same average luminosity as its background, defined by larger sparser speckles (texture cues) moving in a different direction from the background (motion cues)[48]]. It is these generalizing properties in particular that are believed to be responsible for the changes in object recognition following inferior temporal damage.

A fourth development—beginning in area TE, continuing into anterior–ventral areas, such as perirhinal area 36, and also into the frontal lobe—is the appearance of response patterns related not to an object per se but rather to its memory—that is, the fact that an object has been seen before, has been seen recently, or has been seen shortly after the appearance of another object.[49,50] For example, for some neurons in area TE, responses to an object that is presented repeatedly, thus losing its novelty, decrease systematically, possibly signaling that the object has been seen in the recent past and/or redirecting attention toward other, novel objects (Fig. 52.6). Some cells in area TE (and also in

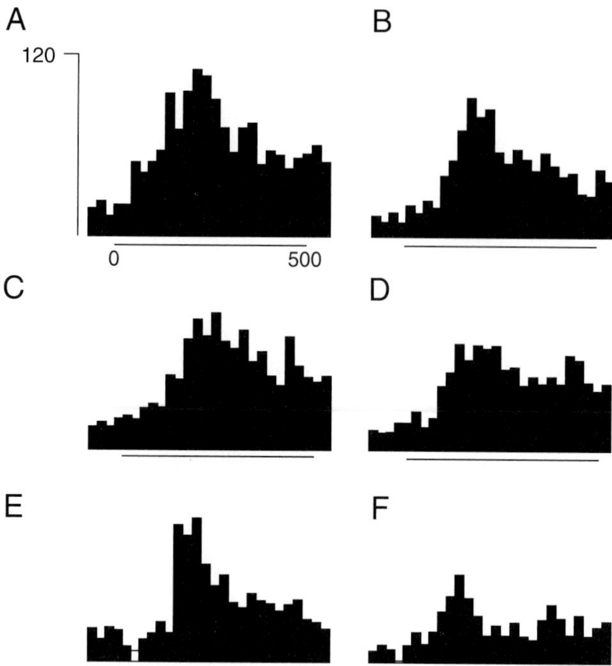

FIGURE 52.6 Examples of responses of an individual IT neuron to a set of 20 initially novel sample visual stimuli. (A, first presentation of 20 novel stimuli; B, second presentation; etc.) Responses to all 20 stimuli have been averaged together into single composite histograms. The six histograms show the average response to the first six presentations of all stimuli. The horizontal line under the histograms indicates the 500-ms time period when the stimuli were on. The vertical scale indicates firing rate in spikes per second, and the bin width is 10 ms. From Li *et al.*[49]

area TE's projection zones in prefrontal cortex) continue to fire during the delay period of a matching task after an object has been removed from view, but still needs to be remembered if the task is to be performed correctly; such activity has been interpreted as a visual memory trace or "holding" signal. Finally, some neurons in area 36, and possibly also area TE, develop conjoint and stable selectivity for unrelated objects that are repeatedly presented together or associated in time.[51]

Functional Imaging and Physiological Studies Demonstrate There Is a Homolog of the Ventral Stream for Object Recognition in Human Cortex

Recent technological advances have made it possible to ask about the neural substrates of perceptual and cognitive abilities in humans by using functional neuroimaging to identify brain regions activated during particular mental and physical states. In particular, **positron emission tomography** (PET) and **functional magnetic resonance imaging** (fMRI) have allowed scientists to start defining areas in the human brain involved in visual object recognition. For example, comparison of patterns of activity during processing of object location on the one hand and physical object features (shape, color) on the other clearly delineates separable dorsal and ventral pathways associated with "what" and "where"[52] in the human brain; as in monkeys, both dorsal and ventral pathways originate in the striate cortex. These studies highlight specific details of object processing in humans. First, much of the tissue devoted to object recognition in humans appears to be considerably more ventral than that in monkeys. Overall, the areas activated during object, color, and form recognition tasks (including identifying faces and naming objects) include the lingual and fusiform gyri (ventral occipitotemporal cortex) and anterior inferior temporal cortex of both hemispheres, the left lateral occipitotemporal cortex, and the right inferior frontal cortex[53,54] (Fig. 52.7). Second, processing of different types of object features activates regions that are only partially coincident, suggesting some localization of function within the human ventral stream at the level of whole areas. For example, foci activated by color processing appear to be located medial to those activated by perception of faces, and foci activated by nonface objects only partially overlap areas that appear to be involved in processing the facial image.[52] Brain imaging work on the neuroanatomy of processing of facial configurations in the human brain is discussed further in the next section.

Researchers have been able to obtain electrophysiological correlates of visual object perception and recognition from human patients with electrodes chronically implanted directly on the occipitotemporal and the inferior temporal cortex for the primary purpose of monitoring epileptic seizures.[56] Evoked potentials recorded by these electrodes when the patients viewed various categories of objects produced a pattern of results highly consistent with the imaging data discussed earlier (Fig. 52.7). Interestingly, potentials evoked specifically by alphanumeric stimuli (letter strings, words, and numbers) were from regions overlapping those associated with potentials related to other types of object stimuli. These findings support the notion that, at least at early levels of processing, linguistic material is treated within the object recognition system.

Summary

In monkeys, the ventral stream consists of a hierarchically organized set of areas with related patterns of anatomical connectivity, physiological response properties, and contributions to object vision. Activity in this ventral stream begins with the coding of simple parameters in early areas (V1 through V4) and progresses to anterior and ventral temporal areas to provide increasingly more abstract representations of visual objects and, ultimately, responses that may code the memory of previously seen objects. Although all areas in the pathway contain populations of cells selective for such simple parameters as edge orientation, color, and texture and for more complex conjunctions of object features, localization of function for components of object processing also exists in the sense that cells selectively responsive to particular stimulus features or to particular types of complex objects are organized into clumps or modules. Studies using functional neuroimaging methods (e.g., PET and fMRI) and direct monitoring of neural activity (event-related potentials) both show that a similar pathway exists within the ventral extrastriate cortex of the human brain.

FACE RECOGNITION: SPECIALIZED CORTICAL CIRCUITS?

Analysis and retention of facial images are crucial cognitive skills for primates. In many primates, the sense of smell is markedly reduced relative to that of

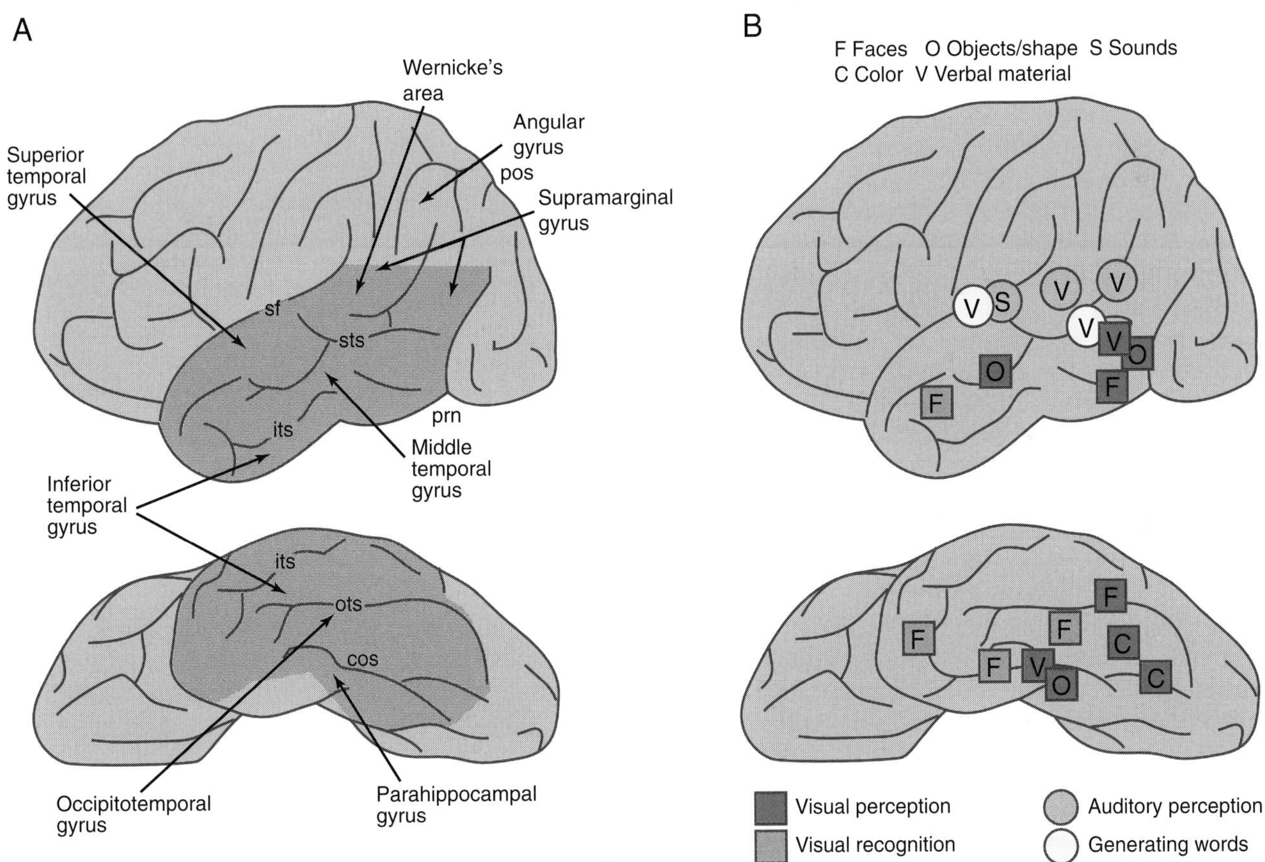

FIGURE 52.7 Schematic lateral (top) and ventral (bottom) views of human cerebral hemispheres. (A) Location of temporal cortex (purple) and major sulci and gyri. The posterior portion of the parahippocampal gyrus is often referred to as the *lingual gyrus,* and the posterior portion of the occipitotemporal gyrus is often referred to as the *fusiform gyrus*. cos, collateral sulcus; its, inferior temporal sulcus; ots, occipitotemporal sulcus; pos, parieto-occipital sulcus; prn, preoccipital notch; sf, sylvian fissure; sts, superior temporal sulcus. (B) Some of the major foci of activation produced in the temporal cortex using stimuli and conditions of the types indicated in neuroimaging and electrical evoked potential studies. Generating words tends to produce a posterior temporal focus of activity only in the left hemisphere, whereas the parahippocampal focus associated with face recognition tends to be found mainly in the right hemisphere. Adapted from Rodman.[55]

other vertebrate groups, and vision is a critical modality for social communication. Visual information inherent in faces thus carries a wealth of critical information about the identity of other individuals, their social positions, emotional states, and intended actions. The survival value of facial-image processing is reflected in the extraordinary memory capacity that humans and other primates show for faces, in the visual preferences for face stimuli shown by infants, and in our remarkable sensitivity to subtle differences among faces. Do face perception and recognition depend on specialized neural circuitry, possibly to some extent inborn, or do they instead reflect general mechanisms of object processing? The major lines of evidence concerning the existence of such dedicated cortical substrates are discussed in this section.

Some Neurons in the Temporal Cortex of Monkeys Respond Selectively to Faces

One of the more striking characteristics of area TE and of the immediately adjacent area STP is the presence of a small population of neurons with responses selective for face stimuli. When these neurons were first reported in 1972,[57] they were interpreted by some as examples of the gnostic units postulated[58] to provide unitary percepts of complex stimuli at the level of single cells.[59] Some years passed between this first report of face-selective neurons and the intensive study of their properties. The question is whether ostensibly face-selective neurons truly respond to visual information unique to the facial configuration or whether their selectivity is more parsimoniously explained as a response to features shared by faces and other types of objects. Although a definitive answer is still elusive, the bulk of the evidence suggests that the former description is more accurate. For example, although face-selective neurons vary in the degree and nature of their preference for face stimuli, many respond to both real faces or pictures of faces, but give nearly no response to any other stimuli tested, including other complex objects, textures, colors, and pictures in which the smaller features making up the face are rearranged or scrambled (Fig. 52.8). Moreover, for many such neurons, the specificity of the response for faces is maintained over a variety of stimulus transformations such as changes in size, position in the RF, angle of lighting of the face, blurring, removal of the natural color of the face, or even replacing the face of a monkey with that of a human. Thus, at least some face-selective neurons appear to be sensitive to very general or global aspects of a face, such as the prototypical arrangement of the eyes and nose into a facelike configuration.

Subsets of Face-Selective Neurons Appear to Participate in Different Aspects of Face Coding

Many face-selective neurons are selective for the orientation of a face relative to the observer; cells tuned to front and profile views are most common. Other face-selective neurons have responses that appear to be specific for particular facial expressions, but which are insensitive to the individual or to other aspects of the face.[60,61] The reverse sort of behavior—face cells that are sensitive to the identity of an individual monkey or human, but which generalize across different facial expressions—has also been documented. However, these cells have been tested with relatively small numbers of different face images, and their preference for a given individual's face within a set of tested stimuli in no way provides evidence for the "grandmother cell" notion of perception. This notion holds that a very specific object, such as one's grandmother, is represented by the activity of a single, very selective neuron. Such neurons may merely be sensitive to one or more distinguishing features within faces. Nevertheless, such cells may well participate in *circuits* responsible for recognizing a particular individual. Some neurons in areas TE and STP do respond to specific face components, such as the presence of eyes per se, the distance between the eyes, or the extent of the forehead.[62] Finally, a subset of face cells that respond to whole faces is particularly sensitive to the direction of gaze of the eyes within a face (looking back or looking to the side), which is an important social signal in both monkeys and humans.[63]

Cells selectively responsive to some aspect of the facial image have a localized distribution within the anterior reaches of the ventral stream in several senses. First, although there are a small number of such neurons (1–5% of all cells recorded) throughout area TE and adjacent areas as a whole, their concentration is much higher in the cortex of the upper and lower banks of the superior temporal sulcus (parts of STP and TE, respectively), where they are found together in clumps and where they may make up as many as 10–20% of all neurons studied. Second, different types of face-selective cells are found in different regions: cells sensitive to facial expression and gaze direction tend to be found within the sulcus, whereas cells more generally selective for faces and for individuals tend to be located in area TE on the inferior temporal gyrus.

Do Face-Selective Cells Indicate a Specialized Neural Machinery?

Do face cells represent a specialized type of neural machinery that has evolved to deal with a specialized

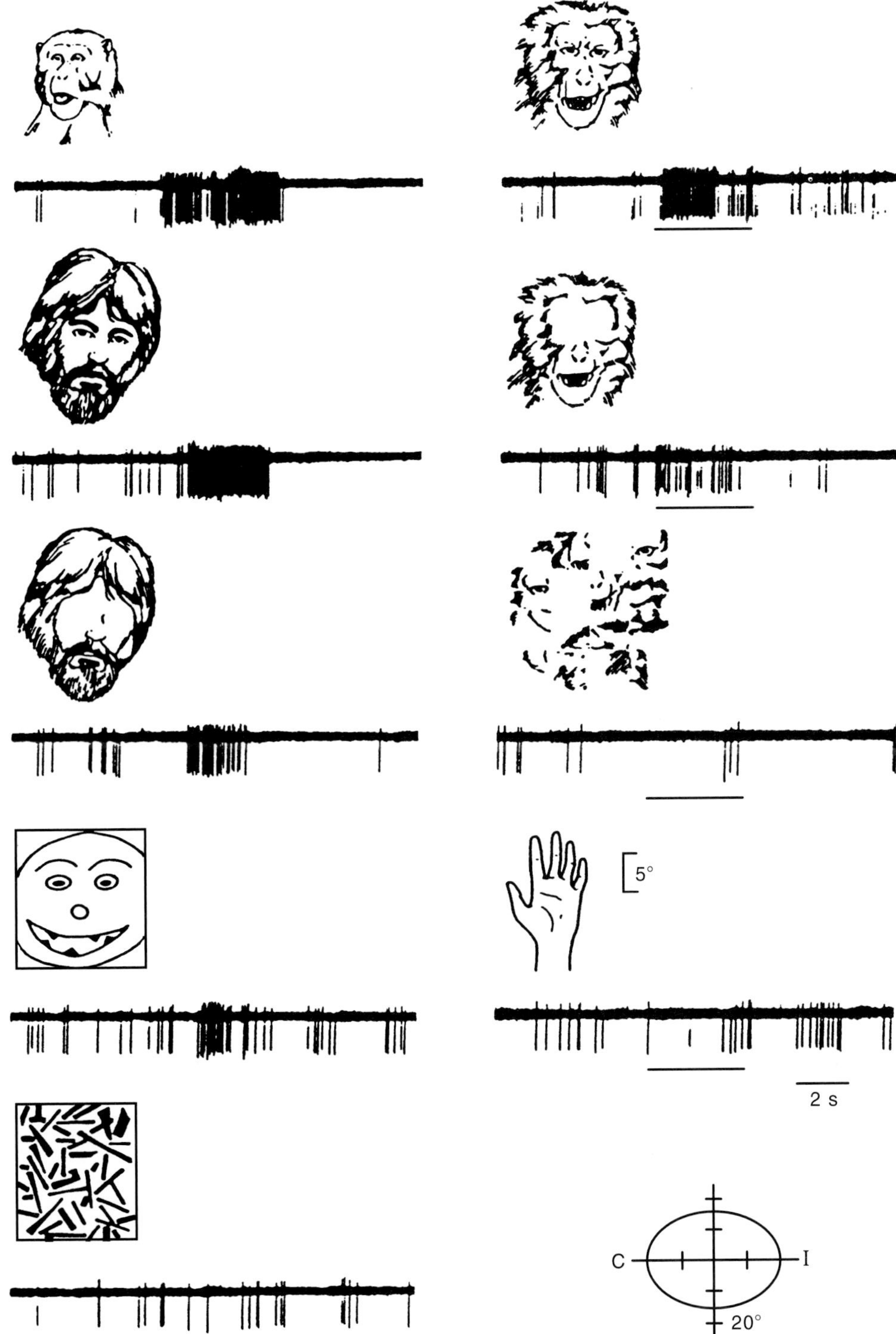

FIGURE 52.8 Activity of an STP neuron that responded better to faces than to all other stimuli tested. Removing eyes on a picture or representing the face as a caricature reduced the response. Cutting the picture into 16 pieces and rearranging pieces eliminated the response. Stimuli represented on the left were traced from a color photograph (monkey face), a black and white photograph (human face), and drawings (caricature and random pattern), which were swept across the fovea at 10 degrees/s. Stimuli represented on the right were traced from color slides, which were projected on the fovea for 3 s (indicated by the horizontal bars). All the unit records are representative ones chosen from a larger number of trials. The receptive field of the neuron is illustrated on the lower right. C, contralateral; I, ipsilateral visual field. From Bruce *et al.*[34]

type of visual stimulus? These neurons can be very selective, and comparably selective cells have yet to be found for other stimulus classes. Moreover, their presence very early in life[64] is consistent with the notion that they represent inborn templates for the detection of faces. However, most cells that respond selectively to faces or face components respond to a variety of individual faces and usually also respond, albeit to a much lesser degree, to other stimuli. In addition, like area TE cells responsive to other given stimulus features (e.g., texture and color), face-selective cells tend to be found together in clumps. Probably, then, the representation of faces, like that of other visual objects, involves a pattern of firing across populations of cells with varying selectivity and some local modular organization. Nevertheless, there may be important quantitative, if not qualitative, differences in the way the ventral stream deals with faces. For example, the large proportion of cells in the anterior portion of the ventral stream that respond to face stimuli, whether in a selective fashion or not, suggests that more cells here may participate in encoding faces than other types of stimuli, reflecting the behavioral significance of this stimulus type. Second, many of the populations or ensembles participating in face recognition may be relatively dedicated to this task, so that they may not participate in coding as many or as wide a variety of nonface patterns as other groups of neurons in the same regions.

Prosopagnosia Is a Specific Deficit of Face Recognition Caused by Brain Damage in Humans

Prosopagnosia, or face agnosia, a selective deficit in recognizing familiar faces, has been documented since at least the turn of the century. Although patients with this syndrome are aware that faces are faces—that is, they know the general type of stimulus category—they fail to reliably identify or even achieve a sense of familiarity from the faces of co-workers, family members, famous persons, and other individuals previously well known to them. Typically, they also have trouble forming memories of new faces, even if other new objects are learned. Accordingly, these persons may resort to remembering individuals by attending to salient details, such as their favorite clothing or their voices. Because the voice of a visually unrecognized person usually enables the patient to identify and feel familiar with that person, prosopagnosia appears to be a specifically visual impairment. A particularly illuminating description of a prosopagnosic patient was given by Pallis.[65] (See Box 52.2.)

A number of explanations for the apparent selectivity of the prosopagnosic deficit have been offered. One explanation is that face perception and recognition are indeed unique behavioral capacities and reflect unique, dedicated neural circuits that can be selectively damaged. A second explanation is that faces are processed and stored in a manner similar to that for other objects, but that the apparent selectivity of prosopagnosia is due to the fact that faces are simply harder to tell apart than other objects; this view is consistent with the observation that prosopagnosia is often accompanied by varying levels of object agnosia of other types. A third and related explanation suggests that face processing reflects subtle discriminations between highly similar exemplars within a category and that it is this general capacity, not the processing of the facial configuration per se, that is disrupted in prosopagnosia. Although there is undoubtedly some truth in these suggestions, one case study[66] has shown that, for at least one patient, processing of faces is still disproportionately impaired when face and nonface stimuli are equated for difficulty or when face discrimination is compared to discrimination of subtly differing exemplars within other classes, such as eyeglass frames or office chairs.

Still another explanation suggests that faces represent a class of stimuli that differ structurally from most other classes of objects, that such structural differences form the basis for different perceptual strategies for faces (such as encoding on the basis of a prototypical configuration), and that these strategies are lost in prosopagnosia. A final and intriguing suggestion, related to the last one, is that face processing represents the acquisition of a type of expertise derived from very protracted experience with a category of complex visual stimuli.[67] Reports of persons with prosopagnosia who have associated deficits in areas of object recognition in which they had previously acquired expertise over long periods of time (e.g., a show dog expert who lost the ability to differentiate breeds) are consistent with this idea.

Different Types of Prosopagnosia Reflect Different Component Subprocesses in Face Recognition

Different patterns of deficits in processing face material occur in prosopagnosia, and these differing patterns have been taken as evidence for a system of dissociable cognitive operations in processing face material by normal subjects. Some patients show considerable sparing of the ability to judge the age, gender, and even the emotional expression of faces whose identity they cannot recognize.[68] In other words, they show intact perception or structural encoding of face infor-

BOX 52.2

CASE STUDY OF PROSOPAGNOSIA

A.H., age 51, a mining engineer and colliery manager, was admitted to the Neurological Department, Cardiff Royal Infirmary, on January 4, 1954. On examination, mitral stenosis and auricular fibrillation were found. The ventricular rate was 70 to 80 per minute. There was a minimal pulse deficit. Blood pressure was 130/90 mm Hg. He was receiving "digoxin." There was no evidence of congestion and no signs of bacterial endocarditis.

He was right-handed. On neurological examination the only abnormalities detected were in the visual fields. There were narrow noncongruous homonymous sector defects in the left and right upper quadrants. (The patient was unaware of these defects.) Confrontation tests revealed no visual inattention. He localized objects accurately in both right and left half-fields. The patient was an excellent witness and gave consistent replies on repeated testing.

He was of above average intelligence and his general level of awareness was extremely keen. His memory was remarkable... His span of digit retention was eight forward and six backward. There was no hesitation in his speech, and he could obey complex orders. He read smoothly, and there was no trouble in understanding and later describing what he had read. He promptly recognized, named, and demonstrated the use of a wide variety of test objects. The significance of line drawings was immediately apparent to him, and he could accurately describe the content of various pictures he was shown.

He mixed readily with the other patients on the ward, but rarely spoke unless spoken to first. He could not identify his medical attendants. "You must be a doctor because of your white coat, but I don't know which one you are. I'll know if you speak." He failed to identify his wife during visiting hours. She was told one day, without his possible knowledge, to walk right past his bed, but he did not show the least sign of recognition. Repeated attempts were made to "catch him out" but none succeeded. If the disability was a feigned one, it was a performance of quite unbelievable virtuosity and consistency. He failed to identify pictures of Mr. Churchill, Mr. Aneurin Bevan, Hitler, Stalin, Miss Marilyn Monroe, or Mr. Groucho Marx. When confronted with such portraits he would proceed deductively, analyzing one feature after another, searching for the "critical detail" that would yield the answer. In human faces, this was rarely forthcoming. He had somewhat less difficulty with animal faces. A goat was eventually recognized by its ears and beard, a giraffe by its neck, a crocodile by its dentition, and a cat by its whiskers.

The patient had analyzed his difficulty in identifying faces with considerable insight. "I can see the eyes, nose, and mouth quite clearly, but they just don't add up. They all seem chalked in, like on a blackboard.... I have to tell by the clothes or by the voice whether it is a man or a woman.... The hair may help a lot, or if there is a mustache.

"At the club I saw someone strange staring at me, and asked the steward who it was. You'll laugh at me. I'd been looking at myself in a mirror." (Excerpted from Pallis.[65])

mation, and their inability to attach these percepts to the appropriate identity of the individual has been interpreted as a deficit in accessing the stored semantic or biographical memories associated with a given facial structure that make possible both identification and the feeling of familiarity. Other patients have severe difficulty with all aspects of face processing; such patients presumably are unable to analyze facial features normally, a necessary precondition to identification. Finally, some patients can perceive structural attributes adequately for judgments about emotion and gender and can even judge whether a face is familiar or not, but have a specific inability to recall the name associated with a familiar individual.[69]

Prosopagnosia Is Caused by Damage to the Ventral Occipitotemporal and Temporal Cortex

Initially, prosopagnosia of various types was associated clinically with right posterior cortical damage, and accordingly face recognition was believed to be dependent exclusively on structures within the posterior right hemisphere, at least in right-handers. In the 1980s, a number of cases came to autopsy. The damage common to these cases lay within the lingual and fusiform gyri, very ventrally and medially within the cortex at the occipitotemporal junction, in roughly the same region of the cortex as that activated in recent neuroimaging studies of object recognition (see Fig. 52.7B). However, in all such cases, this area (or at least the underlying white matter) was damaged bilaterally, and consequently bilateral damage has been thought by many to be a necessary precondition for prosopagnosia.[70] Several cases with prosopagnosia and right cortical damage alone, along with the results of imaging studies, have reopened the debate over the locus of the critical lesion in prosopagnosia. Some of the different patterns of deficits are undoubtedly due to different foci of damage.

A "Monkey Model" of Prosopagnosia Has Not Yet Been Achieved

Prosopagnosia has been conceptualized as the loss of a unique cognitive ability due to localized brain damage. It has often been further interpreted as reflecting the selective loss of ensembles of neurons homologous to face-selective neurons in monkey temporal cortex. Interestingly, the region containing the greatest concentration of face-selective neurons in monkeys—the superior temporal sulcus—is geographically quite distant from the very ventral cortices one would suppose to be homologous to the site of damage revealed in humans with prosopagnosia. Moreover, bilateral ablation of the superior temporal sulcus in monkeys clearly fails to produce more than minor face processing or face recognition impairments on a battery of tasks.[71] Even the minor impairments seen after such lesions—such as a deficit in judging the direction of gaze of a stimulus monkey—appear to be related to the type of behavioral task used and do not appear to be specific to facial material.[72] Face-selective neurons located in more lateral and ventral portions of the temporal lobe (e.g., on the inferior temporal gyrus within area TE) therefore also probably play an important role in face recognition. However, removal of this cortex causes severe impairments not only in face perception but also in perception and recognition of a large number of other classes of objects. One possibility is that the neural substrates for recognizing face and nonface stimuli are not segregated as completely in monkeys as in humans. An alternative possibility is that the still poorly understood ventromedial cortices of monkeys (particularly parahippocampal areas TF and TH) may play a selective role in face recognition that has not yet been appreciated.

Substrates of Dissociable Aspects of Face Recognition in Human Cortex Are Revealed by Functional Imaging and Recording Methods

Neuroimaging studies in normal humans provide strong support both for the involvement of the ventral stream in face recognition and for the existence of dissociable component operations within face processing that are differentially linked to different loci within this pathway and to the two hemispheres. For example, using PET methods, researchers have compared regional activation in normal subjects who were required either to determine the gender of stimulus faces or to judge their identity.[54] In the gender discrimination condition, presumably a perceptual task of facial features, selective activation was found in the right ventral occipitotemporal cortex, to a lesser extent in the same area on the left side, and in a more lateral left focus as well (see foci "F" in Fig. 52.7). These areas overlapped, but were at least partially more anterior to the domains activated by processing of other categories of objects. Judgments of face identity, on the other hand, which presumably require reactivation of specific stored information about individuals, also activated more anterior portions of ventral extrastriate cortex, including the right parahippocampal gyrus, and anterior temporal cortex and the temporal pole on both sides. These studies and those of Haxby and colleagues[53] additionally implicated a portion of the right ventral frontal lobe in perceptual judgments about faces, as well as in working memory for faces.[73] Neuroimaging work also suggests that the frontal cortex is involved in recognizing facial emotion.[74] These functional neuroimaging studies thus show a hierarchical segregation of areas involved with different components of face recognition in humans. The ventral occipitotemporal cortex of the right hemisphere appears to be primarily responsible for the perceptual analysis of faces. Information then appears to be sent forward to more anterior temporal regions for association with stored information about individuals, and frontal cortex appears to contribute both to the analysis of emotional facial content and to holding faces in a short-term memory store. Finally, lesion evidence[69] corroborates the idea that the left lateral focus seen in PET studies of judging face identity does indeed reflect a specialization for attaching stored verbal information (i.e., names) to face percepts.

Electrophysiological correlates of face recognition have also been obtained from patients who have implanted electrodes as part of the preparation for neurosurgery to treat epilepsy (Fig. 52.9).[56,75] A large evoked potential (called the *N200*) is generated by faces (but not by other categories of stimuli) at small sites (i.e., typically at only one electrode within an electrode array) in the ventral occipitotemporal cortex. These small sites, or modules, which vary in their exact location among individuals, are reminiscent of clumps of face neurons found in monkeys. Longer-latency face-specific potentials have also been recorded from the

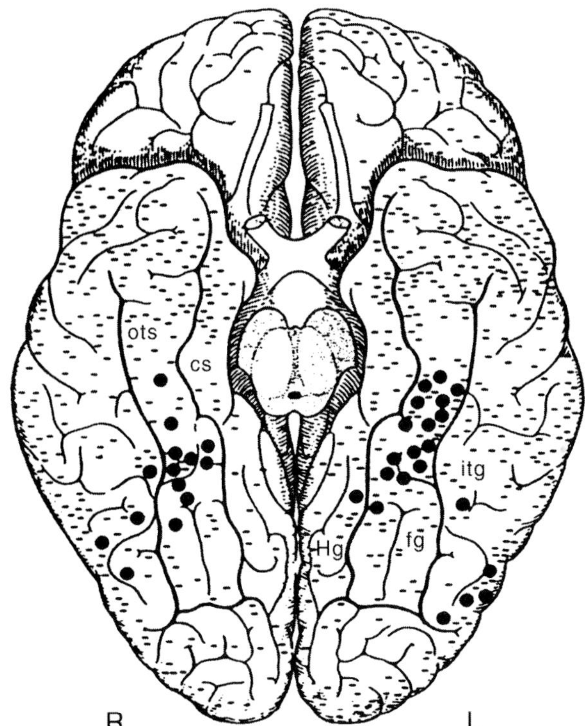

FIGURE 52.9 Summary figure of locations (black dots) on the ventral surface of the human brain from which a surface-negative potential (N200) was recorded only when patients were shown faces and not when other categories of objects were tested. Locations are primarily along the fusiform gyrus. Dashes illustrate other sites tested that were not face-selective. cs, collateral sulcus; fg, fusiform gyrus; itg, inferior temporal gyrus; lg, lingual gyrus; ots, occipitotemporal sulcus. From Allison *et al.*[75]

more anterior portions of inferior temporal cortex that were activated by face recognition in the PET studies. Although sites producing the N200 potential were found bilaterally, there was an interesting hemispheric difference. In normal humans, the right hemisphere tends to process faces as coherent wholes, and accordingly stimuli restricted to the left visual field are processed more slowly when they are presented upside-down, so that the prototypical configuration of features is disrupted. When stimuli are presented to the left hemisphere via the right visual field, no such **inversion effect** is found. Correspondingly, N200 potentials evoked by inverted faces (presented at the center of the visual field) and recorded from the right hemisphere were smaller and longer than those evoked by normally oriented faces; the left hemisphere generated comparable N200s under both conditions. Because of this correspondence between electrophysiology and behavior, the analysis of evoked potentials appears to be a valuable adjunct to other types of functional methods for studying the basis of face and object recognition in humans.

Summary

Striking parallels exist among the results of neurophysiological, neuropsychological, perceptual, and functional neuroanatomical studies of face recognition in primates. These lines of research all indicate that face recognition is a hierarchically organized set of component processes with substrates in the ventral portions of the visual cortex. In both humans and monkeys, faces are processed in subregions of the ventral stream that are at least partially dissociable from those processing other types of visual objects, or the color of objects in isolation. Consequently, the question is now whether the neural machinery dedicated to face recognition represents an adaptation for the processing of faces or for some more general and abstract type of object processing (such as configurational information), of which face recognition is an arbitrary example. In both monkeys and humans, face-processing circuits appear to be localized to relatively small modules, a situation that may reflect a more general tendency of mammalian neocortex to develop category-specific **modules** for behaviorally important classes of stimuli. If so, face recognition could be a valuable model for the understanding of basic mechanisms of object recognition, rather than being a special case.

THEORETICAL ACCOUNTS OF OBJECT RECOGNITION

Biological visual systems are highly successful. Noisy images can be taken as input and, despite the relatively slow firing rate of neurons, objects can be recognized from the images within a few hundred milliseconds.[76] Even the most sophisticated artificial vision systems have still not achieved these capabilities. Yet the goals of biological and artificial visual systems are, in their broadest terms, very similar. For both systems to be successful, processes capable of deriving descriptions of objects from noisy input and of assigning varying input to common categories must be present so that objects are recognized across wide variations in image properties (position, viewing angle, distance, and size). Because of these common goals, theories can address common problems relevant to both biological and artificial visual systems. Full accounts of biological visual systems, however, will also need to explain how the processes of object recognition are implemented in neural terms. Here we discuss several major theories of object recognition, drawing on studies of both artificial and biological visual systems to provide an account of the general processes involved. In addition, we consider proposals about their neural implementation.

Three-Dimensional Representations Arise from "Bottom-Up" Processes (Marr's Approach to Object Recognition)

Perhaps the most influential theoretical account of the processes leading to visual object recognition over the past 15 years is that of David Marr.[77,78] Marr argued that object recognition involves the coding of a series of different representations of objects, with each representation making different kinds of information explicit. Marr's framework starts from the idea that the information used for object recognition is recovered from images on the retina by locating and describing the places where the intensity of the image changes relatively abruptly. These abrupt changes in image intensity signal the presence of edges in the world and can be used to derive useful three-dimensional (3D) attributes such as surface markings on objects, object boundaries, and shadows. Marr proposed that these attributes are specified in something he termed a *primal sketch.* He distinguished two stages of deriving the primal sketch: (1) the raw primal sketch, involving coding and locating individual intensity changes within a map based on the retina; and (2) the full primal sketch, involving a description of the image that is more elaborate, with individual edge fragments being grouped into more meaningful clusters relating to surfaces. Grouping is based on simple physical laws of perceptual organization—for instance, that image elements that are closer or more similar will be grouped more strongly than those that are farther apart and dissimilar. The primal sketch makes explicit information about the presence of two-dimensional (2D) intensity changes in the image. Implicit within this representation is information about the 3D nature of the image features or about the invariant properties of those features across different retinal locations.

At the next stage of coding in Marr's framework, information about the distance and layout of each surface is added, using a variety of depth cues. This representation is termed the *2½D sketch* because it describes only the visible parts of the scene and thus is not fully 3D. The 2½D sketch may be useful for matching actions to objects, because it specifies information about the relative depths of surfaces with respect to the viewer. However, the representation may be problematic for object recognition. To recognize an object, there needs to be contact between the representation encoded and a stored memory for the object concerned. The 2½D sketch for a given object is specific to the particular viewing conditions; for example, if the observer moves position, or if the object is presented at a different angle, then a different 2½D sketch will be derived. For such a representation to serve for object recognition, stored representations for all views of objects would need to exist. This introduced problems of memory storage and of matching. That is, given the immense number of memory representations needed, how can a given image description be matched to an appropriate memory representation? To lessen these problems, Marr suggested that a further representation—the *3D model description*—be constructed.

In the 3D model representation, the parts of the object are coded relative to some salient part of the object itself (e.g., relative to the main axis of the object). Because the parts of objects generally remain in the same location relative to the main axis of the object, the 3D model description remains the same when objects are presented in different views—provided that the same main axis can be recovered in the different images. Consequently, only a single 3D model representation may need to be stored for each known object. Also, for objects to be identified across different viewpoints, the stored 3D model description needs to specify all the parts of an object, even if the parts are not visible in a given image; hence it is truly 3D (unlike the 2½D sketch). Marr further suggested that the parts coded within the 3D model description take the form of **generalized cones.** Generalized cones are the shapes formed by expanding a constant shape in 3D along a main axis—for instance, a vase can be formed from a circular cross section that expands (e.g., at the base) and contracts (e.g., at the stem) along a main axis. Such generalized cone representations makes explicit information about the 3D structure of objects. Figure 52.10 illustrates Marr's framework.

Marr's approach to object recognition stressed that recognition involves **bottom-up processes,** which extract information from the image and build useful descriptions, without incorporating procedures specific to the individual objects concerned. Object descriptions are derived using rules that make general assumptions

FIGURE 52.10 Marr's framework for visual object recognition.

about the nature of the visual world, but do not call on knowledge about specific objects. Marr's approach contrasts with **top-down approaches,** which suggest that knowledge about specific objects is used to facilitate early stages of object processing. As we shall see, a role for top-down mechanisms is favored in some theories dealing with how object recognition might be realized in networks using neuronlike processing units.

Object Recognition Is Achieved by Encoding Relations between Component Parts (Biederman's Approach)

Biederman and colleagues[79–81] have proposed a somewhat different approach to visual object recognition. This approach differs from the one advocated by Marr in at least two significant ways: One is that, according to Biederman, the component parts of objects can be detected directly from the presence of appropriate 2D edge descriptors in images, without it being necessary to encode properties of the surfaces of objects (as would be the case when a 2½D sketch is derived en route to the construction of a 3D model description). The second difference is that recognition involves coding the spatial relations between the component parts, but without the parts necessarily being encoded with respect to a more global property of the whole object, such as its main axis.

Biederman argues that a finite number of volumetric component parts—he terms these "geons," akin to letters of an alphabet—when combined, form many of the objects that we know (Fig. 52.11).[82] Geons can be encoded directly from the presence of "nonaccidental" relations between 2D edge descriptors. Nonaccidental relations are those that are highly unlikely to occur by chance, given random noise in an image[83]; they include relations such as parallel or co-linear edges and closure. The presence of such relations can be used to infer directly the presence of particular geons. Also, because the same nonaccidental features can be derived across a wide range of image variations, the encoding of geons is relatively robust to changes in viewpoint (viewing angle, position, distance, etc.).

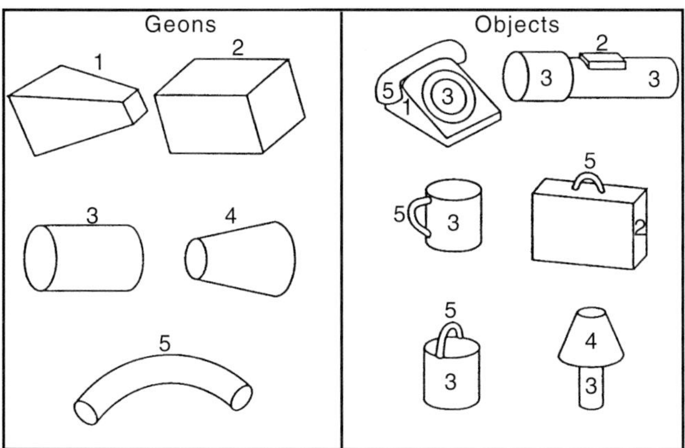

FIGURE 52.11 Illustration of geons and how they are arranged to form objects. (Left) A given view of an object can be represented by an arrangement of simple primitive volumes, or geons, five of which are shown here. (Right) Only two or three geons are required to uniquely specify an object. The relations among the geons matter, as illustrated with the pail and cup. From Biederman.[82]

Experimental Evidence Shows That Both Marr's and Biederman's Approaches Have Validity

Evidence that the spatial relations between component parts are important for object recognition comes from work showing that recognition is impaired when objects are broken into their parts and the spatial relations between the parts are scrambled.[84] Biederman[79] also showed that recognizing line drawings of objects was especially difficult when fragments of the drawings were removed to eliminate regions of discontinuity that might be used to parse the objects into their components (e.g., if the corner regions between the components were removed). This result suggests again that parsing of objects at regions of discontinuity is important for object recognition, although it does not illuminate the nature of the components subsequently encoded.

The approaches of Marr and Biederman differ in the role played by an object's main axis in object recognition. Marr assigns the axis a special role in enabling recognition to become relatively invulnerable to the effects of viewpoint change, whereas Biederman assigns no such special role to the main axis of an object. Biederman and Gerhardstein[81] have reported that large depth rotations produce relatively small effects on object recognition and also that such rotations do not strongly affect the priming effect of one view of an object on the object's subsequent recognition. Strong effects of depth rotation might be expected if the rotations lead to foreshortening of the main axis of the object and if foreshortening is particularly damaging for recognition. On the other hand, researchers[85] have reported that foreshortening disrupts identification even when all the main component parts of objects remain visible. In addition, identification of foreshortened objects is facilitated when the objects are photographed against a textured background giving strong linear perspective cues to the depth of the main axis of the object.[86] These apparently contradictory results may reflect the difficulty of defining the precise component parts used for object recognition, or it may be that recognition is relatively invulnerable to rotations in depth unless the rotations produce severe foreshortening (e.g., when the real main axis of the object is no longer the depicted main axis); evidence[87] indicates such nonlinear effects of foreshortening on people's ability to match different views of objects, thus supporting this view. It may also be that specific component parts and a more global representation of the parts in relation to the main axis of the object can both be used for object recognition[88]; which description is dominant may depend on the task and the context of the discrimination (e.g., whether other similar stimuli may also be presented).

The approaches of Marr and Biederman also differ with respect to the role of surface information in object recognition. Within Marr's framework, surface information can directly affect object recognition, because the $2\frac{1}{2}$D sketch (specifying surface details) is constructed before the 3D model description of an object is generated. In contrast, Biederman's approach emphasizes the role of edge-based information in object recognition. Once again, both approaches appear to be valid to some degree. Biederman and Ju[89] failed to find strong effects of surface information on object recognition and reported that line drawings of objects could be recognized as efficiently as full-color photographs. However, this result depends to some degree on the stimuli used. The effects of surface information on the recognition of man-made objects (*artifacts*) are relatively slight, but are more substantial on the recognition of living things.[90] Living things, as a class, tend to be more visually similar to one another than artifacts and they also tend to have diagnostic colors; surface details appear to be useful when recognition depends on fine-grained discrimination between visually similar items and when surface details are diagnostic for the particular objects involved. The evidence suggests that stored object representations can be accessed directly from edge descriptors, but surface-based representations can contribute when edge-based recognition is relatively inefficient.

Connectionist Approaches Include "Top-Down" Processes for Object Recognition

So far, we have discussed approaches to object recognition that emphasize bottom-up mechanisms, which do not involve knowledge about specific objects in the processes leading up to object recognition. Some attempts to implement object recognition in networks using neuronlike units (so-called connectionist models) move away from this approach, to allow stored knowledge to be used in a top-down manner to guide the recognition process. For instance, Edelman and colleagues[91,92] have trained neural network models (i.e., computer simulations of hypothetical networks constructed of neuronlike units) to recognize wire-framed objects on the basis of a stored set of 2D views. In such models, many different stored representations are formed for a given object, and recognition of the same object from a new view involves interpolation between the stored views. Not only were the models able to recognize the objects they were trained on, but they generated relatively accurate predictions about the success of human recognition of the same objects when rotated. Subjects trained with a set of views in one plane were then presented with the objects either within the same plane of orientation as the old objects (but in new positions) or in a plane orthogonal to that of the old exemplars. There was poor generalization of learning to objects presented in a new, orthogonal plane and much better generalization to objects presented at the new locations in the "old" plane. Bulthoff and Edelman[93] suggest that recognition based on a 3D model of the objects should generalize equally well to objects presented in the old plane and to those presented in the orthogonal plane. In contrast, the finding of a better generalization within the old plane is consistent with the involvement of interpolation based on 2D representations, which is appropriate for stimuli presented in the same plane as the previously presented objects, but not for objects presented in a new plane.

These last results argue against theoretical approaches deriving from Marr's work, which emphasize the utility of having only one stored representation for each known object, along with complex coding procedures to provide accurate access to that object representation. How far Edelman's approach can be taken and whether it will generalize to cover more than the recognition of wire figures are questions awaiting further research.

There Are Open Questions about Objects versus Faces

Most theoretical accounts of object recognition do not make qualitative distinctions between the processes involved in the recognition of different types of objects; nevertheless, neuroscientific evidence suggests that recognition processes can differ for different stimuli.[94] Indeed, surface properties of objects may play a more important role in the recognition of objects belonging to visually homogeneous classes of objects (e.g., living things) than in the recognition of objects from visually more heterogeneous classes (e.g., artifacts). Faces, as a class, are probably more homogeneous than any other general class of visual stimulis, at least with regard to classes of stimuli for which we are able to identify individual exemplars. Does this visual homogeneity mean that face recognition is dependent on the representation of surface features to a greater extent than is the recognition of other types of objects? And, in face recognition, are these surface-based representations differentiated into a parts-based description of the object?[94] These detailed points require further research.

Summary

Lesion studies in monkeys and humans have shown that the ability to identify and recognize objects depends on the inferior temporal cortex. Visual information is relayed to the inferior temporal cortex via a ventrally directed cortical pathway, or "stream," consisting of several functionally distinct visual areas. At successive stations of this ventral stream, the stimulus representation is progressively transformed from one specifying retinal image properties toward one emphasizing intrinsic object shape properties. Functional brain imaging and electrical recording studies in humans suggest that face recognition may involve a specialized neural machinery separate from that responsible for the recognition of other objects. However, it is still unclear whether such a specialized machinery represents an adaptation for the processing of faces per se (e.g., through very protracted experience with faces leading to expert knowledge) or an adaptation for some more abstract type of object processing (e.g., a surface-based representation), of which faces are an especially good example. Theoretical accounts of object recognition have included those of Marr and of Biederman, both of which stress bottom-up mechanisms, as well as that of Edelman and colleagues, in which object recognition is implemented in a network of neuronlike units. One advantage of this latter, connectionist approach is that it allows stored knowledge to be used in a top-down manner to guide the bottom-up recognition process.

References

1. Farah, M. J. (1990). *Visual Agnosia: Disorders of Object Recognition and What They Tell Us About Normal Vision.* MIT Press, Cambridge, MA.
2. Lissauer, H. (1890). Ein fall von seelenblindheit nebst einem beitrage zur theorie derselben. *Arch. Psychiatr. Nervenkr.* **21:** 222–270.
3. Levine, D. N. (1982). Visual agnosia in monkey and man. In *Analysis of Visual Behavior* (D. I. Ingle, M. A. Goodale, and R. J. W. Mansfield, eds.), pp. 629–670. MIT Press, Cambridge, MA.
4. Potzl, O. (1928). *Die Aphasielehre vom Standpunkte der kliniscen Psychiatrie.* Franz Deudicte, Lepzig.
5. Farah, M. J. (1991). Patterns of co-occurrence among the associative agnosias: Implications for visual object representation. *Cognit. Neuropsychol.* **8:** 1–19.
6. Feinberg, T. E., Schindler, R. J., Ochoa, E., Kwan, P. C., and Farah, M. J. (1994). Associative visual agnosia and alexia without prosopagnosia. *Cortex* **30:** 395–411.
7. Klüver, H., and Bucy, P. C. (1937). "Psychic blindness" and other symptoms following bilateral temporal lobectomy in rhesus monkeys. *Am. Physiol. Soc.,* pp. 352–353.
8. Mishkin, M. (1954). Visual discrimination performance following partial ablations of the temporal lobe. II. Ventral surface vs. hippocampus. *J. Comp. Physiol. Psychol.* **47:** 187–193.
9. Mishkin, M. (1966). Visual mechanisms beyond the striate cortex. In *Frontiers in Physiological Psychology* (R. W. Russell, ed.), pp. 93–119. Academic Press, New York.
10. Mishkin, M., and Pribram, K. H. (1954). Visual discrimination performance following partial ablations of the temporal lobe. I. Ventral vs. lateral. *J. Comp. Physiol. Psychol.* **47:** 14–20.
11. Pribram, K. H. (1955). Toward a science of neuropsychology: Method and data. In *Current Trends in Psychology and the Behavioral Sciences* (J. T. Wilson, C. S. Ford, B. F. Skinner, G. Bergmann, F. A. Beach, and K. Pribram, eds.), pp. 115–142. University of Pittsburgh, Pittsburgh, PA.
12. Dean, P. (1982). Visual behavior in monkeys with inferotemporal lesions. In *Analysis of Visual Behavior* (D. J. Ingle, M. A. Goodale, and R. J. W. Mansfield, eds.), pp. 587–628. MIT Press, Cambridge, MA.
13. Gross, C. G., and Mishkin, M. (1977). The neural basis of stimulus equivalence across retinal translation. In *Lateralization in the Nervous System* (S. R. Harnad, R. W. Doty, L. Goldstein, J. Jaynes, and G. Krauthamer, eds.), pp. 109–122. Academic Press, New York.
14. Seacord, L., Gross, C. G., and Mishkin, M. (1979). Role of inferior temporal cortex in interhemispheric transfer. *Brain Res.* **167:** 259–272.
15. Humphrey, N. K., and Weiskrantz, L. (1969). Size constancy in monkeys with inferotemporal lesions. *Q. J. Exp. Psychol.* **21:** 225–238.
16. Weiskrantz, L., and Saunders, R. C. (1984). Impairments of visual object transforms in monkeys. *Brain* **107:** 1033–1072.
17. Rubens, A. B., and Benson, D. F. (1971). Associative visual agnosia. *Arch. Neurol.* (*Chicago*) **24:** 305–316.
18. Bay, E. (1953). Disturbances of visual perception and their examination. *Brain* **76:** 515–550.
19. Bender, M. B., and Feldman, M. (1972). The so-called "visual agnosias." *Brain* **95:** 173–186.
20. Ungerleider, L. G., and Mishkin, M. (1982). Two cortical visual systems. In *Analysis of Visual Behavior* (D. Ingle, M. A. Goodale, and R. J. W. Mansfield, eds.), pp. 549–586. MIT Press, Cambridge, MA.
21. von Bonin, G., and Bailey, P. (1947). *The Neocortex of Macaca mulatia.* University of Illinois Press, Urbana, IL.
22. Mishkin, M., Ungerleider, L. G., and Macko, K. A. (1983). Object vision and spatial vision: Two cortical pathways. *Trends Neurosci.* **6:** 415–417.
23. Gross, C. G., Rodman, H. R., Gochin, P. M., and Colombo, M. W. (1993). Inferior temporal cortex as a pattern recognition device. In *Computational Learning and Cognition* (E. Baum, ed.), pp. 44–73. SIAM Press, Philadelphia.
24. Baizer, J. S., Ungerleider, L. G., and Desimone, R. (1991). Organization of visual inputs to the inferior temporal and posterior parietal cortex in macaques. *J. Neurosci.* **11:** 168–190.
25. Van Essen, D. C. (1985). Functional organization of primate visual cortex. In *Cerebral Cortex* (A. Peters and E. G. Jones, eds.), pp. 259–329. Plenum, New York.

26. Felleman, D. J., and Van Essen, D. C. (1991). Distributed hierarchical processing in the primate cerebral cortex. *Cereb. Cortex* **1:** 1–47.
27. Lewis, M. E., Mishkin, M., Bragin, E., Brown, R. M., Pert, C. B., and Pert, A. (1981). Opiate receptor gradients in monkey cerebral cortex: Correspondence with sensory processing hierarchies. *Science* **211:** 1166–1169.
28. Nelson, R. B., Friedman, D. P., O'Neill, J. B., Mishkin, M., and Routtenberg, A. (1987). Gradients of protein kinase C substrate phosphorylation in primate visual system peak in visual memory storage areas. *Brain Res.* **28:** 387–392.
29. Desimone, R., and Ungerleider, L. G. (1989). Neural mechanisms of visual processing monkeys. In *Handbook of Neuropsychology* (F. Boller and J. Grafman, eds.), pp. 267–299. Elsevier, Amsterdam.
30. Boussaoud, D., Desimone, R., and Ungerleider, L. G. (1991). Visual topography of area TEO in the macaque. *J. Comp. Neurol.* **306:** 554–575.
31. Fenstemaker, S. B., Albright, T. D., and Gross, C. G. (1985). Organization and neuronal properties of visual area TEO. *Soc. Neurosci. Abstr.* **11:** 1012.
32. Gattass, R., Gross, C. G., and Sandell, J. H. (1981). Visual topography of V2 in the macaque. *J. Comp. Neurol.* **201:** 519–539.
33. Gattass, R., Sousa, A. P. B., and Gross, C. G. (1988). Visuotopic organization and extent of V3 and V4 of the macaque. *J. Neurosci.* **8:** 1831–1856.
34. Bruce, C., Desimone, R., and Gross, C. G. (1981). Visual properties of neurons in a polysensory area in superior temporal sulcus of the macaque. *J. Neurophysiol.* **46:** 369–384.
35. Mishkin, M., and Murray, E. A. (1994). Stimulus recognition. *Curr. Opin. Neurobiol.* **4:** 200–206.
36. Baizer, J. S., Robinson, D. L., and Dow, B. M. (1977). Visual responses of area 18 neurons in awake, behaving monkey. *J. Neurophysiol.* **40:** 1024–1037.
37. Burkhalter, A., and Van Essen, D. C. (1986). Processing of color, form and disparity information in visual areas VP and V2 of ventral extrastriate cortex in the macaque monkey. *J. Neurosci.* **6:** 2327–2351.
38. von der Heydt, R., Peterhans, E., and Baumgartner, G. (1984). Illusory contours and cortical neuron responses. *Science* **224:** 1260–1262.
39. Desimone, R., and Schein, S. J. (1987). Visual properties of neurons in area V4 of the macaque: Sensitivity to stimulus form. *J. Neurophysiol.* **57:** 835–868.
40. Gallant, J. L., Braun, J., and Van Essen, D. C. (1993). Selectivity for polar, hyperbolic and Cartesian gratings in macaque visual cortex. *Science* **259:** 100–103.
41. Kobatake, E., and Tanaka, K. (1994). Neuronal selectivities to complex object features in the ventral visual pathway of the macaque cerebral cortex. *J. Neurophysiol.* **71:** 856–867.
42. Zeki, S. (1983). Colour coding in the cerebral cortex: The responses of wavelength-selective and colour-coded cells in monkey visual cortex to changes in wavelength composition. *Neuroscience* **9:** 767–781.
43. Moran, J., and Desimone, R. (1985). Selective attention gates visual processing in the extrastriate cortex. *Science* **229:** 782–784.
44. Haenny, P. E., Maunsell, J. H., and Schiller, P. H. (1988). State dependent activity in monkey visual cortex. II. Retinal and extraretinal factors in V4. *Exp. Brain Res.* **69:** 245–259.
45. Desimone, R., Albright, T. D., Gross, C. G., and Bruce, C. (1984). Stimulus-selective properties of inferior temporal neurons in the macaque. *J. Neurosci.* **4:** 2051–2062.
46. Tanaka, K., Saito, H., Fukada, Y., and Moriya, M. (1991). Coding visual images of objects in the inferotemporal cortex of the macaque monkey. *J. Neurophysiol.* **66:** 170–189.
47. Sato, T., Kawamura, T., and Iwai, E. (1980). Responsiveness of inferotemporal single units to visual pattern stimuli in monkeys performing discrimination. *Exp. Brain Res.* **38:** 313–319.
48. Sary, G., Vogels, S. R., and Orban, G. A. (1993). Cue-invariant shape selectivity of macaque inferior temporal neurons. *Science* **260:** 995–997.
49. Li, L., Miller, E. K., and Desimone, R. (1993). The representation of stimulus familiarity in anterior inferior temporal cortex. *J. Neurophysiol.* **69:** 1918–1929.
50. Miller, E. K., Li, L., and Desimone, R. (1993). Activity of neurons in anterior inferior temporal cortex during a short-term memory task. *J. Neurosci.* **13:** 1460–1478.
51. Miyashita, Y. (1988). Neuronal correlate of visual associative long-term memory in the primate temporal cortex. *Nature (London)* **335:** 817–820.
52. Ungerleider, L. G., and Haxby, J. V. (1994). "What" and "where" in the human brain. *Curr. Opin. Neurobiol.* **4:** 157–165.
53. Haxby, J. V., Horwitz, B., Ungerleider, L. G., Maisog, J. M., Pietrini, P., and Grady, C. L. (1994). The functional organization of human extrastriate cortex: A PET-rCBF study of selective attention to faces and locations. *J. Neurosci.* **14:** 6336–6353.
54. Sergent, J., Ohta, S., and MacDonald, B. (1992). Functional neuroanatomy of face and object processing: A positron emission tomography study. *Brain* **115:** 15–36.
55. Rodman, H. (1998). Temporal cortex. *Encycl. Neurosci.* (in press).
56. Allison, T., McCarthy, C., Nobre, A., Puce, A., and Belger, A. (1994). Human extrastriate visual cortex and the perception of faces, words, numbers, and colors. *Cereb. Cortex* **4:** 544–554.
57. Gross, C. G., Rocha-Miranda, C. E., and Bender, D. B. (1972). Visual properties of neurons in inferotemporal cortex of the Macaque. *J. Neurophysiol.* **35:** 96–111.
58. Konorski, J. (1967). *Integrative Activity of the Brain*. University of Chicago, Chicago.
59. Gross, C. G., and Sergent, J. (1992). Face recognition. *Curr. Opin. Neurobiol.* **2:** 156–161.
60. Baylis, G. C., Rolls, E. T., and Leonard, C. M. (1985). Selectivity between faces in the responses of a population of neurons in the cortex in the superior temporal sulcus of the monkey. *Brain Res.* **342:** 91–102.
61. Hasselmo, M. E., Rolls, E. T., and Baylis, G. C. (1989). The role of expression and identity in the face-selective responses of neurons in the temporal visual cortex of the monkey. *Behav. Brain Res.* **32:** 203–218.
62. Yamane, S., Kaji, S., and Kawano, K. (1988). What facial features activate face neurons in the inferotemporal cortex of the monkey? *Exp. Brain Res.* **73:** 209–214.
63. Perrett, D. I., Smith, P. A., Potter, D. D., Mistlin, A. J., Head, A. S., Milner, A. D., and Jeeves, M. A. (1985). Visual cells in the temporal cortex sensitive to face view and gaze direction. *Proc. R. Soc. London B* **223:** 293–317.
64. Rodman, H. R., Scalaidhe, S. P., and Gross, C. G. (1993). Response properties of neurons in temporal cortical visual areas of infant monkeys. *J. Neurophysiol.* **70:** 1115–1136.
65. Pallis, C. A. (1955). Impaired identification of faces and places with agnosia for colors. *J. Neurol. Neurosurg. Psychiatry* **18:** 218–224.
66. Farah, M. J., Levinson, K. L., and Klein, K. L. (1995). Face perception and within-category discrimination in prosopagnosia. *Neuropsychologia* **33:** 661–674.
67. Diamond, R., and Carey, S. (1986). Why faces are and are not special: An effect of expertise. *J. Exp. Psychol. Gen.* **115:** 107–117.

68. Tranel, D., Damasio, A. R., and Damasio, H. (1988). Intact recognition of facial expression, gender, and age in patients with impaired recognition of face identity. *Neurology* **38:** 690–696.
69. Flude, B. M., Ellis, A. W., and Kay, J. (1989). Face processing and name retrieval in an anemic aphasic: Names are stored separately from semantic information about familiar people. *Brain Cognit.* **11:** 60–72.
70. Damasio, A. R., Tranel, D., and Damasio, H. (1990). Face agnosia and the neural substrates of memory. *Annu. Rev. Neurosci.* **13:** 89–109.
71. Heywood, C. A., and Cowey, A. (1992). The role of the "face cell" area in the discrimination and recognition of faces by monkeys. *Philos. Trans. R. Soc. London B* **335:** 31–37.
72. Eacott, M. J., Heywood, C. A., Gross, C. G., and Cowey, A. (1993). Visual discrimination impairments following lesions of the superior temporal sulcus are not specific for facial stimuli. *Neuropsychologia* **31:** 609–619.
73. Courtney, S. M., Underleider, L. G., Keil, K., and Haxby, J. V. (1997). Transient and sustained activity in a neural system for human working memory. *Nature* **386:** 608–611.
74. George, M. S., Ketter, T. A., Gill, D. S., Haxby, J. V., Ungerleider, L. G., Herscovitch, P., and Post, R. M. (1993). Brain regions involved in recognizing facial emotion or identity: An oxygen-15 PET study. *J. Neuropsychiatry Clin. Neurosci.* **5:** 384–394.
75. Allison, T., Ginter, H., McCarthy, G., Nobre, A., Puce, A., Luby, M., and Spencer, D. D. (1994). Face recognition in human extrastriate cortex. *J. Neurophysiol.* **71:** 821–825.
76. Thorpe, S. J., and Imbert, M. (1989). Biological constraints on connectionist modelling. In *Connectionism in Perspective* (R. Pfeifer, Z. Schreter, F. Fogelman-Soulié, and L. Steels, eds.), pp. 63–92. Elsevier/North-Holland, Amsterdam.
77. Marr, D. (1982). *Vision: A Computational Investigation into the Human Representation and Processing of Visual Information.* Freeman, San Francisco.
78. Marr, D., and Nishihara, H. K. (1978). Representation and recognition of the spatial organization of three-dimensional shapes. *Proc. R. Soc. London B* **200:** 269–294.
79. Biederman, I. (1987). Recognition-by-components: A theory of human image understanding. *Psychol. Rev.* **94:** 115–147.
80. Biederman, I., and Cooper, E. E. (1991). Priming contour-deleted images: Evidence for intermediate representations in visual object recognition. *Cognit. Psychol.* **23:** 393–419.
81. Biederman, I., and Gerhardstein, P. C. (1993). Recognizing depth-rotated objects: Evidence and conditions for three-dimensional viewpoint invariance. *J. Exp. Psychol. Hum. Percept. Perform.* **19:** 1162–1182.
82. Biederman, I. (1990). Higher-level vision. In *Visual Cognition and Action* (D. H. Osherson, S. M. Kosslyn, and J. M. Hollerbach, eds.), Vol. 2, pp. 41–72. MIT Press, Cambridge, MA.
83. Lowe, D. G. (1987). Three-dimensional object recognition from single two-dimensional images. *Artif. Intell.* **31:** 355–395.
84. Cave, C. B., and Kosslyn, S. M. (1993). The role of parts and spatial relations in object identification. *Perception* **22:** 229–248.
85. Humphreys, G. K., and Jolicoeur, P. (1993). An examination of the effects of axis foreshortening, monocular depth cues, and visual field on object identification. *Q. J. Exp. Psychol.* **A 46:** 137–159.
86. Humphreys, G. W., and Riddoch, M. J. (1984). Routes to object constancy: Implications from neurological impairments of object constancy. *Q. J. Exp. Psychol.* **A 36:** 385–415.
87. Lawson, R., and Humphreys, G. W. (1998). View-specificity in object processing: Evidence from picture matching. *J. Exp. Psychol. Hum. Percept. Perform.* (in press).
88. Jolicoeur, P. (1992). Identification of disoriented objects: A dual-systems theory. In *Understanding Vision: An Interdisciplinary Perspective* (G. W. Humphreys, ed.), pp. 180–198. Blackwell, Oxford.
89. Biederman, I., and Ju, G. (1988). Surface versus edge-based determinants of visual recognition. *Cognit. Psychol.* **20:** 38–64.
90. Price, C. J., and Humphreys, G. W. (1989). The effects of surface detail on object categorization and naming. *Q. J. Exp. Psychol.* **A 41:** 797–827.
91. Poggio, T., and Edelman, S. (1990). A network that learns to recognize three-dimensional objects. *Nature (London)* **343:** 263–266.
92. Edelman, S., and Weinshall, D. (1991). A self-organizing multiple-view representation of 3D objects. *Biol. Cybernet.* **64:** 209–219.
93. Bulthoff, H. H., and Edelman, S. (1992). Psychophysical support for a two-dimensional view interpolation theory of object recognition. *Proc. Natl. Acad. Sci. U.S.A.* **89:** 60–64.
94. Bruce, V., and Humphreys, G. W. (1994). Recognizing objects and faces. *Visual Cognit.* **2/3:** 141–180.

CHAPTER

53

Spatial Cognition

Carol L. Colby and Carl R. Olson

As we move through the world, new visual, auditory, vestibular, and somatosensory inputs are continuously presented to the brain. Given such constantly changing input, it is remarkable how easily we are able to keep track of where things are. We can reach for an object, or look at it, or even kick it without making a conscious effort to assess its location in space. But how do we construct a representation of space that allows us to act so effortlessly? This chapter will outline the contributions of several brain areas in the parietal, frontal, and hippocampal cortices to spatial representation, spatial memory, and the generation of actions in space.

THE NEUROANATOMY OF SPATIAL COGNITION

Dorsal Stream Areas Process Visuospatial Information

Within the cerebral hemisphere, visual information is processed serially by a succession of areas progressively more distant from the primary visual cortex of the occipital lobe. Within this hierarchical system, there are two parallel chains, or streams, of areas: the ventral stream, leading downward into the temporal lobe (area TE; see Chapter 52), and the dorsal stream, leading forward into the parietal lobe (area PG; see Chapter 52).[1] Although the two streams are interconnected to some degree, it is a fair first approximation to describe them as separate parallel systems.[2] Areas of the ventral stream play a critical role in the recognition of visual patterns, including faces, whereas areas of the dorsal stream contribute selectively to conscious spatial awareness and to the spatial guidance of actions, like reaching and grasping.[3–6] Dorsal stream areas have at least two distinctive functional traits: first, they contain a comparatively extensive representation of the peripheral visual field; second, they appear to be specialized for the detection and analysis of moving visual images. Both traits would be expected in any system processing visual information for use in spatial awareness and in the visual guidance of behavior.

Although visual input is important for spatial operations, awareness of space is more than just a visual function. We are able to apprehend the shape of an object, and we can tell where it is, regardless of whether we see it or sense it through touch. Accordingly, spatial awareness, considered as a general phenomenon, depends not on visual areas of the dorsal stream but rather on supravisual areas to which they send their output. The transition from areas serving merely visual functions to those mediating generalized spatial awareness is probably gradual, but certainly has been accomplished by the time the dorsal stream reaches its termination in the association cortex of the posterior parietal lobe.

Association Areas Responsible for Spatial Cognition Form a Tightly Interconnected System

The posterior parietal cortex appears to be preeminent among cortical areas responsible for spatial awareness, because lesions of the posterior parietal cortex lead to the most devastating and specific impairments of spatial cognition. However, numerous other

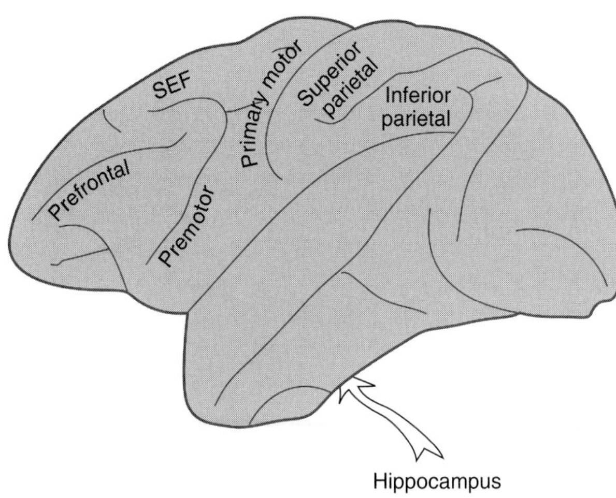

FIGURE 53.1 Lateral view of the left cerebral hemisphere of a rhesus monkey. Areas in the parietal and frontal cortex responsible for motor and cognitive processes of a spatial nature. SEF, supplementary eye field. Brain drawing, courtesy of Laboratory of Neuropsychology, NIMH.

areas in the cerebral hemisphere mediate cognitive functions that depend in some way on the use of spatial information. These **association** areas occupy a continuous swath of the cerebral hemisphere encompassing large parts of the frontal, cingulate, temporal, parahippocampal, and insular cortices. They are anatomically connected to each other and to the parietal cortex by a parallel distributed pathway through which signals are thought to shuttle back and forth in a complex recurrent pattern.[7–9] The functions of some parts of this system are especially well understood. For example, the frontal cortex is involved in the generation of voluntary behavior, and the medial temporal lobe, including the hippocampus, is important for memory. In the following sections, we first consider the spatial functions of the parietal cortex; we then consider how frontal areas program voluntary movements in spatial terms; and finally, we consider how the hippocampus and parahippocampal areas mediate the formation of memories with a spatial component.

In the human brain, the association areas of the nondominant (generally right) hemisphere are particularly important for spatial cognition. The issue of lateralization of function in the human brain is taken up in another chapter (see Chapter 58). We will not be emphasizing it here because the focus of this chapter is on parallels between humans and nonhuman species, and in nonhuman species lateralization is not pronounced. In general, spatial functions are represented in the same cortical areas in humans, monkeys, and rats, but the representation is symmetrically bilateral in lower species, whereas it is biased toward the right hemisphere in humans.

Summary

Spatial functions depend on the parietal cortex and a widely distributed network of areas to which it is linked.

THE PARIETAL CORTEX

The Parietal Cortex Contains Several Divisions

The parietal lobe is divided into the superior and inferior parietal lobules. Within each lobule, several subdivisions are distinguished by anatomical and functional properties.[10–13] In humans, various cytoarchitectural divisions, notably areas 5, 7, 39, and 40, have long been recognized. The functional significance of these divisions and their relation to cytoarchitectural areas recognized in the monkey are not yet well understood. The safest generalization applicable to both humans and monkeys is that the cortex at a more anterior location, corresponding roughly to the superior parietal lobule, serves functions related primarily to **somesthesis,** or tactile cognition, whereas the cortex at a more posterior location, corresponding roughly to the inferior parietal lobule (Fig. 53.1), serves functions related primarily to visuospatial cognition. We will focus our discussion on this more posterior division of the parietal cortex. In the monkey, this posterior division can be further subdivided into functionally distinct regions, including areas LIP (lateral intraparietal) and VIP (ventral intraparietal). Whether there are corresponding subdivisions in the human brain is not known.

Injury to the Human Posterior Parietal Cortex Causes Impairments of Spatial Function

A group of behavioral impairments specifically associated with damage to the parietal lobes was first described by Balint in 1909.[14–16] Balint syndrome includes difficulty in executing eye movements to engage visual targets, inaccuracy in reaching for visual targets, and a tendency not to see things in the peripheral visual field. This collection of symptoms reflects an impairment in the visual guidance of movement and, more generally, in spatial cognition.[17,18] In the following sections, we describe some of the specific impairments of spatial behavior that are known to arise from injury to the parietal lobe.

Simultanagnosia: An Inability to See Multiple Objects Simultaneously

Following injury to the posterior parietal cortex, some patients experience difficulty in the visual perception of spatial relations. They can see objects, but have difficulty making judgments whether two objects are the same size or which of two objects is closer to them. When asked to copy simple line drawings, they may omit or transpose parts, as if unable to judge accurately the spatial arrangement of the object's components. In some patients, failure on visuospatial tests arises from an inability to see more than one object at a time.[19,20] This condition, simultanagnosia, is commonly observed after bilateral damage to the parietal cortex. When looking at the flame of a match, a patient with simultanagnosia may be unable to see the hand holding it. When tested in controlled situations, simultanagnosic patients demonstrate a profound failure of simultaneous vision; for instance, they underestimate the number of dots in a multidot display.[21] See Box 53.1.[22]

Figure 53.2 illustrates the results of a particularly illuminating test carried out on simultanagnosic patients.[23] Presented with a field of randomly intermingled red and green circles (*random* condition in Fig. 53.2), the patients were unable to say whether the circles were of different colors, presumably because they could see only one circle at a time. In contrast, when pairs of circles of different colors were joined by line segments, unifying them into a single object, the patients were able to report that the colors were different (*mixed* condition in Fig. 53.2). This improvement was specific to the condition in which circles of different colors were joined, as shown by the fact that joining circles of the same color produced no improvement (*single* condition in Fig. 53.2). It is important to note that the average distance between circles of different colors was the same in all three conditions. This indicates that the inability of patients to see and compare pairs of circles in the *random* and *single* conditions was the result of the circles' belonging to separate objects and not simply of their being separated by a certain distance.

Simultanagnosia, by preventing simultaneous vision of two objects, gives rise to poor performance on tests requiring a comparison between objects. However, when tests are confined to a single object, it appears to leave spatial perception intact. Simultanagnosic patients are able to make accurate judgments of spatial relations so long as the judgments pertain to a single object; for example, they are able to determine whether a given rectangle is more elongated horizontally or vertically.

Optic Ataxia: An Impairment of Visually Guided Reaching

After damage to the parietal cortex, some patients experience difficulty in making visually guided arm movements. This condition is referred to as **misreach-**

BOX 53.1

SIMULTANAGNOSIA

Disorders of spatial awareness arising from parietal lobe injury are not merely a laboratory phenomenon but can have a profound impact on the patient's daily life, as described in the following case study of simultanagnosia (from Coslett and Saffran, 1991)[22]:

When first examined by the authors 4 months after the right hemisphere infarction, the patient's major complaint was that her environment appeared fragmented; although she saw individual items clearly, they appeared to be isolated and she could not discern any meaningful relationship among them. She stated, for example, that she could find her way in her home (in which she had lived for 25 years) with her eyes closed, but she became confused with her eyes open. On one occasion, for example, she attempted to find her way to her bedroom by using a large lamp as a landmark; while walking toward the lamp, she fell over her dining room table. Although she enjoyed listening to the radio, television programs bewildered her because she could only "see" one person or object at a time and therefore could not determine who was speaking or being spoken to; she reported watching a movie in which, after hearing a heated argument, she noted to her surprise and consternation that the character she had been watching was suddenly sent reeling across the room, apparently as a consequence of a punch thrown by a character she had never seen. Although she was able to read single words effortlessly, she stopped reading because the "competing words" confused her. She was unable to write, as she claimed to be able to see only a single letter; thus when creating a letter, she saw only the tip of the pencil and the letter under construction and "lost" the previously constructed letters.

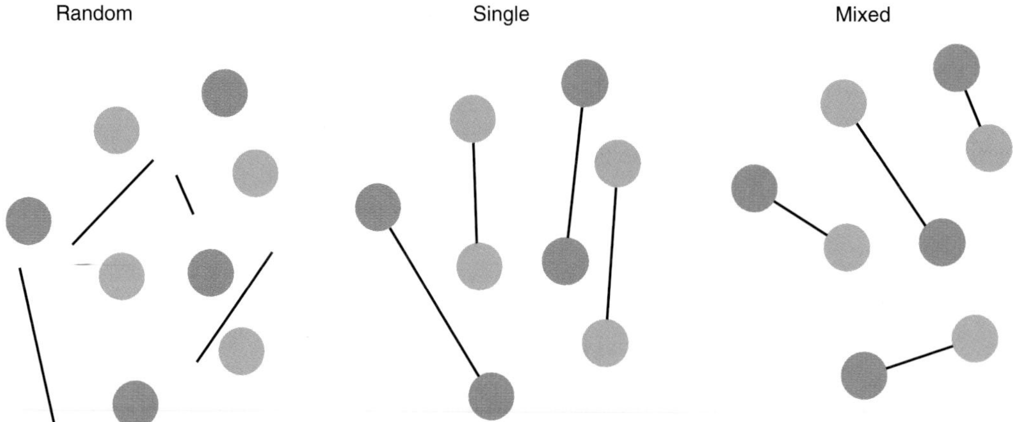

FIGURE 53.2 Three stimuli used for assessing simultanagnosia in human patients. Patients were consistently able to report that circles of different colors were present only in the mixed condition, in which red and green circles were unified into a single object by connecting line segments. From Humphreys and Riddoch.[23]

ing or **optic ataxia.**[24–26] Patients with optic ataxia experience difficulty in real-life situations requiring them to reach accurately under visual guidance. For example, a patient cutting food with a knife and fork may miss the plate altogether and hit the table when attempting to move the knife toward the food.

By testing patients with optic ataxia in controlled situations, neuropsychologists have been able to characterize their reaching deficits in considerable detail. Figure 53.3 illustrates results obtained when patients were required, while looking straight ahead, to reach out and insert one hand into a slot in the center of a disk held by the experimenter. The disk could be held in either the right or the left visual hemifield, and the patient could be asked to reach with either the right or the left hand. To perform the task required both

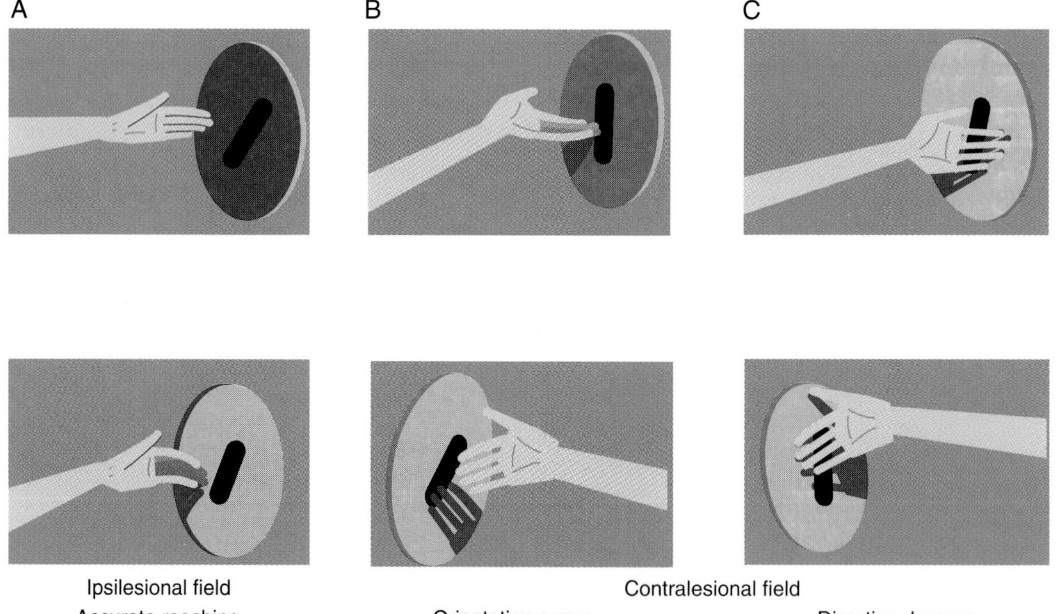

FIGURE 53.3 A test for optic ataxia. Under some conditions, especially when using the ipsilesional hand in the ipsilesional visual field, patients may reach accurately (A). However, under other conditions, especially when reaching into the contralesional visual field, they make errors of hand orientation (B) and of direction (C). The top and bottom rows show the performance of two different patients. From Perenin and Vighetto.[25]

directing the hand toward the center of the slot and orienting the hand so that it would pass into the slot Pictures in the top row of Fig. 53.3 show one patient reaching with the left hand following damage to the right parietal lobe. With the disk positioned in the right—**ipsilesional**—visual field, the patient was able to reach accurately for the slot (Fig. 53.3A). However, with the disk in the left—**contralesional**—visual field, the patient committed errors of hand orientation (Fig. 53.3B) and of reaching direction (Fig. 53.C). The lower row of Fig. 53.3 shows reaching by a patient with damage to the left parietal lobe. When using the left (ipsilesional) hand in the left (ipsilesional) visual field, the patient was able to reach accurately (lower left panel). However, when using the right (contralesional) hand in the right (contralesional) visual field, the patient committed errors of hand orientation (lower middle panel) and of reaching direction (lower right panel).

These results demonstrate that optic ataxia may be lateralized, occurring only when the patient is required to point to targets in one visual hemifield or only when one hand is used for pointing. Generally, in cases where the deficit is restricted to a single hemifield or a single arm, the affected hemifield or arm is opposite the injured parietal lobe. This situation is what would be expected if the parietal lobe of each hemisphere mediates communication between more posterior visual areas (which represent the contralateral half of visual space) and more anterior motor areas (which represent the contralateral arm). However, there are also cases in which the problem is bilateral or occurs for specific combinations of arm and hemifield. Optic ataxia is not simply a problem with visuospatial perception, as indicated by the fact that performance with one arm may be perfectly normal, nor is it simply a motor problem, as indicated by the fact that patients unable to reach accurately for visual targets can commonly touch points on their own bodies accurately under proprioceptive guidance. Optic ataxia is best characterized as a failure in the use of visuospatial information to guide arm movements.

Hemispatial Neglect: Unawareness of the Contralesional Half of Space

Hemispatial neglect is a classic symptom of injury to posterior parietal cortex.[27] It is a condition in which a lateralized failure of spatial awareness is present. Patients fail to notice things in the contralesional half of space (the half of space opposite the injured hemisphere). The most common form of neglect arises from damage to the right parietal lobe and is manifested as a failure to detect things in the left half of space. Patients with neglect experience problems in daily life, such as colliding with obstacles on the contralesional side of the body or mistakenly identifying letters on the contralesional side of a written word. When asked to copy pictures or to draw simple objects from memory, they leave out details on the affected side. When asked to say whether two objects are the same or different, they tend to indicate that two nonidentical objects are the same if the differentiating details are on the contralesional side. Whether the problem underlying neglect is a failure of attention to one half of space or a failure of the ability to form a mental representation of that half of space is not clear.

Neglect certainly is more than just a defect of attention to contralesional sensory events. For example, patients fail to report detail on the left half of an object even when they must form a mental representation of the object by viewing it one part at a time as it passes slowly behind a vertical slit.[28,29] Moreover, when asked to imagine themselves in a familiar public setting and then to report what they see around them, patients fail to report buildings on the contralesional side, regardless of which way they imagine themselves to be facing.[30] Buildings reported accurately when the patient imagines facing east will be neglected when the patient imagines facing west.

Given that neglect affects the half of space opposite an injured parietal lobe, each parietal lobe must represent the opposite half of space. On the face of it, this proposition does not sound particularly surprising. Most visual areas in each hemisphere represent the opposite half of the visual field, most somatosensory areas represent the opposite half of the skin surface, and most motor areas represent muscles on the opposite half of the body. Injury to these areas leads to a sensory loss or motor impairment that affects the opposite half of a functional space defined with respect to some anatomical reference frame (the retina, or the skin surface, or the muscles). In striking contrast, injury to the posterior parietal cortex gives rise to a neglect that is defined in part with respect to external space.

Neglect can be expressed relative to any of several spatial reference frames. These include allocentric frames, in which locations are represented in coordinates extrinsic to the observer; and egocentric reference frames, in which locations are represented relative to the observer. Patients with neglect often show deficits with respect to more than one reference frame. Furthermore, they may show neglect for stimuli presented at particular distances. The following sections describe evidence for impairments of multiple spatial reference frames in neglect.

A patient with left hemispatial neglect, looking straight ahead at the center of some object, will tend not to see detail on its left side. This pattern is open to several interpretations. The simplest interpretation is that stimuli presented in the left visual field tend not to be registered. However, the fundamental problem might actually be with registering stimuli that are to the left of the head, or of the torso, or of the object itself. These possibilities cannot be disentangled without unyoking the various reference frames. Experiments aimed at identifying the reference frame with respect to which neglect is defined have indicated that the patient's failure to detect a stimulus is affected not only by its location relative to the retina but also by its location relative to the object or array within which it is contained, relative to the body, and even relative to a gravitationally defined reference frame.

In many patients, a component of neglect is object-centered. If these patients are presented with an image anywhere in the visual field, they tend to ignore its left side. In one experiment, patients with left hemispatial neglect were required to maintain foveal fixation on a small spot while chimeric faces (images formed by joining at the midline half-images representing the faces of two people) were presented at various visual field locations.[31] Their reports of what they saw were based predominantly on the right halves of the chimeric images. This was true even when the entire composite face was presented within the right visual hemifield. In another experiment, patients with left hemifield neglect were required to maintain foveal fixation on a small spot while four stimuli in a horizontal row were presented.[32] One of the stimuli, was a letter which was to be named. When the letter was in the leftmost location, they were slower to name it, even when the entire array was in the right visual field. Futher demonstrations of object-centered neglect have come from experiments in which, instead of displacing the object away from the visual field midline, one rotates it so that its vertical axis is no longer parallel to the retinal midline.[33] These experiments have demonstrated a form of neglect in which patients ignore detail occupying the left side of the object as defined with respect to the object's (*tilted*) midline rather than with respect to the vertical retinal meridian passing through the center of the object.

A particularly dramatic way of demonstrating the object-centered nature of neglect is to ask patients to make copies of simple line drawings.[34] Results obtained by this procedure are presented in Fig. 53.4, which shows two pictures (left column) and two copies of those pictures (right column) produced by a patient

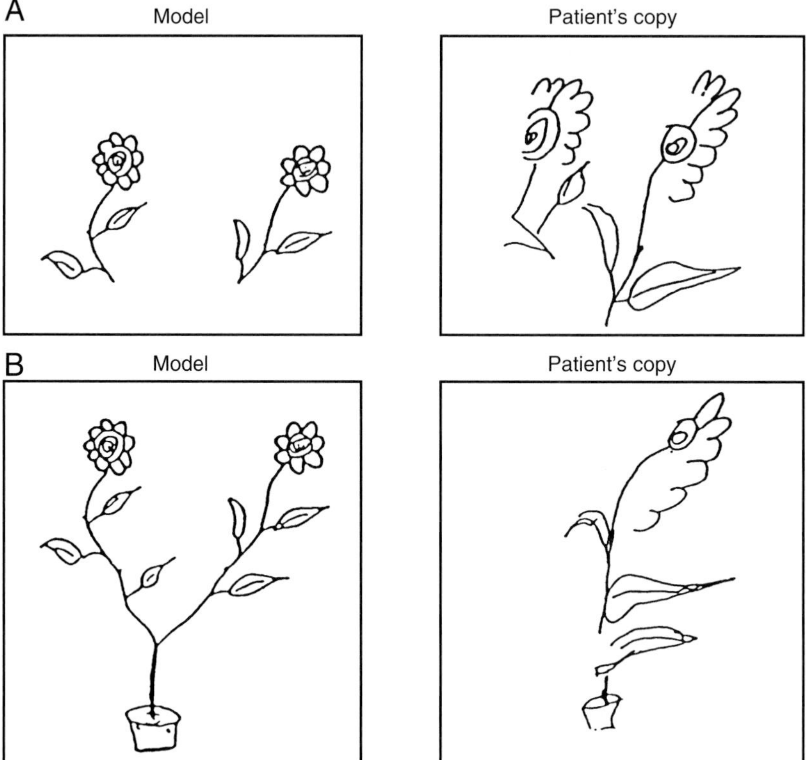

FIGURE 53.4 A test for object-centered neglect. When asked to copy the two drawings on the left, a patient made the two copies on the right. Detail is omitted from the left half of each object rather than from the left half of the drawing as a whole. From Marshall and Halligan.[34]

with right parietal lobe injury. In copying a picture of two flowers (top row, left), the patient saw and copied each flower but omitted the petals on the left half of each, thus showing evidence of left object-centered neglect. When the same two flowers were joined by a common stem (lower row, left), the patient saw and copied the plant, but omitted details on its left side, including all of the leftmost flower, thus showing neglect for the left half of the larger composite object.

Evidence that neglect is defined in part with respect to the midline of the body has come from a reaction-time study in which patients were required to make eye movements in response to suddenly appearing visual targets.[35] When seated with the torso, head, and eyes pointing straight toward the display screen, patients were slower to initiate eye movements into the left visual field than into the right visual field. This difference could be markedly reduced by rotating the patient's chair and torso to the left, while the head and eyes remained stationary and continued to point straight toward the display screen. The effect of this maneuver was to ensure that even stimuli in the left visual field now fell to the right of the midline of the trunk. The simplest interpretation of this result is that neglect in these patients was defined in part with respect to the midline of the trunk.

The role of the gravitational reference frame in neglect has emerged from studies in which patients face a display screen while sitting upright or lying on their side.[36,37] When the patient sits upright while facing the screen, the right and left halves of the screen coincide with the right and left retinal visual fields. However, when the patient lies on one side while facing the screen, the situation is changed. For example, reclining with the right side down, the patient sees the right and left halves of the screen as being in the upper and lower visual fields, respectively. Applying this procedure to patients with left hemispatial neglect enables the investigator to pose the question: Is the neglect specific for the left retinal visual field or is it specific for the left half of the screen? Neglect has turned out to depend in part on each of these factors.

Further evidence that the parietal cortex represents the locations of objects relative to an external, rather than anatomical, framework has come from the observation that neglect, in a few patients, is restricted to stimuli within a certain range of distances from the body.[38,39] The form of neglect termed **peripersonal** or **proximal** is specific for stimuli in the immediate vicinity of the body. Another form of neglect, termed **extrapersonal,** is specific for more distant stimuli. The implication of these findings is that there is a localization of function within the parietal cortex and that neurons in discrete areas process sensory input from objects at different distances. Discrete areas of the parietal cortex may also be specialized for relaying sensory information to different motor systems. Sensory input from peripersonal space is uniquely significant for guiding reaching movements. In contrast, sensory input from greater distances (extrapersonal space) is primarily linked to control of eye movements.

Lesions of the Parietal Cortex in Monkeys Produce Spatial and Attentional Problems

The original distinction between the dorsal and the ventral processing streams in the primate visual system was based in part on differences in the effects of lesions of the posterior parietal cortex and the inferior temporal cortex.[1] Monkeys with posterior parietal lesions are selectively impaired in visuospatial performance, such as judging which of two identical objects is located closer to a visual landmark. In contrast, inferior temporal cortex lesions produce deficits in visual discrimination (for example, shape or pattern recognition; see Chapter 52).

In addition to spatial perceptual deficits, parietal lesions also produce spatial motor deficits. After parietal lesions, monkeys have difficulty directing eye movements toward targets in the hemispace opposite the side of the lesion.[40] Further, when two targets are presented simultaneously in the ipsilesional and contralesional fields, lesioned monkeys tend to ignore the contralesional stimulus, an effect termed **visual extinction**. Parietal lesions also have profound effects on the monkeys' ability to reach toward an object. Lesions confined to inferior parietal cortex impair reaching with the contralesional limb toward a target in contralesional space. Lesions extending across the intraparietal sulcus to include superior parietal cortex produce impairments in reaching with the contralateral arm into either half of space. The deficits observed following parietal lesions indicate that animals are unable either to assess spatial relations between objects or to judge locations of objects relative to themselves.

Parietal Neurons Have Response Properties Related to Spatial Information Processing

To understand more precisely how the parietal cortex contributes to spatial cognition, several groups of investigators have measured the electrical activity of single neurons during the performance of spatial tasks. These studies were done in alert monkeys trained to make eye movements to visual targets. Because brain tissue itself has no sensory receptors, microelectrodes can be introduced into the brain without disturbing the animal's performance on a task. By recording single neuron activity during specially designed tasks, neural activity can be related directly to the sensory, cognitive, and motor processes that underlie spatial behavior.[41,42] The following three sections describe how neurons in different areas within the parietal cortex are selectively activated during spatial tasks and how they contribute to spatial representation.

Area LIP

Neurons in area LIP exhibit many different kinds of task-related activities.[43] First, LIP neurons, like neurons elsewhere in striate and extrastriate visual cortex (Chapter 28), respond to the onset of a visual stimulus in their receptive field, the part of the retina to which they are sensitive.[44]

Second, these visual responses can be enhanced by requiring the monkey to attend to the stimulus in order to detect a faint dimming;[45] that is, the amplitude of the visual response is increased when the stimulus or stimulus location becomes the focus of attention. This enhancement occurs regardless of how the monkey will respond to the stimulus. Whether the task requires a hand movement or an eye movement or requires that the monkey refrain from moving toward the stimulus, the visual response of an LIP neuron becomes larger when the stimulus becomes behaviorally relevant. This means that the same physical stimulus arriving at the retina can evoke very different responses centrally as a result of spatial attention.

A third interesting feature of LIP neuron activity is the prolonged, or tonic, responses observed when the monkey must remember the location at which the stimulus appeared.[46] In this task, a stimulus is flashed only briefly in the *receptive field* but the neuron continues to fire for several seconds after the stimulus is gone, as though the neuron were holding an image of the target location. A particularly interesting question in understanding spatial representation concerns the fate of memory-related activity in area LIP following an eye movement, as will be described later. A fourth kind of activation commonly observed in LIP neurons is specifically related to performance of a **saccade**—a rapid eye movement—toward the receptive field. LIP neurons fire just before the monkey initiates a saccade that would move the fovea onto the target in the receptive field.[47,48] LIP neurons have overlapping sensory and motor fields, just like neurons in the superior colliculus (see Chapter 36). Finally, LIP neuron activity can be modulated by the position of the eye in the orbit.[49] For instance, the visual response of a given cell may become larger when the monkey is looking toward the left part of the screen than when it is looking toward the right. This property is interesting because it suggests that neurons in area LIP may contribute to spatial representations that go beyond simple retinotopy.[50] This idea is discussed in more detail in the next section.

In sum, individual LIP neurons have receptive fields at particular retinal locations and carry visual, memory, and saccade-related signals that can be modulated by attention and by orbital position. Activity in area LIP cannot be characterized as a simple visual or motor signal. Rather, the level of activation in a given LIP neuron reflects the degree to which attention has been allocated to a location within the receptive field.

Spatial Representation in Area LIP

Every time we move our eyes, each object in our surroundings activates a new set of retinal neurons. Despite this constantly changing input, we experience a stable visual world. How is this possible? More than a century ago, Helmholtz[51] proposed that the reason the world appears to stay still when we move our eyes is that the effort of will involved in making a saccade simultaneously adjusts our perception to take that specific eye movement into account. He suggested that when a motor command to shift the eyes in a given direction is issued, a copy of that command, or corollary discharge, is sent to brain areas responsible for generating our internal image of the world. This image is then updated so as to be aligned with the new visual information that will arrive in cortex after the eye movement. A simple experiment convinces most people that Helmholtz's account must be essentially true. When the retina is displaced by pressing on the eye, the world does seem to move, presumably because there is no corollary discharge.

Recent experiments indicate that neurons in area LIP contribute to this updating of the internal image.[52,53] The experiment illustrated in Fig. 53.5 shows that the memory trace of a previous stimulus event is shifted following an eye movement to match the new eye position. The activity of a single LIP neuron was recorded under three different conditions. Under the first set of conditions, shown in Fig. 53.5A, the monkey looked steadily at a fixed point on the screen while a stimulus spot was flashed in the receptive field. In the cartoon at the top, the dot is the fixation point, the dashed circle shows the location of the receptive field when the monkey was looking at the fixation point, and the asterisk represents the visual stimulus. The time lines just below the cartoon show that the vertical and horizontal components of eye position remained steady throughout the trial. The stimulus time line shows that the stimulus started 400 ms after the beginning of the trial and continued for the entire trial. The long vertical line running through the whole panel shows when the stimulus started. The raster display shows the electrical activity of a single LIP neuron in 16 successive trials. In these rasters, each dot indicates

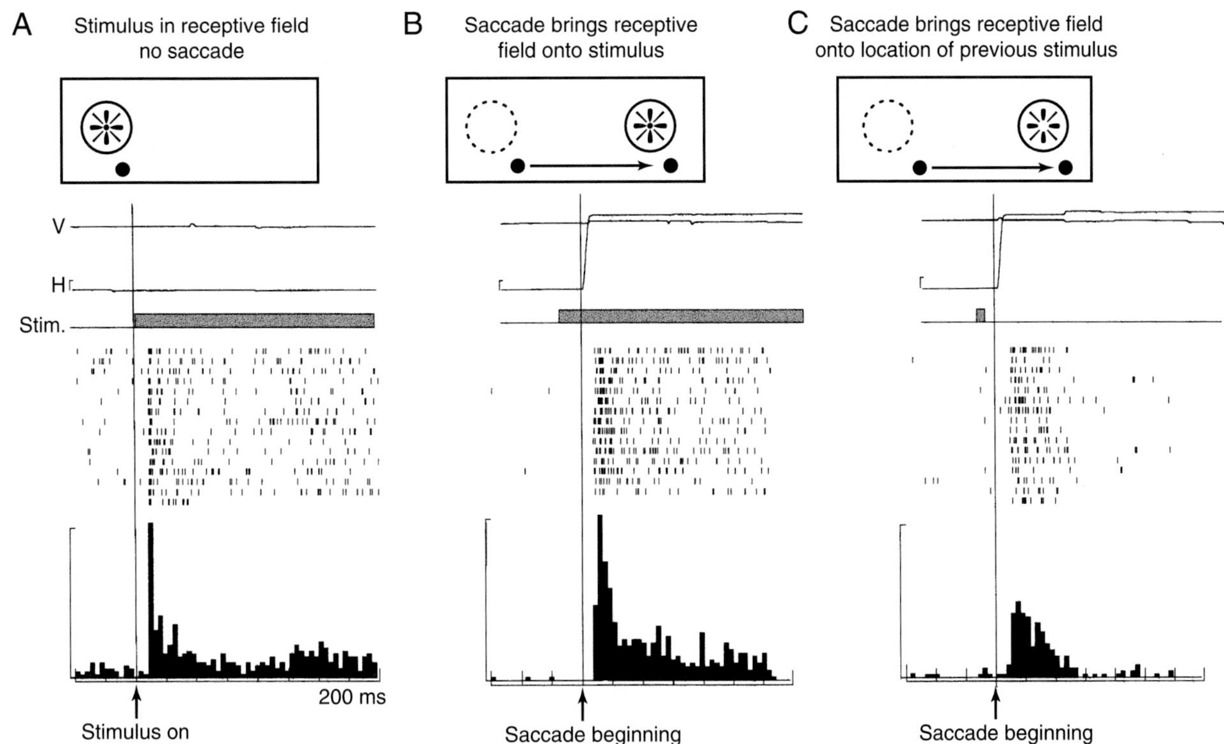

FIGURE 53.5 The remapping of visual memory trace activity in area LIP (see text for a detailed description of the experiment). The activity of a single neuron was recorded under three different conditions. (A) Simple visual response to a constant stimulus in the receptive field, presented while the monkey is fixating. The rasters and histogram are aligned on the time of stimulus onset. (B) Response following a saccade that brings the receptive field onto the location of a constant visual stimulus. (C) Response following a saccade that brings the receptive field onto the location where a stimulus was previously presented. The stimulus is extinguished before the saccade begins, so it is never physically present in the receptive field. The neuron responds to the memory trace of the stimulus. From Duhamel *et al.*[52] V, vertical eye position; H, horizontal eye position.

the time at which an action potential occurred, and each horizontal line of dots represents activity in a single trial. In each trial, there was a brief initial burst of action potentials shortly after the stimulus appeared, followed by continuing neural activity at a lower level. The histogram at the bottom of the panel shows the average firing rate as a function of time. The visual response shown in this left panel is typical of that observed in neurons in many visual areas. Basically, the neuron fired when a stimulus appeared in the particular region of visual space to which that neuron was most sensitive.

In the second set of trials (Fig. 53.5B), the visual response occurred when the stimulus was brought into the receptive field as the result of a saccade. At the beginning of the trial, the monkey was looking at the fixation point on the left, and the rest of the screen was blank. Simultaneously, a new fixation point appeared on the right and a visual stimulus appeared above it. The monkey made a saccade from the old fixation point to the new one, indicated by the arrow in the cartoon. The eye movement was straight to the right, so only the horizontal eye position trace shows a change. At the end of this saccade, the receptive field had been moved to the screen location containing the visual stimulus. The rasters and histogram in this panel are aligned on the time that the saccade began. In each trial, the neuron began to respond after the receptive field had landed on the stimulus. This result is just what would be expected for neurons in any visual area with retinotopic receptive fields.

The surprising finding is shown in Fig. 53.5C. In this set of trials, the monkey made a saccade that would bring a stimulus into the receptive field, just as in the previous experiment (Fig. 53.5B). The only difference was the duration of the stimulus, which lasted for only 50 ms instead of staying on for the entire trial. As can be seen on the stimulus time line, the stimulus actually disappeared before the saccade began. This means that the stimulus was never physically present in the receptive field. Nevertheless, the neuron fired as though there were a stimulus on the screen. This result shows that LIP neurons respond to the memory trace of a previous stimulus and that the representation of the memory trace is updated at the time of a saccade. The general idea of how a memory trace can be updated is as follows: At the beginning of the trial, while the monkey is looking at the initial fixation point, the onset of the stimulus activates those neurons whose receptive fields encompass the stimulated location. Some of these neurons continue to respond after stimulus offset, encoding the location at which the stimulus occurred. When the monkey moves its eyes toward the new fixation point, a copy of the eye movement command is sent to parietal cortex. This corollary discharge causes the active LIP neurons to transmit their activity to another set of neurons whose receptive fields will encompass the stimulated screen location after the saccade. By this means, LIP neurons encode the spatially updated memory trace of a previous stimulus.

The significance of this result lies in what it tells us about spatial representation in area LIP. It suggests that the internal image is dynamic rather than static. Tonic, memory-related activity in area LIP not only allows neurons to encode a salient spatial location after the stimulus is gone but also allows for dynamic remapping of visual information in conjunction with eye movements. This updating of the internal visual image has specific consequences for spatial representation in the parietal cortex. Instead of being encoded in purely retinotopic coordinates, tied to the specific neurons initially activated by the stimulus, the information is encoded in eye-centered coordinates. This is a subtle distinction but a very important one in generating accurate spatial behavior. Maintaining visual information in eye-centered coordinates tells the monkey not just where the stimulus was on the retina when it first appeared, but where it would be now on the retina following an intervening eye movement. The result is that the monkey always has accurate information with which to program an eye movement toward a real or a remembered target. Further results from this series of experiments indicate that humans also depend on this kind of remapping for accurate spatial representation.[54,55]

Area VIP

In contrast to the eye-centered spatial representation found in area LIP, some neurons in the adjacent area VIP encode locations with respect to a head-centered reference frame. These neurons have several interesting properties. They respond strongly to moving stimuli and are selective for both the speed and the direction of the stimulus.[56] In this respect, VIP neurons are similar to those in other dorsal stream visual areas that process stimulus motion, especially areas MT and MST (see Chapter 28). A surprising finding in area VIP is that most of these visually responsive neurons also respond to somatosensory stimuli, such as a light touch.[57] Most of these bimodal neurons have somatosensory receptive fields on the head and face. These neurons are truly bimodal, in the sense that they can be driven equally well by either a visual or a somatosensory stimulus. Further, these neurons have corresponding visual and somatosensory receptive fields. This correspondence is illustrated in Fig. 53.6, which shows visual and somatosensory receptive fields for 14 VIP neurons.

Three kinds of correspondence are shown. First, receptive fields in each modality match in location for a given neuron. For example, a neuron that responds to a visual stimulus in the upper left visual field also responds when the left brow is touched (Fig. 53.6, top right inset). Second, receptive fields match in size. A neuron with a restricted visual receptive field also has a small somatosensory receptive field. Third, preferred directions of movement in the two modalities are matched. For instance, a neuron responsive to a visual stimulus moving toward the right also responds when a small probe is brushed lightly to the right across the monkey's face (Fig. 53.6, lower left inset). In sum, visual and somatosensory receptive fields for individual VIP neurons match in location, size, and directional preference.

This observation of correspondence in receptive field location immediately raises a question: What happens to the relative locations of the visual and somatosensory receptive fields when the eyes move? If the visual receptive field were simply retinotopic, it would move when the eyes do; and if the somatosensory receptive field were purely somatotopic, it would be unchanged by eye movements. There could not be a consistent correspondence in location if visual receptive fields were defined with respect to the retina while somatosensory receptive fields were defined with respect to the skin surface.

The answer is that visual receptive fields shift their location on the retina when the eyes move. A neuron that responds best to a visual stimulus approaching the mouth and has a somatosensory receptive field around the mouth will continue to respond best to a

FIGURE 53.6 Matching of the visual and somatosensory receptive fields of 14 neurons from area VIP. On each outline of the monkey's head, the patch of color corresponds to one neuron's somatosensory receptive field. On the square above the head, the patch of texture corresponds to the same neuron's visual receptive field. The square can be thought of as a screen placed in front of the monkey so that its center is directly ahead of the monkey's eyes. From Duhamel *et al.*[57] by permission of Oxford University Press.

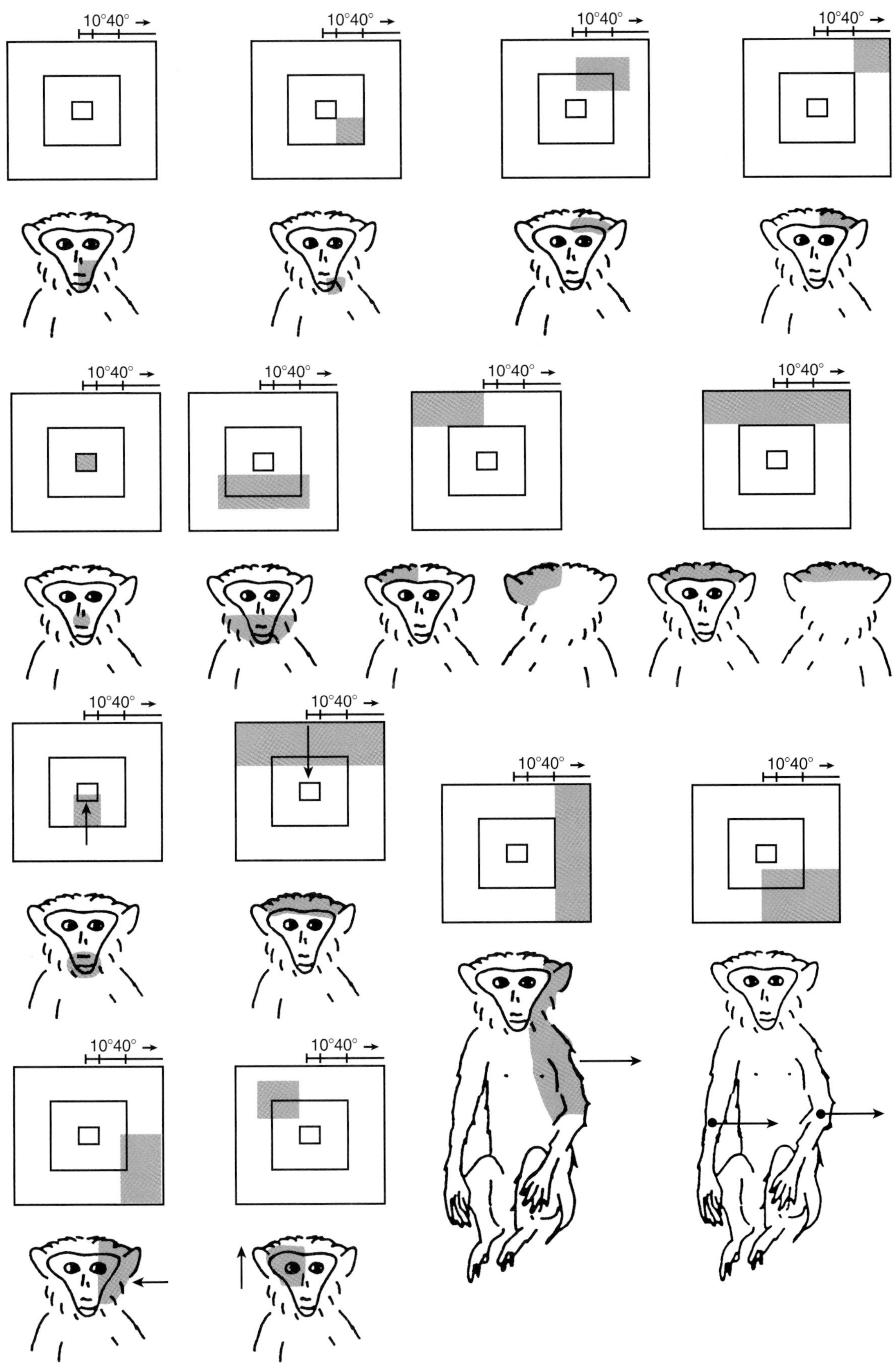

10°40° →

visual stimulus moving toward the mouth regardless of where the monkey is fixating. Thus, both the visual and the somatosensory receptive fields are defined with respect to the skin surface. In this sense, the receptive fields are head-centered: a given VIP neuron responds to stimulation of a certain portion of the skin surface and to the visual stimulus aligned with it, no matter which part of the retina is activated.

In sum, neurons in area VIP encode bimodal sensory information in a head-centered representation of space. This kind of representation would be most useful for guiding head movements. Anatomical studies indicate that area VIP sends information to the specific region of the premotor cortex that is involved in generating head movements. In contrast, neurons in area LIP encode sensory information in an eye-centered representation of space, in a form most useful for guiding eye movements. Area LIP sends projections to both the superior colliculus and the frontal eye fields, regions that are involved in generating eye movements. The parietal cortex contains a number of other areas, especially within the intraparietal sulcus, each of which may be specialized for particular types of stimuli and particular regions of space.[58] The general point is that the problem of spatial representation may be solved in several ways, and each solution may contribute to the generation of a different kind of action.

Summary

The posterior parietal cortex plays a critical role in spatial awareness. Injury to parietal cortex in humans and monkeys leads to deficits in spatial perception and action. Physiological studies in monkeys have shown that parietal neurons construct a representation of space by combining signals from multiple sensory modalities with motor signals. An intriguing physiological finding is that parietal neurons represent spatial locations relative to multiple reference frames, including ones centered on the eye and the head. In accord with the physiology, human neuropsychological studies have shown that neglect resulting from parietal lobe injury can be expressed with respect to several different reference frames.

THE FRONTAL CORTEX

The Frontal Cortex Contributes to Voluntary Movement and the Regulation of Behavior

The cortex at the front of the cerebral hemisphere is involved in spatial functions as a natural result of its being involved in behavioral regulation. The three main divisions of the frontal lobe are the **primary motor cortex** on the precentral gyrus, the **premotor cortex** located in front of the primary motor cortex, and the **prefrontal cortex,** which has the most anterior location (see Fig. 53.1). The motor, premotor, and prefrontal areas all contribute to behavioral regulation, but they differ from each other with respect to the quality of their contribution. This difference is seen in the effects of brain injury. Injury to the primary motor cortex leads to weakness and paralysis of the contralateral muscles.[59] In contrast, injury to the premotor cortex leads to difficulty in producing movements in certain circumstances, for example, when the patient is asked to mime the use of a tool or to learn arbitrary associations between stimuli and responses.[60] Finally, injury to the prefrontal cortex results in a classic syndrome characterized by lack of drive and poor ability to carry through on plans.[61] These effects indicate that progressively more anterior parts of frontal cortex contribute to progressively more abstract aspects of behavioral regulation. Each of these three districts participates in spatial processes insofar as the kind of behavioral regulation to which it is dedicated has a spatial component.

Neurons in the Primary Motor Cortex May Represent Movement Direction Relative to a Spatial Frame

The primary motor cortex contains a map of the muscles of the body in which the leg is represented medially, the head laterally, and other body parts at intermediate locations. Within the map are patches of neurons that represent different muscles. The neurons within a given patch receive proprioceptive input from a muscle or small group of synergistic muscles and send their output back to that muscle or group of synergists by way of a **multisynaptic pathway** traversing the brainstem and spinal cord. There have been many studies in which the electrical activity of neurons in the primary motor cortex is monitored while animals move. The general thrust of these studies is that neurons in the primary motor cortex are active when the corresponding muscles are undergoing active contraction.

Neurons in the primary motor cortex probably do more than simply encode the levels of activation of individual muscles or groups of muscles. One proposal is that they encode movement trajectories. Every voluntary movement can be described in two quite different, but perfectly complementary, ways: in terms of the lengths of the muscles and in terms of the position of the part of the body being moved. For example, during an arm movement, conjoint changes both in the lengths of muscles acting on the arm and in the position of the hand take place. Could it be that neurons in the primary motor cortex encode a spatial variable, such as the direction of movement of the hand, rather than a muscle variable?

Evidence supporting the idea that neurons of the primary motor cortex encode movement direction has come from studies in which monkeys make reaching movements from a central starting point to targets displaced from it in various directions. Individual neurons are selective for movement direction under these conditions; a given neuron may fire most strongly during movements up and to the right and progressively less strongly during movements that deviate by progressively greater angles from the preferred direction.[62,63] The patterns of selectivity are well defined and the preferred directions of different neurons cover the range of possible movements fairly evenly, so that by monitoring the activity of the entire population of neurons one could, in principle, quite accurately describe the movement. However, there are some impediments to concluding that these neurons encode movement trajectories. Over a small range of movements, muscle activation is almost linearly related to movement direction, so that determining whether neuronal activity reflects muscle activation or movement direction is difficult. Moreover, if the two factors are dissociated by inducing a monkey to move its hand along the same trajectory, but with the arm in different postures so that different patterns of muscle activation are required, then the relation between neuronal activity and the direction of movement of the hand seems to break down.[64]

Neurons in the Premotor Cortex Have Head-Centered and Hand-Centered Visual Receptive Fields

One of the functions of premotor cortical areas is to act as a conduit through which sensory signals are relayed to the motor system. The sensory information that reaches these areas has been highly processed already in the posterior cerebral hemisphere and thus it is not surprising, although it is still striking, that the sensory receptive fields of some neurons in premotor cortex are defined with respect to an external spatial framework, in a form suitable for motor use.

Two different forms of spatially organized visual responsiveness have been described in premotor cortex. First, in subdivisions of the premotor cortex representing orofacial movements, neurons respond to visual stimuli at a certain location relative to the head.[65,66] These neurons have been characterized by monitoring their electrical activity while objects approach the monkey's head along various trajectories. A typical experiment is illustrated in Fig. 53.7. In the first phase of the experiment, as shown in Fig. 53.7A, the monkey looked straight ahead at a small fixation target (F) while an object approached the face and receded, following a trajectory that brought it either to the right side of the head (trajectory 1) or to the left side of the head (trajectory 2). Records of neuronal activity (panel C) showed that the neuron fired when the object approached along trajectory 1 (panel A) but not when it approached along trajectory 2 (panel A). We conclude that the neuron had a receptive field located to the right of the monkey's head or at least to the right in his retinal visual field (shaded area in Fig. 53.7A). To determine whether the receptive field was head-centered or retina-centered required a further phase of testing. In this phase, as shown in Fig. 53.7B, the monkey looked far to the left at a small fixation target (F). While he maintained a leftward gaze, objects again approached the face, following trajectories 1 and 2. If the receptive field of the neuron were head-centered, one would predict that it should continue to respond as the object approached along trajectory 1. However, if the receptive field were fixed to the retina, then one would predict that the neuron should respond as the object approached along trajectory 2. Records of the neuron's electrical activity, monitored while the object moved along trajectory 1 (panel B) and trajectory 2 (panel B), clearly indicate that the neuron had a head-centered visual receptive field; it was selective for stimuli presented to the right of the head's midline, not to the right of the retina's midline. The head-centered spatial selectivity of neurons in the premotor cortex is reminiscent of the properties of some neurons in the parietal cortex, as described previously in connection with area VIP. That neurons in the two areas should exhibit similar patterns of spatial selectivity is not surprising because the parietal and premotor cortices are strongly interconnected.

A second pattern has been observed in subdivisions of the premotor cortex representing arm movements. Here, neurons respond to visual stimuli if those stimuli are presented in the vicinity of the hand.[67] When the hand moves to a new location, the visual receptive field moves with it. The visual receptive field remains fixed to the hand regardless of where the monkey is looking and, thus, regardless of the part of the retina on which the image is cast. These two forms of body-centered visual responsiveness presumably reflect the involvement of premotor neurons in visual guidance of orofacial and arm movements.

Neurons in the Supplementary Eye Field Encode the Object-Centered Direction of Eye Movements

The supplementary eye field (SEF; see Fig. 53.1) is a division of the premotor cortex with attentional and

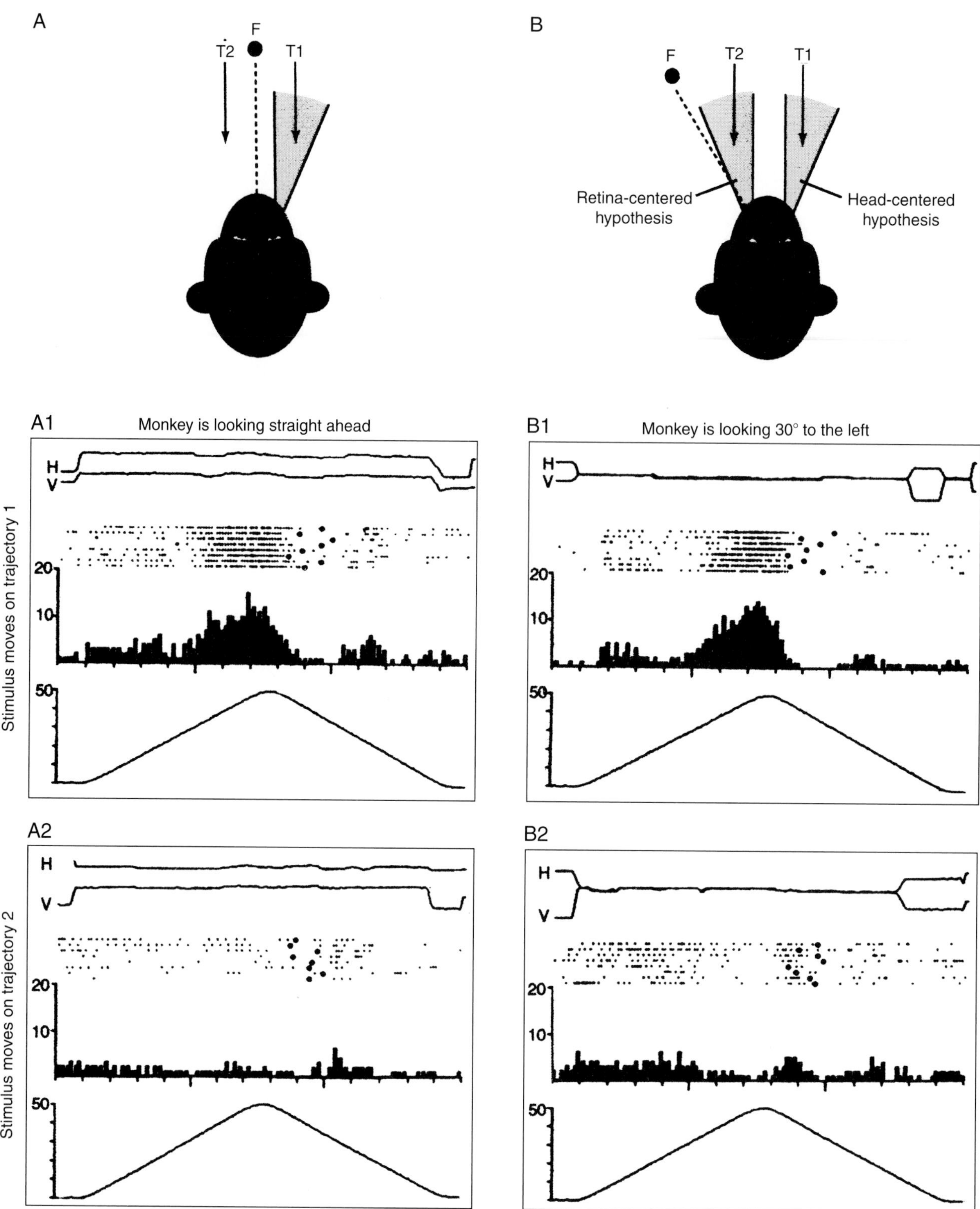

FIGURE 53.7 Data from a neuron in the premotor cortex with a head-centered visual receptive field. While the monkey was looking at a fixation point (F) directly in front of the head (A) or to the left of the head (B), a visible object approached the head and receded, traveling either along trajectory 1 (to the right of the head) or along trajectory 2 (to the left of the head). The neuron fired strongly when the object approached along trajectory 1, regardless of whether the monkey was looking straight ahead (A) or to the left (B). The neuron did not fire strongly when the object approached along trajectory 2, regardless of whether the monkey was looking straight ahead (A) or to the left (B). From Fogassi *et al.*[66]

oculomotor functions. Neurons here fire before and during the execution of saccadic eye movements, the rapid eye movements by which the eye darts from point to point between periods of fixation. In standard tests of oculomotor function, which involve monitoring neuronal activity while monkeys make eye movements between spots of light projected on a screen, neurons of the SEF exhibit directional selectivity. Each neuron has a preferred direction. It fires strongly before and during eye movements in this direction and at a progressively lower rate during eye movements that deviate by a progressively greater angle from this direction. A few traits of the SEF set it apart from brainstem oculomotor centers and suggest that its contribution to eye movement control occurs at a comparatively abstract level. For example, neurons here fire during a period when the monkey is waiting to make an eye movement in the preferred direction, as well as during overt execution of the eye movement. Moveover, some SEF neurons become especially active during a period when the monkey is learning to associate arbitrary visual cues with particular directions of eye movements.[68]

In monkeys trained to make eye movements to particular locations on an object, SEF neurons exhibit a unique form of spatial selectivity: they encode the direction of the impending eye movement as defined relative to an object-centered reference frame.[69,70] An experiment demonstrating this point is presented in Fig. 53.8. This figure shows data collected from a single SEF neuron while the monkey performed a so-called bar task. At the beginning of each 1- to 2-s trial, the monkey fixated a dot at the center of a video screen. While the monkey fixated the central dot, a sample-cue display was presented in the right visual field. The display consisted of a cue spot flashed on either the right or the left end of a short horizontal sample bar. Following extinction of the sample-cue display, the monkey maintained fixation of the central spot for around a second. Then, simultaneously, the central spot was extinguished and a target bar appeared at an unpredictable location in the monkey's upper visual

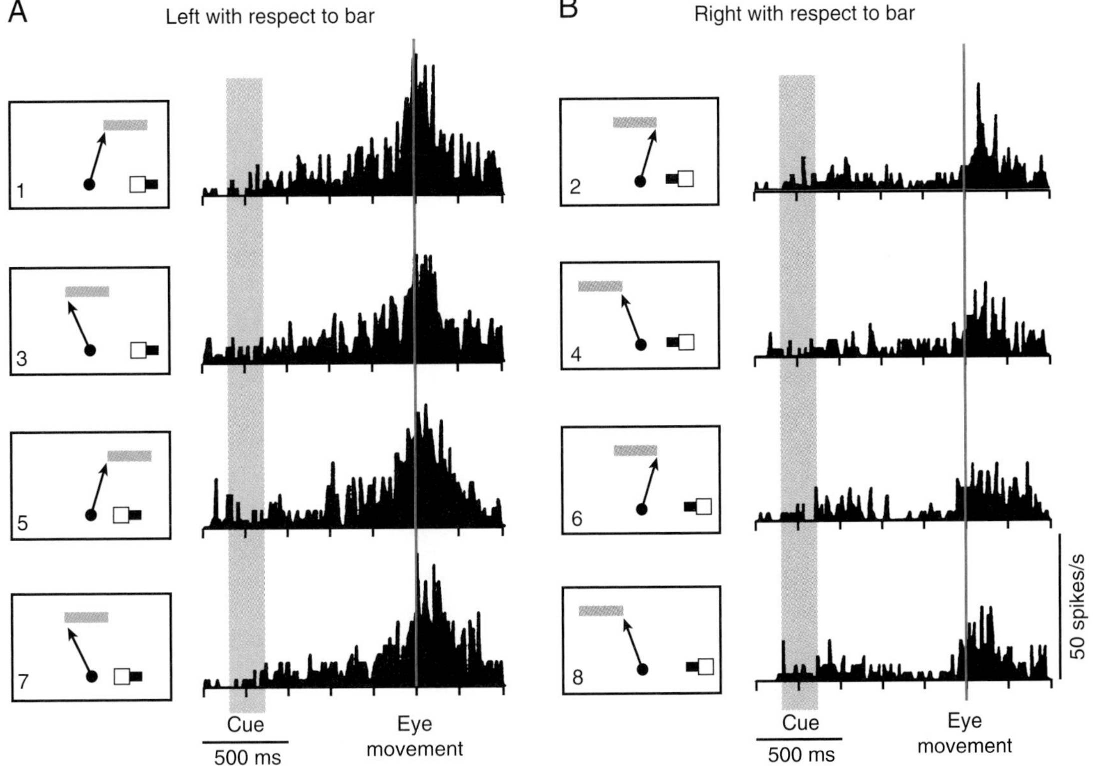

FIGURE 53.8 Data from a neuron in the SEF selective for the object-centered direction of eye movements. The monkey was trained to make eye movements to the right or left end of a horizontal bar that could be presented at several locations. The arrow in the panel next to each histogram indicates the direction of the eye movement. The neuron fired strongly when the eye movement was directed to the left end of the target bar (conditions 1, 3, 5, and 7) regardless of whether the eye's physical movement was up and to the right (conditions 1 and 5) or up and to the left (conditions 3 and 7). From Olson and Gettner.[69]

field. The monkey then had to make an eye movement to the end of the target bar corresponding to the cued end of the sample bar. In a series of trials, the sample bar, cue spot, and target bar were presented at various locations. The eight different conditions are shown in panels 1 through 8 of Fig. 53.8. The dot at the center of each panel represents the central fixation point, the elements at the right of the panel are the sample bar and cue spot, the element at the top of the panel is the target bar, and the arrow indicates the direction of the monkey's eye movement. The physical direction of the eye movement could be either up and to the right (panels 1, 2, 5, and 6) or up and to the left (panels 3, 4, 7, and 8). The object-centered direction of the eye movement could be either to the left end of the target bar (panels 1, 3, 5, and 7) or to the right end of the target bar (panels 2, 4, 6, and 8). Across this set of conditions, the object-centered direction of the eye movement was completely independent of its physical direction.

This situation made it possible to ask whether the electrical activity of the neuron was related to the movement's object-centered direction or to its physical direction. To the right of each panel in Fig. 53.8 is shown the average neuronal firing rate as a function of time during the trial. Regardless of the direction of the eye's physical movement, firing was clearly stronger on trials in which the monkey made an eye movement to the left end of the target bar than on trials in which the target was the bar's right end. For example, in conditions 1 and 2, the physical direction of the eye movement was exactly the same, and yet firing was much stronger when the bar's left end was the target (condition 1) than when the bar's right end was the target (condition 2). This neuron exhibited object-centered direction selectivity in the sense that it fired most strongly before and during movements to a certain location on a reference object. About half of the neurons in the SEF exhibit object-centered direction selectivity, each neuron favoring a particular location on the object, for example, the top, bottom, right end, left end, or center.

Object-centered direction selectivity, although it may at first seem to be an esoteric phenomenon, probably serves an important function in natural settings. In scanning the environment, we sometimes look toward locations where things are expected to appear, but which, at the time, contain no detail—for example, the center of a blank screen or the center of an empty doorway. Our eyes are guided to these featureless locations by surrounding features that define them indirectly. It is specifically in these cases that the SEF may contribute to the selection of the target for an eye movement. If so, then lesions of the SEF should selectively impair eye movements to targets defined indirectly by their spatial relation to visible features. This prediction can be given an even more specific form because the SEF areas of the right and left hemispheres are functionally specialized. In each SEF, neurons selective for eye movements to the contralateral ends of objects are preponderant (e.g., in the right hemisphere for eye movements to the left end of an object). Therefore, injury to one SEF should produce an impairment of eye movements to the contralateral ends of bars or other reference objects, a condition analogous to the objected-centered neglect that arises from unilateral parietal injury.

The Prefrontal Cortex Mediates Working Memory for Spatial Information

Working memory is required to hold a plan in mind and carry it out step by step (see Chapter 56). The fact that this ability is severely impaired in some patients suffering from prefrontal injury indicates that the prefrontal cortex, which forms the anterior pole of the cerebral hemisphere, plays a crucial role in working memory (see Chapter 59). Insofar as plans and working memory have a spatial component, operations carried out by the prefrontal cortex should also be spatial in nature. Single-neuron-recording experiments in monkeys performing delayed-response tasks have demonstrated the importance of the dorsolateral prefrontal cortex for both spatial and nonspatial forms of working memory.[71] A delayed-response task consists of several trials, each several seconds long. At the beginning of each trial, a cue is presented briefly, instructing the monkey which response to make, but the reponse must be withheld until the end of the trial. Delayed-response tasks can be designed so that both cues (for instance, spots flashed to the right or left of fixation) and responses (for instance, eye movements to the right or left) may be spatial. In the context of these spatial tasks, prefrontal neurons are active during the period between the cue and the signal to respond, when the monkey is holding spatial information in working memory. Just as for visual responses, some neurons are selective for the direction of the response. The simple interpretation of this pattern of activity is that it is a neural correlate of the monkey's actively remembering the cue and holding in mind the intended response. This interpretation is also supported by recent experiments based on imaging of brain activation in humans.[72]

The view that prefrontal cortex mediates spatial working memory has received further support from lesion experiments in monkeys. After injury to or inactivation of specific locations in the prefrontal cortex,

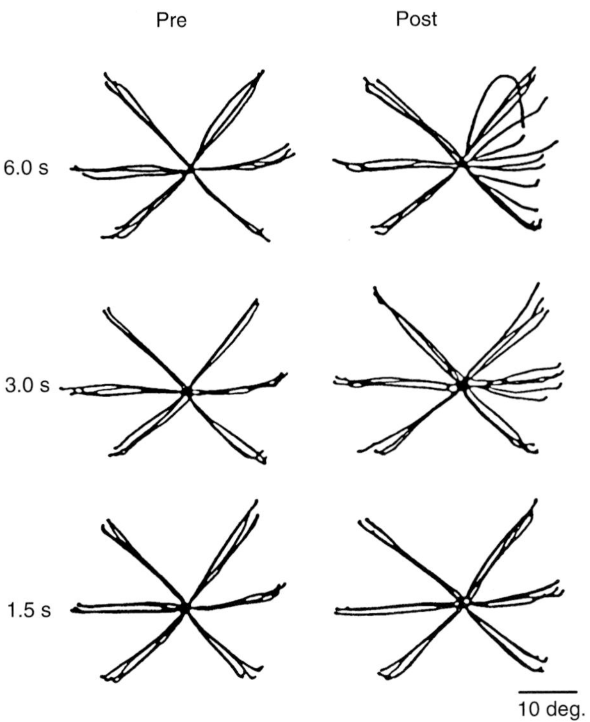

FIGURE 53.9 Inactivation of the left prefrontal cortex disrupts spatial working memory in the right half of space. A monkey was trained to fixate a central spot while a peripheral cue was presented briefly at one of six locations. After an interval of 1.5, 3, or 6 s, the fixation spot was extinguished and the monkey made an eye movement to the remembered location. Each inset of diverging rays shows the trajectories of eye movements executed under a certain set of conditions. Trajectories before and after prefrontal inactivation are shown on the left and right, respectively. Trajectories in the three rows are from trials with three different delay durations. When the cue was in the right hemifield and the monkey was required to remember it over long delays, the movements became highly inaccurate. From Sawaguchi and Goldman-Rakic.[74]

monkeys are poor at remembering locations in the opposite half of space, as indicated by the fact that their delayed responses are inaccurate and by the fact that the inaccuracy is exacerbated by longer delays, which tax active memory more heavily.[73,74] An experiment demonstrating the importance of the prefrontal cortex for spatial working memory is illustrated in Fig. 53.9, which shows behavioral data from a monkey trained to perform an oculomotor delayed-response task. At the outset of each trial, the monkey fixated a spot at the center of the screen. While the monkey maintained central fixation, a cue was flashed at one of six possible locations at positions 1, 3, 5, 7, 9, and 11 o'clock relative to the central spot. Following presentation of the cue, a delay of 1–6 s ensued before the monkey was permitted to make an eye movement to the cued location. Monkeys were able to perform this task with a high degree of accuracy.

Data from a normal monkey are shown in the left column of Fig. 53.9. In each inset, the six bundles of radiating rays represent the eye trajectories on trials when the cue was at the six different locations. The bottom, middle, and top insets represent eye movements on trials when the monkey had to remember the cue for 1.5, 3, and 6 s, respectively. Even when required to remember the cue for 6 s, the monkey made accurate eye movements to the cued location. Data in the right column are from the same monkey after a dopamine antagonist was injected into the left prefrontal cortex. The monkey's ability to remember the location of cue, as evidenced by execution of accurate eye movements to the cued location, remained intact when the cue was in the left (ipsilesional) visual field. However, performance deteriorated on trials when the cue was in the right (contralesional) visual field. Specifically, after long delays (middle and top insets), the direction of the eye movement began to deviate from the location of the cue, as if the monkey's working memory were fading. The fact that this deficit was specific to long delays is noteworthy because it rules out any simple explanation based on interference with visual or motor processes as opposed to working memory itself.

Summary

Neurons in frontal cortex represent spatial information as a natural consequence of their role in controlling behavior. Neurons in primary motor cortex encode the directions of movements. Neurons in premotor cortex encode the locations of objects relative to the body, even when these objects are not the immediate targets of actions. Finally, neurons in prefrontal cortex encode the locations of objects being held in short-term memory.

THE HIPPOCAMPUS AND ADJACENT CORTEX

The Hippocampal System Is Associated with Memory Formation

The hippocampus is an area of primitive cortex, or allocortex, hidden on the underside of the temporal lobe, where it occupies a medial location. The hippocampus is connected to a set of immediately adjacent cortical areas. These cortical areas, closely affiliated with the hippocampus in what might be termed a hippocampal system, include the perirhinal, entorhinal, and parahippocampal cortices.[75,76] The locations of the

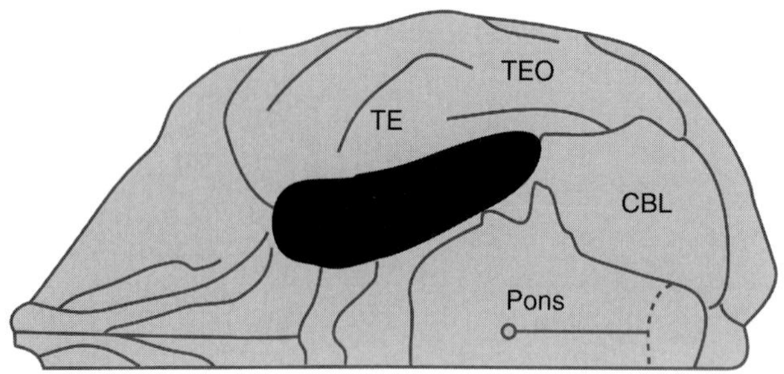

FIGURE 53.10 In this ventral view of the left cerebral hemisphere of a rhesus monkey, shading indicates the location of the hippocampus and the perirhinal and parahippocampal cortical areas. They occupy the ventral and medial aspects of the temporal lobe. This ventral view should be compared with Fig. 53.1, which shows a lateral view of the hemisphere. TE and TEO, visual cortical areas lateral to the parahippocampal cortex. CBL, cerebellum; Pons, pons: brainstem structures ventral and medial to the temporal lobe. Modified from Squire and Zola-Morgan.[77]

hippocampus and adjacent cortex are indicated in Fig. 53.10.[77]

Amnesia Resulting from Hippocampal Injury in Humans Includes a Spatial Component

Extensive evidence implicates the hippocampus and related medial temporal structures in the formation of episodic memories in humans. Memories dependent on the hippocampus include, although they are by no means restricted to, memories for spatial material.[78–80] In addition to other signs, the amnesia of the celebrated patient H.M., who sustained medial temporal lobe surgery, was manifested by his inability to learn to find his way through new neighborhoods. Patients with damage to the hippocampus and especially to the right hippocampus perform poorly on tests requiring them to inspect a scene with many objects and then to recall the locations of individual objects.

Neurons of the Hippocampal System Have Place Fields and Are Sensitive to Directional Orientation of the Head

Neuronal electrical activity has been monitored in the hippocampus of rats running eight-arm radial mazes and performing other tasks that require locomotion within a workspace. These experiments have revealed a remarkable degree of spatial selectivity. Many (perhaps a majority of) neurons throughout the hippocampus have place fields; that is, a given neuron will fire most strongly when the rat is within a certain sector of the workspace.[81–83] Different neurons have different place fields, so that, collectively, they cover the workspace.

Place fields are defined relative to prominent environmental landmarks; if a radially symmetric eight-arm maze is rotated relative to a surrounding room containing salient landmarks, then the place fields remain fixed with respect to the room. However, even in darkness, neurons continue to fire when the rat is in their place field. If the rat is placed in a new environment, hippocampal neurons rapidly manifest place fields relative to that environment. The location of a neuron's place field relative to the new environment is not predictable from its location relative to the old environment. This is true even in cases where the workspace is changed without any change in the surrounding room, for instance, through replacement of an eight-arm radial maze by a free field. Some hippocampal system neurons are sensitive not only to the rat's location but also to the direction in which the head is pointing.[82,84] Sensitivity to heading, although not the most distinctive feature of hippocampal neurons, is dominant in the postsubiculum, a cortical area adjacent to and closely linked to the hippocampus. Each postsubicular neuron fires most strongly when the rat's head is pointing in its preferred direction and fires progressively less strongly as the orientation of the rat's head deviates farther from that direction. In a room plunged into darkness, postsubicular neurons remain sensitive to the rat's heading so long as the rat retains a sense of spatial orientation, as reflected by error-free performance on spatial tests. When the rat's sense of spatial orientation drifts away from **veridicality** during prolonged darkness, as evidenced by the occurrence of systematic errors on spatial tests, then the preferred headings of postsubicular neurons exhibit a commensurate drift. These observations establish that neurons of the hippocampal system are sensitive to the rat's spatial orientation. How the hippocampus uses spatial information, along with nonspatial information, to form new memories is taken up in Chapter 56.

Summary

The hippocampal system mediates the formation of memories, including memories with spatial content. Injury to the hippocampal system, both in humans and in laboratory animals, leads to profound deficits of memory, including navigational memory. In accord with these findings, single-neuron recording in rats has revealed that neurons of the hippocampal system have place fields, encoding the rat's location in its environment, and directional sensitivity, encoding head direction relative to the environment.

SPATIAL COGNITION VERSUS SPATIAL ACTION

We have seen in the preceding sections that spatial information is processed by numerous cortical areas that serve distinct functions, such as motor control, attention, and working memory. Even within the motor system, there appears to be a fractionation of spatial functions, in that neurons controlling movements of the eyes, head, and arm represent the locations of visible targets relative to eye-centered, head-centered, and hand-centered reference frames, respectively. In addition to these distinctions, there may be another fundamental distinction within brain systems mediating spatial functions. Areas mediating conscious awareness of spatial information may be partially separate from those mediating the spatial guidance of motor behavior. These functions may seem inseparable, insofar as one must be aware of the location of a thing in order to look at it or reach for it. However, this is not necessarily the case. An indication that spatial awareness and spatially programmed behavior are distinguishable has come from studies of patients with so-called "blindsight."[85] This condition arises as a result of injury to primary visual cortex. Patients experience a **scotoma**, an area of blindness, in the part of the visual field represented by the injured cortex. The blindness is total in the sense that patients do not report seeing visual stimuli when the stimuli are presented within the confines of the scotoma. Nevertheless, if some patients are asked to look toward or to reach for the unseen stimulus, choosing the target by guesswork, their responses are directed to the correct location.[86] Similar findings have been reported in patients with diffuse pathology affecting widespread areas, including the prestriate visual cortex. When asked to express spatial judgments (for instance, to indicate the size of a visible object by spreading the thumb and forefinger), these patients perform poorly. Nevertheless, when asked to make visually guided movements (for instance, to reach for an object), they accurately adjust the grip size and hand orientation under visual control to grasp the object efficiently.[87,88] The fact that intact visuomotor performance coexists with profoundly impaired visuospatial perception in these patients seems to argue for the existence of distinct brain systems specialized for conscious spatial awareness and motor guidance, respectively.

Summary

Spatial cognition is a function of several different brain areas. No one area is uniquely responsible for our ability to carry out spatial tasks. Nevertheless, some generalizations can be made about the part of the problem that is solved in each brain region.

The parietal lobe plays a crucial role in many aspects of spatial awareness, including spatially focused attention. The representation of space in the parietal cortex takes several forms. Each area within the parietal cortex may have a different kind of representation, designed to help guide different kinds of actions. Beneath the unity of our spatial perception may lie a diversity of specific representations: the frontal lobe transforms spatial awareness into actions; the motor cortex uses a spatial framework to encode intended actions; the premotor cortex contains a set of different spatial representations to generate movement; the prefrontal cortex contains neurons with very high-order, abstract spatial representations and mediates short-term spatial memory; the hippocampus mediates episodic spatial memories, including those which underlie spatial orientation.

The distributed nature of spatial cognition and the many purposes it serves means that we construct internal representations of space not once but many times. A challenge for the future is to understand how these representations function together.

References

1. Ungerleider, L. G., and Mishkin, M. (1982). Two cortical visual systems. In *Analysis of Visual Behavior* (D. J. Ingle, M. A. Goodale, and R. J. W. Mansfield, eds.), pp. 549–586. MIT Press, Cambridge, MA.
2. DeYoe, E. A., and Van Essen, D. C. (1988). Concurrent processing streams in monkey visual cortex. *Trends Neurosci.* **11:** 219–226.
3. Ettlinger, G. (1990). "Object vision" and "spatial vision". The neuropsychological evidence for the distinction. *Cortex* **26:** 319–341.
4. Haxby, J. V., Grady, C. L., Horwitz, B., Ungerleider, L. G., Mishkin, M., Carson, R. E., Herscovitch, P., Shapiro, M. B., and Rapoport, S. I. (1991). Dissociation of object and spatial visual processing pathways in human extrastriate cortex. *Proc. Natl. Acad. Sci. U.S.A.* **88:** 1621–1625.
5. Haxby, J. V., Horwitz, B., Ungerleider, L. G., Maisog, J. M., Pietrini, P., and Grady, C. L. (1994). The functional organization of human extrastriate cortex: A PET-rCBF study of selective attention to faces and locations. *J. Neurosci.* **14:** 6336–6353.
6. Goodale, M. A., and Milner, A. D. (1992). Separate visual pathways for perception and action. *Trends Neurosci.* **15:** 20–25.
7. Pandya, D. N., and Yeterian, E. H. (1985). Architecture and connections of cortical association areas. In *Cerebral Cortex* (A. Peters and E. G. Jones, eds.), Vol. 4, pp. 3–61. Plenum, New York.
8. Goldman-Rakic P. S. (1988). Topography of cognition: Parallel distributed networks in primate association cortex. *Annu. Rev. Neurosci.* **11:** 137–156.
9. Young, M. P. (1993). The organization of neural systems in the primate cerebral cortex. *Proc. R. Soc. London, Ser. B* **252:** 13–18.
10. Andersen, R. A., Asanuma, C., and Cowan, W. M. (1985). Callosal and prefrontal associational projecting cell populations in area 7a of the macaque monkey: A study using retrogradely transported fluorescent dyes. *J. Comp. Neurol.* **232:** 443–445.

11. Andersen, R. A. (1989). Visual and eye movement functions of the posterior parietal cortex. *Annu. Rev. Neurosci.* **12:** 377–403.
12. Cavada, C., and Goldman-Rakic, P. S. (1989). Posterior parietal cortex in rhesus monkey. I: Parcellation of areas based on distinctive limbic and sensory corticocortical connections. *J. Comp. Neurol.* **287:** 393–421.
13. Colby, C. L., and Duhamel, J.-R. (1991). Heterogeneity of extrastriate visual areas and multiple parietal areas in the macaque monkey. *Neuropsychologia* **29:** 517–537.
14. Balint, R. (1909). Seelenlähmung des 'schauens,' optische ataxie, raümliche störung der aufmerksamkeit. *Monatsschr. Psychiatr. Neurol.* **25:** 51–81.
15. Hécaen, H., and de Ajuriaguerra, J. (1954). Balint's syndrome (psychic paralysis of visual fixation) and its minor forms. *Brain* **77:** 373–400.
16. DeRenzi, E. (1985). Disorders of spatial orientation. In *Handbook of Clinical Neurology* (J. A. M. Frederiks, ed.), Vol. 1, pp. 405–422. Elsevier, Amsterdam.
17. Andersen, R. A. (1987). The role of the inferior parietal lobule in spatial perception and visual motor integration. In *The Handbook of Physiology* (F. Plum, V. B. Mountcastle, and S. R. Geiger, eds.), Sect. 1, Vol. IV, Part 2, pp. 483–518. Am. Physiol. Soc., Bethesda, MD.
18. Stein, J. F. (1991). Space and parietal association areas. In *Brain and Space* (J. Paillard, ed.), pp. 185–222. Oxford University Press, Oxford.
19. Kinsbourne, M., and Warrington, E. K. (1962). A disorder of simultaneous form perception. *Brain* **85:** 461–486.
20. Baylis, G. C., Driver, J., Baylis, L. L., and Rafal, R. D. (1994). Reading of letters and words in a patient with Balint's syndrome. *Neuropsychologia* **32:** 1273–1286.
21. Rizzo, M., and Robin, D. A. (1990). Simultanagnosia: A defect of sustained attention yields insights on visual information processing. *Neurology* **40:** 447–455.
22. Coslett, H. B., and Saffran, E. (1991). Simultanagnosia: To see but not two see. *Brain* **114:** 1523–1545.
23. Humphreys, G. W., and Riddoch, M. J. (1993). Interactions between object and space systems revealed through neuropsychology. In *Attention and Performance* (D. E. Meyer and S. Kornblum, eds.), Vol. XIV, pp. 143–162. MIT Press, Cambridge, MA.
24. Jeannerod, M. (1988). Impairments in visuomotor control following cortical lesions. In *The Neural and Behavioural Organization of Goal-Directed Movements* (M. Jeannerod, ed.), pp. 209–271. Clarendon Press, Oxford.
25. Perenin, M.-T., and Vighetto, A. (1988). Optic ataxia: A specific disruption in visuomotor mechanisms. I: Different aspects of the deficit in reaching for objects. *Brain* **111:** 643–674.
26. Jeannerod, M., Decety, J., and Michel, F. (1994). Impairment of grasping movements following a bilateral posterior parietal lesion. *Neuropsychologia* **32:** 369–380.
27. Rafal, R. D. (1994). Neglect. *Curr. Opin. Neurobiol.* **4:** 231–236.
28. Bisiach, E., Luzzatti, C., and Perani, D. (1979). Unilateral neglect, representational schema and consciousness. *Brain* **102:** 609–618.
29. Ogden, J. A. (1985). Contralesional neglect of constructed visual images in right and left brain-damaged patients. *Neuropsychologia* **23:** 273–277.
30. Bisiach, E., and Luzzatti, C. (1978). Unilateral neglect of representational space. *Cortex* **14:** 129–133.
31. Young, A. W., Hellawell, D. J., and Welch, J. (1992). Neglect and visual recognition. *Brain* **115:** 51–71.
32. Arguin, M., and Bub, D. N. (1993). Evidence for an independent stimulus-centered spatial reference frame from a case of visual hemineglect. *Cortex* **29:** 349–357.
33. Driver, J., and Halligan, P. W. (1991). Can visual neglect operate in object-centered coordinates? An affirmative single-case study. *Cognit. Neuropsych.* **8:** 475–496.
34. Marshall, J. C., and Halligan, P. W. (1993). Visuo-spatial neglect: A new copying text to assess perceptual parsing. *J. Neurol.* **240:** 37–40.
35. Karnath, H. O., Schenkel, P., and Fischer, B. (1991). Trunk orientation as the determining factor of the "contralateral" deficit in the neglect syndrome and as the physical anchor of the internal representation of body orientation in space. *Brain* **114:** 1997–2014.
36. Ladavas, E. (1987). Is the hemispatial deficit produced by right parietal lobe damage associated with retinal or gravitational coordinates? *Brain* **110:** 167–180.
37. Farah, M. J., Brunn, J. L., Wong, A. B., Wallace, M. A., and Carpenter, P. A. (1990). Frames of reference for allocating attention to space: Evidence from the neglect syndrome. *Neuropsychologia* **28:** 335–347.
38. Bisiach, E., Perani, D., Vallar, G., and Berti, A. (1986). Unilateral neglect: Personal and extra-personal. *Neuropsychologia* **24:** 759–767.
39. Guariglia, C., and Antonucci, G. (1992). Personal and extrapersonal space: A case of neglect dissociation. *Neuropsychologia* **30:** 1001–1009.
40. Lynch, J. C., and McLaren, J. W. (1989). Deficits of visual attention and saccadic eye movements after lesions of parietooccipital cortex in monkeys. *J. Neurophysiol.* **61:** 74–90.
41. Wurtz, R. H. (1969). Visual receptive fields of striate cortex neurons in awake monkeys. *J. Neurophysiol.* **32:** 727–742.
42. Goldberg, M. E. (1983). Studying the neurophysiology of behavior: Methods for recording single neurons in awake behaving monkeys. In *Methods in Cellular Neurobiology* (J. L. Barker and J. F. McKelvy, eds.), Vol. 3, pp. 225–248. Wiley, New York.
43. Mountcastle, V. B., Lynch, J. C., Georgopoulos, A., Sakata, H., and Acuna, C. (1975). Posterior parietal association cortex of the monkey: Command functions for operations within extrapersonal space. *J. Neurophysiol.* **38:** 871–908.
44. Robinson, D. L., Goldberg, M. E., and Stanton, G. B. (1978). Parietal association cortex in the primate: Sensory mechanisms and behavioral modulations. *J. Neurophysiol.* **41:** 910–932.
45. Bushnell, M. C., Goldberg, M. E., and Robinson, D. L. (1981). Behavioral enhancement of visual responses in monkey cerebral cortex. I: Modulation in posterior parietal cortex related to selective visual attention. *J. Neurophysiol.* **46:** 755–772.
46. Gnadt, J. W., and Andersen, R. A. (1988). Memory related motor planning activity in posterior parietal cortex of macaque. *Exp. Brain Res.* **70:** 216–220.
47. Goldberg, M. E., Colby, C. L., and Duhamel, J.-R. (1990). Representation of visuomotor space in the parietal lobe of the monkey. *Cold Spring Harbor Symp. Quant. Biol.* **55:** 729–739.
48. Barash, S., Bracewell, R. M., Fogassi, L., Gnadt, J. W., and Andersen, R. A. (1991). Saccade-related activity in the lateral intraparietal areas. II: Spatial properties. *J. Neurophysiol.* **66:** 1109–1124.
49. Andersen, R. A., Bracewell, R. M., Barash, S., Gnadt, J. W., and Fogassi, L. (1990). Eye position effects on visual, memory, and saccade-related activity in areas LIP and 7a of macaque. *J. Neurosci.* **10:** 1176–1196.
50. Zipser, D., and Andersen, R. A. (1988). A back-propagation programmed network that simulates response properties of a subset of posterior parietal neurons. *Nature (London)* **331:** 679–684.
51. Helmholtz, H. (1866/1924). *Treatise on physiological optics.* Dover, New York.
52. Duhamel, J.-R., Colby, C. L., and Goldberg, M. E. (1992). The updating of the representation of visual space in parietal cortex by intended eye movements. *Science* **255:** 90–92.

53. Colby, C. L., Duhamel, J.-R., and Goldberg, M. E. (1995). Oculocentric spatial representation in parietal cortex. *Cereb. Cortex* **5:** 470–481.
54. Duhamel, J.-R., Goldberg, M. E., Fitzgibbon, E. J., Sirigu, A., and Grafman, J. (1992). Saccadic dysmetria in a patient with a right frontoparietal lesion: The importance of corollary discharge for accurate spatial behaviour. *Brain* **115:** 1387–1402.
55. Heide, W., Blankenburg, M., Zimmermann, E., and Kömpf, D. (1995). Cortical control of double-step saccades: Implications for spatial orientation. *Ann. Neurol.* **38:** 739–748.
56. Colby, C. L., Duhamel, J.-R., and Goldberg, M. E. (1993). Ventral intraparietal area of the macaque: Anatomic location and visual response properties. *J. Neurophysiol.* **69:** 902–914.
57. Duhamel, J.-R., Colby, C. L., and Goldberg, M. E. (1991). Congruent representations of visual and somatosensory space in single neurons of monkey ventral intra-parietal cortex (area VIP). In *Brain and Space* (J. Paillard, ed.), pp. 223–236. Oxford University Press, Oxford.
58. Colby, C. L., Duhamel, J.-R., and Goldberg, M. E. (1995). Multiple parietal representations of space. In *Brain Theory: Biological Basis and Computational Theory of Vision* (A. Aertsen and V. Braitenberg, eds.), pp. 37–52. Elsevier, Amsterdam.
59. Laplane, D., Talairach, J., Meininger, V., Bancaud, J., and Bouchareine, A. (1977). Motor consequences of motor area ablations in man. *J. Neurol. Sci.* **31:** 29–49.
60. Halsband, U., and Freund, H.-J. (1990). Premotor cortex and conditional motor learning in man. *Brain* **113:** 207–222.
61. Eslinger, P. J., and Damasio, A. R. (1985). Severe disturbance of higher cognition after bilateral frontal lobe ablation: Patient EVR. *Neurology* **35:** 1731–1741.
62. Schwartz, A. B., Kettner, R. E., and Georgopoulos, A. P. (1988). Primate motor cortex and free arm movements to visual targets in three-dimensional space. I: Relations between single cell discharge and direction of movement. *J. Neurosci.* **8:** 2913–2927.
63. Georgopoulos, A. P., Lurito, J. T., Petrides, M., Schwartz, A. B., and Massey, J. T. (1989). Mental rotation of the neuronal population vector. *Science* **243:** 234–236.
64. Scott, S. H., and Kalaska, J. F. (1995). Changes in motor cortex activity during reaching movements with similar hand paths but different arm postures. *J. Neurophysiol.* **73:** 2563–2567.
65. Gentilucci, M., Scandolara, C., Pigarev, I. N., and Rizzolatti, G. (1983). Visual responses in the postarcuate cortex (area 6) of the monkey that are independent of eye position. *Exp. Brain Res.* **50:** 464–468.
66. Fogassi, L., Gallese, V., di Pellegrino, G., Fadiga, L., Gentilucci, M., Luppino, G., Matelli, M., Pedotti, A., and Rizzolatti, G. (1992). Space coding by premotor cortex. *Exp. Brain Res.* **89:** 686–690.
67. Graziano, M. S., Yap, G. S., and Gross, C. G. (1994). Coding of visual space by premotor neurons. *Science* **266:** 1054–1057.
68. Chen, L. L., and Wise, S. P. (1995). Neuronal activity in the supplementary eye field during acquisition of conditional oculomotor associations. *J. Neurophysiol.* **73:** 1101–1121.
69. Olson, C. R., and Gettner, S. N. (1995). Object-centered direction selectivity in the macaque supplementary eye field. *Science* **269:** 985–988.
70. Olson, C. R., and Gettner, S. N. (1996). Brain representation of object-centered space. *Curr. Opin. Neurobiol.* **6:** 165–170.
71. Funahashi, S., Bruce, C. J., and Goldman-Rakic, P. S. (1991). Neuronal activity related to saccadic eye movements in the monkey's dorsolateral prefrontal cortex. *J. Neurophysiol.* **65:** 1464–1483.
72. McCarthy, G., Blamire, A. M., Puce, A., Nobre, A. C., Bloch, G., Hyder, F., Goldman-Rakic, P., and Shulman, R. G. (1994). Functional magnetic resonance imaging of human prefrontal cortex activation during a spatial working memory task. *Proc. Natl. Acad. Sci. U.S.A.* **91:** 8690–8694.
73. Funahashi, S., Bruce, C. J., and Goldman-Rakic, P. S. (1993). Dorsolateral prefrontal lesions and oculomotor delayed-response performance: Evidence for mnemonic scotomas. *J. Neurosci.* **13:** 1479–1497.
74. Sawaguchi, T., and Goldman-Rakic, P. S. (1994). The role of D1-dopamine receptor in working memory: Local injections of dopamine antagonists into the prefrontal cortex of rhesus monkeys performing an oculomotor delayed-response task. *J. Neurophysiol.* **71:** 515–528.
75. Witter, M. P. (1993). Organization of the entorhinal-hippocampal system: A review of current anatomical data. *Hippocampus* **3:** 33–44.
76. Zola-Morgan, S., and Squire, L. R. (1993). Neuroanatomy of memory. *Annu. Rev. Neurosci.* **16:** 547–563.
77. Squire, L. R., and Zola-Morgan, S. (1988). Memory: Brain systems and behavior. *Trends Neurosci.* **11:** 170–175.
78. Milner, B., Corkin, C., and Teuber, H.-L. (1968). Further analysis of the hippocampal amnesic syndrome: 14-year follow-up study of HM. *Neuropsychologia* **6:** 215–234.
79. Jones-Gotman, M., and Milner, B. (1978). Right temporal-lobe contribution to image mediated verbal learning. *Neuropsychologia* **16:** 61–71.
80. Smith, M. L., and Milner, B. (1981). The role of the right hippocampus in the recall of spatial location. *Neuropsychologia* **19:** 781–793.
81. Ranck, J. B., Jr. (1973). Studies on single neurons in dorsal hippocampal formation and septum in unrestrained rats. I: Behavioral correlates and firing repertoires. *Exp. Neurol.* **41:** 461–531.
82. Muller, R. U., Kubie, J. L., Bostock, E. M., Taube, J. S., and Quirk, G. J. (1991). Spatial firing correlates of neurons in the hippocampal formation of freely moving rats. In *Brain and Space* (J. Paillard, ed.), pp. 296–333. Oxford University Press, Oxford.
83. O'Keefe, J., and Burgess, N. (1996). Geometric determinants of the place fields of hippocampal neurons. *Nature (London)* **381:** 425–428.
84. Muller, R. U., Ranck, J. B., Jr., and Taube, J. S. (1996). Head direction cells: Properties and functional significance. *Curr. Opin. Neurobiol.* **6:** 196–206.
85. Weiskrantz, L. (1996). Blindsight revisited. *Curr. Opin. Neurobiol.* **6:** 215–220.
86. Weiskrantz, L., Warrington, E. K., Sanders, M. D., and Marshall, J. (1974). Visual capacity in the hemianoptic field following a restricted occipital ablation. *Brain* **97:** 709–728.
87. O'Keefe, J., and Dostrovsky, J. (1971). The hippocampus as a spatial map. Preliminary evidence from unit activity in the freely-moving rat. *Brain Res.* **34:** 171–175.
88. Goodale, M. A., Meenan, J. P., Bülthoff, H. H., Nicolle, D. A., Murphy, K. J., and Racicot, C. I. (1994). Separate neural pathways for the visual analysis of object shape in perception and prehension. *Curr. Biol.* **4:** 604–610.

CHAPTER

54

Attention

G. S. Aston-Jones, R. Desimone, J. Driver, S. J. Luck, and M. I. Posner

The problem of selective attention is one of the oldest in psychology. William James wrote at the turn of the century, "Everyone knows what attention is. It is the taking possession by the mind in clear and vivid form of one out of what seem several simultaneous objects or trains of thought."[1] This chapter deals with three aspects of attention: (1) the selection of sensory objects, (2) the control of voluntary trains of thought or actions, and (3) the maintenance of the alert state required for attentive processing.

We have chosen to stress those aspects of attention that are closest to the study of neuroscience. Until recently, researchers studying human information processing and neuroscientists have differed in their approaches to attention. The former approach tended to describe attention either in terms of a bottleneck that prevented limited-capacity central systems from overload or as a resource that could be allocated to various processing systems as if they were economic entities. On the other hand, neuroscience, on the basis of animal experiments, emphasized several separate neural mechanisms that might be involved in orienting and maintaining alertness. These two approaches are now being integrated within a cognitive neuroscience of attention. For example, studies of visual search have included a modern neuroscience view of the multichannel visual system, incorporating separate mechanisms for dealing with color, form, and motion with the cognitive idea of a separate visual attention system needed to integrate information from these channels.

An impressive aspect of current developments in this field is the convergence of evidence from studies using various methods. These studies include performance studies of reaction time, dual-task performance studies, recording from scalp electrodes, and studies of lesions in humans and animals, as well as those using various methods for imaging and recording from restricted brain areas, including individual cells.

Current progress in the anatomy of the attention system can be attributed to two important methodological developments. First, the use of microelectrodes with alert animals has made it possible to gather evidence of increased activity in specific cell populations under conditions of selective attention. Second, anatomical (e.g., computerized tomography or magnetic resonance imaging) and physiological (e.g., positron emission tomography, functional magnetic resonance imaging) methods of studying parts of the brain have facilitated investigations of the localization of cognitive function in normal people. In addition, the use of localizing methods has been coupled with methods for tracing the time course of brain activity in the human subject. This combination provides a convenient way to trace the rapid time-dynamic changes that occur in the course of human information processing.

These methods have been applied with special vigor to three general aspects of attention. The first aspect concerns orienting to sensory events, the part of attention for which human and animal investigations are most closely related. The second is the area of executive control that relates attention to semantic memory (Chapter 56) and language (Chapter 57). The third area is arousal or maintaining the alert state, which is closely related to material presented earlier on sleep.

ORIENTING TO AND SELECTING FROM COMPETING STIMULI

Orienting Aligns Attention with a Source of Signals

Most everyday scenes are cluttered, containing numerous objects that stimulate our senses at the same time. For instance, in a busy market the hubbub of many superimposed sounds reaches our ears, while our eyes receive input from innumerable stimuli. We cannot respond to all these objects at once; we cannot pick up every item at one stall in the market simultaneously, nor can we visit every stall at the same time. We also cannot fully perceive all the stimuli reaching our senses at once. For instance, when choosing fruit at a market, we typically inspect the details of each potential purchase one at a time, rather than attempting to judge every fruit simultaneously. Mechanisms of attention address the need for selection that is imposed by the occurrence of multiple concurrent stimuli. These mechanisms allow us to pick out particular stimuli, to control our responses, and to receive fuller perceptual processing.

Covert Orienting Is the Ability to Concentrate Our Attention on a Particular Stimulus without Moving Any Part of Our Bodies

In Chapter 36 we discussed the control of overt orienting in vision through head and eye movements. Orienting can also be achieved by purely internal means, with no external realignments. We can concentrate on particular visual, auditory, or tactile stimuli, without moving our eyes, head, or body around. These abilities are referred to as **covert orienting** and have been extensively examined with a behavioral technique known as spatial cueing (see Fig. 54.1). Covert orienting can be an automatic response to a sensory event **(exogenous orienting)** or voluntary control **(endogenous orienting)**.

Spatial Cueing Has Been Used Extensively to Investigate Covert Orienting

In one version of spatial cueing,[2] the subject's task is to detect the onset of a flash of light, which can appear on the left or on the right, by pressing a single button as fast as possible, without moving the eyes. The critical manipulation is that before the target appears, the experimenter "cues" the person's attention to one side or another—for instance, with a peripheral flash on that side or by an instruction such as a central arrow that indicates the side where the target is most likely to appear. Typically, the person will be faster to respond to targets on the cued side than on the uncued side *even though the eyes do not move from the center.* Since no shift of receptors toward the cued side is permitted, the benefit for the cued side is usually attributed to some *covert* shift in attention toward that side. A common metaphor is that of a mental "spotlight" with limited extent that can be shifted internally, analogous to external shifts of the fovea.

Does the faster target detection on the cued side reflect a genuine effect of covert attention on perception? Subjects might show benefits if they were simply less cautious in responding to the cued side (i.e., prepared to press the button on the basis of less evidence from that side, lowering their "criterion," to use the technical term). The question of whether covert attention affects sensory perception, and if so at what level, is of long standing and has been addressed in a number of ways with the cueing technique. Instead of using a simple detection task, the subject can be required to make some choice discrimination—for example, to press one of several buttons as fast as possible in response to, say, the shape of the target when it arrives. With such techniques, both the speed and the accuracy of a wide range of discriminations at the cued location can be enhanced. If the effect of the cue were simply to induce a less cautious response to the cued location, faster *but less accurate* performance should be observed there. In an alternative behavioral method, near-threshold stimuli are presented for discrimination in the absence of time constraints, so that sophisticated signal-detection analyses can be applied to the data. Several such studies have found that perceptual sensitivity is indeed affected by covert spatial orienting.[4]

One Can Measure Underlying Neural Activity during Covert Spatial Orienting

One of the beauties of the spatial-cueing method is that its simplicity allows spatial orienting to be studied with many converging methods in many different species. For instance, event-related potentials (ERPs) can be measured noninvasively in humans by averaging voltage fluctuations from scalp electrodes in response to particular stimuli over many trials (see Fig. 54.2 and Box 54.1). The same stimuli are presented while the experimenter manipulates whether the subject is cued to attend to them covertly. Several such studies have found that early components of the sensory ERP (those occurring starting around 80 ms after the stimulus onset) can be modulated by covert attention toward or away from the stimulus. Researchers have used the ERP method to show that cueing affects extra striate visual cortex after about 100 ms of input, as shown in Fig. 54.3. The most straightforward interpretation of such findings is that covert attention modulates sensory processing, amplifying the signal for attended stimuli and/or attenuating the signal for unattended stimuli.

Endogenous covert orienting is isolated by using cues that predict the likely target locus (see Fig. 54.1B) but do not appear directly at it (e.g., a central arrow that correctly points to the target side on 80% of trials). Here the aim is to get subjects to shift their covert attention voluntarily toward the side where the target

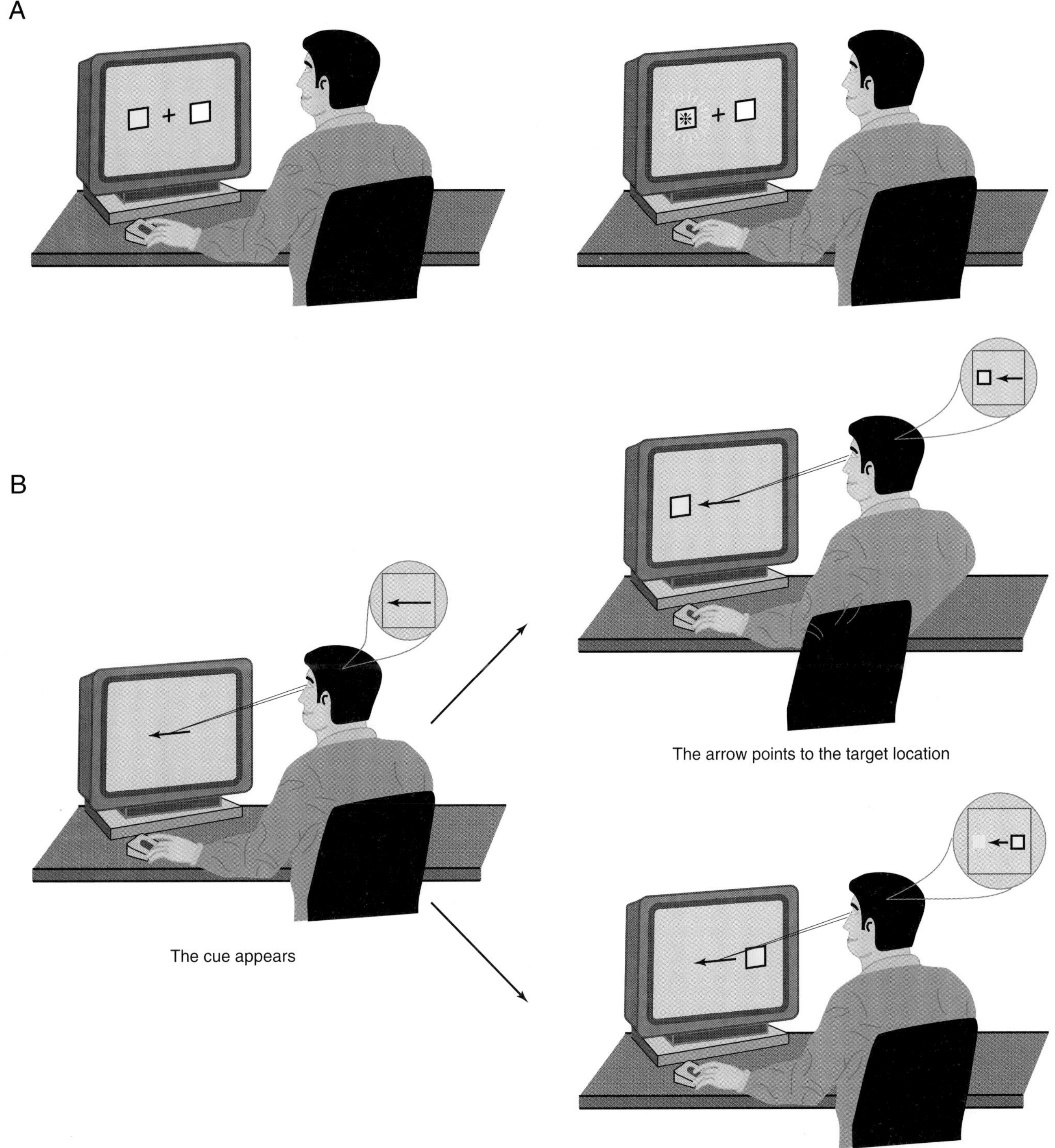

FIGURE 54.1 (A) Exogenous cue. At left, a cue pulls attention covertly to its location, where the subsequent target is presented and is given priority. (B) Endogenous cue. An arrow cue may inform the person where to place attention. Targets at the cued location will be given priority (valid trial), while those at uncued locations will be responded to slowly (invalid trials).

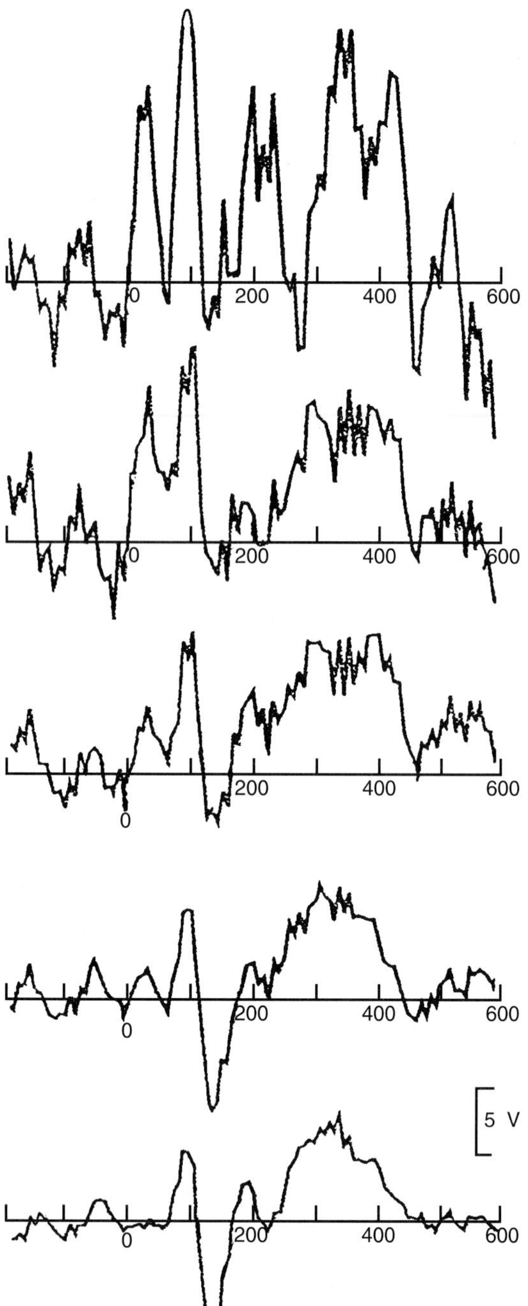

FIGURE 54.2 Electrical activity summed over 1 to 32 trials. The ERP to a visual word tends to stabilize after 16 to 30 trials to produce an average ERP that is distinctive for each person and type of stimulus. The introduction of the stimulus occurs at 0 ms. Electrical activity prior to that is clearly noise.

is most likely. There are subtle differences in the effects of central informative cues and those of peripheral uninformative cues, as well as in the methodology needed to interpret them unambiguously. When using peripheral cues, investigators must implement various control conditions to ensure that any cueing effect is attentional rather than sensory. For example, a benefit in target detection at the location of an uninformative cue might, in principle, be caused by some sensory interaction between the cue and the subsequent target—for example, an energy summation when the targets appear at the same place as the preceding cue. Such sensory effects can be ruled out by comparison with further conditions. For instance, concurrent peripheral cues on *both* sides should produce energy summations with a subsequent target comparable to those with single cues, yet they should not produce any shift of attention toward only one side. Such methodological issues are less problematic in studies of endogenous covert orienting, because the stimulus events can be held constant while only the location where subjects expect to see the targets is varied.

The endogenous effects of such expectations should last as long as the subject's expectancy. In contrast, whereas the exogenous effects of uninformative peripheral cues (e.g., a sudden flash that does not predict target location) usually emerge very rapidly (commencing as soon as the cue appears), the benefit in target detection at the cued location is typically short-lived. Indeed, about 300 ms after an uninformative visual cue, this benefit usually reverses to become a disadvantage for target detection at the cued location.[5] This paradoxical effect has been termed **inhibition of return,** reflecting the hypothesis that covert exogenous attention is first drawn to the location of the uninformative peripheral event and then moves elsewhere with a bias against returning. The phenomenon is not observed with informative peripheral cues—though it may still apply, but be "hidden" under the beneficial effect of continued endogenous attention to the expected target location. Such differences between the effects of informative and uninformative cues suggest that endogenous and exogenous covert orienting may rely on distinct neural mechanisms. For instance, the superior colliculus may be involved only in exogenous covert orienting.[6]

The studies reviewed so far indicate how covert orienting can be measured in normal human subjects and can influence performance by giving the selected signal priority during performance. They also suggest a distinction between endogenous selection under voluntary control and exogenous selection when a sudden event captures attention.

Damage to Specific Areas Disrupts Covert Orienting

Suppose there were indeed two distinct "spotlights" of covert attention, one exogenous and one endogenous, with different neural substrates for each. Then, in principle, lesions in one substrate should be able to

BOX 54.1

MEASURING BRAIN WAVES

Scientists have been measuring brain waves for more than 50 years, ever since Hans Berger showed that electrical activity from the brain could be measured by placing conducting material on the scalp and amplifying the resultant electrical signal so that it could be written out by a pen recorder. His instrument, the electroencephalograph (EEG), has been a standard tool for diagnosing brain damage in the years since.

The EEG did not become suitable for cognitive studies, however, until G. D. Dawson developed a method of averaging the EEG signal following a stimulus. The concept is simple. The stimulus is presented many times to the same subject. At each electrode, the electrical activity is recorded at fixed intervals following the stimulus—say, every 4 ms. The electrical values at each interval are taken from many trials and averaged together so that electrical activity not caused by the stimulus averages to zero and the resultant signal shows only the activity produced by the stimulus. Usually 10 to 100 presentations of the stimulus suffice to produce a reliable potential that reflects characteristics of both the individual brain and the particular stimulus. The waveform can be described by giving the direction (positive or negative) and the delay to the appearance of each of the bumps in the wave (see Fig. 54.2).

To improve the chances of finding an electrical signal from the areas where brain activity has been found with PET or other neuroimaging methods is a complex task. First, a large number of electrodes are used to achieve as thorough a sample of electrical activity from the surface as possible. Second, each electrode's activity is compared to the average activity of all other electrodes. Finally, a subtractive strategy similar to that used in PET studies helps to isolate the effects of a particular mental operation.

For example, one study (Fig. 54.2) measured event-related potentials in tasks similar to those used in PET. One task involves the presentation of visual words. Each trial starts with a fixation cross that serves as a warning signal. During the entire procedure, the subject's eye position is monitored through a TV camera to make sure that the eyes have not wandered from the fixation point. After half a second a word replaces the cross and remains present for another half to one second. Half a second after it is taken away, a prompt tells the subject to press a key to give his or her response. Brain waves are recorded just before the warning signal and continue to be recorded throughout the trial. Later the event-related potentials for a given condition (e.g., words or nonsense strings) are averaged for each subject, and grand averages over all subjects are computed.

---

disrupt exogenous but not endogenous covert orienting, while lesions in the other substrate would have the reverse effect. A widely accepted double dissociation of this kind has not yet been demonstrated, although researchers[7] have suggested that parietal lesions impair primarily exogenous, not endogenous, covert orienting in humans, while frontal lesions may do the reverse. Perhaps we should not expect to find a complete dissociation between exogenous and endogenous mechanisms, because these seem most likely to interact as components in a complex network, as do the superior colliculus and frontal eye fields in overt orienting.

Despite this failure to demonstrate a clear double dissociation as yet, evidence indicates that particular lesions can impair only certain aspects of covert orienting. For instance, inhibition of return after uninformative peripheral cues is absent in patients suffering from progressive supranuclear palsy (PSP), but is present in a variety of control groups with cortical lesions.[8] PSP is a progressive degenerative disease, which, judging by postmortem studies, seems to affect primarily the midbrain. This site for the disease coincides with the suggested collicular substrate for exogenous covert orienting[6] and thus for inhibition of return. On the other hand, whereas cell abnormalities are found only in the midbrain of PSP patients at postmortem, positron emission tomography (PET) reveals a diffuse hypometabolism throughout the frontal cortex *in vivo,* so that linking the effects of PSP on covert orienting to a specific anatomical location is difficult. Within distributed networks, distant areas may interact so that damage to one region can have effects on function elsewhere. For this reason, arguments based on the lesion method need support from converging methods.

Patient Studies Link the Parietal Cortex, Midbrain, and Thalamus to the Component Processes "Disengage–Move–Reengage"

Unilateral *parietal* lesions have long been associated with clinical deficits of attention (such as the neglect syndrome; see Chapter 56). When the effect of these lesions is analyzed with the spatial-cueing techniques,

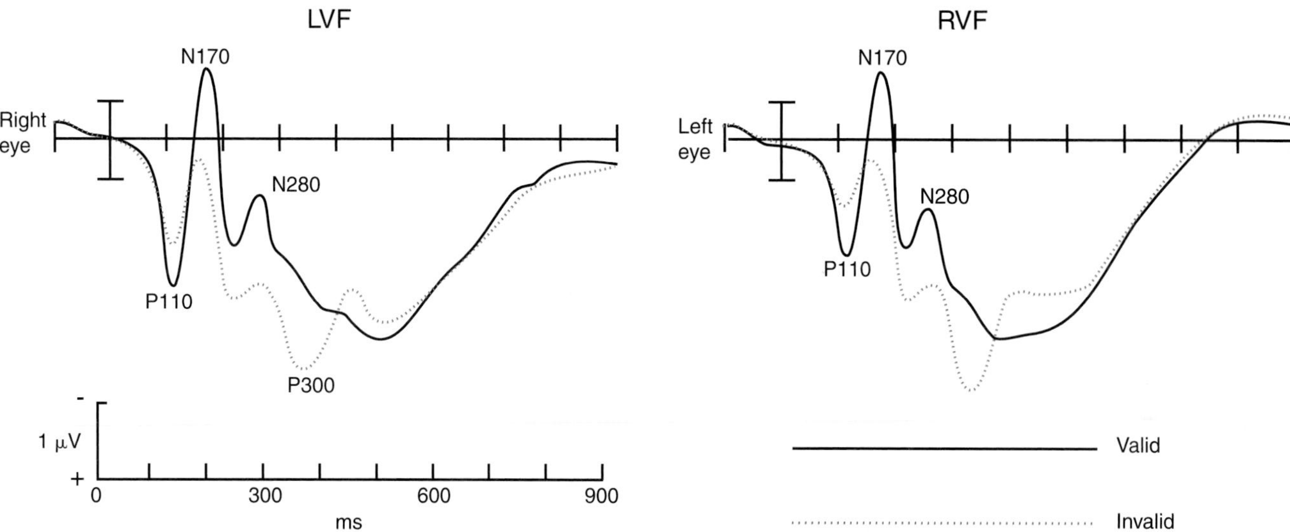

FIGURE 54.3 Recordings of scalp electrical activity show larger event-related potentials (see Box 54.1) to targets after cues to the same visual field (valid trials, solid line) than to targets in the field opposite the cue (invalid trials, dashed line). These effects occur within 80–100 ms after presentation of the target. Components of the electrical activity are given a letter (N or P) to indicate positive or negative electrical activity and a time (e.g., P110 = a positive wave that peaks at about 110 ms after the stimulus). LVF, left visual field; RVF, right visual field.

a characteristic deficit in the behavioral markers of covert orienting is found.[9a] Like normal individuals, patients with unilateral parietal damage show an advantage in visual detection at the cued location, regardless of whether the cue falls on the ipsilesional or contralesional side. This result suggests that the patients can shift their attention covertly to engage it on a new location in either direction. Their abnormality arises specifically on trials where they are cued in the ipsilesional direction and then presented with a target further toward the contralesional side. Responses are then disproportionately slow, and the target is sometimes missed completely. This pattern of results may be due to a specific deficit in disengaging attention from an ipsilesional location once a cue has been perceived there. The "disengage deficit" has been replicated several times across different patients with unilateral parietal damage and the experimental deficit has been successfully correlated with the extent of their everyday attentional difficulties.[9a]

Other groups of patients show other specific abnormalities in spatial cueing. We have already pointed out the PSP patients' lack of inhibition of return. This group shows another abnormality: the usual advantage in target detection for peripherally cued over uncued locations is slow to emerge. This deficit has been attributed to a slowness in "moving" attention to the cued location, rather than to any difficulty in disengaging or engaging attention once there. Finally, patients with unilateral thalamic damage are slow to detect contralesional targets, regardless of where the cue falls. This deficit can be considered a difficulty in "engaging" attention on contralesional targets.

Thus, a model of covert spatial orienting has three components: disengage–move–reengage. Patient studies suggest that these components are localized to the parietal cortex, midbrain, and thalamus, respectively. This model has had considerable influence, but is not without its critics. As it stands, the model says little about potential differences between exogenous and endogenous mechanisms. The success in precisely localizing the three components has also been questioned. For instance, which region of the parietal lobe is critical for the disengage deficit and whether only parietal lesions can produce it remain uncertain. In addition, the hypothesis of three quite distinct components has been debated.[10] For instance, if the disengage operation were truly separate from the move operation, why would the disengage deficit of unilateral parietal patients show up only when they must "move" in a contralesional direction after disengaging?

Despite these potential criticisms, the initial patient studies with cueing techniques provide hope that covert attention can be broken down into component operations, each with a specific function and substrate. The substrates themselves could be localized more certainly by combining different methods, such as relating

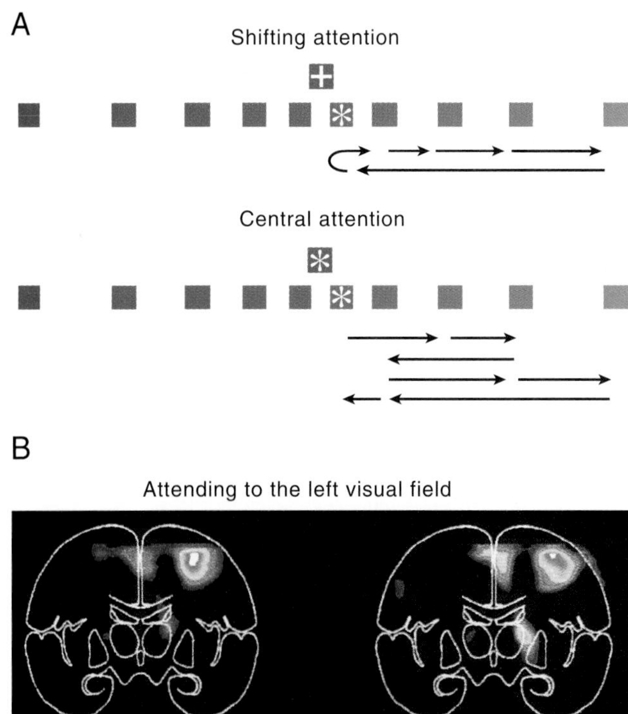

FIGURE 54.4 Subjects are instructed to keep attention at the center (central condition) or to move it in one visual field from box to box to detect targets that occur in each box in turn (shifting condition). The difference between these two conditions shows that there is activation of the superior parietal lobe of the right hemisphere when targets are in the left visual field and in both parietal lobes when targets are in the right visual field. This asymmetry implies a stronger right hemisphere involvement in orienting attention.

lesion effects to the site of activations in normal subjects in neuroimaging or ERP studies. For instance, a recent PET study[11] found bilateral parietal lobe activation when normal subjects attended to the right visual field and right unilateral activation when subjects attended to the left visual field (Fig. 54.4). This result has since been corroborated with the functional magnetic resonance imaging (fMRI) method. When combined with the effect of parietal lesions, these data strongly support the hypothesis that the parietal lobe is an important source of modulation by spatial attention.

Covert Orienting Mechanisms Exist in Other Sensory Modalities

Up to now, we have concentrated on visual covert orienting, but similar mechanisms exist in other modalities, and evidence of strong cross-modal links, as for overt orienting, is emerging. Researchers[12] have found that auditory endogenous attention toward one side tends to be accompanied by visual covert orienting to that side. Subjects in these experiments heard different spoken messages from left and right sides simultaneously. When they had to repeat the words from only one side, their visual sensitivity (for the shape of briefly flashed characters) was greater on that side even though they did not move their eyes. Evidence for audiovisual links in exogenous covert orienting comes from observations that patients with unilateral parietal damage show the characteristic disengage deficit even when an uninformative *sound* is the spatial cue for a subsequent visual target. Covert orienting has also been present with the spatial-cueing technique in purely auditory experiments[13] and purely tactile[14] experiments, thereby allowing the links between the modalities to be explored in full.

The studies described here show how aspects of orienting can be related to the functions of regional brain areas through studies of lesioned patients and by use of neuroimaging methods in healthy individuals.

Covert Orienting Allows for Attending to Locations and Objects

Overt orienting is clearly a spatially selective operation. Although covert attention has a spatial dimension, it also allows us to select a particular object rather than just a region of space. Thus, covert orienting is a part of the process of searching a visual scene for an object.

A number of behavioral results involving vision demonstrate that covert attention does indeed tend to select separate objects, rather than only predetermined regions of the retinal image. In one experiment, subjects were presented with two distinct objects but in the same two-dimensional space: one object was a box and the other a line that crossed the box. These objects were presented briefly (to rule out eye movements) and followed by a nonsense pattern (to make judgments about them difficult). Subjects had to make decisions about one or two attributes in each display without time pressure. When judging two attributes, the subject might have to compare attributes from the same object (e.g., was the box tall, and where was the gap in it?) or one attribute from each object (e.g., was the box tall, and was the line across it dotted or dashed?).

Results showed that subjects could make two judgments about the same object as accurately as one judgment, but could not judge two attributes from separate objects as well as one attribute. The basic result has now been replicated many times[15] and applies for all the visual qualities that have been examined (color, size, shape, movement, position, and so on), even though these dimensions are thought to be processed in separate visual regions of the brain (see Chapter 52). The implication is that covert attention selects all the properties of an individual object. Somehow a selection for the properties of the relevant object must spread across the diverse neural areas in which each of these properties is coded. Certainly, these results are difficult to explain in a purely spatial model of covert attention, since the two objects were superimposed in roughly the same place, and the attributes that had to be judged were no closer when both were in a single object than when they were in different objects.

The idea that covert attention may operate on segmented objects that the visual system has separated from other parts of the retinal image rather than on fixed positions does not apply only to complex judgments; it has also emerged from spatial-cueing experiments. Peripheral cues in exogenous orienting studies have often taken the form of brightening an outline box (see Fig. 54.1). Attention might be applied to this box itself, rather than to its position alone. In experiments in which the outline boxes were moved after the peripheral brightening,[16] attention was found to track the cued box. In other experiments, the performance of unilateral parietal patients was examined in a covert orienting study with two rotating boxes. Again, it was found that attention may track a moving object. This ability to update the position of an attended object would clearly be adaptive, given that most of our visual environments are dynamic.

Although many studies suggest that visual attention tends to select objects, spatial-cueing effects cannot all be object-based. For instance, when subjects are cued to expect targets in one region of an entirely empty display, there is no object for the system to lock onto, and yet covert-orienting effects are still found.[2] Clearly, covert visual attention is both space-based *and* object-based, although these two are often presented as mutually exclusive alternatives. Both components have been measured behaviorally within the same task (see Fig. 54.1). Researchers have spatially cued normal people to expect a visual target at one end of an object (an elongated rectangle). Visual detection was slower when the target subsequently appeared at the other end of the same object than when it appeared at the cued end, demonstrating the time costs of a purely spatial shift. However, the delay was even greater when the target appeared in another object, the same distance away, thus demonstrating the additional time cost of a between-object shift. Patients with parietal lesions to the right or left hemisphere showed the characteristic spatial disengage deficit in this task, as measured for shifts within an object; that is, they were slower to detect targets on the contralesional side after a cue on the ipsilesional side. In addition, the patients with left-hemisphere damage were found to show an object-based disengage deficit; they were exceptionally slow in detecting a contralesional target when they had been previously cued to the wrong object. The possibility that the left hemisphere may be specialized for between-object shifts of covert attention would be consistent with the proposal (see Chapter 58) that this hemisphere may be specialized for categorical representations of space (e.g., same versus different object) rather than for metric representations (e.g., 10 degrees apart).

In Visual Search There Is Competition between Targets

So far we have considered orienting in a simple field with few objects, but important new principles emerge when we consider multiple objects appearing within the same receptive field of a cell (see Fig. 54.5). The two basic phenomena that define the problem of visual search can be illustrated in a simple example. Consider the arrays shown in Fig. 54.5. In a typical search experiment, subjects are asked to report letters in one color (e.g., black letters) and to disregard those in the other color (e.g, white letters). The array is then briefly flashed before the subjects, without any opportunity for eye movements, and the subjects give their report. The display mimics our usual cluttered visual environment. It contains one or more objects that are relevant to current behavior, along with others that are irrelevant.

The first striking point about these experiments with multiple targets is that as long as the distinction between targets and nontargets is based on a simple feature such as black versus white, the difficulty of visual search is a function only of the number of targets. When the targets and distractors differ in a single feature (e.g., a black letter among white letters), the target pops out and responses are independent of the number of distractors.

When subjects have to report features of the targets, or when the distractors share many features with the targets, subjects do not perform as well, because their attention is divided instead of being focused on one feature. When subjects are required to identify simple properties of each object such as size, brightness, orien-

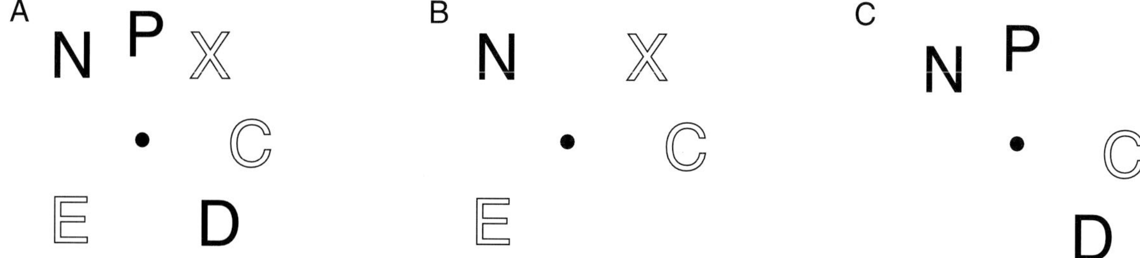

FIGURE 54.5 Conditions of visual search in which subjects are asked to report on the black letters. As the number of black letters increases, reports become less accurate and take longer. The number of white letters (distractors) does not matter.

tation, or spatial position, the result is much the same as when they have to identify more complex properties such as shape.[17] One exception is when subjects can rely on detection of a large change in brightness or energy.[18]

A second point is that as long as exposure to the stimulus is brief and the experiment measures the accuracy with which the stimulus is identified, perception of the stimulus input, rather than subsequent short-term storage and response, seems to be the major limitation on performance. For example, interference from processing two objects is abolished if the objects are shown one after the other, with an interval of perhaps a second between them,[17,18] even though the two responses called for must still be remembered and made together at the end of the trial.

Third, interference is independent of eye movements. Even though the gaze is fixed, it is easier to identify one object in the periphery than two.

An enduring issue is the underlying reason for between-object competition. It has often been argued that full visual analysis of every object in a scene would be impossibly complex.[19,20] Competition reflects the fact that there is a limit on the capacity for visual identification. Equally strong, however, is the view that competition concerns the control of response systems.[21] Certainly, some response activation often occurs from objects a person has been told to ignore,[22] so that unwanted information is not entirely filtered out. Very probably, competition between objects occurs at multiple levels between sensory input and motor output.

The Neural Basis for Competition Depends on Receptive Fields

If the nervous system had an unlimited capacity to process information in parallel throughout the visual field, competition between objects would presumably be necessary only at the motor output stage, where the number of effectors limits the ability to respond to multiple objects simultaneously. However, there do appear to be important limits on the parallel processing of visual information, and we will consider the nature of these limits and the role of attention in biasing the competition between objects within the visual system before discussing the role of attention in controlling motor output.

Receptive fields can be viewed as a critical visual-processing resource for which objects must compete[20,23,24] (see Chapter 28 for explicit definition and discussion of receptive field organization in vision), especially in areas such as V4 and inferior temporal (IT) cortex, where the receptive fields are so large that the neurons typically receive inputs from multiple objects at any given moment. As ever more objects are added to a receptive field in these areas, the information available about any one of them must certainly decrease. This is illustrated in Fig. 54.6 (left), which shows the responses that a typical V4 neuron might give to colored squares. This neuron is selective for color, producing a large response to a red square (50 spikes/s), a small response to a blue square (10 spikes/s), and an intermediate response to a violet square (30 spikes/s). When a neuron in one of these areas is simultaneously presented with a stimulus that normally elicits a large response and a stimulus that normally elicits a small response, the result is usually an intermediate response.[25,26] For example, the neuron in Fig. 54.6 produces a response of 30 spikes/s to the simultaneous presentation of a red stimulus and a blue stimulus. If this cell's computational role is to signal the presence of red, then this intermediate response might be a useful signal that half of the objects within the receptive field are red. However, the neuron's response is ambiguous, because the same firing rate is produced for a single violet square and for the combination of a red square and a blue square.

This ambiguity may be reduced by linking objects and their features to specific retinal locations. For example, if a neuron has a small receptive field, it is likely to contain only a single object and can unambiguously

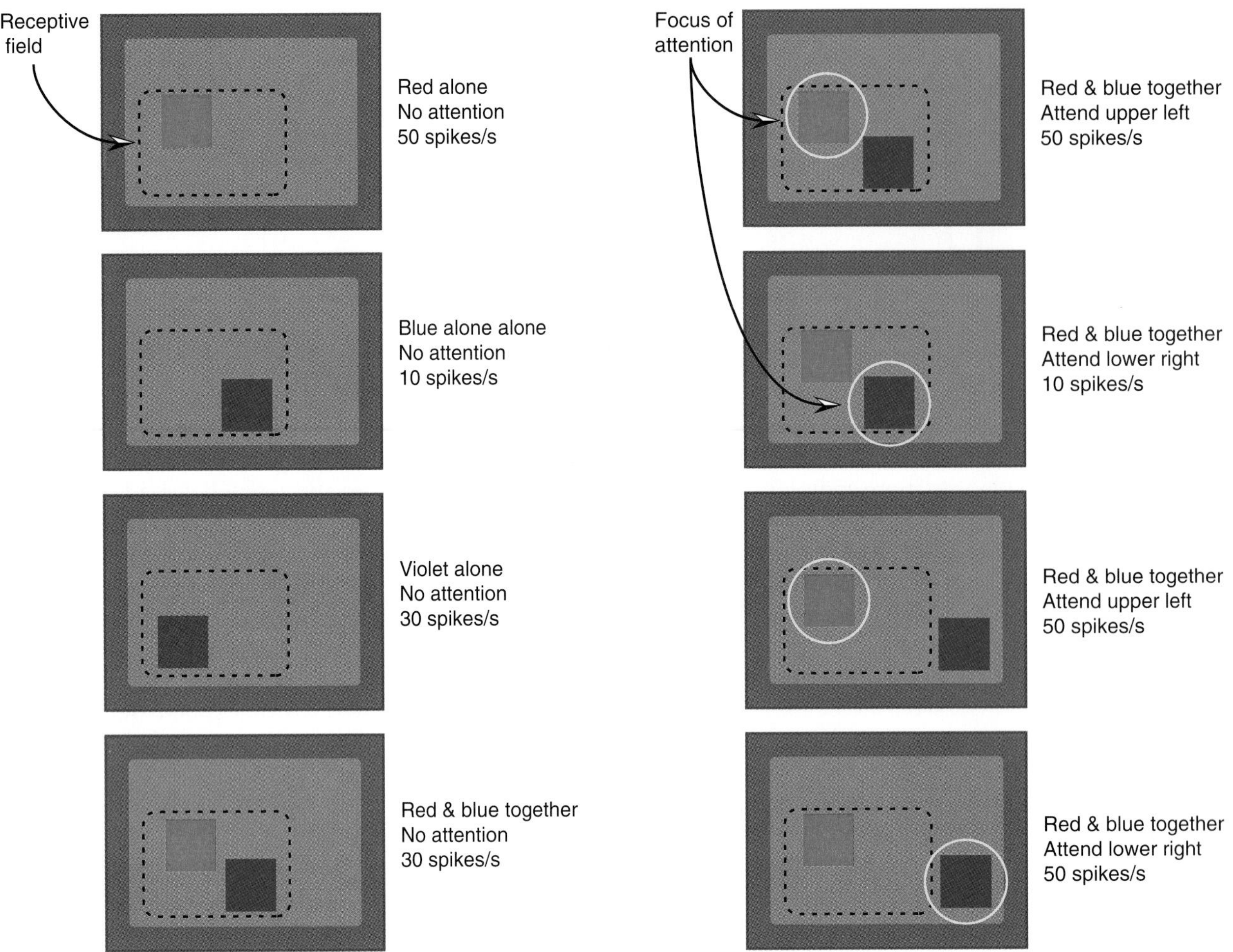

FIGURE 54.6 Responses of a typical neuron in area V4 to colored squares presented on a video monitor. The left column shows typical responses in the absence of explicit attentional instructions, and the right column shows typical responses when attention has been directed to one of the two objects. The firing rate of the neuron is given for each combination of stimulus configuration and attentional instructions.

signal that the feature for which it is sensitive is present at a specific location. However, if all visual neurons had small receptive fields, it might be very difficult to recognize that a given stimulus is the same object no matter where in the visual field it is presented. This potential difficulty may explain why neurons in high-level visual areas tend to have large receptive fields.[27]

Although the coding of spatial location in the dorsal stream has been emphasized,[28] it is important to note that ventral-stream areas such as area V4 and IT cortex also code stimulus location, albeit coarsely. Specifically, although the receptive fields in these areas are large, they are not infinitely large and they are not homogeneous. Thus, it is possible at least in principle to localize an object on the basis of the pattern of responses across many ventral-stream neurons, just as an object's color can be determined very precisely from the pattern of activation it elicits in photoreceptors that are broadly tuned to red, green, and blue (see Chapter 28). However, this sort of coarse coding tends to break down when multiple objects are presented simultaneously, placing limits on the effectiveness of processing the entire visual field in parallel.

Figure 54.6 (right) illustrates the role that attention appears to play in resolving the ambiguities that occur when two or more objects compete for a neuron's receptive field. Specifically, it has been proposed that an attended object will gain control of a neuron such that the neuron's output reflects only the features of the attended object and not the features of the ignored objects.[29,30] For example, if the red and blue squares are presented simultaneously inside the receptive field of the neuron illustrated in Fig. 54.6, but only the red square is attended, then the neuron's output will be the same as if only the red square were present inside the receptive field (i.e., 50 spikes/s). Similarly, if the blue square is attended, the neuron's output will be the same as if only the blue square were present inside the receptive field (i.e., 10 spikes/s). In this manner, the competition between the red and blue squares is biased in favor of the attended square, allowing the neuron's output to unambiguously signal the color of that square.

This proposed role of attention in regulating competition between stimuli leads to an interesting prediction: If attention serves to regulate competition between objects for access to the receptive field, then attention should have little or no effect when competition is eliminated by presenting only one object inside the receptive field. This is illustrated in the bottom two panels of Fig. 54.6 (right), which show the predicted effects of attention when the red square is inside the receptive field and the blue square is outside. In this situation, the red and blue squares do not compete for control of the neuron, and so the neuron's response to the one item inside the receptive field—the red square—should be unaffected by attention. This prediction may seem surprising, but it has now been verified in two separate experiments,[25,31] as will be described in the next section.

Top-Down Control Is Required to Coordinate Selection in Multiple Systems

Several investigators have proposed that the selection of objects by attention is based on a top-down "attentional template" that specifies the characteristics of the objects that are relevant for the current task.[23,32,33] For example, if you are searching for a friend who is wearing a red cap and is sitting somewhere on the left side of a crowded movie theater, your attentional template might specify "red" and "left." The attentional template is then used to coordinate selective processing across the multiple visual areas that are responsible for coding different features, allowing inputs that are red and on the left to have a competitive advantage for the control of perception and action. The concept of an attentional template may also help us to understand the relationship between spatial selection and object selection, because an object's spatial location can be considered one of its features. Indeed, there appear to be similarities between space-based and object-based attention in addition to the differences described earlier in this chapter.

Visual Selection Based on Spatial Location

The proposal that attention regulates competition between objects for access to neural receptive fields (Fig. 54.6) has been supported by experiments in which neural activity in monkeys was recorded while they attended to one of two locations. In one study of cells in area V4 and in IT cortex, the monkeys performed a discrimination task on target stimuli at one location in the visual field, ignoring simultaneously presented distractors at a second location.[31] The target location for a given trial block was indicated to the monkey by special instruction trials at the beginning of each block, and the monkey was required to remember which location to attend throughout the remainder of the block; that is, spatial attention was controlled in a purely top-down manner on the basis of information held in working memory (see Chapter 59). When the attended-location target and the ignored-location distractor were both within the receptive field of the cell being recorded [as in the top two panels of Fig. 54.6 (right)], the neuron's response was determined primarily by the target stimulus and not by the distractor stimulus. In other words, the neurons responded as though their receptive fields had "shrunk" around the target. However, when either the target or the distractor was placed outside the receptive field [as in the bottom two panels of Fig. 54.6 (right)], so that they were no longer in competition for control over the neuron being recorded, attention no longer had any effect on the neuron's response. Thus, attention appears to provide a top-down bias over the competition that occurs when multiple stimuli fall within a receptive field.

Although attention-related modulations of neuronal responses may be observed even when only a single stimulus is placed inside the receptive field,[34–36] every study that has ever compared configurations with one versus two stimuli inside the receptive field has found larger attention-related modulations when two stimuli were presented inside the receptive field.[25,31,36,37] In addition, attention-related modulations appear to be more easily obtained in areas with larger receptive fields, such as area V4, area MT, and IT cortex. For example, with one exception,[34] experiments with monkeys have failed to find consistent effects of spatial attention on neural activity in area V1, where the receptive fields are too small to contain both an attended stimulus and an ignored stimulus.[25,31] Neurophysiological studies in human subjects have similarly failed to observe attentional modulations of responses in area V1, although substantial modulations have been observed in higher level areas where the receptive fields are presumably larger.[38,39] Receptive fields are also small in area V2, and one study of V2 neurons found attentional modulations only in neurons whose receptive fields were large enough to contain both an attended and an ignored stimulus.[25] By the stage of inferotemporal cortex, receptive fields are so large that it is almost impossible to place one stimulus inside and another outside the receptive field, leading to attentional modulations in almost every neuron.[31] These results suggest that target selection is a multistage process, working over small spatial ranges in a small subset of neurons at early stages of the visual system and operating over the entire visual field in the majority of neurons at late stages.

To summarize, spatial attention can strongly modulate neural responses in visual cortex, but these effects are found primarily when multiple stimuli compete for access to a given neuron. Because receptive field sizes increase as information travels anteriorly through the visual system, the probability of multiple stimuli appearing inside a given receptive field also increases at the more anterior areas, which should lead to an increase in the proportion of neurons that are influenced by attention in these areas (although this has never been directly quantified). It might seem strange that the effects of attention are limited to a subset of visual areas and to a subset of the neurons within an area for a given stimulus array. However, it would be inefficient for the visual system to code only a single object at any given moment and suppress the information from the rest of the visual input. Indeed, with the exception of certain neurological patients,[40] most people report that they see the entire visual world rather than a single object at a time, even when attention is strongly focused. This aspect of experience may be the result of the many neurons within the visual system that are not influenced by attention at a given moment.

Mechanisms of Spatial Biasing

Although the synaptic mechanisms mediating the gating of V4 and IT responses are not known, anatomy dictates that they fall into one of two classes.[23] In the first class, spatial bias signals control which specific subset of a given cell's inputs causes the cell to fire, whereas in the second class, the bias signals control which specific cells in a population are allowed to fire. In other words, attention-related modulation of neural activity can be achieved by gating the inputs to individual neurons or by gating entire neurons.

If the gating of V4 and IT responses occurs as a result of an external signal that biases competition in favor of the attended location, some evidence of this signal should be discernible. A possible signal of this nature has been observed in a recent study of spatial attention in areas V1, V2, and V4.[25] In this study, V2 and V4 cells showed a sustained elevation of their baseline (prestimulus) firing rates when the monkey's attention was directed inside rather than outside their receptive fields. The elevation in firing rate can be seen by comparing the firing rates when attention is directed to location 1 with those when attention is directed to location 4 in Fig. 54.7.

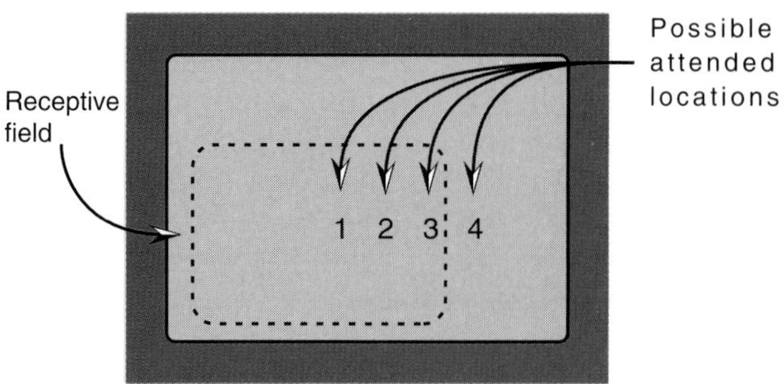

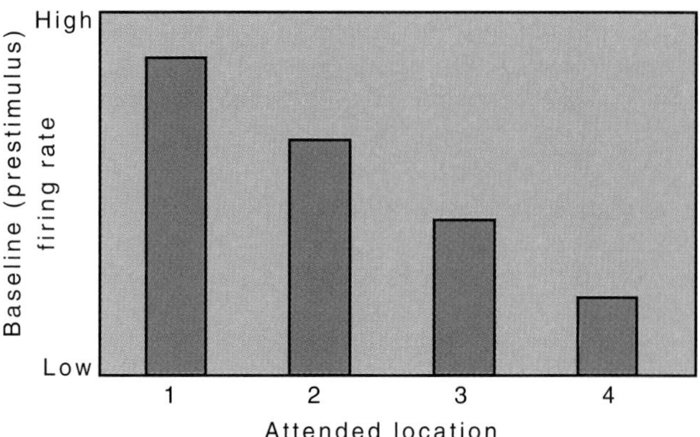

FIGURE 54.7 (Top) Location of attention within the receptive field; (bottom) the typical prestimulus firing rates in area V4 as a function of the position of attention relative to the receptive field of the cell being recorded. Baseline firing rates are highest when attention is directed to the center of the receptive field and decline as attention is directed progressively farther away. This effect may reflect the attentional template that indicates which location is to be attended.

The elevation in tonic neural activity observed when the monkey attended inside the receptive field could reflect the attentional template that specifies which location is to be attended. First, this elevation was present at the beginning of each trial, before any stimuli had appeared, which is consistent with it being a control signal rather than a sensory response. Second, because the only information about where to attend was given to the animal minutes earlier, the elevation of baseline activity must reflect top-down information about the to-be-attended location that is held in working memory. Third, this elevation of baseline neural activity was absent in area V1, where attention was found to have no effects whatsoever. These factors suggest that the elevation of baseline activity reflects an attentional template, although it is not yet known how this signal ultimately influences stimulus-elicited neuronal responses.

Receptive fields in area V4 are moderately large, and the attentional template must have a higher resolution than the diameter of a V4 receptive field to be effective (after all, the animals are able to attend to a target inside the receptive field while ignoring a distractor that is also inside the receptive field). Consistent with this proposal, the attention-related elevation of baseline firing activity appeared to have high spatial resolution. Specifically, when attention was shifted to different regions within the same receptive field, the baseline firing rate varied according to the distance between the attended location and the center of the receptive field (see Fig. 54.7). Thus, visual cortex appears to contain tonic attention-related signals that have a spatial resolution finer than the diameter of V4 receptive fields.

Summary

Orienting to places in the visual field is the aspect of attention that has been studied most extensively in cognitive neuroscience. Much orienting is done overtly by eye movements, but it is also possible to attend to things within a single fixation by covert orienting of attention. When many objects appear together in the visual field, they are in competition for the processing within each cell's receptive field. Recordings from cells in the object pathway indicate how this competition is influenced by attention, which serves to shrink the effective receptive field of the cell around the attended object.

EXECUTIVE CONTROL OF BEHAVIOR

All normal people have a strong subjective feeling of intentional or voluntary control of their behavior. Asking people about goals or intention is probably the single most effective way to obtain information that is predictive of their behavior during problem solving.[41] The importance of intention and goals is illustrated by observations of patients with frontal lesions or mental disorders that cause disruption in either their central control over behavior or the subjective feelings of such control.[42,43]

This section first reviews efforts to develop a cognitive model of executive control and consider how experimental methods can be used to explore conditions under which executive control will operate. We then examine neuroimaging studies that incorporate these cognitive methods to explore the anatomy and circuitry of executive control. Finally, we consider evidence from lesion and developmental studies to further define which areas are involved in executive control.

A Cognitive Model Specifies the Conditions for Executive Attention

Norman and Shallice[44] have created one representative model of executive control that assumes multiple, insoluble subsystems of cognitive processing (Fig. 54.8). These multiple subsystems interact to coordinate goals and actions[21] and are controlled by two qualitatively different mechanisms. The first level of control operates via contention scheduling. The contention-scheduling mechanism corresponds to routine selection—for example, the selection that might be involved in selecting a red stimulus among other visual items, as in the visual search task described previously. When the situation is novel or highly competitive (i.e., requires executive control), a "supervisory system" intervenes and provides additional inhibition or activation to the appropriate schema for the situation (see Fig. 54.8). The supervisory system has access to the overall representation of the environment and the goals of the person, unlike the contention-scheduling mechanism, which involves only competition among subsystems.

Norman and Shallice[44] argued that the supervisory system is necessary for five types of behaviors or situations in which the routine or automatic processes[45] of the contention-scheduling mechanisms are inadequate and the executive control of the supervisory system is required:

1. Situations involving planning or decision-making
2. Situations involving error correction
3. Situations in which the response is novel and not well learned
4. Situations judged to be difficult or dangerous
5. Situations that require overcoming habitual responses

In the following sections, we discuss some evidence of brain systems involved in situations calling for executive control.

Executive Attention Works by Means of Inhibitory Control

In the Norman–Shallice model, contention scheduling works via local inhibition of competing schemas. In the last section visual-subprocessing systems were viewed as selectors of stimuli that were competing locally for receptive fields, which are a critical resource. In addition, it was suggested that the competition be-

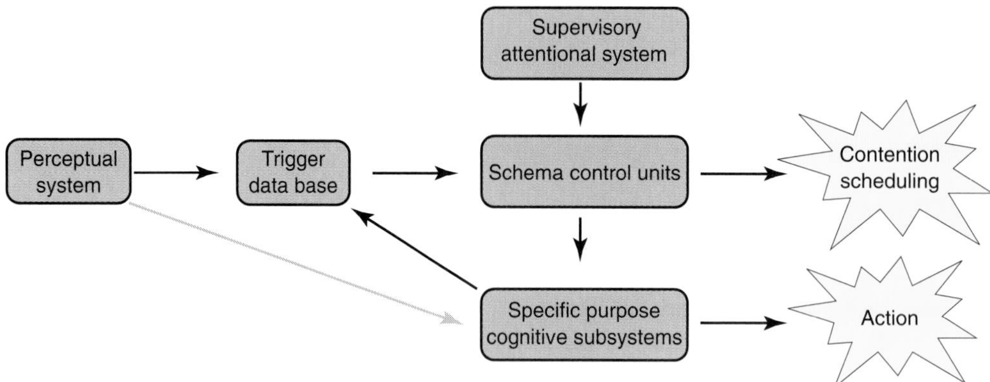

FIGURE 54.8 Diagram of a model of higher-level executive attention proposed by Norman and Shallice.[44] The model is described in the text.

tween stimuli can be biased by a top-down mechanism that selects objects that are important to the current behavior or goal. Like the supervisory system mechanism of the Norman–Shallice model, competition for control of behavior appears to be resolved at local sites by the relative amplification (involving both increases in the selected objects and decreases in the competition) of the selected competitor.

As in Visual Search, Multiple Targets Interfere with Executive Control

To understand the mechanisms of supervisory control, we must have reliable experimental techniques for causing executive control to be employed. A well-established principle of cognitive psychology is that interference will occur whenever two tasks require access to the same underlying systems. Interference between tasks that use quite separate input and output pathways has been taken as a method for measuring central attentional control.

In an early series of experiments, subjects were presented with two separate streams of information, one to each ear, and were required to rivet their attention to one stream by saying each word heard on the ear aloud as quickly as possible. This task is called **shadowing** and requires very intense attention to the message being repeated.[19,46] Most information from the nonshadowed ear is lost. In a basic experiment, Treisman and Geffen[47] asked subjects to tap a key whenever they heard the word "tap." When the word was presented in the attended ear, subjects tapped the key close to 100% of the time, but when the word was presented in the unattended ear, they almost never did. On the other hand, significant events presented to the unattended ear or presented visually during shadowing can still activate the memory trace of a previously presented item **(priming)** or produce a skin response indicating emotional arousal.[48–51]

When the subjects were not required to shadow one of the two messages[18,52,53] and were instead required to monitor a number of channels to detect a target, the number of channels information was coming from did not make a difference. For example, subjects could attend to tone coming to the left or right ear and at the same time monitor for visual and tactile signals. Subjects appeared to have a nearly unlimited capacity to monitor various sensory channels as long as no targets were actually presented. This contrasted sharply with the results obtained with shadowing. Work by Duncan[18] reconciled the shadowing and monitoring studies. He showed that attention could be summoned to one of several input channels with very great effectiveness, but when a target occurred on one channel, processing of targets on any other channel dropped dramatically. In other words, major interference was found between items selected for focal attention (targets).

PET Studies Localize the Functional Anatomy of the Executive Network

Tasks requiring supervisory control[54–57] are severely affected by lesions of the frontal lobes. Because these tasks are quite complex with many components and because the frontal lobes constitute a large part of the brain, neuroimaging methods have been used in an attempt to localize supervisory functions.

Neuroimaging allows examination of brain metabolism during task performance. Many studies involving the detection of targets or the resolution of conflict between targets have found that activation occurs in a midline frontal area called the anterior cingulate. Although this area alone is probably not responsible for executive attention, it is important to consider the efforts to link executive control to anatomical areas. We turn to a consideration of two tasks that have been used to accomplish such linking: the generate-uses task and the Stroop task.

In the generate-uses task, subjects are asked to name a use for a visually or aurally presented noun as quickly as possible (e.g., hammer → pound). In the control condition, subjects read the word name aloud. Blocks of 40 trials, during which blood flow is averaged, are presented. A subtractive strategy is then used in which the blood flow found in the read-aloud task is subtracted from the blood flow in the generate-uses task. The assumption is that this strategy subtracts away the stimulus and response process common to the two tasks and leaves intact the additional activation involved in generating an association. The subtraction of repeat from generate reveals three areas of activation: the anterior cingulate and two left lateral areas, one in a frontal area anterior to Broca's area and one in Wernicke's area. The lateral areas were near classical language areas, so that it seems more likely that the midline anterior cingulate area is involved in attention to the task.

Subjects are then given the same list in a new order and asked to generate the same use. Practice on the same list reduces the mental effort needed to perform the task, and reaction times drop markedly. As the task becomes more automatic, the Normal and Shallice model would suggest that a "schema" formed after practice would trigger when the stimulus was presented. The supervisory system would then not be necessary. Raichle *et al.*[58] had subjects perform the generate-uses task while undergoing PET scans and found the expected activation of the anterior cingulate. In addition, Raichle also had subjects practice the same list repeatedly, generating the same appropriate use for each word until the list was thoroughly learned. After the extended practice, subjects again were scanned. This time, the anterior cingulate and the left lateral activation were gone; instead, there was increased activation in the anterior insula, which now displayed activation similar to that found when a word was read aloud. Following their practice, Raichle *et al.*[58] had subjects generate a use for a new, unpracticed list. Again, the anterior cingulate and left lateral areas were active. Thus, the anterior cingulate is active when the supervisory system is necessary for appropriate behavior, as in the Norman–Shallice model, and the anterior cingulate is inactive when the supervisory system should be inactive and the contention-scheduling mechanisms active. Because both the cingulate and the lateral cortex behaved in the same way with practice, whether they are both part of the supervisory attention system cannot be determined. However, the lateral cortex seems to be rather specific to language tasks, so it may merely be increased in activation when attention is directed to language.

The Stroop tasks involve naming the color of ink in a word that can be congruent (matching the color of the ink in which it is printed; e.g., the word *red* in red ink), neutral (non-color-related; e.g., the word *lot* in red ink), or incongruent (a mismatch of the word with the color of ink in which the word is printed; e.g., the word *red* in blue ink). One analysis of the components of the Stroop task can be outlined as follows: (a) remember the instructions for vocalizing the ink color, (b) attend to the visually presented stimulus, (c) determine the ink color of the word, (d) inhibit the naming of the word, and (e) make the appropriate response (being careful not to name the color word presented). Anterior cingulate activation while carrying out such activities is confirmed by four separate Stroop (or Strooplike) studies (see Fig. 54.9).

As described earlier, the Norman–Shallice[44] model suggests five situations in which the supervisory system is necessary for appropriate behavior or successful execution of a task or goal. The first of these situations involves internally planned, or voluntary actions. Using PET, Passingham and his colleagues[59,60] have shown statistically significant increased activation in the anterior cingulate in voluntary, planned arm and hand movement compared to resting, learned sequence movements and fixed-sequence movements. Two other situations in which the Norman–Shallice model holds the supervisory system to be necessary are those that require overcoming habitual responses and those where responses are not well learned or contain novel sequences of actions. The generate-use and Stroop tasks fit this profile. Another situation in which the Norman–Shallice model necessitates a supervisory system involvement is in error correction or detection (troubleshooting). Studies involving error detection are considered in the next section.

ERPs Can Be Used to Investigate the Time Course of Attention

To perform a supervisory function, a brain area must influence widely distributed parts of the brain where computations related to the task are performed.[61] Anatomical studies suggest that the anterior cingulate, like many brain regions, has close contact with many other cortical areas.[62] One interesting feature of the cingulate is that connections to parietal and prefrontal cortex alternate in a columnar organization. The cingulate has particularly strong anatomical connections to lateral frontal areas involved in word recog-

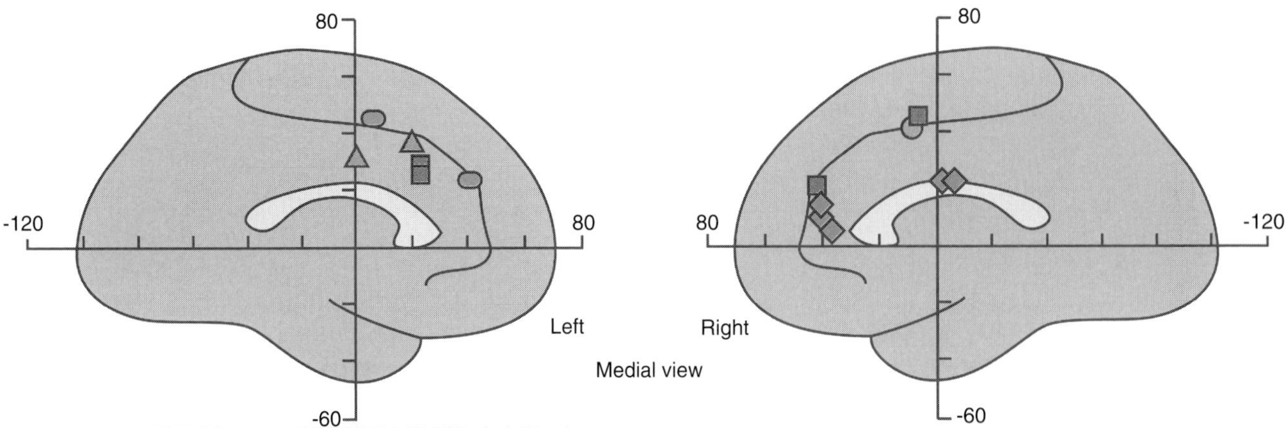

FIGURE 54.9 In the Stroop task subjects are asked to name the ink color in which a word is written. In the incompatible condition the words are different ink colors (e.g., the word *red* in blue ink). In a neutral condition, words are unrelated to color, and in a compatible condition they are the same color as the name of the word. PET experiments have been done in which blood flow in the relatively easy neutral or compatible condition is subtracted from blood flow in the more difficult compatible condition. As shown in the diagram, areas of the left and right cingulate gyrus show stronger activation in the incompatible condition. This has supported the idea that this brain area is related to the resolving of conflict and thus a part of an executive attention network.

nition and posterior parietal areas involved in orienting.

Researchers made efforts to trace the dynamics of these interactions by using ERPs (Fig. 54.10 and Box 54.1).[63,64] Determining the generator of electrical activity from a scalp distribution of such activity can be a difficult task. However, when the generator is identified by PET or fMRI studies, researchers can more easily evaluate whether the scalp distribution could come from that generator (see Heinze *et al.*[38]

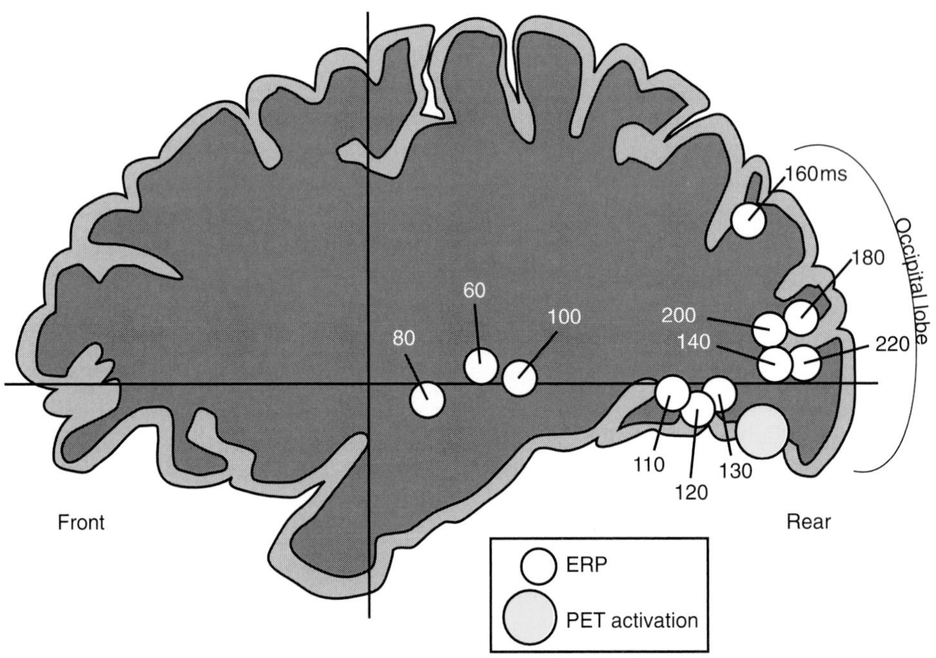

FIGURE 54.10 Subjects are asked to attend to stimuli in one visual field. PET studies (large circle) show activation of the fusiform gyrus opposite to the attended visual field. ERP studies show that the best-fitting dipole generators (at different times) cluster around the PET activation area. The ERPs generators at 110–130 ms are thought to be most closely related to the attention effect. After Heinze *et al.*[38]

for an example of this methodology). The algorithms for relating a generator to the scalp distribution[65] work best when fewer generators are involved. In more complex tasks, it is necessary to use a control condition that allows a subtraction, thus reducing the number of generators active at any time. For example, by subtracting reading aloud from the generate-uses task, researchers can remove sensory and motor sources, allowing a better chance of localizing the sources unique to generating the association.

Making an error gives rise to a negative scalp potential. This negative potential was investigated in an effort to isolate the brain areas generating it. When human subjects were aware of making an error in speeded tasks, recordings of scalp ERPs showed a very strong negativity in a localized area over the mid frontal scalp. Further analysis using the BESA algorithm[65] showed that this error negativity most likely came from the anterior cingulate. Errors can be either slips—incorrect execution of a motor program—or mistakes—selection of an inappropriate intention. The finding that error negativity comes from one of the brain areas involved in the generate-uses task supports the idea of a supervisory system concerned both with response selection and with monitoring the correctness of a response.

Event-related potentials have been used to study the generate-uses task described previously and have provided evidence of an anterior cingulate activation starting about 170 ms after visual presentation of a word.[66] This activation was presumably related to some kind of focal attention. The cingulate activation continued and was joined after 50 ms by a left frontal activation.

This experiment took a further step in replicating the PET results. Subjects generated uses for the same list several times. The left frontal and cingulate activations tended to disappear after practice, but the activations were restored when a new list was presented or when subjects were required to generate a new use for the practiced words (Fig. 54.11). This finding from ERPs fits well with similar results obtained with PET and thus supports the general approach of combining the two methods.

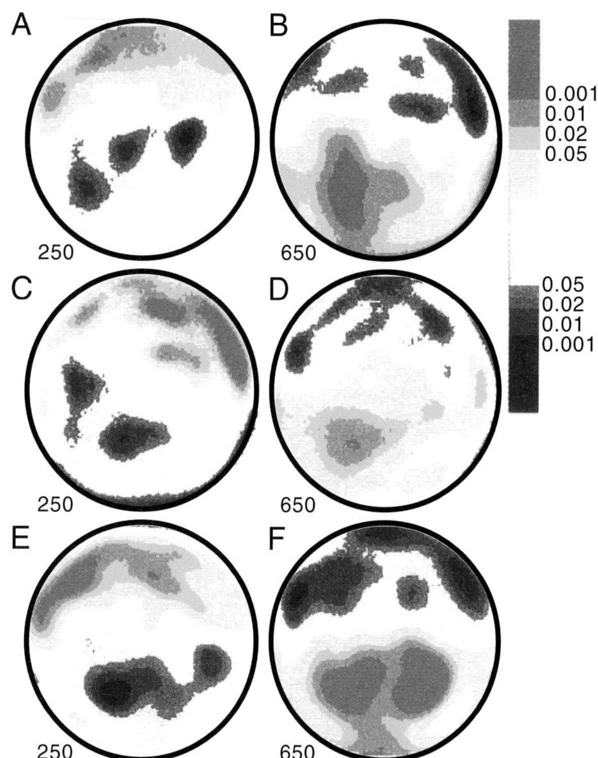

FIGURE 54.11 Statistical maps of difference waves from an ERP study in which the recorded activity when reading a noun aloud is subtracted from the activity associated with generating a use for a noun. When the list is initially studied there is an early left frontal activation (anterior cingulate and left frontal semantic area, A) and a later left posterior activation (Wernicke's area, B). As in PET studies, these go away with practice but are replaced by a right frontal activation (thought to reflect recall of the previously generated word, C and D). When a novel use has to be generated, the left frontal activation returns (E) and the later posterior Wernicke's activation is joined by a mirror image right hemisphere activity (F). After Abdullaev and Posner.[67]

Executive Attention Works by Altering Neuronal Activity in Other Areas of the Brain

These PET and ERP experiments suggest that the anterior cingulate, together with related areas involved in executive attention, is active during tasks that require some thought. Such activity is reduced or disappears as tasks become routine—for example in reading words aloud or after practice generating the same use.

What is the cingulate activation actually doing? According to one analysis, the cingulate is involved in producing the local amplification in neural activity that accompanies top-down selection of items. It is easiest to understand this function in the domain of processing words. It is well known from cognitive studies that a target word is processed more efficiently after presentation of a word that retrieves related information; for example, subjects can pronounce or classify the word "doctor" more rapidly after receiving the related prime "nurse."[68] A portion of this improvement occurs automatically because the prime word activates a pathway shared with the target. However, another portion of the activation is top-down because the attention to the prime leads the subject to expect a particular type of target. Under some conditions, the prime is not attended so that its influence on the target must be primarily bottom-up. Some conditions where the prime will be unattended are when it is followed by a visual mask that prevents subjects from being aware of the identity of the prime; they thus cannot pay attention to its meaning. Also, if the prime does not predict the type of target (low validity), there is little incentive to attend. If the prime is of high validity or subjects are instructed to attend to the prime or to use the prime to think of another category (e.g., animal prime means to expect body parts), top-down or attentional effects dominate. When an ambiguous target is used (e.g., palm can be a tree or body part), top-down priming effects tend to be limited to only one meaning but masked primes that are processed automatically tend to activate both meanings. Executive attention in usually thought to be responsible for the top-down effects by providing a boost to items associated with the expectations indicated by the prime.

Anatomically, these effects may involve the cingulate in contact with areas of the left lateral and posterior cortices that seem to be involved in understanding the meaning of a given target word. Indeed, the time courses of activation of the cingulate (170 ms) and the left lateral frontal (220 ms) cortex during the generate-uses task support the view that attention interacts with the semantic activation pattern.[66]

In addition, cingulate activation may be involved in the voluntarily reactivation of brain areas that can also be driven automatically from input. For example, feature analysis of visual targets appears to involve right lateralized posterior parts of the brain. When subjects are instructed to examine a feature voluntarily, similar electrode sites are activated, but much later. By increasing activation of the brain area that performs a specific computation, one can change the time course of the organization of the component operations.

Frontal Structures Are Important in Executive Function

Lesions of the frontal lobe often produce disorganized or incoherent behavior.[56,57,69] The dysexecutive syndrome that follows closed head injury, stroke, or degenerative disorders of frontal structures is characterized by the loss of the ability to plan coherently, to solve problems, or to organize the routines of daily life. Patients suffering from this syndrome have difficulty with problem-solving tasks such as the Tower of Hanoi, in which planning ahead is an important component.

There has been some controversy about the importance of cingulate involvement in the loss of executive function. Large lesions of the frontal midline produced by strokes can have devastating effects on human behavior. Damasio,[70] who has studied many of these patients, suggests:

> Before leaving the subject of human brain lesions, I would like to propose there is a particular region in the human brain where the systems concerned with emotion, attention and working memory interact so intimately that they constitute the source for the energy for both external action and internal action, thought, animation, and reasoning. This fountain head region, is the anterior cingulate cortex, another piece of the limbic puzzle.

This observation comes from patients who show akinetic mutism after strokes in the general area of the cingulate. These patients can orient to events but initiate little in the way of spontaneous behavior. One woman studied by Damasio recovered and when Damasio asked her what was going on during the time she suffered from the brain injury and why she didn't initiate any behavior, she said, "Well, nothing ever came to mind." The fact that there can be recovery after a brief period of akinetic mutism suggests considerable distribution of executive function both within the cingulate and in other structures related to it. Considerable work with cats and monkeys that have lesions of the cingulate[71,72] produced results similar to those of Damasio's studies. Both cats and monkeys with extensive anterior cingulate lesions show the same failure to initiate voluntary behavior or movement.

In contrast to the profound effects of massive cingulate trauma, more discrete cingulate lesions that have been induced to treat patients with pain or anxiety give little evidence of the gross loss of conscious control reported in the studies cited above.[73] Perhaps this lack of evidence relates to the various subareas of the cingulate that might be involved in different aspects of attention. As shown in Fig. 54.10, even a single task seems to activate different regions of the cingulate in different studies. What is not yet known is whether these are merely errors introduced by different laboratories, subjects, and exact procedure or whether they indicate that parts of the cingulate are differentially influenced by task demands. It is also likely that the cingulate works in close connection with the supplementary motor area and basal ganglia, which may also play a role in executive attention.

Summary

A higher level executive attention system appears to be involved when processing requires careful planning, mediating conflict, or handling novel stimuli. Our understanding of the brain networks involved in this higher form of executive attention is not far advanced. Many tasks that involve conflict, response selection, and / or response monitoring appear to activate the frontal midline, sometimes in conjunction with more lateral frontal cortical areas and the basal ganglia. In generating the use of words, medial and lateral frontal areas show activity within the first 200 ms after input. The midfrontal activity suggests that attention is used in generating and selecting word meanings. As the act of generation becomes automated with practice on the same list and requires little or no attention, the midfrontal activity drops away. Lesions of the frontal areas often produce disorganization of behavior, and large-scale lesions of the frontal midline can produce a complete loss of the initiation of spontaneous behavior.

ATTENTIONAL STATE

At the beginning of this chapter, we described two aspects of attention. The first aspect involves selection and cognitive control, and the second involves the maintenance of an attentive or alert state. Both of these attentional functions depend on input from the monoaminergic transmitter systems. Many basic properties of these systems are described in Chapter 8. As was discussed in Chapter 46, these systems are important in the diurnal rhythm and in the distinction between sleep and wakefulness.[74]

In this section, we focus on the noradrenergic locus ceruleus (NE-LC) system. The other widely projecting modulatory systems (see below) may also have important roles in the regulation of attentional state and alertness, but to date the most evidence in this regard is available for the NE-LC system.

Monoamines Affect Cortical Function

Neurons located in the brainstem are the origin of most of the monoaminergic systems: acetylcholine (ACh), norephinephrine (NE), dopamine (DA), and 5-hydroxytryptamine (5HT). In addition, important modulatory systems that employ ACh or histamine originate in the basal forebrain and hypothalamus, respectively. The anatomy of these systems has been described in Chapter 49.[75] One important attribute of all of these systems is their very widespread projection anatomy. Indeed, these systems project more globally throughout the CNS than is typical of other brain systems (e.g., thalamocortical systems). These systems behave as modulators in that they modulate the responsivity of target (postsynaptic) neurons. Classical neurotransmitters typically simply excite or inhibit neuronal activity. Good examples of nonmodulatory, or "classical," neurotransmitters are glutamate [Glu; especially when acting at non-NMDA (*N*-methyl-D-aspartate) ionotropic receptors] and γ-aminobutyric acid (GABA; especially when acting at $GABA_A$ receptors). In contrast, a neuromodulator may have little effect on its own but act principally by altering the response of neurons to other inputs (often mediated by classical transmitters). A variety of modulatory effects have been found both for these monoamines and for other transmitters acting at certain receptors (see Chapter 9).

NE Modulates Glu and GABA Responses

The cerebellum has been used as a model system for studying the effects of NE on neurons because (i) LC neurons send NE projections into the cerebellum, and (ii) the anatomy and physiological properties of the cerebellum are well understood (see Chapter 35). Several groups have described modulatory effects of NE on the activity of the principal output neuron of the cerebellar cortex—the Purkinje cell (described in Chapter 35). Moises and colleagues[76] (1981) have found that NE, either directly applied from a micropipette or from stimulation of the LC afferents to the cerebellum, increases responses of Purkinje neurons to both excitatory and inhibitory inputs. In both cases, NE acts to increase the Glu- or GABA-evoked response relative to the basal activity of the cell. NE modulation of neuronal responsiveness is found in many target areas, including the cerebral cortex.[77,78] The obvious implications for signal processing have led to the proposal that NE may enhance the **signal-to-noise ratio**—or signal-processing capacity—of neurons. It is interesting that the relative augmentation of Glu and GABA responses in the cerebellum and cerebral cortex is mediated by distinct NE receptors, with β-adrenoceptors implicated in the augmentation of GABA responses[77] and α_1-adrenoceptors linked to the augmentation of Glu responses.[78]

Neurons That Use Neuromodulators as Chemical Transmitters Have Specific Patterns of Activity

The specific patterns of activity of neurons that use neuromodulators presumably reflect times that they release their neuromodulator chemicals onto postsynaptic neurons in the thalamus, in the cerebral cortex, and elsewhere. Most important in this regard is the relationship between behavior and the modulatory influence of these systems; this relationship has been studied by recording impulse activity of the various modulatory source neurons in unanesthetized behaving animals. These and other relevant findings are discussed in this part of the chapter.

Noradrenergic LC Neurons Modulate Activity

Tonic LC activity varies with behavioral state. Aston-Jones and colleagues[79] found that spontaneous LC impulse activity is fastest during waking, slower during slow-wave sleep, and virtually silent during paradoxical sleep (PS). A subpopulation of LC neurons with similar activity has been reported in cat[80] and in unanesthetized monkeys.[81–84] Noradrenergic LC neurons are more difficult to study in some species (e.g., cat, rabbit) because the NE neurons are interdigitated with non-NE neurons within the LC nucleus. For this reason, rats and monkeys, whose noradrenergic LC nucleus is more homogeneous, are the species of choice in such studies.

Neurons of the LC also are strongly activated in association with orienting responses. In both rat[85] and monkey,[81–83] the highest phasic discharge rates observed for LC neurons are consistently associated with spontaneous or evoked behavioral orienting responses. LC activity associated with orienting behavior is most intense when ongoing preprogrammed behavior (e.g., sleep, grooming, or consumption) is suddenly disrupted and the animal orients. Thus, "spontaneous" bursts of LC activity, termination of preprogrammed low-vigilance behaviors, and increased attentiveness are closely connected (see below).

LC neurons exhibit polymodal sensory responsiveness. In addition to fluctuations in tonic activity, LC neurons in unanesthetized rats and monkeys are responsive to a variety of environmental stimuli.[79,81,85] In rats, LC neurons exhibit phasic short-latency (15–50 ms) activation following unconditioned auditory, visual, somatosensory, or olfactory stimuli. Responses are most consistently evoked by intense, conspicuous stimuli.

A particularly salient characteristic of NE-LC neurons is that stimuli effective in eliciting LC responses also disrupt ongoing behavior and elicit a behavioral orienting response in both rats and monkeys. The largest responses are elicited by stimuli that cause an abrupt transition from sleep to waking, with associated behavioral orientation. Also, LC responses to stimuli that do not interrupt grooming or drinking are reduced, whereas stimuli that disrupt such activity and generate orienting behavior elicit strong LC responses.[85] Thus, in rats, as in monkeys, sensory-evoked LC impulse activity is strongly correlated with behavioral responses, and in both species LC responses are associated with behavioral disruption and reorientation.

Monkey LC Neurons Can Be Selectively Activated by Meaningful Stimuli

LC neurons in behaving monkeys readily become conditioned to respond to low-intensity stimuli when the stimuli are made meaningful by serving as CS + (target) cues in operant tasks.[83,86,87] In experiments, monkeys performed a visual discrimination task. First, they viewed a video monitor that presented a central fixation point that the animal was required to look at to ensure attentiveness to the task. After successful visual fixation of this point, a vertical or horizontal bar was presented at the center of gaze. One was chosen to be target (CS+) and the other was nontarget (CS−). Monkeys had to release a lever after CS+ stimuli to receive a drop of juice, but to continue depressing the lever after CS− stimuli. As seen in Fig. 54.12, CS+ stimuli consistently activated all LC neurons examined. These same stimuli presented before conditioning, or similar intensity unconditioned stimuli, elicited no response from LC cells. Interestingly, these responses were selective for CS+ stimuli, as other task stimuli (including CS− stimuli) did not activate LC neurons. These cells also were not activated during lever release outside of the task, indicating that these LC responses were not primarily motor in nature. The latencies of LC responses to target cues were relatively short (~100-ms onset for an overlearned contingency) and preceded behavioral responses by ~200 ms. Moreover, the latencies of response for LC neurons and lever releases were significantly correlated over a number of trials, so that shorter LC responses were associated with shorter behavioral responses to the same cues. These findings indicate that LC target responses could facilitate behavioral responses to target cues.

These responses of LC neurons to target stimuli were not driven strictly by sensory attributes, as either vertical or horizontal bars could evoke responses, depending on which was conditioned to be the target stimulus. Recordings during reversal training further confirmed that these LC responses were independent of sensory attributes.[87] In reversal training, the former CS+ cue is conditioned to be CS−, and the former CS− stimulus is conditioned to become CS+. As shown in Fig. 54.12, such reversal of cue meaning causes LC cells to reverse responsiveness; the cells become selectively activated by the new target cue and lose responsiveness to the old target (new nontarget cue). These data indicate that phasic LC activation in this task is specifically related to the meaning of the stimuli, not to their physical attributes.

The results of experiments with conditioned stimuli show a close relationship between phasic activation of LC neurons and behavioral responding to meaningful

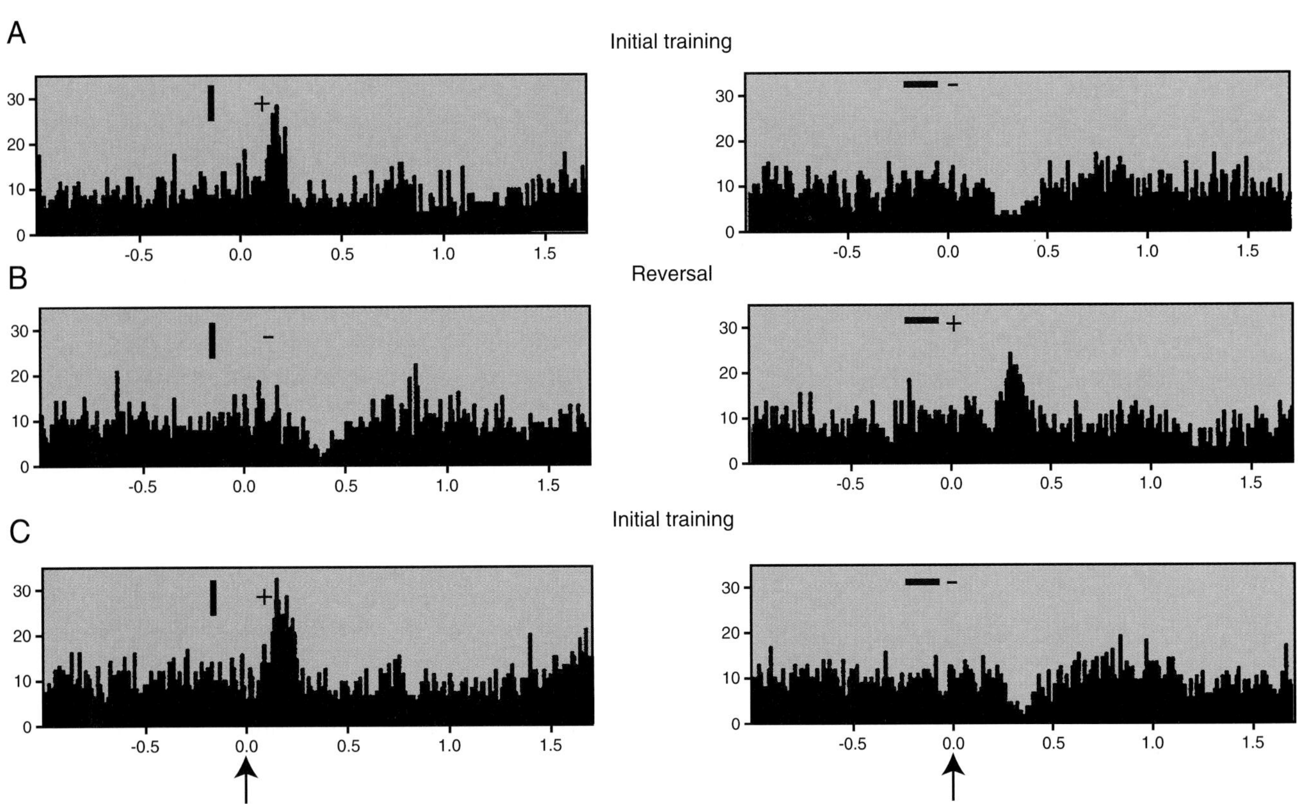

FIGURE 54.12 Reversal of LC response with task reversal. Peristimulus time histograms (PSTHs) showing activity of an LC neuron during reversal of the vigilance task. Note that this neuron is selectively and phasically activated by vertical cues when they are target and inhibited by horizontal cues when they are nontarget (A, initial training), but that this stimulus–response relationship reverses after reversal of cue meaning (B, reversal). Rereversal to initial training reestablishes the original response in the LC cell (C). Inhibition of LC neurons by nontarget cues occurred only in some animals. Stimuli presented at arrows.

sensory cues. These results extend those found earlier in unconditioned animals in which conspicuous stimuli that evoked behavioral orienting responses were most effective in activating LC cells.[82,85,88] These findings indicate that LC responses can readily be conditioned to salient stimuli, an important factor in understanding the role of this system in attentional processing.

Tonic LC Activity Varies with Attentional State

Very low LC activity is accompanied by drowsiness (as noted earlier in the chapter) and cessation of task performance,[84] whereas levels of tonic LC activity during alert task performance vary between "intermediate" and "elevated" discharge rates. The difference between these tonic rates is small, in the range of 1–2 spikes/s. However, similar changes in tonic activity have functional effects (e.g., EEG activation).[89]

These different levels of tonic LC discharge in the intermediate to elevated range are closely associated with differences in behavioral performance on the visual discrimination task.[90] During periods of elevated tonic LC activity, monkeys foveate the central fixation point (required to initiate each trial; described earlier) less frequently, and exhibit more eye movements unrelated to the task. This behavior suggests that at these times monkeys are less focused on the task and are more distracted by nontask stimuli. Consistent with this interpretation, periods of elevated tonic LC activity are consistently accompanied by an increased number of false alarms or errors (erroneous lever responses for nontarget stimuli; Fig. 54.13). In addition, responses to CS+ stimuli (described above) are much reduced in magnitude during periods of elevated tonic LC discharge. Analyses of behavioral performance have revealed that during periods of elevated LC activity the discriminability of stimuli decreases and the animal's tendency to respond behaviorally to any stimulus increases.[86] Researchers[87] speculate that during elevated LC activity the animal may be less focused on task stimuli (making it more difficult to discriminate target

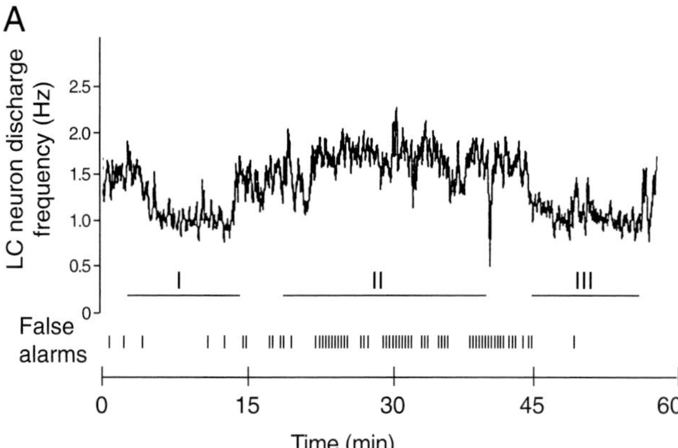

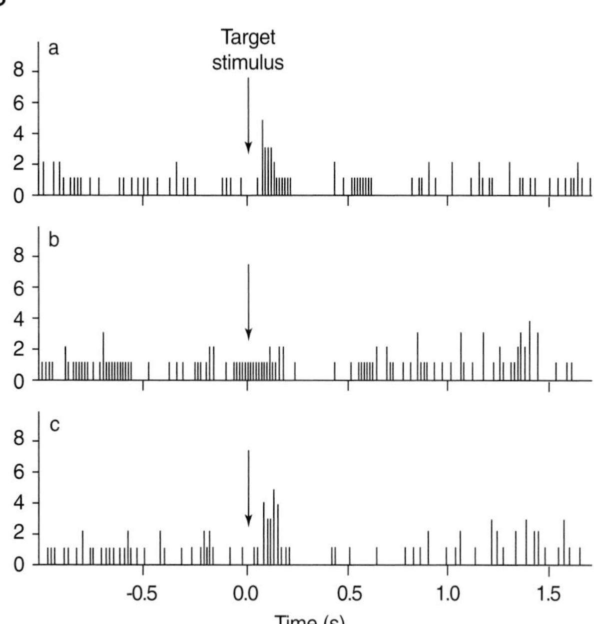

FIGURE 54.13 Tonic activity of monkey LC neurons is correlated with rates of false alarm errors. (A) Upper trace shows discharge frequency of a typical LC neuron during the visual discrimination task. Lower trace shows corresponding occurrences of false alarm errors (bar releases to nontarget stimuli). Note that more false alarms occur during the epochs of elevated LC discharge (e.g., marked II) than during the epochs of intermediate activity (marked I and III). (B) PSTHs of activity of this same LC neuron in response to target stimuli during this session. Epochs for data accumulated into each of the PSTHs in I, II, and III are marked in (A). Note that target responses of LC neurons occur only during epochs of intermediate tonic activity (I and III).

from nontarget stimuli) and that because of this higher attentional lability and distractibility the animal displays a greater tendency to respond to nontarget stimuli (lower response criterion). That is, intermediate levels of LC activity with phasic activation by CS+ stimuli are closely correlated with stable focused attention and good task performance with few errors, whereas elevated LC activity corresponds to less focused, labile attention and poorer task performance with many errors.

The Locus Ceruleus May Regulate Attentional State

When taken together, the cellular properties of the LC-NE system have several functional implications. The broad efferent trajectory of the LC system throughout the CNS (Chapter 8) implies that it has a global function. It is also important to note that LC-NE neurons are physiologically homogeneous, and the properties described here are typical of perhaps all LC neurons. Thus, robust LC activity in many circumstances may result in globally synchronized release of NE onto target neurons located throughout the neuraxis. Areas associated with attentional functioning may receive relatively high NE-LC input. Postsynaptically, NE biases target cells to promote responses to strong inputs while reducing spontaneous or low-level activity. These findings, combined with the specific conditions of LC activation in behaving animals, can be integrated to produce a picture of overall LC function.[88,90,91] In this view, very low LC activity causes relatively low responsivity of many neurons throughout the brain that are innervated by the LC, precluding strong engagement with the sensory environment. This facilitates internally driven vegetative programs such as sleep[79] (Chapter 46). Conversely, high tonic LC activity produces tonically elevated neuronal responsiveness in many CNS regions, resulting in extensive interaction with the sensory environment instantiated as scanning or labile attentiveness. Such a mode of attentiveness is not conducive to focused attention, but rather would be associated with a short attention span and low threshold for distraction by exogenous stimuli. This state may be adaptively suited to behavior in a dangerous or uncertain environment. Intermediate levels of LC tonic activity coupled with selective, phasic LC responsiveness to meaningful stimuli may facilitate performance on tasks that require focused selective attention (such as the visual discrimination task described here). The low tonic NE release would prevent overly high neuronal responsivity and behavioral distractibility, while the phasic LC activation would promote processing selectively for stimuli that are salient or meaningful within the current behavioral context. (Note that phasic activation of LC neurons by CS+ stimuli is much reduced during periods of elevated tonic discharge, as described earlier). This mode of LC activity may thereby produce an attentional state that facilitates focused or selective attention and behavioral performance in accordance with an executive process for planning, described in the preceding pages of this chapter.

Summary

Attentional state varies from sleep to waking and, within the waking state, from low to high levels of alertness. These states relate to widespread effects of neuromodulatory systems originating in the brainstem and influencing the activity of cortical neurons. The norepinephrine system arising in the locus coeruleus is the best understood of these systems. Experiments show that strong activation of this system can lead to premature responding, whereas low levels of activation can produce sleepiness and cause targets to be missed. Target stimuli tend to modify this system, inducing higher levels of activation and increasing alertness.

References

1. James, W. (1890). *Principles of Psychology*. Holt, New York.
2. Posner, M. I. (1980). Orienting of attention: The 7th Sir F. C. Bartlett lectures. *Q. J. Exp. Psychol.* **32:** 3–25.
3. Briand, K., and Klein, R. M. (1987). Is Posner's "beam" the same as Treisman's "glue"?: On the relation between visual orienting and feature integration theory. *J. Exp. Psychol. Hum. Percep. Perform.* **13:** 228–241.
4. Luck, S., Hillyard, S. A., Mouloua, M., Woldorff, M. G., Clark, V. P., and Hawkins, H. L. (1994). Effects of spatial cueing on luminance detectability: Psychophysical and electrophysiological evidence for early selection. *J. Exp. Psychol. Hum. Percep. Perform.* **20:** 87–904.
5. Posner, M. I., and Cohen, Y. (1984). Components of attention. In *Attention and Performance* Vol. X (H. Bouma and D. Bowhuis, eds.), pp. 531–556. Erlbaum, Hillsdale, NJ.
6. Rafal, R., Henik, A., and Smith, J. (1991). Extrageniculate contributions to reflex visual orienting in normal humans: A temporal hemifield advantage. *J. Cognit. Neurosci.* **3:** 322–328.
7. Ladavas, E. (1993). Spatial dimensions of automatic and voluntary components of attention. In *Unilateral Neglect: Clinical and Experimental Studies* (I. Robertson and J. Marshall, eds.), pp. 193–210. Erlbaum, Hillsdale, NJ.
8. Posner, M. I., Rafal, R. D., Choate, L. S., and Vaughan, J. (1985). Inhibition of return: Neural basis and function. *Cognit. Neuropsychol.* **2:** 211–228.
9. Morrow, L. A., and Ratcliff, G. (1987). Attentional mechanisms in clinical neglect. *J. Clin. Exp. Neuropsychol.* **9:** 74–75.

9a. Posner, M. I., Walker, J. A., Friedrich, F. J., and Rafal, R. D. (1984). Effects of parietal lobe injury on covert orienting of visual attention. *J. Neurosci.* **4:** 1863–1874.

10. Cohen, J. C., Farah, M. J., Romero, R. D., and Servan-Schreiber, D. (1994). Mechanisms of spatial attention: The relation of macrostructure to microstructure in parietal neglect. *J. Cognit. Neurosci.* **93:** 1202–1226.
11. Corbetta, M., Miezin, F. M., Shulman, G. L., and Petersen, S. E. (1993). A PET study of visuospatial attention. *J. Neurosci.* **93**(3): 1202–1226.
12. Driver, J., and Spence, C. J. (1994). Spatial synergies between auditory and visual attention. In *Attention and Performance* (C. Umilta and M. Moscovitch, eds.), Vol. XV, pp. 331–331. MIT Press, Cambridge, MA.
13. Spence, C. J., and Driver, J. (1994). Covert spatial orienting in audition: Exogenous and endogenous mechanisms facilitate sound localization. *J. Exp. Psychol. Hum. Percept. Perform.* **22:** 1005–1030.
14. Whang, K. C., Burton, H., and Schulman, G. L. (1991). Selective attention in vibrotactile tasks: Detecting the presence and absence of amplitude change. *Percept. Psychophys.* **50:** 156–165.
15. Duncan, J. (1996). Cooperating brain systems in selective perception and action. In *Attention and Performance* (T. Innui and J. L. McClelland, eds.), Vol. XVI, pp. 549–578. MIT Press, Cambridge, MA.
16. Tipper, S. P., Driver, J., and Weaver, J. (1991). Object-centered inhibition of return of visual attention. *Q. J. Exp. Psychol.* **43A,** 289–298.
17. Duncan, J. (1984). Selective attention and the organization of visual information. *J. Exp. Psychol. Gen.* **113:** 501–517.
18. Duncan, J. (1980). The locus of interference in the perception of simultaneous stimuli. *Psychol. Rev.* **87**(3): 272–300.
19. Broadbent, D. E. (1958). *Perception and Communication.* Plenum, London.
20. Tsotsos, J. K. (1990). Complexity analysis of visual processing. *Behav. Brain Sci.* **13:** 423–469.
21. Allport, D. A. (1980). Attention and performance. In *Cognitive Psychology* (G. Claxton, ed.), pp. 112–153. Routledge & Kegan Paul, London.
22. Eriksen, B. A., and Eriksen, C. W. (1974). Effects of noise letters upon identification of a target letter in a nonsearch task. *Percept. Psychophys.* **16:** 143–149.
23. Desimone, R. (1992). Neural substrates for visual attention in the primate brain. In *Neural Networks for Vision and Image Processing* (G. Carpenter and S. Grossberg, eds.), pp. 343–364. MIT Press, Cambridge, MA.
24. Olshausen, B. A., Anderson, C. H., and Van Essen, D. C. (1993). A neurobiological model of visual attention and invariant pattern recognition based on dynamic routing of information. *J. Neurosci.* **13:** 4700–4719.
25. Luck, S. J., Chelazzi, L., Hillyard, S. A., and Desimone, R. (1997). Neural mechanisms of spatial selective attention in areas V1, V2, and V4 of macaque visual cortex. *J. Neurophysiol.* **77:** 24–42.
26. Miller, E. K., Gochin, P. M., and Gross, C. G. (1993). Suppression of visual responses of neurons in inferior temporal cortex of the awake macaque monkey by addition of a second stimulus. *Brain Res.* **616:** 25–29.
27. Gross, C. G., and Mishkin, M. (1977). The neural basis of stimulus equivalence across retinal translation. In *Lateralization in the Nervous System* (S. Harnad, R. W. Doty, L. Goldstein, J. Jaynes, and G. Krauthamer, eds.), pp. 109–122. Academic Press, New York.
28. Ungerleider, L. G., and Mishkin, M. (1982). Two cortical visual systems. In *The Analysis of Visual Behavior* (D. J. Ingle, R. J. W. Mansfield, and M. A. Goodale, eds.), pp. 549–586. MIT Press, Cambridge, MA.
29. Desimone, R., Wessinger, M., Thomas, L., and Schneider, W. (1990). Attentional control of visual perception: Cortical and subcortical mechanisms. *Cold Spring Harbor Symp. Quant. Biol.* **55:** 963–971.
30. Luck, S. J., Girelli, M., McDermott, M. T., and Ford, M. A. (1997). Bridging the gap between monkey neurophysiology and human perception: An ambiguity resolution theory of visual selective attention. *Cognit. Psychol.* **33:** 64–87.
31. Moran, J., and Desimone, R. (1985). Selective attention gates visual processing in the extrastriate cortex. *Science* **229:** 782–784.

32. Bundesen, C. (1990). A theory of visual attention. *Psychol. Rev.* **97:** 523–547.
33. Duncan, J., and Humphreys, G. (1989). Visual search and stimulus similarity. *Psychol. Rev.* **96:** 433–458.
34. Motter, B. C. (1993). Focal attention produces spatially selective processing in visual cortical areas V1, V2 and V4 in the presence of competing stimuli. *J. Neurophysiol.* **70:** 909–919.
35. Spitzer, H., Desimone, R., and Moran, J. (1988). Increased attention enhances both behavioral and neuronal performance. *Science* **240:** 338–340.
36. Treue, S., and Maunsell, J. H. R. (1996). Attentional modulation of visual motion processing in cortical areas MT and MST. *Nature (London)* **382:** 539–541.
37. Chelazzi, L., and Desimone, R. (1994). Responses of V4 neurons during visual search. *Soc. Neurosci. Abstr.* **20:** 1054.
38. Heinze, H. J., Mangun, G. R., Burchert, W., Hinrichs, H., Scholtz, M., Müntel, T. F., Gös, A., Scherg, M., Johannes, S., Hundeshagen, H., Gazzaniga, M. S., and Hillyard, S. A. (1994). Combined spatial and temporal imaging of brain activity during visual selective attention in humans. *Nature (London)* **372:** 543–546.
39. Mangun, G. R., Hillyard, S. A., and Luck, S. J. (1993). Electrocortical substrates of visual selective attention. In *Attention and Performance* (D. Meyer and S. Kornblum, eds.), Vol. XIV, pp. 219–243. MIT Press, Cambridge, MA.
40. Farah, M. (1990). *Visual Agnosia.* MIT Press, Cambridge, MA.
41. Newell, A., and Simon, H. A. (1972). *Human Problem Solving.* Prentice Hall. Engelwood Cliffs, NJ.
42. Duncan, J. (1986). Disorganization of behavior after frontal lobe lesions. *Cogn. Neuropsychol.* **3:** 271–290.
43. Frith, C. D. (1992). *The Cognitive Neuropsychology of Schizophrenia.* Erlbaum, Hillsdale, NJ.
44. Norman, D. A., and Shallice, T. (1986). Attention to action: Willed and automatic control of behavior. In *Consciousness and Self-Regulation* (R. J. Davidson, G. E. Schwartz, and D. Shapiro, eds.), pp. 1–18. Plenum, New York.
45. Shallice, T. (1994). Multiple levels of control processes. In *Attention and Performance* (C. Umilta and M. Moscovitch, eds.), Vol. XV, pp. 395–420. MIT Press, Cambridge, MA.
46. Broadbent, D. E. (1973). *Decision and Stress.* Academic Press, New York.
47. Treisman, A. M., and Geffen, G. (1967). Selective attention: Perception or response? *Q. J. Exp. Psychol.* **19:** 1–18.
48. Corteen, R. S., and Wood, B. (1972). Autonomic response for shock associated words in an unattended channel. *J. Exp. Psychol.* **94:** 308–313.
49. Corteen, R. S., and Dunn, D. (1974). Shock-associated words in nonattended message: A test for momentary awareness. *J. Exp. Psychol.* **102:** 1143–1144.
50. Dawson, M. E., and Schell, A. M. (1982). Electrodermal responses to attended and unattended significant stimuli during dichotic listening. *J. Exp. Psychol. Hum. Percept. Perform.* **8:** 315–324.
51. Posner, M. I., Sandson, J., Dhawan, M., and Shulmlan, G. L. (1989). Is word recognition automatic? A cognitive anatomical approach. *J. Cognit. Neurosci.* **1:** 50–60.
52. Ostry, D., Moray, N., and Marks, (1976). Attention practice and semantic targets. *J. Exp. Psychol. Hum. Percept. Perform.* **2:** 326–336.
53. Shiffrin, R. M., McKay, D. P. O., and Shaffer, W. O. (1977). Attending to 49 positions at once. *J. Exp. Psychol. Hum. Percept. Perform.* **2:** 14–22.
54. Duncan, J. (1995). Attention, intelligence and frontal lobes. In *The Cognitive Neurosciences* (M. S. Gazzaniga, ed.), pp. 721–733. MIT Press, Cambridge, MA.
55. Shallice, T. (1988). *From Neuropsychology to Mental Structure.* Cambridge University Press, New York.
56. Shallice, T., and Burgess, P. W. (1991). Deficits in strategy applications following frontal lobe damage in man. *Brain* **114:** 727–741.
57. Shallice, T., and Burgess, P. W. (1991). Higher-order cognitive impairments and frontal lobe lesions in man. In *Frontal Lobe Function and Injury* (H. S. Levin, H. M. Eisenberg, and A. I. Benton, eds.), pp. 125–138. Oxford University Press, New York.
58. Raichle, M. E., Fiez, J. A., Videen, T. O., MacLeod, A.-M. K., Pardo, J. V., Fox, P. T. and Petersen, S. E. (1994). Practice-related changes in human brain functional anatomy during nonmotor learning. *Cereb. Cortex* **4:** 8–26.
59. Colebatch, J. M., Cunningham, V. J., Deiber, M.-P., Frackowiak, R. S. J., and Passingham, R. E. (1990). Regional cerebral blood flow during unilateral arm and hand movements in human volunteers. *Physiol. Soc. Abstr.* 9.
60. Deiber, M.-P., Passingham, R. E., Colebach, J. G., Friston, K. J., Nixon, P. D., and Frackowiak, R. S. J. (1991). Cortical areas and the selection of movement: A study with positron emission tomography. *Exp. Brain Res.* **84:** 393–402.
61. Posner, M. I., and Raichle, M. E. (1994). *Images of Mind.* Scientific American Library, New York.
62. Goldman-Rakic, P. S. (1988). Topography of cognition: Parallel distributed networks in primate association cortex. *Annu. Rev. Neurosci.* **11:** 137–156.
63. Näätänen, R. (1992). *Attention and Brain Function.* Erlbaum, Hillsdale, NJ.
64. Rugg, M. D., and Coles, M. D. (1995). *Electrophysiology of Mind.* Oxford University Press, Oxford.
65. Scherg, M., and Berg, P. (1993). *Brain Electrical Source Analysis,* Version 2.0. NeuroScan, Inc., New York.
66. Snyder, A., Abdullaev, Y. G., Posner, M. I., and Raichle, M. E. (1995). Scalp electrical potentials reflect regional cerebral blood flow reponses during processing of written words. *Proc. Natl. Acad. Sci. U.S.A.* **92:** 1689–1693.
67. Abdullaev, Y. G., and Posner, M. I. (1997). Time course of activating brain areas in generating verbal associations. *Psychol. Sci.* **8**(1): 56–59.
68. Posner, M. I. (1978). *Chronometric Explorations of Mind.* Erlbaum, Hillsdale, NJ.
69. Duncan, J., Burgess, P., and Emslie, H. (1995). Fluid intelligence after frontal lobe lesion. *Neuropsychologia* **33**(3): 261–268.
70. Damasio, A. R. (1994). *Descarte's Error: Emotion, Reason, and the Human Brain.* Putnam, New York.
71. Kennard, M. A. (1954). Effect of bilateral ablation of cingulate area on behavior of cats. *J. Neurophysiol.* **18:** 159–169.
72. Kennard, M. A. (1955). The cingulate gyrus in relation to consciousness. *J. Nerv. Ment. Dis.* **121:** 34–39.
73. Corkin, S., Twitchell, T. E., and Sullivan, E. V. (1979). Safety and efficacy of cingulotomy for pain and psychiatric disorders. In *Modern Concepts in Psychiatric Surgery* (E. R. Hitchcock, H. T. Ballantine, and B. A. Meyerson, eds.), pp. 129–163. Elsevier, Amsterdam.
74. Steriade, M., and McCarley, R. (1990). *Brainstem Control of Wakefulness and Sleep.* Plenum, New York.
75. Nieuwenhuys, R. (1985). *Chemoarchitecture of the Brain.* Springer-Verlag, Berlin.
76. Moises, H. C., Waterhouse, B. D., and Woodward, D. J. (1981). Locus coeruleus stimulation potentiates Purkinje cell responses to afferent input: The climbing fiber system. *Brain Res.* **222:** 43–64.
77. Waterhouse, B. D., Moises, H. C., Yeh, H. H., and Woodward, D. J. (1982). Norepinephrine enhancement of inhibitory synaptic

mechanisms in cerebellum and cerebral cortex: Mediation by beta adrenergic receptors. *J. Pharmacol. Exp. Ther.* **221:** 495–506.
78. Mouradian, R. D., Sessler, F. M., and Waterhouse, B. D. (1991). Noradrenergic potentiation of excitatory transmitter action in cerebrocortical slices: Evidence for mediation by an alpha-1 receptor-linked second messenger pathway. *Brain Res.* **546:** 83–95.
79. Aston-Jones, G., and Bloom, F. E. (1981). Activity of norepinephrine-containing locus coeruleus neurons in behaving rats anticipates fluctuations in the sleep-waking cycle. *J. Neurosci.* **1:** 876–886.
80. Hobson, J. A., McCarley, R. W., and Wyzinski, P. W. (1975). Sleep cycle oscillation: Reciprocal discharge by two brainstem neuronal groups. *Science* **189:** 55–58.
81. Foote, S. L., Aston-Jones, G., and Bloom, F. E. (1980). Impulse activity of locus coeruleus neurons in awake rats and monkeys is a function of sensory stimulation and arousal. *Proc. Natl. Acad. Sci. U.S.A.* **77:** 3033–3037.
82. Grant, S. J., Aston-Jones, G., and Redmond, D. E. J. (1988). Responses of primate locus coeruleus neurons to simple and complex sensory stimuli. *Brain Res. Bull.* **21:** 401–410.
83. Rajkowski, J., Kubiak, P., and Aston-Jones, G. (1994). Locus coeruleus activity in monkey: Phasic and tonic changes are associated with altered vigilance. *Brain Res. Bull.* **35:** 607–616.
84. Rajkowski, J., Kubiak, P., Ivanova, S., and Aston-Jones, G. (1998). State related activity and reactivity of locus coeruleus neurons in behaving monkeys. In *Adv. Pharmacol.* (in press).
85. Aston-Jones, G., and Bloom, F. E. (1981). Norepinephrine-containing locus coeruleus neurons in behaving rats exhibit pronounced responses to nonnoxious environmental stimuli. *J. Neurosci.* **1:** 887–900.
86. Aston-Jones, G., Rajkowski, J., Kubiak, P., and Alexinsky, T. (1994). Locus coeruleus neurons in the monkey are selectively activated by attended stimuli in a vigilance task. *J. Neurosci.* **14:** 4467–4480.
87. Aston-Jones, G., Rajkowski, J., and Kubiak, P. (1997). Conditioned responses of monkey locus coeruleus neurons anticipate acquisition of discriminative behavior in a vigilance task. *Neuroscience* **80:** 697–715.
88. Aston-Jones, G., Chiang, C., and Alexinsky, T. (1991). Discharge of noradrenergic locus coeruleus neurons in behaving rats and monkeys suggests a role in vigilance. *Prog. Brain Res.* **88:** 501–520.
89. Foote, S. L., Berridge, C. W., Adams, L. M., and Pineda, J. A. (1991). Electrophysiological evidence for the involvement of the locus coeruleus in alerting, orienting, and attending. *Prog. Brain Res.* **88:** 521–532.
90. Aston-Jones, G., Rajkowski, J., Kubiak, P., Ivanova, S., Usher, M., and Cohen, J. (1998). Neuromodulation and cognitive performance: Recent studies of noradrenergic locus coeruleus neurons in behaving monkeys. *Adv. Pharmacol.* (in press).
91. Aston-Jones, G. (1985). Behavioral functions of locus coeruleus derived from cellular attributes. *Physiol. Psychol.* **13:** 118–126.

CHAPTER

55

Learning and Memory: Basic Mechanisms

John M. Beggs, Thomas H. Brown, John H. Byrne, Terry Crow, Joseph E. LeDoux, Kevin LeBar, and Richard F. Thompson

During the last quarter of this century, we have witnessed remarkable progress in understanding how the nervous system encodes and retrieves information. Current research is focused at the cellular level, where the encoding process entails activity-dependent changes in the strength of synaptic connections among neurons.

Antecedents to modern thinking can be traced back more than a century. The American psychologist William James[1] was among the first to discuss the physiological basis of the manner in which associations become formed. His "law of neural habit" states:

> When two elementary brain processes have been active together or in immediate succession, one of them, on reoccuring, tends to propagate its excitement into the other. (James,[1] p. 226)

According to the law of neural habit, the condition that drives the formation of associations is the coactivity of elementary brain processes (contiguity). Although James did not specifically identify the *locus* of the physiological modifications, others were quick to do so. The Italian anatomist Tanzi[2] appears to be the first to have advanced the hypothesis that the synapse was the locus of the change that encodes experience. The work of the great Spanish neuroanatomist Ramón y Cajál[3] suggested that the nervous system was not a syncytium, but rather a collection of physically separate neurons that signal information to one another only at specialized synaptic points of interaction. If signaling between neurons takes place at synapses, it follows that changes in the signal strength could alter the flow of activity within the brain and, consequently, the way an organism responds to experiences. According to this view, then, learning is the product of synaptic changes. Donald Hebb[4] argued that learning involved coincident synaptic activation of neurons, the "Hebb synapse" (discussed later).

Some general principles have emerged from research on several vertebrate and invertebrate model systems. A list of these principles[5] might include the following:

1. Multiple memory systems are present in the brain.
2. Short-term forms of learning and memory require changes in existing neural circuits.
3. These changes may involve multiple cellular mechanisms within individual neurons.
4. Second-messenger systems appear to play a role in mediating cellular changes.
5. Changes in the properties of membrane channels are often correlated with learning and memory.
6. Long-term memory requires new protein synthesis and growth, whereas short-term memory need not.

In this chapter we describe several selected memory systems and neural and molecular mechanisms implicated in learning. Before doing so, however, we first present an overview of some of the methods that have been used to study learning.

DEFINITIONS AND TYPES OF LEARNING

There Are Multiple Memory Systems

Current views recognize a number of different forms of learning and memory involving different neural systems (Fig. 55.1). Many workers distinguish between "declarative" and "nondeclarative" (or "proce-

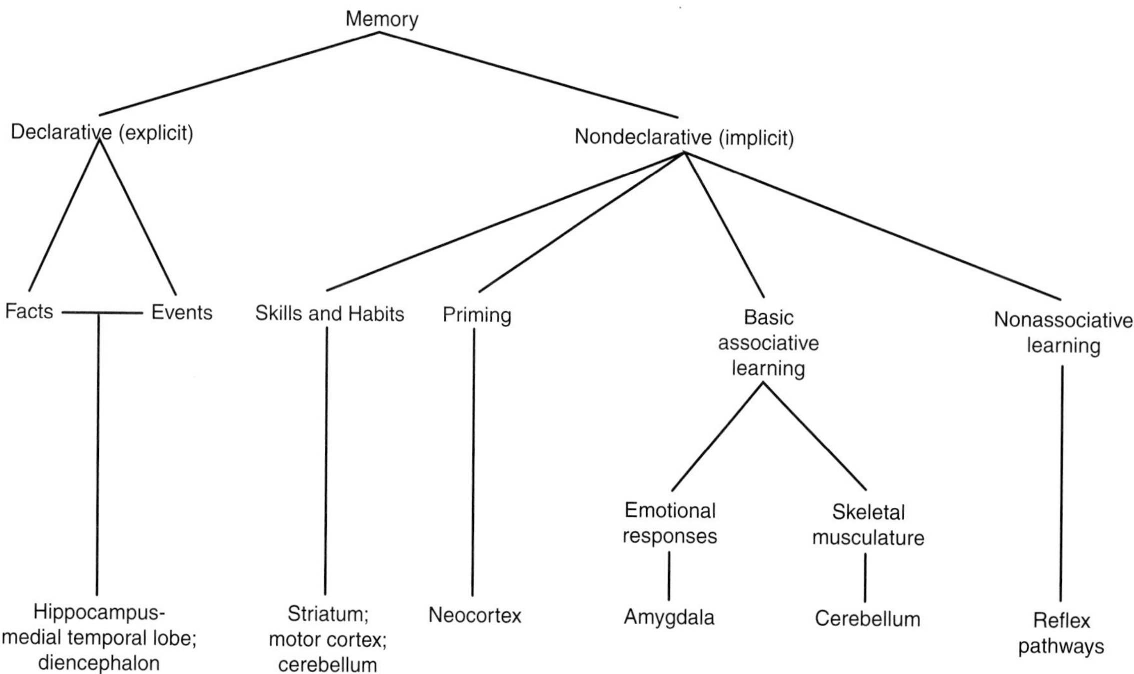

FIGURE 55.1 Multiple memory systems and their associated brain structures. Memory systems in the brain can be categorized into two major types: declarative and nondeclarative. The nondeclarative system is also referred to as implicit or procedural. Sometimes the term *procedural* is reserved for skills and habits. Each system is supported by distinct anatomical regions of the brain. Modified from Squire and Knowlton.[6]

dural'') memory. Declarative memory generally refers to explicit memories of ''what''—that is, one's own previous experiences, recognition of familiar scenes and objects, and so on; some workers have even equated it with the information one can be aware of. Declarative memory is a major topic of the next chapter.

Here we focus on nondeclarative, implicit, or procedural memory—memory of ''how to.'' The vast majority of memory processes in nonhuman animals, and many aspects of memory in humans, are of this sort. Consider all your likes and dislikes, all the skilled movements you perform (tennis, golf, swimming, bicycle riding, not to mention walking and talking), and so on. ''Nondeclarative'' is really a grab bag category; by some terminologies it can include the phenomenon of priming, defined as an increased ability to identify or detect a stimulus as a result of prior exposure. In this chapter we consider certain aspects of implicit memory, particularly nonassociative learning (sensitization), basic associative learning, and mechanisms of memory storage.[7]

The categories of memory shown in Fig. 55.1 are somewhat arbitrary and by no means mutually exclusive. When an organism learns something important, several of these memory systems can become engaged. At a more general level, all aspects of learning share a common thrust. As Rescorla[8] has stressed, basic associative learning is the way organisms, including humans, learn about causal relationships in the world. It results from exposure to relations among events in the world. In both modern Pavlovian and cognitive views of learning and memory, the individual constructs a representation of the causal structure of the world and adjusts this representation through experience to bring it in tune with the real causal structure of the world, striving to reduce any discrepancies or errors between internal representation and external reality.[9]

We will first describe in some detail the paradigms that have been used to study ''procedural'' or nondeclarative learning and provide examples of mechanistic analyses that have been performed in several selected invertebrate and vertebrate model systems. At the end of the chapter, we focus on possible mechanisms of a phenomenon known as long-term potentiation (LTP). LTP is viewed by many as a mechanism of memory storage in the nervous system, particularly in forebrain structures. The process of long-term depression (LTD) also occurs in forebrain structures. In addition, LTD is thought to be the mechanism for memory storage in the cerebellum.

Paradigms Have Been Developed to Study Nondeclarative (Procedural) Learning

Nonassociative Learning

Associative learning involves the establishment of a relationship between *two* events (see later). Nonassociative learning, one of the more basic learning processes, involves the effect of a *single* event on response probability. The three examples of nonassociative learning that have received the most attention are habituation, dishabituation, and sensitization. **Habituation** is defined as a reduction in responding to a repeatedly delivered stimulus. **Dishabituation** refers to the restoration or recovery of a habituated response due to the presentation of another, typically strong, stimulus to the animal. **Sensitization** is an enhancement or augmentation of a response produced by the presentation of a strong stimulus. In vertebrate systems, at least, dishabituation appears to be an instance of sensitization.[10]

Associative Learning

Interest in associative learning has a rich philosophical and experimental tradition, starting with the rules of association—similarity, contrast, and contiguity—formulated by Aristotle around 367 B.C. British associationism of the 17th and 18th centuries provided a more formal statement of the laws of association, emphasizing both simultaneous and successive associations. Associative learning is a very broad category that includes much of the learning we do: learning to be afraid, learning to talk, learning a foreign language, learning to play the piano. In essence, associative learning involves the formation of associations among stimuli and/or responses. It is generally subdivided into classical versus instrumental conditioning or learning. Classical or Pavlovian conditioning is the procedure in which a neutral stimulus, termed a **conditioned stimulus** (CS), is paired with a stimulus that elicits a response, termed an **unconditioned stimulus** (US), for example, food that elicits salivation or a shock to the foot that elicits limb withdrawal.

Ivan Pavlov, a Russian physiologist who had been studying digestion in dogs, discovered classical conditioning by accident—a celebrated case of serendipity. Pavlov received the Nobel Prize, incidentally, for his work on digestion. He noticed that the mere sight of the food dish caused the dogs to salivate and decided to continue the experiments to see if dogs would also salivate in response to a bell at feeding time. Pavlov trained dogs to stand in a harness and, after the sound of a bell, fed them meat powder (Fig. 55.2).[11] He recorded the salivary responses of the dogs. At first, the bell did not elicit any response; the meat powder, of course, elicited reflex salivation, termed the **unconditioned response** (UR). He noted that after a few pairing of the bell and meat powder the dogs began to salivate when the bell rang, before they received the meat powder. This is termed the **conditioned response** (CR). This type of conditioning came to be called reward or appetitive **classical conditioning.** If the bell or another stimulus was followed by an unpleasant event, such as a strong electric shock, then a variety of autonomic responses became conditioned. This type of conditioning is often termed aversive or fear conditioning. Skeletal muscle movements appropriate to deal with the US (e.g., leg flexion with a paw shock US) are also learned in aversive classical conditioning. A key aspect of Pavlovian conditioning is that the animal or human subject cannot control the occurrence of the CS and the US; they are determined by the experimenter. Instrumental learning or **operant conditioning** describes a situation in which the animal or person must perform some response in order to obtain reward or avoid punishment. That is, the subject can control the occurrence of the US. Aspects of instrumental learning are treated in Chapter 56.

Classical (Pavlovian) conditioning According to the traditional view, classical or Pavlovian conditioning is an operation that pairs one stimulus, the conditioned stimulus or CS, with a second stimulus, the unconditioned stimulus or US, as noted earlier. The US reliably elicits a response termed the unconditioned response or UR. Repeated pairings of the CS and US result in the CS eliciting a response, defined as the conditioned response or CR. Critically important variables are:

1. Order: the CS precedes the US.
2. Timing: the interval between CS and US is critical for most examples of conditioning.
3. Contiguity: the pairing or contiguity of the CS and US is necessary for conditioning.

Conditioning procedures in which the CS and US overlap in time are called **delay conditioning,** whereas **trace conditioning** consists of a procedure in which a time interval of no stimulation exists between the CS and the US. These temporal relations for delay and trace conditioning are depicted in Fig. 55.3. Often, the CR is similar to the UR (e.g., in Pavlov's experiment both were salivation).

The contemporary view of Pavlovian conditioning The traditional view of Pavlovian conditioning emphasized the contiguity of the CS and US. A more general and contemporary view of Pavlovian conditioning emphasizes the *relationship* between the CS and

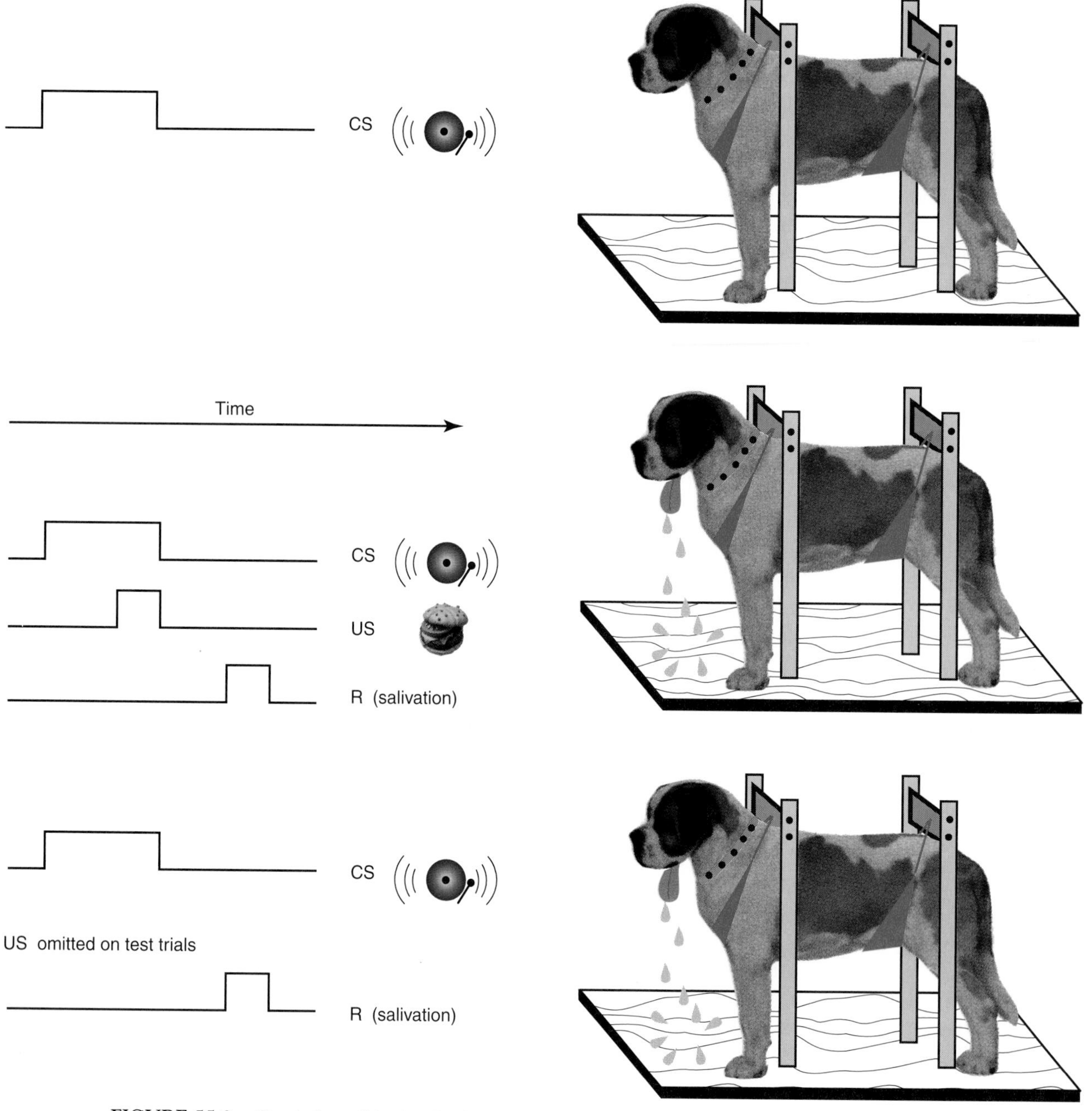

FIGURE 55.2 Classical conditioning. In the procedure introduced by Pavlov, the production of saliva is monitored continuously. Presentation of meat powder reliably leads to salivation, whereas some "neutral" stimulus such as a bell initially does not. With repeated pairings of the bell and meat powder, the animal learns that the bell predicts the food and salivates in response to the bell alone. Modified from Rachlin.[11]

the US. That is, the information that the CS provides about the occurrence of the US is the critical feature for learning. This perspective on Pavlovian conditioning is consistent with current cognitive views of learning and memory, as noted previously. Indeed, in some situations the CR is quite different from the UR: footshock causes an increase in activity (UR) in the rat; fear learned to a tone paired with this same footshock is expressed as freezing (CR). Note, however, that both these responses are adaptive.

As noted earlier, conditioning involves learning about the relations between events in the organism's

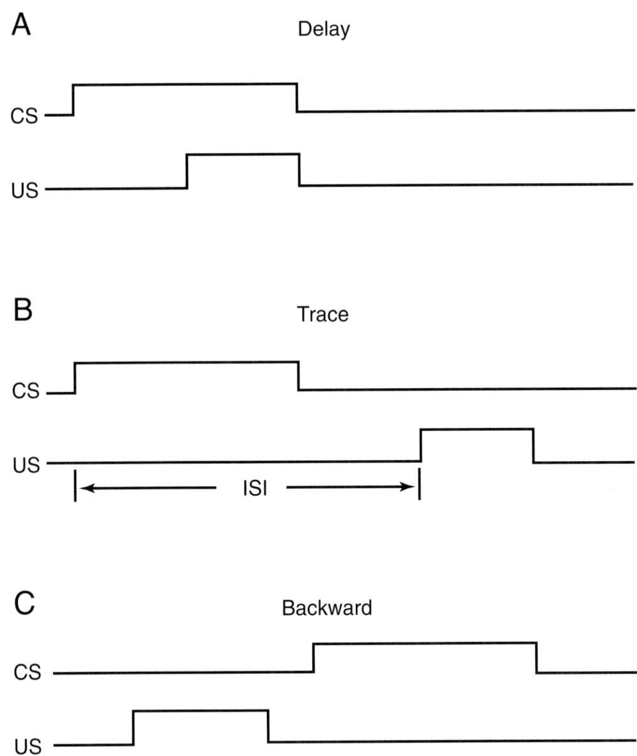

FIGURE 55.3 Classical conditioning procedures. (A) Delayed conditioning. Unconditioned stimulus (US) occurs during conditioned stimulus (CS). (B) Trace conditioning. US occurs after CS has terminated. (C) Backward conditioning. US occurs before CS. Time between onset of CS and onset of US is the interstimulus interval (ISI).

environment. In this view, contingency is a key factor in organizing the organism's environment. Consider the following experiment. A group of rats is given a series of paired stimuli in which tone (CS) and footshock (US) are paired. The animals learn very well to freeze (CR) when the CS occurs. Another group of rats is given the same number of paired CS–US trials but is also given a number of presentations with the US alone. Animals in this group do not learn to freeze to the CS at all. Both groups had the same number of contiguous pairings of CS and US, but the contingency, the probability that the US is predicted by the CS, was very much lower in the group that was also given trials with the US alone.[8]

Summary

Memory systems can be divided into two broad categories; declarative and nondeclarative, with each system being subserved by distinct brain structures. Nondeclarative memory can be further divided into several categories including nonassociative and associative. Nonassociative learning includes habituation, dishabituation and sensitization, whereas associative learning includes classical (Pavlovian) conditioning and instrumental (operant) conditioning.

INVERTEBRATE STUDIES: KEY INSIGHTS INTO BASIC MECHANISMS OF PROCEDURAL LEARNING

The Nervous Systems of Invertebrates Have Simple Circuits, Relatively Large Cells, and Express Both Simple and Complex Forms of Learning

Invertebrates are useful for analyzing the cellular and molecular events that underlie learning. The nervous systems of many invertebrates contain only several thousand neurons compared to the billions of cells in vertebrate nervous systems, yet these neurons have biochemical and biophysical properties similar to those of vertebrates. In some circumstances, a given behavior may be mediated by 100 neurons or less, allowing determination of the entire neural circuit generating the behavior. The neurons of many invertebrates are relatively large and can be repeatedly identified as unique individuals, permitting examination of the functional properties of individual cells. Molecular and biophysical events underlying the changes in cellular properties can then be determined.

For many years, the general belief was that the small number of neurons found in most invertebrates limits their behavioral capabilities to only the simplest forms of behavioral modifications such as habituation and sensitization. However, it has become clear that even invertebrates exhibit more complex behavioral modifications, such as classical conditioning, operant conditioning, and higher-order forms of classical conditioning. Here we review the extensive analyses on *Aplysia* and *Hermissenda,* two gastropod mollusks. These studies have contributed in a major way to our understanding of the neural and molecular mechanisms of simple forms of learning. See Box 55.1[12–20] for a brief description of other invertebrate model systems.

The Marine Mollusk *Aplysia* Is Well Suited to Studying Mechanisms of Learning and Memory

A number of characteristics make *Aplysia* well suited to the examination of the molecular, cellular, morphological, and network mechanisms underlying neuronal

BOX 55.1

SOME INVERTEBRATES THAT ARE USEFUL FOR PROVIDING INSIGHTS INTO THE MECHANISMS UNDERLYING LEARNING

Gastropod Mollusks

Aplysia* and *Hermissenda (see text).

Pleurobranchaea The opisthobranch *Pleurobranchaea* is a voracious marine carnivore. When exposed to food, the animal exhibits a characteristic bite–strike response. After pairing of a food stimulus (CS) with a strong electric shock to the oral veil (US), the CS, instead of eliciting a bite–strike response, elicits a withdrawal and suppression of feeding responses (conditioned response, CR). The CR is acquired within a few trials and is retained for up to 4 weeks. Neural correlates of associative learning have been analyzed by examining responses of various identified neurons in the circuit to chemosensory inputs in animals that have been conditioned. One correlate is an enhanced inhibition of command neurons for feeding.[12]

Tritonia To escape a noxious stimulus, the opisthobranch *Tritonia diomedea* initiates stereotypical rhythmic swimming. This response exhibits both habituation and sensitization and involves changes in many different components of swim behavior in each case.[13] The neural circuit consists of sensory neurons, precentral pattern generating (CPG) neurons, and motor neurons. Habituation appears to involve plasticity at multiple loci, including decrement at the first afferent synapse. Sensitization appears to involve enhanced excitability and synaptic strength in one of the CPG interneurons.

Pond snail (Lymnaea stagnalis) The pulmonate *Lymnaea stagnalis* exhibits fairly rapid nonaversive conditioning of feeding behavior. A neutral chemical or mechanical stimulus (CS) applied to the lips is paired with a strong stimulant of feeding such as sucrose (US).[14] Greater levels of rasping, a component of the feeding behavior, can be produced by a single trial, and this response can persist for at least 19 days. The circuit consists of a network of three types of CPG neurons, 10 types of motor neurons, and a variety of modulatory interneurons. An analog of the behavioral response occurs in the isolated central nervous system. The enhancement of the feeding motor program appears to be due to an increased activation of the CPG cells by mechanosensory inputs from the lips.

Land snail (Helix) Land snails can be conditioned to avoid food using procedures similar to those used with *Pleurobranchaea*. A food stimulus such as a piece of carrot (CS) is paired with an electric shock to the dorsal surface of the snail (US). After 5–15 pairings, the carrot, instead of eliciting a feeding response, elicits withdrawal and suppression of feeding responses. The transmitter serotonin appears to have a critical role in learning. Animals injected with a toxin that destroys serotonergic neurons exhibit normal responses to the food and the shocks alone, but are incapable of learning. *Helix* also exhibit habituation and sensitization of avoidance responses elicited by tactile stimuli.[15]

Limax The pulmonate *Limax* is an herbivore that locomotes toward desirable food odors. This behavior makes it well suited to food-avoidance conditioning. The slug's normal attraction to a preferred food odor (CS) is significantly reduced when the preferred odor is paired with a bitter taste (US). In addition to this example of classical conditioning, food avoidance in *Limax* exhibits higher-order features of classical conditioning, such as blocking and second-order conditioning. An analog of taste-aversion learning occurs in the isolated central nervous system, facilitating subsequent cellular analyses of learning in *Limax*. The procerebral (PC) lobe in the cerebral ganglion processes olfactory information and is a likely site for the plasticity.[16]

Arthropods

Cockroach (Periplaneta americana) and locust (Schistocerca gregaria) Learned modifications of leg positioning in the cockroach and locust may be useful in the cellular analysis of operant conditioning. When the animal is suspended over a dish containing a fluid, initially, it makes many movements, including those that cause the leg to come in contact with the liquid surface. When contact with the fluid is paired with an electric shock, the insect rapidly learns to hold its foot away from the fluid. Neural correlates of the conditioning have been observed in somata of the leg motor neurons. These correlates include changes in intrinsic firing rate and membrane conductance.

Crayfish (Procambarus clarkii) The crayfish tailflip response exhibits habituation and sensitization. A key component of the circuit is a pair of large neurons called the lateral giants (LGs), which run the length of the animal's nerve cord. The LGs are the decision and command cells for the tailflip. Learning is related to changes in the strength of synaptic input driving the LGs.

Honeybee (Apis mellifera) Honeybees, like other insects, are superb at learning. For example, sensitization of the antenna reflex of *Apis mellifera* is produced as a result of presenting gustatory stimuli to the antennae. Classical conditioning of feeding behavior can be produced by pairing visual or olfactory CS with sugar solutions (US) to the antennae. The small size of bee neurons is an obstacle in pursuing detailed cellular analyses of these behavioral modifications. Nevertheless, regions of the brain necessary for associative learning have been identified, and some neural correlates have been described. In particular, intracellular recordings have revealed that one identified cell, the ventral unpaired median (VUM) neuron, is sufficient to mediate the reinforcing effects of the US.[17]

Drosophila Because the neural circuitry in the fruit fly is both complex and inaccessible, the fly might seem to be an unpromising subject for studying the neural basis of learning. However, the ease with which genetic studies are performed compensates for the difficulty in performing electrophysiological studies.[18] A frequently used protocol employs a two-stage differential odor-shock avoidance procedure, which is performed on large groups of animals simultaneously rather than on individual animals. Animals learn to avoid odors paired (CS+) with shock but not one explicitly unpaired (CS−). This learning is typically retained for 4–6 h, but retention for 24 h to 1 week can be produced by a spaced training procedure. Several mutants deficient in learning have been identified. In many of these mutants elements of the cAMP signaling pathway are affected. Experiments using inducible genes demonstrate a role for cAMP-responsive transcription factors in the induction of long-term memory. These transcription factors are also important for long-term memory in *Aplysia* and in vertebrates.

Annelids

Leech Defensive reflexes in the leech *(Hirudo medicinalis)* exhibit habituation, dishabituation, sensitization, and classical conditioning. For example, the shortening response is enhanced following pairing of a light touch to the head (CS) with electric shock to the tail (US). The identified S neurons appear critical for sensitization, as their ablation disrupts sensitization. Interestingly, ablation of the S cells only partly disrupts dishabituation, indicating that separate processes contribute to dishabituation and sensitization.[19] Separate processes also contribute to dishabituation and sensitization in *Aplysia.* The transmitter serotonin (5-HT) appears to mediate at least part of the reinforcing effects of sensitizing stimuli and the US. Serotonin appears to play similar roles in *Aplysia, Helix, Hermissenda,* and *Tritonia.*

Nematoda

Caenorhabditis elegans Although analyses in *C. elegans* are just beginning, this animal promises to be a valuable vehicle for cellular and molecular studies of learning. Its principal advantages are threefold. First, its nervous system is extremely simple. It has a total of 302 neurons, all of which have been described in terms of their locations and synaptic connections. Second, the developmental lineage of each neuron is completely specified. Third, it is amenable to genetic and molecular manipulations. Recently, the animal has been shown to exhibit several forms of learning. When a vibratory stimulus is applied to the medium in which they locomote, adult *C. elegans* will swim backward. This reaction, known as the tap withdrawal reflex, exhibits habituation, dishabituation, sensitization, long-term (24 h) retention of habituation training, and context conditioning. Although the neurons are small and it is difficult to record their electrical activity, aspects of the neural circuit have been described. The particular role of individual neurons is being elucidated using laser ablation to remove specific neurons from the circuit.[20]

modifications (plasticity) and learning and memory. The animal has a relatively simple nervous system with large, identifiable neurons that are accessible for detailed anatomical, biophysical, and biochemical studies. Neurons and neural circuits that mediate many behaviors in *Aplysia* have been identified. In several cases, these behaviors have been shown to be modified by learning. Moreover, specific loci within neural circuits at which modifications occur during learning have been identified, and aspects of the cellular mechanisms underlying these modifications have been analyzed and modeled.[21–23]

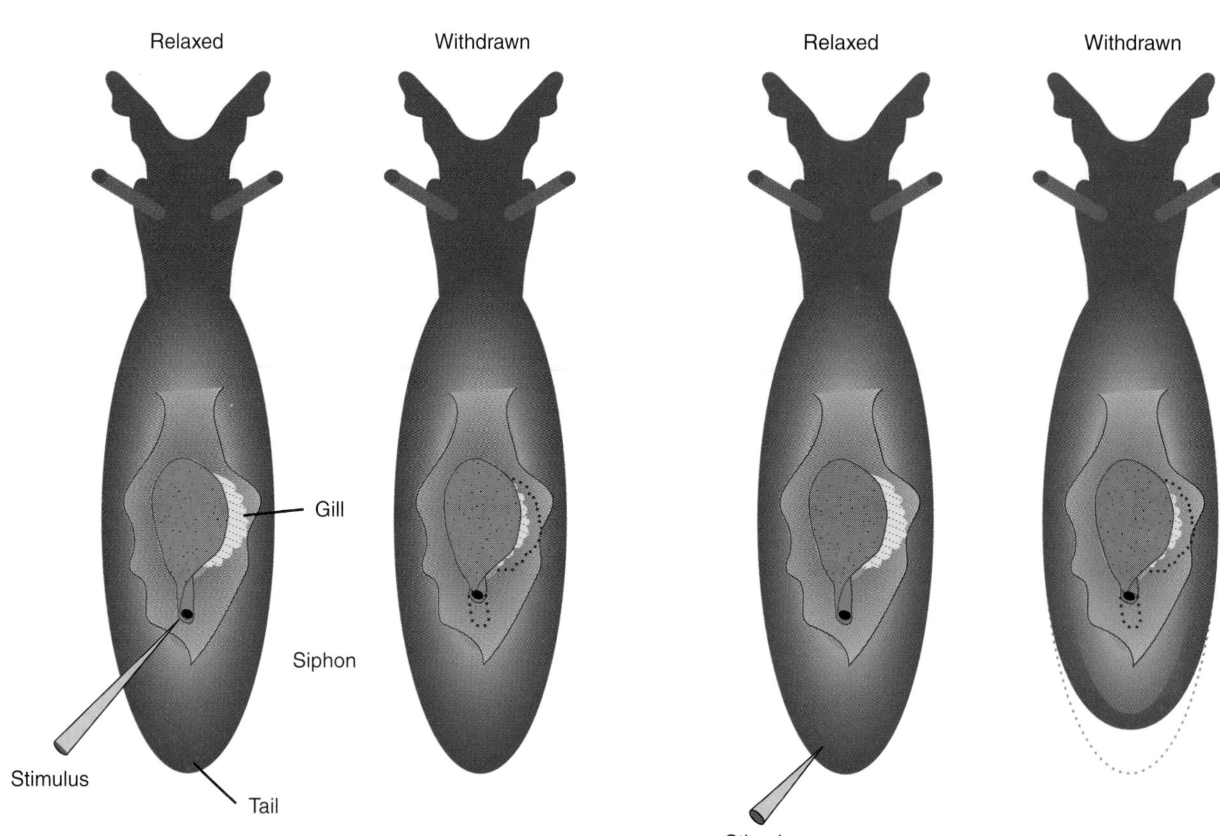

FIGURE 55.4 Siphon–gill and tail–siphon withdrawal reflexes of *Aplysia*. (A) Siphon–gill withdrawal. Dorsal view of *Aplysia:* (1) Relaxed position. (2) A stimulus (e.g., a water jet, brief touch, or weak electric shock) applied to the siphon causes the siphon and the gill to withdraw into the mantle cavity. (B) Tail–siphon withdrawal reflex. (1) Relaxed position. (2) A stimulus applied to the tail elicits a reflex withdrawal of the tail, the siphon, and the gill.

The Siphon–Gill and Tail–Siphon Withdrawal Reflexes of Aplysia

Within the mantle cavity of *Aplysia* is the respiratory organ of the animal, the gill, and protruding from the mantle cavity is the siphon (Fig. 55.4). The siphon–gill withdrawal reflex is elicited when a tactile or electrical stimulus is delivered to the siphon; the stimulus causes withdrawal of the siphon and gill (Fig. 55.4A). A second behavior that has been examined extensively is the tail–siphon withdrawal reflex. Tactile or electrical stimulation of the tail elicits a coordinated set of defensive responses, two components of which are a reflex withdrawal of the tail and the siphon (Fig. 55.4B).

These two defensive reflexes in *Aplysia* exhibit three forms of nonassociative learning: habituation, dishabituation, and sensitization. A single sensitizing stimulus can produce a reflex enhancement that lasts minutes (short-term sensitization), whereas prolonged training (e.g., multiple stimuli) produces an enhancement that lasts days to weeks (long-term sensitization). *Aplysia* also exhibits several forms of associative learning, including classical conditioning and operant conditioning.

A prerequisite for the analysis of the neural and molecular basis of these different forms of learning is an understanding of the neural circuit that controls the behavior. The afferent limb of the siphon–gill withdrawal reflex consists of sensory neurons with somata in the abdominal ganglion. The siphon sensory neurons (SN) monosynaptically excite gill and siphon motor neurons (MN) that are also located in the abdominal ganglion (Fig. 55.5A). Activation of the gill and siphon motor neurons leads to contraction of the gill and siphon. Excitatory, inhibitory, and modulatory interneurons (IN) in the withdrawal circuit have also been identified, although only excitatory interneurons are illustrated in Fig. 55.5. The afferent limb of the

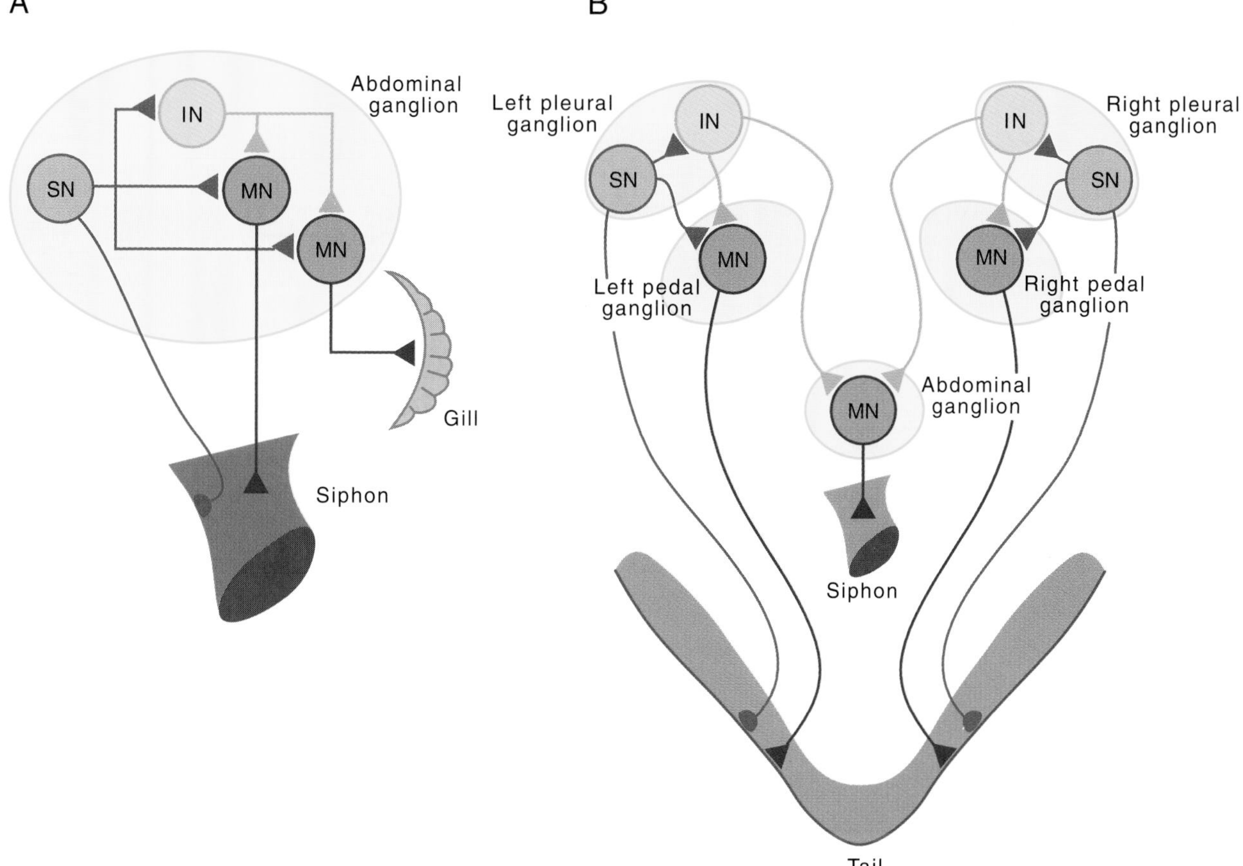

FIGURE 55.5 Simplified circuit diagrams of the siphon–gill (A) and tail–siphon (B) withdrawal reflexes. Stimuli activate the afferent terminals of mechanoreceptor sensory neurons (SN) whose somata are located in central ganglia. The sensory neurons make excitatory synaptic connections (triangles) with interneurons (IN) and motor neurons (MN). The excitatory interneurons provide a parallel pathway for excitation of the motor neurons. Action potentials elicited in the motor neurons, triggered by the combined input from the SNs and INs, propagate out peripheral nerves to activate muscle cells and produce the subsequent reflex withdrawal of the organs. Modulatory neurons (not shown here but see Fig. 55.6A1), such as those containing serotonin (5-HT), regulate the properties of the circuit elements and, consequently, the strength of the behavioral responses.

tail–siphon withdrawal reflex consists of a bilaterally symmetric cluster of sensory neurons located in the left and right pleural ganglia. These sensory neurons make monosynaptic excitatory connections with motor neurons in the adjacent pedal ganglion, which produce withdrawal of the tail (Fig. 55.5B). In addition, the tail sensory neurons form synapses with various identified excitatory and inhibitory interneurons.[24,25] Some of these interneurons activate motor neurons in the abdominal ganglion that control reflex withdrawal of the siphon. Moreover, several additional neurons modulate the tail–siphon withdrawal reflex (see Fig. 55.6A1).

The sensory neurons for both the siphon–gill and tail–siphon withdrawal reflexes are similar and appear to be important plastic elements in the neural circuits. Changes in their membrane properties and the strength of their synaptic connections (synaptic efficacy) are associated with sensitization. Moreover, the properties of these neurons are modulated by procedures that mimic short- and long-term sensitization training.

Multiple Cellular Processes and Short- and Long-Term Sensitization in Aplysia

Short-term sensitization Short-term sensitization is induced when a single brief train of shocks to the body wall results in the release of modulatory transmitters, such as serotonin (5-HT), from a separate class of interneurons referred to as facilitatory neurons (Fig. 55.6A1). These facilitatory neurons regulate the properties of the sensory neurons and the strength of their connections with postsynaptic interneurons and motor neurons, a process called **heterosynaptic facilitation** (Figs. 55.6A2 and 55.6A3). The molecular mechanisms

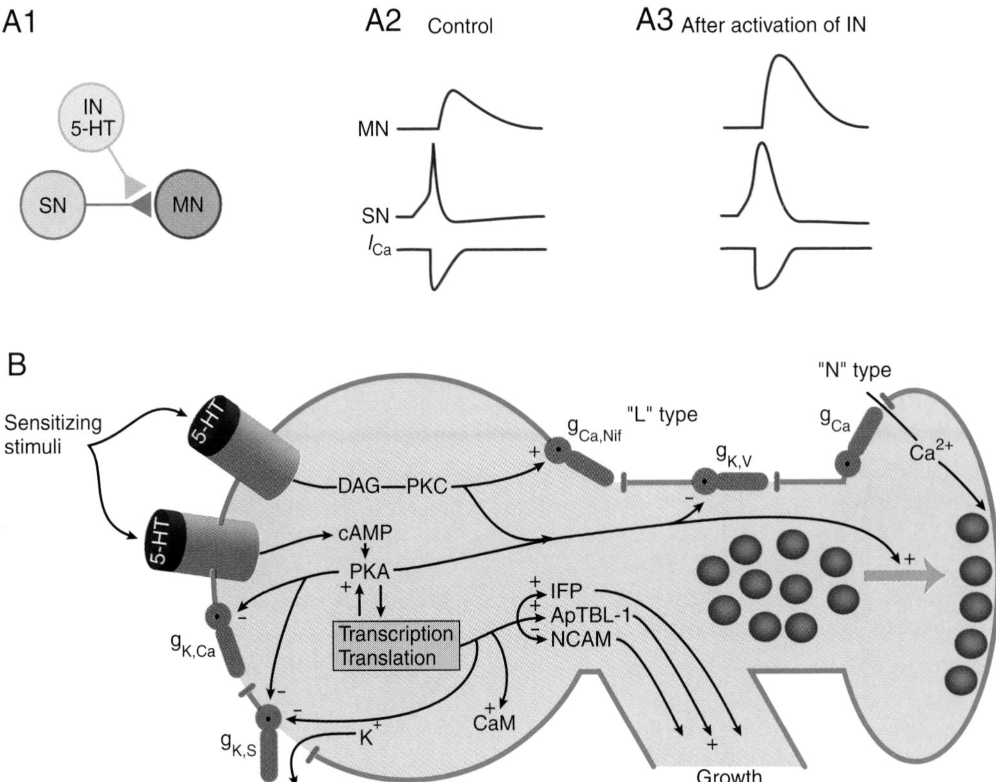

FIGURE 55.6 Model of heterosynaptic facilitation of the sensorimotor connection that contributes to short- and long-term sensitization in *Aplysia.* (A1) Sensitizing stimuli activate facilitatory interneurons (IN) that release modulatory transmitters, one of which is 5-HT. The modulator leads to an alteration of the properties of the sensory neuron (SN). (A2, A3) An action potential in SN after the sensitizing stimulus results in greater transmitter release and hence a larger postsynaptic potential in the motor neuron (MN) than an action potential before the sensitizing stimulus. For short-term sensitization, the enhancement of transmitter release is due, at least in part, to broadening of the action potential and an enhanced flow of Ca^{2+} (I_{Ca}) into the sensory neuron. (B) Molecular events in the sensory neuron. 5-HT released from the facilitatory neuron (A1) binds to at least two distinct classes of receptors on the outer surface of the membrane of the sensory neuron, which leads to the transient activation of two intracellular second messengers, DAG and cAMP. These second messengers, acting through their respective protein kinases, affect multiple cellular processes, the combined effects of which lead to enhanced transmitter release when a subsequent action potential is fired in the sensory neuron. Long-term alterations are achieved through regulation of protein synthesis and growth. Positive (+) and negative (−) signs indicate enhancement and suppression of cellular processes, respectively (see text for additional details).

contributing to heterosynaptic facilitation are illustrated in Fig. 55.6B. The first step is the binding of 5-HT to one class of receptors on the outer surface of the membrane of the sensory neurons. This leads to the activation of adenylate cyclase, which in turn leads to an elevation of the intracellular level of the second messenger cyclic adenosine 3′,5′-monophosphate (cyclic AMP, or cAMP) in sensory neurons. When cAMP binds to the regulatory subunit of cAMP-dependent protein kinase (protein kinase A, or PKA), the catalytic subunit is freed and can now add phosphate groups to specific substrate proteins and, hence, alter their functional properties. One consequence of this protein phosphorylation is an alteration in the properties of membrane channels. Specifically, the increased levels of cAMP lead to a decrease in the serotonin-sensitive potassium current [S–K^+ current ($I_{K,S}$)], a component of the calcium-activated K^+ current ($I_{K,Ca}$) and the delayed K^+ current ($I_{K,V}$). See Chapter 6. These changes in membrane currents lead to depolarization of the membrane potential, enhanced excitability, and an increase in the duration of the action potential.

Cyclic AMP also activates a facilitation process that is independent of membrane potential and spike duration. This process is represented in Fig. 55.6B (large open arrow) as the translocation or mobilization of transmitter vesicles from a storage pool to a releasable pool. The translocation makes more transmitter-containing vesicles available for release, with subsequent action potentials in the sensory neuron. The overall effect is a short-term cAMP-dependent enhancement of transmitter release.

Serotonin also acts through another class of receptors to increase the level of the second messenger diacylglycerol (DAG). DAG activates protein kinase C (PKC), which, like PKA, contributes to facilitation that is independent of spike duration (i.e., mobilization of vesicles). In addition, PKC regulates a nifedipine-sensitive Ca^{2+} channel ($I_{Ca,Nif}$) and the delayed K^+ channel ($I_{K,V}$). Thus, the delayed K^+ channel ($I_{K,V}$) is dually regulated by PKC and PKA. The modulation of $I_{K,V}$ contributes importantly to the increase in duration of the action potential (Fig. 55.6A3). Because of its small magnitude, the modulation of $I_{Ca,Nif}$ appears to play a minor role in the facilitatory process.

The consequences of activating these multiple second-messenger systems and modulating these various cellular processes are demonstrated when test stimuli elicit action potentials in the sensory neuron at various times after the presentation of the sensitizing stimuli (Fig. 55.6A3). More transmitter than normal is available for release as a result of the mobilization process and each action potential is broader, allowing a great influx of Ca^{2+} to trigger release of the available transmitter. The combined effects of mobilization and spike broadening lead to the release of more transmitter from the sensory neuron and consequently a larger postsynaptic potential in the motor neuron. Larger postsynaptic potentials lead to enhanced activation of interneurons and motor neurons and thus an enhanced behavioral response (i.e., sensitization).

Researchers have mathematically modeled and simulated aspects of the modulation of membrane channels and the dynamics of second-messenger systems, namely, calcium regulation and transmitter storage and release.[26–28]

Long-term sensitization Repeated sensitizing stimuli (shocks over a period of $1\frac{1}{2}$ h) induce long-term sensitization, the memory of which can persist for days to weeks. Repeated training leads to more prolonged phosphorylation and activation of nuclear regulatory proteins by PKA. These proteins affect the regulatory regions of DNA, lead to increased transcription of RNA, and hence increase synthesis of specific proteins. Some of the resulting proteins may be transcription factors, which can activate other genes, and some of these genes may be able to maintain their own activation. One of the newly synthesized proteins initiates the internalization and degradation of neuronal cell adhesion molecules (NCAMs), allowing the restructuring of the axon arbor.[29] The sensory neuron can now form additional connections with the same postsynaptic target or make new connections with other cells. Other newly synthesized proteins, such as intermediate filament proteins (IFP) and ApTBL-1, an activator of TGF_{β}, are also likely to contribute to the growth of new processes.[30,31] Increased synthesis of calmodulin (CaM) also occurs, but the functional significance of this effect has not been determined.

Prolonged stimulation and increased levels of cAMP also activate a process that decreases the level of PKA regulatory subunits, further prolonging PKA activation.[32] With fewer regulatory subunits of PKA to bind to catalytic subunits, the catalytic units are persistently active and may contribute to long-term facilitation of transmitter release through the same cAMP-dependent processes seen in the short term. Some of these changes induced by cAMP and PKA include a decrease in $I_{K,S}$ and enhanced excitability, as well as a possible prolongation or amplification of their effects on nuclear regulatory proteins (see previous discussion). As with short-term sensitization, the long-term enhanced responses of the animal to test stimuli are based on the enhanced release of transmitter from existing contacts between sensory neurons and motor neurons or between sensory neurons and interneurons. However, increases in axonal arborization (Fig. 55.6B) and synaptic contacts are unique to long-term sensitization, and these developments may contribute to the enhanced activation of interneurons and motor neurons that receive connections from the sensory neurons (e.g., Fig. 55.5).

Mechanisms Underlying Associative Learning in Aplysia

The withdrawal reflexes of *Aplysia* are subject to classical conditioning.[21,23] The short-term classical conditioning observed at the behavioral level reflects a cellular mechanism called **activity-dependent neuromodulation.** Delivering a US, such as an electric shock to the tail or a peripheral nerve, releases a modulatory neurotransmitter, such as 5-HT, that nonspecifically enhances transmitter release from the sensory neurons. This nonspecific enhancement contributes to short-term sensitization (see prior discussion). The associative learning results from the pairing of a CS (e.g., spike activity in one sensory neuron) with the US, an interaction that causes a selective amplification of the modulatory effects of the US in that specific sensory neuron. Unpaired activity does not amplify the effects of the US. The amplification of the modulatory effects in the paired sensory neuron leads to a pairing-specific enhancement of transmitter release from the sensory neuron.

In this proposed mechanism, increased Ca^{2+} levels resulting from spike activity in the sensory neuron alter adenylate cyclase levels via calmodulin and increase the cAMP level produced by 5-HT. Thus, Ca^{2+} and CaM appear to play a role in the activity-dependent neuromodulation underlying associative conditioning of the tail and gill withdrawal reflexes. In addition, activity and changes in the intracellular levels of Ca^{2+} in the postsynaptic neuron (i.e., motor neuron) may also contribute to associative changes in synaptic strength at the sensory–motor neuron synapse.[33,33a]

An important conclusion is that short-term associative learning operates via a mechanism that is an elaboration of the cAMP-dependent mechanisms contributing to a simpler form of learning—sensitization. This finding raises the interesting possibility that even more complex forms of learning may be achieved by using these simpler forms as building blocks. Indeed, theoretical studies have shown that a mathematical model of the learning rule (activity-dependent neuromodulation) for simple classical conditioning, when incorporated into simple neural circuits, has the capability to simulate higher-order features of classical conditioning such as second-order conditioning and blocking, as well as features of operant conditioning.[28]

The Pacific Nudibranch *Hermissenda* Is Useful for Studying Mechanisms of Pavlovian Conditioning

One organism that has contributed to the development of a cellular and molecular understanding of associative learning and memory is the Pacific nudibranch *Hermissenda crassicornis. Hermissenda* exhibits a robust example of Pavlovian conditioning. The relative simplicity of the pathways supporting the conditioned stimulus and unconditioned stimulus has made it possible to identify neurons and their convergence within the central nervous system. Because the sensory systems activated by the CS and US are central, interactions within and between both pathways can be studied in an isolated nervous system, and, in fact, mechanisms underlying Pavlovian conditioning have been identified in sensory neurons of the CS pathway.[34,35]

Visually Guided Locomotion and Foot Contraction of Hermissenda

Pavlovian conditioning of *Hermissenda* involves changes in locomotion and foot length produced by stimulation of the visual and vestibular systems.[36,37] *Hermissenda* normally exhibits a positive phototaxis when stimulated with light. Light-elicited locomotion, orientation and movement toward a light source, and reduced locomotion in the brightest part of a light gradient can all be observed in response to light. In addition to the effects of illumination on locomotion,

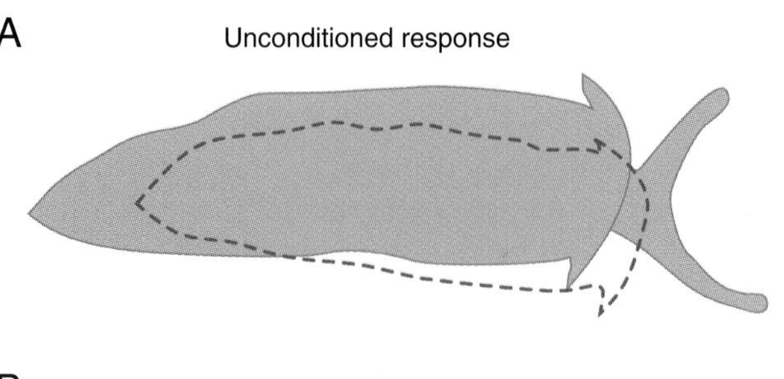

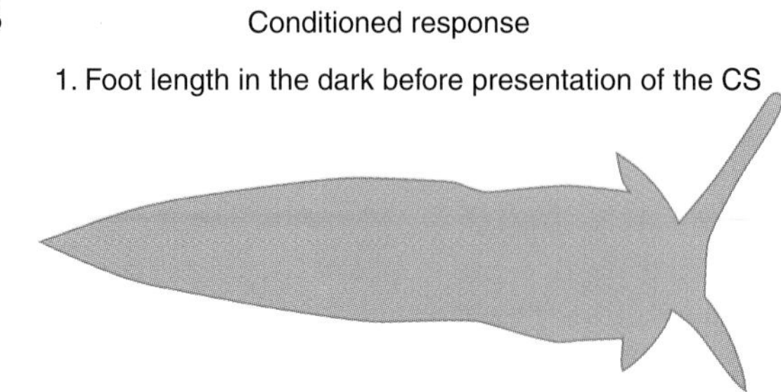

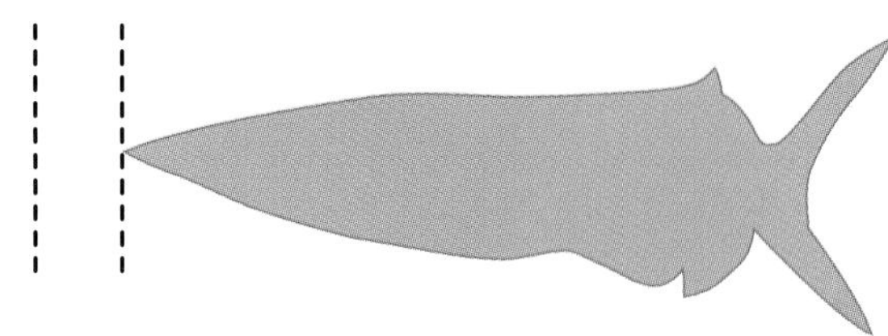

FIGURE 55.7 Conditioned foot-shortening of *Hermissenda*. The unconditioned response (UR) is shown in (A) as the outline of the foot represented by the dashed line in response to rotation of the animal, the unconditioned stimulus (US). Comparison of the length of the foot after Pavlovian conditioning in the dark (B1) and in response to the presentation of the conditioned stimulus (CS) in (B2). The area indicated by the dashed lines represents the foot-shortening conditioned response (CR). Pseudo-random and random presentations of the CS and US do not result in the development of phototactic suppression or foot-shortening. Drawings of the foot adapted from Lederhendler *et al.*[37]

light elicits a lengthening of the foot. Stimulation of the gravity receptors (hair cells) by rotating the animals on a turntable with rotation produces both an inhibition of locomotion and foot-shortening, the unconditioned response (UR). The Pavlovian conditioning procedure consists of pairing light, the CS, with high-speed rotation, the US. After conditioning, the CS suppresses the normal positive phototactic response and elicits foot-shortening (CR). The learning lasts for days to weeks, depending on the number of conditioning trials. A diagram of the conditioning procedure used with *Hermissenda* is shown in Fig. 55.7. The change in behavior elicited by the CS depends on the association of the two sensory stimuli. In addition, unpaired presentations of the US prior to conditioning degrade subsequent conditioning produced by CS–US pairings.[38]

Examples of nonassociative learning, such as habituation and sensitization, have not been a primary focus of investigations in *Hermissenda.* However, short-term nonassociative effects have been identified. These effects are typically expressed in the initial trials of a conditioning session and decrease rapidly after multitrial training is terminated.[39] Because the associative and nonassociative contributions to behavior follow different time courses and are of different magnitudes, the mechanism of classical conditioning in *Hermissenda* is not likely to be an amplification or potentiation of the mechanism of short-term sensitization.

Cellular and subcellular analyses of one-trial conditioning in *Hermissenda* have provided an opportunity to examine time-dependent mechanisms of memory consolidation. In a one-trial conditioning procedure shown to modify phototaxis, serotonin appears to be the neurotransmitter or neuromodulator in the US pathway. Light (CS) paired with direct application of 5-HT (to mimic the US) to the exposed nervous system of otherwise intact *Hermissenda* significantly suppresses phototactic behavior when the animals are tested 1 day after one-trial conditioning.[40] One-trial conditioning also produces cellular change in identified type B photoreceptors, the sites of cellular plasticity produced by multitrial Pavlovian conditioning (see next section).

Mechanisms of Conditioning in Hermissenda

An essential step in the physiological analysis of conditioning is identifying the loci in the animal's nervous system where the memory of the associative experience is stored. In the *Hermissenda* nervous system one site of memory storage is the primary sensory neurons (type A and type B photoreceptors) of the pathway mediating the CS. Each non-image-forming eye of *Hermissenda* is relatively simple, consisting of three type B photoreceptors and two type A photoreceptors.[41]

In type B photoreceptors, conditioning is accompanied by a number of modifications that alter the response of the cells to the CS. These include a significant increase in CS-elicited spike activity, enhanced excitability to extrinsic current, an increase in the input resistance, both increased and decreased amplitudes of light-elicited generator potentials, a decrease in spike frequency accommodation, and reductions in the peak amplitudes of several diverse K^+ currents.[34,42–48] Cellular modifications in conditioned animals are also observed in the type A photoreceptors.[48] Lateral type A photoreceptors of conditioned animals exhibit a significant increase in CS-elicited spike activity, a decrease in generator potential amplitude, and enhanced excitability and decreased spike frequency accommodation to extrinsic current.[46] The enhanced excitability of identified sensory neurons of conditioned animals, expressed by significant increases in both the amplitude of CS-elicited generator potentials and spike activity elicited by the CS, may be a major contributor to changes in the duration and amplitude of complex postsynaptic potentials and enhanced spike activity recorded in postsynaptic targets after conditioning. In addition to the enhanced excitability of type A and B photoreceptors found after conditioning, there are changes in the strength of synaptic connections between identified photoreceptors.[49] Taken collectively, these experiments show that in the CS pathway of conditioned animals cellular changes are found at multiple sites involving changes in both excitability and synaptic strength.

Voltage-clamp studies of type B photoreceptors have identified two K^+ currents, I_A and $I_{K,Ca}$, that are reduced after conditioning.[42,43] Reductions in several diverse K^+ conductances could account for both the enhanced excitability and the enhancement of IPSPs observed in conditioned animals.

Several second-messenger systems appear to be responsible for the reduction in the K^+ currents of type B photoreceptors. Evidence suggests that the phosphoinositide system may contribute to reductions in K^+ currents observed in conditioned *Hermissenda.*[34,50–52] Activation of PKC by phorbol esters and diacylglycerol analogs and intracellular injection of PKC into type B photoreceptors reduced both I_A and $I_{K,Ca}$. Activation of PKC may be initiated by the actions of an agonist released by stimulation of the US pathway[35] and 5-HT and/or γ-aminobutyric acid (GABA) may be released by stimulation of statocyst hair cells by rotation (US). Several 5-HT immunoreactive neurons may provide polysynaptic input to the visual system from stimulation of the US pathway.[53] In addition, the monosynaptic inhibitory input to photoreceptors from statocyst hair cells is presumed to be GABAergic and may be part of the US pathway. The mitogen-activated protein kinase (MAPK) pathway is also activated in Pavlovian conditioning of *Hermissenda.*[60]

One-Trial Conditioning of Hermissenda

One-trial conditioning in *Hermissenda* has provided insights into the mechanisms of time-dependent memory consolidation. The one-trial conditioning procedure described earlier produces CS-elicited short- and long-term enhancement (STE and LTE) of generator potentials recorded from identified type B photoreceptors, as well as enhanced excitability to the CS and extrinsic current.[54,55] LTE depends on protein and messenger RNA (mRNA) synthesis, is expressed only in

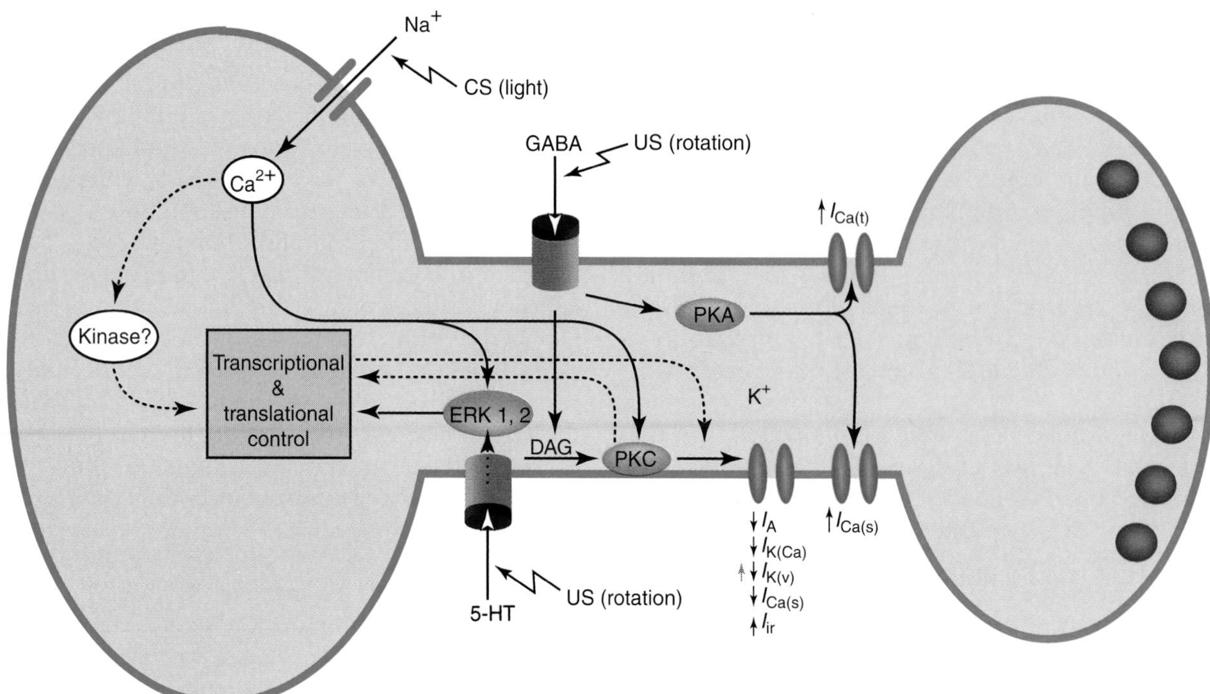

FIGURE 55.8 Cellular model for the mechanism of Pavlovian conditioning of *Hermissenda*. A modulatory transmitter released by stimulation of the US pathway binds to 5-HT and/or γ-aminobutyric acid (GABA) receptors. The receptor-activated signal is transmitted through a G protein to the enzyme phospholipase C (not shown). A precursor lipid, PIP_2 (phosphatidylinositol 4,5-biphosphate), is cleaved to yield inositol trisphosphate and diacylglycerol (DAG). The DAG and Ca^{2+} released by inositol trisphosphate from internal stores activate protein kinase C (PKC), which may reduce K^+ currents and enhance cellular excitability. The CS results in increased levels of intracellular Ca^{2+} produced by the depolarizing generator potential and light-induced release of Ca^{2+} from intracellular stores. Pairing specificity may result from the synergistic action of Ca^{2+} and PKC-dependent phosphorylation by stimulation of the US pathway, or activation of extracellular signal-regulated protein kinases (ERK1,2). Time-dependent activation of second messengers and ionic events have been proposed to account for the reduction of K^+ currents and synaptic enhancement and enhanced excitability. This activation may also be responsible for protein synthesis and gene expression necessary for long-term memory (see text).

lateral B photoreceptors, and is dependent on the contiguity of the CS and US.[40,54,55,56] Figure 55.8 illustrates a cellular model for associative memory in the type B photoreceptors. Changes in these neurons by one-trial conditioning are the result of activation of PKC and MAPK by stimulation of the US pathway and elevated intracellular Ca^{2+} levels produced by the presentation of the CS. This activation of PKC due to elevated intracellular Ca^{2+} may result in phosphorylation of channel proteins.

The induction of short-term enhancement by one-trial conditioning is caused by activation of PKC because pretreatment with broad-spectrum protein kinase inhibitors and downregulation of PKC activity block the induction of short-term enhancement.[57] Moreover, evidence indicates that short- and long-term enhancement may be parallel processes. The conditions that are sufficient to block short-term enhancement—downregulation of PKC and kinase inhibition—do not block long-term enhancement.[58] We conclude from these results that short- and long-term enhancement are not sequential processes, but are parallel processes involving independent mechanisms.

Researchers have developed an *in vitro* conditioning procedure to examine biochemical mechanisms underlying one-trial conditioning.[59] In this procedure, stimulating the isolated eyes and proximal optic nerve of *Hermissenda* with light (CS) paired with 5-HT administration produced an increase in protein phosphorylation detected at different times following *in vitro* conditioning. In addition, the increase in protein phosphorylation detected 2 h after conditioning is dependent on CS–US pairing.

Summary

Invertebrates have an enormous capacity for learning and offer experimental advantages for analyzing the cellular and molecular mechanisms of learning. Each of the animals described has its own unique strengths. Behaviors in the gastropod mollusks and the leech are mediated by relatively simple neural circuits, which can be elucidated with conventional electroanatomical approaches. Once the circuit is specified, the neural locus for the particular example of learning can be found, and biophysical, biochemical, and molecular approaches can be used to identify mechanisms underlying the change. The relatively large size of some of these cells allows these analyses to take place at the level of individual identified neurons. Individual neurons can be surgically removed and assayed for changes in the levels of second messengers, protein phosphorylation, and RNA and protein syntheses. Moreover, peptides and nucleotides can be injected into individual neurons. Invertebrates such as *Drosophila* and *Caenorhabditis elegans* have small neurons but offer tremendous advantages for obtaining insights into mechanisms of learning and memory through genetic approaches.

Despite the differences in the levels of analyses and the examples of learning that have been analyzed, we can make some general observations based on the studies described in this section. First, learning is associated with changes in the properties of individual neurons and synapses. Support for this assertion comes from studies on *Aplysia, Hermissenda, Pleurobranchaea, Lymnaea stagnalis, Tritonia,* cockroach, locust, crayfish, honeybee, and leech. Second, modulatory transmitters appear to be important for inducing cellular changes associated with many examples of learning. Serotonin appears to be particularly important in *Aplysia, Hermissenda, Helix, Tritonia,* crayfish, and leech, whereas other amines are important in the honeybee and *Drosophila.* Third, work in *Aplysia, Hermissenda,* honeybee, and *Drosophila* has shown that second-messenger systems are engaged during learning and that these messengers affect multiple cellular processes. Fourth, changes in the properties of membrane channels are associated with learning. This assertion is supported by findings in *Aplysia, Hermissenda, Pleurobranchaea,* and *Tritonia.* Fifth, studies in *Aplysia, Hermissenda,* and *Drosophila* have shown that long-term memory is associated with changes in protein synthesis. *Aplysia* and *Drosophila* provide evidence that changes in protein synthesis are induced by activation of CREB, a cAMP-dependent transcription factor. The findings from invertebrates are consistent with those now emerging from vertebrates. A universal mechanism for learning, however, does not appear to be present. Rather, different animals and, indeed, different neural circuits within any one animal, draw on a palette of multiple mechanisms supporting plasticity to mediate specific types of learning.

CLASSICAL CONDITIONING IN VERTEBRATES: DISCRETE RESPONSES AND FEAR AS MODELS OF ASSOCIATIVE LEARNING

When animals, including humans, are faced with an aversive or threatening situation, at least two complementary processes of learning occur. Learned fear or arousal develops very rapidly, often in one trial. Subsequently, the organism learns to make the most adaptive behavioral motor responses to deal with the situation. These observations led to so-called two-process theories of learning: development of an initial learned fear or arousal, followed by slower learning of discrete behavioral responses.[61] As the latter learning develops, fear subsides. We now think that, at least in mammals, a third process typically takes place in which declarative memory for the events and their relations develops (see Fig. 55.1 and later discussion). In this section, we focus on the learning of discrete responses, using eyeblink conditioning as the model system, and on conditioned fear.

Eyeblink Is a Model System for Studying the Conditioning of Discrete Behavioral Responses in Vertebrates

A vast amount of research has used Pavlovian conditioning of the eyeblink response in humans and other mammals.[62] The eyeblink response exhibits all the basic laws and properties of Pavlovian conditioning equally in humans and other mammals. The basic procedure is to present a neutral CS, such as a tone or a light, followed a quarter of a second or so later by a puff of air to the eye or by a periorbital (around the eye) shock (US). (This is an example of what is known as a delay procedure, e.g., Fig. 55.3A.) Initially, there is no response to the CS and a reflex eyeblink to the US. After a number of such trials, the eyelid begins to close in response to the CS before the US occurs. In a well-trained subject, the eyelid closure (CR) becomes very precisely timed so that it is maximally closed about

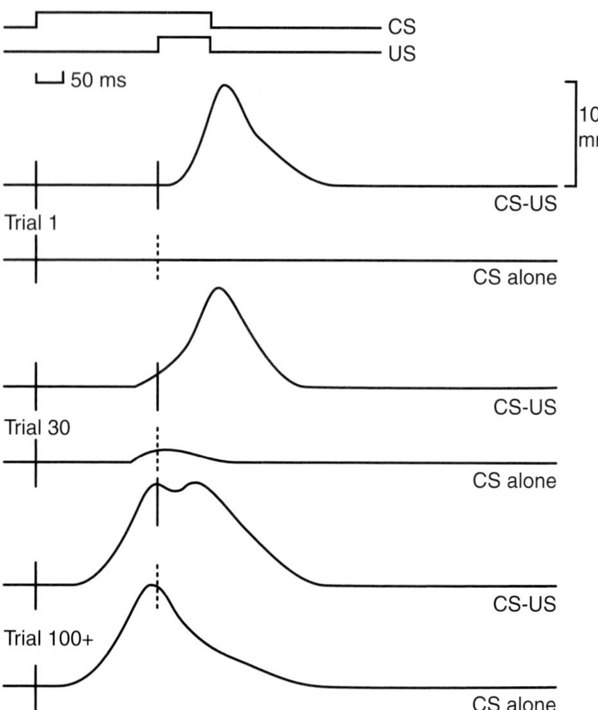

FIGURE 55.9 The adaptive nature of classical conditioning. This example shows the development of the conditioned eyeblink response over the trials of training. The CS is typically a "neutral" light or tone; the US here is a puff of air to the cornea. The eyelid closure response is indicated by upward movement of the tracing. The first marker is tone CS onset; the second is airpuff US onset. In Trial 1 the eyeblink does not move to the CS but closes (blinks) following onset of the US. The conditioned response (CR) is any measurable degree of eyelid closure prior to the onset of the US. Note that after learning, the CR peaks at the onset of the US, i.e., maximum eyelid closure at airpuff onset. If the CS–US onset interval were longer (e.g., 500 ms), the CR would now peak at the onset of the US, 500 ms after CS onset. The conditioned response is adaptive. For this type of learning, a period (ISI) of about 250 ms between CS onset and US onset (shown here) yields the best learning. This best learning time varies widely depending on the type of response (e.g., for fear learning, several seconds is best).

the time that the air puff or shock (US) onset occurs (see Fig. 55.9). This very adaptive timing of the eyeblink CR develops over the range of CS–US onset intervals (i.e., ISI, Fig. 55.3) in which learning occurs, about 100 ms to 1 s. Thus, the conditioned eyeblink response is a very precisely timed elementary learned motor skill. The same is true of other discrete behavioral responses learned to deal with aversive stimuli (e.g., the forelimb or hindlimb flexion response and the head turn).

As noted previously, there are two basic procedures in classical conditioning: delay and trace (Fig. 55.3). Pavlov[63] first described trace classical conditioning. He stressed that the organism must maintain a "trace" of the CS in the brain in order for the CS and the US to become associated. In eyeblink conditioning in animals, a typical trace interval between CS offset and US onset is 500 ms. The trace eyeblink procedure is much more difficult to learn than the delay procedure.

Two brain systems, the hippocampus and the cerebellum, become massively engaged in eyeblink conditioning.[64] When the US is sufficiently aversive to elicit learned fear, the amygdala also plays a role. In an experimental design using a click CS and glabellar (forehead) tap US in restrained cats, a very short latency (<20 ms) eyeblink muscle EMG (electrical response recorded from muscles around the eye) CR involving the motor cortex develops.[65,66] However, bilateral removal of the motor cortex does not appear to affect either learning or expression of the standard longer latency adaptive delay or trace CRs.[67] This short latency EMG response may be a component of the startle response elicited by a sudden acoustic stimulus.[68]

Hippocampus and Classical Conditioning

In eyeblink conditioning, neuronal unit activity in hippocampal fields CA1 and CA3 increases very rapidly in paired (tone CS–corneal airpuff US) training trials, shifts forward in time as learning develops, and forms a predictive "temporal model" of the learned behavioral response both within trials and over the trials of training[69,70] (Fig. 55.10).[71] To summarize a large body of research, the growth of the hippocampal unit response, under normal conditions, invariably and strongly predicts subsequent behavioral learning.[71] This increase in neuronal activity in the hippocampus becomes significant by the second or third trial of training, long before behavioral signs of learning develop. Neurons in the hippocampus become engaged in many other types of learning as well[72] (see Chapter 59).

In eyeblink conditioning, many neurons identified as pyramidal neurons in fields CA1 and CA3 show learning-related increases in discharge frequency during the trial period[73] (Fig. 55.10). Typically, a given neuron models only some limited time period of the trial, although some pyramidal neurons model the entire learned behavioral response, as in Figs. 55.10A and 55.10B. Thus, the pyramidal neuron representation of the behavioral learned response is distributed over both space and time in the hippocampus.[74]

The results just described were obtained using the basic delay procedure, in which hippocampal lesions do not impair simple response acquisition in rabbits. Similarly, humans with hippocampal–temporal lobe anterograde amnesia (Chapter 59) are able to learn simple acquisition of the eyeblink conditioned response, but cannot recall the learning experience.[75] The

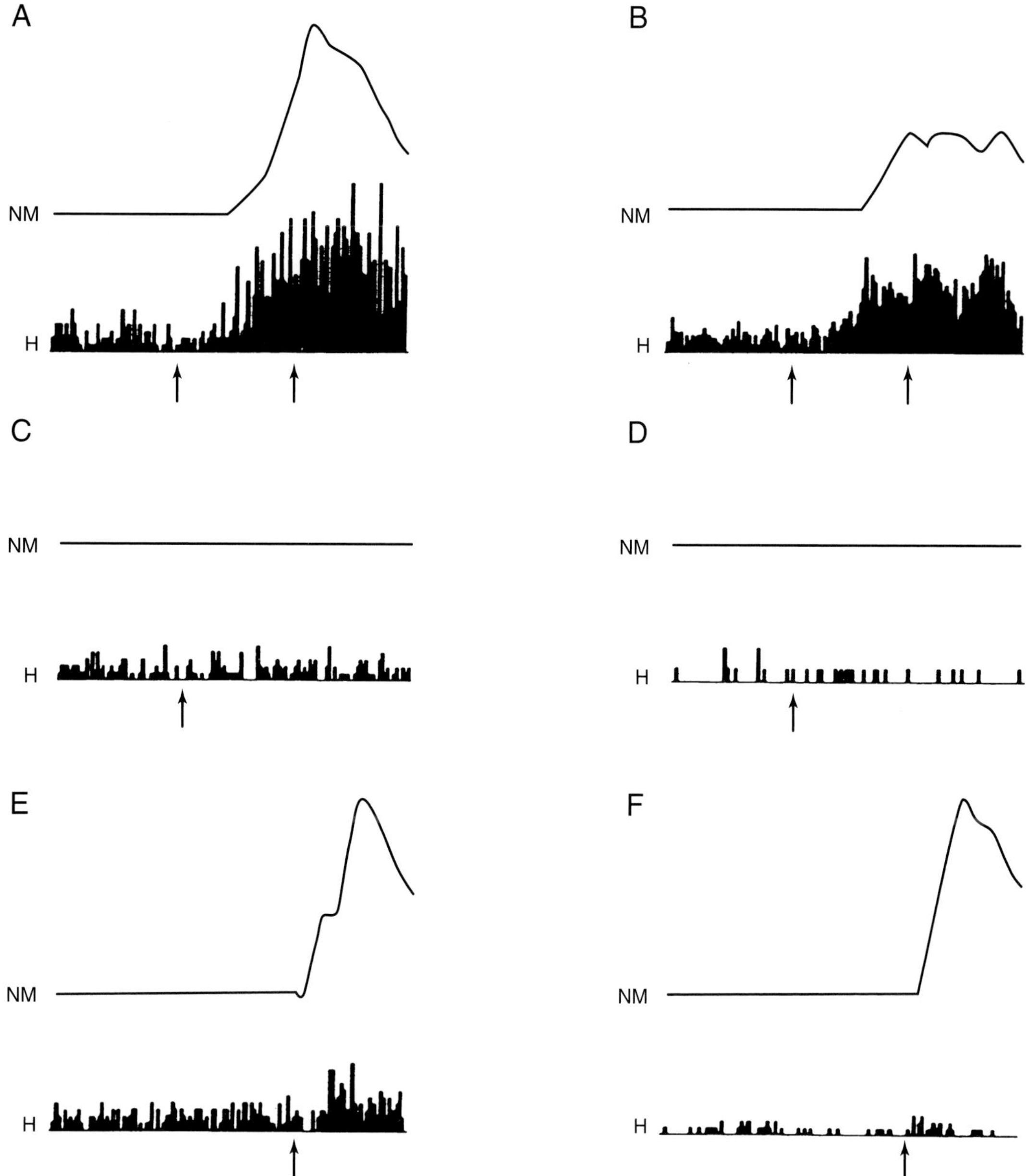

FIGURE 55.10 Engagement of hippocampal neurons in eyeblink conditioning. Responses of identified pyramidal neurons during paired (A and B) and unpaired (C–F) presentations of tone and corneal airpuff. The upper traces show the averaged nictitating membrane (NM, a component of the eyeblink) response for all trials during which a given cell was recorded. The bottom traces show the response of the recorded neuron in the form of a peristimulus time histogram. The total length of both NM responses and histograms was 750 ms. Arrows occurring early in the trial period indicate tone onset; arrows occuring late in the trial period indicate airpuff onset. H, hippocampus. In this particular figure, A and B show examples of responses of two pyramidal neurons recorded from two different animals during delay conditioning. The results in C and E show the response of a pyramidal neuron recorded from an animal given unpaired tone-alone (C) and airpuff-alone (E) presentations. (D and F) Same for a different pyramidal cell recorded from a different control animal. From Berger *et al.*[71]

involvement of the hippocampus depends on the difficulty of the task. For example, such amnesic humans are massively impaired on conditional discriminations in eyeblink conditioning (e.g., blink to tone only if preceded by light) but not on simple discriminations.[76] Bilateral hippocampal lesions in rabbits markedly impair subsequent acquisition of the trace CR.[77,78] Interestingly, when the hippocampal lesion is made immedi-

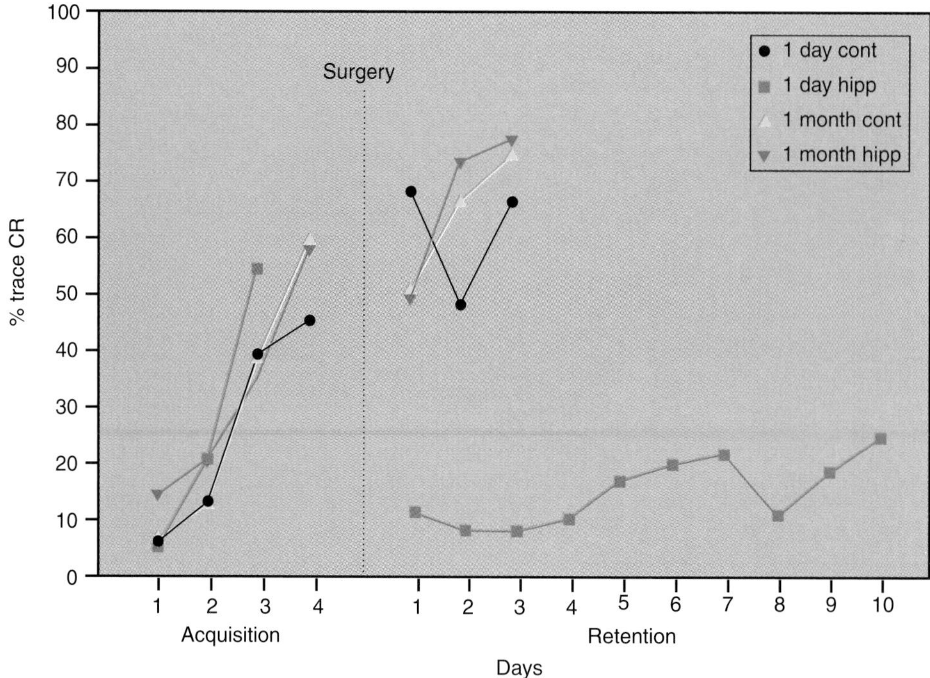

FIGURE 55.11 Effects of hippocampal lesions on retention of trace CRs. Shown are the mean percentage of CRs during initial training and following postoperative training: 1 day cont, controls given cortical or sham lesions 1 day after training; 1 month cont, controls given lesions 1 month after training; 1 day hipp, bilateral hippocampal lesions made 1 day after training; 1 month hipp, hippocampal lesions made 1 month after training. Only the hippocampal lesions made immediately after training abolished the trace CR. From Kim *et al.*[79]

ately after trace learning in rabbits, the CR is abolished; when the lesion is made a month after training, the CR is not impaired (Fig. 55.11).[79]

These results are striking in light of reports of declarative memory deficit following damage to the hippocampal system in humans and monkeys (see Chapter 59). These deficits have two key temporal characteristics: (1) profound and permanent anterograde amnesia and (2) profound but clearly time-limited retrograde amnesia. Subjects have great difficulty learning new declarative tasks and / or information (anterograde amnesia) and have substantial memory loss for events for some period preceding brain damage (retrograde amnesia), but relatively intact memory for earlier events.[80] So even in a simple procedural learning task such as eyeblink conditioning, hippocampal-dependent "declarative" memory processes develop.

What are the mechanisms of the changes in the hippocampus? The process of long-term potentiation is widely considered to be the most likely mechanism of memory storage in the hippocampal system (see later discussion). In the case of classical conditioning, there are a number of parallels between the properties of LTP and the properties of the learning-induced increase in neuronal activity in the hippocampus.[71] Both LTP and the learning-induced increase in hippocampal neuron activity are associated with pyramidal neurons, both begin to develop after very brief periods (e.g., 100 Hz for 1 s for LTP; 1–3 trials of training in eyeblink conditioning), both approach a limit asymptotically over a period of many minutes, both show the same magnitude of increase, and both are developed only with very specific parameters of stimulation. Further, there is a persistent increase in the extracellularly recorded monosynaptic population spike in the dentate gyrus in response to stimulation of the perforant path as a result of eyeblink conditioning, just as occurs when LTP is induced by tetanus of the perforant path.[81]

There are strikingly parallel and persisting increases in glutamate AMPA (α-amino-3-methylsoxazole-4-propionic acid) receptor binding on hippocampal membranes in both eyeblink conditioning (well-trained animals) and *in vivo* expression of LTP by stimulation of the perforant path projection to the hippocampal dentate gyrus. The pattern of increased binding is similar in both.[82–84] Glutamate NMDA (*N*-methyl-D-aspartate) receptors play a critical role in induction of LTP (at least in the dentate gyrus and CA1) and also appear to be involved in acquisition of the trace eye-

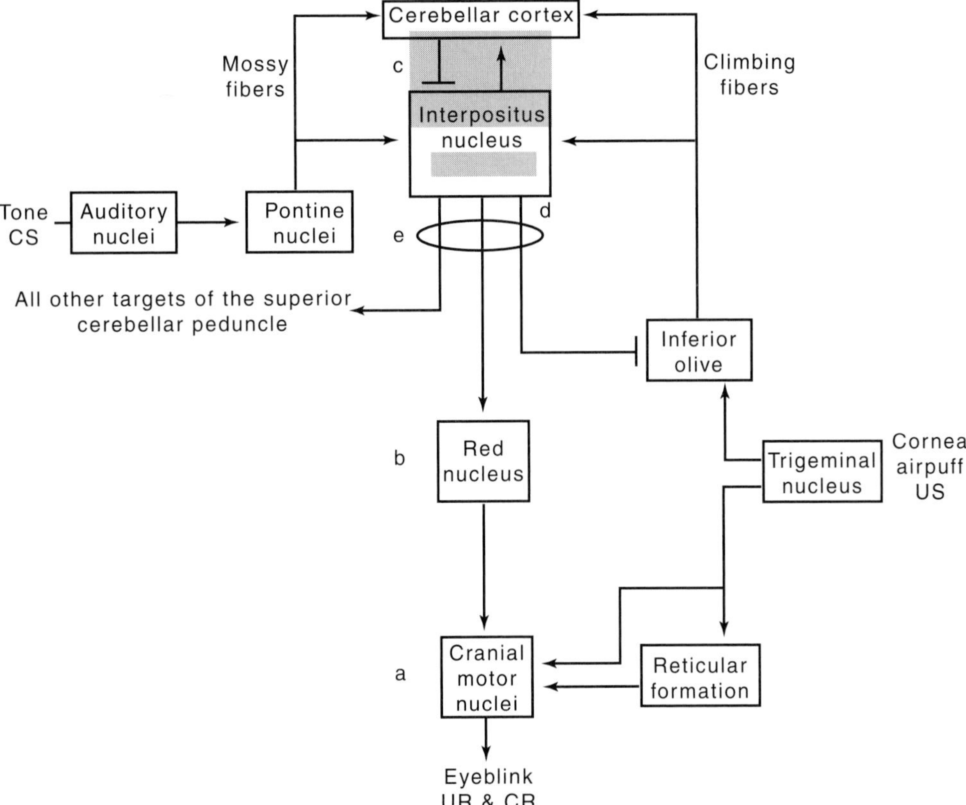

FIGURE 55.12 Simplified schematic of the essential brain circuitry involved in standard delay classical conditioning of discrete responses (e.g., eyeblink response). Shadowed boxes represent areas that have been reversibly inactivated during training. (a) Inactivation of motor nuclei including facial (7th) and accessory 6th. (b) Inactivation of magnocellular red nucleus. (c) Inactivation of dorsal aspect of the anterior interpositus and overlying cerebellar cortex. (d) Inactivation of ventral anterior interpositus nucleus and associated white matter. (e) Complete inactivation of the superior cerebellar peduncle (scp), essentially all output from the cerebellar hemisphere. Inactivation of each of these regions in trained rabbits abolishes performance of the CR. Significantly, inactivation of the motor nuclei (a), the red nucleus (b), the superior cerebellar peduncle (e), and the output of the interpositus nucleus (d) *during training* do not prevent learning at all, but inactivation of a localized region of the anterior interpositus nucleus and overlying cortex (c) during training completely prevents learning. From Thompson and Krupa.[89]

blink CR.[85] Mechanisms of LTP are discussed at length in the following section.

The Cerebellar System and Classical Conditioning of Discrete Responses

Since publication of the classic papers of Marr[86] and Albus,[87] the cerebellum has been favored as a structure for modeling neuronal learning. Figure 55.12 is a highly simplified diagram of a current qualitative working model of the role of the cerebellum in basic classical (delay) conditioning of eyeblink and other discrete responses.[88,89] Laterality is not addressed in Fig. 55.12; the critical region of the cerebellum is ipsilateral to the trained eye (or limb), whereas the critical regions of the pontine nuclei, red nucleus, and inferior olive are contralateral (see Fig. 55.15 for a more realistic representation). In this section, the data refer to the basic delay eyeblink CR, unless otherwise noted.[89–91]

In brief, the reflex eyeblink response pathways activated by corneal airpuff (or periorbital shock) include the trigeminal nucleus, direct projections to the relevant motor nuclei (mostly the seventh and accessory sixth), and indirect projections to the motor nuclei via the brainstem reticular formation (Fig. 55.12). Analysis of response latencies rules out any direct role of the cerebellum in the reflex response. The tone (and light) CS pathways project to the cerebellum as mossy fibers, mostly relaying through the pontine nuclei. The mossy fibers, in turn, activate granule cells and these granule cells project to Purkinje cells via parallel fibers. The US pathway projects from the trigeminal nucleus to the inferior olive and from there to the cerebellum as

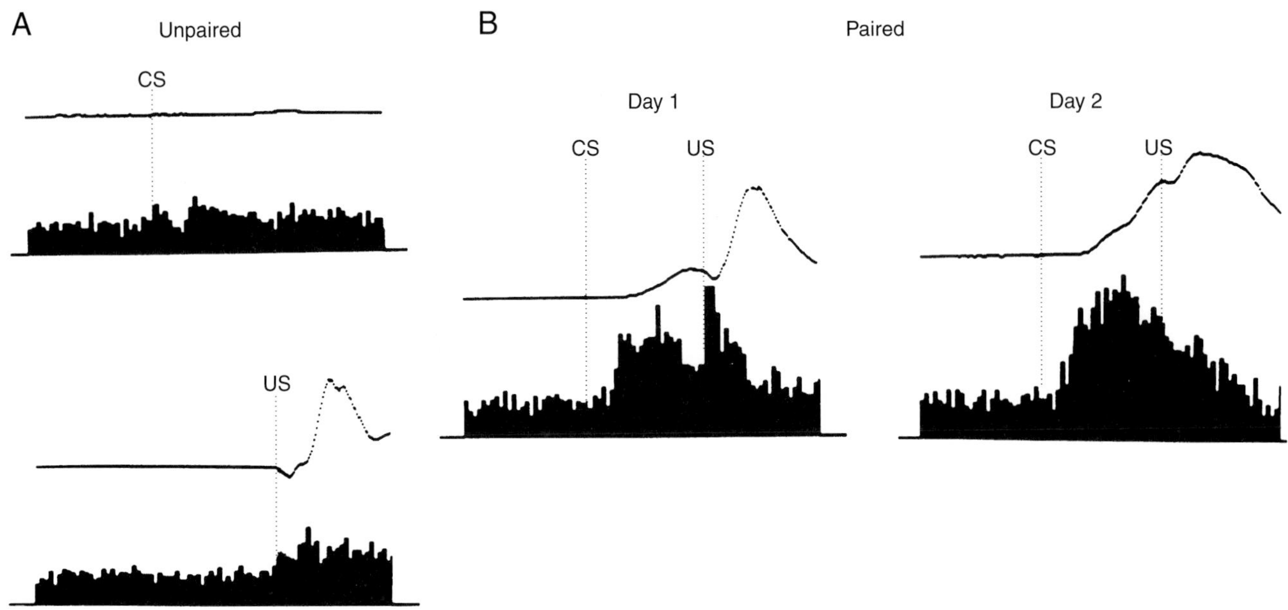

FIGURE 55.13 Engagement of neurons in the cerebellar interpositus nucleus in eyeblink conditioning. Histograms of a unit cluster recording from the anterior interpositus nucleus over the course of training are shown. The eyeblink response (here nictitating membrane extension) is shown on the tracing above each histogram. (A) Results of a day of unpaired CS and US presentations. There is some activity to the US. However, when paired training (B) is given (days 1 and 2), as behavioral learning develops (eyelid closure prior to US onset) there is a massive increase in neuronal discharges in the CS period that precedes and correlates with performance of the conditioned eyeblink response. Total trace duration 750 ms, CS–US onset interval 250 ms. Each trace and histogram is the average or cumulation of 1 day of training (120 trials). From McCormick and Thompson.[92]

climbing fibers. The CS-activated mossy fiber–parallel fiber pathway and the US-activated climbing fiber pathway converge and make synaptic connections on Purkinje neurons in the cerebellar cortex (parallel fiber–climbing fiber) and on neurons in the interpositus nucleus (mossy fiber–climbing fiber). The CR pathway projects from the interpositus nucleus of the cerebellum via the superior cerebellar peduncle to the red nucleus, and from there to the premotor and motor nuclei (mostly seventh and accessory sixth) controlling the eyeblink response.

This circuitry has been identified using a number of methods, including lesion studies, electrophysiological recordings, electrical microstimulation, and anatomical characterization of projection pathways. For example, in animals, neurons in the cerebellar cortex and interpositus nucleus respond to the CS and US before training and develop amplitude–time-course models (e.g. Fig. 55.13) of the learned behavioral response. These models precede and predict the occurrence and form of the CR within trials and over the trials of training (see Fig. 55.13).[92] By inference from PET analysis the same process occurs in humans (see Fig. 55.14).[93] In animals, appropriate lesions of the anterior interpositus nucleus completely and permanently prevent learning. Similar lesions inflicted after training permanently abolish the CR but are without effect on the UR.[92,94,95] In the same way, in humans, cerebellar lesions can completely prevent learning of the CR, but are again without effect on the UR.[96] Interestingly, when the interpositus lesion (in rabbits) is incomplete, resulting in a marked impairment in the CR but not complete abolition, the attenuated CR does not recover with further training.[97,98]

Appropriate lesions of the pontine nuclei (the CS pathway) can selectively abolish the CR to one modality of CS, and stimulation of the pontine nuclei serves as a supernormal CS yielding faster learning than peripheral CSs.[99,100] Finally, lesions of the appropriate region of the inferior olive completely prevent learning if they are made before training. Lesions made after training, at the same location, result in extinction and abolition of the CR.[101–103] Electrical microstimulation of this same region elicits discrete movements, and the exact movements so elicited can be trained to occur to any neutral stimulus.[104] The inferior olive–climbing fiber system, incidentally, is the only system in the brain other than reflex afferents where this occurs.[105]

These results constitute a verification of the theories developed initially in the classic papers of Marr[86] and

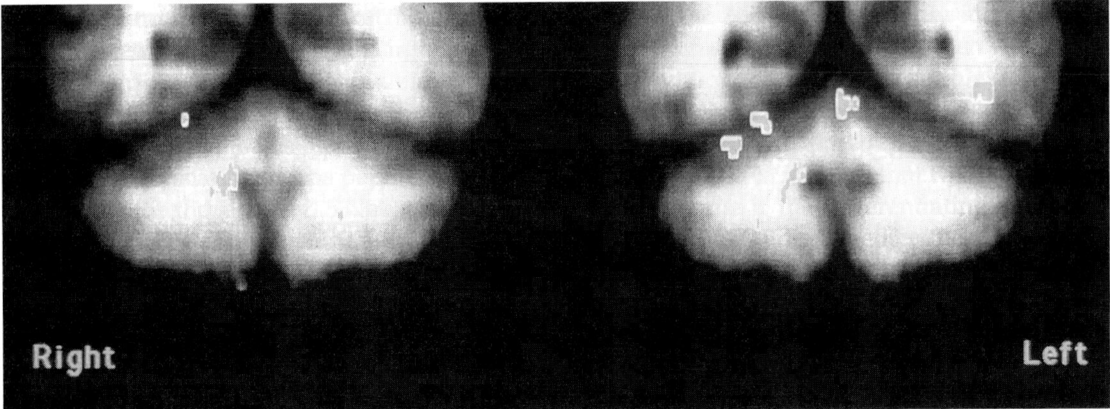

FIGURE 55.14 Functional localization of brain cerebellar activity (PET scan) in human eyeblink conditioning. Regions showing bright yellow are the regions where activation correlated significantly with degree of learning. The cerebellar anterior interpositus nucleus and several regions of cerebellar cortex show highly significant increases in activation with learning. From Logan and Grafton.[93]

Albus[87] and elaborated by Eccles,[106] Ito,[107] and Thach *et al.*[108] These theories proposed that the cerebellum was a neuronal learning system in which there was a convergence of mossy-parallel fibers that conveyed information about stimuli and movement contexts (CSs here) and the climbing fibers that conveyed information about specific movement errors and aversive events (USs here). This convergence might occur on Purkinje neurons in the cerebellar cortex to alter the synaptic efficacy of the parallel fiber synapses on Purkinje dendrites. There is a similar convergence of mossy and climbing fibers on neurons in the interpositus nucleus (see Figs. 55.12 and 55.15).

The Cerebellum: The Locus of the Long-Term Memory Trace

Overall, the results described to this point demonstrate that the cerebellum is necessary for learning, retention, and expression of classical conditioning of the eyeblink and other discrete responses. The next and more critical issue concerns the locus of the memory traces. We will next consider evidence that points to the cerebellum as the location where long-term memory traces for this type of learning are formed and stored.

Reversible inactivation has proved to be a powerful tool to localize sites of memory storage in systems where the essential circuitry is known, as in eyeblink conditioning (Figs. 55.12 and 55.15). In brief, if inactivation of a structure abolishes the learned response, the structure is considered to be part of the circuitry necessary for expression of the learned response. If the structure is inactivated during training and the animal immediately shows complete learning when the inactivation is subsequently removed, then the structure is not involved in acquiring the learned response but lies on the efferent path from the memory trace. However, if the animal shows no evidence of having learned following inactivation training, then either the memory trace is normally located in the structure or the structure is a necessary afferent to the trace. Reversible inactivation can be produced by local cooling using a cold probe or by infusion of a drug. A variety of drugs can produce reversible inactivation, including muscimol, a GABA agonist that inactivates only neuron somas and not axons, and TTX, a sodium channel blocker that blocks both neuron somas and axons (see Chapter 6).

Several parts of the circuit shown in Fig. 55.12 have been reversibly inactivated during training in naive animals.[64,89,90,109–111] In brief, inactivation of the motor nuclei (Fig. 55.12a), red nucleus (Fig. 55.12b), superior cerebellar peduncle (Figs. 58.12d and 58.12e), and a localized region of the anterior interpositus nucleus and overlying cerebellar cortex (Fig. 55.12c) each prevent expression of the CR (only motor nuclei inactivation also prevents expression of the UR). After training carried over during reversible inactivation of motor nuclei, the red nucleus, or the superior cerebellar peduncle, the CR is found to be fully learned as soon as the inactivation has ceased (Figs. 55.12a, 55.12b, 55.12d, and 55.12e). However, localized cerebellar inactivation (Fig. 55.12c) completely prevents learning; animals must learn from scratch as if completely untrained. These results argue strongly for cerebellar localization of the memory trace. This hypothesis is supported by the observation that inhibition of protein synthesis in the cerebellar interpositus nucleus appears to prevent long-term retention of the conditioned eyeblink response.[112]

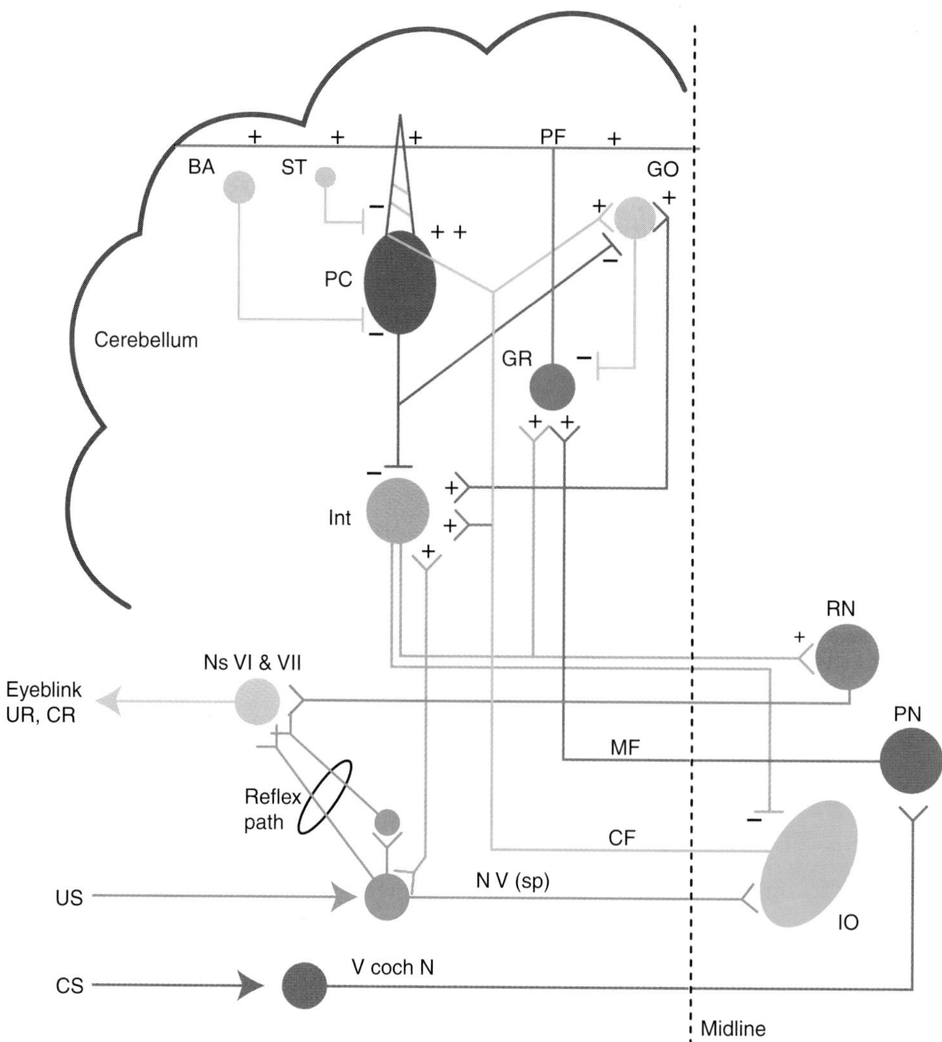

FIGURE 55.15 The commonly accepted eyeblink conditioning circuit based on experimental findings and anatomy of the cerebellum and the brainstem. The conditioned stimulus (CS) pathway consists of excitatory (+) mossy-fiber (MF) projections primarily from the pontine nuclei (PN) to the interpositus nucleus (Int) and to the cerebellar cortex. In the cortex, the mossy fibers form synapses with granule cells (GR), which in turn send excitatory parallel fibers to the Purkinje cells (PC). Purkinje cells are the exclusive output neurons from the cortex and they send inhibitory (−) fibers to deep nuclei such as the interpositus. The unconditioned stimulus (US) pathway consists of excitatory climbing fiber (CF) projections from the inferior olive to the interpositus nucleus and to the Purkinje cells in the cerebellar cortex. Within the cerebellar cortex, Golgi (GO), stellate (ST), and basket (BA) cells exert inhibitory actions on their respective target neurons. The efferent conditioned response (CR) pathway projects from the interpositus nucleus to the red nucleus (RN) and via the descending rubral pathway to act ultimately on the motor neurons generating the eyeblink response. V Coch N, ventral cochlear nucleus; N V (sp), spinal fifth cranial nucleus; N VI, sixth and accessory sixth cranial nuclei; N VII, seventh cranial nucleus; UR, unconditioned response. Note that the reflex pathways do not involve the cerebellar circuitry. From Kim and Thompson.[108a]

Experimentally, it has proved extremely difficult to determine the relative roles of the cerebellar cortex and interpositus nucleus in eyeblink conditioning using the lesion method.[113,114] These difficulties were overcome by making use of the mutant Purkinje cell degeneration (*pcd*) mouse strain.[115] In this mutant, Purkinje neurons (and all other neurons studied) are normal throughout pre- and perinatal development. At about 2–4 weeks after birth, the Purkinje neurons in the cerebellar cortex degenerate and disappear. For about 2 months after this time, other neuronal structures appear relatively normal. Thus, during this period of young adulthood, the animals have a complete, selective functional decortication of the cerebellum.[116]

The *pcd* mice learned very slowly, very poorly, and to a much lower level than wild-type controls and showed extinction with subsequent training to the CS alone. Thus, the cerebellar cortex plays a critically important role in normal learning (of discrete behavioral response), but some degree of learning is possible without the cerebellar cortex.

Putative Mechanisms of Memory Storage in the Cerebellum

Classic theories of the cerebellum as a learning machine (see earlier) proposed that conjoint activation of Purkinje neurons by parallel fibers and climbing fibers would lead to alterations in synaptic strength of the parallel fiber synapses. Ito[117] discovered that such conjoint activation leads to a long-lasting depression in the efficacy of parallel fiber synapses to Purkinje neuron dendrites. This process is known as cerebellar long-term depression. Ito and associates showed that such a process plays a key role in adaptation of the vestibulo-ocular reflex.[107,118–120]

In eyeblink conditioning, many of the Purkinje neurons that exhibit learning-related changes show decreases in simple spike responses in the CS period[74] that are consistent with LTD. The current view at the molecular level is that LTD is due to a persisting decrease in AMPA receptor function at parallel fiber synapses on Purkinje neuron dendrites.[119,121,122] This decrease in AMPA receptor function is, in turn, the result of glutamate activation of AMPA and metabotropic receptors on Purkinje neuron dendrites, together with increased intracellular calcium (normally by climbing fiber activation).

Classical conditioning studies using "gene knockout" mice have strengthened the argument that LTD is a key mechanism of memory storage in the cerebellar cortex.[123] Thus, mice that lack metabotropic glutamate receptors (mGluR1) critical for LTD show marked impairments in cerebellar cortical LTD as expected, but also in eyeblink conditioning.[124] They also show generalized motor impairments, that is, some degree of ataxia, as do the *pcd* mice mentioned previously.

Current studies present evidence supporting the view that LTD is more important for learning (e.g., eyeblink conditioning) than for motor coordination. Thus, the PKCγ knockout mutant mouse maintains to adulthood the perinatal condition of more than one climbing fiber per Purkinje neuron (wild-type adults have only one climbing fiber per Purkinje neuron). This mutant exhibits normal LTD but impaired motor coordination (due, primarily, to the multiple climbing fiber innervation of Purkinje neurons). In striking contrast, these animals learn the conditioned eyeblink response more rapidly than do wild-type controls.[125] This is consistent with the view that the climbing fiber system is the reinforcing or teaching pathway.

In striking contrast, a quite different mutant, the GFAP (glial fibrillary acidic protein) knockout mouse,[126] shows marked deficiency in cerebellar cortical LTD and in eyeblink conditioning. The performance of such mutants is very similar to that of *pcd* mice. Unlike the PKCγ mutants, these animals do not show any obvious impairments in motor coordination or general motor behavior. GFAP, which is expressed following neuronal injury is not present in neurons, only in glial cells. In the cerebellum it is normally present in substantial amounts in the Bergmann glia that surround the parallel fiber and the synapses between the climbing fibers and the Purkinje neuron dendrites. Although the Bergmann glia appear morphologically normal in GFAP knockout mice, they have no GFAP. The point here is that an abnormality limited to glial cells markedly impairs a form of synaptic plasticity (LTD) and a form of basic associative learning and memory, suggesting a key role for glia in processes of learning and memory.

We have focused on the essential role of the cerebellum in the classical conditioning of discrete behavioral responses, a basic form of associative learning and memory. To date, this is perhaps the clearest and most decisive example of evidence for the localization of a memory trace to a particular brain region in mammals (cerebellum). The cerebellum has also been pinpointed as the location where complex, multijoint movements are learned and stored[108] (see Chapter 35 on the cerebellum).

Actually, growing evidence suggests that the cerebellum is critically involved in many other forms of learning and memory, including cardiovascular conditioning,[127] discrete response instrumental avoidance learning,[128] maze learning,[129] spatial learning and memory,[130,131] and adaptive timing.[132] There is even a growing literature implicating the cerebellum in complex cognitive processes.[133]

The type of learning exemplified by the cerebellar circuitry underlying classical conditioning of discrete responses has been termed "supervised learning."[134] Information from one network of neurons acts as an instructive signal (a US) to influence the pattern of connectivity in another network (e.g., CS); other examples include adaptation of the VOR and calibration of the auditory space map in the barn owl (Chapter 22). In eyeblink conditioning, the neutral CSs (e.g., tone or light) influence the activity of neurons in the cerebellum only weakly and do not yield the behavioral response. As a result of training, the strong connections established between networks of neurons are not functionally coupled prior to learning. That is, diffuse cerebellar mossy and/or parallel fibers activated by the CS develop sufficient strength of their synaptic connections to successfully signal the specific circuit initially formed by the very localized climbing fiber projections to the cerebellum activated by the corneal airpuff US. In sum, weak and ineffective anatomical connections become powerful and effective through learning. Note, however, that the connections do exist before training. This may be a general principle in all aspects of learning and memory.

Fear Conditioning Is a Model System for Investigating the Neural Substrates of Emotional Memory

Significant progress has been made in identifying the neural substrates of emotional memory processing, and many of the advances have relied on studies using fear conditioning in animals as a model system.

Classical fear conditioning, also known as aversive classical conditioning or Pavlovian defensive conditioning, consists of repeated temporal pairings of an affectively neutral stimulus (CS) with an aversive event (US; see Fig. 55.16).[135] The US elicits a multitude of physiological and behavioral responses (URs), and over several conditioning trials, conditioned responses (CRs) develop in reaction to the CS itself. In a typical experiment, a rat is presented with a tone followed by a brief electric shock to the feet. After several tone–shock pairings, the tone acquires aversive properties and begins to elicit a set of responses (the CRs) characteristic of a state of fear: freezing; autonomic responses, such as changes in skin conductance, heart rate, blood pressure, or pupillary dilation; and endocrine responses, such as conditioned hormone release.[135–137] The CRs thus form a set of observable indices that can be used to gauge emotional learning and memory as the organism acquires the association between the CS and the US. This emotional stimulus learning becomes extinguished if the subject receives subsequent CS-alone presentations, as evidenced by a decrease in the number of CRs produced (Fig. 55.16).

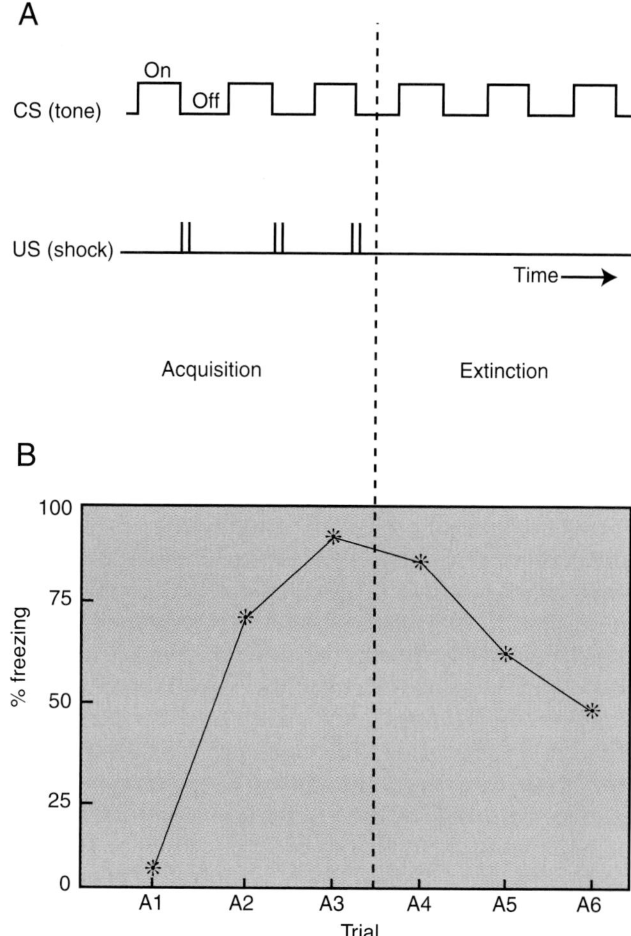

FIGURE 55.16 A hypothetical illustration of fear conditioning. (A) Typical parametric arrangement of stimuli during the acquisition and extinction phases of a simple delay conditioning task. CS, conditioned stimulus; US, unconditioned stimulus. (B) The corresponding acquisition and extinction learning curves as exemplified by conditioned freezing responses. The dependent measure is the percentage of time the animal spends freezing during the CS presentation. Hypothetical data from the first three trials of acquisition (A1–A3) and the first three trials of extinction (E1–E3) are shown. From LeDoux.[135]

Conditioned Fear Involves Specific Neural Circuits

The role of the amygdala Across various paradigms, species, and response measures, the amygdala has consistently emerged as a brain structure essential to the acquisition and expression of conditioned fear.[135–138] Pretraining lesions of the amygdala prevent the development of a CR, whereas posttraining lesions of the amygdala disrupt the expression of a CR that has already been learned, even after extensive overtraining. Single and multiple unit recordings from neurons in the central nucleus of the amygdala reveal changes in neural activity that parallel the emergence of a CR, and responses similar to CRs can be elicited by electrical stimulation of the amygdala.

Anatomical connections of the amygdala In combination with lesion data, neuroanatomical tract-tracing studies have begun to elucidate the afferent and efferent connections of the amygdala to sensory and motor areas involved in transmitting information about the CS and US and generating emotional responses. Most of the work on CS pathways has involved auditory stimuli, although visual CS pathways

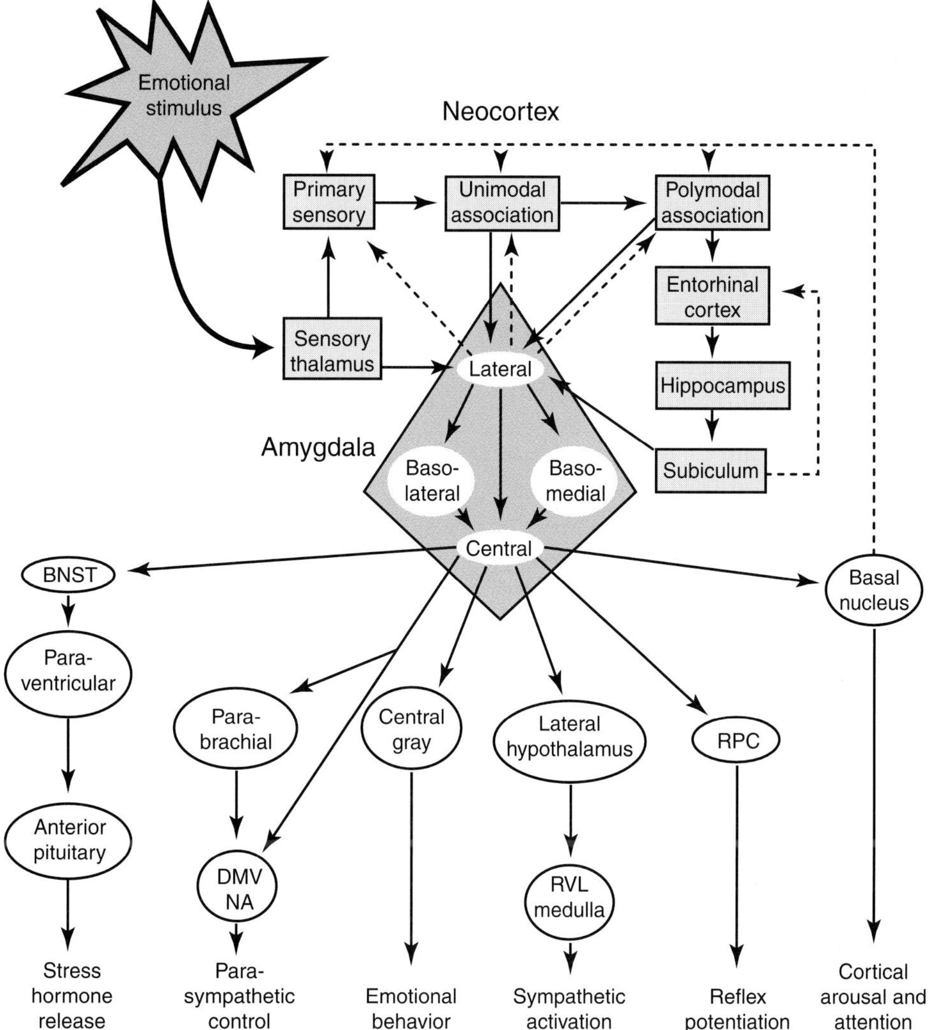

FIGURE 55.17 A model of the neural circuit involved in conditioned fear. A hierarchy of incoming sensory information converges on the lateral nucleus of the amygdala. Through intra-amygdala circuitry, the output of the lateral nucleus is transmitted to the central nucleus, which serves to activate various effector systems involved in the expression of emotional responses. Feedforward projections are indicated by solid lines, and feedback projections are indicated by dashed lines. BNST, bed nucleus of the stria terminalis; DMV, dorsal motor nucleus of the vagus; NA, nucleus ambiguus; RPC, nucleus reticularis pontis caudalis; RVL Medulla, rostral ventrolateral nuclei of the medulla. From LeDoux.[135]

have also been described. Information regarding an auditory CS reaches the amygdala by way of two neural routes: a direct thalamo–amygdala pathway from the auditory thalamus (medial portion of the medial geniculate nucleus and posterior intralaminar nucleus) to the lateral nucleus of the amygdala and an indirect thalamo–cortico–amygdala pathway linking the auditory thalamus with the lateral nucleus of the amygdala by way of connections within the auditory cortex (Fig. 55.17). The direct thalamo–amygdala pathway is more rapid but provides a cruder representation of the incoming sensory stimulus than the indirect thalamo–cortico–amygdala pathway. The direct pathway is thought to function in two ways: first, as a quick route for simple stimulus features to evoke defensive emotional responses; and second, as a method of priming the amygdala to set up appropriate emotional responses to incoming stimuli that are more highly processed by the indirect pathway. Lesion studies have shown that either of these routes in isolation is sufficient to mediate responding in simple conditioning protocols involving one CS. However, the indirect pathway via the cortex appears to be critical for performance on discrimination tasks involving two CSs, where one CS is paired with the US and the other is not. On these tasks, more complex analysis of the incoming acoustic signal by the auditory cortex is required for appropriate responding.

Both of the incoming CS pathways converge in the lateral nucleus of the amygdala, which functions as an interface relaying sensory information to this structure. Although the nature of afferent US pathways has not been fully determined, cells in the lateral nucleus that receive incoming acoustic CS information also respond to somatosensory signals elicited by footshock. Furthermore, stimulation of part of the acoustic thalamus (the posterior intralaminar nucleus), which projects to the lateral nucleus of the amygdala, can serve as an effective US in fear conditioning. Thus, the locus of CS–US convergence may reside in the lateral nucleus of the amygdala, although the acoustic thalamus itself may play a crucial role, at least for auditory fear conditioning.

Incoming sensory information to the lateral nucleus is then projected by intra-amygdala circuitry to the central nucleus, which mediates emotional responses through efferent connections with motor and autonomic centers (Fig. 55.17). Interestingly, lesions of the target structures or transection of fibers projecting to these target areas selectively disrupts CRs expressed in specific response modalities, leaving other CR measures intact. For example, lesions of the central gray region disrupt a freezing CR, but a conditioned increase in blood pressure remains evident. Lesions of the lateral hypothalamus have a complementary effect: conditioned freezing behavior is spared, while blood pressure CRs are impaired. These results, along with others, show the contrasting but ubiquitous effects of amygdala lesions across response modalities. Therefore, along the neural routes involved in fear conditioning, the amygdala appears to function as the key weigh station where emotional significance is assessed independent of stimulus and response measurement.

Contributions of other brain structures Whereas the roles of the amygdala and its projections are well established as being critical for the regulation of conditioned fear associations, the contributions of other brain regions are only now receiving increased attention. Lesions of the hippocampus interfere with contextual fear conditioning[139] and higher-order conditioning processes, such as blocking and latent inhibition. In these situations, the hippocampus may be exerting its influence through its anatomical interactions with the amygdala. Hippocampal lesions, however, have no effect on emotional responses generated to an explicit CS in simple conditioning. These findings are consistent with current theories regarding hippocampal involvement in complex stimulus processing.

Evidence shows that lesions of the medial prefrontal cortex in rats selectively interfere with the extinction of conditioned fear responses.[140] If extended to human populations, this finding is potentially important for clinical applications in which the suppression of acquired fear responses is impaired. Other brain areas appear to selectively influence the acquisition of some CRs but not others. For example, lesions of the cerebellar vermis attenuate acquisition of conditioned bradycardia, but the cerebellum does not appear to have an effect on fear-potentiated startle. This contrasts with the essential role of cerebellar structures in eyeblink conditioning.

Mechanisms of Fear Conditioning

One way to observe changes in CS processing at the cellular level is through changes in the receptive field properties of neurons encoding sensory information. Electrophysiological recordings of single neurons in the medial division of the medial geniculate nucleus of the thalamus, in the auditory cortex, and in the lateral amygdala show receptive field plasticity during fear conditioning, that is, changes in the properties of neurons in the receptive field[141] (see Fig. 55.18).[142] Because the cells in the medial division of the medial geniculate are very broadly tuned, it is unlikely that the changes observed in the auditory cortex and lateral amygdala are simply consequences of the thalamic source—rather, there appears to be active neural tuning at each of these stations. Moreover, the plasticity seen in different regions may reflect different adaptive functions: plasticity in the medial geniculate may allow very rapid evaluation of changes in CS significance; plasticity in the auditory cortex may provide more detailed fine-tuning in the auditory frequency domain; and plasticity in the lateral amygdala may serve as a substrate for central CS–US associative learning. This evidence for receptive field plasticity during fear conditioning is another example of experience-dependent changes observed in sensory areas of the adult brain during learning and memory tasks.

Human Fear and Anxiety

The role of the amygdala Fear conditioning has been readily demonstrated in human subjects, and many experimental preparations for measuring fear in animals can be adapted for use with human populations.[143,144] Fear conditioning in brain-damaged human subjects, however, has not been well studied, although patients with amygdala damage show deficits on fear-conditioning tasks. Selective amygdala damage in humans also leads to deficits in the recognition of facial expressions of fear.[145] Furthermore, in epileptic patients

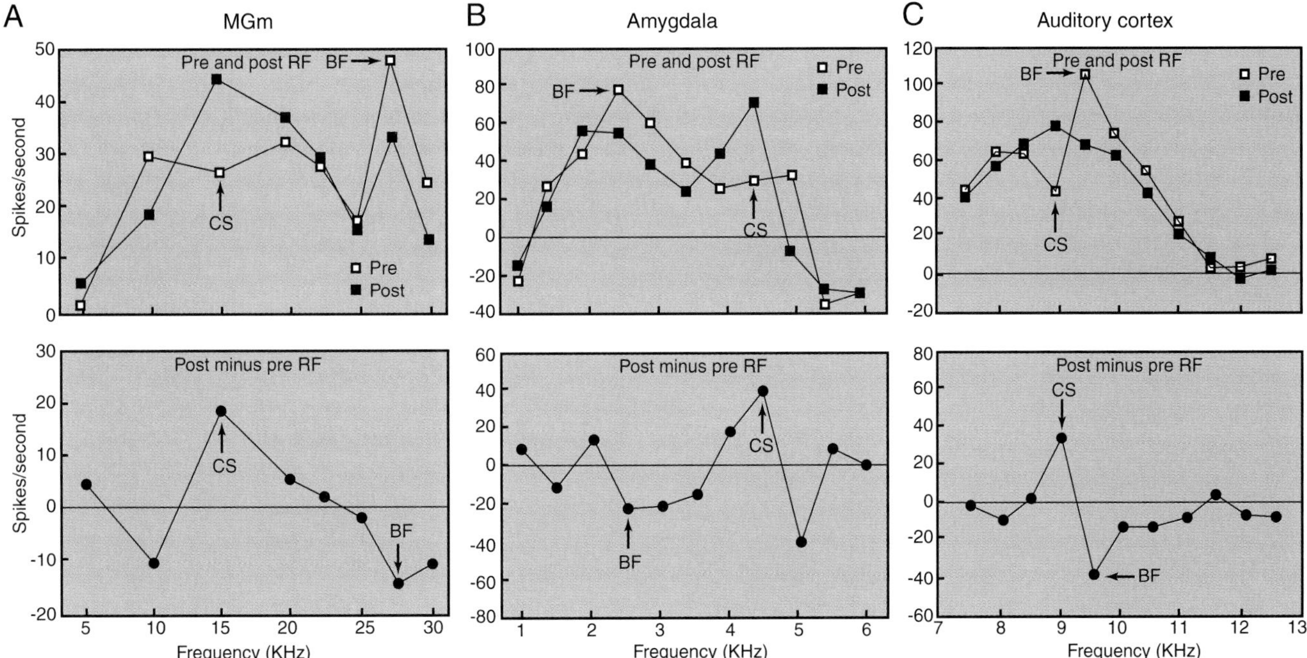

FIGURE 55.18 Conditioned fear-induced changes in receptive field (RF) properties of single neurons in the medial division of the medial geniculate nucleus (MGm), amygdala, and auditory cortex. The auditory receptive field of each neuron was determined prior to conditioning (Pre RF), and the neuron's best frequency (BF) was identified. In each case illustrated here, after conditioning (Post RF), the frequency tuning of the neuron shifted to the CS frequency. The bottom half of each figure depicts the post–pre RF difference plots, showing the relative decrease in firing to the pretraining BF and the relative increase in firing to the CS frequency after conditioning. Adapted from Armony *et al.*[142]

undergoing surgical treatment, electrical stimulation of the amygdala typically evokes feelings of fear and anxiety. Thus, in humans as well as other species, the amygdala appears to be centrally involved in regulating mechanisms of fear.

Human anxiety disorders The marked similarities in the clinical symptomatology of anxiety in humans and measures of conditioned fear in animals[137] have led researchers to propose using fear conditioning as a model for studying human anxiety disorders, such as posttraumatic stress disorder, phobia, and panic. One clinical marker for posttraumatic stress disorder is an increase in startle. Conditioning studies have shown enhanced startle responses in this population in comparison to controls.

In addition, fear conditioning using phobic stimuli generally shows greater resistance to extinction than fear conditioning using nonphobic stimuli, although some acquisition effects have also been reported.[146] Behavioral therapies based on classical conditioning procedures have been relatively successful in the treatment of patients with phobic disorders. These therapies have evolved to incorporate contemporary theories of conditioning, instrumental learning, and cognition.

Summary

Fear conditioning has become extremely useful as a model for understanding the neural basis of emotional learning and memory. Significant progress has been made in revealing the anatomical structures involved in fear conditioning, and studies have demonstrated a critical role for the amygdala in the acquisition and expression of conditioned fear. Other structures, such as the medial prefrontal cortex and the hippocampus, appear to contribute to other aspects of emotional memory, such as learning more intricate emotional associations among stimuli and extinction. Physiological research has revealed corresponding cellular plasticity in the sensory cortex, thalamus, and amygdala during the acquisition of fear conditioning. The neural structures regulating conditioned fear associations may also play a role in other forms of emotional learning, such as instrumental *learning of reward.* Furthermore, research on fear conditioning in animals has been extended to study anxiety in human populations, in which conditioning may provide a useful model for developing and testing behavioral and pharmacological therapies for fear-related affective disorders.

LONG-TERM POTENTIATION

Since the early 1970s we have witnessed stunning progress in understanding how the nervous system encodes and retrieves information. At the cellular level, the usual assumption is that the encoding process entails activity-dependent changes in the strength of synaptic connections among neurons. An extensively studied candidate mechanism is the synaptic phenomenon called long-term potentiation, a persistent increase in synaptic strength (as measured by the amplitude of the EPSP) that can be rapidly induced by brief neural activity.

The intense current experimental interest in LTP is driven by the working hypothesis that this form of synaptic plasticity may participate in the information encoding and/or retrieval process in several brain regions. In this section, we will describe the properties of LTP and how it is studied, review its underlying mechanisms, and conclude with remarks about linkages between LTP and behavior.

Long-Term Potentiation Occurs in a Variety of Neural Synapses

Since the start of the 20th century, scientists from numerous disciplines have hypothesized that learning and memory could be encoded via activity-dependent changes in the strength of the synaptic connections between neurons; yet the evidence that mammalian synapses could undergo an appropriate type of modification began to appear only in the last quarter of the century. The first interesting data appeared in 1973, when Timothy Bliss and Terje Lomo demonstrated LTP in the anesthetized rabbit. In this classic paper, Bliss and Lomo[147] reported that brief, high-frequency stimulation of the perforant-pathway input to the dentate gyrus produced a long-lasting enhancement of the extracellularly recorded field potential. Studies of nonanesthetized animals showed that LTP can last for weeks or months.

Since this discovery, countless LTP studies have been done in numerous laboratories throughout the world. These subsequent studies have been done *in vivo* and *in vitro* on many different synapses and using a variety of recording methods. Originally thought to be unique to the mammalian hippocampal formation, LTP is now known to occur in the mammalian peripheral nervous system, the arthropod neuromuscular junction and other invertebrate synapses, neocortical regions of mammals, and subcortical mammalian nuclei, such as the amygdala.

Brain Slices Are the Preferred Substrate for *in Vitro* Studies of Long-Term Potentiation

During the 1980s, a general appreciation of the numerous experimental advantages of brain slices for studies of synaptic physiology developed.[148] Partly for this reason, most of the research that has been done on LTP thus far has used acute brain slices that remain viable for several hours. The hippocampal brain slice proved to be particularly useful in this respect because much of the intrinsic circuitry, along with the major cell classes, remains intact in a transverse slice. A schematic illustration of a rat hippocampal slice preparation is shown in Fig. 55.19.[149] It is convenient to use as many as two or three stimulating electrodes plus one or two recording electrodes.[150]

Within the hippocampus proper, by far the most commonly studied synapse is the Schaffer collateral/commissural (Sch/com) input to pyramidal neurons of the CA1 region (Fig. 55.19). In fact, *this is probably the most commonly studied synapse in the mammalian brain.* Part of this interest is because the circuitry is relatively simple and its laminar organization makes it possible to extract useful data from extracellular recordings, which are easier to perform than intracellular recordings and preferable for some purposes. A much smaller number of laboratories have also been interested in the mossy-fiber input from the granule cells of the dentate gyrus to the pyramidal neurons of the CA3 region (Fig. 55.19).

The first study of LTP done under voltage-clamp conditions used microelectrodes in concert with a "switch clamp" to study the mossy-fiber synaptic input to CA3 in transverse rat hippocampal slices.[151] More recent work on LTP in these synapses used "whole-cell recordings," with noise levels sufficiently low that unitary synaptic currents can be analyzed.[152]

Examples of unitary mossy-fiber excitatory postsynaptic currents (EPSCs) recorded in rat brain slices before and after LTP induction are illustrated in Fig. 55.20. The upper waveforms are superimposed EPSCs before (Fig. 55.20A) and after (Fig. 55.20B) LTP induction, and the corresponding lower waveforms are their averages. LTP is indicated by the fact that the average responses to both the first and the second pair of stimulations were greater after LTP induction (Fig. 55.20B, bottom traces) than before (Fig. 55.20A, bottom traces). LTP was induced by stimulating the mossy-fiber syn-

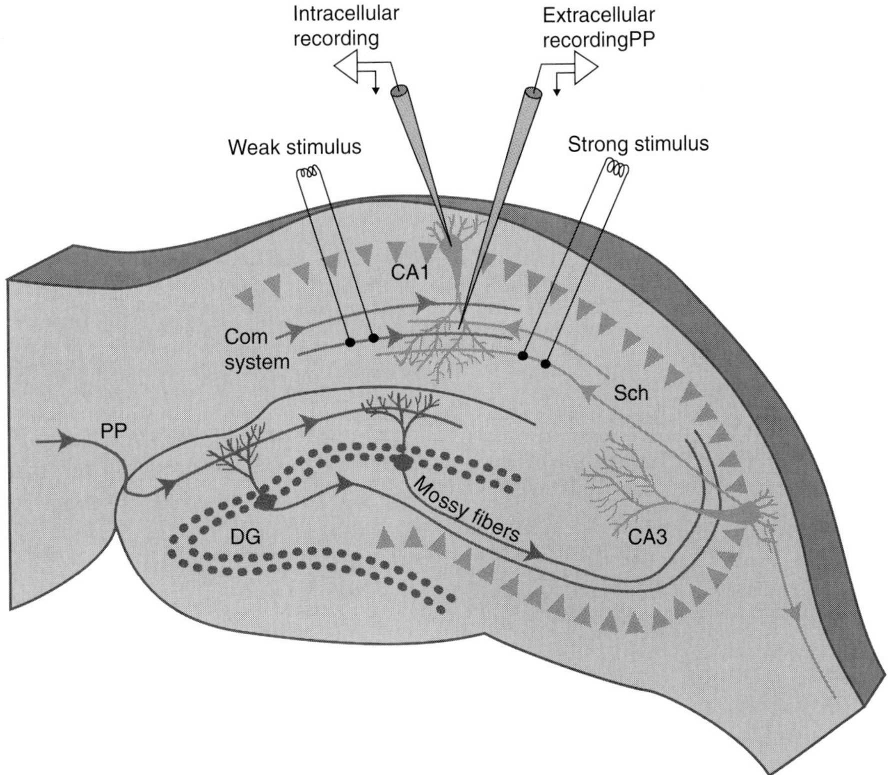

FIGURE 55.19 Schematic of a transverse hippocampal brain slice preparation from the rat. Two extracellular stimulating electrodes are used to activate two nonoverlapping inputs to pyramidal neurons of the CA1 region of the hippocampus. Both inputs consisted of axons of the Schaffer collateral / commissural (Sch / com) system. By suitably adjusting the current intensity delivered to the stimulating electrodes, different numbers of Sch / com axons can be activated. In this way, one stimulating electrode was made to produce a weak postsynaptic response and the other to produce a strong postsynaptic response. Sometimes three or more stimulating electrodes are used. Also illustrated is an extracellular recording electrode placed in the stratum radiatum (the projection zone of the Sch / com inputs) and an intracellular recording electrode in the stratum pyramidal (the cell body layer). Also indicated is the mossy-fiber projection from the granule cells of the dentate gyrus (DG) to the pyramidal neurons of the CA3 region. Adapted from Barrionuevo and Brown.[149]

apses with a short train of stimuli (5–10) at 100 Hz. In rat brain slices, mossy-fiber LTP can last for an hour or more, showing little if any decrement. Because brain slices have a limited life span, to study the full time course of hippocampal LTP typically requires *in vivo* studies. Of course, one gives up some degree of experimental control in such studies, and the measurements are typically limited to extracellular field-potential recordings.

The "Classical Properties" of Long-Term Potentiation Include Cooperativity, Associativity, and Input Specificity

Certain synapses of the hippocampal formation can exhibit a form of LTP characterized by properties that have been variously termed "cooperativity," "associativity," "input specificity," and "spatiotemporal specificity."[153,154] As we shall see, these "classical properties" are not orthogonal but rather are different manifestations of the same underlying mechanism that is responsible for one type of LTP. This form of LTP is most commonly studied in the Sch / com synaptic input to pyramidal neurons of hippocampal region CA1. Other types of LTP, which are less commonly studied, have different signatures.

Cooperativity refers to the fact that the probability of inducing LTP, or the magnitude of the resulting change, increases with the number of stimulated afferents. The latter can be varied by changing the intensity of extracellular stimulation. Smaller or briefer currents (weak stimulation) activate fewer afferents than larger or longer currents (strong stimulation). The finding was that weak high-frequency stimulation often did

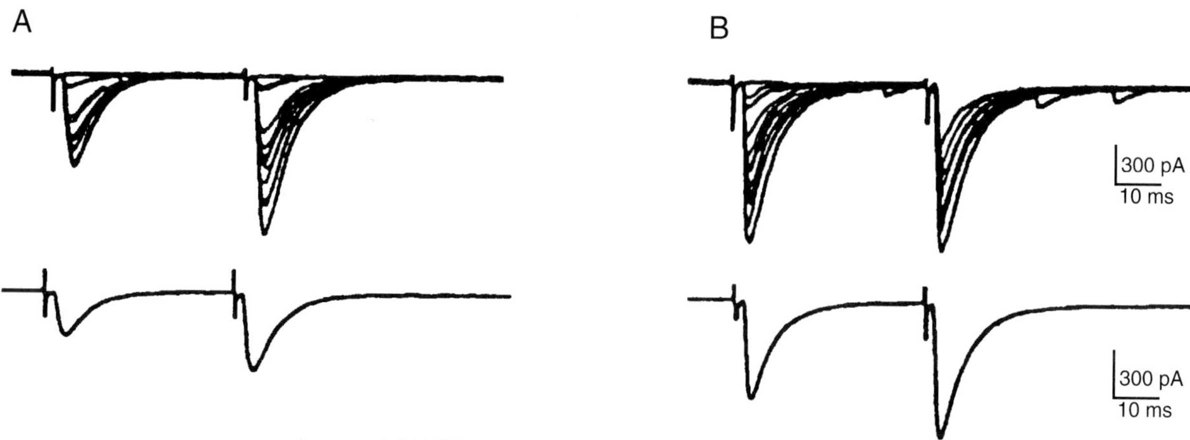

FIGURE 55.20 LTP in the mossy-fiber synapses of the rat hippocampus. Whole-cell recordings were from a CA3 pyramidal cell in which the soma was maintained under voltage clamp at −80 mV during minimal stimulation of dentate gyrus (see Fig. 55.19). Both before and after LTP induction, the synapses were tested using a "paired-pulse" paradigm to reveal "paired-pulse facilitation" (PPF). (A) Upper traces are 15 superimposed records of mossy-fiber EPSCs before LTP induction; lower trace is their average. Note that the amplitude of the response increases in the second of the paired stimulations, demonstrating PPF. (B) Upper traces are 15 superimposed records of EPSCs after LTP induction; lower trace is their average (same cell and conditions). Note that LTP induction increased the average EPSC amplitude in response to both the first and second pulses. Adapted from Xiang *et al.*[152]

not induce LTP, whereas strong stimulation at the same frequency and for the same duration produced LTP more reliably.[155] This finding was termed cooperativity because it was thought that more axons were recruited with higher stimulation intensities, thus "cooperating" to trigger LTP.

Associativity was shown in preparations in which two distinct axonal inputs converged onto the same postsynaptic target. Levy and Steward[156] explored this *in vivo* using the perforant-pathway inputs to the dentate gyrus, and Barrionuevo and Brown[149] explored it *in vitro* using Sch/com inputs to hippocampal region CA1. The experiments were designed to examine interactions between weak (W, small number of stimulated afferents) and strong (S, large number of stimulated afferents) inputs (Fig. 55.19). Tetanic (high-frequency) stimulation of the W input by itself failed to produce LTP in that pathway unless this stimulation was paired with tetanic stimulation of the S input. Thus, LTP was induced in a W input only when its activity was associated with activity in the S input.

Input specificity means that LTP is restricted to only the inputs that received the tetanic stimulation.[157] The spatiotemporal specificity of associative LTP induction was examined in detail in the CA1 region by using two sets of W inputs (W1 and W2) activated by two separate stimulating electrodes.[150] Both W1 and W2 received the same tetanic stimulations, but only one of them was stimulated at the same time as the S input. Tetanic stimulation of the other input did not overlap temporally with tetanic stimulation of the S input. The finding was that LTP was induced only in the W input that was stimulated at the same time as the S input. The high degree of spatial specificity was emphasized by the fact that these W inputs were both Sch/com synapses that were anatomically intermingled on the apical dendrites of the CA1 pyramidal neurons. Temporal specificity was evident from the fact that LTP was not induced in the W input if its tetanic stimulation terminated a fraction of a second before the onset of the S stimulation.

A Hebbian Mechanism Explains the Classical Properties of Long-Term Potentiation in the Hippocampus

How can one explain these classical properties of LTP in the hippocampal formation? In the late 1940s, the Canadian psychologist Donald Hebb[4] advanced an idea regarding the *conditions* that cause synapses to change. His thinking proved to be influential and informed later experiments that probed the mechanisms behind LTP. According to Hebb's now-famous postulate:

> When an axon of cell A is near enough to excite cell B repeatedly or consistently takes place in firing it, some growth process or metabolic change takes place in one or both cells such that A's efficiency, as one of the cells firing B, is increased. (Hebb,[4] p.62)

In short, coincident activity in two, synaptically coupled neurons would cause increases in the synaptic strength between them. Hebb's postulate could be thought of as the synthesis of William James's "law of neural habit" and the synaptic hypothesis for memory.[153] There are numerous modern interpretations of Hebb's postulate, but most of them are captured by the mnemonic: "Cells that fire together, wire together."

Could the classical properties of LTP all be consequences of synapses that obey a Hebbian rule? This could be true if a critical amount of postsynaptic depolarization were a necessary condition for inducing LTP in active synapses. According to this possibility, cooperativity would result when enough input fibers were stimulated to produce the critical amount of postsynaptic depolarization; associativity would emerge from the fact that the strong input (S) caused sufficient depolarization of the postsynaptic membrane during the presynaptic activity in the weak input (W); and the spatiotemporal specificity would occur because LTP was induced only in those W inputs to a neuron that were active at the same time that the cell was sufficiently depolarized by the S input to that neuron. In other words, these classical phenomena could all be manifestations of a single underlying Hebbian mechanism. It was natural, therefore, to ask whether Sch/com synapses were in fact Hebbian.

An explicit effort to examine this possibility[158] yielded unequivocal results based on a simple rationale. If the synapses were Hebbian, then it should be possible to induce LTP under experimental conditions in which one substitutes for the usual S input direct depolarization of the postsynaptic neuron via the recording microelectrode (see Fig. 55.21). On the other hand, if the synapses were non-Hebbian, and the critical role of the S input were instead, for example, to release an "LTP factor," then pairing presynaptic stimulation of a W input with direct depolarization of the postsynaptic cell should fail to induce LTP.

Results of the first of a series of current- and voltage-clamp experiments, done to distinguish between these hypotheses, are shown in Fig. 55.21, which plots the mean amplitude of the excitatory postsynaptic potentials evoked in CA1 pyramidal neurons as a function of time and the various experimental manipulations. The EPSPs were tested every 12 s by delivering a single extracellular stimulation to the Sch/com afferent inputs (Fig. 55.19). After a stable EPSP baseline was established, the postsynaptic cell was depolarized alone (in the absence of presynaptic tetanic stimulation) to demonstrate that this manipulation by itself was without effect (Fig. 55.21, Depol. alone). Next, a tetanic stimulation (100 Hz) was given to the W input while the postsynaptic soma was maintained at −80 mV under voltage-clamp conditions (Fig. 55.21, 100 Hz + voltage clamp). As indicated, this was sometimes done twice, with the same results—no LTP induction. Then the same presynaptic tetanic stimulation was given while the postsynaptic cell was depolarized under current-clamp conditions (Fig. 55.21, 100 Hz + depol.). In agreement with the Hebbian hypothesis, this manipulation did in fact consistently result in LTP induction.

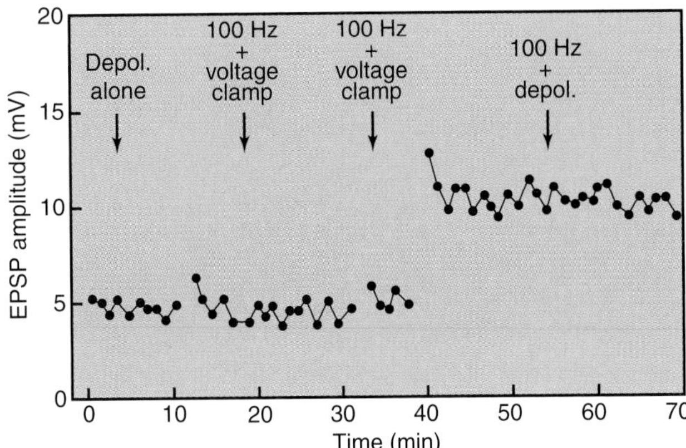

FIGURE 55.21 Demonstration of Hebbian synapses. Intracellular recordings were made from a pyramidal cell in area CA1 of the hippocampus, with stimulation applied to the Sch/com inputs. Excitatory postsynaptic potential (EPSP) amplitudes are plotted as a function of time of occurrence (arrows) of three manipulations—an outward current step alone (Depol. alone) or synaptic stimulation trains delivered while applying either a voltage clamp (100 Hz + voltage clamp) or an outward current step (100 Hz + depol.). Only presynaptic stimulation combined with postsynaptic depolarization resulted in lasting potentiation. Each point is the average of five consecutive EPSP amplitudes. Adapted from Kelso *et al.*[158]

From these studies it is clear that Hebb-type synapses do exist in the hippocampus, a noncontroversial result that has been replicated in many laboratories around the world. Hebbian synapses were later found to exist also in the neocortex, and even in *Aplysia*, suggesting that this mechanism may have developed early in evolution and been conserved across phyla. However, we hasten to point out that not all forms of LTP are Hebbian (see Fig. 55.22), which means that the classical properties are not universal.[159,160]

Mechanisms of Long-Term Potentiation Must Account for Induction, Expression, and Maintenance

Even though a tremendous amount of research has been devoted to LTP, it remains a challenge to explain how this process occurs physiologically. Partly for pedagogical reasons, it is convenient to divide the discussion into three parts: induction, expression, and maintenance of LTP. Induction refers to the initial events

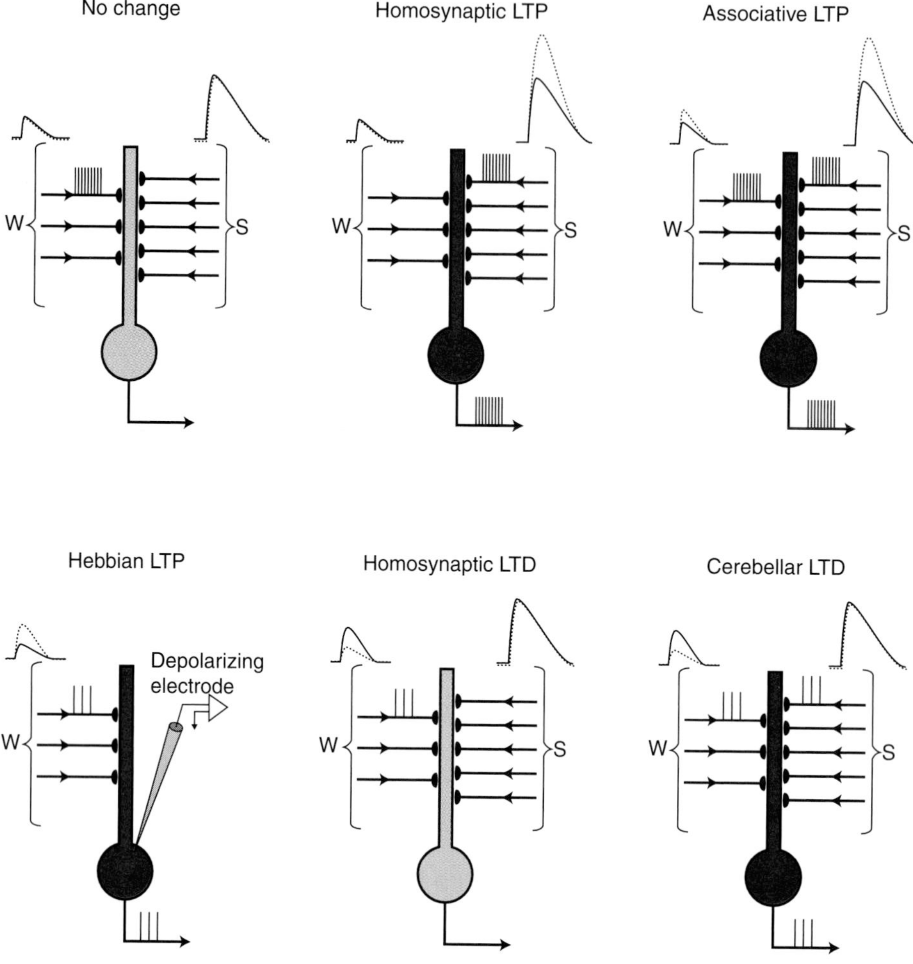

FIGURE 55.22 Varieties of synaptic activity-modification relationships. Schematic neurons are shown receiving nonoverlapping inputs that are either weak (W, few axons) or strong (S, many axons). Action potentials on axons are denoted by short vertical lines that are closely spaced (high frequency) or widely spaced (low frequency). Activity in synapses or cells is indicated by black shading. Postsynaptic potentials before inducing stimulation are given by solid lines; those after are given by dotted lines. No change is produced when a single weak input is stimulated at high frequency. Homosynaptic LTP is induced in the synapses of a strong input when it receives high-frequency stimulation, but the unstimulated synapses of the weak input are unchanged. Associative LTP occurs when a weak input (that would not potentiate if stimulated by itself) is stimulated concurrently with a strong input, resulting in potentiation of both inputs. Hebbian LTP occurs when a weak input (that would not potentiate if stimulated by itself) is stimulated at the same time depolarization is induced in the postsynaptic cell through injection of an intracellular current. Homosynaptic LTD is induced only in synapses receiving low-frequency (1–5 Hz) stimulation; unstimulated synapses are unchanged. Cerebellar LTD occurs when parallel fibers (represented here by the W input) are stimulated simultaneously with climbing fibers (represented here by the S input). Parallel fibers undergo LTD, but climbing fibers do not. Adapted from Brown *et al.*[153]

that trigger or initiate the modification process; expression concerns the proximal cause of the final synaptic enhancement; and maintenance addresses the manner in which the enhancement is made to endure over time.

LTP Induction

With regard to LTP induction, we shall see that there are probably multiple mechanisms or at least multiple pathways that can lead to persistent synaptic enhancement. Multiple pathways may also contribute to expression and maintenance.

Glutamate receptors To understand LTP induction we need to consider the neurotransmitter L-glutamic acid (glutamate) and the receptors that it activates. Most of the systems in which LTP has been studied use glutamate as the neurotransmitter, although there are notable exceptions. In very broad terms, glutamate receptors (GluRs) can be subdivided into two general categories: ionotropic receptors that form ion channels and metabotropic receptors (mGluRs) that are linked via a G protein to phospholipase C (PLC) activation and adenylate cyclase inhibition. The ionotropic receptors in turn can be divided further into two subpopulations: those that respond optimally to *N*-methyl-D-aspartate versus those that respond to kainic acid (KA) or α-amino-3-hydroxy-5-methyl-4-isoxazolepropionic acid (AMPA).

Here, we distinguish between the NMDA receptor (NMDAR) and the AMPA receptor (AMPAR), and we use these terms to refer to both the ligand-binding sites and the ion-conducting channel. In interpreting some of the studies of LTP induction, it is a good idea to bear in mind that within the broad classification of GluRs there are further subtypes, and their pharmacology is more complex and uncertain than can be discussed here. (See Chapter 10 for additional details.)

Calcium ions and LTP There is general agreement that some aspect of LTP induction depends on the intracellular concentration of calcium ions ($[Ca^{2+}]_i$) in some key compartment of the pre- and/or postsynaptic cells.[154,159,160] The exact role of calcium in the induction process depends on the particular form of LTP and the synaptic system. In the CA1 region of the hippocampus, LTP induction in the Sch/com synaptic input seems to depend critically on the postsynaptic $[Ca^{2+}]_i$.

The current view[154,160,161] is that many different routes modulate or control $[Ca^{2+}]_i$ in the critical subcellular compartment(s) (Fig. 55.23). Three routes that have been studied extensively may be implicated in some aspect of LTP induction: calcium influx through ionotropic GluRs, especially the NMDAR; calcium influx through voltage-gated calcium channels (VGCCs); and calcium release from intracellular stores.[154,161,162] We will elaborate on these three routes and their possible interactions.

NMDAR-dependent LTP Recall that the classical form of LTP has properties that can be explained in terms of a Hebbian mechanism. For this form of LTP, considerable evidence shows a role for the NMDAR.[154] Numerous pharmacological studies have shown that competitive antagonists of the NMDA receptor site, such as D-2-amino-5-phosphonopentenoic acid (D-AP5, also termed AP5 or APV) or NMDA ion channel blockers, such as the noncompetitive antagonist (+)-5-methyl-10,11-dihydro-5*H*-dibenzo[*a*,*d*]cyclohepten-5,10-imine (MK-801), can prevent the induction of one type of LTP.

The NMDAR has two properties that immediately suggest the nature of its role in LTP induction at Hebbian synapses.[153,154] First, NMDARs are permeable to Ca^{2+} (in addition to Na^+ and K^+). This is significant given that postsynaptic $[Ca^{2+}]_i$ plays a critical role in inducing this form of LTP. Second, the channel permeability is a function of both pre- and postsynaptic factors. Channel opening requires the neurotransmitter glutamate (or some related agonist) to bind to the NMDA site. This in turn requires presynaptic activity for glutamate release. At the usual resting membrane potential, the ionic channels are normally blocked by magnesium ions (Mg^{2+}), but this channel block is relieved by sufficient depolarization of the postsynaptic membrane containing the NMDAR. Thus, the NMDAR-mediated conductance is voltage dependent, allowing Ca^{2+} entry only when presynaptic release is combined with postsynaptic depolarization.

These interesting gating properties of the NMDAR, combined with a number of other assumptions and facts, easily give rise to quantitative models that can account for much of what is known about this form of LTP.[163,164] Before proceeding further we should distinguish between the properties of the NMDAR and those of the AMPAR. The AMPAR does not exhibit voltage-dependent Mg^{2+} block and has relatively lower Ca^{2+} permeability. The AMPAR-mediated conductance is essentially voltage independent. Released glutamate can potentially act on both the AMPARs and the NMDARs associated with the membrane on the dendritic spine (Fig. 55.23). With this knowledge, it is easy to envision a possible role for the NMDAR in a Hebbian modification. Nearly concurrent presynaptic activity (producing glutamate release and binding) and postsynaptic activity (relieving the Mg^{2+} block) allow Ca^{2+} influx into the dendritic spine of the postsynaptic neuron. The increased $[Ca^{2+}]_i$ in some critical region of the dendritic spine, presumably very close to the NMDAR, is thought to activate Ca^{2+}-dependent enzymes, such as calmodulin-dependent kinase II (CAM kinase II), that are thought to play a key role in LTP induction (Fig. 55.23).

In qualitative terms, we can easily see how these molecular events could help account for the properties of cooperativity, associativity, and spatiotemporal specificity. Active synapses release glutamate, which can bind to the NMDAR, causing Ca^{2+} influx into dendritic spines on the postsynaptic cell. This Ca^{2+} influx acts locally, resulting in *input-specific* LTP. However, the Ca^{2+} influx occurs only when the synaptic input is strong enough to depolarize the postsynaptic membrane sufficiently to relieve the Mg^{2+} block, giving rise

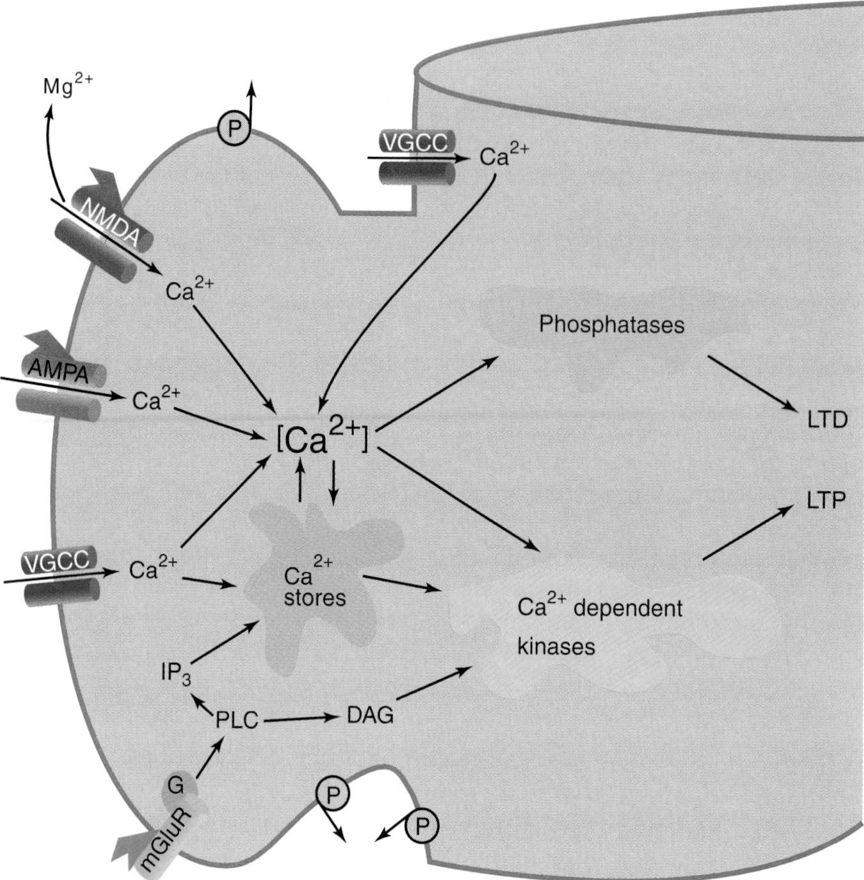

FIGURE 55.23 Events leading to LTP or LTD. The schematic depicts a postsynaptic spine with various sources of Ca^{2+}. The NMDA receptor–channel complex admits Ca^{2+} only after depolarization removes the Mg^{2+} block. Calcium may also enter through the ligand-gated AMPA receptor channel or voltage-gated calcium channels (VGCC), which may be located on the spine head or dendritic shaft. Also, certain subtypes of metabotropic glutamate receptors (mGluRs) are coupled positively to phospholipase C (PLC), which cleaves membrane phospholipids into inositol triphosphate (IP_3) and diacylglycerol (DAG). Increased levels of IP_3 lead to the release of intracellular Ca^{2+} stores, whereas increases in DAG activate Ca^{2+}-dependent enzymes. Calcium pumps, located on the spine head, neck, and dendritic shaft, are hypothesized to help isolate Ca^{2+} concentration changes in the spine head from those in the dendritic shaft (see text for details).

to *cooperativity* (see Fig. 55.22). The depolarization itself is mediated in large part by the (voltage-independent) AMPARs, which are also colocalized on the dendritic spine (Fig. 55.23). Note that activity in a W input by itself would not depolarize the postsynaptic cell sufficiently to relieve the Mg^{2+} block unless this activity were properly timed in relationship to activity in an S input to the same cell. The combined depolarization of the two inputs gives rise to *associativity* and its *spatiotemporal specificity* (Fig. 55.22).

Efforts to create formal models of this process quickly led to the realization that the properties of the NMDAR alone were not sufficient to account for the classical properties of LTP. Characteristics of the dendritic spine itself seem to play a key role. The spine is presumed to compartmentalize and amplify the second-messenger signal ($\Delta[Ca^{2+}]_i$) and to perform a number of other functions, including binding and pumping Ca^{2+}, that enable this mechanism to work[163] (Fig. 55.23). Amplification of $\Delta[Ca^{2+}]_i$ results from the small volume of the spine head coupled with restricted diffusion along the spine neck.[163] Similarly, the restricted diffusion, resulting from the spine geometry, combined with Ca^{2+} binding, help to compartmentalize the largest transient $\Delta[Ca^{2+}]_i$ to the head of the dendritic spine, where the relevant Ca^{2+}-dependent enzymes are presumed to be located.[163,164]

Computer simulations were used to explore the role

of "back-propagating" action potentials—spikes initiated in the soma that actively propagate *antidromically* into the dendrites. The principal finding was that "antidromic" Na^+ spikes had little effect unless they in turn activated VGCCs, in which case they had a pronounced effect. In certain cells, we now know that there are back-propagating spikes, that they do activate voltage-gated calcium channels, and that they may indeed participate in LTP induction.[162]

NMDAR-independent LTP Most of the preceding accounts of the classical (Hebbian, NMDAR-dependent) form of LTP are widely accepted and are assumed to apply quite generally. Nevertheless, this explanation may be applicable only to certain synapses under some conditions, and even then it may be only one piece of the story.[159–162] In many synapses, LTP induction does not appear to require the NMDA receptor.[159,161] Even within the hippocampus, some synapses exhibit NMDAR-independent forms of LTP. The usual example is the mossy-fiber synaptic input to CA3 pyramidal cells.[159]

The Sch/com inputs to CA1 pyramidal neurons, which are known to exhibit the classical Hebbian form of LTP that relies on the NMDAR, can be shown, under the appropriate conditions, to exhibit an NMDAR-independent type of LTP. Grover and Teyler[165] demonstrated that LTP can in fact be induced in these synapses in the presence of the competitive antagonist APV. They were careful to evaluate the possibility that high-frequency tetanic release of glutamate might competitively unblock the APV by using a relatively high concentration of DL-APV (200 m*M*) to saturate the APV-binding site.[165] The onset of NMDAR-independent LTP was relatively slow (20–30 min), it exhibited input specificity, and it was prevented by nifedipine, an L-type Ca^{2+} channel blocker. Thus, they distinguish between "NMDA LTP" and "VGCC LTP."

Using a combination of electrophysiological and $[Ca^{2+}]_i$ imaging methods, Magee and Johnston[162] further examined NMDAR-independent LTP in the Sch/com synaptic input to CA1. They found that back propagating dendritic spikes paired with stimulation of a weak Sch/com synaptic input to CA1 neurons produced LTP in the presence of 100 m*M* DL-APV. Not surprisingly, stimulation of the weak synaptic input by itself failed to induce LTP in the presence of APV. The back propagating spikes produced a strong Ca^{2+} signal in the dendrites, and, interestingly, the LTP produced by pairing was blocked by the Ca^{2+} channel blockers nimodipine and Ni^{2+}. NMDAR-independent LTP is not restricted to the CA1 region of the hippocampus.[159] Other work has suggested that VGCCs are likely to be responsible for certain types of LTP in the CA3 region of the hippocampus and in the visual cortex.

A cautious perspective is to recognize the possibility that both NMDAR-dependent and NMDAR-independent forms of LTP may co-occur in the same brain region, among different classes of synaptic inputs onto the same postsynaptic neuron, and even among the same class of synaptic inputs to the same postsynaptic neuron (Fig. 55.23). Given the possibilities, it is easy to see that application of NMDAR antagonists in behavioral studies should not be expected to block all forms of LTP.

LTP switch and mGluR Another of the more recently investigated LTP induction mechanisms involves the "metabotropic" glutamate receptor (mGluR).[166] Like the NMDAR, this complex is found on the postsynaptic cell, but unlike the NMDAR, it is also found presynaptically. Not surprisingly, there are a variety of mGlu receptors. Class I mGluR subtypes ($mGluR_1$ and $mGluR_5$) are coupled to phospholipase C (PLC), which enzymatically breaks down membrane phospholipids to form diacylglycerol and inositol 1,4,5-trisphosphate (IP_3) (see Fig. 55.23). DAG modulates channel activity through protein kinase C (PKC), while IP_3 mobilizes release of Ca^{2+} from intracellular stores (Fig. 55.23), a process that does not raise intracellular Ca^{2+} concentrations as quickly as the opening of VGCCs. In contrast, class II mGluR subtypes ($mGluR_2$ and $mGluR_3$) are coupled to G-protein-mediated inhibition of adenylate cyclase, an action that causes a depression of the second messenger cAMP (not shown in Fig. 55.23). In studies of synaptic plasticity, there is ample reason to pay close attention to changes in cAMP regulated by neurotransmitters (see earlier discussion and Byrne and Kandel[22]).

The role of the mGluR has been studied most extensively in the Sch/com input to hippocampal region CA1. Collingridge and co-workers reported[166] that application of the mGluR antagonist (+)-α-methyl-4-carboxy-phenylglycine (MCPG) blocked LTP induction in synapses that had not previously received high-frequency stimulation (HFS) but did not prevent the induction of additional LTP at synapses that had prior exposure to HFS. A creative interpretation of these and other experiments is that the mGluR acts as a "molecular switch" that must be activated as a prerequisite to LTP induction.[167] This interesting idea has generated further experiments in other laboratories, but thus far a consistent pattern has not emerged.[168] Clearly, we need to know more about the factors that affect the spatial distribution and relative proportions of the various mGluR subtypes and their ultimate roles in neuronal function.

Long-term depression The mechanisms responsible for inducing LTP also may play a role in triggering another synaptic phenomenon, called long-term depression. First seen in the hippocampus and subsequently in many other brain regions, LTD is thought by many to be the mechanism by which learning is encoded in the cerebellum (see section on eyeblink conditioning), as well as a process whereby LTP could be reversed in the hippocampus and neocortex.[169] In the latter brain regions, brief, high-frequency stimulation (e.g., 4 trains of 10 shocks at 100 Hz) can induce classical LTP, whereas low-frequency stimulation (LFS) over longer periods (1 Hz for 10 min) can induce LTD.

Some forms of LTD appear to be mediated by the NMDAR,[170] and these forms of LTD seem to result from depotentiation (removal of LTP). In addition, there appear to be NMDAR-independent forms of LTD. One example of the latter comes from studies on the frontal cortex. Reports on the layer I/II input to layer V neurons suggest that LTP and LTD are separate and superimposed processes and that LTD induction is not mediated by activation of NMDA receptors.[171] Another example of NMDAR-independent LTD is found in the parallel fiber input to Purkinje cells in the cerebellum.

From our discussion so far, it should be clear that there may be many forms of LTP and LTD and many pathways by which they operate. Furthermore, these forms may vary in different brain regions and sometimes among different inputs to the same brain region. Even within the CA1 region, the Sch/com input may exhibit both NMDAR-dependent[170] and NMDAR-independent forms of LTD, and the latter could be mediated partly by Ca^{2+} entry through VGCCs.

Bidirectional control by calcium ions With regard to NMDAR-dependent LTP, one interesting point on which there has been general agreement in studies of the Sch/com input to CA1 is that *both* LTP and LTD in CA1 appear to be Ca^{2+}-dependent processes that can be blocked by injecting Ca^{2+} chelators into the postsynaptic cell.[172] If both LTP and LTD are triggered by Ca^{2+} entry, then how are their induction processes different? The presumption is that more Ca^{2+} influx occurs during an LTP-inducing HFS than during an LTD-inducing LFS.[161] One formal molecular model incorporates this Ca^{2+}-dependent, bidirectional control of synaptic strength.[173] In this model, high $[Ca^{2+}]_i$ (> 5 m*M*) activates a protein kinase that phosphorylates a protein that leads to LTP induction, whereas low $[Ca^{2+}]_i$ (< 5 m*M*) activates a protein phosphatase that dephosphorylates this protein and causes LTD. The synaptic strength thus depends on which of these competing processes is most active, which in turn will be a function of the pattern of activity experienced by the cell (Fig. 55.23). These ideas have led to testable biochemical predictions.[172]

LTP Expression

Up to this point we have emphasized evidence related to early events in the causal chain that triggers the modification process. Another question follows naturally: What physical changes incorporate this modification once it has been triggered? This question addresses the process of LTP expression. A variety of hypotheses have been proposed to account for the synaptic enhancement associated with LTP expression. Since many of these models have not been conclusively evaluated yet, controversy still surrounds the details of LTP expression. In what follows, we will overview some of the possible expression mechanisms to reveal the logic behind this subfield of LTP research.

Most of the ideas about enhanced synaptic transmission concern either increased transmitter release or increased receptivity to released transmitter. The former entails presynaptic changes; the latter, postsynaptic. Although some of the induction mechanisms discussed previously implicated a postsynaptic increase in $[Ca^{2+}]_i$, this does not necessarily imply that expression also must be postsynaptic. There is ample evidence for ongoing two-way communication across the synaptic cleft, so that a postsynaptic trigger could in principle give rise to a pre- and/or postsynaptic modification. There are a large number of seemingly conflicting accounts in the literature regarding the nature of the changes responsible for the observed increase in synaptic efficacy following LTP induction.[174]

Experimentally, the increase in synaptic efficacy that is characteristic of LTP was shown to be the result of an increase in the measured synaptic conductance (ΔG_e),[151] and not a decrease in inhibition, a lowering of the spike threshold, or an increase in input resistance (see Fig. 55.24).[175] This enhanced synaptic conductance could reflect an increase in either of two quantal parameters—m and q (see Chapter 7). The first parameter m is the mean number of quantal packages of neurotransmitter released per presynaptic action potential. The second parameter q is the average postsynaptic response produced by the release of each quantal package of neurotransmitter. The mean response amplitude is just the product of m and q.

Classical methods of quantal analysis have been used in an attempt to determine whether LTP results from an increase in m or q or both. In certain simple systems, like the crayfish neuromuscular junction, this analysis can be applied with some confidence. In this system, LTP seems to be due to an increase in the quantal parameter m, and there is no change in q.[176]

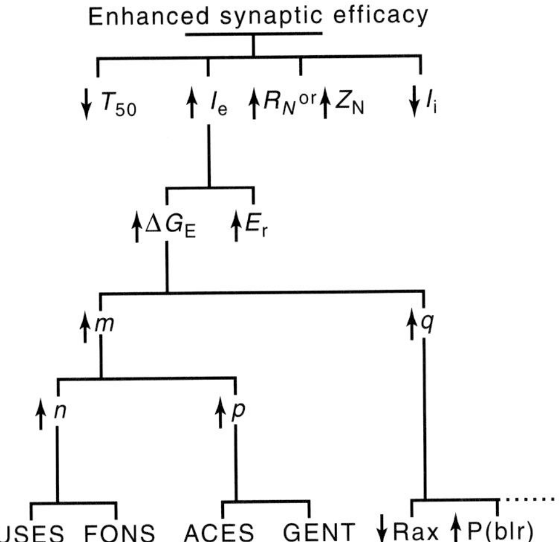

FIGURE 55.24 Logic tree used to direct experimental analysis of LTP expression. Changes in the variables shown could lead to increased synaptic efficacy. Arrows indicate increases or decreases in a variable. Upper terminal branches indicate possibilities that have been ruled out in some synapses: ↓ T_{50}, reduction of spike threshold; ↑ R_n, increased input resistance; ↑ Z_n, increased input impedance; ↓ I_i, decreased inhibitory current. Experimental results suggested an increase in excitatory current ↑ I_e, which could have been caused by either an increase in excitatory synaptic conductance (↑ ΔG_e) or a positive shift in the reversal potential (↑ E_r). Results demonstrating the former lead to investigations of the quantal parameters (m, q, n, and p) responsible for ↑ ΔG_e. Terminal branches at the bottom list possible expression mechanisms: USES, unsilencing existing synapses; FONS, formation of new synapses; ACES, altered coupling between excitation and secretion; GENT, greater excitation of the nerve terminal; ↓ Rax, reduction in the axial resistance of the postsynaptic spine; ↑ P(b|r), increase in the probability of transmitter binding to a receptor, given release. Other possibilities exist, but are beyond the scope of this chapter. Adapted from Brown *et al.*[175]

Application of the methods of quantal analysis to an understanding of LTP in mammalian central synapses has been less successful. Different groups have often obtained seemingly contradictory results.[174] In the mossy-fiber synaptic input to pyramidal neurons in hippocampal region CA3, the results suggest an increase in m,[152] but other synapses of the hippocampus need to be considered separately.

In a simple binomial model of transmitter release, m is the product of two other parameters—n and p (Fig. 55.24). The parameter n can be conceptualized as the number of eligible release sites. Even in the simplest binomial model, an increase in n could reflect any number of causes, two of which are indicated in Fig. 55.24. The first assumes that there are preexisting but "silent" release sites. They could be silent for several reasons—a failure of the neurotransmitter-containing vesicles to dock appropriately at the release site, an absence of functioning postsynaptic receptors opposite the release site,[177] or an absence of functioning VGCCs immediately adjacent to the release site—but the point is that there could be *unsilencing of existing sites* (Fig. 55.24, USES). Alternatively, LTP could result from the *formation of new sites* (Fig. 55.24, FONS), which could even entail sprouting totally new synaptic boutons.

The binomial parameter p is the mean probability for each of the n active release sites of discharging a quantum when a presynaptic nerve impulse occurs. An increase in p could reflect any of a large number of causes, two of which are indicated in Fig. 55.24. First, a number of potentially modifiable causes are involved in coupling the neurotransmitter secretion to the arrival of an action potential in the nerve terminal. Here, there could be *altered coupling of excitation to secretion* (Fig. 55.24, ACES). Alternatively, there might be no alteration in excitation–secretion coupling for a given action potential, but instead, as in *Aplysia*, the action potential in the nerve terminal itself could change. Thus, the obvious alternative possibility entails *greater excitation of the nerve terminal* (Fig. 55.24, GENT).

Similarly, in the case of the binomial parameter q (the postsynaptic response), we can devise a large number of possible mechanisms for increasing its value. These include a decrease in the axial resistance of the dendritic spines (R_{ax}), an increase in the probability that a released molecule of neurotransmitter will bind to a postsynaptic receptor $P(b|r)$, an increase in the number of neurotransmitter molecules in each vesicular packet (not indicated), and several others (see Fig. 55.24). An increase in $P(b|r)$ could be caused, for example, by an increase in the number of AMPA receptors, a possibility suggested by research in several laboratories.[174] There is reason to discount changes in spine resistance, based on the relationship of the reciprocal of the spine axial resistance (G_{ax}) to the peak synaptic conductance (ΔG_{syn}). Theoretical work[151] shows that the role of the spines is negligible if $G_{ax} \gg \Delta G_{syn}$, which may generally be the case. Still, a variety of other hypothesized mechanisms for increasing q remain possible.[160,177] A clear experimental distinction among these hypotheses awaits further research or the development of new technologies.

LTP Maintenance

Regardless of the ultimate nature and locus of the modification that gives rise to LTP expression, the more general problem remains of how a synaptic change can endure over long periods of time in the face of constant molecular turnover. This is the problem of LTP maintenance.

Gene expression and protein synthesis One favorite answer to this problem of how to maintain plastic changes is to assume that it ultimately involves alterations in gene expression. Just as genetic machinery can be used to maintain macroscopic aspects of an organism, such as eye color and height, the genome also could be used to maintain microscopic features of an organism. There is a difference, however, between eye color and synaptic plasticity. The former trait is relatively unchanged throughout the lifetime of an organism and is controlled by inherited genetic material. The latter is a rapid change that is hypothesized to be induced by experience.

Interestingly, there is indeed evidence for changes in gene expression after neuronal stimulation. High-frequency electrical stimulation in the rat hippocampus can raise levels of mRNA, which in turn could be used to maintain persistent structural changes. Furthermore, a large body of literature links protein synthesis to learning and memory.[178] For example, application of protein synthesis inhibitors interferes with the formation and retention of memories.

This naturally raises the question whether protein synthesis inhibitors interfere with the maintenance of LTP. Several studies have revealed that maintaining long-lasting synaptic plasticity involves many stages, and not all of these stages are dependent on protein synthesis. In an illustrative experiment using hippocampal slices,[179] the protein synthesis inhibitor actinomycin D (ACT D) was applied for 2 h, starting just before high-frequency stimulation was delivered. While the synaptic response indicated an enhancement, this increase persisted for only 2 h before steadily declining back to baseline levels. Other slices that did not receive ACT D showed a persistent enhancement lasting over 4 h, and slices that received only ACT D without high-frequency stimulation were unchanged.

These results suggest that synaptic enhancements induced by high-frequency stimulation have at least two stages—an early stage that lasts for about 2 h and is not dependent on protein synthesis, followed by a later stage that is dependent on protein synthesis. Interestingly, slices that received ACT D just 2 h after high-frequency stimulation showed no decline in enhancement, indicating that there is a critical time window during which protein synthesis might be necessary to maintain long-term plasticity. Other work, done *in vivo*, has pointed to a still later stage of LTP that lasts weeks and that also depends on protein synthesis.[180] Similar stages of long-term synaptic plasticity have been identified in *Aplysia*, *Drosophila*, and *Hermissenda*, so that the two-stage process may be a general one present in a range of species.

Immediate-early genes and CREB The learning-related events that turn on gene expression in neurons are uncertain, but a plausible scheme has been put forward by Kandel and colleagues.[181,182] They envision the first step to be Ca^{2+} binding to calmodulin, which activates adenylate cyclase, thereby promoting synthesis of cAMP. Prolonged elevation of cAMP can in turn trigger the activation of PKA, which may ultimately translocate to the nucleus. Once in the nucleus, PKA is thought to activate CREBs (cAMP-responsive element-binding proteins), which initiate the transcription of immediate-early genes such as c-*fos* or c-*jun*. These immediate-early genes could in turn transcribe late-effector genes whose role it would be to encode proteins underlying, for example, structural changes at the synapse. Protein synthesis is, of course, required for each of the above steps that involve transcription.

Gene expression and synaptic specificity Although this scheme is consistent with the data, it immediately raises the problem of synaptic input specificity. If neural activity ultimately affects gene expression in the nucleus, then the proteins produced in the soma could in principle travel to any synapse within the cell. The problem is to modify only the appropriate synapses. While this problem has not been solved experimentally, conceptually there is no shortage of reasonable possibilities. One solution is for the synapse to produce a local "marker" that makes it especially susceptible to proteins sent from the nucleus.[183] To support a more permanent modification might require a self-perpetuating marker and / or an enduring modification in local transport.

Researchers Are Using Genetically Engineered "Knockout" Mice to Investigate the Links between Long-Term Potentiation and Learning

Long-term potentiation has the kinds of properties that have long been considered necessary for the encoding and retrieval of information. Hebbian forms of LTP exhibit associativity, which seems like a desirable property, and all forms of LTP appear to be well suited to aspects of rapid learning. One of the more important and difficult remaining challenges entails linking LTP to learning and memory.[184,185] Given what we now know about the molecular mechanisms underlying synaptic transmission and its modification, one can understand why the matter would not be easy to settle simply through pharmacological studies aimed at interfering with some aspect of LTP.

Some of the more promising work in this area has come from studies of genetically engineered knockout mice. The first generation of knockouts prevented the expression of some factor that was thought to be necessary for LTP, such as CAM kinase II. Although these studies were intriguing, they suffered from the fact that the consequences of a gene knockout could alter brain development and could not be confined to a specific part of the brain under study. Some of these problems have been overcome in a second generation of knockouts that have temporal as well as spatial specificity. In one example of what will surely prove to be a widely used approach, one group[186] has developed a mutant mouse that lacks one form of the NMDAR only in hippocampal region CA1. Furthermore, this mutation is only expressed after the third postnatal week, thereby reducing influences on early development.

Tests of these mice have revealed that they have LTP deficits in hippocampal region CA1, but not in the dentate gyrus, where the NMDAR was expressed. The behavioral effects of this manipulation also are interesting and include impaired performance on tests of spatial memory, as well as altered firing properties of CA1 pyramidal cells during navigational behaviors. The firing rate of a CA1 pyramidal cell commonly increases when the mouse visits certain spatial locations, which constitute the "place field" for that neuron. Cells coding for overlapping place fields also tend to show correlated firing. In knockout mice, however, the place fields were spatially more diffuse than those seen in the controls, and the firing patterns of neurons from overlapping place fields did not correlate with each other as highly. These results are consistent with the hypothesis that the NMDAR participates in some aspect of the formation of place fields through a Hebbian mechanism, and deficits in spatial memory could result, in part, from untuned and/or improperly associated place fields.

Although this knockout study does not directly connect LTP to learning and memory, it is impressive because it combines evidence and ideas from molecular, cellular, systems and behavioral levels into a consistent picture. One looks forward to future variants of knockout mice that have inducible molecular lesions that can be triggered at the will of the investigator. This general approach holds tremendous promise for testing hypotheses about the functional role of various forms of LTP in specific brain regions.

Summary

The search for the biological basis of learning and memory has led many of the 20th century's leading neuroscientists to investigate the synapse. As a result of this focus, tremendous effort has been directed toward understanding the cellular and molecular mechanisms behind changes in synaptic efficacy. Our understanding of synaptic plasticity is rapidly evolving and constantly changing. Whereas the N-methyl-d-aspartate receptor was once the pivotal focus of long-term potentiation (LTP) research, it is now clear that voltage-gated calcium channels and metabotropic glutamate receptors as well as other mechanisms should be considered. It also has become evident that high-frequency stimulation is but one end of a spectrum of stimulations that can induce synaptic changes. Lower stimulation frequencies can induce long-term depression (LTD), which may share some common molecular mechanisms with LTP. Finally, several stages in the maintenance of LTP have been identified, and probably more will be found. The most daunting remaining challenge is to clarify the varieties of LTP and LTD mechanisms and to demonstrate their functional significance by establishing convincing links to the encoding and retrieval of information and to the development and maturation of the nervous system.

References

General

Dash, P. K., Hochner, B., and Kandel, E. R. (1990). Injection of the cAMP-responsive element into the nucleus of *Aplysia* sensory neurons blocks long-term facilitation. *Nature (London)* **345:** 718–721.

Feng, T. P. (1941). Studies on the neuromuscular junction. XXVI. The changes of the endplate potential during and after prolonged stimulation. *Chin. J. Physiol.* **16:** 341–372.

Cited

1. James, W. (1890). *Principles of Psychology.* Dover, New York.
2. Tanzi, E. (1893). I fatti e le induzioni nell'odierna del sistema nervoso. *Riv. Sper. Freniatr. Med. Leg. Alienazioni Ment.* **19:** 419–472.
3. Ramón y Cajál, S. (1911). *Histologie du système nerveux de l'homme et des vertébrés,* Vol. 2. Maloine, Paris. [Republished: *Histologie du système nerveux* (L. Azoulay, transl.). Instituto Ramón y Cajál, Madrid, 1955.]
4. Hebb, D. O. (1949). *The Organization of Behavior.* Wiley (Interscience), New York.
5. Byrne, J. H. (1987). Cellular analysis of associative learning. *Physiol. Rev.* **67:** 329–439.
6. Squire, L. R., and Knowlton, B. J. (1994). Memory, hippocampus and brain systems. In *The Cognitive Neurosciences* (M. S. Gazzaniga, ed.), pp. 825–837. MIT Press, Cambridge, MA.
7. Thompson, R. F., Donegan, N. H., and Lavond, D. G. (1988). The psychobiology of learning and memory. In *Steven's Handbook of Experimental Psychology* (R. C. Atkinson, R. J. Herrnstein, G. Lindzey, and R. D. Duce, eds.), 2nd ed., Vol. 2, pp. 245–347. Wiley, New York.
8. Rescorla, R. A. (1988). Behavioral studies of Pavlovian conditioning. *Annu. Rev. Neurosci.* **11:** 329–352.
9. Dudai, Y. (1989). *The Neurobiology of Memory.* Oxford University Press, New York.
10. Groves, P. M., and Thompson, R. F. (1970). Habituation: A dual-process theory. *Psychol. Rev.* **77:** 419–450.
11. Rachlin, H. (1991). *Introduction to Modern Behaviorism,* 3rd ed. Freeman, New York.
12. London, J. A., and Gillette, R. (1986). Mechanism for food avoidance learning in the central pattern generator of feeding behav-

ior of *Pleurobranchaea californica*. *Proc. Natl. Acad. Sci. U.S.A.* **83:** 4058–4062.

13. Frost, W. N., Brown, G. D., and Getting, P. A. (1996). Parametric features of habituation of swim cycle number in the marine mollusc *Tritonia diomedea*. *Neurobiol. Learn. Mem.* **65:** 125–134.
14. Kemenes, G., and Benjamin, P. R. (1994). Training in a novel environment improves the appetitive learning performance of the snail, *Lymnaea stagnalis*. *Behav. Neural Biol.* **61:** 139–149.
15. Balaban, P. (1993). Behavioral neurobiology of learning in terrestrial snails. *Prog. Neurobiol.* **41:** 1–19.
16. Gelperin, A. (1994). Nitric oxide, odor processing and plasticity. *Neth. J. Zool.* **44**(3–4): 159–169.
17. Hammer, M., and Menzel, R. (1995). Learning and memory in the honeybee. *J. Neurosci.* **15:** 1617–1630.
18. DeZazzo, J., and Tully, T. (1995). Dissection of memory formation: From behavioral pharmacology to molecular genetics. *Trends Neurosci.* **18:** 212–218.
19. Sahley, C. L. (1995). What we have learned from the study of learning in the leech. *J. Neurobiol.* **27:** 434–445.
20. Wicks, S. R., and Rankin, C. H. (1995). Integration of mechanosensory stimuli in *Caenorhabditis elegans*. *J. Neurosci.* **15:** 2434–2444.
21. Byrne, J. H., Zwartjes, R., Homayouni, R., Critz, S., and Eskin, A. (1993). Roles of second messenger pathways in neuronal plasticity and in learning and memory: Insights gained from *Aplysia*. *Adv. Second Messenger Phosphoprotein Res.* **27:** 47–108.
22. Byrne, J. H., and Kandel, E. R. (1996). Presynaptic facilitation revisited: State- and time-dependence. *J. Neurosci.* **16**(2): 425–435.
23. Hawkins, R. D., Kandel, E. R., and Siegelbaum, S. (1993). Learning to modulate transmitter release: Themes and variations in synaptic plasticity. *Annu. Rev. Neurosci.* **16:** 625–665.
24. Cleary, L. J., and Byrne, J. H. (1993). Identification and characterization of a multifunction neuron contributing to defensive arousal in *Aplysia*. *J. Neurophysiol.* **70:** 1767–1776.
25. White, J. A., Ziv, I., Cleary, L. J., Baxter, D. A., and Byrne, J. H. (1993). The role of interneurons in controlling the tail-withdrawal reflex in *Aplysia:* A network model. *J. Neurophysiol.* **70:** 1777–1786.
26. Gingrich, K. J., and Byrne, J. H. (1987). Single-cell neuronal model for associative learning. *J. Neurophysiol.* **57:** 1705–1715.
27. Baxter, D. A., and Byrne, J. H. (1993). Learning rules from neurobiology. In *The Neurobiology of Neural Networks* (D. Gardner, ed.), pp. 71–105. MIT Press, Cambridge, MA.
28. Byrne, J. H., Baxter, D. A., Buonomano, D. V., and Raymond, J. L. (1990). Neuronal and network determinants of simple and higher-order features of associative learning: Experimental and modeling approaches. *Cold Spring Harbor Symp. Quant. Biol.* **55:** 175–186.
29. Bailey, C. H., Chen, M., Keller, F., and Kandel, E. R. (1992). Serotonin-mediated endocytosis of apCAM: An early step of learning-related synaptic growth in *Aplysia*. *Science* **256:** 645–649.
30. Liu, Q.-R., Hatter, S., Endo, S., MacPhee, K., Zhang, H., Cleary, L. J., and Byrne, J. H. (1997). A developmental gene (Tolloid/BMP-1) is regulated in *Aplysia* neurons by treatments that induce long-term sensitization. *J. Neurosci.* **17:** 755–764.
31. Zhang, F., Endo, S., Cleary, L. J., Eskin, A., and Byrne, J. H. (1997). Role of transforming growth factor-β in long-term facilitation in *Aplysia*. *Science* **275:** 1318–1320.
32. Greenberg, S. M., Castellucci, V. F., Bayley, H., and Schwartz, J. H. (1987). A molecular mechanism for long-term sensitization in *Aplysia*. *Nature (London)* **329:** 62–65.
33. Lin, X. Y., and Glanzman, D. L. (1994). Hebbian induction of long-term potentiation of *Aplysia* sensorimotor synapses: Partial requirement for activation of an NMDA-related receptor. *Proc. R. Soc. London, B* **255:** 215–221.

33a. Lechner, H. A., and Byrne, J. H. (1998). New perspectives on classical conditioning: A synthesis of hebbian and nonhebbian mechanisms. *Neuron* **20:** 355–358.

34. Alkon, D. L. (1989). Memory storage and neural systems. *Sci. Am.* **261**(1): 42–50.
35. Crow, T. (1988). Cellular and molecular analysis of associative learning and memory in *Hermissenda*. *Trends Neurosci.* **11:** 136–142.
36. Crow, T., and Alkon, D. L. (1978). Retention of an associative behavioral change in *Hermissenda*. *Science* **201:** 1239–1241.
37. Lederhendler, I., Gart, S., and Alkon, D. L. (1986). Classical conditioning of *Hermissenda:* Origin of a new response. *J. Neurosci.* **6:** 1325–1331.
38. Farley, J. (1987). Contingency learning and causal detection in *Hermissenda*. I. Behavior. *Behav. Neurosci.* **101:** 13–27.
39. Crow, T. (1983). Conditioned modification of locomotions of sensory adaptation in *Hermissenda crassicornis:* Analysis of time dependent associative and nonassociative components. *J. Neurosci.* **3:** 2621–2628.
40. Crow, T., and Forrester, J. (1986). Light paired with serotonin mimics the effects of conditioning on phototactic behavior in *Hermissenda*. *Proc. Natl. Acad. Sci. U.S.A.* **83:** 7975–7978.
41. Alkon, D. L., and Fuortes, M. G. F. (1972). Responses of photoreceptors in *Hermissenda*. *J. Gen. Physiol.* **60:** 631–649.
42. Alkon, D. L., Lederhendler, I., and Shoukimas, J. J. (1982). Primary changes of membrane currents during strength of associative learning. *Science* **215:** 693–695.
43. Alkon, D. L., Sakakibara, M., Forman, R., Harrigan, J., Lederhendler, I., and Farley, J. (1985). Reduction of two voltage-dependent K^+ currents mediates serotonin of a learned association. *Behav. Neural Biol.* **44:** 278–300.
44. Crow, T., and Alkon, D. L. (1980). Associative behavioral modification in *Hermissenda:* Cellular correlates. *Science* **209:** 412–414.
45. Farley, J., and Alkon, D. L. (1982). Associative neural and behavioral change in *Hermissenda:* Consequences of nervous system orientation for light- and pairing-specificity. *J. Neurophysiol.* **48:** 785–807.
46. Frysztak, R. J., and Crow, T. (1993). Differential expression of correlates of classical conditioning in identified medial and lateral type A photoreceptors of *Hermissenda*. *J. Neurosci.* **13:** 2889–2897.
47. West, A., Barnes, E. S., and Alkon, D. L. (1982). Primary changes of voltage responses during retention of associative learning. *J. Neurophysiol.* **48:** 1243–1255.
48. Farley, J., Richards, W. G., and Grover, L. M. (1990). Associative learning causes changes intrinsic to *Hermissenda* type A photoreceptors. *Behav. Neurosci.* **104:** 135–152.
49. Frysztak, R. J., and Crow, T. (1994). Enhancement of type B and A photoreceptor inhibitory synaptic connections in conditioned *Hermissenda*. *J. Neurosci.* **14:** 1245–1250.
50. Farley, J., and Auerbach, S. (1986). Protein kinase C activation induces conductance changes in *Hermissenda* photoreceptors like those seen in associative learning. *Nature (London)* **319:** 220–223.
51. Farley, J., and Schuman, E. (1991). Protein kinase C inhibitors prevent induction and continued expression of cell memory in *Hermissenda* type B photoreceptors. *Proc. Natl. Acad. Sci. U.S.A.* **88:** 2016–2020.
52. Matzel, L. D., Lederhendler, I. I., and Alkon, D. L. (1990). Regulation of short-term associative memory by calcium-dependent protein kinase. *J. Neurosci.* **7:** 1198–1206.
53. Land, P. W., and Crow, T. (1985). Serotonin immunoreactivity in the circumesophageal nervous system of *Hermissenda crassicornis*. *Neurosci. Lett.* **3:** 199–205.
54. Crow, T., and Forrester, J. (1991). Light paired with serotonin *in vivo* produces both short- and long-term enhancement of

generator potentials in identified B photoreceptors in *Hermissenda. J. Neurosci.* **11:** 608–617.
55. Crow, T., Siddiqi, V., and Dash, P. K. (1998). Long-term enhancement but not short-term in *Hermissenda* is dependent upon mRNA synthesis. *Neurobiol. Learn. Mem.* **58:** 343–350.
56. Crow, T., and Forrester, J. (1990). Inhibition of protein synthesis blocks long-term enhancement of generator potentials produced by one-trial *in vivo* conditioning in *Hermissenda. Proc. Natl. Acad. Sci. U.S.A.* **87:** 4490–4494.
57. Crow, T., Forrester, J., Williams, M., Waxham, M. N., and Neary, J. T. (1991). Down-regulation of protein kinase C blocks 5-HT-induced enhancement in *Hermissenda* B-photoreceptors. *Neurosci. Lett.* **12:** 107–110.
58. Crow, T., and Forrester, J. (1993). Down-regulation of protein kinase C and kinase inhibitors dissociate short- and long-term enhancement produced by one-trial conditioning of *Hermissenda. J. Neurophysiol.* **69:** 636–641.
59. Crow, T., Siddiqi, V., Zhu, Q., and Neary, J. T. (1996). Time-dependent increase in protein phosphorylation following one-trial enhancement in *Hermissenda. J. Neurochem.* **66:** 1736–1741.
60. Crow, T., Xue-Bian, J. J., Siddigi, V., Kang, Y., and Neary, J. T. (1998). Phosphorylation of mitogen-activated protein kinase by one-trial and multi-trial classical conditioning. *J. Neurosci.* **18:** 3480–3487.
61. Rescorla, R. A., and Solomon, R. L. (1967). Two process learning theory: Relationships between Pavlovian conditioning and instrumental learning. *Psychol. Rev.* **55:** 151–182.
62. Gormezano, I., Kehoe, E. J., and Marshall-Goodell, B. S. (1983). Twenty years of classical conditioning research with the rabbit. In *Progress in Physiological Psychology* (J. M. Sprague and A. N. Epstein, eds.), pp. 197–275. Academic Press, New York.
63. Pavlov, I. P. (1927). *Conditioned Reflexes: An Investigation of the Physiological Activity of the Cerebral Cortex* (G. V. Anrep, transl.). Oxford University Press, London.
64. Thompson, R. F., and Kim, J. J. (1996). Memory-systems in the brain and localization of a memory. *Proc. Natl. Acad. Sci. U.S.A.* **93:** 13438–13444.
65. Woody, C. D., and Yarowsky, P. J. (1972). Conditioned eyeblink using electrical stimulation of coronal-precruciate cortex of the cat. *J. Neurophysiol.* **35:** 242–252.
66. Woody, C. D., Yarowsky, P., Owens, J., Black-Cleworth, P., and Crow, T. (1974). Effect lesions of cortical motor areas on acquisition of conditioned eye blink in the cat. *J. Neurophysiol.* **37:** 385–394.
67. Ivkovich, D., and Thompson, R. F. (1998). Motor cortex lesions do not effect learning or performance of the eyeblink response in rabbits. *Behav. Neurosci.* (in press).
68. Davis, M. (1984). Mammalian startle response. In *Neural Mechanisms of Startle Behavior* (R. C. Eaton, ed.), pp. 287–351. Plenum, New York.
69. Berger, T. W., Alger, B. E., and Thompson, R. F. (1976). Neuronal substrate of classical conditioning in the hippocampus. *Science* **192:** 483–485.
70. Berger, T. W., and Thompson, R. F. (1978). Identification of pyramidal cells as the critical elements in hippocampal neuronal plasticity during learning. *Proc. Natl. Acad. Sci. U.S.A.* **75**(3): 1572–1576.
71. Berger, T. W., Berry, S. D., and Thompson, R. F. (1986). Role of the hippocampus in classical conditioning of aversive and appetitive behaviors. In *The Hippocampus* (R. L. Isaacson and K. H. Pribram, eds.), Vol. 4, pp. 203–239. Plenum, New York.
72. Isaacson, R. L., and Pribram, K. H., eds. (1986). *The Hippocampus,* Vol. 4. Plenum, New York.
73. Berger, T. W., Rinaldi, P. C., Weisz, D. J., and Thompson, R. F. (1983). Single unit analysis of different hippocampal cell types during classical conditioning of the rabbit nictitating membrane response. *J. Neurophysiol.* **50:** 1197–1219.
74. Thompson, R. F. (1990). Neural mechanisms of classical conditioning in mammals. *Philos. Trans. R. Soc. London B* **329:** 161–170.
75. Weiskrantz, L., and Warrington, E. K. (1979). Conditioning in amnesic patients. *Neuropsychologia* **17:** 187–194.
76. Daum, I., Channon, S., Polkey, C. E., and Gray, J. A. (1991). Classical conditioning after temporal lobe lesions in man: Impairment in conditional discrimination. *Behav. Neurosci.* **105:** 396–408.
77. Moyer, J. R., Jr., Deyo, R. A., and Disterhoft, J. F. (1990). Hippocampectomy disrupts trace eyeblink conditioning in rabbits. *Behav. Neurosci.* **104:** 243–252.
78. Solomon, P. R., Vander Schaaf, E. R., Thompson, R. F., and Weisz, D. J. (1986). Hippocampus and trace conditioning of the rabbit's classically conditioned nictitating membrane response. *Behav. Neurosci.* **100:** 729–744.
79. Kim, J. J., Clark, R. E., and Thompson, R. F. (1995). Hippocampectomy impairs the memory of recently, but not remotely, acquired trace eyeblink conditioned responses. *Behav. Neurosci.* **109:** 195–203.
80. Zola-Morgan, S. M., and Squire, L. R. (1990). The primate hippocampal formation: Evidence for the time-limited role in memory storage. *Science* **250:** 288–290.
81. Weisz, D. J., Clark, G. A., and Thompson, R. F. (1984). Increased activity of dentate granule cells during nictitating membrane response conditioning in rabbits. *Behav. Brain Res.* **12:** 145–154.
82. Baudry, M., Davis, J. L., and Thompson, R. F., eds. (1993). *Synaptic Plasticity: Molecular and Functional Aspects.* MIT Press, Cambridge, MA.
83. Maren, S., Tocco, G., Standley, S., Baudry, M., and Thompson, R. F. (1993). Postsynaptic factors in the expression of long-term potentiation (LTP): Increased glutamate receptor binding following LTP induction *in vivo. Proc. Natl. Acad. Sci. U.S.A.* **90:** 9654–9658.
84. Tocco, G., Maren, S., Shors, T. J., Baudry, M., and Thompson, R. F. (1992). Long-term potentiation is associated with increased ^{3}H-AMPA binding in rat hippocampus. *Brain Res.* **573:** 228–234.
85. Thompson, L. T., Deyo, R. A., and Disterhoft, J. F. (1992). Hippocampus-dependent learning facilitated by a monoclonal antibody or D-cycloserine. *Nature (London)* **359:** 838–841.
86. Marr, D. (1969). A theory of cerebellar cortex. *J. Physiol. (London)* **202:** 437–470.
87. Albus, J. S. (1971). A theory of cerebellar function. *Math. Biosci.* **10:** 25–61.
88. Thompson, R. F. (1986). The neurobiology of learning and memory. *Science* **233:** 941–947.
89. Thompson, R. F., and Krupa, D. J. (1994). Organization of memory traces in the mammalian brain. *Annu. Rev. Neurosci.* **17:** 519–549.
90. Lavond, D. G., Kim, J. J., and Thompson, R. F. (1993). Mammalian brain substrates of aversive classical conditioning. *Annu. Rev. Psychol.* **44:** 317–342.
91. Yeo, C. H. (1991). Cerebellum and classical conditioning of motor response. *Ann. N.Y. Acad. Sci.* **627:** 292–304.
92. McCormick, D. A., and Thompson, R. F. (1984). Cerebellum: Essential involvement in the classically conditioned eyelid response. *Science* **223:** 296–299.
93. Logan, C. G., and Grafton, S. T. (1995). Functional anatomy of human eyeblink conditioning determined with regional cerebral glucose metabolism and positron-emission tomography. *Proc. Natl. Acad. Sci. U.S.A.* **92**(16): 7500–7504.
94. Steinmetz, J. E., Lavond, D. G., Ivkovich, D., Logan, C. G., and Thompson, R. F. (1992). Disruption of classical eyelid conditioning after cerebellar lesions: Damage to a memory trace system or a simple performance deficit? *J. Neurosci.* **12:** 4403–4426.

95. Yeo, C. H., Hardiman, M. J., and Glickstein, M. (1985). Classical conditioning of the nictitating membrane response of the rabbit. I. Lesions of the cerebellar nuclei. *Exp. Brain Res.* **60:** 87–98.
96. Daum, I., Schugens, M. M., Ackerman, H., Lutzenberger, W., Dichgans, J., and Birbaumer, N. (1993). Classical conditioning after cerebellar lesions in human. *Behav. Neurosci.* **107:** 748–756.
97. Clark, G. A., McCormick, D. A., Lavond, D. G., and Thompson, R. F. (1984). Effects of lesions of cerebellar nuclei on conditioned behavioral and hippocampal neuronal response. *Brain Res.* **291:** 125–136.
98. Welsh, J. P., and Harvey, J. A. (1989). Cerebellar lesions and the nictitating membrane reflex: Performance deficits of the conditioned and unconditioned response. *J. Neurosci.* **9:** 299–311.
99. Steinmetz, J. E., Rosen, D. J., Chapman, P. F., Lavond, D. G., and Thompson, R. F. (1986). Classical conditioning of the rabbit eyelid response with a mossy fiber stimulation CS. I. Pontine nuclei and middle cerebellar peduncle stimulation. *Behav. Neurosci.* **100:** 871–880.
100. Steinmetz, J. E., Logan, C. G., Rosen, D. J., Thompson, J. K., Lavond, D. G., and Thompson, R. F. (1987). Initial localization of the acoustic conditioned stimulus projection system to the cerebellum essential for classical eyelid conditioning. *Proc. Natl. Acad. Sci. U.S.A.* **84:** 3531–3535.
101. McCormick, D. A., Steinmetz, J. E., and Thompson, R. F. (1985). Lesions of the inferior olivary complex cause extinction of the classically conditioned eyeblink response. *Brain Res.* **359:** 120–130.
102. Voneida, T., Christie, D., Boganski, R., and Chopko, B. (1990). Changes in instrumentally and classically conditioned limb-flexion responses following inferior olivary lesions and olivocerebellar tractotomy in the cat. *J. Neurosci.* **10:** 3583–3593.
103. Yeo, C. H., Hardiman, M. J., and Glickstein, M. (1986). Classical conditioning of the nictitating membrane response of the rabbit. IV. Lesions of the inferior olive. *Exp. Brain Res.* **63:** 81–92.
104. Mauk, M. D., Steinmetz, J. E., and Thompson, R. F. (1986). Classical conditioning using stimulation of the inferior olive as the unconditioned stimulus. *Proc. Natl. Acad. Sci. U.S.A.* **83:** 5349–5353.
105. Thompson, R. F. (1989). Role of inferior olive in classical conditioning. In *The Olivocerebellar System in Motor Control* (P. Strata, ed.), pp. 347–362. Springer-Verlag, New York.
106. Eccles, J. C. (1977). An instruction-selection theory of learning in the cerebellar cortex. *Brain Res.* **127:** 327–352.
107. Ito, M. (1984). *The Cerebellum and Neural Control.* Appleton Century-Crofts, New York.
108. Thach, W. T., Goodkin, H. G., and Keating, J. G. (1992). The cerebellum and the adaptive coordination of movement. *Annu. Rev. Neurosci.* **15:** 403–442.
109. Clark, R. E., and Lavond, D. G. (1993). Reversible lesions of the red nucleus during acquisition and retention of a classically conditioned behavior in rabbit. *Behav. Neurosci.* **107:** 264–270.
110. Hardiman, M. J., Ramnani, N., and Yeo, C. H. (1996). Reversible inactivations of the cerebellum with muscimol prevent the acquisition and extinction of conditioned nictitating membrane responses in the rabbit. *Exp. Brain Res.* **110:** 235–247.
111. Krupa, D. J., Thompson, J. K., and Thompson, R. F. (1993). Localization of a memory trace in the mammalian brain. *Science* **260:** 989–991.
112. Bracha, V., and Bloedel, J. R. (1996). In *The Acquisition of Motor Behavior in Vertebrates* (J. R. Bloedel, T. J. Ebner, and S. P. Wise, eds.), pp. 175–204. MIT Press, Cambridge, MA.
113. Lavond, D. G., Steinmetz, J. E., Yokaitis, M. H., Lee, J., and Thompson, R. F. (1986). Retention of classical conditioning after removal of cerebellar cortex. *Neurosci. Abstr.* **12:** 753.
114. Yeo, C. H., Hardiman, M. J., and Glickstein, M. (1985). Classical conditioning of the nictitating membrane response of the rabbit. II. Lesions of the cerebellar cortex. *Exp. Brain Res.* **60:** 99–113.
115. Chen, L., Bao, S., Lockard, J. M., Kim, J. J., and Thompson, R. F. (1996). Impaired classical eyeblink conditioning in cerebellar lesioned and Purkinje cell degeneration (pcd) mutant mice. *J. Neurosci.* **16:** 2829–2838.
116. Goldowitz, D., and Eisenman, L. M. (1992). Genetic mutations affecting murine cerebellar structure and function. In *Genetically Defined Animal Models of Neurobehavioral Dysfunctions* (P. Driscoll, ed.), pp. 66–88. Birkhaeuser, Boston.
117. Ito, M., Sukurai, M., and Tongroach, P. (1982). Climbing fibre induced depression of both mossy fibre responsiveness and glutamate sensitivity of cerebellar Purkinje cells. *J. Physiol. London* **324:** 113–134.
118. Ito, M. (1989). Long-term depression. *Annu. Rev. Neurosci.* **12:** 85–102.
119. Ito, M. (1993). Cerebellar mechanisms of long-term depression. In *Synaptic Plasticity: Molecular and Functional Aspects* (M. Baudry, J. L. Davis, and R. F. Thompson, eds.), pp. 117–146. MIT Press, Cambridge, MA.
120. du Lac, S., Raymond, J. L., Sejnowski, T. J., and Lisberger, S. G. (1995). Learning and memory in the vestibulo-ocular reflex. *Annu. Rev. Neurosci.* **18:** 409–441.
121. Linden, D. J., and Conner, J. A. (1991). Participation of postsynaptic PKC in cerebellar long-term depression in culture. *Science* **254:** 1656–1659.
122. Linden, D. J., and Conner, J. A. (1995). Long-term synaptic depression. *Annu. Rev. Neurosci.* **18:** 319–357.
123. Kim, J. J., Chen, L., Bao, S., Sun, W., and Thompson, R. F. (1996). Genetic dissections of the cerebellar circuitry involved in classical eyeblink conditioning. In *Gene Targeting and New Developments in Neurobiology* (S. Nakanishi, A. J. Silva, S. Aizawa, and M. Katsuki, eds.), pp. 3–15. Japan Scientific Societies Press, Tokyo.
124. Aiba, A., Kano, M., Chen, C., Stanton, M. E., Fox, G. D., Herrup, K., Zwingman, T. A., and Tonegawa, S. (1994). Deficient cerebellar long-term depression and impaired motor learning in mGluR1 mutant mice. *Cell (Cambridge, Mass.)* **79:** 377–388.
125. Chen, C., Masanobu, K., Abeliovich, A., Chen, L., Bao, S., Kim, J. J., Hashimoto, K., Thompson, R. F., and Tonegawa, S. (1995). Impaired motor coordination correlates with persistent multiple climbing fiber innervation in PKCγ mutant mice. *Cell (Cambridge, Mass.)* **83:** 1233–1242.
126. Shibuki, K., Gomi, H., Chen, C., Bao, S., Kim, J. J., Wakatsuki, H., Fujisaki, T., Fujimoto, K., Ikeda, T., Chen, C., Thompson, R. F., and Itohara, S. (1996). Deficient cerebellar long-term depression, impaired eyeblink conditioning and normal motor coordination in GFAP mutant mice. *Neuron* **16:** 587–599.
127. Supple, W. F., Jr., and Leaton, R. N. (1990). Lesions of the cerebellar vermis and cerebellar hemispheres: Effects on heart rate conditioning in rats. *Behav. Neurosci.* **104:** 934–947.
128. Steinmetz, J. E., Logue, S. F., and Miller D. P. (1993). Using signaled barpressing tasks to study the neural substrates of appetitive and aversive learning in rats: Behavioral manipulations and cerebellar lesions. *Behav. Neurosci.* **107:** 941–954.
129. Pellegrino, L. J., and Altman, J. (1979). Effects of differential interference with postnatal cerebellar neurogenesis on motor performance, activity level and maze learning of rats: A developmental study. *J. Comp. Physiol. Psychol.* **93:** 1–33.
130. Goodlett, C. R., Hamre, K. M., and West, J. R. (1992). Dissociation of spatial navigation and visual guidance performance in Purkinje cell degeneration (pcd) mutant mice. *Behav. Brain Res.* **47:** 129–141.

131. Lalonde, R., and Botez, M. I. (1990). The cerebellum and learning processes in animals. *Brain Res. Rev.* **15:** 325–332.
132. Keele, S. W., and Ivry, R. B. (1990). Does the cerebellum provide a common computation for diverse tasks: A timing hypothesis. In *The Development and Neural Bases of Higher Cognitive Functions* (A. Diamond, ed.), pp. 179–211. N.Y. Acad. Sci. Press, New York.
133. Schmahmann, J. D., ed. (1997). *International Review of Neurobiology,* Vol. 41. Academic Press, San Diego, CA.
134. Knudsen, E. I. (1994). Supervised learning in the brain. *J. Neurosci.* **14:** 3985–3997.
135. LeDoux, J. E. (1995). Emotion: Clues from the brain. *Annu. Rev. Psychol.* **46:** 209–235.
136. Kapp, B. S., Wilson, A., Pascoe, J., Supple, W., and Whalen, P. J. (1990). A neuroanatomical systems analysis of conditioned bradycardia in the rabbit. In *Learning and Computational Neuroscience: Foundations of Adaptive Networks* (M. Gabriel and J. Moore, eds.), pp. 53–90. MIT Press, Cambridge, MA.
137. Davis, M. (1992). The role of the amygdala in fear and anxiety. *Annu. Rev. Neurosci.* **15:** 353–375.
138. LeDoux, J. E. (1992). Brain mechanisms of emotion and emotional learning. *Curr. Opin. Neurobiol.* **2:** 191–197.
139. Phillips, R. G., and LeDoux, J. E. (1992). Differential contribution of amygdala and hippocampus to cued and contextual fear conditioning. *Behav. Neurosci.* **106:** 274–285.
140. Morgan, M. A., and LeDoux, J. E. (1995). Differential contribution of dorsal and ventral medial prefrontal cortex to the acquisition and extinction of conditioned fear in rats. *Behav. Neurosci.* **109:** 681–688.
141. Weinberger, N. M. (1995). Returning the brain by fear conditioning. In *The Cognitive Neurosciences* (M. S. Gazzaniga, ed.), pp. 1071–1089. MIT Press, Cambridge, MA.
142. Armony, J. L., Servan-Schreiber, D., Cohen, J. D., and LeDoux, J. E. (1995). An anatomically constrained neural network model of fear conditioning. *Behav. Neurosci.* **109:** 246–257.
143. Eysenck, H. J. (1979). The conditioning model of neurosis. *Behav. Brain Sci.* **2:** 155–199.
144. Charney, D. S., Deutch, A. Y., Krystal, J. H., Southwick, S. M., and Davis, M. (1993). Psychobiologic mechanisms of posttraumatic stress disorder. *Arch. Gen. Psychiatry* **50:** 295–305.
145. Adolphs, R., Tranel, D., Damasio, H., and Damasio, A. R. (1994). Impaired recognition of emotion in facial expressions following bilateral damage to the human amygdala. *Nature (London)* **372:** 669–672.
146. Marks, I., and Tobena, A. (1990). Learning and unlearning fear: A clinical and evolutionary perspective. *Neurosci. Biobehav. Rev.* **14:** 365–384.
147. Bliss, T. V. P., and Lomo, T. (1973). Long-lasting potentiation of synaptic transmission in the dentate area of the anaesthetized rabbit following stimulation of the perforant path. *J. Physiol. (London)* **232:** 331–356.
148. Dingledine, R., ed. (1984). *Brain Slices.* Plenum, New York.
149. Barrionuevo, G., and Brown, T. H. (1983). Associative long-term potentiation in hippocampal slices. *Proc. Natl. Acad. Sci. U.S.A.* **80:** 7347–7351.
150. Kelso, S. R., and Brown, T. H. (1986). Differential conditioning of associative synaptic enhancement in hippocampal brain slices. *Science* **232:** 85–87.
151. Barrionuevo, G., Kelso, S., Johnston, D., and Brown, T. H. (1986). Conductance mechanism responsible for long-term potentiation in monosynaptic and isolated excitatory synaptic inputs to the hippocampus. *J. Neurophysiol.* **55:** 540–550.
152. Xiang, Z., Greenwood, A. C., Kairiss, E. W., and Brown, T. H. (1994). Quantal mechanisms of long-term potentiation in hippocampal mossy-fiber synapses. *J. Neurophysiol.* **71:** 2552–2556.
153. Brown, T. H., Ganong, A. H., Kairiss, E. W., and Keenan, C. L. (1990). Hebbian synapses: Biophysical mechanisms and algorithms. *Annu. Rev. Neurosci.* **13:** 475–512.
154. Bliss, T. V. P., and Collingridge, G. L. (1993). A synaptic model of memory: Long-term potentiation in the hippocampus. *Nature (London)* **361:** 31–39.
155. McNaughton, B. L., Douglass, R. M., and Goddard, G. V. (1978). Synaptic enhancements in fascia dentata: Cooperativity among coactive efferents. *Brain Res.* **157:** 277–293.
156. Levy, W. B., and Steward, O. (1983). Temporal contiguity requirements for long-term associative potentiation/depression in the hippocampus. *Neuroscience* **8:** 791–797.
157. Lynch, G. S., Dunwiddie, T., and Gribkoff, V. (1977). Heterosynaptic depression: A postsynaptic correlate of long-term potentiation. *Nature (London)* **266:** 737–739.
158. Kelso, S. R., Ganong, A. H., and Brown, T. H. (1986). Hebbian synapses in hippocampus. *Proc. Natl. Acad. Sci. U.S.A.* **83:** 5326–5330.
159. Johnston, D., Williams, D., Jaffe, D., and Gray, R. (1992). NMDA-receptor-independent long-term potentiation. *Annu. Rev. Physiol.* **54:** 489–505.
160. Nicoll, R. A., and Malenka, R. C. (1995). Contrasting properties of two forms of long-term potentiation in the hippocampus. *Nature (London)* **377:** 115–118.
161. Teyler, T. J., Cavus, I., Coussens, C., DiScenna, P., Grover, L., Lee, Y. P., and Little, Z. (1994). Multideterminant role of calcium in hippocampal synaptic plasticity. *Hippocampus* **4**(6): 623–634.
162. Magee, J., and Johnston, D. (1997). A synaptically controlled, associative signal for Hebbian plasticity in hippocampal neurons. *Science* **275:** 209–213.
163. Zador, A., Koch, C., and Brown, T. H. (1990). Biophysical model of a Hebbian synapse. *Proc. Natl. Acad. Sci. U.S.A.* **87**(16): 6718–6722.
164. Holmes, W. R., and Levy, W. B. (1990). Insights into associative long-term potentiation from computational models of NMDA receptor-mediated calcium influx and intracellular calcium changes. *J. Neurophysiol.* **63:** 1148–1168.
165. Grover, L. M., and Teyler, T. J. (1995). Different mechanisms may be required for maintenance of NMDA receptor-dependent and independent forms of long-term potentiation. *Synapse* **19**(2): 121–133.
166. Bashir, Z. I., Bortolotto, Z. A., Davies, C. H., Beretta, N., Irving, A. J., Seal, A. J., Henley, J. M., Jane, D. E., Watkins, J. C., and Collingridge, G. L. (1993). Induction of LTP in hippocampus needs synaptic activation of glutamate metabotropic receptors. *Nature (London)* **363:** 69–72.
167. Bortolotto, Z. A., Bashir, Z. I., Davies, C. H., and Collingridge, G. L. (1994). A molecular switch activated by metabotropic glutamate receptors regulates induction of long-term potentiation. *Nature (London)* **368:** 740–743.
168. Selig, D. K., Lee, H. K., Bear, M. F., and Malenka, R. C. (1995). Reexamination of the effects of MCPG on hippocampal LTP, LTD, and depotentiation. *J. Neurophysiol.* **74**(3): 1075–1082.
169. Bear, M. F., and Malenka, R. C. (1994). Synaptic plasticity: LTP and LTD. *Curr. Opin. Neurobiol.* **4:** 389–399.
170. Dudek, S. M., and Bear, M. F. (1992). Homosynaptic long-term depression in area CA1 of hippocampus and effects of N-methyl-d-aspartate receptor blockade. *Proc. Natl. Acad. Sci. U.S.A.* **89:** 4363–4367.
171. Hirsch, J. C., and Crepel, F. (1991). Blockade of NMDA receptors unmasks a long-term depression in synaptic efficacy in rat prefrontal neurons *in vitro. Exp. Brain Res.* **85**(3): 621–624.

172. Mulkey, R. M., and Malenka, R. C. (1992). Mechanisms underlying induction of homosynaptic long-term depression in area CA1 of the hippocampus. *Neuron* **9:** 967–975.
173. Lisman, J. (1989). A mechanism for the Hebb and the anti-Hebb processes underlying learning and memory. *Proc. Natl. Acad. Sci. U.S.A.* **86:** 9574–9578.
174. Larkman, A. U., and Jack, J. B. (1995). Synaptic plasticity: Hippocampal LTP. *Curr. Opin. Neurobiol.* **5:** 324–334.
175. Brown, T. H., Ganong, A. H., Kairiss, E. W., Keenan, C. L., and Kelso, S. R. (1989). Long-term potentiation in two synaptic systems of the hippocampal brain slice. In *Neural Models of Plasticity* (J. Byrne and W. Berry, eds.), pp. 266–306. Academic Press, Orlando, FL.
176. Baxter, D. A., Bittner, G. D., and Brown, T. H. (1985). Quantal mechanism of long-term synaptic potentiation. *Proc. Natl. Acad. Sci. U.S.A.* **82:** 5978–5982.
177. Malinow, R. (1994). LTP: Desperately seeking resolution. *Science* **266:** 1195–1196.
178. Matthies, H. (1989). In search of cellular mechanisms of memory. *Prog. Neurobiol.* **32:** 277–349.
179. Nguyen, P. V., Abel, T., and Kandel, E. R. (1994). Requirement of a critical period of transcription for induction of a late phase of LTP. *Science* **265:** 1104–1107.
180. Krug, M., Loessner, B., and Ott, T. (1984). Anisomycin blocks the late phase of long-term potentiation in the dentate gyrus of freely moving rats. *Brain Res. Bull.* **13:** 39–42.
181. Alberini, C. M., Ghirardi, M., Huang, Y. Y., Nguyen, P. V., and Kandel, E. R. (1995). A molecular switch for the consolidation of long-term memory: cAMP-inducible gene expression. *Ann. N.Y. Acad. Sci.* **758:** 261–286.
182. Huang, Y.-Y., Nguyen, P. V., Abel, T., and Kandel, E. R. (1996). Long-lasting forms of synaptic potentiation in the mammalian hippocampus. *Learn. Mem.* **3:** 74–85.
183. Frey, U., and Morris, R. G. M. (1997). Synaptic tagging and long-term potentiation. *Nature (London)* **385:** 533–536.
184. Barnes, C. A. (1995). Involvement of LTP in memory: Are we "Searching under the street light?" *Neuron* **15:** 751–754.
185. Brown, T. H., Chapman, P., Kairiss, E. W., and Keenan, C. L. (1988). Long-term potentiation. *Science* **242:** 724–728.
186. Wilson, M. A., and Tonegawa, S. (1997). Synaptic plasticity, place cells and spatial memory: Study with second generation knockouts. *Trends Neurosci.* **20**(3): 102–106.

C H A P T E R

56

Learning and Memory: Systems Analysis

Howard B. Eichenbaum, Lawrence F. Cahill, Mark A. Gluck, Michael E. Hasselmo, Frank C. Keil, Alex J. Martin, James L. McGaugh, Jaap Murre, Catherine Myers, Michael Petrides, Benno Roozendaal, Daniel L. Schacter, Daniel J. Simons, W. Carter Smith, and Cedric L. Williams

Memory is a remarkable property of the brain. It allows us to accomplish numerous tasks that are essential to our everyday lives: recalling personal experiences, learning facts and gaining conceptual knowledge, recognizing objects and people, and acquiring skills and habits. Scientific thinking about memory was dominated for many years by the assumption that memory is a unitary or monolithic entity—a single faculty of the mind and brain. However, the assumption of a unitary memory has been challenged by converging evidence from psychology and neuroscience pointing toward multiple memory systems that can be dissociated from one another. This chapter provides a historical introduction to the issue and summarizes key concepts and findings pertinent to our current understanding of memory systems. We will first discuss experimental characterizations of **multiple memory systems** in humans and in animals. Following this, we outline four rapidly evolving directions in memory research: development of computational models of hippocampal memory function, progress in understanding the semantic structure of permanent knowledge, identification of frontal lobe functions in working memory, and discoveries about hormonal modulators of memory.

THE NOTION OF MULTIPLE MEMORY SYSTEMS

Although an intensive focus on multiple memory systems is a relatively recent development, the idea that memory is not a monolithic entity has roots in the 19th century (for detailed historical discussions, see Schacter[1] and Zola-Morgan[2]). Two early proponents of the idea were the European thinkers Franz Joseph Gall and Maine de Biran. Gall, founder of the phrenological movement, focused on the notion that each specialized faculty of the mind is concerned with particular contents (e.g., music, mathematics) and maintains its own memory.[3] Gall believed that the differential developmental of these separate faculties accounted for the common observation that some people can remember certain kinds of information very well but have great difficulty remembering other kinds of information. As we shall see, Gall's ideas bear little relation to modern notions of memory systems. The philosopher Maine de Biran distinguished among three different types of memory: *representative memory,* concerned with recollection of ideas and events; *mechanical memory,* concerned with acquisition of habits and skills; and *sensitive memory,* concerned with memory for feelings. In contrast to Gall, Maine de Biran's distinctions in some respect anticipate the modern conceptualizations that are the focus of this chapter.[4] The notion of a nonunitary memory also received some attention from late 19th-century neurologists, who envisaged a series of *memory centers* that are specialized to handle different kinds of information, including centers for auditory, visual, and motor memories. Indeed, in 1881 the French psychologist Theodule Ribot[5] noted that "if, in the normal condition of the organisms, the different forms of memory are relatively independent, it is natural that, if in a morbid state one disappears, the others should remain intact."

After this promising beginning, ideas about multiple forms of memory virtually disappeared during the first half of the 20th century, with the exception of the philosopher Bergson's distinction between recollective memory and habit learning.[6] However, shortly after World War II, a number of proposals appeared: Tolman[7] argued for a distinction between *cognitive maps*

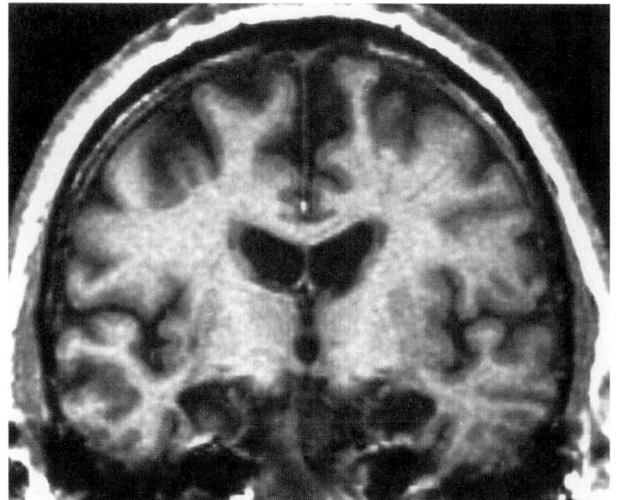

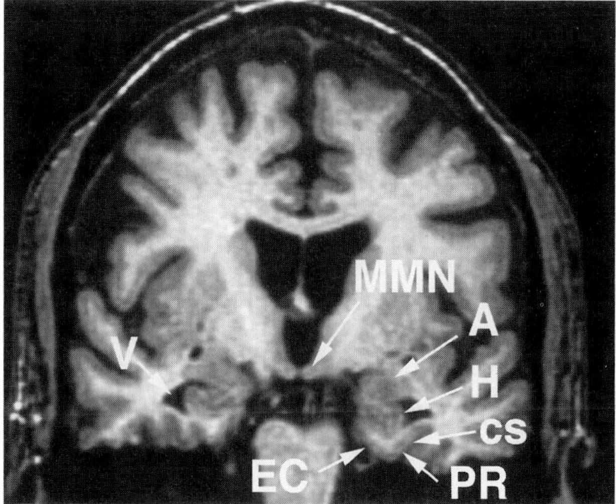

FIGURE 56.1 Left: Magnetic resonance imaging scan showing the removal of medial temporal lobe structures in the patient H.M. The lesion included most of the entorhinal cortex, the amygdala, and about two-thirds of the hippocampus. Right: Scan of a normal control subject showing the structures removed in H.M. A, amygdala; cs, calcarine sulcus; EC, entorhinal cortex; H, hippocampus; MMN, medial mammillary nucleus; PR, perirhinal cortex. From Corkin *et al.*[12]

and *response habits*, the philosopher Ryle[8] distinguished between "knowing how" and "knowing that," psychologists Reiff and Scheerer[9] proposed that "remembrances" (memories of personal experiences) differ fundamentally from "memoria" (general knowledge and skills), and the neurologist Nielsen[10] proposed a similar distinction between "temporal memory" and "categorical memory."

The Discovery of Selective Memory Deficits Supports Distinctions between Memory Systems

It was not until the 1960s and 1970s that efforts to experimentally dissociate memory systems emerged as a central research direction in psychology and neuroscience. Much of the new interest was stimulated by observations concerning the famous amnesic patient H.M., who had a complete bilateral resection of the medial temporal lobes for relief of intractable epilepsy[11] (Fig. 56.1).[12] As first discussed in Chapter 53, although H.M. exhibited little ability to retain and recollect new information across a delay, he had no difficulties with immediate or short-term retention, providing important support for the distinction between short- and long-term memory systems. The observations that H.M. could learn new motor skills and that other amnesic patients sometimes exhibited normal or near-normal learning when tested with special procedures raised the possibility that different kinds of long-term memory could be distinguished. See Box 56.1.

Although the implications of these observations for the notion of dissociable memory systems were not immediately apparent, the finding that amnesic patients could exhibit some kind of new learning despite poor recollection of their recent experiences proved central to the development of later ideas about multiple memory systems.[1,13] At the same time, studies of animals revealed that removing the hippocampus affects performance on some memory tasks while sparing others, leading to a variety of new proposals about dissociable memory systems.[14] In cognitive psychology, Tulving[15] put forth the highly influential distinction between episodic memory and semantic memory, which served to stimulate debate concerning the nature and number of long-term memory systems. Taken together, these developments set the stage for an explosive growth in research and theorizing about dissociable memory systems that has continued into the present. This research involves parallel (and converging) efforts to dissociate memory systems in humans and animals, each of which will be described in turn.

Summary

The notion that there are different forms of memory has a long history, dating at least from phrenology. Several proposals distinguished many faculties of the mind and included ideas about fundamentally distinct

BOX 56.1

CASE HISTORY OF H.M.

This 27-year-old motor winder, a high school graduate, had had minor seizures since the age of 10 and major seizures since the age of 16. Despite heavy and varied anticonvulsant medication, the major attacks had increased in frequency and severity through the years until the patient was quite unable to work. The etiology of this patient's attacks is not clear. He was knocked down by a bicycle at the age of 9 and was unconscious for 5 min afterward, sustaining a laceration of the left supraorbital region. Later radiological studies, however, including two pneumoencephalograms, have been completely normal, and the physical examination has always been negative. Electroencephalographic studies have consistently failed to show any localized epileptogenic area. On September 1, 1953, bilateral medial temporal-lobe resection was carried out, extending posteriorly for a distance of 8 cm from the midpoints of the tips of the temporal lobes, with the temporal horns constituting the lateral edges of resection.

After operation, the patient was drowsy for a few days, but his subsequent recovery was uneventful apart from the grave memory loss already described. There has been no neurological deficit. An electroencephalogram taken 1 year after operation showed increased spike-and-wave activity, which was maximal over the frontal areas and bilaterally synchronous. He continues to have seizures, but these are less incapacitating than before.

A *psychological examination* was performed on April 26, 1955. The memory defect was immediately apparent. The patient gave the date as March 1953, and his age as 27. Just before coming into the examining room, he had been talking to Dr. Karl Pribram, yet he had no recollection of this at all and denied that anyone had spoken to him. In conversation, he reverted constantly to boyhood events and seemed scarcely to realize that he had had an operation.

On formal testing, the contrast between his good general intelligence and his defective memory was most striking. On the Wechsler-Bellevue Intelligence Scale, he achieved a full-scale IQ rating of 112, which compares favorably with the preoperative rating of 104, the improvement in arithmetic being particularly striking. An extensive test battery failed to reveal any deficits in perception, abstract thinking, or reasoning ability, and his motivation remained excellent throughout.

On the Wechsler Memory Scale his immediate recall of stories and drawings fell far below the average level and on the "associate learning" subtest of this scale he obtained zero scores for the hard word associations, low scores for the easy associations, and failed to improve with repeated practice. These findings are reflected in the low memory quotient of 67. Moreover, on all tests we found that once he had turned to a new task the nature of the preceding one could no longer be recalled; nor the test recognized if repeated.

In summary, this patient appears to have a complete loss of memory for events subsequent to bilateral medial temporal lobe resection 19 months before, together with a partial retrograde amnesia for the 3 years leading up to his operation, but early memories are seemingly normal and there is no impairment of personality or general intelligence.

Edited from Scoville and Milner.[11]

types of memory based on philosophical considerations. The modern era of research on multiple memory systems began with the discovery that selective brain damage could result in severe impairment in one form of memory without affecting other learning capacities. This has spawned a large number of proposals about memory systems in the brain.

DISSOCIABLE MEMORY SYSTEMS IN HUMANS

Many researchers have advanced distinctions between various types or forms of memory, but only some of these distinctions refer to dissociable memory systems. Schacter and Tulving[16] have suggested that a *memory system* meets three key criteria:

1. It is a set of interrelated brain processes that allow one to store and retrieve a specific type or class of information.
2. It can be characterized in terms of lists of properties that describe its mode of operation.
3. It can be dissociated from other systems on the basis of converging evidence from psychology and neuroscience.

In contrast, different *forms* of memory can refer to different tasks (e.g., recognition memory versus recall memory) or types of information (visual versus auditory) without any necessary implication that different memory systems are involved. For example, major distinctions have been made between explicit and implicit memory and between declarative and nondeclarative memory.[13] Both explicit and declarative memory are distinctions characterized by conscious recollection of past experiences, whereas implicit and nondeclarative memory are characterized as unconscious influences of those experiences revealed in changes in the speed or biases with which the same or a similar task is performed. Having read this paragraph, for example, you will be able to recall facts about memory and the experience of reading the texbook using explicit, declarative memory. You will also be able to reread the identical paragraph more rapidly, and you will tend to select the same words to describe memory, using your implicit, nondeclarative memory. Schacter focused on implicit and explicit memory as different ways of *expressing* the effects of past experiences, leaving open the question whether it is necessary to postulate dissociable systems to account for differences between the two. Squire[17] characterized declarative memory in terms of a brain system, tying this type of memory to a biologically identifiable substrate, namely, the medial temporal lobe. He distinguished this type of memory from **nondeclarative memory**, a descriptive concept that refers to a collection of different learning abilities mediated by brain structures outside the medial temporal lobe.

Five Major Memory Systems Have Been Identified in Studies on Humans

Although concepts of memory systems are still evolving, converging evidence from psychology and neuroscience points to at least five major systems in humans: episodic memory, semantic memory, the perceptual representation system, procedural memory, and working memory.

Episodic Memory

Episodic memory is the explicit recollection of incidents that occurred at a particular time and place in one's personal past. Episodic memories are characterized by what William James in 1890[18] called "warmth and intimacy," which identify them as personal experiences that are the *property* of the self. In the laboratory, researchers attempt to measure episodic memory by asking people to recollect information acquired at a specific time and place in the past. Damage to the medial or inner parts of temporal lobes, including the hippocampal formation, greatly impairs the acquisition of new episodic memories. Patients with organic amnesic syndromes resulting from damage to the medial temporal region invariably have serious impairments of episodic memory: they are unable to remember ongoing events in their day-to-day lives, and they perform poorly on laboratory tests that require episodic memory.

Regions within the prefrontal cortex play a key role in episodic memory. Although patients with selective damage to prefrontal regions do not develop a profound amnesia for recent events, they have great difficulty remembering when and where recent events occurred—the defining features of episodic memory. For instance, patients with frontal lobe lesions have great difficulty remembering the temporal order of two events.[19] Similarly, frontal lobe damage often produces a phenomenon known as source amnesia, in which patients can acquire new facts but fail to recollect when or where they learned them. Source memory problems have also been noted in elderly adults, who often exhibit signs of frontal lobe pathology, and in young children, who have immature frontal functions. Damage to the frontal lobes can also produce striking distortions of episodic memory in which patients claim to remember events that never occurred.[20]

Episodic memory has been investigated using positron emission tomography (PET scanning) to measure regional cerebral blood flow. These studies have consistently revealed frontal lobe activation during episodic memory tasks.[21,22] In some studies, right frontal regions show greater activation than left frontal regions during episodic retrieval, and left frontal regions show greater activation than right frontal regions during episodic encoding. In contrast, activation in the medial temporal lobe, including the hippocampus, is observed during both encoding and retrieval (Fig. 56.2).[23–25] Prefrontal regions show activation when subjects make extensive efforts to recall recently presented information, whereas the hippocampal formation becomes active during the actual recollection of that information. Thus, both prefrontal and medial temporal regions play important roles in episodic memory, although the exact nature of their contributions appears to differ (see later for further discussions of medial temporal lobe contributions).

Semantic Memory

Semantic memory refers to general knowledge of facts and concepts that is not linked to any particular time and place. Episodic memory is critical for remembering a specific visit to the city of Paris, for example, whereas semantic memory is important for knowing that Paris is the capital of France. The acquisition of new semantic memories (like the acquisition of new episodic memories) depends on the integrity of the

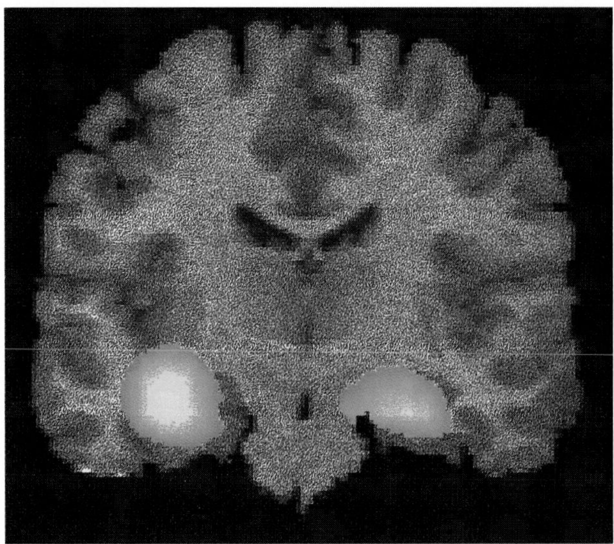

FIGURE 56.2 Brain scan showing activation of the medial temporal lobe during encoding of pictures. From Martin *et al.*[23]

medial temporal lobes. For instance, amnesic patients have great difficulty acquiring new vocabulary and factual knowledge, although they can acquire large amounts of new semantic knowledge when that information is presented repeatedly. Whereas the outputs of episodic memory contribute to an experience of *remembering* the contextual details of a past event, the outputs of semantic memory contribute to an experience of *knowing*, or being familiar with a fact or association.[26] Remembering and knowing can be measured by asking people to judge whether they *remember* details associated with the presentation of a word or picture earlier in an experiment (e.g., what they thought about or what the item looked like) or whether they just *know* that it occurred because it seems familiar. Amnesic patients make fewer *remember* and fewer *know* judgments about recent events than nonamnesic control subjects, a phenomenon that suggests they have impairments in both episodic and semantic memory.

Because the acquisition of new memories, both episodic and semantic, depends on the integrity of the medial temporal region, episodic and semantic memory can be referred to collectively as declarative memory. However, episodic and semantic memory can be dissociated from one another. For example, a profoundly amnesic patient known by the initials K.C. was unable to recollect a single episode from any time in his entire life.[27] K.C. sustained head injuries that resulted in extensive damage to medial temporal and frontal regions. Nonetheless, K.C. possessed extensive semantic knowledge of facts and concepts and was able to acquire novel factual information with repetition, although at a rate slower than normal. In a contrasting case,[28] a patient with damage to the anterior sectors of the temporal lobe appeared to have little difficulty remembering specific past episodes, but had great difficulty understanding the meaning of common words and had lost knowledge of historical events. Similarly, elderly patients characterized by the syndrome of semantic dementia have an extremely impoverished knowledge of the properties of specific objects, yet show generally intact episodic memory. Evidence from neuroimaging studies of such patients has revealed reduced metabolic activity and structural atrophy in the anterior and lateral regions of the temporal lobe, particularly in the left hemisphere, and suggests that these regions play important roles in the semantic memory system.[29] See Box 56.2.

Perceptual Representation System

The perceptual representation system (PRS) plays in important role in the identification of words and objects on the basis of their form and structure. PRS operates at a presemantic level and is not involved in representing associative or conceptual information, which is the province of semantic memory. PRS can be classified into at least three major subsystems: a visual word form subsystem that handles information about physical and orthographic features, an auditory word form system that handles phonological and acoustic information, and a structural description subsystem that handles information about the relations between parts of an object that specify its global form and structure. Even further divisions within subsystems may be necessary—for example, between abstract representations of general properties of words or objects and specific representations of their precise features.

Some evidence for a dissociation between the PRS and semantic memory comes from studies of patients who exhibit relatively intact knowledge of the form and structure of words and objects despite impaired access to their meaning or functional properties (discussed later). In support of this view, PET scanning studies have revealed that specific regions within the extrastriate occipital cortex are involved in processing and representing the visual form of words, whereas regions within the temporal and frontal cortices are involved with word meaning. Likewise, evidence from studies of both monkeys and human patients with brain lesions,[30] as well as PET data,[31,32] suggests that regions near the occipital temporal junction, such as the inferior temporal gyrus and fusiform gyrus, are involved in representing the global structure of an object.

The PRS also appears to play a prominent role in the phenomenon of **priming.** In priming tasks, a sub-

BOX 56.2

CASE HISTORY OF K.C.

K.C. was delivered during the seventh month of pregnancy. The postnatal period and infancy were uneventful. Developmental milestones were normal. However, at age 18, he received a blow to the head that resulted in admission to the Montreal Neurological Institute and observation for 3 days. He was discharged on phenytoin and phenobarbitol and remained on these anticonvulsants for 1 year. He had no seizures, but did not reenter school for 1 year. At age 24, he was involved in a traffic accident, without loss of consciousness, and sustained a fractured mandible. Although painful, neither of the head injuries appeared to have deleterious effects on K.C.'s intellectual functioning. After graduating from high school, he enrolled in a 3-year course in business administration at a community college and graduated at age 25. In the spring of 1978, age 27 years, he became employed at an engineering and manufacturing company. His job consisted of two activities: driving a delivery and pick-up truck and doing quality-control work.

The accident responsible for K.C.'s present condition occurred October 1981, at age 30. Riding his motorcycle home from work, he went off the road. No other vehicles were involved in the accident. He remained unconscious for approximately 72 h, when a subdural hematoma was removed from the left cranium. He then became stuporous, but responded to commands for about the next 4–5 days. At approximately the seventh posttraumatic day he appeared to recognize his mother. The patient remained in an intensive care unit for 4 weeks. He was transferred to a rehabilitation hospital 6 weeks after the accident and exhibited a severe right hemiplegia. He was discharged home in July 1982, where he has remained in the care of his parents.

Neurological examination on December 12, 1986, revealed an alert, cooperative individual who responded appropriately to all questions. The most striking feature was a marked apathy, flattening of affect, and general indifference to his surroundings.

Computerized axial tomography and magnetic resonance imaging scans of the head were performed. There is mild cerebral and cortical atrophy as evidenced by enlargement of the sulci, ventricles, and cerebellar folia. There is evidence of contusion in the deep white matter of the left frontal-parietal region and right parieto-occipital region (magnetic resonance scan). There is an infarct in the distribution of the left posterior cerebral artery and a large defect in the left frontal-parietal region subadjacent to the previous craniotomy.

K.C. is a quiet, polite, and cooperative person. He seldom complains about anything. In response to direct questions, he says that his life is good, although he concedes that he has problems with his memory. When left alone for a longer period of time, he shows no restlessness or agitation. When he is engaged in conversation, he pays close attention to other speakers, his attention does not wander, he stays alert throughout, and he always responds appropriately. He has good manners and displays no social disinhibitions. With the exception of memory-related items and frontal-lobe deficits, K.C. would receive normal ratings on the Neurobehavioral Rating Scale.

Formal neuropsychological testing has shown that outside the domain of memory, K.C.'s intellectual functions are largely preserved. On the Wechsler Adult Intelligence Scale—Revised, he achieved a full-scale IQ of 94 (Verbal, 98, Performance, 91). Language comprehension is intact (Token Test, 33), and performance on the Benton Visual Naming Test falls within the normal range. K.C. does have problems on the Benton Word Fluency (FAS) Test, scoring in the 4th percentile. In contrast, he achieves five categories on the Wisconsin Card Sorting Test. The discrepancy between these two tests, both of which are known to be sensitive to frontal-lobe pathology, may appear surprising, although it is not without precedent. K.C. does exhibit a number of other classic frontal signs: He virtually never initiates any optional activity on his own, has difficulty planning complex actions, and does not respond when given broad directions (e.g., "Write a brief summary of your life.") He cannot describe his own future, regardless of the time span specified in the question—"this afternoon," "tomorrow," or "next summer." When asked to describe the state of his mind when he is trying to think about any part of his past or future, he says that it is "blank."

Most of K.C.'s perceptual functions are normal: his final copy of the Rey figure is perfect, and his performance on the Hooper Visual Organization Test, which requires perceptual integration of fragments of parts of line-drawn objects, is normal. He readily identifies himself, members of the family, and old friends from photographs and snapshots. Even when shown a recent snapshot of himself, his mother, and one of the authors of this article playing cards at the latter's house, he recognizes all people without difficulty (although he has no idea where or when the snapshot was taken). His ability to imagine familiar objects visually and describe these verbally seems to be normal. However, he does have difficulty with the kind of fine perceptual discrimination tested by the Benton Facial Recognition Test: he receives a score of zero on the test.

K.C.'s thought processes are normal: there are no signs of confusion or disorganization of any kind. He does not confabulate. When he does not know the answer to a question, he says so. When he provides an answer and is then asked whether he is sure or only guessing, he may respond either way. Once he makes the response, he cannot be easily dissuaded.

K.C. can provide good descriptions of scripted activities, the kinds of well-organized action sequences in which people frequently engage in their daily life—for instance, going to a restaurant, making a long-distance telephone call, or changing a flat tire. He does all this without any recollection of ever having done any of these things himself.

His short-term memory is essentially normal: His digit span is normal, and he has no difficulty remembering the last two or three items in a meaningful paired-associate list. When he is not distracted, he can hold even a long question in mind for at least up to a minute. His preserved short-term memory capacity is sufficient to play a hand of hearts, or of bridge, without any apparent handicap.

K.C.'s ability to learn new information is very poor. His MQ on the Wechsler Memory Scale is 79.5, which is probably inflated by his good short-term memory. He scores zero on both immediate and delayed tests of the "hard" associates, and also scores zero on delayed story recall and visual reproduction. His performance on Warrington's Recognition Memory Test, measured on two different occasions, was at chance for both faces and words: His false-alarm rate was as high as his hit rate.

Edited from Tulving *et al.*[27]

ject first studies a word or picture and subsequently is presented with only part of the same item. Priming is demonstrated as an improvement in the ability to identify the partial item following the recent exposure to the entire item. Priming appears to operate unconsciously, in the sense that people can exhibit effects of priming under conditions in which they lack explicit memory for having studied a word or object. Most importantly, amnesic patients exhibit intact priming across a wide variety of tasks, materials, and situations, including visual word and nonword priming, auditory word priming, and priming of novel visual objects and patterns. These findings indicate that priming does not depend on the medial temporal structures that mediate explicit remembering and are consistent with the idea that the posterior cortical regions that constitute the PRS are involved in priming.

Procedural Memory

Procedural memory refers to the acquisition of skills and habits, that is, "knowing how" rather than "knowing that." Procedural memories are acquired gradually through repetitive practice. Studies of amnesic patients have revealed that even patients with a profound inability to explicitly remember past experiences can gradually acquire new perceptual, motor, and cognitive skills, habits that are involved in classification and categorization, and implicit knowledge of sequences or grammatical rules. These results show clearly that the acquisition of procedural knowledge does not depend on the medial temporal lobe structures that are damaged in amnesic patients.

A variety of studies support the conclusion that procedural memory depends critically on a corticostriatal system. For instance, patients with Huntington disease, which is characterized by damage to the basal ganglia, have difficulties acquiring new motor skills, despite relatively intact explicit memory—the exact opposite of the pattern exhibited by amnesic patients.[33] Recent neuroimaging evidence also implicates the basal ganglia, as well as the motor cortex, in procedural learning.[34] The cerebellum, too, is involved in some forms of procedural memory: patients with cerebellar damage have great difficulty learning to execute sequences of movements.[35] Because none of these structures is routinely impaired in amnesic patients, procedural memory must depend on a system different from that in either episodic or semantic memory.

Working Memory

The memory systems considered so far are all concerned with long-term retention spanning time periods of minutes, hours, weeks, and years. In contrast, *working memory* is concerned with short-term retention, operating over periods of seconds. Working memory is used to hold information on-line in the service of such basic cognitive activities as comprehending, reasoning, and problem solving.[36,37] The concept of working memory emerged from debates in cognitive psychology during the 1960s concerning short-term memory versus long-term memory. As noted earlier, studies of amnesic patients such as H.M. revealed that the ability to immediately remember small strings of digits is intact. This finding was one of several that led to the idea

BOX 56.3

CASE HISTORY OF K.F.

K.F., a 28-year-old man, had a left parieto-occipital fracture in a motor-bicycle accident 11 years before, when a left parietal subdural hematoma was evacuated. He was unconscious for 10 weeks. At first he was very dysphasic, but his speech gradually improved over the next few years.

At the age of 19 he started having epilepsy and when age 25 he was admitted for the investigation of this. There was a bone defect in the left parieto-occipital region. An air encephalogram showed prominent localized dilatation of the left trigone and occipital horn, with some dilatation of the left temporal horn.

K.F. was tested on the WAIS and obtained a verbal IQ of 79 and a performance IQ of 113. On the Progressive Matrices he scored 40 of 60, which is just below the 50th percentile for his age. His relatively poor language functions were reflected in his verbal IQ. His ability to express himself was halting, and some word-finding difficulty and circumlocutions were noted. Paraphasic errors were rare, and on no occasion were neologisms used. There was a very mild degree of nominal dysphasia, which could be detected only with uncommon names. Receptive speech functions were well preserved. Single instructions were carried out, although there was some difficulty with "longer" messages. Using a task similar to the token test devised by De Renzi, the conceptual difficulty of the message did not impair his performance. Reading a simple test was slow, but reasonably accurate. On Schonell's graded word list he scored just below the 9-year level. Both oral and written spelling were very impaired (at the 6-year level). Memory for day-to-day happenings was good and he had an adequate knowledge of recent and past events.

Immediate memory of the Binet figures was accurate. The most striking feature of his performance was his almost total inability to *repeat* verbal stimuli. His digit span was two, and on repeated attempts at repeating two digits his performance would deteriorate, so that on some trials his digit span was one or even none. His repetition difficulty was not restricted to digits; he had a similar difficulty in repeating letters, disconnected words, and sentences. Single verbal items would be repeated correctly with the exception of polysyllabic words, which were on occasion mispronounced.

Edited from Warrington and Shallice.[38]

of a separate short-term memory system that serves as a gateway to long-term memory. However, other patients, such as K.F., exhibit severely impaired short-term retention of digits and related kinds of verbal information, despite a relatively normal ability to acquire most new long-term memories—the exact opposite of the pattern observed in patient H.M.[38] Such patients typically have damage in a specific part of the left parietal lobe known as the supramarginal gyrus. These findings not only strengthen the distinction between short- and long-term memory, but also indicate that information can *enter* long-term memory even when one kind of short-term memory is profoundly impaired. See Box 56.3

Researchers have explained this pattern of findings by postulating that the working memory system consists of three components: a central executive or limited capacity workspace and two *slave* subsystems that support it.[39] One subsystem, called the **phonological loop,** allows rehearsal or recycling of small amounts of speech-based information, but is not necessary for entering information into long-term memory. According to this model, it is the phonological loop that is impaired in patients who exhibit impaired immediate retention yet show mostly normal long-term memory. Importantly, though, this subsystem is necessary for long-term learning of phonological information.[36] Thus, the findings from patient K.F. can be understood as a selective deficit in one component of short-term memory and a correspondingly selective deficit in long-term memory for information that is ordinarily processed by the defective short-term memory component.

The second slave subsystem of working memory—the **visuospatial sketch pad**—is thought to be involved in the short-term retention of visual and spatial information. Evidence from brain-damaged patients and PET scans suggests that a variety of regions in the right hemisphere, including the visual association cortex, inferior parietal lobule, and inferior prefrontal cortex, are important components of the visuospatial sketch pad.[40]

Summary

The brain has multiple systems for memory. These systems include one for declarative or explicit memory and others for implicit forms of memory expression. Declarative memory is of two forms, episodic and semantic, which are dissociable from each other and from several forms of nondeclarative memory. Episodic memory involves explicit recollection of specific personal events, and semantic memory involves general knowledge of facts and concepts not specified in time or space. Several forms of nondeclarative memory are mediated by other identified brain systems. These systems include perceptual recognition systems that involve biasing or tuning of cortical representations, a procedural or habit memory system that involves a cortical–striatal circuit and the cerebellum, and a working memory system that involves the prefrontal cortex in combination with widespread cortical areas.

DISSOCIABLE MEMORY SYSTEMS IN ANIMALS

Neurobiological studies of memory in animals have several potential advantages. The scope and amount of all learning experiences are under direct experimental control, and basic memory processes can be examined without the potentially overwhelming influences of linguistic competence. In addition, anatomical and behavioral manipulations can be pursued at a level of selectivity and resolution not possible in human subjects, and neural coding mechanisms and cellular plasticity can be characterized directly with physiological recording techniques. Explorations of animal memory can also provide insights into how particular memory mechanisms evolved. At the same time, the ultimate value of studying animal systems depends critically on how well we can characterize human-like memory phenomena in animals. This section first focuses on the success of animal models in improving our understanding of declarative memory and then reviews the full scope of memory systems identified in studies on animals.

Animal Models Have Been Useful for Understanding the Neurobiological Bases of Declarative Memory

Studies of declarative memory in animals have focused on the development of animal models of amnesia and on the characterization of neural coding in animals performing memory tasks. These studies have succeeded in offering preliminary identifications of both the critical brain structures and the fundamental cognitive operations that underlie this kind of memory. However, at the outset it is important to note that some limitations and special challenges are associated with the study of declarative memory in animals. Obviously, animals do not express their memories by verbal declaration. In addition, how to test distinctions between episodic and semantic forms of declarative memory, as well as explicit versus implicit memory expression, is not immediately clear. Efforts to meet these challenges have provided important insights into the nature of declarative memory.

After the initial descriptions of global amnesia in the patient H.M., researchers took two main approaches to developing animal models of amnesia. One approach focused on visual recognition memory in nonhuman primates and on identifying the critical medial temporal lobe structures. The other approach focused on identifying the critical aspects of cognitive processing accomplished by the hippocampus in rats.

The Nonhuman Primate Model of Amnesia

Neuroscientists have used a specific, carefully selected set of behavioral tests in developing a nonhuman primate model of human amnesia.[41,42] The set of tasks involves three-dimensional objects as memory cues. In one type of task, called *delayed non-match-to-sample,* subjects are exposed to an object once and then, after a delay, asked to recognize the object by indicating the unfamiliar one in a two-choice presentation (Fig. 56.3).[43] When the delay is a few seconds, monkeys with experimental lesions of the entire medial temporal area that was damaged in H.M. perform as well as normal monkeys. As the delay is increased, however, the monkeys become progressively more impaired. Thus, monkeys with medial temporal damage, like humans with amnesia, have intact short-term memory but forget abnormally rapidly (Table 56.1).

Monkeys with medial temporal damage also perform poorly when they must retain rapidly acquired object discriminations for a prolonged period. In contrast to these impairments in object memory, monkeys with medial temporal damage have intact capacities for skill acquisition in a task that involves learning to retrieve a candy by manipulating it along a bent rod. In direct comparisons, monkeys with damage to the hippocampal system perform comparably to humans with amnesia on similar tasks. In both monkeys and humans, the ability to acquire individual object discriminations is relatively intact, as is the acquisition of motor learning. Both monkeys and humans are im-

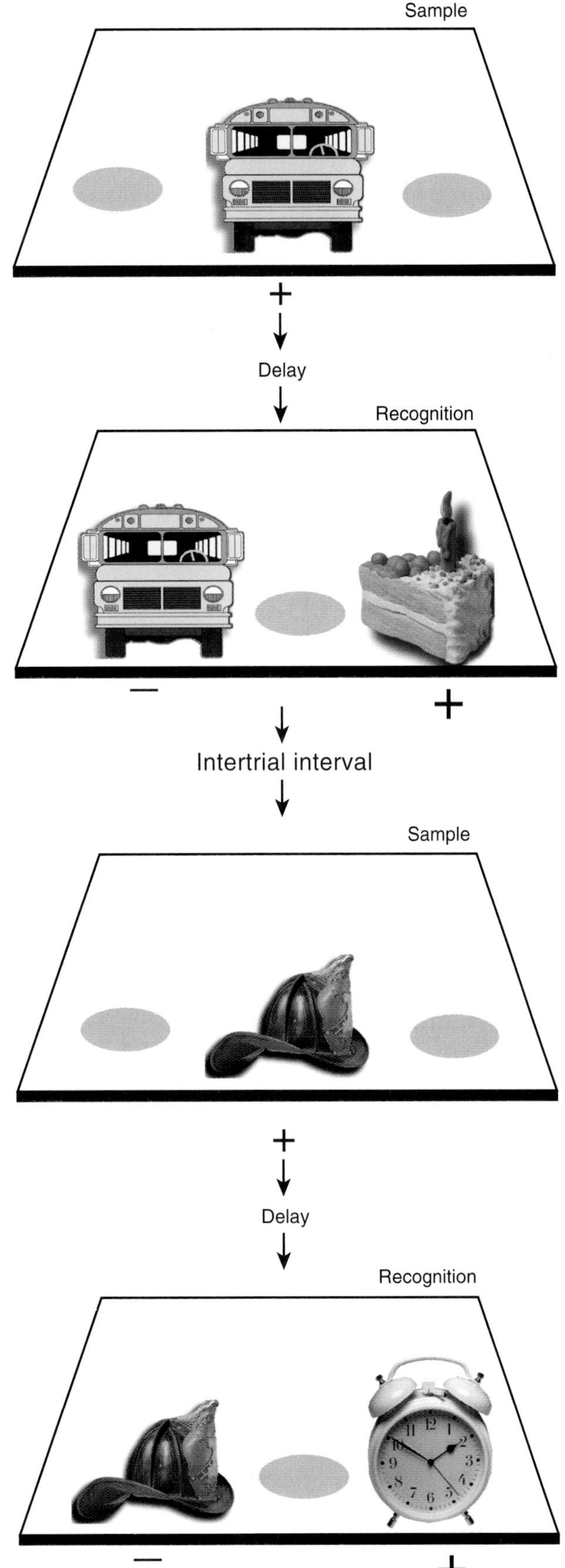

TABLE 59.1 Characteristics of Human Amnesia Produced in Monkeys with Large Bilateral Lesions of the Medial Temporal Lobe

1. Immediate memory is spared
2. Memory for events prior to the onset of amnesia can be affected in a temporally graded fashion (retrograde amnesia)
3. Memory impairment is not limited to one sensory modality
4. Memory is impaired on a variety of tasks, including tasks identical to those failed by amnesic patients
5. Memory impairment is exacerbated by increasing the retention delay or the amount of material to be learned
6. Memory impairment is exacerbated by distraction
7. Memory impairment can be enduring
8. Skill-based memory is spared

From Squire and Zola-Morgan.[46]

paired on delayed performance in non-matching-to-sample acquisition and in delayed retention of object discriminations. Thus, the pattern of both preserved and impaired memory in human amnesics is closely modeled by the performance of monkeys with similar brain damage.

Retrograde amnesia is another aspect of the amnesic syndrome that has been modeled in monkeys. Nearly all patients with amnesia due to medial temporal lobe damage suffer both a deficit in learning new material, called **anterograde amnesia,** and some loss of memories acquired before the brain damage, called **retrograde amnesia.** Importantly, the retrograde deficit is *graded,* and material acquired shortly before the damage is most severely affected, whereas items learned earlier in life are relatively spared.[17] Parallel to these observations, studies have shown that object discriminations learned by monkeys shortly before medial temporal damage are poorly retained, but discriminations learned remotely before the damage are spared.[44] This pattern of amnesic deficit, along with the other characteristics of memory impairment in monkeys with a damaged hippocampal system, validates the nonhuman primate model of human amnesia (Table 56.1).[45]

Using this model, investigators have turned to identifying the structures of the medial temporal lobe critical to supporting memory. In H.M. and in early studies on monkeys, the damage involved the amygdala, the

FIGURE 56.3 The delayed non-match-to-sample task using unique objects as stimuli. The subject is initially presented with a single novel object as sample and must displace the object. This is followed by a variable delay during which the subject cannot see any objects. In the subsequent recognition test two objects are presented, one of which is the same as the sample and the other of which is novel. Correct performance requires the subject to recognize and avoid the sample object and instead choose the novel one to receive a food reward. From Rapp and Amaral.[43]

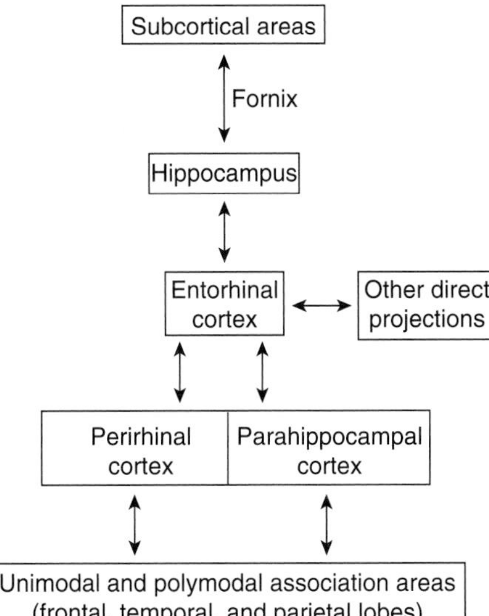

FIGURE 56.4 Structures of the hippocampal region that mediate declarative memory. From Zola-Morgan *et al.*[46]

hippocampus, and the surrounding cortical regions, including the perirhinal, parahippocampal, and entorhinal areas (Fig. 56.4).[46] However, studies using the monkey model have shown definitively that the amygdala is not important to the types of memory described earlier.[41,45] In addition, the impact of damage within the remaining portions of the medial temporal area differs according to the extent and locus of damage. Damage limited to the hippocampus, or to its major connections through the fornix, has only a modest effect. In contrast, damage to the perirhinal and parahippocampal region can produce the full pattern of the amnesic deficit. Clearly, the perirhinal and parahippocampal cortical regions themselves make major contributions to memory. Localized damage to the hippocampus can result in amnesia in humans,[47] but the specific contribution of the hippocampus itself is not yet clearly identified in nonhuman primates.

Models of Hippocampal Function in Rodents

Studies on rodents have identified specific contributions of the hippocampus in this species, and these findings have general implications for hippocampal memory function in humans and nonhuman primates. Most prominent among the theories guiding this research is O'Keefe and Nadel's[48] view that the hippocampus mediates *cognitive mapping*—that is, the establishment of an organized neural representation of the physical environment. They analyzed a large body of literature on the effects of hippocampal damage on different behavioral tasks and concluded that animals with hippocampal system damage are severely impaired in many forms of spatial exploration and learning, but are impaired on a relatively small number of nonspatial tasks. Their analysis went beyond making a simple distinction between *spatial* and *nonspatial* learning. They proposed that the hippocampus mediates a large-scale organization of memories and that this kind of memory is rapid and is driven by curiosity rather than by rewards and punishments. All of these properties are consistent with characterizations of declarative memory in humans.

Among the strongest evidence in favor of the cognitive mapping view is the finding that rats with hippocampal damage are severely impaired in *place* learning. A particularly good example of place learning is the *Morris water-maze task.* In this task, rats are trained to find a hidden escape platform submerged just below the surface in a pool of cloudy water. Because there is no specific cue at the escape site, the rat must learn its place on the basis of spatial relationships among the cues that can be seen outside the maze. Rats with hippocampal damage are severely impaired in this task. However, these rats are completely intact in a *cued* version of the test in which they learn to swim toward a platform that is visible above the water surface and located in any of several different places.[49] This distinction between hippocampal-dependent place learning and hippocampal-independent cued learning has been highly influential in formulating current views on hippocampal function in animals and is exploited in many neurobiological studies of hippocampal function and plasticity.

In addition to the observation that spatial memory depends on the hippocampus, the cognitive mapping theory is strongly supported by the discovery of hippocampal *place cells,* neurons that fire only when the rat is in a particular location in its environment and whose firing is independent of the rat's orientation or ongoing behavior[50] (see Chapter 53). Several lines of evidence indicate that place cell activity reflects an encoding of the spatial relationships among physical stimuli in the environment. Place fields move in concert with rotations of salient visual cues, they *scale* with enlargement of all features of the environment, and they are altered when the spatial arrangement of cues is disrupted. Furthermore, from experiments with rats in a plus-shaped maze, place cell activity can be related to the rat's memory about its spatial location, a result consistent with the view that place cells reflect spatial memory representations (see Fig. 56.5).[51]

Despite strong evidence of a role for the hippocampus in cognitive mapping, the narrow view that hippocampal function is limited strictly to spatial learning in rats does not match the global memory function identified for the hippocampal region in humans. Is the scope of hippocampal memory function more lim-

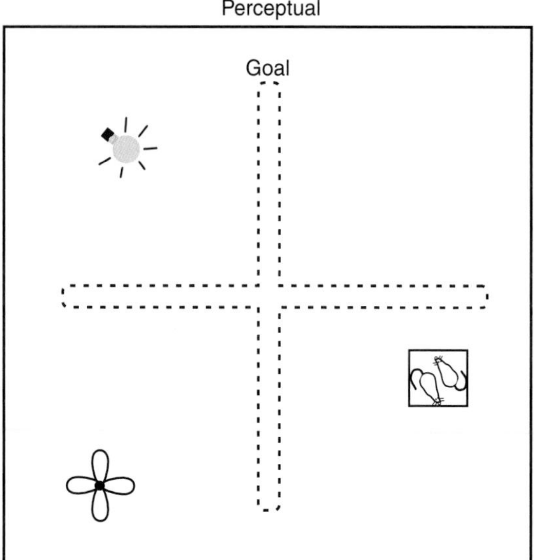

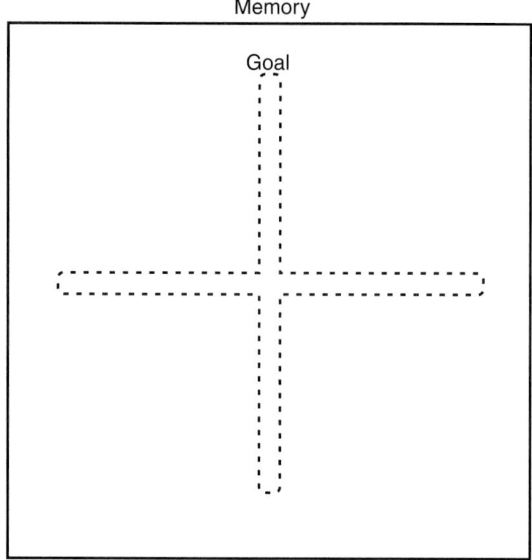

FIGURE 56.5 Firing maps for a hippocampal place cell. The firing patterns of a single pyramidal cell in the hippocampus were recorded as a rat explored a plus-shaped maze. Contour plots illustrate areas of the maze associated with increased firing rate of the hippocampal neuron. The rat had learned to find a reward goal at the end of one arm of the maze guided by various cues outside the maze (left). These areas associated with increased firing are called "place fields." The same place fields were also observed when the cues were removed and the rat correctly found the goal from memory (right). From O'Keefe and Speakman.[51]

ited in rats than in humans? A number of studies using animals have demonstrated deficits in various types of nonspatial learning following hippocampal damage. Several competing theories of hippocampal function have emerged as a result of these studies. For example, one theory[52] postulates that the hippocampus mediates the retrieval of memories that are guided by the context in which they were acquired. In contrast, direct modifications in performance systems that support stimulus–response or stimulus–reward associations proceed without hippocampal involvement. A number of proposals assign the hippocampus a critical role in mediating the representation of items within their spatial or temporal context and in creating unambiguous memory representations for stimuli that differ in significance depending on their configuration with respect to other cues.[14] Although no consensus has emerged, there is general agreement on two points: (1) some type of organized representation of multiple stimuli is dependent on hippocampal function—the nature and scope of the memory organization remain contested; and (2) specific stimulus–reward and stimulus–response associations are mediated by other brain systems.

Experimental evidence indicates that the hippocampus itself is indeed critically involved in both nonspatial and spatial memory organizations and, in particular, in the ability to express memory *flexibly*—that is, in solving novel problems.[53] In experiments using olfactory cues that exploit rats' natural foraging strategies, animals were trained with stimuli that consisted of distinctive odors added to sand under which was buried a cereal reward. The rats had to dig through the sand to obtain the reward (Fig. 56.6). Initially, the rats learned a set of odor "paired associates," a list of associations between pairs of odors (see Fig. 56.6B). Then they learned a second set of paired associates, and each of these associations involved one of the odors used in the first set. Subsequently, the rats were given probe tests to determine the extent to which learned representations supported two forms of *flexible memory expression.* One of these tests, a test for **transitivity,** measured the ability to infer an association between two odors that shared a common associate. For example, having learned that odor A is associated with odor B and that odor B is associated with odor C, could

FIGURE 56.6 Associative transitivity and symmetry in paired associate learning. On each training trial one of two *sample odors* initially presented was followed by two *choice odors,* each assigned as the associate of one of the samples and baited only when preceded by that sample. After training on two sets of paired associates, normal rats showed transitivity in that they preferred indirectly associated odors. They also showed symmetry in that they preferred appropriate pairings presented in reverse order. Rats with selective damage to the hippocampus showed no ability for either form of flexible, inferential memory expression. From Bunsey and Eichenbaum.[53]

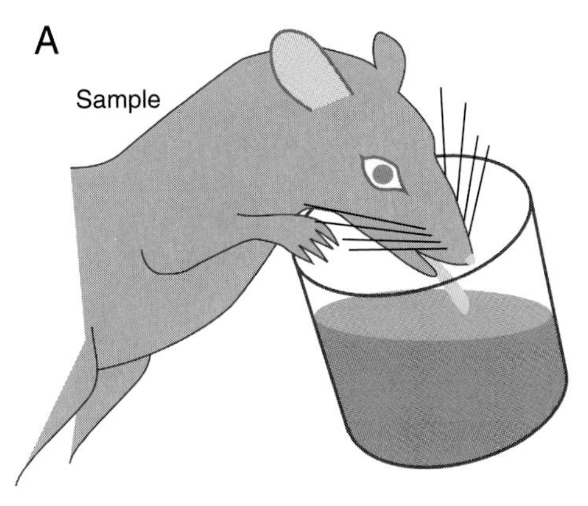
A
Sample

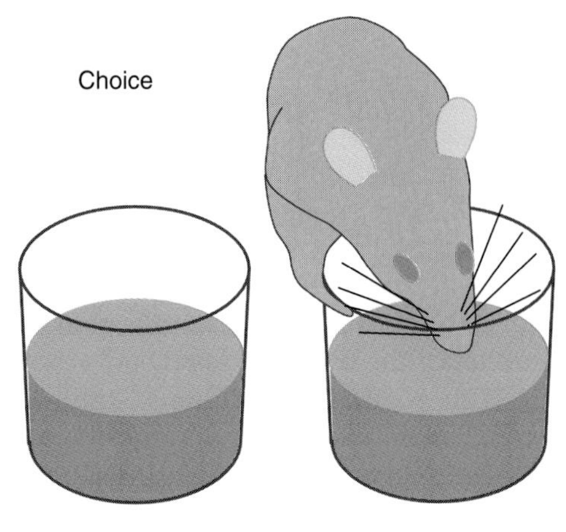
Choice

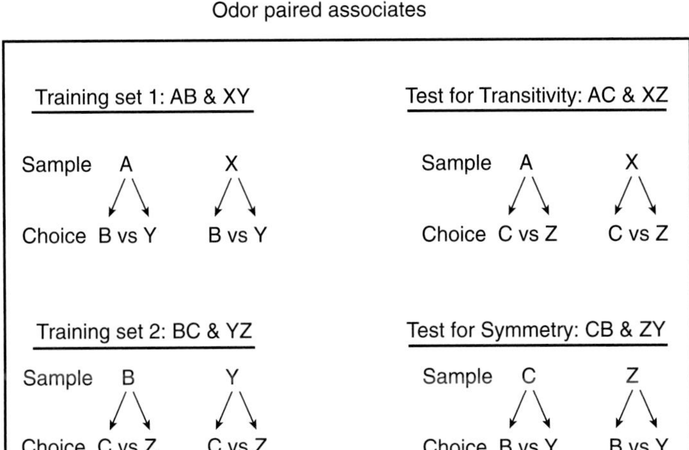
B
Odor paired associates
Training set 1: AB & XY
Sample A X
Choice B vs Y B vs Y
Test for Transitivity: AC & XZ
Sample A X
Choice C vs Z C vs Z
Training set 2: BC & YZ
Sample B Y
Choice C vs Z C vs Z
Test for Symmetry: CB & ZY
Sample C Z
Choice B vs Y B vs Y

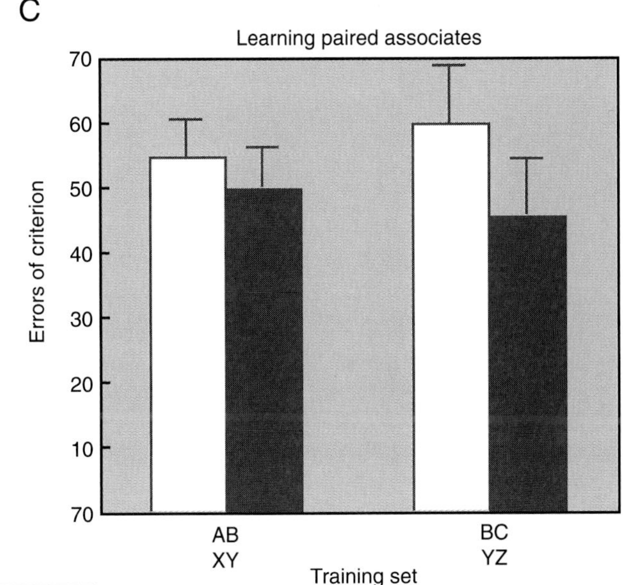
C
Learning paired associates
Errors of criterion
70
60
50
40
30
20
10
70
AB
XY
BC
YZ
Training set
Sham
Hippocampal

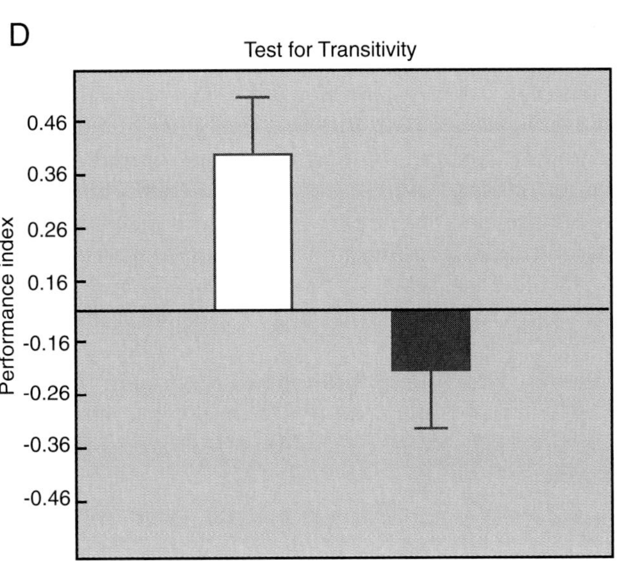
D
Test for Transitivity
Performance index
0.46
0.36
0.26
0.16
-0.16
-0.26
-0.36
-0.46

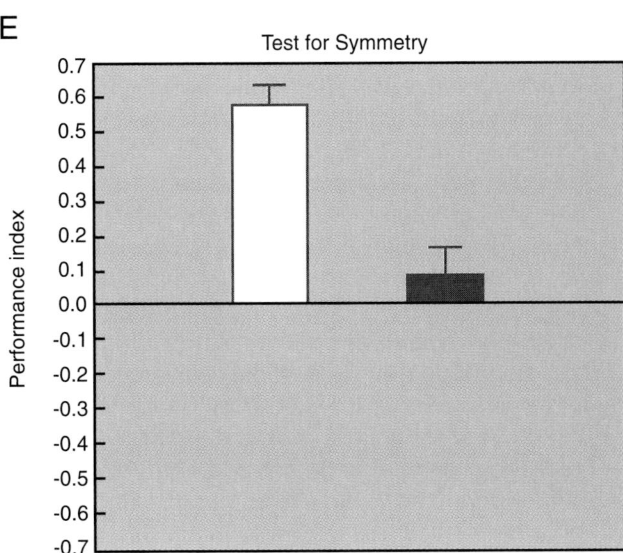
E
Test for Symmetry
Performance index
0.7
0.6
0.5
0.4
0.3
0.2
0.1
0.0
-0.1
-0.2
-0.3
-0.4
-0.5
-0.6
-0.7

they infer that A is indirectly associated with C? The other test, a test for **symmetry,** measured the ability to recognize associated odors when they were presented in the reverse of their training order. For example, if B is associated with C, is C associated with B?

Intact rats learned paired associates rapidly, and hippocampal damage did not affect the acquisition rate on either of the training sets. These results are consistent with reports on stimulus–stimulus association learning in monkeys[54] and amnesic patients.[55] Intact rats also showed strong transitivity across the sets, as reflected in a preference for items only indirectly associated with the sample presented. In contrast, rats with selective hippocampal damage were severely impaired in that they showed no evidence of transitivity. In the symmetry test, intact rats showed their associations were indeed symmetrical. In contrast, rats with hippocampal damage again were severely impaired, showing no significant capacity for symmetry. These findings show that animals share various aspects of human declarative memory. These aspects have been recognized historically: William James' description of memory as involving an elaborated network of associations that can be applied across a broad range of situations; Hebb's[56] proposal that conscious memory supports inferences about indirect relations between stimuli not previously experienced together; and Cohen and Eichenbaum's[14] description of declarative memory as *promiscuous* in its accessibility by novel routes of expression.

How can these findings be reconciled with the findings on hippocampal place cells? A variety of recording studies have shown that in rats hippocampal cells fire in association with conjunctions or combinations of multiple visual, auditory, and olfactory stimuli presented either in different spatial configurations or in temporal sequences during discrmination learning and matching tasks.[57] In monkeys, hippocampal cells fire in association with configurations of pictures and the spatial or temporal positions in which they are presented. Notably, hippocampal cells that have spatial firing properties in some tasks also have other nonspatial firing correlates when the task demands change. Thus, for example, a cell that fired when the rat was in a specific location as the animal performed a spatial task subsequently switched to firing during odor exploration when the animal was performing an olfactory discrimination task in the same environment. Furthermore, in studies on rats performing a radial maze task where both spatial and nonspatial cues were prominent, hippocampal cells encoded both types of information, and the overall hippocampal representation reflected both spatial and nonspatial relations among cues and associated behavioral actions. In other experiments, the spatial firing patterns changed dramatically when the behavioral requirements of the task were altered, even though all the spatial cues were held constant. Thus, a broad range of both spatial and nonspatial relations are prominently represented in the hippocampus, and these representations change rapidly with task demands. The common denominator across the variety of observations on hippocampal neural activity in behaving animals is that hippocampal representations encode any important relationship among cues as well as relationships between stimuli and behavioral responses to those stimuli. This characterization of hippocampal coding is entirely consistent with findings from studies on experimental damage to the hippocampus discussed earlier, and it supports the general view that the hippocampus mediates relational representations, which are the basis of declarative memory.

Distinct Memory Systems Mediate Procedural Memory, Emotional Memory, and Other Memory Functions

So far, our characterization of declarative memory leaves open questions of how many nondeclarative memory systems exist in animals and what brain circuits underlie these other types of learning. McDonald and White[58] addressed these issues in experiments demonstrating a *triple dissociation* among different types of memory depending on the hippocampus, the amygdala, or the striatum. Rats were trained on a radial maze—that is, a maze with a central platform with eight arms radiating outward. By carefully manipulating the task demands, McDonald and White created three different versions of the task for which experimental damage to exactly one of these structures prevented normal learning. The integrity of the striatum, but not the amygdala or hippocampus, was critical to learning when rats were given food reinforcement for approaching any maze arm that was illuminated, regardless of its location. The amygdala, but not the striatum or hippocampus, was critical when the rats were separately confined to an illuminated maze arm with food, or a dark arm without food, and then tested for a preference between the illuminated and dark arms. The hippocampus, but not the amygdala or striatum, was critical when the rats were reinforced only for entering a maze-arm location not previously visited on a particular trial, a task requiring flexible memory expression and spatial mapping known to rely on hippocampal function.

Given these findings, Maine de Biran's 200-year-old proposal for three kinds of memory (outlined at the

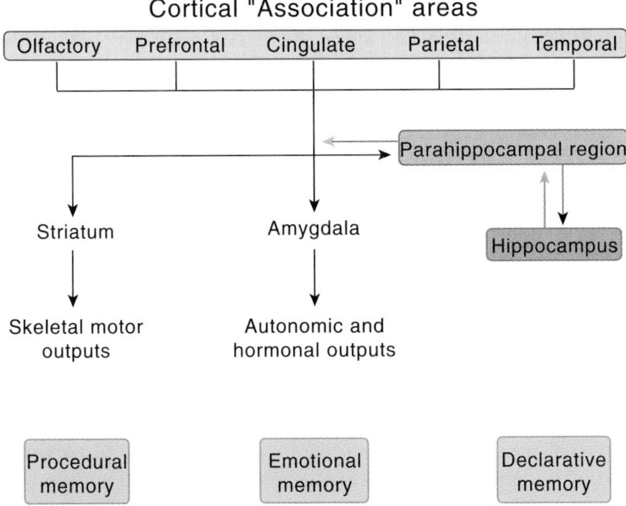

FIGURE 56.7 Circuits of dissociable memory systems.

beginning of this chapter) can now be interpreted as a reflection of the different types of associations supported by separate anatomical circuits (Fig. 56.7): the convergence of sensory inputs and motor system connections in the dorsal striatum supporting procedural memory or habit learning (Maine de Biran's *mechanical memory*), the convergence of sensory and affective inputs in the amygdala supporting emotional (*sensitive*) memory, and the convergence of higher-order sensory inputs in the hippocampus mediating declarative (*representative*) memory.

There is now substantial evidence for localization of the general types of memory functions involved in the task just described. The striatum, which forms part of the basal ganglia, is critical for a variety of forms of response or habit learning. In addition to its role in rats in developing biases toward rewarding stimuli, the amygdala plays a critical role in the acquisition of a variety of positive and negative stimulus biases in monkeys, and it plays a critical role in fear and other types of emotional conditioning in many species (see Chapter 55).

Are there three and only three memory systems in animals? McDonald and White[58] suggested that the designation of separate systems for flexible stimulus–stimulus learning (*hippocampus*), stimulus–reinforcer learning (*amygdala*), and stimulus–response learning (*striatum*) covers all the major forms of association. However, we have looked at a number of other memory systems, including the system for learned motor reflexes that relies critically on the cerebellum (see Chapter 55). In addition, several distinct cortical systems mediate simple forms of perceptual performance, as discussed earlier under the concept of priming. Furthermore, studies of both humans and animals have determined that working memory depends on a distinct system that critically involves prefrontal cortical regions. Finally, in addition to its role in emotional learning per se, the amygdala controls the release of stress-related hormones that modulate the memory of emotionally arousing events in several of the memory systems described in this chapter.[59] Whether this kind of influence should be considered yet another memory system is unclear.

So how many memory systems are there? Although categorizing memory systems according to similarities and distinctions in their psychological characteristics is sometimes useful, it is not always the most appropriate way to view how memory operates in the brain. The alternative view, suggested by the diverse list of **memory systems** and their anatomical pathways in animals, is that memory is not a separate entity, or even multiple entities, but rather a reflection of plasticity within each functional system of the brain. From this perspective, and given that all functional systems demonstrate plasticity, it can be argued that there are as many **memory systems** as there are **functional brain systems,** and that the parallels and distinctions among their operating characteristics are consequences of the similarities and differences in the circuitry and neural coding processes in these functional systems.

Summary

Neurobiological studies on animal models of declarative memory provide a framework for thinking about medial-temporal function in terms of memories that are organized according to relations among stored items and are accessible through a variety of routes and forms of behavioral experssion. The circuit for declarative memory includes all association areas of the neocortex, the parahippocampal region, and the hippocampus, each of which plays a different role in supporting declarative memory. In addition, like the studies on humans, experiments on animals have identified other brain systems that mediate nondeclarative forms of memory. These include a stimulus–response or habit-learning system that centers on the striatum, a stimulus reinforcer or emotional memory system that centers on the amygdala, and still other systems not discussed at length here. The distinctions suggested here for both humans and animals should be regarded as provisional; they will no doubt be modified in light of future findings. This observation both strengthens and expands the fundamental insight of modern cognitive neuroscience that the concept of *memory* is just a convenient expression for describing the variety of ways in which the brain adapts and changes as a result of experience.

COMPUTATIONAL THEORIES OF HIPPOCAMPAL FUNCTION IN LEARNING AND MEMORY

The theories and models of hippocampal function we have discussed up to now are *qualitative,* presenting a central concept or metaphor to summarize the function of the hippocampal region. In contrast, we focus in this section on the development of *formal network models,* often termed *computational* or *connectionist models,* that work out in *quantitative* terms a proposed computational role (or roles) for the hippocampal region. Such models have the advantage that they can be rigorously tested with computer simulations and, occasionally, formal mathematical analysis. Computational or connectionist models simulate information processing in a brain region through analysis of interactions among multiple adaptive processing elements or nodes. Each node takes input information, transforms it in a specific (often modifiable) way, and produces variable output based on the results of this transformation. Nodes may represent simplified characterizations of individual neurons, in which case the input information may represent afferent synaptic transmission and the output may represent axonal firing probabilities. At the other extreme, nodes may be abstractions of the processing that occurs within a collection of neural elements. Both the more realistic and the more abstract connectionist models have proven useful in addressing various questions about the processing in different brain regions, including the hippocampal region. In this section, we provide an overview of connectionist modeling techniques and then briefly describe a few examples of connectionist models of hippocampal function in memory.

Marr's Early Model Considered the Hippocampus to Be a Temporary Store of Associations

One of the early and most influential models of information processing in the hippocampal region was proposed by David Marr.[60] Marr's basic idea was to distinguish separable roles in memory for the hippocampus and for the neocortex and to show how they might interact in memory storage and retrieval. Marr assumed that the chief role of the neocortex was to store large complex event memories as patterns of activities over a large number of neocortical cells, evoked by a particular set of sensory inputs (Fig. 56.8A). Such a pattern is stored by associating its elements so that activation of some of the elements can activate other elements in turn (Fig. 56.8B). Later, if a subset of the pattern is presented to the neocortex, it should be able to retrieve the full pattern (Fig. 56.8C). One difficulty in implementing this pattern completion function in the neocortex is that a large number of very precise connections are required to associate each element with every other relevant element. Further, the associations required to store elements may well disrupt preexisting associations created to store other patterns with common elements. Worse, if another stored pattern shares common elements with the first, then activation of part of either pattern activation will begin to retrieve both. At the extreme, if many overlapping patterns are stored, any attempt to retrieve any stored pattern will result in a pattern of activation that shares elements with all stored patterns, but is identical to none, a situation known as **catastrophic interference.**

Because of this potential for interference in recall, Marr suggested that it would be useful to have a separate processor—the hippocampus—that could rapidly store event memories and then allow gradual transfer of this pattern to the neocortex, which would reorganize and classify this information, incorporating it with existing knowledge in such a way as to reduce interference. More specifically, Marr proposed that the hippocampus is able to store new patterns rapidly, holding them in a temporary memory store, but that it is not able to integrate them with the larger body of existing knowledge. Marr imagined the hippocampus as functionally consisting of two layers or groups of cells (Fig. 56.9A). Inputs cause activity in the first "A" layer of cells, which project onto the second "B" layer of cells. The "B" cells in turn project back to the "A" cells. All synapses between cells are modifiable, but are simplified in the model to allow only binary "on" or "off" values; similarly, cell activity is assumed to be either on or off. This network is essentially the same as that characterized in Fig. 56.8, except that in this network cells are differentiated according to whether they directly receive external input ("A" cells) or not ("B" cells) rather than by whether or not they are activated. A stored pattern can be retrieved if, when part of the pattern is presented to the "A" cells, the evoked activity on the "B" cells feeds back to complete the original firing pattern on the "A" cells.

Later Autoassociative Models Incorporate Hebbian Learning Rules

The network described by Marr is a form of an **autoassociator**. An autoassociator network learns to

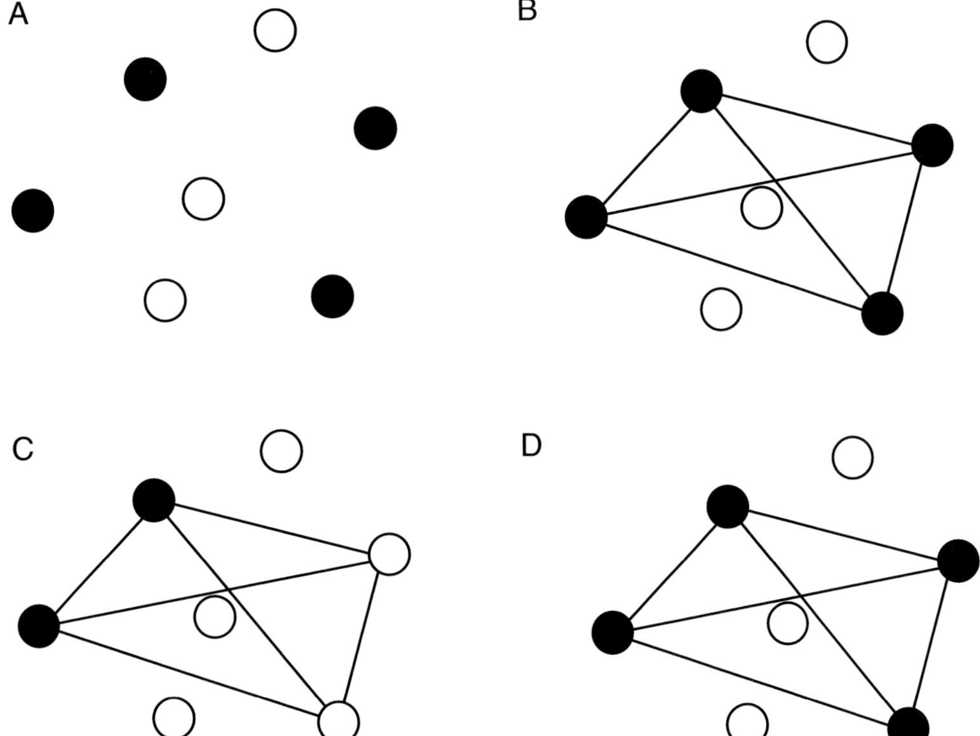

FIGURE 56.8 (A) Storage of an event memory as a pattern of cell activations in the neocortex, according to Marr's[60] model. Initially, the event memory simply evokes a pattern of activations (darkened circles) across a group of unrelated cells. (B) As the pattern is stored, various elements of the pattern are associated by weighted connections (lines). (C) Later, if a partial version of the original pattern is presented (darkened circles), activation spreads along the associations to activate the complete pattern (D).

associate an input pattern with an identical output pattern.[61] A general form of an autoassociator, shown in Fig. 56.9B, consists of a single layer of nodes receiving excitatory connections from external sources as well as from each other. Nodes are assumed to have binary states, either *active* or "firing" (represented by an output value of 1) or *quiescent* (represented by an output value of 0). Node j becomes active if the sum of inputs exceeds some firing threshold. This can be expressed mathematically as

$$y_i = 1 \text{ if } \sum_i w_{ij} y_j > \theta_j,$$

$$y_j = 0 \text{ otherwise,} \tag{56.1}$$

where y_j is the output or activation of cell j, w_{ij} is the weight (or strength) of the synapse on j from another cell i, and θ_j is cell j's threshold. This threshold, θ_j, is then set so that j will become active when the weighted sum of its inputs exceeds some proportion of the total inputs active in the original pattern. Additional inhibitory processes, not shown in Fig. 56.9B, may be required to determine the threshold. More complex networks may also allow continuous (real-valued) inputs and outputs, but the central ideas are the same.

A binary pattern is stored in this network by presenting elements of the pattern to separate nodes in the network, with each elemental input forcing that node to take on its input value. For this reason, the external inputs are often termed *forcing inputs,* and the one synapse each node receives from the forcing input is often termed a *forcing synapse.* The network then undergoes synaptic plasticity at the feedback connections, so that synapses from active presynaptic cells have excitatory effects on other active postsynaptic cells. This can be accomplished by a **Hebbian learning** rule of the form

$$\Delta w_{ij} = \alpha(y_i y_j), \tag{56.2}$$

where y_i and y_j are the activities of presynaptic cell i and postsynaptic cell j, respectively, α is a constant term, and Δw_{ij} is the weight of the synapse between i and j. Note that synaptic mechanisms of long-term potentiation and depression (LTP and LTD) are Heb-

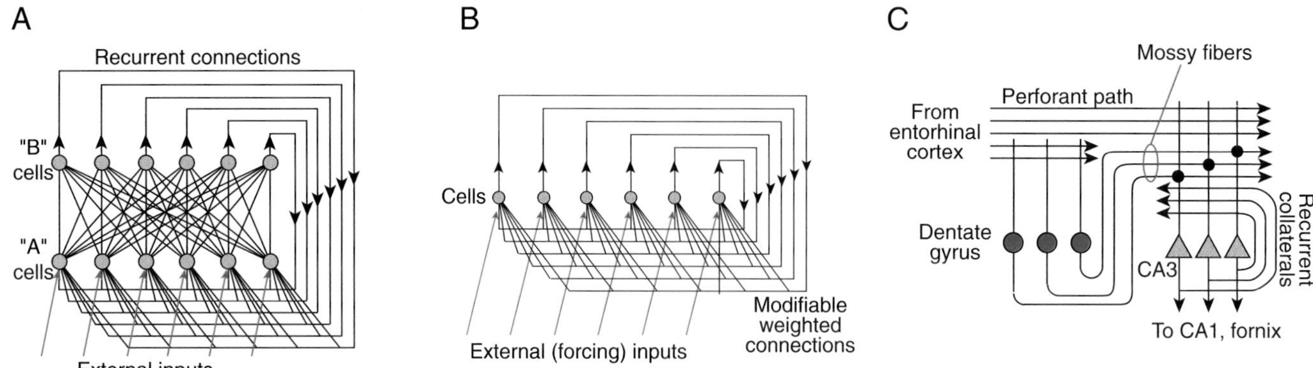

FIGURE 56.9 (A) Simplified schematic of Marr's[60] model. Cells are either "A" cells, which receive direct activation from the external input (heavy lines), or "B" cells, which are driven only by "A" cells and then send their outputs back to "A" cells. Learning consists of strengthening connections between "B" cells and the "A" cells that activate them. Later, if a partial version of a stored pattern is presented to the "A" cells, the feedback from "B" cells activates the remaining "A" cells required to complete the stored pattern. (B) A generalized form of an autoassociative network. There is a single layer of cells with outputs that branch out (ramify) to provide feedback input to the cell layer. These synapses are weighted, and cells become active if the total weighted synaptic input exceeds a threshold [Eq. (56.1)]. Patterns are stored by presenting external (*forcing*) input to the cells; learning then consists of weighing the synapses between all pairs of co-active cells [Eq. (56.2)]. Later, if a partial version of a stored pattern is presented on the external inputs, activity spreads iteratively through the recurrent feedback connections, activating additional cells until the entire pattern is reconstructed. (C) A schematic representation of information flow into the hippocampal field CA3. Inputs to the pyramidal cells arrive directly from entorhinal cortex, as well as indirectly via the mossy fibers from dentate gyrus. The mossy fiber afferents make sparse, presumably strong, synapses onto CA3 dendrites, and so are most likely forcing inputs to the network. CA3 pyramidal cell outputs ramify to become feedback afferents to CA3, as well as exiting to hippocampal field CA1 and through the fornix to other, extrahippocampal targets. From Marr.[60]

bian in nature (see Chapter 55). Later, if some subset of the pattern is presented to the network, activity in the recurrent collaterals will iterate through the network and activate the cells needed to complete the missing parts. Thus, this network performs pattern completion.

Autoassociators and Hippocampal Field CA3 Have Three Common Features

An autoassociator such as the one shown in Fig. 56.9B has three basic requirements:

1. A high degree to which principal cells connect to each other (*internal recurrency*).
2. Strong, sparse synapses from external afferents, which could function as forcing synapses.
3. Plasticity at the synapses exhibits LTP.

These requirements allow the functions of pattern storage, completion, and retrieval. Hippocampal field CA3 satisfies all three requirements (Fig. 56.9C). First, the principal neurons of CA3—pyramidal cells—are perhaps unique in the brain for their high degree of internal recurrency. Each CA3 pyramidal cell may receive contact from about 4% of the other pyramidal cells in the field, a synaptic contact probability high enough to allow autoassociation, that is, the association of elements with a pattern to each other. Second, in addition to recurrent collaterals and sparse entorhinal afferents, CA3 pyramidal cells receive a small number of inputs from mossy fibers, containing entorhinal information, that reaches CA3 via the dentate gyrus. Whereas each CA3 pyramidal cell in the rat may receive 12,000 synapses from recurrent collaterals and 4000 synapses from direct entorhinal afferents, it may receive only about 50 mossy-fiber synapses. However, the mossy-fiber synapses are very large and presumably also very strong (that is, have a larger than usual effect on the post-synaptic cell), so that coincident activity on a relatively small number of mossy-fiber synapses could activate a CA3 pyramidal cell. The mossy-fiber synapses are thus good candidates for forcing synapses in an autoassociator. Third, plasticity in the form of LTP has been demonstrated at the synapses of recurrent collaterals in CA3.

Autoassociative Networks Can Mimic Aspects of Hippocampus Dependent Memory

Marr's important contribution was to conceptualize the hippocampus as an autoassociator network that performs pattern storage and retrieval, and many subsequent models have elaborated on this idea.[62,63] For example, autoassociative networks can operate like declarative memory by first creating unified memories from several component features and then retrieving the entire memory from a partial input. This capacity of an autoassociative memory system also seems ideal for operating a spatial processor, in which the broad memory of a place should be evoked by any of several distinct views of the area, even if some of the usual cues are missing. Sequential learning can be treated similarly; given a partial input consisting of the present state, an autoassociative network is required to perform pattern completion and retrieve the predicted next state. Autoassociative networks have also been used to model the modulation of hippocampal dynamics between storage and recall states.[64] In addition, models of cortical–hippocampal interactions can simulate memory consolidation through the slow transfer to neocortex of rapidly constructed hippocampal memories.[65,66] Finally, these models can recode stimuli and contextual information to simulate how simple stimulus–response learning survives hippocampal damage, but is disrupted if there are more complex configural, contextual, or temporal relationships between stimuli.[67]

Summary

Computational or connectionist models simulate memory processing in the hippocampus by the interaction of multiple adaptive processing elements and their modifications, using Hebbian plasticity rules. Hippocampal field CA3 has all the properties needed to function as an autoassociator performing storage and retrieval of input patterns: high internal recurrency among the principal cells, strong and sparse synapses from external afferents, and plasticity in the form of LTP at the synapses. Autoassociators can implement many hippocampal-dependent functions, including pattern completion, spatial learning, and sequence learning. A consensus is developing that fast, temporary storage in an autoassociator is an important component of an episodic or declarative memory system in which arbitrary patterns are stored. By assuming the existence of a hippocampal autoassociator capable of performing this function, it is possible to account for the severe anterograde amnesia as well as graded retrograde amnesia that follows hippocampal damage.

SEMANTIC MEMORY AND REPRESENTATION OF KNOWLEDGE

The earlier discussion of semantic memory focused on distinctions between this and other memory systems (e.g., procedural memory, declarative memory, working memory) without addressing the content and organization of semantic memory. Much of the early research on this issue was conducted relatively independently by neurobiological and behavioral investigators. More recently, cognitive psychologists working with normal populations and cognitive neuropsychologists studying patients with acquired brain damage have accumulated a large body of data concerning the organization of semantic knowledge. Parallel findings in these two fields suggest that a new model of semantic memory may be synthesized.

Is the Evidence from Cognitive Psychology and Neuropsychology Converging?

There is general agreement that knowledge is organized into categories (animals, plants, rocks, tools, furniture, rivers, stars, body parts, fruits, appliances, etc.) that are embedded in hierarchically structured frameworks. Yet there is little consensus about the precise structures, mechanisms, and processes underlying categorization. Cognitive neuropsychologists have reported numerous cases of category-specific deficits in patients with localized brain damage, suggesting that categorical knowledge may be encoded in circumscribed regions of the brain.[68–70] Here again, though, researchers disagree over the interpretation of these patterns of impairment.

What Is Impaired in Category-Specific Deficits?

In their seminal work on category-specific localization, Warrington and Shallice[71] studied four patients in whom an impaired ability to identify living things (i.e., animals and plants) and foods was coupled with a spared ability to identify nonliving things (i.e., artifacts, gems, weather terms, earth formations). All four patients showed bitemporal damage from herpes simplex virus encephalitis (HSVE). Two patients who were unable to give coherent verbal responses were tested only in a picture and/or word matching task. The other two patients were tested using picture naming, definition, and picture and/or work matching tasks, and one of the patients was asked to mime appropriate actions toward various pieces of fruit and inanimate objects. Across tasks, all patients were selectively impaired in identifying living things.

This pattern of selective impairment in identifying living but not nonliving things has been replicated with several other patients, all suffering from temporal damage; the impairment was often the result of HSVE.[72,73] Moreover, the converse pattern of selective impairment has also been reported in the literature.[74] Such patients show impaired comprehension of nonliving things with relative sparing of their comprehension of living things.

This dissociation between living and nonliving things is consistent with models of semantic memory, based on studies of nonclinical populations, in which knowledge is organized into distinct categories.[75] Furthermore, this neuropsychological evidence suggests that categories may have a functionally, even anatomically, distinct embodiment in neural tissue. Such a provocative hypothesis has generated a variety of attempts to explain selective impairments as the result of differences in the familiarity of different categories of stimulus materials,[76,77] differences in the complexity of items among the categories,[78] or as differences in the modality of information processing (e.g., visual vs auditory) rather than the meanings of the items in the category.[79]

Is Stored Knowledge Category-Specific or Modality-Specific?

Functional brain imaging studies with normal subjects indicate that category-specific deficits may occur after damage to discrete regions of the posterior cortex important for perceiving different attributes of an object (e.g., form, color, motion; see Chapter 52). In experiments designed to explore the organization of stored knowledge about these attributes, subjects were shown pictures of black-and-white line drawings of objects and asked to generate a single word denoting a color or an action commonly associated with the object (e.g., "yellow" or "write" in response to a picture of a pencil[80]). Different regions of the posterior cortex were activated by each of these tasks. Importantly, these regions were close to the areas of the brain known to mediate perception of those attributes. Retrieving information about the color of the object activated a site in the ventral portion of the temporal lobe just anterior to the region of occipital cortex active during the perception of color, whereas retrieving information about actions associated with the object activated a site in the middle temporal gyrus just anterior to the region of occipital cortex active during the perception of motion. These activations occurred even though the simple pictures presented to the subjects were neither colored nor moving. Thus, information about specific attributes may be stored in discrete regions of the cortex, and the organization of these regions may parallel the organization of sensory and motor systems in the human brain. If so, then perhaps identifying tools requires activation of sites for stored knowledge about motion and motor acts, whereas identification of animals requires activation of sites for stored knowledge about visual features.

Brain imaging data collected while subjects named tools and animals are consistent with this view.[8] Naming tools selectively activated two regions of the cortex. One of these regions was in the left middle temporal gyrus, identical to the region active when subjects generated action words. The other region was in the left premotor cortex, identical to an area active when subjects imagined manipulating objects with their right hand. In contrast, naming animals produced selective activation of the medial occipital cortex, a location known to be involved in the early stages of visual processing and active during detailed, object imagery.[82] Thus, identifying and naming tools may require activation of previously acquired information about the pattern of motion and the sequence of motor acts associated with tool use, whereas naming animals may involve the activation of previously acquired visual information needed to distinguish one animal (e.g., a tiger) from another (e.g., a leopard). Within this framework, category-specific disorders would arise when a lesion disrupts storage sites associated with one type of information (e.g., patterns of motion and action), but not the other (e.g., visual features).

Summary

There is a general consensus that permanent semantic knowledge is organized into categories within a hierarchical memory framework. Selective, category-specific impairments in semantic memory are observed in patients with damage to circumscribed brain areas, and the nature of these deficits parallels categorization phenomena in nonclinical populations. However, the dissociated categories also differ in the way items are defined (e.g., living things are defined by visual features and nonliving things by functional features). The eventual description of the hierarchical structure of knowledge will depend on advances in our understanding of several important aspects of how knowledge is defined, including what makes up a category, how to interpret miscategorizations, and how categorization schemes normally arise during language development.

WORKING MEMORY AND THE FRONTAL LOBE

Defining the role of the frontal cortex in memory is a complex issue that requires consideration of both the type of mnemonic process and the precise regions of the frontal cortex involved (Fig. 56.10). In addition to its more direct involvement in certain aspects of memory, the frontal cortex carries out a variety of executive functions concerned with the organization of behavior. It is inevitable that these executive functions will find expression in memory as much as in other aspects of cognitive functioning.[83] The frontal cortex is also a large part of the cerebral cortex and comprises many different architectonic areas that have distinct connections with other cortical and subcortical regions of the brain. These widely differing connections reflect functional differences that must be addressed in any attempt to deal with the function of the frontal cortex. Inputs to specific parts of the prefrontal cortex originate from the visual prestriate cortex, the auditory and the visual temporal association cortex, and the posterior parietal cortex.[84] Most of these connections are reciprocal, indicating that the prefrontal cortex can both influence and be influenced by posterior cortical areas that are involved in the processing of visual, auditory, and somatosensory information. In addition, the frontal cortex is strongly linked with regions of the medial temporal lobe critical for mnemonic processing via two pathways: a large fiber system running from the dorsolateral and dorsomedial frontal cortex and the cingulate cortex to the presubiculum of the hippocampal complex, and another association system that links the caudal orbitofrontal cortex with the entorhinal and perirhinal cortex. The existence of these connections raises the question of the role of the different parts of the frontal cortex in mnemonic processing.

Can a Severe Memory Disorder Result from Damage to Caudal Orbitomedial Parts of the Frontal Cortex?

Combined damage to the orbital frontal and medial limbic frontal cortex (i.e., the *subcallosal* and *cingulate cortex*) in the monkey can result in a severe impairment on the delayed non-matched-to-sample test of recognition memory.[85] In humans, a severe memory disorder often follows ruptured aneurysms of the anterior communicating artery.[86,87] Such patients often have damage to the caudal orbitofrontal and adjacent medial frontal cortex, and this damage can be taken as evidence that these regions of the human frontal cortex participate in basic memory processes. This evidence, however, is not conclusive. In patients with ruptured aneurysms of the anterior communicating artery, the damage extends to several nearby basal forebrain structures (e.g., septal area, nucleus accumbens, and nucleus basalis of Meynert) that are known to contribute to mnemonic processing. In both monkeys and humans, only extensive damage to this orbitomedial frontal region is likely to give rise to an amnesic syndrome.[85]

Damage to the Lateral Prefrontal Cortex Produces Memory Impairments in Monkeys

The study of the role of the lateral frontal cortex in memory was greatly influenced by the work of Jacobsen in 1936.[88] He demonstrated that monkeys with lesions of the prefrontal cortex have severe deficits on the spatial delayed-response and delayed-alteration tasks. Several variations of these spatial short-term memory tasks have since appeared, but the essential requirement in all is that the monkey should remember the location where food was most recently placed. In Jacobsen's studies, the lesion involved the entire prefrontal cortex, but subsequent work showed that severe impairments are present after lesions limited to the cortex lining the sulcus principalis (i.e., area 46; see Fig. 56.10A). Further studies showed that performance of a nonspatial analog of the delayed-alternation task, the object alternation task, is not as severely affected by sulcus principalis lesions. These findings suggest that the cortex of the sulcus principalis (area 46) is predominantly involved in spatial working memory. Additional work in the monkey showed that lesions of the ventrolateral prefrontal cortex yield severe impairments on both spatial delayed-response tasks and nonspatial versions of these tasks, as well as on several other spatial and nonspatial learning tasks. These results suggest that the ventrolateral prefrontal cortex carries out basic executive processes of comparison and active retrieval of various aspects of stimuli (e.g., relative saliency, recency) from both short- and long-term memory.[89] Some single-cell recordings indicate that the cells in the cortex of the sulcus principalis are specifically active during spatial working memory performance, whereas cells in the adjacent ventrolateral frontal cortex seem to be specifically active during visual object working memory performance.[90] However, another study has reported that prefrontal cells with delay activity related to working memory for spatial and object information, respectively, are distrib-

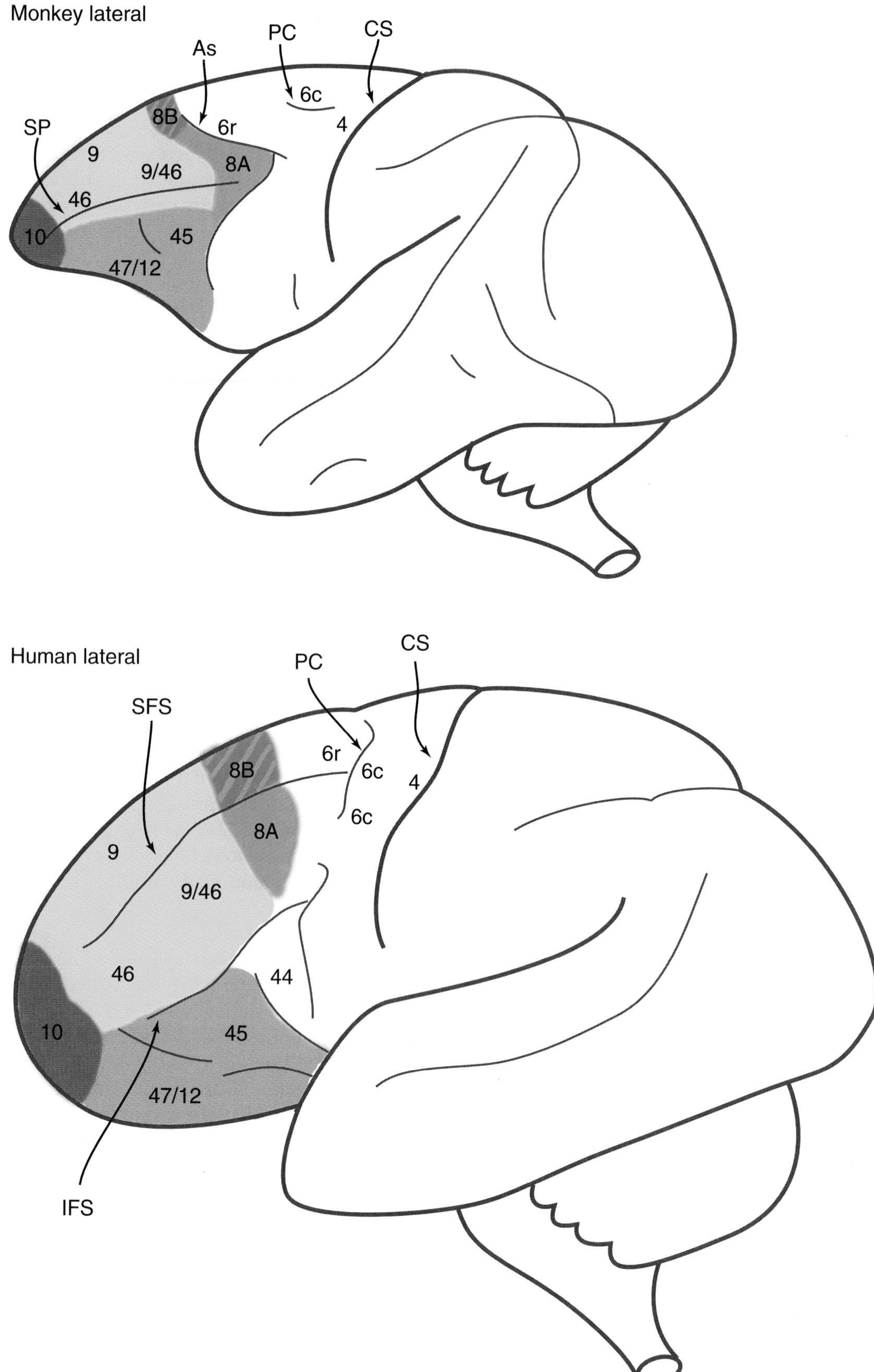

FIGURE 56.10 (A) The frontal lobe refers to the part of the brain that lies anterior to the central sulcus of the primate brain. Its posterior part consists of the primary motor cortex (Brodmann area 4) and the premotor cortex (Brodmann area 6). The vast expanse of cortex that lies further anterior in the primate

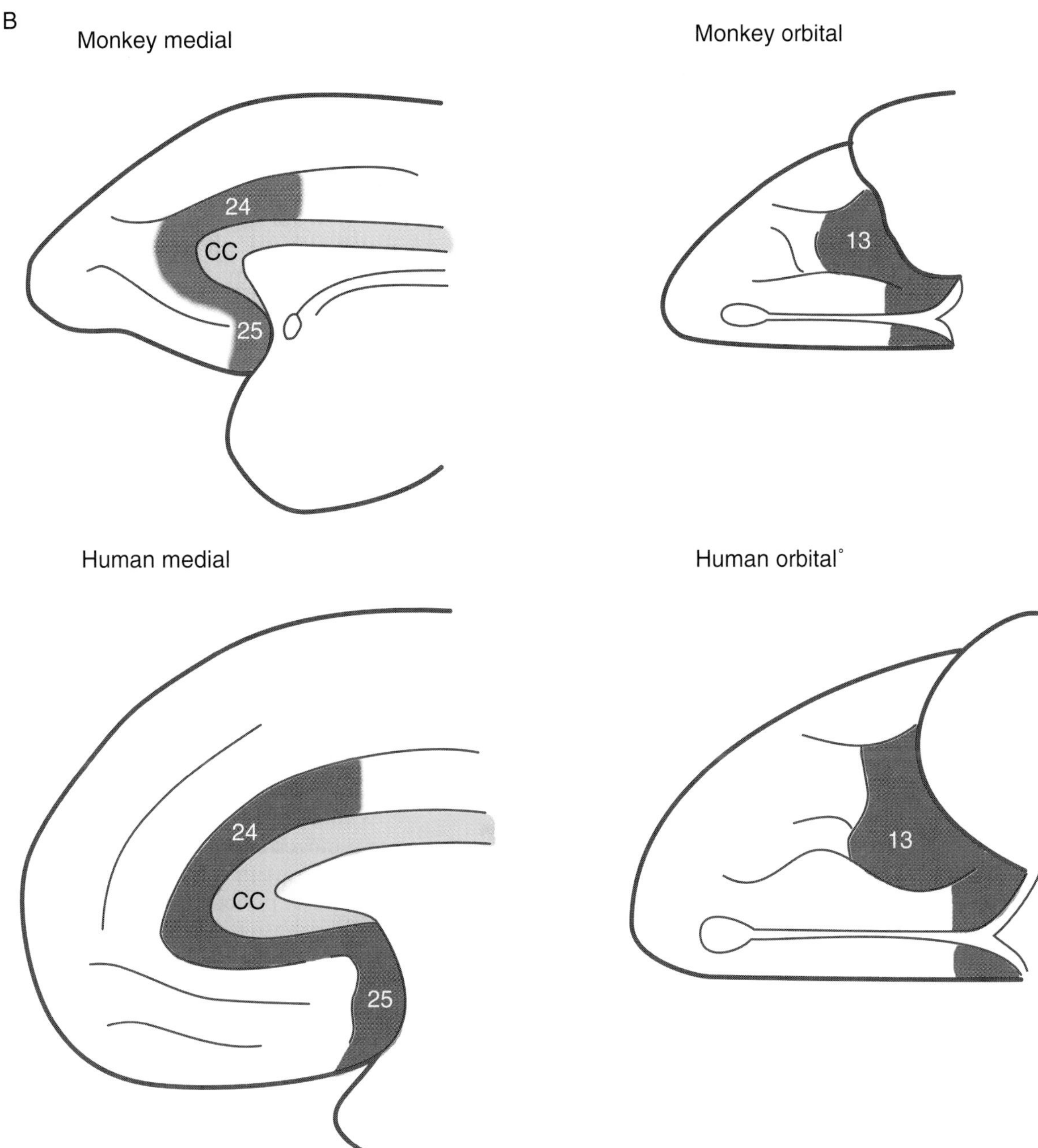

brain is often referred to as the *frontal granular cortex* or the *prefrontal cortex.* The term frontal granular cortex is used to acknowledge the fact that, in the primate brain, a well-developed granular layer IV can be identified in this part of the frontal cortex and clearly distinguishes it from the posteriorly located granular motor and premotor cortical fields. It is important to note that in the scientific literature, especially in studies of the cognitive effects of cerebral lesions, the general term *frontal cortex* is often used to refer to the frontal granular or *prefrontal* cortex. In the monkey brain, the prefrontal cortex lies in front of the arcuate sulcus. The lateral prefrontal cortex comprises several areas: 10 (frontopolar cortex), 9/46 (mid dorsolateral), 8 (posterior dorsolateral), and 47/12 and 45 (ventrolateral). CS, central sulcus; PCS, precentral sulcus; IFS, inferior frontal sulcus; SFS, superior frontal sulcus; SP, sulcus principalis; AS, arcuate sulcus; CC, corpus callosum. (B) The colored area shows the medial and orbital proisocortical region of the frontal cortex, which has architectonic characteristics indicating a close relationship with the limbic structures of the medial temporal lobe. This limbic part of the frontal lobe is intimately connected with the medial temporal region and may be part of the same basic circuit subserving basic declarative mnemonic processing. The numbers shown refer to cytoarchitectonic areas.

uted more equally across dorsolateral and ventrolateral regions.[91]

Monkeys with lesions of the middorsal part of the lateral prefrontal cortex that extend dorsally from above the sulcus principalis to the midline (i.e., dorsal part of area 46 and area 9) do not show impairments on the classic versions of the spatial or nonspatial delayed-response task or on the delayed non-matching-to-sample task of basic recognition memory.[85,92] In other words, both simple recognition judgments of the novelty versus familiarity of stimuli (tested in delayed non-matching-to-sample) and judgments of the relative recency or saliency of constantly recurring recent spatial and nonspatial events (tested in spatial and nonspatial delayed-response tasks) can be normal after lesions of the middorsal part of the prefrontal cortex. However, after such lesions, monkeys show severe impairment when the number of stimuli to be monitored in working memory increases (see Fig. 56.11A)[93] and when the subject must remember the precise serial order in which events have occurred (self-ordered monitoring).[89] These results emphasize that only certain aspects of mnemonic performance can be impaired by middorsal lateral frontal lesions and that other aspects of performance carried out by ventrolateral and orbitomedial frontal areas in association with other brain regions can be normal.

Damage to the Prefrontal Cortex Causes Memory Impairments in Humans

Although performance on several standard tests of verbal and nonverbal memory can be normal in patients with prefrontal cortical damage, mnemonic performance can be severely impaired in certain circumstances, mostly on short-term memory tasks that require comparisons among a small set of recurring stimuli or judgments of the relative recency of stimuli.[94] These tests are very similar in requirements to those of the classical delayed-response tasks, where a few stimuli recur all the time and the main requirement is to discriminate their most recent occurrence from several earlier ones.

Patients with dorsolateral prefrontal lesions have major impairments monitoring events within working memory. These impairments are clearly illustrated in the self-ordered working memory task in which the patients are presented with a set of stimuli and are required to select a different stimulus on each trial until all the stimuli are selected.[87] From the moment they start responding, the subjects must keep track of the stimuli that have already been selected and compare them with the stimuli that remain to be selected (see Fig. 56.11B). In a self-ordered task, the subject is required to give attention to the stimulus currently under consideration while actively considering (i.e., giving attention to) several other stimuli whose current status is essential for the decision to be made. As pointed out previously, lesion studies in monkeys have shown that these monitoring processes within working memory depend on the middorsal part of the lateral frontal cortex (i.e., dorsal area 46 and area 9). Monkeys with such lesions can remember stimuli, as demonstrated by normal performance on recognition memory tests. The fundamental problem for these animals on the self-ordered working memory tasks stems from the monitoring requirements of the task, that is, the number of stimuli that must be kept in mind and considered, as responses are being made.[89]

Single-Cell Recording Studies Characterize Mnemonic Processing in the Prefrontal Cortex

Studies of the activities of single neurons recorded in the frontal cortex in alert behaving monkeys have also provided evidence for the involvement of the lateral frontal cortex in mnemonic processing. These studies were initiated in the early 1970s and, as might be expected, the experimental protocols used were various versions of the delayed-response tasks derived from earlier lesion work.[95,96] Many neurons in the prefrontal cortex change their firing rate when stimuli are presented or removed in a delayed-response task, and these neurons maintain this change in discharge throughout the delay period until the animal responds. This sustained change in firing rate can last for a minute or longer, depending on the delay imposed in the task. In some neurons, the change in the firing rate during the delay occurs regardless of the location that is rewarded. In other neurons, a differential change is observed; that is, the neuron responds during the delay period only when a specific location has been baited. A particularly interesting demonstration of this phenomenon has been seen in an oculomotor delayed-response task.[97] In this task, the monkey was required to maintain eye fixation on a central spot of light. Each trial began with the brief illumination of one of eight locations. The animal had to remember this location because at the end of the delay, it had to direct its eyes to the location of this briefly illuminated cue. Several neurons in prefrontal cortical area 46 showed sustained changes in their firing rates during the delay period, and their firing depended on the specific location that was cued. These results from single-cell recording studies provide further evidence that the prefrontal cortex is important for certain aspects of working memory.

A

Recognition

Monitoring

B

FIGURE 56.11 (A) In one experiment, monkeys with middorsal lateral frontal lesions were tested under two mnemonic conditions. Under one condition, basic recognition memory was tested. The animals were presented with three stimuli and were allowed to choose any one of the three stimuli to receive reward. On the subsequent test trial administered 10 s later, a novel object was introduced, and to obtain a reward the animals were required to select the novel object. Performance on this condition could be based on a simple discrimination between the novel and the familiar item, i.e., simple recognition memory. Monkeys with middorsal lateral frontal lesions were not impaired on this task because performance could be sustained by the orbitomedial frontal cortex and the associated limbic medial temporal lobe system responsible for such judgments. In the other condition, monitoring of choices within working memory was taxed. The monkeys were again shown three objects and were allowed to choose one of them. On the subsequent test trial, however, the animals were presented with the same objects, and the correct response was to select one of the objects not previously chosen. Note that now the animal was faced with equally familiar objects and therefore performance required recall of which one of these objects had previously been selected. Monkeys with middorsal lateral frontal lesions were severely impaired in this condition. (B) In an experiment in humans, the subject was presented with a stack of cards on each of which all stimuli were presented, but in different random orders. The subject had to select one of the stimuli, point to it, and then turn to the next card to select another stimulus and continue like this until all stimuli had been selected. In subsequent testing the subject was required to recognize which object had been selected on each card from a set of equally familiar alternatives. The subject was therefore required to monitor which objects had been selected on each card from a set of equally familiar alternatives. In the example illustrated, the stimuli are abstract designs. Patients with dorsolateral frontal lesions were impaired in this self-ordered monitoring task. However, if familiar stimuli were mixed with novel stimuli, the patients with dorsolateral frontal lesions were able to select the novel from the familiar stimuli. From Petrides.[93]

Summary

The prefrontal cortex plays a critical role in working memory, the ability to hold information on-line for several seconds in the service of comprehension, reasoning, and problem solving. Working memory may be divided into multiple subsystems responsible for executing verbal rehearsal and operating a visuospatial sketch pad. These types of working memory involve different brain circuits, and separate parts of the caudal–medial and lateral prefrontal cortex are linked to different aspects of working memory performance. Parts of the orbital and medial prefrontal cortex play a more general role in memory. Deficits are most prominent when animals or humans with damage to the prefrontal cortex must monitor ordered information in working memory. Correspondingly, single neurons in the prefrontal cortex show sustained activations across memory delays as animals perform working memory tasks.

MODULATORS OF MEMORY STORAGE

Evidence indicates that memories of emotionally arousing events are often more vivid, more accurate, and more stable than memories of more ordinary events. Such evidence makes sense because organisms would benefit from remembering the important events best. Thus, it also makes sense that the brain should have evolved mechanisms for storing information that reflects the degree to which the information is worth remembering. Research suggests that specific neural mechanisms serve to modulate the strength of newly formed memories. These **memory-modulating** mechanisms are thought to underlie, at least in part, the effects of emotional arousal on memory.

Three Lines of Evidence Support the Concept of a Memory-Modulatory System

The concept of memory storage modulation is based on three primary discoveries in experiments with animals.[98] The first discovery was that recently formed memories are susceptible to postlearning influences (e.g., drug injections, electrical brain stimulation) for a limited time after they are formed. It is now well established, for example, that a large variety of drugs and neurotransmitter agents (e.g., treatments affecting adrenergic, cholinergic, dopaminergic, GABAergic, and opioid peptidergic systems) administered after training can alter memory for the training experience. The second discovery was that, in many cases, the same postlearning treatment can either enhance or impair (i.e., modulate) memory, depending on the experimental conditions. Finally, some posttraining treatments (e.g., injection of sympathetic stress hormones) affect memory storage even though they do not directly affect the brain. From these facts, investigators infer the existence of endogenous systems that influence memory storage processes, but which do not serve as the permanent neural locus of memory storage.

A memory-modulatory system has several important characteristics (discussed by Packard *et al.*[99]). Perhaps most critically, the role of a memory-modulatory system in memory is time-limited. As was noted earlier, posttraining treatments affect memory storage for only a limited time after learning. Additionally, the brain regions participating in memory modulation are not required for the retrieval of memories once stored. Finally, memory-modulatory systems are potentially capable of influencing all of the different memory systems described earlier.

Stress Hormones Act as Endogenous Memory Modulators

Extensive evidence supports the view that stress hormones act as endogenous modulators of memory for events that cause their release. For example, removal of the pituitary or the **adrenal glands**, two primary sources of stress hormones, impairs several forms of learning. In this section, we summarize evidence regarding the effects of stress hormones on memory, focusing on the two major classes of adrenal stress hormones, *catecholamines* and *glucocorticoids.*

Catecholamines

Extensive findings implicate the sympathetic adrenomedullary hormones epinephrine and norepinephrine, both classified as catecholamines, as endogenous modulators of memory. Nonemotional training conditions, producing only minimal fluctuations in plasma epinephrine and norepinephrine levels, result in weak memory retention. However, retention for these tasks is significantly improved by systemic posttraining injections of epinephrine or norepinephrine. As is the case for virtually every memory-enhancing hormone or drug tested, the effects of epinephrine and norepinephrine on memory storage are characterized by an inverted-U relationship: moderate doses of these hormones enhance retention performance, whereas both lower and higher doses are less effective. Studies investigating the role of catecholamines in memory in humans[59] provided further evidence that the enhancing influence of arousal (either emotionally or physically induced) on memory depends on β-adrenergic receptor activation.

The mechanism of these effects is indirect. For example, epinephrine, which is released from the adrenal medulla, does not readily enter the brain. Its memory-modulating effects most likely result secondarily from activation of the peripheral nervous system. Systemically administered epinephrine increases the release and turnover of norepinephrine in limbic structures, including the amygdala, and potentiates the firing rates of neurons in the locus ceruleus, a collection of noradrenergic cells that project to brain regions involved in memory storage such as the amygdala and hippocampus.

One mechanism by which epinephrine is thought to enhance memory storage is by activating afferent fibers of the vagus nerve. Vagotomy (ablation of the vagus nerve) or inactivation of the nucleus of the solitary tract (the brainstem nucleus receiving vagal afferents) blocks the memory-enhancing effects of epinephrine. Conversely, electrical stimulation of the vagus nerve immediately after training modulates retention in an inverted-U fashion. In addition, epinephrine likely affects memory, at least in part, via its well-established effects on blood glucose levels. For example, when administered systemically after training, both epinephrine and glucose induce inverted-U dose–response enhancement of memory.[100] Glucose has also been shown to enhance memory in elderly humans and in patients with Alzheimer disease. Because glucose freely enters the brain, it may act directly on brain memory processes. However, fructose, which does not readily pass the blood–brain barrier, also modulates memory at doses similar to those of glucose.

Glucocorticoids

In addition to inducing the release of catecholamines, emotionally stressful events induce a cascade of physiological events involving hormones of the hypothalamic–pituitary–adrenal axis. Both adrenocorticotropin (ACTH) and glucocorticoids modulate memory storage.[101] Unlike adrenomedullary catecholamines, adrenocortical hormones readily enter the brain and can bind to several classes of brain adrenal steroid receptors, including the mineralocorticoid receptor (MR or Type I) and the glucocorticoid receptor (GR or Type II). MR activation facilitates hippocampal neuronal excitability, a form of LTP that may underlie learning and memory (see Chapter 55). In contrast, the effects of GR activation are biphasic: mild GR stimulation generally facilitates electrophysiological responses, whereas high concentrations of glucocorticoids or chronic stimulation with glucocorticoids (resulting in GR saturation) can suppress these processes.[102] Furthermore, the dose-dependent effects of glucocorticoids on memory parallel the electrophysiological dose–response effects: low doses of glucocorticoids generally enhance memory storage via GR activation,[103] whereas high doses of glucocorticoids or chronic exposure to glucocorticoids or stress generally impairs memory. Similarly, sustained hypercortisolemia in human patients suffering from Cushing syndrome results in cognitive impairments.[104] Glucocorticoids interact with peripheral catecholamines to modulate memory storage. For example, adrenocortical suppression blocks the memory-enhancing effects of epinephrine and amphetamine.[105]

Other Memory-Modulating Hormones

The opioid peptides include the endorphins and enkephalins. Enkephalins are found in both the brain and the periphery, where they are coreleased from the adrenal glands with epinephrine and norepinephrine in stressful situations. β-Endorphin is generated from the same parent molecule as ACTH (proopiomelanocortin, or POMC) and is released from the hypothalamus and pituitary with ACTH. In contrast to the adrenomedullary and adrenocortical stress hormones, opioid peptides generally impair memory.[106] Conversely, systemic injections of naloxone, an opiate antagonist, facilitate memory storage.[107] Endorphins are believed to disrupt memory storage by a direct action on the brain, whereas enkephalins are thought to produce their effects by a peripherally initiated mechanism. Other memory-modulatory substances released in response to stress include vasopressin, substance P, and cholecystokinin.[101,108]

The Effects of Drugs and Hormones in Animals Reveal That Memory Modulation Is Mediated by the Amygdaloid Complex

In addition to playing a role in the fear conditioning system, the amygdala is the brain region most clearly implicated to date in the modulatory effects of peripheral drugs and hormones on memory. Direct stimulation of the amygdala can modulate (enhance or impair) memory, and the effects of amygdala stimulation on memory depend on the integrity of the adrenal glands. In addition, evidence from human patients with selective amygdala degeneration resulting from a rare genetic disease indicates that the effects of emotional arousal on conscious memory depend on the amygdala.[109,110]

Evidence from animal studies indicates that lesions of the amygdala or the stria terminalis, a major afferent–efferent pathway of the amygdala, block the mem-

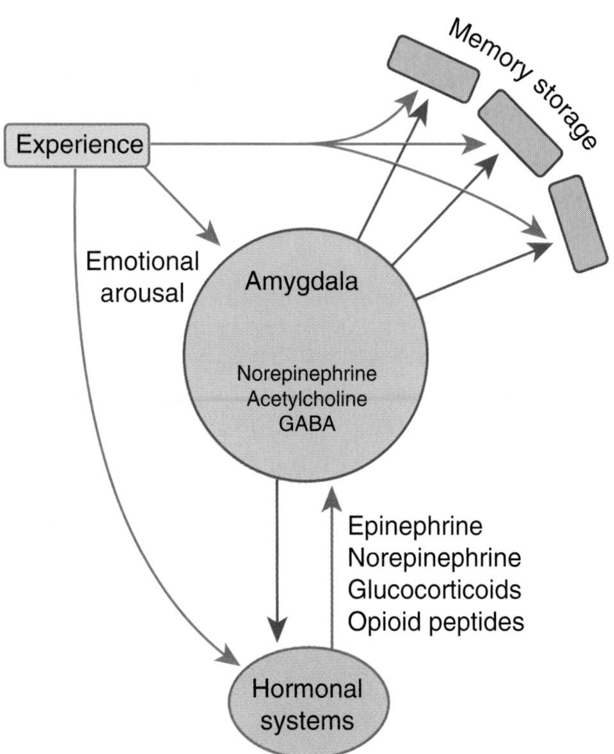

FIGURE 56.12 A schematic representation of how hormonal systems and the amygdala complex can modulate the storage of memory for emotionally arousing events through influences on other brain systems. See text for details. From McGaugh *et al.*[98]

ory-enhancing or memory-impairing effects of many drugs and hormones (Fig. 56.12)[98] and block the memory-impairing effects of adrenalectomy. Moreover, the memory-modulatory effects of many drugs, including treatments affecting adrenergic, GABAergic, and opioid peptidergic mechanisms, are blocked by infusions of the β-adrenergic antagonist propranolol administered into the amygdala. Although infusions of naloxone into the amygdala enhance memory, this enhancement depends on an intact noradrenergic function in the amygdala.[111] These findings indicate that systemically administered drugs and hormones influence memory storage through effects involving noradrenergic mechanisms within the amygdala.

The amygdala consists of many subnuclei, most of which have a specific neuronal architecture and are connected to different brain structures (see Chapter 55). The memory-modulatory effects of glucocorticoids depend on the integrity of the basolateral nucleus of the amygdala, whereas glucocorticoid-induced memory enhancement is not affected by lesions of the central amygdala nucleus.[103] Similarly, the memory-impairing effects of systemic injections of diazepam (valium) are blocked by lesions of the basolateral nucleus, but not of the central or lateral nuclei. Thus, the basolateral nucleus appears to play a crucial role in modulating memory storage. This view is further supported by the finding that infusion of drugs selectively into the basolateral nucleus induces memory modulation, whereas infusions into the central nucleus are ineffective.[112] This specificity is understandable from an anatomical perspective: the basolateral nucleus is reciprocally connected with brain regions involved in memory storage such as the hippocampus and neocortex. In contrast, other amygdaloid nuclei, including the central nucleus, receive only sparse innervation from structures that are involved in long-term memory storage.

As noted previously, one characteristic of a memory-modulatory system is that, although it may participate in memory storage, it is not required for normal retrieval of information once it is stored. Many experiments indicate that the amygdala exhibits this characteristic in memory. For example, amygdala stimulation (via intra-amygdala infusions of amphetamine) modulates memory of both a hippocampal-dependent and a caudate nucleus-dependent task when given immediately after training.[113] However, inactivation of the amygdala (via injection of the local anesthetic lidocaine) prior to retention testing has no effect on the enhancement of memory due to posttraining amygdala stimulation in either task. Findings like these indicate that the amygdala is important in modulating storage in emotionally stressful situations, but not in the maintenance or retrieval of memory. These findings also indicate that the amygdala can modulate memory storage of several forms of learning and does this through influences on the separate brain systems that mediate each kind of memory.

Although the amygdala is the brain region most implicated in drug and hormone effects on memory modulation, other brain regions, including the septohippocampal system, caudate nucleus, and basal forebrain nucleus, are also involved. The time-limited involvement of the septohippocampal system in long-term memory is well established and is consistent with a memory-modulatory role. Moreover, the septohippocampal system is involved in drug-induced modulation of memory storage mediated by agents such as glucocorticoids, opioids, and benzodiazepines.[102,114] Experimental evidence also implicates the caudate nucleus and basal forebrain nucleus. Memory storage is modulated by dopaminergic and cholinergic drugs infused into the caudate nucleus, and substance P has been reported to modulate memory storage via the basal forebrain nucleus.

Summary

A very substantial body of evidence now suggests that endogenous nervous system mechanisms exist to modulate memory storage during and after emotional events. These mechanisms include peripheral mechanisms of the adrenomedullary and adrenocortical stress hormones and central mechanisms mediated by the amygdala. Memory-modulation mechanisms are viewed as an efficient, evolutionarily adaptive method of ensuring that the strength of memories is, generally speaking, proportional to their importance to the individual.

Neurobiological studies on both humans and animals have identified a brain system for declarative memory, the ability to recall our personal history and knowledge of the world, and have distinguished this memory system from several other specialized systems that serve perceptual performance, acquisition of habits, and emotional learning. The hippocampus plays a critical role in declarative memory and performs this function through intimate interactions with areas of the cerebral cortex thought to be the repositories of hierarchically organized category-specific representatives. Experimental studies on animals and computational models indicate that the fundamental role of the hippocampus is to mediate the organization of large-scale networks of cortical associations in support of a capacity for flexible recall of memories from partial or associated information.

In addition to these memory systems, specialized functions of the prefrontal cortex subserve working memory, our capacity to hold information on-line for several seconds and to manipulate and order information. Also, the amygdala provides a special memory function by modulating the strength of long-term storage within all memory systems in accordance with the emotional impact and adaptive importance of specific experiences. These findings support the notion that there are many widely distributed memory systems in the brain, each supporting a particular type of adaptive function.

References

1. Schacter, D. L. (1987). Implicit memory: History and current status. *J. Exp. Psychol. Learn Mem. Cognit.* **13:** 501–518.
2. Zola-Morgan, S. (1995). Localization of brain function: The legacy of Franz Joseph Gall (1758–1828). *Annu. Rev. Neurosci.* **18:** 359–383.
3. Gall, F. J. (1835). *The Influence of the Brain on the Form of the Head* (W. Lewis, translation ed.). Marsh, Capen & Lyon, Boston.
4. Maine de Biran (1929). *The Influence of Habit on the Faculty of Thinking.* Williams & Wilkins, Baltimore, MD (first publication in 1804).
5. Ribot, T. (1881). *Diseases of Memory.* Appleton-Century Crofts, New York.
6. Bergson, H. (1911). *Matter and Memory* (N. M. Paul and W. S. Palmer, translation eds.). Allen & Unwin, London.
7. Tolman, E. C. (1948). Cognitive maps in rats and men. *Psychol. Rev.* **55:** 189–208.
8. Ryle, G. (1949). *The Concept of Mind.* Hutchinson, San Francisco.
9. Reiff, R., and Scheerer, M. (1959). *Memory of Hypnotic Age Regression.* International Universities Press, New York.
10. Nielsen, J. M. (1958). *Memory and Amnesia.* San Lucas Press, Los Angeles.
11. Scoville, W. B., and Milner, B. (1957). Loss of recent memory after bilateral hippocampal lesions. *J. Neurol. Neurosurg. Psychiatry* **20:** 11–21.
12. Corkin, S., Amaral, D. G., Gonzalez, R. G., Johnson, K. A., and Hyman, B. T. (1997). H.M.'s medial temporal lobe lesion. Findings from magnetic resonance imaging. *J. Neurosci.* **17:** 3964–3979.
13. Cohen, N. J., and Squire, L. R. (1980). Preserved learning and retention of pattern analyzing skill in amnesiacs: Dissociation of knowing how and knowing that. *Science* **210:** 207–210.
14. Cohen, N. J., and Eichenbaum, H. (1993). *Memory, Amnesia, and the Hippocampal System.* MIT Press, Cambridge, MA.
15. Tulving, E. (1972). Episodic and semantic memory. *Organization of Memory* (E. Tulving and W. Donaldson, eds.), pp. 381–403. Academic Press, New York.
16. Schacter, D. L., and Tulving, E. (1994). What are the memory systems on 1994? In *Memory Systems 1994* (D. L. Schacter and E. Tulving, eds.), pp. 1–38. MIT Press, Cambridge, MA.
17. Squire, L. R. (1992). Memory and the hippocampus: A synthesis from findings with rats, monkeys, and humans. *Psychol. Rev.* **99:** 195–231.
18. James, W. (1890). *The Principles of Psychology.* Henry Holt, New York.
19. Milner, B., Corsi, P., and Leonard, G. (1991). Frontal lobe contribution to recency judgments. *Neuropsychologia* **29:** 601–618.
20. Moscovitch, M. (1995). Confabulation. In *Memory Distortion: How Minds, Brains and Societies Reconstruct the Past* (D. L. Schacter, J. T. Coyle, G. D. Fischbach, M.-M. Mesulam, and L. E. Sullivan, eds.), pp. 226–254. Harvard University Press, Cambridge, MA.
21. Buckner, R. L., and Tulving, E. (1995). Neuroimaging studies of memory: Theory and recent PET results. In *Handbook of Neuropsychology* (F. Boller and J. Grafman, eds.), pp. 439–466. Elsevier, Amsterdam.
22. Ungerleider, L. G. (1995). Functional brain imaging studies of cortical mechanisms for memory. *Science* **270:** 760–775.
23. Martin, A., Wiggs, C. L., and Weisberg, J. A. (1997). Modulation of human temporal lobe activity by form, meaning, and experience. *Hippocampus* **7:** 587–593.
24. Schacter, D. L., Alpert, N. M., Savage, C. R., Rauch, S. L., and Albert, M. S. (1996). Conscious recollection and the human hippocampal formation: Evidence from positron emission tomography. *Proc. Natl. Acad. Sci. U.S.A.* **93:** 321–325.
25. Stern, C. E., Corkin, S., Gonzalez, R. G., Guimaraes, A. R., Baker, J. R., Jennings, P. J., Carr, C. A., Sugiura, R. M., Vedantham, V., and Rosen, B. R. (1996). The hippocampal formation participates in novel picture encoding: Evidence from functional magnetic resonance imaging. *Proc. Natl. Acad. Sci. U.S.A.* **93:** 8660–8665.
26. Tulving, E. (1985). Memory and consciousness. *Can. Psychologist* **26:** 1–12.
27. Tulving, E., Schacter, D. L., McLachlan, D. R., and Moscovitch,

M. (1988). Priming of semantic autobiographical knowledge: A case study of retrograde amnesia. *Brain Cognit.* **8:** 3–20.

28. De Renzi, E., Liotti, M., and Nichelli, P. (1987). Semantic amnesia with preservation of autobiographic memory: A case report. *Cortex* **23:** 575–597.
29. Patterson, K., and Hodges, J. R. (1995). Disorders of semantic memory. In *Handbook of Memory Disorders* (A. D. Baddeley, B. A. Wilson, and F. N. Watts, eds.), pp. 167–186. Wiley, Chichester.
30. Plaut, D. C., and Farah, M. J. (1990). Visual object representation: Interpreting neurophysiological data within a computational framework. *J. Cognit. Neurosci.* **2:** 320–343.
31. Haxby, J. V., Horwitz, B., Ungerleider, L. G., Maisog, J-Ma, Pietrini, P., and Grady, C. L. (1994). The functional organization of human extrastriate cortex: A PET-rCBF study of selective attention of faces and locations. *J. Neurosci.* **14:** 6336–6353.
32. Schacter, D. L., Reiman, E., Uecker, A., Polster, M. R., Yun, L. S., and Cooper, L. A. (1995). Brain regions associated with retrieval of structurally coherent visual information. *Nature (London)* **376:** 587–590.
33. Butters, N., Heindel, W. C., and Salmon, D. P. (1990). Dissociation of implicit memory in dementia: Neurological implications. *Bull Psychon. Soc.* **28:** 359–366.
34. Karni, A., Meyer, G., Jezzard, P., Adams, M. M., Turner, R., and Ungerleider, L. G. (1995). Functional MRI evidence for adult motor cortex plasticity during motor skill learning. *Nature (London)* **377:** 155–158.
35. Grafman, J., Litvan, I., Massaquoi, S., Stewart, J., Sirigu, A., and Hallett, M. (1992). Cognitive planning deficit in patients with cerebellar degeneration. *Neurology* **42:** 1493–1496.
36. Baddeley, A. (1994). Working memory: The interface between memory and cognition. In *Memory Systems 1994* (D. L. Schacter and E. Tulving, eds.), pp. 351–368. MIT Press, Cambridge, MA.
37. Goldman-Rakic, P. S. (1994). The issue of memory in the study of prefrontal function. In *Motor and Cognitive Functions of the Prefrontal Cortex* (A.-M. Thierry, ed.), pp. 112–121. Springer-Verlag, Berlin.
38. Warrington, E. K., and Shallice, T. (1969). The selective impairment of auditory verbal short-term memory. *Brain* **92:** 885–896.
39. Baddeley, A. D., and Hitch, G. J. (1974). Working memory. In *Recent Advances in Learning and Motivation* (G. H. Bower, ed.), pp. 47–90. Academic Press, New York.
40. Vallar, G., and Papagno, C. (1995). Neuropsychological impairments of short-term memory. In *Handbook of Memory Disorders* (A. D. Baddeley, B. A. Wilson, and F. N. Watts, eds.), pp. 135–165. Wiley, Chichester.
41. Mishkin, M., Malamut, B., and Bachevalier, J. (1984). Memories and habits: Two neural systems. In *The Neurobiology of Learning and Memory* (J. L. McGaugh, G. Lynch, and N. M. Weinberger, eds.), pp. 65–77. Guilford Press, New York.
42. Zola-Morgan, S., and Squire, L. R. (1985). Medial temporal lesions in monkeys impair memory on a variety of tasks sensitive to human amnesia. *Behav. Neurosci.* **99:** 22–34.
43. Rapp, P. R., and Amaral, D. G. (1989). Evidence for task-depenent memory dysfunction in the aged monkey. *J. Neurosci.* **9:** 3568–3576.
44. Zola-Morgan, S., and Squire, L. R. (1990). The primate hippocampal formation: Evidence for a time-limited role in memory storage. *Science* **250:** 288–290.
45. Squire, L. R., and Zola-Morgan, S. (1991). The medial temporal lobe memory system. *Science* **253:** 1380–1386.
46. Zola-Morgan, S., Squire, L. R., and Ramus, S. J. (1994). Severity of memory impairment in monkeys as a function of locus and extent of damage within the medial temporal lobe memory system. *Hippocampus* **4:** 483–495.
47. Zola-Morgan, S., Squire, L. R., and Amaral, D. G. (1986). Human amnesia and the medial-temporal region: Enduring memory impairment following a bilateral lesion limited to field CA1 of the hippocampus. *J. Neurosci* **6:** 2950–2967.
48. O'Keefe, J., and Nadel, L. (1978). *The Hippocampus as a Cognitive Map.* Oxford University Press (Clarendon), London.
49. Morris, R. G. M., Garrud, P., Rawlins, J. N. P., and O'Keefe, J. (1982). Place navigation impaired in rats with hippocampal lesions. *Nature (London)* **297:** 681–683.
50. O'Keefe, J. (1976). Place units in the hippocampus of the freely moving rat. *Exp. Neurol* **51:** 78–109.
51. O'Keefe, J., and Speakman, A. (1987). Single unit activity in the rat hippocampus during spatial memory task. *Exp. Brain Res.* **68:** 1–27.
52. Hirsh, R. (1974). The hippocampus and contextual retrieval of information from memory: A theory. *Behav. Biol.* **12:** 421–444.
53. Bunsey, M., Eichenbaum, H. (1996). Conservation of hippocampal memory function in rats and humans. *Nature (London)* **379:** 255–257.
54. Murray, E. A., Gaffan, D., and Mishkin, M. (1993). Neural substrates of visual stimulus-stimulus association in rhesus monkeys. *J. Neurosci.* **13:** 4549–4561.
55. Moscovitch, M. (1994). Memory and working with memory: Evaluation of a component process model and comparisons with other models. In *Memory Systems 1994* (D. L. Schacter and E. Tulving, eds.), pp. 259–310. MIT Press, Cambridge, MA.
56. Hebb, D. O. (1949). *The Organization of Behavior.* Wiley, New York.
57. Eichenbaum, H. (1996). Is the rodent hippocampus just for "place"? *Curr. Opin. Neurobiol.* **6:** 187–195.
58. McDonald, R. J., and White, N. M. (1993). A triple dissociation of memory systems: Hippocampus, amygdala, and dorsal striatum. *Behav. Neurosci.* **107:** 3–22.
59. Cahill, L., Prins, B., Weber, M., and McGaugh, J. L. (1994). Beta-adrenergic activation and memory for emotional events. *Nature (London)* **371:** 702–704.
60. Marr, D. (1971). Simple memory: A theory for archicortex. *Philos. Trans. R. Soc. London B* **262:** 23–81.
61. Anderson, J. (1977). Neural models with cognitive implications. In *Basic Processes in Reading: Perception and Comprehension* (D. LaBerge and S. Samuels, eds.), pp. 27–90. Erlbaum, Hillsdale, NJ.
62. McNaughton, B., and Morris, R. (1987). Hippocampal synaptic enhancement and information storage. *Trends Neurosci.* **10:** 408–415.
63. Treves, A., and Rolls, E. T. (1994). Computational analysis of the role of the hippocampus in memory. *Hippocampus* **4:** 374–391.
64. Hasselmo, M. E., Wyble, B. P., and Wallenstein, G. V. (1996). Encoding and retrieval of episodic memories: Role of cholinergic and gabaergic modulation in the hypocampus. *Hippocampus* **6:** 693–708.
65. Alvarez, P., and Squire, L. (1994). Memory consolidation and the medial temporal lobe: A simple network model. *Proc. Natl. Acad. Sci. U.S.A.* **91:** 7041–7045.
66. McClelland, J. L., McNaughton, B. L., and O'Reilly, R. C. (1995). Why there are complementary learning systems in the hippocampus and neocortex: Insights from successes and failures of connectionist models of learning and memory. *Psychol. Rev.* **102:** 419.
67. Gluck, M., and Myers, C. (1993). Hippocampal mediation of stimulus representation: A computational theory. *Hippocampus* **3:** 491–516.
68. Shallice, T. (1988). *From Neuropsychology to Mental Structure.* Cambridge University Press, Cambridge, UK.

69. Damasio, A. R. (1990). Category-related recognition deficits as a clue to the neural substrates of knowledge. *Trends Neurosci.* **13:** 95–98.
70. Caramazza, A., Hillis, A. Leek, E. C., and Miozzo, M. (1994). The organization of lexical knowledge in the brain: Evidence from category- and modality-specific deficits. In *Mapping the Mind: Domain Specificity in Cognition and Culture* (L. A. Hirschfeld and S. A. Gelman, eds.), pp. 68–84. Cambridge University Press, New York.
71. Warrington, E. K., and Shallice, T. (1984). Category-specific semantic impairments. *Brain* **107:** 829–854.
72. Sartori, G,. and Job, R. (1988). The oyster with four legs: A neuropsychological study on the interaction of visual and semantic information. *Cognit. Neuropsychol.* **5:** 105–132.
73. Sartori, G., Job, R., Miozzo, M., Zago, S., and Marchiori, G. (1993). Category-specific form-knowledge deficit in a patient with herpes simplex virus encephalitis. *J. Clin. Exp. Neuropsychol.* **15:** 280–299.
74. Hillis, A. E., and Caramazza, A. (1991). Category-specific naming and comprehension impairment: A double dissociation. *Brain* **114:** 2081–2094.
75. Rosch, E., Mervis, C., Gray, W., Johnson, D., and Boyes-Braem, P. (1976). Basic objects in natural categories. *Cognit. Psychol.* **8:** 382–439.
76. Funnell, E., and Sheridan, J. (1992). Categories of knowledge? Unfamiliar aspects of living and non-living things. *Cognit. Neuropsychol.* **9:** 135–153.
77. Stewart, F., Parkin, A. J., and Hunkin, N. M. (1992). Naming impairments following recovery from herpes simplex encephalitis: Category-specific? *Q. J. Exp. Psychol.* **44A:** 261–284.
78. Gaffan, D., and Heywood, C. A. (1993). A spurious category-specific visual agnosia for living things in normal human and nonhuman primates. *J. Cognit. Neurosci.* **5:** 118–128.
79. Warrington, E. K., and McCarthy, R. A. (1987). Categories of knowledge: Further fractionation and an attempted integration. *Brain* **110:** 1273–1296.
80. Martin, A., Haxby, J. V., Lalonde, F. M., Wiggs, C. L., and Ungerleider, L. G. (1995). Discrete cortical regions associated with knowledge of color and knowledge of action. *Science* **270:** 102–105.
81. Martin, A., Wiggs, C. L., Ungerleider, L. G., and Haxby, J. V. (1996). Neural correlates of category-specific knowledge. *Nature (London)* **379:** 649–652.
82. Kosslyn, S. M., Thompson, W. L., Kim, I. J., and Alpert, N. M. (1995). Topographical representations of mental images in primary visual cortex. *Nature (London)* **378:** 496–498.
83. Shimamura, A. P. (1995). Memory and frontal lobe function. In *The Cognitive Neurosciences* (M. S. Gazzaniga, ed.), pp. 803–813. MIT Press, Cambridge, MA.
84. Pandya, D. N., and Barnes, C. L. (1987). Architecture and connections of the frontal cortex. In *The Frontal Lobes Revisited* (E. Perecman, ed.), pp. 41–72. IRBN Press, New York.
85. Bachevalier, J., and Mishkin, M. (1986). Visual recognition impairment follows ventromedial but not dorsolateral prefrontal lesions in monkeys. *Behav. Brain Res.* **20:** 249–261.
86. Corkin, S., Cohen, N. J., Sullicen, E. V., Clegg, R. A., Rosen, T. J., and Ackerman, R. H. (1985). Analyses of global impairments of different etiologies. *Ann. N. Y. Acad. Sci.* **444:** 10–40.
87. Petrides, M. (1989). Frontal lobes and memory. In *Handbook of Neuropsychology* (F. Boller and J. Grafman, eds.), pp. 75–90. Elsevier, New York.
88. Jacobsen, C. E. (1936). Studies of cerebral function in primates. I: The functions of the frontal association areas in monkeys. *Comput. Psychol. Monogr.* **13:** 1–60.
89. Petrides, M. (1994). Frontal lobes and working memory: Evidence from investigations of the effects of cortical excisions in nonhuman primates. In *Handbook of Neuropsychology* (F. Boller and J. Grafman, eds.), pp. 59–82. Elsevier, New York.
90. Wilson, F. A. W., Scalaidhe, S. P. O., and Goldman-Rakis, P. S. (1993). Dissociation of object and spatial processing domains in primate prefrontal cortex. *Science* **260:** 1955–1958.
91. Rao, S. C., Rainer, G., and Miller, E. K. (1997). Integration of what and where in the primate prefrontal cortex. *Science* **276:** 821–824.
92. Petrides, M. (1994). Impairments on non-spatial self-ordered and externally ordered working memory tasks after lesions of the mid-dorsal part of the lateral frontal cortex in the monkey. *J. Neurosci.* **15:** 359–375.
93. Petrides, M. (1996). Lateral frontal cortical contribution to memory. *Semin. Neurosci.* **8:** 57–68.
94. Milner, B. (1964). Some effects of frontal lobectomy in man. In *The Frontal Granular Cortex and Behavior* (J. M. Warren and K. Akert, eds.), pp. 313–334. McGraw-Hill, New York.
95. Goldman-Rakic, P. S. (1987). Circuitry of primate prefrontal cortex and regulation of behavior by representational memory. In *Handbook of Physiology* (V. B. Mountcastle, F. Plum, and S. R. Geiger, eds.), Sect. I, Vol. V, Part I, pp. 373–417. Am. Physiol. Soc., Bethesda, MD.
96. Fuster, J.-M. (1989). *The Prefrontal Cortex: Anatomy, Physiology, and Neuropsychology of the Frontal Lobe.* Raven Press, New York.
97. Funahashi, S., Bruce, C. J., and Goldman-Rakic, P. S. (1993). Dorsolateral prefrontal lesions and oculomotor delayed-response performance: Evidence for mnemonic "*scotomas.*" *J. Neurosci.* **13:** 1479–1497.
98. McGaugh, J. L., Introini-Collison, I. B., Cahill, L., Kim, M., and Liang, K. C. (1992). Involvement of the amygdala in neuromodulatory influences on memory storage. In *The Amygdala: Neurobiological Aspects of Emotion, Memory, and Mental Dysfunction* (J. P. Aggleton, ed.), pp. 431–451. Wiley-Liss, New York.
99. Packard, M., Williams, C. L., Cahill, L., and McGaugh, J. L. (1995). The anatomy of a memory modulatory system: From periphery to brain. In *Neurobehavioral Plasticity* (N. E. Spear, L. P. Spear, and M. L. Woodruff, eds.), pp. 149–185. Erlbaum, Hillsdale, NJ.
100. Gold, P. E. (1995). Modulation of emotional and nonemotional memories: Same pharmacological systems, diffeent neuroanatomical systems. In *Brain and Memory: Modulation and Mediation of Neuralplasticity* (J. L. McGaugh, N. M. Weinberger, and G. S. Lynch, eds.), pp. 41–74. Oxford University Press, New York.
101. Bohus, B. (1994). Humoral modulation of learning and memory processes: Physiological significance of brain and peripheral mechanisms. In *The Memory Systems of the Brain* (J. Delacour, ed.), pp. 337–364. World Scientific, New Jersey.
102. McEwen, B. S., and Sapolsky, R. M. (1995). Stress and cognitive function. *Curr. Opin. Neurobiol.* **5:** 205–216.
103. Roozendaal, B., and McGaugh, J. L. (1996). Amygdaloid nuclei lesions differentially affect glucocorticoid-induced memory enhancement in an inhibitory avoidance task. *Neurobiol. Learn. Mem.* **65:** 1–8.
104. Starkman, M., Gebarski, S., Berent, S., and Schteingart, D. (1992). Hippocampal formation volume, memory dysfunction, and cortisol levels in patients with Cushing's syndrome. *Biol. Psychiatry* **32:** 756–765.
105. Roozendaal, B., Carmi, O., and McGaugh, J. L. (1996). Adrenocortical suppression blocks the memory-enhancing effects of epinephrine and amphetamine. *Proc. Natl. Acad. Sci. U.S.A.* **93:** 1429–1433.
106. Martinez, J. L., Jr., Weinberger, S. B., and Schulteis, G. (1988).

Enkephalins and learning and memory: A review of evidence for a site of action outside the blood-brain barrier. *Behav. Neural Biol.* **49:** 192–221.
107. Gallagher, M. (1982). Naloxone enhancement of memory processes: Effects of other opiate antagonists. *Behav. Neural Biol.* **35:** 375–382.
108. McGaugh, J. L. (1992). Affect, neuromodulatory systems and memory storage. In *Handbook of Emotion and Memory* (S.-A. Christianson, ed.), pp. 245–268. Erlbaum, Hillsdale, NJ.
109. Markowitsch, H. (1994). The amygdala's contribution to memory: A study on two patients with Urbach-Wiethe disease. *NeuroReport* **5:** 1349–1352.
110. Cahill, L., Babinsky, R., Markowitsch, H. J., and McGaugh, J. L. (1995). The amygdala and emotional memory. *Nature (London)* **377:** 295–296.
111. Gallagher, M., Rapp, P. R., and Fanelli, R. J. (1985). Opiate antagonist facilitation of time-dependent memory processes: Dependence upon intact norepinephrine function. *Brain Res.* **347:** 284–290.
112. Silva, M. A., and Tomaz, C. (1995). Amnesia after diazepam infusion into the basolateral but not central amygdala of *Rattus norvegicus. Neuropsychology* **32:** 31–36.
113. Packard, M. G., Cahill, L., and McGaugh, J. L. (1994). Amygdala modulation of hippocampal-dependent and caudate nucleus-dependent memory processes. *Proc. Natl. Acad. Sci. U.S.A.* **91:** 8477–8481.
114. Izquierdo, I. (1994). Pharmacology of memory: Drugs acting upon the neurotransmitter mechanisms involved in memory consolidation. In *The Memory Systems of the Brain* (J. Delacour, ed.), pp. 337–364. World Scientific, New Jersey.

C H A P T E R

57

Language and Communication

David Caplan, Thomas Carr, James Gould, and Randi Martin

Of all the topics in cognitive science, the topic receiving the most attention has been the study of language. In this chapter, we discuss only those aspects of language that make sustained contact with brain mechanisms. These aspects include the study of animal communication, neuroimaging techniques, and brain lesion methods, all of which have been used to connect aspects of language to brain activity.

This chapter begins with a discussion of animal communication. Animal communication combines both innate and learned features, but does not capture the full complexity of human language as it has been defined by linguists. The next section of the chapter provides a brief summary of what is common among human languages as vehicles for communication. Because written language has proven easier to control in cognitive and imaging experiments, many of these studies have used written rather than spoken language. In the third section of this chapter, we turn to these studies to indicate how imaging methods have influenced the analysis of this form of skill learning. The final section deals with deficits in written and spoken language acquired from lesions. In patients with such deficits, it is clear that the language function was present prior to the lesion, but is lost as a result of specific brain injury. The new methods of neuroimaging, together with the more classical approach to language from the perspective of studies of patients, provide most of the current data for understanding the brain mechanisms of human language.

ANIMAL COMMUNICATION

Communication Is Important for Individual Survival

The ultimate goal of most animal communication, like that of behavior in general, is reproduction. Thus, signals that indicate the sender's species, gender, and degree of reproductive readiness account for the vast majority of natural communication. These are the messages being broadcast by chirping crickets, flashing fireflies, pheromone-releasing moths, and singing birds. Frequently, the mate-attraction call is also used to warn off potential rivals; for example, bird and cricket songs are used to identify the boundaries of territories or personal space. Differences in signal quality are the usual basis of mate choice in species for which some degree of discrimination is evident. This competition for the attention of members of the opposite sex has led to the development of more conspicuous signals, and in many cases to the evolution of displays, signaling morphology (i.e., sounds vs shapes vs color vs movement vs odors), and messages that go far beyond the basic needs of species and sexual identification.

Most animals are solitary except when mating; they abandon their eggs or larvae before the offspring are born. But a number of species engage in some degree of parental care. For them, signals between parent and offspring are often very important. Most birds, for instance, have about two dozen calls that communicate mundane messages such as the need to eat, defecate, take cover, and so on. In cases in which both parents tend the young—the usual case in birds, for instance—additional signals are required to agree on a nest site, synchronize brooding shifts, and guard the nestlings.

The minority of species that are highly social have the most elaborate communication systems of all. They need messages for a variety of elements of social coordination, including, in many cases, group hunting or foraging, defense, and working out a social hierarchy.

Animal Communication Strategies May Help in Understanding Human Communication

The potential relevance of animal communication to human language lies in the observation that animals use a limited number of communication strategies and that more complex systems have evolved from less ambitious ones. Although human language appears at first to be a special creation, a wholly cultural construct of incredible complexity, when looked at in the context of conventional animal communication, human language turns out in most respects to differ from animal communication only in degree.[1]

To ensure species specificity in mating, most organisms rely on more than one cue to identify a sexual partner. (Exceptions include some of the species that rely on pheromones.) Thus, multiple signals must be sent, and a choice made between sending simultaneous messages and sending sequential messages (or a combination of the two). The sequential strategy has the advantage that the individual signals must be correct and the order must be appropriate. A female stickleback, for instance, requires the male to have a red ventral stripe, perform a zig-zag dance, poke his nose in a nest, and then vibrate her abdomen; the odds of this concatenation of signals occurring together at all, much less in this order, is remote. But sequential signaling is time-consuming. A faster strategy is to provide all the cues in parallel, but there is a larger chance the cues will occur together by chance. For example, when a parent herring gull waves its bill in front of chicks to see if they need to be fed (which they indicate by pecking) the young see a vertical beak, a red spot, and a horizontal motion, each of which is a discrete cue.

Nearly all animal communication is innate: the sender produces the appropriate signal in the correct context even without any opportunity for learning, and it can be recognized for what it is by equally naive conspecifics. The basis of innate recognition appears to lie with feature detectors in the nervous systems—the inborn circuits that automatically isolate iconic visual or acoustic elements. In the visual system the simplest elements include spots, lines, and movement. To the extent that the issue has been studied, innate responses can usually be correlated with such feature detectors. The clearest instance of this involves prey recognition rather than mate identification, although the principles appear to be the same. In the case of European toads, the signals unwittingly emitted by prey (for example, a line moving along its long axis, as a worm crawling) and the behavior of the predator correlate almost perfectly with neural responses recorded simultaneously from the nervous system (i.e., when the prey-detector neurons fire, the toad snaps at the prey). In the jargon of ethology, innately recognized features with special salience for an organism are known as **sign stimuli;** the roughly equivalent term in psychology, at least in the context of classical conditioning, is unconditioned stimuli.

The availability of the many visual, auditory, tactile, and olfactory feature detectors, which can in theory be used in any specific combination or order, accounts for most of the diversity of animal communication, and reliance on these single feature detectors, rather than pattern detection, accounts for its curious limitations. For instance, female crickets initially select conspecifics on the basis of a calling song. (Additional cues come into play once a female gets close to a male.) The carrier frequency and time intervals within the song are important, but the actual pattern of the song, so memorable to our ears, is lost on the females; the call is equally attractive played forward and backward. This makes sense, because pattern detectors are rare in the nervous system. So, too, young gull chicks find a hand-held knitting needle with several "spots" more stimulating than an adult gull; the ability to recognize a gull head and beak, though it would be adaptive, is absent, reflecting the rarity of complex innate visual pattern recognition.

Innate Communication Can Be Complex

A common misapprehension is that complex behaviors must be learned. In fact, complex behavior in relatively short-lived species is usually innate, reflecting the reality that intricate activities are very difficult to learn and may require more time and risk of errors than an animal can afford. Thus, so far as is known, all bird nests are built on the basis of innate instructions, though some improvement with experience is also evident. Therefore, looking at how complex innate communication can be is a useful calibration exercise before we conclude that something as intricate as human speech must be wholly learned.

In terms of its ability to communicate information, the most complex system of innate communication known at present is the dance language of honey bees. The term "language" seems appropriate because the system uses arbitrary conventions to describe objects distant in both space and time—that is, it does not reflect a real-time emotive readout, as might be the case when a primate gives an alarm call or grunts at a banana. The dance language is a parallel communication system that specifies the distance and direction of a food source, water supply, or potential nest site. The dance consists of a figure eight pattern of movement on the part of the signaling forager, with a simultaneous waggling of the body (at about 13 Hz) and buzzing (consisting of 280 Hz bursts occurring at 30 Hz) during the central parts—the waggle runs— of the dance (Fig. 57.1). The dance normally takes place on the vertical surface of the comb within the darkness of the hive cavity.

Direction is indicated by the orientation of the waggle runs: straight up is taken to be the direction of the sun, so that a dance whose average waggle-run angle is 80 degrees to the left of vertical is indicating a site 80 degrees to the left of the sun's current azimuth (Fig. 57.2). Because the sun moves from east to west over the course of the day, dances indicating a specific site

FIGURE 57.1 The waggle dance of honey bees follows a figure 8; the two intersecting straight runs are emphasized by waggling of the body and the production of sound.

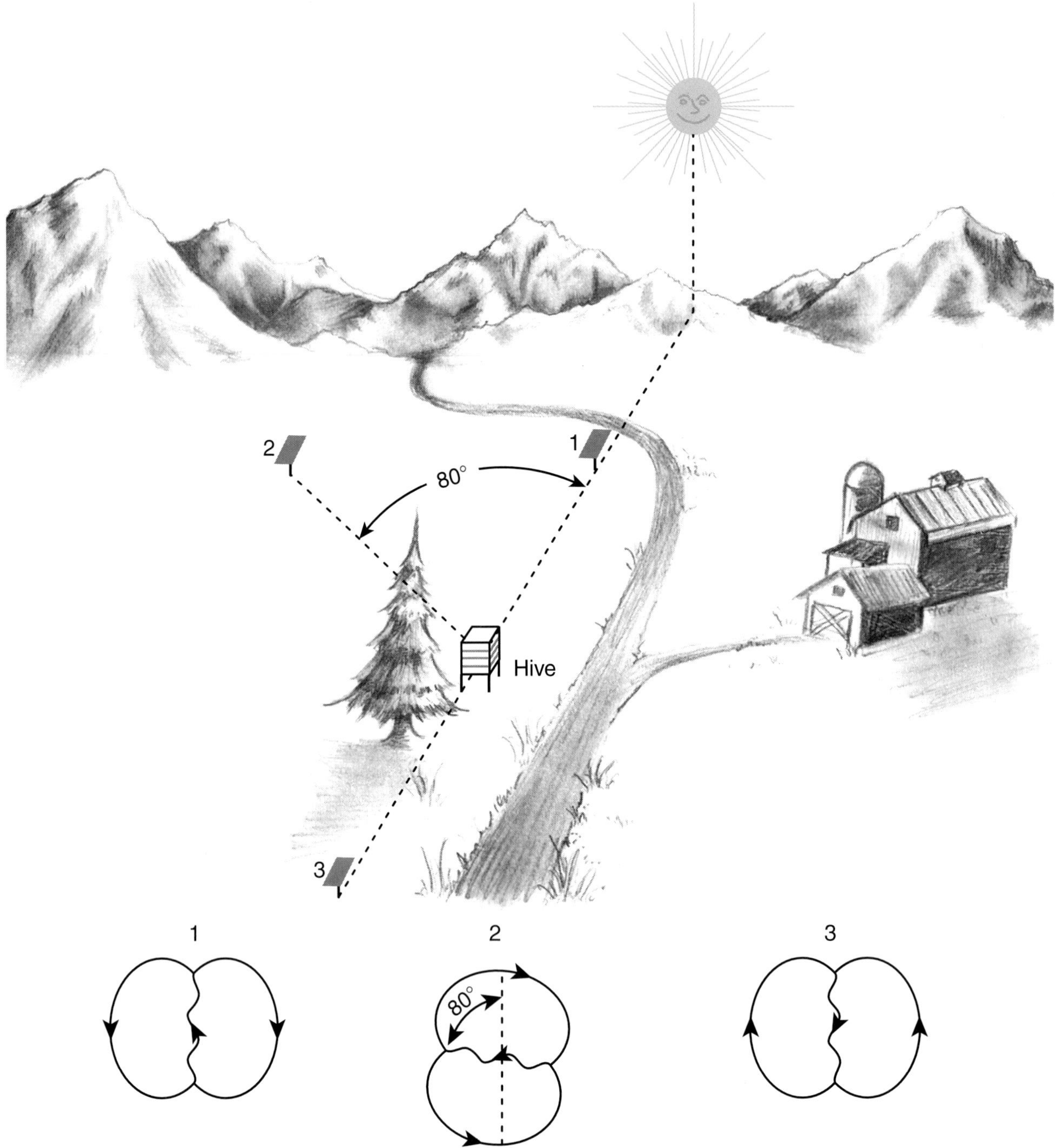

FIGURE 57.2 Direction is encoded into the dance as the angle of the waggle runs left or right of vertical on the comb, which corresponds to the angle to the food relative to the sun's azimuth in the field.

precess counterclockwise to compensate. This compensation is evident in the extended dances of foragers that have had no opportunity to see the sun for minutes or even hours: as time passes, the dance angle shifts counterclockwise at just the rate the sun's azimuth shifts clockwise. That "up" should mean "the direction of the sun" seems arbitrary, since "down" would work equally well, so long as encoder and decoder agreed on the convention; the dance direction could also be referenced to some other cue—magnetic north or the direction the hive entrance faces.

Distance is indicated by the duration of the waggle run or one of the several factors that correlate with it—duration of sound production, number of sound

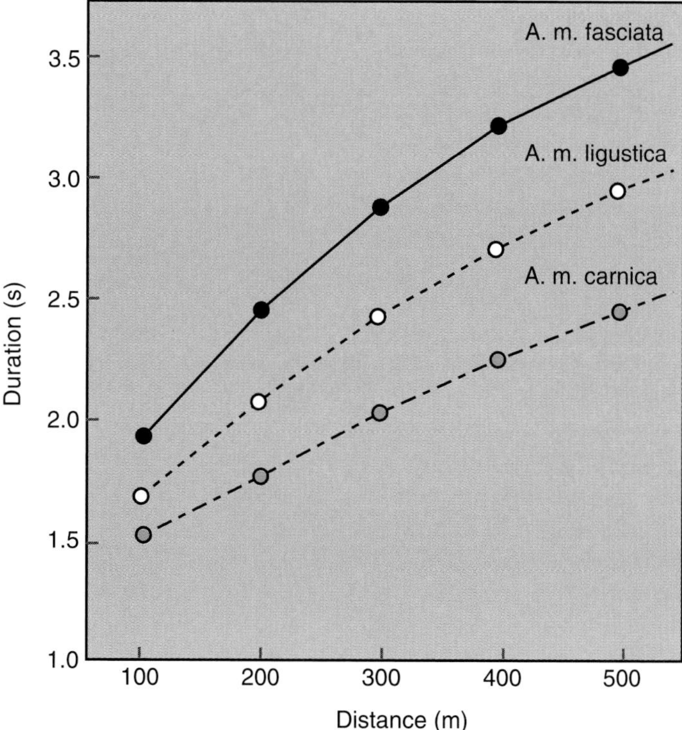

FIGURE 57.3 Distance is encoded as the duration of the waggle run. Different subspecies have different dialects.

bursts, and so on. The conversion of meters flown to waggle duration differs between subspecies: for the Egyptian honey bee a waggle is equivalent to less than 10 m, whereas Italian honey bees value a waggle at about 20 m, and German honey bees peg the exchange rate closer to 50 m (Fig. 57.3). These dialects, which are innate, underscore the languagelike nature of the dance system.

In terms of information content, a honey bee dance is second (albeit a very distant second) only to human speech, and so far as is known is far richer than the language of any primate system. But the dance language suffers from at least two limitations: It is a closed system—there seems to be no way to introduce new conventions to deal with novel needs. It is also graded—instead of discrete signals for different directions or distances, single components are varied over a range of values (angles and durations). The less complex but more flexible systems of birds and primates illustrate the likely evolutionary precursors of speech.

Learning Can Modify Innate Strategies

Bird Songs

Some birds have innate songs. Individuals reared in isolation produce songs that are indistinguishable from their socially reared peers and respond to calls appropriately without prior experience. Chickens, doves, and pigeons are familiar examples. Most songbirds, however, illustrate a different pattern. Isolated chicks sing a schematic form of the species song, but the richness of a normal song is absent. Adult conspecifics can recognize innate songs as coming from members of their species, but in general these impoverished vocalizations produce lower levels of response. Typically, there is a sensitive period during which exposure to song, if it is going to have any impact, must occur (Fig. 57.4). In most species there is a gap between this sensitive period and the process of overt song development—that is, practice and perfection of the adult song are based on the bird's memory of what it heard during its sensitive period.[2]

Given a range of possible song models during isolated rearing, a chick selects an example from its own species and memorizes it. If it hears only songs of other species, the mature song is the unmodified innate song (Fig. 57.4). Thus there is an innate bias in the initial learning. Where this bias has been studied, it appears to depend on acoustic sign stimuli.

Practice is essential in the normal development of birdsong and part of this practice occurs in a babbling phase known as subsong, which begins at a species-

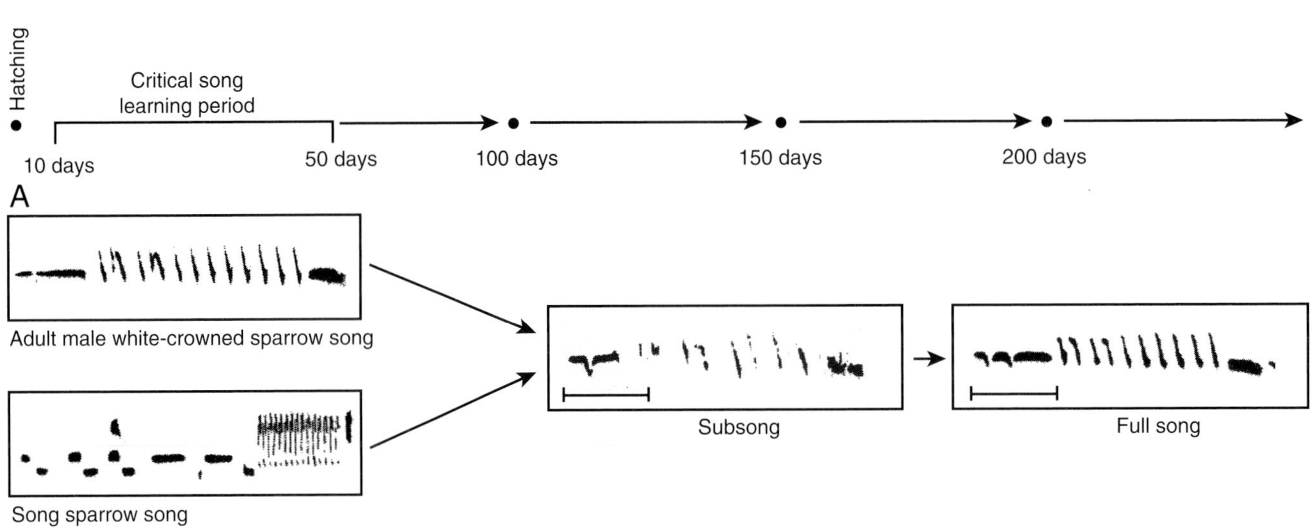

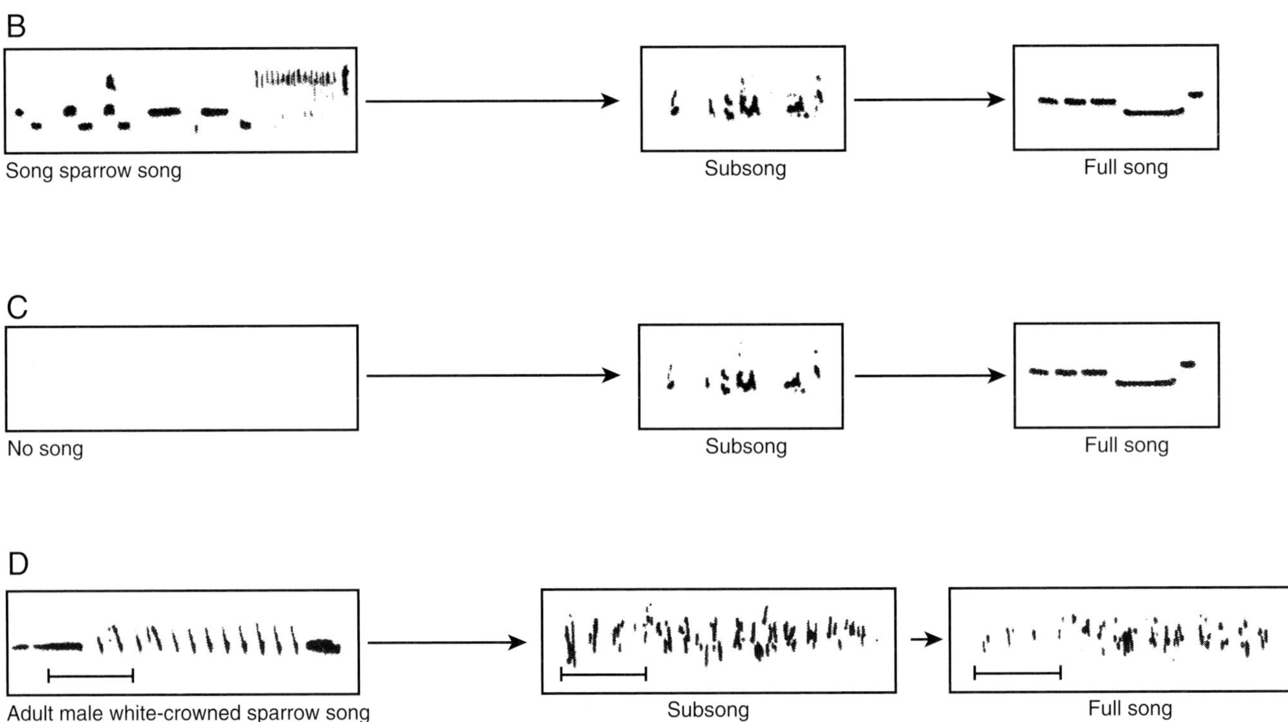

FIGURE 57.4 Bird song development in most species is characterized by a sensitive period during which a song of the species must be heard. Later, during subsong, the bird practices making notes and assembles them into the correct order and pattern (A). Birds not allowed to hear their species' song sing a schematic version of the song (B, C); birds deafened before subsong cannot sing (D).

typical age. A bird deafened after its sensitive period, but before it begins producing notes in preparation for singing (subsong), is unable to produce even an innate song (Fig. 57.4). During the earliest parts of subsong, birds try out a number of notes. These notes are typical of the species, but most are absent from the song they eventually sing. The learning process may involve producing each member of an innate repertoire of notes, listening to them, checking to see if they match any element in the memorized song, discarding the unnecessary ones, and rearranging, scoring, and modifying the others to produce a reasonable copy of the original song heard during the sensitive period. There is some flexibility in song development. For example, when the chick has heard two very different specimens of its own species' song, it will often incorporate elements from each. Similarly, when the chick has been exposed to the sight of a singing conspecific and simultaneously the sound of a heterospecific song, it may pick out elements of the abnormal song and adapt them as best it can into its own species-specific organization.

Birdsong, therefore, depends on two innately orchestrated learning sequences, imprinting the song in memory and learning to perform it. This system is flexible, but only within clear limits.

Vervet Calls

Vervets, like all social primates, have a large repertoire of innate calls used for social communication. Among these approximately three dozen signals are four alarm calls. In some parts of their range, one of the calls is specific for martial eagles; in another the same call is used for certain hawks. In either case, the call causes monkeys to look up; those at the tops of trees drop to the interior, while those on the ground move into bushes or under trees. A second call, specific to leopards in one region and to other solitary hunters elsewhere, sends the warned individuals up to the tree tops. A third, specific for snakes, induces the other members of the troop to stand up and look around in the grass. A fourth call is heard in the presence of humans or group-hunting predators.

The development of calling is revealing. Young vervets appear to understand the class of animals each call refers to, but not the particular species that are dangerous. Thus, infants will give the eagle call to harmless vultures, storks, and even falling leaves, but not to snakes or leopards. Consequently, adults generally respond to the alarm calls of infants with a casual look around, followed by their own alarm if there is a genuine danger. Juveniles make fewer mistakes, and adult errors are confined to calls produced when the bird is so far away that human observers require binoculars to identify the species. In short, young vervets seem to learn the details of how to apply an innate categorical vocabulary.

Human Speech May Have Emerged from Animal Signals

If human speech and language are evolved from animal signals, they could have developed from the repertoire of two to three dozen innate calls typical of birds and primates. In that case we would expect to find that elements such as *phonemes* are innately recognized and distinguished by the sorts of acoustic features that provide the basis for the innate discrimination of signs and stimuli in other species (e.g., a rapid downward FM sweep with a standard starting frequency and duration). Babies have an innate ability to discriminate phonemes, which are thus acoustic sign stimuli. The evolution of human speech could have taken advantage of the sorts of sensitive periods and innate learning biases so evident in song birds and vervet monkeys. In this case, we might expect to see a species-typical babbling phase, and perhaps a sensitive period for easy learning of new languages (see Chapter 51, for example). If the evolution of speech and language makes use of preexisting (innate) semantics, we might expect some sort of default grammar not unlike the unlearned and impoverished songs of birds reared in isolation. Finally, to the extent that speech carries parallel signals (e.g., semantic and emotional messages), we might expect to find parallel processing, perhaps in separate areas of the brain (see section on reading, for example). In short, human language would have cross-cultural universals analogous to the species-specific features of animal communication.[3] It is to an examination of these possibilities that we now turn.

Summary

Animal communication in its most basic form is based on discrete innate sign stimuli used according to an innate "grammar." Even at this level, the communication can be very complex. More advanced systems use imprinting and other variants of programmed learning to modify, extend, and enrich the communicative exchange. When viewed from a biological perspective, the ancestral elements of sign stimuli, innate (or "default") grammar, and programmed learning seem evident in human language.

HUMAN LANGUAGE

Animal communication is quite sophisticated and shares attributes with human language. However, human language has even greater complexity than that found in the animal models. To examine the brain mechanisms of human language, it is first necessary to examine some of the common features that characterize human communication.

There Are Universals in Human Language

Language is a code that relates form to meaning. The complexity of the code is due partly to the presence

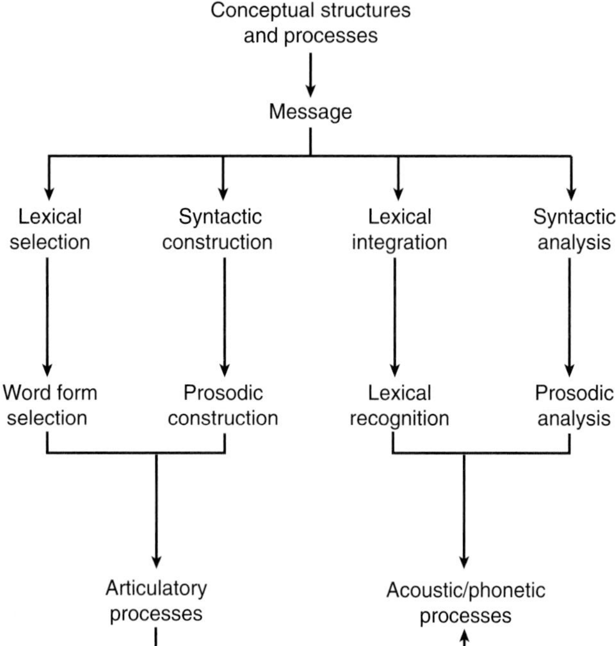

FIGURE 57.5 (Left) Levels of processing in language production (from stored message to speech) and (Right) word comprehension (from auditory input to message).

of several levels of form, each connected to particular aspects of meaning, and each related to one another as shown in Fig. 57.5. The code is also complex because different languages use different forms at each level of the code. For instance, in Italian, sentence subjects that are pronouns are usually omitted, unlike in English. Nevertheless, there appear to be important universal features of human language, so much so that the leading authority in the field, Noam Chomsky, has suggested that a visitor from another planet would conclude that there was only one human language. Below is a brief outline of the universal and language-specific features of words and sentences.

Words Are Composed of Phonemes

Simple words are defined and distinguished from each other primarily by their constituent phonemes. A **phoneme** is a single distinct sound that contrasts with another and makes it possible to determine the existence of a word in a language. For instance, in English (see Fig. 57.6) /p/ and /b/ are different phonemes, because they determine the separate existence of the members of word pairs such as *pat-bat, pale-bale, pull-bull, lap-lab.* The phonemes /p/ and /b/ are minimally different from each other, varying only in whether voicing occurs during the production of the segment (/b/) or not (/p/). Other contrasts involve larger articulatory and acoustic contrasts. For example, the contrast between /p/ and /g/ (*pot/got*) involves both voicing and place of articulation. There are a relatively small number of English phonemes, as illustrated in Table 57.1. Moreover, evidence indicates that the ability to recognize these consonants and vowels is present at birth.

Most phonogists[4–6] have argued that all phonemes consist of sets of "distinctive features"—features of sound production such as voicing, aspiration, roundedness, location and degree of maximal constriction of the vocal tract, and nature of the constriction of the vocal tract (see Fig. 57.5). A phoneme can be classified according to whether it has a positive or negative value for a given feature (Table 57.2).

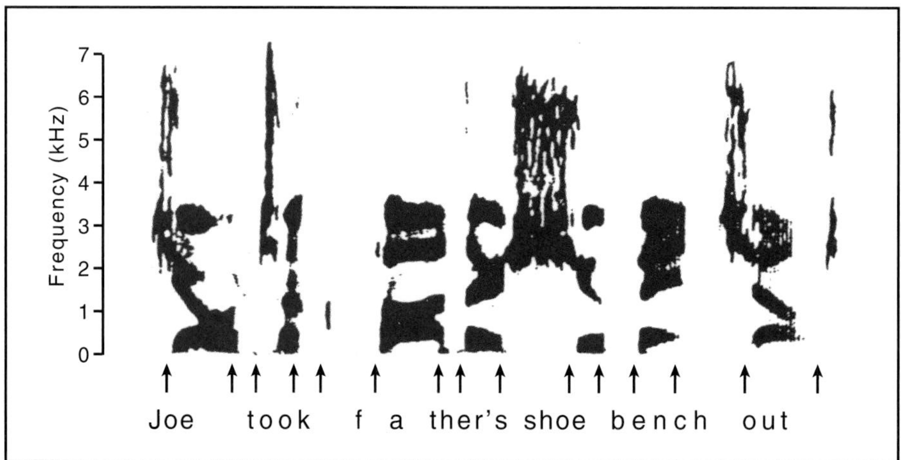

FIGURE 57.6 A speech spectrograph of an English sentence. The arrows indicate places of rapid transition related to the presentations of phonemes. Note that silent places may not be at word boundaries.

TABLE 57.1 The Phonemes of American English

Consonants		Vowels	
Symbol	Example	Symbols	Example
/w/	wet	/i/	heed
/ʍ/	whet	/I/	hid
/b/	bill	/e/ or /ei/	rain
/d/	dig	/ɛ/	head
/g/	give	/æ/	had
/p/	pick	/a/	odd
/t/	tin	/ɔ/	bought
/k/	key	/ʊ/	hood
/m/	men	/u/	too
/n/	nine	/ʌ/	ton
/ŋ/	ring	/ə/	the
/f/	fast	/ɚ/	earth
/v/	vice	/ai/	hide
/θ/	thigh	/ɔi/	boy
/ð/	thy	/au/	out
/s/	sick	/oʊ/	boat
/z/	zip	/iu/	few
/ʃ/	shy		
/ʒ/	measure		
/l/	lie		
/r/	rock		
/j/	you		
/h/	hello		
/tʃ/	charm		
/ʤ/	joke		

Note: The phonemic symbols corresponding to the consonants are shown on the left along with an example of a typical word that includes each sound as indicated by the underlined letter or letters in each word. The right-hand columns present a similar list of vowel sounds and words that include these.

The binary system is used to represent distinctive features. The distinctive features are abstractions—idealizations of the articulatory and acoustic content of the phonemes of languages. Although phrased in terms of positions and manners of articulation of the vocal tract, distinctive features are not easily mapped onto articulatory or acoustic phenomena. This is basically because, although distinctive features are related to articulatory gestures, specific theories of distinctive features have been postulated in an effort to account for regularities in the sound systems of languages, and not in articulation itself. One example of the abstract nature of the way distinctive features are represented is the fact mentioned above that most theories claim that distinctive features are binary (i.e., have only + or − values). Consider the phonemes /p/, /t/, and /k/. They differ in their place of articulation. We could describe them in terms of a three-valued distinctive feature called "place," but current theories do not. Rather, they are described as different combinations of two binary features. The reason a purely binary system is preferred is that it allows linguists to capture other regularities in the sound patterns of languages. In this way, the model of distinctive features is influenced by more than just articulatory or acoustic considerations.

The Words of a Language Are Characterized by an Inventory of Phonemes and Laws Regulating Syllable Structure

Each language uses a restricted number of phonemes—its "phonemic inventory"—to construct

TABLE 57.2 Articulatory Classification of English Consonant Sounds

Place of articulation	Manner of articulation					
			Stop		Fricative	
	Glide	Nasal	Voiced	Unvoiced	Voiced	Unvoiced
Front						
Bilabial	w, ʍ	m	b	p		
Labiodental					v	f
Middle						
Dental					ð	θ
Alveolar	j,l	n	d	t	z	s
Palatal	r				ʒ	ʃ
Back						
Velar	w, ʍ	ŋ	g	k		
Pharyngeal						h
Glottal			ɔ			

Note: The articulatory features of manner, place, and voicing classify the consonant sounds according to similarities and differences that exist in the way in which each sound is produced. Note that the voicing distinction is relevant only for stops and fricatives in English.

words. The phonemes of a given language are partially selected on the basis of language-universal factors and in part by language-specific processes. A language-universal factor dictates that some phonemes are more likely than others to occur in a language for two reasons: they are easier to produce and they represent more extreme contrasts of articulatory gestures. All languages have at least a vowel–consonant distinction, reflecting the extreme contrast between an open vocal tract (the vowel) and a closed tract (the consonant). If a language has only three vowels, it is likely to have the high front unrounded vowel /i/ (as in *beet*), the high back rounded vowel /u/ (as in *pool*), and the low back partially rounded vowel /a/ (as in *father*)—vowels that are maximally distinguished with respect to their articulatory gestures. If a language has a single consonant, it is likely to be /t/—a consonant that differs maximally from the vowels in having a total occlusion of the vocal tract and being voiceless. If a language has a large phonemic inventory, it is likely to have both the more common, basic phonemes and a number of phonemes not found in all languages. For instance, English has phonemes not found in French (e.g., the unvoiced /th/ sounds in words such as *this* and *thimble*), and vice versa (e.g., the high rounded front vowel found in the French word *queue* (*tail*) is not found in English). These are language-specific "choices" that, in part, distinguish one language from another.

Phonemes and their distinctive features are the elementary segments out of which words are built. Simple, underived words consist of sequences of phonemes structured into higher-order units.[7–11] For instance, *cat* is a monosyllabic word, made up of an onset (/k/) and a rime (/at/). The rime is itself made up of a nucleus (/a/) and a coda (/t/). In multisyllabic words, the syllables are further organized into "feet." Phonemes are not easily segmented from ongoing speech, but they can be observed to some degree by examining a picture of the sound pattern in a speech spectrogram of an English sentence as in Fig. 57.6.

The sequence of phonemes in a word is determined partially by the laws regulating syllable structure in a language. Both universal and language-specific features of the organization of sounds are involved in rules determining syllable structure. Universal factors dictate that syllables tend to become more "sonorant" from onset to nucleus, and less sonorant from nucleus to coda. Sonorance reflects the degree of unimpeded flow of air through the vocal tract. Thus, sonorance is related directly to the articulation of the phonemes of a word. Distinctive features such as [high], [back], [low], and [continuant] characterize the degree of closure of the vocal tract during the production of a particular phoneme; features such as [tense] and to a lesser extent [voiced] characterize the force with which air is expelled through the vocal cavity. These distinctive features determine the sonorance of each phoneme of the language and place each phoneme on a "sonorance hierarchy." For instance, unvoiced stop consonants (/p/, /t/, /k/) are nonsonorant, liquids (/l/, /r/) and nasals (/m/, /n/) are intermediately sonorant, and vowels most sonorant. In each syllable, there is a strong tendency for less sonorant items to occur in onset and coda positions relative to the nucleus of a syllable.

Language-specific rules further constrain the internal organization of syllables and thus the order of phonemes in the words of a language. For instance, Italian has a language-specific rule that indicates that almost all word final syllables must end in a vowel; English has a variety of language-specific rules that regulate the possible phonemes in syllabic onsets (such as the rule that indicates that the liquid following an onset /st/ must be /r/ and not /l/). For the most part, these language-specific rules are in keeping with language-universal tendencies such as the sonorance hierarchy, although there are some cases in which they produce exceptions to language-universal factors (e.g., in English, the unusual concatination of consonants that terminates the word *sixths*).

Phonological theory holds that the "underlying" distinctive features and phonemes that phonologists assign to words are not necessarily the phonemes that are produced and heard. Theories of phonology assume that the abstract representation of the phonemes of a word conveys just enough information about distinctive features to allow each phoneme to be uniquely determined by the application of the general phonological rules of the language. In English, this is accomplished by reducing unstressed vowels to a neutral vowel. For example, the vowel sound in the second syllable of *Canada* and *Canadian* is thought to be the same at an underlying level, and to change to the sound that is actually produced because of the different patterns of stress in the two words. The spelling reflects the underlying phonology, not its actual (surface) realization.

Other phonological features of words include stress and tone. Stress and tone contours are determined by the phonemes and syllable structure of words.[10] English has a complex set of rules determining stress assignment that are derived from the stress assignment rules of Romance and Anglo-Saxon languages.

All Languages Have a Mechanism for Forming Words from Other Words

In English, there are basically two processes that create new words: morphological constructions (e.g., the word "construction" formed from "construct" and "tion") and compounding (e.g., the word "hangman" formed from "hang" and "man"). A brief review of English morphological structure will illustrate several universal and language-specific features of this process.[12,13]

English morphological word formation can be divided into two mechanisms: inflectional morphological processes and derivational morphological processes. Roughly, inflections are morphological forms that are related to the syntactic structure of a sentence, such as agreement features between subjects and objects (I see; he sees). For the most part, inflectional morphological processes do not change the category (noun, verb, adjective) of the roots to which they are attached. Though all languages are thought to have some inflection (a universal feature), some, like English or Chinese, are relatively poor in overt inflectional features. Languages such as French and German have more complete and complex agreement systems that affect adjective–noun agreement, verb inflections, and the case markers on nouns.

Derivational processes, in contrast, are those that create new categories of words (i.e., parts of speech) from existing words. Therefore, most derivational processes change the category of a root (e.g., *destroy* → *destruction; happy* → *happiness*), though some do not (e.g., *orphan* → *orphanage*). Once again, languages differ in the frequency with which derivation occurs and in the type of derivation.

Morphological forms also vary. English morphology uses a system of affixes (word endings—suffixes like "tion"—and beginnings—prefixes like "re" or "un"); morphology in Semitic languages is carried in a vowel "tier" that is concatenated with the consonants that define words. For example, in Hebrew, "ochel" means "he is eating" and "achla" means "she ate." There are rules governing the ways that morphological forms attach to roots and to each other. For instance, in English, Latinate suffixes attach to Latinate roots (e.g., derive → derivation), Anglo-Saxon suffixes attach more freely to many simple, underived words (e.g., happy → happiness), as well as to derived words with Latinate suffixes (e.g., respond → responsive → responsiveness), and inflectional suffixes apply after all the derivational suffixes have applied to form a word (e.g., confer → conference → conferenced).[14,15]

Affixation has semantic consequences. Agreement features (e.g., in English, the third-person singular present tense marker *s*) convey the semantic features inherent in the agreement. For example, the third-person present tense marker *s* conveys the information that an action is being accomplished (or is habitually accomplished) by an individual (or a set of individuals considered as whole) who is neither the speaker nor the listener. Universal principles affect the relationship between the specificity of overt morphological markings (e.g., word endings) and the presence of other elements in a sentence. A universal principle of language is that when these markings are sufficiently explicit and distinctive, they stand alone as indications of these semantic values, and certain other elements can be omitted. For instance, Italian has no need for subject pronouns in sentences, as the information expressed by these pronouns is explicitly conveyed by the agreement features on the verb.

Derivational morphology also has effects on semantics. For instance, the thematic roles assigned by a verb (information about who is doing what to whom) are reassigned to different nouns when certain adjective-formation suffixes are added. For instance, a noun modified by the adjective *huggable* is understood as the theme of the action of *hugging,* as in *The boy is huggable.* Both universal and language-specific features produce these effects.[16] Derivation also affects syntactic categorization. In English, the last in a series of derivational suffixes determines the syntactic category of the derived word (e.g., *considerate* is an adjective, because *-ate* is an adjective-forming suffix, while *consideration* is a noun, because *-ion* is a noun-forming suffix).

Grammar Organizes the Sentences of the Language

The semantic values associated with simple words and with words derived from other words consist primarily of objects, actions, and properties of objects and actions. At the sentence level the set of semantic values that language can express greatly expands. Sentences convey aspects of the structure of events and states in the world. These semantic values are collectively known as the **propositional content** of a sentence. These values include thematic roles (information about who did what to whom, such as the fact that in the sentence *The dog chased the cat,* the dog is the agent and the cat is the theme), attribution of modification (information about which adjectives go with which nouns, such as the fact that in the sentence *The big boy chased the little girl,* the boy is big and girl is little), scope of quantification (information about what items are included in the scope of quantifiers, such as the fact that in the sentence, *None of the boys wearing hats were cold,* the quantifier "none" applies to the boys wearing hats, not just to the boys), the reference of pronouns and other anaphoric elements (information about which words in a set of sentences refer to the same items or actions, such as the fact that in the sentence *The brother of the visitor shaved himself,* "himself" refers to "brother" and not to "visitor"), etc. Sentences are a crucial level of the language code because the propositions they express make assertions about the

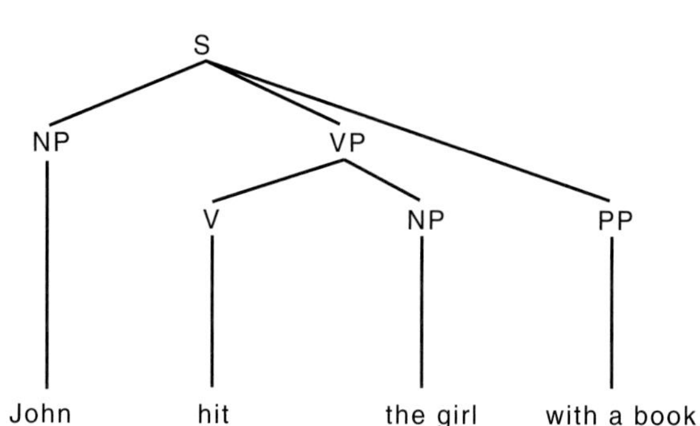

B

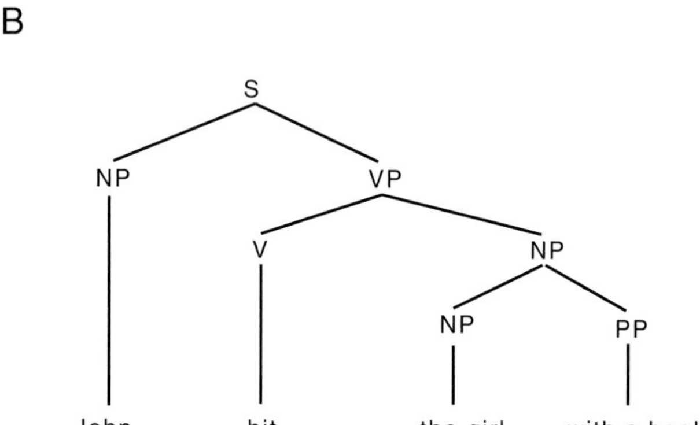

FIGURE 57.7 Two different parsings of a sentence. (A) The book is used to hit the girl, and (B) the girl has a book. S, sentence; NP, noun phrase; V, verb; PP, prepositional phrase.

world. These assertions can be added to an individual's knowledge of the world, be entered into logical systems, serve as the basis for planning actions, and so on.

The propositions conveyed by sentences are entered into higher-order structures that constitute the discourse level of linguistic structure.[17,18] Discourse includes information about the general topic under discussion, the focus of a speaker's attention, the novelty of the information in a given sentence, the temporal order of events, causation, and so on.

At the sentence level, language allows words to be related to one another so that they can convey a potentially infinite number of propositions within the context of a discourse. This is accomplished by the relationships between words that are established by the syntactic structure of a sentence. The syntactic structure of a sentence is a complex hierarchy, in which multiple relationships between units can be defined and each related to different aspects of propositional content. The same sentence may convey very different meanings if the syntax is ambiguous, as in Fig. 57.7.

Languages Have Different Surface Syntactic Forms

Languages vary in their use of agreement, declension, relatively fixed word order, and other features. There are regularities across languages that reflect the co-occurrence of these features.[19] These have been called "universals" of syntactic (or morphosyntactic) structure. However, beginning with the pioneering work of Chomsky,[20–23] linguistics has developed theories of syntactic representations that incorporate more basic universal features. Within the frame of reference of these theories, language-specific features of syntax are those that make "choices" within "parameters" that universally define the possible set of syntactic structures.

The most important universal feature of syntactic structure in Chomsky's and related theories is that the *surface form* of a sentence is an inadequate reflection of the syntactic structure of a sentence. In oversimplified form, Chomsky's theory maintains that a sentence has two levels of syntactic structure: a relatively superficial level of structure (currently called S-structure) that is quite closely related to the spoken form of the sentence, and a second representational level (currently called D-structure), which is related to several sentential semantic features of a sentence. Let us consider an example that illustrates this theory.

According to Chomsky's theory, noun phrases (NPs) and other elements are subject to movement and deletion operations between the D- and the S-structure. One feature of syntactic structure that has received a great deal of attention is the existence of constraints on the movement of noun phrases and other syntactic units. All languages have such constraints. An example from English can illustrate these constraints. Consider sentence 1:

1. The boat that you believed the claim John painted is red.

The sequence of words in Sentence 1 is not a well-formed sentence, even though it is quite clear what it would mean if it were a sentence (the same as sentence 3). The reason it is not well formed is that the relative pronoun *that* is related to a "trace" (t) across two S (sentence) boundaries and an NP boundary, as indicated in sentence 2. This is not allowed by the grammar of English.

2. The boat [$_{NP}$ that$_i$ [$_S$ you believed [$_{NP}$ the claim [$_S$ John painted $_{t_i}$] is red.

Contrast sentence 1 with sentence 3:

3. The boat that you believed John painted is red.

The sequence of words in Sentence 3 is a well-formed sentence, because the relative pronoun *that* is related to its trace across two S boundaries, as indicated in Sentence 4. This is allowed by the grammar of English.

4. The boat $[_{NP}$ that$_i$ $[_S$ you believed $[_S$ John painted $t_i]]]$ is red.

The limit on how far an NP can move differs from language to language (a language-specific choice of the value of a parameter), but it is always expressed in terms of a certain number of major higher-level nodes such as NP and S.[23]

Many other aspects of syntactic structure have both a universal and a language-specific aspect. These become quite technical and need not be reviewed here. Of relevance to this chapter is the fact that both language-universal and language-specific features of syntactic structures differ from the representations in other cognitive and linguistic domains. This has been taken to suggest (but obviously does not prove) that syntactic structures are a special domain of mental representations, whose basic features are likely to be innate.

Summary

Although the communicative functions of human language serve many purposes that are also served by nonhuman communication systems related to survival and procreation, and even though some features of human language (e.g., the fact that it is conveyed by both a sequence of elements and a (phonemes) superimposition of features—stress overlaid on phonemes) are also features of how animal communication systems are conveyed, human language is a vastly more complex code—with vastly great semantic power and flexibility—than any nonhuman communication system. Many aspects of this code are now thought of as constraints on the nature and organization of language elements that an individual language can have. These universal constraints on the nature of human languages are likely to be innate.

READING

Biological Preparation and Cultural Engineering Are Sources of Language Skill

So far we have stressed universal features of human language that have a strong innate component. The human brain is *biologically prepared* to acquire and express language.[24–29] If a neurologically normal human infant enters into a human social group in which language is used for its usual communicative purposes, and if the members of that social group interact with the infant in the ordinary ways that come naturally to humans, then the infant will become a language user. The language the infant develops will be hierarchically organized, and it will map between form and meaning in the ways we have just described. Only a small percentage of human children fail to develop a fully functional and approximately complete language system, despite wide cross-cultural and intracultural variation in the language environments to which they are exposed and the types of linguistic interactions with other people in which they participate. The age span over which language acquisition normally occurs is restricted and quite predictable, as is the basic sequence in which particular language structures and capabilities are added to the child's growing linguistic repertoire. Although vocabulary varies considerably as a function of experience, specific practice, and intelligence, other properties of language do not. In particular, the syntactic repertoires or grammars of speakers of a given language tend to be remarkably similar despite large variations in life experience and large differences in achievement in other cognitive domains.

In addition to these indicators of an innate foundation for grammar, there is clear evidence of innate preferences regarding sensory input and motor output. The brain's preferred sensory-input modality for language perception is audition, and the brain's preferred motor-output modality for language production is the articulatory apparatus—vocal chords, throat, tongue, and mouth. Communities of neurologically normal human beings spontaneously develop *spoken* language.

Another combination of input and output also appears to be rather natural, but its spontaneous development is much more restricted. If auditory stimuli cannot be perceived, as is the case for deaf infants, or if spoken language is unavailable in the environment, as in families in which both parents are deaf and do not speak to one another or to the infant, then alternatives to speech that use visual perception of hand gestures rather than auditory perception of articulatory gestures can be developed. There is even evidence that early in normal development the same regions of prefrontal cortex that plan articulation also plan fine manual gestures of sufficient complexity to be precursors of sign.[30] This evidence invites the speculation that prior to differentiation of the inferior portions of this prefrontal tissue into Broca's area, there is a relatively large zone of cortex that is approximately equipotential for controlling the articulatory apparatus and the hands in linguistically relevant ways. Nevertheless, sign language seems to be a fallback that develops spontaneously only when the raw materials for spoken language—speech available in the social environment and the auditory functions needed to hear it—are missing. It would be interesting to actually quantify the extent to which preference for speech dominates, but to date no one has conducted a rigorous study of the probabilities of acquiring spoken language, sign, or both when speech and sign are equally available in the immediate social environment of neurologically normal infants.

Not all linguistic skills, however, are so biologically natural as speech and sign. Consider literacy. Reading and writing are *culturally engineered* forms of language, rather than biologically prepared ones. Unlike spoken language, literacy does not rely on the biologically preferred sensory-input and motor-output modalities of hearing and articulation. The input modality for written language is visual, rather than auditory as with speech, and the output modality is manual, rather than vocal. These are the same input and output modalities as sign, but the type of visual stimulus that must be perceived in reading—static arrays of two-dimensional patterns distributed in space—is not at all the same as sign's. The hand configurations and arm movements of sign change dynamically in space and time. Comprehending them emphasizes motion perception at least as much as static pattern recognition. In contrast, motion perception is not part of reading, and indeed, if words or texts start moving around in the visual field, reading gets harder. Likewise, whereas the output modality of literacy involves the hands, as in sign, the manual gestures used in typing and handwriting are very different from the ones used in sign. A particularly interesting (and very useful) feature of literacy is that the gestures of production can be separated from the written language products themselves—another major difference between literacy and sign as forms of language. Once writing has been put down on paper, it can be removed in time and space from the writer in a way that is not possible with sign. Even making a videotape of a signed message and putting the tape in a library still preserves the signer as part and parcel of the signed message. Thus, reading and writing have properties quite different from those of the two more biologically prepared linguistic formats, speech and sign.

The way that literacy is learned also differs. Reading and writing commonly require explicit instruction and supervised practice of a type that is not needed and rarely observed in the acquisition of spoken language. Evidence of the special demands of learning to read and write is easy to find. Modern societies invest massive resources in school instruction, much of which is directly aimed at literacy. Even so, literacy is not nearly so certain to be acquired as is spoken language, even when extensive instruction is provided. Many children who are quite competent speakers and listeners turn out to be much less competent readers and writers.

The differences between acquiring spoken language and learning to read and write highlight the unique features of literacy as a cultural rather than a biological invention—new frontiers of linguistic function are opened up, and the communicative powers of language are greatly extended, but at a cost to ease and universality of acquisition. Reading attempts to interface the naturally occurring linguistic system to new sensory and motor systems that have biological specializations for very different functions.[31–33] This interface makes literacy very interesting and complicated theoretically, in addition to being immensely important practically.

Reading has proven to be fertile ground for the development of methods that integrate cognitive psychology's techniques for studying mental processes with neuroscience's techniques for studying anatomy and physiology. We turn now to a discussion of the unique properties of reading as a language skill, focusing on visual information and the role of the eye movement system in controlling visual intake. We then explore the application of neuroimaging methods to the investigation of the functional anatomy of reading, focusing on the recognition of individual words. We conclude with a neuroimaging study of listening that will take us back to the most general issues regarding the localization of language function in the human brain and allow us to consider what features of brain organization are unique to reading as a cultural invention and what features are general properties of the brain's biologically prepared capacities.

A Cognitive Neuroscientific Account of Reading Has Three Levels of Description

For purposes of scientific investigation, a language skill can be treated in three different ways: first as *overt action* or *behavior*, second as *cognition* or *mental computation*, and third as *neural activity*. These three treatments come together and complement one another in the cognitive neuroscientific study of reading. The goal is to build a three-level account consisting of a description of reading behavior, a description of the cognitive processes or mental computations of which the behavior is an expression, and a description of the neural activity that implements the cognitive processes.

With many cognitive skills, including language, overt action constitutes only the external manifestation of what is fundamentally an *internal capacity*. Studying language behavior for its own sake, without concern for mental events and neural activity, would produce an incomplete and highly misleading scientific understanding. Although this point may seem intuitively obvious, it was a difficult insight to achieve scientifically during the first half of the 20th century, when much of linguistics, philosophy, and psychology was dominated by behaviorism. The situation was changed by a series of critiques of the behaviorist approach to language that began to appear around mid-century.[20,34–37] Linguists, psychologists, and neuroscientists argued forcefully that language is a medium of communication and a vehicle for thinking—it is a coding system used to represent and transmit ideas, not a set of behaviors that can be separated from the mental life of the language user. Therefore, language must be conceptualized as a complex cognitive skill in which the controlling or causal activity is described in terms of mental computations that process information, and the mental computations are in turn described in terms of the neural activity that implements them. Much of the scientific achievement in the study of language has consisted of designing measurement situations that allow researchers to "get inside the head" and draw conclusions about mental computations and neural activity.

The empirical data generated in these situations consist of (1) measurements of behavioral performance—the locations and durations of eye fixations during silent reading or the speed and accuracy of responses required in specialized laboratory tasks—and (2) measurements of brain function. The brain measures include electroencephalographic or magnetoencephalographic recordings of gross electrical activity, occasionally microelectrode recordings of single-cell electrical activity (usually taken during brain surgery), and, most important of late, positron emission tomography and functional magnetic resonance imaging of regional cerebral blood flow.

Data are generated in a wide range of reading-related tasks using a wide range of reading-related stimuli. Sometimes the stimulus is text. Other times sentences are presented and people are asked to decide whether each one is grammatical or whether it makes sense. Often the stimuli are single words or word-length strings of letters rather than sentences. If the letter string is not a real word, it might be a pronounceable but unfamiliar and meaningless "pseudoword" (such as *mard, brop,* or *quisper*), or it might be a random string of letters with little or no structure to it at all (*rmda, opbr, qpsurei*). People are asked to make a judgment about some linguistically relevant property of the letter string—its orthography (the spelling of the letter string), phonology (its pronunciation), semantics (its meaning), or syntactic form class (its part of speech, to use an old-fashioned term from high-school English).

In an orthographic task, people might be asked to decide whether a particular target letter is present in each letter string or whether two strings contain the same letters in the same order or differ from one another at one or more letter positions. A phonological task might ask for rhyme judgments, or simply have people pronounce each word or pseudoword aloud as rapidly as they can. A semantic task might ask whether each letter string is meaningful, whether each letter string names a member of a target category, or whether two words are synonyms. These tasks are appealing because it is clear from a logical, task-analytic perspective what kind of linguistically relevant information must be attended and processed in order to make a correct response. Generally, cognitive neuroscientists prefer to employ tasks with intuitively clear information requirements, but this is not always the case. In one very widely used task, called lexical decision, the participant in the experiment has two response buttons, one labeled "word" and the other "nonword." Each time a letter string appears, the participant decides whether or not the letter string is a real word and presses the correct button as quickly as possible. The task sounds simple enough, and even rather young readers can readily perform it. Nevertheless, researchers have had surprising difficulty figuring out exactly what information people use to make such lexical decisions.[38,39] Therefore, although the data obtained in this task are very useful for many purposes,[40,41] they are more difficult to relate to specific linguistic computations than the data from the other tasks we have described.

Ideally, behavioral and neural data are collected at the same time from the same people. The people may be normal adults or children, patients who have suffered brain damage, or people with learning disabilities or other language problems. Sometimes, behavioral and neural data cannot be collected at the same time because the experiment would take too long, because not all the equipment is available in the same laboratory, or because the different kinds of equipment would interfere with one another. Regardless of such methodological details, the goal is always the same: to use two types of data (behavioral and neural) to build a theory with three levels of description (behavior, mental computation, and neural activity).

Reading Can Be Studied in a Relatively Naturalistic Way by Monitoring Eye Movements

Reading text involves a series of eye fixations separated by saccadic eye movements (see Chapter 36). Visual information is taken in during each fixation. Sensory intake is suppressed during the saccade and begins again once the eye is settled at its new location.

A

An example of a moving window

```
1     Xxxxhology means persxxxxxxx xxxxxxxxx xxxx xxxx xxxxxxx.    Xxxx xx
                     *
2     Xxxxxxxxxx xxxxs personality diaxxxxxx xxxx xxxx xxxxxxx.    Xxxx xx
                               *
3     Xxxxxxxxxx xxxxx xxxxxxxxxxx xiagnosis from hanx xxxxxxx.    Xxxx xx
                                              *
4     Xxxxxxxxxx xxxxx xxxxxxxxxxx xxxxxxxxx xxom hand writing.    Xxxx xx
                                                       *
```

B

An example of a line of text and the various text patterns derived from it

```
Text  Graphology means personality diagnonsis from hand writing.  This is a
XS    Xxxxxxxxxx xxxxx xxxxonality diagnonsis xxxx xxxx xxxxxxx.  Xxxx xx x
XF    XXXXXXXXXXXXXXXXXXXXXonality diagnonsisXXXXXXXXXXXXXXXXXXXXXXXXXXXXXX
VS    Cnojkaiazp wsorc jsnconality diagnonsis tnaw kori mnlflrq.  Ykle le o
VF    Cnojkaiaqpawsorcajsnconality diagnonsisatnawakoriamnlflrqaaaYklealeao
DS    Hbfxwysyvo tifdl xiblonality diagnonsis abyt wfdn hbemedv.  Awel el f
DF    Hbfxwysyvoatifdlaxiblonality diagnonsisaabytawfdnahbemedvaaaAwelaelaf
                                   ↑
                                   Reader is fixating on the letter "d" in diagnosis
```

XS = Letters replaced with Xs spaces preserved
XF = Letters replaced with Xs spaces filled
VS = Letters replaced with similar letters spaces preserved
VF = Letters replaced with similar letters spaces filled
DS = Letters replaced with dissimilar letters spaces preserved
DF = Letters replaced with dissimilar letters spaces filled

FIGURE 57.8 A computer is used to sense eye movements. (A) All parts of the display are Xs except where the person is fixated. The display is changed to a real word when the eye lands. (B) A window of 17 spaces about the size of the information available on each fixation. The remainder of the spaces are filled in various ways.

A computer-driven system for monitoring eye movement allows the researcher to change the display during each saccade. See examples in Fig. 57.8. Figure 57.8A shows a moving window of text only at the point of fixation. Figure 57.8B shows various changes in the text that can be imposed during the saccade. After a small amount of practice, reading proceeds relatively comfortably and naturally. The best eye-movement-monitoring systems can resolve the direction in which the eyes are aimed to within a quarter of a degree of visual angle, allowing great precision in locating a fixation. Experimenters can determine which individual letter is at the center of each fixation and how many letter positions each eye movement has covered.[42,43] Standard data compiled in eye movement studies include which words in a text are fixated and which are skipped over, how many fixations are made on each fixated word, the duration of each fixation, the length of each eye movement, and the probability of moving the eyes back to a word after it has been passed.

Three important empirical facts have emerged from analyses of these measures of eye movements. First, eye movement patterns are exquisitely sensitive to linguistic properties of the words being fixated and how the words fit together to make grammatical sentences that tell a sensible story. Here are three examples of findings that demonstrate this sensitivity. (a) Longer words are fixated more times, on average, than shorter words. This means that when a word contains more letters to be recognized, subjects take more time to look at the word. (b) Uncommon words are fixated for a longer duration than common words. This means that when a word has been encountered less frequently in the past and is less familiar, subjects take more time to look at it. (c) Words that are unpredictable given the text that has already been read are fixated longer than words that are predictable. This means that when a word's meaning makes a surprising addition to the reader's understanding of the text, the reader takes more time to look at it. In contrast, a predictable word is looked at for less time, and might even be skipped altogether.[44] These and a long list of other sensitivities[40,43] indicate that eye movements are under tight cognitive control and their pattern reflects an ease or difficulty of reading at each moment in time as the reader moves through the text.

Second, the useful information obtained during any one fixation comes from at most a couple of words beyond the word currently being fixated. Although **closed-class function words** (articles, prepositions, conjunctions, and the like) are often skipped, almost all **content words** (nouns, verbs and modifiers) are fixated. A short content word containing four or five letters will commonly receive a single fixation (although if it is highly predictable from context, it might be skipped). Longer content words often receive two or more fixations before the eyes leave it for another word, and longer content words are rarely skipped. What these facts indicate is that reading proceeds approximately one content word at a time. It is extremely difficult to alter this pattern of information intake and still maintain reasonable comprehension and memory, even after considerable practice. Contrary to the claims of speed-reading enthusiasts, attempting to skim, skip lots of words, or take in lots of words at a single glance all result in lower comprehension and poorer memory. In contrast to what happens in "speed reading," it is possible to double people's normal reading rates in the laboratory by presenting the words of a text one by one at the center of a computer screen, thereby eliminating the need to plan and execute eye movements as a part of reading. This rapid serial visual presentation (RSVP) procedure is essentially the *opposite* of speed reading—each and every word is fixated while the eyes stay at one place. When contrasted with the failure of speed reading, the success of RSVP underscores the conclusion drawn from eye movement studies that reading proceeds approximately one content word at a time.

Third, the duration of a fixation for a skilled adult reader averages only about 250–275 ms. Given the tight cognitive control exerted over how long the eyes fixate, when they move, and how far they go, this means that within about a quarter of a second for shorter words and only about twice that amount of time for longer words—or even faster in the RSVP procedure—sufficient cognitive processing must have taken place to determine enough about the meaning and syntactic role of the word being fixated to recognize it and begin the process of integrating the word into the already-established mental representation of the text that has been read up to that point. The mental computations of word recognition—visual encoding of two-dimensional pattern, orthographic encoding of letter identities and letter order, phonological encoding of pronunciation, semantic encoding of meaning, and syntactic encoding of grammatical form class and related structural information—are thus implemented very rapidly by the brain.

Reading Should Be Described in Terms of Underlying Mental Computations

As indicated by the conclusions we just drew from the characteristics of eye movement patterns, behavioral data serve as tools with which to infer the underlying mental computations that allow words to be recognized, sentences to be parsed and understood, and text representations to be built and stored in memory. Computational analysis—identifying the information-processing operations going on in the mind that take the reader step-by-step from a visual pattern in the outside world to an integrated understanding stored in memory—is central to cognitive neuroscience. From the cognitive neuroscientist's perspective, the nervous system acts as an information-processing machine. The neurons and their organization into brain structures are the "hardware" of the machine ("firmware," actually, because the brain alters its own connectivity as a function of its experience in the world. This firmware implements a "program" by which information processing is performed, analogous to a software program running on the hardware of a computer. The task of the cognitive neuroscientist is to identify the computations in the program, how each computation is carried out in the nervous system, and how the computations are related to one another—whether they happen one-by-one in serial fashion or are occurring simultaneously in parallel—the time course of their execution, and what information is exchanged between them. Behavioral performance in tasks requiring different kinds of decisions—visual, orthographic, phonological, semantic, or syntactic—provides insights into the information-processing properties of the cognitive computations. Blood-flow neuroimaging and electrophysiology provide insights into the brain structures responsible for implementing each computation and the time course of their activity. Finally, as we will see later in the section on language disorders, brain injuries that impair some cognitive functions while sparing others provide converging evidence on the identity and independence of the cognitive computations and the location of brain structures involved in their implementation.

Using Neuroimaging to Study How Neural Systems Implement Cognitive Computations

Advances in functional neuroimaging technology, primarily positron emission tomography and functional magnetic resonance imaging (Chapter 14), make it possible to monitor various indicators of regional brain metabolism—mainly event-related changes in blood flow—while normal people with intact nervous systems perform language tasks. Using these techniques, researchers are making rapid progress in understanding localization of function for the cognitive computations of reading. We illustrate this progress with examples from the study of orthographic, phonological, and semantic encoding of individually presented words.

The Logic of a Neuroimaging Experiment

Suppose a literate adult performs one of several different tasks on a series of nouns presented on a computer screen: read each noun silently, pronounce each noun aloud, decide whether each noun rhymes with a target provided before the series starts (for example, does the noun rhyme with "mat"?), decide whether each noun refers to a member of a target category (for example, does the noun name an animal?), or generate a verb that names an action appropriate to the noun (for example, if the noun is "hammer," think of an action that goes with "hammer" and say it out loud, such as "hit" or "smash" or "pound"). What must be done mentally to meet these different task demands? The silent reading task imposes the fewest specific constraints. As a minimum, the reader passively watches each word appear and disappear; the reader may choose to think about the words in some more active way, but this is not required. The other tasks each direct the reader's attention to a particular type of linguistically relevant information and constrain the reader to use that information to execute a specific performance. The attended information includes phonology in pronunciation and rhyming, semantics in category membership, semantics, and syntactic form class in the generate-verbs task. If the different types of information are computed by different brain structures, and if we could measure how active various brain structures are in each task, then we could find out what brain structures are most heavily involved in each type of computation by comparing measurements of brain activity across tasks.

As discussed in Chapter 14, the amount of work being done by different regions of brain tissue is reflected rather directly in blood flow. A region that is working harder receives an increased supply of oxygenated blood within a few seconds—perhaps as soon as 1–2 s—after the region begins its increased metabolic activity.[45–47] Suppose, then, that we use a neuroimaging technique such as PET or fMRI to measure regional blood flow while groups of readers carry out the different tasks we have described. The measured patterns of blood flow can be averaged across readers within each group to give a generic picture of what the "average" brain is doing, they can be analyzed separately for each individual reader to give a picture of individual differences, and they can be compared across tasks to determine how the distribution of metabolic activity in the brain varies as a function of the type of linguistically relevant information that is needed for each task performance.

This basic logic has been used in a number of studies of word recognition. The results converge on an account of word recognition in which visual, orthographic, phonological, and semantic components are each processed by a different system of brain structures.

Patterns of Brain Activation during Visual Word Recognition

We begin with the activation patterns seen in the silent reading task. Compared to a control condition in which people simply look at a cross or some other visual fixation stimulus, silent reading of a series of words consistently activates primary visual areas (portions of V1 and V2 in left and right striate occipital cortex), a region of left-medial prestriate occipital cortex, regions of left inferior temporal cortex, and a region of left inferior prefrontal cortex. The temporal and inferior prefrontal activations are weaker than the occipital activations and are not found in every study. The left and right striate activations and the left-medial prestriate activation are stronger and quite robust across studies.[31,45,46,48,49]

One might guess that these occipital blood-flow increases have something to do with encoding visual shape and determining the orthography of the word being viewed, because occipital cortex is generally involved in visual perception. Petersen *et al.*[50] confirmed these guesses with a more analytic study using words and three other kinds of stimuli: pseudowords, which are spelled like English words and can be pronounced but are unfamiliar and meaningless; random strings of consonants; and strings of unfamiliar but somewhat letterlike shapes. Again compared to a control condition in which people looked at a fixation cross, all four kinds of stimuli activated left and right striate cortex—the primary visual areas. As in the earlier study, words activated the left-medial prestriate region, but the unfamiliar shapes and the random strings of letters did not. This pattern suggests either that the left-medial prestriate region responds to familiar words or that it responds to well-structured orthographic patterns—sequences of letters that follow English spelling conventions, might be words, and hence deserve further, more specialized linguistic processing.

The inclusion of pseudowords among the stimuli allowed these two hypotheses to be discriminated. Pseudowords also activated the left-medial prestriate region, leading Petersen and colleagues to conclude that this portion of the visual system is an orthographic processor. It creates shape-based representations of well-structured letter strings that are likely to be words and communicates these representations to brain structures that specialize in computing additional linguistic properties.

Carr and Posner[31] extended this idea to reading development. They argued that the left-medial prestriate region is the "primary gateway" by which visual information gains access to the linguistic system and that the principal task facing the beginning reader is to learn the orthographic structure of the written language so that the primary gateway is properly established. This is an example of **procedural learning** (see Chapter 56; see also Squire and Knowlton's chapter in Gazzaniga[51])—the acquisition of a new perceptual skill in which a particular processor in the brain "knows" how to construct a particular kind of representation that can be used by the language system when it receives a particular kind of input from primary visual areas. Gaining this skill provides the interface between the already-existing language-processing machinery and visual perception.

What happens when the task requires pronunciation or rhyme judgments rather than silent reading? Both of these tasks direct attention specifically to phonology, and they create activation in superior temporal and inferior parietal regions near the Sylvan fissure. They also produce activation in frontal regions. Rhyme judgments and pronunciation of words or pseudowords aloud activate regions in and around Broca's area; pronunciation adds activation in primary motor areas.[31,45,48,49,52,53]

Converging evidence on temporoparietal and frontal involvement in computing phonology comes from Shaywitz, Pugh, and colleagues.[54–56] Early in their research, this group found that several tasks requiring phonological information activated left and right temporoparietal and frontal structures, with activation patterns for males tending to be strongly left-lateralized and activation patterns for females tending to be more bilateral. Later evidence indicated that males and females tend to produce differentially lateralized frontal and temporoparietal activation patterns because they tend to rely on different strategies for computing phonology. Pugh *et al.*[55] hypothesized that males rely more on a direct paired-associate retrieval process in which orthographic codes for words act as visual retrieval cues for phonological representations that are already stored in memory, and this process takes place largely in the left hemisphere. They hypothesized that females tend to rely more on "sounding words out," using the rules of phonics, and that this process involves more complicated interactions among frontal and temporoparietal structures in the two hemispheres, resulting in bilateral rather than left-lateralized activation. Pugh *et al.*[55] amassed evidence supporting these hypotheses in a sophisticated example of how measures of brain activation and behavioral measures of performance in word recognition tasks can be combined to draw inferences about the functional anatomy of information processing. Readers, both male and female, who showed greater evidence of sounding words out to help them make lexical decisions showed more bilateral frontal and temporoparietal activation, whereas readers who showed little evidence of relying on the rules of phonics showed left-lateralized frontal and temporoparietal activation. Females were more likely than males to sound words out, thereby accounting for the sex difference in lateralization found in the earlier research.

Taken altogether, the data on pronunciation, rhyme judgments, and phonological effects in lexical decision suggest two broad conclusions. First, computing phonology relies on a rather complex set of processes involving frontal, temporal, and parietal structures in both cortical hemispheres. Second, there appear to be two quite different strategies for computing phonology, with different brain structures supporting them.

What happens when the task specifically requires processing of meaning, as in categorization of a noun or production of a verb appropriate to a noun? These semantically oriented tasks consistently activate regions in left inferior prefrontal cortex, anterior to Broca's area, as shown in Fig. 57.9.[48,49,57] This is the same prefrontal tissue sometimes activated during silent reading, but activation is much stronger when the task specifically requires task-appropriate processing of meaning. Carr and Posner[31] dubbed this region the frontal lexical semantics area (FLSA). As will be seen later in this chapter, evidence from loss of semantics due to brain damage suggests that semantic knowledge is not actually stored in prefrontal cortex; rather, it appears that left inferior prefrontal structures are critical to retrieving semantic knowledge and ensuring that the retrieved knowledge actually meets the needs of whatever task is being performed.[31,48] Where and how semantic knowledge is stored are complicated questions; at this point, loss of semantic knowledge is most often associated with left temporal lesions, while fron-

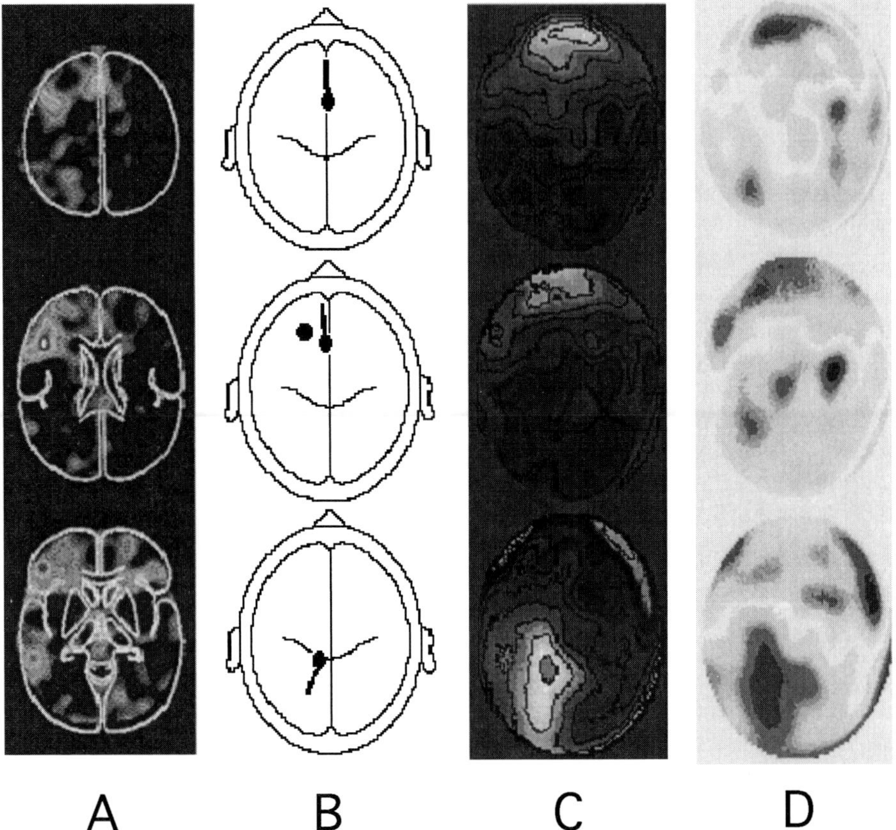

FIGURE 57.9 (A) Results of PET studies of the generate-uses task (minus repeat). Left frontal and posterior semantic areas are active. (B) The dots represent the best-fitting generators for the generate-repeat task. The top picture is about 200 ms after input, the middle about 250 ms, and the bottom about 600 ms. (C) The scalp electrical potentials from which the generators are fit. (D) Significant areas of differences in scalp electrical activity as indicated by t test ($P < 0.01$).

tal lesions are more likely to result in problems of strategic control over the use of knowledge rather than loss of it altogether.[58]

The Time Course of Brain Activation during Visual Word Recognition

These neuroimaging studies indicate that the linguistically relevant properties of written words are computed in different and widely separated brain structures—essentially, word recognition is distributed through the entire cortex. A rough posterior-to-anterior progression can be identified, beginning with encoding of visual shape in posterior striate cortex, moving to encoding of more abstract but still shape-based orthographic information in prestriate cortex, and moving from there to encoding of phonology in structures arrayed around the Sylvan fissure and to retrieving and strategically controlling semantic information in temporal and prefrontal regions. This progression corresponds to the general pattern of information flow in cortex when the sensory stimulus is visual, which begins in posterior occipital areas and projects forward.

One might expect that visual and orthographic information would be available sooner than phonological and semantic information after the appearance of the visual stimulus. The expected order of phonological and semantic activation is more difficult to specify, both because cortical–cortical projections are quite complex and because strategic effects can speed or slow the processing of information as a function of whether it is attended or ignored. Perhaps the order of phonological and semantic activation is not fixed, but varies with task demands. Behavioral evidence from reaction time experiments is consistent with these expectations.[59] More recently, event-related potentials have provided converging evidence that orthographic codes become activated quite early in response to a visually presented word, followed by semantic and phonological codes at variable delays depending on what task is being performed and what information is being attended.[57,60,61]

Neuroimaging Can Be Used to Study Spoken Language

We conclude this section by illustrating how neuroimaging can be applied to the study of spoken language as well as to the study of reading. According to Mazoyer *et al.*:[62]

> To perceive and understand speech, one must deal with the acoustical, phonological, lexical, prosodic, syntactic, and conceptual information conveyed by the signal. The auditory stimulus has first to be mapped into a phonological code. This code is invariant across speakers, speech rate, and accent. When a sequence of phonemes combines into an existing word, the mental lexicon is activated. For example, the word BED is recognized in the mental lexicon as a familiar item with a given meaning. This is not the case when one listens to a pseudoword, e.g., DEB. Eventually, syntactic processes specify the structure of the sentence, making it possible to interpret its meaning. (p 467)

This sequence of mental computations, dealing successively with acoustics, phonology, lexical semantics, syntax, and finally with the meaning of the sentence, was the object of a neuroimaging experiment crafted by this group of researchers working in Paris. They designed a series of stimulus comparisons in a listening task that isolated each level of psycholinguistic processing to discover whether a specific pattern of brain activation was associated with processing of each type of linguistic information. Five different kinds of spoken stimuli were presented to the participants, who were 16 French-speaking, right-handed males. Four of the stimulus types were presented in French. The fifth was in Tamil, a very different language that was unknown to any of the participants. Each listener underwent six PET scans. For 5 of the participants, two scans were taken while they listened to French stories, two were taken while they listened to Tamil stories, and two were taken while they rested quietly with eyes closed. For 5 more participants, the scans were taken while they listened to French stories, listened to lists of unrelated French words, and rested quietly. For the remaining 6 participants, the scans were taken while they listened to French sentences in which the content words were replaced with pseudowords, listened to French sentences in which all the words were real but many did not fit the context, so that the sentences made no sense, and rested quietly. A PET image of regional cerebral blood flow was constructed for each stimulus type by averaging across the images obtained from each participant who received that stimulus (Fig. 57.10).

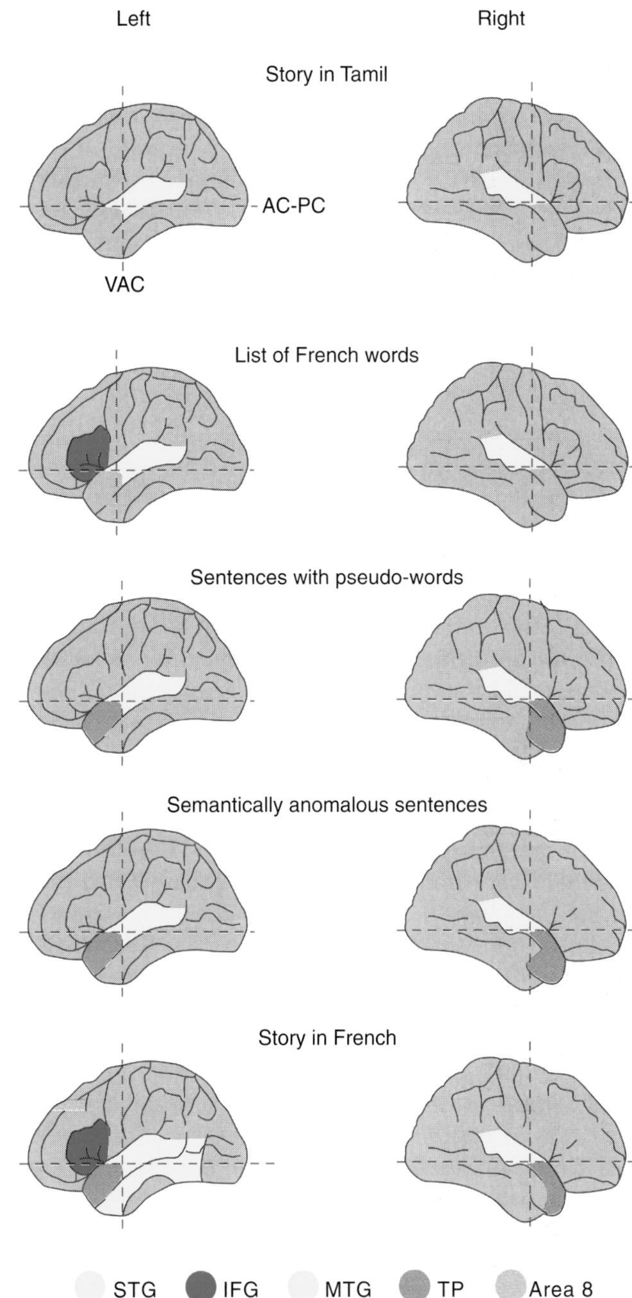

FIGURE 57.10 Areas of brain activation of the left and right hemisphere associated with varying conditions of listening to words and stories. The listeners are fluent in French but do not know Tamil. STG superior temporal sulcus; IFG, inferior frontal gyrus; MTS, middle temporal sulcus; TP, temporal pole.

The remaining conditions in Mazoyer's experiment presented sentences or stories rather than individual words. When an undistorted French story was the stimulus, the primary auditory, left prefrontal, and temporoparietal activations seen with words were present again. Additional temporal activity occurred anterior and inferior to the temporal regions active during word lists, and a region of prefrontal activity appeared anterior and superior to anything observed in response to words. The recruitment of additional brain structures to support syntactic processing and computation of the meaning of phrases, clauses, and sentence seems quite sensible—figuring out sentences and linking sentences together to understand a story are larger, more complicated cognitive jobs than recognizing words. Converging evidence on this conclusion was obtained in a fMRI study of reading.[63] People read sentences that differed in syntactic complexity and hence in how difficult they were to understand. A particularly interesting comparison involved sentences with subject-relative clauses ("The reporter that attacked the senator admitted the error") and syntactically more complex sentences with object-relative clauses ("The reporter that the senator attacked admitted the error"). Although the object-relative sentences were noticeably more difficult to understand, they contained *exactly* the same words as the subject-relative sentences—the difference in difficulty was caused entirely by how the words were arranged. Both types of sentences activated cortical regions in superior temporal lobe and inferior prefrontal cortex, with more activity in the left hemisphere than in the right. However, the amount of tissue activated in these regions and the size of the blood-flow increase relative to control conditions were greater for the more difficult object-relative sentences. In both reading and listening, then, greater demands on syntactic parsing and propositional semantics result in a higher level of cortical activation, especially in left temporal and frontal regions.

Returning to Mazoyer and colleagues' listening task, neither of the two conditions with distorted sentences elicited the complete pattern of activation produced by French stories. When all the words were familiar but the sentences did not make sense, some components of the story pattern were missing. When unfamiliar pseudowords replaced familiar words, right-temporal activation that was not noticeable in any of the other stimulus conditions appeared. This activation was similar in distribution to the right-temporal activity that indicated sounding words out in the Pugh *et al.*[55] study of reading. One of the primary benefits of being able to sound out words is that people can pronounce unfamiliar strings of letters they have not seen before. Of course, a written pseudoword is exactly this kind of stimulus. Thus, when people listen to a pseudoword being pronounced by someone else, some of the brain activity that occurs is the same as the activity that would occur if they saw the pseudoword spelled out and pronounced it to themselves.

Summary

Reading can be broken down into a number of component mental operations. Some of these operations have been localized in different brain areas by neuroimaging studies. Reading and listening have much in common. Differences between them found in imaging studies arise mainly from the separate sensory inputs involved. Once the more abstract linguistic properties of phonology, semantics, and syntax are computed, similarities outweigh differences. This is exactly what one would expect of the relation between reading and listening if reading is a culturally engineered language skill that interfaces a new "perceptual front end," the visual system, to an already-existing language-processing system.

LANGUAGE DISORDERS

A Distinct Cognitive Neuropsychological Approach to Language Disorders Has Emerged

In the cognitive neuropsychological approach to the study of language disorders, there is a close interaction between theories of normal language function and the evidence gained from the study of brain-damaged patients' spared and impaired abilities. As discussed in the previous sections of this chapter, cognitive theories of language assume that there are different cognitive components (e.g., semantic, phonological, syntactic) involved in performing language tasks such as reading or spoken sentence comprehension. Critical data supporting this componential view come from dissociations of function observed in brain-damaged patients—that is, demonstrations that patients perform normally on tasks drawing on one cognitive component, but are impaired on tasks drawing on another cognitive component.

As a specific example, consider the cognitive processes involved in object naming. Most theories of naming assume that after recognition of the object's perceptual form, a semantic description of the object is obtained and then this description is used to access the phonological form corresponding to the object's name. For instance, in naming a picture of a table, recognition of the shape of parts of the table and their spatial relation to each other would lead to retrieval of semantic information—such as "this is a piece of furniture, likely made of wood, with four legs supporting a flat surface, which is used for writing or eating." Access to this semantic information would lead to retrieval of the phonological form that would specify that the name is a two-syllable word with stress on the first syllable and the phonemes /tey/ and /b l/ constituting the two syllables. According to such theories, a patient with preserved visual perceptual abilities might have difficulty with object naming either due to some disruption of semantic processes or due to a disruption of phonological representations (or access to these representations). Consequently, for an individual with a naming deficit, tests would be directed at determining whether the patient had a deficit at the semantic or phonological level or both. Tests for a semantic deficit might include having the patient decide whether a pictured object is an animal or an inanimate object, verify whether certain properties of an object are true (e.g., is this typically found indoors? is this made of metal?), and judge whether two objects (e.g., zipper and button) are similar in function. Tests for a phonological deficit in naming might include having the patient judge whether the names of two pictures rhyme or deciding whether a word matches the name of a picture where some of the incorrect words are phonologically related to the target (e.g., "mat" for "map"). The types of errors that the patient made in naming might also be indicative of a phonological deficit. For example, if the patient said "opuspus" for a picture of an octopus, this would suggest that the patient could access partial, but not complete, phonological information about the name.

Support for a theory assuming separable semantic and phonological components in the naming process would be demonstrated if some patients showed preserved performance on the semantic tasks but impaired performance on the phonological tasks. In this example, the reverse pattern (preserved performance on the phonological tasks, but impaired performance on the semantic tasks) would not be predicted because access to the phonological form is assumed to be dependent on access to the semantic representation. Consequently, a patient who was impaired on the semantic tasks should also be impaired on the phonological tasks involving object names. In fact, evidence against the theory would be obtained if a patient showed poor performance on the semantic tasks and yet performed well on the phonological tasks. A modification to the theory would then be called for. Such a modified theory might hypothesize, for example, that naming could occur by direct access to a phonological form from a visual description of the object.

The cognitive neuropsychological approach contrasts with the syndrome-based approach, in which brain-damaged patients are classed into categories on the basis of partially correlated clusters of behavioral symptoms. In this approach, once patients have been classified into groups, further research seeks to uncover underlying deficits that cause the constellation of symptoms for each group and which explain the differences among the groups.

Aphasias Are Disorders of Spoken Language

The term *aphasia* is used to refer to any language disorder resulting from brain damage; however, subtypes of aphasia are typically defined in terms of the nature of the patients' speech production deficit. In the classic approach to aphasia, patients are classified as exhibiting one of a fairly small number of syndromes defined primarily by a contrast between the patient's ability to produce speech spontaneously and his or her ability to repeat spoken words, phrases, or sentences. Broca's aphasia (motor or expressive aphasia) is characterized by distorted, labored (i.e., nonfluent) speech that is rich in content words but impoverished in function words and grammatical markers. In contrast, patients with Wernicke's aphasia (sensory or receptive aphasia) produce fluent speech that is marked by the absence of content information, together with the presence of grammatical words and inflections. In conduction aphasia, there is relatively preserved spontaneous speech production, but very impaired repetition. The reverse is the case with transcortical aphasia in which repetition is preserved, but spontaneous production is impaired.

These symptoms have been related to models of language production and comprehension that were originally proposed by Lichtheim[64] (often termed the Wernicke–Lichtheim model). This model sees language as consisting of sensory representations for words (stored in Wernicke's area), motor representations for words (stored in Broca's area), and pathways linking these two types of representations to concepts (of unspecified localization) and to each other.

It should be clear, however, from the preceding sections of this chapter that such a model of language is inadequate, primarily because it deals mainly with peripheral aspects of language and has little say about more central semantic and syntactic processes. Figures 57.11 and 57.12 depict more current models of language production and comprehension, respectively.

These models highlight the importance of lexical, semantic, and grammatical processes in production and comprehension. According to the cognitive neuropsychological approach, impairments in language production and comprehension could derive from the disruption of any component of either model, and the consequences of such disruption can be predicted on the basis of the role of the component in the model. Research completed in the past 15 to 20 years has demonstrated that patterns of aphasic performance can be interpreted with respect to such cognitive models, and conversely that findings from such patients can suggest needed revisions to these models. Because of the many different patterns that can be and have been observed, there is insufficient space to discuss all of them. Instead, a few illustrative examples will be discussed in the following sections.

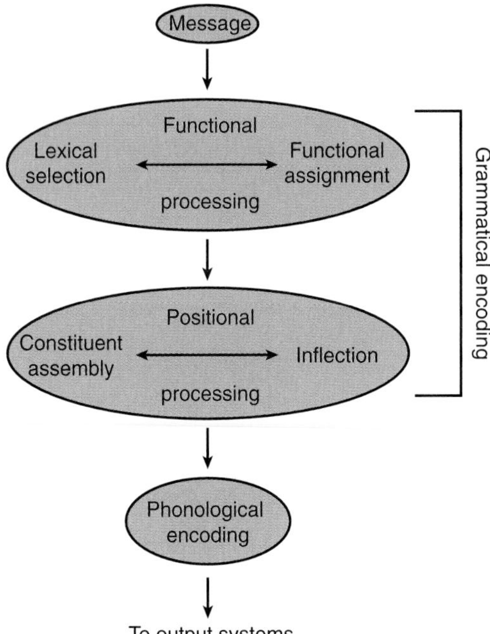

FIGURE 57.11 A model of language production showing the many processes involved. Processing flows in the direction of the arrows. The message level is constructed first and consists of a nonverbal representation of the meaning to be expressed. Functional processing involves selection of the appropriate lexical items to express the intended meaning and relating these lexical items to each other in terms of the functions they play, such as thematic role relations, or relations of place or time. Positional processing involves developing the syntactic form of the sentence, including construction of constituents such as noun phrases and verb phrases and the specification of inflections such as tense or number. Phonological encoding involves the specification of the phonological forms of the words to be produced.

Some Disorders Involve Problems with Word Production and Comprehension

Much of the work on language production deficits has focused on deficits in the production and comprehension of single words. The term *anomia* refers to a disruption in producing substantive words (nouns, verbs, adjectives) and is commonly used in reference to a difficulty in producing concrete nouns. Anomic aphasia is a traditional syndrome category characterized by good comprehension and fluent, grammatically correct speech that is lacking in substantive words (e.g., "thing" might be produced in place of a specific noun and "did" or "made" in place of a more specific verb). On visual confrontation naming (i.e., naming a visually presented object or line drawing), anomic patients perform poorly. The usual account of such a pattern is that the patient has difficulty in retrieving the appropriate phonological form corresponding to a concept but has a preserved ability to access a concept from phonological input. However, in spontaneous speech, producing the correct word depends on having an appropriate semantic representation prior to accessing a phonological form. Naming a visually presented object involves visual analysis as well as access to semantic representations and phonological retrieval. Thus, a naming deficit might result from a disruption of semantic knowledge rather than retrieval. Even for patients who appear to have preserved semantic knowledge because of good performance on clinical assessments of comprehension, a semantic deficit cannot be ruled out because the comprehension test may not have required fine enough distinctions or may not have assessed in a careful fashion those concepts or categories for which the patient demonstrates a naming deficit.

Several studies have demonstrated that some naming deficits may result from a semantic disruption.[65,66] Hillis *et al.*[65] reported that the patient K. E. made semantic errors in oral and written picture naming and that there was a strong correspondence between the items that were misnamed and items that were missed on picture–word matching comprehension tests. The cases reported by Warrington and Shallice[66] showed category-specific deficits in naming (poorer performance for living than nonliving things) and a corresponding deficit in comprehension for items in those categories with the greatest naming errors.

Other patients have demonstrated naming impairments that appear to result from difficulty in retrieving a phonological form from a preserved semantic representation.[67–69] The patient reported by Kay and Ellis[67] showed good comprehension of the words he could not produce and often produced phonological approximations to the target (e.g., "sumberry" for "strawberry"). The cases reported by Lhermitte and Derousne[68] and Caramazza and Hillis[69] are interesting in that their written naming was preserved whereas their oral naming was very disrupted. The preserved written naming demonstrates the preservation of semantic information. In oral naming, the two patients reported by Lhermitte and Derousne produced mainly neologisms (well-articulated nonwords with varying degrees of similarity to the target word) whereas the patients reported by Caramazza and Hillis produced mainly semantic errors. The different error patterns may reflect either different degrees of deficit in the ability to retrieve phonological forms or somewhat different deficits (e.g., a retrieval deficit for the Lhermitte and Derousne patients and a disruption of output phonological forms for the Caramazza and Hillis patients).

Some Naming Deficits Are Category-Specific

The finding that there are patients with category-specific deficits raises a number of interesting issues

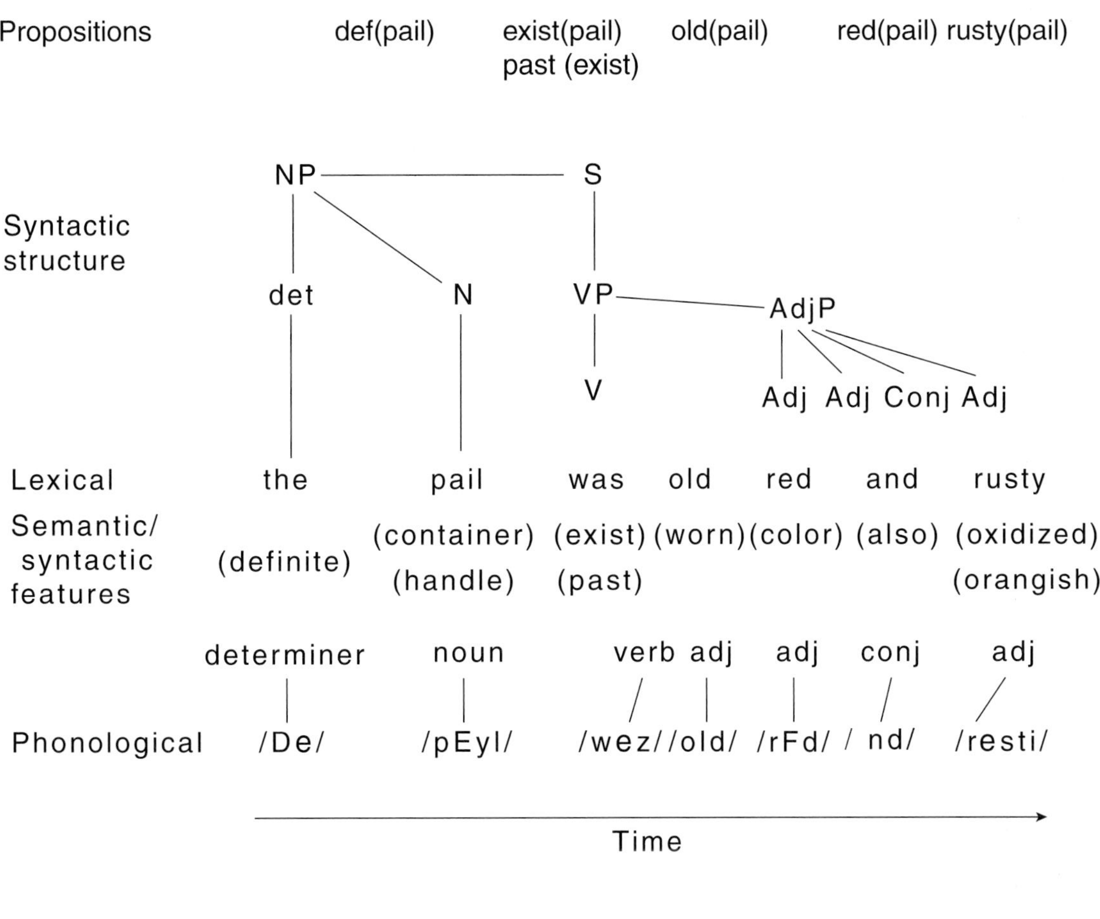

FIGURE 57.12 A view of the computations involved in sentence comprehension. At the bottom, acoustic input is presented over time. The acoustic input is transformed into a phonological representation. These phonological forms are used to access semantic and syntactic information about the words perceived. The syntactic information about the words, that is, word class information (det, determiner; N, noun; V, verb; adj, adjective; conj, conjunction) and information about the typical syntactic structures that the words appear in, is used to construct the syntactic constituent structure of the sentence (the sequence and hierarchical relations between different types of phrases (NP, noun phrases; VP, verb phrase; AdjP, adjective phrase; S, sentence). The constituent structure and semantic representations of the individual words are used to construct propositions that represent the meaning relations among the words in the sentence.

about the nature of the representation of semantic knowledge in the brain. In addition to the deficit specific to living things, category-specific deficits have been reported for a number of other categories, including nonliving things,[70–72] concrete words,[73] abstract words,[74,75] proper names,[76] and body parts.[77] The issue raised by these findings is whether semantic knowledge is organized along these categorical lines in the brain or whether some other underlying factor might account for these dissociations. One argument advanced to account for a deficit specific to living things is that these items tend to be less familiar and more visually confusable than items from nonliving categories.[78] Although these factors could account for some patients' difficulties with living things, they could hardly account for patients who have more difficulty with nonliving things. Another argument is that categories are distinguishable on the basis of the primary type of featural information that distinguishes members of certain categories from other categories. For example, some categories may be defined primarily on the basis of perceptual aspects such as color or shape (e.g., birds, flowers), whereas others might be defined primarily on the basis of their function or the motor movements that are used in conjunction with the object (e.g., tools, weapons). According to this line of reasoning, category-specific deficits reflect damage to knowledge about these different types of features, rather than about categories per se. For example, animals are defined in terms of perceptual features such as shape and color, whereas man-made objects are defined in terms of function. Patients might therefore have a deficit for animals but not for man-made objects because they have a disruption in knowledge of shape and color. The featural account has some appeal because of the known specialization of different primary cortical areas for the processing of certain types of sensory or motor information. However, there is no detailed evidence that a patient who seems to show a deficit in knowledge about, for example, shape or color has a deficit for all categories that might be considered to be defined by that attribute. Also, there is no evidence that such patients have difficulty in making distinctions related to the feature or features hypothesized to have been affected (e.g., a specific loss of knowledge of the color of particular animals). Moreover, the specificity of the deficits noted in some patients (e.g., a deficit with naming fruits and vegetables but not other foods[79]) would seem to defy a featural account.

Some Naming Deficits Are Specific to the Modality of Input

Another set of somewhat related issues has been raised by studies of patients who show naming deficits specific to one modality of input. For instance, in so-called optic aphasia, the patient has a deficit in naming objects from visual input despite demonstrating adequate recognition (for example, by miming its use), but does not have difficulty naming the object from other sensory input (e.g., tactile, auditory). According to a rather complex line of reasoning, some researchers have argued that such findings suggest that there are separate semantic systems for different sensory modalities, and a verbal semantic system separate from these modality-specific systems.[80,81] That is, if there were only one amodal semantic system, then the ability to name an object presented in one sensory modality should indicate that this amodal semantic representation is intact. If an object can be recognized when presented in another modality, there must be access to this amodal representation, and it should be possible to name the object presented in the second modality.

Finding a modality-specific naming deficit such as optic aphasia suggests that although the patient has accessed a visual semantic representation, it has been disconnected from a verbal semantic system, resulting in an inability to access the name. One counterargument has been that the tests of access to semantic information in the modality for which the naming deficit has been demonstrated have not been sufficiently stringent, and thus, the patients may in fact have some deficit in accessing the amodal semantic system from information in a particular sensory modality.[82] In cases of optic aphasia where patients demonstrate impaired naming but good miming for visually presented objects, some researchers have argued that the miming test does not require very specific semantic knowledge. For example, the gestures that one might make for slipper, boot, and shoe might all be very similar. A patient might produce a similar gesture for all three (and these might be judged as correct); however, such gesturing would not demonstrate that the patient was able to access discriminating semantic information for these three concepts for visually presented exemplars. A naming test might reveal a deficit in conceptual discrimination, if, for example, the patient produced "slipper" incorrectly for shoe.

Whether this criticism of insufficiently strong tests of semantic access in the affected modality applies to all cases of modality-specific anomia is currently a matter of debate.[83,84] If the modality-specific naming deficits do not force us to conclude that there are multiple semantic systems, they would at least demonstrate that access routes to an amodal system are modality-specific. That is, if the patient who had difficulty accessing discriminating semantic information for shoe versus slipper with visual presentation could discriminate and name these two objects correctly when allowed to touch (but not see) them, this would demonstrate that access to the amodal semantic system was impaired specifically for visual input. The modality-specific naming deficits also demonstrate that damage to each access route may occur in a partial fashion so that sufficient semantic information may be accessed to support the performance of some tasks (e.g., providing an approximately correct gesture), but not a task, such as naming, that requires a detailed semantic representation.

Some Disorders Are Related to the Production and Comprehension of Sentences

Sentence production deficits have also been a focus of research in aphasia, although in this domain much of the work has originated from a syndrome-based approach, concentrating on patients showing agrammatic speech. Agrammatic speakers produce reduced grammatical structure and a preponderance of content words and tend to omit function words (i.e., grammatical words such as prepositions, articles, pronouns, and conjunctions) and inflections. Although agrammatism occurs predominantly in nonfluent patients who typically are classed as having Broca's aphasia, several studies have documented that features of agrammatism may also appear in fluent speakers.[85,86] Moreover, other studies have shown that the difficulties with sentence structure and those with function words may be dissociated in some patients. That is, some patients may produce sentences that have reduced complexity but which are characterized by accurate production of function words and inflections,[87] whereas other patients may show the reverse.[86,88] The dissociation between difficulties with sentence structure and those with function words implies that these deficits arise at different levels in the production process. Several suggestions have been made as to what these different deficits might be.[89] One interesting approach relates deficits in sentence structure to deficits in the knowledge of verb representation. In Fig. 57.12, at the functional level, the verb plays a major role in structuring the roles of nouns (such as agents, patients, recipients) with respect to the action in the sentence. For example, the functional representation of the message that a woman donated a book to the library would include the verb "donate" and the associated information that "woman" was the agent of donate, "book" was the theme (or the object donated), and "library" was the recipient. Some have claimed that the representation at this level also relates these roles to the grammatical position that the noun will play (e.g., the recipient will be the subject of an active sentence using the verb "receive").[90] A deficit in knowledge of the relations of semantic and grammatical roles played by verbs could lead to a reduction in sentence structure, such as the failure to produce a required indirect object, or to inaccurate sentence structure in which the mapping between semantic and grammatical roles is incorrect.[91,92]

The disruption in the production of function words and inflections might come from a disruption at a different stage, specifically, the positional level in Fig. 57.11. At the positional level, the specific syntactic structure to be used in production is selected, specifying word order, along with the required function words and grammatical markers. Some researchers have postulated that this process involves the selection of grammatical frames that have specified function words (for example, a frame for expressing an indirect object that includes the preposition "to," as in "to Mary"[93]). If a patient could construct a functional representation accurately but not an appropriate positional representation, the patient's production might include the major content words but not the accompanying function words.[94,95] For example, the patient might produce "Sue..toss.. ball... Jim" for the intended sentence "Sue tossed the ball to Jim." Of course, many patients might have a disruption at both levels, resulting in prototypical agrammatic speech.

In Some Patients, Lack of Comprehension Is Related to Syntax

In the domain of sentence comprehension, one finding that generated intense interest was that some patients who understood the content words in a sentence were unable to comprehend the sentence as a whole when comprehension depended on correct interpretation of the syntactic information in the sentence.[96] For example, when asked to match pictures to sentences, these patients were unable to choose between a picture of a dog chasing a girl and one of a girl chasing a dog to match with the sentence "The dog was chased by the girl" or to choose between a picture of a girl carrying a boy with red hair and one of a girl with red hair carrying a boy for the sentence "The boy that the girl carried has red hair." The finding that patients showing this deficit often produced agrammatic speech led Berndt and Caramazza[97] to hypothesize that the underlying source of the comprehension and production patterns was a specific disruption of knowledge of syntax. However, some patients who show this comprehension deficit do not produce agrammatic speech.[98,99] In addition, several patients who showed this comprehension deficit on sentence–picture matching tasks were able to analyze syntactic structure when tested on their ability to distinguish grammatical from ungrammatical sentences.[100]

Because these results are not consistent with a global deficit in syntactic processing, other explanations of the comprehension deficit have been suggested.[101] One prominent theory[102] is that patients with this comprehension deficit can analyze the syntactic structure of the sentence and determine grammatical roles such as subject, object, and indirect object, but have difficulty mapping between this grammatical information and thematic role information (i.e., which noun is the agent, theme, recipient, location). For example, for the sentence "The boys were pushed by the girl," the patient would be able to determine that "boys" was the grammatical subject (and that therefore "were" had to be plural to agree with "boys"), but would be unable to determine that the grammatical subject was not the agent but rather the theme in this sentence. The existence of patients who are impaired on syntactic comprehension tests but who perform well on grammar tests supports the contention that a cognitive process performs the mapping between syntactic and thematic roles, and that this process may be independently affected by brain damage. (Of course, according to the cognitive neuropsychological approach, one would also expect to find some patients who do have a deficit at the syntactic level and who would fail both on the comprehension tests and on the grammaticality judgment tests).

An important offshoot of this theoretical approach has been the development of a "mapping therapy" procedure aimed at retraining aphasic patients to carry out this mapping process.[103,104] This therapy, unlike most traditional approaches, has resulted in significant improvements in sentence comprehension for patients who have exhibited aphasic symptoms over a period of several years. Importantly, the improvement in comprehension often generalizes to sentences with content words or syntactic structures different from those used in training. Sometimes, the training has been found to lead to improved sentence production even though only comprehension was targeted in training.

In addition to syntactic and thematic mapping deficits, restriction in short-term memory capacity may underlie some aphasic patients' sentence comprehension deficits. Aphasic patients often have very restricted short-term memory capacity, being able to recall only 2 or 3 words from a list compared to a normal subjects' ability to recall 5 or 6 words.[105,106] Some patients may be able to remember a single word at best.[107] Many of these patients appear to have a specific deficit in the ability to retain phonological information.[108] Although the idea that restricted short-term memory capacity impedes comprehension seems plausible, some patients with very restricted memory spans show excellent sentence comprehension even for sentences with complex syntactic structures.[109–111] Such findings support the "immediacy of processing" theories of comprehension, which state that syntactic analysis and semantic interpretation are carried out on a word-by-word basis.[112,113] Consequently, a verbatim phonological representation of a clause or sentence is not needed to support comprehension processes. In some patients, however, short-term memory deficits may derive from a deficit in retaining semantic information.[111,115] The restricted ability of such patients to retain semantic information impedes comprehension for certain sentence types that put a strain on the capacity to retain individual word meanings. Specifically, these patients have difficulty comprehending sentences when the structure of the sentence delays the integration of word meanings into more integrated semantic representations (e.g., sentences with several prenominal adjectives such as "The drab old red swimsuit was taken to the beach") but do not have difficulty comprehending similar sentences where the meanings can be integrated immediately (e.g., for sentences with several adjectives following the noun "The swimsuit was old, red, and drab, but she took it along anyway").

Strokes Can Produce a Sudden Inability To Read

The cognitive neuropsychological perspective has been used extensively to study reading disorders after brain damage. Acquired dyslexia may sometimes occur in the absence of obvious spoken language impairments, and thus dyslexia is usually treated as a domain of inquiry separate from aphasia.

The traditional approach, initiated by Dejerine in 1892,[116] distinguishes two syndromes in which reading is severely disrupted: pure alexia (in which reading is impaired but writing preserved) and alexia with agraphia (in which both reading and writing are disrupted). According to Dejerine there is one brain center for the visual images of letters that is critical to both reading and writing. In pure alexia, access to this center from visual input is disrupted, but the center itself is intact, allowing for normal writing. In alexia with agraphia, the center itself is damaged, disrupting both reading and writing. The more recent cognitive neuropsychological approach focuses on patients who show partial impairments of reading, where the pattern of breakdown with respect to such variables as spelling-to-sound regularity (i.e., reading of regularly spelled words such as "basket" or "march" vs reading of irregularly spelled words such as "sword" or "pint") and word concreteness (i.e., reading of concrete words such as "furnace" or "carrot" vs reading of abstract words such as "idea" or "program") has interesting implications for theories of reading. Some work has focused on what has been termed the "peripheral dyslexias," that is, patients whose reading deficits are attributed to disruptions of various aspects of the visual or attentional processes involved in word perception.[117] However, beginning with a seminal paper by Marshall and Newcombe,[118] more work has focused on patients in whom the reading difficulty cannot be attributed to a perceptual deficit but rather is the result of some more central aspect of reading involved in matching a correctly perceived visual representation to a pronunciation or to a meaning.

Surface and Deep Dyslexia Are Due to Impairment of Two Different Reading Routes

Two patterns of central reading impairment initially identified by Marshall and Newcombe[118]—surface and deep dyslexia—continue to be of interest. Patients with **surface dyslexia** appear to rely on grapheme-to-phoneme conversion (i.e., "sounding out") in reading aloud. Consequently, they are able to read regular words and nonwords, but tend to incorrectly read words with irregular grapheme–phoneme correspon-

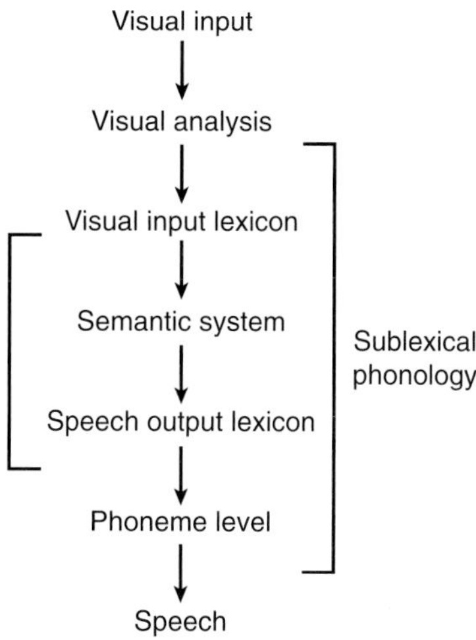

FIGURE 57.13 Processes that may be involved in acquired dyslexia. The top indicates visual input and the bottom speech output. Reading difficulties may arise in any of the intermediate stages.

dences (e.g., island, have), sometimes regularizing the pronunciation (e.g., pronouncing "have" to rhyme with gave). In cases of **deep dyslexia,** patients show a constellation of symptoms, including semantic errors (e.g., reading "sick" as "ill"), better reading of concrete than abstract words, and an inability to read nonwords. These contrasting syndromes fit well with dual-route models of oral reading, in which one route corresponds to a grapheme-to-phoneme correspondence route (or sublexical route) and the second corresponds to a lexical route where the pronunciation is accessed on a whole-word basis.[119] In the cognitive neuropsychological literature, this lexical route is usually assumed to be a semantic route. That is, the whole-word orthographic representation (written form of the word) is assumed to access a semantic representation. The phonological form is then accessed from the semantic representation (see Fig. 57.13). For patients with surface dyslexia, the lexical route is assumed to be impaired, forcing reliance on the sublexical route. For patients with deep dyslexia, the sublexical route is impaired and reading is accomplished by the lexical route. Their substitution of semantically related words (e.g., reading "reflection" as "mirror") is evidence for the semantic nature of this route.

The symptoms of surface dyslexia may be caused by any disruption that prevents the use of the grapheme–phoneme conversion route, which involves access to semantic representations. For example, in one patient with surface dyslexia the severity of disruption in recognizing orthographic representations for words was related to word frequency (i.e., low-frequency words were more difficult to recognize).[120] The patient failed to show a word superiority effect—that is, better recognition of words than pseudowords—for low-frequency words, although he did show such an effect for high-frequency words. In contrast to this form of surface dyslexia is the case of a patient whose symptoms appeared to arise from a general semantic deficit, as her knoweldge of word meanings was very impaired even for spoken words.[121] A third form of surface dyslexia is evident in patients whose comprehension of the meaning of irregularly spelled words is superior to their ability to read such words aloud.[67,122] For example, the patient pronounces "yacht" as "yatched" but yet is able to correctly choose a picture to match the word. For these patients, the disruption in the lexical route appears to be at the stage of retrieving phonological representations from semantic representations.

A Third Reading Route Has Been Proposed

One issue that remains unresolved in the neuropsychological literature is whether oral reading that is not mediated by grapheme–phoneme conversion must be accomplished via access of a semantic representation or whether a whole-word phonological representation can be accessed directly from a visual representation (a so-called "third route" for reading). Patients with phonological dyslexia cannot read nonwords (indicating a disruption of the sublexical route) yet can read words very well and thus do not show the evidence of "semantic" reading implicated in deep dyslexia. Such patients may be reading by this third route. Alternatively, they may be reading by the semantic route, but this route is functioning well, whereas the patients with deep dyslexia are also reading by the semantic route, but the semantic route has been disrupted in some fashion. In fact, most theorists assume that patients with deep dyslexia have some deficit in the semantically based reading route in addition to their deficit in the sublexical route.[123] As with surface dyslexia, deficits at various points in the lexical route give rise to different variations in the form of deep dyslexia.[117]

Better evidence for the existence of the third route would be the existence of patients who cannot perform grapheme–phoneme conversion, yet who can read aloud words for which they have no idea of the meaning. Whether such evidence exists is a matter of dispute. Two groups[124,125] have presented evidence of patients who were able to read aloud irregular words they could not comprehend. However, these patients may have been able to read these words by combining partial semantic information and partial knowledge of letter–sound correspondences.[126]

There have been attempts to model patient deficits

in acquired dyslexia by "lesioning" connectionist models of reading.[123,127,128] These models are computer models with a quasi-neural flavor that consist of nodes and connections between the nodes. The nodes represent orthographic, phonological, and semantic information, and multiple, parallel connections exist between the nodes in different layers. Activation spreads between the nodes in different layers (e.g., between orthographic and phonological nodes) based on the strength of the connections between the layers. Researchers[127] have attempted to replicate the reading patterns observed in patients with surface dyslexia by damaging different aspects of a connectionist model.[129] This model postulates only a single route for reading rather than separate lexical and sublexical routes. The attempt was successful in duplicating aspects of the deficits of some surface dyslexics, but not of surface dyslexics in whom the sublexical route appears to be functioning well. Other models of deep dyslexia assume a dual route in which the sublexical route has been damaged.[123,128] This research focuses on modeling damage to the semantic route and mimicking the different subpatterns of deep dyslexia by damaging different layers of connections in their model. Although the attempts to model both surface and deep dyslexia provide parsimonious accounts of certain constellations of symptoms, they fail to account for others. Thus, whether such models will be successful in accounting for all of the striking dissociations in symptoms documented in acquired dyslexic patients remains to be seen.

Summary

Language is a complex code that contains many component processes. Some of the elements of language appear innately in the communication of animals. Some innate signals can be modified by learning. Some of the universals of human language are not present in animal communication, but are unique to the human being. Phonemes serve as units that can be combined to produce the words of all the world's languages. Grammar serves to organize words into an infinite number of propositions that can be used to express meaning. Most phonemes and the basic structure of grammar appear to be innate.

Neuroimaging studies of spoken and written language have revealed brain areas involved in the sight, sound, and meaning of words. There is still rather little known about how the brain combines words to form the propositions and sentences of natural languages. However, some clues to these mechanisms come from strokes to areas of the brain that damage the abilities for language comprehension, production, and reading. Patient studies constitute natural experiments that provide additional evidence of the computations carried out within particular brain areas. Evidence to date suggests a highly modularized organization.

References

1. Gould, J. L., and Gould, C. G. (1994). *The Animal Mind.* Freeman, New York.
2. Gould, J. L. (1982). *Ethology.* Norton, New York.
3. Gould, J. L., and Marler, P. (1987). The instinct to learn. *Sci. Am.* **256**(1): 74–85.
4. Jakobson, R. (1941). *Kindersprache, Aphasie und Allgemeine Lautgesetze.* Universitets Arsskrift, Uppsala.
5. Trubetzkoy, N. S. (1939). *Grundzuge der Phonologie.* Travaux du Cercle Linguistique de Prague 7, Prague.
6. Jakobson, R., Fant, G. M., and Halle, M. (1963). *Preliminaries to Speech Analysis.* MIT Press, Cambridge, MA.
7. Selkirk, E. (1984). *Phonology and Syntax: The Relation Between Sound and Structure.* MIT Press, Cambridge, MA.
8. McCarthy, J. (1979). *Formal Problems in Semitic Phonology and Morphology.* Ph.D. dissertation, Massachusetts Institute of Technology, Department of Linguistics, Cambridge, MA.
9. Goldsmith, J. (1976). Autosegmental phonology. Ph.D. Dissertation, Massachusetts Institute of Technology, Department of Linguistics, Cambridge, MA.
10. Halle, M., & Vergnaud, J.R. (1980). Three-dimensional phonology. *J. Linguistic Res.* **1:** 83–105.
11. Clements, G. N., and Keyser, S. J. (1983). *CV Phonology: A Generative Theory of the Syllable.* MIT Press, Cambridge, MA.
12. Aronoff, M. (1976). *Word Formation in Generative Grammar.* MIT Press, Cambridge, MA.
13. Baker, M. (1988). *Incorporation.* University of Chicago Press, Chicago.
14. Kiparsky, P. (1982). From cyclic phonology to lexical phonology. In *The Structure of Phonological Representations* (H. van der Hand and N. Smith, eds.), Vol. 1. Foris, Dordrecht, The Netherlands.
15. Anderson, S. R. (1982). Where's morphology. *Linguistic Inquiry* **13:** 571–612.
16. Williams, E. (1981). X features. In *Language Acquisition and Linguistic Theory* (S. Tavakolian, ed.). MIT Press, Cambridge, MA.
17. Van Dijk, T. A., and Kintsch, W. (1983). *Strategies of Discourse Comprehension.* Academic Press, New York.
18. Grosz, B. J., Pollack, M. E., and Sidner, C. L. (1989). Discourse: In *Foundations of Cognitive Science* (M. Posner, ed.), pp. 437–468. MIT Press, Cambridge, MA.
19. Greenberg, J. H., ed. (1963). *Universals of Language.* MIT Press, Cambridge, MA.
20. Chomsky, N. (1957). *Syntactic Structures.* Mouton, The Hague.
21. Chomsky, N. (1965). *Aspects of the Theory of Syntax.* MIT Press, Cambridge, MA.
22. Chomsky, N. (1981). *Lectures on Government and Binding.* Foris, Dordrecht, The Netherlands.
23. Chomsky, N. (1986). *Knowledge of Language.* Praeger, New York.
24. Chomsky, N. (1988). *Language and Problems of Knowledge: The Managua Lectures.* MIT Press, Cambridge, MA.
25. Gleitman, L., and Wanner, E. (1988). Current issues in language learning. In *Developmental Psychology: An Advanced Textbook* (M. H. Bornstein and M. E. Lamb, eds.). Erlbaum, Hillsdale, NJ.
26. Hirsh-Pasek, K., and Golinkoff, R. (1996). *The Origins of Grammar: Evidence from Early Language Comprehension.* MIT Press, Cambridge, MA.
27. Pinker, S. (1994). *The Language Instinct.* Morrow, New York.

28. Pinker, S., and Bloom, P. (1992). Natural language and natural selection. In *The Adapted Mind: Evolutionary Psychology and the Generation of Culture* (J. Barkow, L. Cosmides, and J. Tooby, eds.), pp. 451–493. Oxford University Press, New York.
29. Wexler, K., and Culicover, P. (1980). *Formal Principles of Language Acquisition.* MIT Press, Cambridge, MA.
30. Greenfield, P. M. (1991). Language, tool, and brain: The ontogeny and phylogeny of hierarchically organized sequential behavior. *Behav. Brain Sci.*
31. Carr, T. H., and Posner, M. I. (1995). The impact of learning to read on the functional anatomy of language processing. In *Speech and Reading: A Comparative Approach* (B. de Gelder and J. Morais, eds.), pp. 267–301. Erlbaum, Hove, UK, and Taylor & Frances, London.
32. Rozin, P. (1976). The evolution of intelligence and access to the cognitive unconscious. In *Progress in Psychobiology and Physiological Psychology* (J. M. Sprague and A. N. Epstein, eds.). Academic Press, New York.
33. Rozin, P., and Gleitman, L. (1977). The structure and acquisition of reading: II. The reading process and acquisition of the alphabetic principle. In *Toward a Psychology of Reading* (A. S. Reber and D. L. Scarborough, eds.). Erlbaum, Hillsdale, NJ.
34. Lashley, K. S. (1951). The problem of serial order in behavior. In *Cerebral Mechanisms in Behavior: The Hixon Symposium* (L. A. Jeffres, ed.). Wiley, New York.
35. Chromsky, N. (1959). A review of Skinner's *Verbal Behavior. Language* **35:** 26–58.
36. Austin, J. (1962). *How To Do Things with Words.* Harvard University Press, Cambridge, MA.
37. Gardner, H. (1985). *The Mind's New Science.* Basic Books, New York.
38. Grainger, J., and Jacobs, A. M. (1996). Orthographic processing in visual word recognition: A multiple read-out model. *Psychol. Rev.* **103:** 518–565.
39. Posner, M. I., and Carr, T. H. (1992). Lexical access and the brain: Anatomical constraints on cognitive models of word recognition. *Am. J. Psychol.* **105:** 1–26.
40. Carr, T. H. (1986). Perceiving visual language. In *Handbook of Perception and Human Performance* (K. R. Boff, L. Kaufman, and J. P. Thomas, eds.), pp. 1–92. Wiley, New York.
41. Neely, J. H. (1991). Semantic priming effects in visual word recognition: A selective review of current findings and theories. In *Basic Processes in Reading: Visual Word Recognition* (D. Besner and G. W. Humphreys, eds.), pp. 264–336. Erlbaum, Hillsdale, NJ.
42. Pollatsek, A., and Rayner, K. (1990). Reading. In *Foundations of Cognitive Science* (M. I. Posner, ed.). MIT Press, Cambridge, MA.
43. Rayner, K., and Pollatsek, A. (1989). *The Psychology of Reading.* Prentice-Hall, Englewood Cliff, NJ.
44. Zola, D. (1984). Redundancy and word perception during reading. *Percept. Psychophys.* **36:** 277–284.
45. Frackowiak, R. S. J., Friston, K. J., Frith, C. D., Dolan, R. J., and Mazziota, J. C. (1997). *Human Brain Function.* Academic Press, San Diego, CA.
46. Posner, M. I., and Raichle, M. E. *Images of Mind.* Scientific American Library, New York.
47. Raichle, M. E. (1987). Circulatory and metabolic correlates of brain function in normal humans. In *Higher Functions of the Brain* (F. Plum, ed.), Part 2, pp. 643–674. Williams & Wilkins, Baltimore, MD.
48. Cabeza, R., and Nyberg, L. (1997). Imaging cognition: An empirical review of PET studies with normal subjects. *J. Cognit. Neurosci.* **9:** 1–26.
49. McCandliss, B. D., and Posner, M. I. (in press). Brain circuitry during reading. In *Converging Methods for Understanding Reading and Dyslexia* (R. M. Klein and P. McMullen, eds.). MIT Press, Cambridge, MA.
50. Petersen, S. E., Fox, P. T., Snyder, A. Z., and Raichle, M. E. (1990). Activation of extrastriate and frontal cortical areas by visual words and word-like stimuli. *Science* **249:** 1041–1044.
51. Squire, L. S., and Knowlton, B. J. (1994). Memory, hippocampus, and brain systems. In *The Cognitive Neurosciences* (M. S. Gazzaniga, ed.). MIT Press, Cambridge, MA.
52. Demb, J. B., and Gabrieli, J. D. E. (in press). Functional imaging of word processing. In *Converging Methods for Understanding Reading and Dyslexia* (R. M. Klein and P. McMullen, eds.). MIT Press, Cambridge, MA.
53. Fiez, J. A., Tallal, P., Raichle, M. E., Miezin, F. M., Katz, W. F., and Petersen, S. E. (1995). PET studies of auditory and phonological processing: Effects of stimulus characteristics and task demands. *J. Cognit. Neurosci.* **7:** 357–375.
54. Pugh, K. R., Shaywitz, B. A., Constable, R. T., Shaywitz, S. E., Skudlarski, P., Fulbright, R. K., Bronen, R. A., Shankweiler, D. P., Katz, L., Fletcher, J. M., and Gore, J. C. (1996). Cerebral organization of component processes in reading. *Brain* **119:** 1221–1238.
55. Pugh, K. R., Shaywitz, B. A., Shaywitz, S. E., Shankweiler, D. P., Katz, L., Fletcher, J. M., Skudlarski, P., Fulbright, R. K., Constable, R. T., Bronen, R. A., Lacadie, C., and Gore, J. C. (1997). Predicting reading performance from neuroimaging profiles: The cerebral basis of phonological effects in printed word identification. *J. Exp. Psychol. Hum. Percept. Perform.* **23:** 299–318.
56. Shaywitz, B. A., Shaywitz, S. E., Pugh, K. R., Constable, R. T., Skudlarski, P., Fulbright, R. K., Bronen, R. A., Fletcher, J. M., Shankweiler, D. P., Katz, L., and Gore, J. C. (1995). Sex differences in the functional organization of the brain for language. *Nature (London)* **373:** 607–609.
57. Abdullaev, Y. G., and Posner, M. I. (1997). Time course of activating brain areas in generating verbal associations. *Psychol. Sci.* **8:** 51–59.
58. McCarthy, R. A., and Warrington, E. K. (1990). *Cognitive Neuropsychology: A Clinical Introduction.* Academic Press, San Diego, CA.
59. Posner, M. I. (1986). *Chronometric Explorations of Mind,* 2nd ed. Oxford University Press, New York. (1st ed. Erlbaum, Hillsdale, NJ, 1978.)
60. Snyder, A. Z., Abdullaev, Y. G., Posner, M. I., and Raichle, M. E. (1995). Scalp electrical potentials reflect regional cerebral blood flow responses during processing of written words. *Proc. Nat. Acad. Sci. U.S.A.* **92:** 1689–1693.
61. Ziegler, J. C., Besson, M., Jacobs, A. M., Nazir, T., and Carr, T. H. (1997). Word, pseudoword, and nonword processing: A multitask comparison using event-related brain potentials. *J. Cognit. Neurosci.* (in press).
62. Mazoyer, B. M., Tzourio, N., Frak, V., Syrota, A., Murayama, N., Levrier, O., Salamon, G., Dehaene, S., Cohen, L., and Mehler, J. (1993). The cortical representation of speech. *J. Cognit. Neurosci.* **5:** 467–479.
63. Just, M. A., Carpenter, P. A., Keller, T. A., Eddy, W. F., and Thulborn, K. R. (1996). Brain activation modulated by sentence comprehension. *Science* **274:** 114–116.
64. Lichtheim, H. (1885). On aphasia. *Brain* **7:** 433–484.
65. Hillis, A., Rapp, B., Romani, C., and Caramazza, A. (1990). Selective impairment of semantics in lexical processing. *Cognit. Neuropsychol.* **7:** 191–243.
66. Warrington, E. K., and Shallice, T. (1984). Category specific semantic impairments. *Brain* **107:** 829–853.

67. Kay, J., and Ellis, A. W. (1987). A cognitive neuropsychological case study of anomia: Implications for psychological models of word retrieval. *Brain* **110:** 613–629.
68. Lhermitte, F., and Derouesne, J. (1974). Paraphasies et jargonaphasies dans le langage oral avec conservation du langage écrit. Génèse des néologismes. *Rev. Neurol.* **130:** 21–38.
69. Caramazza, A., and Hillis, A. (1990). Where do semantic errors come from? *Cortex* **26:** 95–122.
70. Hillis, A., and Caramazza, A. (1991). Category specific naming and comprehension impairment: A double dissociation. *Brain* **114:** 2081–2094.
71. Sacchett, C., and Humphreys, G. W. (1992). Calling a squirrel a squirrel but a canoe a wigwam: A category-specific deficit for artifactual objects and body parts. *Cognit. Neuropsychol.* **9:** 73–86.
72. Warrington, E. K., and McCarthy, R. (1983). Category specific access dysphasia. *Brain* **106:** 859–878.
73. Goodglass, H., Hyde, M. R., and Blumstein, J. (1969). Frequency, picturability, and availability of nouns in aphasia. *Cortex* **5:** 104–119.
74. Breedin, S., Saffran, E., and Coslett, H. B. (1994). Reversal of the concreteness effect in a patient with semantic dementia. *Cognit. Neuropsychol.* **11:** 617–660.
75. Warrington, E. K. (1975). The selective impairment of semantic memory. *Q. J. Exp. Psychol.* **27:** 635–657.
76. Semenza, C., and Zettin, M. (1988). Generating proper names: A case of selective inability. *Cognit. Neuropsychol.* **5:** 711–721.
77. Dennis, M. (1976). Dissociated naming and locating of body parts after left anterior temporal lobe resection: An experimental case study. *Brain Language* **3:** 147–163.
78. Funnell, E., and Sheridan, J. (1992). Categories of knowledge? Unfamiliar aspects of living and non living things. *Cognit. Neuropsychol.* **9:** 135–153.
79. Hart, J., Berndt, R., and Caramazza, A. (1985). Category-specific naming deficit following cerebral infarction. *Nature* (*London*) **316:** 439–440.
80. Beauvois, M. F. (1982). Optic aphasia: A process of interaction between vision and language. *Philos. Trans. R. Soc. London, Ser. B* **289:** 35–47.
81. Shallice, T. (1988). Specialization within the semantic system. *Cognit. Neuropsychol.* **5:** 133–142.
82. Riddoch, M. J., Humphreys, G. W., Coltheart, M., and Funnell, E. (1988). Semantic systems or system? Neuropsychological evidence re-examined. *Cognit. Neuropsychol.* **5:** 3–25.
83. Coslett, H. B., and Saffran, E. M. (1989). Optic aphasia and the right hemisphere: A replication and extension. *Brain Language* **43:** 148–161.
84. Hillis, A., and Caramazza, A. (1997). Cognitive and neural mechanisms underlying visual and semantic processing: Implications from "Optic Aphasia." *J. Cognit. Neurosci.* (in press).
85. Butterworth, B., and Howard, D. (1987). Paragrammatisms. *Cognition* **26:** 1–37.
86. Miceli, G., Mazzucci, A., Menn, L., and Goodglass, H. (1983). Contrasting cases of Italian agrammatic aphasia without comprehension disorder. *Brain Language* **19:** 65–97.
87. Saffran, E. M., Berndt, R. S., and Schwartz, M. F. (1989). The quantitative analysis of agrammatic production: Procedure and data. *Brain Language* **37:** 440–479.
88. Kolk, H., van Grunsven, M., and Keyser, A. (1985). On parallelism between production and comprehension in agrammatism. In *Agrammatism* (M. L. Kean, ed.). Academic Press, Orlando, FL.
89. Berndt, R. (1991). Sentence processing in aphasia. In *Acquired Aphasia* (M. T. Sarno, ed.). Academic Press, San Diego, CA.
90. Bock, K., and Levelt, W. (1994). Language production: Grammatical encoding. In *Handbook of Psycholinguistics* (M. Gernsbacher, ed.). Academic Press, San Diego, CA.
91. Saffran, E. M., Schwartz, M. F., and Marin, O. S. M. (1980). Evidence from aphasia: Isolating the components of a production model. In *Language Production* (B. Butterworth, ed.), Vol. 1. Academic Press, London.
92. Mitchum, C., and Berndt, R. S. (1989). Verb retrieval and sentence production. Paper presented at the Academy of Aphasia, Santa Fe, NM.
93. Lapointe, S. G., and Dell, G. S. (1989). A synthesis of some recent work in sentence production. In *Linguistic Structure in Language Processing* (G. N. Carlson and M. K. Tanenhaus, eds.). Kluwer Academic Publishers, Dordrecht, The Netherlands.
94. Caramazza, A., and Hillis, A. (1989). The disruption of sentence production: Some dissociations. *Brain Language* **36:** 625–650.
95. Stemberger, J. P. (1984). Structural errors in normal and agrammatic speech. *Cognit. Neuropsychol.* **1:** 281–313.
96. Caramazza, A., and Zurif, E. B. (1976). Dissociation of algorithmic and heuristic processes in language comprehension: Evidence from aphasia. *Brain Language* **3:** 572–582.
97. Berndt, R. S., and Caramazza, A. (1980). A redefinition of the syndrome of Broca's aphasia: Implications from a neuropsychological model of language. *Appl. Psycholinguistics* **1:** 225–278.
98. Caramazza, A., and Miceli, G. (1991). Selective impairment of thematic role assignment in sentence processing. *Brain Language* **41:** 402–436.
99. Martin, R. C., and Blossom-Stach, C. (1986). Evidence of syntactic deficits in a fluent aphasiac. *Brain Language* **28:** 196–234.
100. Linebarger, M., Schwartz, M. F., and Saffran, E. M. (1983). Sensitivity to grammatical structure in so-called agrammatic aphasics. *Cognition* **13:** 361–392.
101. Zurif, E. B., Swinney, D., Prather, P., Solomon, J., and Bushnell, C. (1993). An on-line analysis of syntactic processing in Broca's and Wernicke's aphasia. *Brain Language* **45:** 448–464.
102. Schwartz, M. F., Linebarger, M. C., Saffran, E. M., and Pate, D. S. (1987). Syntactic transparency and sentence interpretation in aphasia. *Language Cognit. Process.* **2:** 85–113.
103. Byng, S. (1988). Sentence processing deficits: Theory and therapy. *Cognit. Neuropsychol.* **5:** 629–676.
104. Schwartz, M., Saffran, E., Fink, R., Myers, J., and Martin, N. (1994). Mapping therapy: A treatment programme for agrammatism. *Aphasiology* **8:** 19–54.
105. Martin, R. C. (1987). Articulatory and phonological deficits in short-term memory and their relation to syntactic processing. *Brain Language* **32:** 137–158.
106. Caplan, D., and Hildebrandt, N. (1988). *Disorders of Syntactic Comprehension.* MIT Press, Cambridge, MA.
107. Martin, N., and Saffran, E. M. (1992). A computational account of deep dysphasia: Evidence from a single case study. *Brain Language* **43:** 240–274.
108. Shallice, T., and Vallar, G. (1990). The impairment of auditory-verbal short-term storage. In *Neuropsychological Impairments of Short-Term Memory* (G. Vallar and T. Shallice, eds.), pp. 11–53. Cambridge University Press, Cambridge, UK.
109. Butterworth, B., Campbell, R., and Howard, D. (1986). The uses of short-term memory: A case study. *Q. J. Exp. Psychol.* **38A:** 705–737.
110. Martin, R. C. (1993). Short-term memory and sentence processing: Evidence from neuropsychology. *Memory Cognit.* **21:** 176–183.
111. Waters, G., Caplan, D., and Hildebrandt, N. (1988). On the structure of verbal short-term memory and its functional role in sentence comprehension: Evidence from neuropsychology. *Cognit. Neuropsychol.* **8:** 81–126.

112. Carpenter, P. A., and Daneman, M. (1981). Lexical retrieval and error recovery in reading: A model based on eye fixations. *J. Verb. Learn. Verb. Behav.* **20:** 137–160.
113. Marslen-Wilson, W. D., Brown, C. M., and Tyler, L. K. (1988). Lexical representations in spoken language comprehension. *Language Cognit. Process.* **3:** 1–16.
114. Martin, R. C., Shelton, J., and Yaffee, L. (1994). Language processing and working memory: Evidence for separate phonological and semantic capacities. *J. Memory Language* **33:** 83–111.
115. Martin, R. C., and Romani, C. (1984). Verbal working memory and sentence comprehension: A multiple-components view. *Neuropsychology* **8:** 506–523.
116. Dejerine, J. (1892). Contribution à l'étude anatomoclinique et cliniques des différentes variétés de cécité verbale. *Mem. Soc. Biol.* **4:** 61–90.
117. Ellis, A. W., and Young, A. W. (1988). *Human Cognitive Neuropsychology.* Erlbaum, London.
118. Marshall, J. C., and Newcombe, F. (1973). Patterns of paralexia: A psycholinguistic approach. *J. Psycholinguistic Res.* **2:** 175–199.
119. Coltheart, M. (1978). Lexical access in simple reading tasks. In *Strategies of Information Processing* (G. Underwood, ed.), pp. 151–216. Academic Press, London.
120. Behrman, M., and Bub, D. (1992). Surface dyslexia and dysgraphia: Dual routes, single lexicon. *Cognit. Neuropsychol.* **9:** 209–251.
121. Bub, D., Cancelliere, A., and Kertesz, A. (1985). Whole word and analytic translation of spelling to sound in a non-semantic reader. In *Surface Dyslexia: Neuropsychological and Cognitive Studies of Phonological Reading* (K. E. Patterson, J. C. Marshall, and M. Coltheart, eds.). Erlbaum, London.
122. Howard, D., and Franklin, S. (1987). Three ways for understanding written words and their use in two contrasting cases of surface dyslexia. In *Language Perception and Production: Common Processes in Listening, Speaking, Reading and Writing* (D. A. Allport, D. MacKay, W. Prinz, and E. Sheerer, eds.). Academic Press, London.
123. Hinton, G. E., and Shallice, T. (1991). Lesioning an attractor network: Investigations of acquired dyslexia. *Psychol. Rev.* **98:** 74–95.
124. Schwartz, M. F., Saffran, E. M., and Marin, O. S. M. (1980). Fractionating the reading process in dementia: Evidence for word-specific print-to-sound associations. In *Deep Dyslexia* (M. Coltheart, K. E. Patterson, and J. C. Marshall, eds.). Routledge & Kegan Paul, London.
125. Funnell, E. (1983). Phonological processes in reading: New evidence from acquired dysgraphia. *Br. J. Psychol.* **74:** 159–180.
126. Miceli, G., Giustolisi, L., and Caramazza, A. (1991). The interaction of lexical and non-lexical processing mechanisms: Evidence from anomia. *Cortex* **27:** 57–80.
127. Patterson, K. E., Seidenberg, M. S., and McClelland, J. L. (1989). Connections and disconnections in a computational model of reading processes. In *Parallel Distributed Processing: Implications for Psychology and Neurobiology* (R. G. M. Morris, ed.). Oxford University Press (Clarendon), London and New York.
128. Plaut, D., and Shallice, T. (1993). Deep dyslexia: A case study of connectionist neuropsychology. *Cognit. Neuropsychol.* **10:** 377–500.
129. Seidenberg, M. S., and McClelland, J. L. (1988). A distributed, developmental model of visual word recognition and naming. *Psychol. Rev.* **96:** 523–568.

C H A P T E R

58

Hemispheric Specialization

Stephen M. Kosslyn, Michael S. Gazzaniga, Albert M. Galaburda, and Carolyn Rabin

The study of cerebral *lateralization* examines the localization of function on one side of the brain in preference to the other. It is dependent on the more general study of the functions of various parts and systems within the brain. Efforts to characterize the hemispheres in terms of dichotomies—the left is analytic, the right holistic, the left is verbal, the right perceptual, and so on—have failed to characterize hemispheric differences. An historic representation of brain lateralization is depicted in Fig. 58.1.

The literature on cerebral lateralization contains an unusually large number of irreproducible and apparently contradictory results. This state of affairs probably reflects at least three difficulties: First, any complex function is likely to be accomplished by a host of more specialized processes, not all of which need be lateralized the same way. Second, the methodologies used to study lateralization are sometimes unreliable. Third, at least some hemispheric differences may depend on attention, and attention can be altered by the precise requirements of the task.

In this chapter, we focus on the two areas that have been studied most intensively and from which the most coherent picture of lateralization has emerged—namely, vision (including visual attention) and language. We begin with a description of the methods used to assess cerebral specialization. We then briefly review key anatomical features that differ between the hemispheres; these structural differences may, at least in some cases, have direct implications for function. We then turn to key theories and findings of how the hemispheres differ in their abilities to encode visual and spatial information, and to key findings about the lateralization of language, including speech encoding, comprehension, and production. We conclude with brief observations about the status of this field.

METHODS OF STUDYING CEREBRAL SPECIALIZATION

The literature on cerebral asymmetry is fraught with inconsistencies and seeming contradictions. Because part of the problem may stem from the nature of the methods used, it is worth considering the primary methods used to study hemispheric specialization. Studies have been carried out on subjects with various types of localized brain damage and on normal subjects, and rely on anatomical investigations, carefully designed behavioral experiments, and various imaging techniques.

Brain Damage from Stroke Is Often Unilateral

Brain damage disrupts the behavior of those who suffer it. Consequently, some researchers attempt to infer the nature of hemispheric specialization by observing the selective deficits exhibited in patients who have had strokes, injury, brain surgery, or disease. Neuroimaging methods make it possible to select patient groups whose lesions are rather precisely localized to a specific anatomical region, as shown in Fig. 58.2.

It is tempting to presume a direct mapping between a behavioral dysfunction and the processing carried out by the damaged structures. (Wernicke, Broca, and the other founders of founders of behavioral neurology established this tradition.) The fact that an ability is disrupted following brain damage, however, does not imply that the lesioned area is responsible for that ability. Consider Gregory's[1] classic example: if one removes a resistor from a radio and it squawks, this does not mean that the resistor is a squawk suppressor.

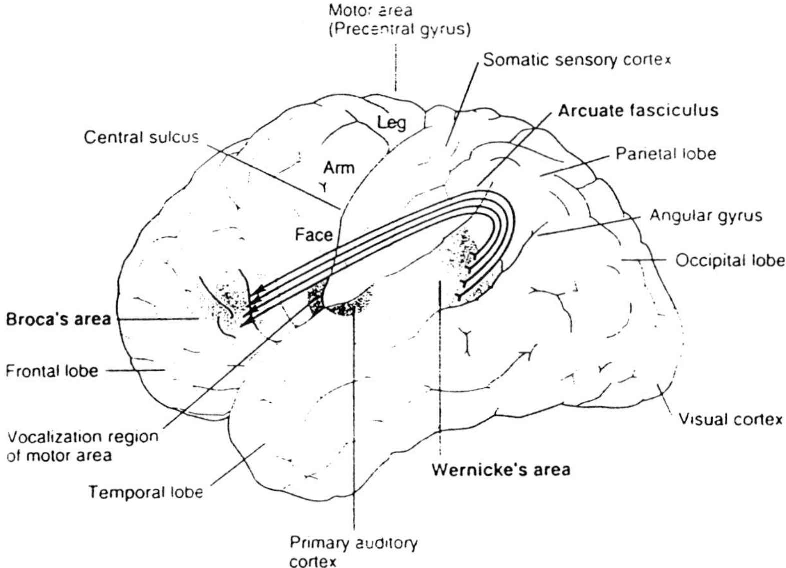

FIGURE 58.1 The classical view of hemispheric function. Language areas assigned at the end of the 19th century.

The functional consequences of brain damage may not directly reflect the function of the damaged tissue for several reasons. For example, nondamaged regions may suffer a kind of shock when they are deprived of their normal inputs from the damaged area, which causes them to perform poorly and produce symptoms. In addition, nondamaged parts of the brain sometimes may be capable of compensating, at least in part, for damaged regions, and deficits may reflect the operation of these compensatory processes. Furthermore, the activities of most brain-damaged people are slowed down. The cortico–subcortical feedback loops that are necessary for alertness are disrupted. Because such activation is essential for information processing throughout the brain, a reduction in activation can produce numerous deficits. More complex processing typically requires greater amounts of activation than less complex processing; hence, more complex processing may be more severely impaired than less complex processing if the activation level is decreased. The appearance of a hemisphere-specific deficit can occur if more complex processing typically takes place in one hemisphere. Such processing requires more activation and hence is affected when less complex processing is not. Thus, the appearance of specificity can be misleading.

The Study of Patients with Surgical Division of the Hemispheres Has Provided Valuable Insights into Hemispheric Specialization

Intractable epileptics who have undergone surgical division of the major fiber track between the hemispheres, the corpus callosum (split-brain surgery), form a group tailor-made for the study of hemispheric lateralization. In certain cases, when extensive efforts to medically control a patient's epileptic seizures have been unsuccessful, surgical division of the corpus callosum and anterior commissure is carried out, effectively severing communication between the hemispheres of the forebrain. In 1961, a series of studies was initiated on patients who had undergone this procedure, with the object of investigating the lateralization of hemispheric function.[2,3] Because the callosal surgery inflicted discrete damage to a fiber system and not to nuclear areas, one of the immediate appeals of such a study was that it presented an opportunity to study the separate functions of the two cerebral hemispheres in the absence of focal damage.

Studies of Subjects with Split Brains Frequently Rely on Separate Visual or Auditory Inputs to the Left and Right Visual or Auditory Fields

Researchers often use one of two methods to test hemisphere function in people in whom the corpus callosum has been severed. When **divided-visual-field presentation** is used, a stimulus is presented briefly to the left or right of a fixation point. The stimulus is presented so briefly that the subject cannot move his or her eyes; consequently, the image of the stimulus will strike only a single hemiretina (in both eyes). Each hemiretina projects to a single hemisphere. Therefore, a visual stimulus presented to the right visual field

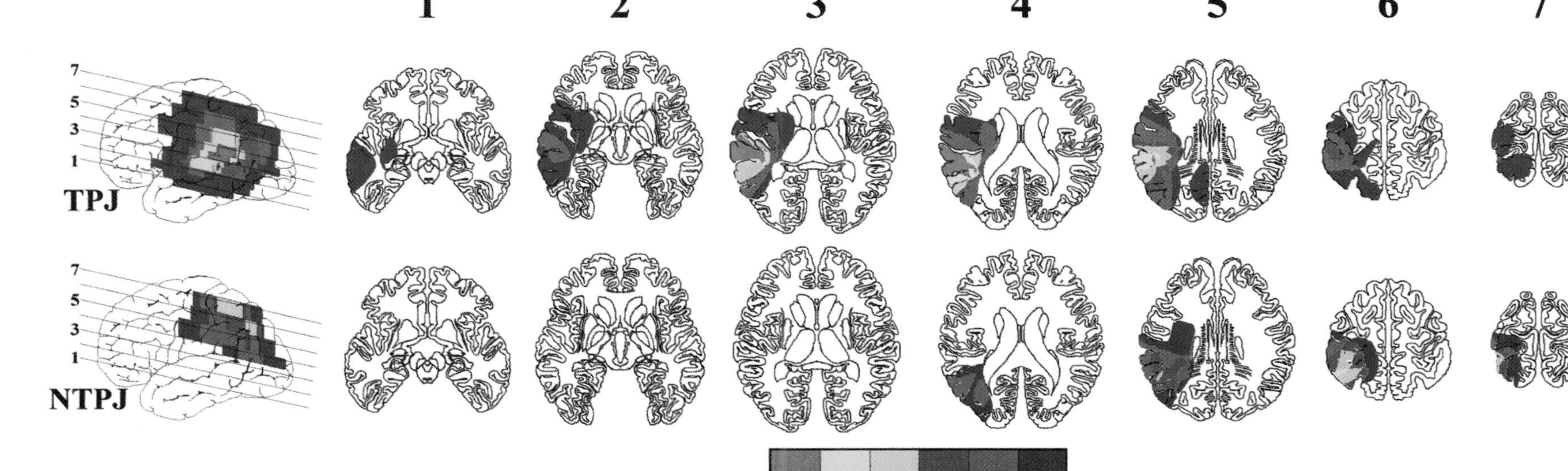

FIGURE 58.2 Modern methods of neuroimaging of brain structure allow combining lesions over subjects to study the function of a brain area as is done here for studies of the temporal–parietal junction (TPJ). The methods allow researchers to specify the location of a lesion in different brains using the same reference points and hence to be able to compare lesions and their effects across different patients. (Reproduced by courtesy of Robert Rafal, University of California—Davis.

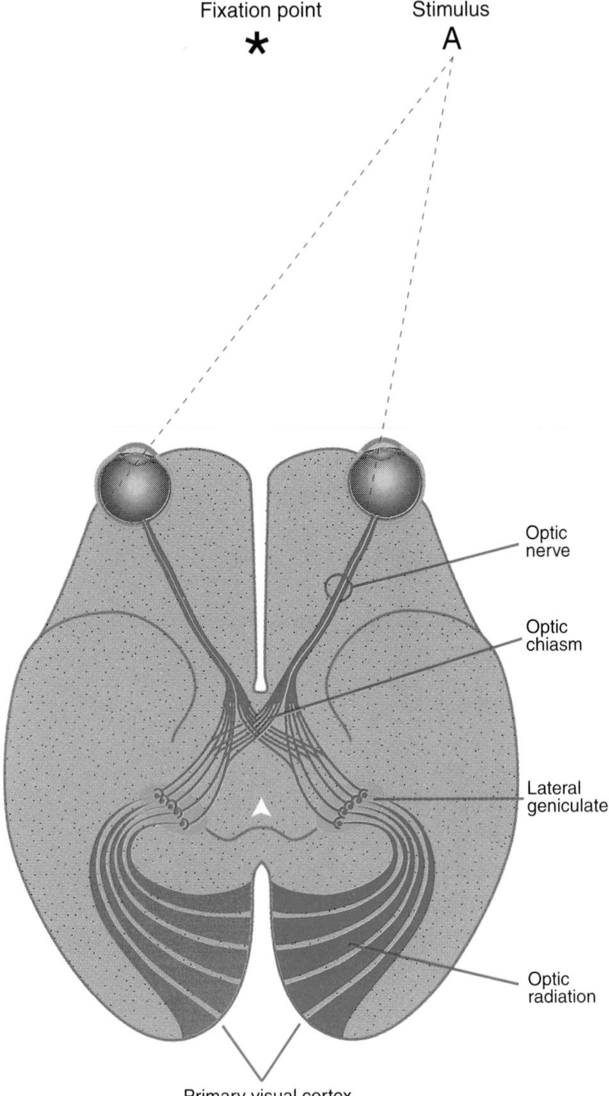

FIGURE 58.3 Connections of the retina to the visual cortex in the human brain showing how the visual fields project to separate primary visual areas of the two hemispheres. Signals from the right side of the retinas (left visual field) of both eyes travel through the optic nerve, optic tract, and optic radiations to the primary visual cortex in the right hemisphere, whereas signals from the left retinas (right visual field) travel to the left hemisphere.

will be processed initially by the left hemisphere and one projected to the left visual field by the right hemisphere (see Fig. 58.3). When **dichotic listening** is used, speech is presented to both ears simultaneously; one ear receives a specific stimulus that must be recalled or evaluated in some way. If subjects are listening to different messages in the two ears, one message is more likely to be processed by the left hemisphere and one by the right. However, the projections are not segregated as sharply as those involved in vision: approximately 40% of the projections from each ear go to the ipsilateral (i.e., same side) hemisphere. In contrast, a visual stimulus whose location is removed from the fixation point by 1.5° or so of visual angle will be projected almost exclusively to the contralateral hemisphere. Dichotic listening studies are not used as often as divided-visual-field studies with patients with split brains.

Regardless of the method used, caution must be excercised in interpreting results from such patients. These subjects do not have normal brains. After suffering for years from severe epilepsy (and proving to be unresponsive to traditional drug therapy), they have undergone a treatment of last resort—surgical severence of the corpus callosum. Even if their brains had been normal at the outset (which they were not), they clearly were not normal after the surgery. The normal brain exists as an integrated system, so that when the hemispheres are isolated, certain regions of the brain probably do not operate as they usually do. Furthermore, functional specialization may be masked by attentional deficits in patients with split brains. Such patients are interesting to study, however, because their brains reveal what kinds of functions can be performed by distinct processes; the same process cannot be performing two different tasks if each of those tasks is accomplished more efficiently by the opposite hemisphere. In addition, findings with such patients can indicate the kinds of information that cross between hemispheres via subcortical connections.

Behavioral Studies with Normal Subjects Have Also Indicated Hemispheric Specialization

Normal subjects have also been tested in divided-visual-field and dichotic listening experiments. Normal subjects tested in divided-visual-field studies should be faster and / or more accurate when the stimulus is initially presented to the hemisphere specialized for the appropriate processing. When the stimulus is presented to the other hemisphere, more time should be required: this hemisphere is less efficient at this type of processing, and the more efficient hemisphere does not receive information about the stimulus until it has crossed the callosum (which takes approximately 15 ms). Moreover, when information is transmitted across the corpus callosum, it may be somewhat degraded.[4] The logic underlying a dichotic listening study is similar. When a stimulus is presented to the ear projecting primarily to the hemisphere that is best at performing the task, the subject should perform better than when the stimulus is presented to the other ear.

The logic of these studies has several problems. Perhaps most crucially, as will be discussed later, differences in attention may overwhelm processing specialization.[5-7] Thus, the results from divided-visual-field and dichotic listening studies are sometimes difficult to replicate.[8] Not only may the outcomes of divided-visual-field experiments be affected by many different factors,[9,10] but these biases may vary between individuals.[11] In addition, people differ in the characteristic "level of arousal" of the hemispheres; the level of arousal may selectively affect the ease of performing different types of processing, with more complex processing requiring a greater level of arousal. By analogy, if one is sleepy, difficult tasks (e.g., complex math problems) are even more difficult to do, but simple ones (e.g., adding 2 + 2) are barely affected.

Imaging Methods Can Also Indicate Hemispheric Differences

Another way of investigating lateralization is measuring brain activity at specific sites while a person performs a task. Some of these methods, such as electroencephalography (EEG) and event-related potentials (ERPs), entail recording electrical activity from scalp electrodes (see Chapter 54, Box 54.1 and Fig. 54.2). These methods are noninvasive, have good temporal resolution, and are inexpensive. However, the electric current that these methods record is distorted as it travels across the brain, through the skull, and across the scalp. This distortion makes it difficult to infer the locus of the neural generator.

Such distortion can be circumvented by the use of magnetoencephalography (MEG), which relies on recording magnetic fields; these fields do not traverse the cortex or scalp, and they are not distorted by bone. Moreover, MEG allows one to infer the location of the dipole that gives rise to a specific field. Hence, this procedure has good temporal and spatial resolution. The main drawback of using MEG, aside from the high cost, is that the alignment of the dendrites that produce the magnetic dipoles does not allow one to record from gyri. Nevertheless, the technique is useful for studying events in sulci.

Cerebral laterality has also been measured with a variety of relatively invasive, radiation-based techniques that measure cerebral blood flow. These techniques differ in both temporal and spatial resolution, as well as in cost and availability. Positron emission tomography (PET) is one such method and single photon emission tomography (SPECT) another. Functional magnetic resonance imaging (fMRI) is also showing great promise as a noninvasive method (see Chapter 14).

These methods allow researchers to observe neural activity in awake, behaving human beings. However, the finding of greater activation in a specific locus is often difficult to interpret. Does the activation indicate excitatory processes or inhibitory processes? Does the activation arise in a location or is it an indirect consequence of activity in another location, which releases inhibition? Moreover, it is not clear that more blood flow always arises following more processing: If an individual is very efficient at a specific kind of processing, relatively few additional nutrients or little oxygen may be required by the neural substrate.

In addition, many of the brain-scanning techniques often rely on averaging data across subjects; however, brains differ enormously, both in the sizes of specific regions and in their relative locations. Thus, the best possible level of spatial resolution is decreased by averaging data from different brains. Furthermore, most brain-scanning studies involve a comparison of activity in two tasks that are designed to differ in a specific way. However, there is no guarantee that researchers actually understand how the tasks differ. If there is no difference in blood flow between two tasks, whether a given process was present in both or in neither task cannot be determined; "automatic" processes, such as those involved in naming that give rise to the Stroop effect, may be very difficult to study using these techniques. The Stroop effect occurs when the color named by a word interferes with the ease of naming a different colored ink that is used to print the word; for example, if the word "RED" were written in blue ink, people would have trouble naming the color of the ink compared to when the ink is the color named by the word (see Chapter 54).

Despite these potential problems, combinations of methods can lead to firm conclusions at the level of hemispheric function. If the same hemispheric difference is found with multiple methods, it is unlikely to reflect methodological differences.

Summary

Brain damage can selectively impair the functioning of one or the other cerebral hemisphere. Thus, we can learn about the functions of the hemispheres in part by studying patients who have suffered lateralized (i.e., restricted to one side) brain damage. However, it is an error to assume that the deficits patients show directly reflect damage to the processes that normally carry out the impaired function. Patients who have had the two hemispheres disconnected (for medical reasons) provide an opportunity to study the functions of the isolated hemispheres. However, the mere fact that the hemispheres are isolated is not normal; the normal brain functions as a single system. Dichotic listening (where different inputs are presented to different ears) can also be used to study the specializations of the cerebral hemispheres; however, auditory information is not delivered solely to one or the other hemisphere. Normal subjects can be studied using divided visual field techniques (i.e., presenting a stimulus to one side quickly, so that subjects cannot move their eyes to see it) or dichotic listening techniques, but the results may reflect attentional processes as well as differences in the functioning of the cerebral hemispheres. Brain imaging methods (such as PET and fMRI) provide powerful tools for studying cerebral lateralization, but even they have limitations (such as in the study of automatic or very efficient processes, which do not produce large increases in cerebral blood flow). The best strategy for studying the functioning of the cerebral hemispheres is to use multiple techniques. Because each technique has different potential drawbacks, a result found using more than one technique probably reflects actual differences in the functioning of the hemispheres.

DIFFERENCES IN HEMISPHERIC ANATOMY

The cerebral hemispheres differ in their anatomical characteristics in several ways, and these anatomical differences probably give rise to different functional properties.

Anatomical Asymmetry Is Found in the Temporal Lobe

In 1968, Norman Geschwind and Walter Levitsky[12] reported their findings of asymmetry in the planum temporale in 100 autopsied human brains. They found that 65% of the sample showed a longer left planum temporale, whereas the right planum was longer in only 11%; both plana were equal in the remaining 24%. The results were highly significant and were essentially replicated by subsequent studies.[13,14] In a study that included the brains of newborns,[15] the left planum was larger in 64% and the right in 10%. A more recent cadaver study[16] found that two-thirds of 106 brains showed a larger left planum.

Asymmetry is also found in Heschl's gyrus and the sylvian fissure. Heschl's gyrus represents the anterior border of the planum temporale and contains the primary auditory cortex. Asymmetry is seen in the orientation of Heschl's gyri: The left one is usually more oblique, less transverse than the right one.[17] In addition, in right-handers, the left sylvian fissure is more horizontal than the right.[18] (Fig. 58.4). Where the fissures are asymmetric the pattern is that of two left, rather than two right, sylvian fissures. This is by and large also true for the planum temporale. Left-handers often present this pattern.

Hemispheric Asymmetries Are Also Found in Fetal and Infant Brains

Gross anatomical asymmetries are present in the cerebral cortex before birth. The sylvian fissures are visibly asymmetric from about the middle of gestation, demonstrating the pattern usually seen in the adult human. The planum temporale is also grossly asymmetric before the end of pregnancy.[19] In a study that examined 14 brains from newborns, the planum temporale was larger on the left side in 79% of the cases.[20]

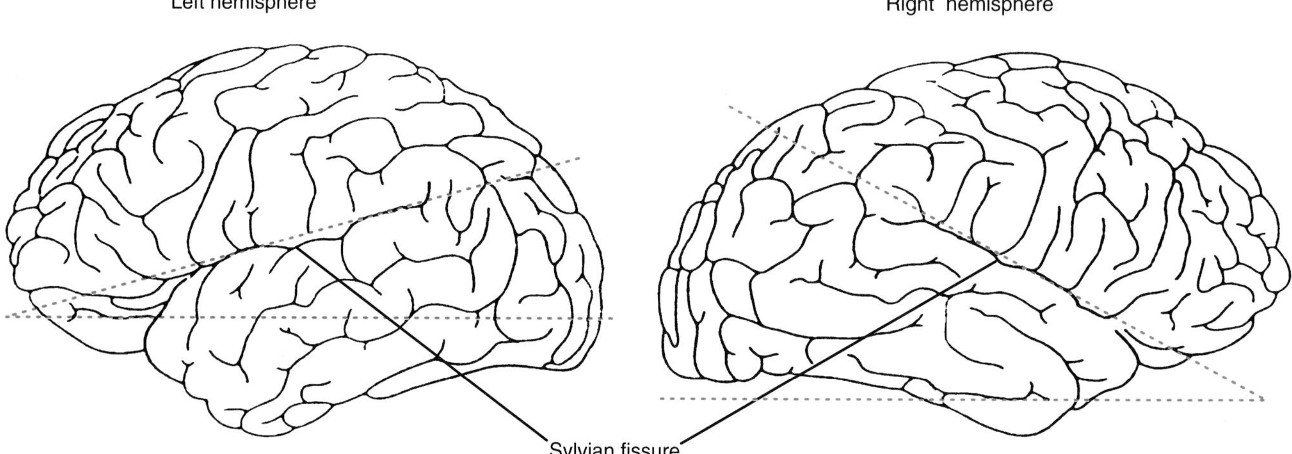

FIGURE 58.4 Differences between the temporal areas of the left and right hemisphere. In most right-handed people, the sylvian fissure in the left hemisphere is longer and runs at a shallower angle than the fissure in the right hemisphere. In left-handers, the fissures are more often symmetric. Adapted from Geschwind.[19]

Planimetric measurements of 100 adult and 100 newborn and fetal brains showed that the average surface area of the right planum temporale was 55% of the left in adults and 67% in the younger brains.[14] If this difference is significant, does this indicate that more individuals with larger right plana do not make it to adulthood? The authors of this study also noted that the planum temporale asymmetry was visible beginning in the 29th week of gestation. The right Heschl's gyrus was doubled on the right side in 54% of the cases and on the left in 18%.[19]

Hemispheric Asymmetries May Reflect Specializations for Language

Several cortical areas implicated in language function show asymmetry. For instance, area Tpt, which is located on the posterior one-third of the superior temporal gyrus extending onto the planum temporale, is larger on the left side in the majority of brains.[21] Asymmetry of area Tpt correlates positively with asymmetry of the planum temporale. The frontal operculum contains predominantly cytoarchitectonic areas 44 and 45; the former covers most of the pars opercularis (the foot of Broca) and the latter covers mainly the pars triangularis (the cape of Broca). In a collection of neurologically normal brains, area 44 was larger in 6 of 10 brains, nearly symmetric in 3, and larger on the right side in 1 brain.[21]

Hemispheric Asymmetries Have Been Demonstrated by Imaging Devices in Living Subjects

Pneumoencephalograms, by which air is injected into the cerebral ventricles and X rays are taken, show that the left occipital horn of the lateral ventricle is larger in 57% of subjects, whereas 13% show the opposite asymmetry. Among right-handed subjects, the standard asymmetry is found 60% of the time, whereas in left-handed subjects, it is seen only 38% of the time. Symmetric horns are seen in right-handers 40% of the time compared to 62% of the time in left-handers. The left sylvian fissure is longer and straighter than the right in carotid arteriograms in 67% of right-handers compared to only 29% of left-handed or ambidextrous individuals.[22] Note that these findings in living subjects undergoing special X rays are comparable to those seen in autopsy studies (Fig. 58.4).

The Wada test reveals a correlation between the side of the longer and straighter sylvian fissure and language lateralization. In this test, amobarbital is injected into the internal carotid artery to produce transient aphasia. A study found that 66% of subjects having left hemisphere lateralization as measured by the Wada test showed a longer sylvian fissure on the left, whereas only 35% of those having right hemisphere specialization for language had this pattern.[23]

In computerized axial tomograms of the brain, the right frontal lobe is often seen to protrude ahead of the left (right frontal petalia), whereas the left occipital lobe tends to protrude farther toward the back than the right (left occipital petalia). Left occipital petalia is seen in 78% of right-handers, whereas the lobes in left-handers are once again more often symmetric.

Magnetic resonance imaging (MRI) lends itself to accurate reconstructions of the planum temporale and measurements of asymmetry. By this technique, the planum temporale was larger in the left for righthanders but not lefthanders.[27] However, another study using MRI[16] did not find the left planum asymmetry when a method that included (and perhaps overestimated) folding of the cortex was used.

Asymmetries Can Extend to the Cellular Level

In general, no obvious qualitative differences between the two sides of asymmetric architectonic areas are apparent at the cellular level. However, the distributions of one neuronal type may differ in the two hemispheres in areas of cerebral asymmetry.[25] This difference was revealed on examining cell packing densities of several types of neurons stained by immunohistochemical methods in the rat brain and comparing the left and right sides in areas of asymmetry. There was no overall relationship between cell packing density and asymmetry; however, the density of parvalbumin-positive neurons was greater on the larger side in asymmetric cases. Parvalbumin-positive neurons are characterized by having long projections, so that a preponderance of these would indicate that the larger (dominant?) side is more connected to subcortical structures and to the opposite hemisphere than the smaller side. This difference in cellular distribution would be compatible with a different functional capacity on the two sides.

Hemispheric differences in connections have been found only in the parietal eye of the lizard and in other nonmammalian brains. However, most research on connectivity has not specifically compared the two sides. Track tracing methods for studying connections do not lend themselves easily to the kind of quantitative comparisons needed for asymmetry work. On the other hand, the findings with regard to parvalbumin-positive neurons suggest that these are subtle connectional hemispheric differences.

In an attempt to circumvent methodological limitations that make equivalent tracer injections in the two hemispheres impossible, researchers sectioned the corpus callosum in the rat and looked at degenerating axonal terminals on the two sides of the brain in relation to the asymmetry of targeted architectonic areas, for instance, areas 18.[26] They found that there were fewer callosal connections between hemispheres for asymmetric areas than for similar areas that are more symmetric. Cortical areas receive callosal projections in only some locations, others being acallosal. Developmentally, the number of callosal connections that reach under the cortical plate is larger than the number that ultimately penetrate it and establish connectivity with neurons in the cortex.[27–30] Of those that do not penetrate, some are withdrawn and disappear, while others are rerouted. In symmetric areas fewer neurons appear to be withdrawn, while in asymmetric areas more are withdrawn. In the latter, whether neurons are rerouted or simply disappear is not known. More rerouting in the asymmetric cases would mean that such areas would connect within the same hemisphere rather than across the hemispheres. Asymmetric areas would be more intrahemispherically connected, while symmetric areas would be more interhemispherically connected. This difference could produce important differences in inter- and intrahemispheric communication.

Researchers do not know how various regions of the two hemispheres come to be of a different size. Furthermore, they do not know what determines variability in side differences. For instance, why is it that some areas are severalfold larger on one side than the other, whereas in other areas, the sizes of the two sides differ by only a few percentage points? And why is an area only slightly asymmetric in some individuals but strikingly asymmetric in anothers? Another important question is whether variability in the directionality and magnitude of asymmetry alters the functional characteristics of the brain.

Summary

Asymmetry in cortical areas encompasses changes in the volume of architectonic areas, differences between sides in overall numbers and densities of some neurons, and variation in the patterns of callosal connections. Indirect evidence suggests that asymmetry is determined early during corticogenesis, probably when the neuroblast pools are being established on the two sides of the midline of the neural tube. The gross anatomical and histological characteristics of symmetric and asymmetric cortical areas do not support the notion that cerebral dominance reflects simply the existence of the appropriate anatomical substrate in the left hemisphere, the right hemisphere, or a bit of each. Instead, symmetric and asymmetric brain regions appear to differ in the size and composition of their neural and connectional elements, so that in the intact brain, they are likely to perform tasks in a different way rather than with just different degrees of hemispheric participation. Thus, pinpointing cerebral dominance is important not only in understanding the effects of injury to one or the other hemisphere, but also in elucidating functional properties of symmetric and asymmetric cortical areas. It is this latter variation that provides the species with desirable and sometimes problematic individual variation.

LATERALIZATION IN VISUAL INFORMATION PROCESSING

The discovery that the cerebral hemispheres differ in their visual abilities was made at about the same time that the lateralization of language ability was discovered. Since then, scientists have learned an enormous amount about vision, and this knowledge has in turn promoted discoveries of how visual processing is lateralized in the cerebral hemispheres.

Visual Attention Studies Reflect Differences between the Hemispheres

The attentional and perceptual abilities of split-brain patients have been extensively explored, and visual perception has been the easiest faculty to study. After cortical disconnection, perceptual information does not pass between the two cerebral hemispheres, but the supporting cognitive processes of attentional mechanisms do sometimes interact. Findings from visual perception studies of split-brain patients are summarized in this section.

Simple perceptual interactions are not seen. Split-brain patients are not able to cross-integrate visual information between the two halves of their visual fields. When visual information is lateralized, to either the left or the right disconnected hemisphere (see Fig. 58.2) by presentation of stimuli to either the left or right visual field only, the unstimulated hemisphere cannot use the information for perceptual analysis. This is also true for stereognostic information presented to each hand. While the general presence or absence of touch stimulation to any part of the body is noted by either hemisphere, patterned somatosensory information is lateralized. Thus, an object held in the left hand cannot help the right hand find an identical object.

Humans show visual midline overlap phenomenon. There is some nasotemporal overlap at the retinal vertical meridian in cat and monkey.[31,32] In a striped display that straddles the two visual half fields, visual information is sent to both the left and the right visual cortices. Whether the anatomical projections have any functional significance has never been examined in animal studies, but the issue has been examined in split-brain subjects.[33,34] An image stabilizer combined with a Purkinje eye-tracker, used for careful assessment of the visual midline of two split-brain patients, revealed an area, no more than 2° wide, at the veridical midline where visual information appears to be available to both halves of the brain. Within this strip of overlap, the signals conveyed to each hemisphere from the contralateral hemiretina appear to be weak or degraded. Stimuli could not be compared across the vertical meridian if these comparisons required detailed shape information or if the stimuli were presented for only 200 m. Thus, a "square" could not be compared to a "circle." Interhemispheric transfer is seen for crude spatial location information. Unlike the input visual and somatosensory cues, crude information concerning spatial locations can be cross-integrated.[35–37] In one set of experiments, a four-point grid was presented to each visual field. On a given trial, one of the positions on the grid was highlighted, and the subject was asked to move the eyes to the highlighted point within the visual field stimulated (Fig. 58.5A). Subsequently, the subject was required to move his eyes to the same relative point in the opposite visual field (Fig. 58.5B). Split-brain subjects were easily able to do this, thereby suggesting that some crude cross-integration of spatial information takes places. This was true even when the grid was randomly positioned in the tested field.

Spatial attention can be directed but not divided between the hemispheres. The finding that some type of spatial information remains integrated between the two halves of the brain raises the question: Are the attentional processes associated with spatial information affected by cortical disconnection surgery? A study using a protocol (see Chapter 54, Fig. 54.1) that capitalizes on priming phenomena[38] found that each hemisphere can direct attention to a point in either the left or the right visual field. The response latency to a peripheral visual target is reduced when observers have prior information regarding its spatial location, even when eye movements are prevented. Presumably, the spatial cue allows observers to direct their attention to the appropriate location prior to the onset of the target (see Fig. 58.5). When this protocol was used in split-brain subjects to measure the extent to which such attentional cues affect performance, the separated hemispheres were found not to be strictly independent in their control of spatial orientation. Rather, the two hemispheres rely on a common orienting system to maintain a single focus of attention. Thus, as with normal people, a cue to direct attention to a particular point in the visual field is used no matter which hemisphere is presented with the spatial cue.

The discovery that spatial attention can be directed with ease to either visual field raised the question whether each separate cognitive system in the split-brain patient could, if instructed to do so, independently direct attention to a particular part of its own visual field.[39] Can the right hemisphere direct attention to a point in the left visual field while the left brain simultaneously directs attention to a point in the right visual field? Normal subjects cannot so divide their attention. Can split-brain subjects with evident cognition in both hemispheres do so?

Results from several studies show that the split-brain patient is unable to divide spatial attention between the two halves of the brain. Only one integrated spatial attention system appears to remain intact following cortical disconnection. Thus, like neurologically intact observers, split-brain patients have a unifocal attentional system. They are unable to prepare for events in two spatially disparate locations.

Central Attentional Resources Are Shared by the Two Hemispheres

The dramatic effects of disconnecting the cerebral hemispheres on perception and cognition might suggest that each half of the brain possesses its own attentional resources. If this is true, one would predict that the cognitive operations of one half brain would little influence the cognitive activities of the other. The competing view is that the brain has a set of limited resources that manage such processes and when they are being applied to task A, fewer are available for task B. This model would predict that the harder hemisphere A worked on a task, the worse hemisphere B would do on a task of constant complexity.

Many studies have been carried out to investigate this issue and all confirm the notion that the central resources are limited.[40,41] In the original experiment, two series of geometric shapes were displayed concurrently to the left and right of central fixation and thus were lateralized to the right and left hemispheres, respectively. A unilateral probe figure subsequently appeared, and the observer indicated with a forced-choice key press whether it matched any of the items in the probed field. On half of the trials the same three figures were displayed in the two fields (the hard condition). On the other half, one hemisphere saw three items while the other saw only one stimulus presented three times (the easy condition). The results clearly

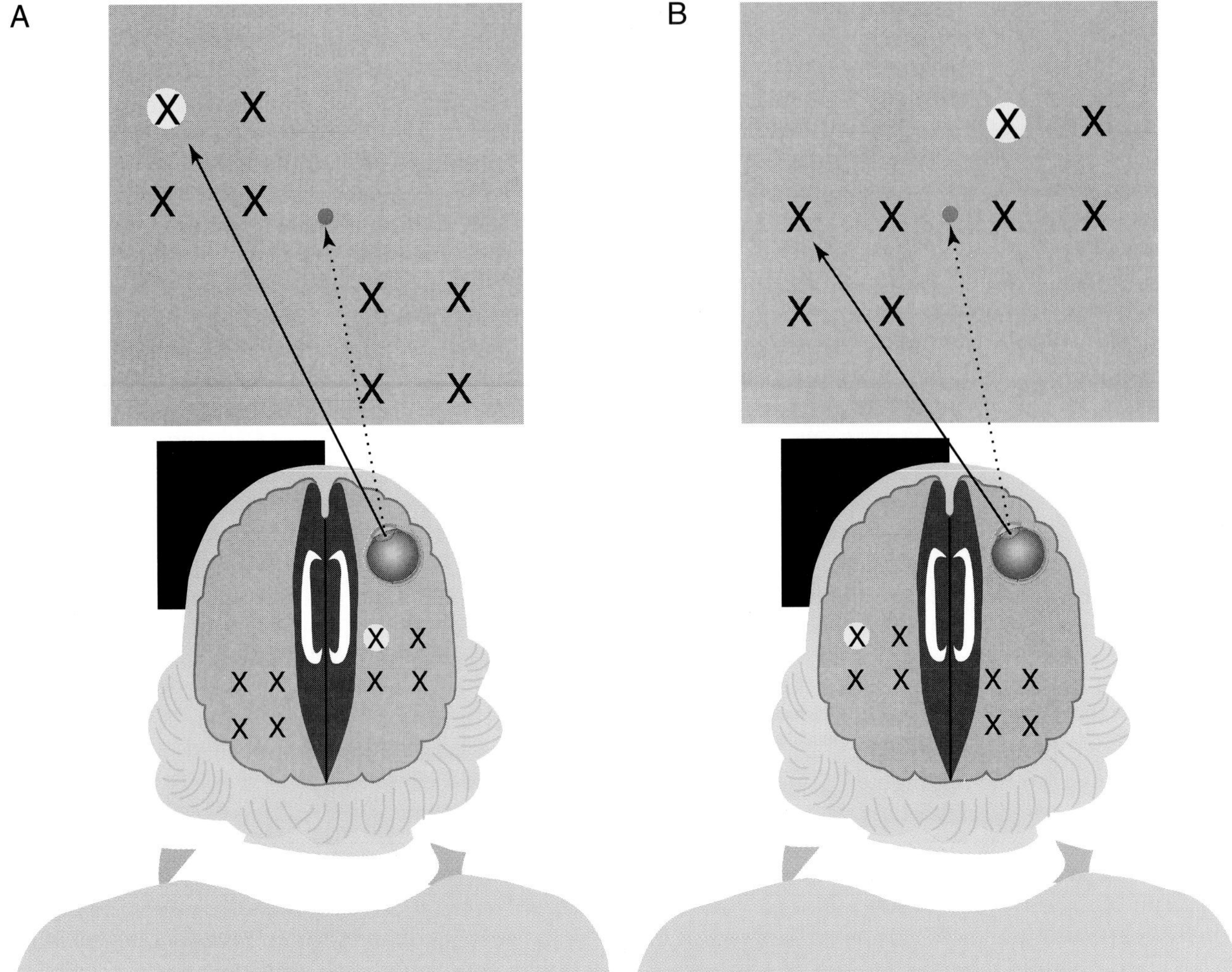

FIGURE 58.5 The method of cueing within and between visual fields used to study eye movements and covert attention in split-brain patients. On within-field trials (A) the eyes moved to the stimulus that was surrounded by the highlighted probe. On the between-field trials (B) the eyes also moved to the corresponding stimulus in the other hemifield.

showed that when one half of the brain was working on processing only one repeated stimulus, the opposite hemisphere performed better at recalling whether the probed stimulus was part of the original set of three stimuli. When both hemispheres were trying to process three stimuli, the performance of each was impaired. These overall findings have recently been replicated in a monkey model of these tasks.[42]

Visual Search Is Independent and Different in the Two Halves of the Brain

While the overall resources a brain commits to a task appear constant, the method by which they are deployed can vary. The more items presented to be analyzed in a visual array, the longer the analysis takes. Thus, after a baseline reaction time is established, normal controls require an additional 70 ms to respond to two more items and another 70 ms for an additional two items and so on. In split-brain subjects, when the items are distributed across the midline of the visual field (guided search) as opposed to all being in one visual field (Fig. 58.6A), the reaction time to added stimuli is cut almost in half.[43,44]

Each hemisphere uses a different strategy to examine the contents of its visual field.[45] The left dominant hemisphere utilizes a "guided" or "smart" strategy, whereas the right hemisphere does not (Fig. 58.6B). This means that the left hemisphere adopts a helpful cognitive strategy in solving the problem, whereas the right hemisphere does not possess those extra cognitive skills.

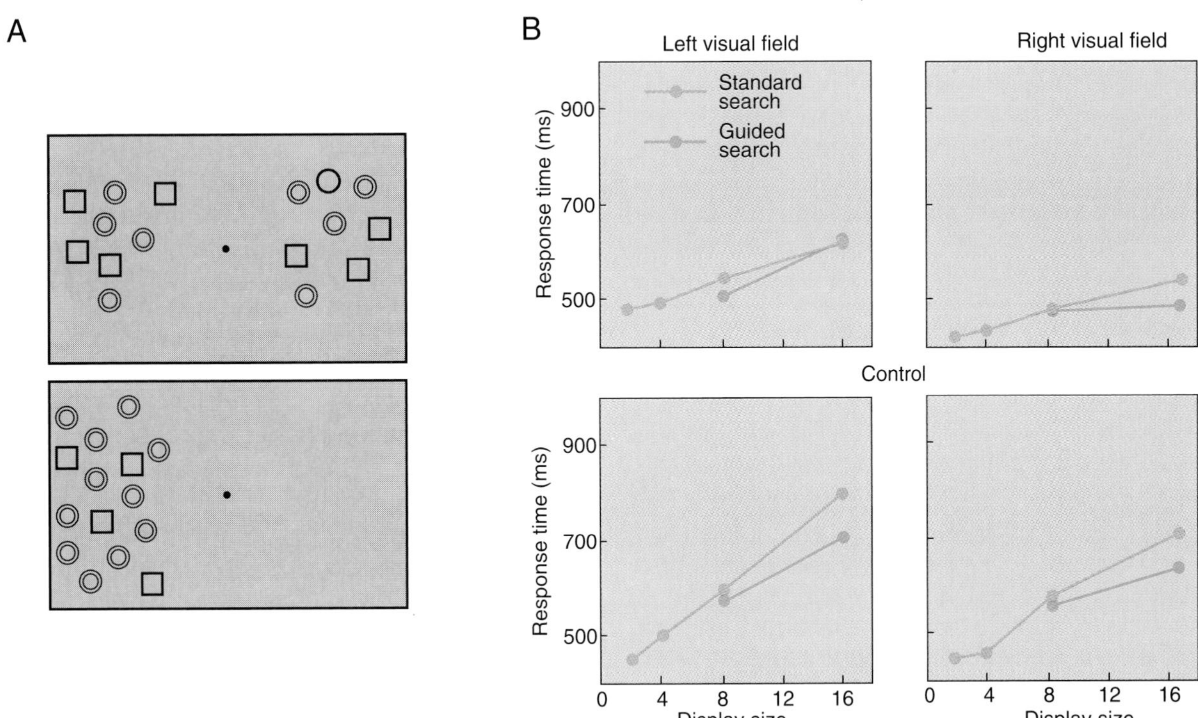

FIGURE 58.6 Illustrative data of visual search between and within visual fields in split-brain patients. (A) Normal subjects search the visual display for a difficult target at the same rate when targets are in one visual field (bottom display) or two visual fields (top display) as though they have only a single focus of attention. However, split-brain subjects search twice as fast when the display is split between the two fields as though they have one focus of attention in each hemisphere. (B) Illustration of "guided" strategy. See text for details.

The Hemispheres Differ in their Coding of Visual Shape

Researchers have proposed two major hypotheses regarding hemispheric differences in shape encoding. One theory posits that the left hemisphere stores categories of shapes (perhaps represented by prototypes), and the right hemisphere stores specific exemplars.[46,47] The other theory proposes that the hemispheres differ in the resolution of the information encoded, as defined by "spatial frequency."[48] These two hypotheses are not mutually exclusive.

The Right Temporal Lobe Stores Specific Visual Exemplars While the Left Stores Categories

The inferior temporal lobe apparently stores visual representations of shape.[47,49,50] It now appears likely that the right and left temporal lobes have different specializations. Whereas the right hemisphere may be better at storing specific exemplars (e.g., a specific image of a dog), the left hemisphere may be more adept at storing categorical visual information regarding shape (e.g., a prototype of the shape of a typical dog). Frequently, simple dot patterns are used to study the storage of prototypes (see Fig. 58.7). Typically, two different patterns of dots are created (the prototypes) and then variations of each are produced by moving the dots slightly in random directions. Later, subjects are shown the patterns that were so generated and are told which of two categories each one belongs to (these categories are based on which of the two original patterns was used to produce each variation). Following this, the patterns are again presented and the subjects are asked to categorize them. One interesting finding is that in the final phase, the subjects can correctly categorize the original patterns (the "prototypes," the ones that all the others were based on) despite the fact that these stimuli were never actually shown before. Indeed, the subjects correctly categorize the prototypes more quickly and accurately than the variations that were actually studied.

Evidence that specific examples and prototypes are processed differently in the two hemispheres was provided by experiments[49] in which subjects were

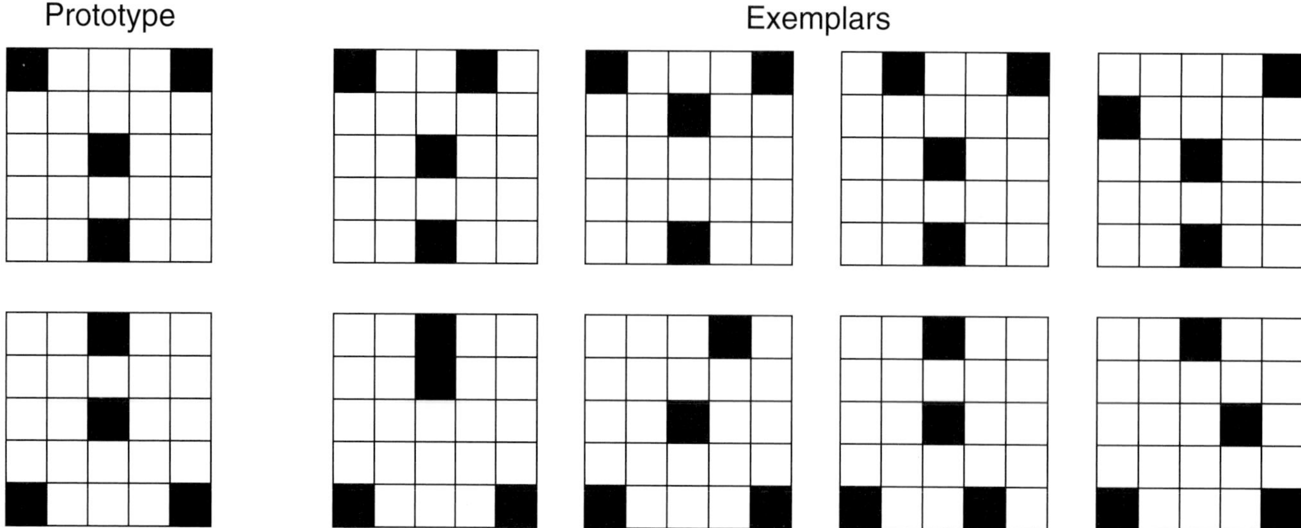

FIGURE 58.7 Prototypes of two patterns and various exemplars used to study differences in visual storage by right and left hemispheres.

shown lateralized word stems in a standard stem-completion task (a word stem is the first few letters of a word; e.g., CAS__ for castle). In this procedure, subjects were first primed with a set of words that they either read or heard. The subjects then stared at a central fixation point and saw a word stem briefly in one visual field. Only half of these stems were from words that were primed (by having been seen at the outset). The task was to say the first word that came to mind that would complete the stem. As expected, the subjects produced more of the words on the initial list when they had seen the list than when they had not, which reflects priming. This effect of priming was greater when subjects read words initially than when they heard those words. Moreover, all of the additional priming was in the right hemisphere (i.e., when the stems were presented to the left visual field and hence initially encoded in the right hemisphere). In addition, when subjects saw the stems in the same case (upper- or lowercase, depending on how the word had been originally presented) as the original words, there was more priming (more words from the primed list) than when they saw the words in a different case. And again, this added priming was exclusively in the right hemisphere. The fact that the right hemisphere exhibited priming that was specific for a particular typefont suggests that the right hemisphere plays a special role in the representation of specific exemplars.

A visual pattern categorization task was used to demonstrate that the left hemisphere is in fact better than the right at storing information about visual categories. In a series of experiments, subjects were shown eight sets of simple line patterns. Each set contained six members based on a prototypical pattern; the six members of a set were created by shifting the locations of individual parts of the prototype. Subjects were not initially shown the prototypical patterns, however. Their task was later to categorize patterns, including the prototype for each set. The subjects were better able to determine the category of the previously unseen prototypes when the stimuli were in the right visual field (shown to the left hemisphere) than when they were shown to the left visual field.

In other experiments,[51] subjects were shown pictures of objects and nonobjects (created by combining parts of real objects in novel ways in either the left or the right visual field). Subjects were better able to distinguish objects from nonobjects if the pictures were presented to the right visual field (initially to the left hemisphere). An implicit memory task of this sort requires stored categorical representations of objects to be accessed for comparison, and hence the left-hemisphere advantage is consistent with the claim that the left hemisphere stores representations of visual categories. No hemispheric difference was found for nonobjects, which presumably would not have matched any representation in either hemisphere.

Further studies[52] using PET discovered predominantly left-hemisphere activation when subjects categorized objects as living or nonliving. A portion of this activation was in the left, but not the right, middle temporal gyrus. Similarly, primarily left-hemisphere activation was detected[53] in the left middle temporal gyrus when subjects heard a word each time a picture of an object was presented and decided whether the words named the objects (half the time they did, and half the time they did not).

Numerous other findings support the claim that the right hemisphere is more adept at storing specific exemplars of shapes and the left hemisphere is more adept at storing categories of shapes. For example, studies using a divided-visual-field paradigm showed that the left hemisphere encodes standard typographic fonts better than the right, whereas the right hemisphere encodes script better than the left. Another interpretation of these findings, however, is that the right hemisphere more effectively encodes subtle variations in shape.[54] Patients who have had their anterior right temporal lobes removed (for treatment of otherwise intractable epilepsy) experience a selective deficit in memory for pictures.[55] Because the subjects were always asked to memorize specific pictures, the subsequent test always involved matching specific exemplars. Thus, this finding is consistent with results summarized earlier that the right hemisphere stores visual representations of specific exemplars. In addition, the right hemispheres of split-brain patients could match an arc to a circle more accurately than the left hemispheres.[56,57] Although this finding was interpreted in terms of part–whole relations, it also supports the claim that the right hemisphere stores a more precise representation of a particular circle.

It is important to note that other results are not consistent with the category/exemplar distinction. For example, when stimuli were initially presented to the left visual field (right hemisphere),[58] subjects were able to judge more quickly that two differently shaped versions of the same geometric figure (e.g., triangles) were the same; this task requires categorizing the stimuli.[59] It is not clear how to explain such findings, but they may have depended on the specific properties of the stimuli, such as their intensity and contrast (e.g., low-contrast stimuli typically are processed better by the right hemisphere).[9,10] Moreover, attention may be the limiting factor and it may shift to a stimulus in either visual field with equal effectiveness.[60] Furthermore, when stimuli are very easy to encode, a ceiling effect may occur so that either hemisphere can process the stimuli as fast as possible (for an elaboration of this account, see Kosslyn[47]; for similar findings, see also Sergent and Lorber[61]).

The Right Hemisphere Appears Specialized for Encoding Low Spatial Frequencies and the Left for High Spatial Frequencies

The cerebral hemispheres may be tuned to encode different ranges of spatial frequencies.[48] Spatial frequency corresponds to the number of regular alterations of dark and light per unit of space (usually a degree of visual angle). Thus, thin alternating black-and-white stripes have a higher spatial frequency than thick alternating black-and-white stripes. To test this hypothesis,[48] subjects were presented separately with versions of the Navon[62] stimuli in each visual half-field. The Navon stimuli consist of a large letter (the global level) made up of smaller versions of another letter (the local level). The subjects were asked to determine whether a target letter was present, which could be the global, overall shape, or the smaller, constituent letters that made up the overall shape. When the stimuli were initially presented to the left visual field, subjects could better encode the global (lower spatial frequency) pattern, whereas when stimuli were initially presented to the right visual field, they could better encode the local (higher spatial frequency) pattern. In addition, patients with right-hemisphere lesions tend to reproduce only the local level, whereas patients with left-hemisphere lesions tend to reproduce only the global level (Fig. 58.8). Further, when subjects prepare to encode the global level of one of these composite figures,[63] their ability to see low-spatial-frequency stripes is relatively better than when they prepare for the local level, thus providing a link between local versus global processing and processing of spatial frequencies. Although replication of these results has occasionally proved difficult,[64,65] meta-analysis[64] disclosed that these findings[48] were consistent across the reported studies.

Similarly, other groups have studied perceptual encoding in brain-damaged patients using the Navon figures.[66–68] These researchers found that patients with damage to the right hemisphere have difficulty encoding the global shape, whereas patients with left-hemisphere damage have difficulty encoding the constituent parts. Moreover, patients with damage to the left superior temporal gyrus (which may well have also affected the middle temporal gyrus) demonstrate a strong bias toward encoding the global patterns, whereas patients with damage to the inferior parietal lobule do not demonstrate such a bias.[68] However, as illustrated in Fig. 58.9, patients with damaged left inferior parietal lobules have difficulty allocating attention selectively to one level or the other. These results suggest that when patterns are encoded at different levels of scale, at least two processes are at work—one that involves attentional allocation in the parietal lobes and another involving specialization for encoding different levels of scale in the temporal lobe.

An interesting and related discovery was that a split-brain patient can better recognize and draw smaller component shapes using his right hand (controlled primarily by the left hemisphere), whereas he can

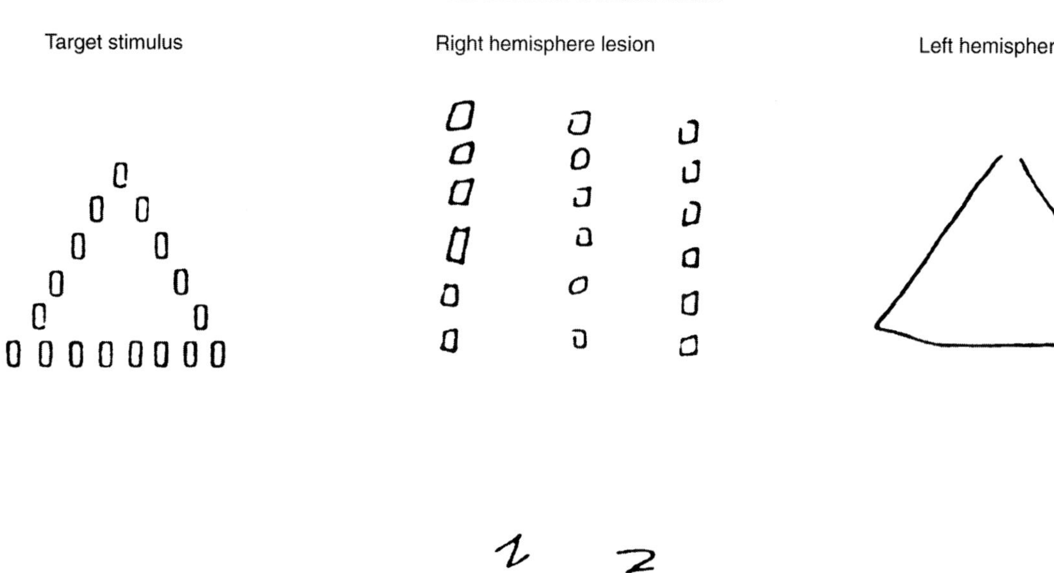

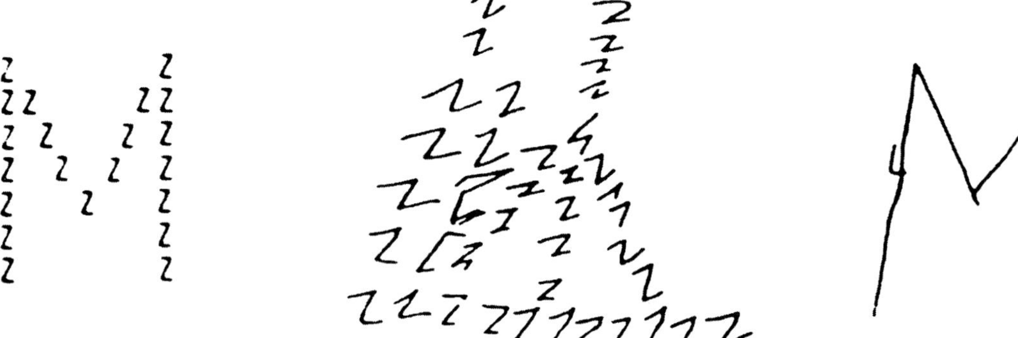

FIGURE 58.8 On the left of each row are global patterns (triangle and letter M) made of local elements (rectangles and Zs). These are the so-called Navon figures, named after the investigator who first used them. The middle column shows reproductions by patients with right hemisphere lesions, and the right column shows reproductions by patients with left hemisphere lesions.

better recognize and draw global shapes using his left hand (which is controlled primarily by the right hemisphere).[69]

In other studies, subjects have been asked to determine whether a set of evenly spaced, equally wide black-and-white stripes matches one stored in memory. These subjects are better able to assess thinner (higher spatial frequency) stripes in their right visual field (left hemisphere) and thicker (lower spatial frequency) stripes in their left visual field (right hemisphere).[70–73]

Laterality differences in encoding spatial frequency occur only when subjects are required to recognize a pattern. When one simply is asked to discriminate between black-and-white stripes and a homogeneous gray field, the hemispheres have the same sensitivity to different spatial frequencies.[71–73]

Differences in spatial frequency may be related to the ease of encoding categories versus exemplars, but this hypothesis has yet to be explored in detail; computer simulation models lend credence to this possibility.[74]

The Hemispheres Differ in Encoding Spatial Properties

Spatial properties are encoded primarily by the parietal lobes, and hemispheric specialization occurs here as well. PET studies[75] indicate that the right hemisphere does indeed represent both visual fields (whereas the left represents only the contralateral field). It has become evident in recent years, however, that both hemispheres play a role in encoding spatial properties.

A distinction can be made between two methods for encoding spatial information.[46] One method involves grouping positions into broad classes; for example, an object can be described as "above" another regardless of its position on the horizontal axis. The other method involves specifying precise metric locations; such

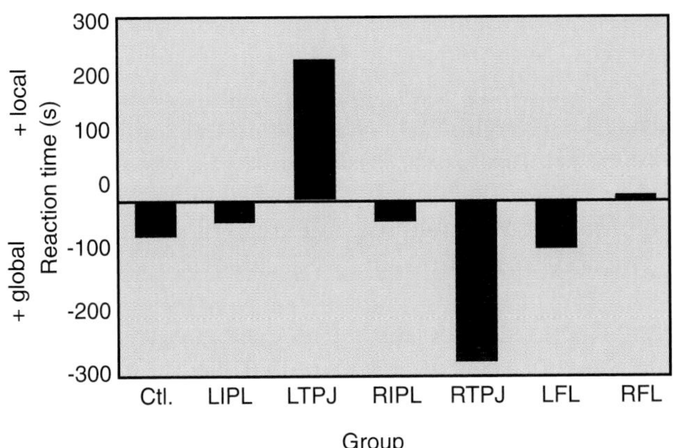

FIGURE 58.9 Differences in reaction time favoring either global or local processing. Notice the large effects in patients with lesions of left (LTPJ) and right (RTPJ) temporal-parietal junctions. Other groups are normal (nonlesion) controls (CTL) and patients with lesions of the inferior parietal lobe (LIPL or RIPL) or prefrontal (LPFC or RPFC).

"metric" (or "coordinate") representations of spatial relations specify location in a way that is useful for guiding actions.

It is possible to view categorical spatial relations as language-like, and hence the left hemisphere should encode them better than the right; in contrast, because metric spatial relations are useful for navigation (and the right hemisphere appears to play a special role in such processing), one might expect the right hemisphere to be better than the left at encoding coordinate spatial relations.

In fact, subjects were better at determining whether one stimulus was within a criterion distance of another (e.g., 0.5 in, 1 cm, or 1 in, in different experiments) when stimuli were presented in the left visual field (initially to the right hemisphere) than when they were presented in the right visual field (initially to the left hemisphere); on the other hand, they could better determine whether one stimulus was on or off, to the left or right, or above or below another (in different experiments) when stimuli were in the right visual field[76] (see Fig. 58.10).

Hellige and Michimata[77] developed the above/below task and reported the same results. These conclusions have been substantiated by studies[78] showing that patients with damage to the posterior left hemisphere have difficulty encoding categorical spatial relations, whereas patients with damage to the posterior right hemisphere have difficulty encoding metric spatial information.

Previous neuropsychological findings are also consistent with a distinction between processes that encode two types of spatial relations. For example, normal subjects were asked to judge the orientation of narrow rectangles.[79] The rectangles were oriented horizontally, vertically, and at 45° diagonals in one experiment. The subjects judged these easily categorized orientations better when stimuli were presented in the right visual field and hence encoded first in the left hemisphere. In contrast, when rectangles were presented at other, less easily categorized, oblique orientations (15°, 30°, 45°, and 60° from the vertical) in another experiment, the subjects judged orientation best when the stimuli were presented initially to the left visual field and hence encoded first by the right hemisphere (see also Ref. 80).

Much of the clinical literature corroborates this distinction between the two subsystems encoding spatial relations. For example, several groups[81–84] discovered that damage to the right hemisphere impairs a patient's ability to encode the precise position of a dot more than does damage to the left hemisphere. Similarly, patients with posterior right-hemisphere damage had difficulty performing a task that required utilization of coordinate spatial relations (because the orientations involved were not easily categorized).[85] These patients were asked to point a rod in the same orientation as a sample rod. The patients not only performed more poorly than control subjects, but also performed more poorly than patients with damage to the anterior right hemisphere or the anterior or posterior left hemisphere. Moreover, patients with damage to the right hemisphere were impaired at determining whether two angles were the same, whereas patients with damage to the left hemisphere accomplished this task normally.[86]

In the same vein, damage to the left hemisphere in the region of the angular gyrus may result in Gerstmann's syndrome,[87,88] which impairs a patient's ability to distinguish right from left. In one such case,[89] the patient could point accurately to a target, yet could

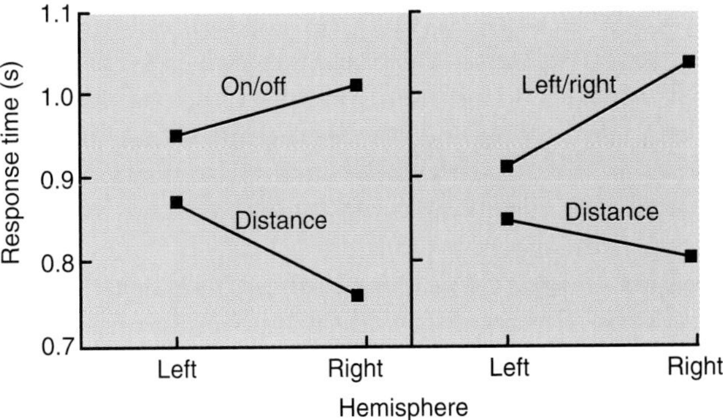

FIGURE 58.10 Response time for normal subjects with stimuli in projected directly to the left or right hemisphere for categorical (on/off or left/right) and metric judgments.

not judge right from left; this patient demonstrated a pure dissociation between the processing of "categorical" and "coordinate" spatial relations. Similarly, patients with left occipital-parietal lesions were unable to determine categorical spatial relations such as "on top of" or "under."[90]

Thus, damage to the left hemisphere can impair the ability to categorize spatial relations, whereas damage to the right hemisphere can impair the ability to localize objects precisely. Although this is a useful generalization, we must note that many tasks can be accomplished using either method of representing spatial relations. For example, in one spatial encoding task,[85] no difference was observed between patients with left- and right-hemisphere damage (although patients with posterior lesions performed more poorly than those with anterior lesions). In this task, subjects observed six cards arranged into two rows of three; each card contained a geometric shape. The shapes were then covered, and the subjects were shown a copy of each shape and asked to point to the location of the corresponding card. Because the row and the position in the row are easily categorized, this task could be performed using either method of representing spatial relations.

Finally, it is also crucial to recognize that more than one process is required to carry out all tasks, and each hemisphere may be more adept at performing some of these processes. Thus, damage to either hemisphere may disrupt task performance in certain cases. For example, patients with damage to the left hemisphere had difficulty encoding line orientation.[86,91] Subjects were asked to study two oriented line segments and then pick the equivalent segments from an array of oriented lines. The array of lines resembled spokes extending out from a circle, progressively tilted in 18° increments. It seems reasonable that the right hemisphere should have been required for this discrimination because the orientations were difficult to categorize; however, patients with damage to the right hemisphere were no worse at the task than those with damage to the left hemisphere. Possibly, "the intervention of the LH [left hemisphere] is necessary in handling extraneous and/or distracting visual information,"[86] and, in this task, such processing may be needed "to disentangle the target two lines of given slope from the decoys in the array." Indeed, several groups[92–95] have demonstrated that when target figures are embedded in other patterns, the left hemisphere is critically involved in detecting them.

Summary

Most interactions between the hemispheres depend on the corpus callosum, as evident by their absence in split-brain patients. However, central attentional resources are shared by the two hemispheres; thus when one hemisphere must process more fully, the other becomes less efficient. Nevertheless, the hemispheres can sometimes use different strategies, which are more or less effective for a given task. Evidence indicates that the left hemisphere is relatively good at encoding visual representations of categories of shapes, whereas the right hemisphere is relatively good at encoding visual representations of specific exemplars. These visual memories apparently are localized to the left and right temporal lobes, respectively. In addition, and not inconsistent with these findings, evidence indicates that the left hemisphere is better able to encode into memory high-spatial-frequency patterns, whereas the right hemisphere is relatively better able to encode into memory low-spatial-frequency patterns. Perhaps counterintuitively, computer stimulation models have shown that high spatial frequencies are relatively important for encoding prototypes, whereas low spatial frequencies are relatively important for encoding individual exemplars. In addition, the hemispheres differ in the kinds of spatial information they most effectively encode. The left is relatively good at encoding categorical spatial relations (such as above/below or left/right), whereas the right is relatively good at encoding metric spatial relations. The posterior parietal lobe appears to play a special role in these functions.

LATERALIZATION OF LANGUAGE ABILITIES

Like vision, language is not accomplished by a single mechanism. Rather, a host of distinct processes underlie our ability both to comprehend and to produce speech.

Lexical and Grammatical Knowledge Show Hemispheric Specialization

A dichotomy that is useful in trying to understand language is the distinction between how the brain enables grammar and how it enables a lexicon (see Chapter 57). The distinction between grammar and lexicon[96] is different from the more traditional distinction between syntax and semantics. The latter is commonly invoked to understand the differential effects of brain lesions on language processes. In general terms, grammar refers to the rule-based system for arranging words to communicate effectively. The lexicon, on the other hand, is the mind's dictionary, where specific words are associated with particular meanings. The reason for using the distinction between grammar and lexicon is that it takes into account such factors as memory, which allows word strings such as idioms to be learned by rote. Although the lexicon (memory) cannot underlie most phrases and sentences because of the endless ability to generate unique sentences (such as the one you are currently reading), memory does play a role in many short phrases. Thus, when such word strings are uttered, they do not reflect an underlying interaction of syntax and semantic systems. They are, instead, essentially an entry from the lexicon. In more general terms, the grammar system ought to be discrete and therefore localizable. The lexicon should be distributed and therefore more difficult to completely damage.

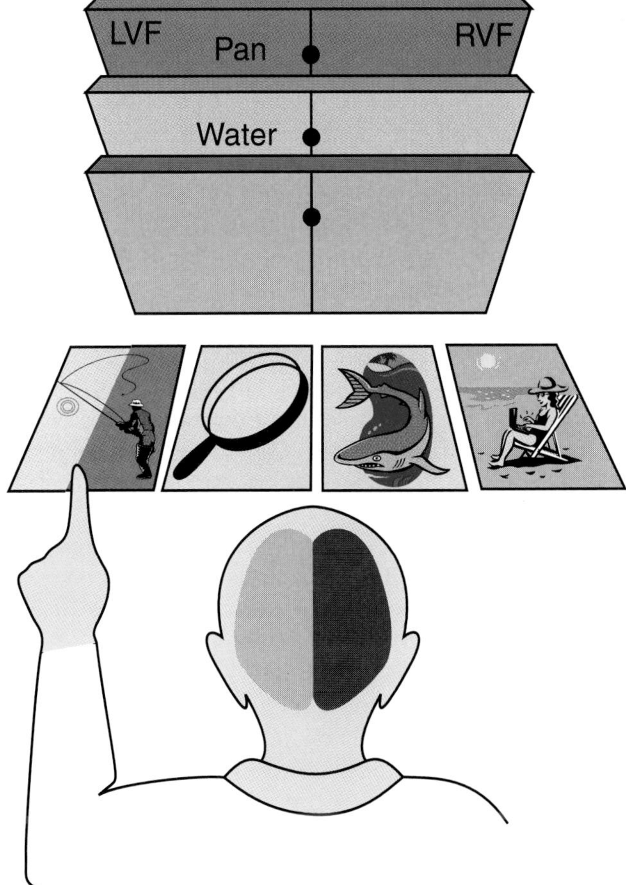

FIGURE 58.11 Even language-rich right half brains are poor at thinking. In this simple task, all that is required is that each half brain see the relationship between the two pictures and choose which of the four are most related. The left brain finds these tasks as simple as a 2-year-old would find them, while the right stumbles along and makes many errors.

Language and Speech Processes Can Rarely Be Present in Both Hemispheres

Right-hemisphere language has a different organizational structure from left-hemisphere language: The separated left hemisphere alone is fully capable of normal comprehension of all aspects of language, but the right hemisphere can also possess language capability. Although there has been evidence of right-hemisphere language capability, these disconnected right hemispheres were severely limited in the kinds of linguistic and thought processes they possess[97,98] (see Fig. 58.11).

Over the last 30 years, there have been very few cases that demonstrated some kind of language capability in the right hemisphere. In the early 1980s, only five split-brain patients had proven to have a lexicon in the right hemisphere. Since that time only one more normally right-handed split-brain patient has been found with a lexicon in both the left and the right hemispheres.[99]

The left and the right lexicons of these special patients can be nearly equal in their capacity but they are organized quite differently. For example, no priming phenomena have been discovered in the disconnected right hemisphere, and letter processing appears to be serial—not parallel—in nature.[100] Moreover, these patients have a variety of other deficiencies, such as not recognizing when one word is superordinate to another or judging antonyms.

In sum, the findings from split-brain patients suggest there can be two lexicons, one in each hemisphere, but this lexical organization is rare. When it is present, the right-hemisphere lexicon seems organized differently from the left-hemisphere lexicon. These observations are consistent with the view that lexicons reflect learning processes and as such have a wider distribution in the cerebral cortex. Still, we must note that in the general population, the lexicon seems to be in the left hemisphere. A right-hemisphere lexicon is rarely present and stores information in no particular pattern or hierarchy.

A number of illuminating studies have also been performed using the divided-visual-field method with normal subjects. In one lexical decision task, subjects were asked to identify, as rapidly as possible, whether a string of letters constituted a word. Subjects correctly identified the "target" string as a word more often when it was displayed in the right visual field (left hemisphere) than when it was displayed in the left visual field (right hemisphere). This finding was obtained even when subjects were encouraged to pay more attention to the left visual field and thus the effect probably reflects the operation of processes implemented in the left hemisphere and not simply the operation of attentional biases.[101] Furthermore, subjects were more adept at recognizing the target as a word when they had been primed with a semantically related word. Therefore, displaying one word (the prime) appears to activate a number of semantically similar words (one of which may be the target) in the brain. Interestingly, although patients with Wernicke's aphasia tend to show normal priming in this sort of task, they are impaired when they attempt to make semantic judgments about the stimuli.[101] For example, even though patients with Wernicke's aphasia may be able to identify the string H-A-I-R after being primed with the word "comb," they may not understand what the word "hair" means. From this, one might conclude[101] that "there seems to be a dissociation between tasks that measure the nature and integrity of structural relations in the lexicon and tasks that require active decisions about semantic relations between words."

Generative Syntax Is Present in Only One Hemisphere

Although the right hemisphere of some split-brain patients clearly has a lexicon, these right hemispheres have shown erratic performance on other aspects of language such as understanding verbs, pluralizations, the possessive, differences between active and passive, and so on.[97] The right hemisphere in the patients that possess some language has also not demonstrated a capacity to use word order to assist in deciphering meaning. At the same time these right hemispheres can indicate when a sentence ends with a semantically odd word.[102] Additionally, right hemispheres that reveal language capacities are able to make grammatical judgments.[103,104] Thus, even though they cannot use syntax to remove ambiguity from verbal stimuli, they can judge that one set of utterances is grammatical while another set is not. This rather startling finding suggests that patterns of speech are learned by rote. Yet, recognizing the pattern of acceptable utterances does not mean a neural system can use this information to assist in the understanding of word strings.

In right-handed people, the left hemisphere plays a special role in syntactic processing. For instance, when stimuli are presented initially to a single hemisphere in normal right-handed people, only the left hemisphere decomposes words into their simpler meaning constituents (e.g., "walking," which can be decomposed into "walk" and "ing"[105,106]); the right hemisphere has particular trouble using the rules of grammar to understand combinations of words. Indeed, the distinct representations of roots (e.g., the French stem "agit") and suffixes (e.g., the French suffix "at") are processed in the left hemisphere. These findings are consistent with the huge literature on the aphasias that reveals a special role for the left hemisphere (in right-handed people) in language.[107] Both speech production and comprehension are disrupted following left-hemisphere lesions. More anterior lesions typically disrupt production more than comprehension, whereas for more posterior lesions the situation is reversed.

Some Right Hemispheres Can Develop Speech

One of the hallmarks of most split-brain patients is that they speak out of the left hemisphere and not the right.[108] This observation has been consistent with the neurologic literature and with amytal studies, which have shown that the left hemisphere is the dominant hemisphere for both language and speech.[109]

There are now three and possibly four split-brain patients who seem able to speak out of either hemisphere. While there is always an initially dominant hemisphere following brain bisection, some patients have developed the capacity to make one-word utterances from the disconnected right hemisphere.[110] This rather startling development in these patients shows that two of the three major systems in human language—the lexicon and speech—can be managed to some extent by either hemisphere. It also illustrates an extraordinary plasticity occurring sometimes over 10 years after callosal surgery.

These observations of split-brain patients are consistent with those from other brain-damaged patients. It has long been known that brain-damaged patients with lesions in Broca's area, in the left prefrontal cortex, typically have an "expressive aphasia," an impaired ability to generate speech. One source of this problem has been identified[111]: Broca's aphasics have difficulty using syntactic information—they are, for example, unable to make use of auxiliary verbs and prepositions. Their speech is, therefore, choppy and "telegraphic."

Researchers have isolated the brain areas involved in speech production by using PET techniques.[112] The first step in these studies was to determine which areas of the brain were activated when subjects did not speak, but merely perceived words. The researchers then monitored blood flow in the brain while subjects also pronounced the words. The activation caused by speaking the word was then determined by subtracting the pattern of blood flow evoked when the words were presented but not pronounced from that evoked when they were also pronounced. Speaking words selectively activated a number of areas of the brain, including the mouth region of the primary motor area of the left hemisphere (area M1, which controls fine motor movements), the left buried sylvian cortex, the left premotor cortex (area 6), the right primary motor area, the right lateral sylvian cortex, and the supplementary motor area (SMA). The same areas were activated when the words were presented visually or auditorily. Subjects were then asked to move their mouths and tongues without speaking, which activated the sylvian cortex in both hemispheres; this result suggests that the sylvian cortex is really specialized for motor programming or monitoring of the mouth and tongue in general, rather than for speech output.

Phonological Encoding Is Lateralized in Monkeys and Humans

Even monkeys apparently have lateralized encoding of speechlike sounds. For example, in one experiment[113] an electric shock was administered through a water spout while one monkey vocalization occurred, but no shock was presented when a different monkey "coo" occurred. Japanese macacque monkeys learned to discriminate between the two vocalizations and avoided drinking the water when they would be shocked. Once the monkeys had been trained, different parts of their brains were removed. Lesioning the left superior temporal gyrus impaired the monkeys' ability to discriminate the vocalizations; in contrast, when the equivalent portion of the right hemispherre was taken out, the monkeys did not have difficulty discriminating among the vocalizations. However, only 10 additional training sessions were required, on average, for the monkeys with lesions in the left hemisphere to once again be able to discriminate among the sounds. When a second lesion was made in the intact right hemisphere, all of the monkeys lost their ability to discriminate between the vocalizations. Even after practice they were unable to regain this ability. These results suggest that both hemispheres can accomplish phonological processing, though one is typically "dominant."

The results from human PET scanning experiments indicate that the temporal regions of the brain outside area A1 are needed for speech encoding. When subjects' brains were monitored by PET as they simply listened to words, six critical brain areas were activated.[112] In the left hemisphere, the anterior superior temporal cortex, the posterior superior temporal cortex, the temporal–parietal cortex, and the inferior anterior cingulate cortex were active. Two regions of temporal cortex were also activated in the right hemisphere. When words were presented visually, however, none of these six areas was activated. It is worth noting that other experimenters have found many of these areas to be active when subjects hear speech and nonspeech auditory stimuli; the temporal–parietal and anterior superior temporal areas were the only ones activated by speech but not by nonspeech sounds.[114–116] The other regions of the temporal lobe seem to encode both sorts of sounds. Indeed, patients with temporal lobe lesions often have trouble encoding both speech and nonspeech sounds.[115]

Other PET studies implicate left-hemisphere temporal–parietal areas in the storage of auditory word forms. Subjects determined whether two simultaneously presented written words rhymed. Auditory memories ought to be activated by this task because it requires the subject to form an auditory mental image of the sounds in sequence. This task evoked activation in an area close to the left supramarginal gyrus; this area is distinct from, but close to, the temporal areas that were activated when subjects listened to words and nonwords. Consistent with this finding, patients with lesions in the left temporal–parietal areas (the angular gyrus and the supramarginal gyrus) often encounter difficulty in recognizing speech sounds (i.e., they have phonological deficits[117]). An area of the left frontal lobe is often active during rhyming tasks.[115]

Summary

Gone are the days when hemispheric differences were characterized by simple dichotomies, such as verbal versus perceptual or analytic versus intuitive. Complex processing of the sort used in vision or language is accomplished by a host of distinct processes, each of which can be lateralized in a different way. Cerebral lateralization apparently has resulted in a kind of "division of labor." Indeed, computational models have shown that two similar computations will interfere with each other in the same network, and hence are more effectively carried out by separate networks. For example, the information needed to compute a precise metric spatial relation must be discarded when one computes a categorical spatial relation (one object is equally "left of" another, regardless of the precise distance), but this metric information is crucial for computing a coordinate spatial relation. When computations have opposing requirements, it is more efficient for different networks to carry them out. Nevertheless, we should not lose sight of the fact that the hemispheres complement each other, and by necessity must work together in many tasks.

Research on cerebral lateralization has made progress in part because it has become more tightly linked to research in specific content domains, such as vision and language. Computational modeling will play an increasingly important role in the study of laterality, if only because a number of different principles may simultaneously operate to determine cerebral specialization and hence it will be difficult to predict specific outcomes without such models.

References

1. Gregory, R. L. (1966). *Eye and Brain.* McGraw-Hill, New York.
2. Bogen, J. E., Fisher, E. D., and Vogel, P. J. (1965). Cerebral commissurotomy: A second case report. *JAMA* **194:** 1328–1329.
3. Bogen, J. E., and Gazzaniga, M. S. (1965). Cerebral commissurotomy in man: Minor hemisphere dominance for certain visuospatial functions. *J. Neurosurg.* **23:** 394–399.

4. Springer, S. P., and Deutsch, G. (1985). *Left Brain, Right Brain.* Freeman, New York.
5. Kosslyn, S. M., Anderson, A. K., Hillger, L. A., and Hamilton, S. E. (1994). Hemispheric differences in sizes of receptive fields or attentional biases? *Neuropsychology* **8:** 139–147.
6. Peterzell, D. H., Harvey, L. O., and Hardyck, C. D. (1989). Spatial frequencies and the cerebral hemispheres: Contrast sensitivity, visible persistence and letter classification. *Percep. Psychophys.* **46:** 443–455.
7. Schwartz, S., and Kirsner, K. (1982). Laterality effects in visual information processing: Hemispheric specialization or the orienting of attention? *Q. J. Exp. Psychol.* **34A:** 61–77.
8. White, M. J. (1969). Laterality differences in perception: A review. *Psychol. Bull.* **72:** 387–405.
9. Sergent, J., and Hellige, J. B. (1986). Role of input factors in visual-field asymmetries. *Brain Cognit.* **5:** 174–199.
10. Hellige, J. B., and Sergent, J. (1986). Role of task factors in visual field asymmetries. *Brain Cognit.* **5:** 200–222.
11. Levy, J., Heller, W., Banich, M. T., and Burton, L. A. (1983). Are variations among right-handed individuals in perceptual asymmetries caused by characteristic arousal differences between hemispheres? *J. Exp. Psychol. Hum. Percep. Perform.* **9:** 329–359.
12. Geschwind, N., and Levitsky, W. (1968). Human brain: Left-right asymmetries in temporal speech region. *Science* **161:** 186–187.
13. Campain, R., and Minckler, J. (1976). A note on the gross configurations of the human auditory cortex. *Brain Lang.* **3:** 318–323.
14. Wada, J. A., Clarke, R., and Hamm, A. (1975). Cerebral hemispheric asymmetry in humans. *Arch. Neurol.* (*Chicago*) **32:** 239–246.
15. Teszner, D., Tzavaras, A., Gruner, J., and Hécaen, H. (1972). L'asymmétrie droite-gauche du planum temporale: A propos de l'étude anatomique de 100 cervaeux. *Rev. Neurol.* **126:** 444–449.
16. Loftus, W. C., Tramo, M. J., Thomas, C. E., Green, R. L., Nordgren, R. A., and Gazzaniga, M. S. (1993). Three-dimensional quantitative analysis of hemispheric asymmetry in the human superior temporal region. *Cereb. Cortex* **3:** 348–355.
17. Galabarda, A. M. (1997). Personal observations.
18. Cunningham, D. J. (1892). *Contribution to the Surface Anatomy of the Cerebral Hemispheres.* Royal Irish Academy, Dublin.
19. Chi, J. G., Dooling, E. C., and Gilles, F. H. (1977). Gyral development of the human brain. *Ann. Neurol.* **1:** 86–93.
20. Witelson, S. F., and Pallie, W. (1973). Left hemisphere specialization for language in the newborn: Neuroanatomical evidence of asymmetry. *Brain* **96:** 641–646.
21. Galaburda, A. M., and Sanides, F. (1980). Cytoarchitectonic organization of the human auditory cortex. *J. Comp. Neurol.* **190:** 597–610.
22. Hochberg, F. H., and LeMay, M. (1975). Arteriographic correlates of handedness. *Neurology* **25:** 218–222.
23. Ratcliff, G., Dila, C., Taylor, L., and Milner, B. (1980). The morphological asymmetry of the hemispheres and cerebral dominance for speech: A possible relationship. *Brain Language* **11:** 87–98.
24. Steinmetz, H., Volkmann, J., Jancke, L., and Freund, H. J. (1991). Anatomical left-right asymmetry of language-related temporal cortex is different in left-handers and right-handers. *Ann. Neurol.* **29:** 315–319.
25. Rosen, G. D., Sherman, G. F., and Galaburda, A. M. (1993). Neuronal subtypes and anatomic asymmetry: Changes in neuronal numbers and cell-packing density. *Neuroscience* **56:** 833–839.
26. Rosen, G. D., Sherman, G. F., and Galaburda, A. M. (1989). Interhemispheric connections differ betwen symmetrical and asymmetrical brain regions. *Neuroscience* **33:** 525–533.
27. Innocenti, G. M. (1981). Growth and reshaping of axons in the establishment of visual callosal connections. *Science* **212:** 824–827.
28. Innocenti, G. M., and Frost, D. O. (1980). The postnatal development of visual callosal connections in the absence of visual experience or of the eyes. *Exp. Brain Res.* **39:** 365–375.
29. Ivy, G. O., and Killackey, H. P. (1981). The ontogeny of the distribution of callosal projection neurons in the rat parietal cortex. *J. Comp. Neurol.* **195:** 367–389.
30. Ivy, G. O., and Killackey, H. P. (1982). Ontogenetic changes in the projections of neocortical neurons. *J. Neurosci.* **2:** 735–743.
31. Stone, J. (1966). The naso-temporal division of the cat's retina. *J. Comp. Neurol.* **126:** 585–600.
32. Stone, J., Leicester, J., and Sherman, S. M. (1973). The naso-temporal division of the monkey's retina. *J. Comp. Neurol.* **150:** 333–348.
33. Fendrich, R., and Gazzaniga, M. S. (1989). Evidence of foveal splitting in a commissurotomy patient. *Neuropsychologia* **27**(3): 273–281.
34. Fendrich, R., Wessinger, C. M., and Gazzaniga, M. S. (1994). Processing profiles at the retinal vertical midline of the callosotomy patient. *Soc. Neurosci. Abstr.* **20:** 1579.
35. Trevarthen, C. (1970). Experimental evidence for a brain-stem contribution to visual perception in man. *Brain Behav. Evol.* **3:** 338–352.
36. Trevarthen, C., and Sperry, R. W. (1973). Perceptual unity of the ambient visual field in human commissurotomy patients. *Brain* **96:** 547–570.
37. Holtzman, J. D. (1984). Interactions between cortical and subcortical areas: Evidence from human commissurotomy patients. *Vision Res.* **24:** 801–813.
38. Holtzman, J. D. Sidtis, J. J., Volpe, B. T., Wilson, D. H., and Gazzaniga, M. S. (1981). Dissociation of spatial information for stimulus localization and the control of attention. *Brain* **104:** 861–872.
39. Holtzman, J. D., Volpe, B. T., and Gazzaniga, M. S. (1984). Spatial orientation following commissural section. In *Varieties of Attention* (R. Parasuraman and D. R. Davies, eds.), pp. 375–394. Academic Press, New York.
40. Holtzman, J. D., and Gazzaniga, M. S. (1982). Dual task interactions due exclusively to limits in processing resources. *Science* **218:** 1325–1327.
41. Deleted.
42. Lewine, J. D., Doty, R. W., Astur, R. S., and Provencal, S. L. (1994). Role of the forebrain commissures in bihemispheric mnemonic integration in macaques. *J. Neurosci.* **14**(5, Pt.1): 2515–2530.
43. Luck, S. J., Hillyard, S. A., Mangun, G. R., and Gazzaniga, M. S. (1989). Independent hemispheric attentional systems mediate visual search in split-brain patients. *Nature* (*London*) **342:** 543–545.
44. Luck, S. J., Hillyard, S. A., Mangun, G. R., and Gazzaniga, M. S. (1994). Independent hemispheric attentional systems mediate visual search in split-brain patients. *J. Cognit. Neurosci.* **6:** 84–91.
45. Kingstone, A., Enns, J., Mangun, G. R., and Gazzaniga, M. S. (1994). Guided visual search is a left hemisphere process in split-brain patients. *Psychol. Sci.*
46. Kosslyn, S. M. (1987). Seeing and imagining in the cerebral hemispheres: A computational approach. *Psychol. Rev.* **94:** 148–175.

47. Kosslyn, S. M. (1994). *Image and Brain: The Resolution of the Imagery Debate.* MIT Press, Cambridge, MA.
48. Sergent, J. (1987). Failures to confirm the spatial-frequency hypothesis: Fatal blow or healthy complication? *Can. J. Psyuchol.* **41:** 412–428.
49. Ungerleider, L. G., and Mishkin, M. (1982). Two cortical visual systems. In *Analysis of Visual Behavior* (D. J. Ingle, M. A. Goodale, and R. J. W. Mansfield, eds.), pp. 549–586. MIT Press, Cambridge, MA.
50. Marsolek, C. J., Kosslyn, S. M., and Squire, L. R. (1992). Form-specific priming in the right cerebral hemisphere. *J. Exp. Psychol. Learning Memory Cognit.* **18:** 492–508.
51. Vitkovitch, M., and Underwood, G. (1992). Visual field differences in an object decision task. *Brain Cognit.* **19:** 195–207.
52. Sergent, J., Ohta, S., and MacDonald, B. (1992). Functional neuroanatomy of face and object processing: A positron emission tomography study. *Brain* **115:** 15–36.
53. Kosslyn, S. M., Alpert, N. M., Thompson, W. L., Chabris, C. F., Rauch, S. L., and Anderson, A. K. (1994). Identifying objects seen from different viewpoints: A PET investigation. *Brain* **117:** 1055–1071.
54. Bryden, M. P., and Allard, F. (1976). Visual hemifield differences depend on typeface. *Brain Lang.* **3:** 191–200.
55. Milner, B. (1968). Visual recognition and recall after right temporal-lobe excision in man. *Neuropsychologia* **6:** 191–209.
56. Nebes, R. D. (1971). Superiority of the minor hemisphere in commissurotomized man for the perception of part-whole relations. *Cortex* **7:** 333–349.
57. Hatta, T. (1977). Functional hemisphere asymmetries in an inferential thought task. *Psychologia* **20:** 145–150.
58. Simion, F., Bagnara, S., Bisiacchi, P., Roncato, S., and Umilta, C. (1980). Laterality effects, levels of processing, and stimulus properties. *J. Exp. Psychol. Hum. Percep. Perform.* **6:** 184–195.
59. Sergent, J., Zuck, E., Lévesque, M., and MacDonald, B. (1992). Positron emission tomography study of letter and object processing: Empirical findings and methodological considerations. *Cereb. Cortex* **2:** 68–80.
60. Pollatsek, A., Rayner, K., and Henderson, J. M. (1990). Role of spatial location in integration of pictorial information across saccades. *J. Exp. Psychol. Hum. Percep. Perform.* **16:** 199–210.
61. Sergent, J., and Lorber, E. (1983). Perceptual categorization in the cerebral hemispheres. *Brain Cognit.* **2:** 39–54.
62. Navon, D. (1977). Forest before trees: The precedence of global features in visual perception. *Cognit. Psychol.* **9:** 353–383.
63. Shulman, G. L., and Wilson, J. (1987). Spatial frequency and selective attention to local and global information. *Perception* **16:** 89–101.
64. Van Kleeck, M. H. (1989). Hemispheric differences in global versus local processing of hierarchical visual stimuli by normal subjects: New data and a meta-analysis of previous studies. *Neuropsychologia* **27:** 1165–1178.
65. Brown, H., and Kosslyn, S. M. (1998). Cerebral specialization for size versus level of hierarchy. In *Handbook of Cerebral Lateralization* (R. Davidson and K. Hugdahl, eds.). MIT Press, Cambridge, MA (in press).
66. Delis, D. C., Robertson, L. C., and Efron, R. (1986). Hemispheric specialization of memory for visual hierarchical stimuli. *Neuropsychologia* **24:** 205–214.
67. Robertson, L. C., and Delis, D. C. (1986). "Part-whole" processing in unilateral brain damaged patients: Dysfunction of hierarchical organization. *Neuropsychologia* **24:** 363–370.
68. Robertson, L. C., Lamb, M. R., and Knight, R. T. (1988). Effects of lesions of temporal-parietal junction on perceptual and attentional processing in humans. *J. Neurosci.* **8:** 3757–3769.
69. Delis, D. C., Kramer, J. H., and Kiefner, M. G. (1988). Visuospatial functioning before and after commissurotomy: Disconnection in hierarchical processing. *Arch. Neurol. (Chicago)* **45:** 662–465.
70. Christman, S., Kitterle, F., and Hellige, J. (1991). Hemispheric asymmetry in the processing of absolute versus relative spatial frequency. *Brain Cognit.* **16:** 62–73.
71. Kitterle, F. L., ed. (1991). *Cerebral Laterality: Theory and Research.* Erlbaum, Hillsdale, NJ.
72. Kitterle, F. L., and Selig, L. (1991). Visual field effects in the discrimination of sine wave gratings. *Percep. Psychophys.* **50:** 15–18.
73. Kitterle, F. L., Christman, S., and Hellige, J. (1990). Hemispheric differences are found in the identification, but not the detection, of low versus high spatial frequencies. *Percep. Psychophys.* **48:** 297–306.
74. Jacobs, R. A., and Kosslyn, S. M. (1998). Encoding shape and spatial relations: The role of receptive field size in coordinating complementary representations. *Cognit. Sci.* **18:** 361–386.
75. Corbetta, M., Miezen, F. M., Schulman, G. L., and Petersen, S. E. (1993). A PET study of visuospatial attention. *J. Neurosci.* **13:** 1202–1226.
76. Kosslyn, S. M., Koenig, O., Barrett, A., Cave, C. B., Tang, J., and Gabrieli, J. D. E. (1989). Evidence for two types of spatial representations: Hemispheric specialization for categorical and coordinate relations. *J. Exp. Psychol. Hum. Percep. Perform.* **15:** 723–735.
77. Hellige, J. B., and Michimata, C. (1989). Categorization versus distance: Hemispheric differences for processing spatial information. *Memory Cognit.* **17:** 770–776.
78. Laeng, B. (1994). Lateralization of categorical and coordinate spatial functions: A study of unilateral stroke patients. *J. Cognit. Neurosci.* **6**(3): 189–203.
79. Umilta, C., Rizzolatti, G., Marzi, C. A., Zamboni, G., Franzini, C., Camarda, R., and Berlucchi, G. (1974). Hemispheric differences in the discrimination of line orientation. *Neuropsychologia* **12:** 165–174.
80. White, M. J. (1971). Visual hemifield differences in the perception of letter and contour orientation. *Can. J. Psychol.* **25:** 207–212.
81. Goldenberg, G. (1989). The ability of patients with brain damage to generate mental visual images. *Brain* **112:** 305–325.
82. Hannay, H. J., Varney, N. R., and Benton, A. L. (1976). Visual localization in patients with unilateral brain disease. *J. Neurol. Neurosurg. Psychiatry* **39:** 307–313.
83. Taylor, A. M., and Warrington, E. K. (1973). Visual discrimination in patients with localized brain lesions. *Cortex* **9:** 82–93.
84. Warrington, E. K., and Rabin, P. (1970). Perceptual matching in patients with cerebral lesions. *Neuropsychologia* **8:** 475–487.
85. De Renzi, E., Faglioni, P., and Scotti, G. (1971). Judgment of spatial orientation in patients with focal brain damage. *J. Neurol. Neurosurg. Psychiatry* **34:** 489–495.
86. Mehta, Z., and Newcombe, F. (1991). A role for the left hemisphere in spatial processing. *Cortex* **27:** 153–167.
87. Critchley, M. (1953). *The Parietal Lobes.* Hafner, New York.
88. De Renzi, E. (1982). *Disorders of Space Exploration and Cognition.* Wiley, New York.
89. Levine, D. N., Maini, R. B., and Calvanio, R. (1988). Pure agraphia and Gerstmann's syndrome as a visuospatial-language dissociation: An experimental case study. *Brain Lang.* **35:** 172–196.
90. Luria, A. R. (1980). *Higher Cortical Functions in Man.* Basic Books, New York.

91. Mehta, Z., Newcombe, F., and Damasio, H. (1987). A left hemisphere contribution to visuospatial processing. *Cortex* **23:** 447–461.
92. Corkin, S. (1979). Hidden-figures test performance: Lasting effects of unilateral penetrating head injury and transient effects of bilateral cingulotomy. *Neuropsychologia* **17:** 585–605.
93. Russo, M., and Vignolo, L. A. (1967). Visual figure-ground discrimination in patients with unilateral cerebral disease. *Cortex* **3:** 113–127.
94. Teuber, H. L., and Weinstein, S. (1956). Ability to discover hidden figures after cerebral lesions. *Arch. Neurol. Psychiatry* **76:** 369–379.
95. Van Kleeck, M. H., and Kosslyn, S. M. (1989). Gestalt laws of perceptual organization in an embedded figures task: Evidence for hemispheric specialization. *Neuropsychologia* **27:** 1179–1186.
96. Pinker, S. (1993). *The Language Instinct.* Wm. Morrow, New York.
97. Gazzaniga, M. S. (1970). *The Bisected Brain.* Appleton-Century-Crofts, New York.
98. Zaidel, E., Clarke, J. M., and Suyenobo, B. (1990). Hemispheric independence: A paradigm case for cognitive neuroscience. In *Neurobiology of Higher Cognitive Function* (A. B. Scheibel and A. F. Wechsler, eds.), pp. 880–890. Guilford, New York.
99. Baynes, K., Tramo, M. J., and Gazzaniga, M. S. (1992). Reading with a limited lexicon in the right hemisphere of a callosotomy patient. *Neuropsychologia* **30**(2): 187–200.
100. Deleted.
101. Hellige, J. B. (1993). *Hemispheric Asymmetry: What's Right and What's Left.* Harvard University Press, Cambridge, MA.
102. Kutas *et al.* (1990).
103. Baynes, K. (1990). Language and reading in the right hemisphere: Highways and biways of the brain? *J. Cognit. Neurosci.* **2:** 159–179.
104. Baynes, K., and Gazzaniga, M. S. (1988). Right hemisphere language: Insights into normal language mechanisms? In *Language, Communication and the Brain* (F. Plum, ed.) Raven Press, New York.
105. Code, C. (1987). *Language, Aphasia and the Right Hemisphere.* Wiley, Chichester.
106. Koenig, O., Wetzel, C., and Caramazza, A. (1992). Evidence for different types of lexical representations in the cerebral hemispheres. *Cognit. Neuropsychol.* **9:** 33–45.
107. Hécaen, H., and Albert, M. L. (1978). *Human Neuropsychology.* Wiley, New York.
108. Deleted.
109. Lenneberg, E. H. (1967). *Biological Foundations of Language.* Wiley, London.
110. Gazzaniga, M. S., LeDoux, J. E., Smylie, C. S., and Volpe, B. T. (1979). Plasticity in speech organization following commissurotomy. *Brain* **102:** 805–815.
111. Berndt, R. S., Carmazza, A., and Zurif, E. (1983). Language functions: Syntax and semantics. In *Language Function and Brain Organization* (S. J. Segalowitz, ed.), pp. 5–28. Academic Press, New York.
112. Petersen, S. E., Fox, P. T., Posner, M. I., Mintun, M., and Raichle, M. E. (1988). Positron emission tomographic studies of the cortical anatomy of single-word processing. *Nature (London)* **331:** 585–589.
113. Heffner, H. E., and Heffner, R. S. (1984). Temporal lobe lesions and perception of species-specific vocalizations by macaques. *Science* **226:** 76–76.
114. Petersen, S. E., Fox, P. T., Snyder, A. Z., and Raichle, M. E. (1990). Activation of extrastriate and frontal cortical areas by visual words and word-like stimuli. *Science* **249:** 1041–1044.
115. Lauter, J. L., Herscovitch, P., Formby, C., and Raichle, M. E. (1985). Tonotopic organization in human auditory cortex revealed by positron emission tomography. *Hear. Res.* **20:** 199–205.
116. Mazziotta, J. C., Phelps, M. E., Carson, R. E., and Kuhl, D. E. (1982). Tomographic mapping of human cerebral metabolism: Auditory stimulation. *Neurology* **32:** 921–937.
117. Shallice, T. (1981). Phonological agraphia and the lexical route in writing. *Brain* **104:** 413–429.

CHAPTER

59

Thinking and Problem Solving

Stanislas Dehaene, John Jonides, Edward E. Smith, and Manfred Spitzer

The higher mental processes include mental calculation, reasoning, problem solving, and the understanding of language. Virtually all instances of these processes require the use of stored information (see Chapters 55 and 56). Consider two examples, one involving mental arithmetic and the other geometric analogies.

1. Mentally calculate the running total of the following series of numbers: 28, 17, 33, 19, 22.
2. Inspect the 3 × 3 matrix in Fig. 59.1, in which the bottom right entry is missing, and determine which of the 8 alternatives given below the matrix is the missing entry. (To do this, you have to determine the rules that specify how the forms vary across the rows and columns.)

You cannot do the mental arithmetic problem without accessing the relevant arithmetic facts from **long-term memory,** nor can you solve the geometric analogy without retrieving from memory the instructions about choosing among alternatives and analyzing the rows and columns. But more than long-term memory is involved here. In the mental arithmetic example you have to keep accessing the current running total before you can add a new number to it; the constantly changing running total is presumably active, maintained in short-term or **working memory** (in contrast to long-term memory). In the geometric analogy, in each row or column you have to determine the similarities and differences between pairs of items, and then keep these similarities and differences active in working memory (see Chapter 56).

The general point is that thought processes typically generate a number of intermediate mental products that must be held "on-line" for successful performance to occur. This on-line storage system is working memory, and earlier work has established some of its key computational properties (at least for verbal contents like digits, letters, or words). Specifically, working memory:

1. Requires on the order of a few hundred milliseconds to encode a new item.
2. Has a limited storage capacity that has been estimated at 7 ± 2 items.[1]
3. Loses information in a matter of seconds.[2]
4. Requires about 50–100 ms for retrieval of each item.[3]

The system is thus well suited to briefly holding a limited amount of material that must be rapidly accessible, just the kind of system needed to expedite thinking.

The fact that working memory is involved in many forms of thought suggests the following two-step strategy for studying the neural basis of thought:

1. Start by focusing on tasks that require just working memory, and try to characterize the neural circuitry of this system.
2. Then consider tasks that require the involvement of working memory in increasingly complex ways, and use what has been learned about working memory to bootstrap our understanding of the neural basis of these more complex tasks.

In what follows, we adopt this strategy. Specifically:

1. First we consider relatively pure memory tasks and provide an account of a neural network for working memory.
2. Then we move up one step in complexity, looking at tasks in which subjects not only store items in working memory but also code each one with respect to temporal order.
3. Next we consider tasks in which subjects perform a few operations on information stored in work-

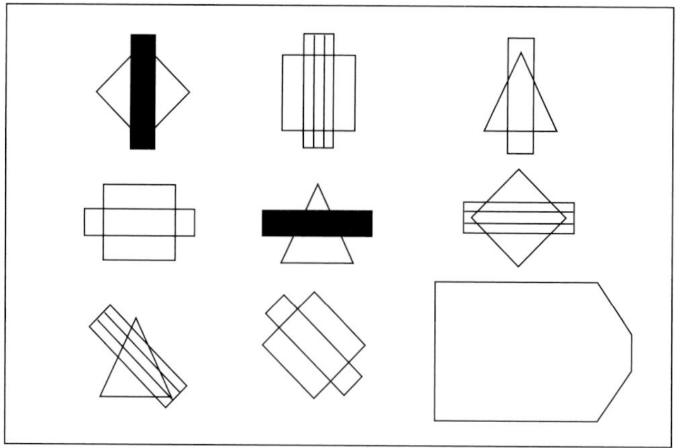

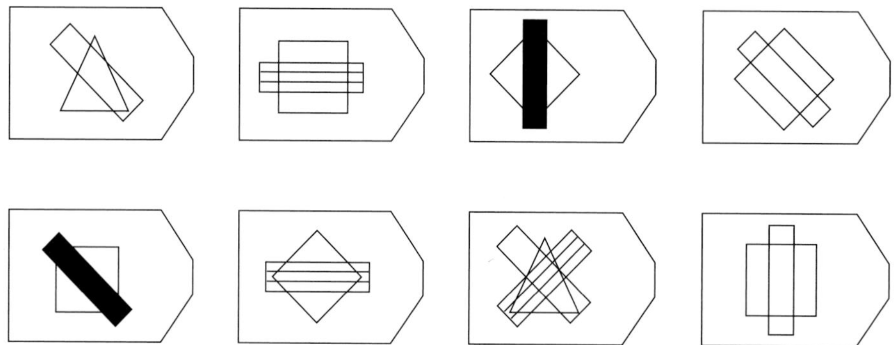

FIGURE 59.1 Example of a geometric analogies problem (from the Ravens Progressive Matrices Test). The task is to determine which of the eight alternatives presented beneath the matrix is the missing bottom-right entry in the matrix. See text for further explanation.

ing memory to accomplish a meaningful goal. Here, we consider two kinds of tasks—language understanding and mental arithmetic.

In discussing the tasks used in steps 2–3 we will be interested in whether the neural basis of performance involves the network for working memory. In addition, we will be interested in what other neural networks are recruited for task performance.

VERBAL WORKING MEMORY

Before beginning our discussion, one more introductory issue must be addressed. We have talked as if there is just one working memory, as if the same storage system is used regardless of the contents that have to be maintained. This assumption is almost certainly incorrect, as shown by single-cell studies of nonhuman primates and neuroimaging studies of humans. Recordings from the dorsolateral prefrontal cortex of adult monkeys[4] showed that some neurons responded only when spatial information had to be stored, and other neurons responded only when visual-object information had to be briefly maintained. In addition, positron emission tomography (PET) studies with humans have found different patterns of activation depending on whether the material stored briefly is spatial, visual object, or verbal in nature.[5,6] Thus, we need to specify *which* working memory we are discussing. In what follows we focus on verbal working memory because so many problem-solving and reasoning tasks have a verbal component.

Verbal Working Memory Retains Items in a Speech-Based Code

Verbal working memory is the system involved when one must briefly remember a series of numbers, letters, words, or other verbal items. For example, after reading the following letters, look away from the text for about 5 s and then report these letters in order:

E B T G V C P. Most people who do this task report that during the 5-s retention interval they implicitly spoke or "rehearsed" the names of the letters to themselves. This introspection is supported by objective behavioral data. For example, the faster one's rate of implicit speech, the better one performs the task (because it is less likely that a letter will have faded before it can be rehearsed again[7]). The upshot of this line of behavioral research is that verbal working memory represents items in a phonological code (the sounds of the items), and these phonological representations can be maintained by a rehearsal process that consists of internal speech.

Rehearsal and Storage Components of Working Memory Have Separate Anatomy

With regard to the neural basis of working memory, consider first some evidence from neuropsychology. Brain damage can result in an impairment known as the **short-term memory syndrome,**[8] in which the primary deficit is an inability to store verbal information for a period of seconds (the deficit is particularly severe for the auditory presentation of material). We can illustrate with one frequently studied patient, KF (see Box 56.3, Chapter 56). When KF is presented with a sequence of 1 to 7 digits and is required to immediately repeat them back in order, he gets only 1 digit correct (normal is 7). In contrast, when KF is given a long-term memory task—say, learning a list of 20 words over a number of trials—he performs normally. Thus, KF's memory deficit is confined to verbal working memory. Importantly, part of KF's brain damage includes the posterior parietal cortex of the left hemisphere. This region is the most frequent site of damage in patients manifesting the short-term memory syndrome.

PET scanning studies with normal subjects provide additional support for the involvement of the left-hemisphere posterior parietal cortex. In one study[9] subjects were scanned while they were performing two different tasks. One task, *item recognition,* is presented schematically in Fig. 59.2, top. On each trial, a target set of four letters is presented briefly (200 ms), followed by a blank retention interval of 3000 ms, followed by presentation of a *probe* letter. The subject's task is to decide as quickly as possible whether the probe names one of the target letters (subjects indicate their decision by pressing one of two response buttons). This is a standard test of verbal working memory,[3] and the pattern of observed activation should reveal the brain structures involved in this system. However, the task also includes components that are not part of working memory—perceiving the letters, selecting a response, and executing a response—and the activation due to these unwanted components needs to be subtracted out if a clear "picture" of working memory is to be gained. This problem is routine in PET research and there is a routine solution: scan the same subjects on a task that is thought to involve the same perceptual and response components as the memory task of interest but not the working memory component, and then subtract the activation pattern obtained in this control task from that obtained in the memory task. The control task used in this study is sketched in Fig. 59.2, bottom. In this task, a set of four letters again is presented on each trial, but now the letters remain in view while the probe is presented so that the subject need not rely on memory in making a decision.

The data obtained from the memory and control tasks consist of sets of images, each image showing the relative changes in blood flow in a particular horizontal slice of cortex. Since increases in blood flow are assumed to be monotonic with increases in neural activity, each brain image reveals which regions have relative increases in neural activity during performance of the task of interest. When the images of the control task are subtracted from those of the memory task, a number of regions are significantly active; presumably these regions mediate verbal working memory. Importantly, one of these regions in the posterior cortex of the left hemisphere is the same region implicated by the neuropsychological studies of the short-term memory syndrome. However, other regions are active as well. They include anterior left-hemisphere regions known to be involved in the production and planning of speech,[10] including Broca's area, the premotor area, and the supplementary motor area (or SMA). Given their role in overt speech, it seems plausible they may mediate covert speech (i.e., rehearsal) as well.

PET experiments in other laboratories provide corroborative evidence for this distinction between posterior storage mechanisms and anterior rehearsal mechanisms. For example, the item-recognition task was associated with activation in the left-hemisphere posterior parietal cortex as well as in anterior speech-related regions.[11] In this same study, when activation in a task requiring rehearsal but not storage was subtracted from the activation associated with the item-recognition task, significant activation remained in the posterior region but not in the anterior regions. This pattern of results gives us a picture of verbal working memory that includes a storage component in the posterior cortex and a rehearsal component in the anterior cortex, both in the left hemisphere.

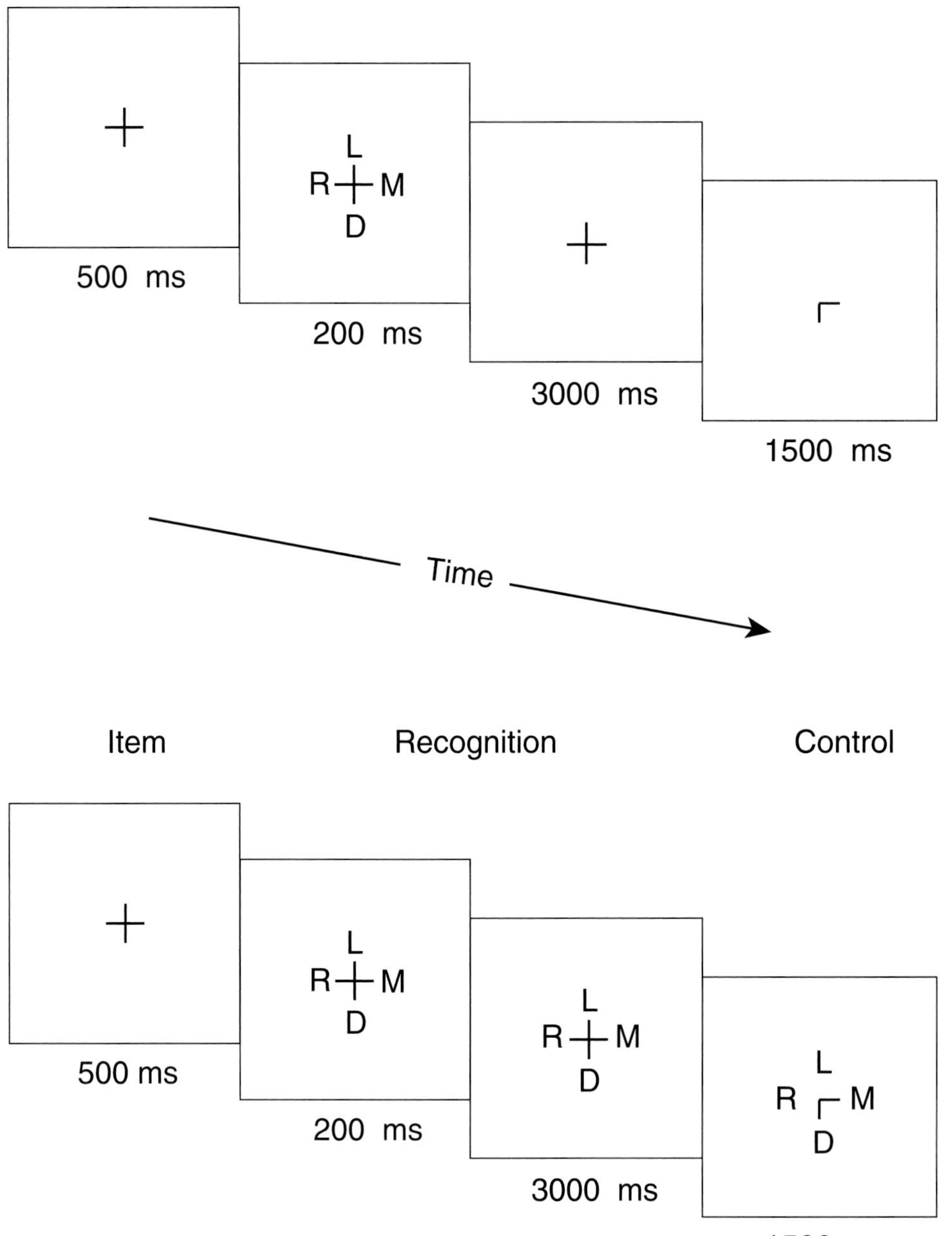

FIGURE 59.2 Schematic representations of the item recognition task (top) and its control condition (bottom).

Working Memory Can Include Temporal Tags to Order Information

Recent neuroimaging research has focused on tasks that required subjects not only to maintain items in working memory but also to code them with respect to their temporal order.[5,9,12,13] Such tasks are of interest because they are further along the continuum from pure memory tasks to tasks that involve working memory in more complex cognition (in accordance with the strategy laid out earlier).

In one such study,[9] subjects saw a continuous sequence of letters, and for each one they had to decide whether it was identical to the one presented two letters earlier or two back. This "two back" task requires a working memory load of two to three items (the last two letters presented plus the current one). It also requires subjects to temporally code the items currently in working memory—because only the letter that entered two back is a proper match—and to continually change these codes as new items enter working memory. The questions of interest are: Do PET images for this task show evidence of the working-memory neural network described earlier, and do new regions of activation emerge that may correspond to the coding operations needed in this task? The answer to both questions is "yes." When activation under a suitable control condition is subtracted from that in the two back memory condition, the resulting PET images again show activation in the left-hemisphere posterior parietal region that presumably mediates storage, as well as the left-hemisphere anterior regions that presumably mediate inner speech (Broca's area, the premotor area, and SMA).

Importantly, some regions that are not active in pure memory tasks (like item recognition) are active in this memory-plus-coding task. Some of the additional regions are right-hemisphere homologs of left-hemisphere areas already described, including right-hemisphere SMA. These additional regions may reflect mainly the added difficulty of this task compared to the item recognition tasks; the right-hemisphere homologs are helping out in a particularly difficult version of what is normally a left-hemisphere task. Another result, however, suggests that the current task is qualitatively different from a pure memory task. When more sensitive statistical analyses are conducted, an area in the dorsolateral prefrontal cortex (area 46) also shows evidence of activation. This area is known to be involved in the temporal coding of information.[14]

Thinking Includes Working Memory and Executive Attention

So far we have considered working memory in isolation. PET studies have revealed specific brain areas that mediate components of working memory such as storage and active rehearsal.

Let us take a bigger step up the complexity scale and consider tasks in which subjects perform some operations on the information stored in working memory so as to accomplish a meaningful goal. This involves not only the problem of representing information in memory that has been considered in this chapter but also the issue of executive control discussed in Chapter 54. Two kinds of tasks will be considered: certain situations requiring an understanding of language and standard mental arithmetic problems. Both kinds of tasks clearly exemplify thinking.

Working Memory Mediates Communication

The best behavioral evidence for the involvement of working memory in language understanding comes from correlational studies.[15,16] There is a positive correlation between a measure of an individual's working-memory capacity and that individual's performance in a language-understanding task, such as answering true–false questions about previously read paragraphs. (Such correlations, though, are obtained with measures of working memory that require the subject to store material while concurrently engaging in some processing, for example, storing the last word of each of a series of sentences that the subject also has to understand.)

Some neuropsychological evidence for the involvement of working memory in language understanding comes from patients with the short-term memory syndrome (impairment in short-term memory tasks associated with damage in left posterior parietal cortex). Although such patients have no difficulty understanding most kinds of sentences, they perform poorly when they also have to carry out a mental operation based on the verbatim content of the sentence.[17] Presumably, storing the verbatim content—the exact words—requires verbal working memory, and this is why the patients' capacity to understand sentences breaks down. Thus, the patients are impaired in answering orally presented comparative questions like: "Which is green, a poppy or lettuce?" Successful performance here depends on maintaining the exact words ("green," "poppy," and "lettuce") and performing mental operations on the representations of these words.

Another kind of sentence on which the patients show impairment is an orally presented instruction with high information content.[18] An example is "Before picking up the green circle, touch the red square," where the patient is expected to carry out the instruction. In this case, understanding requires setting up a plan, and the generation of this plan requires verbatim memory of some of the information; the latter requirement presumably causes the patients' problems. Other sentence types that people with short-term memory syndrome have difficulty with show the same general characteristics.[17]

Given that we are dealing with language understanding, regions other than the left posterior parietal cortex—namely, the language regions in the perisylvian area of the left posterior temporal cortex (including Wernicke's area)—are also involved. These are the regions that are damaged in many patients who show language disturbances (e.g., Wernicke's aphasia). The left-hemisphere posterior temporal cortex apparently houses our normal language understanding system. However, when verbatim memory of language is required, the verbal working memory system in left-hemisphere parietal and frontal cortices is called into play as well.

Arithmetic Also Requires Working Memory

Extensive behavioral evidence indicates that verbal working memory is used in mental arithmetic. For instance, the longer partial sums must be held before they can be reported, the poorer mental-calculation performance will be, which suggests that the outputs of mental calculation undergo decay just as any other information in working memory. Thus, when subjects must mentally add a 3-digit and a 2-digit number, their accuracy is greater when they can report their answers in reverse order (units, tens, hundreds) than in forward order.[19] Another piece of behavioral evidence for the link between working memory and calculation comes from studies on the cognitive effects of aging. It is well known that working memory declines with age.[20] It has also been established that the ability to mentally execute a multistep numerical calculation declines with age. Neither of these two findings is surprising. What is newsworthy is that the age-based decline in mental calculation is almost totally attributable to those steps of the calculation that require storage in working memory.[21]

Turning to the neural underpinnings of mental calculation, we find that patients with the short-term memory syndrome also show impairment on arithmetic tests.[17] In addition, early neuroimaging work[22] showed that when subjects engaged in a mental arithmetic task (subtracting successive 3s from 50), the left-hemisphere parietal cortex was activated. These same imaging results also showed extensive activation in the frontal cortex, including the dorsolateral prefrontal cortex. More recent neuroimaging work has confirmed that mental calculations recruit both inferior parietal regions associated with number processing and dorsolateral prefrontal ones associated with working memory.[23] Again, working memory seems to be an important component in a thinking task, but it is only one component of the total neural system recruited for the task.

Summary

Neuroimaging tasks that look at verbal working memory show activation of left-hemisphere frontal and parietal sites. The frontal area is closely related to rehearsal of the items in working memory, whereas the posterior area is related to storing items. Things can be viewed as a combination of these working memory areas with high-level executive attention networks that were reviewed in Chapter 54.

MODELS OF PROBLEM SOLVING

Nearly all the areas of the brain can be said to be involved in some form of problem solving. For instance, some visual areas solve the problem of recovering the 3D shape of objects from their retinal projection. As already noticed by Helmholtz at the end of the 19th century, such "perceptual problems" can be extremely difficult and ambiguous and require a sophisticated apparatus, adequately called by Helmholtz an "unconscious inference," in order to solve them. However, the kind of problem solving that is performed in perception (and also in simple motor control) has the characteristic of being highly inflexible. No matter how long we look at many visual illusions, our percepts do not change. This is because our perceptual apparatus is dedicated to solving a single restricted problem, and almost always solves it in the same way.

The kind of problem solving that we consider in this chapter, however, is quite different and is characterized by a considerable amount of flexibility. Mammals (especially the higher primates and, of course, humans) can find a solution to problems that they have never encountered before and for which evolution has not developed dedicated "wired-in" solutions. For instance, a rat can find the way out of a maze, a chimpanzee can figure out how to use a stick to unhook a banana from the ceiling, and a human adult can subtract 356 from 644, play chess, or plan a trip to Mexico. Such activities involve (a) constructing an accurate mental representation of the goal to be achieved, (b) selecting appropriate means for achieving this goal, and (c) executing the planned strategy and monitoring how successful it is.

Obviously, models of problem solving can be aimed at several different levels of analysis. Mathematics (especially graph theory and game theory), computer science, and artificial intelligence have mostly been concerned with designing and evaluating different computational strategies for solving problems. Although some insights have been gained through this approach, it will only be minimally discussed here because, for the most part and until recently, it has shown little concern for the actual solutions that humans and animals use or for the neural apparatus underlying them. We shall deal more deeply with models, originating from cognitive psychology and/or neuropsychology, that have examined the mental architectures underlying simple reasoning. Finally, we shall discuss recent models that have made specific proposals about the neuronal or even the molecular systems underlying flexible problem solving.

Artificial Intelligence Studies Aid Us in Describing Problem Domains

From its early inception, artificial intelligence has been trying to copy the flexibility that humans, and

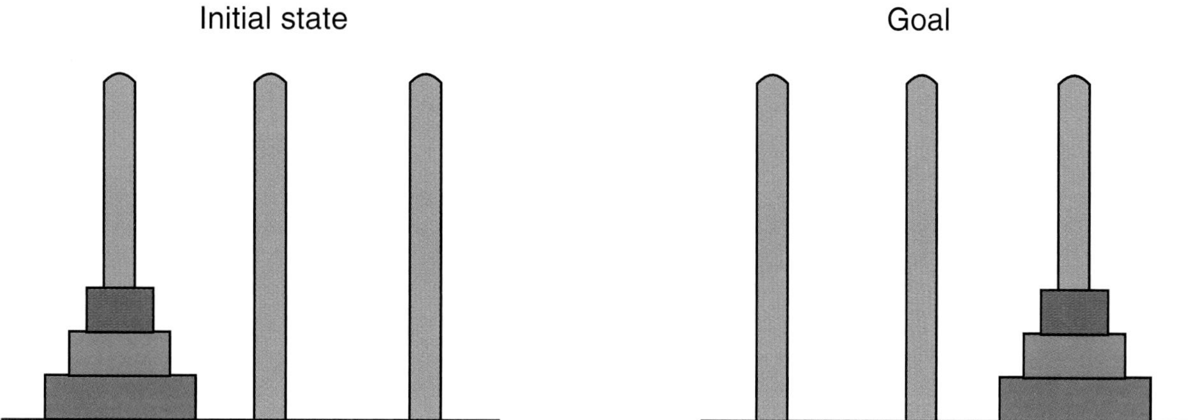

FIGURE 59.3 Example of a simple Tower of Hanoi problem. The task is to move the stack of disks over to the right hand peg, moving one at a time, and being sure not to stack a larger disk on a smaller one.

to some extent animals, show in abstract problem solving as exemplified by chess playing or theorem proving. One problem task that has been widely studied is the Tower of Hanoi, illustrated in Fig. 59.3. In this task an optimal solution can be specified, and yet the task captures some of the decision-making strategies involved in common games such as chess.

An important insight from studies of the Tower of Hanoi and of chess is that such problems can be abstractly represented by **decision trees:** at each point in time, there are many options for action, some of them leading closer to the goal and most of the others diverging from the solution (Fig. 59.4). Thus, solving a problem becomes equivalent to exploring a large tree of possibilities and trying to find the shortest path toward the goal.

In the most interesting cases, the tree of possibilities is so large that it cannot be explored, or even known, in its entirety. Hence, **heuristics** or rules of thumb must be devised to guide the search. One possibility is to reason from the goal backward, defining a chain of achievable subgoals that become progressively easier to reach from the current starting situation. Another useful device is an evaluation function that, for each given situation, computes an approximation of how remote the goal is. If the evaluation function is adequate, simply picking, whenever a decision needs to be made, the action that leads to the most valuable situation will be a successful strategy.

Another useful problem-solving trick in artificial intelligence (AI) is using learning to progressively reduce and focus the search. One of the earlier successes of AI, Samuel's checker-playing program, progressively adapted its evaluation function so that, in the end, the evaluation of a very large tree of possibilities could be predicted by a single "look" at the checker deck. Similarly, frequently used action sequences may be compiled into a more or less fixed scenario or script.[24] Upon later encounteres with a similar situation, the script can be reused. The role of the controller program is then confined to checking the execution of the script and reacting appropriately if it becomes inadapted or ends prematurely. In the course of solving more and more problems, some AI programs thus learn to compile a repertoire of strategies for solving different problems. When a relatively novel problem-solving situation occurs, and when the known strategies seem to fail, such a program still needs to resort to tree exploration heuristics as above. However, it can automatically detect recurring regularities in its exploration behavior and add them to its list of available strategies. Progressively, then, problem solving comes to rely more and more on precompiled strategies, with calls to a higher-level controller becoming less and less frequent.

Although most AI approaches are aimed at developing efficient programs rather than at simulating human problem-solving behavior, it is remarkable that in so doing, they have developed concepts that often provide adequate characterizations of the actual mental architectures for abstract thought. There is considerable evidence for a dissociation, in humans, between "routine" and "creative" problem solving. The greatest chess players, for instance, have developed highly efficient routines for "parsing" any chess situation and immediately getting excellent hunches as to what the best moves may be. Before becoming experts, however, we all have to painfully explore a tree of possibilities that taxes our working memory, error detection, and backtracking abilities. Areas of the prefrontal cortex are instrumental in the creative form of reasoning and problem solving.

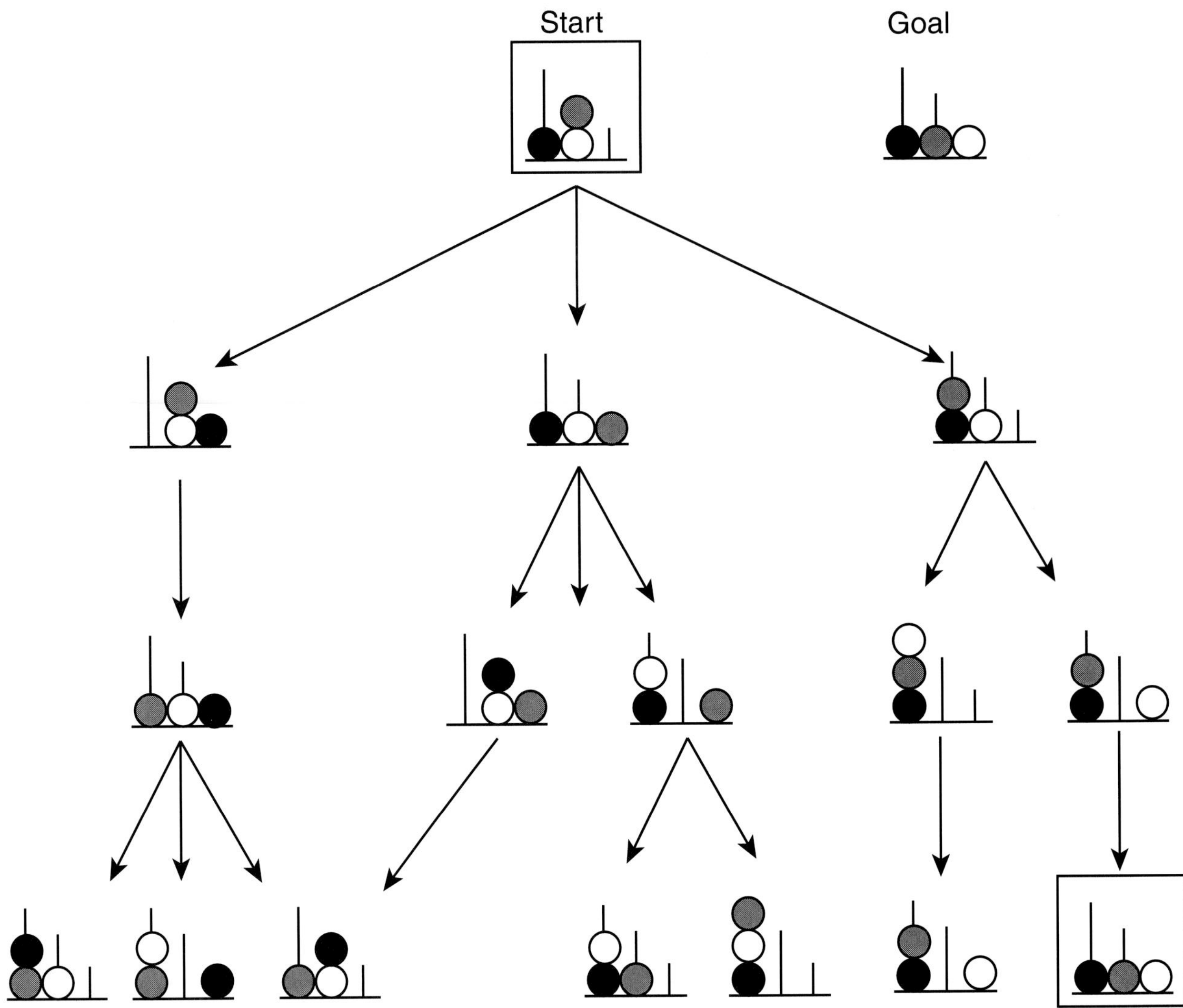

FIGURE 59.4 A small portion of the decision tree for Shallice's Tower of London test, which requires planning a series of moves of balls on three pegs[8].

There Is a Common Human Architecture for Problem Solving

One of the more influential models of the architecture of human problem solving was developed by Norman and Shallice (see also Chapter 54 for a review of this model). The Norman–Shallice model belongs to cognitive neuropsychology. Although it nicely captures the behavioral data on problem solving in normal human adults and in patients with damage to the frontal lobe, it provides no means of predicting the neuronal circuits and the activity of cells involved in problem-solving tasks. However, as described in Chapter 54, tasks involving conflict usually activate frontal areas. A number of neuronal network models have been proposed on the basis of these findings.

The Prefrontal Cortex May Play a Role in the Flexible Adaptation of an Organism to Various Tasks

A classical set of task tapping prefrontal functions in animals is the delayed-response task. Depending on the version of the task, the animal must pay attention to and store in working memory different aspects of its environment, such as the identity of an object (in delayed matching-to-sample tasks) or its location (in spatial delayed-response tasks). Following a delay, the animal is given a choice between two objects and is asked to find the one that matches the description stored in memory. Dehaene and Changeux[25,26] have proposed a simple model of how the prefrontal cortex contributes to such delayed-response tasks. The model is based on a hierarchy of neural layers, each of which modulates the level immediately lower to it (Fig. 59.5). When the object to be memorized is presented for input, a low-level direct mapping between sensory data and corresponding actions allows it to be grasped. This lower level input–output system, which corresponds to the triggering of action schemata in the Norman–Shallice model, has no memory, however, so it cannot support delayed-response performance. A higher level mapping includes working memory units with long-lasting firing properties that can modulate and select among actions triggered at the lower level. This indirect mapping coarsely maps onto the dorsolateral prefrontal cortex, and the activity of the simulated units mimics the long-lasting, delayed related firing of actual prefrontal cells.

In the Dehaene–Changeux model, behavioral flexibility is achieved because the nature of the task to be performed (spatial delayed-response or delayed matching-to-sample) is encoded in cell activities rather than in connection strengths and can therefore be modified "on the fly" as required, without requiring slow modifications of synaptic strengths. As noted, some units in the model code for aspects of past experience stored in working memory. The activity of other units, called "rule-coding units," encodes the behavioral set of plans that the organism is currently following. The network might change, for instance, from performing spatial delayed response to performing delayed matching-to-sample by the mere switching on or off of some rule-coding units.

In human adults, a classical task tapping the ability to switch between mental sets is the Wisconsin Card Sorting Test. A deck of cards bearing colored symbols must be sorted, but at different stages of the test the sorting criterion changes abruptly from, say, color to shape or to number of stimuli on the cards. Patients with lesioned prefrontal cortext fail to change their sorting criterion and perseverate sorting by color. Such perseveration behavior can be mimicked by the Dehaene–Changeux network (Fig. 59.5B).

A group of units (color rule-coding units), when

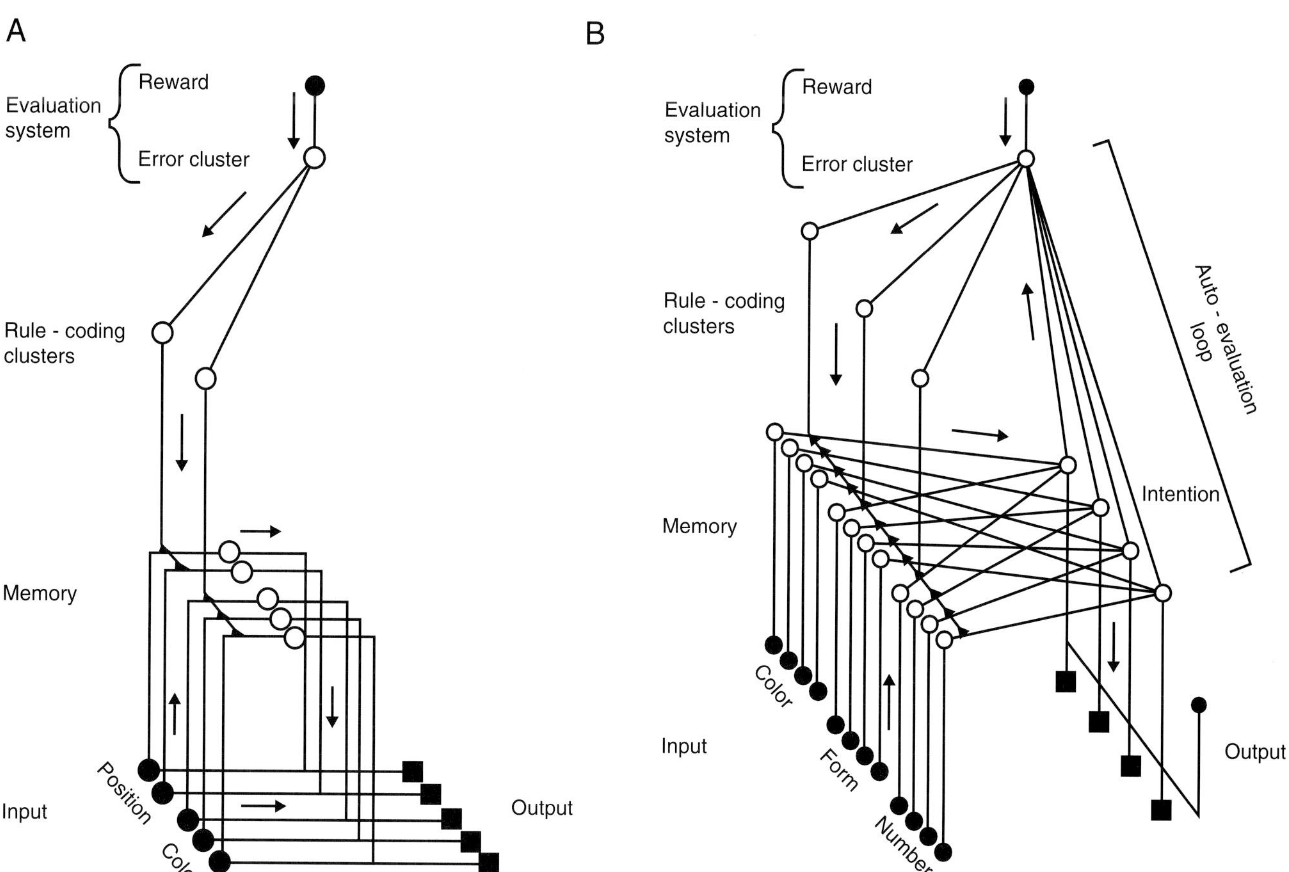

FIGURE 59.5 Architecture of two simple model neuronal networks that have been used to simulate functions of the prefrontal cortex. Left: Delayed-response tasks. Right: Wisconsin Card Sorting Task. Redrawn from Dehaene and Changeux.[26]

active, directs the lower levels of the system to orient to color and therefore to sort the stimulus cards according to their color. The overall sorting plan can be rapidly changed if needed, for instance, if negative external reward signals that the current rule is likely to be invalid. It is assumed that the different rule-coding units are organized in a specialized neuronal network that functions as a generator of diversity. That is, units coding for different rules have a strong level of spontaneous firing that enables them to spontaneously come into play and propose a new hypothetical rule or plan to be followed. Normally, the units inhibit each other so that only one can be active at a given time. Negative reward, however, has the effect of destabilizing the currently active unit and therefore of releasing all the others from inhibition. Spontaneous firing then ensures that new rules will be tried out until a fitting one is found. The model was shown to be able to pass tests of cognitive flexibility such as the Wisconsin Card Sorting Test, and impairments similar to those found in patients with damage to the frontal lobes were observed when parts of the control structure were lesioned. More generally, Dehaene and Changeux[25] have suggested that much of high-level human problem solving rests on "mental Darwinism." Just as Darwin modeled the apparition of new species by random variation followed by selective elimination, the flexible emergence of new problem-solving strategies can be modeled by the random production of novel hypotheses followed by their elimination or selection as a function of their usefulness for solving the problem at hand.

Several gaps in the Dehaene–Changeux models have been filled by models of other groups. Levine and Prueitt[27] have described a network that also solves the Wisconsin Card Sorting Test and embodies a distinction between habits (circuits that cannot be modulated by external reinforcement) and biases (which can learn, using reinforcement, to overcome habits). There is indeed good physiological and anatomical evidence for a separate neural circuity for habit formation.[28] Another important issue is whether the neuronal architecture for learning complex tasks must be prewired from the start (as in the Dehaene–Changeux and Levine–Prueitt models), or whether it can be partially acquired by learning. Other structured models still embody the distinction between a lower level of direct sensory–motor mapping and a higher level of controlled processing, in which the higher level is capable of learning.[29–31] One model starts with a semirandom connectivity. The simulated prefrontal cells then learn to store and keep "on-line" bits of information related to the task at hand.

It is important to note that most current models either are prewired to solve a specific task or require thousands of learning trials before they can master a novel task. No model to date has shown anything close to the specifically human capacity for switching tasks by mere exposure to a few seconds of instructions. The most flexible of current models can only switch between a small number of local circuits. To put such "flexibility" into perspective, brain-imaging techniques in humans have shown that the pattern of regional activation of the entire brain can be radically altered by attention, intention, and instruction. Much more research is needed to understand how the selection of active circuits is controlled in the human brain.

Emotions Are Involved in Models of Reasoning

An interesting feature of current neuronal models of problem solving and decision making is that they have led to a renewed interest in reward, evaluation, and emotion systems and to a reconsideration of their role in reasoning. In most of the above models, flexibility comes from the prompt behavioral reaction of the system to a change in the positive or negative reinforcement signals that it receives. This is achieved by a dedicated architecture in which the "value" of an action is rapidly signaled to several areas and is allowed to affect neuronal activity and synaptic strengths in the circuits that it projects to. Dehaene and Changeux[26] have proposed one possible molecular mechanism for the rapid effect of reward signals. Negative reward would be signaled by an elevated concentration of a diffuse neuromodulator (e.g., dopamine or acetylcholine) in prefrontal areas. In the presence of this neuromodulator, currently active postsynaptic receptor molecules (ion channel open) would undergo allosteric transitions to a slowly desensitized state in which the ion channel is closed. This would have the effect of temporarily inactivating neurons and circuits that were active just before negative reward was received. It would therefore impose a change in the internal activity of prefrontal neurons and hence a switch to a new plan of behavior.

Negative or positive reward signals, however, need not come exclusively from the external world. Rather, the organism itself may learn to predict the occurrence of reward and may activate reward circuits internally when the appropriate conditions are met. Such a mechanism is called an "adaptative critic"[32] or an "auto-evaluation loop."[26] It empowers the system with an ability to evaluate its current choices and intentions spontaneously without waiting for an external reaction, and in some cases, without even actually performing actions. Reasoning, in effect, becomes a mental simulation of possible actions and an internal evaluation of their predicted consequences. Unlike a more basic system, a network possessing an auto-evaluation loop can use reasoning to avoid making the same error twice in the Wisconsin Card Sorting Test. When a new rule is selected, the network first tries it internally to see if it yields the same error as on the previous trial. If it does, negative reward is predicted and triggers the elimination of this rule, as would a normal external reward.

Summary

Artificial intelligence models problem solving as the exploration of a vast tree of possibilities under the guidance of various heuristics and evaluation functions. Prefrontal cortex is heavily involved in this active exploration. Neuronal models of planning and problem solving suggest at least three functions for prefrontal cortex areas. Some prefrontal circuits are involved in the active maintenance of problem information in working memory. Other circuits may be involved in maintaining specific mental strategies and in rapidly switching from one strategy to another. Evaluation circuits, finally, may contribute to the internal monitoring of ongoing plans. Evaluation circuits may cause the release of reward signals, for instance, from catecholaminergic projection systems, which may modulate the activity of other units and thus influence decision making.

DISORDERS OF THOUGHT IN SCHIZOPHRENIA

Psychopathology is the science and the art of describing what is wrong with a mentally ill patient. Schizophrenia (see Box 59.1),[33] which is arguably the most disruptive and at the same time enigmatic of the psychiatric disorders, has a lifetime prevalence of 1 to 1.5% and about 1 person in 3000 is treated for schizophrenia in any one year in the United States. Most patients become ill in their twenties, although there are rare cases of childhood onset and onset past the age of 55.

Schizophrenia Is Associated with Impaired Access to the Mental Lexicon and Working Memory and by Disordered Thought Content

The concept of schizophrenia was formed 90 years ago. At that time, disrupted thought processes were described in terms of association psychology, the prevailing school of thought in psychology. Currently, these changed processes of thinking are considered in a framework linked to the basic cognitive functions of working memory and thought discussed previously.

Schizophrenic thought disorder can be characterized by a *decreased accuracy of lexical access* combined with *decreased working memory.* Both dysfunctions may be related, and they may be caused by dysfunctional maplike semantic networks that can be localized in frontal and temporal cortical areas. Disorders of the content of thought (i.e., delusions) are discussed within a framework of **neuromodulation** and **neuroplasticity** in cortical networks processing semantic and possibly other high-level information. The structures of semantic networks as revealed by experimental psychological, neuropsychological, and functional magnetic resonance imaging (fMRI) studies bear a close resemblance to self-organizing feature maps (i.e., a type of neural network). In these maps, the influence of noise on plasticity can be demonstrated, and these findings can be related to the neuromodulatory function of dopamine, which appears to regulate the signal-to-noise ratio in network information processing. In sum, different methods and strategies provided by cognitive neuroscience are combined to bridge the gap between psychopathology and underlying brain pathology and to provide a comprehensive and parsimonious explanation of a number of otherwise inexplicable or unrelated phenomena.

The Mental Lexicon Is a Maplike Network

The store of words in the mind is called the **mental lexicon.** Words have a number of features regarding meaning, grammar, sound, writing, and aspects of use. Word associations and various ways to study them have played a major role in research on how the mental lexicon is organized—that is, how semantic, grammatical, phonetic, graphemic, and pragmatic information is stored and accessed when language is produced or understood.[34–36]

One of the more important methods for studying word-related computations is the **lexical decision experiment.** The subject must decide whether or not a given string of characters is a word. To investigate specific types of associations, two words are presented one at a time, and the effect of the relation between the words on the reaction time is measured. Figure 59.6 shows the series of events in a typical lexical decision experiment. A robust phenomenon that has been discovered using this technique of lexical decision is **semantic priming.**[37,38] A word is recognized faster if a meaningfully related word is shown immediately before. For example, "black" is recognized faster as a word if it is presented shortly after "white" than if it is presented shortly after a nonrelated word such as "soft."

BOX 59.1

SCHIZOPHRENIA

The Swiss psychiatrist Eugen Bleuler coined the term "schizophrenia" in a famous book, first published in 1911.[33] In this book, which is full of clinical descriptions, Bleuler made the point that this disorder is characterized by four types of symptoms regarding:

(1) thinking (disordered associative processes),
(2) affect (inappropriate, depressed, or manic affect),
(3) will (ambivalence, i.e., indecisiveness), and
(4) social behavior (autism, social withdrawal).

The following writing of a patient examplifies the disturbed thought processes in schizophrenic patients, driven by associative links between concepts rather than goal-directed thinking.

> I am writing on paper. The pen which I am using is from a factory called 'Perry & Co.' This factory is in England. I assume this. Behind the name of Perry & Co. the city of London is inscribed; but not the city. The city of London is in England. I know this from my school-days. Then, I always liked geography. My last teacher in that subject was Professor August A. He was a man with black eyes. I also like black eyes. There are also blue and gray eyes and other sorts, too. I have heard it said that snakes have green eyes. All people have eyes. There are some, too, who are blind. These blind people are led about by a boy. It must be very terrible not to be able to see. There are people who can't see and, in addition, can't hear. I know some who hear too much. One can hear too much. There are many sick people in Burgholzli; they are called patients. One of them I like a great deal. His name is E. Sch. He taught me that in Burgholzli there are many kinds, patients, inmates, attendants. Then there are some who are not here at all. They are all peculiar people. . . . (Bleuler 1911/1950, p. 80).[33]

Schizophrenia poses a major public health problem worldwide, with a lifetime prevalence of about 1% in most cultures and geographic locations studied. Its clinical manifestations usually appear in adolescence and early adulthood. Prognosis varies widely, with some patients showing a stable illness course with minimal disability during maintenance treatment and others a more severe, deteriorating course which eventually stabilizes at a level of marked disability.

While the etiology of schizophrenia is unknown, several lines of converging evidence suggest that schizophrenia is a neurodevelopmental disorder (or group of disorders) resulting from a combination of genetic susceptibility and acquired neuropathology arising early in life. Family, twin, and adoption studies have established the importance of genetic factors in the etiology of schizophrenia, but have also suggested a role for acquired factors.[11,12,14] For example, the concordance rates among monozygotic and dizygotic twins are about 50 and 20%, respectively.

The most compelling evidence for a neurodevelopmental process in schizophrenia comes from *postmortem* studies that show cytoarchitectural disorganization of the cerebral cortex, which if confirmed by future studies would imply a defect in cortical development arising during the second trimester of gestation. Recent neurodevelopmental models proposed for approaching the pathogenesis of schizophrenia attempt to account for these histopathological findings and the several-year latency between the developmental period and the onset of clinical symptoms. For example, some groups have shown that lesions placed in specific frontal cortical or hippocampal areas during the perinatal period in experimental animals result in cognitive impairment and hyperdopaminergic behaviors (see below) which are not pronounced until after puberty. Another model capitalizes on the observation that NMDA–glutamatergic receptor antagonists (e.g., phencyclidine) can produce the spectrum of psychotic, behavioral/social, and cognitive symptoms seen in schizophrenia in nonschizophrenic, postpubertal humans. In contrast, such reactions rarely if ever occur in children who receive NMDA antagonists as part of anesthetic regimens, suggesting that the development of sensitivity to the psychotomimetic effects of NMDA hypofunction has an age dependency similar to that seen for the onset of psychosis in schizophrenia. Moreover, when introduced *in utero* to rats at critical developmental stages, NMDA antagonists produce neurodegenerative changes in the limbic cortex. These observations led to the hypothesis that schizophrenia is associated with NMDA receptor hypofunction, which, during cortical development, produces excitotoxic damage and consequent microscopic abnormalities, and during the postpubertal period, produces susceptibility to psychosis.

Wayne C. Drevets

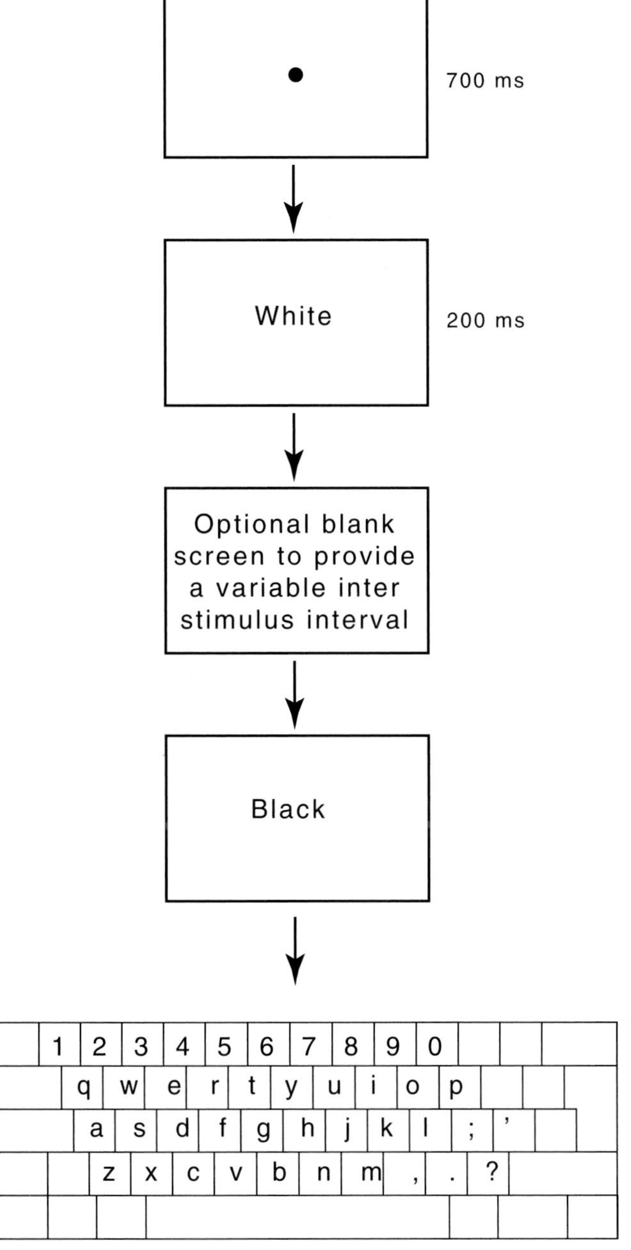

FIGURE 59.6 A typical sequence of events in semantic priming. Time runs vertically from top to bottom. The prime (e.g., white) stays on for 200 ms and the target (e.g., black) until the subjects responds.

Lexical Decision Experiments and Related Techniques Suggest That Word-Related Information Is Stored in the Form of an Associative Network

According to current network models of the mental lexicon, semantic (and possibly other) features of words are represented as "nodes" (which have been called "logogens") in a neuronal network (see Fig. 59.7). In the course of an utterance, these semantic units become activated for a short period of time and thereafter either decay rapidly or are actively inhibited.[38–40] This model of access to the mental lexicon further asserts that concepts activated in a semantic network by a prime serve as a source of activation that spreads to other related concepts. Such spreading of activation to nearby nodes in the semantic network lowers their thresholds of activation, that is, increases their probability of becoming used in the production or understanding of a subsequent utterance. If one of these concepts is denoted by a word that is a target in a lexical decision experiment, this target will be recognized faster because its processing is facilitated by its being already activated to some degree.

Ritter and Kohonen[41] have proposed a biologically and computationally plausible mechanism for the formation of semantic networks. They used a special type of neural network, a so-called self-organizing feature map, to simulate the organization of semantic input. This type of network is highly biologically plausible, since its basic features—lateral inhibition, a high degree of connectivity, and Hebbian learning—are features of the neuronal organization of the neocortex.[42,43] When the neural network is presented with any kind of coherent input, it will create an orderly, maplike representation of this input.[44,45] Ritter and Kohonen presented such a network with the names and characteristics of animals. This was done by using an arbitrary binary code for the animals' names and a binary representation of the presence or absence of the animals' crucial features. Upon presentation of the input, the network formed a map, on which 16 animals were represented in such a way that animals with similar features were close together and dissimilar animals were far apart. In their second experiment, the authors presented short sentences to a similar network. This time, the network organized this input not only according to semantic but also according to grammatical features of the words. Nouns, adverbs, and verbs were put on distinctive areas on the map, and within these areas, the words were organized according to semantic features.

The Brain Maps Semantic Concepts

Very different aspects of the outside world are represented in a maplike manner in the human cortex. Multiple somatosensory and motor maps were described even several decades ago.[46,47] Moreover, multiple retinotopic and tonotopic maps have been discovered in the primate cortex, and evidence indicates that

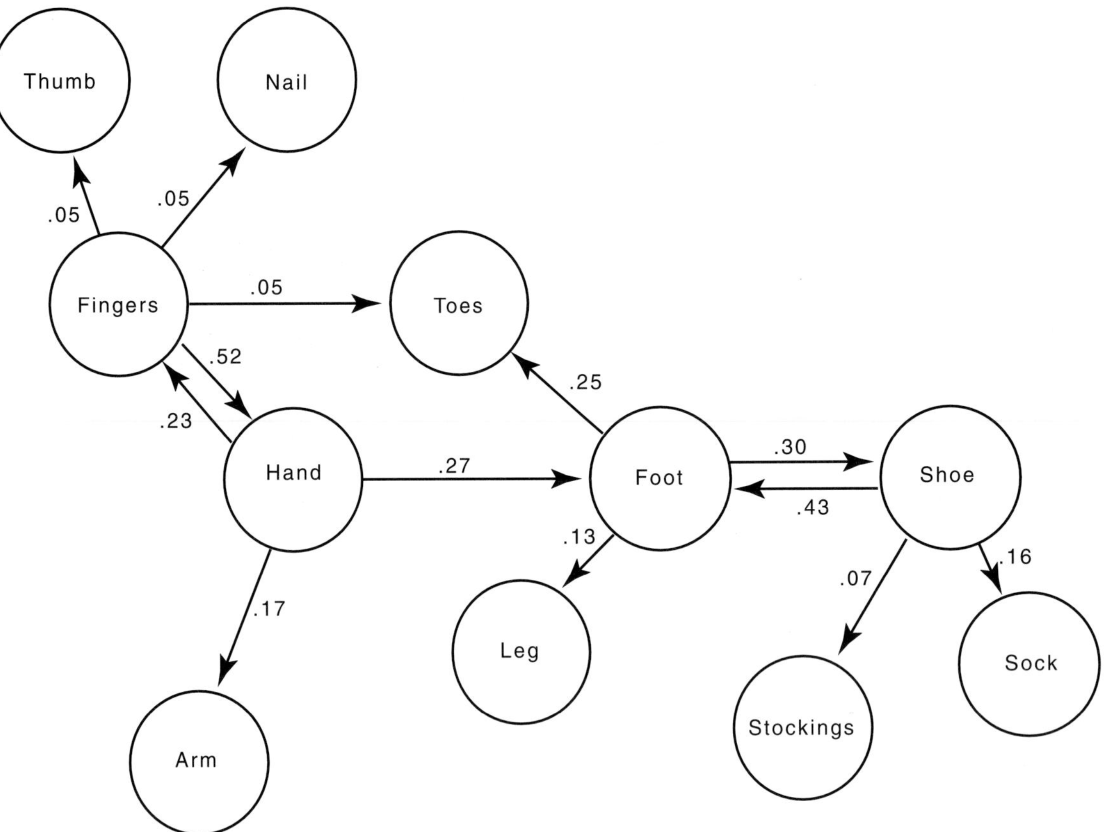

FIGURE 59.7 Semantic network (sketch) derived from word association norms (Palermo & Jenkins, 1963). Words that normal college students associated with stimulus words were put in adjacent nodes.

such maps exist in the human cortex[48–50] (see Chapter 50).

Data accumulated over the past decade from brain damaged-patients point to the existence of *semantic* maps in cortical areas. Some patients with aphasia related to brain damage display a loss of only a small fraction of their semantic memory. Some patients have no cognitive deficit except for the naming of, for example, living things. Others are unable to name vegetables or items inside the house.[18,51,52] These cases appear to be rare, but an increasing number of descriptions of patients with category-specific naming deficits suggests that a negative observation bias may have contributed, and may still be contributing, to the rarity of the phenomenon (see Chapter 57). In fact, as early as 1966, a high incidence of deficits in naming items of a specific category was found in a quantitative study of category-specific word comprehension deficits. This finding led to the conclusion that in aphasic patients such category-specific deficits may be the rule rather than the exception. The fact that the lesions in most of these cases were not small, but rather extended or even diffuse, suggests the existence of multiple semantic maps, so that selective category-specific deficits occur only when the localized representations of the category in each map are lost. In any event, we can conclude from the neuropsychological evidence gathered so far that the representations are organized at least in part by semantics, and these representations must be localized to some degree.[52]

Functional Imaging Studies Support a Maplike Organization of the Mental Lexicon

In one fMRI study, normal subjects were asked to covertly name pictures of items from four categories that had been chosen on the basis of previous neuropsychological evidence (i.e., animals, furniture, fruit, and tools). Color images of 20 items from each category were digitized and processed so that they were about equal in luminance and contrast and could be projected onto a screen mounted within the fMRI scanner. The stimuli were projected one at a time for 1.5 s each, resulting in 30-s stimulation epochs per category. One 6-min data acquisition run consisted of three presentations of each series of category-specific items, that is, of 12 epochs, in fixed succession (animals / furniture / fruit / tools / animals / furniture, etc.). Four such runs were executed by each subject, with a pause of about 15 min between runs. Each run was preceded by a 30-s "warm-up" phase in which 20 items from the four categories (5 of each) had to be named. The purpose of this warm-up was to exclude activation caused by the mere beginning of the task, a phenomenon that was seen in a pilot experiment. The stimuli were different from those in the subsequent tasks. While the subjects performed the task, they were scanned with a 1.5-T (Tesla) MR scanner equipped with echo planar imaging and a surface coil placed over the left frontotemporal region of the head. During each 30-s epoch, 15 images were taken in 5 planes.

Data were analyzed on a unit volume basis (i.e., voxel by voxel). Figure 59.8 displays the time course of activation for the furniture and tool categories. Most subjects showed areas of increased cortical activation caused by naming items of one of the categories. Because of the way images were obtained, only the left frontal temporal areas could be assessed.[54] In another study involving subjects naming only animals or furniture items, activated areas were located not too far apart within the brain of each subject. Several such areas were found in each subject, in the *left* frontal and temporal lobes. Therefore, this study provides further evidence for distributed maplike semantic representations of semantic information. Two positron emission tomography studies of category-specific brain activation found further evidence of localized storage of high-level representations. Both studies involved the categories of animals and tools and provide converging evidence for the localized storage of aspects of these representations.

Associative Disorders Are Revealed by Abnormal Semantic Priming in Schizophrenic Patients

Schizophrenic patients suffering from thought disorders exhibit a number of language-related abnormalities.[55] Their utterances in normal conversations contain more repetitions, which may occur at the level of syllables, words, or phrases, as well as more **associative intrusions**—inappropriate intrusions of words that are often very remotely associated with some previous words of the utterance. The finding that schizophrenic patients produce more nonstandard associations in the word association test has been replicated a number of times.[56]

To investigate the associative processes of schizophrenic patients in more detail, researchers have used the above-mentioned semantic priming protocol.[57] When one study was run, a most unexpected result was obtained: an *increased* semantic priming effect in schizophrenic patients who suffered from formal thought disorder (TD) compared to the effect in non-thought-disordered (NTD) schizophrenic patients and normal control subjects.[57,58]

This experimental result is highly unexpected, because the very patients who by definition suffer from strange and unexpected associations benefit more from normal associations in the lexical decision experiment. The increased semantic priming effect (due to normal associations) can be reconciled with the presence of thought disorder (i.e., pathology of associations) by the spreading activation hypothesis of lexical access, if it is assumed that activation during lexical access

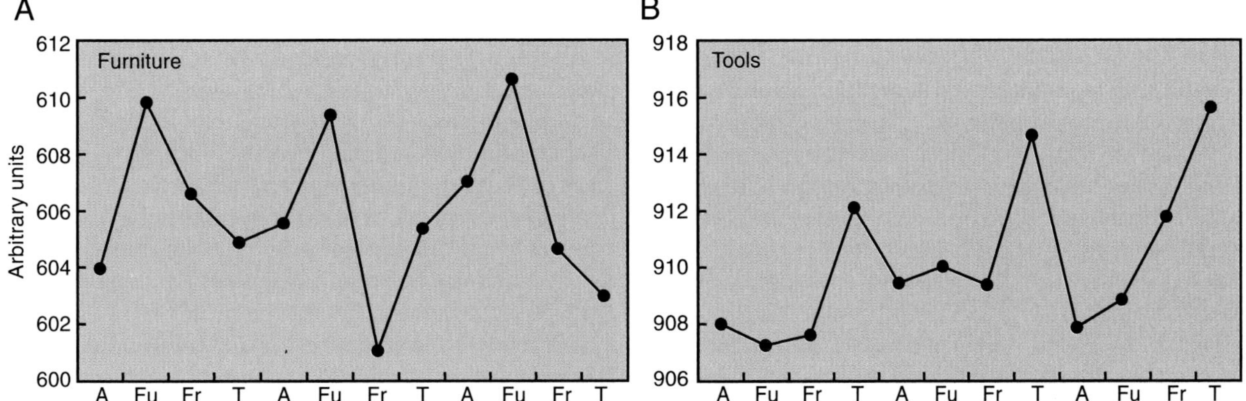

FIGURE 59.8 Results of MRI studies using picture naming as the primary task. Within a left frontal brain area related to semantic processing different sites become active depending on whether the subject sees pictures of furniture (Fu), animals (A), fruit (Fr), or tools (T). (A) Activity level of one set of sites during presentation of different types of pictures. These sites are most sensitive to furniture. (B) Activity level of another set of sites that most sensitive to tools.

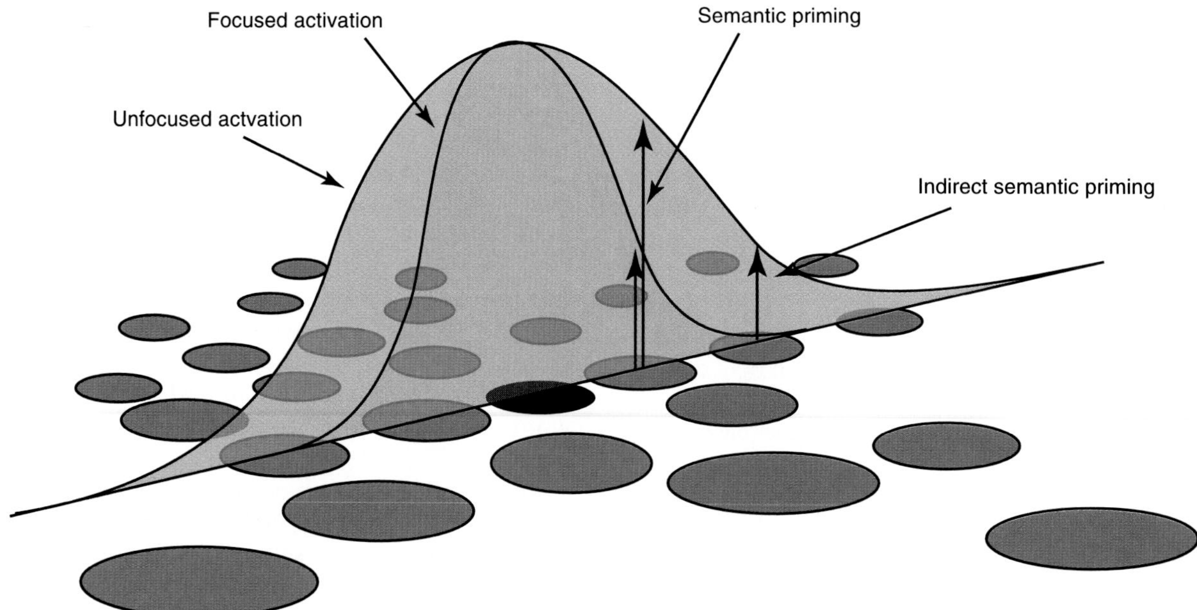

FIGURE 59.9 Illustration of how direct and indirect priming help us to study the spread of semantic activation. The elipses represent nodes in memory that code semantic information. Activation of the solid elipse is driven by an input item (e.g., the prime "white" in Fig. 59.6). The activation spreads to closely related nodes (which include "black" as one example), activated nodes within the focused gray curve. However, there may also be unfocused activation beyond the gray area, shown by the white area. Indirect priming (for example, of "night," which is associated to black but only indirectly to white) can be used to study activation that spreads beyond the focused area.

spreads faster and farther in the semantic network in TD schizophrenic patients than in normal subjects. This causes the increased activation of normal associations on the one hand (and hence an increased semantic priming effect) and the intrusion of oblique and unusual associations into utterances, because activity spreads out quickly to farther nodes, causing pathological intrusions.

Indirect Priming Is Improved in Schizophrenia

The finding of an increased semantic priming effect in TD schizophrenic patients was an important first step. However, careful clinical observation provided the clue for another measure of increased spreading of activation in TD schizophrenic patients. Whereas schizophrenic patients produce *fewer close associates* in word association tests,[59] they tend to produce *more indirect*, or *mediated, associations.* Many years ago, Bleuler[33] (p. 26) noted: "In experimental investigations of association, we find a notable frequency of 'mediate associations.'" Bleuler's results were recently replicated using a standard word association task given to 20 normal control subjects and 20 schizophrenic patients.[53] Compared to the normal control subjects, the TD schizophrenic patients showed fewer standard associations, fewer associations driven by meaning, and more indirect associations.

Finally, the following line of argument, derived from the associative network model of semantic priming, can be made to suggest a better measure for the spreading of activation in such networks. According to this model, activation is postulated to dissipate with distance. Empirical evidence indicates that such an inverse relationship between semantic distance and the amount of activation exists in normal subjects.[60] Therefore, from a psycholinguistic perspective, closely associated words, which are automatically activated in normal control subjects and in schizophrenic patients, may not be the best stimuli for proving the faster and farther spread of activation in associative networks of schizophrenic patients. Instead, far associations should be more effective discriminators between normal and activated associative networks (Fig. 59.9). Examples of such far, or indirect, associations are "chalk (white)–black" and "lemon (sour)–sweet." In general, indirect associations can be defined as word pairs where the connection between the words is obvious only via a mediating associated word. Applied to lexical decision experiments, this means that the target is an association to an association of the prime.

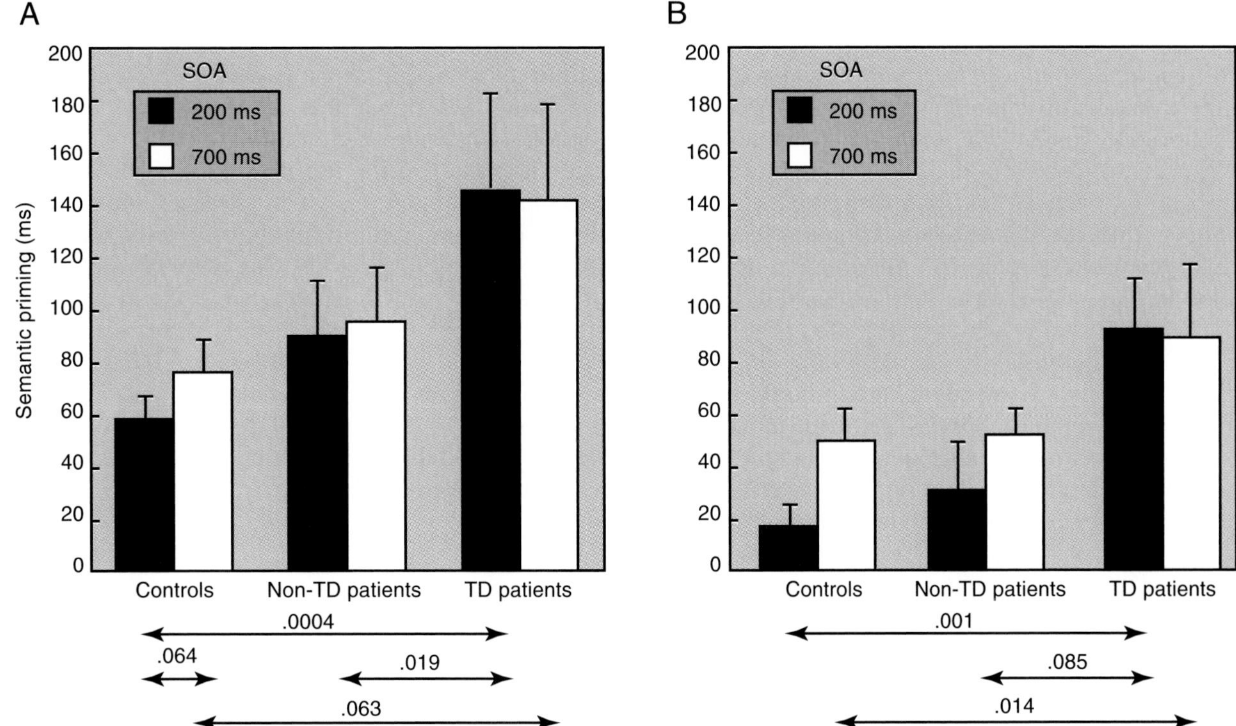

FIGURE 59.10 Direct (A) and indirect (B) priming score (difference between RT to related and unrelated words) for 50 normal controls, 21 non-thought-disordered schizophrenics, and 29 thought-disordered schizophrenics. Reproduced with permission from Spitzer.[62]

Indirect Semantic Priming Proved to Be a Better Measure of Spreading Activation Than Direct Semantic Priming

Two studies of indirect and direct semantic priming in normal control subjects and schizophrenic patients clearly confirmed the validity of these ideas. As can be seen in Fig. 59.10, the spreading of activation reaches more distant nodes only after several hundred milliseconds in normal subjects. In this group a significant indirect semantic priming effect was observed only when the target word appeared 700 ms after the prime word. This interval between the beginning of the prime and the beginning of the target is called stimulus onset asynchrony (SOA). In contrast, TD schizophrenic patients displayed a significant indirect semantic priming effect when the SOA was short, i.e., only 200 ms. This was interpreted as a sign of the fast and far spreading of activation in this group.

Differences in (direct) semantic priming between TD schizophrenic patients and normal subjects—particularly at the long SOA—can be attributed exclusively to the general slowness of the patients. When this slowness was taken into account, no difference in the priming effect was visible. This was not the case, however, for the indirect semantic priming effect. This study not only provided support for the spreading activation model of thought disorder but also suggested that indirect semantic priming in lexical decision tasks with a short SOA is a good measure of spatiotemporal characteristics of the spreading of activation in semantic networks.

SCHIZOPHRENIA AND DOPAMINE

The Modulatory Activity of Neurons Changes Relatively Slowly Compared to the Rate of Neurotransmission

Most neurons in the brain are engaged in excitatory or inhibitory point-to-point fast signal transmission (see Chapter 8). Only a small fraction of all brain neurons do not engage in fast information processing of signals. These cells have connections that are diffusely and widely spread across the cortex. They use substances such as monoamines (norepinephrine, dopamine), serotonin, and acetylcholine for transmission, and receptor sites for these substances can be found in many cortical areas and within the various layers of the cortex. The transmitters do not act on ion channels, but rather activate comparatively slow second-messenger systems (see Chapter 9).

The distinction between fast neurotransmission and slow neuromodulation is a matter of degree. Consider the following analogy: In a color TV set, fast information processing corresponds to the screen being refreshed about every 30 ms, according to the signals coming in through the antenna. In contrast, neuromodulation corresponds to slow, hand-operated changes in general variables such as contrast, brightness, and color saturation, affecting the entire screen display.

Just as there is a clear advantage in being able to control general qualities of TV pictures, it must be advantageous for the organism to set general variables controlling information processing. For example, when we relax we may enjoy a seemingly endless and rather unusual stream of "free" associations. Such "wandering in mind" may eventually generate rather unusual thoughts, or even creative solutions to problems we have long carried with us. On the other hand, in the presence of a threat, we had better do what we know is best and quickly implement the necessary behavior to get out of the situation. To wander in mind in such circumstances would clearly be disadvantageous. In other words, just as the adjustment of contrast or brightness of a TV improves the overall quality of the display in various circumstances (such as conditions of lighting or picture displayed), the adjustment of general processing features is advantageous for the organism because it allows better adaptation to the varying demand characteristics of an ever-changing environment.

Which General Processing Features Can Be Assumed to Be under the Control of Neuromodulators?

From a subjective point of view, we are all familiar with such general functional characteristics of mentation as vigilance and mood. We are more or less alert and do things in our mind with more or less ease; we find ourselves in various mood states and accordingly think differently about different aspects of the environment. Vigilance and affect are two concepts derived from subjective experience that can be reframed in neuromodulatory terms. Of course, it is unlikely that there is a clear-cut match between verbal abstractions from subjective accounts of mental processes and neuronal modulatory systems; however, it is important to realize that just as vigilance and affect are general aspects of mentation, neuromodulatory systems control general aspects of fast neural transmission.

One such general aspect of mentation concerns the strength of neural signals. At various sites in the cortex serotonin (5-hydroxytryptamine; 5HT) functions as an enhancer of neural transmission. In contrast, norepinephrine and dopamine do not act as general enhancers; instead, they amplify strong signals and dampen weak ones.[63] The net effect of this function is to enhance the ratio between a transmitted signal and the background activity of the neurons. In computational terms, the effect of these two neuromodulators has been referred to as enhancing the ratio between signal and noise. To go back to our TV example: Whereas 5HT appears to control "brightness" (i.e., the general strength of input signals to cortical areas), norepinephrine and dopamine appear to control "contrast," that is, the relation between the signal and the random background activity of the system.[64,65]

Elevated Dopamine Levels Have Been Implicated in the Pathology of Schizophrenia

The basis for implicating dopamine in schizophrenia is the finding that psychoactive agents that alleviate symptoms of schizophrenia, such as hallucinations and delusions, block dopamine receptors in the brain.[66] Moreover, a side effect of these agents is parkinsonism, a disorder chacterized by motor phenomena that are caused by a hypodopaminergic state.

These findings led to the so-called **dopamine hypothesis of schizophrenia.** The standard dopamine hypothesis of schizophrenic psychopathology attributes schizophrenic psychopathology to elevated dopamine levels in the brain. Although this hypothesis dominated the literature for decades, much evidence has accrued to challenge it. First, it never fit several clinical observations. For example, whereas neuroleptic drugs, as dopamine-receptor antagonists are called in the context of psychopharmacology, produce Parkinsonlike symptoms almost immediately, their action on psychopathological symptoms is delayed by days or sometimes even weeks. Second, some symptoms of schizophrenia do not respond to neuroleptic drugs and sometimes even become worse under therapy. In particular, so-called "positive" symptoms such as hallucinations and delusions may respond favorably to neuroleptic drugs, whereas this is not the case with most "negative" symptoms such as social withdrawal, anhedonia, and apathy. Third, if schizophrenia were necessarily associated with a hyperactive dopamine system, one would expect increases in the levels of dopamine and its metabolites in the brain of schizophrenic patients. Yet neither *in vivo* nor postmortem studies have produced consistent results in this regard. Finally, homeostatic mechanisms that are built into the dopamine system would act to restore dopamine equilibrium following destabilization.

Negative symptoms in schizophrenia may be due to a *decrease* in dopaminergic activity rather than to an increase.[66–72] Various proposals have been based on this concept. For example, negative symptoms may be caused by low prefrontal dopamine activity, which leads to excessive dopamine activity in mesolimbic dopaminergic neurons, which in turn may eventually lead to positive symptoms.[68]

Dopamine May Modulate Signal-to-Noise Ratios in the Neuronal Network

Several lines of evidence suggest that dopamine modulates one general parameter of cortical information processing, namely, its signal-to-noise ratio.[65] According to this model, a decreased dopaminergic activation of cortical areas leads to a decrease in the functional focus of cortical neuronal network activity, thereby reducing the ability to produce appropriate output.

Whereas a high signal-to-noise ratio may at first appear to be desirable under any conditions, it can also at times be counterproductive. As discussed earlier, network models suggest that noise is an important factor driving neuroplasticity. In semantic networks, the relative absence of noise, for example, that produced by a state of moderate anxiety, may cause a more focused activation of ideas, concepts, and meanings. The upside of this effect is that under a given threat, human beings will engage in the one behavior they have learned to be appropriate. With regard to language, it has been demonstrated that stress and anxiety can lead to the production of an increased number of standard associations (such as black–white, doctor–nurse) in normal subjects.[73] In other words, anxiety may order the thoughts of normal subjects, turning them in the opposite direction of the type of thought disorders discussed above. The downside of such highly focused activation characteristics of semantic networks is that creativity is less likely to occur. We all know that anxious candidates will not do too well on an examination because they will not be able to produce creative solutions of problems that require more than the reproduction of rote-learned facts. To come up with "creative" solutions, we need to "unfocus" our mental activity to some extent and allow for the intrusion of unusual thoughts. In sum, the capacity to modulate the relative amount of signal and noise appears to be highly advantageous to an organism, and therefore neuromodulatory systems may have evolved.

L-Dopa Has Been Used to Study the Effects of Dopamine in the Central Nervous System

If dopamine modulates the signal-to-noise ratio in cortical networks, if such networks are involved in the storage of semantic information in the form of maps, and if these maps are accessed during semantic information processing more or less reliably (i.e., with more or less noise involved), the ingestion of L-dopa, a precursor of dopamine and norepinephrine (see Chapter 8), should cause an increase in the focus of activation in semantic networks, and hence, a decrease in the effects of spreading activation, which are represented in Fig. 59.9. (L-dopa is used because dopamine itself cannot pass the blood–brain barrier.)

Because L-dopa is a precursor of dopamine and norepinephrine and both substances have been implicated in modulating the signal-to-noise ratio in cortical networks,[64,69,74] the effects of the two catecholamines are difficult to discern. However, neuroanatomical considerations render dopamine the more likely candidate when it comes to the modulation of semantic processes. The noradrenergic system originates in the locus ceruleus and projects mainly to primary sensory cortical areas, modulating sensory input from the thalamus. In contrast, the dopaminergic projections arise from the ventral tegmental area and terminate predominantly in frontal areas, which are involved in language processing. Moreover, dopamine receptors (mainly D1 receptors) have been demonstrated on spines of pyramidal cells in cortical layer III, where corticocortical projection neurons are located, linking association cortices with each other.[75–77] Anatomical properties thus make the dopaminergic mesocortical neurons particulaarly suited to exerting a modulatory effect on the processing of semantic information.

The hypothesis of a dopaminergic neuromodulatory influence on semantic networks was directly tested in a study on indirect semantic priming in normal volunteers.[78] In a double-blind placebo-controlled design, a speeded lexical decision task and indirectly related word pairs as well as nonrelated word pairs were used to assess the effect of 100 mg of L-dopa (plus 25 mg benserazide, a peripheral decarboxylase inhibitor) on the time course of spreading activation in 31 normal subjects. If dopamine causes a sharper focus of lexical activation, the small indirect priming effect that normal subjects display at longer SOAs should decrease. The results of the study were in line with this hypothesis: When a long stimulus onset asynchrony was used to elicit indirect priming in normals, L-dopa produced a significant decrease of the indirect semantic priming effect from 28 to 14 ms. A small, nonsignificant reduction in semantic priming indicated again that this measure may be less sensitive to changes in the spreading of activation in semantic networks. This study provided direct support for the hypothesis that dopamine increases the signal-to-noise-ratio in semantic networks, that is, causes a decreased spreading of activation during the process of lexical access. Indirectly, these data provide some support for the hypothesis that formal thought disorder is the result of a decreased dopaminergic tone.

Schizophrenics Also Show Working Memory Deficits

Since the time of the German psychiatrist Emil Kraepelin (1856–1926), the prefrontal cortex has been linked to schizophrenic psychopathology. However, until the advent of recent neuroimaging methods, little clear-cut evidence had been produced in support of this notion. This changed when single-photon emission tomography (SPECT) and positron emission tomography (PET) were used to image the brains of schizophrenic patients. The majority of the SPECT studies and quite a few of the PET studies suggest that schizophrenic patients suffer from a lower blood flow through the prefrontal cortex. In particular, more recent studies demonstrated a failure of activation of the prefrontal cortex in patients performing a task that is known to activate the prefrontal cortex in normal subjects, such as the Wisconsin Card Sorting Test, the Continuous Performance Test, the Porteus Mazes, or the Tower of London Test.[79,80] This observation led to the somewhat vague notion of "hypofrontality" in schizophrenia.[81]

The frontal lobes can be conceived as the site of the psychological function of working memory as discussed earlier in this chapter (also see Chapter 56). Working memory has been linked to dopamine activity in this brain area in human beings.[82] Because dopamine functioning is clearly involved in the pathogenesis of schizophrenia, because frontal cortex dysfunction in schizophrenia has been demonstrated by neuroimaging studies, and because delayed response tasks require subjects to guide their responses by memory of information newly stored for each trial, such tasks seem suitable for tapping working memory deficits in schizophrenic patients.[83] Moreover, working memory deficits have been demonstrated directly in schizophrenic patients using various delayed-response tasks.[63,84,85]

Features of schizophrenic thought may also be explained as a combined dysfunction of associative semantic and working memory. As we have already seen, the particular kind of schizophrenic concretism, that is, the tendency to make a remote aspect of a concept overly concrete, can easily be explained as the combined effect of a disinhibited (unfocused) associative memory and a reduced capacity of working memory. Furthermore, the clinically relevant aspect of schizophrenic thought and behavior, the patients' ubiquitous lack of sensitivity to context,[86,87] can easily be accounted for in terms of working and associative memory. The patients' failure to make appropriate use of contextual evidence in the production and understanding of language and in goal-directed behavior may be caused by the inability to keep relevant information "in mind" while pursuing a certain project. This relevant information must be represented in working memory, because it must be permanently used to guide behavior in the absence of immediate perceptual cues or even despite perceptual cues that suggest some alternative behavior.

Summary

Cognitive neuroscience is the most recent name for the human endeavor to understand the nature of mind and how it is related to the brain. Cognitive neuroscience provides a framework for the study of higher mental processes. In this chapter we reviewed the concepts of working memory, problem solving, and psychopathology. In doing so, we have drawn on concepts and knowledge of attention, language, memory, and emotion described in previous chapters of this section. Concepts such as neuroplasticity and neuromodulation have been used to understand the changes in such systems over long and short periods of time. We believe that there remains very great potential for the use of this framework in understanding higher mental functional and its pathologies.

References

1. Miller, G. A. (1956). The magical number seven plus or minus two: Some limits on our capacity for processing information. *Psychol. Rev.* **63:** 81–97.
2. Peterson L. R., and Peterson, M. J. (1959). Short-term retention of individual verbal items. *J. Exp. Psychol.* **58:** 193–198.
3. Sternberg, S. (1966). High speed scaning in human memory. *Science* **153:** 652–654.
4. Wilson, F. A. W., O'Scalaidhe, S. P., and Goldman-Rakic, P. S. (1993). Dissociation of object and spatial processing domains in primate prefrontal cortex. *Science* **260:** 1955–1958.
5. Smith, E. E., and Jonides, J. (1997). Working memory: A view from neuroimaging. *Cognit. Psychol.* **33:** 5–42.
6. Smith, E. E., Jonides, J., and Koeppe, R. A. (1996). Dissociating verbal and spatial memory using PET. *Cereb. Cortex* **6:** 11–20.
7. Baddeley, A. D., Thompson, N., and Buchanan, M. (1975). Word length and the structure of short term memory. *J. Verb. Learn. Verb. Behav.* **14:** 578–589.
8. Shallice, T. (1988). *From Neuropsychology to Mental Structure.* Cambridge University Press, Cambridge, UK.

9. Awh, E., Jonides, J., Smith, E. E., Schumacher, E., Koeppe, R., and Katz, S. (1996). Dissociation of storage and rehearsal in verbal working memory: Evidence from PET. *Psychol. Sci.* **7:** 25–31.
10. Petersen, S. E., Fox, P. T., Posner, M. I., Mintun, M., and Raichle, M. E. (1988). Positron emission tomographic studies of the cortical anatomy of single-word processing. *Nature (London)* **331:** 585–589.
11. Paulesu, E., Frith, C. D., and Frackowiak, R. S. (1993). The neural correlates of the verbal component of working memory. *Nature (London)* **362:** 342–345.
12. Gevins, A., and Cutillo, B. (1993). Spatiotemporal dynamics of component processing in human working memory. *Electroencephalogr. Clin. Neurophysiol.* **1:** 1–17.
13. Cohen, J., Forman, S. D., Braver, S., Casey, B. J., Servan-Schreiber, D., and Noll, D.C. (1995). Activation of prefrontal cotex in a nonspatial working memory task with functional MRI. *Hum. Brain Mapp.* **1:** 291–304.
14. Fuster, J. (1995). *Memory in the Cerebral Cortex.* MIT Press, Cambridge, MA.
15. Daneman, M., and Carpenter, P. A. (1980). Individual differences in working memory and reading. *J. Verb. Learn. Verb. Behav.* **19:** 450–466.
16. Just, M. A., and Carpenter, P. A. (1992). A capacity theory of comprehension: Individual differences in working memory. *Psychol. Rev.* **99:** 122–149.
17. McCarthy, R., and Warrington, E. K. (1990). *Cognitive Neuropsychology: A Clinical Introduction.* Academic Press, San Diego. CA.
18. De Renzi, E., and Lucchelli, F. (1994). Are semantic systems separately represented in the brain? The case of living category impairment. *Cortex* **30:** 3–25.
19. Hitch, G. J. (1978). The role of short-term working memory in mental arithmetic. *Cognit. Psychol.* **10:** 302–323.
20. Craik, F. I. M., and Jennings, J. M. (1992). Human memory. In *Handbook of Aging and Cognition* (F. I. M. Craik and T. A. Salthouse, eds.). Erlbaum, Hillsdale, NJ.
21. Campbell, J. I. D., and Charness, N. (1990). Age-related declines in working memory skills: Evidence from a complex calculation task. *Dev. Psychol.* **26:** 879–888.
22. Roland, P. C., and Friberg, L. (1985). Localization of cortical areasmactivated by thinking. *J. Neuropsychol.* **53:** 1219–1243.
23. Dehaene, S., and Cohen, L. (1995). Towards an anatomical and functional model of number processing. *Math. Cognition* **1:** 83–120.
24. Schank, R. C., and Abelson, R. P. (1977). *Scripts, Plans, Goals and Understanding: An Inquiry into Human Knowledge Structures.* Erlbaum, Hillsdale, NJ.
25. Dehaene, S., and Changeux, J. P. (1989). A simple model of prefrontal cortex function in delayed-response tasks. *J. Cognit. Neurosci.* **1:** 244–261.
26. Dehaene, S., and Changeux, J. P. (1991). The Wisconsin Card Sorting Test: Theoretical analysis and modelling in a neuronal network. *Cereb. Cortex* **1:** 62–79.
27. Levine, D. S., and Prueitt, P. S. (1989). Modelling some effects of frontal lobe damage—novelty and perseveration. *Neural Networks* **2:** 103–116.
28. Mishkin, M., and Appenzeller, T. (1987). The anatomy of memory. *Sci. Am.* **256**(6): 80–89.
29. Cohen, J. D., Dunbar, K., and McClelland, J. (1990). On the control of automatic processes: A parallel distributed processing model of the Stroop effect. *Psychol. Rev.* **97:** 332–361.
30. Dominey, P., Arbib, M., and Joseph, J. P. (1995). A model of cortico-striatal plasticity for learning occulomotor associations and sequences. *J. Cognit. Neurosci.* **7:** 311–337.
31. Guigon, E., Dorizzi, B., Burnod, Y., and Schultz, W. (1995). Neural correlates of learning in the prefrontal cortex of the monkey: A predictive model. *Cereb. Cortex* **2:** 135–147.
32. Barto, A. G., Sutton, R. S., and Anderson, C. W. (1983). Neuronlike elements that can solve difficult learning control problems. *JEEE Trans. Syst. Man. Cybernetic.* **13:** 834–846.
33. Bleuler, E. (1911/1950). *Dementia praecox or the Group of Schizophrenias* (J. Ziskin and N. D. Lewis, transl.). International Universities Press, New York.
34. Aitchison, J. (1987). *Words in the Mind.* Blackwell, Oxford, and Cambridge, MA.
35. Levelt, W. J. M. (1989), *Speaking: From Intention to Articulation.* MIT Press, Cambridge, MA and London.
36. Miller, G. A., and Glucksberg, S. (1988). Psycholinguistic aspects of pragmatics and semantics. In *Steven's Handbook of Experimental Psychology* (R. C. Atkinson, R. J. Herrnstein, G. Lindzey, and R. D. Luce, eds.), Vol. 2, pp. 417–472. Wiley, New York.
37. Meyer, D. E., and Schvaneveldt, R. W. (1971). Facilitation in recognizing pairs of words: Evidence of a dependence between retrieval operations. *J. Exp. Psychol.* **20:** 227–234.
38. Neely, J. H. (1991). Semantic priming effects in visual word recognition: A selective review of current findings and theories. In *Basic Progresses in Reading and Visual Word Recognition* (D. Besner and G. W. Humphreys, eds.), pp. 264–333. Erlbaum, Hillsdale, NJ.
39. Collins, A. M., and Loftus, E. F. (1975). A spreading activation theory of semantic processing. *Psychol. Rev.* **82:** 407–428.
40. Neely, J. H. (1977). Semantic priming and retrieval from lexical memory: Roles of inhibitionless spreading activation and limited capacity attention. *J. Exp. Psychol. Gen.* **106:** 226–254.
41. Ritter, H., and Kohonen, T. (1989). Self-organizing semantic maps. *Biol. Cybernet.* **61:** 241–254.
42. Creutzfeld, D. O. (1995). *Cortex Cerebri.* Oxford University Press, Oxford.
43. Thomson, A. M., and Deuchars, J. (1994). Temporal and spatial properties of local circuits in neocortex. *Trends Neurosci.* **17**(3): 119–126.
44. Kohonen, T. (1982). Self-organized formation of topologically correct feature maps. *Biol. Cybernet.* **43:** 59–69.
45. Kohonen, T. (1989). *Self-Organization and Associative Memory,* 3rd ed. Springer, Berlin.
46. Penfield, W., and Rasmussen, T. (1950). *The Cerebral Cortex of Man: A Clinical Study of Localization and Function.* Macmillan, New York.
47. Merzenich, M. M., and Sameshima, K. (1993). Cortical plasticity and memory. *Curr. Opin. Neurol.* **3:** 187–196.
48. Zeki, S. (1993). *A Vision of the Brain.* Blackwell, Oxford.
49. Tootell, R., Kwong, K., Belliveau, J., Baker, J., Stern, C., Hockfield, S., Breiter, H., Born, R., Benson, R., Brady, T., and Rosen, B. (1993). Mapping human visual cortex: Evidence from functional MRI and histology. *Invest. Ophthalmol. Visual Sci.* 813.
50. Woolsey, T. A., and van der Loos, H. (1970). The structural organization of layer IV in the somato-sensory region of the mouse cerebral cortex. *Brain Res.* **17:** 204–242.
51. Caramazza, A., Hillis, A., Leek, E. C., and Miozzo, M. (1994). The organization of lexical knowledge in the brain: Evidence from category- and modality-specific deficits. In *Mapping the Mind* (L. A. Hirschfeld and S. A. Gelman, eds.), pp. 68–84. Cambridge University Press, Cambridge, UK.
52. Farah, M. J., and Wallace, M. A. (1992). Semantically-bounded anomia: Implications for the neural implementation of naming. *Neuropsychologia* **30:** 609–621.
53. Spitzer, M., Kwong, K. K., Kennedy, W., Rosen, B. R., and Belli-

veau, J. W. (1995). Category specific brain activation of fMRI during picture naming. *Neuroreport* **6:** 2109–2112.
54. Martin, A., Haxby, J. V., Lalonde, F. M., Wiggs, C. L., and Ungerleider, L. G. (1995). Discrete cortical regions associate with knowledge of color and knowledge of action. *Science* **270:** 102–105.
55. Maher, B. A., and Spitzer, M. (1993). Thought disorder and language behavior in schizophrenia. In *Linguistic Disorders and Pathologies. Handbücher der Sprach-und Kommunikationswissenschaft* (G. Blanken, J. Dittmann, H. Grimm, J. C. Marshal, and C. W. Wallesch, eds.), Vol. 9, pp. 522–533. de Gruyter, New York and Berlin.
56. Cramer, P. (1968). *Word Association.* Academic Press, New York and London.
57. Maher, B. A., Manschreck, T. C., Hoover, T. M., and Weisstein, C. C. (1987). Thought disorder and measured features of language production in schizophrenia. In *Positive and Negative Symptoms in Psychosis: Description, Research and Future Directions* (P. Harvey and E. Walker, eds.), pp. 195–215. Erlbaum, Hillsdale, NJ.
58. Manschreck, T. C., Maher, B. A., Milavetz, J. J., Ames, D., Weisstein, C. C., and Schneyer, M. L. (1988). Semantic priming in thought disordered schizophrenic patients. *Schizophr. Res.* **1:** 61–66.
59. Kent, G. H., and Rosenoff, A. J. (1910). A study of associations in insanity. *Am. J. Insanity* **66/67** (Part I): 7–47; (Part II): 317–390.
60. den Heyer, and Briand, K. (1986). Priming single digit numbers: Automatic spreading activation dissipates as a function of semantic distance. *Am. J. Psychol.* **99:** 315–339.
61. Spitzer, M. (1993). Assoziative Netzwerke, formale Denkstörungen und Schizophrenie. *Nervenarzt* **64:** 147–159.
62. Spitzer, M. (1993). The psychopathology, neuropsychology and neurobiology of associative and working memory in schizophrenia. *Eur. Arch. Psychiatry Clin. Neurosci.* **243:** 57–70.
63. Morrison, J. H., and Hof, P. R. (1992). The organization of the cerebral cortex: From molecules to circuits. *Discuss. Neurosci.* **9**(2): 7–79.
64. Servan-Schreiber, D., Printz, H., and Cohen, J. D. (1990). A network model of catecholamine effects: Gain, signal-to-noise ratio and behavior. *Science* **249:** 892–895.
65. Cohen, J., and Servan-Schreiber, D. (1992). Context, cortex and dopamine: A connectionist approach to behavior and biology in schizophrenia. *Psychol. Rev.* **12:** 45–77.
66. Carlsson, A. (1988). The current status of the dopamine hypothesis of schizophrenia. *Neuropsychopharmacology* **1:** 179–203.
67. Crow, T. J. (1980). Molecular pathology of schizophrenia: More than one disease process? *Br. Med. J.* **137:** 383–386.
68. Davis, K. L., Kahn, R. S., Ko, G., and Davidson, M. (1991). Dopamine in schizophrenia: A review and reconceptualization. *Am. J. Psychiatry* **148:** 1474–1486.
69. Grace, A. A. (1991). Phasic versus tonic dopamine release and the modulation of dopamine system responsivity: A hypothesis for the etiology of schizophrenia. *Neuroscience* **41:** 1–24.
70. Heritch, A. J. (1990). Evidence for reduced and dysregulated turnover of dopamine in schizophrenia. *Schizophr. Bull.* **16:** 605–615.
71. Mackay, A. V. P. (1980). Positive and negative schizophrenic symptoms and the role of dopamine. *Br. J. Psychiatry* **137:** 379–386.
72. Weinberger, D. R., Berman, K. F., and Illowsky, B. P. (1988). Physiological dysfunction of dorsolateral prefrontal cortex in schizophrenia: A new cohort of evidence for a monoaminergic mechanism. *Arch. Gen. Psychiatry* **45:** 606–615.
73. Mintz, S. (1969). Effect of actual stress on word associations. *J. Abnorm. Psychol.* **74:** 293–295.
74. Chiodo, L. A., and Berger, T. W. (1986). Interactions between dopamine and amino acid-induced excitation and inhibition in the striatum. *Brain Res.* **375:** 198–203.
75. Goldman-Rakic, P. S., Leranth, C., Williams, S. M., Mons, N., and Geffard, M. (1989). Dopamine synaptic complex with pyramidal neurons in primate cerebral cortex. *Proc. Natl. Acad. Sci. U.S.A.* **86:** 9015–9019.
76. Smiley, J. F., and Goldman-Rakic, P. S. (1993). Heterogeneous targets of dopamine synapses in monkey prefrontal cortex demonstrated by serial section electron microscopy. *Cereb. Cortex* **3:** 223–238.
77. Smiley, J. F., Levey, A. I., Ciliax, B. J., and Goldman-Rakic, P. S. (1994). D1 dopamine receptor immunoreactivity in human and monkey cerebral cortex: Predominant and extrasynaptic localization in dendritic spines. *Proc. Natl. Acad. Sci. U.S.A.* **91**(12): 5720–5724.
78. Kischka, U., Kammer, T., Weisbrod, M., Meier, S., Thimm, M., and Spitzer, M. (1996). Dopaminergic modulation of semantic network activation. *Neuropsychologia* **34:** 1107–1113.
79. Andrasen, N. C., Rezai, K. R., Alliger, R., Swayze, V. W., Flaum, M., Kirchner, P., Cohen, G., and O'Leary, D. S. (1992). Hypofrontality in neuroleptic-naive patients and in patients with chronic schizophrenia. Assessment with Xenon 133 single-photon emission computed tomography and the Tower of London. *Arch. Gen. Psychiatry,* **49:** 943–948.
80. Andreasen, N. C., Swayze, V. W., Flaum, M., O'Leary, D. S., and Alliger, R. (1994). The neural mechanisms of mental phenomena. In *Schizophrenia: From Mind to Molecule* (N. C. Andreasen, ed.), pp. 49–91. American Psychiatric Press, Washington, DC.
81. Winn, P. (1994). Schizophrenia research moves to the prefrontal cortex. *Trends Neurosci.* **17:** 265–268.
82. Luciana, M., Depue, R. A., Arbisi, P., and Leon, A. (1992). Facilitation of working memory in humans by a D2 dopamine receptor agonist. *J. Cognit. Neurosci.* **4:** 58–68.
83. Goldman-Rakic, P. S. (1991). Cortical dysfunction in schizophrenia: The relevance of working memory. In *Psychopathology and the Brain* (B. J. Carroll and J. E. Barrett, eds.). Raven Press, New York.
84. Park, S., and Holzman, P. S. (1992). Schizophrenic show spatial working memory deficits. *Archi. Gen. Psychiatry* **49:** 975–982.
85. Park, S. (1995). Spatial working memory function in schizophrenia. In *Experimental Psychopathology* (M. Spitzer and B. A. Maher, eds.). Cambridge University Press, New York.
86. Chapman, L. J., Chapman, J. P., and Miller, G. A. (1964). A theory of verbal behavior in schizophrenia. In *Progress in Experimental Personality Research* (B. A. Maher, ed.), Vol. 1, pp. 49–77. Academic Press, New York and London.
87. de Silva, W. P., and Hemsley, D. R. (1977). The influence of context on language perception in schizophrenia. *Br. J. Clin. Psychol.* **16:** 337–345.

Appendix: Using the Ethics Cases

The ethics cases included in this book were chosen to reflect some of the issues that neuroscientists encounter as professionals. As you explore *Fundamental Neuroscience,* we encourage you to examine these cases and discuss them with your colleagues.

Working through ethical dilemmas is challenging. Often we may feel that we do not have adequate information upon which to base a decision. We also may be unnerved by the reality that there often are no "right" answers to such dilemmas, and that instead, we frequently need to choose from imperfect solutions. Fortunately, ethicists have developed tools to aid us in working through such situations. One method for systematically examining the key components of an ethical dilemma has been outlined by Bebeau and colleagues (1995). This approach relies on answering the following four questions:

1. What conflicting rights or obligations form the source of the dilemma?
2. Who are the individuals that will be affected by the central character's decision? (The list may include some individuals, groups, or organizations not named in the case.)
3. What actions can the central character take, and what are the likely outcomes of each of these actions?
4. What are the moral obligations of the central character?

We recommend that you apply these four questions to each of the ethics cases in this book (see Box for example). Then after you have given a case some thought, we invite you to refer back to this appendix, where you will find supplemental questions tailored to the individual cases. These questions are meant to further stimulate your exploration of the issues raised in the case. For the purpose of these exercises, the final decision you make is less important than learning how to think through the scenarios, as the ability to reason through such dilemmas is a skill that will serve you well throughout your career.

Reference

Bebeau, M. J., Pimple, K. D., Muskavitch, K. M. T., and Smith, D. H. (1995). *Moral Reasoning in Scientific Research: Cases for Teaching and Assessment.* Bloomington, IN: The Poynter Center, Indiana University.

SUPPLEMENTAL QUESTIONS TO ETHICS CASES

Case 1: Promotional Pressures (page 6)

1. What does it mean to say that Dr. Alexander has "demonstrated" a phenomenon but still needs to do more "replications"?

2. Suppose that Dr. Alexander artificially inflated the number of replications and submitted her manuscript for publication. What options would she have if the work was quickly accepted for publication with no revisions necessary?

3. Knowing that she needed to publish in order to be promoted, should Dr. Alexander have attempted such a long-term study? If not, then at what point can one undertake such long-term experiments, given that publications are important not only for obtaining tenure but also for acquiring grants and other promotions?

4. Is there any other way that Dr. Alexander can demonstrate her productivity short of providing an accepted manuscript?

5. Did the chairperson and/or senior faculty of Dr. Alexander's department have a responsibility to mentor her?

Case 2: To Be or Not to Be . . . a Consultant? (page 50)

1. Does this situation represent a conflict of interest? If so, how?

2. How does this situation compare with obtaining a research grant from a federal granting agency?

HEINZ AND THE DRUG
(A classical ethical dilemma)

A long time ago in a small village lived a man named Heinz, whose wife was dying. The local druggist produced a drug known to cure her disease, but he was only willing to sell it at a considerable profit—ten times what it cost him to produce it. Even with the financial help of his friends and relatives, Heinz could not raise even half of the money needed to purchase the drug. Heinz asked the druggist if he could pay for the drug over a period of time, but the druggist would not agree to this. Heinz then contemplated stealing the drug. What should he do?

Case Analysis

1. **What conflicting rights or obligations form the source of the dilemma?** His wife's right to her life is in conflict with the druggist's rights to his property.

2. **Who are the individuals that will be affected by the central character's decision?** Heinz's decision may affect himself, his wife, other members of his family, the druggist, and members of his community.

3. **What actions can the central character take, and what are the likely outcomes of each of these actions?** Either Heinz could steal the drug or he could refrain from stealing the drug. If he steals, he may or may not get caught. Some of the outcomes are listed in the table below.

4. **What are the moral obligations of the central character?** Heinz is morally obligated to try to save his wife's life, to respect the property of others, and to obey the laws of the society in which he lives.

Beth A. Fischer

	Heinz steals the drug and gets caught.	**Heinz steals the drug but does not get caught.**	**Heinz does not steal the drug.**
Heinz	May be jailed, his reputation and career damaged.	May suffer guilt; may be encouraged to try other unlawful acts (slippery slope).	May find a legitimate way of obtaining the drug; if not and wife dies he may feel badly about not being able to help.
Heinz's wife	May not have received the drug and thus may die. If he is jailed, she may suffer from lack of further assistance.	Will have the medicine she needs. However, if she finds out that Heinz stole it, she may feel guilty, angry, or both.	Would not have access to the drug and may die.
Heinz's children (if any)	May retain support of their mother, feel pleased with their father's sacrifice or upset by his guilt. May lose their father to jail and/or their mother to illness.	May retain support of mother.	May lose mother and resent father for not helping her.
The druggist	May feel violated by theft; may feel guilty for not letting Heinz make gradual payments.	May feel violated by theft.	May feel partly responsible for death of Heinz's wife.
Members of Heinz's community	May be proud/upset by Heinz's actions, partly responsible for not helping Heinz purchase the drug. May lose respect for druggist.	May lose respect for druggist if they learn of his behavior.	May be hurt by the death of Heinz's wife and may lose respect for druggist if they learn of his behavior.

3. Should academic scientists make their expertise available to verify the claims of a company?

4. Should academic scientists be compensated for consulting?

5. If Parker Pharmaceuticals funds Dr. Wong's research on the drug, should the company have the right to review the manuscript? Why or why not?

6. By insisting on the right to review Dr. Wong's results, is Parker Pharmaceuticals infringing on his right to submit those results for peer review or disseminate that information?

7. Are there any situations in which a publication lag of 60 days would be problematic?

8. If Dr. Wong publishes his work on the drug, should readers be informed that Parker Pharmaceuticals funded the study?

9. What regulations does your institution have regarding financial arrangements between university faculty and private companies?

Case 3: A Political Powderkeg (page 447)

1. What are some of the questions that neuroscientists might address that have social implications?

2. Should the social implications of a scientific project be decided before or after a proposal is solicited and / or reviewed? For example, should peer reviewers be asked to consider the social implications of a project in addition to rating its scientific and technical merit?

3. Should neuroscientists refrain from studying topics that may have politically unpopular ramifications? If such topics are to be studied, should public funds be used to support the research? And, if they are not to be studied, what is the proper balance between the social constraints on research and academic freedom?

4. What responsibilities, if any, does a scientist have for the social consequences of their research?

5. Should one federal employee be able to override the decision of a group of peer reviewers, thereby suppressing (or promoting) funding for a project?

Case 4: Sound Practices (page 668)

1. Would it have made any difference if the situation were the same except that: (a) the speaker's work had already been published? (b) Dr. O'Hara was the speaker and Ms. Shields a member of the audience?

2. Is it prudent to orally present work that has not yet been published?

3. What responsibilities, if any, does one have when using ideas presented by someone making an oral presentation? What about ideas obtained in a private conversation?

4. If Dr. O'Hara publishes a paper that contains some ideas that parallel those of Ms. Shields, did he necessarily obtain the ideas from her? Under what circumstances should he cite her?

5. If Dr. O'Hara uses Ms. Shields' ideas in his paper and does not cite her, would that constitute plagiarism? If so, would she have any recourse?

6. Could / Should Ms. Shields' advisor have better prepared her to deal with a situation like the one that she encountered?

Case 5: Concerning Confidentiality (page 860)

1. Is it ever reasonable to use information contained in a manuscript or grant application under review? If so, under what conditions and for what purpose?

2. Is there a difference in using confidential information to terminate a line of scientific inquiry versus to initiate one?

3. One might argue that Dr. Hernandez could just wait until the paper she reviewed is published and then share the information with Dr. Robbins. However, editors tend not to print studies with negative results. What if the manuscript that Dr. Hernandez reviewed was such a study and therefore might not ever get published? Would that change your decision?

4. What if Dr. Hernandez was a member of a thesis committee and Mark Robbins was proposing the work to be done for his dissertation? What if Dr. Hernandez was a lab director and Mark Robbins was her graduate student?

5. Can you think of any circumstances in which the apparent innocent sharing of information can lead to negative consequences for the person providing the information? For the person receiving it? For a third party?

Case 6: A Subject of Discussion (page 1024)

1. What are the restrictions at your institution on the use of animals for research?

2. Do you feel that the use of animals in research is always justified so long as their discomfort is minimized? Explain.

3. Are you surprised that Mr. Lewis feels a conflict working with the cats but not about working with the rats? Are the ethical considerations of using rats and cats different? If so, how and why? What about other species?

4. Should someone leave neuroscience if they are unwilling to perform research on animals?

5. Might Dr. Gorkin have handled the matter differently? Explain.

6. What recourse do students have if there is an impasse between them and their advisor?

Case 7: Cotter's Quandary (page 1306)

1. Should one expect some loss of independence while in training? If so, where does one draw the line and refuse to carry out a directive from a supervisor?

2. What is the procedure at your institution for getting approval from the Institutional Review Board (IRB) to use human subjects? Is IRB approval adequate assurance for Dr. Cotter to recruit subjects or must she evaluate the request on her own?

3. What are the essential components of "informed consent"?

4. Can individuals who suffer from mental illness provide informed consent?

5. Is there a conflict between the need for clinical research and the best interest of patients?

6. Should research be done on patients who will not derive any clinical benefit from the project?

7. Free treatment and/or monetary compensation is often used as a tool for recruiting subjects for clinical studies. Consequently, poor people may be more likely to participate in such studies. Is this a form of coercion? Is it ethically acceptable to use the poor in research studies to develop treatments that fellow members of their socioeconomic community will not be able to afford (for example, AIDS cocktails)?

8. Does Dr. Cotter have any choices other than simply accepting or rejecting the request?

Permissions

Neuroscience is a collective endeavor that has blossomed through the activities and pursuits of researchers and scholars from a wide variety of backgrounds and interests. Their findings are reported in a great number of general and specialized scientific journals and books, published by a large number of organizations and publishers. These all play a role in developing and distributing advances in the field.

The Editors, Contributors, and Academic Press thank all the providers of original sources of text and figures that have been used throughout to enhance and illustrate this book. We have tried to identify the original source of material and the correct reference to that material in order for the volume to be as scholarly a work as possible.

The publishers who have provided permissions include: AAAS, American Association of Clinical Chemists, American Medical Association, American Physiological Society, American Society of Biochemistry & Molecular Biology, American Scientist, Annual Reviews, Biophysical Society, Blackwell Science Publishers, Cambridge University Press, Cell Press, The Company of Biologists, CRC Press, Elsevier Science Publishers, the Endocrine Society, Federation of American Societies for Experimental Biology, Harvard University Press, Humana Press, Igaku-Shoin, Indiana University Press, John Wiley & Sons, Lippincott Williams & Wilkins, MacMillan Magazines, McGraw–Hill, the MIT Press, the National Academy of Sciences, the New York Academy of Sciences, Nature, Ornithological Societies of North America, Oxford University Press, The Physiological Society, Plenum Press, Rapid Science Publishers, Rockefeller University Press, the Royal Society, S. Karger, SIAM Press, Sinauer Associates, Society for Neuroscience, Springer-Verlag, Stanford University Press, University of Chicago Press, W.B. Saunders, W.H. Freeman, and Yale University Press.

We thank them for their cooperation and contribution.

Contributors

Huda Akil University of Michigan, Ann Arbor, MI

Marilyn S. Albert Massachusetts General Hospital, Boston, MA

Frances M. Ashcroft University Laboratory of Physiology, Oxford, United Kingdom

G. S. Aston-Jones University of Pennsylvania, Philadelphia, PA

J. Baker Northwestern University School of Medicine, Chicago, IL

Robert W. Baloh University of California School of Medicine, Los Angeles, CA

Amy J. Bastian Washington University Medical School, St. Louis, MO

Michael J. Baum Boston University, Boston, MA

John M. Beggs Yale University, New Haven, CT

Mark Bennett University of California, Berkeley, CA

Scott T. Brady University of Texas Southwestern Medical Center, Dallas, TX

Peter Brophy University of Edinburgh, Edinburgh, Scotland

M. Christian Brown Massachusetts Eye and Ear Infirmary, Boston, MA

Thomas H. Brown Yale University, New Haven, CT

Steven J. Burden New York University Medical Center, New York, NY

Mary C. Bushnell McGill University, Montreal, Quebec, Canada

John H. Byrne University of Texas Medical School, Houston, TX

Lawrence F. Cahill University of California, Irvine, CA

Judy Cameron University of Pittsburgh School of Medicine, Pittsburgh, PA

Serge Campeau University of Michigan, Ann Arbor, MI

David Caplan Massachusetts General Hospital, Boston, MA

J. Patrick Card University of Pittsburgh, Pittsburgh, PA

Thomas Carr Michigan State University, East Lansing, MI

Luz Claudio Mount Sinai Hospital, New York, NY

Carol L. Colby University of Pittsburgh, Pittsburgh, PA

David R. Colman The Mount Sinai Medical Center, New York, NY

Terry J. Crow University of Texas Medical School, Houston, TX

Susan M. Culican Washington University, St. Louis, MO

William E. Cullinan Marquette University, Milwaukee, WI

Jean de Vellis University of California School of Medicine, Los Angeles, CA

Stanislas Dehaene Service Hospitalier Frederic Joliot, Orsay cedex, France

R. Desimone National Institute of Mental Health, Bethesda, MD

Ariel Y. Deutch Vanderbilt University School of Medicine, Nashville, TN

Adele D. Diamond Eunice Kennedy Shriver Center, Waltham, MA

Wayne C. Drevets University of Pittsburgh Medical Center, Pittsburgh, PA

J. Driver University College London, London, United Kingdom

Howard B. Eichenbaum Boston University, Boston, MA

Andrew G. Engel Mayo Clinic, Rochester, MN

Barry J. Everitt University of Cambridge, Cambridge, United Kingdom

Martha J. Farah University of Pennsylvania, Philadelphia, PA

Jack L. Feldman University of California, Los Angeles, CA

Beth A. Fischer University of Pittsburgh, Pittsburgh, PA

Roslyn Holly Fitch Rutgers University, Newark, NJ

M. K. Floeter National Institute of Neurological Disorders and Stroke, Bethesda, MD

Lawrence A. Frohman University of Illinois, Chicago, IL

Albert M. Galaburda Beth Israel Hospital, Boston, MA

Michael S. Gazzaniga Dartmouth College, Hanover, NH

Alfred G. Gilman University of Texas Southwestern Medical Center, Dallas, TX

Paul W. Glimcher New York University, New York, NY

Mark A. Gluck Rutgers University, Newark, NJ

James Gould Princeton University, Princeton, NJ

Paul Greengard Rockefeller University, New York, NY

William A. Harris University of Cambridge, Cambridge, United Kingdom

Volker Hartenstein University of California School of Medicine, Los Angeles, CA

Michael E. Hasselmo Harvard University, Cambridge, MA

Mary E. Hatten Rockefeller University, New York, NY

Nathaniel Heintz Rockefeller University, New York, NY

Stewart H. C. Hendry Johns Hopkins University, Baltimore, MD

Karl Herrup Case Western Reserve School of Medicine, Cleveland, OH

J. Allen Hobson Harvard Medical School, Boston, MA

Patrick R. Hof Mount Sinai School of Medicine, New York, NY

Steven S. Hsiao Johns Hopkins University School of Medicine, Baltimore, MD

Glynn Humphreys Birmingham University, Edgbaston, Birmingham, United Kingdom

Steven E. Hyman National Institute of Mental Health, Rockville, MD

James E. Johnson Wake Forest University, Winston-Salem, NC

John Jonides University of Michigan, Ann Arbor, MI

Jon H. Kaas Vanderbilt University, Nashville, TN

Michael G. Kaplitt New York Hospital–Cornell University Medical College, New York, NY

Seymour Kaufman National Institutes of Health, Bethesda, MD

Frank C. Keil Cornell University, Ithaca, NY

Sue C. Kinnamon Colorado State University, Ft. Collins, CO

Christopher Kintner Salk Institute, La Jolla, CA

Eric I. Knudsen Stanford University School of Medicine, Stanford, CA

George F. Koob Scripps Research Institute, La Jolla, CA

Stephen M. Kosslyn Harvard University, Cambridge, MA

Dimitri M. Kullmann Institute of Neurology, London, United Kingdom

Kevin S. LaBar Northwestern University School of Medicine, Chicago, IL

Gabrielle G. Leblanc National Institute of Neurological Disorders and Stroke, Bethesda, MD

Ronald M. Lechan Tufts University School of Medicine, Boston, MA

Joseph E. LeDoux New York University, New York, NY

Jeff W. Lichtman Washington University School of Medicine, St. Louis, MO

Arthur D. Loewy Washington University School of Medicine, St. Louis, MO

S. J. Luck University of Iowa, Iowa City, IA

Thomas Lufkin The Mount Sinai Medical Center, New York, NY

Andrew Lumsden United Medical and Dental School, Guy's Hospital, London, United Kingdom

Peter R. Mac Leish Morehouse School of Medicine, Atlanta, GA

Pierre J. Magistretti University of Lausanne, Lausanne, Switzerland

Alex J. Martin National Institute of Mental Health, Bethesda, MD

Randi Martin Rice University, Houston, TX

David A. McCormick Yale University School of Medicine, New Haven, CT

Donald R. McCrimmon Northwestern University Medical School, Chicago, IL

James L. McGaugh University of California, Irvine, CA

Robert W. Meech School of Medical Science, Bristol, United Kingdom

Jonathan W. Mink Washington University Medical School, St. Louis, MO

Aage R. Møller The University of Texas, Dallas, TX

Robert Y. Moore University of Pittsburgh School of Medicine, Pittsburgh, PA

Enrico Mugnaini Northwestern University, Chicago, IL

Jaap Murre University of Amsterdam, Amsterdam, The Netherlands

Catherine Myers Rutgers University, Newark, NJ

Helen J. Neville University of Oregon, Eugene, OR

Carl R. Olson Carnegie Mellon University, Pittsburgh, PA

Ronald W. Oppenheim Wake Forest University, Winston-Salem, NC

Michael Petrides McGill University, Montreal, Quebec, Canada

M. I. Posner University of Oregon, Eugene, OR

Terry L. Powley Purdue University, West Lafayette, IN

Todd M. Preuss University of Southwestern Louisiana, New Iberia, LA

Carolyn Rabin Highland Park, NJ

Jonathan A. Raper University of Pennsylvania School of Medicine, Philadelphia, PA

Peter R. Rapp Mount Sinai School of Medicine, New York, NY

R. Clay Reid Harvard Medical School, Boston, MA

Trevor W. Robbins University of Cambridge, Cambridge, United Kingdom

Hillary R. Rodman Emory University, Atlanta, GA

Benno Roozendaal University of California, Irvine, CA

Robert H. Roth Yale University School of Medicine, New Haven, CT

Renato Rozental Albert Einstein College of Medicine, Bronx, New York, and Federal University of Goias, Goiania, Brazil

Joseph Santos-Sacchi Yale University Medical School, New Haven, CT

Eliana Scemes Albert Einstein College of Medicine, Bronx, NY

Daniel L. Schacter Harvard University, Cambridge, MA

Marc H. Schieber University of Rochester Medical Center, Rochester, NY

Jeremy D. Schmahman Massachusetts General Hospital, Boston, MA

Howard Schulman Stanford University Medical Center, Stanford, CA

Martin E. Schwab University of Zurich, Zurich, Switzerland

Gordon M. Shepherd Yale University School of Medicine, New Haven, CT

Daniel J. Simons Harvard University, Cambridge, MA

David V. Smith University of Maryland School of Medicine, Baltimore, MD

W. Carter Smith Cornell University, Ithaca, NY

Edward E. Smith University of Michigan, Ann Arbor, MI

Solomon H. Snyder Johns Hopkins University School of Medicine, Baltimore, MD

Manfred Spitzer Psychiatrische University, Heidelberg, D Germany

Stephen R. Sprang University of Texas Southwestern Medical Center, Dallas, TX

David C. Spray Albert Einstein College of Medicine, Bronx, NY

Edward M. Stricker University of Pittsburgh, Pittsburgh, PA

Ueli Suter Switzerland Federal Institute of Technology, Zurich, Switzerland

Alan F. Sved University of Pittsburgh, Pittsburgh, PA

Larry W. Swanson University of Southern California, Los Angeles, CA

Paula A. Tallal Rutgers University, Newark, NJ

Marc Tessier-Lavigne University of California, San Francisco, CA

W. Thomas Thach Washington University, St. Louis, MO

Richard F. Thompson University of Southern California, Los Angeles, CA

Roberto Toni University of Bologna School of Medicine, Bologna, Italy

Bruce D. Trapp Cleveland Clinic Foundation, Cleveland, OH

Joseph G. Verbalis Georgetown University, Washington, DC

Stanley J. Watson University of Michigan, Ann Arbor, MI

M. Neal Waxham University of Texas Health Science Center, Houston, TX

Cedric L. Williams University of Virginia, Charlottesville, VA

Phyllis M. Wise University of Kentucky College of Medicine, Lexington, KY

Rachel O. L. Wong Washington University School of Medicine, St. Louis, MO

Stephen C. Woods University of Cincinnati Medical Center, Cincinnati, OH

Susan Wray National Institutes of Health, Bethesda, MD

Robert S. Zucker University of California, Berkeley, CA

Index

B

C

D

E

F

J

K

L

M

N

O

T

U

V